SCHOLARSHIPS,

FELLOWSHIPS

AND LOANS

ISSN 1058-5699

SCHOLARSHIPS, FELLOWSHIPS AND LOANS

A GUIDE TO EDUCATION-RELATED FINANCIAL AID PROGRAMS FOR STUDENTS AND PROFESSIONALS

Volume Three

Sponsors and Their Scholarships: U–Z
and Indexes

Thirty-Eighth Edition

GALE
A Cengage Company

Scholarships, Fellowships and Loans, 38th Edition

Project Editor: Anthony Boussie

Editorial Support Services: Scott Flaugher

Composition and Electronic Prepress:
  Charlie Montney

Manufacturing: Cynde Lentz

For product information and technology assistance, contact us at
Gale Customer Support, 1-800-877-4253.
For permission to use material from this text or product,
submit all requests online at **www.cengage.com/permissions.**
Further permissions questions can be emailed to
permissionrequest@cengage.com

Gale
27500 Drake Rd.
Farmington Hills, MI, 48331-3535

ISBN-13: 978-0-02-867033-1 (3 vol. set)
ISBN-13: 978-0-02-867034-8 (vol. 1)
ISBN-13: 978-0-02-867035-5 (vol. 2)
ISBN-13: 978-0-02-867036-2 (vol. 3)

ISSN 1058-5699

This title is also available as an e-book.
ISBN-13: 978-0-02-867038-6
Contact your Gale sales representative for ordering information.

Printed in the United States of America
1 2 3 4 5   25 24 23 22 21

Contents

This edition of *Scholarships, Fellowships and Loans (SFL)* provides access to over 3,400 sources of education-related financial aid for students and professionals at all levels. *SFL*'s scope ranges from undergraduate and vocational/technical education through post-doctoral and professional studies. Students and others interested in education funding will find comprehensive information on a variety of programs in all educational areas, including:

- Architecture
- Area and Ethnic Studies
- Art
- Business
- Communications
- Computer Science
- Education
- Engineering
- Health Science
- Humanities
- Industrial Arts
- Language
- Law
- Literature
- Liberal Arts
- Library Science
- Life Science
- Medicine
- Mathematics
- Performing Arts
- Philosophy
- Physical Sciences
- Social Sciences
- Theology and Religion

SFL Provides Detailed Information on Awards

SFL provides all the information students need to complete their financial aid search. Entries include: administering organization name and address; purpose of award; qualifications and restrictions; selection criteria; award amount and number of awards granted; application details and deadlines; detailed contact information.

Additionally, look for the section on federal financial aid following the User's Guide for a quick summary of programs sponsored by the U.S. government, as well as information on the AmeriCorps program. There is also a section that lists higher education agencies by state.

Five Indexes Allow Quick and Easy Access to Awards

Whether you are a high school student looking for basic undergraduate financial aid, a scientist investigating research grants, or a professional attempting to finance additional career training, SFL aids your search by providing access to awards through the following indexes:

Field of Study Index categorizes awards by very specific subject fields.

Legal Resident Index targets awards restricted to applicants from specific geographic locations.

Place of Study Index provides a handy guide to awards granted for study within specific states, provinces, or countries.

Special Recipient Index lists awards that are reserved for candidates who qualify by virtue of their gender, organizational affiliation, minority or ethnic background.

Sponsor and Scholarship Index provides a complete alphabetical listing of all awards and their administering organizations.

Catchwords

SFL includes catchwords of the organization on each corresponding page, to aid the user in finding a particular entry.

As we make our way through difficult economic times, there is a growing need for a more highly-trained and educated work force. From political discussions and debates to reports from future-oriented think tanks and other groups, there is agreement that postsecondary education is a key to success. Yet how are students and their families to afford the already high (and constantly rising) cost of higher education? Searching for financial aid can be very tedious and difficult, even though hundreds of millions of dollars in aid reportedly go unclaimed every year.

Scholarships, Fellowships and Loans (SFL), the most comprehensive single directory of education-related financial aid available, can save you time, effort, and money by helping you to focus your search within the largest pool of awards and avoid pursuing aid for which you do not qualify. In most cases, the detailed descriptions contain enough information to allow you to decide if a particular scholarship is right for you to begin the application process. *SFL* lists over 8,900 major awards available to U.S. and Canadian students for study throughout the world. Included are:

- scholarships, fellowships, and grants, which do not require repayment;

- loans, which require repayment either monetarily or through service;

- scholarship loans, which are scholarships that become loans if the recipient does not comply with the award's terms;

- internships and work study programs, which provide training, work experience, and (usually) monetary compensation; and

- awards and prizes that recognize excellence in a particular field.

Also included are other forms of assistance offered by associations, corporations, religious groups, fraternal organizations, foundations, and other private organizations and companies. *SFL* includes a broad representation of government-funded awards at the national and state levels, as well as a representative sampling of lesser-known and more narrowly focused awards, such as those of a strictly local nature or programs sponsored by small organizations. Some financial aid programs administered and funded by individual colleges or universities are included in *SFL*. Both need- and merit-based awards are included. Competition-based awards and prizes are included when they offer funds that support study or research and are intended to encourage further educational or professional growth.

Students of All Types Can Benefit

Traditional students as well as those returning to school, non-degree learners, those in need of retraining, and established professionals can use the funding sources listed in *SFL* for formal and non-formal programs of study at all levels:

- high school
- vocational
- undergraduate
- graduate
- postgraduate
- doctorate
- postdoctorate
- professional development

Content and Arrangement

Scholarships, Fellowships and Loans is organized into a main section containing descriptive listings of award programs and their administering organizations, and five indexes.

The main section, Sponsors and Their Scholarships, is arranged alphabetically by name of administering organization. Entries for each organization's awards appear immediately following the entry on the organization. Each entry contains detailed contact and descriptive information, often providing users with all the information they need to make a decision about applying.

The indexes provide a variety of specific access points to the information contained within the organization and award listings, allowing users to easily identify awards of interest.

Practical Tips on How to Find Financial Aid

While there are many education-related financial aid programs for students of all types and study levels, the competition for available funds is steadily increasing. You will improve the likelihood of meeting your financial aid goals if you:

- carefully assess your particular needs and preferences;

- consider any special circumstances or conditions that might qualify you for aid; and

- carefully research available aid programs.

The following pages list some general guidelines for making your way through the search and application process.

Start Your Search Early

Any search for financial aid is likely to be more successful if you begin early. If you allow enough time to complete all of the necessary steps, you will be more likely to identify a wide variety of awards for which you qualify with plenty of time to meet their application deadlines. This can increase your chances of obtaining aid.

Some experts recommend that you start this process up to two years before you think you will need financial assistance. While you will probably be able to obtain some support if you allow less time, you might overlook some important opportunities.

Some awards are given on a first-come, first-served basis, and if you do not file your application early enough, the aid will already be distributed. In many cases, if your application is late you will not be considered, even if you have met all of the other criteria.

An early start will also allow you to identify organizations that offer scholarships to members or participants, such as student or professional associations, in time to establish membership or otherwise meet their qualifying criteria.

Assess Your Needs and Goals

The intended recipients for financial aid programs and the purposes for which awards are established can vary greatly. Some programs are open to almost anyone, while others are restricted to very specific categories of recipients. The majority of awards fall somewhere in between. Your first step in seeking financial aid is to establish your basic qualifications as a potential recipient. The following are some general questions to ask yourself to help define your educational and financial needs and goals:

- What kinds of colleges or universities interest me?

- What careers or fields of study interest me?

- Do I plan to earn a degree?

- Am I only interested in financial aid that is a gift, or will I consider a loan or work study?

- In what parts of the country am I willing to live and study?

Leave No Stone Unturned

After you have defined your goals, the next step is to identify any special factors that might make you eligible for aid programs offered only to a restricted group. Examine this area carefully, and remember that even minor or unlikely connections may be worth checking. The most common qualifications and restrictions involve:

- citizenship

- community involvement or volunteer work

- creative or professional accomplishment

- employer

- financial need

- gender

- merit or academic achievement

- military or veteran status

- organization membership (such as a union, association, or fraternal group)

- place of residence

- race or ethnic group

- religious affiliation

With many awards, you may be eligible if your spouse, parents, or guardians meet certain criteria by status or affiliations. You should be aware of your parents' affiliations even if you don't live with one (or both) of them, or if they are deceased. And given enough lead time, it may be possible for you (or your parents) to join a particular organization, or establish necessary residence, in time for you to be eligible for certain funds.

Contact Financial Aid Offices

Most colleges, universities, and other educational institutions offer their own financial aid programs. Their financial aid offices may also have information on privately sponsored awards that are specifically designated for students at those institutions. Contact their respective financial aid offices to request applications and details for all of the aid programs they sponsor and/or administer.

Use *SFL* to Identify Awards Sponsored by Private Organizations and Corporations

Scholarships, Fellowships and Loans (SFL) is the most comprehensive single source of information on major education-related financial aid programs sponsored and administered by private organizations and companies for use by students and professionals. Using *SFL* as a starting point, you can quickly compile a substantial list of financial aid programs for which you may qualify by following these simple steps:

- Compile an initial list of awards offered in your field of study.

- If you have already chosen your field of study, look in the Field of Study Index to find listings of awards grouped by more precise disciplines (such as Accounting or Journalism). If you choose this approach, your initial list is likely to be shorter but more focused. Eliminate awards that cannot be used at your chosen level of study or that do not meet your financial needs. Are you an undergraduate only interested in scholarships? Are you a graduate student willing to participate in an internship or take out a loan? Consult the User's Guide to determine which of the study level categories and award types apply to your particular situation. Both indexes clearly note the study levels at which awards may be used. The Field of Study Index also lists the type of financial aid provided.

- Eliminate awards by citizenship, residence, and other restrictions (minority status, ethnic background, gender, organizational affiliation) that make you ineligible.

- If your list is based on the Field of Study Index, you will need to look under the section for qualifications in each descriptive listing to see what requirements apply.

- Read the descriptive listings for each of the award programs left on your list. The descriptive listings should contain all the information you need to decide if you qualify and should apply for each of the awards on your list.

Expand Your List of Possibilities

If you are willing to take the initiative and do a little extra digging, you should be able to add to your list of institution-related and privately sponsored programs. In most cases, the best possibilities fall into these two areas:

Government Agencies and Programs. The Sponsors and Their Scholarships main section includes a broad representation of award programs sponsored by federal and state governments. Since these listings are not meant to be exhaustive, you should be able to identify additional programs by contacting the government agencies responsible for education-related financial aid programs listed here. On the federal level, contact the U.S. Department of Education at 400 Maryland Ave., SW, Washington, DC 20202, or on their website at https://www.ed.gov, for up-to-date information on U.S. Government award programs. For a broad overview of federal financial aid, consult the Federal Programs section. Similarly, you may contact your state department of education for details on what is offered in your particular state. Please see the State Higher Education Agencies section for state-by-state listings.

Local Sources of Awards. A surprisingly large number of financial aid programs are sponsored by small and/or lo-cal organizations. *SFL* contains a representative sampling of such programs to encourage you to seek similar programs in your own geographic area. High school guidance counselors are often aware of local programs as well, and they can usually tell you how to get in touch with the sponsoring or administering organizations. Local newspapers are also rich sources of information on financial aid programs.

Allow Enough Time for the Application Process

The amount of time needed to complete the application process for individual awards will vary, so you should pay close attention to application deadlines. Some awards carry application deadlines that require you to apply a year or more before your studies will begin. In general, allow plenty of time to:

- Write for official applications. You may not be considered for some awards unless you apply with the correct forms.

- Read all instructions carefully.

- Take note of application deadlines.

- Accurately and completely file all required supporting material, such as essays, school transcripts, and financial records. If you fail to answer certain questions, you may be disqualified even if you are a worthy candidate.

- Give references enough time to submit their recommendations. Teachers in particular get many requests for letters of recommendation and should be given as much advance notice as possible.

Make Sure You Qualify

Finally, don't needlessly submerge yourself in paperwork. If you find you don't qualify for a particular award, don't apply for it. Instead, use your time and energy to find and apply for more likely sources of aid.

Available in Electronic Format

Scholarships, Fellowships and Loans is also available online as part of Gale Directory Library and Gale eBooks. For more information, call 1-800-877-GALE.

Comments and Suggestions Welcome

We welcome reader suggestions regarding new and previously unlisted organizations and awards. Please send your suggestions to:

Scholarships, Fellowships and Loans

Gale, a Cengage Company

27500 Drake Rd.

Farmington Hills, MI 48331-3535

Phone: (248) 699-4253

Toll-free: 800-347-4253

Fax: (248) 699-8070

Email: Anthony.Boussie@cengage.com

Scholarships, Fellowships and Loans is comprised of a main section containing descriptive listings on award programs and their administering organizations, and five indexes that aid users in identifying relevant information. Each of these sections is described in detail below.

Sponsors and Their Scholarships

SFL contains two types of descriptive listings:

- brief entries on the organizations that sponsor or administer specific award programs

- descriptive entries on the award programs themselves

Entries are arranged alphabetically by administering organization; awards administered by each organization follow that organization's listings. Entries contain detailed contact and descriptive information. Users are strongly encouraged to read the descriptions carefully and pay particular attention to the various eligibility requirements before applying for awards.

The following sample organization and award entries illustrate the kind of information that is or might be included in these entries. Each item of information is preceded by a number, and is explained in the paragraph with the same number on the following pages.

Sample Entry

▮ 1 ▮ 3445
▮ 2 ▮ Microscopy Society of America
▮ 3 ▮ 4 Barlows Landing Rd., Ste. 8 Woods Hole, MA 02543
▮ 4 ▮ *Ph:* (508) 563-1155
▮ 5 ▮ *Fax:* (508) 563-1211
▮ 6 ▮ *Free:* 800-538-3672
▮ 7 ▮ *E-mail:* businessofficemsa.microscopy.com
▮ 8 ▮ *URL:* http://www.msa.microscopy.com
▮ 9 ▮ 3446
▮ 10 ▮ MSA Presidential Student Awards
▮ 11 ▮ *(Graduate, Undergraduate/*
▮ 12 ▮ *Award*

> ▮ 13 ▮ Purpose: To recognize outstanding original research by students. ▮ 14 ▮ Focus: Biological Clinical Sciences—Microscopy, Physical Sciences—Microscopy. ▮ 15 ▮ Qualif.: Candidate may be of any nationality, but must be enrolled at a recognized college or university in the United States at the time of the MSA annual meeting. ▮ 16 ▮ Criteria: Selection is done based on the applicant's

career objectives, academic record, and financial need. ▮ 17 ▮ Funds Avail.: Registration and round-trip travel to the MSA annual meeting, plus a stipend to defray lodging and other expenses. ▮ 18 ▮ Duration: Annual. ▮ 19 ▮ Number awarded: 5. ▮ 20 ▮ To Apply: Write to MSA for application form and guidelines. ▮ 21 ▮ Deadline: March 15. ▮ 22 ▮ Remarks: Established in 1979. ▮ 23 ▮ Contact: Alternate phone number: 800-538-EMSA.

Descriptions of Numbered Elements

▮ 1 ▮ **Organization Entry Number.** Administering organizations are listed alphabetically. Each entry is followed by an alphabetical listing of its awards. All entries (organization and award) are numbered in a single sequence. These numbers are used as references in the indexes.

▮ 2 ▮ **Organization Name.** The name of the organization administering the awards that follow.

▮ 3 ▮ **Mailing Address.** The organization's permanent mailing address is listed when known; in some cases an award address is given.

▮ 4 ▮ **Telephone Number.** The general telephone number for the administering organization. Phone numbers pertaining to specific awards are listed under "Contact" in the award description.

▮ 5 ▮ **Fax Number.** The facsimile number for the administering organization. Fax numbers pertaining to specific awards are included under "Contact" in the award description.

▮ 6 ▮ **Toll-free Number.** The toll-free number for the administering organization. Toll-free numbers pertaining to specific awards are included under "Contact" in the award description.

▮ 7 ▮ **E-mail Address.** The electronic mail address for the administering organization. Electronic mail addresses pertaining to specific awards are included under "Contact" in the award description.

▮ 8 ▮ **URL and Social Media.** The web address(es) for the administering organization.

▮ 9 ▮ **Award Entry Number.** Awards are listed alphabetically following the entry for their administering organizations. All entries (organization and award) are numbered in a single sequence. These numbers are used as references in the indexes.

▮ 10 ▮ **Award Name.** Names of awards are always listed. Organization titles or acronyms have been added to generic award names (for example, MSA Undergraduate Scholarships, Canadian Council Fiction Writing Grant, etc.) to avoid confusion.

❚11❚ Study Level. The level of study for which the award may be used. One or more of the following terms will be listed:

- All: not restricted to a particular level.
- High School: study at the secondary level.
- Vocational: study leading to postsecondary awards, certificates, or diplomas requiring less than two years of study.
- 2 Year: study leading to a bachelor's degree within two years
- 4 Year: study leading to a bachelor's degree within four years
- Undergraduate: study immediately beyond the secondary level, including associate, colleges and universities, junior colleges, technical institutes leading to a bachelor's degree, and vocational technical schools.
- Graduate: study leading to an M.A., M.S., LL.B., LL.M., and other intermediate degrees.
- Master's: study leading specifically to a master's degree, such as a M.A., M.S., or M.B.A.
- Postgraduate: study beyond the graduate level not specifically leading to a degree.
- Doctorate: study leading to a Ph.D., Ed.D., Sc.D., M.D., D.D.S., D.O., J.D., and other terminal degrees.
- Postdoctorate: study beyond the doctorate level; includes awards intended for professional development when candidates must hold a doctoral degree to qualify.
- Professional Development: career development not necessarily restricted by study.

❚12❚ Award Type. The type or category of award. One or more of the following terms will be listed:

- Award: generally includes aid given in recognition and support of excellence, including awards given through music and arts competitions. Non-monetary awards and awards given strictly for recognition are not included.
- Fellowship: awards granted for graduate- or postgraduate-level research or education that do not require repayment.
- Grant: includes support for research, travel, and creative, experimental, or innovative projects.
- Internship: training and work experience programs. Internships that do not include compensation of some type are not included.
- Loan: aid that must be repaid either monetarily or through service. Some loans are interest-free, others are not.
- Prize: funds awarded as the result of a competition or contest. Prizes that are not intended to be used for

study or to support professional development are not included.

- Scholarships: support for formal educational programs that does not require repayment.
- Scholarship Loan: a scholarship that becomes a loan if the recipient does not comply with the terms.
- Work Study: combined study and work program for which payment is received.
- Other: anything that does not fit the other categories, such as a travel award.

❚13❚ Purpose. The purpose for which the award is granted is listed here when known.

❚14❚ Focus. The field(s) of study that the recipient must be pursuing.

❚15❚ Qualif. Information regarding applicant eligibility. Some examples of qualification requirements include the following: academic record, citizenship, financial need, organizational affiliation, minority or ethnic background, residency, and gender.

❚16❚ Criteria Information concerning selection criteria.

❚17❚ Funds Avail. The award dollar amounts are included here along with other relevant funding information, such as the time period covered by the award, a breakdown of expenses covered (e.g., stipends, tuition and fees, travel and living allowances, equipment funds, etc.), the amount awarded to the institution, loan repayment schedules, service-in-return-for-funding agreements, and other obligations.

❚18❚ Duration. Frequency of the award.

❚19❚ Number awarded. Typical number of awards distributed.

❚20❚ To Apply. Application guidelines, requirements, and other information.

❚21❚ Deadline. Application due dates, notification dates (the date when the applicant will be notified of receipt or denial of award), disbursement dates, and other relevant dates.

❚22❚ Remarks. Any additional information concerning the award.

❚23❚ Contact. When contact information differs from that given for the administering organization, relevant addresses, telephone and fax numbers, and names of specific contact persons are listed here. When the address is that of the administering organization, the entry number for the organization is provided.

Indexes

Field of Study Index classifies awards by one or more of 450 specific subject categories, allowing users to easily target their search by specific area of study. Citations are arranged alphabetically under all appropriate subject terms. Each citation is followed by the study level and award type, which appear in parentheses and can be used to narrow the search even further.

Legal Residence Index lists awards that are restricted by the applicant's residence of legal record. Award citations are arranged alphabetically by country and subarranged by region, state or province (for U.S. and Canada). Each citation is followed by the study level and award type, which appear in parentheses and can be used to eliminate inappropriate awards.

Place of Study Index lists awards that carry restrictions on where study can take place. Award citations are arranged alphabetically under the following geographic headings:

- United States
- United States—by Region
- United States—by State
- Canada
- Canada—by Province
- International
- International—by Region
- International—by Country

Each citation is followed by the study level and award type, which appear in parentheses.

Special Recipient Index lists awards that carry restrictions or special qualifying factors relating to applicant affiliation. This index allows users to quickly identify awards relating to the following categories:

- African American
- Asian American
- Association Membership
- Disabled
- Employer Affiliation
- Ethnic Group Membership
- Fraternal Organization Membership
- Hispanic American
- Military
- Minority
- Native American
- Religious Affiliation
- Union Affiliation
- Veteran

Awards are listed under all appropriate headings. Each citation includes information on study level and award type, which appear in parentheses and can be used to further narrow the search. Users interested in awards restricted to particular minorities should also look under the general Minorities heading, which lists awards targeted for minorities but not restricted to any particular minority group.

Sponsor and Scholarship Index lists, in a single alphabetic sequence, all of the administering organizations, awards, and acronyms included in *SFL*.

Federal aid for college students is available through a variety of programs administered by the U.S. Department of Education. Most colleges and universities participate in federal programs, but there are exceptions. Contact a school's financial aid office to find out if it is a participating institution. If it participates, the student works with financial aid counselors to determine how much aid can be obtained.

Aid for students comes in three forms: grants (gifts to the student), loans (which must be repaid), and work-study jobs (a job for the student while enrolled in which his/her pay is applied to his school account). These types of aid are further explained below. More information can be found at https://www.ed.gov.

Grants

Pell Grants are intended to provide funds for any undergraduate student (who does not already have a degree) who wishes to attend college regardless of family financial background. They are available through the financial aid office at the school. The maximum Pell Grant award for the 2020-2021 award year (July 1, 2020 to June 30, 2021) is $6,345.

Federal Supplemental Educational Opportunity Grants (FSEOG) are intended for students with exceptional financial need, these grants are typically for smaller amounts (between $100 and $4,000) than Pell Grants. They are available on a limited basis.

Loans

Student loans are available a variety of ways. Loans may not be taken out for more than the cost of attendance at the school, which is determined by the financial aid administrator. Grants and other forms of aid are taken into consideration when determining the amount a student will be allowed to borrow. Loan amounts may be reduced if a student receives other forms of aid. Loans are divided into two types, subsidized and unsubsidized:

Subsidized loans: the federal government pays the interest on the loan until after schooling is complete.

Unsubsidized loans: the student incurs the interest charges while in school, but payment of the charges may be deferred until schooling is complete. The advantage of unsubsidized loans is that there are usually fewer restrictions against obtaining them. Amounts available through these programs vary depending on academic level. The total debt a student or a student's parents may accumulate for that student is $31,000 for a dependent undergraduate student, $57,500 for an independent undergraduate student (with a limit of $23,000 in subsidized loans), and $138,500 for a graduate or professional student (with a limit of $65,500 in subsidized loans) or $224,000 for health professionals.

Available Funding Programs Direct Loan Program

These low-interest loans bypass lending institutions such as banks. They are a direct arrangement between the government and the student (administered by the school). There are four repayment options for the Direct Loan program: the Income Contingent Repayment Plan, the Extended Repayment Plan, the Graduated Repayment Plan, and the Standard Repayment Plan.

Direct subsidized loans may be taken out for a maximum of $3,500 by incoming freshmen, $4,500 for sophomores, and $5,500 for juniors and seniors. The amounts for independent undergraduate students range from $9,500 to $12,500 per year for direct loans. Independent students face some restrictions on the amount of subsidized funds they can receive from the program. At least half of the funds borrowed through the Direct Loan program by independent students must come from unsubsidized loans. Graduate students may borrow up to $20,500 directly in unsubsidized loans.

Direct PLUS Loans Direct PLUS loans are federal loans that graduate or professional degree students and parents of dependent undergraduate students can use to help pay education expenses. The U.S. Department of Education makes Direct PLUS loans to eligible borrowers through schools participating in the program. The Maximum amount to be borrowed is the cost of attending the shool minus other forms of aid already obtained. For 2020-2021 the fixed rate for a Direct PLUS loan is 5.30%.

With the Direct PLUS loan, students or parents fill out a Direct PLUS Loan Application, available at the school's financial aid office. The funds are disbursed to the school. Students and parents may choose from three repayment plans: Standard, Extended, or Graduated.

Perkins Loan Program Under federal law, the authorty for schools to make new Perkins Loans ended on Sept. 30, 2017, and final disbursements were permitted through June 30, 2018. As a result, students can no longer receive Perkins Loans. A borrower who received a Perkins Loan can learn more about managing the repayment of the loan by contacting either the school that made the loan or the school's loan servicer.

Federal Work-Study Program Work-study is an arrangement that allows students to work on campus while they are enrolled to help pay their expenses. The federal government pays the majority of the student's wages, although the department where the student works also contributes. The employment must be relevant to the student's field of study and only so much time per semester may be devoted to the job. If the student earns the amount of aid prior to the end of the semester, work is terminated for the duration of the award period.

Other Considerations

Application: Applying for federal student aid is free. All federal aid is obtained by first completing a Free Application for Federal Student Aid (FAFSA). After the application is submitted, it will be processed by the Department of Education. The student then receives a Student Aid Report (SAR), which contains a figure for Expected Family Contribution. This is the amount that the student should plan on providing from non-federal sources in order to attend school.

Dependency: If a student is eligible for independent status, more money may be available in the form of loans. The interest rates and the programs for repayment, however, are the same. Independent status provides more financial aid for students who do not have the benefit of parental financial contributions.

Deadline: FAFSA deadlines are set by federal and state agencies, as well as individual schools, and vary widely. Applicants are encouraged to apply as soon as possible after January 1 of the year they plan to enroll, but no earlier.

Special Circumstances: The financial aid counselor at the school will often listen to extenuating circumstances such as unexpected medical expenses, private education expenses for other family members, or recent unemployment when evaluating requests for assistance.

Contact Information for Federal Financial Aid Programs

Call (800)433-3243 to have questions answered; (319) 337-5665 to find out if your application has been processed; (800) 730-8913 (TTY) if you are hearing impaired; (800) 647-8733 to report fraud, waste, or abuse of federal student aid funds; or visit https://www.ed.gov for application forms, guidelines, and general information.

President Clinton launched this volunteer community service program in September 1993 through the *National and Community Service Trust Act*, aimed at helping college-bound young people pay for their education while serving their communities. AmeriCorps volunteers receive minimum wage, health benefits, and a grant toward college for up to two years.

Funds for the program are distributed by the federal government in the form of grants to qualifying organizations and community groups with the goal of achieving direct results in addressing the nation's critical education, human services, public safety, and environmental needs at the community level. The program provides meaningful opportunities for Americans to serve their country in organized efforts, fostering citizen responsibility, building community, and providing educational opportunities for those who make a substantial commitment to service.

The AmeriCorps programs are run by not-for-profit organizations or partnerships, institutions of higher learning, local governments, school or police districts, states, Native American tribes, and federal agencies. Examples of participating programs include Habitat for Humanity, the American Red Cross, Boys and Girls Clubs, and local community centers and places of worship. Volunteers have nearly 1,000 different groups from which to choose. The AmeriCorps Pledge: "I will get things done for America to make our people safer, smarter, and healthier. I will bring Americans together to strengthen our communities. Faced with apathy, I will take action. Faced with conflict, I will seek a common ground. Faced with adversity, I will persevere. I will carry this commitment with me this year and beyond. I am an AmeriCorps Member and I am going to get things done."

Eligibility and Selection for Service in AmeriCorps

Citizens and legal resident aliens who are 17 years of age or older are eligible to serve in AmeriCorps before, during, or after post-secondary education. In general, participants must be high school graduates or agree to achieve their GED prior to receiving education awards. Individual programs select service participants on a nondiscriminatory and nonpolitical basis. There are national and state-wide recruiting information systems and a national pool of potential service volunteers.

Term of Service

One full-time term of service is a minimum of 1,700 hours over the course of one year or less; or a part-time term, which can range from 300 hours to 900 hours. Short-term service (such as a summer program) provides eligibility for reduced part-time status.

Compensation

You will receive a modest living allowance, health insurance, student loan deferment, and training. After you complete your term of service, you will receive an education award to help pay for your education. Serve part-time and you will receive a portion of the full amount. The amount is tied to the maximum amount of the U.S. Department of Education's Pell Grant. Since the amount of a Pell Grant can change from year to year, the amount of an education award can vary from year to year. Currently, AmeriCorps members may earn up to the value of two full-time education awards and have seven years from the date they earned each award to use it. For fiscal 2021, which began October 1, 2020, the award is $6,345 for a year of full-time service, and is pro rated for part-time service.

How Can I Use an Award?

These awards may be used to repay qualified existing or future student loans, to pay all or part of the cost of attending a qualified institute of higher education (including some vocational programs), or to pay expenses while participating in an approved school-to-work program. Awards must be used within seven years of completion of service.

Contact

Individuals interested in participating in AmeriCorps national service programs should apply directly. For basic program information, individuals can call the AmeriCorps Information Hotline at 1-800-942-2677 or visit their Web site at https://www.nationalservice.gov/programs/americorps.

The following is an alphabetic state-by-state listing of agencies located in the United States. Many of these agencies administer special federal award programs, as well as state-specific awards, such as the Tuition Incentive Program (TIP) offered by the state of Michigan for low-income students to receive free tuition at community colleges. Financial aid seekers should contact the agency in their home state for more information.

ALABAMA

Alabama Comm. on Higher Education
100 N. Union St.
P.O. Box 302000
Montgomery, AL 36104
(334)242-1998
https://ache.edu

ALASKA

Alaska Comm. on Postsecondary Education
P.O. Box 110505
Juneau, AK 99811-0505
(907)465-2962
https://acpesecure.alaska.gov

ARIZONA

Arizona Comm. for Postsecondary Education
2020 N. Central Ave.,
Ste. 650
Phoenix, AZ 85004-4503
(602)542-7230
https://highered.az.gov

ARKANSAS

Arkansas Div. of Higher Education
423 Main St., Ste. 400
Little Rock, AR 72201
(501)371-2000
https://www.adhe.edu

CALIFORNIA

California Student Aid Comm.
PO Box 419027
Rancho Cordova, CA 95741-9027
(888)224-7268
https://www.csac.ca.gov

COLORADO

Colorado Dept. of Higher Education
1600 Broadway, Ste. 2200
Denver, CO 80202
(303)862-3001
https://highered.colorado.gov

CONNECTICUT

Connecticut Office of Higher Education
450 Columbus Blvd. Ste. 707
Hartford, CT 06103-1841
(860)947-1800
www.ctohe.org

DELAWARE

Delaware Dept. of Higher Education Scholarship Incentive Program
The Townsend Building
401 Federal St., Ste. 2
Dover, DE 19901-3639
(302)735-4000
https://www.doe.k12.de.us/Page/316

DISTRICT OF COLUMBIA

District of Columbia Office of the State Superintendent of Education
1050 First Street, NE
Washington, DC 20002
(202)727-6436
https://osse.dc.gov

FLORIDA

Office of Student Financial Assistance
Dept. of Education
325 W. Gaines St.

Turlington Bldg., Ste. 1514
Tallahassee, FL 32399-0400
(800)366-3475
www.floridastudentfinancialaid.org

GEORGIA

Georgia Student Finance Comm.
2082 E. Exchange Pl.
Tucker, GA 30084
(800)505-4732
https://gsfc.georgia.gov

HAWAII

Hawaii Board of Regents
2444 Dole St.,
Bachman Hall, Rm. 209
Honolulu, HI 96822
(808)956-8213
www.hawaii.edu/offices/bor/

IDAHO

Idaho State Board of Education
PO Box 83720
Boise, ID 83720-0037
(208)334-2270
https://www.boardofed.idaho.gov

ILLINOIS

Illinois Student Assistance Comm.
1755 Lake Cook Rd.
Deerfield, IL 60015-5209
(800)899-4722
https://www.isac.org

INDIANA

Indiana Comm. for Higher Education
101 W. Ohio St., Ste. 300
Indianapolis, IN 46204-4206

(888)528-4719
https://www.in.gov/che

IOWA

Iowa College Student Aid Comm.
475 SW Fifth St., Ste. D
Des Moines, IA 50309
(877)272-4456
https://www.iowacollegeaid.gov

KANSAS

Kansas Board of Regents
1000 SW Jackson St., Ste. 520
Topeka, KS 66612-1368
(785)430-4240
https://www.kansasregents.org

KENTUCKY

Kentucky Higher Education Assistance Authority
P.O. Box 798
Frankfort, KY 40602-0798
(800)928-8926
https://www.kheaa.com/website/
kheaa/home

LOUISIANA

Louisiana Office of Student Financial Assistance
602 N. Fifth St.
Baton Rouge, LA 70802
(225)219-1012
https://mylosfa.la.gov

MAINE

Finance Authority of Maine (FAME)
5 Community Dr.
P.O. Box 949
Augusta, ME 04332-0949
(207)623-3263
https://www.famemaine.com

MARYLAND

Maryland Higher Education Comm.
6 N. Liberty St.
Baltimore, MD 21201
(410)767-3300
https://mhec.state.md.us/Pages/
default.aspx

MASSACHUSETTS

Massachusetts Dept. of Higher Education
One Ashburton Pl., Rm. 1401
Boston, MA 02108-1696

(617)994-6950
https://www.mass.edu/home.asp

MICHIGAN

MI Student Aid
Student Scholarships and Grants
P.O. Box 30462
Lansing, MI 48909-7962
(888)447-2687
https://www.michigan.gov/
mistudentaid

MINNESOTA

Minnesota Office of Higher Education
1450 Energy Park Dr., Ste. 350
St. Paul, MN 55108-5227
(651)642-0567
www.ohe.state.mn.us/index.cfm

MISSISSIPPI

Mississippi Institutions of Higher Learning
3825 Ridgewood Rd.
Jackson, MS 39211
(601)432-6198
www.ihl.state.ms.us

MISSOURI

Missouri Dept. of Higher Education
301 W. High St.
Jefferson City, MO 65101
(573)751-2361
https://dhewd.mo.gov/

MONTANA

Montana Board of Regents
Office of Commissioner of Higher Education
Montana University System
560 N. Park, 4th Fl.
PO Box 203201
Helena, MT 59620-3201
(406)449-9124
https://www.mus.edu

NEBRASKA

Nebraska Coordinating Comm. for Postsecondary Education
P.O. Box 95005
Lincoln, NE 68509-5005
(402)471-2847
https://ccpe.nebraska.gov

NEVADA

Nevada Department of Education
700 E. Fifth St.
Carson City, NV 89701
(775)687-9115
www.doe.nv.gov

Las Vegas Office
2080 E. Flamingo Rd., Ste. 210
Las Vegas, NV 89119
(702)486-6458

NEW HAMPSHIRE

New Hampshire Dept. of Education
101 Pleasant St.
Concord, NH 03301-3494
(603)271-3494
https://www.education.nh.gov/

NEW JERSEY

Higher Education Student Assistance Authority
P.O. Box 545
Trenton, NJ 08625-0545
(800)792-8670
https://www.hesaa.org/Pages/
Default.aspx

NEW MEXICO

New Mexico Higher Education Dept.
2044 Galisteo St., Ste. 4
Santa Fe, NM 87505-2100
(505)476-8400
https://hed.state.nm.us

NEW YORK

New York State Higher Education Svcs. Corp.
99 Washington Ave.
Albany, NY 12255
(888)697-4372
https://www.hesc.ny.gov

NORTH CAROLINA

North Carolina State Education Assistance Authority
PO Box 14103
Research Triangle Park, NC 27709

(919)549-8614
www.ncseaa.edu

NORTH DAKOTA

North Dakota University System
10th Fl., State Capitol
600 E. Boulevard Ave., Dept. 215
Bismarck, ND 58505-0230
(701)328-2960
https://www.ndus.edu

OHIO

Ohio Department of Higher Education
25 S. Front St.
Columbus, OH 43215
(614)466-6000
https://www.ohiohighered.org

OKLAHOMA

Oklahoma State Regents for Higher Education
655 Research Pkwy.
Suite 200
Oklahoma City, OK 73104
(405)225-9100
https://www.okhighered.org

OREGON

Oregon Student Access Comm.
1500 Valley River Dr., Ste. 100
Eugene, OR 97401
(541)687-7400
https://oregonstudentaid.gov

PENNSYLVANIA

Pennsylvania Higher Education Assistance Agency
1200 N. 7th St.
Harrisburg, PA 17102-1444
(800)692-7392
https://www.pheaa.org

RHODE ISLAND

Rhode Island Office of the Postsecondary Commissioner
560 Jefferson Blvd., Ste. 100
Warwick, RI 02886-1304

(401)736-1100
https://www.riopc.edu

SOUTH CAROLINA

South Carolina Comm. on Higher Education
1122 Lady St., Ste. 300
Columbia, SC 29201
(803)737-2260
https://www.che.sc.gov/

SOUTH DAKOTA

South Dakota Board of Regents
306 E. Capitol Ave., Ste. 200
Pierre, SD 57501
(605)773-3455
https://www.sdbor.edu/Pages/default.aspx

TENNESSEE

Tennessee Higher Education Comm.
312 Rosa Parks Ave., 9th Floor
Nashville, TN 37243
(615)741-3605
https://www.tn.gov/thec.html

TEXAS

Texas Higher Education Coordinating Board
1200 E. Anderson Ln.
Austin, TX 78752
(512)427-6101
https://www.highered.texas.gov

UTAH

Utah System of Higher Education
Two Gateway
60 South 400 West
Salt Lake City, UT 84101-1284
(800)418-8757
https://ushe.edu

VERMONT

Vermont Student Assistance Corp.
10 E. Allen St.
P.O. Box 2000

Winooski, VT 05404
(800)642--3177
https://www.vsac.org/

VIRGINIA

State Council of Higher Education for Virginia
James Monroe Bldg.
101 N. 14th St., 10th Fl.
Richmond, VA 23219
(804)225-2600
https://www.schev.edu

WASHINGTON

Washington Student Achievement Council
917 Lakeridge Way SW
Olympia, WA 98502
(360)753-7800
https://wsac.wa.gov

WEST VIRGINIA

West Virginia Higher Education Policy Comm.
1018 Kanawha Blvd., E., Ste. 700
Charleston, WV 25301
(304)558-2101
www.wvhepc.edu

WISCONSIN

Wisconsin Higher Education Aids Board
P.O. Box 7885
Madison, WI 53707-7885
(608)267-2206
heab.state.wi.us

WYOMING

Wyoming Community College Comm.
2300 Capitol Ave., 5th Fl., Ste. B
Cheyenne, WY 82002
(307)777-7763
https://communitycolleges.wy.edu

U.S. State Abbreviations

AK	Alaska
AL	Alabama
AR	Arkansas
AZ	Arizona
CA	California
CO	Colorado
CT	Connecticut
DC	District of Columbia
DE	Delaware
FL	Florida
GA	Georgia
GU	Guam
HI	Hawaii
IA	Iowa
ID	Idaho
IL	Illinois
IN	Indiana
KS	Kansas
KY	Kentucky
LA	Louisiana
MA	Massachusetts
MD	Maryland
ME	Maine
MI	Michigan
MN	Minnesota
MO	Missouri
MS	Mississippi
MT	Montana
NC	North Carolina
ND	North Dakota
NE	Nebraska
NH	New Hampshire
NJ	New Jersey
NM	New Mexico
NV	Nevada
NY	New York
OH	Ohio
OK	Oklahoma
OR	Oregon
PA	Pennsylvania
PR	Puerto Rico
RI	Rhode Island
SC	South Carolina
SD	South Dakota
TN	Tennessee
TX	Texas
UT	Utah
VA	Virginia
VI	Virgin Islands
VT	Vermont
WA	Washington
WI	Wisconsin
WV	West Virginia
WY	Wyoming

Canadian Province Abbreviations

AB	Alberta
BC	British Columbia
MB	Manitoba
NB	New Brunswick
NL	Newfoundland and Labrador
NS	Nova Scotia
NT	Northwest Territories
ON	Ontario
PE	Prince Edward Island
QC	Quebec
SK	Saskatchewan
YT	Yukon Territory

Other Abbreviations

ACT	American College Testing Program
B.A.	Bachelor of Arts
B.Arch.	Bachelor of Architecture
B.F.A.	Bachelor of Fine Arts
B.S.	Bachelor of Science
B.Sc.	Bachelor of Science
CSS	College Scholarship Service
D.D.S.	Doctor of Dental Science/Surgery
D.O.	Doctor of Osteopathy
D.Sc.	Doctor of Science
D.S.W.	Doctor of Social Work
D.V.M.	Doctor of Veterinary Medicine
D.V.M.S.	Doctor of Veterinary Medicine and Surgery
D.V.S.	Doctor of Veterinary Science
FAFSA	Free Application for Federal Student Aid
FWS	Federal Work Study
GED	General Education Development Certificate
GPA	Grade Point Average
GRE	Graduate Record Examination
J.D.	Doctor of Jurisprudence
LL.B.	Bachelor of Law
LL.M.	Master of Law
LSAT	Law School Admission Test
M.A.	Master of Arts
M.Arch.	Master of Architecture
M.B.A.	Master of Business Administration
M.D.	Doctor of Medicine
M.Div.	Master of Divinity
M.F.A.	Master of Fine Arts
MIA	Missing in Action
M.L.S.	Master of Library Science
M.N.	Master of Nursing
M.S.	Master of Science
M.S.W.	Master of Social Work
O.D.	Doctor of Optometry
Pharm.D.	Doctor of Pharmacy
Ph.D.	Doctor of Philosophy
POW	Prisoner of War
PSAT	Preliminary Scholastic Aptitude Test
ROTC	Reserve Officers Training Corps
SAR	Student Aid Report
SAT	Scholastic Aptitude Test
Sc.D.	Doctor of Science
TDD	Telephone Device for the Deaf
Th.d.	Doctor of Theology
U.N.	United Nations
U.S.	United States

11161 ■ UAF Community and Technical College (UAF CTC)

604 Barnette St.
Fairbanks, AK 99701
Ph: (907)455-2800
Free: 877-882-8827
URL: www.ctc.uaf.edu
Social Media: www.facebook.com/uafctc
instagram.com/uafctc
twitter.com/UAFCTC
youtube.com/user/UAFCTC

11162 ■ CTC Culinary Arts Scholarship Endowment
(Undergraduate, Vocational/Occupational/Scholarship)

Purpose: To provide support for deserving students intending to pursue their study in culinary arts. **Focus:** Culinary arts. **Qualif.:** Applicants must be students enrolled in the Culinary Arts Program at the Community and Technical College, University of Alaska Fairbanks.

Funds Avail.: $500. **Duration:** Annual. **To Apply:** Application details are available at: uaf.edu/finaid/scholarships.php. **Contact:** Email: uaf-financialaid@alaska.edu.

11163 ■ William C. Leary Memorial Emergency Services Scholarship *(Undergraduate, Vocational/ Occupational/Scholarship)*

Purpose: To encourage students to pursue their career in emergency service program. **Focus:** Emergency and disaster services. **Qualif.:** Applicants must be students majoring in Emergency Services enrolled at the University of Alaska Fairbanks. **Criteria:** Selection of applicants will be based on demonstrated motivation, and academic and leadership potential

Funds Avail.: $500. **Duration:** Annual. **To Apply:** Application details are available at: uaf.edu/finaid/scholarships.php. **Deadline:** February 15. **Contact:** Email: uaf-financialaid@alaska.edu.

11164 ■ Udall Foundation

130 South Scott Avenue
Tucson, AZ 85701-1922
Ph: (520)901-8500
Fax: (520)670-5530
URL: www.udall.gov
Social Media: www.facebook.com/udallfoundation
www.instagram.com/udallfoundation
twitter.com/udallfoundation

11165 ■ Udall Undergraduate Scholarship
(Undergraduate/Scholarship)

Purpose: To provide students the innovative ideas, professional advice, job and internship opportunities that will help them grow educationally. **Focus:** Environmental technology; Native American studies.

Funds Avail.: Up to $7,000 each. **Duration:** Annual. **To Apply:** Applicants must complete and sign Udall Scholarship Application and submit along with an 800-word essay (signed and dated), a current official college transcript and transcripts for other colleges attended, and three letters of recommendation; Additional documentation is required for applicants in tribal public policy and health care, and for U.S. permanent residents. **Deadline:** March 5. **Remarks:** Established in 1992.

11166 ■ The Ulman Cancer Fund for Young Adults

921 E Fort Ave., Ste. 325
Baltimore, MD 21230
Ph: (410)964-0202
Free: 888-393-FUND
E-mail: info@ulmanfund.org
URL: ulmanfund.org
Social Media: www.facebook.com/ulmancancerfund
www.linkedin.com/company/the-ulman-cancer-fund-for
-young-adults
twitter.com/ulmancancerfnd

11167 ■ Body of Young Adult Advisors Scholarship (BOYAA) *(Graduate, Master's, Doctorate/Scholarship)*

Purpose: To recognize Baltimore, MD, or Washington, DC, area residents who have battled cancer or selflessly supported a parent or sibling through their cancer experience. **Focus:** Health sciences; Medicine. **Criteria:** Selection will be based on the committee's criteria.

Funds Avail.: $2,500. **Duration:** Annual. **Number Awarded:** 1. **To Apply:** Applicants must submit a complete online application form together with letter of recommendation, an essay and physician verification form or death certificate as applicable. **Deadline:** March 1.

11168 ■ Marilyn Yetso Memorial Scholarship *(Graduate, Master's, Doctorate/Scholarship)*

Purpose: To support the financial needs of college students who have lost a parent to cancer or have a parent with cancer. **Focus:** Health sciences; Medicine. **Qualif.:** Ap-

Awards are arranged alphabetically below their administering organizations

plicants must be support the financial needs of a college student who has lost a parent to cancer or has a parent with cancer and who displays financial need. **Criteria:** Selection will be based on the committee's criteria.

Funds Avail.: $2,500. **Duration:** Annual. **To Apply:** Applicants must submit a complete online application form together with letter of recommendation, an essay. **Deadline:** November 2.

11169 ■ Olivia M. Marquart Scholarships *(Graduate, Master's, Doctorate/Scholarship)*

Purpose: To support young adults who are either cancer survivors or currently undergoing treatment. **Focus:** Health sciences; Medicine.

Funds Avail.: $2,500. **Duration:** Annual. **To Apply:** Applicants must submit a complete online application form together with letter of recommendation, an essay and physician verification form or death certificate as applicable. **Deadline:** February 11.

11170 ■ Ultrasound Schools Info

PO Box 3026
Bellingham, WA 98225
Ph: (360)389-3203
E-mail: info@UltrasoundSchoolsInfo.com
URL: www.ultrasoundschoolsinfo.com
Social Media: www.facebook.com/
  MedicalImagingEducation
www.instagram.com/sonographyedu
www.linkedin.com/company/ultrasound-schools-info
twitter.com/SonographyEdu

11171 ■ Ultrsound Schools Info Student Scholarship *(Two Year College, Undergraduate/Scholarship)*

Purpose: To support students interested in pursuing degrees as diagnostic medical sonographers. **Focus:** Radiology. **Qualif.:** Must be at least 18 years old, a U.S. citizen or hold a student visa, be a current or intended student in a sonography program that has been accredited by the Commission on Accreditation of Allied Health Education Programs (CAAHEP). **Criteria:** Selection will be based on the essay which will be judged on originality, content, accuracy, and inspirational value.

Funds Avail.: $1,000 each. **Duration:** Annual. **Number Awarded:** 2 per year. **To Apply:** Completed application and essay must be submitted via mail. **Deadline:** March 15; October 15. **Contact:** Phone: 360-389-3203; Email: Scholarship@ultrasoundschoolsinfo.com; URL: www.ultrasoundschoolsinfo.com/sonography-student-scholarship/.

11172 ■ UNC Hussman School of Journalism and Media

PO Box 3365
Chapel Hill, NC 27514
Ph: (919)962-1204
Fax: (919)962-0620
URL: hussman.unc.edu
Social Media: www.facebook.com/pg/unchussman
www.instagram.com/unchussman
www.linkedin.com/school/unc-hussman-school-of
  -journalism-and-media
twitter.com/unchussman

11173 ■ Floyd S. Alford Jr. Scholarships *(Undergraduate/Scholarship)*

Purpose: To educate journalists; to recognize students who demonstrate outstanding journalistic talent and a strong commitment to improve the community through honest and accurate work. **Focus:** Journalism. **Qualif.:** Applicants must be students who have pre-declared or are enrolled in the School of Media and Journalism. **Criteria:** Recipients will be selected based on their academic interests, geographic location, financial need and programs of study.

To Apply: Applicants must submit a completed general application form, available at the website. **Contact:** mjschoolscholarships@unc.edu.

11174 ■ Ameel J. Fisher Scholarship *(Undergraduate/Scholarship)*

Purpose: To support an undergraduate student in the School of Media and Journalism. **Focus:** Communications; Journalism. **Qualif.:** Applicant must be undergraduate student in the UNC School of Media and Journalism. **Criteria:** Selection will be based on academic performance and overall excellence.

Funds Avail.: $5,000. **Duration:** Annual. **Number Awarded:** 3. **To Apply:** Applicants must submit a completed general application form, available on the website. **Deadline:** February 1. **Contact:** Email: mjschoolscholarships@unc.edu.

11175 ■ Ardis Kipp Cohoon Scholarship *(Undergraduate/Scholarship)*

Purpose: To support and encourage a student in the School of Media and Journalism. **Focus:** Communications; Journalism. **Qualif.:** Applicant must be student in the School of Media and Journalism. **Criteria:** Recipients will be selected based on their academic interests, geographic location, financial need and programs of study.

Duration: Annual. **To Apply:** Applicants must submit a completed general application form, available at the website. **Contact:** Email: mjschoolscholarships@unc.edu.

11176 ■ AT&T Business Internship Awards *(Undergraduate, Graduate/Internship)*

Purpose: To provide financial assistance to undergraduate or graduate students interested in business journalism. **Focus:** Journalism. **Qualif.:** Applicants must be an undergraduate major interested in business journalism; must have arranged a business journalism internship. **Criteria:** Preference given to students from the AT&T service area: California, Nevada, Kansas, Oklahoma, Texas, Missouri, Arkansas, Louisiana, Wisconsin, Michigan, Illinois, Indiana, Ohio, Connecticut, North Carolina, South Carolina, Georgia, Alabama, Florida, Kentucky and Tennessee.

Funds Avail.: $1,000. **Duration:** Annual. **To Apply:** Applications can be submitted through online. **Deadline:** November 1. **Contact:** Professor Chris Roush, Phone: 919-962-409; Email: croush@email.unc.edu; Return applications to Roush in Carroll 211.

11177 ■ Jim Batten Community Newspaper Internship *(Undergraduate/Internship)*

Purpose: To fund living expenses of MJ-school undergraduate majors during a summer internship at a community newspaper. **Focus:** Communications; Journalism. **Qualif.:** Applicants must be UNC MJ-school undergraduate majors. **Criteria:** Recipients will be selected based on the

Awards are arranged alphabetically below their administering organizations

academic interests, geographic location, financial need and programs of study.

Funds Avail.: $3,000. **Duration:** Annual. **Number Awarded:** 2. **To Apply:** Applicants must submit a completed general application form, available at the website. **Remarks:** The Internship was created to honor the memory of James Allen Batten, editor of several N.C. newspapers and the owner of Emerald Isle Realty, one of the largest real estate agencies in the state. **Contact:** Email: uncmjawards@unc.edu.

11178 ▪ Bob Quincy Scholarship *(Undergraduate/ Scholarship)*

Purpose: To support and encourage a student in the School of Media and Journalism. **Focus:** Communications; Journalism. **Qualif.:** Applicant must be student in the School of Media and Journalism. **Criteria:** Recipients will be selected based on academic interests, geographic location, financial need and programs of study.

Funds Avail.: No specific amount. **Duration:** Annual. **To Apply:** Applicants must submit a completed general application form, available on the website. **Contact:** Email: mjschoolscholarships@unc.edu.

11179 ▪ Charles McCorkle Hauser Scholarship *(Undergraduate/Scholarship)*

Purpose: To support and encourage a student in the School of Media and Journalism. **Focus:** Communications; Journalism.

Duration: Annual.

11180 ▪ David Julian Whichard Scholarship *(Undergraduate/Scholarship)*

Purpose: To recognize outstanding juniors or seniors of the school who are from North Carolina and planning to start a career in newspaper journalism. **Focus:** Communications; Journalism. **Qualif.:** Applicants must be outstanding juniors or seniors in the school; must be from North Carolina and plan careers in newspaper journalism. **Criteria:** Preference is given to N.C. residents in the reporting specialization.

Funds Avail.: No specific amount. **Duration:** Annual. **To Apply:** Applicants must submit a completed general application form, available at the website. **Contact:** Email: mjschoolscholarships@unc.edu.

11181 ▪ Don and Barbara Curtis Excellence Fund for Extracurricular Activities *(Undergraduate/ Scholarship)*

Purpose: To support undergraduate majors in the School of Media and Journalism who participate in meaningful out-of-class activities that will help them in their careers. **Focus:** Communications. **Qualif.:** Applicants must be undergraduate majors in the School of Media and Journalism; must participate in meaningful out-of-class activities. **Criteria:** Recipients are selected based on the academic performance, financial need, and potential for journalism-mass communication careers.

Funds Avail.: $1,000. **Duration:** Annual. **To Apply:** Applicants must visit the website to complete the online application process. **Deadline:** Last day of each month; August through March. **Contact:** Louise Spieler, Senior Associate Dean for Strategy and Administration, Phone: 919-843-8137 (Carroll 119); Email: lspieler@unc.edu.

11182 ▪ Don S. Maurer Advertising Scholarship *(Undergraduate/Scholarship)*

Purpose: To provide outstanding student in the school who is interested in a career in advertising. **Focus:** Advertising.

Qualif.: Applicant must be an outstanding student in School of Media and Journalism; must have an interest in a career in advertising. **Criteria:** Special Considerations will be given to a rising junior in the advertising program.

Funds Avail.: No specific amount. **Duration:** Annual. **Number Awarded:** 1. **To Apply:** Applicants must submit a completed general application form, available on the website. **Contact:** Email: mjschoolscholarships@unc.edu.

11183 ▪ Edward Heywood Megson Scholarship *(Undergraduate/Scholarship)*

Purpose: To support and encourage a student in the School of Media and Journalism. **Focus:** Communications; Journalism. **Qualif.:** Applicant must be student in the School of Media and Journalism. **Criteria:** Recipients will be selected based on their academic interests, geographic location, financial need and programs of study.

Funds Avail.: No specific amount. **Duration:** Annual. **Number Awarded:** 1. **To Apply:** Applicants must submit a completed general application form, available at the website. **Deadline:** February 1. **Contact:** Email: mjschoolscholarships@unc.edu.

11184 ▪ Edward Jackson International Travel Award *(Undergraduate/Award)*

Purpose: To support students of MJ-school undegraduate journalism major from North Carolina. **Focus:** Communications; Journalism. **Qualif.:** Applicants must be current UNC students who have pre-declared or are enrolled in the school of media and journalism; must be a resident of North Carolina. **Criteria:** Selection will be based on their academic interests, geographic location, financial need and programs of study.

Funds Avail.: No specific amount. **Duration:** Annual. **Number Awarded:** 1. **To Apply:** Applicants must submit a completed special application form, available at the website. **Deadline:** February 1. **Contact:** Email: mjschoolscholarships@unc.edu.

11185 ▪ Elton Casey Scholarship *(Undergraduate/ Scholarship)*

Purpose: To support a student in the school who is interested in a career as a sports reporter. **Focus:** Communications. **Qualif.:** Applicant must be student in the School of Media and Journalism; must be interested in pursuing a career in sports journalism. **Criteria:** Preference will be given to students from Durham or Orange counties (North Carolina).

Funds Avail.: No specific amount. **Duration:** Annual. **To Apply:** Applicants must submit a completed general application form, available on the website. **Contact:** Email: mjschoolscholarships@unc.edu.

11186 ▪ Erwin Potts Scholarship *(Undergraduate/ Scholarship)*

Purpose: To provide educational assistance to current MJ-school students. **Focus:** Communications; Journalism. **Qualif.:** Applicant must be student in the School of Media and Journalism. **Criteria:** Preference is given to a student studying newspaper journalism.

Duration: Annual. **To Apply:** Applicants must submit a completed general application form, available on the website. **Contact:** Email: mjschoolscholarships@unc.edu.

11187 ▪ Reese Felts Scholarships *(Undergraduate/ Scholarship)*

Purpose: To support a student in the School of Media and Journalism who is in the broadcast and electronic journal-

Awards are arranged alphabetically below their administering organizations

ism specialization. **Focus:** Communications; Journalism. **Qualif.:** Applicant must be student in the UNC School of Media and Journalism; must be in the broadcast and electronic journalism specialization. **Criteria:** Selection will be based on their academic interests, geographic location, financial need and programs of study.

Funds Avail.: No specific amount. **Duration:** Annual. **To Apply:** Applicants must submit a completed general application form, available at the website. **Contact:** Email: mjschoolscholarships@unc.edu.

11188 ■ Joy Gibson MATC Cohort Award
(Undergraduate/Scholarship)

Purpose: To provide educational assistance to students who are studying journalism. **Focus:** Communications; Journalism. **Qualif.:** Applicants must be students who have pre-declared or are enrolled in the School of Media and Journalism. **Criteria:** Recipients will be selected based on their academic interests, geographic location, financial need and programs of study.

Funds Avail.: $1,000. **Duration:** Annual. **To Apply:** Applicants must submit a completed general application form, available at the website. **Contact:** mjschoolscholarships@unc.edu.

11189 ■ Glenn Keever Scholarship *(Undergraduate/Scholarship)*

Purpose: To support and encourage a student in the School of Media and Journalism. **Focus:** Communications; Journalism. **Qualif.:** Applicant must be student in the UNC School of Media and Journalism. **Criteria:** Selection will be based on their academic interests, geographic location, financial need and programs of study.

Funds Avail.: No specific amount. **Duration:** Annual. **To Apply:** Applicants must submit a completed general application form, available at the website. **Contact:** Email: mjschoolscholarships@unc.edu.

11190 ■ James Davis Scholarship *(Undergraduate/Scholarship)*

Purpose: To support a student who is North Carolina natives and has demonstrated a commitment to the study of state history. **Focus:** Communications; Journalism. **Qualif.:** Applicant must be student in the School of Media and Journalism. **Criteria:** Preference given to North Carolina natives who have demonstrated a commitment to the study of state history.

Funds Avail.: No specific amount. **Duration:** Annual. **Number Awarded:** 2. **To Apply:** Applicants must submit a completed general application form, available on the website. **Deadline:** February 1. **Contact:** Email: mjschoolscholarships@unc.edu.

11191 ■ James F. Hurley III Bicentennial Merit Scholarship *(Undergraduate/Scholarship)*

Purpose: To support rising junior or rising senior in the school who is in the reporting specialization. **Focus:** Communications; Journalism. **Qualif.:** Applicants must be rising juniors or seniors in the school who are in the reporting specialization. **Criteria:** Preference is given to students with a newspaper career interest.

Funds Avail.: $2,500 each. **Duration:** Annual. **To Apply:** Applicants must submit a completed general application form, available at the website. **Contact:** Email: hussman@unc.edu.

11192 ■ Kathryn M. Cronin Scholarship *(Undergraduate, Graduate/Scholarship)*

Purpose: To support outstanding students who shows through coursework and other activities an intent to pursue a career in medical journalism or health communication. **Focus:** Communications; Journalism. **Criteria:** Selection will be based on academic interests and financial need.

Funds Avail.: No specific amount. **Duration:** Annual. **Deadline:** February 1. **Contact:** Tom Linden, Director, M.A. in Media and Communication Glaxo Wellcome Distinguished Professor of Medical Journalism, Phone: 919-962-4078(Carroll 328); Email: linden@unc.edu.

11193 ■ Kays Gary Scholarship *(Undergraduate/Scholarship)*

Purpose: To support and encourage a student in the School of Media and Journalism. **Focus:** Communications; Journalism. **Qualif.:** Applicant must be student in the School of Media and Journalism. **Criteria:** Recipients will be selected based on their academic interests, geographic location, financial need and programs of study.

Funds Avail.: No specific amount. **Duration:** Annual. **To Apply:** Applicants must submit a completed general application form, available at the website. **Contact:** Email: mjschoolscholarships@unc.edu.

11194 ■ Louis M. Connor, Jr. Scholarship *(Undergraduate/Scholarship)*

Purpose: To provide educational assistance to students in the public relations specialization. **Focus:** Public relations. **Qualif.:** Applicant must be outstanding student in the UNC School of Media and Journalism in the public relations specialization. **Criteria:** Preference is given to public relations students.

Funds Avail.: No specific amount. **Duration:** Annual. **To Apply:** Applicants must submit a completed general application form, available at the website. **Contact:** Email: mjschoolscholarships@unc.edu.

11195 ■ Mackey-Byars Scholarship for Communication Excellence *(Undergraduate/Scholarship)*

Purpose: To provide educational assistance to students who are studying journalism. **Focus:** Communications. **Qualif.:** Applicant must be student in the School of Media and Journalism. **Criteria:** Preference will be given to minorities or students with financial need.

Duration: Annual. **Number Awarded:** 1. **To Apply:** Applicants must submit a completed general application form, available at the website. **Contact:** Email: mjschoolscholarships@unc.edu.

11196 ■ Margaret A. Blanchard Scholarship *(Graduate/Scholarship)*

Purpose: To support and encourage a student in the School of Media and Journalism. **Focus:** Communications. **Qualif.:** Applicants must be current UNC students who have pre-declared or are enrolled in the school of media and journalism. **Criteria:** Selection will be based on their academic interests, geographic location, financial need and programs of study.

Funds Avail.: No specific amount. **Duration:** Annual. **To Apply:** Applicants must submit a completed special application form, available at the website. **Deadline:** February 1. **Contact:** Heidi Hennink-Kaminski; Senior Associate Dean for Graduate Studies; Associate Professor; Carroll

Awards are arranged alphabetically below their administering organizations

361; Phone: 919-962-2555; Email: h2kamins@email.unc.edu or mjschoolscholarships@unc.edu.

11197 ■ Marjorie Usher Ragan Scholarship
(Undergraduate/Scholarship)

Purpose: To support and encourage a student in the School of Media and Journalism. **Focus:** Communications; Journalism. **Qualif.:** Applicant must be student in the UNC School of Media and Journalism.

Funds Avail.: No specific amount. **Duration:** Annual. **Number Awarded:** 1. **Contact:** Email: mjschoolscholarships@unc.edu.

11198 ■ The Maxwell Scholarship in Graduate Medical Journalism *(Graduate/Scholarship)*

Purpose: To provide educational assistance to current MJ-school students. **Focus:** Journalism. **Qualif.:** Applicant must be a graduate student entering the school. **Criteria:** Selection will be based on academic interests, geographic location, financial need and programs of study.

Funds Avail.: No specific amount. **Duration:** Annual. **To Apply:** Potential applicants should contact Tom Linden for more information. **Contact:** Tom Linden, Director, M.A. in Media and Communication Glaxo Wellcome Distinguished Professor of Medical Journalism; Phone: 919-962-4078(Carroll 328); Email: linden@unc.edu.

11199 ■ C.A. "Pete" McKnight Scholarships *(High School/Scholarship)*

Purpose: To support and encourage a student in the School of Media and Journalism. **Focus:** Journalism. **Qualif.:** Applicant must be student in the School of Media and Journalism. **Criteria:** Recipients will be selected based on academic interests, geographic location, financial need and programs of study.

Funds Avail.: No specific amount. **Duration:** Annual. **To Apply:** Applicants must submit a completed general application form, available on the website. **Deadline:** February 1. **Contact:** Email: mjschoolscholarships@unc.edu.

11200 ■ Molly McKay Scholarship *(Undergraduate/Scholarship)*

Purpose: To support and encourage a student in the School of Media and Journalism. **Focus:** Religion. **Qualif.:** Applicant must be student in the School of Media and Journalism. **Criteria:** Recipients will be selected based on their academic interests, geographic location, financial need and programs of study.

Funds Avail.: No specific amount. **Duration:** Annual. **To Apply:** Applicants must submit a completed general application form, available at the website. **Contact:** Email: mjschoolscholarships@unc.edu.

11201 ■ Paul Green Houston Scholarship *(Undergraduate/Scholarship)*

Purpose: To provide educational assistance to students who are studying journalism. **Focus:** Communications; Journalism. **Qualif.:** Applicant must be an outstanding student School of Media and Journalism; must be in the reporting specialization. **Criteria:** Recipients will be selected based on their academic interests, geographic location, financial need and programs of study.

Funds Avail.: No specific amount. **Duration:** Annual. **Number Awarded:** 1. **To Apply:** Applicants must submit a completed general application form, available at the website. **Deadline:** February 1. **Contact:** Email: mjschoolscholarships@unc.edu.

11202 ■ Peter DeWitt Pruden and Phyllis Harrill Pruden Scholarship *(Undergraduate/Scholarship)*

Purpose: To support and encourage a student in the School of Media and Journalism. **Focus:** Communications; Journalism. **Qualif.:** Applicant must be student in the UNC School of Media and Journalism; must be from one of the following states: Virginia, Tennessee, North Carolina or South Carolina. **Criteria:** Preference goes to students from Virginia, Tennessee, South Carolina or North Carolina with strong character, excellent academic performance and financial need.

Funds Avail.: No specific amount. **Duration:** Annual. **To Apply:** Applicants must submit a completed general application form, available on the website. **Contact:** Email: mjschoolscholarships@unc.edu.

11203 ■ Philip Alston Scholarship *(Undergraduate/Scholarship)*

Purpose: To provide financial assistance to students interested in sports communication program. **Focus:** Communications; Journalism. **Qualif.:** Applicant must be student in the School of Media and Journalism. **Criteria:** Preference will be given to a students in the sports communication program.

Duration: Annual. **To Apply:** Applicants must submit a completed general application form, available at the website. **Contact:** Email: mjschoolscholarships@unc.edu.

11204 ■ Robert Pittman Scholarships-Internships *(Undergraduate/Scholarship, Internship)*

Purpose: To provide educational assistance to current MJ-school students. **Focus:** Communications; Journalism. **Qualif.:** Applicants must be outstanding students in the school who are in the reporting specialization; must have a strong interest in a newspaper career and excellence in academic and journalistic accomplishments. **Criteria:** Recipients will be selected based on the academic interests, geographic location, financial need and programs of study.

Funds Avail.: No specific amount. **Duration:** Annual. **To Apply:** Applicants must submit a completed general application form, available at the website. **Deadline:** Varies. **Contact:** Robin Jackson, Director of Alumni Affairs and Donor Relations at mjschoolscholarships@unc.edu.

11205 ■ Quincy Sharpe Mills Memorial Scholarship *(Undergraduate/Scholarship)*

Purpose: To provide educational assistance to current MJ-school students. **Focus:** Communications; Journalism. **Qualif.:** Applicants must be a student in School of Media and Journalism.

Funds Avail.: No specific amount. **Number Awarded:** Varies. **Contact:** Email: mjschoolscholarships@unc.edu.

11206 ■ Raleigh Mann Scholarship *(Undergraduate/Scholarship)*

Purpose: To support a student in the school in the reporting specialization who excel at copy editing. **Focus:** Communications; Journalism. **Qualif.:** Applicant must be a students in the school in the reporting specialization who excel at copy editing. **Criteria:** Recipients will be selected based on their academic interests, geographic location, financial need and programs of study.

Awards are arranged alphabetically below their administering organizations

Duration: Annual. **Number Awarded:** 1. **To Apply:** Applicants must submit a completed general application form, available at the website.

11207 ■ Rick Brewer Scholarship *(Undergraduate/ Scholarship)*

Purpose: To provide educational assistance to students who have expressed an interest in pursuing a career in the field of sports journalism, broadcasting or public relations on the collegiate, amateur or professional levels. **Focus:** Broadcasting; Journalism; Public relations. **Qualif.:** Applicants must be a student in School of Media and Journalism; must have expressed an interest in pursuing a career in the field of sports journalism, broadcasting or public relations on the collegiate, amateur or professional levels. **Criteria:** Recipients will be selected based on their academic interests, geographic location, financial need and programs of study.

Duration: Annual. **Number Awarded:** 1. **To Apply:** Applicants must submit a completed general application form, available at the website. **Deadline:** February 1. **Contact:** Email: mjschoolscholarships@unc.edu.

11208 ■ Robert Winchester Dodson Scholarship *(Undergraduate/Scholarship)*

Purpose: To support and encourage a student in the School of Media and Journalism. **Focus:** Communications; Journalism.

Duration: Annual. **To Apply:** Applicants must submit a completed general application form, available on the website. **Contact:** Email: hussman@unc.edu.

11209 ■ Eugene L. Roberts, Jr. Prize *(Undergraduate/ Prize)*

Purpose: To encourage students who has demonstrated a career interest in journalism. **Focus:** Journalism. **Qualif.:** Applicants must be undergraduate students interested in print journalism who propose the best idea for a Gene Roberts-type story; applicants must be returning to School for at least one semester to research and write a story in MEJO 596; the course is "Independent Study" supervised by a faculty member for three credits. **Criteria:** Selection is based on demonstrated ability to report and write a story and academic standing.

Duration: Annual. **Remarks:** The award honors Eugene L. Roberts Jr., former managing editor of The New York Times and former executive editor of The Philadelphia Inquirer. **Contact:** Charlie Tuggle, Senior Associate Dean, Phone: 919-962-5694; Email: catuggle@unc.edu.

11210 ■ A.C. Snow and Katherine Snow Smith Scholarship *(High School/Scholarship)*

Purpose: To provide educational assistance to students who are studying journalism. **Focus:** Journalism. **Qualif.:** Applicant must be student in the School of Media and Journalism; must be news-editorial student with an interest in grammar. **Criteria:** Preference will be given to reporting students with an interest in grammar.

Funds Avail.: $1,500. **Duration:** Annual. **Number Awarded:** 1. **To Apply:** Applicants must submit a completed general application form, available at the website. **Deadline:** February 1. **Contact:** Email: mjschoolscholarships@unc.edu.

11211 ■ Stephen Gates Memorial Scholarship *(Undergraduate/Scholarship)*

Purpose: To support students who are studying electronic communication specialization with an interest in sports journalism. **Focus:** Broadcasting; Communications. **Qualif.:** Applicant must be a student in the school in the broadcast and electronic journalism specialization with an interest in sports journalism. **Criteria:** Recipients will be selected based on academic interests, geographic location, financial need and programs of study.

Duration: Annual. **Number Awarded:** 1. **To Apply:** Applicants must submit a completed general application form, available on the website.

11212 ■ Jim and Pat Thacker Sports Communication Internship *(Undergraduate/Internship)*

Purpose: To provide Hussman School undergraduate majors to intern with a professional sports organization during the summer. **Focus:** Communications. **Qualif.:** Applicant must be MJ-school undergraduate majors; must have at least a 3.0 GPA. **Criteria:** Recipients will be selected based on their academic interests, geographic location, financial need and programs of study.

Funds Avail.: No specific amount. **Duration:** Annual. **Number Awarded:** 3 in 2019. **To Apply:** Applicants must submit a completed general application form, available at the website. **Remarks:** The award honors Jim and Pat Thacker of Charlotte. **Contact:** Email: uncmjawards@unc.edu.

11213 ■ Tom Bost Scholarship *(Undergraduate/ Scholarship)*

Purpose: To support and encourage a student in the School of Media and Journalism. **Focus:** Communications; Journalism. **Qualif.:** Applicant must be student in the School of Media and Journalism.

Duration: Annual. **Number Awarded:** 1. **To Apply:** Applicants must submit a completed general application form, available at the website. **Contact:** Email: mjschoolscholarships@unc.edu.

11214 ■ Tucker Family Scholarship *(Undergraduate/ Scholarship)*

Purpose: To provide financial assistance for students who are interested in print or broadcast journalism. **Focus:** Communications; Journalism.

Funds Avail.: No specific amount. **Duration:** Annual. **Number Awarded:** 2.

11215 ■ Victoria M. Gardner Scholarship *(Undergraduate/Scholarship)*

Purpose: To provide educational assistance to students who have an interest in health and family issues in the field of medical journalism. **Focus:** Education, Medical. **Qualif.:** Applicant must be student in the School of Media and Journalism; must have interested in health and family issues in the field of medical journalism. **Criteria:** Selection will be based on the committee's criteria.

Duration: Annual. **Contact:** Email: mjschoolscholarships@unc.edu.

11216 ■ Tom Wicker Award *(Graduate/Award)*

Purpose: To support to recognize and reward these students for their outstanding accomplishments. **Focus:** Communications; Journalism.

Funds Avail.: No specific amount. **Duration:** Annual. **To Apply:** Potential applicants should contact Heidi Hennink-Kaminski for more information. **Contact:** Heidi Hennink-Kaminski, Senior Associate Dean for Graduate Studies Associate Professor; Phone: 919-962-2555(Carroll 361);

Awards are arranged alphabetically below their administering organizations

Email: h2kamins@email.unc.edu.

11217 ■ WTVD Scholarship *(Undergraduate/ Scholarship)*

Purpose: To provide educational assistance to students who have demonstrated excellence in their studies in journalism and mass communication. **Focus:** Communications; Journalism. **Qualif.:** Applicant must be student in the School of Media and Journalism; must have demonstrated excellence in studies in media and journalism. **Criteria:** Preference will be given to students from North Carolina.

Duration: Annual. **To Apply:** Applicants must submit a completed general application form, available at the website. **Contact:** Email: mjschoolscholarships@unc.edu.

11218 ■ UNICO Merrimack Valley Foundation
40 Bayfield Dr.
North Andover, MA 01845
Ph: (847)255-0210
Free: 866-457-2582
URL: www.unicomerrimackvalley.org

11219 ■ UNICO Merrimack Valley Scholarships
(Graduate/Scholarship)

Purpose: To grant scholarships to deserving Merrimack Valley, higher education-bound, Italian-American students. **Focus:** General studies/Field of study not specified. **Qualif.:** Applicant must be graduating senior of a greater Merrimack Valley area high school; must have high moral character and ranked within the top 25% of their class; involved in extra-curricular activities; must be of Italian descent; no member of the candidate's family (parent, grandparent, aunt/uncle, first cousin) may be a member of Merrimack Valley area high school. **Criteria:** Selection will be based on scholarship committee members.

Funds Avail.: $2,500. **Duration:** Annual. **Number Awarded:** 5. **To Apply:** Applicant must include the UNICO application form, High School Transcript, SAT or ACT scores, a letter of recommendation. **Deadline:** March 15. **Remarks:** Established in 1990. **Contact:** Email: scholarships@unicomerrimackvalley.org.

11220 ■ Unico National (UN)
271 US Hwy. 46, Ste. F-103
Fairfield, NJ 07004
Ph: (973)808-0035
Fax: (973)808-0043
E-mail: uniconational@unico.org
URL: www.unico.org

11221 ■ Ella T. Grasso Literary Scholarship
(Undergraduate/Scholarship)

Purpose: To support matriculated college students, of Italian heritage, in their education. **Focus:** General studies/ Field of study not specified. **Qualif.:** Applicants should be matriculated college students.

Funds Avail.: $1,000 each. **Duration:** Annual. **Number Awarded:** 2. **To Apply:** Applicants terms of submission require the candidate to present, in writing, an original short story or essay celebrating their Italian heritage.

11222 ■ Unifor
205 Placer Ct.
Toronto, ON, Canada M2H 3H9

Ph: (416)497-4110
Free: 800-268-5763
E-mail: communications@unifor.org
URL: www.unifor.org
Social Media: www.facebook.com/UniforCanada
twitter.com/UniforTheUnion
www.youtube.com/user/UniforCanada

11223 ■ Unifor Scholarship *(Professional development, Undergraduate/Scholarship)*

Purpose: To support members who are pursuing higher education. **Focus:** Education. **Qualif.:** Applicant must be entering their first year of full-time post-secondary education (university, community college, technological institute, trade school, etc.) in a public Canadian institution.

Funds Avail.: 2,000 Canadian Dollars each. **Number Awarded:** 28. **To Apply:** Applicants must submit a online application; current high school transcript (children of Unifor members only); reference letter; local Union Officer signature form; essay. **Deadline:** June 15. **Contact:** Email: scholarships@unifor.org.

11224 ■ UNIGO Group
c/o Education Dynamics
111 River St.
Hoboken, NJ 07030
Ph: (201)377-3000
URL: www.unigo.com
Social Media: www.facebook.com/myunigo
www.instagram.com/myunigo
twitter.com/unigo

11225 ■ All About Education Scholarship
(Undergraduate, High School/Scholarship)

Purpose: To help students pursue education. **Focus:** General studies/Field of study not specified. **Qualif.:** Applicants must be 13 years of age or older at the time of application; must be legal residents of the 50 United States or the District of Columbia; must be students.

Funds Avail.: $3,000. **Duration:** Annual. **Number Awarded:** 1. **To Apply:** Applicants must visit the website for the online application and must submit a short written response, 250 words or less, for the topic: "How will a $3,000 scholarship for education make a difference in your life?" **Deadline:** April 30.

11226 ■ Do-Over Scholarship *(Undergraduate, High School/Scholarship)*

Purpose: To help students pursue education. **Focus:** General studies/Field of study not specified. **Qualif.:** Applicants must be 13 years of age or older at the time of application; must be legal residents of the 50 United States or the District of Columbia; must be students.

Funds Avail.: $1,500. **Duration:** Annual. **Number Awarded:** 1. **To Apply:** Applicants must visit the website for the online application and must submit a short written response, 250 words or less, for the question: "If you could get one 'Do-Over' in life, what would it be and why?" **Deadline:** June 30.

11227 ■ Education Matters Scholarship *(Undergraduate, High School/Scholarship)*

Purpose: To serve the needs of students seeking further education. **Focus:** General studies/Field of study not speci-

Awards are arranged alphabetically below their administering organizations

fied. **Qualif.:** Applicants must be 13 years of age or older at the time of application; must be legal resident of the 50 United States or the District of Columbia. **Criteria:** Selection will be based on the committee's criteria.

Funds Avail.: $5,000. **Duration:** Annual. **Number Awarded:** 1. **To Apply:** Applicants must visit the website for the online application and must submit a short written response, 250 words or less, for the question "What would you say to someone who thinks education doesn't matter, or that college is a waste of time and money?" **Deadline:** November 30. **Contact:** URL: www.unigo.com/scholarships/our-scholarships/education-matters-5k-scholarship.

11228 ■ Fifth Month Scholarship *(Undergraduate, High School/Scholarship)*

Purpose: To help students pursue education. **Focus:** General studies/Field of study not specified. **Qualif.:** Applicants must be 13 years of age or older at the time of application; must be legal residents of the 50 United States or the District of Columbia; must be students. **Criteria:** Selection will be based on the committee's criteria.

Funds Avail.: $1,500. **Number Awarded:** 1. **To Apply:** Applicants must visit the website for the online application and must submit a short written response, 250 words or less, for the question: "May is the fifth month of the year. Write a letter to the number five explaining why five is important. Be serious or be funny. Either way, here's a high five to you just for being original." **Deadline:** May 31.

11229 ■ Flavor of the Month Scholarship *(Undergraduate, High School/Scholarship)*

Purpose: To serve the needs of college undergraduate and graduate students and high school students as they look for ways to pay for their education. **Focus:** General studies/Field of study not specified. **Qualif.:** Applicants must be 13 years of age or older at the time of application; must be legal residents of the 50 United States or the District of Columbia; must be students. **Criteria:** Selection will be based on the committee's criteria.

Funds Avail.: $1,500. **Duration:** Annual. **Number Awarded:** 1. **To Apply:** Applicants must visit the website for the online application and must submit a short written response, 250 words or less, for the question: "Summer and ice cream go hand-in-hand. In fact, July is National Ice Cream Month and that's the inspiration behind this award. We think people are very similar to ice cream; some are nutty, others a little exotic, while some are very comforting. If you were an ice cream flavor, which would you be and why?" **Deadline:** July 31.

11230 ■ I Have a Dream Scholarship *(Graduate, High School/Scholarship)*

Purpose: To help students make their educational dreams come true. **Focus:** General studies/Field of study not specified. **Qualif.:** Applicants must be 14 years of age or older at the time of application; must be legal residents of the 50 United States or the District of Columbia; must be currently enrolled in an accredited post-secondary institution of higher education.

Funds Avail.: $1,500. **Duration:** Annual. **To Apply:** Applicant must submit an online response to the following question: What do you dream about? Whether it's some bizarre dream you had last week, or your hopes for the future, share your dreams with us. **Deadline:** January 31.

11231 ■ Make Me Laugh Scholarship *(Undergraduate, High School/Scholarship)*

Purpose: To serve the needs of students seeking further education. **Focus:** General studies/Field of study not speci-

fied. **Qualif.:** Applicants must be 13 years of age or older at the time of application; must be legal resident of the 50 United States or the District of Columbia.

Funds Avail.: $1,500. **Duration:** Annual. **Number Awarded:** 1. **To Apply:** Applicants must visit the website for the online application and must submit a short written response, 250 words or less, for the question "OMG, finding and applying for scholarships is serious business, but it's time to lighten things up a little. We don't want to know why you deserve $1,500 or how great your grades are, we simply want to LOL. Describe an incident in your life, funny or embarrassing (fact or fiction), and make us laugh!" **Deadline:** August 31. **Contact:** URL: www.unigo.com/scholarships/our-scholarships/make-me-laugh-scholarship.

11232 ■ Shout It Out Scholarship *(Undergraduate, High School/Scholarship)*

Purpose: To serve the needs of students seeking further education. **Focus:** General studies/Field of study not specified. **Qualif.:** Applicants must be 13 years of age or older at the time of application; must be legal resident of the 50 United States or the District of Columbia.

Funds Avail.: $1,500. **Duration:** Annual. **Number Awarded:** 1. **To Apply:** Applicants must visit the website for the online application and must submit a short written response, 250 words or less, for the question "If you could say one thing to the entire world at once, what would it be and why?". **Deadline:** September 30. **Contact:** URL: www.unigo.com/scholarships/our-scholarships/shout-it-out-scholarship.

11233 ■ Superpower Scholarship *(Undergraduate, High School/Scholarship)*

Purpose: To help students pursue education. **Focus:** General studies/Field of study not specified. **Qualif.:** Applicants must be 13 years of age or older at the time of application; must be legal residents of the 50 United States or the District of Columbia; must be students.

Funds Avail.: $2,500. **Duration:** Annual. **Number Awarded:** 1. **To Apply:** Applicants must visit the website for the online application and must submit a short written response, 250 words or less, for the question: "Which superhero or villain would you want to changes places with for a day and why?" **Deadline:** March 31.

11234 ■ Sweet and Simple Scholarship *(Undergraduate, High School/Scholarship)*

Purpose: To help students afford a college education. **Focus:** General studies/Field of study not specified. **Qualif.:** Applicants must be 13 years of age or older at the time of application; must be legal residents of the 50 United States or the District of Columbia; must be currently enrolled in an accredited post-secondary institution of higher education.

Funds Avail.: $1,500. **Duration:** Annual. **To Apply:** Applicant must submit an online response (250 words or less) to the following question: Not every gift has to be expensive or extravagant. In fact, sometimes it's the sweet and simple things that make a real difference in our lives. Think back and tell us about something you received as a gift and why it meant so much to you. **Deadline:** February 28.

11235 ■ Top Ten List Scholarship *(Undergraduate, High School/Scholarship)*

Purpose: To serve the needs of students seeking further education. **Focus:** General studies/Field of study not speci-

Awards are arranged alphabetically below their administering organizations

fied. **Qualif.:** Applicants must be 13 years of age or older at the time of application; must be legal residents of the 50 United States or the District of Columbia.

Funds Avail.: $1,500. **Duration:** Annual. **Number Awarded:** 1. **To Apply:** Applicants must visit the website for the online application and must submit a short written response, 250 words or less, for the question "Create a Top Ten List of the top ten reasons you should get this scholarship." **Deadline:** December 31. **Contact:** URL: www.unigo.com/scholarships/our-scholarships/top-ten-list-scholarship.

11236 ■ Unigo $10K Scholarship (Undergraduate, High School/Scholarship)

Purpose: To help students pursue education. **Focus:** General studies/Field of study not specified. **Qualif.:** Applicants must be 13 years of age or older at the time of application; must be legal residents of the 50 United States or the District of Columbia; must be students.

Funds Avail.: $10,000. **Duration:** Annual. **Number Awarded:** December 31. **To Apply:** Applicant must submit an online response (less than 250 words) to the following question: "Imagine a historical figure is brought back to life. Who is it? What's their favorite mobile app?"

11237 ■ Zombie Apocalypse Scholarship (Undergraduate, High School/Scholarship)

Purpose: To serve the needs of students seeking further education. **Focus:** General studies/Field of study not specified. **Qualif.:** Applicants must be 13 years of age or older at the time of application; must be legal residents of the 50 United States or the District of Columbia.

Funds Avail.: $2,000. **Duration:** Annual. **Number Awarded:** 1. **To Apply:** Applications are available online; must complete a 250-word answer to the following: "Imagine that your high school or college has been overrun with zombies. Your math professor, the cafeteria ladies, and even your best friend have all joined the walking dead. Flesh out a plan to avoid the zombies, including where you'd hide and the top-five things you'd bring to stay alive." **Deadline:** October 31. **Contact:** URL: www.unigo.com/scholarships/our-scholarships/zombie-apocalypse-scholarship.

11238 ■ Union Internationale de la Marionnette (UNIMA-USA)

1404 Spring St. NW
Atlanta, GA 30309
Ph: (404)881-5110
Fax: (404)873-9907
E-mail: unimausa@gmail.com
URL: www.unima-usa.org
Social Media: www.facebook.com/UNIMA.USA

11239 ■ UNIMA-USA Scholarship (Professional development/Scholarship)

Purpose: To help cover tuition fees for American puppeteers who wish to study puppetry outside the U.S. **Focus:** Puppetry. **Qualif.:** Candidates must be citizens or permanent residents of the United States who are over 18 years old and have some experience in puppetry or/and a university degree showing an interest in puppetry. **Criteria:** Applicants are judged upon the committee's criteria.

Funds Avail.: $1,000. **Duration:** Annual. **Deadline:** December 15. **Remarks:** Established in 1982.

11240 ■ Union of Marash Armenian Student Fund

252-39 Leeds Rd.
Little Neck, NY 11362
E-mail: info@umastudentfund.org
URL: www.umastudentfund.org

11241 ■ Union of Marash Armenian Student Funds (Undergraduate, Graduate/Scholarship)

Purpose: To promote the education of Armenian students by granting scholarships to any Armenian or any descendant of an Armenian, and to encourage the educational, cultural, and athletic endeavors of Armenian Youth. **Focus:** General studies/Field of study not specified. **Qualif.:** Applicant must be a matriculated, full-time undergraduate or graduate student accepted at an accredited institution of higher education; must demonstrate academic excellence; be of good moral character; be in financial need and show involvement in community and must be a descendant of a Marashtsi (a part of Armenia/Asia Minor). **Criteria:** Selection will be based on the committee's criteria.

To Apply: Application form available on sponsor's website. **Deadline:** July 15.

11242 ■ Union Plus Education Foundation

1100 First St., NE, Ste. 850
Washington, DC 20002
Free: 800-472-2005
URL: www.unionplus.org

11243 ■ Union Plus Scholarship Program (Undergraduate, Graduate/Scholarship)

Purpose: To provide scholarships to union members and dependents or spouses who are attending or planning to attend a four-year college or university, a community college, technical college, or trade school. **Focus:** General studies/Field of study not specified. **Qualif.:** Applicant must be current or retired members of participating unions, their spouses and their dependent children (as defined by IRS regulations); must have at least one year of continuous union membership by the applicant, applicant's spouse or parent (if applicant is a dependent). One year membership minimum must be satisfied by May 31 of the scholarship year. Applicants must also be undergraduate or graduate students accepted into a U.S. accredited college or university, community college, or technical or trade school at the time the award is issued. **Criteria:** Applicants are evaluated according to academic ability, social awareness, financial need and appreciation of labor; GPA of 3.0 or higher is recommended.

Funds Avail.: $500 to $4,000. **Duration:** Annual. **To Apply:** Applicant must submit an online application form at www.unionplus.org/benefits/education/union-plus-scholarships. **Deadline:** January 31. **Remarks:** Established in 1991. **Contact:** E-mail: scholarships@unionplus.org.

11244 ■ Unitarian Universalist Association (UUA)

24 Farnsworth St.
Boston, MA 02210-1409
Ph: (617)742-2100
Fax: (617)367-3237
E-mail: info@uua.org
URL: www.uua.org
Social Media: www.facebook.com/TheUUA
twitter.com/uua

Awards are arranged alphabetically below their administering organizations

www.youtube.com/c/
UnitarianUniversalistAssociationBoston

11245 ■ Martha and Robert Atherton Ministerial Scholarship *(Master's/Scholarship)*

Purpose: To provide financial assistance to promising ministerial students in pursuing their education. **Focus:** Religion. **Qualif.:** Applicants must be students enrolled full-time or at least half-time in a Masters of Divinity degree program leading to fellowship as Unitarian Universalist (UU) ministers; must be citizens of the United States or Canada. **Criteria:** Priority is given to students who have demonstrated outstanding ministerial ability, secondarily to students with the greatest financial need, especially persons of color.

Funds Avail.: No specific amount. **Duration:** Annual. **Number Awarded:** 1. **To Apply:** Application must be completed, describe your call to the unitarian universalist ministry in 250 words. **Deadline:** August 15. **Remarks:** The scholarship was established to honor Martha and Robert Atherton for their generous contributions. Established in 1997. **Contact:** Ministerial Credentialing Office, 24 Farnsworth St., Boston, MA 02210-1409; Email: mco@uua.org.

11246 ■ Children of Unitarian Universalist Religious Professionals Grant *(Undergraduate/Grant)*

Purpose: To provide educational support to the children of Unitarian Universalist Ministers, Credentialed Religious Professionals, and Certified Musicians who are attending college. **Focus:** General studies/Field of study not specified. **Qualif.:** Applicants must be college undergraduates and children of Fellowshipped Unitarian Universalist Ministers, Credentialed Religious Professionals, and Certified Musicians who are attending college.

Funds Avail.: $1,000. **Duration:** Annual. **To Apply:** Applications can be submitted online; must submit proof of college enrollment. **Deadline:** October 15. **Contact:** Rev. Richard Nugent, UUA Office of Church Staff Finances, 24 Farnsworth St., Boston, MA 02210; Fax: 617-742-2875; Email: ocsf@uua.org.

11247 ■ David Pohl Scholarship *(Master's/Scholarship)*

Purpose: To support the intellectual, spiritual, and professional development of individuals studying for the Unitarian Universalist ministry. **Focus:** Religion. **Qualif.:** Applicants must be students enrolled full-time or at least half-time in a Masters of Divinity degree program leading to fellowship as Unitarian Universalist (UU) ministers; must be citizens of the United States or Canada. **Criteria:** Priority is given to students that have demonstrated outstanding ministerial ability, secondarily to students with the greatest financial need, especially persons of color.

Funds Avail.: No specific amount. **Duration:** Annual. **To Apply:** Applicants must apply for financial aid to be automatically considered for scholarships with no additional material required, except when noted. **Deadline:** March 23. **Remarks:** The scholarship was established by the Unitarian Universalist Association of Congregations (UUA) upon Rev. Pohl's retirement as Unitarian Universalist Association Director of Ministry. Established in 1993. **Contact:** Ministerial Credentialing Office, 24 Farnsworth St., Boston, MA 02210-1409; Email: mco@uua.org.

11248 ■ Pauly D'Orlando Memorial Art Scholarship *(Graduate, Undergraduate/Scholarship)*

Purpose: To support Unitarian Universalist students with their educational pursuit. **Focus:** Art. **Qualif.:** Applicants must be Unitarian Universalist graduate or undergraduate students pursuing a career in fine arts, except those who are performing arts majors. **Criteria:** Selection is based on active relationship with Unitarian Universalism, financial need, and enrollment in an accredited institution.

Duration: Annual. **Number Awarded:** Varies. **To Apply:** Applicants must submit a completed application form along with the personal information, essay, personal financial statement, transcripts, recommendation from educator and recommendation from church. **Deadline:** February 15. **Contact:** Email: uufp@uua.org.

11249 ■ David Eaton Scholarship *(Master's/Scholarship)*

Purpose: To women from a historically marginalized group who share the same vision as David Eaton. **Focus:** Religion. **Qualif.:** Applicants must be students enrolled full-time or at least half time in a Masters of Divinity degree program leading to fellowship as Unitarian Universalist (UU) ministers; citizens of the United States or Canada; women from a historically marginalized group who share the same vision as David Eaton. **Criteria:** Priority is given to students that have demonstrated outstanding ministerial ability secondarily to students with the greatest financial need, especially persons of color.

Funds Avail.: No specific amount. **Duration:** Annual. **To Apply:** Applicants must apply for financial aid to be automatically considered for scholarships with no additional materials required, except where noted. **Deadline:** April 15. **Remarks:** The scholarship was established to honor Rev. David Hilliard Eaton. **Contact:** Ministerial Credentialing Office, 24 Farnsworth St., Boston, MA 02210-1409; Email: mco@uua.org.

11250 ■ Joseph Sumner Smith Scholarship *(Undergraduate/Scholarship)*

Purpose: To support the education of a Unitarian Universalist (UU) student. **Focus:** General studies/Field of study not specified. **Qualif.:** Applicants must be Unitarian Universalist students attending Harvard University. **Criteria:** Priority is given to students who will pursue the ministry after graduation.

Funds Avail.: $250 - $1,000. **Duration:** Annual. **To Apply:** Applicants must contact the Scholarship Administrator of the UU Funding Program for the application process. **Deadline:** July 31. **Contact:** Scholarship Administrator, c/o UU Funding Program, PO Box 3011149, Jamaica Plain, MA 02130; Phone: 617-971-9600; Email: uufp@uua.org, ocsf@uua.org.

11251 ■ The Olympia Brown and Max Kapp Award *(Master's/Scholarship)*

Purpose: To support the education of a student in a Masters of Divinity degree program. **Focus:** Religion. **Qualif.:** Applicants must be students enrolled full-time or at least half-time in a Masters of Divinity degree program leading to fellowship as Unitarian Universalist (UU) ministers; must be citizens of the United States or Canada. **Criteria:** Priority will be given to students who have demonstrated outstanding ministerial ability, secondarily to students with the greatest financial need, especially persons of color; entries will be evaluated by an outside reader.

Funds Avail.: $2,500. **Duration:** Annual. **Number Awarded:** 1. **To Apply:** Applicants must apply for financial aid to be automatically considered for scholarships; must

Awards are arranged alphabetically below their administering organizations

submit a winning paper, sermon, or other special project on some aspect of Universalism. **Deadline:** April 15. **Contact:** Ministerial Credentialing Office, 24 Farnsworth St., Boston, MA 02210-1409; Email: mco@uua.org.

11252 ■ Marion Barr Stanfield Art Scholarship
(Graduate, Undergraduate/Scholarship)

Purpose: To support Unitarian Universalist students with their educational pursuit. **Focus:** Art. **Qualif.:** Applicants must be Unitarian Universalist graduate or undergraduate students pursuing a career in fine arts, except those who are performing arts majors. **Criteria:** Selection is based on active relationship with Unitarian Universalism, financial need, and enrollment in an accredited institution.

Funds Avail.: No specific amount. **Duration:** Annual. **Number Awarded:** Varies. **To Apply:** Applicants must submit a completed application form along with the personal information, essay, personal financial statement, transcripts, recommendation from educator and recommendation from church. **Deadline:** February 15. **Contact:** Email: uufp@uua.org.

11253 ■ Otto M. Stanfield Law Scholarship
(Graduate/Scholarship)

Purpose: To support student's education entering law school at graduate level. **Focus:** Law. **Qualif.:** Applicants must be Unitarian Universalist students who are about to enter or already in law school, except those pre-law students or Political Science majors. **Criteria:** Selection is based on active relationship with Unitarian Universalism, financial need, and enrollment in an accredited institution.

Funds Avail.: No specific amount. **Duration:** Annual. **Number Awarded:** Varies. **To Apply:** Applicants must submit a completed application form along with the personal information, essay, personal financial statement, tax information, slide portfolio, list of works; transcripts, recommendation from educator, recommendation from church. **Deadline:** February 15. **Remarks:** The award was established by Marion Barr Stanfield in memory of her husband Otto M. Stanfield. **Contact:** Email: uufp@uua.org.

11254 ■ Roy H. Pollack Scholarship *(Graduate, Master's/Scholarship)*

Purpose: To students who have strong academic records and are a promising candidate for the Unitarian Universalist ministry. **Focus:** Religion. **Criteria:** Priority is given to students who have demonstrated outstanding ministerial ability. secondarily to students with the greatest financial need, especially persons of color.

Funds Avail.: No specific amount. **Duration:** Annual. **To Apply:** Applicants must apply for financial aid to be automatically considered for scholarships with no additional material required, except where noted. **Remarks:** Established in 1998. **Contact:** Ministerial Credentialing Office, 24 Farnsworth St., Boston, MA 02210-1409; Email: mco@uua.org.

11255 ■ Alice Southworth Schulman, Class of 1954, Simmons Scholarships for Unitarian Universalist Women *(Undergraduate/Scholarship)*

Purpose: To provide educational support to Unitarian Universalist women attending Simmons College in Boston. **Focus:** General studies/Field of study not specified. **Qualif.:** Applicants must be Unitarian Universalist Women members attending Simmons College in Boston. **Criteria:** Selection will be made by UUA committee.

Funds Avail.: No specific amount. **Duration:** Annual. **Number Awarded:** 2. **To Apply:** Applicants must apply and submit the information profile for Endowed scholarships through the office of Student Financial Services at Simmons College; letter of recommendation from a member or leader. **Contact:** Email: legacy@uua.org.

11256 ■ The Rev. Chuck and Nancy Thomas Scholarship *(Professional development/Scholarship)*

Purpose: To individual who has shown an outstanding commitment to Unitarian Universalism as a lay leader to support the first year of seminary or pre-seminary academic work at the undergraduate level. **Focus:** Religion. **Qualif.:** Applicants must be first-year students showing an outstanding commitment to Unitarian Universalism as lay leaders before preparing for ordained ministry. **Criteria:** Selection will be based on the committee's criteria.

Funds Avail.: No specific amount. **Duration:** Annual. **Number Awarded:** 1. **To Apply:** Applicants must submit two letters of recommendation, two to three page essay, and a recent resume. **Deadline:** March 23. **Remarks:** The award was established in honor of Chuck Thomas' career in the Unitarian Universalist ministry and his family's long-standing commitment to lay leadership. Established in 1998. **Contact:** Unitarian Universalist Association, Ministerial Credentialing Office, 24 Farnsworth St., Boston, MA 02210-1409; Email: mco@uua.org.

11257 ■ Von Ogden Vogt Scholarship *(Master's/Scholarship)*

Purpose: To support the intellectual, spiritual, and professional development of future Unitarian Universalist ministers who are attending Meadville Lombard Theological School. **Focus:** Religion. **Qualif.:** Available to students enrolled full-time or half time in a Masters of Divinity degree program leading to fellowship as a Unitarian Universalist minister. **Criteria:** First priority is given those grantees that have demonstrated outstanding ministerial ability, second to students with the greatest financial need.

Funds Avail.: No specific amount. **Duration:** Annual. **Deadline:** April 15. **Remarks:** The scholarship was established by Walter and Carolyn Vogt to honor Walter's father The Rev. Dr. Von Ogden Vogt and his dedication and commitment to Unitarian Universalism. Established in 2001.

11258 ■ United Engineering Foundation (UEF)
1650 Market St., Ste. 1200
Philadelphia, PA 19103
URL: www.uefoundation.org

11259 ■ United Engineering Foundation Grants *(All/Grant)*

Purpose: To support engineering and education for the advancement of engineering arts and sciences. **Focus:** Engineering. **Qualif.:** Any non-profit organization, individual and group is eligible for the grant. **Criteria:** The UEF Grants Committee will prioritize the proposals and forward prioritized proposals to the UEF Board of Trustees. Preference will be given to proposals demonstrating U.S. based organizations having 501(c)(3) status, established deadlines and with page limitation.

Funds Avail.: No specific amount. **Number Awarded:** Up to 10. **To Apply:** Applicants must submit a detailed proposal and a two-page concept paper in PDF format. **Deadline:** June 1. **Contact:** Email: grants@UnitedEngineeringFnd.org.

Awards are arranged alphabetically below their administering organizations

11260 ■ United Food and Commercial Workers International Union (UFCW)

1775 K St. NW
Washington, DC 20006
URL: www.ufcw.org

11261 ■ UFCW Local Union Scholarships *(All/Scholarship)*

Purpose: To aid UFCW local community members in their educational pursuit. **Focus:** General studies/Field of study not specified. **Qualif.:** Applicants must be UFCW members in their respective localities. **Criteria:** Selection is based on scholastic achievements, community involvement and on the submitted essay.

Funds Avail.: No specific amount. **Duration:** Annual. **Number Awarded:** Varies. **To Apply:** Applicants may visit the program website or verify the scholarship at their local union offices. **Deadline:** May 10.

11262 ■ United Methodist Young People's Ministries

1908 Grand Ave.
Nashville, TN 37212
Ph: (615)340-7079
Free: 877-899-2780
E-mail: youngpeople@gbod.org
URL: www.umcyoungpeople.org
Social Media: www.facebook.com/umcyoungpeople
www.instagram.com/umcyoungpeople
twitter.com/umcyoungpeople
www.youtube.com/user/YoungPeopleMinistry

11263 ■ David W. Self Scholarship *(Undergraduate/Scholarship)*Focus: General studies/Field of study not specified. **Qualif.:** Applicant must be a United Methodist youth that has been active in his/her local church for at least one year prior to application, a U.S. citizen or permanent resident, admitted to a full-time degree program in an accredited college/university, pursuing a "church-related" career, maintained at least a "C" average throughout high school, and be able to establish financial need.

Funds Avail.: No specific amount. **Duration:** Annual. **To Apply:** Complete application online. **Deadline:** March 1. **Contact:** URL: www.umcyoungpeople.org/david-w-self-scholarship.

11264 ■ Richard S. Smith Scholarships *(Undergraduate/Scholarship)*

Purpose: To support students in pursuing their church-related career. **Focus:** General studies/Field of study not specified. **Qualif.:** Applicants must be graduating high school seniors entering first year of undergraduate study; must be racial-ethnic minorities; must have a minimum GPA of 2.5, active membership in UMC; must be U.S. citizens or permanent residents; must be admitted to a full-time degree program in an accredited college/university pursuing a "church-related" career. **Criteria:** Selection is based on the submitted application.

Funds Avail.: $1,000. **Duration:** One year. **To Apply:** Complete application online. **Deadline:** March 1. **Contact:** URL: www.umcyoungpeople.org/richard-w-smith-scholarship.

11265 ■ United Mitochondrial Disease Foundation (UMDF)

8085 Saltsburg Rd., Ste. 201
Pittsburgh, PA 15239
Ph: (412)793-8077
Fax: (412)793-6477
Free: 888-317-8633
E-mail: info@umdf.org
URL: www.umdf.org
Social Media: www.facebook.com/theUMDF
www.instagram.com/umdf
twitter.com/UMDF
www.youtube.com/channel/UCIvkleCr0XI7oum4Cibb0ug

11266 ■ UMDF Clinical Research Fellowship Training Awards *(Professional development/Fellowship)*

Purpose: To support the training of physician scientists who plan to practice clinical management of patients with mitochondrial disorders and to conduct clinically oriented research in the field of mitochondrial medicine. **Focus:** Health sciences. **Qualif.:** Applicants must hold a Doctor of Medicine or equivalent degree and have completed an ACGME or Canadian LMCC accredited residency program by the date of grant funding. **Criteria:** Selection will be based on the committee's criteria. Preference will be given to applicants who intend to remain in the US or Canada after completing training.

Funds Avail.: No specific amount. **To Apply:** Applicants must download the Statement of Intent form available at the website. Fill out the preceding form and then save it as a normal Word document. Use only the NIH biographical sketch format, maximum of four pages. Completed Statement of Intent and all NIH biographical sketches must be submitted through email for applicants and mentors as one document. In addition, applicants must also send a signed hard copy to Jean Bassett.

11267 ■ United Nations Educational, Scientific and Cultural Organization (UNESCO)

7 Pl. de Fontenoy
75007 Paris, France
Ph: 33 1 45681000
URL: en.unesco.org
Social Media: www.facebook.com/unesco
www.instagram.com/unesco
www.linkedin.com/company/unesco
twitter.com/unesco
www.youtube.com/user/unesco

11268 ■ L'Oréal-UNESCO For Women in Science International Rising Talents *(Doctorate, Postdoctorate/Fellowship)*

Purpose: To support and encourage promising young women to pursue their scientific careers. **Focus:** Life sciences. **Qualif.:** Applicants must be at their doctoral or postdoctoral level.**Criteria:** Selection will be based on the committee's criteria.

Funds Avail.: 110,055.18 USD. **Duration:** Annual. **Number Awarded:** 15. **Remarks:** Established in 1998.

11269 ■ United Negro College Fund (UNCF)

1805 7th St. NW
Washington, DC 20001

Awards are arranged alphabetically below their administering organizations

Free: 800-331-2244
URL: www.uncf.org
Social Media: www.facebook.com/UNCF
www.instagram.com/uncf
www.linkedin.com/company/united-negro-college-fund
twitter.com/UNCF

11270 ■ UNCF Merck Graduate Science Research Dissertation Fellowships *(Graduate/Fellowship)*

Purpose: To increase the number of African Americans in the pipeline of biomedical science education and research in the fields of biological and physical sciences. **Focus:** Engineering; Life sciences; Physical sciences. **Qualif.:** Candidates must be African-American; must be citizens or permanent residents of the United States; must be enrolled full-time in a PhD or equivalent doctoral degree program majoring in a life science, physical science or engineering; must be engaged in and within 1-3 years of completing dissertation research; and must successfully complete all qualifying exams. **Criteria:** Selection will be based on academic ability and record of accomplishment of the Applicants and the soundness of the proposed doctoral research plan.

Funds Avail.: Up to $53,500. **Duration:** Annual. **Number Awarded:** 10. **To Apply:** Applicants may contact the UNCF or the Merck Company Foundation for the application process and other information. **Contact:** United Negro College Fund, 8260 Willow Oaks Corporate Dr., Ste 510, Fairfax, VA 22031-8044; Phone: 800-331-2244, E-mail: uncfmerck@uncf.org.

11271 ■ UNCF/Merck Postdoctoral Science Research Fellowships *(Postdoctorate/Scholarship)*

Purpose: To support post-graduate students to obtain postdoctoral training and to prepare for a career in biomedical research. **Focus:** Engineering; Life sciences; Physical sciences. **Qualif.:** Applicants must be African-Americans; must be citizens or permanent residents of the United States; must be PhD or equivalent doctoral degree recipients in a life or physical science by the end of the current academic year; must be appointed as new or continuing postdoctoral fellows at an academic or on-academic research institution in the USA (private industrial laboratories are excluded). **Criteria:** Selection will be based on academic ability and record of accomplishment of the Applicants and the soundness of the proposed doctoral research plan.

Funds Avail.: Up to $92,000. **Duration:** Annual. **Number Awarded:** 10. **To Apply:** Applicants may contact the UNCF or the Merck Company Foundation for the application process and other information.

11272 ■ United Parent Support for Down Syndrome

1070 S Roselle Rd.
Schaumburg, IL 60193
E-mail: info@upsfordowns.org
URL: www.upsfordowns.org
Social Media: www.facebook.com/upsfordowns
www.instagram.com/upsfordowns
twitter.com/ups4downs

11273 ■ Katie MacDonald Memorial Scholarships *(Graduate, Undergraduate/Scholarship)*

Purpose: To provide financial assistance to those individuals with Down syndrome who are pursuing their education.

Focus: Disabilities. **Qualif.:** Applicants must be U.S. citizens; pursuing junior college, undergraduate or graduate degrees in disability-related fields. **Criteria:** Selection will be based on the committee's criteria.

Funds Avail.: $2,500 each. **Number Awarded:** 5. **Deadline:** April 1. **Contact:** Email: scholarship@ upsfordowns.org.

11274 ■ Eric Martinez Memorial Scholarships *(Graduate, Undergraduate/Scholarship)*

Purpose: To provide financial assistance to individuals or siblings affected by down syndrome pursuing their education. **Focus:** General studies/Field of study not specified. **Qualif.:** Applicants must be U.S. citizens; must be individuals with Down syndrome or siblings of individuals with Down syndrome pursuing full or part-time educational or job training opportunities beyond high school or must be pursuing junior college, undergraduate or graduate degrees. **Criteria:** Selection will be based on demonstrated accomplishments; obstacles overcome; leadership and community involvement; life goals.

Funds Avail.: $2,500 each. **Number Awarded:** 2. **To Apply:** Applicants must submit a completed application form; essay/personal statement; two recommendation letters; additional documentation (transcripts, extra-curricular activities, etc). Two copies of the application packet should be submitted. **Deadline:** June 1. **Contact:** Beth Barrett, Scholarship Committee Chairman; Email: embarrett@ upsfordowns.org.

11275 ■ United Services Automobile Association (USAA)

9800 Fredericksburg Rd.
San Antonio, TX 78288
Free: 800-531-8722
URL: www.usaa.com
Social Media: www.facebook.com/USAA
twitter.com/USAA
www.youtube.com/user/usaa

11276 ■ CSM Virgil R. Williams Scholarship *(Undergraduate/Scholarship)*

Purpose: To support the education of EANGUS members, their spouses and their unmarried children. **Focus:** General studies/Field of study not specified. **Qualif.:** Applicants must be EANGUS Auxiliary members; must be unmarried, dependent sons and daughters of EANGUS Auxiliary members; must be spouses of EANGUS Auxiliary members. **Criteria:** Selection will be made based on the applicant's character, leadership and financial need.

Funds Avail.: $2,000. **To Apply:** Applicants must submit a transcript of high school credits and/or a transcript of college credits for applicants already in an institution of higher learning; a letter from the applicants with personal, specific facts as to why financial assistance is required; must have three letters of academic recommendation verifying the application and giving moral, personal and leadership traits. Application form and other documents must be submitted electronically via the internet to the Chairman of the Scholarship Committee except the school transcript. **Deadline:** June 1.

11277 ■ United South and Eastern Tribes (USET)

711 Stewarts Ferry Pke.
Nashville, TN 37214

Awards are arranged alphabetically below their administering organizations

Ph: (615)872-7900
Fax: (615)872-7417
URL: www.usetinc.org
Social Media: www.facebook.com/USETInc
www.instagram.com/uset.inc
twitter.com/USETINC
www.youtube.com/channel/UCYadd2Y--nEl5hWuZiNcXPA

11278 ■ USET Scholarship Fund (Undergraduate/ Scholarship)

Purpose: To provide financial assistance to Indian students in the USET service area. **Focus:** General studies/Field of study not specified. **Qualif.:** Applicants must be Indian students who are enrolled members of one of the twenty-seven USET Member Tribal Nations. **Criteria:** Applicants will be judged based on satisfactory scholastic standing and current enrollment or acceptance in a post-secondary educational institution.

Funds Avail.: $750- $1,000. **Duration:** Annual. **To Apply:** Applicants must submit the completed application form, three (3) letters of recommendation, verification of tribal enrollment in a USET Tribal Nation. **Deadline:** January 15. **Contact:** USET Scholarship Fund, Melisa Stephens, 711 Stewarts Ferry Pike Ste 100, Nashville TN 37214; Fax: 615-872-7417.

11279 ■ U.S. Air Force ROTC
551 E Maxwell Blvd.
Montgomery, AL 36112
Free: 866-423-7682
URL: www.afrotc.com
Social Media: www.facebook.com/afrotcofficial
www.instagram.com/usafrotc
twitter.com/usafrotc
www.youtube.com/user/AFBlueTube

11280 ■ Hispanic Serving Institution Scholarships (HSIS) (Undergraduate/Scholarship)

Purpose: To meet officer production requirements and enhance enrollment at HSIs. **Focus:** General studies/Field of study not specified. **Qualif.:** Applicant must be a U.S. citizen pass the AFROTC Physical Fitness Assessment (PFA); have at least a 2.5 cumulative college GPA; not already be a contracted scholarship recipient; must meet the age, moral, and medical requirements for AFROTC. **Criteria:** Applicants do not have to meet a selection board for this scholarship.

Funds Avail.: Amount varies. **Duration:** Annual. **To Apply:** Applicants may start the application process for the scholarship program by contacting the Air Force ROTC detachment at the school that they wish to attend.

11281 ■ Historically Black College or University Scholarships (HBCUS) (Undergraduate/Scholarship)

Purpose: To meet officer production requirements and enhance enrollment at HBCUs. **Focus:** General studies/ Field of study not specified. **Qualif.:** Applicants must be a U.S. citizen, pass the AFOQT and a physical fitness test, have a minimum 2.5 GPA and pass the height, weight and medical requirements. **Criteria:** Applicants do not have to meet a selection board.

Funds Avail.: Amount varies. **Duration:** Annual. **To Apply:** Applications for the HBCU Scholarship are processed and approved at the detachment level. Applicant must contact

the detachment serving the school, and the school will work to nominate the applicant for the appropriate scholarship program. Applications are accepted at any time each year.

11282 ■ U.S. Air Force ROTC High School Scholarship - Type 1 (High School/Scholarship)

Purpose: To provide financial assistance for college students enrolled in specific fields. **Focus:** Aeronautics; Aerospace sciences; Atmospheric science; Engineering. **Criteria:** Selection is based on leadership and work experience, extracurricular activities, results from the personal interview, questionnaire results, and academic scores.

Funds Avail.: Pays full (100 percent). **Duration:** Annual. **To Apply:** Applicants must submit complete application form with counselor certification/copy of transcripts, extracurricular activity sheet, physical Fitness Test, and SAT and/or ACT scores.

11283 ■ U.S. Air Force ROTC High School Scholarship - Type 2 (High School/Scholarship)

Purpose: To provide financial assistance to high school seniors. **Focus:** General studies/Field of study not specified. **Criteria:** Selection will be based on leadership and work experience; extracurricular activities; results from the personal interview; questionnaire results; and academic scores.

Funds Avail.: Up to $18,000 plus stipend of $900. **Duration:** Annual; Up to three and four years. **Number Awarded:** Varies. **To Apply:** Applicants must submit their application online and include the following forms counselor certification, personal Statement, physical fitness assessment, and resume; must have their high school transcripts with raised seal or signature as well as their SAT or ACT scores. **Deadline:** January 14.

11284 ■ U.S. Air Force ROTC In-College Scholarships - Type 2 (High School/Scholarship)

Purpose: To provide scholarships to college freshmen and sophomores in any major. **Focus:** General studies/Field of study not specified. **Criteria:** Selection will be based on academic performance.

Funds Avail.: Up to $18,000. **Duration:** Annual; Up to 3 years. **To Apply:** Applications can be submitted online.

11285 ■ United States Army (U.S. ARMY) - Center of Miltary History (CMH)
102 4th Ave., Bldg. 35
Fort McNair, DC 20024
URL: www.history.army.mil
Social Media: www.facebook.com/armyhistory
www.instagram.com/armyhistory
twitter.com/USArmyCMH
www.youtube.com/channel/UC
_UnoWe8iQAZVoD3LR6gKIA/featured

11286 ■ CMH Dissertation Fellowships (Graduate/ Fellowship)

Purpose: To support scholarly research and writing among qualified civilian graduate students preparing dissertations in the history of warfare. **Focus:** History, Military. **Qualif.:** Applicants must be civilian citizens of the United States unaffiliated with the U.S. government; that is, they must not be military personnel, not in federal service as civilian employees, and not under contract to the U.S. government.

Awards are arranged alphabetically below their administering organizations

Criteria: Selection of applicants on the basis of academic achievement, faculty recommendations, demonstrated writing ability, and the nature and location of the proposed research.

Funds Avail.: $10,000. **Duration:** Annual. **Number Awarded:** 3. **To Apply:** Applicants must submit the official transcripts from all undergraduate and graduate schools attended; proposed plan of research; letter of recommendation from their academic director that includes a statement approving the dissertation topic; two other letters of recommendation from individuals who can attest to their qualifications for the fellowship; and writing sample of approximately 25 pages. **Deadline:** January 15. **Contact:** Dissertation Fellowship Committee U.S. Army Center of Military History 102 4th Avenue, Building 35 Fort McNair, DC 20319-5060; Email: usarmy.mcnair.cmh.mbx.dissfellow@mail.mil.

11287 ■ U.S. Army Health Care

2040 Babcock Rd., Ste. 406
San Antonio, TX 78229
Ph: (210)945-2303
URL: www.goarmy.com
Social Media: facebook.com/goarmy
instagram.com/goarmy
pinterest.com/goarmypins
twitter.com/goarmy
youtube.com/goarmy

11288 ■ Army Health Professions Scholarship Program (HPSP) *(Professional development/ Scholarship)*

Purpose: To help students fulfill their dreams of becoming a doctor, dentist, veterinarian, clinical psychologist, or optometrist. **Focus:** Dentistry; Medicine; Ophthalmology; Optometry; Psychology; Veterinary science and medicine. **Criteria:** Selection will be based on the Board's criteria.

Funds Avail.: Minimum of $2,200. **To Apply:** Applicants must apply through an Army Recruiter.

11289 ■ United States Army Warrant Officers Association (USAWOA)

462 Herndon Pky., Ste. 207
Herndon, VA 20170-5235
Ph: (703)742-7727
Fax: (703)742-7728
Free: 800-587-2962
URL: www.usawoa.org
Social Media: www.facebook.com/USAWOA
twitter.com/usawoa_social

11290 ■ USAWOASF/Grantham University On-Line Scholarship *(Graduate/Scholarship)*

Purpose: To support the education of the relatives or dependents of USAWOA members. **Focus:** General studies/Field of study not specified. **Qualif.:** Applicants should be association regular members in good standing, their spouses and their children (natural and adopted) and stepchildren (seniors in high school or above). All must have a cumulative GPA of 3.0 or higher on a 4.0 scale. **Criteria:** Selection will be based on the committee's criteria.

Funds Avail.: No specific amount. **Duration:** Annual. **Number Awarded:** Varies. **To Apply:** Application form is available on the website. Applicants must submit a complete

application packet consisting of: the application form (typewritten format); an essay (800-100 words, include word count) on educational goals; special circumstances which may affect the applicants' school attendance; list of extracurricular activities; a recommendation letter (from instructor, faculty advisor, etc.); National Test Scores, SAT, ACT, etc.; and a 4x6 photograph (view head and shoulders). **Deadline:** May 1. **Contact:** Email: Nisker@verizon.net; Toll Free: 800-587-2962.

11291 ■ USAWOASF Regular Scholarship *(Graduate/ Scholarship)*

Purpose: To support the education of the relatives or dependents of USAWOA members. **Focus:** General studies/Field of study not specified. **Qualif.:** Applicants must be spouses, children (natural and adopted), grandchildren and dependent stepchildren, under the age of 23 years (seniors in high school or above); of members in good standing in the USAWOA; and must be in their senior year of high school (or higher) and plan to attend, or continue their education, in an accredited American college or university, vocational technical institution on a full time basis. All must have a cumulative GPA of 3.0 or higher on a 4.0 scale. The school must be a degree or certificate granting institution. **Criteria:** Selection will be based on the committee's criteria.

Funds Avail.: No specific amount. **Duration:** Annual. **Number Awarded:** Varies. **To Apply:** Application form is available on the website. Applicants must submit a complete application packet consisting of: the application form (typewritten format); an essay (800-100 words, include word count) on educational goals; special circumstances which may affect the applicants' school attendance; list of extracurricular activities; a recommendation letter (from instructor, faculty advisor, etc.); National Test Scores, SAT, ACT, etc.; and a 4x6 photograph (view head and shoulders). **Deadline:** May 1.

11292 ■ United States Association of Blind Athletes (USABA)

1 Olympic Plz.
Colorado Springs, CO 80909
Ph: (719)866-3224
Fax: (719)866-3400
URL: www.usaba.org
Social Media: www.facebook.com/UnitedStatesABA
www.instagram.com/usaba1
www.linkedin.com/company/united-states-association-of
-blind-athletes
twitter.com/usaba
www.youtube.com/user/USABA1976/feed

11293 ■ Arthur E. Copeland Scholarship *(Four Year College, Two Year College/Scholarship)*

Purpose: To provide financial assistance to a male USABA member based on athletic participation and academic achievement. **Focus:** General studies/Field of study not specified. **Qualif.:** Applicant must be a current USABA member; must have been an active participant in a USABA event; legally blind; enrolled or enrolling in a 2- or 4-year college, university or technical school as a full-time student; citizen of the United States. **Criteria:** Selection will be based on the committee's criteria.

Funds Avail.: $500. **Duration:** Annual. **Number Awarded:** 2. **To Apply:** Application should include the current college

Awards are arranged alphabetically below their administering organizations

or university name; brief cover letter and personal biography including your involvement with sport and USABA;essay of no more than 300 words about the role and importance of sport in your life. **Deadline:** July 31. **Contact:** Cat Bouwkamp, Email:cbouwkamp@usaba.org; Phone:(719) 866-3210.

11294 ■ Helen Copeland Scholarship *(Professional development, Undergraduate, Vocational/Occupational/ Scholarship)*

Purpose: To provide financial assistance to a female USABA member based on athletic participation and academic achievement. **Focus:** General studies/Field of study not specified. **Qualif.:** Legally blind scholar/athletes, active with the association during the current year, and entering or already in an academic, vocational, technical, professional, or certification program at the postsecondary level may apply.

Funds Avail.: $500. **Duration:** Annual. **To Apply:** Applications should include; name of current college/university; brief cover letter and personal biography including your involvement with sport and USABA; and essay of no more than 300 words about the role and importance of sport in your life. **Deadline:** July 31. **Contact:** Kevin Brousard, Email: kbrousard@usaba.org; Phone: 719-866-3019.

11295 ■ United States Association for Energy Economics (USAEE)
28790 Chagrin Blvd., Ste. 350
Cleveland, OH 44122-4642
Ph: (216)464-2785
Fax: (216)464-2768
E-mail: usaee@usaee.org
URL: www.usaee.org
Social Media: www.facebook.com/USEnergyEcon
www.linkedin.com/groups/7058531/profile
twitter.com/USEnergyEcon

11296 ■ Dennis J. O'Brien USAEE Best Student Paper Award *(Undergraduate/Award)*

Purpose: To showcase and reward the best student work in the profession. **Focus:** Energy-related areas. **Qualif.:** Applicants must be full-time students or have completed a degree within the past 12 months; must also be members of IAEE in good standing. **Criteria:** Recipients will be selected based on the submitted papers.

Funds Avail.: Varies. **Number Awarded:** Varies. **To Apply:** Applicants must submit an abstract; a qualification letter with photocopy of student ID; and advisor's letter or letter from a faculty member confirming that the applicant's paper meets the qualifications. Papers must be original. Only papers co-authored by students will be given consideration. **Deadline:** June 29. **Contact:** Email: usaee@ usaee.org.

11297 ■ USAEE/IAEE North American Conference Registration Fee Scholarships *(Undergraduate/ Scholarship)*

Purpose: To offset the conference registration costs for students who will be presenting a paper or poster at the conference. **Focus:** Energy-related areas. **Qualif.:** Applicants must be full-time students. **Criteria:** Awards will be awarded on a rolling basis.

Duration: Annual. **To Apply:** Applicant must submit a personal letter as well as a letter from their advisor or

another faculty member familiar with their research. Personal letter must include the following information: meets all the required qualifications; describes the energy interests and future accomplishments of attending the conference; and provides name and contact information of a faculty member. Advisor's letter should describe the applicant's research interests, nature of the academic program and progress, and recommendation for the award. **Deadline:** June 14. **Contact:** Dave Williams, USAEE Executive Director; usaee@usaee.org.

11298 ■ U.S. Capitol Historical Society (USCHS)
200 Maryland Ave. NE
Washington, DC 20002
Ph: (202)543-8919
Fax: (202)525-2790
Free: 800-887-9318
URL: www.uschs.org

11299 ■ United States Capitol Historical Society Fellowships *(Graduate/Fellowship)*

Purpose: To provide financial support to scholars researching important topics in the art and architectural history of the United States Capitol Complex. **Focus:** Art history; History, American; Museum science; United States studies. **Qualif.:** Applicant must be a graduate student enrolled in a degree program in art or architectural history, American history, American studies, museum studies, or decorative arts, and scholars with a proven record of research and publication.

Funds Avail.: $2,500 per month, up to $30,000 for a full year. **Duration:** One month and a maximum of one year. **To Apply:** Applicants must submit a curriculum vitae; transcripts of graduate work; two supporting letters; dates for which the fellowship is requested, with estimated time period for each phase of the proposed research; list of expected sources of income during the proposed period; and research proposal (maximum 5 pages). Submit materials by regular mail to Dr. Donald Kennon, or by fax, or email to Dr. Barbara Wolanin. **Deadline:** May 1. **Remarks:** Established in 1986. **Contact:** Dr. Michele Cohen, Curator, Architect of the Capitol, Phone: (202) 228-1222.

11300 ■ United States Department of Agriculture Animal and Plant Health Inspection Service (USDA APHIS)
4700 River Rd.
Riverdale, MD 20737
Ph: (301)851-2046
Fax: (301)734-5786
Free: 877-770-5990
E-mail: plantproducts.permits@aphis.usda.gov
URL: www.aphis.usda.gov
Social Media: www.linkedin.com/company/usda-aphis
twitter.com/usda_aphis
www.youtube.com/user/USDAAPHIS

11301 ■ Saul T. Wilson, Jr. Internship *(Graduate, Undergraduate/Internship)*
Purpose: To provide financial assistance to those students who are in a veterinary medicine and biomedical sciences. **Focus:** Biomedical sciences; Veterinary science and medicine. **Criteria:** Applicants are evaluated based on academic achievement.

Awards are arranged alphabetically below their administering organizations

Funds Avail.: Up to $5,000 for undergraduate studies; Up to $10,000 for graduate studies. **Duration:** Annual. **To Apply:** Applicants must submit an online application form along with a resume, transcript for all completed college work to date, proof of current enrollment on a full-time basis or if applicable, a letter of acceptance to the veterinary school, and a copy of DD-214, if claiming Veterans' Preference. **Remarks:** The Internship was established in honor of Saul T. Wilson, Jr. **Contact:** Phone: 301-851-3573.

11302 ■ U.S. Department of Commerce - National Oceanic and Atmospheric Administration (NOAA)

1401 Constitution Ave. NW, Rm. 5128
Washington, DC 20230
Ph: (301)713-1208
E-mail: noaa.staff.directory@noaa.gov
URL: www.noaa.gov

11303 ■ EPP/MSI Undergraduate Scholarship Program (USP) *(Undergraduate/Scholarship)*

Purpose: To increase the number of undergraduate and graduate students who undertake target areas integral to NOAA's mission; to train students in NOAA-related sciences. **Focus:** Atmospheric science; Oceanography. **Criteria:** Selection will be based on evaluation of relevant course work; education plan and statement of career interest; academic recommendations or endorsements; additional relevant experience related to diversity of education.

Funds Avail.: $45,000(including travel and conference participation). **Duration:** Annual. **To Apply:** Applicants must submit a completed application form; The completed application and supporting materials, including required references, must be submitted directly through the online system. **Contact:** Email: epp.usp@noaa.gov.

11304 ■ John A. Knauss Marine Policy Fellowship *(Graduate/Fellowship)*

Purpose: To provide educational experience to students who have interest in marine/ocean/Great Lakes resources and in the national policy decisions affecting those resources. **Focus:** Water resources. **Qualif.:** Applicants must be graduate students with hosts in the legislative branch, executive branch or appropriate associations/institutions located in the Washington, DC area. **Criteria:** Recipients will be selected based on submitted materials.

Funds Avail.: $45,000 for stipend and living expenses, $9,000 to cover health insurance, moving expenses, academic degree-related activities, and fellowship-related activities. **Duration:** Annual. **To Apply:** Applicants must submit curriculum vitae, a personal education and career goals statement, two letters of recommendation, copy of all official undergraduate and graduate transcripts, listing of classes and career plan(s).

11305 ■ NOAA Graduate Sciences Scholarships *(Graduate/Scholarship)*

Purpose: To provide financial assistance to graduate students pursuing a degree in atmospheric and oceanic-related sciences. **Focus:** Atmospheric science; Oceanography. **Criteria:** Selection will be based on academic records; statement of career interests and goals; compatibility of the applicant's background with the interests of NOAA.

To Apply: Applicants must submit a completed application form; essay on, "How Your Course of Study will Benefit or Complement NOAA's Mission"; statement of the applicant's

academic and career goals; letter of acceptance to an accredited graduate school/university; official college transcripts; three references from individuals who know the student in a professional capacity; list of current and planned courses.

11306 ■ U.S. Department of Education

400 Maryland Ave. SW
Washington, DC 20202
Free: 800-872-5327
URL: www2.ed.gov
Social Media: facebook.com/ed.gov
www.facebook.com/ED.gov
twitter.com/usedgov
youtube.com/user/usedgov

11307 ■ ARIT Summer Fellowships for Intensive Advanced Turkish Language Study *(Graduate, Undergraduate/Fellowship)*

Purpose: To promote American and Turkish research and exchange related to Turkey. **Focus:** Foreign languages; General studies/Field of study not specified. **Qualif.:** Applicant must be a full-time students and scholars affiliated at academic institutions; must be citizen, national, or permanent resident of the United States; must currently enrolled in an undergraduate or graduate level academic program, or be faculty; must have minimum B average in current program of study; must perform at the high-intermediate level on a proficiency-based admissions examination.

Funds Avail.: No specific amount. **Duration:** Annual. **Number Awarded:** Approximately 18. **To Apply:** Applicants must submit complete application information; transcripts and three letters of reference; application fee in the amount of $25. **Deadline:** 'February. **Contact:** Dr. Sylvia Önder, Director; Division of Eastern Mediterranean Languages Department of Arabic and Islamic Studies, Georgetown University; 210 North Poulton Hall, 1437 - 37th Street N.W., Washington, D.C. 20007; Email:aritfellowship@georgetown.edu or aritoffice@gmail.com.

11308 ■ U.S. Department of Education - Office of Postsecondary Education

LBJ Building
400 Maryland Ave., SW
Washington, DC 20202
Ph: (202)453-6914
E-mail: customerservice@inet.ed.gov
URL: www2.ed.gov
Social Media: www.facebook.com/ed.gov
twitter.com/usedgov
www.youtube.com/user/usedgov

11309 ■ ARIT Summer Fellowships for Intensive Advanced Turkish Language Study *(Graduate, Undergraduate/Fellowship)*

Purpose: To promote American and Turkish research and exchange related to Turkey. **Focus:** Foreign languages; General studies/Field of study not specified. **Qualif.:** Applicant must be a full-time students and scholars affiliated at academic institutions; must be citizen, national, or permanent resident of the United States; must currently enrolled in an undergraduate or graduate level academic program, or be faculty; must have minimum B average in

Awards are arranged alphabetically below their administering organizations

current program of study; must perform at the high-intermediate level on a proficiency-based admissions examination.

Funds Avail.: No specific amount. **Duration:** Annual. **Number Awarded:** Approximately 18. **To Apply:** Applicants must submit complete application information; transcripts and three letters of reference; application fee in the amount of $25. **Deadline:** 'February. **Contact:** Dr. Sylvia Önder, Director; Division of Eastern Mediterranean Languages Department of Arabic and Islamic Studies, Georgetown University; 210 North Poulton Hall, 1437 - 37th Street N.W., Washington, D.C. 20007; Email:aritfellowship@georgetown.edu or aritoffice@gmail.com.

11310 ■ Jacob K. Javits Fellowships Program
(Master's, Doctorate/Fellowship)

Purpose: To provide fellowships to students of superior academic ability to undertake study at the Doctoral and Master of Fine Arts level in selected fields of arts, humanities, and social sciences. **Focus:** Arts; Humanities; Social sciences. **Criteria:** Selection will be based on demonstrated achievement, financial need and exceptional promise.

Funds Avail.: No specific amount. **To Apply:** Applicants may obtain a copy of FAFSA online or from their institution's financial aid office and are encouraged to submit their FAFSA electronically. **Deadline:** September 30. **Contact:** Carmen Gordon, program officer; U.S. Department of Education, OPE Student Service, Jacob K. Javits Fellowships Program, 400 Maryland Ave. S W, Washington, DC, 20202; Phone: 202-453-7311; Email: carmen.gordon@ed.gov, OPE_Javits_Program@ed.gov.

11311 ■ U.S. Department of Education - Office of Special Education and Rehabilitative Services - National Institute on Disability and Rehabilitation Research (NIDRR)
400 Maryland Ave. SW, MS 2700
Washington, DC 20202
Ph: (202)245-7640
Fax: (202)245-7643
URL: www2.ed.gov/about/offices/list/om/fs_po/osers/home.html?src=oc

11312 ■ Mary Switzer Research Fellowships - Distinguished Fellowships *(Doctorate/Fellowship)*

Purpose: To support qualified individuals to engage in scientific research relating to the rehabilitation of individuals with disabilities. **Focus:** Disabilities; Rehabilitation, Physical/Psychological. **Qualif.:** Applicants must be individuals with a doctorate, other terminal degree or comparable academic qualifications who have seven or more years of research experience in subject areas, methods or techniques directly relevant to rehabilitation research. **Criteria:** Applications are subjected to a competitive peer review process that is dictated by federal regulation.

To Apply: Applicants information is available from Grants.gov; may download an application package online. **Contact:** Marlene Spencer, U.S. Department of Education, OSERS, National Institute on disability and Rehabilitation Research, 550 12th St. SW, RM. 5133, Washington, DC 20202-2700; Email: marlene.spencer@ed.gov; Phone: 202-245-7532.

11313 ■ Mary Switzer Research Fellowships - Merit Fellowships *(Professional development/Fellowship)*

Purpose: To support qualified individuals to engage in scientific research relating to the rehabilitation of individu-

als with disabilities. **Focus:** Disabilities; Rehabilitation, Physical/Psychological. **Qualif.:** Applicants must be individuals with advanced professional training or research experience in an independent study in appropriate areas that are directly pertinent to disability and rehabilitation, but who are in earlier stages of their research career, with less than the required seven years experience, or who do not have a doctorate. **Criteria:** Selection will be based on the committee's criteria.

To Apply: Applicants information is available from Grants.gov; may download an application package online. **Contact:** Marlene Spencer, U.S. Department of Education, OSERS, National Institute on disability and Rehabilitation Research, 550 12th St. SW, RM. 5133, Washington, DC 20202-2700; Email: marlene.spencer@ed.gov; Phone: 202-245-7532.

11314 ■ U.S. Department of Energy - Fermi National Accelerator Laboratory
PO Box 500
Batavia, IL 60510-5011
Ph: (630)840-3000
Fax: (630)840-4343
E-mail: fermilab@fnal.gov
URL: www.fnal.gov
Social Media: www.facebook.com/Fermilab
twitter.com/Fermilab

11315 ■ Fermilab Internships for Physics Majors
(Undergraduate/Internship)

Purpose: To familiarize students with opportunities at the frontiers of scientific research in particle physics. **Focus:** Physics. **Qualif.:** Applicants must be undergraduate foreign students, major in physics and attending U.S. or non-U.S. universities; must provide evidence of identity and eligibility to work in the U.S.; must have medical insurance while at Fermilab. **Criteria:** Selection will be based on the committee's criteria.

Funds Avail.: No specific amount. **Duration:** Annual. **To Apply:** Applicants must submit names of two people who are willing to provide references; they will receive a link to the site where the letters can be submitted; preference is for letters from internship mentors or university professors. **Deadline:** January 9. **Contact:** internship@fnal.gov.

11316 ■ Fermilab Science Undergraduate Laboratory Internship *(Undergraduate/Internship)*

Purpose: To offer outstanding students a chance to work with Fermilab scientists or engineers on a project within the context of laboratory research. **Focus:** Engineering; Physics. **Qualif.:** Applicants must be at least 18 years of age, permanent residents or U.S. citizens currently enrolled as full-time undergraduate physics or engineering major, at least one year as matriculating undergraduate students with minimum cumulative grade point average (GPA) of 3.0 on a 4.0 scale and must have high school diplomas or certificate of general education development; must provide evidence of identity and eligibility to work in the U.S.

Funds Avail.: Stipend of $540 per 40-hour week. **Duration:** Annual. **To Apply:** Applicants must have the following requirements complete entrance and exit surveys; must make a poster presentation to mentors and peers; must submit a one-page peer review of another SULI Intern's poster or oral presentation and; must submit an abstract and a 1500-3000 word research project report in the required format.

Awards are arranged alphabetically below their administering organizations

11317 ■ Fermilab Summer Internships in Science & Technology (SIST) (Undergraduate/Internship)

Purpose: To offer outstanding students a chance to work with Fermilab scientists or engineers on a project within the context of laboratory research. **Focus:** Engineering; Physics. **Qualif.:** Applicants must be undergraduate college students currently enrolled in four-year U.S. colleges or universities, major in Physics, Engineering (mechanical, electrical and computer), Materials Science, Mathematics and Computer Science and must be members of under-represented group (Black, Hispanic, Native, American and women); must provide evidence of identity and eligibility to work in the U.S.

Funds Avail.: No specific amount.

11318 ■ Lee Teng Undergraduate Fellowship in Accelerator Science and Engineering (Undergraduate/Fellowship)

Purpose: To support and promote the exciting and challenging world of particle accelerator physics and technology to the students. **Focus:** Physics. **Qualif.:** Applicants must be sophomores or junior students who are currently, legally enrolled full time at US universities, regardless of their nationality; must provide identification, as well as evidence of citizenship or visa status.

Funds Avail.: U.S. Citizens and Permanent Residents Wage of $13.50 per 40-hour work week and Foreign Students: Wage of $12.50 per hour for a standard 40-hour work week. **Duration:** Annual. **To Apply:** Applicants must submit a curriculum vitae, a Copy of Unofficial University Transcript, and two Reference Letters. **Deadline:** January 22.

11319 ■ Helen Edwards Summer Internship (Undergraduate/Internship)

Purpose: To offer students a chance to work with Fermilab scientists and engineers regarding on the scientific research in physics and technology of particle accelerators. **Focus:** Engineering; Physics. **Qualif.:** Applicants must be at least 18 years of age, students of university in a country in Europe, majoring in Physics or Engineering and fluent in English; must be at least one full year at the university at the moment of applying and must have a minimum of 4.0 Grade Point Average (in 2-5 grading system). **Criteria:** Specialization in Accelerator Physics and Technology is preferred.

Funds Avail.: Wage of $12.50 per hour for a standard 40-hour work week. **Duration:** Annual. **To Apply:** Applicants must submit names of two people who are wiling to provide references; they will receive a link to the site where the letters can be submitted; preference is for letters from internship mentors or university professors. **Deadline:** January 8. **Contact:** Fermilab Helen Edwards Internship, PO Box 500, MS 229, Batavia, IL, 60510, USA; Phone: 630-840-3929; Email: HE-Intership@fnal.gov.

11320 ■ U.S. Department of Energy - Lawrence Livermore National Laboratory (LLNL)

7000 East Ave.
Livermore, CA 94550-9234
Ph: (925)422-1100
Fax: (925)422-1370
URL: www.llnl.gov
Social Media: www.facebook.com/livermore.lab
www.instagram.com/livermore_lab
www.linkedin.com/company/lawrence-livermore-national-laboratory
twitter.com/Livermore_Lab
www.youtube.com/user/LivermoreLab

11321 ■ Lawrence Fellowship (Doctorate/Fellowship)

Purpose: To support PhD student to broaden their education, continue their training, and participate in leading-edge scientific research. **Focus:** Clinical laboratory sciences. **Qualif.:** Applicants must either be in the process of completing their Ph.D. (within one year and employment may not start until Ph.D. requirements have been verified), or have received their Ph.D. degree within five-years of being hired as a Lawrence Fellow. **Criteria:** Selection is based on the statement of technical interests, letters of recommendation, and your scientific track record (publication record).

Funds Avail.: $9,713 per month. **Duration:** Annual; Three years. **To Apply:** Applicants should submit the information Via online along with CV, a project relevance statement, Interest Statement, three letters of recommendation, and transcripts. **Deadline:** October 10. **Contact:** Mildred Lambrecht; P.O. Box 808, L-019, Livermore, CA 94551, Phone: 925-424-4839; Email: lambrecht1@llnl.gov.

11322 ■ U.S. Department of Energy - Office of Science

1000 Independence Ave. SW
Washington, DC 20585
Ph: (202)586-5430
URL: science.energy.gov

11323 ■ Office of Science Graduate Student Research (SCGSR) Program (Graduate, Master's, Postdoctorate/Fellowship)

Purpose: To support outstanding students to pursue graduate training in basic research in areas of physics, non-medical biology; chemistry, mathematics, engineering, computer and computational sciences, and environmental sciences relevant to the Office of Science. **Focus:** Science. **Qualif.:** Applicant must be a graduate students currently pursuing Ph.D. degrees in areas of physics, chemistry, material sciences, biology (non-medical), mathematics, engineering, computer or computational sciences, or specific areas of environmental sciences that are aligned with the mission of the Office of Science are eligible to apply for the research awards provided by the SCGSR program; the research projects are expected to advance the graduate awardees' overall doctoral work while providing access to the expertise, resources, and capabilities available at the DOE laboratories. **Criteria:** Selection will be based on the committee's criteria.

Funds Avail.: No specific amount. **Duration:** Annual. **Number Awarded:** 70. **To Apply:** In addition to meeting the eligibility requirements, applicants must provide the following: a completed online application with all relevant fields answered, including three essays; an academic transcript for every institution listed by the applicants on the application; General Record Examination (GRE) scores for the General Test and a Subject Test. GRE scores are not required but second-year encouraged; three letters of recommendation from individuals that can speak to the applicants' abilities and potential.

Awards are arranged alphabetically below their administering organizations

11324 ■ U.S. Department of Health and Human Services - Agency for Healthcare Research and Quality (AHRQ)

5600 Fishers Ln.
Rockville, MD 20857
Ph: (301)427-1364
URL: www.ahrq.gov
Social Media: www.facebook.com/ahrq.gov
www.linkedin.com/company/agency-for-healthcare
  -research-and-quality
twitter.com/ahrqnews
www.youtube.com/user/AHRQHealthTV

11325 ■ AHRQ Mentored Clinical Scientist Research Career Development Award *(Doctorate, Master's/ Award)*

Purpose: To support an intensive mentored research career development experience, comprised of didactic study and/or mentored research opportunities in health services research, for individuals with clinical doctoral degrees. **Focus:** Health care services. **Qualif.:** Candidates for the K08 award must have a clinical doctoral degree. Such degrees include, but are not limited to, the MD, DO, DDS, DMD, OD, DC, PharmD, ND (Doctor of Naturopathy), and DVM. Individuals with the PhD or other doctoral degree in clinical disciplines such as clinical psychology, nursing, clinical genetics, speech-language pathology, audiology or rehabilitation are also eligible. **Criteria:** Selection process in which only those applications deemed to have the highest scientific and technical merit (generally the top half of applications under review) will be discussed and assigned an overall impact score.

Duration: Annual. **To Apply:** Applicant organizations must complete and maintain the following registrations as described in the SF 424 (R&R) Application Guide to be eligible to apply for or receive an award. All registrations must be completed prior to the application being submitted. Registration can take 6 weeks or more, so applicants should begin the registration process as soon as possible. All registrations require that applicants be issued a DUNS number. After obtaining a DUNS number, applicants can begin both SAM and eRA Commons registrations. The same DUNS number must be used for all registrations, as well as on the grant application. Applicants must complete and maintain an active registration, which requires renewal at least annually. must have an active DUNS number and SAM registration in order to complete the eRA Commons registration. must have an active DUNS number and SAM registration in order to complete the Grants.gov registration. **Deadline:** January 10; March10. **Contact:** Tamara Willis, PhD, MPH Agency for Healthcare Research and Quality (AHRQ) Telephone: 301-427-1011 Email: Tamara.Willis@ahrq.hhs.gov.

11326 ■ Health Services Research Dissertation Awards *(Doctorate/Award)*

Purpose: To support students in developing their career and research skills regarding health services. **Focus:** Health care services. **Qualif.:** Applicants must be U.S. citizens, non-citizen nationals, or permanent residents by the time of the grant award; be full-time academic students in good standing, who are enrolled in an accredited research doctoral program in such fields as behavioral sciences, health services research, nursing, social sciences, epidemiology, biostatistics, health policy, health informatics, engineering and mathematics; have completed all non-dissertation requirements for their doctoral degree by the time of submission of the application, including completion of their qualifying exams. (The only exception allowable will be the completion of required clinical internships that follow completion of the dissertation.); not have more than part-time employment in addition to the requirements of their current, full-time academic student appointments (defined as greater than 20 hours per week); not be recipients of mentored career development awards; institution is any of the following: public or non-profit private institution (such as a university, college, faith-based or community-based organization), units of local or State government, eligible agencies of the Federal Government and Indian/Native American Tribal Government or Designated Organizations.

Funds Avail.: Up to $40,000 in direct costs. **Duration:** Annual; minimum 9 months up to 17 months. **To Apply:** Applicants must visit the Grants.gov website for the online application process and other required materials. **Deadline:** February 1; May 1; August 1 and November 1. **Contact:** For application submission, Email: journalpublishing@ahrq.hhs.gov; Division of Research EducationOffice of Extramural Research, Education and Priority Populations (OEREP) Agency for Healthcare Research and Quality; Phone: (301) 427-1391; Email:GregoryStu-ard@ahrq.hhs.gov.

11327 ■ U.S. Department of Health and Human Services - Centers for Disease Control and Prevention (CDC)

1600 Clifton Rd.
Atlanta, GA 30329
Free: 800-232-4636
URL: www.cdc.gov
Social Media: www.facebook.com/CDC
www.instagram.com/CDCgov
twitter.com/CDCgov
www.youtube.com/user/CDCstreamingHealth

11328 ■ CDC Steven M. Teutsch Prevention Effectiveness (PE) *(Doctorate/Fellowship)*

Purpose: To establish a cadre of quantitative policy analysts at CDC whose work provides information for health policy decision-makers regarding allocation and use of resources to maximize health impact. **Focus:** Economics; Engineering, Industrial; Health sciences; Health services administration; Operations research. **Qualif.:** Applicants must hold a doctoral degree in economics or applied economics, decision sciences, health services research or related health sciences, industrial engineering or operations research, public policy or policy analysis or related quantitatively-oriented field; non-US citizens must be legal permanent residents or eligible for J-1 status.

Funds Avail.: No specific amount. **Duration:** Annual. **To Apply:** Applicants must apply from the online; must submit three signed letters of recommendation, Signed by the letter writer. **Deadline:** January 22. **Contact:** CDC Steven M. Teutsch Prevention Effectiveness Fellowship; Phone: 404-498-6324; Email: PEF@cdc.gov.

11329 ■ The National Center for Health Statistics Postdoctoral Research Program (NCHS) *(Postdoctorate/Fellowship)*

Purpose: To provide information to develop programs and policies that will improve the health of the American people. **Focus:** General studies/Field of study not specified.

Awards are arranged alphabetically below their administering organizations

Funds Avail.: No specific amount. **Duration:** Irregular. **Number Awarded:** 1. **Contact:** Luigia Franks, Centers for Disease Control and Prevention, National Center for Health Statistics, 3311 Toledo Rd., Mail Stop-P-08, Rm. 183, Hyattsville, MD, 20782; Phone: 301-458-4217; Email: NCHSPostDoc@cdc.gov.

11330 ■ Presidential Management Fellows (PMF)
(Graduate, Master's/Fellowship)

Purpose: To attract outstanding graduates from different academic discipline who are committed to excellence in leadership and management of public policies and programs. **Focus:** Management. **Qualif.:** Applicants must be ready to graduate or be a recent graduate within two years of earning a master's, law, or doctoral degree from any academic discipline; display a strong interest in, and commitment to, a career in public health policy, leadership, and management. **Criteria:** Selection will be based on the committee criteria.

Funds Avail.: No specific amount. **Duration:** Annual; Two years. **To Apply:** Application must submit online. **Deadline:** October 14.

11331 ■ Preventive Medicine Residency and Fellowship (PMR) *(Other/Fellowship)*

Purpose: To provide hands-on experiences in public health agencies at the federal, state and local levels. **Focus:** Medicine. **Qualif.:** Applicants must commit to a one or two-year full-time training period (depending on the program); be willing to relocate throughout the duration of the training; meet the professional and licensing requirements for hiring by the U.S. government according to the U.S; office of personnel management; be U.S. citizens or permanent residents; have trained in the Epidemic Intelligence Service (EIS) program or have comparable applied epidemiology experience; have completed at least 12 months of ACGME-accredited postgraduate clinical training involving at least 11 months of direct patient care; have a current, full and unrestricted medical license from a U.S. licensing jurisdiction; have a Master of Public Health or equivalent accredited degree, per ACGME requirement.

Funds Avail.: No specific amount. **Duration:** Annual. **To Apply:** Applicants must apply from the online; Letters of recommendation; official transcripts for all degrees earned since high school; proof of a current, full and unrestricted license to practice their qualifying clinical specialty in a US licensing jurisdiction. **Deadline:** July 31. **Contact:** Email: PrevMed@cdc.gov.

11332 ■ Public Health Informatics Fellowship Program (PHIFP) *(Professional development, Master's, Graduate/Fellowship)*

Purpose: To provide training and experience in applying computer and information science and technology to real public health problems. **Focus:** Computer and information sciences.

Funds Avail.: No specific amount. **Duration:** Two years. **To Apply:** Applicants must apply from the online; must submit three letters of recommendation; work and volunteer experience; Post-graduate training and skills; publications, presentations, and grants; Unofficial college or university transcripts. **Deadline:** November 8. **Contact:** Email: phifp@cdc.gov.

11333 ■ U.S. Department of Health and Human Services - Health Resources and Services Administration (HRSA)
5600 Fishers Ln.
Rockville, MD 20852-1750
Ph: (301)443-2216
Fax: (301)443-1246
Free: 888-ASK-HRSA
E-mail: ask@hrsa.gov
URL: www.hrsa.gov

11334 ■ HRSA Scholarships for Disadvantaged Students *(Undergraduate/Scholarship)*

Purpose: To provide scholarships for full-time, financially needy students from disadvantaged backgrounds who are enrolled in health professions and nursing programs. **Focus:** Health sciences; Medicine; Mental health; Nursing; Public health. **Qualif.:** Applicants must be enrolled in and apply for aid to participating health professions training program.

Duration: Annual.

11335 ■ NURSE Corps Scholarship Program
(Professional development/Scholarship)

Purpose: To provide scholarships to nursing students in exchange for a minimum two year full-time service commitment (or part-time equivalent), at an eligible health care facility with a critical shortage of nurses. **Focus:** Nursing. **Qualif.:** Applicants must be U.S. citizen (born or naturalized), a national, or a lawful permanent resident; must have enrolled--or accepted for enrollment--in a professional nursing degree program at an accredited school of nursing in the U.S. **Criteria:** Preference will depend on financial need.

Funds Avail.: $1,363 monthly stipend. **Duration:** Annual. **Deadline:** June 14. **Contact:** Phone: 800-221-9393.

11336 ■ U.S. Department of Health and Human Services - National Heart, Lung, and Blood Institute (NHLBI)
31 Center Dr., Rm. 5B10
Bethesda, MD
Ph: (301)592-8573
Fax: (301)592-8563
E-mail: nhlbiinfo@nhlbi.nih.gov
URL: www.nhlbi.nih.gov
Social Media: www.facebook.com/NHLBI
twitter.com/nih_nhlbi?lang=en

11337 ■ Ruth L. Kirschstein Individual Predoctoral NRSA for MD/PhD and other Dual Degree Fellowships *(Doctorate, Master's/Fellowship)*

Purpose: To enhance the integrated research and clinical training of promising predoctoral students, who are matriculated in a combined MD/PhD or other dual-doctoral degree training program. **Focus:** Behavioral sciences; Biomedical sciences.

11338 ■ U.S. Department of Health and Human Services - National Institutes of Health - National Library of Medicine (NLM)
8600 Rockville Pke.
Bethesda, MD 20894

Awards are arranged alphabetically below their administering organizations

Ph: (301)594-5983
Fax: (301)402-1384
Free: 888-346-3656
URL: www.nlm.nih.gov
Social Media: www.facebook.com/nationallibraryofmedicine
twitter.com/nlm_news
youtube.com/user/NLMNIH

11339 ■ NLM Associate Fellowship *(Postgraduate/ Fellowship)*

Purpose: To provide a broad foundation in health sciences information services, and to prepare librarians for future leadership roles in health sciences libraries and in health services research. **Focus:** Health sciences. **Qualif.:** Applicants must be master's degree in an ALA-accredited library/information science program, earned by August of the year of appointment or within 2 years. (Undergraduate degree can be in any major.); must be United States or Canadian citizenship. **Criteria:** Preference will be given to U.S citizens.

Duration: Annual. **Number Awarded:** Up to 5. **To Apply:** Applicants must submit an application using an online application system; both undergraduate and graduate transcripts must be uploaded. Must provide three educational or professional references; one must be from a library school professor. All documents must be in English or include an official English translation. **Deadline:** January 26. **Remarks:** Established in 1957. **Contact:** ORISE; 1299 Bethel Valley Road, MC-100-36, Oak Ridge, TN, 37830-0117; Phone: 865-576-9975; Fax: 865-574-2846; Email: nlm.associate.fellowship@orau.org.

11340 ■ U.S. Department of Health and Human Services - U.S. Public Health Service - National Institutes of Health (NIH)

9000 Rockville Pke.
Bethesda, MD 20892
Ph: (301)496-4000
URL: www.nih.gov
Social Media: www.instagram.com/nihgov/
twitter.com/nih
www.youtube.com/user/nihod

11341 ■ National Institute of Health Undergraduate Scholarship Program (NIH UGSP) *(Undergraduate/ Scholarship)*

Purpose: To aid students from disadvantaged backgrounds who are committed to careers in biomedical, behavioral, and social science health-related research. **Focus:** Behavioral sciences; Biomedical research; Social sciences. **Criteria:** Selection will be based on competitive scholarships to students from disadvantaged backgrounds who are committed to careers in biomedical, behavioral, and social science health-related research.

Funds Avail.: $20,000. **Duration:** Annual; up to four years. **To Apply:** Applicants must complete the online application form; must complete the Certification for Exceptional Financial Need (EFN) Form and submit it to applicant's financial aid office to determine if applicant meet the financial need eligibility guidelines. **Contact:** Email: ugsp@od.nih.gov.

11342 ■ U.S. Department of Labor - Bureau of Labor Statistics (BLS)

2 Massachusetts Avenue NE
Washington, DC 20212-0001

Ph: (202)691-5200
E-mail: blsdata_staff@bls.gov
URL: www.bls.gov

11343 ■ ASA/NSF/BLS Fellowships *(Graduate/ Fellowship, Recognition, Grant)*

Purpose: To improve the collaboration between government and academic research. **Focus:** Government; Statistics. **Qualif.:** Applicants should have academically recognized research records and considerable expertise in their areas of proposed research. Moreover, applicants must be affiliated with a U.S. institution. **Criteria:** Recipients will be selected based on the proposed research project; preference will be given to those who meet the criteria.

Funds Avail.: No specific amount. **Duration:** Annual. **Number Awarded:** Varies. **To Apply:** Applicants must submit the following information via email: a curriculum vitae; names and addresses of three references; a detailed research proposal that includes background information about research topic, significance of expected results; advantages of conducting research at the bls; and detailed budget estimate (salary, relocation, travel expenses, research support). all of these must be compiled in one pdf file. **Deadline:** January 3. **Contact:** Email: joyce@amstat.org.

11344 ■ U.S. Department of State

Rm. 2236, 2201 C St. NW
Washington, DC 20520
Ph: (202)895-3500
E-mail: ofm-info@state.gov
URL: www.state.gov

11345 ■ ARIT Fellowships in the Humanities and Social Sciences in Turkey *(Postdoctorate, Graduate/ Fellowship)*

Purpose: To help applicant's research and study facilities for researchers, as well as connections with colleagues, institutions, and authorities through its centers in Istanbul and Ankara. **Focus:** History, Ancient; Humanities; Medieval studies; Modern languages; Social sciences. **Qualif.:** Applicants must be scholars and advanced graduate students engaged in research on ancient, medieval, or modern times in turkey, in any field of the humanities and social sciences; student applicants must have fulfilled all requirements for the doctorate except the dissertation by June of the current year, and before beginning any ARIT-sponsored research; non-U.S. applicants who reside in the U.S. or Canada are expected to maintain an affiliation with an educational institution in the U.S. or Canada.

Funds Avail.: No specific amount. **Duration:** Annual. **To Apply:** Applicants must provide complete application information; three letters of recommendation; letters of reference; copy of graduate transcript; supporting documents. **Deadline:** November 1. **Contact:** University of Pennsylvania Museum, 3260 South Street, Philadelphia PA 19104-6324. For further information call (215) 898-3474, fax (215) 898-0657, or e-mail to aritoffice@gmail.com.

11346 ■ The Thomas R. Pickering Foreign Affairs Fellowship *(Graduate, Undergraduate/Fellowship)*

Purpose: To provide funding to participants as they are prepared academically and professionally to enter the United States Department of State Foreign Service. **Focus:** Business; Economics; Foreign languages; International af-

Awards are arranged alphabetically below their administering organizations

fairs and relations; Political science; Public administration; Sociology.

Remarks: The fellowship is named in honor of Ambassador Pickering, one of the most distinguished and capable American diplomats of the latter half of the 20th century.

11347 ■ U.S. Department of State - Bureau of Educational and Cultural Affairs - Fulbright U.S. Student Program

809 United Nations Plz.
New York, NY 10017-3850
Ph: (202)632-3238
E-mail: fulbright@state.gov
URL: eca.state.gov/fulbright
Social Media: www.facebook.com/fulbright
www.linkedin.com/company/the-fulbright-program
twitter.com/FulbrightPrgrm

11348 ■ ARIT Fellowships in the Humanities and Social Sciences in Turkey *(Postdoctorate, Graduate/ Fellowship)*

Purpose: To help applicant's research and study facilities for researchers, as well as connections with colleagues, institutions, and authorities through its centers in Istanbul and Ankara. **Focus:** History, Ancient; Humanities; Medieval studies; Modern languages; Social sciences. **Qualif.:** Applicants must be scholars and advanced graduate students engaged in research on ancient, medieval, or modern times in turkey, in any field of the humanities and social sciences; student applicants must have fulfilled all requirements for the doctorate except the dissertation by June of the current year, and before beginning any ARIT-sponsored research; non-U.S. applicants who reside in the U.S. or Canada are expected to maintain an affiliation with an educational institution in the U.S. or Canada.

Funds Avail.: No specific amount. **Duration:** Annual. **To Apply:** Applicants must provide complete application information; three letters of recommendation; letters of reference; copy of graduate transcript; supporting documents. **Deadline:** November 1. **Contact:** University of Pennsylvania Museum, 3260 South Street, Philadelphia PA 19104-6324. For further information call (215) 898-3474, fax (215) 898-0657, or e-mail to aritoffice@gmail.com.

11349 ■ U.S. Environmental Protection Agency (EPA)

1200 Pennsylvania Ave.
Washington, DC 20460
Ph: (202)272-0167
Free: 888-372-8255
E-mail: acres_help@epa.gov
URL: www.epa.gov
Social Media: www.facebook.com/EPA
www.instagram.com/epagov
twitter.com/epa
youtube.com/user/USEPAgov

11350 ■ EPA Science to Achieve Results Fellowships (STAR) *(Graduate/Fellowship)*

Purpose: To encourage students to obtain advanced degrees and pursue careers in an environmental field. **Focus:** Environmental science. **Qualif.:** Applicants must attend a fully accredited U.S. college or university for their

graduate studies; must be U.S. citizens or legal residents; must be a masters' students and doctoral candidates in environmental studies. **Criteria:** Selection will be based on evaluation of the submitted requirements and specific criteria.

Funds Avail.: Up to $44,000 per year. **Duration:** Annual. **To Apply:** Applicants must submit a completed application form. **Contact:** U.S. Environmental Protection Agency, at the above address.

11351 ■ U.S. Environmental Protection Agency - National Exposure Research Laboratory (NERL)

1200 Pennsylvania Avenue NW
Washington, DC 20004
Ph: (919)541-2106
URL: www.epa.gov
Social Media: www.instagram.com/epagov
twitter.com/epa
www.youtube.com/user/USEPAgov

11352 ■ NERL Postdoctoral Research Program *(Postdoctorate, Advanced Professional, Professional development/Fellowship)*

Purpose: To provide scientific leadership, understanding, and tools necessary to quantify exposure for humans and ecosystems. **Focus:** Ecology; Remote sensing. **Qualif.:** Applicants must be U.S. citizens or permanent residents; must be scientists interested in conducting high priority research in areas such as: atmospheric modeling; watershed/hydrological modeling; genomics; geospatial and statistical analyses; human exposure modeling; informatics; and remote sensing. Only in the absence of qualified U.S. citizens will permanent residents be considered, and permanent resident applicants must be seeking citizenship as outlined in 8 U.S.C. 1324b(a)(3)(B). **Criteria:** Selection of candidates will be based on the aforementioned qualifications and compliance with the application details.

Funds Avail.: $77,382 to $100,784. **Duration:** Up to three years. **Number Awarded:** Varies. **To Apply:** Applicants must submit the following: up-to-date curriculum vitae; letter of recommendation from their senior research advisors or comparable officials (this may be emailed with their application or separately, whichever the advisors prefer); cover letter indicating positions/project descriptions and locations of interest, their email address, U.S. citizenship status, and how the candidates learned of the program; form DD-214, if claiming veteran's preference. Please take note that applications sent via email must be submitted in a format readable by the office, such as MS Word, portable document format (PDF), rich text format (RTF), or plain text. Use of any format the office cannot read may invalidate the candidates' application. Online applications from journal websites will not be accepted. Please include "NCEA Post-Doctoral Program" in the email subject line. **Contact:** Candidates may email their application materials to US EPA, HRMD-C639-02 Attn: Ms. Danielle Weiker, NERL Post Doctoral Program Research Triangle Park, NC 27711; Email: ordpostdocapps@epa.gov; For express courier, send to: Attn: Ms. Danielle Weiker, NERL Post Doctoral Program Mail Drop C639-02 HRMD/Suite C635 4930 Page Road Durham, NC 27703; questions, contact Ms. Danielle Weiker at (800) 433-9633.

Awards are arranged alphabetically below their administering organizations

11353 ■ U.S. Environmental Protection Agency - National Health and Environmental Effects Research Laboratory (NHEERL)

109 T.W. Alexander Dr.
Research Triangle Park, NC 27709
URL: archive.epa.gov

11354 ■ NHEERL Postdoctoral Research Program
(Postdoctorate, Advanced Professional, Professional development/Fellowship)

Purpose: To support research that may contribute to the protection of human health and the environment. **Focus:** General studies/Field of study not specified. **Qualif.:** Candidates must be U.S. citizens or permanent residents; must be scientists interested in conducting high priority research that contributes to protecting human health and the environment. Only in the absence of qualified U.S. citizens will permanent residents be considered, and permanent resident applicants must be seeking citizenship as outlined in 8 U.S.C. 1324b(a)(3)(B). **Criteria:** Selection of candidates will be based on the aforementioned qualifications and compliance with the application details.

Funds Avail.: $74,596 to $107,542. **Duration:** Up to 3 year appointment. **Number Awarded:** Varies. **To Apply:** Candidates must submit the following: up-to-date curriculum vitae; letter of recommendation from their senior research advisors or comparable officials (this may be emailed with their application or separately, whichever the advisors prefer); cover letter indicating positions/project descriptions and locations of interest, their email address, U.S. citizenship status, and how the candidates learned of the program; form DD-214, if claiming veteran's preference. Please take note that applications sent via email must be submitted in a format readable by the office, such as MS Word, portable document format (PDF), rich text format (RTF), or plain text. Use of any format the office cannot read may invalidate the candidates' application. Online applications from journal websites will not be accepted. Please include "NHEERL Post-Doctoral Program" in the email subject line. **Contact:** Candidates may email their application materials to US EPA, HRMD-C639-02 Attn: Ms. Danielle Weiker, NHEERL Post Doctoral Program Research Triangle Park, NC 27711; Email: ordpostdocapps@epa.gov; For express courier, send to: Attn: Ms. Danielle Weiker, NHEERL Post Doctoral Program Mail Drop C639-02 HRMD/Suite C635 4930 Page Road Durham, NC 27703; questions, contact Ms. Danielle Weiker at (800) 433-9633.

11355 ■ U.S. Environmental Protection Agency - National Risk Management Research Laboratory (NRMRL)

Rm No. D310-G
Cincinnati, OH 45268
Ph: (513)569-7900
Fax: (580)436-8500
E-mail: tri.help@epa.gov
URL: www.epa.gov/aboutepa/national-risk-management
 -research-laboratory-nrmrl
Social Media: facebook.com/EPA
instagram.com/epagov
twitter.com/epa
youtube.com/user/USEPAgov

11356 ■ NRMRL Postdoctoral Research Program
(Postdoctorate, Advanced Professional, Professional development/Fellowship)

Purpose: To aid aspiring postdoctoral researchers in conducting significant studies on risk management research. **Focus:** Risk management. **Qualif.:** Applicants must be U.S. citizens or permanent residents. Only in the absence of qualified U.S. citizens will permanent residents be considered, and permanent resident applicants must be seeking citizenship as outlined in 8 U.S.C. 1324b(a)(3)(B).**Criteria:** Selection of candidates will be based on the aforementioned qualifications and compliance with the application details.

Funds Avail.: $73,242-$95,876. **Duration:** Up to three years.**Number Awarded:** Varies. **To Apply:** Applicants must submit the following: up-to-date curriculum vitae; letter of recommendation from their senior research advisors or comparable officials (this may be emailed with their application or separately, whichever the advisors prefer); cover letter indicating positions/project descriptions and locations of interest, their email address, U.S. citizenship status, and how the candidates learned of the program; form DD-214, if claiming veteran's preference. Please take note that applications sent via email must be submitted in a format readable by the office, such as MS Word, portable document format (PDF), rich text format (RTF), or plain text. Use of any format the office cannot read may invalidate the candidates' application. Online applications from journal websites will not be accepted. Please include "NCEA Post-Doctoral Program" in the email subject line. **Contact:** Candidates may email their respective application materials to ordpostdocapps@epa.gov.

11357 ■ U.S. Environmental Protection Agency - Office of Research and Development - National Center for Computational Toxicology (NCCT)

109 T.W. Alexander Dr., MD-D-143-02
Research Triangle Park, NC 27711
Ph: (919)541-4219
URL: www2.epa.gov/aboutepa/about-national-center
 -computational-toxicology-ncct
Social Media: www.facebook.com/EPA

11358 ■ NCCT Postdoctoral Research Program
(Postdoctorate, Advanced Professional, Professional development/Fellowship)

Purpose: To aid the next generation of exceptionally qualified scientists with outstanding talent and credentials by encouraging them to fill EPA postdoctoral positions. **Focus:** Medical research; Toxicology. **Criteria:** Selection of candidates will be based on the aforementioned qualifications and compliance with the application details.

Funds Avail.: No specific amount. **To Apply:** Candidates must submit the following: up-to-date curriculum vitae; letter of recommendation from their senior research advisors or comparable officials (this may be emailed with their application or separately, whichever the advisors prefer); cover letter indicating positions/project descriptions and locations of interest, their email address, U.S. citizenship status, and how the candidates learned of the program; form DD-214, if claiming veteran's preference. Please take note that applications sent via email must be submitted in a format readable by the office, such as MS Word, portable document format (PDF), rich text format (RTF), or plain text. Use of any format the office cannot read may invalidate

Awards are arranged alphabetically below their administering organizations

the candidates' application. Online applications from journal websites will not be accepted. Please include "NCCT Post-Doctoral Program" in the email subject line. **Contact:** Candidates may email their respective application materials to ordpostdocapps@epa.gov.

11359 ■ U.S. Environmental Protection Agency - Office of Research and Development - National Center for Environmental Assessment

Two Potomac Yard
2733 S Crystal Dr.
Arlington, VA 22202-3553
URL: epa.gov
Social Media: www.facebook.com/EPA
www.instagram.com/epagov
twitter.com/epa
www.youtube.com/user/USEPAgov

11360 ■ NCEA Postdoctoral Research Program
(Postdoctorate/Fellowship)

Purpose: To provide federal research experience to up-and-coming environmental scientists. **Focus:** Conservation of natural resources; Risk management. **Criteria:** Selection of candidates will be based on the aforementioned qualifications and compliance with the application details.

Funds Avail.: $72,332-$99,296. **Duration:** Annual; Up to three years. **Number Awarded:** Varies. **To Apply:** Applicants must submit the following: up-to-date curriculum vitae; letter of recommendation from their senior research advisors or comparable officials (this may be emailed with their application or separately, whichever the advisors prefer); cover letter indicating positions/project descriptions and locations of interest, their email address, U.S. citizenship status, and how the candidates learned of the program; form DD-214, if claiming veteran's preference. Please take note that applications sent via email must be submitted in a format readable by the office, such as MS Word, portable document format (PDF), rich text format (RTF), or plain text. Use of any format the office cannot read may invalidate the candidates' application. Online applications from journal websites will not be accepted. Please include "NCEA Post-Doctoral Program" in the email subject line. **Contact:** Email:ordpostdocapps@epa.gov.

11361 ■ U.S. Federal Emergency Management Agency - Federal Insurance & Mitigation Administration (FIMA)

500 C St. SW
Washington, DC 20472
URL: www.fema.gov

11362 ■ EERI/FEMA NEHRP Graduate Fellowship in Earthquake Hazard Reduction *(Graduate/Fellowship)*

Purpose: To support study and research that may contribute to the science and practice of earthquake hazard mitigation. **Focus:** Earth sciences. **Qualif.:** Applicants must be enrolled in a graduate degree program at an accredited U.S. college/university and must hold U.S. citizenship or permanent resident status. **Criteria:** Selection is based All application materials must be submitted electronically to EERI, including a letter of nomination from a faculty sponsor at the student's institution and two additional reference letters.

Funds Avail.: $12,000. **Duration:** Annual. **Number Awarded:** 2. **To Apply:** Applicants must include an academic transcript; a statement of educational and career goals that also describes involvement in EERI; letter of nomination from a faculty sponsor at the student's institution and two additional reference letters.

11363 ■ United States Geospatial Intelligence Foundation (USGIF)

13665 Dulles Technology Drive, Suite 100
Herndon, VA 20171
Fax: (703)793-9069
Free: 888-698-7443
E-mail: info@usgif.org
URL: www.usgif.org
Social Media: www.facebook.com/USGIF
twitter.com/usgif

11364 ■ United States Geospatial Intelligence Foundation Graduate Scholarships *(Graduate/Scholarship)*

Purpose: To further the advancement of the geospatial tradecraft, USGIF is dedicated to assist promising students studying GEOINT, geospatial sciences, and related fields. **Focus:** Geosciences. **Qualif.:** Applicants must be graduate students interested in geospatial sciences. **Criteria:** Selection based on their academic and professional excellence.

Funds Avail.: $5,000. **Duration:** Annual. **Number Awarded:** Multiple. **Remarks:** Established in 2004. **Contact:** E-mail: scholarships@usgif.org.

11365 ■ United States Geospatial Intelligence Foundation High School Scholarships *(Undergraduate, Doctorate, Graduate, High School/Scholarship)*

Purpose: To further the advancement of the geospatial tradecraft, USGIF is dedicated to assist promising students studying GEOINT, geospatial sciences, and related fields. **Focus:** Geosciences. **Qualif.:** Applicants must be graduating high school students interested in geospatial sciences. **Criteria:** Selection based on their academic and professional excellence.

Funds Avail.: $2,000. **Duration:** Annual. **Number Awarded:** Multiple. **Contact:** E-mail: scholarships@usgif.org.

11366 ■ United States Geospatial Intelligence Foundation Undergraduate Scholarships *(Undergraduate/Scholarship)*

Purpose: To help further the geospatial tradecraft and to assist promising students interested in the geospatial sciences. **Focus:** Geosciences. **Qualif.:** Applicants must be undergraduate students interested in geospatial sciences. **Criteria:** Selection based on their academic and professional excellence.

Funds Avail.: $5,000. **Duration:** Annual. **Number Awarded:** Multiple. **Remarks:** Established in 2004. **Contact:** E-mail: scholarships@usgif.org.

11367 ■ U.S. Global Leadership Coalition

1129 20th St. NW, Ste. 600
Washington, DC 20036
Ph: (202)689-8911
Fax: (202)689-8910
E-mail: info@usglc.org
URL: www.usglc.org

Awards are arranged alphabetically below their administering organizations

Social Media: www.facebook.com/USGLC
twitter.com/USGLC

11368 ■ USGLC Internships - Communications
(Undergraduate, Doctorate/Internship)

Purpose: To help individuals in their career development by means of providing on-job training for them to make their marks on foreign policy. **Focus:** Communications; International affairs and relations. **Qualif.:** Applicants must be juniors, seniors, graduate students, and recent graduates who are able to commit at least 20 hours/week in the Communications Department of USGLC. **Criteria:** Selection of interns will be based on the Communications Department's criteria.

Funds Avail.: No specific amount. **To Apply:** Applicants must send their resume and cover letter. **Deadline:** August 1 (fall term); November 1 (spring term); April1 (summer term). **Contact:** Email: intern@usglc.org.

11369 ■ USGLC Internships - Government Relations
(Undergraduate, Graduate/Internship)

Purpose: To help individuals in their career development by means of providing on-job training for them to make their marks on foreign policy. **Focus:** Government; International affairs and relations. **Qualif.:** Applicants must be juniors, seniors, graduate students, and recent graduates who are able to commit at least 20 hours/week in the Communications Department of USGLC. **Criteria:** Selection of interns will be based on the Government Relations Department's criteria.

Funds Avail.: No specific amount. **To Apply:** Applicants must send their resume and cover letter. **Deadline:** August 1 (fall term); November 1 (spring term); April1 (summer term). **Contact:** Email: intern@usglc.org.

11370 ■ USGLC Internships - Outreach *(Undergraduate, Graduate/Internship)*

Purpose: To help individuals in their career development by means of providing on-job training for them to make their marks on foreign policy. **Focus:** International affairs and relations; Leadership, Institutional and community. **Qualif.:** Applicants must be juniors, seniors, graduate students, and recent graduates who are able to commit at least 20 hours/week in the Communications Department of USGLC. **Criteria:** Selection of interns will be based on the Outreach Department's criteria.

Funds Avail.: No specific amount. **To Apply:** Applicants must send their resume and cover letter. **Deadline:** August 1 (fall term); November 1 (spring term); April1 (summer term). **Contact:** Email: intern@usglc.org.

11371 ■ USGLC Internships - Policy *(Undergraduate, Graduate/Internship)*

Purpose: To assist individuals by providing them trainings and career developments for them to make their marks on foreign policy. **Focus:** Government; International affairs and relations. **Qualif.:** Applicants must be juniors, seniors, graduate students, and recent graduates who are able to commit at least 20 hours/week in the Communications Department of USGLC. **Criteria:** Selection of interns will be based on the Policy Department's criteria.

Funds Avail.: No specific amount. **To Apply:** Applicants must send their resume and cover letter. **Deadline:** August 1 (fall term); November 1 (spring term); April1 (summer term). **Contact:** Email: intern@usglc.org.

11372 ■ United States Golf Association (USGA)
PO Box 708
Far Hills, NJ 07931
Ph: (908)234-2300
Fax: (908)234-9687
URL: www.usga.org
Social Media: www.facebook.com/USGA
www.instagram.com/usga
www.linkedin.com/company/united-states-golf-association
twitter.com/usga
www.youtube.com/user/TheUSGA

11373 ■ USGA/Chevron STEM Scholarship Program
(Undergraduate/Scholarship)

Purpose: To support students seeking their respective careers in STEM courses. **Focus:** Engineering; Mathematics and mathematical sciences; Science; Technology.

11374 ■ United States Hunter Jumper Association (USHJA)
3870 Cigar Ln.
Lexington, KY 40511
Ph: (859)225-6700
Fax: (859)258-9033
E-mail: membership@ushja.org
URL: www.ushja.org
Social Media: www.facebook.com/USHJA
www.instagram.com/ushunterjumper
twitter.com/ushja

11375 ■ USHJA Foundation Hamel Scholarship for Further Education *(Undergraduate/Scholarship)*
Purpose: To provide financial support to those students who are in need. **Focus:** General studies/Field of study not specified. **Qualif.:** Applicants must be current USHJA members who have been members for at least three consecutive years; must be a US citizen or legal resident accepted to a college, university, trade or professional school in the United States for the current school year; must have GPA of 3.0 (or better) on a 4.0 scale; for those not recently in school, equivalent employment history will be considered; must demonstrate financial need.
Funds Avail.: $25,000. **Duration:** Annual. **Number Awarded:** 1. **To Apply:** Applicant must submit application form. **Deadline:** July 31.

11376 ■ United States Institute of Peace (USIP)
2301 Constitution Ave. NW
Washington, DC 20037
Ph: (202)457-1700
Fax: (202)429-6063
E-mail: eventinquiries@usip.org
URL: www.usip.org
Social Media: www.facebook.com/usinstituteofpeace
www.instagram.com/usipeace/
www.linkedin.com/company/united-states-institute-of
  -peace/
www.linkedin.com/company/united-states-institute-of-peace
twitter.com/USIP
www.youtube.com/user/usinstituteofpeace

11377 ■ Learning from Peace in Sub-Saharan Africa
(Professional development/Grant)
Purpose: To support research in Africa that focus on the peacebuilding field. **Focus:** African studies; Peace studies.

Awards are arranged alphabetically below their administering organizations

Qualif.: All U.S. and foreign non-profit organizations and universities are eligible. Applicants must be able to demonstrate that they have personnel and organizational capacity in the area where the project would be implemented. **Criteria:** Preference will be given to local organizations in the region.

Funds Avail.: $25,000-$100,000. **Number Awarded:** 2 to 3. **To Apply:** There is a two step application process. The first step in the process is to submit a mandatory concept note. Sample concept note forms are available on the web site. Concept notes should be no longer than 3 pages. The concept note template will guide you through the process and help you formulate your proposal narrative in the following sections: research question and how the proposed project seeks to address the topic of learning from examples of peace; proposed research approach and dissemination plan; anticipated impact of the project on filling a gap in knowledge, advancing practice and/or improving policy making; project monitoring and evaluation; qualifications of the organization and the project team; and estimated cost and timeline of the project. **Deadline:** November 9. **Contact:** E-mail: africagrants@usip.org.

11378 ■ Peace Dissertation Prize Grant
(Postgraduate/Grant)

Purpose: To recognize the outstanding dissertation on the analysis of violent conflict, conflict resolution, peacemaking, or peacebuilding completed in a United States graduate program. **Focus:** Peace studies. **Qualif.:** A dissertation must be completed at a U.S. graduate institution in the previous academic year (June to May) and nominated by the head of the department in which the dissertation has been accepted.

Funds Avail.: $1,000. **Duration:** Annual. **To Apply:** Applications must include: nomination letter from department head; candidate's curriculum vitae (including contact information); and dissertation. **Deadline:** September 30.

11379 ■ Promoting the Rule of Law and Access to Justice *(Other/Grant)*

Purpose: To support Afghanistan's civil society organizations in promoting the rule of law and citizen's access to justice. **Focus:** Law; Peace studies. **Qualif.:** Applicants must be legally registered Afghan civil society organizations. **Criteria:** Decisions will be made on a rolling basis.

Funds Avail.: $25,000 to $150,000. **Number Awarded:** 10-12. **To Apply:** Applicants must submit a three-page concept note that should include: a brief description of the proposed activity or project; how will the applicants evaluate whether the project has achieved its stated objectives (one paragraph) and; if the applicants' project is successful, briefly explain what changes will have been created as a result of the project; a short statement describing the applicants' organization, including its purpose and status as a non-profit NGO; names of project directors and staff, their qualification and relevant experience and contact information (email and telephone). **Deadline:** January 21.

11380 ■ Jennings Randolph Peace Scholarship Dissertation Program *(Doctorate/Scholarship, Fellowship)*

Purpose: To support research from top academics in a variety of fields that contribute to a wider understanding of how to manage conflict and build sustainable peace effectively. **Focus:** Peace studies. **Qualif.:** Applicants must be citizens of any country; must be enrolled in recognized doctoral programs in accredited universities in the United States. **Criteria:** Recipients will be selected based on

project significance; project design; implementation; potential as a peace scholar.

Funds Avail.: $20,000 per academic year. **Duration:** Annual. **To Apply:** Applications must be submitted through the Fluxx online application system. On the application form, please indicate the scholarship(s) for which you would like to be considered. Three letters of recommendation must be attached to your application in the Fluxx system. One letter must be from the dissertation advisor, and two from current professors. **Deadline:** October 15. **Remarks:** Established in 1988.

11381 ■ United States Institute of Peace Jennings Randolph Senior Fellowship Program *(Advanced Professional/Fellowship)*

Purpose: To support targeted research, analysis and writing that is more closely integrated with the work of the Institute. **Focus:** Peace studies. **Qualif.:** Applicants $10,000 per month. They may be academics, independent writers and researchers, journalists, or practitioners. Citizens of any country are eligible to be senior fellows. Former senior fellows are eligible to reapply for Senior Fellowships after 4 years of holding a Senior Fellowship; fellowships may not be used to cover tuition or other costs related to obtaining a degree. **Criteria:** Recipients will be selected based on: overall project significance; project design; implementation; track record and reputation; potential as fellows.

Funds Avail.: $10,000 per month. **Duration:** Annual. **To Apply:** Applicants must complete and submit the application form together with their proposed project. **Deadline:** March 30. **Remarks:** Established in 1986.

11382 ■ United States Judo Federation (USJF)
PO Box 338
Ontario, OR 97914
Ph: (541)889-8753
Fax: (541)889-5836
E-mail: no@usjf.com
URL: www.usjf.com
Social Media: www.facebook.com/usjudofederation
www.instagram.com/usjudofederation
www.linkedin.com/company/united-states-judo-federation
twitter.com/usjudofed
www.youtube.com/playlist?list=PL566240AAD1B6F468

11383 ■ George C. Balch Scholarship *(Graduate/ Scholarship)*

Purpose: To provide financial assistance to judo students. **Focus:** Education. **Qualif.:** Applicants must be judo students who are high school seniors or graduate students pursuing a college degree in Education. **Criteria:** Recipients will be judged based on academic records.

Funds Avail.: $1,000. **Duration:** Annual; 4 years. **Number Awarded:** 1. **To Apply:** Applicants must submit a filled-out application form. **Deadline:** August 15. **Contact:** USJF National Office Email: no@usjf.com.

11384 ■ Joseph J. Fitzsimmons Scholarship Fund *(Doctorate/Scholarship)*

Purpose: To USJF members who are pursing a medical degree in a recognized academic institution. **Focus:** Medicine. **Criteria:** Selection will be based on committee's criteria.

Awards are arranged alphabetically below their administering organizations

Funds Avail.: No specific amount. **To Apply:** Applicants must submit a filled-out application form which can be obtained online; and must send a copy of their acceptance letter from the medical school. **Deadline:** July 15.

11385 ■ Keiko Fukuda Scholarship *(Undergraduate, Postgraduate/Scholarship)*

Purpose: To encourage female judoka to continue their formal education and to further their training in judo. **Focus:** General studies/Field of study not specified. **Qualif.:** Applicants must be female judoka and must be U.S. Citizens; post-secondary education must have at least a "B" average. **Criteria:** Selection will be based on outstanding contribution to the development of judo on a local, yudan-shakai, or national level; good competition records (shiai or kata); good moral character and social conduct; and dedication to judo.

Funds Avail.: $400 - $500. **Duration:** Annual. **To Apply:** Applicants must submit a completed application form.

11386 ■ Tamo Kitaura Scholarships *(Other/ Scholarship)*

Purpose: To provide financial assistance to USJF referees. **Focus:** General studies/Field of study not specified. **Qualif.:** Applicants must be USJF referees who have reached a degree of technical proficiency; must show an interest in developing themselves through testing and certification. **Criteria:** Recipients will be selected based on submitted application materials.

Funds Avail.: No specific amount. **To Apply:** Applicants must complete the application form which can be obtained online.

11387 ■ Ben Palacio Scholarships *(Undergraduate/ Scholarship)*

Purpose: To financially assist students who wish to continue their judo education. **Focus:** General studies/Field of study not specified. **Qualif.:** Applicants must have plans to enroll in the City College of San Francisco. **Criteria:** Recipients will be selected based on submitted application materials.

Funds Avail.: No specific amount. **To Apply:** Applicants must contact the Board of Trustees for further information.

11388 ■ United States Naval Research Laboratory (NRL)

4555 Overlook Ave. SW
Washington, DC 20375
Ph: (202)767-3200
Fax: (202)265-8504
E-mail: asee@hro1.nrl.navy.mil
URL: www.nrl.navy.mil
Social Media: www.facebook.com/USNRL
twitter.com/usnrl
www.youtube.com/user/USNRL

11389 ■ ASEE-NRL Postdoctoral Fellowship Program *(Postdoctorate/Fellowship)*

Purpose: To increase the involvement of scientists and engineers from academia and industry to scientific and technical areas of interest and relevance to the Navy. **Focus:** Architecture, Naval; Naval art and science. **Qualif.:** Applicants must be U.S. citizens or legal permanent residents and have received the PhD, ScD, or other research doctoral degree recognized in U.S. academic

circles as equivalent to the PhD within seven years of the date of application. **Criteria:** Selection is based on the technical quality and relevance of the proposed research, recommendations by the Navy laboratories or centers, academic qualifications, reference reports, and availability of funds.

Funds Avail.: The stipend level is currently $79,720 annually. Travel and relocation expenses are paid, with limited funds available for professional travel if approved by NRL. **Duration:** Annual. **To Apply:** Applicants are required to register online to apply. **Deadline:** February 1; May 1; August 1.

11390 ■ U.S. News & World Report, LP

120 Fifth Ave., 7th Fl.
New York, NY 10011
Ph: (212)716-6800
URL: www.usnews.com
Social Media: www.facebook.com/usnewsandworldreport
twitter.com/usnews

11391 ■ U.S. News Path to College Scholarship *(Undergraduate/Scholarship)*

Purpose: To assist high school students who plan to continue their education at a four-year U.S. college or university. **Focus:** General studies/Field of study not specified.

11392 ■ U.S. Office of Personnel Management (USOPM)

1900 E St. NW
Washington, DC 20415-1000
Ph: (202)606-1800
URL: www.opm.gov
Social Media: www.facebook.com/USOPM
twitter.com/USOPM

11393 ■ CyberCorps (R): Scholarship For Service *(Undergraduate, Graduate, Doctorate/Scholarship)*

Purpose: To increase and strengthen the cadre of federal information assurance professionals that protect the U.S. government's critical information infrastructure. **Focus:** Computer and information sciences. **Qualif.:** Applicant must be a full-time student pursuing a bachelor's or master's degree in a coherent formal program that is focused on cyber security at an awardee institution, or research-based doctoral student; be a citizen or a lawful permanent resident of the U.S.; meet criteria for federal employment; and be able to obtain a security clearance, if required.

Funds Avail.: $22,500 for undergraduate students and $34,000 for graduate students. **To Apply:** Each participating university manages their own application/selection process. After deciding upon a university, contact directly for application/selection procedures. **Remarks:** Provides scholarships that may fully fund the typical costs incurred by full-time students at a participating institution, including tuition and education and related fees. Additionally, participants receive stipends of $22, 500 for undergraduate students and $34, 000 for graduate students. In return, recipients must agree to work after graduation for a government agency or a federally funded research and development center in a position related to cybersecurity for a period equal to the length of the scholarship. **Contact:** SFS

Awards are arranged alphabetically below their administering organizations

Program Office: sfs@opm.gov (757-441-3186) or Kathy Roberson, SFS Program Manager (405-259-8277).

11394 ■ U.S. Pan Asian American Chamber of Commerce (USPAACC)

1329 18th St. NW
Washington, DC 20036
Ph: (202)296-5221
Fax: (202)296-5225
Free: 800-696-7818
E-mail: info@uspaacc.com
URL: uspaacc.com
Social Media: www.facebook.com/
   UsPanAsianAmericanChamberOfCommerce
www.linkedin.com/company/uspaacc-ef
twitter.com/uspaacc

11395 ■ USPAACC Ampcus Hallmark Scholarship
(Undergraduate/Scholarship)

Purpose: To support high school seniors nationwide for their post-secondary education. **Focus:** General studies/ Field of study not specified. **Qualif.:** Applicants must be at least 16 years of age at the time of application; must be high school seniors; must be of Asian Pacific Island heritage; must be citizens or permanent residents of the United States; must be beginning full-time study at an accredited post-secondary educational institution in the United States; must be able to attend the current CelebrAsian Procurement Conference. **Criteria:** Selection will be based on the applicants' academic achievement of 3.3 GPA or higher, leadership in extracurricular activities, involvement in community service and financial need.

Funds Avail.: $3,000 to $5,000. **Duration:** Annual. **To Apply:** Application form must be completed online and submitted with the following: a 2x2 photo; an essay of 350 to 400 words answering the question "Why Should I Be Awarded this Scholarship?"; high school transcript; a copy of most recent household tax return signed by taxpayer(s); two letters of recommendation; post-secondary information. **Deadline:** May 15. **Remarks:** Established in 1989.

11396 ■ USPAACC College Hallmark Scholarships
(Undergraduate/Scholarship)

Purpose: To support high school seniors nationwide for their post-secondary education. **Focus:** General studies/ Field of study not specified. **Qualif.:** Applicants must be at least 16 years old and high school seniors; must be of Asian Pacific Island heritage (for most scholarships); must be U.S. citizens or permanent residents beginning full-time study at an accredited post-secondary educational institute in the fall; must have a minimum 3.3 GPA, leadership in extracurricular activities, involvement in community service, and financial need.

Funds Avail.: $3,000 to $5,000. **Duration:** Annual. **Number Awarded:** 10 to 20. **To Apply:** Application form must be completed online and submitted with the following: a 2x2 photo; an essay of 350 to 400 words answering the question "Why Should I Be Awarded this Scholarship?"; high school transcript; a copy of most recent household tax return signed by taxpayer(s); two letters of recommendation; post-secondary information. **Deadline:** May 15. **Remarks:** Established in 1989.

11397 ■ USPAACC Denny's Hungry for Education Scholarship *(Undergraduate/Scholarship)*

Purpose: To support students by giving them higher educational opportunities in order to learn and succeed.

Focus: General studies/Field of study not specified. **Qualif.:** Applicants must be at least 16 years old and high school seniors; must be of Asian Pacific Island heritage (for most scholarships); must be U.S. citizens or permanent residents beginning full-time study at an accredited post-secondary educational institute in the fall; must have a minimum 3.3 GPA, leadership in extracurricular activities, involvement in community service, and financial need.

Funds Avail.: $3,000 to $5,000. **To Apply:** Application form must be completed online and submitted with the following: a 2x2 photo; an essay of 350 to 400 words; high school transcript; a copy of most recent household tax return signed by taxpayer(s); two letters of recommendation; post-secondary information. **Deadline:** May 15.

11398 ■ United States Society on Dams (USSD)

1616 17th St., Ste. 483
Denver, CO 80202
Ph: (303)628-5430
Fax: (303)628-5431
E-mail: info@ussdams.org
URL: www.ussdams.org
Social Media: www.facebook.com/ussocietyondams
www.linkedin.com/company/ussd
twitter.com/ussdams

11399 ■ United States Society on Dams Scholarships *(Graduate, Undergraduate/Scholarship)*

Purpose: To help students pursue their education. **Focus:** Construction. **Qualif.:** Student Members whose academic program has a potential for developing practical solutions to design and construction problems and other dam-related issues. **Criteria:** Selection will be based on the committee's criteria.

Duration: Annual. **To Apply:** Applications can be submitted online.

11400 ■ United States Tennis Association Foundation

70 W Red Oak Ln.
White Plains, NY 10604
Ph: (914)696-7223
E-mail: foundation@usta.com
URL: www.ustafoundation.com
Social Media: www.linkedin.com/company/usta-foundation/
   about

11401 ■ Marian Wood Baird Scholarship
(Undergraduate/Scholarship)

Purpose: To provide scholarships to deserving young individuals who have participated in the United States Tennis Association. **Focus:** General studies/Field of study not specified. **Criteria:** Selection will be based on the aforesaid qualifications.

Funds Avail.: Total of $15,000 for 4 years. **Duration:** Annual; up to 4 years. **Number Awarded:** 2 (1 male; 1 female). **To Apply:** Applicants are requested to provide the following additional information; which is to be uploaded directly to students application (by logging onto their USTA Foundation Scholarship account): letters of recommendation; one from a teacher or guidance counselor or mentor; one from a tennis coach; federal tax returns or FAFSA; and, recent photo (.jpg format, no larger than 2 MB).

Awards are arranged alphabetically below their administering organizations

Remarks: The scholarship is named in honor of the late Marian Wood Baird, who had been recognized by the USTA for over 40 years of volunteer service. **Contact:** Email: scholarships@usta.com.

11402 ■ Dwight F. Davis Memorial Scholarship
(Undergraduate/Scholarship)

Purpose: To provide scholarships to qualified high school seniors. **Focus:** General studies/Field of study not specified. **Criteria:** Selection will be based on the aforesaid qualifications.

Funds Avail.: $10,000 ($2,500 per annum). **Duration:** Annual; up to 4 years. **Number Awarded:** 2 (1 male; 1 female). **To Apply:** Applicants are requested to provide the following additional information; which is to be uploaded directly to students application (by logging onto their USTA Foundation Scholarship account): letters of recommendation; one from a teacher or guidance counselor or mentor; one from a tennis coach; federal tax returns or FAFSA; and, recent photo (.jpg format, no larger than 2 MB). **Deadline:** March 21. **Remarks:** The scholarship is named in honor of Dwight Filey Davis, who became president of the U.S. Lawn Tennis Association in 1923. **Contact:** Email: scholarships@usta.com.

11403 ■ Dwight Mosley Scholarship Award
(Undergraduate/Scholarship)

Purpose: To provide scholarship to high school seniors of ethnically diverse heritage. **Focus:** General studies/Field of study not specified. **Criteria:** Selection will be based on the aforesaid qualifications.

Funds Avail.: $10,000 ($2,500 per annum). **Duration:** Annual; up to 4 years. **Number Awarded:** 2 (1 male; 1 female). **To Apply:** Applicants are requested to provide the following additional information; which is to be uploaded directly to students application (by logging onto their USTA Foundation Scholarship account): letters of recommendation; one from a teacher or guidance counselor or mentor; one from a tennis coach; federal tax returns or FAFSA; and, recent photo (.jpg format, no larger than 2 MB). **Deadline:** March 30. **Remarks:** The scholarship was named in memory of Dwight A. Mosley, the first African American elected to the USTA Board of Directors. **Contact:** E-mail: scholarships@usta.com.

11404 ■ Eve Kraft Education & College Scholarship
(Undergraduate/Scholarship)

Purpose: To provide scholarships to qualified high school seniors. **Focus:** General studies/Field of study not specified.

Funds Avail.: $2,500 each. **Duration:** Annual; up to 4 years. **Number Awarded:** 2 (one male and one female). **To Apply:** Applicants are requested to provide the following additional information; which is to be uploaded directly to students application (by logging onto their USTA Foundation Scholarship account): letters of recommendation; one from a teacher/guidance counselor or mentor; one from a tennis coach; federal tax returns and/or FAFSA; and, recent photo (.jpg format, no larger than 2 MB). **Deadline:** March 30. **Remarks:** The scholarship is named in memory of Eve Kraft of Princeton, New Jersey, a tennis pioneer who introduced thousands of young people to the game of tennis, particularly in disadvantaged communities. **Contact:** Email: scholarships@usta.com.

11405 ■ USTA Serves College Education Scholarship
(Undergraduate/Scholarship)

Purpose: To support high school seniors who have excelled academically, demonstrated community service and participated in an organized tennis program. **Focus:** General studies/Field of study not specified. **Qualif.:** Applicants must be high school senior students entering a two- or four-year college or university. **Criteria:** Selection will be based on the committee's criteria.

Funds Avail.: $8,000. **Duration:** Annual; up to 4 years. **To Apply:** Applicants may contact the Foundation for further information. **Deadline:** March 30. **Contact:** E-mail: scholarships@usta.com.

11406 ■ USTA Serves College Textbook Scholarship
(Undergraduate/Scholarship)

Purpose: To assist students in purchasing textbooks or supplies. **Focus:** General studies/Field of study not specified. **Qualif.:** Applicants must be high school senior students who are entering a two- or four-year college or university program. **Criteria:** Selection will be based on the committee's criteria.

Funds Avail.: $1,000. **Duration:** Annual. **To Apply:** Applicants may contact the Foundation for further information. **Deadline:** March 30.

11407 ■ U.S. Travel Association
1100 New York Ave. NW, Ste. 450
Washington, DC 20005
Ph: (202)408-8422
URL: ustravel.org
Social Media: www.facebook.com/U.S.TravelAssociation
www.facebook.com/U.S.TravelAssociation?fref=ts
www.instagram.com/ustravel_association/
www.linkedin.com/company/ustravelassociation
twitter.com/USTravel

11408 ■ Ronald H. Brown Memorial Scholarship
(Undergraduate/Scholarship)

Purpose: To financially support undergraduate students who are committed to the pursuit of a career in any segment of the travel industry. **Focus:** General studies/Field of study not specified.

Funds Avail.: $3,000. **Deadline:** June 13.

11409 ■ U.S.-Ukraine Foundation (USUF)
1660 L St. NW, Ste. 1000
Washington, DC 20036-5634
Ph: (202)524-6555
Fax: (202)280-1989
E-mail: info@usukraine.org
URL: www.usukraine.org
Social Media: www.facebook.com/usukraine
instagram.com/usukraine
www.linkedin.com/company/66228
twitter.com/usukraine
youtube.com/c/usukraine

11410 ■ Mychajlo Dmytrenko Fine Arts Foundation Scholarships *(Undergraduate/Scholarship)*

Purpose: To support the education of Art students from the Academy of Fine Arts in Kyiv. **Focus:** Art. **Qualif.:** Applicants must be art students at the academy of Fine Arts in Kyiv. **Criteria:** Selection is based on criteria.

Funds Avail.: No specific amount. **Duration:** Annual. **To Apply:** Applicants must submit a completed application

---

Awards are arranged alphabetically below their administering organizations

form. **Remarks:** Established in 2000. **Contact:** 1425 La Perla Long Beach CA 90815 USA and look for Mark Dmytrenko, President or call at Phone: 877-813-4591; Fax: 562-986-5770; Email: foundation@dmytrenko.org.

11411 ■ European College of Liberal Arts Scholarships (ECLA) *(Undergraduate/Scholarship)*

Purpose: To offer full scholarships on a need-blind basis. **Focus:** General studies/Field of study not specified. **Qualif.:** Applicants must study German while attending ECLA; must have earned 30 credit hours in a full year program and 8 credits in the summer program; should be between ages 18-24 with the right background and interests, proficient academic performance and good values. **Criteria:** Preference will be given to those students who meet the criteria.

Funds Avail.: No specific amount. **To Apply:** Applicants must check the available website for more information. **Deadline:** April. **Contact:** Dick Shriver; Email: at rhsusa@yahoo.com.

11412 ■ Kovaluk Scholarship Fund *(Undergraduate/Scholarship)*

Purpose: To help deserving students from the village of Zabolotivci to continue their education on a university level. **Focus:** Education; Human rights. **Qualif.:** Applicants must be students from the village of Zabolotivci.

Funds Avail.: No specific amount. **Remarks:** Established in 2000.

11413 ■ USA/USA-Ukramerazha Scholarships *(Undergraduate/Scholarship)*

Purpose: To provide financial support to talented high school students in Ukraine. **Focus:** General studies/Field of study not specified. **Qualif.:** Applicants must be talented high school students in Ukraine heading to preparatory schools and colleges in the U.S., Canada or the United Kingdom. **Criteria:** Preference will be given to those students who meet the criteria.

Funds Avail.: No specific amount. **To Apply:** Applicants must check the available website for more information. **Contact:** U.S.-Ukraine Foundation, at the above address.

11414 ■ UnitedAg

54 Corporate Pk.
Irvine, CA 92606-5105
Fax: (949)975-1671
Free: 800-223-4590
URL: www.unitedag.org
Social Media: www.facebook.com/UnitedAgOrg
www.instagram.com/unitedagorg
www.linkedin.com/company/unitedag
twitter.com/UnitedAgOrg

11415 ■ UnitedAg Scholarship Program *(Undergraduate/Scholarship)*

Purpose: To provide financial assistance to students who wish to pursue their education. **Focus:** General studies/Field of study not specified.

Funds Avail.: Up to $75,000. **Duration:** Annual. **Number Awarded:** Varies.

11416 ■ Université de Montréal - Centre de Recherches Mathematiques (CRM)

Pavillon Andre-Aisenstadt
2920 Chemin de la tour, bur. 5357

Montreal, QC, Canada H3T 1J4
Ph: (514)343-7501
Fax: (514)343-2254
E-mail: crm@crm.umontreal.ca
URL: crm.umontreal.ca
Social Media: www.facebook.com/Centrederecherches mathematiques
www.linkedin.com/company/centre-de-recherches -mathématiques
twitter.com/CRM_Montreal
www.youtube.com/channel/UCyj7mR88ut2AYobXtnWRhJg

11417 ■ CRM-ISM Postdoctoral Fellowship *(Postdoctorate/Fellowship)*

Purpose: To support promising researchers who have recently obtained or are expected to obtain a PhD in the mathematical science. **Focus:** Mathematics and mathematical sciences. **Qualif.:** Candidate must be supported by a scientific group. Exceptionally, support from individual professors will be accepted if, for example, the candidate's field of research is poorly represented by scientific groups. **Criteria:** Selection is based on the excellence of the file, integration of the person into a research team, guaranteed funding from a team.

11418 ■ Universite du Quebec - Institut National de la Recherche Scientifique (INRS)

490, Rue de la Couronne
Quebec, QC, Canada G1K 9A9
URL: www.inrs.ca

11419 ■ Postdoctoral Fellowship *(Postdoctorate, Doctorate/Fellowship)*

Purpose: To expand student's horizons and sharpen their research skills, enhance their ability to design and carry out projects, and advance doctoral training. **Focus:** Engineering; Environmental science; Social sciences.

Duration: Annual. **To Apply:** Application forms must be filled out online. **Contact:** Mohamed Chaker; E-mail: chaker@emt.inrs.ca; Charles Calmettes: E-mail: charles.calmettes@iaf.inrs.ca;Jean-Francois Blais; Email: jean-francois.blais@ete.inrs.ca.

11420 ■ Universités Canada

1710-350 Albert St.
Ottawa, ON, Canada K1R 1B1
URL: www.univcan.ca

11421 ■ Vale Manitoba Operations Post-secondary Scholarship *(Undergraduate/Scholarship, Internship)*

Purpose: To promote mining industry related fields of study, attracting students in the region to pursue careers in mining as part of the Northern Employment Strategy which supports initiatives to "grow our own". **Focus:** General studies/Field of study not specified. **Qualif.:** Applicants must be residing in Manitoba and living in a community that is North of the 52 parallel; entering the first year or already enrolled in a first bachelor degree or first diploma program. **Criteria:** Selection will be based on the committee's criteria. **Number Awarded:** 1.

11422 ■ Universities Space Research Association (USRA)

7178 Columbia Gateway Dr.
Columbia, MD 21046

Awards are arranged alphabetically below their administering organizations

Ph: (410)730-2656
E-mail: info@usra.edu
URL: www.usra.edu
Social Media: www.facebook.com/USRAedu
www.linkedin.com/usra
twitter.com/USRAedu

11423 ■ Thomas R. McGetchin Memorial Scholarship Award *(Undergraduate/Scholarship)*

Purpose: To support students who have shown a career interest in science or engineering with an emphasis on space research or space science education. **Focus:** Aerospace sciences; Engineering; Science; Space and planetary sciences. **Qualif.:** Applicants must be full-time undergraduate students attending a four-year accredited college or university that offers courses leading to a degree in science or engineering; must be within two years of earning a B.S. in a field of science and engineering, including life science and science education by the time the award is received. **Criteria:** Selection will be based on the following criteria demonstrated or expressed interest in space research and/or space science education; student essay, both in its reflection of students interest and its writing quality; letters of recommendation; academic standing (minimum required cumulative GPA of 3.50); as needed, school and community activities may be used to distinguish otherwise equally qualified candidates.

Funds Avail.: $5,000. **Duration:** Annual. **Number Awarded:** 1. **To Apply:** Applicants must complete the online application form; must include two letters of recommendation with at least one from a teacher or school official at the college level; an official college transcript showing two or more years of college credits including GPA; a one page (maximum of 500 words) statement stating the qualification and educational career goals in the field of space research or space science education. **Deadline:** August 7. **Remarks:** Honors the late Thomas R. McGetchin, former Lunar and Planetary Institute Director, for his significant contributions in the area of volcanic and igneous processes. **Contact:** Email: scholarship@usra.ed; URL: www.usra.edu/educational-activities-and-opportunities/usra-distinguished-undergraduate-awards.

11424 ■ John R. Sevier Memorial Scholarship Award *(Undergraduate/Scholarship)*

Purpose: To support students who have shown a career interest in science or engineering with an emphasis on space research or space science education. **Focus:** Aerospace sciences; Engineering; Science; Space and planetary sciences. **Qualif.:** Applicants must be full-time undergraduate students attending a four-year accredited college or university that offers courses leading to a degree in science or engineering; must be within two years of earning a B.S. in a field of science and engineering, including life science and science education by the time the award is received. **Criteria:** Selection will be based on the following criteria demonstrated or expressed interest in space research and/or space science education; student essay, both in its reflection of students interest and its writing quality; letters of recommendation; academic standing (minimum required cumulative GPA of 3.50); as needed, school and community activities may be used to distinguish otherwise equally qualified candidates.

Funds Avail.: $5,000. **Duration:** Annual. **Number Awarded:** 1. **To Apply:** Applicants must complete the online application form; must include two letters of recommendation with at least one from a teacher or school official at the college level; an official college transcript showing two or more years of college credits including GPA; a one page (maximum of 500 words) statement stating the qualification and educational career goals in the field of space research or space science education. **Deadline:** August 7. **Remarks:** The scholarship was established to honor John R. Sevier, for his dedication to education and advancements in aerospace technology. **Contact:** Email: scholarship@usra.ed; URL: www.usra.edu/educational-activities-and-opportunities/usra-distinguished-undergraduate-awards.

11425 ■ Frederick A. Tarantino Memorial Scholarship Award *(Undergraduate/Scholarship)*

Purpose: To support students who have shown a career interest in science or engineering with an emphasis on space research or space science education. **Focus:** Aerospace sciences; Engineering; Science; Space and planetary sciences. **Qualif.:** Applicants must be full-time undergraduate students attending a four-year accredited college or university that offers courses leading to a degree in science or engineering; must be within two years of earning a B.S. in a field of science and engineering, including life science and science education by the time the award is received. **Criteria:** Selection will be based on the following criteria demonstrated or expressed interest in space research and/or space science education; student essay, both in its reflection of students interest and its writing quality; letters of recommendation; academic standing (minimum required cumulative GPA of 3.50); as needed, school and community activities may be used to distinguish otherwise equally qualified candidates.

Funds Avail.: $5,000. **Duration:** Annual. **Number Awarded:** 1. **To Apply:** Applicants must complete the online application form; must include two letters of recommendation with at least one from a teacher or school official at the college level; an official college transcript showing two or more years of college credits including GPA; a one page (maximum of 500 words) statement stating the qualification and educational career goals in the field of space research or space science education. **Deadline:** August 7. **Remarks:** The scholarship was established to honor the late Frederick A. Tarantino, USRA President and CEO from 2006 - 2014. **Contact:** Email: scholarship@usra.ed; URL: www.usra.edu/educational-activities-and-opportunities/usra-distinguished-undergraduate-awards.

11426 ■ James B. Willett Educational Memorial Scholarship Award *(Undergraduate/Scholarship)*

Purpose: To support students who have shown a career interest in science or engineering with an emphasis on space research or space science education. **Focus:** Aerospace sciences; Engineering; Science; Space and planetary sciences. **Qualif.:** Applicants must be full-time undergraduate students attending a four-year accredited college or university that offers courses leading to a degree in science or engineering; must be within two years of earning a B.S. in a field of science and engineering, including life science and science education by the time the award is received.**Criteria:** Selection will be based on the following criteria demonstrated or expressed interest in space research and/or space science education; student essay, both in its reflection of students interest and its writing quality; letters of recommendation; academic standing (minimum required cumulative GPA of 3.50); as needed, school and community activities may be used to distinguish otherwise equally qualified candidates.

Funds Avail.: $5,000. **Duration:** Annual. **Number Awarded:** 1. **To Apply:** Applicants must complete the

Awards are arranged alphabetically below their administering organizations

online application form; must include two letters of recommendation with at least one from a teacher or school official at the college level; an official college transcript showing two or more years of college credits including GPA; a one page (maximum of 500 words) statement stating the qualification and educational career goals in the field of space research or space science education. **Deadline:** August 7. **Remarks:** The scholarship was established to honor the efforts of the late James B. Willett, a noted astrophysicist who worked with USRA. **Contact:** Email: scholarship@usra.ed; URL: www.usra.edu/educational-activities-and-opportunities/usra-distinguished-undergraduate-awards.

11427 ■ University of the Aftermarket Foundation (UAF)

7101 Wisconsin Ave., Ste. 1300
Bethesda, MD 20814
URL: www.automotivescholarships.com

11428 ■ University of the Aftermarket Foundation Scholarship *(Community College/Scholarship)*

Purpose: To help develop a strong, knowledgeable aftermarket work force. **Focus:** Automotive technology; Engineering, Automotive. **Qualif.:** Applicant must be enrolled in an accredited two- or four-year college/university in the United States or Canada and must be pursuing a career in a certified automotive, collision, or heavy duty technician program, or the automotive aftermarket field. **Criteria:** Selection is made by a team of industry veterans who evaluate the applications.

Funds Avail.: $1,000 tp $10,000. **Duration:** Annual. **To Apply:** Applicant should apply online at www.automotive-scholarships.com. **Deadline:** March 31.

11429 ■ University of Alabama at Birmingham School of Public Health - Lister Hill Center for Health Policy

1665 University Blvd.
Birmingham, AL 35233
E-mail: lhc@uab.edu
URL: www.uab.edu/listerhillcenter
Social Media: www.facebook.com/UABLHC
instagram.com/sophuab
www.linkedin.com/company/uab-school-of-public-health
twitter.com/intent/follow?source=followbutton&variant=1
  .0&screen_name=uabSOPH
www.youtube.com/user/uabSOPH?sub_confirmation=1

11430 ■ UAB Health Policy Fellowship *(Graduate, Master's, Doctorate/Scholarship)*

Purpose: To assist in the transfer of health policy and health services research skills to the policy making setting, and to provide graduate students with a unique opportunity to learn about the political system through direct exposure to public or private sector roles in health policy development. **Focus:** Health services administration; Public health. **Qualif.:** Applicants must be students from any masters or doctoral program at UAB who have a demonstrated interest in health policy; an interest in learning more about health policy through direct experience; and the skills to make a contribution in the organization in which they will serve; should be within twelve months of completing all the requirements for their degree.

Funds Avail.: up to $28,800. **Duration:** Annual. **Number Awarded:** 2. **Deadline:** February 18.

11431 ■ UAB Lister Hill Center Intramural Grant Program *(Professional development, Postdoctorate/Grant)*

Purpose: To encourage and foster health policy/health services research on the UAB campus. **Focus:** Medical research; Public health. **Qualif.:** All faculty with primary appointments at the University of Alabama at Birmingham are eligible to apply.

Duration: Annual.

11432 ■ University of Alaska (UA)

Butrovich Bldg., Ste. 209
910 Yukon Dr.
Fairbanks, AK 99775-5340
Ph: (907)450-8100
Fax: (907)450-8101
E-mail: helpdesk@alaska.edu
URL: www.alaska.edu

11433 ■ Alaska Aerospace Development Corporation Scholarships *(Undergraduate/Scholarship)*

Purpose: To provide financial support to deserving students in Alaska who want to pursue an education in any campus of the University of Alaska. **Focus:** Business; Engineering; Mathematics and mathematical sciences; Physics; Technical communications. **Qualif.:** Applicants must be freshmen majoring in mathematics, physics, engineering, business, or a technical science field such as computer science who have graduated from the Kodiak Island Borough School District; must be full-time students attending any UA campus (whether at Fairbanks, at Anchorage, or at Southeast), and enrolled in 14 credits and in good academic standing. **Criteria:** Selection will be based on their academic standing and application documents.

Funds Avail.: Minimum $5,000. **Duration:** Annual. **To Apply:** Applicants should submit a written statement verifying that they have not been convicted of a crime other than a minor traffic violation; must complete and submit the application form available at the website together with a personal essay, two letters of recommendation, and current transcripts. **Deadline:** February 15.

11434 ■ Alaska Native Medical Center Auxiliary Scholarships *(Undergraduate/Scholarship)*

Purpose: To provide financial support to deserving students in Alaska who want to pursue an education in any campus of the University of Alaska. **Focus:** General studies/Field of study not specified. **Qualif.:** Applicants must be a graduate of a rural Alaska high school that is off the Alaska highway system; a minimum cumulative GPA of 2.5; enrolled full-time; a resident of Alaska. **Criteria:** Selection will be based on merit, financial need, outstanding achievement in specialized fields.

Funds Avail.: No specific amount. **To Apply:** Applications can be submitted online. **Deadline:** February 15.

11435 ■ Alaska Press Club Scholarships *(Undergraduate/Scholarship)*

Purpose: To provide financial support to deserving students in Alaska who want to pursue an education in any campus of the University of Alaska. **Focus:** Journalism.

Awards are arranged alphabetically below their administering organizations

Qualif.: Applicants must be students attending any campus of the University of Alaska (Anchorage, Fairbanks, Southeast and all community campuses). **Criteria:** Selection will be based on merit, financial need, outstanding achievement in specialized fields.

Funds Avail.: No specific amount. **Duration:** Annual. **Number Awarded:** 1. **To Apply:** Applications can be submitted online. **Deadline:** February 15.

11436 ■ Mike Ardaw Scholarships *(Undergraduate/ Scholarship)*

Purpose: To provide support to deserving students in Alaska who want to pursue an education in any campus of the University of Alaska. **Focus:** Education; Engineering; Science. **Qualif.:** Applicants must be full-time students attending at any of the UA campus (whether at Fairbanks, at Anchorage, or at Southeast) and have a minimum GPA of 2.5. **Criteria:** Preference will be given to students studying science, education or engineering and to students who have been Alaska residents for at least one year and are from the Navy Lake area.

Funds Avail.: Minimum $1,000. **Duration:** Annual. **To Apply:** Applicants must: complete the application forms available at the website; must attach a personal essay, two letters of recommendation, and current transcripts; must also submit a paragraph describing their connection to and love for the Nacy Lake area. **Deadline:** February 15.

11437 ■ Lawrence Bayer Business Administration Scholarships *(Undergraduate/Scholarship)*

Purpose: To provide financial support to deserving students in Alaska who want to pursue an education in any campus of the University of Alaska. **Focus:** Business administration. **Qualif.:** Applicants must be a Business Administration major active in clubs and/or sports. **Criteria:** Selection will be based on merit, financial need, outstanding achievement in specialized fields.

Funds Avail.: No specific amount. **To Apply:** Applications can be submitted online and must submit a list of clubs and/or sports in which he/she is an active participant. **Deadline:** February 15. **Contact:** UA Foundation, at the above address.

11438 ■ Charles E. Behlke Engineering Memorial Scholarships *(Undergraduate/Scholarship)*

Purpose: To provide financial support to deserving students in Alaska who want to pursue an education in any campus of the University of Alaska. **Focus:** Engineering. **Qualif.:** Applicants must be full-time students entering his/her sophomore, junior or senior year and must be an Engineering major. Recipients must be in good academic standing with a minimum GPA of 2.5. **Criteria:** Selection will be based on merit, financial need, outstanding achievement in specialized fields.

Funds Avail.: No specific amount. **To Apply:** Applications can be submitted online. **Contact:** UA Foundation, at the above address.

11439 ■ Bolick Foreign Student Scholarships *(Undergraduate/Scholarship)*

Purpose: To provide financial support to deserving students in Alaska who want to pursue an education in any campus of the University of Alaska. **Focus:** General studies/Field of study not specified. **Qualif.:** Applicants must be full-time students attending at any of the UA campus (whether at Fairbanks, at Anchorage, or at Southeast) who are also holding exclusive citizenship in another country. **Criteria:** Preference will be given to Swedish citizens.

Funds Avail.: Minimum $1,000. **Duration:** Annual. **To Apply:** Applicants must complete the application forms available at the website; must attach a personal essay, two letters of recommendation, and current transcripts. **Contact:** Email:robbie.graham@alaska.edu.

11440 ■ Dr. Betty J. Boyd-Beu and Edwin G. Beu, Jr. Scholarships *(Undergraduate/Scholarship)*

Purpose: To provide financial assistance for tuition and other educational expenses to non-traditional students who are seeking degree completion or retraining at the University of Alaska in Anchorage. **Focus:** General studies/Field of study not specified. **Qualif.:** Applicants must be non-traditional students and have graduated from high school who want or will attend at University of Alaska in Anchorage; must have worked prior to enrolling or returning to college, thus re-entering college to complete a degree or enrolling to retrain for another position in the workplace, and be in good academic standing with a minimum cumulative GPA of 3.0; must be formally admitted to a degree seeking program, and enrolled in the semester(s) for which the award is made. **Criteria:** Selection will be based on the applicants' academic performance and application documents.

Funds Avail.: No specific amount. **Duration:** Annual. **To Apply:** Applicants must visit the website for the UA Online Scholarship application process. **Deadline:** February 15. **Contact:** UA Foundation, at the above address.

11441 ■ Bunnell Scholarships *(Undergraduate/ Scholarship)*

Purpose: To provide financial support to deserving students in Alaska who want to pursue an education in any campus of the University of Alaska. **Focus:** General studies/Field of study not specified. **Qualif.:** Applicants must be full-time students entering his/her junior or senior year with a declared major in an accredited field and have a minimum GPA of 3.2. **Criteria:** Preference will be given to applicants who graduated from an Alaska high school and have lived in Alaska for 3 or more years.

Funds Avail.: Minimum $1,000. **Duration:** Annual. **To Apply:** Applicants must submit an additional paragraph describing how they emulate the ideals of persistence, vision, self sacrifice, concern for others and love of the North; must complete the application forms available at the website; must attach a personal essay, two letters of recommendation, and current transcripts. **Deadline:** February 15. **Contact:** UA Foundation, at the above address.

11442 ■ Loyal D. Burkett Memorial Scholarships *(Undergraduate/Scholarship)*

Purpose: To provide financial support to deserving students in Alaska who want to pursue an education in any campus of the University of Alaska. **Focus:** General studies/Field of study not specified. **Qualif.:** Applicants must be full-time students attending at any of the UA campuses; in good academic standing; and demonstrate motivation, academic and leadership potential. **Criteria:** Selection will be based on the submitted application and academic standing.

Funds Avail.: No specific amount. **Duration:** Annual. **To Apply:** Applicants must complete the application forms available at the website; must attach a personal essay, two

Awards are arranged alphabetically below their administering organizations

letters of recommendation, and current transcripts. **Contact:** UA Foundation, at the above address.

11443 ■ Lyle Carlson Wildlife Management Scholarships (Undergraduate/Scholarship)

Purpose: To provide financial support to deserving students in Alaska who want to pursue an education in any campus of the University of Alaska. **Focus:** Wildlife conservation, management, and science. **Qualif.:** Applicants must be students majoring in Wildlife Management, Wildlife Biology or another closely related major who have a minimum GPA of 3.0. **Criteria:** Selection will be based on merit, financial need, outstanding achievement in specialized fields.

Funds Avail.: No specific amount. **To Apply:** Applications can be submitted online. **Contact:** UA Foundation, at the above address. Butrovich Building Suite 209 2025 Yukon Drive P.O. Box 755340 Fairbanks, AK 99775-5340; Phone: 907.450.8100; Fax: 907.450.8101; Emal:.

11444 ■ Mable B. Crawford Memorial Scholarships (Undergraduate/Scholarship)

Purpose: To provide financial support to deserving students in Alaska who want to pursue an education in any campus of the University of Alaska. **Focus:** Accounting; Business; Economics; Law. **Qualif.:** Applicants must be full-time students attending at any UA campus (whether at Fairbanks, at Anchorage, or at Southeast) who have been residents of Alaska for at least two years. **Criteria:** Selection will be awarded on the basis of both scholastic ability and need; preference will be given to applicants majoring in accounting, economics, law or business.

Funds Avail.: Minimum $500. **Duration:** Annual. **To Apply:** Applicants must complete the application form available at the website; must attach a personal essay, two letters of recommendation, and current transcripts. **Contact:** UA Foundation, at the above address.

11445 ■ Patricia Hughes Eastaugh Teaching Scholarship (Undergraduate/Scholarship)

Purpose: To provide financial support to deserving students in Alaska who want to pursue an education in any campus of the University of Alaska. **Focus:** Teaching. **Qualif.:** Applicants must be first-time incoming freshman students enrolled in a baccalaureate degree program at any of UA campus (whether at Fairbanks, at Anchorage, or at Southeast); must have the intent to become elementary or secondary school teachers in Alaska and be enrolled in academic programs leading toward that end; must be Alaska residents and graduates of a public or private school in Alaska. **Criteria:** Preference will be given to students who shows a desire to teach and are in the top 25% of their class.

Funds Avail.: Minimum $8,000. **Duration:** Annual. **To Apply:** Applicants must complete and submit the application form available at the website together with two letters of recommendation, and current transcripts; must also attach an additional statement of 1,000 words or less entitled "Why I Want to become a Teacher of Children in Alaska"; should also briefly express their opinion of Alaska's educational system(s) and their thoughts on changes they would embrace therein. **Deadline:** February 15. **Contact:** UA Foundation, at the above address.

11446 ■ Excellence in Geographic Information Systems Scholarships (Graduate/Scholarship)

Purpose: To provide financial support to deserving students in Alaska who want to pursue an education in any

campus of the University of Alaska. **Focus:** Geography. **Qualif.:** Applicants must be students attending any campus of the University of Alaska (Anchorage, Fairbanks, Southeast and all community campuses). **Criteria:** Selection will be based on merit, financial need, outstanding achievement in specialized fields.

Funds Avail.: No specific amount. **To Apply:** Applications can be submitted online. **Contact:** UA Foundation, at the above address.

11447 ■ Lydia Fohn-Hansen/Lola Hill Memorial Scholarships (Undergraduate, Graduate/Scholarship)

Purpose: To provide financial support to deserving students in Alaska who want to pursue an education in any campus of the University of Alaska. **Focus:** Consumer affairs; Family planning. **Criteria:** Selection will be based on the applicants' academic performance.

Funds Avail.: Minimum $1,000. **Duration:** Annual. **To Apply:** Applicants must complete the application forms available at the website; must attach a personal essay, two letters of recommendation, and current transcripts. **Contact:** UA Foundation, at the above address.

11448 ■ Johnny & Sarah Frank Scholarships (Undergraduate/Scholarship)

Purpose: To provide financial support to deserving students in Alaska who want to pursue an education in any campus of the University of Alaska. **Focus:** General studies/Field of study not specified. **Qualif.:** Applicants must be of Gwich in Athabaskan descents; be full-time students attending any UA campus (whether at Fairbanks, at Anchorage, or at Southeast); have a minimum 2.5 GPA; and, enroll for at least six credit hours. **Criteria:** Preference will be given to students from Arctic Village or Venetie and students from Ft. Yukon, Chalkyitsik, Birch Creek, Circle, Beaver or Eagle.

Funds Avail.: No specific amount. **Duration:** Annual. **To Apply:** Applicants must complete the application forms available at the website; must attach a personal essay, two letters of recommendation, and current transcripts. **Contact:** UA Foundation, at the above address.

11449 ■ Charles F. Gould Endowment Scholarships (Undergraduate/Scholarship)

Purpose: To provide financial support to deserving students in Alaska who want to pursue an education in any campus of the University of Alaska. **Focus:** General studies/Field of study not specified. **Qualif.:** Applicants must be students attending any campus of the University of Alaska (Anchorage, Fairbanks, Southeast and all community campuses). **Criteria:** Selection will be based on merit, financial need, outstanding achievement in specialized fields.

Funds Avail.: No specific amount. **Duration:** Annual. **To Apply:** Applications can be submitted online. **Deadline:** February 15. **Contact:** UA Foundation, at the above address.

11450 ■ Patty Hamilton Early Childhood Development Scholarships (Undergraduate/Scholarship)

Purpose: To provide financial support to deserving students in Alaska who want to pursue an education in any campus of the University of Alaska. **Focus:** Education, Early childhood. **Qualif.:** Applicants must be an Alaska resident entering his/her junior or senior year and majoring in Early Childhood Development/Education. Preference will

Awards are arranged alphabetically below their administering organizations

be given to students who have prior experience working with or volunteering with young children. **Criteria:** Preference will be given to students who are working with or volunteering for young children.

Funds Avail.: No specific amount. **Duration:** Annual. **To Apply:** Applicants must complete the application forms available at the website; must attach a personal essay, two letters of recommendation, and current transcripts; must also submit a paragraph describing experience working with or volunteering with young children. **Deadline:** February 15. **Contact:** UA Foundation, at the above address.

11451 ■ John Henderson Endowment Scholarships
(Undergraduate/Scholarship)

Purpose: To provide support to deserving students in Alaska who want to pursue an education in any campus of the University of Alaska. **Focus:** General studies/Field of study not specified. **Qualif.:** Applicants must be students attending any campus of the University of Alaska (Anchorage, Fairbanks, Southeast and all community campuses). **Criteria:** Selection will be based on merit, financial need, outstanding achievement in specialized fields.

Funds Avail.: No specific amount. **To Apply:** Applications can be submitted online. **Deadline:** February 15. **Contact:** UA Foundation, at the above address.

11452 ■ Donald Wills Jacobs Scholarships
(Undergraduate/Scholarship)

Purpose: To provide financial support to deserving students in Alaska who want to pursue an education in any campus of the University of Alaska. **Focus:** Art. **Qualif.:** Applicants must be full-time junior or senior students enrolled in a Bachelor of Fine Arts program at any UA campus (whether at Fairbanks, at Anchorage, or at Southeast). **Criteria:** Selection will be based on their academic performance and application documents.

Funds Avail.: Minimum $500. **Duration:** Annual. **To Apply:** Applicants must complete the application forms available at the website; must also attach a personal essay, two letters of recommendation, and current transcripts. **Deadline:** February 15.

11453 ■ Iver and Cora Knapstad Scholarships
(Undergraduate/Scholarship)

Purpose: To provide financial support to deserving students in Alaska who want to pursue an education in any campus of the University of Alaska. **Focus:** General studies/Field of study not specified. **Qualif.:** Applicants must be students attending any campus of the University of Alaska. **Criteria:** Selection will be based on merit, financial need, outstanding achievement in specialized fields.

Funds Avail.: No specific amount. **To Apply:** Applications can be submitted online. **Contact:** UA Foundation, at the above address.

11454 ■ Austin E. Lathrop Scholarships
(Undergraduate/Scholarship)

Purpose: To provide financial support to deserving students in Alaska who want to pursue an education in any campus of the University of Alaska. **Focus:** General studies/Field of study not specified. **Qualif.:** Applicants must be full-time students attending at any UA campus (whether at Fairbanks, at Anchorage, or at Southeast). **Criteria:** Preference will be given to students who show a need for financial assistance.

Funds Avail.: Minimum $1,000. **Duration:** Annual. **To Apply:** Applicants must complete and submit the application

form available at the website; must also attach a personal essay, two letters of recommendation, and current transcripts. **Deadline:** February 15. **Contact:** UA Foundation, at the above address.

11455 ■ Franklin M. Leach Scholarships
(Undergraduate/Scholarship)

Purpose: To provide financial support to deserving students in Alaska who want to pursue an education in any campus of the University of Alaska. **Focus:** General studies/Field of study not specified. **Qualif.:** Applicants must be full-time students attending any campus of the University of Alaska. **Criteria:** Selection will be based on the applicants' academic standing.

Funds Avail.: No specific amount. **Duration:** Annual. **To Apply:** Applicants must complete and submit the application form available at the website; must also attach a personal essay, two letters of recommendation, and current transcripts. **Deadline:** February 15. **Contact:** UA Foundation, at the above address.

11456 ■ Dave McCloud Aviation Memorial Scholarships *(Undergraduate/Scholarship)*

Purpose: To provide financial support to deserving students in Alaska who want to pursue an education in any campus of the University of Alaska. **Focus:** General studies/Field of study not specified. **Qualif.:** Applicants must be degree in Aviation and have a minimum cumulative GPA of 2.0. **Criteria:** Preference will be given to those students who are affiliated with the military.

Funds Avail.: No specific amount. **To Apply:** Applications can be submitted online and must submit a statement verifying his/her military affiliation. **Deadline:** February 15. **Remarks:** UA Foundation, at the above address.

11457 ■ Molly Ann Mishler Memorial Scholarships
(College/Scholarship)

Purpose: To provide financial assistance for tuition and other educational expenses to students who are admitted into the Early Childhood Development or Elementary Education Program. **Focus:** Education, Early childhood. **Criteria:** Preference will be given to applicants formally admitted into the Early Childhood Development program.

Funds Avail.: No specific amount. **Duration:** Annual. **To Apply:** Applicants must complete the MSC scholarship application form; must attach a list of activities/community service in which they have participated; must attach a resume of their work experience they have held over the past four years; must attach a personal essay (not more than 500 words); must have two letters of recommendation and transcripts. Application documents must be submitted to Molly Ann Mishler Memorial Scholarships, Matanuska-Susitna College, Student Services. **Deadline:** February 15.

11458 ■ Andrew Nerland Scholarships
(Undergraduate/Scholarship)

Purpose: To provide financial support to deserving students in Alaska who want to pursue an education in any campus of the University of Alaska. **Focus:** General studies/Field of study not specified. **Qualif.:** Applicants must be enrolled full-time student; minimum cumulative GPA of 2.0. **Criteria:** Preference will be given to students who demonstrate a need for financial assistance.

Funds Avail.: Minimum $1,000. **Duration:** Annual. **To Apply:** Applicants must complete and submit the application form available at the website; must also submit a personal

Awards are arranged alphabetically below their administering organizations

essay, two letters of recommendation, and current transcripts. **Contact:** UA Foundation, at the above address.

11459 ■ Maureen E. Nolan-Cahill Memorial Scholarship *(Undergraduate/Scholarship)*

Purpose: To provide financial support to deserving students in Alaska who want to pursue an education in any campus of the University of Alaska. **Focus:** Science. **Qualif.:** Applicant must be majoring in science to include Biological Science, Biology, Health Science, Chemistry or Physics; demonstrate financial need; minimum cumulative GPA of 3.0. **Criteria:** Selection committee preference will be given to students in priority order 1) residents of Southeast Alaska, 2) Alaska High School Graduates.

Funds Avail.: No specific amount. **Duration:** Annual. **Number Awarded:** 1. **To Apply:** Applicants must complete and submit the application form available at the website; must also submit a personal essay, two letters of recommendation, and current transcripts. **Deadline:** February 15.

11460 ■ Don and Jan O'Dowd/SAA Statewide Scholarships *(Undergraduate/Scholarship)*

Purpose: To provide financial support to deserving students in Alaska who want to pursue an education in any campus of the University of Alaska. **Focus:** General studies/Field of study not specified. **Qualif.:** Applicants must be full-time incoming freshmen students attending any UA campus (whether at Fairbanks, at Anchorage, or at Southeast) with a minimum GPA of 3.0, and Alaska residents and graduates of an Alaska high school. **Criteria:** Applicants will be selected based on their academic standing.

Funds Avail.: No specific amount. **Duration:** Annual. **To Apply:** Applicants must complete and submit the application form available at the website; must also submit a personal essay, two letters of recommendation, and current transcripts. **Deadline:** February 15. **Contact:** UA Foundation, at the above address.

11461 ■ Alvin G. Ott Fish & Wildlife Scholarship *(Undergraduate/Scholarship)*

Purpose: To provide financial support to deserving students in Alaska who want to pursue an education in any campus of the University of Alaska. **Focus:** General studies/Field of study not specified. **Qualif.:** Applicants must be full-time students with a minimum GPA of 3.0 and majoring in a field related to Fish and Wildlife. **Criteria:** Selection will be based on merit, financial need, outstanding achievement in specialized fields.

Funds Avail.: No specific amount. **Duration:** Annual. **To Apply:** Applications can be submitted online.

11462 ■ Pt. Lay Memorial Scholarships *(Undergraduate/Scholarship)*

Purpose: To provide support to deserving students in Alaska who want to pursue an education in any campus of the University of Alaska. **Focus:** General studies/Field of study not specified. **Qualif.:** Applicants must be students attending any campus of the University of Alaska (Anchorage, Fairbanks, Southeast and all community campuses). **Criteria:** Selection will be based on merit, financial need, outstanding achievement in specialized fields.

Funds Avail.: No specific amount. **To Apply:** Applications can be submitted online. **Deadline:** February 15. **Contact:** UA Foundation, at the above address.

11463 ■ A.D. Al and Maxine Robertson Memorial Scholarship *(Undergraduate/Scholarship)*

Purpose: To provide financial support to deserving students in Alaska who want to pursue an education in any campus of the University of Alaska. **Focus:** General studies/Field of study not specified. **Qualif.:** Applicants must be full-time students in his/her junior or senior year of a nursing program at any institution within the UA system.

Funds Avail.: No specific amount. **To Apply:** Applications can be submitted online. **Contact:** UA Foundation, at the above address.

11464 ■ Clair Shirey Scholarships *(Undergraduate/Scholarship)*

Purpose: To provide financial support to deserving students in Alaska who want to pursue an education in any campus of the University of Alaska. **Focus:** Classical studies. **Qualif.:** Applicants must be Music majors at any UA campus (whether at Fairbanks, at Anchorage, or at Southeast) with a demonstrated interest or emphasis in classical/liturgical organ. **Criteria:** Preference will be given to students who are residents of the following geographical areas: Anchorage Archdiocese, Alaska and the Pacific Northwest.

Funds Avail.: No specific amount. **Duration:** Annual. **To Apply:** Applicants must complete and submit the application form available at the website; must also submit a personal essay describing their interest or emphasis in classical/liturgical organ, two letters of recommendation, and current transcripts. **Deadline:** February 15. **Contact:** UA Foundation, at the above address.

11465 ■ Guy A. Woodings Scholarships *(Undergraduate/Scholarship)*

Purpose: To provide financial support to deserving students in Alaska who want to pursue an education in any campus of the University of Alaska. **Focus:** Natural resources. **Qualif.:** Applicants must be majoring in Natural Resource Management with a 3.1 GPA and must have been enrolled for at least two years pursuing a four-year degree. Preference will be given to students pursuing a degree in Natural Resource Management with an emphasis on planning and land use and those who have performed community service. **Criteria:** Selection will be based on merit, financial need, outstanding achievement in specialized fields.

Funds Avail.: No specific amount. **To Apply:** Applications can be submitted online. **Deadline:** February 15.

11466 ■ Ralph Yetka Memorial Scholarships *(Undergraduate/Scholarship)*

Purpose: To provide financial support to deserving students in Alaska who want to pursue an education in any campus of the University of Alaska. **Focus:** Computer and information sciences; Education, Elementary; Education, Secondary; Engineering. **Qualif.:** Applicants must be full-time students and graduates of Ketchikan or Revilla High School who are attending any UA campus (whether at Fairbanks, at Anchorage, or at Southeast), with a minimum GPA of 2.5 and majoring in engineering, elementary or secondary education, computer science or aviation. **Criteria:** Selection will be based on their application materials and academic standing.

Funds Avail.: Minimum $500. **Duration:** Annual. **To Apply:** Applicants must complete and submit the application form available at the website; must also submit a personal

Awards are arranged alphabetically below their administering organizations

essay, two letters of recommendation, and current transcripts. **Deadline:** April 30.

11467 ■ Joan C. Yoder Memorial Nursing Scholarships (Undergraduate/Scholarship)

Purpose: To provide financial support to deserving students in Alaska who want to pursue an education in any campus of the University of Alaska. **Focus:** Nursing. **Qualif.:** Applicants must enrolled in the nursing program at the University of Alaska; Graduate student -a minimum cumulative GPA of 3.0, declared specialty course; Undergraduate – a minimum cumulative GPA of 2.5, while their major GPA must be a minimum of 2.0. **Criteria:** Preference will be given to full-time students.

Funds Avail.: No specific amount. **Duration:** Annual. **To Apply:** Applicants must complete and submit the application form available at the website; must also submit a personal essay, two letters of recommendation, and current transcripts. **Deadline:** August 15.

11468 ■ University of Alaska Anchorage

3211 Providence Dr.
Anchorage, AK 99508
Ph: (907)786-1800
URL: www.uaa.alaska.edu
Social Media: www.facebook.com/UAAnchorage
www.linkedin.com/school/university-of-alaska-anchorage
twitter.com/uaanchorage
www.youtube.com/user/UAAnchorage

11469 ■ Accounting Club Scholarship (Undergraduate/Scholarship)

Purpose: To offer financial assistance for tuition and other related educational expenses to University of Alaska Anchorage students with a declared major in Accounting, as well as to encourage non-traditional students to pursue academic endeavors. **Focus:** Accounting. **Criteria:** Selection of applicants will be based on their demonstrated motivation, talent, academic, and leadership potential; preference will be given to applicants demonstrating financial need and to non-traditional students.

Funds Avail.: $500. **Duration:** Annual. **To Apply:** Applicants must make sure that they meet all of the aforementioned qualifications before proceeding to apply online through Online and completing the scholarship application. **Deadline:** February 2. **Contact:** Email: scholarships@uaa.alaska.edu.

11470 ■ Elaine Atwood Scholarship (Undergraduate, Graduate/Scholarship)

Purpose: To provide financial assistance to University of Alaska Anchorage students who are formally admitted into the Journalism and Public Communications degree seeking program. **Focus:** Journalism; Public affairs. **Criteria:** Selection of applicants will be based on their demonstrated motivation, talent, academic, and leadership potential.

Funds Avail.: $5,000. **Duration:** Annual. **Number Awarded:** 2. **To Apply:** Applicants must make sure that they meet all of the aforementioned qualifications before proceeding to apply online through Online and completing the scholarship application. Must submit an essay responding to these questions how do you see yourself further advancing education in Alaska?; How do your extracurricular activities enhance your educational experience?; must complete the electronic scholarship application available online. **Deadline:** February 15. **Contact:** Email: scholarships@uaa.alaska.edu.

11471 ■ Dr. Jon Baker Memorial Scholarship (Other/Scholarship)

Purpose: To offer financial assistance for tuition and other educational expenses to full-time University of Alaska Anchorage students who are admitted into a degree-seeking program, with preference will be given to students majoring in Psychology. **Focus:** Psychology. **Qualif.:** Applicants must be in good academic standing with a minimum cumulative GPA of 2.0; must be enrolled full-time. **Criteria:** Selection of applicants will be based on their demonstrated motivation, talent, academic, and leadership potential; preference will be given to students who are formally admitted to the Psychology program.

Funds Avail.: Minimum of $500. **Duration:** Annual. **Number Awarded:** 1. **To Apply:** Applicants must make sure that they meet all of the aforementioned qualifications before proceeding to apply online through Online and completing the scholarship application. **Deadline:** February 15. **Remarks:** The scholarship was established in the remembrance of Dr. Jon Baker. **Contact:** Email: scholarships@uaa.alaska.edu.

11472 ■ UAA Michael Baring-Gould Memorial Scholarship (Graduate, Undergraduate/Scholarship)

Purpose: To provide financial assistance for tuition and other related educational expenses to the University of Alaska Anchorage students with Sociology or a related social science major. **Focus:** Social sciences; Sociology. **Qualif.:** Applicants must be in good academic standing with a minimum cumulative grade point average of 2.5 for undergraduate and 3.0 for graduate and formally admitted into an undergraduate Social Sciences major or an Interdisciplinary Masters degree-seeking program that includes sociology as one of the disciplines; must have completed at least thirty (30) credits; must also have completed at least six (6) credits prior to the semester of the award at the University of Alaska Anchorage, and planning to enroll full time (twelve (12) credits for undergraduate and nine (9) credits for graduate); lastly, they must demonstrate involvement in a project or area of study which reflects a commitment to social justice, peace, equality, and/or empowerment of minorities. **Criteria:** Selection of applicants will be based on their demonstrated motivation, talent, academic, and leadership potential.

Funds Avail.: $1,000. **Duration:** Annual. **To Apply:** Applicants must make sure that they meet all of the aforementioned qualifications before proceeding to apply online through Online and completing the scholarship application. must submit a personal essay which should be no more than 500 words and two letters of recommendation. **Deadline:** February 15. **Contact:** Email: scholarships@uaa.alaska.edu.

11473 ■ Mark A. Beltz Scholarship (Graduate, Undergraduate/Scholarship)

Purpose: To offer financial assistance for tuition and other educational expenses to students who are in financial need and have declared majors for an undergraduate, graduate, or a vocational program in any of the following fields: Political Science, Economics, Business Administration, Business and Corporate Law, and Science and Technology. **Focus:** Business administration; Economics; Political science; Science technologies. **Criteria:** Selection will be based on the students who demonstrate financial need, residents of

Awards are arranged alphabetically below their administering organizations

Alaska, and who intend to pursue a career in Alaska are given preference.

Funds Avail.: Minimum of $2,000. **Duration:** Annual. **To Apply:** Applicants must make sure that they meet all of the aforementioned qualifications before proceeding to apply online through Online and completing the scholarship application. **Deadline:** February 15. **Remarks:** The scholarship was established in the remembrance of Mark A. Beltz.

11474 ■ Pat Brakke Political Science Scholarship
(Undergraduate/Scholarship)

Purpose: To offer financial assistance for tuition and other educational expenses to a full-time student majoring in Political Science. **Focus:** Political science. **Qualif.:** Applicant must have a full-time undergraduate students majoring in Political Science; must have a minimum cumulative GPA of 3.0. **Criteria:** Selection of applicants will be based on their demonstrated motivation, talent, academic, and leadership potential.

Funds Avail.: $500. **Duration:** Annual. **Number Awarded:** Varies. **To Apply:** Applicants must make sure that they meet all of the aforementioned qualifications before proceeding to apply online through Online and completing the scholarship application. Must submit an essay responding to these questions How do you see yourself further advancing education in Alaska?; How do your extracurricular activities enhance your educational experience?; must complete the electronic scholarship application available online. **Deadline:** February 15. **Contact:** Email: web_team@uaa.alaska.edu.

11475 ■ Emi Chance for Aspiring Artists Scholarship *(Undergraduate/Scholarship)*

Purpose: To offer financial assistance for tuition and other related educational expenses to full-time students attending the University of Alaska Anchorage who have declared a major in Art (for Drawing and/or Painting) who have Junior class standing. **Focus:** Art. **Criteria:** Selection of applicants will be based on their demonstrated motivation, talent, academic, and leadership potential.

Funds Avail.: $500. **Duration:** Annual. **To Apply:** Applicants must submit one drawing and/or painting with application. **Deadline:** February 15. **Remarks:** The scholarship was established in the remembrance of Emi Chance.

11476 ■ Edward Rollin Clinton Memorial for Music Scholarship *(Undergraduate/Scholarship)*

Purpose: To offer financial assistance for tuition and other educational expenses to full-time students who are formally admitted into a Music degree-seeking program at the University of Alaska Anchorage. **Focus:** Music. **Qualif.:** Applicants must be in good academic standing with a minimum cumulative grade point average of 3.0 and must be a University of Alaska Anchorage music student; enrolled full-time. **Criteria:** Preference will be given to entering freshmen planning to study piano; upper division students studying piano; freshman planning to study any instrument; upper division students studying any instrument; and students who demonstrate financial need.

Funds Avail.: Minimum of $500. **Duration:** Annual. **To Apply:** Applicants must make sure that they meet all of the aforementioned qualifications before proceeding to apply online through Online and completing the scholarship application. **Deadline:** February 15. **Remarks:** The scholarship was established in the remembrance of Edward Rollin Clinton. **Contact:** Email: scholarships@uaa.alaska.edu.

11477 ■ Michael D. Ford Memorial Scholarship
(Graduate, Undergraduate/Scholarship)

Purpose: To provide a scholarship as a memorial to Michael D. Ford as a way to encourage Alaskan students to enter the field of business. **Focus:** Business.

Funds Avail.: $1,000. **Duration:** Annual.

11478 ■ Jan and Glenn Fredericks Scholarship
(Graduate, Undergraduate/Scholarship)

Purpose: https://alaska.academicworks.com/opportunities/9801To offer financial assistance for tuition and other related educational expenses to University of Alaska Anchorage students who are majoring in Business. **Focus:** Business. **Qualif.:** Applicants must have a minimum cumulative GPA of 2.0. Recipient must be enrolled full-time. Recipient must be a junior or higher. **Criteria:** Preference will be given to students that are of Alaska Native ethnicity.

Funds Avail.: $1,000. **Duration:** Annual. **To Apply:** Applicants must make sure that they meet all of the aforementioned qualifications before proceeding to apply online through Online and completing the scholarship application. **Deadline:** February 15.

11479 ■ Benjamin A. Gilman International Scholarship *(Undergraduate/Scholarship)*

Purpose: To diversify the kinds of students who study and intern abroad and the countries and regions where they go. **Focus:** Engineering; General studies/Field of study not specified; Science. **Qualif.:** Applicants must be U.S. citizen undergraduate students who are receiving Federal Pell Grant funding at a 2-year or 4-year college or university to participate in study abroad programs worldwide; must be receiving a Federal Pell Grant or provide proof that they will be receiving a Pell Grant at the time of application or during the term of their study abroad; applying to or have been accepted into a study abroad program eligible for credit by the student's accredited institution of higher education in the U.S; studying abroad for at least 4 weeks in one country. **Criteria:** Selection criteria are based on the Gilman Scholarship Program goals that may differ from other scholarship programs; recipients are selected using the following criteria: (1) Diversity of the Applicant; (2) Statement of Purpose Essay; (3) Follow-on Project Proposal Essay; (4) Academic Progress and Performance;(5) Fields of Study; (6) Country of Destination; (7) U.S. Institution and State Distribution; (8) Length of Study; (9) Lack of Previous Undergraduate Study Abroad.

Funds Avail.: Up to $5,000. **Duration:** Annual. **Number Awarded:** 2, 900+. **To Apply:** Applicants must submit a completed application form with other requirements or supporting documents. **Deadline:** Campus deadline(Early February & early September); National deadline(Early March & early October). **Contact:** Leslie Tuovinen; Email: latuovinen@alaska.edu; Phone: 907-786-4135.

11480 ■ Governor William A. Egan Award
(Undergraduate/Award)

Purpose: To provide financial assistance to students who are formally admitted to a political science or history degree-seeking program at the University of Alaska Anchorage. **Focus:** History; Political science. **Qualif.:** Applicants must demonstrate motivation, academic and leadership potential; must demonstrate a commitment to their community; must be in good academic standing with a minimum cumulative GPA of 2.0; must be formally admitted to a political science or history degree-seeking program at the

Awards are arranged alphabetically below their administering organizations

University of Alaska Anchorage; must plan to enroll full-time (12 credits) at the University of Alaska Anchorage; must be incoming or continuing students at the University of Alaska Anchorage. **Criteria:** Preference will be given to applicants who are Alaska residents and have shown a potential for public service.

Funds Avail.: Minimum of $2,000. **Duration:** Annual. **To Apply:** Applicants must complete the electronic scholarship application available online. **Deadline:** February 15. **Contact:** Ivy Spohnholz at 907-786-1944 or anias2@uaa.alaska.edu.

11481 ■ Ken Gray Scholarship *(Undergraduate/ Scholarship)*

Purpose: To offer financial assistance for tuition and other educational expenses to full-time junior or senior students who are formally admitted into a Bachelor of Arts or Bachelor of Fine Arts degree-seeking program in the area of sculpture and/or performance art as it relates to the visual art field at the University of Alaska Anchorage. **Focus:** Performing arts; Sculpture. **Qualif.:** Applicants must be in good academic standing with a minimum cumulative grade point average of 3.0; formally admitted into a Bachelor of Art or Bachelor of Fine Art degree-seeking program in the area of sculpture and/or performance art as it relates to the visual art field at the University of Alaska Anchorage; must be a junior or senior. **Criteria:** Selection of applicants will be based on their demonstrated motivation, talent, academic, and leadership potential.

Funds Avail.: Minimum of $500. **Duration:** Annual. **To Apply:** Applicants should submit 20 slides of your artwork, two-page artist's statement reflecting the criteria for selection and three (3) letters of reference from practitioners in the sculptural area. **Deadline:** February 15. **Contact:** Email: scholarships@uaa.alaska.edu.

11482 ■ Lenore and George Hedla Accounting Scholarship *(Undergraduate/Scholarship)*

Purpose: To offer financial assistance for tuition and other related educational expenses to University of Alaska Anchorage students who are enrolled full-time or part-time with a declared major in Accounting. **Focus:** Accounting. **Qualif.:** Applicants must be in good academic standing with a minimum cumulative grade point average of 2.0; formally admitted into an undergraduate Accounting degree-seeking program. **Criteria:** Selection of applicants will be based on their demonstrated motivation, talent, academic, and leadership potential.

Funds Avail.: $1,000. **Duration:** Annual. **To Apply:** Applicants must make sure that they meet all of the aforementioned qualifications before proceeding to apply online through Online and completing the scholarship application. **Deadline:** February 15. **Contact:** Email: scholarships@uaa.alaska.edu.

11483 ■ Chris L. Kleinke Scholarship *(Graduate/ Scholarship)*

Purpose: To provide a monetary award to an outstanding student at the University of Alaska Anchorage Master of Science Program in Clinical Psychology. **Focus:** Psychology. **Qualif.:** Applicants must be in good academic standing with a minimum cumulative grade point average of 3.0; formally admitted into the Master's Program in Clinical Psychology degree-seeking program at the University of Alaska Anchorage; and, incoming or continuing students at the University planning to enroll full-time (nine (9) credits of graduate course work); must be U.S. citizens, non-U.S.

citizens, Alaska residents, or out-of-state residents. **Criteria:** Selection of applicants will be based on their demonstrated motivation, talent, academic, and leadership potential; preference will be given to students who have completed at least one year in the Master of Science in Clinical Psychology program; must be an outstanding student in the University of Alaska Anchorage Master of Science Program in Clinical Psychology.

Funds Avail.: Minimum of $500. **Duration:** Annual. **To Apply:** Applicants must make sure that they meet all of the aforementioned qualifications before proceeding to apply online through Online and completing the scholarship application. **Deadline:** February 15. **Contact:** Email: scholarships@uaa.alaska.edu.

11484 ■ Kris Knudson Memorial Scholarship *(Graduate, Undergraduate/Scholarship)*

Purpose: To offer financial assistance for tuition and other educational expenses to full-time students who are formally admitted into a degree-seeking program in the area of biochemistry, immunology, or microbiology at the University of Alaska Anchorage. **Focus:** Biochemistry; Immunology; Microbiology. **Qualif.:** Applicant must have an earned baccalaureate degree, completed at least 15 credits undergraduate in Chemistry, Biological Sciences, or Natural Sciences and be admitted to a graduate program in one of those disciplines. An undergraduate recipient must have declared a major in and completed 15 credit hours in Chemistry, Biological Sciences, or Natural Sciences. Graduate student recipients must be involved in a research project within the area of biochemistry, immunology, or microbiology and must state the title of their research project on the application form for the scholarship. Recipient must be a full-time student at the University of Alaska Anchorage (minimum 12 credits for undergraduate or minimum of 9 credits for graduate student). Recipient must have a minimum grade point average of 3.0 in major field of study. Recipient must have a minimum overall cumulative GPA of 3.0. **Criteria:** Selection will be based on the committee criteria.

Funds Avail.: Minimum $500 Undergrad; $750 Graduate. **Duration:** Annual. **Number Awarded:** Varies. **To Apply:** Applicant must describe involvement in a research project related to biochemistry, immunology, or microbiology and state the title of research project. **Deadline:** February 15. **Contact:** Email:dsstraight@alaska.edu.

11485 ■ Arlene Kuhner Memorial Scholarship *(Undergraduate/Scholarship)*

Purpose: To offer financial assistance in the name of Dr. Arlene Kuhner for tuition and other related educational expenses to University of Alaska Anchorage students who have a declared major in English. **Focus:** Education, English as a second language. **Qualif.:** Applicants should demonstrate academic excellence; must be in good academic standing with at least a cumulative GPA of 3.0; must be a student attending the University of Alaska Anchorage; must have a declared major in English; must take a minimum of six credits per semester; in the event that two or more students are equally qualified for the scholarship, the scholarship will be awarded to the student with the most financial need. **Criteria:** Preference will be given to students who have been in residence at UAA for at least a year.

Funds Avail.: Minimum of $500. **Duration:** Annual. **Number Awarded:** 1. **To Apply:** Applicants must make sure that they meet all of the aforementioned qualifications

Awards are arranged alphabetically below their administering organizations

before proceeding to apply online through Online and completing the scholarship application. **Deadline:** February 15. **Remarks:** The scholarship was established in the remembrance of Dr. Arlene Kuhner. **Contact:** Email: scholarships@uaa.alaska.edu.

11486 ■ Melissa J. Wolf Accounting Scholarship
(Undergraduate/Scholarship)

Purpose: To offer financial assistance for tuition and other educational expenses to full-time students who are formally admitted into an Accounting degree-seeking program at the University of Alaska Anchorage. **Focus:** Accounting. **Qualif.:** Applicants must be in good academic standing with a minimum cumulative grade point average of 2.0; formally admitted into an Accounting degree-seeking program at the University of Alaska Anchorage. **Criteria:** Selection of applicants will be based on their demonstrated motivation, talent, academic, and leadership potential; preference will be given to students who demonstrate a financial need.

Funds Avail.: Minimum of $500. **Duration:** Annual. **To Apply:** Applicants must make sure that they meet all of the aforementioned qualifications before proceeding to apply online through Online and completing the scholarship application. **Deadline:** February 15. **Contact:** Email: scholarships@uaa.alaska.edu.

11487 ■ Muriel Hannah Scholarship in Art
(Undergraduate, Graduate/Scholarship)

Purpose: To offer financial assistance for tuition and other educational expenses to full-time students who are formally admitted into a degree-seeking program at the University of Alaska Anchorage and who have a demonstrated talent in art. **Focus:** Art. **Qualif.:** Applicants should be a full-time students attending the University of Alaska Anchorage with a demonstrated talent in Art; must have a minimum cumulative GPA of 2.0. **Criteria:** Applicant must be student of one-quarter or more Alaska Native.

Funds Avail.: Minimum of $500. **Duration:** Annual. **To Apply:** Applicants should provide a minimum of five (5) digital slides of your artwork and a digital slide of your artwork. **Deadline:** February 15. **Contact:** Email: scholarships@uaa.alaska.edu.

11488 ■ Diane Olsen Memorial Scholarship
(Undergraduate/Scholarship)

Purpose: To offer financial assistance to junior and senior students at UAA to help them pay for tuition and other related expenses. **Focus:** Economics. **Qualif.:** Applicants must be economics students or have a demonstrated interest in economics by the completion of at least 12 credits in economic courses. They must be: in good academic standing with a minimum cumulative grade point average of 2.75. **Criteria:** Selection of applicants will be based on their demonstrated motivation, talent, academic, and leadership potential; preference will be given to non-traditional students; must be enrolled full-time.

Funds Avail.: Minimum of $500. **Duration:** Annual. **To Apply:** Applicants must make sure that they meet all of the aforementioned qualifications before proceeding to apply online through Online and completing the scholarship application. **Deadline:** February 15. **Remarks:** The scholarship was established in the remembrance of Diane Olsen. **Contact:** Email: scholarships@uaa.alaska.edu.

11489 ■ Pignalberi Public Policy Scholarship
(Graduate/Scholarship)

Purpose: To provide financial assistance for tuition and other educational expenses to students enrolled in a gradu-

ate degree program in the UAA College of Business and Public Policy. **Focus:** Business; Public service.

Funds Avail.: $500. **Duration:** Annual. **To Apply:** Applicants must make sure that they meet all of the aforementioned qualifications before proceeding to apply online through Online and completing the scholarship application. Afterwards, they must submit a brief essay (250 words) answering the question: "In your opinion, what is the most important political issue in Alaska today?". **Deadline:** February 15.

11490 ■ April Relyea Scholarship *(Graduate, Undergraduate/Scholarship)*

Purpose: To offer financial assistance for tuition and other educational expenses to students who are formally admitted into a degree-seeking program at the University of Alaska Anchorage and who have intent to explore human-nature relationships through writing or other creative expression. **Focus:** Human relations. **Criteria:** Preference will be given to students with an intent to produce work for the Student Showcase and students with a demonstrated interest in writing nature books for children.

Funds Avail.: Minimum of $500. **Duration:** Annual. **To Apply:** The application process is online. **Deadline:** February 15. **Contact:** Email: scholarships@uaa.alaska.edu.

11491 ■ RRANN Program Scholarship
(Undergraduate/Scholarship)

Purpose: To provide financial assistance for tuition and other educational expenses to students currently enrolled in a nursing degree program through the Recruitment and Retention of Alaska Natives into Nursing (RRANN Program) at the University of Alaska Anchorage. **Focus:** Nursing. **Qualif.:** Applicants must be in good academic standing with a minimum cumulative grade point average of 2.0; formally admitted into a degree program within the School of Nursing through the RRANN program; Alaskan residents. **Criteria:** Selection of applicants will be based on their demonstrated motivation, talent, academic, and leadership potential; preference will be given to Alaska Natives or American Indian students.

Funds Avail.: Minimum of $500. **Duration:** Annual. **To Apply:** Applicants must make sure that they meet all of the aforementioned qualifications before proceeding to apply online through Online and completing the scholarship application. Must submit an essay responding to these questions How do you see yourself further advancing education in Alaska?; How do your extracurricular activities enhance your educational experience?; must complete the electronic scholarship application available online. **Deadline:** February 15. **Contact:** Email: scholarships@uaa.alaska.edu.

11492 ■ Brown Schoenheit Memorial Scholarship
(Undergraduate/Scholarship)

Purpose: To offer financial assistance for tuition and other educational expenses to students who are formally admitted into a Music degree-seeking program at the University of Alaska Anchorage. **Focus:** Music. **Criteria:** Selection of applicants will be based on their demonstrated motivation, talent, academic, and leadership potential; preference will be given to flute students and to applicants who intend to pursue a career in Alaska upon graduating.

Funds Avail.: $500. **Duration:** Annual. **To Apply:** Applicants must make sure that they meet all of the aforementioned qualifications before proceeding to apply online through Online and completing the scholarship application.

Awards are arranged alphabetically below their administering organizations

Must submit an essay responding to these questions: How do you see yourself further advancing education in Alaska?; How do your extracurricular activities enhance your educational experience?; must complete the electronic scholarship application available online. **Deadline:** February 15. **Remarks:** The scholarship was established in the remembrance of Brown Schoenheit. **Contact:** Email: scholarships@uaa.alaska.edu.

11493 ■ Lillian Smith Scholarship for Teaching Students *(Graduate, Undergraduate/Scholarship)*

Purpose: To provide financial assistance to students at UAA who are studying to become teachers. **Focus:** Education.

Funds Avail.: $500. **Duration:** Annual.

11494 ■ Sheri Stears Education Scholarship *(Undergraduate/Scholarship)*

Purpose: To provide tuition and other related assistance to students in preservice teacher education programs at UAA. Preservice teacher education programs include undergraduate degree programs in elementary and early childhood education. **Focus:** Education. **Criteria:** Preference will be given to students who best address how they see themselves advancing education in Alaska.

Deadline: April 29. **Remarks:** The donors wish for this scholarship to benefit baccalaureate students only.

11495 ■ Sturgulewski Family Scholarship *(Graduate, Undergraduate/Scholarship)*

Purpose: To provide financial assistance for tuition and other related educational expenses to the University of Alaska Anchorage students majoring in the areas of Journalism, Engineering, Teacher Education or Nursing. **Focus:** Education; Engineering; Journalism. **Qualif.:** Applicants must be in good academic standing with a minimum cumulative grade point average of 2.0 for undergraduate and 3.0 for graduate; formally admitted into a Journalism, Engineering, or Education undergraduate, graduate, certificate, and/or vocational degree-seeking program at the University of Alaska Anchorage; planning to enroll full-time (twelve credits for undergraduate and nine credits for graduate) at the University of Alaska Anchorage; and, incoming or continuing students at the University of Alaska Anchorage; must be U.S. citizens, non-U.S. citizens, Alaska residents, or out-of-state residents. **Criteria:** Selection of applicants will be based on their demonstrated motivation, talent, academic, and leadership potential.

Funds Avail.: Minimum of $500. **Duration:** Annual. **To Apply:** Applicants must make sure that they meet all of the aforementioned qualifications before proceeding to apply online through Online and completing the scholarship application. Must submit an essay responding to these questions: How do you see yourself further advancing education in Alaska?; How do your extracurricular activities enhance your educational experience?; must complete the electronic scholarship application available online. **Deadline:** February 15. **Contact:** Email: scholarships@uaa.alaska.edu.

11496 ■ UAA Alaska Kidney Foundation Scholarship *(Graduate, Undergraduate/Scholarship)*

Purpose: To provide scholarships in the name of the Alaska Kidney Foundation to prepare new nurses to provide safe and effective care to individuals experiencing chronic kidney disease in Alaska. **Focus:** Nursing.

Funds Avail.: $1,000. **Duration:** Annual. **To Apply:** Applicants must make sure that they meet all of the aforemen-

tioned qualifications before proceeding to apply online through Online and completing the scholarship application. **Deadline:** February 15. **Contact:** Email: scholarships@uaa.alaska.edu.

11497 ■ UAA Alumni Association Scholarship *(Undergraduate/Scholarship)*

Purpose: To provide financial assistance for tuition, registration fees, books and related educational expenses. **Focus:** General studies/Field of study not specified. **Qualif.:** Applicants must be in financial assistance for tuition, registration fees, books and related educational expenses. Recipient must be maintaining progress toward a degree program either beginning or continuing college education. Recipient must have a minimum cumulative GPA of 2.0. **Criteria:** Preference will be given to students who are Alaska High School graduates.

Funds Avail.: $48,000 in annual ($2,000 to four students in each college). **Duration:** Annual. **Number Awarded:** 4. **Deadline:** February 15.

11498 ■ UAA Ardell French Memorial Scholarship *(Undergraduate/Scholarship)*

Purpose: To offer financial assistance for tuition and other educational expenses to full-time students who are formally admitted into a Chemistry degree-seeking program at the University of Alaska Anchorage. **Focus:** Chemistry. **Qualif.:** Applicants should be a full-time students who are majoring in Chemistry. Recipient must have a minimum cumulative GPA of 3.0. Recipient must be a sophomore or higher. **Criteria:** Preference will be given to applicants who demonstrate financial need and are from Alaska.

Funds Avail.: Minimum of $500. **Duration:** Annual. **To Apply:** Applicants must make sure that they meet all of the aforementioned qualifications before proceeding to apply online through Online and completing the scholarship application. Must submit an essay responding to these questions: How do you see yourself further advancing education in Alaska?; How do your extracurricular activities enhance your educational experience?; must complete the electronic scholarship application available online. **Deadline:** February 15. **Remarks:** The scholarship was established in the remembrance of Ardell French. **Contact:** Email: scholarships@uaa.alaska.edu.

11499 ■ UAA College of Business and Public Policy Scholarships - American Marketing Association & F.X. Dale Tran Memorial Scholarship *(Graduate, Undergraduate/Scholarship)*

Purpose: To offer financial assistance for tuition and other educational expenses to full-time students who are formally admitted into a degree-seeking program within the College of Business and Public Policy at the University of Alaska Anchorage. **Focus:** Business; Public service. **Qualif.:** Applicant must be enrolled full-time in any major within the College of Business and Public Policy. Recipient must have a minimum cumulative GPA of 3.0. **Criteria:** Preference will be given to applicants who demonstrate community involvement.

Funds Avail.: $1,000. **Duration:** Annual. **To Apply:** Applicants must make sure that they meet all of the aforementioned qualifications before proceeding to apply online through Online and completing the scholarship application. **Deadline:** February 15. **Remarks:** The scholarship was established in the remembrance of F.X. Dale Tran. **Contact:** Email: suaa_financialaid@uaa.alaska.edu. Phone: 907-786-1480.

Awards are arranged alphabetically below their administering organizations

11500 ■ UAA Eveline Schuster Memorial Award/ Scholarship *(Graduate, Undergraduate/Scholarship)*

Purpose: To provide financial assistance for tuition and other related educational expenses to sociology students at the University of Alaska Anchorage. **Focus:** Sociology. **Criteria:** Selection of applicants will be based on their demonstrated motivation, talent, academic, and leadership potential.

Funds Avail.: Minimum of $500. **Duration:** Annual. **To Apply:** Applicants must make sure that they meet all of the aforementioned qualifications before proceeding to apply online through Online and completing the scholarship application. **Remarks:** The scholarship was established in the remembrance of Eveline Schuster.

11501 ■ UAA Friends of the Performing Arts Scholarship *(Undergraduate/Scholarship)*

Purpose: To offer financial assistance for tuition and other education related expenses to a full-time University of Alaska Anchorage student who has shown a proven interest in the Performing Arts. **Focus:** Performing arts. **Qualif.:** Applicants must be in good academic standing with a minimum cumulative grade point average of 2.0; formally admitted into an undergraduate Performing Arts (Theatre, Music, etc.) degree-seeking program at the University of Alaska Anchorage. **Criteria:** Selection of applicants will be based on their demonstrated motivation, talent, academic, and leadership potential.

Funds Avail.: Minimum of $500. **Duration:** Annual. **To Apply:** Applicant must upload a 1 - 2 minute recording of one of your performances with the application form through Online. **Deadline:** February 15. **Contact:** Email: scholarships@uaa.alaska.edu.

11502 ■ UAA GCI Scholarship *(Undergraduate/ Scholarship)*

Purpose: To offer financial assistance for tuition and other educational expenses to full-time students who are formally admitted into a Journalism and Public Communications degree-seeking program at the University of Alaska Anchorage and who are in financial need. **Focus:** Journalism; Public affairs. **Qualif.:** Applicants must be in good academic standing with a minimum cumulative grade point average of 3.0; formally admitted into a Journalism and Public Communications degree-seeking program at the University of Alaska Anchorage. **Criteria:** Selection of applicants will be based on their demonstrated motivation, talent, academic, and leadership potential.

Funds Avail.: Minimum of $500. **Duration:** Annual. **To Apply:** Applicants must make sure that they meet all of the aforementioned qualifications before proceeding to apply online through Online and completing the scholarship application. **Deadline:** February 15. **Contact:** Email: scholarships@uaa.alaska.edu.

11503 ■ UAA Kimura Scholarship Fund for Illustration *(Undergraduate/Scholarship)*

Purpose: To provide financial assistance for tuition and other related educational expenses to full-time students at the University of Alaska Anchorage majoring in art. **Focus:** Illustrators and illustrations. **Qualif.:** Applicants must be full time students attending the University of Alaska Anchorage with a declared major in Art or with a declared major in Journalism and Public Communication with an emphasis in illustration; in their Junior year and have completed at least nine credits in studio photography classes at the 200 level

or above; and, in good academic standing with at least a 3.0 GPA. **Criteria:** Selection will be based on the aforesaid qualifications and compliance with the application process.

Funds Avail.: Minimum of $500. **Duration:** Annual. **Number Awarded:** 1. **To Apply:** Applicants must upload 5 digital image of your illustration work through Online and completing the scholarship application. **Deadline:** February 15. **Contact:** UAA Office of Student Financial Assistance, Kimura Scholarships; Address: PO Box 141608, Anchorage, AK 99514.

11504 ■ UAA Kimura Scholarship Fund for Photography *(Undergraduate/Scholarship)*

Purpose: To provide financial assistance for tuition and other related educational expenses to full-time students at the University of Alaska Anchorage majoring in art. **Focus:** Art; Journalism; Photography. **Qualif.:** Applicants must be full time students attending the University of Alaska Anchorage with a declared major in Art or with a declared major in Journalism and Public Communication with an emphasis in photography; in their Junior year and have completed at least nine credits in studio photography classes at the 200 level or above; and, in good academic standing with at least a 3.0 GPA. **Criteria:** Selection will be based on the aforesaid qualifications and compliance with the application process.

Funds Avail.: Minimum of $500. **Duration:** Annual. **To Apply:** Applicants must upload 5 digital image of your photography work through Online and completing the scholarship application. **Deadline:** February 15. **Contact:** UAA Office of Student Financial Assistance, Kimura Scholarships; Address: PO Box 141608, Anchorage, AK 99514.

11505 ■ UAA Quanterra Scholarship *(Master's, Doctorate/Scholarship)*

Purpose: To provide financial assistance to students who are formally admitted to an engineering or science degree-seeking program at the University of Alaska Anchorage. **Focus:** Engineering; Science. **Qualif.:** Applicants must be Alaska natives planning to obtain a Master's or Doctoral degree. **Criteria:** Selection will be based on the scholarship committee's criteria.

Funds Avail.: No specific amount. **Duration:** Annual. **To Apply:** Applicants must complete the online scholarship application process and must provide all required materials.

11506 ■ Wells Fargo Career Scholarship *(Undergraduate/Scholarship)*

Purpose: To provide financial assistance for tuition and other educational expenses to students who are interested in a career with Wells Fargo. **Focus:** Accounting; Business; Economics; Finance; Management. **Qualif.:** Applicants must be in good academic standing with a minimum cumulative grade point average of 3.0; interested in a career with Wells Fargo; junior or senior students attending the University of Alaska Anchorage; enrolled full-time (12 credits) during the semester of the award; and, admitted into an undergraduate degree program within the College of Business and Public Policy. **Criteria:** Selection of applicants will be based on their demonstrated motivation, talent, academic, and leadership potential; preference will be given to candidates in Business Management, Finance, Economics, or Accounting majors or minors, as well as to candidates who have completed accounting, economics, and finance courses.

Awards are arranged alphabetically below their administering organizations

Funds Avail.: No specific amount. **Duration:** Annual. **To Apply:** Applicants must make sure that they meet all of the aforementioned qualifications before proceeding to apply online through Online and completing the scholarship application.

11507 ■ University of Alaska Anchorage - Matanuska-Susitna College

8295 E College Dr.
Palmer, AK 99645
Ph: (907)745-9774
Fax: (907)745-9711
E-mail: info@matsu.alaska.edu
URL: matsu.alaska.edu
Social Media: www.facebook.com/MSCDragons
twitter.com/matsucollege
www.youtube.com/user/MatSuCollege

11508 ■ Bill and Nell Biggs Scholarship
(Undergraduate/Scholarship)

Purpose: To provide financial support to deserving students in Alaska who want to pursue an education in any campus of the University of Alaska. **Focus:** Accounting; Business administration; Engineering; Mathematics and mathematical sciences; Science. **Qualif.:** Applicants must either a graduate from an accredited high school in the Juneau School District or Juneau residents who have completed a high school equivalency program; a minimum cumulative GPA of 2.0. **Criteria:** Preference will be given to applicants majoring in accounting, business administration, engineering, science and mathematics, related science subjects or foreign languages areas such as Spanish, German or French who demonstrate financial need.

Funds Avail.: $500. **To Apply:** Applicant must submit general application. **Deadline:** February 15.

11509 ■ Pat and Cliff Rogers Nursing Scholarship
(Undergraduate/Scholarship)

Purpose: To provide financial support to deserving students in Alaska who want to pursue an education in any campus of the University of Alaska. **Focus:** General studies/Field of study not specified. **Qualif.:** Applicants must enrolled in the junior or senior year of any nursing programs conducted at any institution within the University of Alaska system; a minimum cumulative GPA of 2.0; enrolled full-time.

Funds Avail.: $500.

11510 ■ Dr. Orrin Rongstad Wildlife Scholarship
(Undergraduate/Scholarship)

Purpose: To provide financial support to deserving students in Alaska who want to pursue an education in any campus of the University of Alaska. **Focus:** Wildlife conservation, management, and science. **Qualif.:** Applicants must be a full-time students attending any campus of the University of Alaska majoring in Wildlife Management; a minimum cumulative GPA of 2.0. **Criteria:** Selection is based on their academic standing and application documents.

Funds Avail.: $500. **Deadline:** February 15.

11511 ■ Russian Student Scholarship
(Undergraduate/Scholarship)

Purpose: To provide support to deserving students in Alaska who want to pursue an education in any campus of the University of Alaska. **Focus:** Wildlife conservation, management, and science. **Qualif.:** Applicants must be residents of Russia, Central Asia or the former Soviet Union, Russia, Kazakhstan, Uzbekistan, Turkmenistan, or Kirgizstan; a minimum cumulative GPA of 2.0. **Criteria:** Preference will be given to residents of the Russian Far East.

Funds Avail.: $500. **Deadline:** February 15.

11512 ■ University of Alaska Regents' Scholarship
(Undergraduate/Scholarship)

Purpose: To provide support to deserving students in Alaska who want to pursue an education in any campus of the University of Alaska. **Focus:** General studies/Field of study not specified. **Qualif.:** Applicants must be a junior, senior, or graduate students attending any campus of the University of Alaska; must demonstrate commitment and involvement in leadership, civic, or professional service activities and recognized academic achievement; a minimum cumulative GPA of 3.0; be enrolled full-time; a resident of Alaska. **Criteria:** Selection will be based on the committee's criteria.

Funds Avail.: $5,000. **To Apply:** Applicants must submit a listing of his/her demonstrated commitment and involvement.

11513 ■ University of Alaska Fairbanks (UAF)

1731 South Chandalar Dr.
Fairbanks, AK 99775
Ph: (907)474-7034
URL: www.uaf.edu
Social Media: www.facebook.com/uafairbanks
www.instagram.com/uafairbanks
www.pinterest.com/uafairbanks
twitter.com/uafairbanks
www.youtube.com/c/UafEduNaturallyInspiring

11514 ■ UAF College of Liberal Arts - Anchorage Daily News Journalism Awards *(Undergraduate/Scholarship)*

Purpose: To provide financial assistance students who are formally admitted to the journalism degree-seeking program at the University of Alaska Fairbanks. **Focus:** Journalism. **Qualif.:** Applicants must demonstrate motivation, academic and leadership potential; must be in good academic standing with a minimum cumulative GPA of 2.0; must be formally admitted to a journalism degree-seeking program at the University of Alaska Fairbanks; may be incoming or continuing students at the University of Alaska Fairbanks. **Criteria:** Preference will be given to Alaska Native students.

Funds Avail.: No specific amount. **Duration:** Annual. **To Apply:** Applicants must complete the electronic scholarship application available online. **Deadline:** February 15.

11515 ■ University of Alaska Fairbanks Alumni Association (UAFAA)

201 Constitution Hall
Fairbanks, AK 99775
Ph: (907)474-7081
Fax: (907)474-6712
Free: 844-474-6706
E-mail: uaf-alumni@alaska.edu
URL: www.uaf.edu

Awards are arranged alphabetically below their administering organizations

Social Media: www.facebook.com/uafalum
www.instagram.com/uafairbanks
www.pinterest.com/uafairbanks
twitter.com/uafairbanks
www.youtube.com/uafairbanks

11516 ■ Audrey Loftus Memorial Scholarship
(University/Scholarship)

Purpose: To support students with their educational pursuit. **Focus:** General studies/Field of study not specified. **Qualif.:** Applicants must be freshmen or transfer students with demonstrated experience in and future commitment to extracurricular/ community activities, and have a GPA of 3.0 and above. **Criteria:** Selection is based on leadership skills and potentiality.

Funds Avail.: No specific amount. **Number Awarded:** 1. **To Apply:** Applicants may visit the program website for other details regarding application process.

11517 ■ Fairbanks Chapter Legacy Scholarship
(Undergraduate/Scholarship)

Purpose: To support students in their educational pursuits. **Focus:** General studies/Field of study not specified. **Qualif.:** Applicants must be UAF sophomore students, or above, with a 3.5 GPA or above who are relatives of active, dues-paying members.

Funds Avail.: No specific amount. **Duration:** Annual. **Number Awarded:** 1. **To Apply:** Applicants may visit the program website for other details regarding application process.

11518 ■ Jay Hammond Memorial Scholarship
(Graduate/Scholarship)

Purpose: To support students who exhibit leadership and desire to make a difference in Alaska. **Focus:** General studies/Field of study not specified. **Qualif.:** Applicants must be students at the University of Alaska Fairbanks. **Criteria:** Selection shall be based on the aforementioned qualifications and compliance with the application details.

Funds Avail.: No specific amount. **Number Awarded:** 1. **To Apply:** Applicants may visit the program website for other details regarding application process.

11519 ■ Jim Doogan Memorial Scholarship
(Undergraduate/Scholarship)

Purpose: To support students in their pursuit of higher education. **Focus:** General studies/Field of study not specified. **Qualif.:** Applicants must be sophomore students or above.

Funds Avail.: No specific amount. **Number Awarded:** 1. **To Apply:** Applicants may visit the program website for other details regarding application process.

11520 ■ UAF Alumni Association Scholarship
(Undergraduate/Scholarship)

Purpose: To support the education of a dependent of an alumni. **Focus:** General studies/Field of study not specified. **Qualif.:** Applicants must be undergraduate sophomores, juniors and seniors who are dependents of active alumni association members; and have a GPA of 2.5-3.5 range. **Criteria:** Selection shall be based on the aforementioned qualifications and compliance with the application details.

Funds Avail.: No specific amount. **Duration:** Annual. **To Apply:** Applicants may visit the program website for other

details regarding application process.

11521 ■ University at Albany, State University of New York (CWGCS) - Center for Women in Government and Civil Society
Draper 312
135 Western Ave.
Albany, NY 12222
Ph: (518)442-3300
E-mail: cwgcs@albany.edu
URL: www.albany.edu

11522 ■ Fellowship on Women & Public Policy
(Graduate/Fellowship)

Purpose: To maximize the skills and contributions of women to achieve excellence in public service. **Focus:** Government; Public administration; Women's studies. **Qualif.:** Applicants must be graduate students and working professionals who have successfully completed a minimum of 12 graduate credits in any academic discipline and have a minimum of 3-5 years work experience.

Funds Avail.: $10,000. **Duration:** Annual. **To Apply:** Applicants completed; an official transcript from each college or university you have attended; a current résumé that includes information about your paid work and voluntary activity. **Deadline:** September 30. **Remarks:** Established in 1983. **Contact:** Center for Women in Government & Civil Society, Rockefeller College of Public Affairs & Policy, University at Albany, 135 Western Ave., Draper 302, Albany, NY 12222; Phone: 518-442-3900; Email: cwgcs@uamail.albany.edu.

11523 ■ University of Alberta - UAlberta North
Ring House 3
University of Alberta
Edmonton, AB, Canada T6G 2E1
Ph: (780)492-5717
E-mail: uanorth@ualberta.ca
URL: www.ualberta.ca/north
Social Media: www.facebook.com/UAlbertaNorth
twitter.com/UAlbertaNorth

11524 ■ The Kennett Y. Spencer Memorial Scholarship *(Graduate/Scholarship)*

Purpose: To support students at the University of Alberta for high academic attainment and original research carried out in any discipline pertaining to northern studies. **Focus:** Canadian studies. **Qualif.:** Applicants must be residents of northern Alberta (as defined by Northern Alberta Development Council), Yukon, Northwest Territories and Nunavut; must be student registered full-time in a graduate degree program at the University of Alberta whose focus of enquiry is in the field of northern studies. **Criteria:** Selection is based on superior academic achievement (equivalent to a grade point average of 3.5 or greater on the University of Alberta grading scale).

Funds Avail.: $2,100. **Duration:** Annual. **Number Awarded:** 1. **To Apply:** Applicants must submit original and 1 copy of the completed application forms; transcript; 3 copies of evidence of original research (e.g., course paper, thesis, research paper), and reference letters (minimum of 3). **Deadline:** September 15. **Contact:** UAlberta North, University of Alberta, Ring House 3, Edmonton, T6G 2E1,

Awards are arranged alphabetically below their administering organizations

Phone: 780-492-9089; Email: anitad@ualberta.ca.

11525 ■ University Aviation Association (UAA)
2787 North 2nd Street
Memphis, TN 38127
Ph: (901)563-0505
E-mail: hello@uaa.aero
URL: www.uaa.aero
Social Media: www.facebook.com/
UniversityAviationAssociation
www.linkedin.com/company/university-aviation-association
twitter.com/UAATweets

11526 ■ Eugene S. Kropf Scholarship
(Undergraduate/Scholarship)

Purpose: To encourage careers in aviation and other related fields through educational assistance. **Focus:** Aviation. **Qualif.:** Applicants must be U.S. citizens; enrolled in or planning to pursue two- or four-year degrees in the field of aviation; must be officially enrolled in a UAA member institution; and have a 3.0 GPA or above on a 4.0 scale.

Funds Avail.: $500. **Duration:** Annual. **To Apply:** Applicants must submit application form; proof of enrollment; transcript; an essay (250 words typewritten, double-spaced) on "How Can I Improve Aviation Education". **Deadline:** June 30. **Contact:** Prof. Kevin R. Kuhlmann, Metropolitan State College of Denver, Campus Box 30, PO Box 173362, Denver, CO 80217-3362.

11527 ■ Joseph Frasca Excellence in Aviation Scholarship *(Undergraduate, Graduate/Scholarship)*

Purpose: To encourage students to reach the highest level of achievement in the field of aviation. **Focus:** Aviation. **Qualif.:** Applicants should be undergraduates with a cumulative 3.0 GPA or better in aviation studies; must have FAA certification in flight or aviation maintenance and have attained junior or senior standing, must belong to an aviation-related organizations like Alpha Eta Rho. **Criteria:** Preference is given to applicants with demonstrated interest or experience in aviation simulation; aircraft restoration; aerobatics; with work experience in aviation; with work experience while in school; and exhibits financial need.

Funds Avail.: $1,000 each. **Duration:** Annual. **Number Awarded:** 2. **To Apply:** Applicants must submit completed application form; essay and letter of reference. **Deadline:** June 30. **Contact:** Dave NewMyer, SIU Transportation Education Center, 545 N. Airport Rd., Murphysboro, IL 62966; Email: newmyer@siu.edu.

11528 ■ Paul A. Whelan Aviation and Aerospace Scholarship *(Graduate, Undergraduate/Scholarship)*

Purpose: To promote educational pursuits in the field of aviation or space-related fields through financial assistance. **Focus:** Aviation. **Qualif.:** Applicants must be U.S. citizens; sophomore, junior, senior or graduate students; enrolled in a UAA member institution; must have 2.5 overall GPA and 3.0 in Aviation; and must demonstrate a love of aviation, leadership and extracurricular involvement/community involvement. **Criteria:** Selection is given to applicants who have an FAA certification as a pilot or mechanic; formerly or currently in military service via active duty, ROTC, the Air National Guard or Reserves while in school; and member of an aviation-related association or professional group such as the UAA.

Funds Avail.: $2,000. **Duration:** Annual. **Number Awarded:** 1. **To Apply:** Applicants must submit original copies and five copies of application form; official transcript; and recommendation letter from the institution. **Deadline:** June 30. **Remarks:** Established in memory of Paul A. Whelan, an aviation educator. **Contact:** Dr. David A. NewMyer, Chair, University Aviation Association Scholarship Committee, Southern Illinois University Carbondale, 1365 Douglas Drive, ASA Carbondale, IL 62901-6623.

11529 ■ University of Calgary - Centre for Military, Security and Strategic Studies (CMSS)
Social Sciences 856
2500 University Way NW
Calgary, AB, Canada T2N 1N4
E-mail: cmssgrad@ucalgary.ca
URL: cmss.ucalgary.ca

11530 ■ J.L. Granatstein Post-Doctoral Fellowship
(Postdoctorate/Fellowship)

Purpose: To provide students an opportunity to work with some of Canada's best international military historians and political scientists in the fields of strategy and military analysis. **Focus:** History, Military. **Criteria:** Selection will be based on the committee's criteria.

Funds Avail.: 38,000 Canadian Dollars; $5,000 travel and research allowance. **Duration:** Annual.

11531 ■ University of California, Berkeley
210 Stadium Rim Way
Berkeley, CA 94720-4206
Ph: (510)642-5215
E-mail: azettl@physics.berkeley.edu
URL: www.berkeley.edu
Social Media: www.facebook.com/UCBerkeley
instagram.com/ucberkeleyofficial
twitter.com/UCBerkeley

11532 ■ The Donald A. Strauss Scholarship
(Undergraduate/Scholarship)

Purpose: To support students in pursuing their career in the field of public service. **Focus:** Public service. **Qualif.:** Applicants must be full-time sophomores and juniors; must be in the upper third class (typically a minimum 3.3 GPA); must have outstanding leadership potential; and Passion for public service and making a difference. **Criteria:** Selection will be evaluated based their public service project proposal, outstanding leadership potential, effective communication skills and who "wish to make a difference" in local, regional, or national communities.

Funds Avail.: $15,000 award, consisting of a $7,000 scholarship and $8,000 project grant. **Duration:** Annual. **Number Awarded:** 14. **To Apply:** Applicants must complete the application form (available online); must have one-page resume that includes work history and community service experience; must have one-page autobiographical statement; must have four-page proposal for a community service project; must have completed the acceptance form; must have two or three letters of recommendation from individuals who are well-acquainted with the student's academic and/or service work; must have official copies of all college transcripts. **Contact:** Alicia Hayes, Email: ourscholarships@berkeley.edu.

11533 ■ Udall Scholarship *(Undergraduate/ Scholarship)*

Purpose: To support students in college sophomores and juniors for leadership, public service, and commitment to is-

Awards are arranged alphabetically below their administering organizations

sues related to Native American nations or to the environment. **Focus:** Environmental science; Health care services. **Criteria:** Selection will be selected based on who best demonstrates commitment to one of the areas of study through public or community service and potential for making significant contributions to their field.

Funds Avail.: $7,000. **Number Awarded:** 55. **To Apply:** Applicants must complete the application form; must have an 800-word essay discussing a significant public speech, legislative act, or public policy statement by Congressman Udall and its relationship to the applicant's interest or coursework; must have three letters of recommendation. **Deadline:** March 5. **Contact:** Program Manager Jason Curley curley@udall.gov (520) 901-8564.

11534 ■ University of California, Berkeley - Institute of East Asian Studies - Center for Chinese Studies (CCS)

1995 University Ave., Rm. 520J
Berkeley, CA 94720-2318
Ph: (510)643-6321
Fax: (510)642-5035
E-mail: ccs@berkeley.edu
URL: ieas.berkeley.edu

11535 ■ UC-Berkeley/ISEEES/CCS Postdoctoral Fellowships *(Postdoctorate/Fellowship)*

Purpose: To encourage individuals to pursue their research on Chinese studies. **Focus:** Asian studies. **Qualif.:** Applicant must have no more than four years of post-Ph.D. research experience prior to the appointment start date; must have their Ph.D. or equivalent degree in hand by their start date.

Funds Avail.: $49,188 plus benefits. **Duration:** Annual. **To Apply:** Applicants should submit a curriculum vitae with a list of publications; research proposal no longer than two pages, double-spaced; an English-language writing sample (such as a partial dissertation chapter) no longer than 20 pages, double-spaced; should supply a letter from their home institution confirming their schedule to completion; should request two letters of recommendation and the dissertation table of contents. **Deadline:** January 31. **Contact:** Email: ccs@berkeley.edu.

11536 ■ University of California, Berkeley - Institute of Governmental Studies (IGS)

109 Moses Hall
Berkeley, CA 94720-2370
Ph: (510)642-1474
Fax: (510)642-3020
E-mail: igs@berkeley.edu
URL: www.igs.berkeley.edu
Social Media: twitter.com/BerkeleyIGS

11537 ■ IGS John Gardner Fellowship *(Undergraduate/Fellowship)*

Purpose: To encourage U.C. Berkeley's and Stanford's best students to pursue a career in public service. **Focus:** Public service. **Qualif.:** Applicants must be graduating seniors from UC Berkeley in the current academic year (December or May) who have a strong interest in public service.

Funds Avail.: $32,500. **Duration:** Annual. **Number Awarded:** 6. **Deadline:** January 29. **Remarks:** Gardner's

legacy includes a vast array of public service accomplishments. The John Gardner Fellowship Program is honored to be part of that legacy. **Contact:** For more information contact Program director Terri Bimes.

11538 ■ University of California Institute for Mexico and the United States

University of California
3324 Olmsted Hall
Riverside, CA 92521-0147
Ph: (951)827-3519
Fax: (951)827-3856
E-mail: ucmexus@ucr.edu
URL: ucmexus.ucr.edu

11539 ■ UC MEXUS-CICESE Graduate Student Short-Term Research and Training Program *(Master's, Doctorate, Postdoctorate/Grant)*

Purpose: To accomplish specific laboratory, library or field research or to support short-term stays for graduate student research and training. **Focus:** Latin American studies. **Qualif.:** Applicants must be University of California graduate students fellows an opportunity to conduct research and acquire training. **Criteria:** Recipients will be selected based on submitted proposal.

Funds Avail.: $1,700 per month. **Duration:** Annual. **To Apply:** Applicants must complete the application form; must submit a cover page, project plan, detailed budget, curriculum vitae, UC faculty sponsor's abbreviated curriculum vitae, letter of support, Mexican academic host's letter of invitation and curriculum vitae, letter of acceptance and two sets of the proposal. **Contact:** Wendy DeBoer, PhD, at 951-827-7339 or wendyd@ucr.edu; Alvaro Armenta, PhD, at aarmenta@cicese.mx.

11540 ■ University of California, Los Angeles - Center for the Study of Women (CSW)

1500 Public Affairs Bldg.
Los Angeles, CA 90095-7222
Ph: (310)825-0590
E-mail: csw@csw.ucla.edu
URL: www.csw.ucla.edu
Social Media: twitter.com/UCLA_CSW
www.youtube.com/UCLACSW

11541 ■ Penny Kanner Dissertation Research Fellowship *(Doctorate/Fellowship)*

Purpose: To support an exceptional dissertation research project pertaining to women or gender that uses historical materials and methods. **Focus:** Women's studies. **Qualif.:** Applicants must be registered in a doctoral program at UCLA; must be dissertation prospectus must pertain to women and/or gender and research must use historical materials.

Funds Avail.: $3,000. **Duration:** Annual. **Number Awarded:** Varies. **To Apply:** Applicant must submit dissertation Abstract or Proposal (maximum 5 single-spaced pages); curriculum Vitae; unofficial UCLA Transcripts; two Letters of Recommendation from faculty members of any university. **Deadline:** March 29. **Contact:** Email: csw@csw.ucla.edu.

11542 ■ UCLA-CSW Travel Grants *(Graduate, Undergraduate/Grant)*

Purpose: To assist graduate and undergraduate UCLA students with air and ground transportation expenses

Awards are arranged alphabetically below their administering organizations

related to research on women, gender, and sexuality, including transportation for academic or professional conference presentation. **Focus:** Sexuality; Women's studies. **Qualif.:** Awardees must be registered UCLA students and preferably a woman. Awardees must also be registered during the quarter when travel occurs and when the reimbursement is processed. For summer, students must be enrolled in the preceding spring quarter and subsequent fall or winter quarters. **Criteria:** Selection will be on the basis of merit.

Funds Avail.: Maximum of $400. **Duration:** Semiannual. **To Apply:** Applicants must submit proposal describing research project or conference paper (maximum 2 single-spaced pages); curriculum vitae/resume; unofficial UCLA transcripts; one Letter of recommendation from a faculty member familiar with the research for which you are applying. **Deadline:** November 9 (fall); March 29 (spring). **Contact:** Email: csw@csw.ucla.edu.

11543 ■ University of California, Los Angeles - Near Eastern Languages and Cultures - UCLA Graduate Division Privately Endowed Fellowships
378 Kaplan Hall
Los Angeles, CA 90095
Ph: (310)825-4165
Fax: (310)206-6456
URL: nelc.ucla.edu

11544 ■ Mangasar M. Mangasarian Scholarship Fund *(Graduate/Scholarship)*

Purpose: To provide financial assistance students of Armenian descent. **Focus:** Area and ethnic studies. **Qualif.:** Applicants must be full-time graduate students of Armenian parentage attending the University of California. Scholarship is also offered to international students of Armenian descent.

To Apply: Interested applicants may contact the sponsor for the application process and other required materials.

11545 ■ University of California, Los Angeles - Ronald W. Burkle Center for International Relations
11353 Bunche Hall
Los Angeles, CA 90095
Ph: (310)206-6365
Fax: (310)206-6365
E-mail: burkle@international.ucla.edu
URL: www.international.ucla.edu
Social Media: www.facebook.com/burklecenter
twitter.com/burklecenter
www.youtube.com/channel/UCGjvkLpwLRI9FIkFRJvFV5g

11546 ■ Burkle Center Funding for Faculty Research Working Group Projects *(Graduate/Grant)*

Purpose: To encourage faculty to work in teams to define and develop research related to international affairs and global issues; foster collaborative scholarly exchange; promote interdisciplinary scholarship; and encourage intellectual discourse among faculty and graduate students. **Focus:** International affairs and relations. **Qualif.:** Applicants must be Principal Investigators on each project and must be UCLA ladder faculty.

Funds Avail.: Maximum of $10,000. **Duration:** Annual. **Deadline:** August 31. **Contact:** Email: burkle@international.ucla.edu.

11547 ■ University of California, Riverside - Bourns College of Engineering - Center for Environmental Research and Technology (CE-CERT)
1084 Columbia Ave.
Riverside, CA 92507
Ph: (951)781-5730
Fax: (951)781-5790
E-mail: certinfo@cert.ucr.edu
URL: www.cert.ucr.edu

11548 ■ Ford Motor Company Undergraduate Scholarship Award *(Undergraduate/Scholarship)*

Purpose: To encourage and aid undergraduate students in pursuit of careers in engineering. **Focus:** Engineering. **Qualif.:** Applicant must be a full-time undergraduate student at the University of California, Riverside, currently pursuing a B.S. degree, and have maintained at least a 3.0 grade point average; should have, or plan to have, a working relationship with CE-CERT. **Criteria:** Judgment criteria include the applicant's academic record, recommendations from faculty, promise in developing a successful career in a field of engineering, and financial need.

Funds Avail.: $5,000. **Duration:** Annual. **To Apply:** Applicants can view information and form is available online.

11549 ■ University of California - Riverside - Institute for Mexico and the United States
UC Mexus
3324 Olmsted Hall
900 University Ave.
Riverside, CA 92521-0147
Ph: (951)827-3519
E-mail: ucmexus@ucr.edu
URL: www.ucmexus.ucr.edu

11550 ■ UC MEXUS - CICESE Graduate Student Short-Term Research and Non-degree Training *(Graduate/Grant)*

Purpose: To accomplish laboratory, library or field research or to undertake specialized training. **Focus:** General studies/Field of study not specified. **Qualif.:** Applicants must be enrolled for the duration of the stay in a master's or doctoral level program at the University of California; must be enrolled for the duration of the stay in a master's or doctoral level program at CICESE; must have been continuously enrolled in their graduate program for at least one academic year by the time the proposed stay begins and be considered in good standing within their program. **Criteria:** Selection will be based on the submitted application materials.

Duration: Annual; 2-12 months. **Number Awarded:** 1. **To Apply:** Application must include UC MEXUS-CICESE Graduate Student Training Application Form (available in PDF or request form by email to veronica.sandoval@ucr.edu); curriculum vitae of graduate student applicant (not to exceed five pages); letter from the applicant's current faculty advisor; letter of intent from the faculty host; project plan written in English or Spanish. **Deadline:** March 31.

Awards are arranged alphabetically below their administering organizations

11551 ■ UC MEXUS-CONACYT Collaborative Grants
(Professional development/Grant)

Purpose: To provide seed funding to teams of UC and Mexican researchers with beginning projects in basic and applied collaborative research, instructional development, and public service and education projects that apply research to public issues. **Focus:** General studies/Field of study not specified. **Qualif.:** Applicants must be investigators from a UC campus and from a Mexican institution of higher education and/or research center that is part of the Registro Nacional de Institutions y Empresas Cientificas y Tecnologicas (RENIECYT). **Criteria:** Selection will be based on the submitted proposals.

Funds Avail.: $25,000. **Duration:** Annual. **To Apply:** Applications must be jointly submitted by eligible UC and Mexican collaborators using the online application site. All proposals must include a complete original set of the following items: application cover sheet; project co-principal investigator/institutional approval sheet, University of California; Project Co-Principal Investigator/Institutional Approval Sheet, Mexican Institution; Budget Request; abbreviated curriculum vitae; letters of intent to participate; project plan (maximum 10 pages); bibliography; attachments; must retain a copy of all application materials submitted; a complete proposal packet with two hard copies (original plus one copy) of all the information must be received by UC MEXUS within 10 days of the electronic submission deadline. **Deadline:** February 24.

11552 ■ UC MEXUS-CONACYT Doctoral Fellowship
(Doctorate/Fellowship)

Purpose: To provide non-resident tuition, fees, a stipend and support towards health insurance. **Focus:** Architecture; Biological and clinical sciences; Earth sciences; Engineering; Environmental science; Humanities; Law; Physical sciences; Social sciences; Urban affairs/design/planning. **Qualif.:** Applicants must be Mexican students doing their doctoral studies at any one of the ten University of California campuses; students may pursue doctoral studies in most of the academic disciplines, with the exception of the arts; eligible areas of study include the following Architecture; Biological Sciences; Earth Sciences; Engineering; Environmental Studies; Humanities; Law; Physical Sciences; Social Sciences; Urban Planning. **Criteria:** Selection will be based on the submitted application materials.

Duration: Annual; five years. **To Apply:** Applicants must submit UC MEXUS contact information form; web copy of fall quarter transcript; official transcript; UC MEXUS Academic; report form (Due in June); exit form (Due in June); questionnaire. **Deadline:** June 5. **Contact:** Maestra Marcela Cruz Caballero; Email: mcruzca@conacyt.mx.

11553 ■ UC MEXUS-CONACYT Postdoctoral
Research Fellowships *(Postdoctorate/Fellowship)*

Purpose: To advance academic scholarship by emerging Mexican researchers and UC scientists and scholars in the early stages of their careers, after obtaining their PhD. **Focus:** General studies/Field of study not specified. **Qualif.:** Applicants must earn their PhD by April of the current year; Mexican citizens who have earned their doctorate from an institution other than the University of California may apply only for residencies at a UC campus and must be hosted by eligible UC faculty or researchers; UC doctoral graduates may apply only for residencies at Mexican research institutions and must be hosted by a Mexican faculty member or researcher who holds a full-time academic/research appointment in a Mexican institution of higher education and/or research. **Criteria:** Selection will be reviewed, evaluated, and rated by a committee of faculty members and/or teachers from Mexican and UC institutions representing expertise in relevant topics; in addition to such standard review criteria as clarity, quality, and feasibility of the proposal, UC MEXUS will assign importance to the significant of the proposed activities for the students' academic advancement and training and quality of supervision from UC or Mexican faculty and researchers.

Funds Avail.: Minimum of $46,677 and maximum of $52,156. **Duration:** Annual; one year. **To Apply:** Applicants must include hard copies of all files uploaded to the electronic submission site; the following items are required as part of the proposal packet, for both the online submission and the two hard copies sent to UC MEXUS online application cover sheet; curriculum vitae; abbreviated curriculum vitae of faculty host; letter of intent from the faculty host; project plan; timeline; official letter of invitation; if applicable, official evidence that the postdoctoral candidate belongs to the Sistema Nacional de Investigators of Mexico with the registration number, and/or official letter from the home institution indicating that they hold a full-time appointment and will be released for the time requested; certification of completion of the PhD degree; two letters of reference must be uploaded and sent separately. **Deadline:** March 19. **Contact:** Dr. Wendy DeBoer, Director of Academic Program; Phone: 951-827-7339; Email: wendy.deboer@ucr.edu. or Mtro. Alejandro Uribe Castillo, Director de Planeacion de Ciencia; Phone: 55-53-22-7700; ext. 4060; Email: auuribeca@conacyt.mx.

11554 ■ UC MEXUS Dissertation Research Grants
(Graduate/Grant)

Purpose: To support a dissertation research or MFA final projects by UC graduate students. **Focus:** Latin American studies. **Qualif.:** Applicants must be California graduate students in good standing, or Mexican nationals currently enrolled in UC graduate programs, including UC MEXUS-CONACYT Doctoral Fellows. **Criteria:** Selection will be based on the submitted proposal; each proposal will be reviewed, evaluated, and rated by a committee of UC and Mexican scientists and scholars representing expertise in relevant academic disciplines and topics in the physical, natural and social science, humanities, and arts; preference will be given to projects that hold significant promise for the advance of science or scholarship in areas of interest to UC MEXUS.

Funds Avail.: $12,000. **Duration:** Annual; one academic year. **Number Awarded:** Varies. **To Apply:** Applicants must submit a proposal using the online application site; the following items are required to complete the application: cover sheet; project institutional approval sheet; project plan (maximum 5 pages); bibliography; budget request; abbreviated curriculum vitae; letters of intent to participate; attachments; support letters; must retain a copy of all application materials submitted; within 10 days following the online application deadline, send two hard copies (original plus one copy) of a complete application set with all required materials. **Deadline:** September 12. **Contact:** Andrea Kaus, PhD, Director of Research Programs; Phone: 951-827-3519; Email: andrea.kaus@ucr.edu.

11555 ■ UC MEXUS Scholars in Residence Program
- Graduate *(Graduate/Scholarship)*

Purpose: To offer an academic residency program for scholars at critical junctures in their academic careers. **Focus:** Arts. **Qualif.:** Applicants must be graduate students in the write-up phase of their dissertations, master's thesis,

Awards are arranged alphabetically below their administering organizations

or final phase of production for a Master of Fine Arts; fellows are expected to interact with UCR faculty and students, and also with other visiting researchers at UC MEXUS. **Criteria:** Selection will be based on the submitted application materials.

Funds Avail.: Up to $4,000. **Duration:** Annual; up to 3 years. **To Apply:** Applications require a short prospectus (no more than 3 pages) indicating what the fellows hopes to accomplish with respect to their career development during the residency, how they expects to interact with the UCR campus community, and what the specific end products will be include a current curriculum vitae and request three letters of recommendation to be sent independently to the Director of Academic Programs; fellows must provide proof health insurance prior to beginning their residency. **Contact:** Wendy DeBoer, PhD, Director of Academic Programs; Phone: 951-827-7339; Email: wendy.deboer@ucr.edu.

11556 ■ UC MEXUS Scholars in Residence Program - Recent University Graduates *(Postgraduate, Graduate/Scholarship)*

Purpose: To provide an opportunity for individuals to establish themselves and broaden the research or activities initiated in the last phase of their graduate career or to expand on activities begun as postgraduates. **Focus:** General studies/Field of study not specified. **Qualif.:** Applicants must be researchers, artists, or scholars within 5 years of receiving their graduate degree (PhD, MA, MS or MFA). **Criteria:** Selection will be based on the submitted application materials.

Funds Avail.: Up to $4,000. **Duration:** Annual; Up to 1 year appointments. **To Apply:** Applications require a short prospectus (no more than 3 pages) indicating what the fellows hopes to accomplish with respect to their career development during the residency, how they expects to interact with the UCR campus community, and what the specific end products will be. Include a current curriculum vitae and request three letters of recommendation to be sent independently to the Director of Academic Programs. Fellows must provide proof health insurance prior to beginning their residency. **Contact:** Wendy DeBoer, PhD, Director of Academic Programs; Phone: 951-827-7339; Email: wendy.deboer@ucr.edu.

11557 ■ UC MEXUS Scholars in Residence Program - Visiting Faculty *(Professional development/ Scholarship)*

Purpose: To provide an opportunity for individuals to reflect and dedicate themselves to a specific project and collaborate with UCR faculty. **Focus:** General studies/Field of study not specified. **Qualif.:** Applicants must be visiting faculty researchers or artists. **Criteria:** Selection will be based on the submitted application materials.

Funds Avail.: Up to $4,000. **Duration:** Annual; 4-12 months. **To Apply:** Applications require a short prospectus (no more than 3 pages) indicating what the fellow hopes to accomplish with respect to their career development during the residency, how they expect to interact with the UCR campus community, and what the specific end products will be. Applicant should include a current curriculum vitae and request three letters of recommendation to be sent independently to the Director of Academic Programs; fellows must provide proof of health insurance prior to beginning their residency. **Contact:** Wendy DeBoer, Ph.D. Director of Academic Programs, UC MEXUS tel: (951) 827-7339 e-mail: wendy.deboer@ucr.edu.

11558 ■ UC MEXUS Small Grants for UC Postdocs *(Postdoctorate/Grant)*

Purpose: To support students or researchers for their activities in all disciplines as related to academic exchange, research training, and scholarly development in areas of interest to UC MEXUS. **Focus:** Latin American studies. **Criteria:** Selection will be reviewed by an internal committee and award decisions made by the director of UC MEXUS; in addition to such standard review criteria as clarity, quality, and feasibility of the proposal, UC MEXUS will assign importance to the significant of the proposed activities for the students' academic advancement and training quality from the UC or Mexican faculty and researchers; reviews are based on the proposed project or activity only and the thematic fit UC MEXUS goals, independent of the nationality of the applicants.

Funds Avail.: $1,500. **Duration:** Monthly; up to four years. **To Apply:** Applicants must submit a completed application form, available at the website, and must include the following required attachments a project plan; a detailed budget; curriculum vitae; for projects that will take place in Mexico, a copy of the letter of invitation from a Mexican faculty member or researcher; a signature of the students' UC faculty sponsor is required and academic standing in a graduate program or postdoctoral position must be certified by the chair of the applicants' department. **Deadline:** January 8, February 5, March 5, April 2, May 7, June 4, July 2, August 6, September 4, October 1, November 5, and December 3. **Contact:** Martha Ponce, UC MEXUS, 3324 Olmsted Hall, University of California, Riverside, CA, 92521. or Andrea Kaus, PhD, Director of Grants Programs; Phone: 951-827-3586; Email: andrea.kaus@ucr.edu.

11559 ■ UC MEXUS Small Grants for UC Students *(Graduate, Postdoctorate/Grant)*

Purpose: To assist the activities of individuals in all disciplines as related to academic exchange, research training, and scholarly development in areas of interest to UC MEXUS. **Focus:** Latin American studies.

Funds Avail.: $1,500. **Duration:** 6 month. **To Apply:** Applicant must submit a completed application form, available at the website, and must include the following required attachments: a project plan; a detailed budget; curriculum vitae; for projects that will take place in Mexico, a copy of the letter of invitation from a Mexican faculty member or researcher. **Contact:** Martha Ponce, UC MEXUS, 3324 Olmsted Hall, University of California, Riverside, CA, 92521. or Andrea Kaus, PhD, Director of Grants Programs; Phone: 951-827-3586; Email: andrea.kaus@ucr.edu.

11560 ■ University of California, San Diego - California Sea Grant College Program (CASG)

9500 Gilman Dr.
La Jolla, CA 92093-0232
Ph: (858)534-4440
URL: caseagrant.ucsd.edu
Social Media: www.facebook.com/pages/California-Sea -Grant/152434827994
www.instagram.com/caseagrant
www.linkedin.com/school/caseagrant
twitter.com/CASeaGrant
www.youtube.com/user/CASGnews

11561 ■ John D. Isaacs Marine Undergraduate Research Assistant Program *(Undergraduate/Grant)*

Purpose: To provide undergraduate students interested in marine science with high-quality summer research experience while also assisting investigators to further their marine research projects. **Focus:** Science.

Funds Avail.: $2,500. **Duration:** Annual.

11562 ■ University of California, Santa Barbara - Institute for Social, Behavioral, and Economic Research - Center for Nanotechnology in Society (CNS_UCSB)

Center for Nanotechnology in Society University of California Santa Barbara
Santa Barbara, CA 93106-2150
Fax: (805)893-7995
E-mail: cns@cns.ucsb.edu
URL: www.cns.ucsb.edu

11563 ■ CNS-UCSB Graduate Fellowships for Science and Engineering *(Postdoctorate/Fellowship)*

Purpose: To support outstanding graduate students who want to pursue research in science and engineering. **Focus:** Biology; Chemistry; Physics; Technology. **Qualif.:** Applicant must PhD student (U.S. citizen or permanent resident); must currently enrolled and in good standing in a relevant graduate program ant UCSB; must have interest in and ability to work productively in a collaborative, interdisciplinary environment.

Duration: Annual. **To Apply:** Applicant must include cover sheet; statement of Interest relevant to CNS-UCSB; curriculum vitae; unofficial transcript; recommendation from current academic advisor (must be sent from advisor's email address).

11564 ■ University of Colorado at Boulder - Natural Hazards Center

1440 15th St.
Boulder, CO 80309
Ph: (303)735-5844
Fax: (303)492-2151
E-mail: hazctr@colorado.edu
URL: www.colorado.edu/hazards
Social Media: www.facebook.com/hazcenter
twitter.com/HazCenter

11565 ■ Mary Fran Myers Scholarship *(Professional development, Undergraduate, Graduate, Doctorate/ Scholarship)*

Purpose: To support individual commitment to disaster research. **Focus:** Emergency and disaster services. **Qualif.:** Applicants must be hazards practitioners, students, and researchers with a strong commitment to disaster management and mitigation and who reside in North America or the Caribbean. **Criteria:** Preference is given to those who can demonstrate financial need.

Duration: Annual. **To Apply:** Application details are available online at: hazards.colorado.edu/awards/myers-scholarship. **Deadline:** March 15. **Remarks:** Established to fulfill Myers' request that qualified and talented individuals receive support to attend, ensuring that representatives of all ages, professions, and communities be represented at the Workshop. Established in 2003. **Contact:** For questions, contact committee chair Ponmile Olonilua; Email: oluponmileoOlonilua@tsu.edu.

11566 ■ University Film and Video Association (UFVA)

E-mail: home@ufva.org
URL: www.ufva.org

Social Media: www.facebook.com/ufvaconnection
twitter.com/UFVAtweets

11567 ■ Carole Fielding Student Grant *(Undergraduate, Graduate/Grant)*

Purpose: To support the education aspect of students in the film and video discipline. **Focus:** Filmmaking; Video. **Qualif.:** Applicant must be a graduate or undergraduate student at the time the application is made; faculty member who is an active member of the University Film & Video Association or staff at a UFVA member institution must sponsor the applicant. **Criteria:** Selection will be based on the committee's criteria.

Funds Avail.: $1,000. **Duration:** Annual. **To Apply:** Applicant must submit a one-page description of the project that includes a statement of purpose, an indication of the resources available to complete the work, and a summary of the proposed production or research project; one page resume, including information on past film/video/new media work, and/or publications; a statement by the sponsoring UFVA Member, assessing the feasibility of the project and indicating their willingness to serve as faculty supervisor or consultant; a one-page budget, clearly indicating what portion of the total project will be supported by the grant. Additional following documents include: narrative (a copy of the script for 30 minutes); documentary (a short treatment for 45 minutes); and experimental/animation/New Media (a treatment or script, and/or a storyboard). **Deadline:** December 15.

11568 ■ University of Florida - Center for Latin American Studies

319 Grinter Hall
Gainesville, FL 32611-5530
Ph: (352)273-4705
Fax: (352)392-7682
E-mail: Communications@latam.ufl.edu
URL: www.latam.ufl.edu
Social Media: www.facebook.com/
  UFLatinAmericanStudies
www.instagram.com/uf_latam/
twitter.com/LatamUF
www.youtube.com/user/UFLatinAmerica

11569 ■ FLAS Academic Year Fellowships *(Graduate, Undergraduate/Fellowship)*

Purpose: To support training in Brazilian Portuguese and Haitian Creole. **Focus:** Foreign languages. **Qualif.:** Applicants must be full-time UF graduate or undergraduate students who are U.S. citizens or permanent residents; undergraduate applicants must have at least intermediate proficiency in Portuguese or Haitian Creole; there is no proficiency requirement for graduate applicants; however, graduate students proposing to study a language at the beginning level must demonstrate that they already possess advanced proficiency in at least one other Latin American language; they should also address in their statement of purpose the reasons for studying the new language in connection to their academic and/or career goals. Also accepting applications from students interested in learning Yoruba in the context of the Caribbean and Latin America. **Criteria:** Preference will be given to applicants pursuing a Master's degree, graduate certificate, or undergraduate minor/certificate in Latin American Studies; professional school students are also encouraged to apply; applications

Awards are arranged alphabetically below their administering organizations

are reviewed by the Center's Financial Aid Committee.

Duration: Annual. **To Apply:** Applicants must submit FLAS academic year fellowship application with two-page statement of purpose describing how the study of Brazilian Portuguese or Haitian Creole and Latin American area studies will benefit your program of study and career plans; two letters of recommendation accompanied by release form; for graduate students, one of the letters should be from your adviser, unless you are a new UF applicant; official UF academic transcript; new UF applicants may submit photocopies from previous universities or colleges; determination of financial need - FLAS fellowship form -OR- a copy of most recent FAFSA form (if submitted to UF for financial aid). **Deadline:** February 1. **Contact:** Wanda Carter, Academic Programs Assistant, Email: wcarter@latam.ufl.edu; URL: http://www.latam.ufl.edu/academics/student-funding/flas-academic-year-fellowships/.

11570 ■ UF Center for Latin American Studies FLAS Summer Fellowships *(Master's, Graduate, Undergraduate/Award, Fellowship)*

Purpose: To support individuals who participate or willing to participate in an intensive study program of a less-commonly-taught Latin American Language. **Focus:** Foreign languages; Latin American studies. **Qualif.:** Applicants must be U.S. citizens or permanent residents who are currently enrolled at the University of Florida as full-time undergraduate or graduate students; must have at least intermediate proficiency in their selected language of study for undergraduate students; non-University of Florida graduate students with citizenship or permanent residency who are planning to attend the University of Florida Language and Culture Program in Rio de Janeiro are also eligible.

To Apply: Applicants must submit the following requirements completed FLAS Summer Fellowship application; two-page statement of purpose describing how the study of the less-commonly-taught language will benefit your program of study and career plans; one academic letter of recommendation accompanied by Release Form. For graduate students, the letter should be from your main adviser; one Language Recommendation Form; official academic transcripts; budget with information on program fees; determination of Financial Need - FLAS Fellowship form -OR- a copy of most recent FAFSA form. **Deadline:** March 13. **Contact:** Wanda Carter, Academic Programs Assistant; Email: wcarter@latam.ufl.edu; URL: http://www.latam.ufl.edu/academics/student-funding/flas-summer-fellowships/.

11571 ■ University of Florida College of Liberal Arts and Sciences - Center for Women's Studies and Gender Research

200 Ustler Hall
Gainesville, FL 32611
Ph: (352)392-3365
Fax: (352)392-4873
URL: www.wst.ufl.edu
Social Media: www.facebook.com/UF.CGSWSR
twitter.com/UF_CGSWSR

11572 ■ O. Ruth McQuown Scholarship - Graduate Award for Current Students *(Graduate/Scholarship)*

Purpose: To provide educational support to outstanding students enrolled in the College of Liberal Arts and Sci-

ences at the University of Florida. **Focus:** Humanities; Interdisciplinary studies; Social sciences; Women's studies. **Qualif.:** Applicants must be graduate students who have completed at least one semester of graduate work in the College of Liberal Arts and Sciences. **Criteria:** Selection scholarships will be awarded on a competitive basis in the fields of Humanities, Social Sciences, Individual Interdisciplinary Studies and Women's Studies.

To Apply: Applicants submit the information through the mail along with the two letters of recommendation and an essay paper. **Deadline:** February 22. **Contact:** Arlene Williams, Emai; arlenew@ufl.edu.

11573 ■ University of Louisville Alumni Association (UOFL ALUMNI.)

University Club and Alumni Ctr.
200 E Brandeis Ave.
Louisville, KY 40208
Ph: (502)852-6186
Fax: (502)852-6920
Free: 800-813-8635
E-mail: alumni@louisville.edu
URL: www.uoflalumni.org
Social Media: www.facebook.com/UofLAlumniAssociation
www.instagram.com/uoflalumni
twitter.com/uoflalum
www.youtube.com/user/uoflalumni

11574 ■ Beth K. Fields Scholarship *(University/Scholarship)*

Purpose: To support students in their educational pursuit. **Focus:** General studies/Field of study not specified. **Qualif.:** Applicants must be at least 25 years of age; provide support for at least one dependent; have a minimum of 12 semester hours college credit; have a cumulative GPA of 3.0; and, be full-time students at the university for the semester in which the scholarship is awarded. **Criteria:** Selection is based on the submitted applications.

Funds Avail.: Amount varies. **Duration:** Annual; four years. **To Apply:** Applicants must submit a completed application form together with their resume or list of school, community and civic activities; one-page essay explaining their interest in the award and why they should receive the scholarship; and two letters of recommendation from a professor or teacher, while the other may be from their respective employers, community leaders, friends or relatives. **Deadline:** February 15. **Contact:** sfaoscholarships@louisville.edu.

11575 ■ Covington-Cincinnati/Northern Kentucky Alumni Chapter - Dane Wagge Scholarships *(University/Scholarship)*

Purpose: To provide financial assistance to students in Northern Kentucky/Greater Cincinnati area. **Focus:** General studies/Field of study not specified. **Qualif.:** Applicants must residents in the state of Kentucky (specifically in Boone, Kenton, Campbelle, Grant, Carroll, Pendleton and Gallatin counties) or in Hamilton County in Ohio, and must have a cumulative GPA of 3.0 and an ACT/SAT equivalent of 20 or above. **Criteria:** Selection will be based on the aforementioned qualifications and compliance with the application details.

Funds Avail.: Amount varies. **Number Awarded:** Varies. **Deadline:** February 15. **Contact:** Rachel Kirk, Student

Awards are arranged alphabetically below their administering organizations

Financial Aid Office; Phone: 502-852-8379; Email: rachel.kirk@louisville.edu.

11576 ■ Frankfort/Capital Region Alumni Chapter
(University/Scholarship)

Purpose: To support students in their educational pursuits. **Focus:** General studies/Field of study not specified. **Qualif.:** Applicants must be residents in the state of Kentucky (specifically in Anderson, Franklin, Henry, Owen, Mercer, Shelby and Spencer counties) pursuing a degree at the University of Louisville, and must maintain a GPA of 3.0. **Criteria:** Selection will be based on the basis of financial need.

Funds Avail.: Amount varies. **Duration:** up to 4 years. **Number Awarded:** Varies. **Deadline:** February 15. **Contact:** Rachel Kirk, Student Financial Aid Office; Phone: 502-852-8379; Email: rachel.kirk@louisville.edu.

11577 ■ Kentucky Alumni Club Scholarships - Lexington/Central Kentucky Alumni Chapter *(Graduate, High School/Scholarship)*

Purpose: To support students in their educational pursuits. **Focus:** General studies/Field of study not specified. **Qualif.:** Applicants must be students pursuing a degree at University of Louisville; have 3.0 GPA; and, residents in the state of Kentucky specifically in Fayette, Jessamine, Woodford, Clark, Bourbon, Scott, Harrison and Madison counties. **Criteria:** Students will be selected on the basis of financial need.

Funds Avail.: No specific amount. **Number Awarded:** Varies. **Deadline:** February 15. **Contact:** Rachel Kirk, Student Financial Aid Office; Phone: 502-852-8379; Email: rachel.kirk@louisville.edu.

11578 ■ Kentucky Alumni Club Scholarships - Somerset/Lake Cumberland Area Alumni Chapter
(University/Scholarship)

Purpose: To support students in their educational pursuits. **Focus:** General studies/Field of study not specified. **Qualif.:** Applicants must be students from Adair, Casey, Clinton, Cumberland, Laurel, McCreary, Pulaski, Rockcastle, Rusell, and Wayne counties pursuing a degree at the University of Louisville who meet the minimum admission requirements; must also have a cumulative GPA of 3.5 or higher on a 4.0 scale and an ACT score of 24 or better. **Criteria:** Selection will be based on the aforementioned qualifications and compliance with the application details.

Funds Avail.: Amount varies. **Number Awarded:** Varies. **Deadline:** February 15. **Contact:** Rachel Kirk, Student Financial Aid Office; Phone: 502-852-8379; Email: rachel.kirk@louisville.edu.

11579 ■ Raymond A. Kent-Navy V-12/ROTC
(Undergraduate/Scholarship)

Purpose: To support direct descendants of an individuals who served in the Navy V-12 program or the Naval ROTC program at UofL. **Focus:** General studies/Field of study not specified. **Qualif.:** Applicants must be a direct descendant of an individual who served the Navy V-12 program or the Naval ROTC program; must have a 3.0 GPA. **Criteria:** Applications will be reviewed by the Scholarship Committee of the Board of Directors.

Funds Avail.: No specific amount. **Duration:** Annual. **Deadline:** March 15.

11580 ■ Rodney Williams Legacy Scholarship
(Graduate/Scholarship)

Purpose: To support the children and grandchildren of UofL alumni. **Focus:** General studies/Field of study not

specified. **Qualif.:** Applicant must be related to a U of L graduate; incoming freshman or transfer student; have a 3.0 GPA; and must be a full-time student for the semester. **Criteria:** Selection is based on the submitted applications.

Funds Avail.: No specific amount. **Duration:** Up to four years. **To Apply:** Applicants must submit a completed application form together with a copy of an official transcript of records; resume or list of school, community and civic activities; a (300-word) essay; and two letters of recommendation. **Deadline:** February 15. **Contact:** sfaoscholarships@louisville.edu.

11581 ■ University of Manitoba (UM)
424 University Ctr.
Winnipeg, MB, Canada R3T 2N2
URL: www.umanitoba.ca

11582 ■ Kathleen and Winnifred Ruane Graduate Student Research Grant for Nurses *(Undergraduate/ Grant)*

Purpose: To support nursing students' academic and research objectives. **Focus:** Nursing. **Qualif.:** Applicants must be enrolled full-time in the Faculty of Graduate Studies, Master of Nursing program in the Nurse Practitioner stream, minimum cumulative grade point average of 3.5. **Criteria:** Selection based on not be limited to:innovative past practices in nursing,sound, innovative ideas for future practices,clear articulation of ideas in writing; and demonstrated leadership skills.

Funds Avail.: $3,000. **Duration:** Annual. **Number Awarded:** 2. **To Apply:** Applicants will be required to submit a letter of application, a copy of their official transcript, and two letters of reference, one of which should be from a faculty member. **Deadline:** April 30.

11583 ■ University of Manitoba - Centre on Aging
338 Isbister Bldg.
Winnipeg, MB, Canada R3T 2N2
Ph: (204)474-8754
E-mail: coaman@ad.umanitoba.ca
URL: umanitoba.ca
Social Media: www.facebook.com/CentreOnAging.umanitoba
www.instagram.com/umanitoba
twitter.com/umanitoba
youtube.com/user/YouManitoba

11584 ■ Centre on Aging Betty Havens Memorial Graduate Fellowship *(Graduate, Doctorate, Master's/ Fellowship)*

Purpose: To encourage the furthering of studies in aging and gerontology by supporting aging-related research in any discipline. **Focus:** Gerontology.

Funds Avail.: 4,000 Canadian Dollars. **Duration:** Annual.

11585 ■ Jack MacDonell Scholarship for Research in Aging *(Graduate, Doctorate, Master's/Scholarship)*

Purpose: To encourage the furthering of studies in aging and gerontology by supporting aging-related research in any discipline. **Focus:** Gerontology.

Funds Avail.: 4,000 Canadian Dollars. **Duration:** Annual. **Number Awarded:** 1. **Deadline:** March 20.

Awards are arranged alphabetically below their administering organizations

11586 ■ Esther and Samuel Milmot Scholarship *(Graduate, Undergraduate/Scholarship)*

Purpose: To encourage the furthering of studies in aging and gerontology by supporting aging-related research in any discipline. **Focus:** Gerontology. **Qualif.:** Applicants must be full-time students pursuing a program which bears on gerontology either in the Faculty of Arts or in the Faculty of Graduate Studies with the principal field of study in a department of the Faculty of Arts, University of Manitoba.

Funds Avail.: 500 Canadian Dollars. **Duration:** Annual. **Number Awarded:** 1. **Deadline:** March 20. **Remarks:** Established in 1987.

11587 ■ University of Manitoba Centre on Aging Research Fellowship *(Advanced Professional/Fellowship)*

Purpose: To encourage the furthering of studies in aging and gerontology by supporting aging-related research in any discipline. **Focus:** Gerontology. **Qualif.:** Applicants must be University of Manitoba faculty members.

Funds Avail.: 11,000 Canadian Dollars. **Duration:** Annual. **To Apply:** Applicants must submit one electronic copy of original completed application form (www.umanitoba.ca/aging); three-page research proposal written in a language that allows all members of the selection committee, who may not be specialists in the applicant's field, to have a clear understanding of its scope and nature; financial data including a budget summary and budget justification. **Deadline:** October 18. **Contact:** Dr. Michelle Porter, Director, Centre on Aging, 338 Isbister Bldg., Phone: 204- 474-8754; Email: coaman@umanitoba.ca.

11588 ■ University of Manitoba - Health, Leisure and Human Performance Research Institute
207A Max Bell Centre
Winnipeg, MB, Canada R3T 2N2
URL: www.umanitoba.ca

11589 ■ Health, Leisure and Human Performance Research Institute Graduate Student Travel Award *(Graduate/Grant, Award)*

Purpose: To provide graduate students in the Faculty of Kinesiology and Recreation Management with the opportunity to participate in and to present their research at academic conferences. **Focus:** Medical research. **Qualif.:** Must be enrolled in Faculty of Kinesiology and Recreation Management or a maximum of 4 months after convocation day to attend and submit application giving the opportunity to present final findings; must be the first author and be presenting a paper at a conference based on research conducted while a student in the Faculty of Kinesiology and Recreation Management.

Funds Avail.: $500. **To Apply:** Applicants must complete and submit the application form. **Contact:** Application must submitted to: Jody Bohonos, Graduate Program Coordinator, 203 Active Living Centre, 474-7806; Email: jody.bohonos@umanitoba.ca; More information: Tracey Clifton-Hanslip; Email: tracey.clifton-hanslip@umanitoba.ca.

11590 ■ University of Maryland at College Park - Journalism Center on Children and Families (JCCF)
University of Maryland at College Park
Knight Hall, Rm. 1100
College Park, MD 20742

Ph: (301)405-8808
URL: www.journalismcenter.org

11591 ■ JCCF Equal Voice Journalism Scholarship *(Professional development/Scholarship)*

Purpose: To recognize outstanding individuals who helped to increase public's understanding of poverty in the United States. **Focus:** Journalism. **Qualif.:** Applicants must be individuals in the field of journalism who have the urge to enlighten citizens of the United States in the issues that can affect their lives through the use of media. **Criteria:** Selection will be based on the committees' criteria.

Funds Avail.: No specific amount. **To Apply:** Applicants may contact the Center for application process and other information.

11592 ■ University of Massachusetts Dartmouth - Public Policy Center
285 Old Westport Rd.
North Dartmouth, MA 02747
Ph: (508)990-9660
Fax: (508)999-8374
E-mail: online@umassd.edu
URL: www.umassd.edu/cas/centers/cfpa

11593 ■ Philip H. Melanson Memorial Scholarship *(Undergraduate, Graduate/Scholarship)*

Purpose: To provide financial assistance to graduate students who are enrolled at UMass Dartmouth and maintain an active interest in public policy. **Focus:** Social sciences. **Criteria:** Scholarships will be awarded on a combination of academic merit and public service.

Funds Avail.: $500 - $1,000. **Number Awarded:** Varies. **To Apply:** Applications can be submitted online. **Deadline:** November 1. **Remarks:** The scholarship was established by friends, colleagues, and former students of Dr. Philip H. Melanson, who taught at UMass Dartmouth for thirty-four years and was widely regarded as one of the institution's best and most popular teachers; he was a founding member of the department of public policy at UMass dartmouth and its first department chair. Established in 2006.

11594 ■ University of Memphis - Cecil C. Humphreys School of Law
1 N Front St.
Memphis, TN 38103-2189
Ph: (901)678-2421
Fax: (901)678-5210
E-mail: lawadmissions@memphis.edu
URL: www.memphis.edu/law
Social Media: www.facebook.com/memphislawschool
www.instagram.com/memphis_law/
twitter.com/memlawschool
www.youtube.com/user/uofmemphislawschool

11595 ■ Tillie B. Alperin Scholarship *(Graduate/Scholarship)*

Purpose: To support the education of female law students at the University of Memphis. **Focus:** Law. **Qualif.:** Applicants must be female law students who have successfully completed their first year with a B average; have demonstrated a commitment to the legal profession; and demonstrate financial need. **Criteria:** Selection will be

Awards are arranged alphabetically below their administering organizations

based on academic performance, leadership, character, personal achievements and financial need; preference will be given to applicants who have overcome significant obstacles in pursuit of their education.

Funds Avail.: No specific amount. **Duration:** Annual. **To Apply:** Applicants must complete the online scholarship application; provide a brief description (not to exceed 500 words). **Deadline:** March 15. **Remarks:** The scholarship is named in honor of the late Tillie Blen Alperin, a 1935 graduate of the old University of Memphis Law School and one of the first women to practice law in Tennessee.

11596 ■ Claude T Coffman Scholarship *(Graduate/Scholarship)*

Purpose: To support the education of law students at the University of Memphis. **Focus:** Law. **Qualif.:** Applicants must be admitted at the University of Memphis Cecil C. Humphreys school of law. **Criteria:** Selection will be based on academic merit and financial need.

Funds Avail.: No specific amount. **Duration:** Annual. **To Apply:** Applicants must complete the online scholarship application form along with a resume. **Deadline:** March 15. **Remarks:** The scholarship is named in honor of the late Professor and former interim Dean of the Cecil C. Humphreys School of Law.

11597 ■ C. Cleveland Drennon, Jr. Memorial Scholarship *(Graduate/Scholarship)*

Purpose: To support the education of law students at the University of Memphis. **Focus:** Law. **Qualif.:** Applicants must be admitted as full-time students at the University of Memphis Cecil C. Humphreys School of Law. **Criteria:** Selection will be based on academic merit and financial need.

Funds Avail.: No specific amount. **Duration:** Annual. **To Apply:** Applicants must complete the online scholarship application; provide a brief description (not to exceed 500 words). **Deadline:** March 15. **Remarks:** The scholarship is funded by Humphrey E. Folk, Jr. and the Drennon family and friends.

11598 ■ Evans and Petree Law Firm Scholarship *(Graduate/Scholarship)*

Purpose: To support the education of law students at the University of Memphis. **Focus:** Law. **Qualif.:** Applicants must be Tennessee residents enrolled full-time at the Cecil C. Humphreys School of Law at the University of Memphis. **Criteria:** Selection will be based academic performance, leadership, character, personal achievements, and financial need; preference will be given to returning African American students with financial need.

Funds Avail.: No specific amount. **Duration:** Annual. **To Apply:** Applicants must complete the online scholarship application; provide a brief description (not to exceed 500 words). **Deadline:** March 15.

11599 ■ Federal Court Bench and Bar Scholarships *(Graduate/Scholarship)*

Purpose: To support economically disadvantaged law students from the Middle District of Tennessee. **Focus:** Law. **Qualif.:** Applicants must be economically disadvantaged law students from the Middle District of Tennessee in good academic standing at the law school or the most recent school attended; have demonstrated financial need; and must have graduated from a high school in, or resided for the previous three years as a non-full time student in

one of the following Tennessee Counties Cannon, Cheatham, Clay, Cumberland, Davidson, DeKalb, Dickson, Fentress, Giles, Hickman, Houston, Humphreys, Jackson, Lawrence, Lewis, Macon, Marshall, Maury, Montgomery, Overton, Pickett, Putnam, Robertson, Rutherford, Smith, Stewart, Sumner, Trousdale, Wayne, White, Williamson, or Wilson. **Criteria:** Recipients will be selected based on financial need.

Funds Avail.: No specific amount. **Duration:** Annual. **To Apply:** Applicants must complete the online scholarship application form along with a personal statement, resume, scholarship statement and recommendation letters; must also complete the FAFSA Form. **Deadline:** March 15.

11600 ■ Wilford Hayes Gowen Scholarship Fund *(Undergraduate/Scholarship)*

Purpose: To support the education of law students at the University of Memphis. **Focus:** Law. **Qualif.:** Applicants must be second or third year law students enrolled at the University of Memphis School of Law. **Criteria:** Selection will be based on academic performance, financial need and personal determination.

Funds Avail.: No specific amount. **Duration:** Annual. **To Apply:** Applicants must complete the online scholarship application form along with a personal statement; resume; scholarship statement; and recommendation letters; must also complete the FAFSA Form. **Remarks:** The scholarship was established in memory of Wilford Hayes Gowen, through the Community Foundation of Western North Carolina, in memory of Wilford Hayes Gowen.

11601 ■ Herbert Herff Presidential Law Scholarships *(Graduate/Scholarship)*

Purpose: To support students who have demonstrated high academic or professional achievement and who show potential for an outstanding law career. **Focus:** Law. **Qualif.:** Applicants must be students of the University of Memphis Cecil C. Humphreys School of Law who have demonstrated high academic or professional achievement and who show potential for an outstanding law career. **Criteria:** Selection will be based on academic merit and financial need.

Funds Avail.: No specific amount. **Duration:** Annual; renewable up to two years. **To Apply:** Applicants must complete the online scholarship application form along with a personal statement; resume; scholarship statement; and recommendation letters; must also complete the FAFSA Form.

11602 ■ Robert and Elaine Hoffman Memorial Scholarships *(Graduate/Scholarship)*

Purpose: To support students who have demonstrated high academic or professional achievement and who show potential for an outstanding law career. **Focus:** Law. **Qualif.:** Applicants must be admitted at the University of Memphis Cecil C. Humphreys School of Law as first year law students. **Criteria:** Selection will be based on academic merit.

Funds Avail.: No specific amount. **Duration:** Annual. **Number Awarded:** 2. **To Apply:** Applicants must complete the online scholarship application form along with a resume. **Deadline:** March 15. **Remarks:** The scholarship is named in honor of the late Chancellor Robert Hoffmann and his sister Elaine.

11603 ■ Kathryn Hookanson Law Fellowship *(Graduate/Fellowship)*

Purpose: To support the education of female law students at the University of Memphis. **Focus:** Law. **Qualif.:** Ap-

Awards are arranged alphabetically below their administering organizations

plicant must be a student at the University of Memphis School of Law and in good standing. **Criteria:** Preference will be given to female students and those in financial need.

Funds Avail.: No specific amount. **Duration:** Annual. **To Apply:** Applicants must complete the online scholarship application; provide a brief description (not to exceed 500 words). **Deadline:** March 15.

11604 ■ John C. "Jack" Hough Memorial Law Scholarship *(Graduate/Scholarship)*

Purpose: To support the education of law students at the University of Memphis. **Focus:** Law. **Qualif.:** Applicants must be second or third year law students who demonstrate financial need and are working as volunteers or in a law school externship in the office of the Shelby County Public Defender. **Criteria:** Selection will be based on academic performance, leadership, character, personal achievements and financial need; preference will be given to applicants who express an interest in a career in government service as a public defender or prosecutor, or in the field of criminal law.

Funds Avail.: No specific amount. **Duration:** Annual. **To Apply:** Applicants must complete the online scholarship application; provide a brief description (not to exceed 500 words). **Deadline:** March 15. **Remarks:** The scholarship is named in honor of the late John C. "Jack" Hough, a former member of the Shelby County Public Defender's Office.

11605 ■ Cecil C. Humphreys Law Fellowships *(Graduate/Fellowship, Internship)*

Purpose: To support students who have demonstrated outstanding academic performance, leadership, good citizenship, and scholarly achievements. **Focus:** Law. **Qualif.:** Applicants must be second or third year students; those selected as Fellows are required to work 15 hours per week as research assistants to faculty members. **Criteria:** Selection will be based on demonstrated outstanding academic performance, leadership, good citizenship and scholarly achievements.

Funds Avail.: No specific amount. **Duration:** Annual. **To Apply:** Applicants must complete the online scholarship application form along with a personal statement; resume; scholarship statement; and recommendation letters; must also complete the FAFSA Form. **Contact:** URL: www.memphis.edu/law/admissions/scholarships.php.

11606 ■ The Law Alumni Honor Student Scholarship *(Graduate/Scholarship)*

Purpose: To support the education of law students at the University of Memphis. **Focus:** Law. **Qualif.:** Applicants must be entering students accepted to the University of Memphis Cecil C. Humphreys School of Law who reflect the Law School's commitment to excellence and demonstrates an ability to succeed in the legal profession through leadership, scholarships, community service, or other attributes or achievements. **Criteria:** .

Funds Avail.: $1,000. **Duration:** Annual. **Number Awarded:** 1. **To Apply:** Applicants must complete the online scholarship application; provide a brief description (not to exceed 500 words). **Deadline:** March 15.

11607 ■ Judge William B. Leffler Scholarship *(Graduate/Scholarship)*

Purpose: To support the education of law students at the University of Memphis. **Focus:** Law. **Qualif.:** Applicants must be enrolled at the University of Memphis Cecil C.

Humphreys School of Law and have both academic merit and financial need. **Criteria:** Selection will be based on academic merit and financial need.

Funds Avail.: No specific amount. **Duration:** Annual; up to 2 years. **To Apply:** Applicants must complete the online scholarship application form along with a resume. **Deadline:** March 15. **Remarks:** The scholarship is funded through the Leffler family, the donations of friends, and proceeds from the annual bankruptcy law seminar in Judge Leffler's memory.

11608 ■ H. H. McKnight Memorial Scholarship *(Graduate/Scholarship)*

Purpose: To support veterans of the United States Armed Forces with financial need and who are interested in pursuing a career in criminal law. **Focus:** Law. **Qualif.:** Applicants must be Veterans of the United States Armed Forces interested in pursuing a career in criminal law. **Criteria:** Selection will be based on academic merit and financial need; final selection is made by the donor committee.

Funds Avail.: No specific amount. **Duration:** Annual. **Number Awarded:** 2. **To Apply:** Applicants must complete the online scholarship application form along with a resume. **Deadline:** March 15.

11609 ■ Memphis Access and Diversity Scholarships *(Graduate/Scholarship)*

Purpose: To support the education of law students at the University of Memphis. **Focus:** Law. **Qualif.:** Applicants must be Tennessee residents enrolled at the University of Memphis School of Law who would increase the diversity of the law school. Diversity eligibility for this scholarship includes socioeconomic disadvantage, race, ethnicity, disability, or whether the applicant is a first generation U.S. citizen, whether the applicant is a first generation college graduate, or whether the applicant attended an HBCU, HSI, or Tribal College. Applicants must be residents of Tennessee or neighboring border counties in Arkansas (Crittenden) and Mississippi (De Soto, Tate, Tunica, and Marshall counties). **Criteria:** Selection will be based on academic merit and financial need.

Duration: Annual. **To Apply:** Applicants need to complete the tiger scholarship manager application; they will be asked to complete a 250 word essay on how they will contribute to diversity at the University of Memphis School of Law. **Deadline:** March 16.

11610 ■ Sam A. Myar, Jr. Law Scholarship *(Graduate/Scholarship)*

Purpose: To support the education of law students at the University of Memphis. **Focus:** Law. **Criteria:** Recipients shall be students selected as Editor-in-Chief and Associate Editor of the Law Review as determined by the Dean's Office of the CCH School of Law.

Funds Avail.: No specific amount. **Duration:** Annual. **To Apply:** Applicants must complete the online scholarship application; provide a brief description (not to exceed 500 words). **Deadline:** March 15. **Remarks:** Named in honor of the late Sam A. Myar, Jr. who was a highly regarded Memphis attorney and Professor of Law. Established in 1960.

11611 ■ Donald and Susie Polden Dean's Scholarships *(Graduate/Scholarship)*

Purpose: To support deserving law students who have demonstrated a commitment to community or public service

Awards are arranged alphabetically below their administering organizations

or who express their desire to serve their community during or following law school. **Focus:** Law. **Qualif.:** Applicants must be first year law students committed to community or public service and express a desire to serve the community during or following law school. **Criteria:** Recipients will be selected based on academic merit and financial need; preference will be given to minority students.

Funds Avail.: No specific amount. **Duration:** Annual; renewable up to four years. **To Apply:** Applicants must complete the online scholarship application form along with a resume. **Deadline:** March 15.

11612 ■ Ratner and Sugarmon Scholarship
(Graduate/Scholarship)

Purpose: To support the education of law students at the University of Memphis. **Focus:** Law. **Qualif.:** Applicants must be second or third year law students. **Criteria:** Selection will be given to students who best exemplify a commitment to the needs of the underrepresented in society.

Funds Avail.: No specific amount. **Duration:** Annual. **To Apply:** Applicants must complete the online scholarship application; provide a brief description (not to exceed 500 words). **Deadline:** March 15.

11613 ■ Joseph Henry Shepherd Scholarship
(Graduate/Scholarship)

Purpose: To support the education of law students at the University of Memphis. **Focus:** Law. **Qualif.:** Applicants must be full-time students enrolled in the Cecil C. Humphrey's School of Law. **Criteria:** Selection is based on academic performance and financial need.

Duration: Annual. **Number Awarded:** 3. **To Apply:** Applicants must complete the online scholarship application; provide a brief description (not to exceed 500 words). **Deadline:** March 15. **Remarks:** The scholarship is made possible by an endowment fund established by Dorothy S. Shepherd.

11614 ■ Amy E. Spain Memorial Scholarships
(Graduate/Scholarship)

Purpose: To support law students who have demonstrated academic merit, a commitment to community/professional service, and personal industriousness. **Focus:** Law. **Qualif.:** Applicants must be first year law students with demonstrated academic merit. **Criteria:** Recipients will be selected based on academic merit; commitment to community/professional service; and personal industriousness.

Funds Avail.: No specific amount. **Duration:** Annual. **To Apply:** Applicants must complete the online scholarship application form along with a resume. **Deadline:** March 15. **Remarks:** The scholarship was established by the family and friends of Amy Elizabeth Spain who, at age 30, died in a car accident in 1995.

11615 ■ Springfield Family Scholarship *(Graduate/Scholarship)*

Purpose: To support the education of law students at the University of Memphis. **Focus:** Law. **Qualif.:** Applicants must be entering students who graduated from Rhodes College and who demonstrate academic merit/excellence.

Duration: Annual. **Number Awarded:** 1. **To Apply:** Applicants must complete the online scholarship application form along with a resume. **Deadline:** March 15.

11616 ■ Wyatt, Tarrant & Combs, LLP, Dr. Benjamin L. Hooks Scholarship *(Graduate/Scholarship)*

Purpose: To support the education of law students at the University of Memphis. **Focus:** Law. **Qualif.:** Applicants

must be admitted as full-time students at the University of Memphis Cecil C. Humphreys School of Law; have a minimum GPA of 3.0 and a minimum LSAT score of 153; must maintain a cumulative law school grade point average that places him/her in the top50% of the class. **Criteria:** Selection will be based on academic merit and financial need; preference will be given to Tennessee residents.

Funds Avail.: No specific amount. **Duration:** Triennial. **To Apply:** Applicants must complete the online scholarship application form along with a personal statement; resume; scholarship statement; and recommendation letters; must also complete the FAFSA Form. **Deadline:** March 1. **Remarks:** Established in memory of Dr. Benjamin L. Hooks, and made possible by the law firm of Wyatt, Tarrant & Combs, LLP. **Contact:** University of Memphis School of Law, 1 N. Front St., Memphis, TN, 38103; Phone: 901-678-5403; Email: lawadmissions@memphis.edu.

11617 ■ University of Michigan - Biological Station (UMBS)
2541 Chemistry Bldg.
930 N University Ave.
Ann Arbor, MI 48109-1055
Ph: (734)763-4461
Fax: (734)647-1952
E-mail: umbs@umich.edu
URL: www.lsa.umich.edu/umbs
Social Media: www.facebook.com/umichBIOSTATION
twitter.com/UMBS

11618 ■ Dr. Edward G. Voss Memorial Scholarship
(Undergraduate/Scholarship)

Purpose: To support individuals who wants to enhance their knowledge in the field of biology and related courses. **Focus:** Biology. **Qualif.:** Applicants must be undergraduate students planning to attend at UMBS. **Criteria:** Preference will be given to students interested in botany or entomology.

Funds Avail.: No specific amount. **Deadline:** March 31.

11619 ■ Douglas Lake Improvement Association Scholarship *(Undergraduate/Scholarship)*

Purpose: To support individuals who wants to enhance their knowledge in the field of biology and related courses. **Focus:** Biology. **Qualif.:** Applicants must be students who are residents of Northern Michigan planning to attend the spring or summer session.

Funds Avail.: No specific amount. **Deadline:** March 31.

11620 ■ Fred and Avery Test Scholarship
(Undergraduate/Scholarship)

Purpose: To support individuals who wants to enhance their knowledge in the field of biology and related courses. **Focus:** Biology. **Qualif.:** Applicants must be students at UMBS with financial need.

Funds Avail.: No specific amount. **Deadline:** March 31.

11621 ■ Gary and Gussie Williams Scholarship
(Undergraduate/Scholarship)

Purpose: To support individuals who wants to enhance their knowledge in the field of biology and related courses. **Focus:** Biology. **Qualif.:** Applicants must be students who are teaching science or pursuing a degree in science education.

Awards are arranged alphabetically below their administering organizations

Funds Avail.: No specific amount. **Deadline:** March 31.

11622 ■ Marian P. and David M. Gates Scholarship for Non-Residents *(Undergraduate/Scholarship)*

Purpose: To support individuals who wants to enhance their knowledge in the field of biology and related courses. **Focus:** Biology. **Qualif.:** Applicants must be out-of-state students interested to study at UMBS.

Funds Avail.: No specific amount. **Deadline:** March 31.

11623 ■ Frank Caleb & Margaret Thompson Gates Student Scholarships *(Undergraduate/Scholarship)*

Purpose: To support individuals who wants to enhance their knowledge in the field of biology and related courses. **Focus:** Biology. **Qualif.:** Applicants must be students at UMBS.

Funds Avail.: No specific amount. **Duration:** Annual. **Deadline:** March 31.

11624 ■ George E. Nichols Undergraduate Scholarship *(Undergraduate/Scholarship)*

Purpose: To support individuals who wants to enhance their knowledge in the field of biology and related courses. **Focus:** Biology. **Qualif.:** Applicants must be out-of-state or international undergraduate students in LSA who are studying at UMBS.

Funds Avail.: No specific amount. **Deadline:** March 31.

11625 ■ Howard A. Crum Memorial Scholarship *(Undergraduate/Scholarship)*

Purpose: To support individuals who wants to enhance their knowledge in the field of biology and related courses. **Focus:** Biology. **Qualif.:** Applicants must be students attending UMBS.

Funds Avail.: No specific amount.

11626 ■ James L. Plafkin Memorial Scholarship *(Undergraduate/Scholarship)*

Purpose: To support individuals who wants to enhance their knowledge in the field of biology and related courses. **Focus:** Biology. **Qualif.:** Applicants must be students studying aquatic ecology.

Funds Avail.: No specific amount. **Duration:** Annual. **Deadline:** March 31.

11627 ■ J.B. and Marilyn McKenzie Graduate Student Fellowship *(Graduate/Fellowship)*

Purpose: To support outstanding students engaged in their research. **Focus:** Environmental science; Natural sciences. **Qualif.:** Applicants must be graduate students.

Funds Avail.: No specific amount.

11628 ■ Joel T. Heinen Student Research Fellowship *(Undergraduate, Graduate/Fellowship)*

Purpose: To support outstanding individuals engaged in environmental research at UMBS. **Focus:** Environmental science; Natural sciences. **Qualif.:** Applicants must be graduate or undergraduate students of research at UMBS.

Funds Avail.: No specific amount.

11629 ■ Joel T. Heinen Undergraduate Support Scholarship *(Undergraduate/Scholarship)*

Purpose: To support individuals who wants to enhance their knowledge in the field of biology and related courses.

Focus: Biology. **Qualif.:** Applicants must be undergraduate students taking classes at biological station.

Funds Avail.: No specific amount. **Deadline:** March 31.

11630 ■ Lowe Family First Summer Student Scholarship *(Undergraduate/Scholarship)*

Purpose: To support individuals who wants to enhance their knowledge in the field of biology and related courses. **Focus:** Biology. **Qualif.:** Applicants must be students spending their first summer at the biological station.

Funds Avail.: No specific amount. **Deadline:** March 31.

11631 ■ Schrank Family Scholarship *(Undergraduate/Scholarship)*

Purpose: To support individuals who wants to enhance their knowledge in the field of biology and related courses. **Focus:** Biology. **Qualif.:** Applicants must be students.

Funds Avail.: No specific amount. **Duration:** Annual. **Deadline:** March 31.

11632 ■ UMBS Istock Family Scholarship *(Undergraduate/Scholarship)*

Purpose: To support individuals who wants to enhance their knowledge in the field of biology and related courses. **Focus:** Biology. **Qualif.:** Applicants must be UMBS students with financial need.

Funds Avail.: No specific amount. **Deadline:** March 31.

11633 ■ UMBS Returning Student Award *(Undergraduate/Scholarship)*

Purpose: To support individuals who wants to enhance their knowledge in the field of biology and related courses. **Focus:** Biology. **Qualif.:** Applicants must be returning students who are in their second or subsequent summer at the Biological Station.

Funds Avail.: No specific amount. **Deadline:** March 31.

11634 ■ University of Michigan - Center for the Education of Women
330 E Liberty St.
Ann Arbor, MI 48104-2274
Ph: (734)764-6005
E-mail: contactcew@umich.edu
URL: www.cew.umich.edu
Social Media: www.facebook.com/CEWatUM
twitter.com/CEWatUM

11635 ■ Center for the Education of Women Scholarships *(Graduate, Undergraduate/Scholarship)*

Purpose: To provide educational support to students who are completing their degree. **Focus:** General studies/Field of study not specified. **Qualif.:** Applicants must be undergraduates, graduates and full-time or part-time students attending the University of Michigan (Ann Arbor, Flint, Dearborn Campuses); must have experienced a lapse in education of at least 48 consecutive months and 48 nonconsecutive, and must have not yet received a scholarship. **Criteria:** Recipients are selected based on strength of motivation; impact on the chosen field; academic record and potential; creativity; and contributions.

Funds Avail.: $1,000 to $10,000. **Duration:** Annual. **Number Awarded:** 40. **To Apply:** Applicants must submit a filled-out application form; transcript of records from all

Awards are arranged alphabetically below their administering organizations

previous educational institutions attended; three letters of recommendation from either professors or supervisors; and completed financial statement; provide the needed materials with five completed copies (original and four copies). **Deadline:** February 15. **Contact:** Phone: 734-764-6360; Email: cew-scholarships@umich.edu.

11636 ■ Center for the Education of Women Student Research Grants (Graduate, Undergraduate/Grant)

Purpose: To promote every woman's career, leadership, education, growth and development, healing and well-being. **Focus:** Women's studies. **Qualif.:** Applicants must be graduates and upper division undergraduate students attending University of Michigan-Ann Arbor who are doing dissertation, thesis, or research. **Criteria:** Recipients are selected based on submitted proposals.

Funds Avail.: $1,000 to $10,000. **Duration:** Annual. **Number Awarded:** 40. **To Apply:** Applicants must submit a filled-out application form with student ID number; two-page proposal accompanied by project budget; a letter of support from an advisor; a curriculum vitae; and proof of IRB approval for the project (if relevant). **Deadline:** February 15. **Contact:** Submit application packets to: Susan Kaufmann; E-mail: kaufmann@umich.edu; Call at 734-764-7640.

11637 ■ University of Michigan - Dearborn - Armenian Research Center (ARC)

136 Fairlane Ctr. N.
Dearborn, MI 48128
Ph: (313)593-5181
Fax: (313)593-5219
URL: www.umdearborn.edu/673901
Social Media: www.facebook.com/UMDearbornCASL
www.instagram.com/umdearborn
www.linkedin.com/school/university-of-michigan-dearborn/
twitter.com/UMDearbornCASL
www.youtube.com/user/umdearborn

11638 ■ Dr. George and Isabelle Elanjian Scholarship (Undergraduate/Scholarship)

Purpose: To provide financial assistance to those students who are in need. **Focus:** General studies/Field of study not specified. **Qualif.:** Applicants can be either current UM-Dearborn students or transfer students who have completed 12 credits at UM-Dearborn or another college; recipients should be enrolled full-time (a minimum of 12 credit hours during the fall and winter semesters); minimum GPA requirement is 3.0 (4.0 scale) or better; must demonstrate financial need. **Criteria:** Applicants are selected on the basis of financial need, scholastic achievement, involvement in the community and letters of recommendation.

To Apply: Applicants should submit two letters of recommendation; eligible applicants must describe their leadership/community service, academic goals, and awards/honors received.

11639 ■ University of Minnesota - Charles Babbage Institute Center for the History of Information Technology

University of Minnesota, Charles Babbage Institute
211 Andersen Library
222 21st Avenue South
Minneapolis, MN 55455

Ph: (612)624-5050
Fax: (612)625-8054
E-mail: cbi@umn.edu
URL: www.cbi.umn.edu
Social Media: www.facebook.com/babbageinstitute
twitter.com/BabbageInst

11640 ■ Arthur L. Norberg Travel Fund (Advanced Professional/Grant)

Purpose: To help scholars with travel expenses to use archival collections at the Charles Babbage Institute. **Focus:** Information science and technology. **Qualif.:** Applicants must be scholars intending to use CBI collections for research projects; they must be residents outside the Twin Cities metropolitan region. **Criteria:** Recipients will be selected based on eligibility.

Funds Avail.: $1,000. **Duration:** Annual. **Number Awarded:** 3. **To Apply:** Applicants must submit a two-page CV as well as a 500-word project description that describes the overall research project, identifies the importance of specific CBI collections and discusses the projected outcome (journal article, book chapter, museum exhibit, etc.). **Deadline:** January 15. **Remarks:** The Norberg Travel Fund is named for CBI's founding director, Arthur L. Norberg, and is funded by generous gifts from his friends and colleagues. **Contact:** Jeffrey Yost, CBI Associate Director; Phone:612-624-5050; Email: yostx003@umn.edu.

11641 ■ The Adelle and Erwin Tomash Fellowship in the History of Information Technology (Doctorate, Graduate/Fellowship)

Purpose: To assist graduate students for doctoral dissertation research in the history of computing. **Focus:** Information science and technology. **Qualif.:** Applicants must be CBI students who have completed all requirements for the doctoral degree except the research and writing of the dissertation. **Criteria:** Selection will be given to applicants indicating a need to use CBI materials, planning research in residence at CBI, and willing to make a brief presentation of their research findings to CBI staff.

Funds Avail.: $14,000. **Number Awarded:** 1. **To Apply:** Applicants should send to CBI a curriculum vitae and a five-page (single-spaced) statement and justification of the research project including a discussion of methods, research materials, evidence of faculty support for the project, and bibliography (bibliography does not count toward page count); applicants should also arrange for three letters of reference and certified copies of graduate school transcripts to be sent directly to CBI. **Deadline:** January 15. **Contact:** Charles Babbage Institute: Tomash Fellowship, 211 Andersen Library, University of Minnesota, 222 - 21st Ave. S, Minneapolis, MN, 55455; Questions: Jeffrey Yost, CBI Associate Director; Phone: 612-624-5050; Email: yostx003@umn.edu or cbi@umn.edu.

11642 ■ University of Minnesota - Children's Literature Research Collections (CLRC)

113 Elmer L. Andersen Library
222 21st Ave. S
Minneapolis, MN 55455
Ph: (612)624-4576
URL: www.lib.umn.edu

11643 ■ Ezra Jack Keats/Kerlan Memorial Fellowship (Professional development/Fellowship)

Purpose: Award is given in recognition of outstanding research utilizing original resources available in the Kerlan

Awards are arranged alphabetically below their administering organizations

Collection. **Focus:** Literature, Children's. **Qualif.:** Applicants must be writers and illustrators who wish to use the original manuscripts, illustrations, and books of the Kerlan Collection in course of their professional development. **Criteria:** Special consideration will be given to those who would find it difficult to finance a visit to the Kerlan Collection.

Funds Avail.: $1,500. **Number Awarded:** 1. **To Apply:** Applicants must send an e-mail with the subject heading. **Deadline:** January 30. **Remarks:** Established in 1985.

11644 ■ University of Minnesota Office for Equity and Diversity - Women's Center

432 Morrill Hall
Minneapolis, MN 55455
Ph: (612)624-0594
E-mail: oedidea@umn.edu
URL: diversity.umn.edu

11645 ■ Carol E. Macpherson Memorial Scholarship
(Graduate, Undergraduate/Scholarship)

Purpose: To provide support for qualified individuals intending to pursue an educational career. **Focus:** General studies/Field of study not specified. **Criteria:** Selection will be based on applicant's strength of personal statement, reference letters indicating educational goals and academic promise, status as a student parent, academic achievement and education status.

Funds Avail.: $1,000 - $6,000. **Duration:** Annual. **To Apply:** Applicants must submit the complete scholarship application, including the following: their personal statements; reference letters indicating educational goals and academic promise; academic transcripts of all related college/post-secondary enrollment; completed FAFSA for the academic year they are applying for (to be filed at least three weeks before the scholarship deadline). **Deadline:** July 17. **Remarks:** Established in 1970. **Contact:** Women's Center, Phone: 612-625-9837; Email: women@umn.edu.

11646 ■ University of Nebraska--Lincoln - Institute of Agriculture and Natural Resources - Agricultural Research Division (ARD)

207 Agricultural Hall
Lincoln, NE 68583
Ph: (402)472-2045
E-mail: ardgrants@unl.edu
URL: ard.unl.edu
Social Media: www.facebook.com/UNLAgResearch
www.instagram.com/UNL_AgResearch
www.linkedin.com/school/university-of-nebraska-lincoln
twitter.com/UNLincoln
twitter.com/UNL_AgResearch

11647 ■ Shear-Miles Agricultural Scholarship
(Graduate, Doctorate/Scholarship)

Purpose: To provide funds to individuals conducting basic research in agriculture. **Focus:** Agricultural sciences. **Qualif.:** Applicants must be graduate research assistantships students, may be either beginning graduate students or students in progress, but all nominees must have identified a thesis topic that would clearly be considered "basic research in agriculture"; only students with high scholastic merit and research potential should be nominated. **Criteria:**

Selection will be given to Ph.D. graduate research assistants, although exceptional M.S. students may also be considered.

Funds Avail.: $2,000. **Duration:** Annual. **To Apply:** Applicants may contact the Center for application process and other information. **Deadline:** June 23. **Remarks:** Established in 1975.

11648 ■ Shear-Miles Agricultural Scholarship/ Fellowship *(Graduate, Doctorate/Fellowship, Scholarship)*

Purpose: To provide funds to individuals conducting basic research in agriculture. **Focus:** Agricultural sciences. **Qualif.:** Applicants must be students on Graduate Research Assistantships are eligible for consideration; students paid from fellowship funds are not eligible. **Criteria:** Preference will be given to Ph.D. graduate research assistants, although exceptional M.S. students may also be considered.

Funds Avail.: $2,000. **Duration:** Annual. **Number Awarded:** 1. **Deadline:** June 29. **Remarks:** Established in 1975.

11649 ■ University of New Hampshire (UNH)

105 Main St.
Durham, NH 03824
URL: www.unh.edu
Social Media: www.facebook.com/
universityofnewhampshire
www.pinterest.com/unh
twitter.com/uofnh
www.youtube.com/unhvideo

11650 ■ College of Engineering and Physical Sciences Industry Scholarship *(Undergraduate/ Scholarship)*

Purpose: To provide financial assistance to students who want to continue their education at UNH. **Focus:** Engineering; Physical sciences.

Funds Avail.: No specific amount. **Duration:** Annual. **Number Awarded:** 2. **To Apply:** Applicants must have an application for admission to a major within the College of Engineering and Physical Sciences at the University of New Hampshire; must have official high school transcripts, including the first marking period of senior year; must have the official test scores for either the SAT Reasoning Test or ACT with writing test; must submit an additional scholarship essay through the online form; must submit a Free Application for Federal Student Aid (FAFSA) form. **Deadline:** November 15. **Contact:** Charles Zercher, Associate Dean; Email: chuck.zercher@unh.edu; Wayne Jones, Dean; Email: wayne.jones@unh.edu; Caitlin Baldwin, Academic Counselor; Email: caitlin.baldwin@unh.edu.

11651 ■ The UNH Alumni Association Legacy Scholarship *(Undergraduate/Scholarship)*

Purpose: To provide financial assistance to students who want to continue their education at UNH. **Focus:** General studies/Field of study not specified. **Criteria:** Selection will be based on merit; applicants shall be chosen based on the following criteria: leadership skills; academic record; broad extracurricular interests.

Funds Avail.: $3,000 per year. **Duration:** Annual. **Deadline:** March 31.

Awards are arranged alphabetically below their administering organizations

11652 ■ UNH Parents Association Endowed Scholarship (Undergraduate/Scholarship)

Purpose: To provide financial assistance to students who want to continue their education at UNH. **Focus:** General studies/Field of study not specified. **Criteria:** Selection of recipients will be based on financial need.

Funds Avail.: $3,000 each. **Duration:** Annual. **Number Awarded:** 1. **To Apply:** Applicants must submit the FAFSA for initial qualification; completed application form provided by UNH Program; employment verification letter or community service verification letter; background information statement; and, faculty recommendation. **Deadline:** March 1. **Remarks:** Established in 1999. **Contact:** Phone: 603-862-2040.

11653 ■ University of Oregon (UO)

1585 E 13th Ave.
Eugene, OR 97403
Ph: (541)346-1000
URL: www.uoregon.edu
Social Media: www.facebook.com/universityoforegon
www.linkedin.com/edu/school?id=19207
pinterest.com/uoregon
twitter.com/uoregon
youtube.com/user/UOregon

11654 ■ Robert W. and Bernice Ingalls Staton Scholarships (Undergraduate/Scholarship)

Purpose: To provide financial support to students who desire to further their education without financial burden at the University of Oregon. **Focus:** Education; Humanities; Music; Visual arts. **Qualif.:** Applicant must be an Oregon resident; have extraordinary financial need. **Criteria:** Selection will be based on financial need and other factors include the student's major, professional objective, academic performance, and family educational history with priority given to first-generation college students.

Funds Avail.: $6,550. **Duration:** Annual; up to 4 years. **Number Awarded:** 12. **To Apply:** Applicants must submit the admission application and free application for Federal Student Aid (FAFSA) available online to the office of admission. **Deadline:** February 15. **Remarks:** Established in 2001. **Contact:** Office of Student Financial Aid & Scholarships, 260 Oregon Hall, 1278 University of Oregon, Eugene, OR, 97403-1278; Phone: 541-346-3221 or 800-760-6953; Email: financialaid@uoregon.edu.

11655 ■ University of Oregon Dean's Scholarships (Undergraduate/Scholarship)

Purpose: To encourage qualified individuals to pursue their studies at University of Oregon. **Focus:** General studies/Field of study not specified. **Qualif.:** Applicants must be entering freshmen who have a minimum cumulative high school GPA of 3.0 and meet all current UO freshman admission requirements; must have not attended another college after graduation from high school. **Criteria:** Recipients will be selected based on high school GPA and coursework.

Funds Avail.: No specific amount. **Duration:** Annual. **To Apply:** Applicants may visit the University of Oregon website for further information.

11656 ■ University of Oregon Diversity Excellence Scholarship (Undergraduate/Scholarship)

Purpose: To encourage the undergraduate and graduate students to enhance their educational experience by shar-

ing diverse cultural experiences at the University of Oregon. **Focus:** General studies/Field of study not specified. **Qualif.:** Applicants must be U.S citizens or permanent residents of U.S. and have minimum 3.00 cumulative GPA. **Criteria:** Selection past academic performance; participation in campus or community activities; racial/ethnic background; financial need as determined by the FAFSA; first generation of the family to attend college.

Funds Avail.: $6,500 (undergraduate); $9,000 (graduate). **Duration:** Annual. **To Apply:** Applicants must complete the scholarship application forms available online and transfer students must meet standard admission requirements. **Deadline:** January 31. **Contact:** Office of Student Financial Aid & Scholarships, 260 Oregon Hall, 1278 University of Oregon, Eugene, OR, 97403-1278; Phone: 541-346-3221 or 800-760-6953; Email: financialaid@uoregon.edu.

11657 ■ University of Oregon General University Scholarship (Undergraduate, Graduate/Scholarship)

Purpose: To support qualified individuals who wish to pursue their education at the University of Oregon. **Focus:** General studies/Field of study not specified.

Funds Avail.: $2,000 to $3,000. **Duration:** Annual. **Number Awarded:** 1. **To Apply:** Applicants must complete the scholarship application forms available online. **Deadline:** March 1.

11658 ■ University of Oregon Presidential Scholarship (Undergraduate/Scholarship)

Purpose: To provide financial support to the state's brightest students entering University of Oregon. **Focus:** General studies/Field of study not specified. **Criteria:** Selection will be based on academic preparation as demonstrated by transcripts; test scores; activities and talents; leadership; volunteer service; work experience and four short-answer essay questions.

Funds Avail.: $9,000 per year. **Duration:** Annual; up to 4 years. **Number Awarded:** 50. **To Apply:** Applicant must submit your high school transcripts and standardized test scores to the Admissions Office. **Deadline:** February 15. **Contact:** Office of Student Financial Aid & Scholarships, 260 Oregon Hall, 1278 University of Oregon, Eugene, OR, 97403-1278; Phone: 541-346-3221 or 800-760-6953; Email: financialaid@uoregon.edu.

11659 ■ University of Oxford Department of Politics and International Relations - Reuters Institute for the Study of Journalism

13 Norham Gardens
Oxford OX2 6PS, United Kingdom
Ph: 44 1865 611080
E-mail: reuters.institute@politics.ox.ac.uk
URL: reutersinstitute.politics.ox.ac.uk
Social Media: www.facebook.com/ReutersInstitute
twitter.com/risj_oxford
www.youtube.com/channel/UC3unDTYFa3QD1-e
-dyzBHyQ

11660 ■ Reuters Institute Visiting Fellowships (Professional development/Fellowship)

Purpose: To promote the educational and research interests of the Reuters Institute through relationships with people employed by other institutions. **Focus:** Journalism.

Funds Avail.: No specific amount.

Awards are arranged alphabetically below their administering organizations

11661 ■ University of Pennsylvania - Risk Management and Decision Processes Center

St. Leonard's Court ,3819Chestnut St,Ste130.
Philadelphia, PA 19104
Ph: (215)898-5688
Fax: (215)573-2130
E-mail: hellerc@wharton.upenn.edu
URL: riskcenter.wharton.upenn.edu

11662 ■ Russell Ackoff Doctoral Student Fellowship *(Doctorate/Fellowship)*

Purpose: To provide support to students who are pursuing research in decision making under risk and uncertainly. **Focus:** Management; Risk management. **Qualif.:** Applicants must be Ph.D. students who are pursuing research in decision making under risk and uncertainty; topics to receive funding include insurability and risk management; managing environmental, health and safety risks; psychology; Communications; behavioral economics; and decision processes; doctoral students throughout Penn engaged in ongoing research that relates to problems in decision making under risk and uncertainty are encouraged to apply. **Criteria:** Selection will be based on the committee's criteria.

Funds Avail.: $1,000-$4,000. **Duration:** Annual. **Number Awarded:** Varies. **To Apply:** Applications must include a proposal and the application form; Proposals should be 4 pages in length and must include the required information listed in the application form. **Deadline:** March 20. **Remarks:** The research fellowships are named in honor of an endowment provided to the Wharton School by the Anheuser-Busch Charitable Trust. Established in 2006. **Contact:** Dana Allison; Email: danaalli@wharton.upenn.edu.

11663 ■ University of Pennsylvania - School of Nursing - Center for Health Outcomes and Policy Research (CHOPR)

Claire M.Fagin Hall
418 Curie Blvd.
Philadelphia, PA 19104-4217
Ph: (215)746-3951
Fax: (215)573-9449
E-mail: research@nursing.upenn.edu
URL: www.nursing.upenn.edu/chopr
Social Media: www.facebook.com/PennNursing
www.instagram.com/pennnursing
www.linkedin.com/school/university-of-pennsylvania-school
-of-nursing
twitter.com/PennNursing
www.youtube.com/user/pennnursingscience

11664 ■ CHOPR Fellowship Program *(Postdoctorate/ Fellowship)*

Purpose: To further develop the individuals' research career in the area of health outcomes. **Focus:** Medical research; Nursing; Nursing administration. **Qualif.:** Applicanta must be US Citizens or permanent residents only; to nurses who have received a doctoral degree from an accredited university in nursing or a field relevant to nursing outcomes research and would like the opportunity to further develop their research career in the area of health outcomes. **Criteria:** Selection will be based on the following criteria: match with the overall goals and objectives of the training grant and affiliated Center.; atm with the T32

and Centc-affiliated faculty advisor. Sch; potential for nursing science inquiry; Commitmentco a research career; Scholarly productivity during and after the training.

To Apply: Applicants should submit a cover letter describing goals for the postdoc training, their career goals; CV with a list of publications; copies of any publications or samples of academic writing; 3 references with email who can speak about the candidate's research experience. **Contact:** Center for Health Outcomes and Policy Research University of Pennsylvania School of Nursing, 375 Claire M. Fagin Hall, 418 Curie Blvd., Philadelphia, PA, 19104-4217; Irene D. Hung, MPH; Email: irenedh@nursing.upenn.edu.

11665 ■ University of Pittsburgh Department of Biological Sciences - Pymatuning Laboratory of Ecology

c/o Chris Davis, Assistant Director
13142 Hartstown Rd.
Linesville, PA 16424
Ph: (814)273-0416
E-mail: pymlab@pitt.edu
URL: www.biology.pitt.edu

11666 ■ Arthur and Barbara Pape Endowment *(Graduate/Grant)*

Purpose: To support early stages of ecological and evolutionary research conducted at PLE. **Focus:** Biological and clinical sciences; Ecology. **Qualif.:** Applicants must be graduate students in good standing.

Duration: Annual. **Deadline:** February 19.

11667 ■ University of Prince Edward Island - L.M. Montgomery Institute (LMMI)

550 University Ave.
Charlottetown, PE, Canada C1A 4P3
URL: www.lmmontgomery.ca

11668 ■ Avery Award *(Undergraduate, High School/ Award)*

Purpose: To support UPEI students who have an interest in L. M. Montgomery and have a desire to pursue excellence in writing while working with a mentor from the Lucy Maud Montgomery Institute (LMMI) at UPEI. **Focus:** English language and literature. **Qualif.:** Applicants must be returning UPEI student in their first degree program of undergraduate studies in any faculty who has an interest in L.M. Montgomery; must have a demonstrated aptitude for social media initiatives.

Funds Avail.: $1,000. **Duration:** Annual. **To Apply:** Applicant must complete and submit the application form; Application Personal Statement; personal statement should reference how the candidate meets the criteria, including their interest in L.M. Montgomery, social media initiatives and display effective communication and writing skills; Two Letters of Reference. **Remarks:** Scholarship was established by the owners of Cavendish Figurines Ltd., Jeannette Arsenault and Don Maxfield and their staff as a contribution to their Island community in appreciation of the legacy of L. M. Montgomery on PEI and in tribute to the "Spirit of Anne". The fictional Avery Scholarship in L. M. Montgomery's famous novel Anne of Green Gables was the object of fierce competition between Anne Shirley and Gilbert Blythe and was also the factor that caused them to

Awards are arranged alphabetically below their administering organizations

end their long feud. **Contact:** University of Prince Edward Island Scholarships and Awards Committee, 550 University Ave., Charlottetown, PE C1A 4P3; Phone: 902-620-5187; Email: scholarships@upei.ca.

11669 ■ University of Quebec - Institute of Marine Sciences of Rimouski
310, allée des Ursulines
Rimouski, QC, Canada G5L 3A1
URL: www.ismer.ca

11670 ■ ISMER Student Financial Assistance
(Master's, Doctorate/Monetary, Grant)

Purpose: To provide financial assistance to students for their study in oceanography program. **Focus:** Oceanography. **Qualif.:** Applicants must be new students enrolled full-time in an oceanography Master's or PhD program.

Funds Avail.: $1,000 Master's program; $1,300 PhD program. **Duration:** Annual.

11671 ■ University of Saskatchewan - Centre for the Study of Co-operatives
101 Diefenbaker Bldg.
Saskatoon, SK, Canada S7N 5B8
URL: usaskstudies.coop

11672 ■ Norm Bromberger Research Bursary
(Undergraduate, Graduate/Scholarship)

Purpose: To support research relating to co-operatives and/or credit unions. **Focus:** Banking. **Qualif.:** Applicants must be involved in co-operatives and/or credit unions as volunteers or employees; those who have unable to secure sponsorship for their study from the co-operative or credit union with which they are associated are also urged to apply.

Funds Avail.: 2,000 Canadian Dollars. **Duration:** Annual. **To Apply:** Applicants must complete the application form; must also submit a supporting statement explaining how the proposed study will contribute to credit unions and/or co-operatives and an understanding that a copy of the completed work will be submitted to canadian credit union and co-op resource centers. **Deadline:** June 30. **Remarks:** The Scholarship was established in honor of Norm Bromberger.

11673 ■ University of Saskatchewan - Native Law Centre of Canada
Law Bldg., Rm. 160
15 Campus Dr.
Saskatoon, SK, Canada S7N 5A6
Ph: (306)966-6189
Fax: (306)966-6207
E-mail: native.law@usask.ca
URL: www.usask.ca/nativelaw
Social Media: www.facebook.com/nativelawcentre
www.instagram.com/usask
www.linkedin.com/in/nativelawcentre
twitter.com/NativeLawCentre
www.youtube.com/usask

11674 ■ Harvey Bell Memorial Prize *(Graduate/Prize, Scholarship)*

Purpose: To assist students in order to receive their bachelor of laws degree in Canada. **Focus:** Law. **Qualif.:**

Applicants must be students of Native Canadian ancestry receiving their LL.B. degree in Canada. **Criteria:** Applications will be evaluated based on the contributions from which students might be expected in establishing the right of Native people in Canada; academic records in Law studies.

Funds Avail.: Up to 1,000 Canadian Dollars. **Duration:** Annual. **To Apply:** Applicants must enclose a resume of their career and education; must submit a transcript of records and letter of application concerning their academic achievement. **Deadline:** July 31. **Contact:** Native Law Centre, University of Saskatchewan Rm. 160 Law Bldg., 15 Campus Dr., Saskatoon SK S7N 5A6 Canada.

11675 ■ Poundmaker Memorial Scholarships
(Undergraduate/Scholarship)

Purpose: To support a status of an Indian student born in Saskatchewan pursue their education. **Focus:** Education; Teaching. **Qualif.:** Applicants must be Indian students born in Saskatchewan; must have completed two years of a direct entry teacher education program or currently in their third or fourth year at the University of Saskatchewan, University of Regina, or the First Nation University of Canada. **Criteria:** Evaluation will be based on academic achievement, leadership ability and aspirations to Indian community.

Funds Avail.: 750 Canadian Dollars. **Duration:** Annual. **To Apply:** Applicants must submit a completed application form. **Deadline:** July 31.

11676 ■ University of Tennessee at Knoxville College of Arts & Sciences (CSWS) - Center for the Study of War and Society
217 Hoskins Library
University of Tennessee
Knoxville, TN 37996-4008
Ph: (865)974-0128
E-mail: csws@utk.edu
URL: csws.utk.edu
Social Media: www.facebook.com/danamorrislaw
www.instagram.com/hhmijanelia
twitter.com/utk_csws

11677 ■ The Wilson Fellowship *(Postdoctorate/Fellowship)*

Purpose: To promote the study of American military history. **Focus:** History, Military. **Qualif.:** Must have completed all the requirements for a Ph.D. at University of Tennessee, except for dissertation; must be a student in good standing and making sufficient progress toward the completion of the degree. **Criteria:** Selection preference is given to those who focus on some aspect of the Second World War.

Funds Avail.: $1,000. **Duration:** Annual. **Number Awarded:** 1. **To Apply:** Applicants must submit a dissertation focusing of American military history; a letter of application no longer than two pages that outlines the dissertation topic and the progress toward degree; two letters of recommendation outlining the progress to the degree. At least one letter must be from a faculty member in the History Department of the University of Tennessee. **Deadline:** March 15. **Contact:** Director Center for the Study of War and Society, 220 Hoskins Library, Knoxville, Tennessee, 37996-4008.

Awards are arranged alphabetically below their administering organizations

11678 ■ University of Texas at Austin - Office of the Vice President for Research

110 Inner Campus Drive
Austin, TX 78705
Ph: (512)471-8871
Fax: (512)471-8873
URL: research.utexas.edu

11679 ■ University of Texas at Austin Special Research Grants *(Professional development/Grant)*

Purpose: To cover unanticipated costs or special needs of individuals whose conducting research. **Focus:** Operations research. **Qualif.:** Applicants must be individual tenured and tenure-track faculty members who are planning to conduct modest research for specific project. **Criteria:** Selection will be basis of merit to the discipline and relevance to the University of Texas atAustin's research mission; only one SRG per academic year andno more than three in any five-year period.

Funds Avail.: Up to $750. **To Apply:** Applicants must submit complete, signed application, via email to the office of the Vice President for Research and required one-page curriculum vitae. **Deadline:** November 29. **Contact:** Email: VPRcompetitions@austin.utexas.edu.

11680 ■ University of Toronto (U OF T)

27 King's College Cir.
Toronto, ON, Canada M5S 1A1
Ph: (416)978-2011
E-mail: admissions.help@utoronto.ca
URL: www.utoronto.ca
Social Media: www.facebook.com/universitytoronto
www.instagram.com/uoft
twitter.com/uoft

11681 ■ Dr. Anderson Abbott Awards
(Undergraduate/Scholarship)

Purpose: To support students in pursuing their educational career. **Focus:** Health sciences; Medicine. **Qualif.:** Applicant must be a black undergraduate student in any program of study; show high academic achievement; demonstrate financial need; present evidence of contribution to the black community. **Criteria:** Selection committee may give preference to a student in the medical program or in a related health science program.

Funds Avail.: 4,000 Canadian Dollars. **Duration:** Annual. **Number Awarded:** 1. **To Apply:** Applicants must submit a completed Abbot application form along with the required materials and information. **Deadline:** February 10.

11682 ■ Stephanie Ali Memorial Scholarships
(Undergraduate/Scholarship)

Purpose: To provide educational support to students who are in need. **Focus:** Computer and information sciences; Engineering. **Qualif.:** Applicant must be an undergraduate student; must have demonstrated commitment to community work and/or participation in charitable activities; must be Canadian citizen/permanent resident and resident of Ontario. **Criteria:** Preference will be given to students who are past or present members of the University of Toronto Gospel Choir.

Funds Avail.: Approximately $1,800. **Duration:** Annual; up to 2 years. **Number Awarded:** Varies. **To Apply:** Applicants must submit a completed application form along with the

required materials and information. **Deadline:** February 10. **Contact:** Enrolment Services: 172 Saint George St., Toronto, ON M5R 0A3.

11683 ■ Leon C. Bynoe Memorial Scholarships
(Undergraduate/Scholarship)

Purpose: To provide educational support to students who are in need. **Focus:** General studies/Field of study not specified. **Qualif.:** Applicant must be an undergraduate student; be a Canadian citizen/permanent resident and a resident of Ontario; must demonstrate financial need; must demonstrate outstanding academic achievement. **Criteria:** Preference will be given to candidates from the Afro-Canadian community and Metro Toronto Housing Authority residents.

Funds Avail.: 1,700 Canadian Dollars. **Duration:** Annual. **To Apply:** Applicants must submit a completed application form along with personal statement; two letters of reference. **Deadline:** November 1. **Contact:** Enrolment Services; Email:awards.uoft@utoronto.ca.

11684 ■ Canadian Federation of University Women Etobicoke Bursary *(Undergraduate/Scholarship)*

Purpose: To provide educational support to students who are in need. **Focus:** General studies/Field of study not specified. **Qualif.:** Applicants must be female undergraduate students; must be residents of Etobicoke. **Criteria:** Selection will be based on financial need.

Funds Avail.: 1,500 Canadian Dollars each. **Duration:** Annual. **Number Awarded:** 2. **To Apply:** Applicants must submit a completed application form along with the required materials and information. **Deadline:** November 1. **Contact:** Enrolment Services: 172 Saint George St., Toronto, ON M5R 0A3.

11685 ■ City of Toronto Graduate Scholarships for Women in Mathematics *(Master's, Doctorate/ Scholarship)*

Purpose: To provide financial support to students who are pursuing their educational career. **Focus:** Mathematics and mathematical sciences. **Qualif.:** Applicant must be a Canadian citizen/permanent resident and resident of Ontario; must be a female student enrolled in a master's or doctoral program in mathematics. **Criteria:** Selection will be based on the applicants' financial need, academic merit and demonstrated interest in issues related to women in mathematics.

Funds Avail.: Approximately $8,500. **Duration:** Annual; up to 3 years. **Number Awarded:** 1. **To Apply:** Applicants must submit a completed application form along with the required materials and information. **Deadline:** November 1. **Contact:** Enrolment Services: 172 Saint George St., Toronto, ON M5R 0A3.

11686 ■ City of Toronto Queen Elizabeth II Sesquicentennial Scholarships in Community Health Nursing for Graduates *(Graduate/Scholarship)*

Purpose: To support students with their educational pursuit. **Focus:** Nursing. **Qualif.:** Applicants must be graduate students enrolled in the Graduate Department of Nursing Science; must have completed courses in community health and demonstrate a commitment to the aspect of nursing. **Criteria:** Selection will be based on the general proficiency or outstanding achievements and and financial need.

Funds Avail.: 1,200 Canadian Dollars. **Duration:** Annual. **Number Awarded:** 1. **To Apply:** Applicants must submit a

Awards are arranged alphabetically below their administering organizations

completed application form along with the required materials and information. **Deadline:** October 1. **Contact:** Enrolment Services: 172 Saint George St., Toronto, ON M5R 0A3.

11687 ■ City of Toronto Queen Elizabeth II Sesquicentennial Scholarships in Community Health Nursing for Undergraduates *(Undergraduate/ Scholarship)*

Purpose: To provide financial support to students who are in need. **Focus:** Nursing. **Qualif.:** Applicants must be Canadian citizen/permanent resident and resident of Ontario; be completing the first year of a second-entry, two-year BScN program. **Criteria:** Selection will be demonstrate both academic achievement and financial need.

Funds Avail.: 5,000 Canadian Dollars. **Duration:** Annual. **Number Awarded:** 1. **To Apply:** Applicants must submit a completed application form along with the required materials and information. **Deadline:** November 1. **Contact:** Enrolment Services: 172 Saint George St., Toronto, ON M5R 0A3.

11688 ■ City of Toronto Scholarships for Aboriginal Health *(Graduate, Undergraduate/Scholarship)*

Purpose: To provide financial support to students who are in need. **Focus:** Health services administration. **Qualif.:** Applicants must be Aboriginal students who are studying in any of the undergraduate or graduate health-related professional programs; be Canadian citizen/permanent resident and resident of Ontario. **Criteria:** Selection will be based on the financial need, academic merit and demonstrated community leadership skills.

Funds Avail.: 5,000 Canadian Dollars. **Duration:** Annual. **Number Awarded:** 2. **To Apply:** Applicants must submit a completed application form along with the required materials and information. **Deadline:** November 1. **Contact:** Enrolment Services: 172 Saint George St., Toronto, ON M5R 0A3.

11689 ■ City of Toronto Women's Studies Scholarships *(Graduate, Undergraduate/Scholarship)*

Purpose: To support students with their educational pursuits. **Focus:** Women's studies. **Qualif.:** Applicants must be a Canadian citizen /permanent resident and resident of Ontario; have completed year three, and be enrolled in a major or specialist program in women's studies. **Criteria:** Selection is based on financial need and academic merit.

Funds Avail.: 5,000 Canadian Dollars. **Duration:** Annual. **Number Awarded:** 1. **To Apply:** Applicants must submit a completed application form along with the required materials and information. **Deadline:** November 1. **Contact:** E-mail:awards.uoft@utoronto.ca.

11690 ■ Mary Jane Hendrie Memorial Scholarships *(Graduate, Undergraduate/Scholarship)*

Purpose: To provide financial support to students who are in need. **Focus:** Japanese studies. **Qualif.:** Applicant must be an undergraduate or graduate student; demonstrate an Interest in relations between Japan and Canada; study business, economics, or international relations. **Criteria:** Selection is based on general proficiency or outstanding achievements.

Funds Avail.: 6,000 Canadian Dollars. **Duration:** Annual. **To Apply:** Applicants must submit a completed application form along with the required materials and information. **Deadline:** November. **Contact:** Enrolment Services: 172

Saint George St., Toronto, ON M5R 0A3.

11691 ■ Irving J. Hoffman Memorial Scholarships *(Undergraduate/Scholarship)*

Purpose: To provide financial support to students who are in need. **Focus:** General studies/Field of study not specified. **Criteria:** Selection will be based on academic achievement and financial need.

Funds Avail.: 1,000 Canadian Dollars. **Duration:** Annual. **To Apply:** Applicants must submit a completed application form along with the required materials and information. **Deadline:** November 1. **Contact:** Enrolment Services: 172 Saint George St., Toronto, ON M5R 0A3.

11692 ■ Hosinec Family Scholarships *(Graduate, Undergraduate/Grant)*

Purpose: To support students with their educational pursuits. **Focus:** General studies/Field of study not specified. **Qualif.:** Applicants must be undergraduate or graduate students of the University of Toronto. **Criteria:** Selection will be based on financial need and academic merit.

Funds Avail.: $1,000-$2,500 each. **Duration:** Annual. **Number Awarded:** Varies. **To Apply:** Applicants must submit a completed application form and required materials and information. **Deadline:** November 30. **Contact:** Enrolment Services: 172 Saint George St., Toronto, ON M5R 0A3.

11693 ■ In-course Scholarships - Chinese Dance Workshop Scholarships *(Undergraduate/Scholarship)*

Purpose: To provide educational support to students who are in need. **Focus:** Dance. **Qualif.:** Applicant must be an undergraduate student with at least three years of demonstrated dance experience. **Criteria:** Selection is based on academic excellence and demonstrated dance experience.

Funds Avail.: Approximately $2,800. **Duration:** Annual; up to 4 years. **To Apply:** Applicants must submit a letter of application verifying at least three years of attendance at a recognized dance institute along with a transcript of marks. **Deadline:** November 20. **Contact:** Enrolment Services: 172 Saint George St., Toronto, ON M5R 0A3.

11694 ■ Khaki University and Y.M.C.A. Memorial Scholarships *(Undergraduate/Scholarship)*

Purpose: To provide financial support to students who are in need. **Focus:** General studies/Field of study not specified. **Qualif.:** Applicant must be an undergraduate student. **Criteria:** Selection will be based on students who are descendent from one who has served in the armed forces.

Funds Avail.: 3,000 Canadian Dollars. **Duration:** Annual. **To Apply:** Applicants must submit completed application form along with the required materials and information. **Deadline:** November 1. **Contact:** Enrolment Services: 172 Saint George St., Toronto, ON M5R 0A3.

11695 ■ Joseph McCulley Educational Trust Fund *(Graduate, Undergraduate/Grant)*

Purpose: To provide financial support to students who are in need. **Focus:** Social work. **Qualif.:** Applicants must be graduate or undergraduate students, whose programs of study and career interests lie in the area of public life or social work, emphasizing on penology. demonstrate financial need. **Criteria:** Selection will be based on financial need.

Funds Avail.: 1,000 Canadian Dollars. **Duration:** Annual. **To Apply:** Applicants must submit a completed application

Awards are arranged alphabetically below their administering organizations

form together with the required materials and information. **Deadline:** November 1.

11696 ■ Al Mercury Scholarships *(Undergraduate/ Scholarship)*

Purpose: To provide educational support to students who are in need. **Focus:** General studies/Field of study not specified. **Qualif.:** Applicants must be University of Toronto students with demonstrated community involvement, academic excellence, integrity and an appreciation and interest in music. **Criteria:** Selection will be based on general proficiency or outstanding achievements of the applicants.

Funds Avail.: 500 Canadian Dollars each. **Duration:** Annual. **To Apply:** Submit your application form: Complete the U of T Student Award Application Form Email the completed form (in PDF format) as an email attachment to Enrolment Services (awards.uoft@utoronto.ca). **Deadline:** November 1. **Contact:** Enrolment Services: 172 Saint George St., Toronto, ON M5R 0A3.

11697 ■ John H. Moss Scholarships *(Undergraduate/ Scholarship)*

Purpose: To provide educational support to students who are in need. **Focus:** Arts; Science.

Funds Avail.: 16,650 Canadian Dollars. **Duration:** Annual. **To Apply:** Applicants must submit a completed application form together with the required materials and information.

11698 ■ Taylor Statten Memorial Fellowships *(Graduate/Scholarship)*

Purpose: To provide educational support to students who are in need. **Focus:** Education, Physical; Psychology; Social work. **Qualif.:** Applicants must be post-baccalaureate students in professional field or career related to youth services (such as physical and health education, psychology, teaching, the ministry and social work). **Criteria:** Selection is based on general proficiency or outstanding achievements.

Funds Avail.: 2,500 Canadian Dollars. **Duration:** Annual. **To Apply:** Applicants must submit a completed application form together with Attach a description of your training and experience, including summer vacation employment, and in particular any experience you have with youth activities. Attach a statement which includes the name of the University and your proposed program of study (included plans for vocation). Attach a statement detailing the required extracurricular activities, personal statement and a statement describing your community involvement. Submit two letters of reference from individuals in support of your application who can attest to your academic achievements, extracurricular activities, community involvement and/or participation in volunteer activities. Email the completed form (in PDF format), reference letters and all supporting documents as an email attachments to Enrolment Services. **Deadline:** February 10.

11699 ■ Evald Torokvei Foundation Scholarships *(Graduate/Scholarship)*

Purpose: To provide educational support to students who are in need. **Focus:** Engineering, Chemical. **Qualif.:** Applicants must be PhD student community involvement and academic excellence. **Criteria:** Selection will be based on the committee's criteria.

Funds Avail.: 1,000 Canadian Dollars each. **Duration:** Annual. **Number Awarded:** 2. **Contact:** Enrolment Services:

172 Saint George St., Toronto, ON M5R 0A3.

11700 ■ University of Toronto Accenture Scholarships *(Undergraduate/Scholarship)*

Purpose: To support students with their educational pursuits. **Focus:** Computer and information sciences; Engineering. **Qualif.:** Applicants must be students of University of Ontario enrolled in an Engineering, Computer Science or Bachelor of Commerce Degree; must be third year students entering the final year of study; must have maintained a strong academic background - minimum GPA of 3.0; and must be actively involved in two or more extracurricular activities. **Criteria:** Selection will be based on general proficiency or outstanding achievements of the applicants.

Funds Avail.: 1,500 Canadian Dollars. **Duration:** Annual. **To Apply:** Applicants must submit a completed application form along with the required materials and information. **Deadline:** October 1. **Contact:** Enrolment Services: 172 Saint George St., Toronto, ON M5R 0A3.

11701 ■ University of Toronto Nortel Institute Undergraduate Scholarships *(Undergraduate/ Scholarship)*

Purpose: To provide educational support to students who are in need. **Focus:** Art industries and trade; Engineering. **Criteria:** Selection is based on financial need, academic merit and on the essay.

Funds Avail.: 5,000 Canadian Dollars. **Duration:** Annual. **To Apply:** Applicants must submit a completed application form along with two references and an essay on a given topic (maximum of 500 words). **Deadline:** November 1. **Contact:** Enrolment Services: 172 Saint George St., Toronto, ON M5R 0A3. awards.uoft@utoronto.ca.

11702 ■ University of Toronto Student Union (UTSU) Undergraduate Grant *(Undergraduate/Grant)*

Purpose: To provide educational support to students who are in need. **Focus:** General studies/Field of study not specified. **Qualif.:** Applicants must be a full-time undergraduate student; demonstrate financial need; demonstrate extracurricular involvement in the university community; have maintained a minimum academic standing of "C". **Criteria:** Selection will be based on financial need, and extracurricular involvement in the university community.

Funds Avail.: 1,300 Canadian Dollars. **Duration:** Annual. **Number Awarded:** Varies. **To Apply:** Applicants must submit a completed application form together with the required materials and information. **Deadline:** November 1. **Contact:** Enrolment Services: 172 Saint George St., Toronto, ON M5R 0A3.

11703 ■ University of Toronto - Department for the Study of Religion (DSR)

Jackman Humanities Bldg.
170 St. George St., 3rd Fl.
Toronto, ON, Canada M5R 2M8
Ph: (416)978-0877
Fax: (416)978-1610
E-mail: religion.grad@utoronto.ca
URL: religion.utoronto.ca
Social Media: www.facebook.com/UofTReligion
twitter.com/UofTReligion

11704 ■ Connaught Fellowship *(Graduate/Fellowship)*

Purpose: To assist selected incoming international students with outstanding records who have applied for graduate

Awards are arranged alphabetically below their administering organizations

study. **Focus:** General studies/Field of study not specified. **Qualif.:** Applicants must applied for graduate study; must be nominated by the Department and selected in an SGS competition.

Funds Avail.: $35,000. **Duration:** Periodic; 5 years.

11705 ■ University of Toronto - Edward S. Rogers Sr. Department of Electrical and Computer Engineering - Emerging Communications Technology Institute - Nortel Institute for Telecommunications

Sandford Fleming, Rm. 1102
10 King's College Rd.
Toronto, ON, Canada M5S 3G4
URL: www.nit.utoronto.ca

11706 ■ Nortel Institute for Telecommunications Graduate Scholarship *(Graduate, Master's/Scholarship)*

Purpose: To support outstanding students in the Nortel Institute's Master of Engineering in Telecommunications program. **Focus:** Communications technologies.

Funds Avail.: $15,000. **Duration:** Annual.

11707 ■ Nortel Scholarship *(Undergraduate/Scholarship)*

Purpose: To support undergraduate students in the Faculties of Applied Science and Engineering, Arts and Science, and Management. **Focus:** Communications technologies. **Qualif.:** Applicants must be undergraduate student at the University of Toronto.

Funds Avail.: $5,000. **Duration:** Annual. **Number Awarded:** 1. **Remarks:** Established in 1997.

11708 ■ University of Toronto Faculty of Social Work - Institute for Life Course and Aging

246 Bloor St. W, Room 238
Toronto, ON, Canada M5S 1V4
Ph: (416)978-0377
E-mail: aging@utoronto.ca
URL: www.aging.utoronto.ca
Social Media: www.facebook.com/agingutoronto.ca
twitter.com/lifecourseUofT
www.youtube.com/watch?v=eXtnm4sxV9A

11709 ■ Helene and George Coward Award in Gerontology *(Graduate/Award)*

Purpose: To support a University of Toronto graduate student who is engaged in research in the field of aging. **Focus:** Gerontology. **Qualif.:** Applicants must be University of Toronto graduate student who is engaged in research in the field of aging. **Criteria:** Preference will be given to students registered in the Collaborative Specialization in Aging and the Life Course who have demonstrated high academic achievement.

Funds Avail.: 848 Canadian Dollars. **Duration:** Annual. **To Apply:** Applicants should include two sealed letters of reference. **Deadline:** June 30. **Contact:** Awards Committee, Institute for Life Course and Aging, 246 Bloor St. W., Room 238, Toronto, ON M5S 1V4, Susan Murphy, Admin; Phone: 416-978-7037 or Nina Carlton, Secretary, Phone: 416-978-0377.

11710 ■ Wilfred George Scott Fellowship in Gerontology *(Graduate/Fellowship)*

Purpose: To support a University of Toronto graduate student doing research in the fields of social, psychological and economic aspects of aging. **Focus:** Gerontology. **Qualif.:** Applicants must be University of Toronto graduate student doing research in the fields of social, psychological and economic aspects of aging. **Criteria:** Preference will be given to students registered in the Collaborative Specialization in Aging and the Life Course who have demonstrated high academic achievement.

Funds Avail.: $2,327. **Duration:** Annual. **Deadline:** June 30.

11711 ■ University of Virginia (UVA)

PO Box 400160
Charlottesville, VA 22904-4160
Ph: (434)982-3200
URL: www.virginia.edu
Social Media: www.facebook.com/UniversityofVirginia
www.instagram.com/uva
www.pinterest.com/eampem/university-of-virginia
twitter.com/UVA
www.youtube.com/user/uvamagazine

11712 ■ Bayly-Tiffany Scholarships *(Undergraduate/Scholarship)*

Purpose: To support students at the University of Virginia in their educational pursuits. **Focus:** General studies/Field of study not specified. **Qualif.:** Applicants must be students of the University of Virginia and residents of Accomack or Northampton counties in Virginia. **Criteria:** Selection will be based on the committee's criteria.

Funds Avail.: No specific amount. **Duration:** Annual; renewable for up to four consecutive years. **To Apply:** Students do not need to complete a separate application form but will be considered automatically when admitted. **Remarks:** Established in 1930.

11713 ■ Charles Fred Wonson Scholarship *(Graduate/Scholarship)*

Purpose: To support students at the University of Virginia in their educational pursuits. **Focus:** General studies/Field of study not specified. **Qualif.:** Applicants must be students who are graduates of Robert E. Lee High School in Staunton, Virginia. **Criteria:** Selection will be based on need.

Funds Avail.: No specific amount. **Duration:** Annual. **To Apply:** Students do not need to complete a separate application form but will be considered automatically when admitted.

11714 ■ H. Kruger Kaprielian Scholarship *(Undergraduate/Scholarship)*

Purpose: To support Armenian-descent students at the University of Virginia in their educational pursuits. **Focus:** General studies/Field of study not specified. **Qualif.:** An applicant must prove Armenian descent. All applicants must be U.S. citizens or permanent residents. **Criteria:** Selection will be based on demonstrate financial need.

Funds Avail.: No specific amount. **Duration:** Annual; one year only. **Number Awarded:** 1. **To Apply:** All applications must include at least three (3) forms of proof of Armenian

Awards are arranged alphabetically below their administering organizations

descent (see sidebar for list of acceptable documents). **Deadline:** July 15. **Remarks:** Established in 1951.

11715 ■ John Allen Love Scholarship *(Graduate, Undergraduate/Scholarship)*

Purpose: To support students at the University of Virginia in their educational pursuits. **Focus:** Government; International affairs and relations. **Qualif.:** Applicants must be University of Virginia undergraduate or graduate students residing in Missouri. **Criteria:** Preference will be given to applicants residing in St. Louis or St. Louis County, and also to those enrolled in courses in the Department of Government and Foreign Affairs.

Funds Avail.: No specific amount. **Duration:** Annual. **To Apply:** Students do not need to complete a separate application form but will be considered automatically when admitted.

11716 ■ Margaret E. Phillips Scholarship *(Undergraduate/Scholarship)*

Purpose: To support deserving students who shall be preparing for and who propose to become ministers of the Protestant Episcopal Church in America. **Focus:** Religion. **Qualif.:** Applicants must be University of Virginia students preparing for and proposing to become ministers of the Protestant Episcopal Church in America. **Criteria:** Selection will be based on need.

Funds Avail.: No specific amount. **Duration:** Annual. **To Apply:** Applicants must provide a letter of recommendation from a minister or a member of an organization and any other documentation that validates interest in becoming a minister of the Protestant Episcopal Church in America. **Remarks:** Established in 1965.

11717 ■ V. Thomas Forehand, Jr. Scholarship *(Undergraduate/Scholarship)*

Purpose: To support students at the University of Virginia in their educational pursuits. **Focus:** General studies/Field of study not specified. **Qualif.:** Applicants must be UVA undergraduate students from the city of Chesapeake who attended Oscar F. Smith High School, Norfolk Academy, or Nansemond-Suffolk Academy. **Criteria:** Selection is based on need.

Funds Avail.: No specific amount. **Duration:** Annual. **To Apply:** Students do not need to complete a separate application form but will be considered automatically when admitted.

11718 ■ University of Virginia - Institute for Advanced Studies in Culture (IASC)

Watson Manor
3 University Cir.
Charlottesville, VA 22903
Ph: (434)924-7705
Fax: (434)243-5590
E-mail: iasc@virginia.edu
URL: www.iasc-culture.org
Social Media: twitter.com/iasculture

11719 ■ IASC Associate Fellowships *(Doctorate/ Fellowship)*

Purpose: To support students doing course work in the first years of their doctoral work. **Focus:** Culture. **Qualif.:** Applicants must be students doing course work in the first

years of their doctoral work. **Criteria:** Selection will be based on the committee's criteria.

To Apply: Interested applicants must visit the website for the application process.

11720 ■ IASC Doctoral Fellowships - Dissertation *(Doctorate/Fellowship)*

Purpose: To support students through the research and writing stages of their dissertations. **Focus:** Culture. **Qualif.:** Applicants must be students through the research and writing stages of their dissertations. **Criteria:** Selection will be based on the demonstrated academic promise and how closely their scholarly interests fit with the Institute research priorities.

Funds Avail.: No specific amount. **Duration:** Annual. **To Apply:** Applicants must submit a project abstract, including title (not to exceed 50 words) as a well as a project description, including title, not to exceed 5 double-spaced pages (1, 250 words); cover letter; curriculum vitae; one confidential letter of reference (signed original only); reference letters. **Contact:** Institute for Advanced Studies in Culture, University of Virginia, ? P.O. Box 400816, Charlottesville, VA 22903; Email: IASCFellowsInfo@virginia.edu.

11721 ■ IASC Doctoral Fellowships - Pre-Dissertation *(Doctorate/Fellowship)*

Purpose: To support students through the research and writing stages of their dissertations. **Focus:** Culture. **Qualif.:** Applicants must be in their comprehensive examination and proposal-writing year. **Criteria:** Selection will be based on the demonstrated academic promise and how closely their scholarly interest fit with the Institute's research priorities.

Funds Avail.: No specific amount. **Duration:** Annual. **To Apply:** Applicants must contact the Institute for the application process.

11722 ■ IASC Postdoctoral Fellowships *(Postdoctorate/Fellowship)*

Purpose: To support work on first books by aspiring postdoctoral students. **Focus:** Culture. **Qualif.:** Applicants must be recent PhDs whose research directly contributes to the research priorities of the Institute. Applicants must successfully defend dissertations prior to the start of the academic year in which they have been awarded a fellowship. **Criteria:** Selection will be on a competitive basis.

Funds Avail.: No specific amount. **Duration:** Annual. **To Apply:** Applicants must provide the following: cover letter of application (250-word maximum); curriculum vitae; project abstract, including title (not to exceed 50 words); project description, including title; contact information for at least three references. **Deadline:** December 31.

11723 ■ IASC Visiting Fellowships *(Professional development/Fellowship)*

Purpose: To support established scholars in their advanced studies in culture. **Focus:** Culture. **Qualif.:** Applicants must be scholars looking for semester and year-long sabbaticals and whose work directly contributes to the intellectual priorities of the Institute's research programs. **Criteria:** Selection will be on a competitive basis.

Funds Avail.: No specific amount. **Duration:** Annual. **To Apply:** Applicants must contact the Institute for the application process.

11724 ■ U.V.A. Faculty Fellowships *(Professional development/Fellowship)*

Purpose: To support the next generation of scholars. **Focus:** Culture. **Qualif.:** Applicants must be members of the

Awards are arranged alphabetically below their administering organizations

UVA Faculty. **Criteria:** Selection will be based on the interest and fit with the Institute's intellectual mission.

To Apply: Interested applicants must contact the Institute for the application process.

11725 ■ University of Virginia - The Institute for Nanoscale and Quantum Scientific and Technological Advanced Research
395 McCormick Rd.
Charlottesville, VA 22904
Ph: (434)982-5892
Fax: (434)982-5851
E-mail: nanostar@virginia.edu
URL: nanostar.virginia.edu
Social Media: www.facebook.com/NanostarInstitute

11726 ■ NanoSTAR Seed Fund Program *(Advanced Professional/Grant)*

Purpose: To support promising new interdisciplinary research collaborations in the Institute's three thrust areas: electronics, biomedicine, and energy and the environment. **Focus:** Electronics; Energy-related areas.

Funds Avail.: $30,000 to $60,000. **Duration:** Annual. **Deadline:** May 1.

11727 ■ University of Waterloo
200 University Ave. W
Waterloo, ON, Canada N2L 3G1
URL: www.uwaterloo.ca

11728 ■ Dominion of Canada General Insurance Company Graduate Scholarship in Actuarial Science *(Graduate, Master's, Doctorate/Scholarship)*

Purpose: To provide scholarships for students involved in a research project. **Focus:** Physiology. **Qualif.:** Applicants must be full-time graduate students of the University of Waterloo who are pursuing a Master's or Ph.D. degree in Actuarial Science; must be Canadian/Permanent resident, International/study permit student. **Criteria:** Selection will be determined by the Graduate Studies Office.

Funds Avail.: $20,000. **Contact:** Contact Department/program Graduate Co-ordinator for further information regarding this award.

11729 ■ University of Western Ontario - Centre for Research and Education on Violence Against Women and Children
1151 Richmond Street
London, ON, Canada N6A 3K7
Ph: (519)661-4040
Fax: (519)850-2464
E-mail: crevawc@uwo.ca
URL: learningtoendabuse.ca
Social Media: www.facebook.com/CREVAWC
twitter.com/learntoendabuse
www.youtube.com/channel/
  UCFjlfYQY3QTUIuwW0MOeLcQ

11730 ■ Scotiabank Undergraduate Award for Studies in Violence Against Women and Children *(Undergraduate/Award)*

Purpose: To provide financial support to undergraduate students with an interest in the area of anti-violence advocacy and/or research on violence against women and children. **Focus:** Aggression and violence; Women's studies. **Qualif.:** Applicant must be an undergraduate student; must have an interest in research and education regarding violence against women and children; and be involved with the Centre for Research & Education on Violence Against Women & Children (CREVAWC).

Funds Avail.: $3,250. **Duration:** Annual. **Number Awarded:** 2. **To Apply:** Applicant must submit cover sheet, Personal letter (1 page), Letter of support from an academic leader, Letter of support from a community member and Short CV (four pages). **Deadline:** March 31. **Contact:** Maly Bun, Email: mbun@uwo.ca; Phone: 519-661-4040.

11731 ■ University of Wisconsin Madison
500 Lincoln Dr.
Madison, WI 53706
Ph: (608)263-2400
E-mail: askbucky@uwmad.wisc.edu
URL: www.facebook.com
Social Media: www.facebook.com/UWMadison
twitter.com/uwmadison

11732 ■ Ahlswede, Norman & Marie Endowed Engineering Scholarship *(Undergraduate/Scholarship)*

Purpose: To support UW-Madison engineering students in their education. **Focus:** Engineering. **Qualif.:** Applicants must be UW-Madison undergraduate students enrolled in any engineering major; they must be in good academic standing, be enrolled full-time in the College of Engineering and have completed at least two semesters (excluding Summer Session) on the UW-Madison campus at the time of the award. **Criteria:** Selection will be based on the aforesaid qualifications and compliance with the application process.

Funds Avail.: No specific amount. **Duration:** Annual. **Number Awarded:** Varies. **To Apply:** Applicants must apply by the scholarship deadline; completed applications will be read and evaluated using criteria designated by the donor and the values of the College; in addition, scholarships with a required financial need component use information provided on the completed FAFSA form. **Deadline:** May 1. **Remarks:** The scholarship is part of the UW-Madison College of Engineering scholarships. There are other various scholarships offered.

11733 ■ Barry M. Goldwater Scholarship *(Undergraduate/Scholarship)*

Purpose: To support and recognize promising undergraduates who plan to pursue a PhD or MD/PhD followed by a research career in engineering, mathematics or the natural sciences. **Focus:** Engineering; Mathematics and mathematical sciences; Science. **Qualif.:** Applicants must be full-time sophomores or juniors during academic year of application (defined as two years or one year of undergraduate study remaining after application year) who are also planning to pursue a PhD and research career in mathematics, natural sciences or engineering research (MD alone does not qualify, but MD/PhD does); they must also have an outstanding undergraduate academic record (GPA greater than 3.8), engaged in undergraduate research, and be U.S. citizens, nationals or permanent residents. **Criteria:** Selection will be based on academic achievement, progress toward research goals, research essay, and letters of recommendation.

Funds Avail.: $7,500. **Duration:** Annual; four years. **Number Awarded:** 300. **To Apply:** Applicants must submit all

Awards are arranged alphabetically below their administering organizations

application materials to the UAA Office by the campus deadline. **Remarks:** Established in 1986. **Contact:** Office of Undergraduate Academic Awards, at awards@provost.wisc.edu.

11734 ■ The Bascom Hill Society Scholarship
(Undergraduate/Scholarship)

Purpose: To support a student with financial need who combines academic excellence with demonstrated leadership ability and outstanding service to the university or their community. **Focus:** General studies/Field of study not specified. **Qualif.:** Applicant must have a GPA of 3.2 or above, sophomore or junior status at the time of application, and unmet financial need of at least $1,000 for Wisconsin or Minnesota residents, or at least $5,000 for out-of-state residents. **Criteria:** Selection will be based on the following: outstanding record of campus or community service; demonstrated leadership capacity; and academic ability and achievement.

Funds Avail.: No specific amount. **Duration:** Annual. **To Apply:** Applicant must submit application and transcript from each university attended. Two letters of recommendation required, one attesting to your academic success, the other commenting on your leadership ability and potential. **Contact:** Phone: 608-265-2428; Email: awards@provost.wisc.edu.

11735 ■ Mary Ann Brichta Scholarships
(Undergraduate/Scholarship)

Purpose: To support underrepresented UW-Madison students in their education. **Focus:** Education, Secondary. **Qualif.:** Applicants must be undergraduate students in the final year of an elementary teacher certification program based on financial need of students of underrepresented groups showing academic promise. **Criteria:** Selection will be based on the aforesaid qualifications.

Funds Avail.: No specific amount. **Duration:** Annual. **To Apply:** Interested applicants may contact the Office of the Dean to obtain an application form. **Remarks:** The scholarship was established to help students in the Department of Curriculum & Instruction. Ms. Brichta was a 1938 graduate from the School of Education and became a librarian at Milwaukee County General Hospital. **Contact:** Email: scholarships-soe@education.wisc.edu.

11736 ■ John P. and Tashia F. Morgridge Scholarship *(Undergraduate, Graduate/Scholarship)*

Purpose: To support UW-Madison underrepresented students in their education. **Focus:** Education, Elementary. **Qualif.:** Applicants must be underrepresented undergraduate or graduate students preparing to become teachers, preferably at the elementary level who have proven success in academic achievement and who have demonstrated financial need. **Criteria:** Selection will be based on academic achievement and financial need, with preference given to graduates of Wisconsin high schools; recipients are selected by the All School minority/underserved population scholarship committee.

Funds Avail.: No specific amount. **Duration:** Annual. **Number Awarded:** 6. **To Apply:** Scholarship applications are available from the Office of the Dean. **Deadline:** March 31. **Contact:** Phone: 608-264-4357; Email: scholarship_support@em.wisc.edu.

11737 ■ Kemper K. Knapp Scholarship
(Undergraduate/Scholarship)

Purpose: To support UW-Madison students in their education. **Focus:** General studies/Field of study not specified.

Qualif.: Applicants must be National Merit finalists who are Wisconsin residents and designate UW-Madison as their first-choice institution; other finalists who notify the office of student financial services are eligible as funds permit. **Criteria:** Selection will be based on academic excellence.

Funds Avail.: No specific amount. **Duration:** Annual. **To Apply:** No application for the award. Students will be automatically considered when admitted. **Deadline:** may 31. **Contact:** Phone: 608-264-4357; Email: scholarship_support@em.wisc.edu.

11738 ■ George Koeppel Scholarship/All School
(Undergraduate/Scholarship)

Purpose: To support UW-Madison students in their education. **Focus:** Education, Secondary. **Qualif.:** Applicants must be full-time undergraduates in the School of Education who intend to become elementary school teachers. Scholarships are awarded based on a student's academic record, need, and the department's recommendation. **Criteria:** Preference given to prospective elementary teachers from Milwaukee County. Financial need is considered.

Funds Avail.: No specific amount. **To Apply:** Interested applicant may contact the Office of the Dean to obtain an application form. **Deadline:** May 26. **Remarks:** The scholarship was established by the late Charlotte E. Zinns in honor of her father, a grade school principal in Milwaukee. **Contact:** Email: scholarships-soe@education.wisc.edu.

11739 ■ Kraft Foods Food Science Minority Scholarship *(Undergraduate/Scholarship)*

Purpose: To support UW-Madison students in their education. **Focus:** Agricultural sciences; Life sciences. **Qualif.:** Applicants must be UW-Madison students of color enrolled in the College of Agricultural and Life Sciences (CALS). **Criteria:** Selection is based on academic excellence.

Number Awarded: Varies. **To Apply:** Students must submit a completed CALS scholarship application along with the letter of recommendation. **Contact:** Email: Scholarships@UW-Madison.

11740 ■ Abby Marlatt Scholarship *(Undergraduate/Scholarship)*

Purpose: To support UW-Madison students in their education. **Focus:** Ecology. **Qualif.:** Applicants must be current School of Human Ecology majors at the UW-Madison. **Criteria:** Preference will be given to applicants with good academic standing, who have participated in extracurricular or leadership activities or who have performed community service.

Funds Avail.: No specific amount. **Duration:** Annual. **Number Awarded:** Varies. **To Apply:** Applicants must submit the School of Human Ecology Continuing undergraduate student scholarship online application along with one letter of recommendation and two short essays. **Deadline:** February 18. **Remarks:** The scholarship is provided in honor of Abby Marlatt. **Contact:** Email: scholarships@sohe.wisc.edu.

11741 ■ McBurney Disability Resource Center General Scholarships *(Undergraduate/Scholarship)*

Purpose: To support UW-Madison disabled students in their education. **Focus:** General studies/Field of study not specified. **Qualif.:** Applicants must be UW-Madison undergraduate, graduate and professional students whose disabilities have been verified through the McBurney Disability Resource Center. **Criteria:** Recipients will be

Awards are arranged alphabetically below their administering organizations

selected based on the application materials submitted.

Funds Avail.: $500 to $2,000. **Duration:** Annual. **To Apply:** Applicants must submit a completed McBurney Scholarship; along with two letters of recommendation and a current transcript. **Deadline:** December 1.

11742 ■ Patricia Buchanan Memorial Scholarship
(Undergraduate/Scholarship)

Purpose: To support UW-Madison students in their education. **Focus:** Education, Secondary. **Qualif.:** Applicants must be undergraduate students in underrepresented groups from Madison Metropolitan School District high schools who are preparing to become teachers. **Criteria:** Selection will be based on academic record, need, evidence of community service, and the recommendation of the students' academic department.

Duration: Annual. **To Apply:** Interested applicants may contact the Office of the Dean to obtain an application form. **Deadline:** May 26. **Remarks:** The scholarship was established by the family and friends of the award's namesake. Established in 1991. **Contact:** Email: scholarships-soe@education.wisc.edu.

11743 ■ Pi Lambda Theta Scholarship
(Undergraduate/Scholarship)

Purpose: To support UW-Madison students in their education. **Focus:** Education. **Qualif.:** Applicants must be UW-Madison junior students having the highest GPA in the School of Education, and have completed at least one full semester (12 credits). **Criteria:** Selection will be based on students with highest GPA in junior year enrolled in a teacher preparation program; one award is given to majority student with highest GPA and one award to a student of an underrepresented group.

Funds Avail.: No specific amount. **Duration:** Annual. **Number Awarded:** 2. **To Apply:** Scholarship applications are available from the Office of the Dean. **Contact:** Phone: 608-264-4357; Email: scholarship_support@em.wisc.edu.

11744 ■ Powers-Knapp Scholarship Program
(Undergraduate/Scholarship)

Purpose: To support UW-Madison students in their education. **Focus:** General studies/Field of study not specified. **Qualif.:** Applicants must be U.S. citizens who plan to enroll as new freshmen in the fall following graduation from high school, and be members of one of the following groups; African American; American Indian; Hispanic/Latino; Southeast Asian (Cambodian, Hmong, Laotian, or Vietnamese); socioeconomically disadvantaged; they should demonstrate outstanding academic performance (3.0/4.0 GPA or higher in academic units). **Criteria:** Selection will be based on the demonstrated academic success in high school, involvement in school/community organizations, leadership skills, and abilities to excel in the university's rigorous educational environment.

Funds Avail.: $400 each semester. **Duration:** Annual. **Number Awarded:** 2. **To Apply:** Applicant must complete the general application through https://wisc.academicworks.com/users/sign_in; After completing the general application, applicant will be able to apply for the award. **Deadline:** February 1.

11745 ■ Returning Adult and Single-Parent Scholarships
(Undergraduate/Scholarship)

Purpose: To support single parent students in their education. **Focus:** General studies/Field of study not specified. **Qualif.:** Applicants must be the sole head of their household and the single parent of at least one dependent child supported by and living in that household; a new or continuing student pursuing their first undergraduate degree; able to demonstrate financial need; and, a U.S. citizen, permanent resident, asylee, or other eligible non-citizen. **Criteria:** Preference will be given to undergraduates who have completed at least 30 degree credits with a cumulative GPA of 3.0 or better.

Duration: Annual; one time per year. **To Apply:** Applications can be submitted online. **Deadline:** February 20. **Remarks:** Established in 1993. **Contact:** Division of Continuing Studies, Adult Career and Special Student Services, 21 N Park St., Ste., 7101, Madison, WI, 53715; Phone: 608-263-6960; Email: advising@dcs.wisc.edu.

11746 ■ University of Wisconsin-Madison Chancellor's Scholarship Program *(Undergraduate/Scholarship)*

Purpose: To support UW-Madison students in their education. **Focus:** General studies/Field of study not specified. **Criteria:** Selection will be based on the demonstrated academic success in high school, involvement in school/community organizations, leadership skills, and abilities to excel in the university's rigorous educational environment.

Funds Avail.: $400 each semester. **Duration:** Annual. **To Apply:** Applicants must complete the online scholarship application form. **Deadline:** February 1.

11747 ■ University of Wisconsin-Madison National Merit Scholarship *(Undergraduate/Scholarship)*

Purpose: To support UW-Madison students in their education. **Focus:** General studies/Field of study not specified. **Qualif.:** Applicants must be National Merit finalists who designate UW-Madison as their first-choice institution. **Criteria:** Recipients will be selected based on a review of all applications.

Funds Avail.: No specific amount. **Duration:** Annual. **Number Awarded:** 5. **To Apply:** There is no application for the scholarship. **Deadline:** December 5. **Contact:** 500 Lincoln Drive Madison, WI 53706 United States.

11748 ■ UW-Madison Engineering Diversity Scholarship *(Undergraduate/Scholarship)*

Purpose: To encourage broadened participation in Engineering. **Focus:** Engineering. **Qualif.:** Applicants must be US Citizen or Permanent Resident; incoming freshman, enrolled full-time in any major in the College of Engineering; remain in engineering and maintain a 2.8 term and cumulative GPA. **Criteria:** Selection will be based on academic merit, quality of application, match to the Diversity Affairs Office mission of broadening participation in engineering, and financial need.

Funds Avail.: $500 to $3,000. **Duration:** Annual. **Number Awarded:** Varies. **To Apply:** Application is via online; A FASFA is also required and should be submitted to the Office of Student Financial Aid as soon as possible to allow for verification prior to award disbursement.

11749 ■ UW-Madison GLBT Alumni Council Scholarships *(Undergraduate, Graduate/Scholarship)*

Purpose: To support UW-Madison LGBTQ students in their education. **Focus:** General studies/Field of study not specified. **Qualif.:** Applicants must demonstrate a commitment to LGBTQ communities; must be enrolled 12 or more credits per term or the graduate equivalent. **Criteria:** Prefer-

Awards are arranged alphabetically below their administering organizations

ence will be given to students with financial need.

Funds Avail.: No specific amount. **Duration:** Annual; three years. **To Apply:** Applicants must complete the online scholarship application form. **Deadline:** April 27. **Contact:** Katherine Charek Briggs, Assistant Director, LGBT Campus Center; Email: katherine.charekbriggs@wisc.edu.

11750 ■ UW-Madison Reserve Officers Training Corps Scholarships (ROTC) *(Undergraduate/ Scholarship)*

Purpose: To support UW-Madison ROTC students in their education. **Focus:** Military science and education.

11751 ■ UW-Madison School of Education Minority Scholarship *(Undergraduate/Scholarship)*

Purpose: To support UW-Madison minority students in their education. **Focus:** Education. **Qualif.:** Applicants must be undergraduate students from underrepresented groups pursuing degrees in the School of Education. **Criteria:** Selection will be based on academic achievement and financial need; recipients are chosen by the School's Minority/Underserved Scholarship Committee.

Funds Avail.: No specific amount. **Duration:** Annual. **To Apply:** Applications are available from the Office of the Dean. **Contact:** Phone: 608-264-4357; Email: scholarship_support@em.wisc.edu.

11752 ■ William F. Vilas Merit Scholarship *(Undergraduate/Scholarship)*

Purpose: To support UW-Madison students in their education. **Focus:** General studies/Field of study not specified. **Qualif.:** Applicants must be students who demonstrate strong academic performance based on class rank and GPA. **Criteria:** Selection is based on academic excellence.

Funds Avail.: Up to $1,600. **Duration:** Annual. **To Apply:** Students will be automatically considered when admitted. **Deadline:** January 2. **Contact:** Office of Student Financial Aid, Phone: 608-262-3060; Email: finaid@finaid.wisc.edu.

11753 ■ Wisconsin Lawton Minority Retention Grants *(Undergraduate/Grant)*

Purpose: To support UW-Madison students in their education. **Focus:** General studies/Field of study not specified. **Qualif.:** Applicants must be sophomores, juniors, and seniors who are of African-American, Latino/a, American Indian, Vietnamese, Cambodian, Laotian, or Hmong heritage; have a minimum cumulative 2.0 grade point average; be enrolled full-time, pass 24 credits each academic year; have a program affiliation; and be United States citizens and residents of Wisconsin (current Minnesota recipients are grandfathered in through the current year). **Criteria:** Recipients will be selected based on financial need.

Funds Avail.: $1,000 to $3,000. **Duration:** Annual; one academic year. **To Apply:** Applicants must file an application at FAFSA in order to be considered. In addition, applicants must contact the Minority and Disadvantaged Coordinator in the UW-Madison school or college where they are enrolled. **Deadline:** March 30.

11754 ■ Unpakt LLC
555 W 25th St.
New York, NY 10001
Ph: (212)677-5333
Free: 855-286-7258

E-mail: support@unpakt.com
URL: www.unpakt.com
Social Media: www.facebook.com/Unpakt
twitter.com/unpakt

11755 ■ Unpakt College Scholarship *(Undergraduate, Graduate/Scholarship)*

Purpose: To help college students and recent graduates with current educational expenses and plan for life after college. **Focus:** General studies/Field of study not specified. **Qualif.:** Applicants must be current college students or recent college graduates (within one year) at time of award announcement. **Criteria:** Selection will be made by the judges.

Funds Avail.: $1,000 grand prize; $500 first runner-up; $100 second runner-up. **To Apply:** Submit essay up to 500 words that describes where you plan to move once you finish your education and why. **Deadline:** December 31. **Contact:** Unpakt, 555 W 25th St., Fl. 3, New York, NY, 10001; Email: scholarship@unpakt.com.

11756 ■ Upakar Indian-American Scholarship Foundation
9101 Friars Rd.
Bethesda, MD 20817
E-mail: upakarfoundation@hotmail.com
URL: www.upakarfoundation.org

11757 ■ Geeta Rastogi Memorial Scholarship *(Undergraduate/Scholarship)*

Purpose: To support the educational and career aspirations of the Indian-American community. **Focus:** Dance; Music. **Qualif.:** Applicants must be students entering a Fine Arts (Music, Dance, Drama, etc.) undergraduate program in the United States; must have either been born or have at least one parent in the Republic of India; must either be U.S. citizens or U.S. Green Card holders; must have latest Family Adjusted Gross Income (AGI) on the IRS form 1040, 1040EZ or 1040A of less than $75, 000; and must be graduating high school seniors living in the United States with a cumulative unweighted GPA of 3.6 or higher on a 4.0 scale.

Funds Avail.: $8,000. **Duration:** Annual; up to 4 years. **Deadline:** April. **Remarks:** Established in 2011.

11758 ■ W.E. Upjohn Institute for Employment Research
300 S Westnedge Ave.
Kalamazoo, MI 49007-4686
Ph: (269)343-5541
Fax: (269)343-3308
E-mail: communications@upjohn.org
URL: www.upjohn.org
Social Media: www.linkedin.com/company/w.e.-upjohn
 -institute-for-employment-research
twitter.com/UpjohnInstitute
www.youtube.com/channel/UCs816XgzMdyFP8O
 -3Z34ecQ

11759 ■ Upjohn Institute Early Career Research Awards (ECRA) *(Professional development/Grant, Award)*

Purpose: To provide resources for junior faculty to carry out policy-related research on labor market issues. **Focus:**

Awards are arranged alphabetically below their administering organizations

Employment; Labor. **Criteria:** Applicants should submit a proposal of, at most, 1, 200 words, must also include a current curriculum vitae.

Funds Avail.: No specific amount. **Duration:** Annual. **Number Awarded:** Varies. **To Apply:** Proposals Contribution to important labor market policy issues and to the professional literature, technical merit, professional qualifications. **Deadline:** January 24.

11760 ■ uPONICS
110 Templeton Pkwy.
Watertown, MA 02472
Ph: (910)987-7877
URL: uponics.com
Social Media: www.facebook.com/uponics
pinterest.com/uponics
twitter.com/myuponics

11761 ■ $1000 uPONICS Hydroponics/Aquaponics Scholarship *(Undergraduate/Scholarship)*

Purpose: To support a student interested in hydroponics and aquaponics as a sustainable form of agriculture. **Focus:** General studies/Field of study not specified. **Qualif.:** Applicant must be a U.S. citizen currently enrolled in an accredited U.S. college or university; minimum GPA of 2.5; and interested in hydroponics, aquaponics, and/or LED grow light technology.

Funds Avail.: $1,000. **Duration:** Annual. **Number Awarded:** 1. **To Apply:** Applicant must include the following using the form below: First and last name; Contact information (email address and phone number); Name of college or university; GPA; Major/Minor (if declared); Estimated graduation year; 1000-3500 word essay on the topic. **Deadline:** November 1. **Contact:** URL: uponics.com/aquaponics-scholarship/.

11762 ■ Upper Left, Inc.
540 N Willow Dr.
Long Lake, MN 55356
URL: www.enhancedinsurance.com

11763 ■ Enhanced Insurance Scholarships Program *(Undergraduate/Scholarship)*

Purpose: To promote insurance industry as positive force. **Focus:** General studies/Field of study not specified. **Qualif.:** Applicants must be high school seniors or current undergraduate students who will be enrolled full-time in a two- or four-year public or private college or university located in the United States and/or in the District of Columbia for an academic school year. **Criteria:** Selection will be based on the following criteria grammar, spelling, punctuation, content, creativity, clarity, and thoughtfulness.

Funds Avail.: $2,500. **Duration:** Annual. **Number Awarded:** Varies. **To Apply:** Students are encouraged to apply online; essays with fewer than 750 words or more than 1,250 words will be disqualified.

11764 ■ Upsilon Pi Epsilon Association
158 Wetlands Edge Rd.
American Canyon, CA 94503
Ph: (530)518-8488
Fax: (707)647-3560
E-mail: upe@acm.org

URL: upe.acm.org
Social Media: www.facebook.com/pages/Upsilon-Pi -Epsilon/113367998673934

11765 ■ UPE Scholarship Awards *(Graduate, Undergraduate/Scholarship)*

Purpose: To provide educational support to students who are in need. **Focus:** Computer and information sciences. **Qualif.:** Applicants must be graduate or undergraduate students. **Criteria:** Recipients will be selected based on the academic records; application form and other documents will be evaluated by the executive council of UPE.

Funds Avail.: $1,000 to $2,500. **Duration:** Annual. **Number Awarded:** 1. **To Apply:** Applications must be submitted as pdf files and must include a Chapter Advisor recommendation. **Deadline:** October 1. **Contact:** Upsilon Pi Epsilon 158 Wetlands Edge Road American Canyon, CA 94503; Email: upe@acm.org.

11766 ■ Urban Affairs Association (UAA)
c/o Urban Studies Program University of Wisconsin-Milwaukee Bolton Hall, Rm. 702 3210 N Maryland Ave.
Milwaukee, WI 53211
Ph: (414)229-3025
E-mail: info@uaamail.org
URL: urbanaffairsassociation.org
Social Media: www.linkedin.com/company/2393900
twitter.com/UAAnews

11767 ■ Alma H. Young Emerging Scholar Award *(Doctorate/Award)*

Purpose: To honor and support emerging scholars whose work exemplifies outstanding scholarship in urban affairs. **Focus:** General studies/Field of study not specified. **Qualif.:** Applicant must be pursuing doctoral research in urban affairs, regardless of academic discipline; must have finished the required course work and passed the comprehensive examinations; must have an approved dissertation proposal. **Criteria:** Recipients will be selected based on scholarship and commitment to urban issues.

Funds Avail.: $1,000. **Duration:** Annual. **Number Awarded:** 1. **To Apply:** Applicants must submit the nomination letter from current UAA members; provide (two-to-three page, double-spaced) personal statement describing urban interests, engagement and career plans; a curriculum vitae; a prospectus for the dissertation of (1, 500 to 2, 000 words) that indicate the research questions, argument or hypotheses, literature and data resources, methodology and nature of expected findings. **Deadline:** October 15. **Remarks:** The award was established in honor of Alma H. Young to commemorate her longstanding service to UAA, and her particular commitment to mentoring graduate students and junior faculty. Established in 1997. **Contact:** Email: awards@uaamail.org; Phone: 414-229-3025.

11768 ■ Urgently
8609 Westwood Center Dr., Ste. 810
Vienna, VA 22182
Free: 888-461-3621
E-mail: help@urgent.ly
URL: www.geturgently.com
Social Media: www.facebook.com/geturgently
www.instagram.com/geturgently
twitter.com/geturgently

Awards are arranged alphabetically below their administering organizations

11769 ■ Urgent.ly Driving Transportation Innovation Scholarship *(Undergraduate, Graduate, Vocational/Occupational/Scholarship)*

Purpose: To promote continued education and innovation within the transportation industry. **Focus:** General studies/Field of study not specified; Transportation. **Qualif.:** Applicants must be enrolled in an accredited U.S. institution of postsecondary education. **Criteria:** Academic performance, extracurricular engagement, and quality of prepared materials. Preference may be given to students enrolled in programs relating to transportation, engineering, technology, logistics, business, and management.

Funds Avail.: $500. **To Apply:** Submit essay between 400 and 600 words that demonstrates interest in the transportation sector. **Deadline:** March 31.

11770 ■ Urology Care Foundation
1000 Corporate Blvd.
Linthicum, MD 21090
Ph: (410)689-3700
Fax: (410)689-3998
Free: 800-828-7866
E-mail: info@urologycarefoundation.org
URL: www.urologyhealth.org
Social Media: www.facebook.com/UrologyCareFoundation
www.instagram.com/urologycarefdn
twitter.com/UrologyCareFdn
www.youtube.com/channel/
UCHCZ1sbVTYhpM1qmKFiOJJQ

11771 ■ AUA Foundation Urology Research Bridge Awards *(Postgraduate/Award)*

Purpose: To provide funds to individuals for interim support for a research grant that was competitive but did not get funded. **Focus:** Urology. **Qualif.:** Applicants must be a member of AUA; not a previous recipient of the award; must have competed for a peer-reviewed external funding for the project during the current federal fiscal year. **Criteria:** Applicants are selected based on the jury's review of the application materials.

Funds Avail.: No specific amount. **Duration:** Annual. **To Apply:** Applicants must register online at the AUA Foundation website in order to apply and submit the following materials: a completed application form; a registration summary form; an application agreement form; a NIH-style biosketch; a statement of support; letter from the applicants; budget justification worksheet; and a letter from the department chair. The form must be signed by the applicants, department chair and sponsoring institution representative. Scan all materials into one complete pdf file. **Remarks:** Established in 1975.

11772 ■ Urology Care Foundation/Astellas Rising Star in Urology Research Awards *(Postdoctorate, Other/Award)*

Purpose: To encourage a young urology faculty to go into, or continue a research career. **Focus:** Urology. **Qualif.:** Applicants must be Board certified or eligible urologists and must have successfully competed for a career development award within the current federal fiscal year. **Criteria:** Applicants will be selected based on scholarship panel's review of the application materials.

Funds Avail.: No specific amount. **Duration:** Annual. **To Apply:** Applicants must complete the online application

form; must also prepare a registration summary form; curriculum vitae; application agreement form with all necessary signatures; letter of support from each mentor; letter from urology department chair; current NIH-style biosketch of each mentor; copy of career development grant award letter; copy of career development grant; and copy of career development grant review summary sheets and scores. All materials must be uploaded and scanned into a single pdf file.

11773 ■ US-Ireland Alliance
3110 Tenth Street North
Arlington, VA 22201
URL: www.us-irelandalliance.org
Social Media: www.facebook.com/USIrelandAlliance
www.instagram.com/mitchellscholars
twitter.com/mitchellscholar

11774 ■ George J. Mitchell Scholarship *(Postgraduate/Scholarship)*

Purpose: To introduce and connect generations of future American leaders to the island of Ireland, while recognizing and fostering intellectual achievement, leadership, and a commitment to public service and community. **Focus:** General studies/Field of study not specified. **Qualif.:** Applicants must be U.S. citizens between 18-30 years old and hold a bachelor's degree from an accredited college or university. **Criteria:** Applicants will be judged based on scholarship; leadership and a sustained commitment to community and public service.

Funds Avail.: No specific amount. **Duration:** Annual. **Number Awarded:** Up to 12. **To Apply:** Applicant must submit an online application form along with four recommendations (plus an institutional endorsement if you are an undergraduate student); Passport-style photo (in PDF); All transcripts scanned into a single PDF (please block out your Social Security number if visible). This should include any undergraduate and graduate work you have completed. Unofficial transcripts are sufficient for the initial application. Finalists will be required to provide official transcripts during the interview process in Washington DC; Personal statement (1,000 words maximum - most applicants find it helpful to write this in advance); The personal statement or essay is your opportunity to share your personality, passion, and drive with the selection committee that cannot be communicated elsewhere in the application materials. You will be required to affirm that this is your original work and that no one has assisted you with the personal statement in any way; a scan of your signature (in PDF); Proof of US Citizenship. **Remarks:** Named to honor former US Senator George Mitchell's pivotal contribution to the Northern Ireland peace process. **Contact:** Contact: Trina Vargo, Founder & President, vargo@us-irelandalliance.org; Carolina Chavez, Director, George Mitchell Scholarship Program, chavez@us-irelandalliance.org; Email: Director director@mitchellscholars.org.

11775 ■ USA Cargo Trailer
1100 Thompson Dr.
Douglas, GA 31535
Free: 800-674-9890
URL: www.usacargotrailersales.com

11776 ■ USA Cargo Trailer Scholarship *(Undergraduate, Graduate/Scholarship)*

Purpose: To assist engineering students in the United States in furthering their educations. **Focus:** Engineering.

Awards are arranged alphabetically below their administering organizations

Qualif.: Applicants must be U.S. citizens attending college or university in the United States and studying engineering. **Criteria:** Selection is randomly drawn.

Funds Avail.: $500. **Duration:** Annual. **Number Awarded:** 1. **To Apply:** Application is available on sponsor's website. **Deadline:** November 30.

11777 ■ USA Water Ski & Wake Sports Foundation

6039 Cypress Gardens Blvd. Ste. 481
Winter Haven, FL 33884
E-mail: info@waterskihalloffame.com
URL: www.usa-wwf.org
Social Media: www.facebook.com/USAWWF1
www.instagram.com/usawwf
twitter.com/USAWSF

11778 ■ American Water Ski Educational Foundation Scholarships *(Undergraduate/Scholarship)*

Purpose: To preserve the traditions of one of America's most popular family recreational activities; to encourage and to educate the safe enjoyment of the challenges of water skiing. **Focus:** General studies/Field of study not specified. **Qualif.:** Applicant must be an incoming freshman, sophomore, junior or senior enrolled at two or four-year school; must be a U.S. citizen; and a current member of USA Water Ski foundation. **Criteria:** Applicants will be evaluated based upon the academic qualifications, leadership, extracurricular involvement, recommendations and financial need.

Funds Avail.: No specific amount. **Duration:** Three years. **To Apply:** Applicants must submit the following: application form; two letters of reference; a 500-word essay on topic, "AWSEF has a beautiful new facility"; an official transcript of grades; or high school transcript (if college freshman). **Deadline:** Mid March 1. **Remarks:** Incomplete applications will not be accepted. Established in 1983.

11779 ■ USAttorneys.com

1001 W Cypress Creek Rd., Ste. 405
Fort Lauderdale, FL 33309
Free: 800-672-3103
URL: divorce.usattorneys.com
Social Media: www.facebook.com/usattorneys
www.linkedin.com/company/us-attorneys
twitter.com/usattorneycom

11780 ■ USAttorneys.com Immigration Scholarships Essay Contest *(Undergraduate/Scholarship)*

Purpose: To assist students with the costs of college tuition and books. **Focus:** General studies/Field of study not specified. **Qualif.:** Applicants must be U.S. citizens who are accepted or currently attending an accredited American university or college. **Criteria:** Selection will be based on the committee's criteria.

Funds Avail.: $500. **To Apply:** Applicants must prepare a 1,000 word legal essay on any of the following topics: Immigration Reform; How to Apply for a Work Visa; The Importance of Having an Immigration Lawyer; How to Apply for Asylum; must submit their essay as an attachment, in PDF or Word format, including their full name, school they will be or are attending, and contact information. **Deadline:** July 14. **Contact:** USAttorneys.com; Email: scholarships@usattorneys.com.

11781 ■ USAttorneys.com National Scholarships Essay Contest *(Undergraduate/Scholarship)*

Purpose: To assist students with the costs of tuition and books. **Focus:** General studies/Field of study not specified. **Qualif.:** Applicants must be U.S. citizens, planning to attend an accredited American university or college. **Criteria:** Selection will be based on the committee's criteria.

Funds Avail.: $2,500. **Duration:** Annual. **To Apply:** Applicants must prepare a 800 to 1,000 word legal essay on any of the following topics: Divorce Law; Child Custody; Divorce Mediation. Applicants must submit their essay as an attachment in PDF or Word format, including their full name, school they will attending and contact information. **Deadline:** June 1.

11782 ■ USC Latino Alumni Association

Epstein Family Alumni Ctr., 3607 Trousdale Pky., TCC 324
Los Angeles, CA 90089-3104
Ph: (213)740-4735
E-mail: latinoalumni@usc.edu
URL: latinoalumni.usc.edu
Social Media: www.facebook.com/USCLAA
www.linkedin.com/company/usclaa
twitter.com/USCLatinoAlumni

11783 ■ USC Latino Alumni Association Scholarships *(Graduate, Undergraduate/Scholarship)*

Purpose: To support financially those students who are pursuing undergraduate and graduate degrees at University of Southern California. **Focus:** General studies/Field of study not specified.

Funds Avail.: $2,000 to $5,000 per academic year for undergraduate students and $1,000 to $5,000 per academic year for graduate students. **Duration:** Annual. **Number Awarded:** 1. **To Apply:** Applicants must submit a completed USC MAAA Scholarship application form together with a typed essay of no more than two pages, double spaced; a resume; original letter(s) of recommendation; and unofficial transcripts. Applications must be sent complete. **Deadline:** March 1. **Contact:** USC Latino Alumni Associaton; Phone: 213 740-473.

11784 ■ USS Coral Sea CVA-43 Association

52 Woodland Pl.
Fort Thomas, KY 41075-1605
URL: www.usscoralsea.org

11785 ■ USS Coral Sea - Scholarship Program *(Undergraduate/Scholarship)*

Purpose: To help the beneficiaries of an individual working at USS Coral Sea CVA-43 Association. **Focus:** General studies/Field of study not specified. **Criteria:** Selection will be based on originality of thought, adherence to topic, completeness, quality, spelling and punctuation; with the highest GPA will be announced as the winner.

Funds Avail.: $500 and $2,000. **Duration:** Annual. **To Apply:** Applicants must submit an original essay; two dated and signed letters of recommendation; and an official transcript of records; essay must be typed and double-spaced; reference sources must be listed and footnoted. **Contact:** Jon Lickey, 2321 N. Delaware St., Peoria, IL 616003-2645; Phone: 309-688-3939; Email: jjlickey47@yahoo.com.

Awards are arranged alphabetically below their administering organizations

11786 ■ Utah Chiefs of Police Association
98 East 5600 South
Ogden, UT 84405
E-mail: vshupe@utahchiefs.org
URL: www.utahchiefs.org

11787 ■ Utah Chiefs of Police Scholarship Program
(College, Undergraduate, University/Scholarship)

Purpose: To assist students in furthering their education and preparing to make a positive contribution to their communities and society in general. **Focus:** General studies/Field of study not specified. **Qualif.:** Applicant must be the child of a full-time Utah police officer employed by one of the following: a Utah municipal police department or municipal public safety organization; a Utah institution of Higher Education police department; a Utah school district police department; the Utah Transit Authority police department; or the Airport police department. Children of a retired police officer formerly employed by any of these entities may also apply. Applicant must attend an accredited college or university, or a Utah POST certified satellite police academy for which college level credit is awarded; be enrolled for at least 12 credit hours per semester; and have and maintain a 3.0 GPA throughout the duration of the scholarship award. **Criteria:** One award recipient will be the child of a Utah municipal police chief, however, if no child of a police chief applies then both scholarships will be awarded to children of police officers. Winners may reapply for the scholarship each year, but first time applicants will be given first priority.

Funds Avail.: $1,000 ($500 per semester). **Duration:** Annual. **To Apply:** Applicant must submit parent's name and employing agency or agency rom which parent is retired; a 250-word essay describing their goals, accomplishment, and explaining why they re the best candidate to receive this scholarship; most recent transcript of college or high school work; and a photograph. **Deadline:** June 20. **Contact:** Val Shupe, Executive Director, Utah Chiefs of Police Association 98 East 5600 South Ogden, Utah 84405.

11788 ■ Utility Workers Union of America (UWUA)
1300 L St. NW No. 1200
Washington, DC 20005
Ph: (202)899-2851
Fax: (202)899-2852
URL: uwua.net
Social Media: www.facebook.com/theUWUA
twitter.com/The_UWUA
www.youtube.com/user/theuwua

11789 ■ Utility Workers Union of America Scholarship Program *(Undergraduate/Scholarship)*

Purpose: To provide a system of services for corporations, foundations and other organizations that wish to sponsor college undergraduate scholarships for outstanding students who interest them. **Focus:** General studies/Field of study not specified. **Qualif.:** Applicants must be high school students who are sons and daughters of active members of UWUA; must be U.S. citizens and have a permanent residence in the United States. **Criteria:** Recipients will be selected based on academic record throughout high school, significant activities and contributions to the school community, test scores, recommendations and the student's essay about personal characteristics, activities, plan and goals.

Funds Avail.: $500 - $2,000. **Duration:** Annual. **To Apply:** Applicants must fill out the application form; must take the PSAT/NMSQT; must obtain a copy of the Official Student Guide to the PSAT/NMSQT from the high school counselor and make arrangements with the school to take the PSAT/NMSQT. **Remarks:** Established in 1961.

11790 ■ ValuePenguin
597 5th Ave. Fl 5
New York, NY 10016
E-mail: media@valuepenguin.com
URL: www.valuepenguin.com
Social Media: www.facebook.com/pg/ValuePenguin
twitter.com/ValuePenguin

11791 ■ ValuePenguin Scholarships *(Undergraduate/Scholarship)*

Purpose: To provide financial assistance for students to afford basic necessities. **Focus:** General studies/Field of study not specified. **Qualif.:** Applicants must be enrolled in an accredited U.S. undergraduate program. **Criteria:** Selection will be based on the following criteria; creativity, novelty and thoughtfulness of the essay responses.

To Apply: Applicants must submit a 500 to 750 word response (for a total word count of 1,000 to 1,500) to each of the following two questions: 1) Students encounter financial pitfalls of all types while attending colleges and universities; Explain a situation in which you spent too much (or not enough) money on a student expense and explain a creative solution you would share with future students. This could be something you did on your own or as part of a group. 2) How did you choose your college and/or major? submit all responses along with the following information: name, school attending, expected graduation date, major and career goal, email address, phone number, and picture. **Deadline:** December 15.

11792 ■ Vector Marketing Corp. (VMC)
1116 East State St.
Olean, NY 14760
Ph: (716)373-6141
E-mail: vectorpr@cutco.com
URL: www.vectorscholarships.com

11793 ■ All-American Vector Marketing Scholarship Program *(Undergraduate/Scholarship)*

Purpose: To support the education of students who are also top sales performers. **Focus:** Marketing and distribution. **Qualif.:** Applicants must be full-time undergraduate students at an accredited college or university. **Criteria:** Selection will be based on the committee's criteria.

Funds Avail.: $50,000. **Duration:** Annual. **Number Awarded:** Varies. **To Apply:** Applicants must submit an online application form.

11794 ■ Vector Marketing Canadian Scholarship Award *(Undergraduate/Scholarship)*

Purpose: To provide financial assistance to student sales representatives and the institutions of higher education they attend. **Focus:** Marketing and distribution. **Qualif.:** Applicants must be full-time university or college students working with vector; and must be currently active on vector marketing All-American program tracking system.

Awards are arranged alphabetically below their administering organizations

Duration: Annual. **To Apply:** Applicants must submit an online application form.

11795 ■ Vectorworks Inc.

7150 Riverwood Dr.
Columbia, MD 21046-1295
Ph: (410)290-5114
Fax: (410)290-8050
Free: 888-646-4223
E-mail: sales@vectorworks.net
URL: www.vectorworks.net
Social Media: www.facebook.com/Vectorworks
www.instagram.com/vectorworks
www.linkedin.com/company/vectorworks-inc
twitter.com/vectorworks
www.youtube.com/user/vectorworks

11796 ■ Vectorworks Design Scholarship
(Undergraduate, Graduate/Scholarship)

Purpose: To support the next generation of creative potential by providing resources and scholarships to those with great designs. **Focus:** Architecture; Construction; Design; Engineering; Environmental design; Graphic art and design; Industrial design; Interior design; Landscape architecture and design; Urban affairs/design/planning. **Qualif.:** Applicants must be student enrolled in a design-based program who are 18 years of age or older at the time of entry and who do NOT reside in Cuba, Iran, North Korea, Sudan, or Syria. **Criteria:** Selection will be based on the submitted designs of the applicants. Criteria includes: design quality, technology, concept and originality, presentation, and explanation of design.

Funds Avail.: $3,000. **Duration:** Annual. **Number Awarded:** Varies. **To Apply:** Submit completed application and a project file. **Deadline:** September 19.

11797 ■ Vegetarian Resource Group (VRG)

PO Box 1463
Baltimore, MD 21203
Ph: (410)366-8343
E-mail: vrg@vrg.org
URL: www.vrg.org
Social Media: www.facebook.com/
thevegetarianresourcegroup
www.instagram.com/vegetarianresourcegroup
twitter.com/VegResourceGrp

11798 ■ Vegetarian Resource Group College Scholarship *(Undergraduate, High School/Scholarship, Monetary, Award)*

Purpose: To assist graduating U.S. high school students who have promoted vegetarianism in their schools and/or communities. **Focus:** General studies/Field of study not specified; Vegetarianism. **Qualif.:** Applicants must be graduating U.S. high school students who have promoted vegetarianism in their schools and or communities. **Criteria:** Applicants will be judged on having shown compassion, courage, and a strong commitment to promoting a peaceful world through a vegetarian diet/lifestyle.

Funds Avail.: One $10,000; two $5,000. **Duration:** Annual. **Number Awarded:** 3. **To Apply:** Applicants must submit a copy of their transcripts or report cards for the past two years; three or more recommendations; any

documentation related to their promotion of vegetarianism in high school and/or community including photographs, a newspaper story. **Deadline:** February 20.

11799 ■ VelvetJobs

1400 N Martel Ave., Ste. 108
Los Angeles, CA 90046
E-mail: support@velvetjobs.com
URL: www.velvetjobs.com
Social Media: www.facebook.com/velvetjobs
www.linkedin.com/company/velvetjobs
pinterest.com/velvetjobs
twitter.com/velvetjobs

11800 ■ Resume Template Design Scholarships
(Undergraduate, Graduate/Scholarship)

Purpose: To support students to achieved their educational goals. **Focus:** General studies/Field of study not specified. **Qualif.:** Applicants must be U.S. or international college or university undergraduate and graduate students. **Criteria:** Selection will be based on the committee's criteria.

Funds Avail.: $1,000. **Duration:** Annual. **To Apply:** Applicants must submit a resume in Microsoft Word format; and must submit their essay and resume template online, including the following information full name, phone number, college or university where the are enrolled or plan to attend, and current school year. **Deadline:** December 31. **Contact:** Email: scholarship@velvetjobs.com.

11801 ■ Vermont Paralegal Organization (VPO)

PO Box 5755
Burlington, VT 05402-5755
E-mail: vermont@paralegals.org
URL: www.vtparalegal.org
Social Media: www.facebook.com/Vermont-Paralegal
-Organization-163232993708517

11802 ■ Vermont Paralegal Organization Paralegal Certification Scholarship *(Undergraduate/ Scholarship)*

Purpose: To promote excellence in the paralegal profession, and support those who are want to take the paralegal certification. **Focus:** Paralegal studies. **Qualif.:** Applicants must be a member of the VPO; meeting educational and experience requirements for the Paralegal Advance Competency Exam. **Criteria:** Selection will be based on the quality of submitted essays, individual's academic achievement, and financial need.

Funds Avail.: $250. **To Apply:** Applicants will be required to submit a written application; scholarship recipient will have one (1) year to utilize this scholarship and complete the process of taking the exam. **Deadline:** March 30; June 30; September 30; December 30. **Contact:** Submissions must be sent to the following:VPO Paralegal Certification Ambassador, at the above address.

11803 ■ Vesalius Trust (VT)

1 Ridge Ct.
Placitas, NM 87043
Fax: (888)519-4088
Free: 888-844-5755
URL: www.vesaliustrust.org

Awards are arranged alphabetically below their administering organizations

Social Media: www.facebook.com/VesaliusTrust
www.instagram.com/vesaliustrust

11804 ■ Inez Demonet Scholarship (Graduate/ Scholarship)

Purpose: To support students with promising contributions to the profession of medical illustration. **Focus:** Illustrators and illustrations. **Qualif.:** Applicant must be a second year graduate student enrolled in a medical illustration program accredited by the accreditation review committee for the medical illustrators (ARC-MI) and commission on accreditation of the Allied Health Education Program (CAAHEP).**Criteria:** Selection is based on academic breadth and depth, academic performance, quality of artwork, quality of references and evidence of broad-based interests and accomplishments.

Funds Avail.: $2,000. **Duration:** One academic year. **To Apply:** Applicant must prepare a resume (one page); transcripts; references; portfolio of five portfolio pieces; and an essay. Application form is available on the website.

11805 ■ Vesalius Trust Student Research Scholarship Program (Graduate, Undergraduate/Scholarship)

Purpose: To support students enrolled in medical illustration programs. **Focus:** Illustrators and illustrations. **Qualif.:** Applicants must be enrolled in a undergraduate or graduate program in biocommunication at the time of award (spring of the following year) or medical illustration program and must have completed one year of the curriculum. **Criteria:** Applicants are judged based on background, education and project concept, design and production plan.

Funds Avail.: No specific amount. **Duration:** Annual. **To Apply:** Applicants must submit an application form; a resume; graduate project description; budget and timeline; transcripts; preceptor form and faculty advisor form. **Deadline:** November 15. **Contact:** Chris Smith Co-Chair 404 E 73rd St. Apt. 5 New York, NY 10021 Josh Bird Co-Chair vtscholarship2018@gmail.com.

11806 ■ VeteranAid.org
77560 Northcross Dr., Ste. 101
Austin, TX 78757
Free: 866-584-7191
URL: www.veteranaid.org

11807 ■ Veteran Benefits Scholarship (Community College, Four Year College, Graduate/Scholarship)

Purpose: To provide students with financial help to expand their knowledge. **Focus:** General studies/Field of study not specified. **Qualif.:** Applicants must be a citizen or a permanent resident of the United States or Canada; currently enrolled in a certificate program, associate's degree, bachelor's degree, or graduate-level program at an accredited 2-year college or 4-year university.

Funds Avail.: $2,000. **Duration:** Annual. **To Apply:** Write a short (up to 150 words) autobiography as well as an essay (500-750 words) responding to the prompt, "Give an example of one veterans benefit and explain how it helps senior veterans. Then propose your own benefit to help senior veterans".

11808 ■ Veterans of Foreign Wars (VFW)
406 W 34th St.
Kansas City, MO 64111
Ph: (816)756-3390

E-mail: foundation@vfw.org
URL: www.vfw.org
Social Media: www.facebook.com/VFWFans
instagram.com/vfwhq
www.linkedin.com/company/vfwhq
youtube.com/c/vfwhq

11809 ■ VFW Voice of Democracy (Undergraduate/ Scholarship)

Purpose: To provide students the opportunity to pursue their next level of education. **Focus:** Youth. **Qualif.:** Applicants must be students in grades 9-12; enrolled in a public, private or parochial high school or home study program in the United States and its territories. **Criteria:** Selection will be based on treatment of the theme should show imagination and human interest; clearly express ideas in an organized manner; and speak in a clear and credible manner.

Funds Avail.: $30,000. **Duration:** Annual. **Number Awarded:** Varies. **To Apply:** Applicants must complete an application form; record their reading of the draft to an audio CD or flash drive; recording can be no shorter than three minutes and no longer than five minutes (plus or minus five seconds). **Deadline:** October 31. **Remarks:** Established in 1947.

11810 ■ Veterans Health Administration - Office of Research and Development - Health Services Research and Development Service - Center for Organization, Leadership, and Management Research (COLMR)
VA Boston Health Care System (152M)
150 S Huntington Ave.
Boston, MA 02130
URL: www.colmr.research.va.gov
Social Media: www.facebook.com/VeteransAffairs
twitter.com/DeptVetAffairs

11811 ■ CHOIR MD Post-Residency Fellowship in Health Services Research (Postdoctorate/Fellowship)

Purpose: To provide post-residency training and research opportunities for physicians and other health professionals. **Focus:** Health care services. **Qualif.:** Applicants must be US citizens and must have completed an ACGME-approved residency. **Criteria:** Selection will be based on the committee's criteria.

To Apply: Applicants must submit a letter of interest with a CV and a brief statement of prior research training and experience, reasons for seeking fellowships, specific health services research interests, goals for the fellowship and overall career objectives; must also indicates whether they are applying to the Boston or Bedford site.

11812 ■ Veterinary Orthopedic Society (VOS)
PO Box 705
Okemos, MI 48805
Ph: (517)597-0047
E-mail: secretary@vosdvm.org
URL: www.vosdvm.org
Social Media: www.facebook.com/Veterinary-Orthopedic
-Society-136061949852076
twitter.com/vosdvm

Awards are arranged alphabetically below their administering organizations

11813 ■ Wade O. Brinker Resident Research Award
(Postgraduate, Professional development/Grant)

Purpose: To foster research related to musculoskeletal problems confronting veterinarians today. **Focus:** Veterinary science and medicine. **Qualif.:** Applicants must be individuals planning or conducting research in the field of orthopedics; principal investigators must be active members of the VOS as of 1st of September in the year of application (resident is designated as the principal investigator); proposed research should be completed during the Principal Investigator's residency training program. **Criteria:** Selection will be evaluated for the following criteria: scientific and technical quality of the idea; scientific and technological quality of the method; relevance to VOS goals and priorities; feasibility of accomplishing objectives within the proposed time line and; relevance of objectives to current literature.

Funds Avail.: $12,000. **Duration:** Annual. **Number Awarded:** 1. **To Apply:** Application form and details are available at www.vosdvm.org/hohn-johnson-brinker-awards. **Deadline:** September 15. **Contact:** Ashlee Watts, VOS Research Chairman; Email: awatts@cvm.tamu.edu.

11814 ■ Hohn-Johnson Research Award *(Professional development/Grant)*

Purpose: To foster research related to musculoskeletal problems confronting veterinarians. **Focus:** Veterinary science and medicine. **Qualif.:** Applicants must be active members of the VOS as of 1st of September in the year of application. **Criteria:** Selection will be evaluated for the following criteria: scientific and technical quality of the idea; scientific and technological quality of the method; relevance to VOS goals and priorities; feasibility of accomplishing objectives within the proposed time line and; relevance of objectives to current literature.

Funds Avail.: $40,000. **Duration:** Annual. **Number Awarded:** 1. **To Apply:** Application form and details are available at www.vosdvm.org/hohn-johnson-brinker-awards. **Deadline:** September 15. **Contact:** Ashlee Watts, VOS Research Chairman; Email: awatts@cvm.tamu.edu.

11815 ■ Viber Out
800 Concar Dr.
San Mateo, CA 94402
Ph: (415)852-6400
URL: viber.com
Social Media: facebook.com/viber
instagram.com/viber
linkedin.com/company/rakuten-viber
twitter.com/Viber

11816 ■ Viber Mobile Technology Scholarship
(Graduate/Scholarship)

Purpose: To help students gain a college education. **Focus:** General studies/Field of study not specified. **Qualif.:** Applicant must be a U.S. citizen and enrolled in higher education in an undergraduate or graduate program. **Criteria:** Selection is based on the essay which should be factual, original, and engaging.

Funds Avail.: $1,000. **Number Awarded:** 3. **To Apply:** Applicant must submit a 400-500 word essay on how they believe mobile technology will change in the next ten years. Essay should be in a Word document and emailed to scholarship@viber.com along with a 50-100 word personal introduction. **Deadline:** June 1. **Contact:** URL: account.viber.com/en/scholarship.

11817 ■ Victoria University - Centre for Reformation and Renaissance Studies (CRRS)
E. J. Pratt Library, Rm. 301
71 Queen's Park Cres. E
Toronto, ON, Canada M5S 1K7
Ph: (416)585-4468
Fax: (416)585-4430
E-mail: crrs.info@utoronto.ca
URL: crrs.ca
Social Media: www.facebook.com/crrs.utoronto

11818 ■ The RSA-Centre for Reformation and Renaissance Studies (CRRS) Grant (CRRS)
(Doctorate/Grant)

Purpose: To support one-month residence of full-time research in the Centre for Reformation and Renaissance Studies collection. **Focus:** European studies. **Qualif.:** Applicants must be faculty and other individuals who have completed their graduate training.

Funds Avail.: $3,000 (for a researcher traveling from within North America); $4,000 (for a researcher traveling from outside of North America). **Duration:** Annual. **To Apply:** Applicants must submit project description, curriculum vitae, relevance of collection(s) to project. **Deadline:** September 7.

11819 ■ Vietnamese American Bar Association of Northern California (VABANC)
772 N 1st St.
San Jose, CA 95112
Ph: (408)975-9321
URL: vabanc.org
Social Media: www.facebook.com/VABANC
www.linkedin.com/company/vabanc-law-foundation/about
twitter.com/vabanc

11820 ■ VABANC Scholarships *(Graduate, Undergraduate/Scholarship)*

Purpose: To provide assistance to students with their public interest or social justice goals. **Focus:** Law. **Qualif.:** Applicants must be all currently enrolled law students who have demonstrated a commitment to serving the needs of the Vietnamese-American and Vietnamese communities. **Criteria:** Priority will be given to those who have demonstrated a commitment to serving the Vietnamese-American community in Northern California and to those who will be using the scholarship award to further their public interest or social justice work, either by pursuing post-graduate work or for a summer position.

Funds Avail.: $1,000 to $4,000 each. **Duration:** Annual. **Number Awarded:** 2. **To Apply:** Applicants must submit a completed application form along with a resume; three academic and/or professional references; and a personal statement of no more than 800 words describing the following: pressing concerns faced by the Vietnamese-American community, and how they will contribute to or engage in addressing such concerns. and/or; their contributions to or activism within the Vietnamese-American community, and/or; their experiences in overcoming socioeconomic and/or other barriers, and/or; identifying a public-service legal project (internship, fellowship, etc.) which you are or will be

Awards are arranged alphabetically below their administering organizations

involved in, and how this scholarship would enable you to execute that project. **Deadline:** July 2. **Contact:** E-mail: scholarships@vabanc.org.

11821 ■ Vietnamese American Scholarship Foundation (VASF)

PO Box 429
Stafford, TX 77497
E-mail: scholarships@vietscholarships.org
URL: www.vietscholarships.org

11822 ■ Danny T. Le Memorial Scholarship
(Undergraduate/Scholarship)

Purpose: To provide financial assistance to students of Vietnamese descent from the Greater Houston area for pursuing further education. **Focus:** General studies/Field of study not specified. **Qualif.:** Applicant must be graduated or who will be graduating from a high school in the Greater Houston Area; pursuing a degree at an accredited 4-year college or university; of Vietnamese descent. **Criteria:** Selection will be based on academic excellence;compassion and desire to help others;strong will and determination to achieve your goals.

Funds Avail.: $2,000. **Duration:** Annual. **Number Awarded:** 1. **Deadline:** June 30. **Remarks:** The Scholarship was established in honor of Danny Thanh Le by his friends and family. **Contact:** Email: dannylescholarship@vietscholarships.org.

11823 ■ Le Hoang Nguyen College Scholarships (LHN) *(Undergraduate/Scholarship)*

Purpose: To provide financial assistance to outstanding graduating high school seniors attending college in the upcoming fall semester. **Focus:** General studies/Field of study not specified. **Criteria:** Applicants are evaluated based on academic achievement and financial need.

Funds Avail.: $500. **Duration:** Annual. **Number Awarded:** 1. **To Apply:** Applicants must submit online application form along with resume, three essays in one word document, high school transcript (unofficial transcripts are acceptable) and a letter of recommendation. **Deadline:** June 30. **Contact:** Email: scholarship@vietscholarships.org.

11824 ■ The Thuy Nguyen Scholarships *(High School/Scholarship)*

Purpose: To provide financial assistance to high school senior students for furthering their education. **Focus:** General studies/Field of study not specified. **Qualif.:** Applicants must be graduating high school seniors from Houston or the surrounding area; must have a cumulative GPA of 3.5 or higher; must be descendants of at least one Vietnamese parent; and must have a family annual income of less than $40,000. **Criteria:** Applicants are evaluated based on financial need.

Funds Avail.: $2,000. **Number Awarded:** 1. **To Apply:** Applicants must complete the online application with resume, essay with a cover letter; must submit a transcript of records, recommendation and a copy of their parent's W-2 forms and a photo. **Contact:** All questions can be directed to scholarships; Email: katielyntrinh@hotmail.com.

11825 ■ Vera Tran Memorial Scholarships
(Undergraduate/Scholarship)

Purpose: To provide financial assistance to graduating high school seniors of Vietnamese descent wishing to pursue further education. **Focus:** General studies/Field of study not specified. **Qualif.:** Applicants must be of Vietnamese descent, graduating high school seniors from Houston or the surrounding area who are planning to pursue an education at an accredited four-year college or university. **Criteria:** Applicants are evaluated based on demonstrated dedication to academic excellence; passion for learning; compassion and desire to help others; pursuit of their dreams; and proven leadership.

Funds Avail.: $2,000. **Duration:** Annual. **Number Awarded:** 1. **To Apply:** Applicants must complete the online application and submit it with their resume; must also send one transcript and recommendation. **Deadline:** May 31. **Contact:** All questions can be directed to scholarships@vietscholarships.org.

11826 ■ Violin Society of America (VSA)

14070 Proton Rd., Ste. 100
Dallas, TX 75244
Ph: (972)233-9107
E-mail: info@vsaweb.org
URL: www.vsaweb.org
Social Media: www.instagram.com/violinsocietyofamerica/

11827 ■ Violin Society of America Scholarships
(Undergraduate/Scholarship)

Purpose: To provide financial assistance for needy and deserving students of the art of violin and bow-making and restoration. **Focus:** Music. **Qualif.:** Applicant must be a U.S. citizen; a student who has satisfactorily completed at least one full year of study in the program and has shown serious effort, talent and future promise and has financial need. **Criteria:** Selection will be evaluated by the administrator of the program and will be recommended to the VSA.

Funds Avail.: No specific amount. **Duration:** Annual. **Number Awarded:** Varies. **To Apply:** The application process is online. **Remarks:** The scholarship was renamed to honor Ann Shaw who distinguished herself as writer, speaker, researcher, consultant and program developer, college and university teacher and an extraordinary international organizer.

11828 ■ Virgin Islands Bar Association (VIBA)

2155 King Cross St., Ste. 2
Christiansted, VI 00822
Ph: (340)778-7497
Fax: (340)773-5060
E-mail: info@vibar.org
URL: www.vibar.org
Social Media: www.facebook.com/VIBarAssociation

11829 ■ Almeric L. Christian Memorial Scholarship
(Graduate/Scholarship)

Purpose: To provide financial assistance to Virgin Islands residents who desire to attend law school and to return home to live and work. **Focus:** Law. **Qualif.:** Applicant must be a college graduate who has been accepted to or is attending a law school accredited by the American Bar Association; must be permanent resident of the United States Virgin Islands and plan to engage in the practice of law in the United States Virgin Islands within three years of graduation from law school; those already attending law school must have a 2.75 GPA and those who have not yet started law study must have at least 3.25 GPA. **Criteria:** Selection is based on the application.

Awards are arranged alphabetically below their administering organizations

Funds Avail.: $15,000. **Duration:** Annual. **To Apply:** Applicants must submit a completed application form along with a letter of acceptance to a law school or most recent transcript if already enrolled in a law school; three letters of recommendation, one from a former college or law school professor and the rest from individuals that are not related to the applicants by blood or marriage; an essay on career objectives and how the schooling plan will prepare the applicants to attain these goals (typewritten); official copy of undergraduate college transcript (if entering the first year of law school) or a copy of latest official transcript (if presently attending law school); and a copy of student financial aid form (FAF), or the equivalent thereof. **Deadline:** 'June 30; November 15. **Contact:** Scholarship Committee, Virgin Islands Bar Association, PO Box 224108, Christiansted, VI, 00822.

11830 ■ Virginia Association of Chiefs of Police (VACP)

880 Technology Pk. Dr., Ste. 100
Glen Allen, VA 23059
Ph: (804)285-8227
Fax: (804)285-3363
URL: www.vachiefs.org
Social Media: www.facebook.com/vachiefs
twitter.com/vachiefs

11831 ■ Lex T. Eckenrode Scholarship for PELS
(Professional development/Scholarship)

Purpose: To support individuals attending the Professional Executive Leadership School (PELS). **Focus:** Education; Law enforcement. **Qualif.:** Applications are available for small departments (35 or less sworn force); and/or graduate of the Institute for Leadership in Changing Times (ILCT); must be a sworn law-enforcement officer employed in the Commonwealth of Virginia. **Criteria:** Selection will be based on community/civic involvement; essay; chief executive's endorsement; letter of recommendation; and financial need.

Funds Avail.: Up to $1,000. **Duration:** Annual. **Number Awarded:** 1. **To Apply:** Applicants must submit an original typed application endorsed by the chief executive of their agency; an original typed essay (1, 000 words or less, double-spaced and typed using Times New Roman font, type size 11, black ink - See "Submit an Essay" section of application); and letter of recommendation from the agency chief executive (or the city/town manager if the applicant is the agency chief executive).

11832 ■ Virginia Dental Hygienist's Association Foundation

638 Independence Pkwy., Ste. 100
Chesapeake, VA 23320
Ph: (757)609-3661
E-mail: cmatthews@managegroup.com
URL: vdha.wildapricot.org
Social Media: twitter.com/VDHA

11833 ■ Alice Hinchcliffe Williams, RDH, MS Merit Scholarship *(Graduate/Scholarship)*

Purpose: To provide support and serve as the primary provider of lifelong learning for dental hygienists throughout Virginia. **Focus:** Dental hygiene. **Criteria:** Applicants will be evaluated based on merit, fulfillment of the required criteria and approval of the written narrative.

Funds Avail.: $1,500. **Duration:** Annual. **To Apply:** Applicants must complete the application form and must submit a narrative. **Deadline:** February 1. **Remarks:** The Scholarship is honored in the memory of Alice Hinchcliffe Williams.

11834 ■ Virginia Historical Society

428 N Arthur Ashe Boulevard
Richmond, VA 23220
Ph: (804)340-1800
Free: 800-358-8701
URL: www.virginiahistory.org
Social Media: www.facebook.com/Virginia-Historical
   -Society-29594152350
www.instagram.com/virginiahistory
www.pinterest.com/virginiahistory
twitter.com/virginiamuseum

11835 ■ Betty Sams Christian Fellowships
(Doctorate/Fellowship)

Purpose: To help scholars with their research and travel expenses. **Focus:** History, American. **Qualif.:** Applicants must be doctoral candidates; undergraduates, master's students, and graduate students not yet admitted to Ph.D. candidacy are not eligible. **Criteria:** Selection is based on scholarly qualifications, the merits of the proposals and the appropriateness of the topics as demonstrated by citation to specific sources in the collections.

Funds Avail.: $150/week for mileage to commuting researchers who live outside the area; $500/week for those who live farther away. **Duration:** Three weeks. **To Apply:** Applicants must submit an original and three copies of a cover letter; a resume; two letters of recommendation (may be sent separately); and a description of the research project (not longer than two double-spaced pages). **Deadline:** January 24. **Contact:** Email: fellowships@VirginiaHistory.org.

11836 ■ Virginia Lakes and Watershed Association (VLWA)

c/o Shelly Frie
5700 Cleveland St., Ste. 101
Virginia Beach, VA 23462
Ph: (757)671-6222
URL: www.vlwa.org
Social Media: www.facebook.com/
   virginialakesandwatersheds/
twitter.com/VLWA

11837 ■ Leo Bourassa Scholarship *(Undergraduate, Graduate/Scholarship)*

Purpose: To support and acknowledge students for academic and personal accomplishments in the field of water resources. **Focus:** Water resources. **Qualif.:** Applicants must be full-time undergraduate or full- or part-time graduate students enrolled in a curriculum related to water resources; must be students in good standing at any Virginia accredited college or university; must be residents of Virginia at the time of application and at the time of award; undergraduate students must have successfully completed at least two semesters. **Criteria:** Recipients will be evaluated based on academic performance, educational plans and contribution to the field of water resources, and related extra-curricular activities.

Awards are arranged alphabetically below their administering organizations

Funds Avail.: From $500 to $3,000. **Duration:** Annual. **Number Awarded:** Up to 8. **To Apply:** Applicant must complete the application form; must attach a copy of current college transcripts, list of clubs and organizations related to water resources as proof of being a member, description of experience(s) in water resources and watershed management, no more than one-page explaining why applicant deserves to get the scholarship. A minimum of two letters of recommendations from non-family members should be signed and mailed. **Deadline:** April 1. **Contact:** Shelly Frie; Phone: 757-671-6222, Email: scholarship@vlwa.org.

11838 ■ Virginia Museum of Fine Arts (VMFA)

200 N Arthur Ashe Blvd
Richmond, VA 23220-4007
Ph: (804)340-1400
E-mail: visitorservices@vmfa.museum
URL: www.vmfa.museum
Social Media: www.facebook.com/myVMFA
www.instagram.com/vmfamuseum
twitter.com/vmfa
www.youtube.com/user/virginiamuseum

11839 ■ Virginia Museum of Fine Arts Visual Arts Fellowships *(Graduate, Other, Undergraduate/ Fellowship)*

Purpose: To support professional artists and art students who demonstrate exceptional creative ability in their chosen field. **Focus:** Art history; Visual arts. **Qualif.:** Applicants must be undergraduate or graduate students enrolled full-time in a degree-seeking program at an accredited university, college, or school of the arts; professional applicants must not be enrolled in a degree-seeking program; college-bound high school seniors are also eligible to apply; must be legal residents of Virginia. **Criteria:** Awards will be given to those applicants of the highest artistic merit.

Funds Avail.: $4,000 (undergraduates); $6,000 (graduates); $8,000 (professionals). **To Apply:** Applicants must complete the required fields on the application form. Crafts, Drawing, Painting, Photography and Sculpture applicants must submit a work sample consists of eight digital images, at least six must represent individual works and two images for details; professional applicants must submit all works that have been completed in the past three years; must submit at least four sample works. Submit images on a PC-formatted CD-R, labeled with the applicant's name; format digital images as JPEGs, no larger than 2 MB and 1000 pixels on the longest side; Mixed Media applicants must submit six images representing individual works plus two images for details; Film/Video applicants must submit a 15-minute (maximum) DVD sample of three work; should be on a PC-formatted DVD, labeled with applicant's name and must include a menu on a DVD with links to each work and running times; format submissions as files that are compatible with both QuickTime and RealPlayer; Art History applicants must submit two hard copies of the three research papers or published articles; must submit a current resume, one-page artistic statement for professionals and transcript of records for students; SASE envelope and confirmation postcard are optional. **Deadline:** November 6. **Remarks:** Established in 1940. **Contact:** Sara Mazullo l Fellowship Program Coordinator; Phone: 804-204-2685; Email: vmfafellowships@vmfa.museum.

11840 ■ Virginia Section: American Water Works Association (VAAWWA)

PO Box 11992
Lynchburg, VA 24506
Ph: (434)386-3190
URL: www.vaawwa.org

11841 ■ VA AWWA Graduate Student Scholarships *(Graduate/Scholarship)*

Purpose: To provide assistance to students pursuing a career in the water industry. **Focus:** Water resources; Water supply industry. **Qualif.:** Applicants must be full- or part-time graduate students who are also members of AWWA, attending school in Virginia, with the intention of a career in the water industry. **Criteria:** Selection will be based on merit.

Funds Avail.: $2,500. **Duration:** Annual. **Number Awarded:** 2. **To Apply:** Applicants should submit the following requirements resume indicating their academic and extracurricular performance and activities; unofficial or official up-to-date transcript or official semester schedule of school currently attending; completed VAAWWA Student Scholarship application; membership in the American Water Works Association; a reference letter from an instructor or professor; and 1000 word essay on a water topic of their choice; should be submitted electronically. **Deadline:** May 29. **Contact:** Mark Titcomb; Email: mtitcomb@nnva.gov; geneva.hudgins@vaawwa.org; or Geneva Hudgins; Email: geneva.hudgins@vaawwa.org.

11842 ■ Virginia Society of Certified Public Accountants (VSCPA)

4309 Cox Rd.
Glen Allen, VA 23060
Fax: (804)273-1741
Free: 800-733-8272
E-mail: vscpa@vscpa.com
URL: www.vscpa.com
Social Media: www.facebook.com/VSCPA
www.instagram.com/vscpa
www.linkedin.com/company/vscpa
twitter.com/VSCPANews
www.youtube.com/user/VSCPAVideos

11843 ■ H. Burton Bates Jr. Scholarships *(Graduate, Undergraduate/Scholarship)*

Purpose: To provide financial support to students pursuing a degree in accounting. **Focus:** Accounting. **Qualif.:** Applicants must be U.S. citizens; must have successfully completed 3 credit hours of accounting prior to the fall semester; current enrollment in an accredited Virginia college or university with the intent to pursue a degree in accounting; must be enrolled full-time in the semester as a junior or senior undergraduate accounting major or have earned an undergraduate degree from an accredited Virginia college or university and enrolled at least part-time (as defined by the institution) in the semester completing additional coursework in order to take the CPA Exam and must demonstrate a minimum overall and accounting GPA of 3.0. **Criteria:** Selection is based on the application materials submitted.

Funds Avail.: $2,250 each. **Duration:** Annual; one academic year. **To Apply:** Applicants must submit a completed application including the following: college

Awards are arranged alphabetically below their administering organizations

transcript(s), unofficial transcripts are acceptable; one-page resume, include info on community service, academic organizations and activities; recommendation from an accounting faculty member. **Remarks:** The scholarship is funded by the children of H. Burton Bates Jr., CPA, a VSCPA life member.

11844 ■ Thomas M. Berry Jr. Scholarships *(Graduate, Undergraduate/Scholarship)*

Purpose: To provide financial support to students pursuing a degree in accounting. **Focus:** Accounting. **Qualif.:** Applicants must be U.S. citizens; must have successfully completed 3 credit hours of accounting prior to the fall semester; current enrollment in an accredited Virginia college or university with the intent to pursue a degree in accounting; must be enrolled in the semester as an accounting major with intent to take the CPA exam and must demonstrate a minimum overall and accounting GPA of 3.0.

Funds Avail.: $3,000 each. **Duration:** Annual; one academic year. **Number Awarded:** 2. **To Apply:** Applicants must submit a completed application including the following: college transcript(s), unofficial transcripts are acceptable; one-page resume, include info on community service, academic organizations and activities; recommendation from an accounting faculty member. **Deadline:** April 1. **Remarks:** The scholarship is funded by friends, family and colleagues of Thomas M. Berry Jr., who retired as president & CEO of the VSCPA in April 2007.

11845 ■ Dixon Hughes Goodman Scholarships *(Undergraduate, Graduate/Scholarship)*

Purpose: To financially support undergraduate accounting students. **Focus:** Accounting. **Qualif.:** Applicants must be U.S. citizens; applicants must be currently enrolled or have been accepted in an accounting program at a Virginia college or university. **Criteria:** selection criteria for the awards include overall academic performance, entry essay, faculty recommendation(s) and community and/or extracurricular activities.

Funds Avail.: $2,250 each. **Duration:** Annual. **Number Awarded:** 2. **Remarks:** Two scholarships are funded by Dixon Hughes Goodman.

11846 ■ Virginia Tech Doctoral Scholarship *(Doctorate/Scholarship)*

Purpose: To provide financial support to students pursuing a doctoral degree in accounting. **Focus:** Accounting. **Qualif.:** Applicants must be U.S. citizens; must be accepted or currently enrolled in the doctoral accounting program at Virginia Tech. **Criteria:** Selection is based on the application materials submitted.

Funds Avail.: $3,000. **Duration:** Annual; one academic year. **Number Awarded:** 2. **To Apply:** Applicants must contact Tracey Zink to be considered for the scholarship. **Contact:** Molly Wash; Email: mwash@vscpa.com.

11847 ■ VSCPA Educational Foundation Minority Accounting Scholarship *(Graduate, Undergraduate/Scholarship)*

Purpose: To financially support minority accounting students. **Focus:** Accounting.

Funds Avail.: range of $1,500 to $2,000. **Duration:** Annual; one academic year. **To Apply:** Applicants must submit a completed application including the following: college transcript(s), unofficial transcripts are acceptable; one-page

resume, include info on community service, academic organizations and activities; recommendation from an accounting faculty member. **Contact:** VSCPA Educational Foundation, Inc, PO Box 4620, Glen Allen, VA, 23058-4620.

11848 ■ VSCPA Educational Foundation Undergraduate Accounting Scholarships *(Undergraduate/Scholarship)*

Purpose: To financially support undergraduate accounting students. **Focus:** Accounting. **Qualif.:** Applicants must be U.S. citizens; currently enrolled in an accredited Virginia college/university undergraduate program with the intent to pursue a bachelor's degree in accounting; must have completed at least three hours of accounting and be currently registered for at least three more accounting credit hours (supporting documentation required) and must demonstrate a minimum overall and accounting GPA of 3.0. **Criteria:** Selection is based on demonstrated academic excellence and financial need.

Funds Avail.: $1,500. **Duration:** Annual; one academic year. **Number Awarded:** Varies. **To Apply:** Applicants must submit a completed application including the following: college transcript(s), unofficial transcripts are acceptable; one-page resume, include info on community service, academic organizations and activities; recommendation from an accounting faculty member.

11849 ■ VSCPA Graduate and PhD Accounting Scholarship *(Doctorate, Graduate/Scholarship)*

Purpose: To financially support graduate and PhD students pursuing an advanced degree in accounting. **Focus:** Accounting. **Qualif.:** Applicants must be U.S. citizens; must have successfully completed 3 credit hours of accounting prior to the fall semester; current enrollment in an accredited Virginia college or university with the intent to pursue a degree in accounting; must demonstrate a minimum overall and accounting GPA of 3.0 and must be enrolled in a graduate or Ph.D. program. **Criteria:** Selection is based on demonstrated academic excellence and financial need.

Funds Avail.: $2,000. **Duration:** Annual; one academic year. **To Apply:** Applicants must submit a completed application including the following: college transcript(s), unofficial transcripts are acceptable; one-page resume, include info on community service, academic organizations and activities; recommendation from an accounting faculty member. **Deadline:** April 1.

11850 ■ Yount, Hyde & Barbour Scholarships *(Undergraduate, Graduate/Scholarship)*

Purpose: To provide financial support to students pursuing a degree in accounting. **Focus:** Accounting. **Qualif.:** Applicants must be U.S. citizens; must be juniors or seniors accounting majors currently enrolled at an accredited Virginia college/university with the intent of taking the CPA exam; must be enrolled in the fall semester as a junior, senior or "fifth year" undergraduate or graduate accounting major with the intent to take the CPA exam; and must demonstrate a minimum overall and accounting GPA of 3.0. **Criteria:** Selection is based on demonstrated academic excellence and financial need.

Funds Avail.: $3,000. **Duration:** Annual. **Remarks:** This scholarship is funded by Yount, Hyde & Barbour.

11851 ■ Virtuous Prom
2088 E Lakeshore Dr.
Lake Elsinore, CA 92530

Awards are arranged alphabetically below their administering organizations

Ph: (801)349-9758
E-mail: virtuousprom@gmail.com
URL: www.virtuousprom.com
Social Media: www.facebook.com/virtuousprom
instagram.com/virtuousprom
twitter.com/Virtuous_Prom

11852 ■ The Virtuous Prom Peace Scholarship
(Undergraduate, Graduate, Postgraduate/Scholarship)

Purpose: To provide financial assistance to female college students studying theology, anthropology, psychology, or sociology. **Focus:** Anthropology; Psychology; Sociology; Theology. **Qualif.:** Applicants must be female; planning to or currently pursuing studies in theology, anthropology, psychology, or sociology, either at the undergraduate, graduate, or post-graduate level. **Criteria:** Coherency and persuasiveness of essay.

Funds Avail.: $250. **Duration:** Annual. **To Apply:** Submit essay of at least 500 words answering the prompt, "In a world that is devastated almost daily by acts of extreme violence in the name of religion or against those of different ethnicity, how can a solid education in theology, anthropology, psychology, or sociology enable you to promote peace, understanding, tolerance and kindness not only at an academic level, but also in your day to day life?". **Deadline:** January 31. **Contact:** Email: scholarships@virtuousprom.com.

11853 ■ Vision Tech Camps
117 Town & Country Dr., Ste. B
Danville, CA 94526
Ph: (925)699-9602
E-mail: inquiry@visiontechcamps.com
URL: www.visiontechcamps.com
Social Media: www.facebook.com/vtcamps
www.linkedin.com/company/vision-tech-camps
twitter.com/visiontechcamps

11854 ■ Vision Tech Camps Scholarship *(Community College, Four Year College/Scholarship)*

Purpose: To encourage more students to make technology a part of their education. **Focus:** Computer and information sciences; Engineering; Graphic art and design; Science. **Qualif.:** Applicants must be enrolled at a university or community college in a field related to technology, including computer science, computer engineering, sciences, engineering, graphic design, or a closely related field; must not have a close relative working at Vision Tech Camps. **Criteria:** Selection will be made by the selection committee.

Funds Avail.: $500-$1,000. **Number Awarded:** 3. **To Apply:** Applicant must include a completed version of the Vision Tech application form; a resume; academic transcripts; optional letters of recommendation (up to 3); optional submission describing your work or a Youtube Video showcasing your work (2 minutes or shorter); access application at www.visiontechcamps.com/scholarship. **Deadline:** August 1. **Contact:** Email: scholarships@visiontechcamps.com.

11855 ■ Visionary Integration Professionals L.L.C.
80 Iron Point Cir., Ste. 100
Folsom, CA 95630

Ph: (916)985-9625
URL: www.trustvip.com
Social Media: www.facebook.com/VisionaryIntegrationProfessionalsVIP
www.linkedin.com/company/visionary-integration-professionals-vip-
twitter.com/trustvip

11856 ■ VIP Women in Technology Scholarship
(Two Year College, Undergraduate, Graduate/Scholarship)

Purpose: To interest, encourage, and assist women in entering into careers in computer science, cybersecurity, information technology, management information systems, or related fields. **Focus:** Computer and information sciences; Information science and technology. **Qualif.:** Applicants must be women enrolled at or accepted into either a two or four-year college or university in the United States for the upcoming school year and planning a career in computer science, information technology, management information services, or related fields; must have a minimum 3.0 GPA. **Criteria:** Selection will be based on GPA, thoughtful answers to the essay question, and level of participation in community service and/or extracurricular activities.

Funds Avail.: $1,000 to $2,500. **Duration:** Annual. **Number Awarded:** 12. **To Apply:** Downloaded at www.trustvip.com/company/community-service-and-support or requested through email. Completed applications, transcripts, essay,and other required documentation should be submitted via email. **Deadline:** April 1. **Contact:** Email: VITS@trustvip.com.

11857 ■ John D. Voelker Foundation
PO Box 15222
Lansing, MI 48901-5222
Ph: (616)897-4036
URL: www.voelkerfoundation.com
Social Media: www.facebook.com/The-John-D-Voelker-Foundation-169598579739889
twitter.com/jdvoelkerfdn

11858 ■ John D. Voelker Foundation Native American Scholarships *(Undergraduate/Scholarship)*
Purpose: To assist Native American students to pursue the dream of a legal education. **Focus:** Law; Paralegal studies. **Qualif.:** Applicants must be Native American students attending law school.

Duration: Annual. **To Apply:** Application information available by contacting the foundation.

11859 ■ Voice Talent Online
52 Bath St.
Gravesend DA11 0DF, United Kingdom
Ph: 44 1474 747 231
Free: 800-423-7048
E-mail: studio@voicetalentonline.com
URL: voicetalentonline.com
Social Media: www.facebook.com/VoiceTalentOnline
twitter.com/VoiceTalentVTO

11860 ■ Voice Talent Online Scholarship *(College, University, Undergraduate/Scholarship)*
Purpose: To assist students with education costs. **Focus:** General studies/Field of study not specified. **Qualif.:** Ap-

Awards are arranged alphabetically below their administering organizations

plicant must be enrolled in a college or university. **Criteria:** Entries will be judged based on entertainment value, quality, and popularity.

Funds Avail.: $1,000. **Number Awarded:** 2. **To Apply:** Application must be completed online; write a 300-600 word blog post. **Deadline:** January 31. **Contact:** Email:marketing@voicetalentonline.com; URL: www.voicetalentonline.com/voice-over-agency/scholarship-entry.

11861 ■ Voluntary Protection Programs Participants' Association (VPPPA)

7600E Leesburg Pke., Ste. 100
Falls Church, VA 22043-2004
Ph: (703)761-1146
Fax: (703)761-1148
URL: www.vpppa.org
Social Media: www.facebook.com/VPPPA
www.instagram.com/vpppa_inc
www.linkedin.com/company/vpppa-inc-
twitter.com/VPPPA
www.youtube.com/user/VPPPA

11862 ■ VPPPA June Brothers Scholarship *(Graduate, Undergraduate/Scholarship)*

Purpose: To recognizes students who are leaders and role models in their schools and communities and who are entering either the environmental, safety and health areas or the trades (respectively). **Focus:** Environmental conservation; Occupational safety and health. **Qualif.:** Applicants must be students pursuing a degree (undergraduate or graduate) in the environmental, safety and health areas (either part-time or full-time); must have at least a 2.5 GPA on a scale of 4.0. **Criteria:** Recipients are chosen on the basis of demonstrated occupational safety, health and/or environmental outreach efforts in their schools, communities and/or workplace, leadership skills, extracurricular activities, involvement in professional organizations, communication skills and other awards and honors earned at educational institutions or at their place of employment.

Funds Avail.: $3,500. **Duration:** Annual. **To Apply:** Applicants must submit completed application form available in the website; copy of current transcript; reference letters from the VPPPA site employee and from a high school teacher, university's department head, professor or supervisor at current job. **Deadline:** June 1. **Remarks:** Established in 2005.

11863 ■ VPPPA Stephen Brown Scholarship *(Graduate, Undergraduate/Scholarship)*

Purpose: To recognizes students who are leaders and role models in their schools and communities and who are the trades. **Focus:** Environmental conservation; Occupational safety and health. **Qualif.:** Applicants must be students pursuing a degree (undergraduate or graduate) in either trades or the environmental, safety and health areas; must be enrolled in or enrolling in a vocational, college or university; must have at least a 2.5 GPA on a scale of 4.0. **Criteria:** Recipients are chosen on the basis of demonstrated occupational safety, health and/or environmental outreach efforts in their schools, communities and/or workplace, leadership skills, extracurricular activities, involvement in professional organizations, communication skills and other awards and honors earned at educational institutions or at their place of employment.

Funds Avail.: $3,500. **Duration:** Annual. **To Apply:** Applicants must submit completed application form available in the website; a typewritten biography of at least 300 words describing interests and accomplishments or current resume; copy of current transcript; reference letters from the VPPPA site employee and from a high school teacher, university's department head, professor or supervisor at current job. **Deadline:** June 1. **Remarks:** Established in 2005.

11864 ■ William "Sully" Sullivan Scholarship *(Graduate, Undergraduate/Scholarship)*

Purpose: To recognize and support employee at a VPPPA full member site who has made significant contributions to the VPP program. **Focus:** Environmental conservation; Occupational safety and health. **Qualif.:** Applicants must be employees enrolled in or enrolling in a vocational school, college or university; must be pursuing a degree (undergraduate or graduate) in the environmental, safety and health areas (either part-time or full-time); must have at least a 2.5 GPA on a scale of 4.0.

Funds Avail.: $3,500. **Duration:** Annual. **To Apply:** Applicants must submit completed application form available in the website; a typewritten biography of at least 300 words describing interests and accomplishments or current resume; copy of current transcript; reference letters from the VPPPA site employee and from a high school teacher, university's department head, professor or supervisor at current job. **Deadline:** June 1. **Remarks:** Established in 2007.

11865 ■ Wakeford Gelini

1388 Sutter Street Suite 810
San Francisco, CA 94109
Ph: (415)569-7495
Social Media: www.facebook.com/wakefordlaw
www.linkedin.com/company/the-wakeford-law-firm

11866 ■ Wakeford Gelini Driver Safety Scholarship *(Undergraduate, Graduate, Vocational/Occupational, College/Scholarship)*

Purpose: To promote driver safety to students. **Focus:** General studies/Field of study not specified. **Qualif.:** Applicant must be a high school senior in the United States who is accepted or waiting acceptance to a university, college, or trade school, or who is currently an undergraduate or graduate student. Applicant must be enrolled by Fall Semester of the awarding year. **Criteria:** Selection will be based on the blog submitted.

Funds Avail.: $1,000. **Number Awarded:** 1. **To Apply:** Applicant must write a 1,000 word blog covering the subject of driver safety; blog should include at least one original graphic or image. Blog should be submitted via: wakefordlaw.com/wakeford-gelini-scholarship/. **Deadline:** August 1.

11867 ■ Wal-Mart Foundation, Inc.

702 SW 8th St.
Bentonville, AR 72716-0555
URL: walmart.org
Social Media: twitter.com/WalmartOrg

11868 ■ Walmart Associate Scholarship *(Undergraduate/Scholarship)*

Purpose: To provide educational grants to deserving students who want to pursue their studies. **Focus:** General

Awards are arranged alphabetically below their administering organizations

studies/Field of study not specified. **Criteria:** Selection will be based on the committee's criteria.

Duration: Quarterly. **To Apply:** Applicants must submit a completed scholarship application available online. **Deadline:** August 31. **Contact:** Phone: 800 311-6823; Email: walmartassociate@applyISTS.com.

11869 ■ Wallace House - University of Michigan

University of Michigan
620 Oxford Rd.
Ann Arbor, MI 48104-2635
Ph: (734)998-7666
Fax: (734)998-7979
URL: wallacehouse.umich.edu

11870 ■ Knight-Wallace Reporting Fellowships
(Professional development/Fellowship)

Purpose: To provide a life-changing experience to journalists from US and abroad. **Focus:** Journalism. **Qualif.:** Applicants must have at least five years of professional experience; must be either a U.S. resident or hold a U.S. passport if working abroad.

Funds Avail.: $80,000. **Duration:** Annual. **Number Awarded:** 10. **To Apply:** Write a reporting proposal of up to 800 words, a personal statement of up to 600 words; provide names, affiliations and email addresses of two professional references; written confirmation from the employer that the applicant will be permitted to make the fellowship reporting their primary focus or written confirmation from a news organization agreeing to publish the work or details on securing a publishing partner.

11871 ■ WarFighters Motorcycle Club, Captain John Odber Chapter

154 E Lafayette Ave., Ste. E
Laurel, MD 20707
Ph: (240)241-4189
URL: www.facebook.com/OdberWFMC
Social Media: facebook.com/help/2687943754764396

11872 ■ WFMC Ride for the Fallen Memorial Scholarship *(Two Year College, Four Year College, Vocational/Occupational/Scholarship)*

Purpose: To help fund college for veterans and their families. **Focus:** General studies/Field of study not specified. **Qualif.:** Applicants must be veterans or family members of a veteran. **Criteria:** Quality of essay.

Funds Avail.: $1,000. **Duration:** Annual. **Number Awarded:** 1. **To Apply:** Submit essay to odberscholarship@gmail.com. **Deadline:** May 26. **Contact:** odberscholarship@gmail.com.

11873 ■ Warner Norcross and Judd L.L.P.

1500 Warner Building 150 Ottawa Avenue, NW
Grand Rapids, MI 49503-2832
Ph: (616)752-2000
Fax: (616)752-2500
URL: www.wnj.com
Social Media: twitter.com/WNJLLP

11874 ■ Warner Norcross & Judd Minority Scholarships *(Undergraduate/Scholarship)*

Purpose: To provide encouragement and financial assistance to students of racial and ethnic minority heritage

pursuing a career in law. **Focus:** Law; Paralegal studies. **Criteria:** Applicants will be selected based on academic standing and financial need.

Funds Avail.: $5,000 to law school students; $2,000 to paralegals/legal assistant students;$1,000 to legal secretarial students. **Duration:** Annual. **To Apply:** Applicants must submit completed application forms; a statement of goals and aspirations related to their studies in the legal profession, and must indicate the reason why they choose the legal profession/field as their area of study; and two letters of reference. **Contact:** Ruth Bishop, Grand Rapids Community Foundation; Email: rbishop@grfoundation.org, or to Rodney Martin, Warner Norcross & Judd LLP; Email: rmartin@wnj.com.

11875 ■ Washburn University School of Law

1700 SW College Ave.
Topeka, KS 66621
Ph: (785)670-1060
Fax: (785)670-3249
URL: washburnlaw.edu
Social Media: www.facebook.com/washburnlawschool
www.linkedin.com/school/washburn-university-school-of
 -law
twitter.com/washburnlaw
www.youtube.com/user/Washburnlaw

11876 ■ J.L. Weigand, Jr. Legal Education Trust Scholarship *(Undergraduate/Scholarship)*

Purpose: To promote excellence in legal education and encourage the most scholastically qualified students who are long-term Kansas residents to remain in or return to Kansas to practice law. **Focus:** Law. **Qualif.:** Applicants must be admitted full-time to Washburn Law; be in the top ten percent of the class; and, have been a legal residents of Kansas for at least ten years prior to their admission to law school. **Criteria:** Selection will be based on merit.

Funds Avail.: No specific amount. **Duration:** Annual. **Number Awarded:** Varies. **To Apply:** Applicants must apply through the Weigand website. **Deadline:** February 15. **Contact:** Preston Nicholson, Assistant Dean for Admissions; Phone: 785-670-1706; Email: preston.nicholson@washburn.edu.

11877 ■ Judge Delmas C. Hill Scholarship *(Undergraduate/Scholarship)*

Purpose: To assist Washburn University students in their education. **Focus:** Law. **Criteria:** Selection will be based on the aforesaid qualifications and other criteria.

Funds Avail.: $15,000 per year. **Duration:** Annual. **Number Awarded:** 1. **To Apply:** Applicants must submit a statement showing the reason for interest in the law as a profession; public and community service activities; leadership activities; and potential for leadership.

11878 ■ Koch Scholars Program *(Undergraduate/ Scholarship)*

Purpose: To assist Washburn University students in their education. **Focus:** Law. **Qualif.:** Applicants to Washburn University School of Law for each fall semester whose credentials qualify for the top 10% of the class are invited to apply for the award; moreover, eligibility requirements to maintain the award after the first year are: maintain a 3.0 grade-point average; no sanctions under the School of Law

---

Awards are arranged alphabetically below their administering organizations

Honor Code, and, enrolled full-time at the School of Law. **Criteria:** Selection will be made by school of law's Financial Aid Committee reviews the applications; and selects no more that five finalists; koch scholar is made by the Financial Aid Committee after interviewing the finalists; made prior to the admission seat deposit deadline.

Funds Avail.: Total of $45,000 ($15,000 per year). **Duration:** Annual. **To Apply:** Applicants must submit a statement showing the reason for interest in the law as a profession; public and community service activities; and, leadership activities and potential for leadership. **Remarks:** Established in 1994.

11879 ■ Shamberg Scholars Program
(Undergraduate/Scholarship)

Purpose: To assist Washburn University students in their education. **Focus:** Law. **Qualif.:** Applicants to Washburn University School of Law for each fall semester whose credentials qualify for the top 10% of the applicant pool are invited to apply for the Shamberg Scholar Award; maintain a 3.0 grade-point average. **Criteria:** Selection of the Shamberg Scholar is made by the Financial Aid Committee.

Funds Avail.: $15,000 per year. **Duration:** Annual. **Number Awarded:** 3. **To Apply:** The applicant must submit a statement showing: the reason for interest in the law as a profession; public and community service activities; and leadership activities and potential for leadership.

11880 ■ Washburn University School of Law Business and Transactional Law Center Scholarships
(Undergraduate/Scholarship)

Purpose: To assist Washburn University law students in their education. **Focus:** Law. **Qualif.:** Applicants must be admitted to Washburn Law and have an interest in business law or transactional law. **Criteria:** Recipients will be selected based on the aforesaid qualifications and other criteria.

Funds Avail.: Maximum of $28,000. **Duration:** Annual; one to two months during the period June 1, 2017 to May 31, 2018. **To Apply:** Applicants to be considered for the scholarship, must indicate their interest on the Washburn Law application; they will be automatically considered for the award upon admission and will be notified within two weeks of admission by letter if selected for the award. **Contact:** Washburn University School of Law Business and Transactional Law Center, 1700 SW College Ave., Topeka, Kansas 66621; phone: 785-670-1676; e-mail: transactional@washburnlaw.edu.

11881 ■ Washburn University School of Law Child and Family Advocacy Fellowships *(Undergraduate/Fellowship)*

Purpose: To assist Washburn University students in their education. **Focus:** Law. **Qualif.:** Applicants must be entering Washburn law students who are also intending to pursue careers in child and family advocacy. **Criteria:** Selection will be based on the aforesaid qualifications and other criteria.

Funds Avail.: Maximum of $27,000, plus stipend of $3,000 for summer externship. **Duration:** Annual; two-year cycle. **To Apply:** Applicants must indicate their interest on the Washburn Law application; they will be automatically considered for the award upon admission and will be notified within two weeks of admission by letter if selected for the award. **Contact:** Washburn University School of Law Children and Family Law Center, 1700 SW College Ave.,

Topeka, Kansas 66621; phone: 785-670-1676; e-mail: children@washburnlaw.edu.

11882 ■ Washington Association of School Business Officials (WASBO)
284 Lee St. SW, Ste. 132
Tumwater, WA 98501
Ph: (360)528-2025
Fax: (360)528-2028
Free: 800-524-4706
E-mail: admin@wasbo.org
URL: www.wasbo.org
Social Media: www.facebook.com/WASBO.Organization
www.instagram.com/wasbo_/
www.linkedin.com/company/washington-association-of
 -school-business-officials
twitter.com/WASBO9

11883 ■ WASBO Scholarship Program
(Undergraduate/Scholarship)

Purpose: To support WASBO members, to enable them to continue their higher education in school business courses offered by colleges or universities. **Focus:** Business. **Qualif.:** Applicants must be WASBO members. **Criteria:** Selection will be based on the committee's criteria.

Funds Avail.: Up to $500. **Duration:** Annual. **To Apply:** Interested applicant may contact the Washington Association of School Business Officials for the application process and other information. **Remarks:** Established in 1993. **Contact:** Email: admin@wasbo.org.

11884 ■ Washington City/County Management Association (WCMA)
625 Swift Blvd.
Richland, WA 99352
URL: wccma.org

11885 ■ Washington City/County Management Association Scholarships *(Graduate/Scholarship)*

Purpose: To provide financial assistance to students who have chosen to pursue a graduate degree in public administration and who have a desire to work in city or county management. **Focus:** Public administration. **Criteria:** Selection will be based on graduate students pursuing a degree in public administration, public affairs, or public policy.

Funds Avail.: $5,000. **Duration:** Annual; one academic year. **To Apply:** Applicants must submit a completed application form along with one official copy of undergraduate transcripts; one official copy of graduate transcripts (if applicable); two letters of reference, one from a previous or current undergraduate or graduate academic instructor and the other from a previous or current work supervisor; and a letter of application (no more than two pages); an initial unofficial copy of transcripts is sufficient to meet the deadline but must be followed by an official copy of them. **Deadline:** April 30. **Contact:** Adam Lincoln, City Of Pullman, 325 Se Paradise St., Pullman, WA, 99163; Fax: 509-334-2751; Email: adam.lincoln@pullman-wa.gov.

11886 ■ The Washington Group (TWG)
3311 Toledo Rd
Hyattsville, MD 20782-2064

Awards are arranged alphabetically below their administering organizations

E-mail: wg_secretariat@cdc.gov
URL: www.washingtongroup-disability.com

11887 ■ Alberta Ukrainian Centennial Commemorative Scholarship *(Graduate/Scholarship)*

Purpose: To encourage active participation in the Ukrainian community. **Focus:** General studies/Field of study not specified. **Qualif.:** Applicants must be graduate students intending to study in Alberta or Canadian graduate students from Alberta intending to study in Ukraine. **Criteria:** Recipients are chosen by a selection committee appointed by the Presidents of the universities in Alberta. Applicants are judged on previous academic accomplishments, program of study, appraiser's evaluations, answers to the essay question, and general impressions from the application form.

Funds Avail.: No specific amount. **Duration:** Annual. **Number Awarded:** 2. **To Apply:** Interested applicants may contact The Washington Group for the application process and other requirements. **Deadline:** February 1. **Remarks:** Established in 1991. **Contact:** Student Aid Alberta, PO Box 28000, Station Main, Edmonton, AB, T5J 4R4; Toll free: 855-606-2096.

11888 ■ Canada-Ukraine Parliamentary Program Internship Scholarships (CUPP) *(Undergraduate/ Scholarship, Internship)*

Purpose: To encourage active participation in the Ukrainian community. **Focus:** General studies/Field of study not specified. **Qualif.:** Applicants must be Ukrainian citizens seeking scholarships for a three-month internship for Ukrainian undergraduates with a Member of Parliament of the House of Commons in Ottawa, Canada. **Criteria:** Recipients are selected based on academic records. Proficiency in English or French as well as in Ukrainian is a requirement.

Funds Avail.: No specific amount. **Duration:** Annual; every three months. **To Apply:** Interested applicants may contact The Washington Group for the application process and other requirements.**Remarks:** The internship is run by the Chair of Ukrainian Studies Foundation.

11889 ■ Chopivsky Fellowships *(Graduate/ Fellowship)*

Purpose: To encourage active participation in the Ukrainian community. **Focus:** Economics; Environmental science; Forestry. **Criteria:** Recipients are selected based on academic records.

Funds Avail.: No specific amount. **Duration:** Annual. **To Apply:** Interested applicants may contact The Washington Group for the application process and other requirements. **Deadline:** January 1. **Contact:** Chopivsky Fellowships, Yale-Ukraine Initiative Committee, Russian and East European Studies, PO Box 208206, New Haven, CT 06520-8606; Phone: 203-432-3423; Fax: 203-432-5963; Email: rees@yale.edu.

11890 ■ Washington Hospital Healthcare System (WHHS)

2000 Mowry Ave.
Fremont, CA 94538
Ph: (510)797-1111
URL: www.whhs.com
Social Media: www.facebook.com/WashingtonHosp
www.instagram.com/washingtonhosp

www.linkedin.com/company/washington-hospital
-healthcare-system
twitter.com/WashingtonHosp
www.youtube.com/user/WHHSInHealth

11891 ■ Service League Volunteer Scholarships *(Undergraduate/Scholarship)*

Purpose: To support Washington Hospital District students who are pursuing studies in a health-related field. **Focus:** Health care services. **Criteria:** Selection will be based on committee's criteria.

Funds Avail.: $1,000 (per year for four years). **Duration:** One year, renewable each year for three additional years. **Number Awarded:** 2. **To Apply:** Applicants must submit completed application form; current letters of recommendation from a Director of Volunteer Services, employer, counselor, advisor or teacher; high school or college transcript and proof of citizenship. **Deadline:** April 1. **Contact:** Washington Hospital Service League, 2000 Mowry Ave, Fremont, CA, 94538.

11892 ■ Washington Hospital Employee Association Scholarship *(Undergraduate/Scholarship)*

Purpose: To support students residing in the District who are pursuing careers in the health sciences field. **Focus:** Health sciences. **Qualif.:** Applicants must be students residing within the Washington Township Health Care District who are pursuing careers in the health sciences field; must be students enrolled in the nursing program at San Jose State University or Ohlone College.

Funds Avail.: $2,000. **Duration:** Annual. **To Apply:** Applicants must submit a completed application form. **Deadline:** April 1. **Contact:** Medical Staff office at 510-791-3446.

11893 ■ Washington Indian Gaming Association (WIGA)

525 Pear St. S.E.
Olympia, WA 98501
Ph: (360)352-3248
Fax: (360)352-4819
E-mail: info@washingtonindiangaming.org
URL: www.washingtonindiangaming.org

11894 ■ WIGA College Scholarships *(Postgraduate, Graduate, Undergraduate/Scholarship)*

Purpose: To promote tribal economic development and self-sufficiency. **Focus:** General studies/Field of study not specified.

Funds Avail.: $100,000. **Duration:** Annual. **Number Awarded:** Varies. **To Apply:** Applicants must submit personal information/tribal affiliationalong with proof of enrollment or statement from a tribal enrollment officer; must submit two (2) letters ofRecommendation; and a personal essay that is between 250-500 words. **Contact:** Rebecca Kaldor, Deputy Director, at 360-352-3248 or email at rebeccakaldor@reachone.com.

11895 ■ Washington Library Association (WLA)

PO Box 33808
Seattle, WA 98133
Ph: (206)823-1138
E-mail: info@wla.org
URL: www.wla.org

Awards are arranged alphabetically below their administering organizations

Social Media: www.facebook.com/WashingtonLibraryAssociation?filter=2
www.linkedin.com/company/washington-library-association
twitter.com/WALIBASSN

11896 ■ WLA Conference Attendance Grants
(Undergraduate, Professional development/Grant)

Purpose: To defray the expense of attending the WLA Annual Conference. **Focus:** Library and archival sciences. **Qualif.:** Applicant must member of WLA.

Funds Avail.: $400. **Duration:** Annual. **Number Awarded:** 1. **Deadline:** June 4.

11897 ■ Washington Society of Certified Public Accountants (WSCPA)
902 140th Ave. NE
Bellevue, WA 98005-3480
Ph: (425)644-4800
Fax: (425)562-8853
Free: 800-272-8273
E-mail: memberservices@wscpa.org
URL: www.wscpa.org/home?Site=WSCPA
Social Media: www.facebook.com/WashingtonCPAs
twitter.com/wscpa

11898 ■ George J.Waterman Memorial Scholarship
(Undergraduate/Scholarship)

Purpose: To support accounting students. **Focus:** Accounting.

Contact: Kimberly Scott at kscott@wscpa.org.

11899 ■ Washington CPA Foundation Scholarship
(Undergraduate/Scholarship)

Purpose: To support accounting students. **Focus:** Accounting.

Funds Avail.: $5,000. **Number Awarded:** 70. **Deadline:** February 17.

11900 ■ Washington Space Grant Consortium (WSGC)
PO Box 351310
Seattle, WA 98195-1310
Ph: (206)543-1943
Fax: (206)543-0179
Free: 800-659-1943
E-mail: nasa@uw.edu
URL: www.waspacegrant.org
Social Media: www.facebook.com/Washington-NASA
  -Space-Grant-Consortium-116910748327473
twitter.com/WaSpaceGrant
www.youtube.com/user/waspacegrant

11901 ■ WSGC Community College Transfer Scholarships *(Undergraduate/Scholarship)*

Purpose: To provide opportunities to deserving college students in Washington who are planning to continue their studies in science, technology and engineering. **Focus:** Engineering; Mathematics and mathematical sciences; Science; Technology. **Qualif.:** Applicants must be residents of Washington state and U.S. citizens; must have a minimum GPA of 3.3; must have applied to transfer into Washington

University; must be pursuing an undergraduate degree in science, technology, engineering or mathematics. **Criteria:** Selection will be based on the committee's criteria.

Funds Avail.: $2,000 to $5,000. **Duration:** Annual. **To Apply:** Applicants may contact the University of Washington for the application process and other information.

11902 ■ WSGC Scholarships for Incoming Freshmen *(Undergraduate/Scholarship)*

Purpose: To provide opportunities to deserving students in Washington who are planning to study science, technology and engineering. **Focus:** Science. **Qualif.:** Applicants must be Washington state residents and U.S. citizens; must have a minimum GPA of 3.3. **Criteria:** Selection will be based on the committee's criteria.

Funds Avail.: $2,000 to $5,000. **Duration:** Annual. **To Apply:** Applications can be submitted online.

11903 ■ Washington State Association for Justice (WSAJ)
1809 7th Ave., Ste. 1500
Seattle, WA 98101
Ph: (206)464-1011
E-mail: wsaj@washingtonjustice.org
URL: www.washingtonjustice.org
Social Media: www.facebook.com/washingtonjustice
www.instagram.com/washingtonjustice
www.linkedin.com/groups/152475/profile
twitter.com/wajustice
www.youtube.com/user/washingtonjustice

11904 ■ Women of WSAJ Bar Preparation Scholarship *(Undergraduate/Scholarship)*

Purpose: To provide law school graduates a scholarship to defray the cost of bar review courses. **Focus:** Law. **Qualif.:** Applicants must be female individuals who will take the Washington State bar exam. **Criteria:** Recipients will be selected based on financial need, demonstrated interest and intent to practice in the plaintiff's bar.

Funds Avail.: No specific amount. **Duration:** Annual. **To Apply:** Applicants must submit a resume and an essay (not to exceed two pages, typed and double-spaced). Additional documents that will support the application are acceptable. **Deadline:** November 17. **Contact:** Applications should be mailed to: WSAJ, WOW Scholarship, 1809 7th Ave., Ste. 1500, Seattle, WA, 98101-1328; Raphaela Weissman, Email: raphaela@washingtonjustice.org.

11905 ■ WSAJ American Justice Essay Scholarships *(Undergraduate/Scholarship)*

Purpose: To help students pursue a post-secondary education. **Focus:** General studies/Field of study not specified. **Qualif.:** Applicants must be high school seniors who are currently attending high school in Washington and also residents of the state of Washington. **Criteria:** Recipients will be chosen based on excellence in writing and eloquence in addressing the essay topic.

Funds Avail.: No specific amount. **Duration:** Annual; non-renewable. **To Apply:** Applicants must submit an essay; it should be four-to-five pages, typewritten and double-spaced, original and should pertain to any subject within the scope of the topic; must also provide a cover sheet with the name and contact information.

11906 ■ WSAJ Diversity Bar Preparation Scholarship *(Undergraduate/Scholarship)*

Purpose: To provide scholarship monies for diverse individuals who are under-represented in the legal profes-

Awards are arranged alphabetically below their administering organizations

sion. **Focus:** Law. **Qualif.:** Applicants must be individuals who are under-represented in the legal profession based on disability, gender identity and expression, race, ethnicity, religion and sexual orientation. **Criteria:** Selection will be based on qualifications and submitted materials.

Funds Avail.: No specific amount. **Duration:** Annual. **To Apply:** Applicants must submit a resume and a brief essay (not to exceed two pages, typed and double-spaced); additional documents that will support the application are accepted. **Deadline:** November 17. **Contact:** Applications should be mailed to: WSAJ, WOW Scholarship, 1809 7th Ave., Ste. 1500, Seattle, WA, 98101-1328; Raphaela Weissman, Email: raphaela@washingtonjustice.org.

11907 ■ WSAJ Presidents' Scholarships
(Undergraduate/Scholarship)

Purpose: To support and encourage the efforts of high school students who have overcome obstacles to pursue their education. **Focus:** General studies/Field of study not specified. **Qualif.:** Applicants must be high school senior students who are residents of the state of Washington. **Criteria:** Selected will be based on the following criteria demonstrated academic achievements and planned advancement toward a degree in an institution of higher learning; documented need for financial assistance; history of achievement despite disability; record of commitment in helping needy people or protecting the rights of injured persons; plan or commitment to apply the education in helping people; and residency.

Funds Avail.: No specific amount. **Duration:** Annual; nine-month program. **To Apply:** Applicants must submit all high school and community college academic transcripts; name, address and telephone numbers of two references, at least one of which must be outside the school environment; a brief written financial statement; and any other documentation that will support the application; also required to send a letter to the scholarship committee describing the qualifications and explaining the reasons why they deserve the scholarship. **Deadline:** March 17. **Contact:** Washington State Association for Justice, at the above address.

11908 ■ Washington State Business Education Association (WSBEA)
PO Box 729
Goldendale, WA 98620
Ph: (541)980-0960
E-mail: info@wsbea.org
URL: www.wsbea.org

11909 ■ Dr. F. Ross Byrd Scholarship *(Graduate/Scholarship)*

Purpose: To provide financial support to those students who are in need. **Focus:** Business. **Criteria:** Preference will be given to those who meet the criteria.

Duration: Annual. **Number Awarded:** Varies. **To Apply:** Applicants must submit a completed application form and 3 letters of recommendation, one of which must be from a member of the student's graduate advisory committee, another one from a local vocational director/vocational administrator/administrator, and one from a member of WSBEA. **Deadline:** May 1. **Contact:** Jackie Floetke, WSBEA Scholarship Chair PO Box 138 Wilson Creek, WA 98860 OR, jfloetke@wilsoncreek.org.

11910 ■ Doris Y. and John J. Gerber Scholarship
(Undergraduate/Scholarship)

Purpose: To provide financial assistance to those students who significant contribution to business education in

Washington State. **Focus:** Business. **Qualif.:** Applicants must be junior or senior standing; majoring in business education; nominated by an advisor who is a current dues paying member of Washington State Business Education Association (WSBEA). **Criteria:** Selection will be based on statement of need; leadership; community service.

Duration: Annual. **To Apply:** Applicants must complete an application form; must submit at least three letters of recommendation, one of which must be from the nominating advisor; 300 words or less, explain why becoming a business educator is important. **Deadline:** December 1. **Remarks:** The Scholarship is named in honor of Doris Y. and John J. Gerber's significant contribution to business education in Washington State. **Contact:** Jackie Floetke, WSBEA Scholarship Chair, PO Box 138, Wilson Creek, WA 98860; Email: jfloetke@wilsoncreek.org.

11911 ■ Washington State Lake Protection Association (WALPA)
PO Box 4245
Seattle, WA 98194
E-mail: info@walpa.org
URL: www.walpa.org
Social Media: www.facebook.com/walpa.org

11912 ■ Dave Lamb Scholarship *(Graduate/Scholarship)*

Purpose: To promote the study of limnology, hydrology, ecology, and management or restoration of lakes and watersheds in Washington or Idaho. **Focus:** Environmental science. **Criteria:** Selection will be based on the quality of research topic, its significance to the fields of Environmental Science, particularly limnology and hydrology, and relevance to the applicant's interests and career goals.

Funds Avail.: $1,000 each. **Duration:** Annual. **Number Awarded:** 1. **To Apply:** Applicants must provide a two-page statement of personal and research interests; include a 1-2 page resume and recent transcripts of all college/university course work (transcripts need not be official copies); recommendation from someone in the applicant's field of study is encouraged, but not required; reference letters should be sent as PDF files directly to the committee chair. **Deadline:** May 15. **Contact:** Email: gabriela@cwu.edu.

11913 ■ Washington State Nurses Association (WSNA)
575 Andover Pk. W, Ste. 101
Seattle, WA 98188
Ph: (206)575-7979
Free: 800-231-8482
E-mail: wsna@wsna.org
URL: www.wsna.org

11914 ■ Washington State Nurses Association Foundation Scholarships (WSNF) *(Graduate, Undergraduate/Scholarship)*

Purpose: To support the education of students preparing for a career as registered nurses in Washington State. **Focus:** Nursing. **Criteria:** Selection is based on academic performance, nursing leadership, school and community involvement, professional activities and commitment to WSNA.

Funds Avail.: $1,000 each. **Duration:** Annual. **Number Awarded:** Varies. **To Apply:** Applicants must download the

---

Awards are arranged alphabetically below their administering organizations

application form provided at the scholarship website; other documents to be submitted are also enumerated on the website.

11915 ■ Washington Student Achievement Council (WSAC)
917 Lakeridge Way SW
Olympia, WA 98502
Ph: (360)753-7800
E-mail: info@wsac.wa.gov
URL: www.wsac.wa.gov
Social Media: www.facebook.com/WSACouncil
twitter.com/WSACouncil
www.youtube.com/channel/UC7h4oFRyYKhzfE5i3cS-xKg

11916 ■ American Indian Endowed Scholarship
(Graduate, Undergraduate/Scholarship)

Purpose: To provide financial support to students who are academically competitive. **Focus:** General studies/Field of study not specified. **Qualif.:** Applicants must be Washington state residents; must be enrolled full-time as undergraduate or graduate students in an eligible program. **Criteria:** Selection is based on academic merit and commitment to serve the American Indian communities in Washington.

Funds Avail.: $500-$2,000. **Duration:** Annual. **To Apply:** Applicants must submit an American Indian Endowed Scholarship application form together with the required materials and information.

11917 ■ The College Bound Scholarship
(Undergraduate/Scholarship)

Purpose: To provide financial assistance to low-income students who want to achieve the dream of a college education. **Focus:** General studies/Field of study not specified.

Funds Avail.: No specific amount. **Duration:** Annual. **To Apply:** Applicants must submit the complete application. **Deadline:** August 31. **Remarks:** Established in 2007.

11918 ■ Educator Conditional Scholarship And Repayment Programs *(Other, Undergraduate/Loan, Scholarship)*

Purpose: To encourage outstanding students and paraprofessionals to become teachers, and to encourage current teachers to obtain additional endorsements in teacher shortage subjects. **Focus:** Teaching.

Funds Avail.: No specific amount. **To Apply:** Applicant must contact the Future Teachers Conditional Scholarship and Loan Repayment Program in order to apply. **Contact:** Mary Knutson, Program Manager at futureteachers@hecb.wa.gov.

11919 ■ Washington College Grant (SNG)
(Undergraduate/Grant)

Purpose: To help state's lowest-income undergraduate students pursue degrees, hone skills, or retrain for new careers. **Focus:** General studies/Field of study not specified. **Qualif.:** Applicants must have a family income of equal to or less than 70 percent of the state median; must be Washington State residents; must be enrolled as undergraduate students in an eligible program. **Criteria:** Selection will be based on the applicant's family income.

Funds Avail.: Varies. **Duration:** Annual. **Number Awarded:** Varies. **To Apply:** Applicant should complete a state or federal financial aid application, which colleges will use to determine eligibility and make awards. Application processes for non-campus-based apprenticeship programs have not yet been established.

11920 ■ Washington University School of Law
One Brookings Drive
Saint Louis, MO 63130-4899
Ph: (314)935-6400
URL: law.wustl.edu
Social Media: www.facebook.com/WashULaw
www.instagram.com/washulawlife
twitter.com/washulaw

11921 ■ Buder Scholarships for American Indian Law Students *(Undergraduate/Scholarship)*

Purpose: To provide financial assistance to American Indian law students. **Focus:** Law. **Criteria:** Selection will be based on the applicants' demonstrated potential for success in law school as evidenced by undergraduate academic performance, performance on the law school admission test, and other relevant factors.

Funds Avail.: No specific amount. **Duration:** Annual; up to 3 years. **To Apply:** Applicants must submit an application letter and other requirements to the office. **Contact:** Carrie Burns, Assistant Director of Financial Aid & Student Services; Phone: 314-935-4605; Email: cjburns@wustl.edu.

11922 ■ Walter Moran Farmer Scholarships *(Juris Doctorate/Scholarship)*

Purpose: To offer financial support to students of color with intellectual, leadership and community service achievements. **Focus:** Law; Public service. **Qualif.:** Applicants must be Washington University Law students of color. **Criteria:** Selection will be based on intellectual, leadership and community service achievement; demonstrated commitment of bringing diverse people together; and demonstrated achievement in the face of personal challenges.

Funds Avail.: No specific amount. **Duration:** Annual. **To Apply:** Applicants must submit the application letter and other requirements.

11923 ■ Chancellor's Graduate Fellowship
(Advanced Professional/Fellowship)

Purpose: To provide academic and generous financial support to outstanding and diverse students interested in careers as college or university professors. **Focus:** Arts; Business; Engineering; Law; Social work. **Qualif.:** Applicants must be graduate students who are interested in becoming college or university professors. **Criteria:** Recipients will be selected based on potential contributions to the diversity of graduate education at Washington University.

Funds Avail.: No specific amount. **To Apply:** Applicants may download an application form from the website. **Deadline:** January 25. **Remarks:** Established in 1991. **Contact:** Carrie Burns, Assistant Director of Financial Aid & Student Services; Phone: 314-935-4605; Email: cjburns@wustl.edu.

11924 ■ Washington University Law School Olin Fellowships for Women *(Advanced Professional/ Fellowship)*

Purpose: To provide financial assistance to women who wish to have careers in higher education. **Focus:** Architecture; Art; Business; Engineering; Law; Medicine; Social

Awards are arranged alphabetically below their administering organizations

work. **Qualif.:** Applicants must be women. **Criteria:** Recipients will be selected based on the committee's review of all applications.

Funds Avail.: No specific amount. **Deadline:** January 25. **Contact:** Carrie Burns, Assistant Director of Financial Aid & Student Services; Phone: 314-935-4605; Email: cjburns@wustl.edu.

11925 ■ Webster Society Scholarships *(Juris Doctorate, Undergraduate/Scholarship)*

Purpose: To offer financial support to students with outstanding credentials and a demonstrated commitment to public service. **Focus:** Law; Public service. **Qualif.:** Applicants must be entering first-year J.D. students with exemplary academic credentials and an established commitment to public service.

Funds Avail.: $ 5,000. **Duration:** Annual. **To Apply:** Applicants should write a short statement summarizing their involvement in public service activities. **Contact:** Carrie Burns, Assistant Director of Financial Aid & Student Services; Phone: 314-935-4605; Email: cjburns@wustl.edu.

11926 ■ Water Environment Federation (WEF)
601 Wythe St.
Alexandria, VA 22314
Ph: (703)684-2400
Free: 800-666-0206
E-mail: csc@wef.org
URL: www.wef.org
Social Media: www.facebook.com/
 WaterEnvironmentFederation
www.instagram.com/wef_org
www.linkedin.com/company/water-environment-federation/
twitter.com/WEForg
www.youtube.com/user/WaterEnvironmentFed

11927 ■ Canham Graduate Studies Scholarship *(Graduate/Scholarship)*

Purpose: To provide financial assistance to those post-baccalaureate students who are in the water environment field. **Focus:** Water resources. **Qualif.:** Applicant must be a WEF member working on post-baccalaureate studies in the water environment field. **Criteria:** Selection will be based on evaluation of submitted documents and specific criteria.

Funds Avail.: $25,000. **Duration:** Annual. **Number Awarded:** 1. **To Apply:** Applicants must submit a completed application form providing a summary of academic and practical experience in the environmental field; official college/university transcripts; letter of acceptance to a graduate program in the water environment field; recommendations from three persons; detailed statement of degree objectives as related to career goals and intent to work in the water environment field (750-1000 words). **Deadline:** March 1. **Remarks:** Established in 1987. **Contact:** Water Environment Federation, Awards Program, Attn: Kelsey Hurst, 601 Wythe St., Alexandria, VA, 22314-1994; Email: awards@wef.org.

11928 ■ Water and Sewer Distributors of America (WASDA)
800 Roosevelt Rd, C-312
Glen Ellyn, IL 60137
Ph: (630)672-3670

Fax: (630)790-3095
E-mail: info@wasda.com
URL: www.wasda.com
Social Media: www.facebook.com/JoinWASDA
www.linkedin.com/company/water-&-sewer-distributors-of
 -america
twitter.com/joinwasda
www.youtube.com/user/joinwasda

11929 ■ Matt Stager Memorial Scholarship *(Undergraduate/Scholarship)*

Purpose: To provide financial support to students who are pursuing their educational career. **Focus:** General studies/Field of study not specified. **Qualif.:** Applicants must be children of employees of distributor companies whose membership is in good standing with WASDA; must maintain a GPA of 3.0 or higher and a minimum of 12credits per semester as a full-time student.

Funds Avail.: $1,000. **Duration:** Annual. **To Apply:** Applicants must prepare a one-page detailed narrative description of the academic plans for the future and the career goals; must have two letters of recommendation from persons who are not related to you but have knowledge of your academic achievements; standardized test score; official copy of high school transcript; must have a signature from a WASDA member contact verifying parent's employment and completed counselor's report.

11930 ■ Waterbury Bar Association
PO Box 1767
Waterbury, CT 06721
URL: www.waterburybar.org
Social Media: facebook.com/pages/Waterbury-Bar
 -Association/118639578211368

11931 ■ Bar President's Scholarship *(Undergraduate/Scholarship)*

Purpose: To provide financial support to deceased members' children who wish to continue their educations. **Focus:** Law; Paralegal studies. **Qualif.:** Applicants must be residents of the Waterbury Judicial District (Middlebury, Naugatuck, Prospect, Southbury, Watertown, Wolcott, Woodbury or Waterbury) and be in or entering their final year of study at an accredited law school. **Criteria:** Selection will be based on the association's scholarship committee's criteria.

Funds Avail.: $1,000. **Duration:** Annual. **To Apply:** Applicant must submit an online application form along with transcript. **Deadline:** October 11. **Contact:** Attorney Gina M. Petrokaitis, 678 Chase Parkway, Waterbury, CT 06708; Phone: 203 756-6955.

11932 ■ Edward Traurig Scholarship *(Undergraduate/Scholarship)*

Purpose: To provide financial support to deceased members' children who wish to continue their educations. **Focus:** Law; Paralegal studies. **Qualif.:** Applicants must be residents of the Waterbury Judicial District (Middlebury, Naugatuck, Prospect, Southbury, Watertown, Wolcott, Woodbury or Waterbury) but can be entering their second or final year of study as full or part-time students at an accredited institution. **Criteria:** Selection will be based on the association's scholarship committee's criteria.

Funds Avail.: $1,000. **Duration:** Annual. **To Apply:** Applicant must submit an online application form along with

Awards are arranged alphabetically below their administering organizations

transcript. **Deadline:** October 11. **Contact:** Attorney Gina M. Petrokaitis, 678 Chase Parkway, Waterbury, CT 06708; Phone: 203 756-6955.

11933 ■ Waterbury Bar Association Scholarship
(Undergraduate/Scholarship)

Purpose: To provide financial support to deceased members' children who wish to continue their educations. **Focus:** Law; Paralegal studies. **Qualif.:** Applicants must be residents of the Waterbury Judicial District (Middlebury, Naugatuck, Prospect, Southbury, Watertown, Wolcott, Woodbury or Waterbury) and be in or entering their final year of study at an accredited law school. **Criteria:** Selection will be based on the association's scholarship committee's criteria.

Funds Avail.: $1,500. **Duration:** Annual. **To Apply:** Applicant must submit an online application form along with transcript. **Deadline:** October 11. **Contact:** Attorney Gina M. Petrokaitis, 678 Chase Parkway, Waterbury, CT 06708; Phone: 203 756-6955.

11934 ■ WBA Paralegal/Legal Assistant Scholarship
(Undergraduate/Scholarship)

Purpose: To provide financial support to deceased members' children who wish to continue their educations. **Focus:** Paralegal studies. **Qualif.:** Applicants must be residents of the Waterbury Judicial District (Middlebury, Naugatuck, Prospect, Southbury, Watertown, Wolcott, Woodbury or Waterbury) and must be enrolled in an accredited paralegal or legal assistant program. Applicants must have completed, or will complete within the current school year, at least 30 credit hours toward the completion of the program and intend to seek employment within the Judicial District of Waterbury. **Criteria:** Selection will be based on applicants' academic record, demonstrated interest in community affairs and professional and personal integrity.

Funds Avail.: $500. **Duration:** Annual. **To Apply:** Applicant must submit an online application form along with transcript. **Deadline:** October 11. **Contact:** Attorney Gina M. Petrokaitis, 678 Chase Parkway, Waterbury, CT 06708; Phone: 203 756-6955.

11935 ■ Watson-Brown Foundation
310 Tom Watson Way
Thomson, GA 30824
Ph: (706)595-8886
Fax: (706)595-3948
URL: www.watson-brown.org
Social Media: www.facebook.com/Watson-Brown
  -Foundation-277102390498
www.instagram.com/watson_brown_foundation/?hl=en
twitter.com/wbf_scholars

11936 ■ Watson-Brown Scholarship *(Undergraduate/Scholarship)*

Purpose: To provide assistance to those who are pursuing their educational goals. **Focus:** General studies/Field of study not specified. **Qualif.:** Applicants must be students from Georgia or South Carolina who are high school seniors or current undergraduate students in their respective colleges or universities; must plan to attend a 4 year, accredited, non-profit college. **Criteria:** Recipients are selected based on merit and need.

Duration: Annual. **To Apply:** Applicants must complete the online application and submit high school/college transcript,

SACT and /or ACT score; letters of recommendation and IRS Form 1040 or 1040 EZ. **Contact:** Director of Scholarships, 310 Tom Watson Way, Thomson, GA, 30824.

11937 ■ Thomas J. Watson Foundation (TJW)
233 Broadway, 27th Flr.
New York, NY 10279
URL: watson.foundation

11938 ■ Jeannette K. Watson Fellowship
(Undergraduate/Fellowship)

Purpose: To provide internships, mentoring, and enriched educational opportunities to promising New York City undergraduates with the goal of increasing their life choices and developing their capacity to make a difference in their own and other people's lives. **Focus:** Liberal arts. **Criteria:** Selection is based on Leadership, Ability to work in groups, Openness, Desire to explore diverse cultures and new professional fields, Strong academic record.

Funds Avail.: $5,500; $6,500; $7,000. **Duration:** Annual; up to three years. **Number Awarded:** Varies. **To Apply:** Applicants must submit two short essay and one long essay of 500 word with two letters of recommendation (sent directly to the Campus Representatives), resume, and transcript. **Deadline:** February 19.

11939 ■ Thomas J. Watson Fellowship
(Undergraduate/Fellowship)

Purpose: To support individuals in their purposeful, independent studies outside the United States. **Focus:** General studies/Field of study not specified. **Qualif.:** applicants must be graduating seniors nominated by one of the 41 partner institutions. **Criteria:** Selection will be based on leadership; imagination; independence; emotional maturity; courage; integrity; resourcefulness; and responsibility.

Funds Avail.: $30,000. **Duration:** Annual. **To Apply:** Applicants nominated by a participating college must submit the following: personal statement; project statement; 2 recommendation letters; and transcripts.

11940 ■ Wayne County Foundation, Inc.
33 S 7th St.
Richmond, IN 47374
Ph: (765)962-1638
E-mail: info@waynecountyfoundation.org
URL: www.waynecountyfoundation.org
Social Media: www.facebook.com/
  WayneCountyFoundation
twitter.com/waynecountyfdtn

11941 ■ Jonathan Alan Scholarship Fund
(Undergraduate/Scholarship)

Purpose: To provide support student who plans to enter a medical field and demonstrates financial need. **Focus:** Education, Medical. **Qualif.:** Applicants must be Richmond high school graduates who have plans to enter a medical field and must demonstrate financial need.

Remarks: Established in 1999.

11942 ■ Ralph Burkhardt Scholarship Fund
(Undergraduate, High School/Scholarship)

Purpose: To support students in pursuing their career in the music industry. **Focus:** Music. **Qualif.:** Applicants must

Awards are arranged alphabetically below their administering organizations

be graduating Richmond High School seniors who have been outstanding orchestra students and intend to study music in college.

Duration: Annual. **Number Awarded:** 1. **Remarks:** Established in 1997.

11943 ■ Lucille Campbell Scholarship Fund
(Undergraduate, High School/Scholarship)

Purpose: To support graduating high school seniors of Wayne County obtain a higher education. **Focus:** General studies/Field. of study not specified. **Qualif.:** Applicants must be Wayne County high school graduating seniors. **Criteria:** Applicants are selected based on proof of eligibility and relative financial need.

Funds Avail.: No specific amount. **Duration:** Annual. **Remarks:** Established in 2004.

11944 ■ Betty J. Cecere Memorial Scholarship Endowment Fund *(Graduate/Scholarship)*

Purpose: To benefit an RHS graduating female who demonstrates a financial need and is planning to attend an accredited post-secondary school. **Focus:** General studies/ Field of study not specified. **Qualif.:** Applicants must be Richmond High School graduating female seniors.

Duration: Annual. **Number Awarded:** 1. **Remarks:** Established in 2006.

11945 ■ Centerville-Abington Dollars for Scholars
(Undergraduate/Scholarship)

Purpose: To provide financial assistance to those students who are in need. **Focus:** General studies/Field of study not specified. **Qualif.:** Applicants must be a youth or adults enrolled in an accredited post-secondary institution pursuing a two or four year degree or attending a vocational or technical college. **Criteria:** Selections made by Centerville-Abington Dollars for Scholars Committee and will be determined by a point system that includes a variety of qualities such as work experience, school and community service activities and academic record.

To Apply: Applicants for further information about the application form and materials, are advised to contact the Wayne County Foundation at the above address or visit the website. **Remarks:** Established in 2004.

11946 ■ Melba Dawn Chiarenza Scholarship Fund
(Undergraduate/Scholarship)

Purpose: To provide financial support for Lincoln High School graduates. **Focus:** Business; Criticism (Art, Drama, Literary); Nursing. **Qualif.:** Applicants must be Lincoln High School graduates who plan to obtain a degree in business, nursing, or drama. **Criteria:** Selection will be evaluated based on criteria designed by the Scholarship Selection Committee.

Funds Avail.: $3,500. **Duration:** Annual. **To Apply:** Applicants for further information about the application form and materials, are advised to contact the Wayne County Foundation at the above address or visit the website. **Remarks:** Established in 1998.

11947 ■ Erika A. and George E. Brattain, Sr. Donor Advised Scholarship Fund *(Undergraduate, High School/Scholarship)*

Purpose: To financially support students in pursuing their education in music. **Focus:** Music. **Qualif.:** Applicants must be Lincoln High School graduating seniors who are pursuing an education in music.

Remarks: Established in 2005.

11948 ■ Jason Chaney Memorial Scholarship *(High School/Scholarship)*

Purpose: To provide scholarship assistance to male student who wants to pursue his education. **Focus:** General studies/Field of study not specified. **Qualif.:** Applicants must be Hagerstown High School graduating male seniors.

Funds Avail.: No specific amount. **Duration:** Annual. **Number Awarded:** 2. **Remarks:** Established in 1999.

11949 ■ Niqui McCown Honor and Memorial Scholarship Fund *(Undergraduate/Scholarship)*

Purpose: To provide scholarships to graduating seniors who intend to pursue careers relating to the law or criminal justice. **Focus:** Criminal justice; Law. **Qualif.:** Applicants must be graduating seniors of Richmond High School who intend to pursue careers relating to the law or criminal justice. **Criteria:** Selection will be based on the moral character and academic achievements.

Funds Avail.: No specific amount. **Remarks:** Established in 2010.

11950 ■ Nixon Family Scholarship Fund
(Undergraduate, High School/Scholarship)

Purpose: To assist students pursuing a degree in engineering, technology or related fields. **Focus:** Construction; Engineering; Technology; Welding. **Qualif.:** Applicants must be graduating seniors of Centerville High School; must have completed a two-year course of vocational study at the Whitewater Technical Career in Computer Assisted Design, Precision Machining, Welding, Electricity, Construction, or Project Lead the Way Programs.

Number Awarded: 2. **Remarks:** Established in 2010.

11951 ■ Reid Hospital Graduate Student Scholarships *(Graduate/Scholarship)*

Purpose: To provide scholarship opportunities and assistance for students engaged in practical nursing, pharmacy, physical therapy, occupational therapy, speech and language pathology. **Focus:** Health care services.

Funds Avail.: $250 each. **Number Awarded:** 4. **To Apply:** Applicants must complete the application form available online; must provide an official transcript of grades and letter of recommendation from a professor, guidance counselor, or dean of program that they have known for at least one year; must submit a two-page maximum statement including their future plans, why they should be selected for the scholarship, and what inspired them to pursue a health care profession.

11952 ■ Wayne County College Fund *(Graduate/ Scholarship)*

Purpose: To provide college scholarships to graduates of Lincoln, Hagerstown, Northeastern or Centerville High Schools. **Focus:** Music.

Remarks: Established in 1990.

11953 ■ Websauce Studio
2110 K St., No. 1
Sacramento, CA 95817
Ph: (916)759-3762
URL: www.websaucestudio.com
Social Media: www.facebook.com/websaucestudio
www.instagram.com/websaucestudio

Awards are arranged alphabetically below their administering organizations

www.linkedin.com/company/websauce-studio
www.pinterest.com/websaucestudio
twitter.com/websaucestudio
www.youtube.com/channel/
UCfUmX61Ab7YBDBRN1r4S41Q

11954 ■ Websauce Web Design Scholarship
(Undergraduate/Scholarship)

Purpose: To see how the next generation views the shift to a mobile first world and how web designers will need to adapt their design and user experience to smaller screens and different expectations from users. **Focus:** Design; Marketing and distribution; Technology. **Qualif.:** Applicant must be a student enrolled in an undergraduate program at an accredited U.S. college or university. **Criteria:** Selection will be based on submitted essay.

Funds Avail.: $500. **Number Awarded:** 1. **To Apply:** Applicant must submit a 250-word essay outlining how web design must adapt to a mobile world, an example of a website that works well on mobile, and an explanation of why its a good mobile experience. Applications should be submitted to scholarship@websaucestudio.com. **Deadline:** December 11. **Contact:** Email scholarship@websaucestudio.com.

11955 ■ Weiss & Paarz P.C.
1735 Market St., Ste. 3750
Philadelphia, PA 19103
Ph: (215)238-9200
E-mail: sweiss@weisspaarz.com
URL: www.weisspaarz.com
Social Media: www.facebook.com/weiss.paarz
www.linkedin.com/company/weiss-

11956 ■ Weiss & Paarz Annual Rising Star Scholarship (Undergraduate/Scholarship)

Purpose: To provide financial support to young individuals who plan to realize their full potential on a career path that helps others. **Focus:** General studies/Field of study not specified. **Qualif.:** Applicant must be a graduating senior in high school. **Criteria:** Financial need, exceptional work ethic, strength in the face of adversity, outstanding academic achievement, commitment to the local community and charitable giving, ability to lead others, and overall moral character.

Funds Avail.: $1,000. **Duration:** Annual. **To Apply:** Submit the following: curriculum vitae or resume listing work experience, educational background, and high school and college GPA and class rank (if applicable); personal statement, which includes a description of your career goals and what you plan to use the scholarship funding for (2 pages maximum); confirmation of enrollment in an undergraduate institution or copy of your current student ID; and copy of state ID or driver's license. **Contact:** Sarah Weiss Rozalis; Email: sweiss@weisspaarz.com.

11957 ■ Rob and Bessie Welder Wildlife Foundation
PO Box 1400
Sinton, TX 78387
Ph: (361)364-2643
E-mail: sglasscock@welderwildlife.org
URL: www.welderwildlife.org

11958 ■ Rob and Bessie Welder Wildlife Foundation's graduate research fellowship (Graduate, Master's, Doctorate/Fellowship)

Purpose: To promote the education of exceptionally qualified students and provide research information to manage wildlife populations. **Focus:** Animal science and behavior; Biology; Botany; Conservation of natural resources; Ecology; Genetics; Ornithology; Veterinary science and medicine; Wildlife conservation, management, and science. **Qualif.:** Applicants must be graduate students, at the M.S. and Ph.D. levels, from the continental United States; must have a GPA of 3.0 or 4.0 and a combined verbal and analytical GRE score of 300 or above.

Funds Avail.: $1,600 full-time students; $1,800 M.S. candidates. **Duration:** Annual. **To Apply:** Applicants must provide and submit their respective research proposals in the following areas of study: animal behavior, biology, botany, conservation education, ecology, genetics, mammalogy, ornithology, parasitology, range science, veterinary pathology, and wildlife and fisheries sciences. The complete proposal should include the following; objectives, background and relevance, study site, methods, analytical procedures, itemized budget, and timetable, biographical data, degree sought, three letters of recommendation, complete academic record, and GRE score (verbal and quantitative). **Remarks:** Established in 1956. **Contact:** Director, Rob & Bessie Welder Wildlife Foundation, PO Box 1400, Terry Sinton, TX, 78387; Phone: 361-364-2643, Terry Blankenship, Director; Email: tblankenship@welderwildlife.org.

11959 ■ Wenner-Gren Foundation (WGF)
655 Third Avenue, 23rd Floor
New York, NY 10017
Ph: (212)683-5000
Fax: (212)532-1492
E-mail: inquiries@wennergren.org
URL: www.wennergren.org
Social Media: www.facebook.com/wennergrenfoundation
twitter.com/WennerGrenOrg

11960 ■ Conference and Workshop Grants (Professional development/Grant)

Purpose: To foster the creation of an international community of research scholars in anthropology and advance significant and innovative anthropological research. **Focus:** Anthropology. **Qualif.:** Applicants must be professional anthropologists who will be the primary organizers of the proposed conference or workshop; co-applicants can be specified on the application and must have a doctorate and hold an established academic position. **Criteria:** Selection will be given to those events with the broadest international and disciplinary participation; it is important to justify the potential contribution of invited scholars; priority is given to those events that bring together scholars who can offer new or insightful perspectives on topical anthropological issues; events that bring together scholars who frequently meet to discuss a particular topic of interest are not normally competitive for funding.

Funds Avail.: Up to $20,000. **Duration:** Annual. **To Apply:** Applications must be submitted on the most recent official application form; application forms and guidelines for completing these forms are available three months before each application deadline; all application forms and other required application materials must be submitted online; if it

Awards are arranged alphabetically below their administering organizations

is not possible to submit your application online because of inadequate internet access in your country of origin, you must notify the foundation at least one week before the deadline to arrange to submit an application by conventional mail; in addition to the online submission; must send one printed copy of the application form and attachments, PLUS four additional copies of the application form only, to the foundation offices to complete the filing process; this material must be postmarked by the application deadline (and received by the Foundation no later than two weeks after the deadline) or your application will not be reviewed; applications can only be made within 3 months of the application deadline; applications must be in English. **Deadline:** June 1; December 1. **Contact:** 655 Third Avenue, 23rd Floor New York, NY 10017 USA; Phone: 212.683.5000; Email: inquiries@wennergren.org.

11961 ■ Engaged Anthropology Grant (Doctorate, Postdoctorate/Grant)

Purpose: To enable grantees to return to their research locale to share their research results. **Focus:** Anthropology. **Qualif.:** Applicants must have been funded previously through a Dissertation Fieldwork or Post-Ph.D. Research Grant and the proposed engagement activities must be a direct outgrowth of this Wenner-Gren funded research; must have completed their Dissertation Fieldwork or Post-Ph.D. Research Grant and fulfilled the final reporting requirements before applying for the Engaged Anthropology Grant; must apply within six years of the original approve date of their Dissertation Fieldwork or Post-Ph.D. Research Grant. If you do not know your official approve date, it can be accessed by looking up your name on the Grantees Section of the Wenner Gren website; may apply multiple times for the same or different engagement projects within the stipulated six-year period. **Criteria:** Applications are evaluated according to the project's capacity for producing engaged participation, cultivating mutually beneficial collaborations and forging equitable relationships among all parties involved; priority will be given to proposals that are well developed and based on research results that are in advanced stages of completion and publication; priority will also be given to proposals that involve face-to-face engagement.

Funds Avail.: $5,000. **Duration:** Annual. **To Apply:** Applications must be submitted on the most recent official application form online, along with all other required materials; if it is not possible to submit the application online because of inadequate access in your country of origin, must notify the foundation at least one week before the deadline to arrange to submit an application by conventional mail; a complete application must have the following categories of information; general information about yourself, your prior Wenner-Gren grant and your proposed project; an abstract of the proposed project; project description questions; all responses should be carefully prepared. Applicants are advised to read the questions and instructions as they develop their answers; a detailed budget; curriculum vitae. **Deadline:** August 1.

11962 ■ Fejos Postdoctoral Fellowships in Ethnographic Film (Postdoctorate/Fellowship)

Purpose: To support the completion of ethnographic films based on anthropological research. **Focus:** Anthropology; Ethnography. **Qualif.:** Applicants must have a Ph.D. or equivalent in anthropology or a related discipline at the time of application; and must have received a Ph.D. or equivalent within ten years of the application deadline; must qualified scholars are eligible without regard to nationality,

institutional, or departmental affiliation, although preference is given to applicants who are untenured or do not yet have a permanent academic position; independent scholars are eligible to apply. **Criteria:** Selection will be based mainly on the evaluation of the quality of the research underlying the film project and its potential contribution to anthropological knowledge, theory, and debate; furthermore, applications for the fellowship will also be judged on the following criteria; the degree to which the proposed film reflects and communicates the results of the research upon which it is based; the innovative aspects of the film project; integration of film/video with other media forms and/or written publication; and the quality of the film sample submitted by the applicants; whose applications that were unsuccessful in a prior funding cycle may be resubmitted only twice.

Funds Avail.: $40,000. **Duration:** Annual. **Number Awarded:** 4. **To Apply:** Applications must be submitted using the foundation's online application submission procedure by midnight (Eastern Standard Time) on the day of the deadline; In addition, five printed copies of the complete application must be postmarked by the application deadline and received by the foundation no later than two weeks after the deadline or your application will not be reviewed; if it is not possible to submit application online because of inadequate internet access in applicant's country of origin, applicant must notify the foundation at least one week before the deadline. **Deadline:** May 1. **Remarks:** The fellowship is named after Paul Fejos, who was an early ethnographic film maker (1935-1941) and the first director of the Wenner-Gren Foundation (1941-1963). **Contact:** Email: applications@wennergren.org.

11963 ■ Hunt Postdoctoral Fellowships (Postdoctorate/Fellowship)

Purpose: To support basic research in anthropology. **Focus:** Anthropology. **Qualif.:** Applicants must have received a PhD or equivalent within ten years of the application deadline; and qualified scholars are eligible without regard to nationality or institutional or departmental affiliation. **Criteria:** Selection will be evaluated upon the quality of the research and its potential contribution to anthropological knowledge, theory and debate.

Funds Avail.: $40,000. **Duration:** Annual. **Number Awarded:** Maximum of 8. **To Apply:** The foundation operates an online application submission procedure; all application forms and other required application materials must be submitted online; if it is not possible to submit an application online because of inadequate internet access in country of origin, must notify the foundation at least one week before the deadline to arrange a submission of application by conventional mail; in addition to online submission, five printed copies of the application form and other required materials must be sent to the foundation. **Deadline:** May 1.

11964 ■ Wadsworth African Fellowships (Doctorate/ Fellowship)

Purpose: To support African students undertaking study leading to a PhD at a South African university that can provide them with international-level training in anthropology. **Focus:** Anthropology. **Qualif.:** Applicants must be African scholars who may not otherwise be able to pursue a doctoral degree in anthropology; must be under 35 years of age at the time they begin their fellowship; they must be citizens and residents of an African country at the time of application and also be members of an underrepresented group in academic anthropology/archaeology; must be prepared to demonstrate their reasons for choosing their

Awards are arranged alphabetically below their administering organizations

host institution; priority will be given to applications from the University of Witwatersrand and the University of Cape Town. At the time they submit their application, must have an application for doctoral admission pending at a South African institution that will provide training; must have a host sponsor who is a member of the institution at which the applicants received their prior degrees. **Criteria:** Selection will priority is given to well-articulated training and research goals; it is also important to demonstrate a good fit between the host institution, host sponsor and research goals of applicant; priority will be given to underrepresented groups in academic anthropology; must show evidence of academic excellence in their prior training in anthropology or a related discipline.

Funds Avail.: $17,500. **Duration:** Annual. **To Apply:** Application forms and other required application materials must be submitted online in a format compatible with Microsoft Word 2003, 2007 or 2010 or as an Adobe PDF; acceptable document formats include doc, docx, txt, xls and pdf extensions; two printed copies of the materials must also be mailed to the foundation; application and all supporting materials, such as CVs and transcripts, must be in English. Complete applications must have the following categories of information: general information about the applicant; the home institution sponsor and the host institution sponsor; the answers to three questions about the applicant's background and their proposed plan of study; their research interests and their professional goals or plans - applicants are advised to read the questions and instructions carefully as they develop their answers. Applicants must also provide a detailed budget; copies of official transcripts from their home institution; proof of language competency; curriculum vitae for the applicants and host sponsor; and reference letters from both the home sponsor and the host sponsor, to be sent directly to the foundation. **Deadline:** December 15. **Contact:** Email: internationalprograms@wennergren.org.

11965 ■ Wadsworth International Fellowships
(Graduate/Fellowship)

Purpose: To offer support for students who are in the early stages of their doctoral programs. **Focus:** Anthropology. **Qualif.:** Applicants must be from countries where anthropology is underrepresented and where there are limited resources to send students overseas for training; must be under 35 years of age at the time they begin their fellowship; must have a Host Sponsor who holds an academic position at the Host Institution and in the department where the Applicants will be registered. **Criteria:** Selection will focus on: those who have not already earned a prior degree from an institution outside of their home country and have not already begun their graduate training outside of their home country; must show evidence of academic excellence in their prior training in anthropology or a related discipline; priority is given to applicants with well-articulated training and research goals; it is also important to demonstrate a good fit between the Host Institution, Host Sponsor, and the applicant's research goals.

Funds Avail.: $17,500. **Duration:** Annual. **To Apply:** Applications can be submitted online. **Deadline:** March 1.

11966 ■ Wenner-Gren Foundation Dissertation Fieldwork Grants *(Doctorate/Grant)*

Purpose: To support students who are enrolled in a doctoral program in anthropology. **Focus:** Anthropology. **Qualif.:** Applicants must be currently enrolled for a doctoral degree; must be made jointly with a dissertation supervisor or other scholar who will undertake responsibility for

supervising the project; must be qualified doctoral students are eligible without regard to nationality or institutional or departmental affiliation. **Criteria:** Selection will focus upon: the quality of the research and its potential contribution to anthropological knowledge, theory and debate; submit a well-defined research question; a detailed description of appropriate evidence to answer the research question; a feasible plan for gathering and analyzing this evidence; the significance of the research to important theoretical and methodological issues in anthropology here is no preference for particular geographic areas or topics.

Funds Avail.: $20,000. **Duration:** Annual. **Number Awarded:** 1. **To Apply:** Applications must be submitted using the Foundation's online. **Deadline:** May 1; November 1. **Contact:** Email: applications@wennergren.org.

11967 ■ Wenner-Gren Foundation Post-PhD Research Grants *(Doctorate, Postdoctorate/Grant)*

Purpose: To support individuals who are holding a Ph.D. or equivalent degree with their research projects. **Focus:** Anthropology. **Qualif.:** Applicants must be individuals holding a Ph.D. or equivalent degree to support individual research projects; must qualified scholars are eligible without regard to nationality, or institutional or departmental affiliation. **Criteria:** Selection will be evaluated upon the quality of the research and its potential contribution to anthropological knowledge, theory, and debate.

Funds Avail.: $20,000. **Duration:** Annual. **To Apply:** The foundation operates an online application submission procedure; all application forms and other required application materials must be submitted online; if it is not possible to submit an application online because of inadequate internet access in applicant's country of origin, applicants must notify the foundation at least one week before the deadline to arrange a submission of application by conventional mail. In addition to online submission, five printed copies of the application form and other required materials must be sent to the foundation; and submit curriculum vitae. **Contact:** Email: inquiries@wennergren.orgren.org.

11968 ■ WESCO International, Inc.
225 W Station Square Dr., Ste. 700
Pittsburgh, PA 15219
Ph: (412)454-2200
E-mail: marketing@wesco.com
URL: www.wesco.com
Social Media: www.facebook.com/wesco.corp
www.linkedin.com/company/wesco.corp
twitter.com/wescocorp

11969 ■ The WESCO Student Achievement Award
(Undergraduate/Scholarship)

Purpose: To help students across Canada reach their education and career objectives. **Focus:** Business administration; Electronics; Engineering, Electrical. **Qualif.:** Applicants must be university or college students who have completed at least their first year of study in electrical engineering, electrical technology, or business administration, and maintained a minimum cumulative average of 80%. **Criteria:** Selection will be based on the applicants' eligibility and other criteria of the committee.

Funds Avail.: 3,500 Canadian Dollars. **Duration:** Annual. **To Apply:** Applicants may visit the website for them to create an account to apply for the scholarship, as well as for the other application materials required. **Deadline:** May 31.

Awards are arranged alphabetically below their administering organizations

Remarks: The scholarship is co-sponsored by the WESCO Distribution Canada.

11970 ■ West Virginia Coal Association (WVCA)

200 Association Dr., Ste. 160
Charleston, WV 25311
Ph: (304)342-4153
URL: www.wvcoal.com

11971 ■ Friends of Coal Scholarships
(Undergraduate/Scholarship)

Purpose: To support students with financial needs. **Focus:** General studies/Field of study not specified. **Qualif.:** Applicants must be high school honor graduates; must have high GPA's in high school; must be living in West Virginia. **Criteria:** Recipients are selected based on academic performance and financial need.

To Apply: Applicants must submit a filled-out application form.

11972 ■ West Virginia PTA (WV PTA)

PO Box 3557
Parkersburg, WV 26103-3557
Ph: (304)420-9576
Fax: (304)420-9577
E-mail: info@westvirginiapta.org
URL: www.wvpta.net
Social Media: www.facebook.com/westvirginiapta
twitter.com/westvirginiapta
www.youtube.com/channel/
UCf8n8uQMabQacAyQH8NKAJA

11973 ■ West Virginia PTA Scholarship
(Undergraduate/Scholarship)

Purpose: To support the education of WV students. **Focus:** General studies/Field of study not specified. **Qualif.:** Applicants must be graduating seniors from West Virginia's public high school with a 2.0 GPA.

Funds Avail.: $500. **Duration:** Annual. **Number Awarded:** Varies. **To Apply:** Applicants must accomplish the application form and submit it along with the official transcript, PTA reflection, long-term goals essay with a one-page limit and letters of recommendation. **Deadline:** December 31. **Contact:** Belinda Hite, Scholarship Chair; West Virginia PTA, PO Box, 3557, Parkersburg, WV, 26103; Email: scholarship@westvirginiapta.org.

11974 ■ West Virginia Space Grant Consortium (WVSGC)

Engineering Science Bldg., Rm. G-68
Morgantown, WV 26506-6070
Ph: (304)293-4099
Fax: (304)293-4970
URL: www.wvspacegrant.org
Social Media: www.facebook.com/WVSGC
www.linkedin.com/company/nasa-wv-space-grant
-consortium
twitter.com/NASAWVSGC

11975 ■ NASA WVSGC Undergraduate Research Fellowship *(Undergraduate/Fellowship)*

Purpose: To provide support for undergraduate students to become involved in a research project under the supervi-

sion of their academic supervisor. **Focus:** Space and planetary sciences. **Qualif.:** Applicants must be undergraduate students in the Science, Technology, Engineering and Mathematics (STEM) fields enrolled in a WVSGC affiliate institution; female and minority students are strongly encouraged to apply; must be U.S. citizens. **Criteria:** Selection will be based on soundness and technical merit of the proposed research; student's academic and extracurricular achievements; budget and plans for dissemination and publicizing of the results.

Funds Avail.: $4,500. **To Apply:** Applications can be submitted online; must include research experience and career interests; plans for sharing research findings through participation in a professional conference and/or publication; list of planned expenditures and justification for the expenditures; acknowledgement of prior WVSGC funding and brief description of previous projects funded.

11976 ■ West Virginia University - Center for Women's and Gender Studies

345 Price St.
Morgantown, WV 26506-6450
Ph: (304)293-2339
Fax: (304)293-3041
E-mail: wgst@mail.wvu.edu
URL: womensgenderstudies.wvu.edu
Social Media: www.facebook.com/wgst.wvu
www.instagram.com/wvueberly
twitter.com/WGST_WVU

11977 ■ Judith Gold Stitzel Endowment for Excellence in Women's Studies Teaching and Learning
(Professional development/Grant)

Purpose: To ensure a continuing and vital presence for women's studies as an academic discipline. **Focus:** Teaching; Women's studies.

Funds Avail.: $3,000. **Duration:** Annual. **Remarks:** Established in 1998.

11978 ■ Western Equipment Dealers Association (WEDA)

10100 N Ambassador Dr., Ste. 310
Kansas City, MO 64153
Ph: (816)561-5323
Fax: (816)561-1249
Free: 800-762-5616
URL: www.westerneda.com
Social Media: www.facebook.com/westerneda
www.linkedin.com/company/
westernequipmentdealersassociation/
twitter.com/WesternEDA

11979 ■ WEDA Scholarship Program *(Professional development/Scholarship)*

Purpose: To assist in the training, re-training, or advancement of employees or potential employees of the United States farm, industrial, and outdoor power equipment dealers. **Focus:** Agribusiness; Industry and trade. **Qualif.:** Applicants must be employees or potential employees of United States farm, outdoor power and industrial equipment dealers, subject to the following conditions such applicants must be approved by the dealer principal for training, re-training or professional advancement; enrolled or

Awards are arranged alphabetically below their administering organizations

accepted in a higher education curriculum, which is approved by the dealer principal as training applicable to the dealership's needs; and, enrolled full-time in the approved course of study; lastly, dealer principals must be willing to provide matching scholarship funds in the amount fixed by the WEDA and must be current members of Western Equipment Dealers Association. Recipients may reapply in subsequent years. **Criteria:** At the WEDF Trustees Meeting, awards from each category will be assigned. If scholarship requests exceed funds available in any category, the scholarship awards will be made by random drawing. Funds remaining in any category may be re-directed to another scholarship category at the discretion of the Trustees.

Funds Avail.: Up to $1,000. **Duration:** Annual. **To Apply:** Scholarship form and application are available online at www.westernequipfoundation.org/scholarships **Deadline:** April 30.

11980 ■ Western Golf Association (WGA)

2501 Patriot Blvd
Glenview, IL 60026-8022
Ph: (847)724-4600
URL: www.wgaesf.org
Social Media: www.facebook.com/EvansScholars
www.instagram.com/wgaesf
twitter.com/wgaesf

11981 ■ Chick Evans Caddie Scholarships
(Undergraduate/Scholarship)

Purpose: To help caddies to pursue education. **Focus:** General studies/Field of study not specified. **Qualif.:** Applicants must be caddies nominated by their club and have caddied, successfully and regularly, for a minimum of two years and also expected to caddie or work at their sponsoring club during the summer prior to the application; have completed junior year of high school with above B average in college preparatory courses and are required to take the ACT and/or the SAT; have clearly established their need for financial assistance; and have an outstanding character. **Criteria:** Selection will be outstanding in character, integrity and leadership; must clearly have a need for financial assistance.

Funds Avail.: No specific amount. **Duration:** Annual. **To Apply:** Applications can be submitted online; must submit personal information; high school information; caddie information; academic & extracurricular information; family financial information; photo; essay; additional application requirements. **Deadline:** September 30.

11982 ■ Western Governors' Association (WGA)

1600 Broadway, Ste. 1700
Denver, CO 80202-4901
Ph: (303)623-9378
Fax: (303)534-7309
URL: www.westgov.org
Social Media: www.facebook.com/westgov
www.linkedin.com/company/westgov
twitter.com/westgov
www.youtube.com/user/WestGov

11983 ■ Western Governors' Association "Celebrate the West" High School Art Competition *(High School/Award)*

Purpose: To recognize 2-D high school artists in the Western U.S. **Focus:** Art. **Qualif.:** Applicant must be a cur-

rently enrolled high school student residing in the Western U.S. states served by the Western Governors' Association. **Criteria:** Art submissions are judged based on originality, artistic skill, and the depiction of the theme.

Funds Avail.: $1,000 (Grand Prize); $500 (second place); $300 (third place); and 20 $200 awards for remaining state finalists. **Number Awarded:** 23. **To Apply:** Applicants can submit digital copy of 2-D artwork and entry for via email to the contact. Application form available online at westgov.org/celebrate-the-west/. **Deadline:** April 30.

11984 ■ Western Michigan Society Of Health Systems Pharmacists (WMSHP)

100 Michigan St., NE
Grand Rapids, MI 49503
E-mail: webmaster@wmshp.net
URL: www.wmshp.net
Social Media: facebook.com/wmshp
twitter.com/wmshp

11985 ■ WMSHP Scholarship *(Graduate/Scholarship)*

Purpose: To support the financial needs of a local pharmacy student. **Focus:** Pharmacy. **Criteria:** Recipients are selected based on demonstrated interest in health-system pharmacy and involvement in or leadership positions with professional organizations.

Funds Avail.: One $1,000 and one $500. **Duration:** Annual. **Number Awarded:** 1. **Deadline:** April 3. **Contact:** Stacy Brousseau; Phone: 269-341-7962; Email: brousses@bronsonhg.org.

11986 ■ Western Social Science Association (WSSA)

c/o Larry A. Gould, Professor Emeritus
2307 Chof Trl.
Flagstaff, AZ 86005
Ph: (928)606-2248
Fax: (928)525-2304
URL: www.wssaweb.com
Social Media: www.facebook.com/wssapage

11987 ■ WSSA Student Paper Competition *(Undergraduate, Graduate/Award, Monetary)*

Purpose: To encourage undergraduate and graduate students to present their research papers. **Focus:** General studies/Field of study not specified. **Qualif.:** Applicants must be undergraduate or graduate students. **Criteria:** Selection will be based on the committee's criteria.

Funds Avail.: No specific amount. **Number Awarded:** 1. **To Apply:** Applicants must be via email; subject line. Competitors must register.

11988 ■ Western Society of Criminology (WSC)

La Sierra Univ.
Department of Criminal Justice
1305 Corona Pointe Ct.
Corona, CA 92879
E-mail: secretary-treasurer@westerncriminology.org
URL: westerncriminology.org
Social Media: www.facebook.com/
westernsocietyofcriminology
twitter.com/WSCriminology

Awards are arranged alphabetically below their administering organizations

11989 ■ Libby Deschenes Prize for Applied Research *(Undergraduate/Prize)*

Purpose: To support criminology or criminal justice students. **Focus:** Criminal justice; Criminology. **Qualif.:** Applicants must be students interested in criminal justice or criminology field of study. **Criteria:** Selection will be based on who have demonstrated commitment in improving policy, practice, or programs in criminal justice through research or the application of research.

Funds Avail.: $500. **Duration:** Annual; up to 2 months. **To Apply:** Applicants must contact WSC office for further information and other required documents. **Contact:** WSC Awards Committee Chairperson: Charles Katz, at Charles.Katz@asu.edu.

11990 ■ June Morrison Scholarship Fund *(Undergraduate/Scholarship)*

Purpose: To financially assist undergraduate students and help defray the cost of attending the annual meeting. **Focus:** Criminal justice; Criminology. **Qualif.:** Applicants currently enrolled full-time or part-time in an academic degree program at either the undergraduate or graduate level is eligible to apply for this award; conference registration and student membership dues must be paid prior to the scholarship being awarded. **Criteria:** Recipients will be selected based on submitted materials.

Funds Avail.: $200-$300. **Duration:** Annual. **Number Awarded:** 1-2. **To Apply:** Applicants must submit a paper and must contact WSC office for further information and other required documents. **Deadline:** October 11. **Contact:** Dr. Hadar Aviram, Chairperson of the Awards Committee; E-mail: aviramh@uchastings.edu.

11991 ■ Miki Vohryzek-Bolden Student Paper Competition *(Undergraduate/Prize)*

Purpose: To support undergraduate students who are involved in criminal justice or criminology field. **Focus:** Criminal justice; Criminology. **Qualif.:** Applicants from all majors who are related to criminology, criminal justice, or criminal law and society; currently enrolled full-time or part-time in an academic degree program at either the undergraduate or graduate level is eligible to submit a paper; Papers must not exceed 30 pages, including abstract, text, references, tables and figures, notes; apers exceeding this limit will not be considered; apers must be double-spaced, typed in 12-point font on pages using one-inch margins, and conform to a standard format for the organization of papers and citation. **Criteria:** Recipients will be selected based on submitted materials.

Funds Avail.: $125-$250 (First place); $100 (Second place). **Duration:** Annual; up to 1 year. **To Apply:** Applicants must submit an original manuscript and must contact WSC office for further information and other required documents. **Deadline:** October 11. **Contact:** Dr. Hadar Aviram, Chairperson of the Awards Committee; E-mail: aviramh@uchastings.edu.

11992 ■ Western Society of Weed Science (WSWS)
Bldg. 4, Ste. 5
205 W Boutz Rd.
Las Cruces, NM 88005
URL: www.wsweedscience.org

11993 ■ Elena Sanchez Memorial WSWS Outstanding Student Scholarship Program *(Graduate, Undergraduate/Scholarship)*

Purpose: To encourage new weed science research and future weed science careers. **Focus:** Agricultural sciences; General studies/Field of study not specified. **Qualif.:** Applicants must be undergraduate or graduate students enrolled in a degree program (B.S., M.S., or PhD) at an accredited college or university in the western region; applicants must be current WSWS members at the time of application.

Funds Avail.: A total of $3,000. **Duration:** Annual. **Number Awarded:** 3. **To Apply:** Applicants must submit a completed and signed application form; one-page cover letter describing how applicants became interested in weed science, how applicant's research will contribute to the field of weed science and the WSWS objectives, and what future contributions applicants hopes to make to the field of weed science including career goals; 1 or 2-page resume highlighting recent relevant experience through school, work and/or internships; abstract submitted for paper or poster presentation at WSWS annual meeting; two letters of support, at least one of which must be from a college/university faculty member (preferably major advisor) familiar with the applicant's abilities, interests, and career goals; academic transcripts (unofficial copy is acceptable). **Deadline:** October 1. **Contact:** WSWS Student Liaison Chair Lucas Kopecky Bobadilla; Email: lucask3@illinois.edu.

11994 ■ Western Thoracic Surgical Association (WTSA)
500 Cummings Ctr., Ste. 4550
Beverly, MA 01915
Ph: (978)927-8330
Fax: (978)524-0498
URL: www.westernthoracic.org

11995 ■ Donald B. Doty Educational Award *(Advanced Professional/Award, Grant)*

Purpose: To foster innovative educational initiatives in cardiothoracic surgery by WTSA members, and encourage the dissemination of the information to academic institutions and training centers. **Focus:** Education, Medical; Medicine; Surgery. **Qualif.:** Applicants must be active senior WTSA members in good standing.

Funds Avail.: $10,000. **Duration:** Annual. **Number Awarded:** 1. **To Apply:** Applicants must submit a completed WTSA Donald B. Doty Education Award Application to the WTSA Administrative Officers no later than the deadline. **Deadline:** march 31. **Remarks:** Established in 2005.

11996 ■ Western Washington University Alumni Association
516 High St., MS 9199
Bellingham, WA 98225
Ph: (360)650-3353
Free: 800-676-6885
E-mail: alumni@wwu.edu
URL: alumni.wwu.edu
Social Media: www.facebook.com/WWUAlumni
www.instagram.com/wwu_alumni
twitter.com/WWUAlumni
www.youtube.com/user/WWUalumni

Awards are arranged alphabetically below their administering organizations

11997 ■ Why Get Your Blue On? Video Scholarships (Graduate, Undergraduate/Award, Scholarship)

Purpose: To support current, full-time students enrolled at Western Washington University. **Focus:** General studies/Field of study not specified. **Qualif.:** Applicant must be a current, full-time student at Western Washington University, and must have a valid user account with YouTube. **Criteria:** Scholarship Committee will take into consideration the following factors when evaluating the video submission: creativity, originality, uniqueness, and ingenuity demonstrated in the video; relevance, how well the video related to wearing the blue and WWU.

Funds Avail.: $250-$1,000. **Number Awarded:** 3. **To Apply:** Applicants must create a 5 minute (or less) video response to the question, "Why Get Your Blue On?"; submit a completed Official Entry Form, after successfully uploaded the video on YouTube.

11998 ■ W. Garfield Weston Foundation

22 St. Clair Ave. E Ste. 2001
Toronto, ON, Canada M4T 2S3
E-mail: foundation@westonfoundation.ca
URL: www.westonfoundation.org

11999 ■ Weston Family Awards in Northern Research (Doctorate, Master's/Award)

Purpose: To support significant research and studies about scientific issues facing the North. **Focus:** Canadian studies. **Qualif.:** Applicants must be a Canadian citizen or permanent resident; be enrolled full time in college or university at the time of application and over the tenure of your award. **Criteria:** Selection will be based on academic record, research ability, leadership skills, the potential benefit of the research, referees' reports, and the applicants' interest in, and commitment to the North and northern studies.

Funds Avail.: No specific amount. **To Apply:** Applicants must submit the application form, referee's reports, transcripts and additional questions. **Remarks:** The awards are also administered by the Association of Canadian Universities for Northern Science and the Wildlife Conservation Society Canada.

12000 ■ Weston Brain Institute International Fellowships in Neuroscience (Graduate/Fellowship)

Purpose: To provide funding to students who wish to advance their research on neurodegenerative disease of aging abroad in world-renowned labs and research universities. **Focus:** Neuroscience. **Qualif.:** Applicants must be registered full-time senior Ph.D. graduate students at University of Toronto; must be Canadian citizens or permanent residents in Canada. **Criteria:** Selection will be based on distinguished record of academic achievement, as well as the ability to demonstrate their promise as top-tier researchers and future leaders of their respective field.

Funds Avail.: 60,000 Canadian Dollars per year. **Duration:** Annual. **Number Awarded:** 1. **To Apply:** Applicants must submit completed and signed application form; Transcripts from all attended universities (certified photocopies permitted); Letter of support from current supervisor; Letter of support from receiving/hosting institution. **Deadline:** March 1. **Remarks:** The fellowships are administered through the Weston Brain Institute.

12001 ■ Weston Brain Institute Rapid Response Program (Postdoctorate, Advanced Professional, Professional development/Grant)

Purpose: To catalyze and jumpstart the development of safe and effective treatments for neurodegenerative diseases of aging. **Focus:** Neuroscience. **Qualif.:** Applicants must be researchers working in Canada at least 30% of the time at or above the level of Postdoctoral Fellow, and affiliated with a Canada Revenue Agency-qualified donee institution located in Canada. **Criteria:** Selection will be based on the letters of intent, research proposals and other criteria of the committee.

Funds Avail.: $10,000 to $200,000 Canadian Dollars. **Duration:** Annual. **To Apply:** Applicants must submit a letter of intent, and they will receive feedback from the scientific review committee. Applicants with high potential projects will be invited to submit a proposal; instructions for submitting the proposal will be forwarded to those invited in July current year. **Remarks:** The grants are administered through the Weston Brain Institute.

12002 ■ Wexner Foundation

8000 Walton Pky., Ste. 110
New Albany, OH 43054
Ph: (614)939-6060
E-mail: info@wexner.net
URL: www.wexnerfoundation.org
Social Media: www.facebook.com/WexnerFoundation
www.linkedin.com/company/wexner-foundation
twitter.com/Wexnertweets

12003 ■ Wexner Graduate Fellowship / Davidson Scholars Program (Graduate/Fellowship)

Purpose: To encourage promising candidates to successfully meet the challenges of professional Jewish leadership in the North American Jewish community. **Focus:** Jewish studies; Religion.

Duration: Annual. **Number Awarded:** 20. **To Apply:** Applicants must complete the application online; must submit academic transcripts (undergraduate and, if applicable, graduate); scores from the General Test of the Graduate Record Examination (Institution No. 3134); three letters of recommendation; and confirmation letter or acceptance letter. **Remarks:** Established in 1988.

12004 ■ Weyburn Credit Union

PO Box 1117
Weyburn, SK, Canada S4H 2L3
Ph: (306)842-6641
Fax: (306)842-2135
Free: 800-567-8111
E-mail: info@weyburn.cu.sk.ca
URL: www.weyburncu.ca
Social Media: facebook.com/weyburncu
instagram.com/weyburncreditunion
linkedin.com/company/weyburn-credit-union
twitter.com/WeyburnCU

12005 ■ C.H.(Chuck) Hodgson Scholarships (Undergraduate/Scholarship)

Purpose: To provide financial assistance to students who want to pursue their college education. **Focus:** General studies/Field of study not specified. **Qualif.:** Applicants

---

Awards are arranged alphabetically below their administering organizations

must be recently graduated grade 12 students under age 21 who have been out of High School for at least one year; must be a member of Weyburn Credit Union; must be enrolled full time (3 or more classes) at the Southeast Regional College. **Criteria:** Selection will be given on the basis of academic excellence, good citizenship, and effort.

Funds Avail.: $750 Canadian Dollars. **Duration:** Annual. **Number Awarded:** 2. **To Apply:** Applicants must submit the following application form; resume; a brief description of any clubs, groups, organizations, etc. in which they are involved, what the group achieved and, most important, what part they played, time which they invested in working with the group and what they contributed to the group's success; on an individual level, should include: any individual achievements over the past years and how they achieved them; how and why they chose their particular area of post-secondary study; future goals and ambitions. Must also include letters of reference; these letters should come from people who can give a good evaluation and recommendation of the character (i.e. school counselors, principals, homeroom teachers, youth leaders, part-time employer; or any other individual); the application may include as many letters of reference as applicants wish. **Deadline:** November 15.

12006 ■ Q. O. (Quint) Patrick Scholarships
(Undergraduate/Scholarship)

Purpose: To provide financial assistance to graduated high school students who want to pursue their college education. **Focus:** General studies/Field of study not specified. **Qualif.:** Applicants must be mature students, defined as someone age 21 or older; must be members of Weyburn Credit Union; must be enrolled full time (3 or more classes) at the Southeast Regional College. **Criteria:** Selection will be given on the basis of academic excellence, good citizenship, and effort.

Funds Avail.: $750 Canadian Dollars. **Duration:** Annual. **Number Awarded:** 2. **To Apply:** Applicants must submit the following application form; resume; a brief description of any clubs, groups, organizations, etc. in which they are involved, what the group achieved and, most important, what part they played, time which they invested in working with the group and what they contributed to the group's success; on an individual level, applicants should include: any individual achievements over the past years and how they achieved them; how and why they chose their particular area of post-secondary study; future goals and ambitions; must also include letters of reference; these letters should come from people who can give a good evaluation and recommendation of the character (i.e. school counselors, principals, homeroom teachers, youth leaders, part-time employer; or any other individual); the application may include as many letters of reference as applicants wish. **Deadline:** November 15.

12007 ■ R.S. Williamson & Eliford Mott Memorial Scholarships *(Undergraduate/Scholarship)*

Purpose: To provide financial assistance to graduating high school students. **Focus:** General studies/Field of study not specified. **Qualif.:** Applicants must be post-secondary education, with a preference to institutions in Saskatchewan; must be members of Weyburn Credit Union. **Criteria:** Selection will be given on the basis of academic excellence, good citizenship and effort.

Funds Avail.: 1,000 Canadian Dollars each. **Duration:** Annual; up to 2 years. **Number Awarded:** 3. **To Apply:** Applicants must submit the following application form; resume;

a brief description of any clubs, groups, organizations, etc. in which they are involved, what the group achieved and, most important, what part they played, time which they invested in working with the group and what they contributed to the group's success; on an individual level, applicants should include: any individual achievements over the past years and how they achieved them; how and why they chose their particular area of post-secondary study; future goals and ambitions; must also include letters of reference; these letters should come from people who can give a good evaluation and recommendation of the character (i.e. school counselors, principals, homeroom teachers, youth leaders, part-time employer; or any other individual); the application may include as many letters of reference as wish.

12008 ■ Whirly-Girls International Women Helicopter Pilots
Tryon, NC
URL: www.whirlygirls.org
Social Media: www.facebook.com/whirlygirlsinternational
www.instagram.com/whirly_girls_intl
twitter.com/whirlygirlsintl

12009 ■ Advanced Mountain Flight Training Scholarship *(Professional development, Vocational/Occupational/Scholarship)*

Purpose: To provide Whirly-Girl members the skills to cope with turbulence, rugged terrain, landing zone selection, in mountainous and canyon areas, with special emphasis placed on decision making. **Focus:** Aviation. **Qualif.:** Must be a helicopter pilot with at least a private certificate/license; be a member in good standing at the time of application submission, award of scholarship, during training. **Criteria:** Goal for the flight training specified, experience, achievements, attitude; neatness, ability to follow instructions, completeness and accuracy of your application; reliability, motivation, and commitment to success; dedication to career; ability to accept responsibility and teamwork; financial need.

Funds Avail.: $6,500. **Duration:** Annual. **To Apply:** Complete online application. **Deadline:** October 12.

12010 ■ Flight Safety International Bell 206/Bell 407 Scholarship *(Professional development, Vocational/Occupational/Scholarship)*

Purpose: To pay for training available at FlightSafety's Helicopter Learning Center of Excellence in Lafayette, Louisiana, USA. **Focus:** Aviation. **Qualif.:** Must be a helicopter pilot with at least a private certificate/license; be a member in good standing at the time of application submission, award of scholarship, during training. **Criteria:** Goal for the flight training specified, experience, achievements, attitude; neatness, ability to follow instructions, completeness and accuracy of your application; reliability, motivation, and commitment to success; dedication to career; ability to accept responsibility and teamwork; financial need.

Funds Avail.: $10,000. **Duration:** Annual. **To Apply:** Complete online application. **Deadline:** October 12.

12011 ■ James Wisecup Memorial Flight Training Scholarship *(Vocational/Occupational, Advanced Professional/Scholarship)*

Purpose: This scholarship may be applied towards the cost of upgrading or advancing a current helicopter rating.

Awards are arranged alphabetically below their administering organizations

Focus: Aviation. **Qualif.:** Must be a helicopter pilot with at least a private certificate/license; be a member in good standing at the time of application submission, award of scholarship, during training. **Criteria:** Goal for the flight training specified, experience, achievements, attitude; neatness, ability to follow instructions, completeness and accuracy of your application; reliability, motivation, and commitment to success; dedication to career; ability to accept responsibility and teamwork; financial need.

Funds Avail.: $10,000. **Duration:** Annual. **To Apply:** Complete online application. **Deadline:** October 12.

12012 ■ Robinson Helicopter R22/R44 Safety Course Scholarship (*Professional development/ Scholarship*)

Purpose: To provide Whirly-Girl members the opportunity to attend the Robinson Helicopter Safety Course and build R44 time. **Focus:** Aviation. **Qualif.:** Must be a helicopter pilot with at least a private certificate/license; be a member in good standing at the time of application submission, award of scholarship, during training. **Criteria:** Goal for the flight training specified, experience, achievements, attitude; neatness, ability to follow instructions, completeness and accuracy of your application; reliability, motivation, and commitment to success; dedication to career; ability to accept responsibility and teamwork; financial need.

Funds Avail.: $3,000. **Duration:** Annual. **To Apply:** Complete online application. **Deadline:** December 31.

12013 ■ Whirly-Girls Helicopter Add-On Flight Training Scholarship (*Professional development, Vocational/Occupational/Scholarship*)

Purpose: To assist a certificated female pilot who does not currently have a helicopter rating. **Focus:** Aviation; Women's studies. **Qualif.:** Applicants must be members of Whirly-Girl in good standing for one year. **Criteria:** Goal for the flight training specified, experience, achievements, attitude; neatness, ability to follow instructions, completeness and accuracy of your application; reliability, motivation, and commitment to success; dedication to career; ability to accept responsibility and teamwork; financial need.

Funds Avail.: $8,000. **Duration:** Annual. **To Apply:** Complete online application. **Deadline:** October 12.

12014 ■ Whirly-Girls Jean Tinsley Memorial HELI-EXPO Scholarship (*Professional development, Vocational/Occupational/Scholarship*)

Purpose: To finance a trip to the annual awards banquet and access to the expo floor, training seminars, and associated events at the HAI HELI-EXPO. **Focus:** Aviation. **Qualif.:** Must be a helicopter pilot with at least a private certificate/license; be a member in good standing at the time of application submission, award of scholarship, during training. **Criteria:** Goal for the flight training specified, experience, achievements, attitude; neatness, ability to follow instructions, completeness and accuracy of your application; reliability, motivation, and commitment to success; dedication to career; ability to accept responsibility and teamwork; financial need. Preference will be given to a Whirly-Girl who has not previously attended HAI HELI-EXPO.

Funds Avail.: $2,400. **Duration:** Annual. **To Apply:** Complete online application. **Deadline:** October 12.

12015 ■ White Glove Moving
235 West 1st St.
Bayonne, NJ 07002

Free: 800-340-1911
URL: www.whiteglovemoving.us
Social Media: www.facebook.com/WhiteGloveMoving
twitter.com/WGMoving
www.youtube.com/channel/UCDTgTpJUjHzm31A3tHOITAg

12016 ■ White Gloves Scholarship (*Undergraduate/ Scholarship*)

Purpose: To provide financial support to students who have a stories to tell and who have overcome obstacles in their lives. **Focus:** General studies/Field of study not specified. **Qualif.:** Applicant must be freshman or sophomore enrolled or registered at a post-secondary institution. **Criteria:** Selection will be based on financial need and the applicant's story on overcoming obstacles.

Funds Avail.: $1,000. **Duration:** Annual. **Number Awarded:** 1. **To Apply:** Applicant must submit the following: all personal information; parent/guardian information if under 18 years old; all financial information regarding tuition and other college costs; all financial information regarding other scholarships, grants, loans, and other methods of income); copy of college acceptance letter; copy of high school/college transcripts; personal essay explaining why applicant is deserving of the scholarship; and a copy of the FAFSA. Applications available online at www.whiteglovemoving.us/scholarship/. **Deadline:** July 15. **Contact:** Dan Szwed, 235 West 1st St., Bayonne, NJ, 07002; Phone: 201-705-1996; Email: dan@ whiteglovemoving.us.

12017 ■ Whitfield Bryson & Mason LLP
518 Monroe St.
Nashville, TN 37208
Ph: (615)921-6500
E-mail: info@wbmllp.com
URL: www.nashvillepersonalinjurylawyerwbm.com
Social Media: www.facebook.com/wbmllp/
www.linkedin.com/company/whitfield-bryson-&-mason-llp
twitter.com/WBMattorneys
www.youtube.com/user/wbmllp

12018 ■ Disabled Veteran Student Scholarship (*Two Year College, Four Year College/Scholarship*)

Purpose: To give back to those who have served by helping them achieve their dreams of obtaining an education. **Focus:** General studies/Field of study not specified. **Qualif.:** Veterans of any branch of the U.S. Armed Forces who have a disability rating of 30% or higher. **Criteria:** Selection will be made by scholarship committee.

Funds Avail.: $1,000. **Number Awarded:** 2. **To Apply:** Complete and submit online application. Optional: submit essay up to 800 words about how your military service has changed your life. **Deadline:** January 26. **Contact:** Whitfield, Bryson & Mason LLP,1205 4th Ave. N, Nashville, TN, 37208; Phone: 615-921-6500.

12019 ■ Helen Hay Whitney Foundation (HHWF)
20 Squadron Blvd., Ste. 630
New City, NY 10956
Ph: (845)639-6799
Fax: (845)639-6798
E-mail: hhwf@earthlink.net
URL: www.hhwf.org

Awards are arranged alphabetically below their administering organizations

12020 ■ Helen Hay Whitney Foundation Postdoctoral Research Fellowship *(Postdoctorate, Master's/Fellowship)*

Purpose: To support early postdoctoral research training in all basic biomedical sciences. **Focus:** Biomedical research. **Criteria:** Selection will be based on committee's criteria; personal interview reports and applications will be reviewed.

Funds Avail.: Amount varies. **Duration:** Annual; up to three years. **Number Awarded:** Varies. **To Apply:** Applications must be submitted through online; following items are to be sent directly to the Foundation by the referee or supervisor, not to be uploaded along with the application: 4 Reference Letters; 1 Letter from Prospective Supervisor; following items are to be submitted by the applicant, and uploaded along with the application: 2-Page Application Cover; Form Application Items 1-6; If applicable, up to three significant publications; If applicable, a Financial Officer's Letter; If applicable, Collaboration Letter; If applicable, If applicable, a Copy of Proof of US Citizenship (only for US citizens working outside USA). **Deadline:** June 15. **Remarks:** Established in 1947. **Contact:** The Helen Hay Whitney Foundation, 20 Squadron Blvd., Ste. 630, New City, NY, 10956; Phone: 845-639-6799; Fax: 845-639-6798; Email: office@hhwf.org.

12021 ■ Elie Wiesel Foundation for Humanity

555 Madison Ave.
New York, NY 10022
Ph: (212)490-7788
E-mail: info@eliewieselfoundation.org
URL: www.eliewieselfoundation.org
Social Media: www.facebook.com/eliewieselfdn
www.instagram.com/explore/locations/1018416175/united -states/new-york-new-york/the-elie-wiesel-foundation-for -humanity
www.in.pinterest.com/pin/192669690287680966

12022 ■ Elie Wiesel Prize in Ethics *(Undergraduate/ Prize, Award)*

Purpose: To challenge students to examine and analyze urgent ethical issues confronting them in today's complex world. **Focus:** General studies/Field of study not specified. **Qualif.:** Applicants must be full-time undergraduate juniors and seniors at accredited four-year colleges and universities in the United States.

Funds Avail.: 1st Prize-$5,000; 2nd Prize-$2,500; 3rd Prize-$1,500; Two Honorable Mentions-$500 each. **Duration:** Annual. **Number Awarded:** 3. **Deadline:** January 21. **Remarks:** Established in 1989. **Contact:** The Elie Wiesel Foundation For Humanity, 555 Madison Ave., 20th Fl., New York, NY, 10022; Phone: 212-490-7788.

12023 ■ Wigs.com

12001 N Central Expy., Ste. 950
Dallas, TX 75243
Free: 800-581-2001
URL: www.wigs.com
Social Media: www.facebook.com/wigsonline
twitter.com/wigscom

12024 ■ Hair Loss Scholarship *(College, University, Undergraduate, Graduate, Two Year College, Vocational/Occupational/Scholarship)*

Purpose: To provide support for students suffering from any form of hair loss. **Focus:** General studies/Field of study

not specified. **Qualif.:** Applicant must have a form of hair loss (such as alopecia, trichotillomania, chemotherapy, and illness-related hair loss) and be currently enrolled in a college or university (either attending classes or waiting for classes to begin); and have a minimum 3.0 GPA. **Criteria:** Entries will be judged based on ambitions, GPA, writings skills and/or creativity, goals, stories, and any other outstanding criteria.

Funds Avail.: $1,000. **Number Awarded:** 1. **To Apply:** Applicants must submit the following via email: essay, high school transcripts, proof of college or university enrollment, and a completed scholarship application (which can be downloaded online). **Deadline:** July 16. **Contact:** Email:marketing@beautyandhair.com.

12025 ■ Wild Felid Research and Management Association (WFA)

PO Box 3335
Montrose, CO 81402-3335
URL: www.wildfelid.org

12026 ■ Wild Felid Legacy Scholarship *(Graduate/ Scholarship)*

Purpose: To provide financial support to a graduate-level university student conducting research on wild fields. **Focus:** Wildlife conservation, management, and science. **Criteria:** Selection will be based on demonstrated need for financial aid; participation in a research project that aims to improve our understanding of wild field biology, management and/or conservation; undergraduate and graduate GPA.

Duration: Annual. **To Apply:** Applicants must submit a completed application form; current resume; Bachelor's Degree transcript; graduate studies transcript or copy of acceptance letter into a graduate program in wildlife biology, wildlife management or any related natural resource fields; two reference letters from professor and supervisor; short essay (500-750 words) describing interests in wild field research, career goals and usage of award to further professional development, demonstration of financial need. **Deadline:** March 30.

12027 ■ Wilderness Medical Society (WMS)

6705 W. Hwy 290, Suite 502-243
Austin, TX 78735
Ph: (512)379-5399
Fax: (512)379-5388
URL: www.wms.org

12028 ■ Charles S. Houston Grant *(Advanced Professional/Grant)*

Purpose: To support medical students who are taking research in the field of wilderness and environmental medicine. **Focus:** Medical research. **Qualif.:** Applicants must be medical students. **Criteria:** Selection will be on a competitive basis.

Funds Avail.: $5,000. **Duration:** Annual. **To Apply:** Applicants should submit their proposal by electronically. **Deadline:** October 1. **Contact:** contact: Gabi Glass, Email: gabi@wms.org.

12029 ■ Research-in-Training Grant *(Doctorate/ Grant)*

Purpose: To provide funding for a research project in the field of wilderness medicine. **Focus:** Health care services;

Awards are arranged alphabetically below their administering organizations

Medicine. **Qualif.:** Applicants must be a member in good standing of the WMS; applicant has not received a WMS grant in the past year (previous grant cycle), the project should completed within one year of grant award.

Funds Avail.: $5,000. **Duration:** Annual. **To Apply:** Applicants should submit their proposal by electronically. **Deadline:** October 1. **Contact:** Email:gabi@wms.org.

12030 ■ The Wilderness Society

1615 M St. NW
Washington, DC 20036
Free: 800-843-9453
E-mail: member@tws.org
URL: wilderness.org
Social Media: www.facebook.com/TheWildernessSociety
www.linkedin.com/company/the-wilderness-society
twitter.com/Wilderness

12031 ■ Gloria Barron Wilderness Society Scholarship *(Graduate, Undergraduate/Scholarship)*

Purpose: To encourage individuals who have the potential to make a significant positive difference in the long term protection of wilderness in North America. **Focus:** Conservation of natural resources. **Criteria:** Selection is based on submitted application materials.

Funds Avail.: $10,000. **Duration:** Annual. **Number Awarded:** 1. **To Apply:** Applicants must submit a two-page double-spaced cover letter; 3-5 page double-spaced proposal; current resume or curriculum vitae; two letters of recommendation describing the applicant's ability to meet the objectives of the scholarship and proposed work; and undergraduate and graduate transcripts (official or unofficial). **Remarks:** The scholarship was created by T. A. Barron. **Contact:** Application E-mail: barron_scholarship@tws.org; Query E-mail: barbara_young@tws.org.

12032 ■ Wilkinson & Company L.L.P.

888 Sidney St.
Belleville, ON, Canada K8N 4Z5
Ph: (613)966-5105
Fax: (613)962-7072
Free: 888-728-3890
E-mail: belleville@wilkinson.net
URL: www.wilkinson.net
Social Media: www.facebook.com/
WilkinsonAndCompanyLLP

12033 ■ Wilkinson and Company LLP Scholarships *(Undergraduate/Scholarship)*

Purpose: To provide financial support to students with the highest marks in a business-related course so they may pursue further education. **Focus:** Business. **Qualif.:** Scholarships are presented to each of the secondary schools in the Quinte and Kingston area. **Criteria:** Selection will be based on the committee's criteria.

Funds Avail.: 300 Canadian Dollars. **Duration:** Annual. **Contact:** Email: hrdept@wilkinson.net.

12034 ■ Willamette University

900 State St.
Salem, OR 97301
Ph: (503)370-6300

E-mail: ask@willamette.edu
URL: www.willamette.edu
Social Media: www.facebook.com/Willamette
www.linkedin.com/school/willamette-university
www.pinterest.com/LibrarianOddities/willamette-university
twitter.com/willamette_u

12035 ■ Mary Stuart Rogers Scholarship *(Undergraduate/Scholarship)*

Purpose: To provide financial support to individuals who wish to pursue their studies. **Focus:** General studies/Field of study not specified. **Qualif.:** Applicants must be Sophomore and junior students who demonstrate sufficient financial need and meet the minimum 3.20 GPA.

Funds Avail.: $5,000. **Duration:** Annual. **To Apply:** Applicants must submit a two prompts (maximum of 1,000 words) and save the document as Lastname.Firstname.MSR.pdf; a faculty letter of evaluation. **Deadline:** April 13. **Contact:** Office of Financial Aid, 0615 SW Palatine Hill Rd., Portland, OR 97219-7899; Phone: 503-768-7090; Fax: 503-768-7074; E-mail: fao@lclark.edu.

12036 ■ The Williams Chorale

PO Box 3267
Attleboro, MA 02703
URL: www.thewilliamschorale.org

12037 ■ Williams Chorale Bacardi Fallon Scholarships *(High School/Award, Scholarship)*

Purpose: To help area high school juniors or seniors in their pursuit of a musical education. **Focus:** Education, Music. **Qualif.:** Applicants must be a high school junior or senior pursuing vocal or instrumental studies. **Criteria:** Selection is based on the application recording.

Funds Avail.: Varies. **Duration:** Annual. **Number Awarded:** Varies. **To Apply:** Application recording must include at least 5 minutes of total playing time and must include at least two movements of contrasting style. All recording submissions must be on compact discs. **Deadline:** March 5. **Contact:** Mr. Peter J. Williams, c/o The Williams Chorale; P.O. Box 3267, South Attleboro, MA 02703.

12038 ■ John G. Williams Scholarship Foundation

PO Box 1229
Camp Hill, PA 17001-1229
Ph: (717)795-9880
URL: www.jgwfoundation.org

12039 ■ John G. Williams Scholarship Foundation *(Undergraduate/Scholarship)*

Purpose: To provide financial assistance to deserving students for their pursuit of college and/or post-graduate educational opportunities. **Focus:** General studies/Field of study not specified. **Criteria:** Recipients of financial assistance from the Foundation shall be encouraged to recognize their responsibility as citizens and encouraged to perform services of a civic and humanitarian nature.

Funds Avail.: No specific amount. **Duration:** Annual. **Deadline:** June 15. **Remarks:** Established in 1985.

12040 ■ Wilshire Law Firm, PLC

3055 Wilshire Blvd., 12th Fl.
Los Angeles, CA 90010

Awards are arranged alphabetically below their administering organizations

Ph: (213)381-9988
Fax: (213)381-9989
URL: wilshirelawfirm.com
Social Media: www.facebook.com/WilshireLawFirm
instagram.com/wilshirelawfirmplc
www.linkedin.com/company/wilshire-law-firm-plc
twitter.com/wilshirelawfirm

12041 ■ Wilshire Law Firm Scholarship *(Undergraduate, Graduate/Scholarship)*

Purpose: To encourage and assist a motivated student who has demonstrated academic excellence and a commitment to the community, and wants to become a lawyer. **Focus:** Law. **Qualif.:** Applicant must be planning to pursue a career in the legal field; U.S. citizen or permanent resident. **Criteria:** Strong academic achievements, demonstrated commitment to the community.

Funds Avail.: $1,000. **To Apply:** Submit complete application with a typed essay and unofficial copy of college transcripts via fax or email. **Deadline:** June 30. **Contact:** Email: scholarship@wilshirelawfirm.com.

12042 ■ Woodrow Wilson International Center for Scholars (WWICS)

1 Woodrow Wilson Plz.
1300 Pennsylvania Ave. NW
Washington, DC 20004-3027
Ph: (202)691-4000
Fax: (202)691-4001
E-mail: wwics@wilsoncenter.org
URL: www.wilsoncenter.org
Social Media: www.facebook.com/woodrowwilsoncenter
www.instagram.com/thewilsoncenter
www.linkedin.com/company/woodrow-wilson-international
  -center-for-scholars
twitter.com/thewilsoncenter
www.youtube.com/user/woodrowwilsoncenter

12043 ■ Woodrow Wilson International Center for Scholars Fellowships *(Doctorate, Postdoctorate/Fellowship)*

Purpose: To support individuals conduct an independent research on national and/or international issues addressing key public policy challenges. **Focus:** General studies/Field of study not specified.

Funds Avail.: No specific amount. **Duration:** Annual; nine months. **To Apply:** Applicants may submit their applications online; if submitted by mail, a complete application must include the following a two-page, single-sided Fellowship application form; not to exceed three page list of publications that include exact titles, names of the publishers, dates of publication and status of forthcoming publications; not to exceed five single-spaced typed pages, using 12-point, typed project proposal; maximum of three pages of bibliography for the project that includes primary sources and relevant secondary sources; and a one-page financial information form; all application materials must be submitted in English; two reference letters must be submitted directly to the Center by the referees or mailed with the application. **Deadline:** October 1.

12044 ■ Woodrow Wilson National Fellowship Foundation (WW)

104 Carnegie Ctr., Ste. 301
Princeton, NJ 08540

Ph: (609)452-7007
Fax: (609)452-0066
E-mail: communications@woodrow.org
URL: www.woodrow.org

12045 ■ Leonore Annenberg Teaching Fellowships *(Graduate/Fellowship)*

Purpose: To support future leaders who are developing their career in several critical fields. **Focus:** Education, Secondary. **Qualif.:** Applicants must be recent college graduates and career-changers who agree to work in urban and rural secondary schools serving high proportions of disadvantaged students. **Criteria:** Selection will be based on the committee's criteria.

Funds Avail.: $30,000. **Duration:** Annual. **To Apply:** Applicants may visit the website for further details and application information. **Contact:** Email: wwteachingfellowship@woodrow.org; Phone: 609-452-7007 ext. 141.

12046 ■ Doris Duke Conservation Fellows Program *(Master's/Fellowship)*

Purpose: To support future conservation leaders. **Focus:** Conservation of natural resources; General studies/Field of study not specified. **Qualif.:** Applicants must be students enrolled in multidisciplinary master's programs at a selected group of partner universities. **Criteria:** Selection will be based on the committee's criteria.

To Apply: Applicants must submit a completed application form available on the website. **Remarks:** Established in 1997. **Contact:** Woodrow Wilson National Fellowship Foundation, at the above address.

12047 ■ MMUF Dissertation Grants *(Graduate/Grant)*

Purpose: To support students who are in their critical juncture of completing their graduate degrees. **Focus:** General studies/Field of study not specified. **Qualif.:** Applicants must be at least 35 years old and have a demonstrated record of outstanding professional accomplishments, service to community, service to the legal profession, and developments of subordinates. **Criteria:** Selection will be based on the committee's criteria.

Funds Avail.: Up to $20,000. **Duration:** 12-month period. **To Apply:** Applications must include the following a three-page prospectus; a draft dissertation chapter; a three-page personal statement; an official graduate transcript; two letters of recommendation - one from the dissertation director and one from another academic knowledgeable about the Fellow's academic performance and/or familiar with the Fellow's dissertation project and its contribution to the field of scholarship; official budget form; a declaration of previous fellowship awards. **Deadline:** December 1. **Contact:** Danielle McColgan, Program Associate; Email: mccolgan@woodrow.org.

12048 ■ MMUF Travel and Research Grants *(Graduate, Undergraduate/Grant)*

Purpose: To provide eligible graduate students with the financial means to complete their research prior to the start of dissertation writing. **Focus:** General studies/Field of study not specified. **Qualif.:** Applicants must be Mellon Mays Undergraduate Fellows and candidates for the PhD degree in the fields recognized under the terms of the Mellon Mays Undergraduate Fellowship Program; all candidates must have passed all comprehensive examinations, completed all course work for the degree and selected a

Awards are arranged alphabetically below their administering organizations

dissertation topic that has been approved by the dissertation advisor. **Criteria:** Selection will be based on the committee's criteria.

Funds Avail.: Up to $5,000. **Duration:** One summer or one semester. **To Apply:** Applications must include the following official application form; a resume; a personal statement as outlined in the application; an official budget form (funding may be applied to travel to research sites, cost of meals and lodging at research sites, photocopying or microfilming of documents, purchase of access to research databases, fees for use of research facilities, and other research-related expenses); an official graduate transcript; and a brief letter of recommendation (two-page maximum) from the dissertation advisor endorsing the request for funding. **Deadline:** March 13.

12049 ■ Charlotte W. Newcombe Doctoral Dissertation Fellowship *(Graduate/Fellowship)*

Purpose: To support students in the final stages of doctoral study whose work offers significant potential for advancing academic scholarship related to ethics or religion. **Focus:** Ethics and bioethics; Religion. **Criteria:** Selection will be based on the committee's criteria.

Funds Avail.: $25,000. **Duration:** Annual. **Remarks:** Established in 1981. **Contact:** Newcombe Doctoral Dissertation Fellowships: The Woodrow Wilson National Fellowship Foundation, P.O. Box, 5281, Princeton, NJ, 08543-5281 Phone: (609) 452-7007 Email: www.woodrow.org/newcombe.

12050 ■ The Thomas R. Pickering Foreign Affairs Fellowship *(Graduate, Undergraduate/Fellowship)*

Purpose: To provide funding to participants as they are prepared academically and professionally to enter the United States Department of State Foreign Service. **Focus:** Business; Economics; Foreign languages; International affairs and relations; Political science; Public administration; Sociology.

Remarks: The fellowship is named in honor of Ambassador Pickering, one of the most distinguished and capable American diplomats of the latter half of the 20th century.

12051 ■ Woodrow Wilson Dissertation Fellowship in Women's Studies *(Doctorate/Fellowship)*

Purpose: To encourage original and significant research about women that crosses disciplinary, regional, or cultural boundaries. **Focus:** Women's studies.

Funds Avail.: $5,000 each. **Duration:** Annual. **To Apply:** Applications must be submitted online along with doctoral transcript; two (2) letters of recommendation. **Deadline:** October 15. **Remarks:** Established in 1974.

12052 ■ Woodrow Wilson-Rockefeller Brothers Fund Fellowships for Aspiring Teachers of Color *(Undergraduate/Fellowship)*

Purpose: To support future leaders who are developing their career stages in several critical fields. **Focus:** Education, Secondary. **Qualif.:** Applicant must: be a person of color (African American/Black, Asian, Hispanic, Latino(a), Native American) in senior year of high school or undergraduate preparation; be nominated by an eligible nominating institution; demonstrate a commitment to the program and its goals; have US citizenship or permanent residency; have substantial background in the arts and sciences and high academic performance with a cumulative undergraduate GPA of 3.0 or better on a 4.0 scale (negotiable for ap-

plicants from institutions that do not employ a 4.0 GPA scale); not currently in a teacher preparation program which leads to initial teacher certification. **Criteria:** Selection will be based on the committee's criteria.

Funds Avail.: $30,000. **To Apply:** Applicant must visit the website for application and registration; information required on the application includes educational background; preference(s) of master's program(s); two 500-word essays; contact information for the two recommenders applicant asked to write letters for them; personal information; additional information; in addition to online application, applicants must submit a resume, two recommendations, and official transcripts. **Contact:** Woodrow Wilson National Fellowship Foundation, at the above address.

12053 ■ Wilson Ornithological Society (WOS)

E-mail: woscommunications@gmail.com
URL: www.wilsonsociety.org
Social Media: www.facebook.com/WilsonOrnithSoc
twitter.com/WilsonOrnithSoc

12054 ■ George A. Hall / Harold F. Mayfield Grant *(Undergraduate, Professional development/Grant)*

Purpose: To support avian research by independent and non-professional researchers. **Focus:** Ornithology. **Qualif.:** Applicant must be an independent researchers without access to funds and facilities available at colleges, universities, or governmental agencies, and is restricted to non-professionals, including high school students; must be any kind of avian research is eligible. **Criteria:** Selection will be based on the committee criteria.

Funds Avail.: $1,000. **Duration:** Annual. **Number Awarded:** 1. **To Apply:** Application must submit online. **Deadline:** February 15.

12055 ■ Louis Agassiz Fuertes Grant *(Professional development/Grant)*

Purpose: To promote avian research by any ornithologist. **Focus:** Ornithology. **Qualif.:** Applicants must be members of Wilson Ornithological Society, and may be citizens of any country. **Criteria:** Preference will be given to graduate students and young professionals.

Funds Avail.: $2,500. **Duration:** Annual. **Number Awarded:** Up to 2. **Deadline:** February 15. **Contact:** Department of Biology and Biomedical Sciences, Dr. Jameson Chace, associate professor, E-mail: wos@salve.edu.

12056 ■ Paul A. Stewart Grant *(Professional development/Grant)*

Purpose: To support studies of bird movements based on banding, analysis of recoveries, and returns of banded birds, with an emphasis on economic ornithology. **Focus:** Ornithology. **Criteria:** Preference will be given to proposals for studies of bird movements (based on banding, radio or satellite telemetry, or similar methods) or an emphasis on economic ornithology.

Funds Avail.: $1,000. **Duration:** Annual. **Number Awarded:** Up to 4. **Deadline:** February 15. **Contact:** Department of Biology and Biomedical Sciences, Dr. Jameson Chace, associate professor, E-mail: wos@salve.edu.

12057 ■ Wingate, Russotti, Shapiro & Halperin LLP

420 Lexington Ave., Ste. 2750
New York, NY 10170

Awards are arranged alphabetically below their administering organizations

URL: www.wrshlaw.com
Social Media: www.facebook.com/nyinjurylawyers
www.linkedin.com/company/wingate-russotti-shapiro-&
  -halperin-llp
twitter.com/wrshlaw

12058 ■ Foundation for Your Future Scholarship
(College/Scholarship)

Purpose: To provide financial aid to students seeking an undergraduate degree. **Focus:** General studies/Field of study not specified. **Qualif.:** Applicant must be a high school senior on track to graduate (this calendar year) or a college student enrolled in an accredited four-year university or college, or currently enrolled in a two-year college and planning to transfer to a four-year university or college on completion; have maintained a 3.0 GPA or higher; and be a citizen or permanent resident of the United States (DACA recipients are welcome to apply).

Funds Avail.: $2,500. **Number Awarded:** 1. **Deadline:** May 6.

12059 ■ Winston-Salem Foundation
751 West Fourth Street, Suite 200
Winston Salem, NC 27101
Ph: (336)725-2382
Fax: (336)727-0581
E-mail: info@wsfoundation.org
URL: www.wsfoundation.org
Social Media: www.facebook.com/winstonsalemfoundation
www.linkedin.com/company/wsfoundation
twitter.com/wsfoundation

12060 ■ Alice Conger Patterson Scholarship
(Undergraduate/Scholarship)

Purpose: To help deserving adult women achieve their educational goals. **Focus:** General studies/Field of study not specified. **Criteria:** Selection will be based on the committee's criteria; preference will be given to students at Salem College.

Funds Avail.: $1,000. **Duration:** Annual. **To Apply:** Applicants must submit completed application online and provide signed copy of student's federal tax return; grade transcript (most recent for all postsecondary schools or high school grade transcript if no postsecondary attendance); one recommendation. **Deadline:** April 1. **Remarks:** The Scholarship was established as a tribute to the work of Alice Conger Patterson as Dean of Continuing Studies at Salem College. Established in 2007. **Contact:** Winston-Salem Foundation's Student Aid Department; Phone: 336-714-3445; E-mail: students@wsfoundation.org.

12061 ■ Art and Dannie Weber Scholarship
(Undergraduate/Scholarship)

Purpose: To provide financial support to graduating high school seniors who attend a Forsyth County high school and reside in the Foundation's service area. **Focus:** Education. **Criteria:** Selection will be based on the committee's criteria.

Funds Avail.: $750. **Duration:** Annual. **To Apply:** Applicants must complete online application form providing high school grade transcript through at least the first semester of the 12th grade; one recommendation as described in the online Student Aid Application; signed copy of parents' federal tax return. **Deadline:** April 1. **Remarks:**

Established in 2007. **Contact:** Winston-Salem Foundation's Student Aid Department; Phone: 336-714-3445; E-mail: studentaid@wsfoundation.org.

12062 ■ Blanche Raper Zimmerman Scholarship
(Other/Scholarship)

Purpose: To provide assistance for teachers to increase their understanding of and appreciation for various world cultures, with preference for teachers of social studies and history. **Focus:** History. **Qualif.:** Applicants must be history or social studies teachers of any grade in Forsyth County. **Criteria:** preference for teachers of social studies or history.

Remarks: Established in 1986.

12063 ■ Sam L. Booke, Sr. Scholarship
(Undergraduate/Scholarship)

Purpose: To encourage outstanding students to pursue careers in the mathematics field. **Focus:** Mathematics and mathematical sciences. **Qualif.:** Applicants must be graduating seniors from public high schools in the Winston-Salem/Forsyth County School; must demonstrate interest in mathematics. **Criteria:** Recipients will be selected based on the following; evidence of excellence in mathematics through both course selection and grades; intent to pursue a career in mathematics; potential to achieve career goal; evidence of scholarship including appropriate selection of high school curriculum and academic standing; evidence that students have shown interest and concern for being members of the society.

Funds Avail.: $1,500. **Duration:** Annual. **Number Awarded:** 1. **To Apply:** Applications must be submitted online; applicants must submit a high school grade transcript through the first semester of the 12th grade; one recommendation as described in the application. **Deadline:** April 1. **Remarks:** The scholarship was established in honor of Sam L. Booke. Established in 1989. **Contact:** Winston-Salem Foundation's Student Aid Department; Phone: 336-714-3445; E-mail: studentaid@wsfoundation.org.

12064 ■ Bruce Shelton Scholarship (Undergraduate, High School/Scholarship)

Purpose: To provide financial support to graduating high school seniors from a Forsyth County public high school, who have excelled in at least one varsity sport. **Focus:** General studies/Field of study not specified. **Criteria:** Selection committee reserves the right to rescind an award should a recipient's circumstances change, such as failure to graduate from high school or failure to enroll at an accredited institution.

Funds Avail.: $1,000. **Duration:** Annual; up to 4 years. **To Apply:** Applications must be submitted online; applicants must submit official high school grade transcript through at least the first semester of the 12th grade or most recent college grade transcript; signed copy of parents' federal tax return from previous year; applicant's tax return from previous year; one recommendation. **Deadline:** April 1. **Remarks:** Established in 1991. **Contact:** Winston-Salem Foundation's Student Aid Department; Phone: 336-714-3445; E-mail: studentaid@wsfoundation.org.

12065 ■ Chester Arzell and Helen Miller Montgomery Scholarship (Undergraduate/Scholarship)

Purpose: To provide educational support to deserving students from Stokes County public high schools. **Focus:**

Awards are arranged alphabetically below their administering organizations

General studies/Field of study not specified. **Qualif.:** Applicants must be graduating high school senior at a Stokes County public high school; must have a minimum and cumulative GPA of 2.0; must participate in community service and extracurricular activities; must demonstrate good character and financial need but not restricted to lower income. **Criteria:** Selection will be based on the committee's criteria include Academic Achievement; Community Service and Involvement; Good Character; Extracurricular Activities; Financial Need.

Funds Avail.: $1,000. **Duration:** Annual. **To Apply:** Application must be submitted online; must include high school grade transcript through at least the first semester of the 12th grade; Two recommendations; A recent photograph of the applicant. **Deadline:** April 1. **Remarks:** The Chester Arzell and Helen Miller Montgomery Scholarship was established with a gift from Chester Arzell Montgomery. Established in 2007. **Contact:** Winston-Salem Foundation's Student Aid Department; Phone: 336-714-3445; E-mail: studentaid@wsfoundation.org.

12066 ■ Claude B. Hart Memorial Scholarship
(Undergraduate/Scholarship)

Purpose: To provide financial assistance to graduating high school seniors from Elkin High School in Elkin, NC who will major in mathematics or engineering in college. **Focus:** Engineering; Mathematics and mathematical sciences. **Qualif.:** Applicants must demonstrate significant promise in academics, leadership, community service and school service; must be graduating seniors from Elkin High School and intend to major in mathematics (accounting, computer science, business administration) and/or engineering (mechanical, civil, chemical, etc.) in college; must demonstrate financial need, but not restricted to lower income; renewal of the award after the first year will require that the student be a full-time undergraduate student at an accredited four-year institution, maintain a minimum cumulative grade point average of 2.5, and continue to major in mathematics or engineering. **Criteria:** Selection will be based on the committee's criteria.

Funds Avail.: $1,200. **Duration:** Annual; renewable for four years. **Number Awarded:** 1. **To Apply:** Application must be submitted online; must provide grade transcript through the first semester of the 12th grade. **Deadline:** April 1. **Remarks:** Established in 1994. **Contact:** For submissions: Elkin High School, Attention: Claude B. Hart Memorial Scholarship, 334 Elk Spur St., Elkin, NC 28621; For Questions: Elkin High School Phone: 336-835-3858; or The Winston-Salem Foundation's Student Aid Department, Phone: 336-714-3445; Email: students@wsfoundation.org.

12067 ■ Lloyd E. and Rachel S. Collins Scholarship
(Undergraduate, Graduate, High School/Scholarship)

Purpose: To provide scholarships to graduating high school seniors from North, South, and West Stokes High Schools to be applied to the cost of undergraduate tuition, fees, on-campus room and board, books and other college expenses. **Focus:** General studies/Field of study not specified. **Criteria:** The committee reserves the right to rescind an award should a recipient's circumstances change, such as failure to graduate from high school or failure to enroll at an accredited institution.

Funds Avail.: $2,000. **Duration:** Annual; 4 years. **To Apply:** Applicants must submit complete application form online including high school grade transcript through the first semester of the 12th grade; one recommendation letter and signed copy of parents' federal tax return from previ-

ous year. **Deadline:** April 1. **Remarks:** The scholarship was established by former students of Lloyd E. Collins in honor of Mr. Collins' dedication to education through his service as a teacher, principal, and member of the Stokes County Schools' Board of Education for 50 years. Established in 1991. **Contact:** Winston-Salem Foundation's Student Aid Department; Phone: 336-714-3445; E-mail: studentaid@wsfoundation.org.

12068 ■ D.C. Cornelius Memorial Scholarship
(Undergraduate, Graduate/Scholarship)

Purpose: To provide students the educational support they need in pursuing a two-year associate degree, or a certificate or diploma. **Focus:** General studies/Field of study not specified. **Qualif.:** Applicants must be graduating high school seniors from Forbush High School; must have a minimum cumulative unweighted GPA of 2.8; must demonstrate dedication to school and community service; must demonstrate character, leadership, and compassion for all people; must attend one of the following community colleges: Alamance, Catawba Valley, Davidson County, Forsyth Technical, Guilford Technical, Mitchell, Rowan-Cabarrus, Surry Community, or Wilkes Community; must be U.S. citizens; must demonstrate financial need, but not restricted to lower family incomes. **Criteria:** Selection will be given based on the committee's criteria.

Funds Avail.: $1,000. **Duration:** Annual; Up to 2 years. **Number Awarded:** 1. **To Apply:** Applications can be submitted online including high school grade transcript through the first semester of 12th grade and two recommendations. **Deadline:** April 1. **Remarks:** Established in 2005. **Contact:** Mrs. Donna Myers; Chairman, D.C. Cornelius Scholarship Committee, 2828 Tom's Ridge Lane, E Bend, NC, 27018; Phone: 336-699-4852; Email: donna.myers@me.com; Winston-Salem Foundation's Student Aid Department; Phone: 336-714-3445; E-mail: studentaid@wsfoundation.org.

12069 ■ The Dean Prim Scholarship
(Undergraduate/Scholarship)

Purpose: To promote education, and to provide scholarships and China travel for rising junior and rising senior students from Davie, Forsyth, or Yadkin County high schools. **Focus:** General studies/Field of study not specified. **Qualif.:** Applicants must be high school sophomores and juniors attending Davie County, Forsyth County, or Yadkin County high schools; demonstrate excellence in schoolwork as evidenced by course selection and grades (minimum GPA of 3.0); participate in extracurricular school activities, community and/or church activities, and school or community athletics; demonstrate good character and show interest in and concern for being an active member of society; be committed to traveling and studying in China and have the full support of parent(s) to participate. **Criteria:** Selection will be based on the committee's criteria.

Funds Avail.: $1,500. **Duration:** Annual; up to four years. **To Apply:** Applications must be submitted online; application materials should include a grade transcript, through 10th grade for juniors and 11th grade for seniors; one recommendation as described in the application; signed Dean Prim Scholarship Applicant/Parent Signature page. **Deadline:** August 15. **Remarks:** The Scholarship was established by Dean Prim family in honor of his dedication to promoting education as a member of the Yadkin County Board of Education. Established in 1975. **Contact:** Winston-Salem Foundation's Student Aid Department; Phone: 336-714-3445; E-mail: studentaid@wsfoundation.org.

Awards are arranged alphabetically below their administering organizations

12070 ■ Wade and Marcelene Duncan Scholarship
(Undergraduate/Scholarship)

Purpose: To provide scholarships to worthy graduating high school seniors from either North or South Stokes high schools in Stokes County. **Focus:** General studies/Field of study not specified. **Qualif.:** Applicants must be graduating seniors from either North Stokes or South Stokes high schools; must have a minimum cumulative GPA of 2.0; must demonstrate financial need, leadership, participation in community service, or in athletics. **Criteria:** Selection will be based on the committee's criteria.

Funds Avail.: $500. **Duration:** Annual; up to 4 years. **Number Awarded:** 1. **To Apply:** Applications can be submitted online; must provide high school grade transcript through 1st semester of the 12th grade; one teacher recommendation; signed copy of parent's federal tax return from previous year. **Deadline:** March 15. **Remarks:** The scholarship was established in honor of Wade and Marcelene Duncan. Established in 1996.

12071 ■ Edward Kent Welch Memorial Scholarship
(Undergraduate/Scholarship)

Purpose: To provide college scholarships to graduating high school seniors at Mt. Tabor High School who will attend the University of North Carolina at Chapel Hill. **Focus:** General studies/Field of study not specified. **Criteria:** Selection will be based on the committee's criteria.

Funds Avail.: $500. **Duration:** Annual; up to 4 years. **To Apply:** The Mt. Tabor Guidance Office will select the recipient of this award from its pool of students admitted by and planning to attend UNC-Chapel Hill. **Deadline:** April 1. **Remarks:** The Scholarship was established in memory of Kent Welch with gifts from his family and friends. Established in 2009. **Contact:** Mt. Tabor High School Guidance Office, Phone: 336-703-6728; Questions: Winston-Salem Foundation's Student Aid Department; Phone: 336-714-3445; E-mail: studentaid@wsfoundation.org.

12072 ■ Edwin H. and Louise N. Williamson Endowed Scholarship *(Undergraduate/Scholarship)*

Purpose: To provide scholarships to a graduating high school senior who will pursue a bachelor's degree at the University of North Carolina-Greensboro. **Focus:** General studies/Field of study not specified. **Qualif.:** Applicants must be graduating high school seniors who attend Forsyth County high school and reside in The Winston-Salem Foundation's service area; must demonstrate a minimum cumulative GPA of 3.0; demonstrate financial need but not restricted to lower incomes (students' merit will be considered to a greater degree); attending the University of North Carolina at Greensboro. **Criteria:** Selection will be based on the committee's criteria.

Funds Avail.: $1,500. **Duration:** Annual; 4 years. **To Apply:** Applicants must complete application online; must provide high school grade transcript through the 1st semester of 12th grade; one recommendation; signed copy of parents' federal tax return from previous year. **Deadline:** April 1. **Remarks:** Established in 2007. **Contact:** Winston-Salem Foundation's Student Aid Department; Phone: 336-714-3445; E-mail: studentaid@wsfoundation.org.

12073 ■ Virginia Elizabeth and Alma Vane Taylor Nursing Scholarship *(Undergraduate/Scholarship)*

Purpose: To financially support North Carolina residents seeking associate or baccalaureate nursing degrees. **Focus:** Nursing. **Qualif.:** Applicants must be enrolled in an associate, baccalaureate, or graduate nursing degree program; must be accepted in an accredited North Carolina school of nursing program; must have a high school/college cumulative GPA of at least 2.5; must be North Carolina residents; must demonstrate financial need (not restricted to lower incomes). **Criteria:** Selection will be based on the committee's criteria; preference will be given to students seeking first-time nursing degrees and students living in Davidson, Davie, Forsyth, Stokes, Surry, Wilkes, and Yadkin counties.

Funds Avail.: $1,500. **Duration:** Annual. **Number Awarded:** 1. **To Apply:** Applications must be submitted online; applicants must submit a high school grade transcript through 1st semester of the 12th grade or most recent college grade transcript; signed copy of previous year's federal tax return for parent(s) or student's federal tax return if student is independent; copy of the Student Aid Report (SAR) if applicant has applied for federal aid; copy of the financial aid award letter; letter of acceptance into a nursing program in North Carolina. **Deadline:** July 31. **Remarks:** Established in 1966. **Contact:** Winston-Salem Foundation's Student Aid Department; Phone: 336-714-3445; E-mail: studentaid@wsfoundation.org.

12074 ■ Elizabeth T. Williams Memorial Scholarship
(Undergraduate/Scholarship)

Purpose: To provide students undergraduate tuition, fees, room and board who will pursue full-time undergraduate degrees from UNC-Chapel Hill. **Focus:** General studies/Field of study not specified. **Qualif.:** Applicants must be US citizens and residents of Forsyth County, North Carolina; graduating high school seniors who demonstrate academic success (minimum cumulative unweighted GPA of 3.0 through the first semester of the 12th grade with appropriate course selection); demonstrate participation in student service clubs, non-school community service and/or other school activities; participates in athletics or support positions for athletics; and have good moral character; must be pursuing a full-time undergraduate degree from UNC-Chapel Hill. **Criteria:** Selection will be based on the committee's criteria.

Funds Avail.: $10,000. **Duration:** Annual; up to 4 years. **Number Awarded:** 1. **To Apply:** Applicants must complete online application form providing high school grade transcript through the first semester of the 12th grade; one recommendation as described in the online Common Application. **Deadline:** April 1. **Remarks:** The Scholarship was established by the family of Elizabeth T. Williams to memorialize her life. Established in 1999. **Contact:** Winston-Salem Foundation's Student Aid Department; Phone: 336-714-3445; E-mail: studentaid@wsfoundation.org.

12075 ■ Elmer and Rosa Lee Collins Scholarship
(Undergraduate/Scholarship)

Purpose: To provide a college scholarship to graduating high school senior from a Forsyth County high school who will attend an accredited four-year college or university to be applied to the cost of tuition, fees, room and board, and other college expenses. **Focus:** General studies/Field of study not specified. **Qualif.:** Applicants must be graduating high school seniors attending a Forsyth County high school and residents in the Winston-Salem's Foundation service area; demonstrate character and purpose as evidenced in school, community, church, and work activities; achieved a minimum cumulative GPA of 3.5 with strong course selection; demonstrate financial need (however, the scholarship is not restricted to lower family incomes). **Criteria:** Selec-

Awards are arranged alphabetically below their administering organizations

tion will be based on the committee's criteria.

Funds Avail.: $3,000. **Duration:** Annual; up to 4 years. **To Apply:** Applicants must complete online application form providing high school grade transcript through at least the first semester of the 12th grade; one recommendation as described in the online Student Aid Application; signed copy of parents' federal tax return from previous year. **Deadline:** April 1. **Remarks:** Established in 2006. **Contact:** Winston-Salem Foundation's Student Aid Department; Phone: 336-714-3445; E-mail: studentaid@wsfoundation.org.

12076 ■ F.A. and Charlotte Blount Scholarship
(Undergraduate/Scholarship)

Purpose: To support Forsyth County high school seniors who will pursue a four-year baccalaureate degree at an accredited college or university. **Focus:** General studies/Field of study not specified. **Criteria:** Preference will be given to minority students and selection will be based on the committee's criteria.

Funds Avail.: $4,000. **Duration:** Annual. **To Apply:** Applicants must submit a completed application form Online; must provide high school grade transcript through the first semester of the 12th grade; signed copy of parents' federal tax return; one letter of recommendation. **Deadline:** March 15. **Remarks:** Established in 2007. **Contact:** Winston-Salem Foundation's Student Aid Department; Phone: 336-714-3445; E-mail: students@wsfoundation.org.

12077 ■ Forsyth County Nursing Scholarship
(Undergraduate/Scholarship)

Purpose: To support students seeking first-time RN degrees at accredited two and four-year colleges. **Focus:** Nursing. **Qualif.:** Applicants must be US citizens; must be residents of Forsyth County, NC; must have achieved a current cumulative GPA of at least 2.0; must demonstrate financial need (but not restricted to lowest incomes); must be accepted into a nursing program. **Criteria:** Selection will be based on the committee's criteria; Preference will be given to those seeking the RN degree.

Funds Avail.: No specific amount. **Duration:** Annual. **Number Awarded:** Varies. **To Apply:** Applications can be submitted online; must provide high school grade transcript through at least the first semester of the 12th grade or year-end college grade transcript; parent's federal tax return from last year; applicant's federal tax return from last year; a letter of acceptance into a nursing program; copy of the Student Aid Report (SAR) if applicant has applied for federal aid; copy of the financial aid award letter. **Remarks:** Established in 1969. **Contact:** Winston-Salem Foundation's Student Aid Department; Phone: 336-714-3445; Email: students@wsfoundation.org.

12078 ■ Joe E. Gaddy, Jr. and Margaret W. Gaddy Scholarship *(Undergraduate/Scholarship)*

Purpose: To provide scholarships to graduating high school seniors from R.J. Reynolds High School. **Focus:** General studies/Field of study not specified. **Qualif.:** Applicants must be students who are graduating high school seniors from R.J. Reynolds High School; demonstrate academic promise; must have participated as athletes or in support positions in high school athletics (broad consideration); must demonstrate financial need but not restricted to lower family incomes (student's merit will be considered to a greater degree); must demonstrate school and community service during high school. **Criteria:** Selection will be based on the committee's criteria; preference will be given to students who will attend Davidson College or Wake Forest University.

Funds Avail.: $1,000. **Duration:** Annual; renewable for four years. **Number Awarded:** 1. **To Apply:** Applications can be submitted online; must provide high school grade transcript through at least the first semester of the 12th grade; parent's federal tax return from last year; one recommendation. **Deadline:** March 15. **Remarks:** The Gaddy Scholarship for R.J. Reynolds High School students was established by Dr. Joe E. Gaddy in honor of present and former Reynolds High School educators. Established in 1997. **Contact:** Winston-Salem Foundation's Student Aid Department, Phone: 336-714-3445; Email: studentaid@wsfoundation.org.

12079 ■ The Garden Club Council of Winston-Salem and Forsyth County Scholarship *(Undergraduate/Scholarship)*

Purpose: To provide financial support to students in the Foundation's service area who will enroll in a horticulture or landscape curriculum at post-secondary schools in NC. **Focus:** Horticulture; Landscape architecture and design. **Qualif.:** Applicants must be residents of Forsyth County, NC or one of the other counties in the Winston-Salem Foundation's service area; must maintain at least part-time enrollment; must have a minimum cumulative GPA of 2.0; must demonstrate financial need, but not restricted to lower incomes (student's financial need and merit will be equally weighted); must be in pursuit of undergraduate associate or baccalaureate degree (first-time degrees preferred); must be enrolled in a horticulture or landscaping curriculum. **Criteria:** Selection will be based on the committee's criteria.

Funds Avail.: $1,500. **Duration:** Annual; renewable for two years. **To Apply:** Applications can be submitted online; must submit high school grade transcript through the first semester of 12th grade or most recent college grade transcript; signed copy of parents' federal income tax return from previous year; signed copy of student's federal income tax return from previous year. **Deadline:** April 1. **Remarks:** Established in 2004. **Contact:** Winston-Salem Foundation's Student Aid Department, Phone: 336-714-3445; Email: studentaid@wsfoundation.org.

12080 ■ Johnny Lineberry Memorial Scholarship
(Undergraduate, Vocational/Occupational/Scholarship)

Purpose: To provide educational support to a worthy Forbush High School senior who will go directly to an accredited vocational/technical school, community college, or college/university in pursuit of a certificate, diploma or baccalaureate degree. **Focus:** Electronics. **Qualif.:** Applicants must be graduating high school seniors from Forsbush High School in East Bend, N.C.; must demonstrate a minimum and cumulative GPA of at least 2.5; must demonstrate strong character and compassion for others; must attend an accredited vocational/technical school, community college or college/university; must demonstrate financial need, but not restricted to lower incomes. **Criteria:** Selection will be based on the committee's criteria.

Funds Avail.: $600. **Duration:** Annual. **Number Awarded:** 1. **To Apply:** Applications can be submitted online; must submit high school grade transcript through the first semester of 12th grade and one teacher recommendation. **Deadline:** April 1. **Remarks:** Established in 2008. **Contact:** Winston-Salem Foundation's Student Aid Department; Phone: 336-714-3445; E-mail: students@wsfoundation.org.

12081 ■ Douglas Gray Kimel Scholarship
(Undergraduate/Scholarship)

Purpose: To provide a financial support to students in Forsyth County seeking a degree in Music. **Focus:** Music.

Awards are arranged alphabetically below their administering organizations

Criteria: Selection will be based on the committee's criteria.

Funds Avail.: $700. **Duration:** Annual; up to 4 years. **Number Awarded:** 1. **To Apply:** Applicants must complete the scholarship application online; provide high school grade transcript through the 1st semester of 12th grade; submit one recommendation as outlined on the application; signed copy of parents and students federal tax return from previous year. **Deadline:** April 1. **Remarks:** The Douglas Gray Kimel Scholarship was established by Calvary Moravian Church to honor Doug Kimel's service in the area of music ministry. Established in 2007. **Contact:** Winston-Salem Foundation's Student Aid Department; Phone: 336-714-3445; E-mail: studentaid@wsfoundation.org.

12082 ■ L. Gordon, Jr. and June D. Pfefferkorn Scholarship *(Undergraduate/Scholarship)*

Purpose: To provide financial support to students who are attending a Forsyth County high school and reside in the Foundation's service area of Davidson, Davie, Forsyth, Stokes, Surry, Yadkin, and Wilkes counties. **Focus:** General studies/Field of study not specified. **Qualif.:** Applicants must attend an accredited four-year college or university in North Carolina; must attend a Forsyth County high school and reside in The Winston-Salem Foundation's service area; must be U.S. citizens; must be graduating high school seniors; must have a minimum cumulative unweighted GPA of 3.5 through the first semester of 12th grade; must demonstrate significant promise in leadership, community service, and school service; must demonstrate financial need, but not restricted to lowest incomes (student's merit will be considered to a greater degree). **Criteria:** Selection will be based on the committee's criteria.

Funds Avail.: $5,000. **Duration:** Annual; up to 4 years. **To Apply:** Applicants must submit completed application online; along with must include high school grade transcript through the first semester of the 12th grade; one recommendation as described in the online Student Aid Application; signed copy of parents' federal tax return from previous year. **Deadline:** April 1. **Remarks:** Established in 2004. **Contact:** Winston-Salem Foundation's Student Aid Department; Phone: 336-714-3445; E-mail: studentaid@wsfoundation.org.

12083 ■ L.D. and Elsie Long Memorial Scholarship *(Graduate/Scholarship)*

Purpose: To provide financial support for Forsyth County residents who demonstrate financial need to attend Wake Forest University. **Focus:** General studies/Field of study not specified. **Qualif.:** Applicants must be Forsyth County residents; must demonstrate financial need to attend Wake Forest University. **Criteria:** Preference will be given to students enrolled or planning to enroll in graduate programs on the Reynolda Campus.

Duration: Annual. **Remarks:** Established in 1980.

12084 ■ Nell and Spencer Waggoner Scholarship *(Undergraduate/Scholarship)*

Purpose: To provide financial assistance to graduating high school seniors who attend a Forsyth County high school and reside in the Foundation's service area. **Focus:** General studies/Field of study not specified. **Criteria:** Selection will be based on the committee's criteria.

Funds Avail.: $3,000. **Duration:** Annual; renewable for four years. **To Apply:** In addition to a completed application, the following items are required: a high school grade transcript through at least the first semester of the 12th

grade; an interview if so advised; one recommendation; and signed certification signature page. **Deadline:** April 1. **Remarks:** Established in 2005. **Contact:** Winston-Salem Foundation's Student Aid Department; Phone: 336-714-3445; E-mail: studentaid@wsfoundation.org.

12085 ■ Oliver Joel and Ellen Pell Denny Healthcare Scholarship *(Undergraduate/Scholarship)*

Purpose: To support students who are seeking a first-time associate or baccalaureate degree, certificate or diploma in a health field. **Focus:** Health care services. **Criteria:** Selection will be based on the committee's criteria; preference will be given to those living in Forsyth, Davidson, Davie, and Stokes, Surry, Yadkin and Wilkes counties.

Funds Avail.: $1,500. **Duration:** Annual. **To Apply:** Applications can be submitted online; must provide high school grade transcript through 1st semester of the 12th grade or most recent college grade transcript; signed copy of previous year's federal tax return; copy of the Student Aid Report (SAR); copy of the financial aid award letter. **Deadline:** July 31. **Remarks:** Established in 1985. **Contact:** Winston-Salem Foundation's Student Aid Department; Phone: 336-714-3445; Email: studentsaid@wsfoundation.org.

12086 ■ Orthopaedic Specialists of the Carolinas Nursing Scholarship *(Undergraduate/Scholarship)*

Purpose: To provide financial support for students who have been accepted into the nursing program at Forsyth Technical Community College or Winston-Salem State University. **Focus:** Nursing. **Qualif.:** Applicants must be enrolled on a full-time basis in the pursuit of a first associate degree or a bachelors degree in nursing; must have a minimum cumulative unweighted GPA of at least 3.0 for graduating high school seniors, or a cumulative GPA of at least 2.6 for students already in college; must demonstrate financial need. **Criteria:** Committee reserves the right to rescind an award should a recipient's circumstances change, such as failure to graduate from high school or failure to enroll at an accredited institution. The Foundation reserves the right to withhold the award in the event that no applicants are deemed to meet the qualifications.

Funds Avail.: $1,000. **Duration:** Annual. **To Apply:** Applications can be submitted online; must submit high school grade transcript through the first semester of 12th grade or college grade transcript, whichever is the most recent; copy of the letter of admission into the nursing program, signed copy of previous year's federal tax return for parent(s) or student's federal tax return if student is independent, copy of the Student Aid Report (SAR) if applicant has applied for federal financial aid, copy of the financial aid award notice. **Deadline:** July 31. **Remarks:** Established in 2002. **Contact:** Winston-Salem Foundation's Student Aid Department; Phone: 336-714-3445; E-mail: students@wsfoundation.org.

12087 ■ William H. and Lena M. Petree Scholarship *(Graduate/Scholarship)*

Purpose: To financially support the worthy Forsyth County residents who are graduating high school seniors. **Focus:** General studies/Field of study not specified. **Criteria:** Selection will be based on the committee's criteria.

Funds Avail.: $5,000. **Duration:** Annual; renewable for four years. **To Apply:** Applicants must submit completed application online and provide signed copy of parents federal tax return; one recommendation; high school grade transcript through the first semester of the 12th grade. **Deadline:** August 31. **Remarks:** The scholarship was

Awards are arranged alphabetically below their administering organizations

established in honor of William H. and Lena M. Petree. Established in 1996. **Contact:** Winston-Salem Foundation's Student Aid Department; Phone: 336-714-3445; E-mail: studentaid@wsfoundation.org.

12088 ■ Pfafftown Jaycees/Lynn Canada Memorial Scholarship *(Undergraduate/Scholarship, Award)*

Purpose: To assist students who will pursue a first-time associate's degree in nursing at Forsyth Technical Community College. **Focus:** General studies/Field of study not specified. **Qualif.:** Applicants must be enrolled on a full-time basis in the pursuit of a first associate or a first baccalaureate degree; must provide copy of admission letter into the nursing program at FTCC (ineligible until accepted into the nursing program) and maintain high school or college cumulative GPA of 2.5. **Criteria:** Selection will be based on the committee's criteria.

Funds Avail.: $1,000. **Duration:** Annual. **Number Awarded:** 1. **To Apply:** Applicants may obtain a scholarship application from the Winston-Salem Foundation's website. In addition to the completed/signed application, applicants are responsible for providing the following required supplemental items: signed copy of parent/guardian's federal income tax return; signed copy of student's federal income tax return, if applicable; official high school (as of 1st semester, 12th grade) or official college grade transcript (as of academic year-end); student Aid Report; financial Aid Award Letter; provide a letter of acceptance into a nursing program. **Deadline:** July 31. **Remarks:** Established in 2005. **Contact:** Winston-Salem Foundations Student Aid Department; Phone: 336-714-3445; E-mail: students@wsfoundation.org.

12089 ■ Ray and Pearl Sams Scholarship *(Undergraduate/Scholarship)*

Purpose: To financially support graduating high school seniors who attend a Forsyth County high school and reside in the Foundation's service area. **Focus:** General studies/Field of study not specified. **Criteria:** Selection will be based on the committee's criteria.

Funds Avail.: $2,500. **Duration:** Annual. **To Apply:** Applications must be submitted online; must include high school grade transcript through the first semester of the 12th grade; one recommendation as described in the online student aid application; signed copy of parents' federal tax return from previous year. **Remarks:** Established in 1999. **Contact:** Winston-Salem Foundation's Student Aid Department; Phone: 336-714-3445; E-mail: studentaid@wsfoundation.org.

12090 ■ Rider Family Scholarship *(Undergraduate/Scholarship, Award)*

Purpose: To provide financial support to a student who attend a Forsyth County high school. **Focus:** General studies/Field of study not specified. **Qualif.:** Applicant must be residents of Forsyth County; must be graduating high school senior; must have achieved a current cumulative unweighted GPA of at least 3.5; must demonstrate financial need not restricted to lower family incomes (student's merit will be considered to a greater degree); must pursue full-time two or four year degrees, certificates, or diplomas from accredited post-secondary institutions. **Criteria:** Selection will be based on the committee's criteria and merit and financial need though need is not restricted to lower incomes.

Funds Avail.: $500. **Duration:** Annual; up to 4 years. **Number Awarded:** 1. **To Apply:** Applications must be submitted online; application materials should include high school grade transcript through the first semester of the 12th grade; one recommendation as described in the online Student Aid application; signed copy of parents' federal tax return from previous year. **Deadline:** April 1. **Remarks:** The Scholarship was established by Sally Rider McLeod in 2004 in honor of her parents. Established in 2004. **Contact:** Winston-Salem Foundation's Student Aid Department; Phone: 336-714-3445; E-mail: studentaid@wsfoundation.org.

12091 ■ Serena D. Dalton Scholarship *(Undergraduate/Scholarship)*

Purpose: To provide educational aid for college students who are residents of Forsyth County. **Focus:** General studies/Field of study not specified. **Qualif.:** Applicant must have a family adjusted gross income of up to 300% of the Federal Poverty Guidelines; must be resident of Forsyth County; must have achieved a current cumulative GPA of at least 2.0; must be enrolled in a minimum of six credit hours/semester during the academic year in a program leading to a first time two- or four-year degree, certificate, or diploma from an accredited institution which participates in the federal student aid program. **Criteria:** Selection will be based on the committee's criteria.

Duration: Annual. **Number Awarded:** 16. **To Apply:** Applications can be submitted online; along with high school grade transcript through at least the first semester of the 12th grade or year-end college grade transcript; parent's federal tax return from previous year (if applicant is a dependent student) or applicant's federal tax return from previous year; copy of the Student Aid Report (SAR); copy of the financial aid award letter. **Deadline:** July 31. **Remarks:** Established by the estate of Serena D. Dalton. Established in 1977. **Contact:** Winston-Salem Foundation's Student Aid Department; Phone: 336-714-3445; Email: students@wsfoundation.org.

12092 ■ Stella B. Johnson Scholarship *(Undergraduate/Scholarship)*

Purpose: To provide to provide scholarships to students in Forsyth County. **Focus:** General studies/Field of study not specified.

Funds Avail.: Amount varies. **Duration:** Annual. **To Apply:** Application must be submitted online; must include high school grade transcript through at least the first semester of the 12th grade or year-end college grade transcript; must provide parent's federal tax return from previous year (if applicant is a dependent student) or applicant's federal tax return from previous year; copy of the Student Aid Report (SAR) if applicant has applied for federal aid; copy of the financial aid award letter. **Remarks:** The scholarship was established by Helen Johnson McMurray, in memory of her mother, Stella B. Johnson. Established in 1987. **Contact:** Winston-Salem Foundation's Student Aid Department; Phone: 336-714-3445; E-mail: students@wsfoundation.org.

12093 ■ Stultz Scholarship *(Undergraduate/Scholarship)*

Purpose: To provide educational aid for college to qualified traditional and non-traditional applicants. **Focus:** General studies/Field of study not specified. **Qualif.:** Applicants must be residents of Forsyth County, NC; must have achieved a current cumulative unweighted grade point average (GPA) of at least 2.0; must demonstrate financial need and be enrolled in a minimum of six credit hours/semester during the academic year in a program leading to a first-

Awards are arranged alphabetically below their administering organizations

time two-year or four-year degree, certificate, or diploma from an accredited institution that participates in the federal student aid program. **Criteria:** Selection will be based on the committee's criteria.

Funds Avail.: Amount varies. **Duration:** Annual. **To Apply:** Applicants must complete online application form providing high school grade transcript through at least the first semester of the 12th grade or year-end college grade transcript; parent's federal tax return from previous year (if applicant is a dependent student) or applicant's federal tax return from previous year; copy of the Student Aid Report (SAR) and copy of the financial aid award letter. **Deadline:** August 15. **Remarks:** Established by the estate of Lillian S. Stultz. Established in 1982. **Contact:** Student Aid Department, 751 West Fourth St., Ste., 200, Winston-Salem, NC, 27101-2702; Email: studentaid@wsfoundation.org; Phone: 336-714-3445.

12094 ■ Thomas E. Shown, M.D. Memorial Scholarship (Undergraduate/Scholarship)

Purpose: To support worthy students from the counties of Forsyth, Wikes, Surry, Yahkin, and Davie who plan to attend an accredited two or four year college or university, preferably in North Carolina. **Focus:** General studies/Field of study not specified. **Criteria:** Selection will be based on the committee's criteria.

Funds Avail.: $1,000. **Duration:** Annual; up to 4 years. **To Apply:** Applications must be submitted online; applicants must submit official high school grade transcript through at least the first semester of the 12th grade; grade transcript must include SAT scores and class rank; one recommendation as described in the application. **Deadline:** April 1. **Contact:** Winston-Salem Foundation's Student Aid Department; Phone: 336-714-3445; E-mail: students.aid@wsfoundation.org.

12095 ■ Tien Bui Memorial Scholarship (Undergraduate/Scholarship)

Purpose: To provide financial support to graduating high school seniors who attend a North Carolina high school, reside in North Carolina, and will attend North Carolina State University's College of Engineering. **Focus:** General studies/Field of study not specified. **Qualif.:** Applicants must be a graduating high school senior in North Carolina; must have a minimum unweighted GPA of 3.5, with a challenging course selection; must score high on SAT or ACT test; demonstrate financial need, but not restricted to lower family incomes; plan to attend North Carolina State University's College of Engineering. **Criteria:** Recipients will be selected based on the committee's review of application materials.

Funds Avail.: $1,000. **Duration:** Annual. **To Apply:** Applicants must complete the Tien Bui Memorial Scholarship online application; must submit high school grade transcript through 1st semester of 12th grade; signed copy of parents' federal tax return from previous year. **Deadline:** April 1. **Remarks:** Established by the family of Tien Bui. Established in 2007. **Contact:** Winston-Salem Foundation's Student Aid Department; Phone: 336-714-3445; E-mail: students@wsfoundation.org.

12096 ■ Jeff Turner-Forsyth Audubon Society Scholarship (Undergraduate/Scholarship)

Purpose: To provide financial support graduating high school seniors in Forsyth County who have participated in the Forsyth Audubon Society or who have been involved in wildlife or other environmental activities. **Focus:** General

studies/Field of study not specified. **Qualif.:** Applicants must be a graduating high school senior; must attend a Forsyth County high school and reside in The Winston-Salem Foundation's service area; must demonstrate character and leadership; must demonstrate solid academic skills by achieving a cumulative unweighted GPA of at least 3.0 through first semester of the 12th grade; must attend an accredited post-secondary four year educational institution; must demonstrate participation in the Forsyth Audubon Society or involvement in wildlife or other environmental activities. **Criteria:** Recipients will be evaluated on submitted materials and result of the interview.

Funds Avail.: $500. **Duration:** Annual. **To Apply:** Applications must be submitted online; applicants must submit grade transcript through the first semester of the 12th grade must be submitted to the scholarship committee; one recommendation addressing the applicant's character as well as environmental interests/experiences must be submitted to the scholarship committee. **Deadline:** April 1. **Remarks:** The scholarship was established in honor of Jeff Turner, who was active in the Audubon Society of Forsyth County and other environmental causes while he was a student at Mt. Tabor High School. Established in 2005. **Contact:** Application submission: The Jeff Turner - Forsyth Audubon Society Scholarship, Attention: Michael Turner, Questions: Winston-Salem Foundation's Student Aid Department; Phone: 336-714-3445; E-mail: studentaid@wsfoundation.org; Michael Turner, Phone: 336-924-4952; Email: mcturner553@gmail.com.

12097 ■ Wes Burton Memorial Scholarship (Undergraduate/Scholarship)

Purpose: To provide financial support to worthy graduating high school seniors from Mt. Tabor High School to be applied to cost of undergraduate tuition, fees, and room and board at an accredited college or university. **Focus:** Business administration; Computer and information sciences; Engineering; Mathematics and mathematical sciences. **Qualif.:** Applicants must have a minimum GPA of 3.5; must be high school seniors from Mt. Tabor High School; must demonstrate community and school service; must be graduating high school seniors who have an intent to pursue a career in Mathematics, Computer Science, Business Administration, or Engineering; demonstrate financial need (award is not restricted to lowest family incomes). **Criteria:** Selection will be based on the committee's criteria.

Funds Avail.: $500. **Duration:** Annual. **To Apply:** Applicants must complete application online; must provide high school grade transcript through at least the first semester of the 12th grade; one letter of recommendation from a math teacher, business teacher, or computer science teacher; copy of parents' federal tax return from previous year. **Deadline:** April 1. **Remarks:** Established by Beverly B. Burton and Blaine Burton, Jr. in memory of their son, Wes Burton. Established in 2005. **Contact:** Winston-Salem Foundation's Student Aid Department; Phone: 336-714-3445; E-mail: students@wsfoundation.org.

12098 ■ William H. Andrews/HAWS Scholarship (Undergraduate/Scholarship)

Purpose: To assist with the cost of post-secondary undergraduate education for students residing in the Winston-Salem public housing community. **Focus:** General studies/Field of study not specified. **Qualif.:** Applicant must reside on the property owned or managed by HAWS; must have a minimum cumulative unweighted GPA of 2.0; traditional age students must be enrolled full-time each semester (minimum of 12 hours); non-traditional age

Awards are arranged alphabetically below their administering organizations

students are encouraged to be enrolled full-time, but must be enrolled a minimum of six hours each semester. **Criteria:** Recipients will be selected based on the committee's review of applications.

Funds Avail.: $600-$1,200. **Duration:** Annual; in odd-numbered years. **To Apply:** Applications can be submitted online including high school grade transcript; copy of GED diploma; college grade transcript. **Deadline:** April 1. **Remarks:** The scholarship was established in honor of William H. Andrews. Established in 1992. **Contact:** Winston-Salem Foundation's Student Aid Department; Phone: 336-714-3445; Email: students@wsfoundation.org.

12099 ■ The Winston-Salem Foundation Scholarship (Undergraduate/Scholarship)

Purpose: To provide scholarships to Forsyth County graduating seniors who will pursue post-secondary education at accredited institutions. **Focus:** Education. **Qualif.:** Applicants must attend a Forsyth County high school and reside in the Winston-Salem's Foundation service area; must be graduating high school seniors; must have a minimum unweighted cumulative GPA of 3.5; must demonstrate outstanding leadership, school service, and community involvement; must exemplify the Foundation's core values of generosity, integrity, inclusion, and excellence. **Criteria:** Selection will be based on the committee's criteria.

Funds Avail.: $4,000. **Duration:** Annual; renewable for four years. **To Apply:** Application is available online; must complete the scholarship application in its entirety; must provide high school grade transcripts through the 1st semester of the 12th grade. **Deadline:** April 1. **Contact:** Winston-Salem Foundation's Student Aid Department; Phone: 336-714-3445; E-mail: studentaid@wsfoundation.org.

12100 ■ Winterthur Museum, Garden and Library

5105 Kennett Pke.
Winterthur, DE 19735
Ph: (302)888-4600
Free: 800-448-3883
E-mail: membershipinfo@winterthur.org
URL: www.winterthur.org
Social Media: www.facebook.com/winterthurmuse
www.linkedin.com/company/winterthur-museum/about
www.in.pinterest.com/pin/732820170588145502

12101 ■ Winterthur Research Fellowships (Graduate/Fellowship)

Purpose: To support student's research in many areas of social and cultural history, including material culture, architecture, decorative arts, design, consumer culture, garden and landscape studies, Shaker studies, travel and tourism, the Atlantic World, and objects in literature. **Focus:** Humanities. **Qualif.:** Applicants must be academic, independent or museum scholars and graduate students conducting a research in the areas of social and cultural history. **Criteria:** Recipients are selected based on the significance of the research.

Duration: Annual; from one to three months. **Number Awarded:** Varies. **To Apply:** Applicants must submit the application cover sheet; an application essay of no more than 1500 words which opens a concise overview of the project; a copy of the curriculum vitae; maximum of two pages bibliography; and two letters of reference addressing the previous scholarly record and current project. **Deadline:**

January 15. **Remarks:** Fellowships are divided into certain awards where the successful applicants be designated as: Faith Andrews Fellowships for the study of Shaker life and material culture; Robert Lee Gill Fellowships for research on American decorative arts, painting, architecture, or historic preservation; and the Cheryl A. Robertson Fellowships for the study of American domestic life and material culture.

12102 ■ Wire Reinforcement Institute (WRI)

942 Main St.
Hartford, CT 06103
Ph: (860)240-9545
URL: www.wirereinforcementinstitute.org
Social Media: www.facebook.com/pages/Wire
-Reinforcement-Institute/621715014649171
www.linkedin.com/company/wire-reinforcement-institute

12103 ■ WRI Education Foundation Scholarships - Graduate (Graduate/Scholarship)

Purpose: To support students pursuing graduate level degrees in structural and/or civil engineering. **Focus:** Engineering, Civil.

Funds Avail.: $2,000-$4,000. **Duration:** Annual. **Contact:** wrischolar@wirereinforcementinstitute.org, or 1-860-240-9545.

12104 ■ WRI Education Foundation Scholarships - High School Seniors (Undergraduate/Scholarship)

Purpose: To support students pursuing undergraduate degrees in structural and/or civil engineering. **Focus:** Engineering, Civil. **Criteria:** Selection is based on the application materials submitted for review.

Funds Avail.: $2,000-$4,000. **Duration:** Annual. **To Apply:** Applicants must complete the application form available in website.

12105 ■ WRI Education Foundation Scholarships - Undergraduate (Undergraduate/Scholarship)

Purpose: To support undergraduate students pursuing structural and/or civil engineering. **Focus:** Engineering, Civil. **Qualif.:** Applicants must be currently enrolled/registered undergraduate level student presently pursuing a four year undergraduate level degree in structural and/or civil engineering; or either be enrolled full-time in a four year accredited university/college program in the United States or Canada. **Criteria:** Selection is based on submitted application.

Funds Avail.: $2,000-$4,000. **Duration:** Annual. **To Apply:** Applicants must complete the application form available in website. **Deadline:** April 15. **Contact:** wrischolar@wirereinforcementinstitute.org, or 1-860-240-9545.

12106 ■ Wirefly.com

101 W Broadway, St. 1420
San Diego, CA 92101
URL: www.wirefly.com
Social Media: www.facebook.com/Wirefly
twitter.com/Wirefly

12107 ■ Wirefly.com Scholarhip: Wireless Technology and Society (Undergraduate, Graduate/Scholarship)

Purpose: To help reduce the financial burden associated with attending college. **Focus:** General studies/Field of study not specified. **Qualif.:** Applicant must be an incoming college freshman, graduate student, or current undergraduate student enrolled in an accredited college or university in the United States; must be a U.S. resident. **Criteria:** Selection will be based on quality of the content, amount of insightful research, fresh insight, and original ideas presented in the applicant's essay.

Funds Avail.: $3,000 First Place; $1,500 Second Place. **Duration:** Annual. **Number Awarded:** 2. **To Apply:** Applicant must submit an essay (800 to 1,100 words) explaining how the invention, adoption, and widespread use of cell phones has affected society. If chosen as a finalist, applicant will need to submit either a current college transcript or college acceptance letter. Application details are available online at www.wirefly.com/scholarship/. **Deadline:** September 1. **Contact:** Logan Abbott; Email: admin@wirefly.com.

12108 ■ Wisconsin Association for Food Protection (WAFP)
PO Box 620705
Middleton, WI 53562
E-mail: wafp17@gmail.com
URL: www.wifoodprotection.org

12109 ■ E. H. Marth Food Protection And Food Sciences Scholarship *(Undergraduate/Scholarship)*

Purpose: To promote and sustain interest in fields of study that may lead to a career in dairy, food, or environmental sanitation. **Focus:** Food science and technology. **Criteria:** Selection will be based on academic performance, professional potential, activities and financial need; work experience; and extra-curricular activities.

Funds Avail.: $3,000. **Duration:** Annual. **To Apply:** Applicants must submit a complete application form; a copy of official transcript; recommendation of advisor or instructor which should address scholastic ability, professional potential, applicable work experience, extra-curricular activities, financial need and other relevant information.

12110 ■ Wisconsin Association of School Business Officials (WASBO)
4797 Hayes Rd., Ste. 101
Madison, WI 53704
Ph: (608)249-8588
Fax: (608)249-3163
E-mail: wasbo@wasbo.com
URL: www.wasbo.com
Social Media: www.linkedin.com/company/wisconsin
-association-of-school-business-officials
twitter.com/WisconsinASBO
www.youtube.com/user/WisconsinASBO

12111 ■ WASBO Safety, Security and Wellness Grant *(Other/Grant)*

Purpose: To recognize and promote Wisconsin school districts for their efforts in creating safe and healthy learning environments for students and staff. **Focus:** Business. **Qualif.:** All Wisconsin public school districts are eligible.

Funds Avail.: $1,500. **Duration:** Annual. **To Apply:** An executive summary explaining the problem/challenge the district faced with a description of the solution and how it was Implemented; An explanation of how this bright idea

benefits students and staff. **Deadline:** January 11.

12112 ■ Wisconsin Athletic Trainers' Association (WATA)
11801 W Silver Spring Dr, Ste. 200
Milwaukee, WI 53225
Ph: (414)271-9456
E-mail: watainc.website@gmail.com
URL: watainc.org
Social Media: www.facebook.com/Wisconsin-Athletic
-Trainers-Association-123452497693176
twitter.com/WATA_inc

12113 ■ Founding Fathers Leadership Scholarships *(Undergraduate/Scholarship)*

Purpose: To support athletic training students who have distinguished themselves academically and performed with distinction as a member of the Athletic Training Program. **Focus:** Athletics. **Qualif.:** Applicants must be members of the NATA and WATA; currently enrolled in the first year of an athletic training curriculum program at a college or university in Wisconsin; distinguished academically with an overall minimum accumulative GPA of 3.0 on a 4.0 scale or its equivalent; demonstrated qualities of leadership as members of the Athletic Training Student program. **Criteria:** Selection will be based on application.

Funds Avail.: $1,000. **Duration:** Annual. **To Apply:** Applicants must be nominated by a Licensed/Certified Athletic Trainer. Submit the following with the application: (signed by the nominating Licensed/Certified Athletic Trainer) Embossed undergraduate transcript at completion of the semester preceding the filing of the application; Letter of recommendation completed by the nominating Licensed/Certified Athletic Trainer (Section II); a second letter of recommendation completed by a nominating physician or coach. **Deadline:** March 1. **Remarks:** Established in 2006. **Contact:** Anna Linstedt, LAT, Awards & Scholarship Committee Chair; or Email: anna.linstedt@thedacare.org.

12114 ■ Jeff Oliphant Memorial Post-Graduate Scholarship *(Postgraduate/Scholarship)*

Purpose: To support athletic training students who have distinguished themselves academically and performed with distinction as a member of the Athletic Training Program. **Focus:** Athletics. **Criteria:** Preference will be given to students who will demonstrate qualities of leadership.

Funds Avail.: $1,000. **Duration:** Annual. **To Apply:** Applicants must complete all required sections in the application form; section I General Information (to be completed and signed by the applicant); section II nomination form (to be completed and signed by a BOC certified athletic trainer, who can attest to the skills, abilities and scholarly activities as they relate to the application); section III institutional endorsement (to be completed and signed by the dean of the college or the department head responsible for the academic program); section IV Essay (to be written and signed by the applicant). **Deadline:** March 1. **Remarks:** Established in 2006. **Contact:** Anna Linstedt, LAT, Awards & Scholarship Committee Chair; or Email: anna.linstedt@thedacare.org.

12115 ■ Mueller Undergraduate Scholarship *(Undergraduate/Scholarship)*

Purpose: To provide support for future athletic training professionals. **Focus:** Athletics. **Criteria:** Preference will

Awards are arranged alphabetically below their administering organizations

be given to students who will demonstrate qualities of leadership.

Funds Avail.: $1,000 each. **Duration:** Annual. **Number Awarded:** 2. **To Apply:** Applicants must be nominated by a Licensed/Certified Athletic Trainer; must submit a completed and signed application form together with the essay and embossed transcript; evaluation form must be completed and signed by the Licensed/Certified Athletic Trainer supervisor. **Deadline:** March 1. **Remarks:** Established in 2006. **Contact:** Anna Linstedt, LAT, Awards & Scholarship Committee Chair, at the above address; or Email: anna.linstedt@thedacare.org.

12116 ■ Wisconsin Broadcasters Association (WBA)
44 E Mifflin St., Ste. 900
Madison, WI 53703
Ph: (608)255-2600
Free: 800-236-1922
E-mail: mvetterkind@wi-broadcasters.org
URL: www.wi-broadcasters.org
Social Media: www.facebook.com/Wisconsin.Broadcasters
.Association
twitter.com/MVetterkind

12117 ■ Wisconsin Broadcasters Association Foundation Student Scholarships *(Graduate/ Scholarship)*
Purpose: To assist students enrolled in broadcasting-related educational programs. **Focus:** Broadcasting.

Funds Avail.: $1,000-$2,000. **Number Awarded:** 2. **To Apply:** Applicants must submit a completed application form; a current official transcript of college/university grades; two brief letters of recommendation supporting the application; an original essay written by the applicants forecasting what the broadcasting industry will be like in five years, and how the applicants believes he or she will contribute to radio or television during that time. **Deadline:** November 1. **Contact:** WBA, 44 E Mifflin St., Ste. 900, Madison, WI 53703; Phone: 608-255-2600.

12118 ■ Wisconsin Health Information Management Association (WHIMA)
113 N. Bradley Dr.
Salina, KS 67401
Ph: (785)531-0647
E-mail: whima@whima.org
URL: www.whima.org
Social Media: www.facebook.com/WHIMA.ORG
twitter.com/WHIMAHIM

12119 ■ WHIMA Established Professional Development Scholarship *(Graduate/Scholarship)*
Purpose: To support and recognize Wisconsin students pursuing graduate education as health information professionals and members needing financial assistance for professional development. **Focus:** General studies/Field of study not specified. **Qualif.:** Applicant must be active member of WHIMA and AHIMA; must submit evidence of attendance at continuing education program and personal payment for program or successful completion of credentialing examination; must complete the application procedure; professional or personal references. **Criteria:** Selec-

tion will be made contributions showing leadership, innovation and creativity with the HIM professio n.

Duration: Annual. **Number Awarded:** 1. **To Apply:** Applicants must provide evidence of attendance at a continuing education program and personal payment for program or successful completion of credentialing examination; must complete the application procedure; provide professional or personal references. **Deadline:** February 28. **Contact:** Contact WHIMA at (785) 531-0647 or e-mail whima@whima.org.

12120 ■ Wisconsin Indian Education Association (WIEA)
PO Box 910
Keshena, WI 54135
Ph: (715)799-5110
Fax: (715)799-5102
URL: wiea.net
Social Media: www.facebook.com/wieapage
twitter.com/wieaorg

12121 ■ WIEA Scholarships *(Doctorate, Graduate, Undergraduate, Vocational/Occupational, Master's, Doctorate/Scholarship)*
Purpose: To provide financial assistance to American Indian students attending institutes of higher education. **Focus:** General studies/Field of study not specified. **Qualif.:** Applicant must be in a one to two year program; a graduating high school senior, four-year college (second semester freshman, sophomore, junior or senior) or graduate/Ph.D. student maintaining at least a 2.5 semester GPA. **Criteria:** Achievement based; transcripts, letters of recommendation, essays are also scored.

Funds Avail.: $1,000 each. **Duration:** Annual. **Number Awarded:** 4. **To Apply:** Completed application; two sealed letters of recommendation, one from a teacher, employer or other professional familiar with your academic potential; a one to two-page personal essay focusing on how applicant will apply their education and if they are involved in community and/or extracurricular activities; proof of tribal enrollment. **Deadline:** June 1. **Contact:** Virginia Nuske, WIEA Treasurer, N5448 Broder Road, Shawano, WI 54166.

12122 ■ Wisconsin Laboratory Association (WLA)
PO Box 436
Sun Prairie, WI 53590
URL: www.wisconsinlabassociation.org
Social Media: www.linkedin.com/company/wisconsin
-laboratories-association

12123 ■ Wisconsin Laboratory Association Graduate Student Scholarships *(Graduate/Scholarship)*
Purpose: To financially support students to pursue a career in a non-medical laboratory related field. **Focus:** Technology. **Criteria:** Selection is based on submitted application.

Funds Avail.: $1,000. **Duration:** Annual; up to 3 years. **Number Awarded:** 2. **To Apply:** Applicants must submit completed WLA application form, current transcript from the school, and two letters of recommendation from the student's instructors. **Deadline:** March 31. **Contact:** Gina Steiner, Address: PO Box 808, Fort Atkinson, WI 53538; Email: ginas@jonesdairyfarm.com.

Awards are arranged alphabetically below their administering organizations

12124 ■ WLA Scholarships (Undergraduate, Graduate/Scholarship)

Purpose: To financially support students who plan to pursue a career in a non-medical laboratory related field. **Focus:** Technology. **Criteria:** Selection is based on submitted application materials.

Funds Avail.: $1,000. **Duration:** Annual. **Number Awarded:** 2. **Deadline:** March 31. **Contact:** Gina Steiner, PO Box 808, Fort Atkinson, WI, 53538; Email: ginas@jonesdairyfarm.com; Amanda Matcynski, 3256 E. Twin Pines Ct., Green Bay, WI, 54311; Email: cherneyfoundation@gmail.com.

12125 ■ Wisconsin Laboratory Association Undergraduate University Student Scholarships (Undergraduate/Scholarship)

Purpose: To financially support students who plan to pursue a career in a non-medical laboratory related field. **Focus:** Technology. **Criteria:** Selection is based on application.

Funds Avail.: $1,000. **Duration:** Annual; up to 3 years. **Number Awarded:** 2. **To Apply:** Applicants must submit completed WLA application form, current transcript from the school, and two letters of recommendation from the student's instructors. **Deadline:** March 31. **Contact:** Gina Steiner, Address: PO Box 808, Fort Atkinson, WI 53538; Email: ginas@jonesdairyfarm.com.

12126 ■ Wolf Trap Foundation for the Performing Arts

1645 Trap Rd.
Vienna, VA 22182
Ph: (703)255-1868
Free: 877-965-3872
E-mail: wolftrap@wolftrap.org
URL: www.wolftrap.org

12127 ■ The Wolf Trap Accounting Internship Program (Graduate, Other, Undergraduate/Internship)

Purpose: To provide a training program for the performing arts. **Focus:** Performing arts. **Qualif.:** Applicant must be an Accounting major or minor; must know how to prepare excel spreadsheets; must be detail-oriented and organized.

Funds Avail.: $5,000. **Duration:** Annual; 12 weeks internship program. **To Apply:** Applicants must submit a cover letter with a brief personal statement and an outline of career goals; a resume; two academic or professional recommendations; two contrasting writing samples, (maximum of 3 pages each). **Deadline:** February 1. **Contact:** Phone: 703-937-6304; Tollfree: 800-404-8461; Email: internships@wolftrap.org.

12128 ■ Wolf Trap's Grants for High School Performing Arts Teachers (Other/Grant)

Purpose: To reward and assist the teachers who make it all possible - particularly those creating innovative new programs. **Focus:** Performing arts. **Qualif.:** Applicants must be performing arts public high school teachers in Washington, DC; Montgomery County, MD; Prince George's County, MD; and Fairfax County, VA. **Criteria:** Consideration will be given for artist residencies; commissions; master classes; Science, Technology, Engineering or Math through an artistic discipline; technology in the arts; going Green.

Funds Avail.: $5,000. **Duration:** Annual. **Number Awarded:** 6. **Deadline:** June 30. **Contact:** Phone: 703-937-6304; Email: edugrants@wolftrap.org.

12129 ■ Thomas Wolfe Society (TWS)

PO Box 1146
Bloomington, IN 47402-1146
URL: www.thomaswolfe.org
Social Media: www.facebook.com/The-Thomas-Wolfe-Society-139828276033808

12130 ■ The William B. Wisdom Grants in Aid of Research (Undergraduate, Graduate/Grant)

Purpose: To provide funds for travel and living expenses for scholars and students engages in research on Thomas Wolfe, especially those working out of the William B. Wisdom Collection in the Houghton Library, Harvard University. **Focus:** Literature. **Qualif.:** Applicants must be scholars and students engaged in research on Thomas Wolfe; graduate students at work on PhD dissertations are especially encouraged to apply. **Criteria:** Selection will be based on the committee's criteria; consideration will also be given to applicants who wish to use the Thomas Wolfe Collection in the University of North Carolina at Chapel Hill.

Funds Avail.: $1,000. **Duration:** Annual. **To Apply:** Applicants must provide letters of application, to be submitted in triplicate, and should include a description of the proposed research project; an estimate of expenses; curriculum vitae; list of publications; submit a final report on the research at the following Thomas Wolfe Society meeting and two copies of any publication resulting from the research. **Deadline:** April 1. **Remarks:** Established in 1991. **Contact:** Dr. Joseph M. Flora, Chair of the Grants Committee; Email: jflora@email.unc.edu.

12131 ■ The Thomas Wolfe Student Travel Grants in Honor of Richard S. Kennedy (Graduate, Undergraduate/Grant)

Purpose: To recognize scholarship about Thomas Wolfe by undergraduate and graduate students and foster participation in the Thomas Wolfe Society's annual conferences. **Focus:** Literature. **Qualif.:** Students must be currently enrolled at an institution of higher learning or have graduated in the past year. Essays must be the original work of the submitting students. **Criteria:** Preference will be given to students who demonstrate in the abstract a serious engagement of Wolfe's writing and of relevant scholarship.

Funds Avail.: $300. **Duration:** Annual. **Number Awarded:** Up to three. **To Apply:** Applicants must submit an abstract of at least 300 words, along with a brief biographical statement, CV, list of relevant academic awards, or coursework. **Deadline:** January 10. **Contact:** Send submissions to Thomas Wolfe Society, George Hovis; Email: George.Hovis@oneonta.edu.

12132 ■ Women in Defense, a National Security Organization (WID)

2101 Wilson Blvd., Ste. 400
Arlington, VA 22201-3061
Ph: (703)522-1820
Fax: (703)522-1885
E-mail: rmccaffrey@ndia.org
URL: www.womenindefense.net
Social Media: www.facebook.com/WIDNational
www.instagram.com/widnational

Awards are arranged alphabetically below their administering organizations

www.linkedin.com/company-beta/9396086
twitter.com/WIDNational

12133 ■ Women In Defense HORIZONS Scholarship
(Graduate, Undergraduate/Scholarship)

Purpose: To provide financial assistance to further educational objectives of women either employed or planning careers in defense or national security areas. **Focus:** Business; Computer and information sciences; Economics; Engineering; Government; History, Military; International affairs and relations; Law; Mathematics and mathematical sciences; National security; Physics; Political science. **Criteria:** Selection will be based on academic achievement, participation in defense and national security activities, field of study, work experience, statements of objectives, recommendations and financial need.

Funds Avail.: No specific amount. **Duration:** Annual. **To Apply:** Applicants must submit a completed scholarship application form with the essays, recommendations, and transcripts. **Deadline:** March 15. **Remarks:** Established in 1988. **Contact:** Send complete application packets to: Women In Defense, Attn: HORIZONS Applications, 2101, Wilson Blvd., Ste. 700, Arlington, VA 22201-3061.

12134 ■ Women Divers Hall of Fame (WDHOF)
1412 Neuport Path
The Villages, FL 32163
E-mail: info@wdhof.org
URL: www.wdhof.org

12135 ■ Cecelia Connelly Graduate Scholarship in Underwater Archaeology *(Graduate, Undergraduate/ Scholarship)*

Purpose: To provide financial and educational support to individuals of all ages, particularly those who are preparing for professional careers which involve scuba diving. **Focus:** Aquaculture; Archeology. **Criteria:** Selection will be based on the aforementioned qualifications and compliance with the application details.

Funds Avail.: $2,000 (Graduate). **Duration:** Annual; one year. **Number Awarded:** 2. **To Apply:** Applicants may visit the website to verify the application process and other pieces of information. **Contact:** Women Divers Hall of Fame, 503 Via Florida, San Clemente, CA, 92672.

12136 ■ Elizabeth Greenhalgh Memorial Scholarships in Journalism, Graphic Arts, or Photography
(Undergraduate/Scholarship)

Purpose: To provide financial and educational support to individuals of all ages, particularly those who are preparing for professional careers in scuba diving. **Focus:** Graphic art and design; Journalism; Photography. **Qualif.:** Applicants must be women divers who are furthering their education beyond high school in the field of journalism, graphic arts, or photography to better serve the ocean environment or ocean community. **Criteria:** Selection will be based on the aforementioned qualifications and compliance with the application details.

Funds Avail.: $1,500. **Duration:** Annual; one to two months during the period June 1, 2017 to May 31, 2018. **To Apply:** Applicants may visit the website to verify the application process and other pieces of information. **Contact:** Women Divers Hall of Fame, at the above address.

12137 ■ WDHOF Undergraduate Scholarships in Marine Conservation *(Undergraduate/Scholarship)*

Purpose: To provide financial and educational support to individuals of all ages, particularly those who are preparing for professional careers in scuba diving. **Focus:** Conservation of natural resources. **Qualif.:** Applicants must be undergraduate women enrolled in an accredited academic or research program in the field of marine conservation. **Criteria:** Selection will be based on the aforementioned qualifications and compliance with the application details.

Funds Avail.: $1,000. **Duration:** Annual; one to two months during the period June 1, 2017 to May 31, 2018. **To Apply:** Applicants may visit the website to verify the application process and other pieces of information.

12138 ■ Women in Federal Law Enforcement, Inc. (WIFLE)
2200 Wilson Blvd. PMB-204 Suite 102
Arlington, VA 22201
Ph: (301)805-2180
E-mail: wifle@comcast.net
URL: www.wifle.org
Social Media: www.facebook.com/wifleinc
twitter.com/wifle

12139 ■ WIFLE Regular Scholarship Program
(Graduate, Postdoctorate, Undergraduate/Scholarship)

Purpose: To support women who are interested in pursuing a career in law enforcement. **Focus:** Law enforcement. **Qualif.:** Applicants must be citizens of the United States; be full-time students at an accredited four-year college or university, or be currently enrolled in a full-time in a fully accredited community college with the intention of transferring to a four-year degree; have completed at least one full academic year of college work at an accredited college or university or community college; have a minimum 3.0 overall grade point (GPA) average; and, be majoring in Criminal Justice or related discipline such as social sciences, public administration, computer science, finance, linguistic arts, chemistry, physics, etc., leading to a four-year degree. (Students in graduate and postgraduate programs are also eligible; students pursuing Associate degrees are not eligible, unless as stated above, fully articulate in the application of their intention to transfer to a four-year program). **Criteria:** Selection will be based on academic potential, achievement and commitment to serving communities in the field of law enforcement.

Funds Avail.: No specific amount. **Duration:** Annual. **To Apply:** Applicants must complete the application with a 500-word essay describing the applicant's involvement in a community project and the results or impact of that involvement to the community; if they are currently serving or have served an internship with a law enforcement agency, preferably a federal law enforcement agency, they must provide details including the name of the agency, the dates served and the value of the experience in a 500-word essay; must have at least one community leader or member of a community or police official sponsor their application with a written statement of support. **Deadline:** February 1.

12140 ■ Women Lawyers' Association of Greater St. Louis (WLA)
PO Box 775512
Saint Louis, MO 63177
E-mail: wla@wlastl.org
URL: wlastl.org
Social Media: twitter.com/WLAstlouis

Awards are arranged alphabetically below their administering organizations

12141 ■ Linda J. Murphy Scholarship
(Undergraduate/Scholarship)

Purpose: To support students who are pursuing the legal education. **Focus:** Law. **Criteria:** Selection of recipients is based on demonstrated commitment to causes that are consistent with the Mission of the WLA; academic achievement and financial need are taken into account to a lesser extent.

Funds Avail.: $1,000 - $10,000 .**Duration:** Annual. **To Apply:** Applicants must submit a completed application form along with the personal statement and official or unofficial law school transcripts; accompanying materials must be submitted via e-mail. **Deadline:** February 1. **Remarks:** The Scholarship was named after Linda J. Murphy, who passed away in 1999. Linda was an outstanding member of the WLA, and served as its President in 1987-1988. Established in 1996. **Contact:** The Women Lawyers' Association of Greater St. Louis, PO Box 775512, St. Louis, MO 63177.

12142 ■ Women Lawyers Association of Los Angeles (WLALA)
634 S Spring St., Ste. 617
Los Angeles, CA 90014-3906
Ph: (213)892-8982
Fax: (213)892-8948
E-mail: info@wlala.org
URL: www.wlala.org
Social Media: www.facebook.com/WomenLawyersLA
www.instagram.com/womenlawyersla
www.linkedin.com/company/women-lawyers-association-of
  -los-angeles
twitter.com/WLALAtweets

12143 ■ WLALA Fran Kandel Public Interest Grants
(Postgraduate/Grant)

Purpose: To support law students for projects that make governmental and social institutions and agencies more accessible and responsive to members of society whose interests are not otherwise adequately recognized or asserted. **Focus:** Law; Public service. **Qualif.:** Applicants must be law students who have the interest to know and gain experience about public interest. **Criteria:** Selection will be based on the committee's criteria; strong preference will be given to those who have the support of a sponsoring organization.

Funds Avail.: Maximum of $5,000. **Duration:** Annual. **To Apply:** Applicants should submit the completed application form which consists of personal information; project information; and references (academic, personal, and work); additional requirements include essays of no more than 500 words, single-spaced, on separate sheets of paper (each discussing the specific proposal and the applicants' background); budget; resume; and letter of recommendation. **Deadline:** March 26. **Contact:** Submission: Women Lawyers Association of Los Angeles, 634 S. Spring St., Ste., 617, Los Angeles, CA, 90014; Email: info@wlala.org; Questions: Co-Chairs of WLALA's Grant Committee, Hon. Nancy Ramirez; Phone: 661-483-5986; Email: nramirez@lacourt.org; Sarah Quist; Phone: 213-894-0609; Email: sarah.quist@usdoj.gov.

12144 ■ WLALA Scholarships *(Postgraduate/Scholarship)*

Purpose: To assist law students whose prior and current activities and future plans demonstrate a commitment to is-

sues affecting women and/or children. **Focus:** Law; Women's studies; Youth. **Criteria:** Selection of recipients will be based on the applicants' demonstrated commitment to issues affecting women and/or children.

Funds Avail.: Upto $5,000. **To Apply:** Applicants must submit a personal statement addressing their commitment to issues affecting women and/or children (they must be sure to address how their commitment will continue after law school graduation); the personal statement should also explain why they need the scholarship and how it will benefit them; technical formats are typed, double-spaced, and no longer than 2 pages; additional documents include resume; certified law school transcript, including grades for fall semester last year; and minimum one letter of recommendation (no more than three). **Deadline:** May 1.

12145 ■ Women Marines Association (WMA)
PO Box 377
Oaks, PA 19456-0377
Free: 888-525-1943
E-mail: wma@womenmarines.org
URL: www.womenmarines.org
Social Media: www.facebook.com/womenmarines

12146 ■ The Agnes Sopcak Memorial Scholarship
(Undergraduate/Scholarship)

Purpose: To support students financially in pursuing their educational career. **Focus:** Maritime studies. **Criteria:** Selection board of five members will review qualified applications.

Funds Avail.: $1,500 - $3,000. **Duration:** Annual. **To Apply:** Applicants must submit complete application form (typewritten form); readable copy of Sponsor's National Membership Card; 2x2 passport photos; two letters from school personnel; and proof of relationship to a U.S. Marine; male applicants must submit proof of draft registration; applicants must submit SAT or ACT Scores and official transcripts with grading key. **Deadline:** February 28. **Contact:** Dorothy Stover-Kendrick,PO Box 134, Stilwell, KS, 66085; Email: scholarship@womenmarines.org.

12147 ■ Ethyl and Armin Wiebke Memorial Scholarship *(Undergraduate/Scholarship)*

Purpose: To financially support those students who are in need. **Focus:** Maritime studies. **Criteria:** Selection board of five members will review qualified applications.

Funds Avail.: $1,500. **Duration:** Annual. **Number Awarded:** 1. **To Apply:** Applicants must submit complete application form (typewritten form); readable copy of Sponsor's National Membership Card; 2x2 passport photos; two letters from school personnel; and proof of relationship to a U.S. Marine; male applicants must submit proof of draft registration; applicants must submit SAT or ACT Scores and official transcripts with grading key. **Deadline:** February 28. **Contact:** Dottie Stover-Kendrick, PO Box 134, Stilwell, KS, 66085; Email: scholarship@womenmarines.org.

12148 ■ LaRue A. Ditmore Music Scholarship
(Undergraduate/Scholarship)

Purpose: To financially support those students who are in need. **Focus:** Maritime studies. **Criteria:** Selection board of five members will review qualified applications.

Funds Avail.: $1,500 - $3,000. **Duration:** Annual. **To Apply:** Applicants must submit complete application form

Awards are arranged alphabetically below their administering organizations

(typewritten form); readable copy of Sponsor's National Membership Card; 2x2 passport photos; two letters from school personnel; and proof of relationship to a U.S. Marine; male applicants must submit proof of draft registration; applicants must submit SAT or ACT Scores and official transcripts with grading key. **Deadline:** February 28. **Contact:** Dottie Stover-Kendrick, PO Box 134, Stilwell, KS, 66085; Email: scholarship@womenmarines.org.

12149 ■ Lily H. Gridley Memorial Scholarship
(Undergraduate/Scholarship)

Purpose: To financially support those students who are in need. **Focus:** Maritime studies. **Criteria:** Selection board of five members will review qualified applications.

Funds Avail.: $1,500. **Duration:** Annual. **To Apply:** Applicants must submit complete application form (typewritten form); readable copy of Sponsor's National Membership Card; 2x2 passport photos; two letters from school personnel; and proof of relationship to a U.S. Marine; male applicants must submit proof of draft registration; applicants must submit SAT or ACT Scores and official transcripts with grading key. **Deadline:** February 28. **Contact:** Dottie Stover-Kendrick, PO Box 134, Stilwell, KS, 66085; Email: scholarship@womenmarines.org.

12150 ■ Women Marines Association Edith Macias Vann Southern California Chapter CA-7
1617 Mission Ave.
Oceanside, CA 92052
E-mail: ca7@womenmarines.org

12151 ■ Edith Macias Vann Southern California
(Undergraduate/Scholarship)

Purpose: To support students preparing to attend accredited four-year-colleges, universities, or community colleges. **Focus:** General studies/Field of study not specified. **Qualif.:** Applicants must be students preparing to attend accredited four-year colleges, universities, or community colleges. **Criteria:** Selection will be based on the committee's criteria.

Funds Avail.: $1,000. **Duration:** Annual. **Number Awarded:** 3 in 2019. **To Apply:** Applicants must submit a three letters of reference from adults not related to applicant; two letters may be from school personnel; extracurricular activities, volunteer services, and employment history; Enclose letter(s) of acceptance. **Contact:** Mary Anthony, Chapter Scholarship Committee Chair, Phone: 760-433-6054; Email: m3anthony@cox.net.

12152 ■ Women's Army Corps Veterans' Association (WACVA)
PO Box 663
Weaver, AL 36277
Ph: (256)820-6824
E-mail: info@armywomen.org
URL: www.armywomen.org

12153 ■ Women's Army Corps Veterans Association Scholarships *(Undergraduate/Scholarship)*

Purpose: To provide educational assistance to relatives of Army Service Women. **Focus:** General studies/Field of study not specified. **Qualif.:** Applicants must be relatives of Army Service Women who are U.S. citizens; must be high school graduating seniors or planning to enroll as full-time

students at an accredited college or university; and have 3.5 GPA on a 4.0 scale. **Criteria:** Selection is based on academic achievement; leadership as expressed through co-curricular activities and community involvement; biographical sketch; and recommendations.

Funds Avail.: $1,500. **Duration:** One year. **To Apply:** Applicants must submit the completed application form available from the website, an official 7-semester high school transcript, three letters of recommendation (one of which must be written by a teacher, counselor or principal); biographical sketch; and documentation of sponsor's military service. **Deadline:** February 2. **Contact:** Women's Army Corps Veterans' Association; Women's Army Corps Veterans' Scholarship; PO Box 663, Weaver, AL 36277.

12154 ■ Women's Business Enterprise National Council (WBENC)
1120 Connecticut Ave. NW, Ste. 1000
Washington, DC 20036
Ph: (202)872-5515
Fax: (202)872-5505
URL: www.wbenc.org
Social Media: www.facebook.com/WBENC
www.instagram.com/wbenc
www.linkedin.com/company/wbenc
twitter.com/WBENCLive

12155 ■ Dorothy B. Brothers Executive Scholarship Program *(Undergraduate/Scholarship)*

Purpose: To provide financial assistance and opportunities for women to attend an executive level course. **Focus:** General studies/Field of study not specified. **Criteria:** Selection will be based on the quality of the essay.

Duration: Annual. **Number Awarded:** Varies. **To Apply:** Applications can be submitted online.

12156 ■ Women's Health Research Foundation of Canada (WHRFC)
PO Box 61019
Winnipeg, MB, Canada R3M 3X8
E-mail: whrfc_inc@yahoo.ca
URL: whrfcinc.com
Social Media: www.facebook.com/Womens-Health
-Research-Foundation-of-Canada-WHRFC
-162785307114178/?ref=hl
twitter.com/WHRFCinc

12157 ■ Women's Health Research Foundation of Canada Scholarship Program *(Graduate/Scholarship)*

Purpose: To support graduate students who demonstrate academic excellence in the area of women's health. **Focus:** Women's studies. **Qualif.:** Applicants must be registered in a graduate program at the University of Manitoba; must have research concentration in some area of women's health. **Criteria:** Selection of applicants will be based on their research studies and application requirements.

Funds Avail.: 3,000 Canadian Dollars. **Duration:** Annual. **Number Awarded:** Varies. **To Apply:** Applicants must complete the application form available online; must submit an official transcript or student history; must have an official transcript from all other universities attended; must have two letters of reference. **Deadline:** April 15. **Remarks:** Established in 1992. **Contact:** Mrs. Rosemary Visevic,

Awards are arranged alphabetically below their administering organizations

Awards Assistant, Faculty of Graduate Studies, 500 University Ctr., Winnipeg, Manitoba, Canada, R3T 2N2; Phone: 204- 474-6827; Fax: 204- 474-7553.

12158 ■ Women's International Network of Utility Professionals (WINUP)

2795 E Bidwell St. no. 100-209
Folsom, CA 95630
Ph: (847)255-0210
URL: www.winup.org
Social Media: www.facebook.com/WiNUPINT
linkedin.com/groups/WiNUP-7489510
twitter.com/winupint

12159 ■ Julia Kiene Fellowships in Electrical Energy *(Graduate/Fellowship)*

Purpose: To support students engaging in graduate work toward an advanced degree in any phase of electrical energy. **Focus:** Engineering, Electrical. **Qualif.:** Applicant must be a graduate student earning an advanced degree in electrical energy; must be active member of several professional organizations, including WiNUP. **Criteria:** Selection is based on the application.

Funds Avail.: $2,000. **Duration:** Annual. **To Apply:** Applicants must submit a completed application form along with the required materials. **Deadline:** May 1. **Remarks:** Established in memory of Julia Kiene, past president of the organization.

12160 ■ Lyle Mamer Fellowship *(Graduate/ Fellowship)*

Purpose: To support students engaging in graduate work toward an advanced degree in any phase of electrical energy. **Focus:** Engineering, Electrical. **Qualif.:** Applicant must be a graduate student earning an advanced degree in electrical energy; must be active member of several professional organizations, including Windup. **Criteria:** Selection is based on the application.

Funds Avail.: $1,000. **Duration:** Annual. **To Apply:** Applicants must submit a completed application form along with the required materials; transcripts; letters of reference. **Remarks:** Established in memory of Lyle Mamer who served as an Associate Professor at the University of Tennessee College of Home Economics for 35 years.

12161 ■ Louisan Mamer Fellowship *(Postgraduate/ Fellowship)*

Purpose: To support students who are engaging in graduate work toward an advances degree in any phase of electrical energy. **Focus:** Energy-related areas. **Qualif.:** Applicant must be a WiNUP Members and non-members are eligible to apply for the fellowships. **Criteria:** Selection is based on the application.

Funds Avail.: $500. **Duration:** Annual. **To Apply:** Applicants must submit a completed application form along with the required materials; transcripts; letters of reference. **Deadline:** May 1.

12162 ■ Women's Jewelry Association (WJA)

125 Park Avenue, 25th Floor, Suite 2511
New York, NY 10017
Ph: (845)473-7324
Fax: (646)355-0219
E-mail: info@womensjewelryassociation.com

URL: www.womensjewelryassociation.com
Social Media: www.facebook.com/
  WomensJewelryAssociation
www.instagram.com/womensjewelryassociation
www.linkedin.com/groups/145172/profile
twitter.com/WomensJewelry

12163 ■ Women's Jewelry Association Member Grants *(Professional development/Grant)*

Purpose: To provide educational assistance to students in the international jewelry, watch and related industries. **Focus:** Design; Fashion design. **Qualif.:** Applicants must be members in good standing. Student-level members are NOT eligible for member grants and are encouraged to apply for WJA Scholarships. **Criteria:** Applicants are selected through a random drawing of the WJA Member Grant Committee.

Funds Avail.: $500. **Duration:** Annual. **To Apply:** Applicants must provide in a printed text limited to one 8 1/2 x 11 page a short statement about applicant's personal information, work, the course and how the grant will benefit the applicants (mandatory); applicant's signature to accept all terms and conditions of the WJA Grants (mandatory); a brief description of the applicant's contributions to the jewelry and/or related industries (optional); applicants must submit a completed application form and all supporting documents to WJA Member Grant Committee. **Deadline:** January 31. **Contact:** Email Rachel Jurisz, WJA Membership Coordinator, at rachel@ womensjewelryassociation.com.

12164 ■ Women's Missionary Council of the Christian Methodist Episcopal Church

c/o Dr. Princess A. Pegues, President
2309 Bonnie Ave.
Bastrop, LA 71220
Ph: (318)281-3044
URL: www.cmewmc.org
Social Media: www.facebook.com/Womens-Missionary
  -Council-of-the-Christian-Methodist-Episcopal-Church
  -125840330805430

12165 ■ Helena B. Cobb Higher Education (four Year) Scholarship *(Undergraduate, Vocational/ Occupational/Scholarship)*

Purpose: To support students with their studies by emphasizing the importance of educational training beyond the high school level. **Focus:** General studies/Field of study not specified. **Qualif.:** Applicants must be a member of the Christian Methodist Episcopal Church for atleast seven years; must be a high school graduate.

Funds Avail.: $1,000 - $4,000. **Duration:** Quadrennial. **To Apply:** Applicant must submit a completed application form along with official high school academic transcript; letter of certification from the applicant's Pastor, Local and Region Presidents and Local and Region Vice Presidents must be attached to the letter (a total of five letters); a letter of recommendations from two (2) different persons who are not related to the applicant recommending the applicant for the grant; must write an essay of 500-1,000 words from the subject, "My Goals and Objectives for the Next Four Years".

12166 ■ The Helena B. Cobb Scholarships *(Undergraduate, Vocational/Occupational/Scholarship)*

Purpose: To support students with their studies by emphasizing the importance of educational training beyond

Awards are arranged alphabetically below their administering organizations

the high school level. **Focus:** General studies/Field of study not specified. **Qualif.:** Applicants must be a member of the Christian Methodist Episcopal Church; a high school graduate; and enrolled in a college, university, or vocational-technical school. **Criteria:** Selection is based on the application.

Funds Avail.: $100. **Duration:** Annual. **Number Awarded:** 6. **To Apply:** Applicant must submit a completed application form and applicant must write an essay of 500 – 1,000 words from the subject. **Deadline:** December 31. **Remarks:** Established in 1975.

12167 ■ Women's Overseas Service League (WOSL)

PO Box 124
Cedar Knolls, NJ 07927-0124
URL: www.wosl.org

12168 ■ Women's Overseas and Service League Scholarships for Women *(Undergraduate/Scholarship)*

Purpose: To financially assist women who have served overseas in or with the Armed Forces. **Focus:** General studies/Field of study not specified. **Criteria:** Selection Committee of the Women's Overseas Service League Board of Directors will evaluate the student's application based on academic records.

Funds Avail.: $500 - $1,000. **Duration:** Annual. **To Apply:** Applicants must fill out the application form; must include all needed documents such as resume, transcripts, essays and references.

12169 ■ Women's Transportation Seminar (WTS)

1501 M St., NW Ste. 240
Washington, DC 20005
URL: www.wtsinternational.org
Social Media: www.facebook.com/
  womenstransportationseminar
www.instagram.com/wtsinternational
pinterest.com/wtsprojects
twitter.com/wts_org

12170 ■ Helene M. Overly Memorial Graduate Scholarship *(Graduate/Scholarship)*

Purpose: To encourage and assist women who are beginning professional careers or advancing their existing transportation careers to consider the field of transportation. **Focus:** Finance; Logistics. **Qualif.:** Applicants must be women pursuing graduate studies in transportation engineering, planning, finance or logistics, or related fields; applicants must have at least a GPA of 3.0 or higher. **Criteria:** Recipients are selected based on specific transportation goals, academic record, transportation-related activities, or job skills.

Funds Avail.: $10,000. **Duration:** Annual. **To Apply:** Applicants must fill out the scholarship application form. Contact your local WTS chapter for more information. All applications are submitted through a chapter. **Deadline:** November 29. **Remarks:** The Scholarship was established to honor the first Executive Secretary of WTS for her dedicated service to the organization. Established in 1981.

12171 ■ Sharon D. Banks Memorial Undergraduate Scholarship *(Undergraduate/Scholarship)*

Purpose: To introduce cultural and organizational changes aimed at motivating the public transit work force. **Focus:**

Finance; Logistics; Transportation. **Qualif.:** Applicants selected by WTS Central Florida to receive the local scholarships will then be submitted to WTS International. GPA of 3.0 or higher. Currently enrolled in an undergraduate degree program in a transportation-related field, such as transportation engineering, planning, finance, or logistics. Plans to pursue a career in a transportation-related field. **Criteria:** Recipients are selected based on specific transportation goals, academic record, transportation-related activities, or job skills.

Funds Avail.: $3,000. **Duration:** Annual. **To Apply:** Applicants must submit electronically all application materials including forms, letters, transcripts. **Deadline:** June 12. **Contact:** Tracey Slochover Attn: Scholarship 605 Third Ave., 3rd Floor New York, NY 10158; Email: wtsgnyscholarship@gmail.com.

12172 ■ Women's Transportation Seminar - Greater Dallas/Fort Worth Chapter

Hayden Consultants, Inc.
Dallas, TX 75206
Ph: (214)753-8107
Fax: (214)753-8100
URL: www.wtsinternational.org/greaterdallas
Social Media: facebook.com/womenstransportationseminar
instagram.com/wtsinternational

12173 ■ Dallas/Fort Worth Chapter WTS Undergraduate Scholarship *(Undergraduate/Scholarship)*

Purpose: To encourage bright new female professionals to undertake careers in the area of transportation. **Focus:** Transportation.

Funds Avail.: $2,000. **Duration:** Annual. **Contact:** Daphne King, Hayden Consultants, Inc.; Phone: 214-753-8107; Email: dking@haydenconsultants.com; Angela Hranicky, Hayden Consultants, Inc.; Phone: 214-753-8119; Email: ahranicky@haydenconsultants.com.

12174 ■ Gorrondona & Associates, Inc. / WTS High School Scholarships *(Two Year College, Four Year College/Scholarship)*

Purpose: To encourage female high school seniors to pursue science, technology, engineering, and math (STEM) studies at the community college or university level. **Focus:** Engineering; Mathematics and mathematical sciences; Science; Technology. **Qualif.:** Applicants must be high school senior girls; currently enrolled in a high school in the Dallas-Fort Worth region; have a demonstrated financial need; working to contribute to family budget or participating in extracurricular activities; are among the first of their family members to attend college; considering a career in a transportation-related field; have a GPA of 2.0 or higher. **Criteria:** Applicant's financial need, specific education goals, academic record, and activities or job skills; Minority candidates are encouraged.

Funds Avail.: $2,500. **Duration:** Annual. **Deadline:** October 27. **Remarks:** Established in 2015. **Contact:** Hayden Consultants, Inc, Phone: 214-753-8107; Daphne King, Email: dking@haydenconsultants.com; Angela Hranicky, Phone: 214-753-8119, Email: ahranicky@haydenconsultants.com.

12175 ■ Greater DFW WTS Undergraduate Leadership Scholarship *(Undergraduate/Scholarship)*

Purpose: To motivate and reward women who demonstrate leadership in the transportation industry. **Focus:** Transportation.

Awards are arranged alphabetically below their administering organizations

Funds Avail.: $2,500. **Duration:** Annual.

12176 ■ Greater DFW WTS Monique Pegues Graduate Leadership Scholarship *(Graduate/Scholarship)*

Purpose: To support women pursuing graduate studies in transportation or a related field. **Focus:** Transportation.

Funds Avail.: $2,500. **Duration:** Annual. **Remarks:** Named in honor of Monique Pegues, past president of the Dallas/Fort Worth Chapter of WTS. **Contact:** Daphne King, Hayden Consultants, Inc.; Phone: 214-753-8107; Email: dking@haydenconsultants.com; Angela Hranicky, Hayden Consultants, Inc.; Phone: 214-753-8119; Email: ahranicky@haydenconsultants.com.

12177 ■ Wanda J. Schafer Graduate Scholarship *(Graduate/Scholarship)*

Purpose: To encourage women to pursue career paths in transportation. **Focus:** Transportation.

Funds Avail.: $2,500. **Duration:** Annual. **Remarks:** Named in honor of Ms. Wanda Schafer, the first president of the DFW Chapter of WTS. Established in 2002. **Contact:** Daphne King, Hayden Consultants, Inc.; Phone: 214-753-8107; Email: dking@haydenconsultants.com; Angela Hranicky, Hayden Consultants, Inc.; Phone: 214-753-8119; Email: ahranicky@haydenconsultants.com.

12178 ■ Transportation YOU High School Scholarship *(High School/Scholarship)*

Purpose: To encourage bright new female professionals and students to undertake careers in the area of transportation by supporting girls pursuing high school studies in science, technology, engineering, and math. **Focus:** Transportation.

Funds Avail.: $2,500. **Duration:** Annual. **Contact:** Daphne King, Hayden Consultants, Inc.; Phone: 214-753-8107; Email: dking@haydenconsultants.com; Angela Hranicky, Hayden Consultants, Inc.; Phone: 214-753-8119; Email: ahranicky@haydenconsultants.com.

12179 ■ WTS Community College/Technical/Trade School Scholarship *(Two Year College, Vocational/Occupational/Scholarship)*

Purpose: To foster the development of women in the transportation field by encouraging bright new professionals to undertake careers in the area of transportation. **Focus:** Transportation. **Qualif.:** Applicants must be female; currently enrolled in an Associates or technical degree program in a transportation-related field (such as transportation engineering, planning, finance, or logistics) in certain community colleges/trade/technical schools in in Texas and Oklahoma; have a GPA of 3.0 or higher. **Criteria:** Applicant's specific transportation goals, academic record, and transportation-related activities or job skills. Minority candidates are encouraged to apply.

Funds Avail.: $1,000. **Duration:** Annual. **To Apply:** Submit applications through local WTS chapters. Include official transcript. Applications submitted by mail are preferred, but e-mailed applications will be considered if original signatures are present on the application. **Deadline:** June 26. **Contact:** Elvia Valdez, WTS-SAR Scholarship Chair, c/o Civil Engineering Consultants, 11550 IH 10 W, Ste. 395, San Antonio, TX, 78230; Email: evaldez@cectexas.com.

12180 ■ Wondershare Software Company Ltd.
10/F, Block D, 5th Bldg., Shenzhen Software Industrial Base, Haitian 2nd Rd, Nanshan District

Shenzhen 518057, Guangdong, China
Ph: 86 755 8666-5000
E-mail: media@wondershare.com
URL: www.wondershare.com
Social Media: www.facebook.com/wondershare
www.instagram.com/wondershare
twitter.com/wondershare
www.youtube.com/user/wondershare

12181 ■ PDFelement Scholarship *(Undergraduate, Graduate/Scholarship)*

Purpose: To provide financial assistance to a student with a demonstrated interest in digital document processing skills. **Focus:** General studies/Field of study not specified. **Qualif.:** Applicants must be enrolled in an accredited post-secondary institution, located anywhere in the world. **Criteria:** Selection will be based on the overall quality of the submitted video.

Funds Avail.: $1,000. **To Apply:** Application details are available online at: pdf.wondershare.com/scholarship.html. **Contact:** Email: Scholarship@wondershare.com.

12182 ■ Carter G. Woodson Institute for African-American and African Studies
University of Virginia
108 Minor Hall
Charlottesville, VA 22904-4162
Ph: (434)924-3109
Fax: (434)924-8820
E-mail: woodson@virginia.edu
URL: artsandsciences.virginia.edu
Social Media: www.facebook.com/The-Carter-G-Woodson-Institute-for-African-American-and-African-Studies-266466867235
twitter.com/WoodsonUVA

12183 ■ Carter G. Woodson Institute Post-doctoral Residential Research & Teaching Fellowship *(Postdoctorate/Fellowship)*

Purpose: To facilitate the writing of dissertations or manuscripts and provide successful applicants the opportunity to discuss and exchange works-in-progress both with each other and the larger intellectual community of the University. **Focus:** Humanities; Social sciences. **Qualif.:** Applicants for the post-doctoral fellowship must have been awarded their Ph.D. by the time of application or furnish proof from the relevant registrar that all documentation required for the Ph.D. has been submitted.

Funds Avail.: $47,476. **Duration:** Annual; up to 2 years. **To Apply:** Applicants must submit a Candidate Profile online through Jobs@UVA and must attach the following: a maximum of 250-word letter of application stating interest in the program; a curriculum vitae which must include the personal information, date(s) and location(s) of degree(s) earned, honors and awards, lectures and conference presentations, publications and the names of three referees. Applicants must also submit the following: a project abstract, including title, not to exceed 50 words as well as a project description, including title, not to exceed seven double-spaced pages (1,750 words). It must indicate the nature of the research to be completed during the period of the fellowship award, as well as the significance of this work; the project description must include a detailed research plan giving concrete objectives to be achieved

Awards are arranged alphabetically below their administering organizations

during the award period; project descriptions must be attached through Jobs@ under Writing Sample 1; a working bibliography not to exceed four double-spaced pages; the bibliography must list those scholarly works that the applicants considers most important to the intellectual development of the project; the working bibliography must be attached through Jobs@ under Writing Sample 2; an original, signed three confidential letters of reference sent directly to the Woodson Institute by persons qualified to evaluate the proposals for which support is being sought. **Deadline:** December 1. **Contact:** Selection Committee, Residential Research Fellowships, The Carter G. Woodson Institute, University of Virginia, PO Box 400162, Charlottesville, VA, 22904-4162; Deborah E. McDowell/Director of the Fellowship Program; Email: dem8z@virginia.edu.

12184 ■ Carter G. Woodson Institute Pre-doctoral Fellowship (Doctorate/Fellowship)

Purpose: To facilitate the writing of dissertations or manuscripts and provide successful applicants the opportunity to discuss and exchange works-in-progress both with each other and the larger intellectual community of the University. **Focus:** Humanities; Social sciences. **Qualif.:** Applicants must be qualified candidates without restriction as to citizenship or current residence whose work focused on Africa and/or African Diaspora.

Funds Avail.: $24,000 plus health insurance. **Duration:** Annual; up to 2 years. **To Apply:** Applicants must submit a Candidate Profile on-line through Jobs@UVA and must attach the following: a maximum of 250-word letter of application stating interest in the program; a curriculum vitae which must include the personal information, date(s) and location(s) of degree(s) earned, honors and awards, lectures and conference presentations, publications and the names of three referees; applicants must also submit the following: a project abstract, including title, not to exceed 50 words as well as a project description, including title, not to exceed seven double-spaced pages (1,750 words). It must indicate the nature of the research to be completed during the period of the fellowship award, as well as the significance of this work; the project description must include a detailed research plan giving concrete objectives to be achieved during the award period; project descriptions must be attached through Jobs@ under Writing Sample 1; a working bibliography not to exceed four double-spaced pages; the bibliography must list those scholarly works that the applicants considers most important to the intellectual development of the project; the working bibliography must be attached through Jobs@ under Writing Sample 2; an original, signed three confidential letters of reference sent directly to the Woodson Institute by persons qualified to evaluate the proposals for which support is being sought. **Deadline:** December 1. **Contact:** Selection Committee, Residential Research Fellowships, The Carter G. Woodson Institute, University of Virginia, PO Box 400162, Charlottesville, VA, 22904-4162; Deborah E. McDowell/Director of the Fellowship Program; Email: dem8z@virginia.edu.

12185 ■ Worcester County Conservation District (WCCD)

52 Boyden Rd., Ste. 107
Holden, MA 01520
Ph: (508)829-4477
URL: worcesterconservation.org
Social Media: www.facebook.com/
  WorcesterCountyConservationDistrict

12186 ■ Worcester County Conservation District Annual Scholarships Program (Undergraduate/Scholarship)

Purpose: To promote the conservation of the natural resources throughout all of Massachusetts. **Focus:** Agricultural sciences; Conservation of natural resources; Environmental conservation. **Qualif.:** Applicants must be Worcester County, MA residents; must be high school seniors who will be entering college and majoring in Natural Resource Conservation, Agriculture or Environmental Science. **Criteria:** Selection will be based on the submitted application and essay.

Duration: Annual. **To Apply:** Applicants need to provide the following: an essay consisting of at least 300 words explaining why they are interested in pursuing the chosen degree program and hot it will apply to their career plans; a signed and sealed transcript from the applicants current high school; on e letter of recommendation from a teacher, guidance counselor, athletic coach or employer. **Deadline:** June 14. **Contact:** WCCD Board of Supervisors, 52 Boyden Rd., Ste. 107, Holden, MA 01520.

12187 ■ Worcester District Medical Society (WDMS)

Mechanics Hall
321 Main St.
Worcester, MA 01608-1532
Ph: (508)753-1579
Fax: (508)754-6246
E-mail: info@wdms.org
URL: www.wdms.org

12188 ■ Worcester District Medical Society Scholarship Fund (Undergraduate/Scholarship)

Purpose: To provide educational assistance to medical students. **Focus:** Medicine. **Qualif.:** Applicants must be second, third or fourth- year students enrolled (with tuition obligation) in an accredited medical or osteopathic school; and must be legal residents of Central Massachusetts at the time of applying to medical school. **Criteria:** Selection will be based on academic achievement; community service; and financial need.

Funds Avail.: No specific amount. **Duration:** Annual. **To Apply:** Applicants must submit a completed application form; current transcript; two letters of recommendation; and an essay stating the reasons for selecting a career in medicine and why they deserve the award. **Deadline:** August 3. **Contact:** Scholarship Fund of WDMS, 321 Main St., Mechanics Hall, Worcester, MA, 01608; Michele Pugnaire, MD.

12189 ■ World Association for Cooperative Education (WACE)

c/o Dr. Norah McRae, Assoc. Provost
University of Waterloo
200 University Ave. W
Waterloo, ON, Canada N2L 3G1
E-mail: admin@waceinc.org
URL: www.waceinc.org

12190 ■ National Co-op Scholarship Program (Undergraduate/Scholarship)

Purpose: To help high school seniors and transfer students who plan to participate in college cooperative education at

Awards are arranged alphabetically below their administering organizations

one of our Partner Institutions listed on the Scholarship Partners tab. **Focus:** Engineering; Mathematics and mathematical sciences; Science. **Qualif.:** Applicants must have a cumulative high school GPA of 3.5 or better on a 4.0 scale, and have applied and be accepted for the academic year at one of the WACE partner institutions; must be current high school seniors or transfer students. **Criteria:** Selection shall be based on the aforementioned qualifications and compliance with the application details.

Funds Avail.: $4,200,000. **Duration:** Annual. **Number Awarded:** Varies. **To Apply:** Applicants must submit a complete National Co-op Scholarship program Application including a typed, one-page essay (200 words). **Deadline:** February 15. **Remarks:** Established in 2003. **Contact:** Michelle Hansford; Email: michellehansford@waceinc.org.

12191 ■ World Bank Group (WBG)

1818 H St. NW
Washington, DC 20433
Ph: (202)473-1000
Fax: (202)477-6391
E-mail: info_us@worldbank.org
URL: www.worldbank.org
Social Media: www.facebook.com/worldbank
www.instagram.com/worldbank
www.linkedin.com/company/the-world-bank
twitter.com/worldbank
www.youtube.com/user/WorldBank

12192 ■ Joint Japan/World Bank Graduate Scholarship Program for Developing Country National (JJ/WBGSP) *(Graduate/Scholarship)*

Purpose: To enable mid-career professionals from developing countries to access the latest techniques and knowledge through graduate studies at universities worldwide. **Focus:** General studies/Field of study not specified. **Qualif.:** Applicants must be a national of a World Bank member country eligible to borrow; must not be a dual citizen of any developed country; must not be an Executive Director, Executive Director's alternate staff, or consultant of the World Bank Group (the World Bank, International Finance Corporation, International Development Association, Multilateral Investment Guarantee Agency, and International Center for Settlement of Investments Disputes) or have any relatives or in-laws who are employed by the World Bank Group in any capacity; must hold a bachelor's degree (or equivalent university degree); and must have at least 3 years of development-related experience since earning a bachelor's degree. **Criteria:** Selection will be based on quality of professional experience; quality of professional recommendations; quality of commitment to your home country; quality of education background.

Funds Avail.: $500. **Duration:** Annual. **Number Awarded:** Varies. **To Apply:** Applicants must submit a completed application form (either in English or in the language of their Master's degree program) and recommendation letters from two people who have direct knowledge of the applicants' professional experience. **Deadline:** April 23. **Remarks:** Established in 1987.

12193 ■ Joint Japan/World Bank Graduate Scholarship Program for Japanese National (JJ/WBGSP) *(Graduate, Master's, Doctorate/Scholarship)*

Purpose: To enable mid-career professionals from developing countries to access the latest techniques and knowledge through graduate studies at universities worldwide. **Focus:** General studies/Field of study not specified. **Qualif.:** Applicants must be Japanese national; must hold a bachelor's degree (or its equivalent university degree) earned at least three years prior to the application deadline; must be in good health with respect to the capacity to be a productive graduate student; must have, by the application deadline, at least 3 years but no more than 25 years of full time paid employment acquired after receiving the first bachelor's degree; must not be employed by the Government of Japan or its related agencies, including local governments and the Central Bank at the time of application; must not be an Executive Director, Executive Director's alternate staff, or consultant of the World Bank Group (the World Bank, International Finance Corporation, International Development Association, Multilateral Investment Guarantee Agency, and International Center for Settlement of Investments Disputes) or have any relatives or in-laws who are employed by the World Bank Group in any capacity; and have not received any scholarship funds from the Government of Japan to help finance a graduate degree. **Criteria:** Selection is based on two qualified assessors independently reviewing each eligible application and scoring the application on a scale of 1 to 10, taking into account three main factors and the degree of cohesion among them: quality of academic experience and recommendations; quality of professional experience and recommendations; and quality of commitment to development.

Funds Avail.: No specific amount. **Duration:** Two years. **To Apply:** Application will be accepted and reviewed if the applicant submits only one completed application electronically; Two recommendation letters; One completed Application Form. **Deadline:** April 23.

12194 ■ Robert S. McNamara Fellowships Program (RSMFP) *(Doctorate/Fellowship, Monetary)*

Purpose: To provide financial assistance to PhD students from developing countries for them to conduct innovative, development-related, PhD research under the supervision of a research advisor at a host institution abroad. **Focus:** General studies/Field of study not specified. **Qualif.:** Applicants must be a national of a World Bank member developing country; must not be a dual citizen of a developed country that is not a World Bank member; must be currently enrolled in a Ph.D. program in a World Bank member country; must have completed all course work and exam requirements for Ph.D. at the time of application; must have a master's degree or equivalent; must be 35 years old or younger; must not be an Executive Director, Executive Director's alternate staff, or consultant of the World Bank Group (the World Bank, International Finance Corporation, International Development Association, Multilateral Investment Guarantee Agency, and International Center for Settlement of Investments Disputes) or have any relatives or in-laws who are employed by the World Bank Group in any capacity, including consulting; must not previously been the recipient of the World Bank Robert S. McNamara Fellowship; and must be accepted as a visiting scholar for a period of six to ten months by a university or research center in a World Bank member country other than the applicants' home country. **Criteria:** Selection will be based on the committee's criteria.

Funds Avail.: Up to $25,000. **Duration:** Annual. **To Apply:** Applicants must submit all the required documents together with application form and reference letters official document from host institution stating current enrollment as a Ph. D. student and already completed all coursework and exam requirements for the applicant's doctoral program; proof of

Awards are arranged alphabetically below their administering organizations

employment if the applicants is currently employed; official diploma of the applicant's highest degree earned; and a proposed budget for the fellowship using their own world bank fellowship budget template; all documents must submit in the language in which the applicants is completing application, and should also translate it into English; both the document in the original language and the translated document must be uploaded into the application form; finalists must submit an additional document, a copy of a passport or other legal document (birth or marriage certificate), with the name identical to the one submitted on the application form. **Remarks:** Established in 1982.

12195 ■ World Council of Credit Unions (WOCCU)

5710 Mineral Point Rd.
Madison, WI 53705-4454
Ph: (608)395-2000
Fax: (608)395-2001
E-mail: mail@woccu.org
URL: www.woccu.org
Social Media: www.facebook.com/woccu
www.instagram.com/woccu
www.linkedin.com/company/world-council-of-credit-unions
twitter.com/woccu
www.youtube.com/user/WOCCU/featured

12196 ■ WYCUP Scholarship Program *(Other/Scholarship)*

Purpose: To promote the next generation of credit union professionals and volunteers in the international credit union movement. **Focus:** General studies/Field of study not specified. **Criteria:** nominations and select up to five scholarship recipients based on the criteria included in the eligibility requirements.

Funds Avail.: No specific amount. **Duration:** Annual. **Number Awarded:** 5. **To Apply:** Applicants must have Nomination Forms (attached) completed by the nominee and the sponsor; must provide the proof of age (photocopy of passport, driver's license, birth certificate or other official document); must prepare a brief 300-word essay describing the contribution made to the development of the candidate's credit union or credit union organization. **Deadline:** May 29. **Contact:** Email: wycup@woccu.org.

12197 ■ World Forest Institute (WFI)

World Forestry Ctr.
4033 SW Canyon Rd.
Portland, OR 97221
Ph: (503)228-1367
E-mail: info@worldforestry.org
URL: www.worldforestry.org
Social Media: www.facebook.com/worldforestrycenter
www.instagram.com/worldforestrycenter
twitter.com/World_Forestry

12198 ■ The World Forest Institute International Fellowship *(Undergraduate/Fellowship)*

Purpose: To provide assistance to students interested in the forestry field. **Focus:** Forestry. **Criteria:** Selection will be based on submitted documents and specific criteria.

Duration: Annual. **To Apply:** Applicants should submit a completed application form; project proposal; and cur-

riculum vitae; project should take advantage of being located in the Pacific Northwest which involves collaboration with forest industry, local organizations, researchers, or communities. **Deadline:** October 15. **Contact:** Shadia Duery, International Fellowship Program Manager; Email: sduery@worldforestry.org.

12199 ■ World Leisure Organization (WLO)

Central Michigan University
Warriner Hall 210
Mount Pleasant, MI 48859-0001
E-mail: secretariat@worldleisure.org
URL: www.worldleisure.org
Social Media: www.facebook.com/wordleisure/?ref=hl
www.linkedin.com/company/world-leisure-organization
twitter.com/WorldLeisureOrg
www.youtube.com/user/WorldLeisureOrg

12200 ■ George Torkildsen Literary Award *(Professional development/Award, Trophy)*

Purpose: To recognize individuals who made a significant contribution to the recreation, parks and leisure service literature by advancing innovative ideas, thoughts and/or philosophical perspectives. **Focus:** Parks and recreation. **Qualif.:** Applicants must be individuals who have made contributions in recreation, parks and leisure service literatures. **Criteria:** Applicants will be evaluated based on literary contributions to advance leisure concerns worldwide; impact of the contributions to influence the general public and/or profession; clarity, solutions and insights brought to emerging trends, issues and concepts.

Funds Avail.: No specific amount. **Duration:** Biennial. **To Apply:** Applicants must include their full name, title, organizational affiliation and full contact details; must submit a written statement of no more than 1000 words that addresses the nominees scholarly efforts and other professional contributions, referencing the impact that the nominees contributions have made to the literature; and must submit a curriculum vitae. **Remarks:** The award seeks to perpetuate the memory of George Torkildsen who served as Chair of the World Leisure Board of Directors (1996 - 2004). **Contact:** Please send nominations in pdf format via email to World Leisure Secretariat: secretariat@worldleisure.org.

12201 ■ Thomas and Ruth River International Scholarship *(Undergraduate, Graduate/Scholarship)*

Purpose: To provide opportunities for seniors or graduate students who are studying recreation or tourism studies related fields to attend and present a scholarly paper at the biennial international World Leisure Congress. **Focus:** Parks and recreation; Travel and tourism. **Qualif.:** Applicants must be undergraduate or final year graduate students majoring in recreation, leisure studies, leisure services and resources, or tourism studies; must have a GPA of 3.5 on a 4.0 scale for undergraduates and 3.8 on a 4.0 scale if graduate students; must be recommended by two faculty members; must have demonstrated interest in recreation, leisure and/or tourism internationally; must have had either volunteer or paid work experience in the recreation, leisure services or tourism fields. **Criteria:** Applicants will be selected based on submitted application and supporting documents.

Funds Avail.: No specific amount. **Duration:** Biennial. **To Apply:** Applicants must complete the application form; must

Awards are arranged alphabetically below their administering organizations

submit the Faculty Validation of Student applicants form and a copy of the abstract submitted to the World Congress Program Committee; if the college or university does not have a major in required fields, applicants must obtain a letter from their major professor indicating the area of study. If the college or university does not require coursework, applicants must obtain a letter indicating the required learning/ research activities and performance evaluation. **Remarks:** The award is given in remembrance of Tom Rivers who served as the first Director General of the International Recreation Association (IRA), later known as the World Leisure and Recreation Association (WLRA) from 1956 - 1974. Established in 1970. **Contact:** Dr. Cari E. Autry, CTRS, Program Manger, Thomas and Ruth Rivers International Scholarship Award Committee, Florida International University, 11200 SW 8th St., ZEB 335B, Miami, Florida, USA 33199; Telephone: 305-348-3472; E-mail: cari.autry@ fiu.edu.

12202 ■ World Wildlife Fund (WWF)

1250 24th St. NW
Washington, DC 20037-1193
Ph: (202)293-4800
Free: 800-960-0993
E-mail: membership@wwfus.org
URL: www.worldwildlife.org
Social Media: www.facebook.com/worldwildlifefund
www.pinterest.com/wwfus
twitter.com/world_wildlife
www.youtube.com/channel/
UCZZIdeOoWhKe7SaisbCPk5Q

12203 ■ Kathryn Fuller Science for Nature Fund *(Graduate, Postdoctorate/Fellowship)*

Purpose: To support early-career scientists working on issues of exceptional importance and relevance to conservation. **Focus:** Conservation of natural resources.

Funds Avail.: No specific amount.

12204 ■ Worldstudio Foundation

1239 Broadway, Penthouse
New York, NY 10011
Ph: (212)366-1317
URL: worldstudioinc.com

12205 ■ Worldstudio AIGA Scholarships *(Graduate, Undergraduate/Scholarship)*

Purpose: To help the next generation of artists, architects and designers realize their dreams while being pro-actively involved in their communities. **Focus:** Advertising; Architecture; Art; Art, Caricatures and cartoons; Crafts; Environmental design; Fashion design; Filmmaking; Graphic art and design; Illustrators and illustrations; Industrial design; Interior design; Landscape architecture and design; Photography; Urban affairs/design/planning. **Criteria:** Selection is based on the quality of submitted work, financial need, minority status, academic record, recommendations and strength of written statement.

Funds Avail.: No specific amount. **Duration:** Annual. **To Apply:** Applicants must submit up to ten examples of their work and must follow the format indicated at the website; must mail the disks with film, motion graphics or interactive; transcript(s); and letters of recommendation. **Deadline:** April 22.

12206 ■ Worldwide Assurance for Employees of Public Agencies (WAEPA)

433 Park Ave.
Falls Church, VA 22046
Ph: (703)790-8010
Free: 800-368-3484
E-mail: info@waepa.org
URL: www.waepa.org
Social Media: www.facebook.com/waepanews
www.linkedin.com/company/waepa
twitter.com/WAEPA_News
www.youtube.com/channel/
UCfL6Cg48mZ1Qr8a4cWscbnQ

12207 ■ WAEPA Scholarship Program *(Undergraduate, Vocational/Occupational/Scholarship)*

Purpose: To assist policy holders' children who plan to continue education in college or vocational school programs. **Focus:** General studies/Field of study not specified.

Funds Avail.: $2,500 to 70 students attending four-year colleges or universities; $1,250 to 5 students attending two-year colleges or vocational-technical schools. **Duration:** Annual. **Number Awarded:** Up to 75. **To Apply:** Applicant must submit an online application form. **Remarks:** Established in 2007. **Contact:** WAEPA Scholarship Program, Scholarship Management Services, 1 Scholarship Way, Saint Peter, MN 56082; Phone: 507-931-1682.

12208 ■ Worthington Industries Inc.

1400 Division Rd.
West Warwick, RI 02893-2323
URL: amtrol.com
Social Media: twitter.com/amtroltankstour
www.youtube.com/user/AmtrolUSA

12209 ■ AANP Education Advancement Scholarships *(Graduate/Scholarship, Grant)*

Purpose: To provide education assistance to the members of the organization and to enhance their skills in the field of nursing. **Focus:** Nursing.

Contact: Email: admin@aanp.org, Phone Number: (512)442-4262, Fax Number: (512)442-6469.

12210 ■ Worthy Inc.

20 W 37 st., 12 Fl.
New York, NY 10018
Free: 888-222-0208
E-mail: info@worthy.com
URL: www.worthy.com
Social Media: www.facebook.com/worthyInc
www.linkedin.com/company/worthy-com
www.pinterest.com/worthyluxury/
twitter.com/WorthyInc
www.youtube.com/channel/UC2FXgX7PzZedlrl11VxqSgQ

12211 ■ Worthy Gemological Scholarships *(Undergraduate/Scholarship)*

Purpose: To enhance the students' knowledge and expertise regarding jewelry and its industry. **Focus:** Gemology. **Qualif.:** Applicants must be students with creative, informative and innovative mind about jewelry and jewelry industry. **Criteria:** Selection will be based on the committee's criteria.

Awards are arranged alphabetically below their administering organizations

Funds Avail.: $1,500. **Number Awarded:** 1. **To Apply:** Applicants must complete and submit the application and provide a research paper in PDF format with the name template: LastName_FirstName_Date.pdf. **Contact:** scholarships@worthy.com.

12212 ■ Worthy Women's Professional Studies Scholarship *(Vocational/Occupational/Scholarship)*

Purpose: To support women who have decided to go back to school to pursue their passion and further their professional career. **Focus:** General studies/Field of study not specified. **Qualif.:** Applicants must be enrolled in a continuing education professional studies program; must identify as a female; be at least 30 years old; permanent resident of the United States. **Criteria:** Essays that are honest, thoughtful, and well-written.

Funds Avail.: $2,500 for first place; $1,500 for second; $1,000 for third. **Duration:** Annual. **Number Awarded:** 3. **To Apply:** Submit essay answers (totaling 300-500 words) on one of three topics given at www.worthy.com/about/scholarship. **Deadline:** December 15. **Contact:** Email: scholarships@worthy.com.

12213 ■ Wound Healing Society (WHS)

500 Cummings Ctr, Ste. 4400
Beverly, MA 01915
Ph: (978)927-8330
Fax: (978)524-0461
URL: woundheal.org
Social Media: www.facebook.com/woundheal
www.linkedin.com/pub/wound-healing-society/4b/0/303
twitter.com/woundheal

12214 ■ 3M Fellowship Award *(Postdoctorate/ Fellowship)*

Purpose: To stimulate scientific research and career development of young investigators or junior faculty who are pursuing a career in academic research in wound healing. **Focus:** Education. **Qualif.:** Applicant must be a scientific research and career development of young investigators or junior faculty.

Funds Avail.: $15,000. **Duration:** Annual. **Number Awarded:** 1. **To Apply:** Applicants must submit completed application form along with curriculum vitae and bibliography (two page limit, Pre-May 2015, old NIH format style; description of the research proposal: Use Arial 11 or Times New Roman 12 font; proposal is limited to six single-spaced pages with the left margin of 1.5 inches and all other margins at least 3/4 inch; the proposal should include the following: title of the research project, synopsis (200 word limit), significance of this research, background information, preliminary observations, methods and design, data analysis; literature cited (2 page limit); plans for appropriate institutional approvals; letter of support from either the Sponsor or the Department Chair; copy of the current Conflict of Interest Statement provided to the Sponsor in the normal course of that relationship in pdf. **Deadline:** November 24. **Contact:** Manuela Martins-Green, WHF VP Research and chair of WHF Awards Committee.awards@woundhealingfoundation.org.

12215 ■ Wound, Ostomy and Continence Nurses Society (WOCN)

1120 Rte. 73, Ste. 200
Mount Laurel, NJ 08054
Fax: (856)439-0525
Free: 888-224-9626
E-mail: info@wocn.org
URL: www.wocn.org
Social Media: www.facebook.com/WOCNSociety
www.instagram.com/wocnsociety
www.linkedin.com/company/wocnsociety
www.pinterest.com/wocnsociety
www.youtube.com/c/thewocnsociety

12216 ■ WOCN Society Accredited Educational Scholarship *(Graduate, Undergraduate/Scholarship)*

Purpose: To support individuals seeking education in wound, ostomy and continence nursing specialties. **Focus:** Nursing. **Qualif.:** Applicants must be accepted into a WOCN Society Accredited Nursing Education Program. **Criteria:** Selection will be based on the committee's criteria.

Funds Avail.: No specific amount. **Duration:** two years. **Number Awarded:** Varies. **To Apply:** Applicants must have a certificate of completion from a WOCN-accredited WOC-NEP or Specialty Course, within three months of graduation; must complete the application and submit three satisfactory letters of recommendation from professional associates who have known them for at least one year (one from current employer is preferred); has not received an educational scholarship award from the WOCN Society Foundation in the last three years. **Deadline:** May 1;November 1.

12217 ■ WOCN Society Advanced Educational Scholarship *(Graduate/Scholarship)*

Purpose: To support individual seeking education in wound, ostomy and continence nursing specialties. **Focus:** Nursing. **Qualif.:** Applicants must be obtaining a Baccalaureate, Master's or Doctoral Degree or NP Certificate. **Criteria:** Selection will be based on the committee's criteria.

Funds Avail.: No specific amount. **Duration:** two years. **Number Awarded:** Varies. **To Apply:** Applicants must have a Certification by the Wound, Ostomy and Continence Nursing Certification Board (WOCNCB) in one or more areas of WOCN nursing; must complete the application and submit the following: three letters of recommendation; proof of current RN license; proof of WOCN membership; proof of current or previous employment as a wound, ostomy or continence nurse for three years within the past five years; proof of current enrollment, acceptance, or completion or graduation from an NLN accredited nursing program or other accredited program for non-nursing degree. **Deadline:** May 1;November 1.

12218 ■ Wpromote Inc.

2100 E Grand Ave., First Fl.
El Segundo, CA 90245
Fax: (310)356-3228
Free: 866-977-6668
E-mail: sales@wpromote.com
URL: www.wpromote.com
Social Media: www.facebook.com/wpromote
www.instagram.com/wpromoteofficial
www.linkedin.com/company/wpromote
twitter.com/wpromote
www.youtube.com/user/wpromote

12219 ■ Wpromote Digital Marketing Scholarship *(Undergraduate, Graduate/Scholarship)*

Purpose: To support students with a passion for online marketing. **Focus:** General studies/Field of study not speci-

Awards are arranged alphabetically below their administering organizations

fied. **Qualif.:** Applicants must be undergraduate or graduate students enrolled full-time at an accredited university in the U.S.; 3.0 or higher cumulative GPA; legal U.S. residents. **Criteria:** Selection will be based on originality, professionalism, and GPA.

Duration: Semiannual. **Number Awarded:** 3. **To Apply:** Applicants must submit 200-400 word short answer responses for each post explaining the rationale behind the image and caption and upload your images and captions along with your applications. **Deadline:** May 31.

12220 ■ Xavier University

3800 Victory Pky.
Cincinnati, OH 45207
Ph: (513)745-3000
Free: 800-344-4698
URL: www.xavier.edu
Social Media: www.facebook.com/XavierUniversity
www.instagram.com/xavieruniversity
twitter.com/XavierUniv
www.youtube.com/user/xavieruniversity

12221 ■ Edgecliff McAuley Art Scholarships
(Undergraduate/Scholarship)

Purpose: To provide financial support to students who are in need. **Focus:** Arts. **Qualif.:** Applicants must be incoming first-year students with good academic achievement and outstanding artistic talent. **Criteria:** Selection will be based upon artistic talent and achievement.

Funds Avail.: $250,000. **Duration:** Annual; up to 4 years. **To Apply:** Applicants at the Xavier University are automatically considered; must submit a portfolio (minimum of eight or maximum of twelve examples of best work); portfolios must be clearly labeled with the name, home phone number, school, and must include an inventory list and a one page personal resume; all pieces must be matted (white mats are mandatory) unless in slide/digital format; all work must be original.

12222 ■ Edgecliff McAuley Music Scholarship
(Undergraduate/Scholarship)

Purpose: To support outstanding musicians who intend to major in music or music education. **Focus:** Music. **Qualif.:** Applicants must be incoming freshmen students; must be admitted to Xavier University. **Criteria:** Selection will be based on the competitive basis to outstanding musicians who intend to major in music or music education.

Duration: Annual. **To Apply:** Applicants admitted to Xavier University are automatically considered and must pass the audition.

12223 ■ James E. Hoff, S.J. Scholar *(Undergraduate/Scholarship)*

Purpose: To provide financial support to students who are in need. **Focus:** General studies/Field of study not specified. **Qualif.:** Applicants must be Edgecliff alumni relatives (sons, daughters, brothers, sisters, nieces, nephews and Grandchildren); must demonstrate exceptional leadership, vision, courage, service and compassion in academic and personal life. **Criteria:** Selection is based on academic merit and financial need.

Funds Avail.: Varies. **Duration:** Annual. **To Apply:** Applicants submit the completed application to Xavier University's office of student financial assistance. **Deadline:**

February 1. **Contact:** Xavier University, Office of Student Financial Assistance, 3800 Victory Parkway, Cincinnati, OH, 45207-5111; Phone: 513-745-3142; Fax: 513-745-2806.

12224 ■ Miguel Pro Scholarships *(Undergraduate/Scholarship)*

Purpose: To provide support to students in promoting diversity in the society and demonstrating leadership in the classroom, on campus, and in the greater community. **Focus:** General studies/Field of study not specified. **Qualif.:** Applicants must be students ranking in the top 25 percent of their high school class with at least 3.0 GPA and a minimum SAT of 1070 (23 ACT); admitted students are eligible.

Funds Avail.: No specific amount. **Duration:** Annual. **Deadline:** December 1.

12225 ■ St. Francis Xavier Scholarship
(Undergraduate/Scholarship)

Purpose: To provide financial support to Xavier University students who are in need. **Focus:** General studies/Field of study not specified. **Qualif.:** Applicants must be incoming first-year students with exceptional academic achievement and outstanding leadership involvement in the community or school; only admitted students are eligible; must have at least 3.75GPA and a minimum SAT of 1360 (ACT of 31).

Funds Avail.: No specific amount. **Duration:** Annual; up to 4 years. **Number Awarded:** Up to 10. **To Apply:** Must submit your application for admission to Xavier; test scores are required for competitive scholarship consideration. **Deadline:** December 1.

12226 ■ Francis X. Weninger Scholarships
(Undergraduate/Scholarship)

Purpose: To provide support to Xavier University students who are committed to the promotion of diversity in the society and who demonstrated leadership in the classroom, on campus and in the greater community. **Focus:** General studies/Field of study not specified. **Qualif.:** Applicants must be students ranking in the top 25 percent of their high school class with at least 3.0 GPA and a minimum SAT of 1070 (23 ACT); admitted students are eligible.

Funds Avail.: No specific amount. **Duration:** Four years. **To Apply:** Must submit your application for admission to Xavier, test scores are required for competitive scholarship consideration. **Deadline:** December 1. **Remarks:** Named in honor of Francis Xavier Weninger, S.J., founder of St. Ann Parish in 1865, the first Catholic church and school with a ministry committed to Cincinnati's black community.

12227 ■ Xavier Community-Engaged Fellowships
(Undergraduate/Fellowship)

Purpose: To support students who have demonstrated extraordinary leadership or initiative in the area of community engagement or service through their school, community or church. **Focus:** General studies/Field of study not specified. **Qualif.:** Applicants must be incoming freshmen who excelled in service and chose engagement as part of their undergraduate experience; recipients have at least a 3.0 GPA and an SAT of 1280. **Criteria:** Selection based on interest in social issues; passion for social justice; initiative in responding to community conditions; leadership in inspiring others to action; a collaborative work style; and a willingness to take risks.

Funds Avail.: $22,000. **Duration:** Annual. **Number Awarded:** 8. **Deadline:** December 1. **Remarks:** Established in 1989.

Awards are arranged alphabetically below their administering organizations

12228 ■ Xavier University Presidential Scholarships
(Undergraduate/Scholarship)

Purpose: To financially support students pursuing higher education. **Focus:** General studies/Field of study not specified. **Qualif.:** Applicants who have completed at least 24 credit hours at Xavier, who have a cumulative GPA of 3.0. financial need. **Criteria:** Selection will be based on merit.

Funds Avail.: No specific amount. **Duration:** Annual. **Number Awarded:** Varies. **To Apply:** Students admitted at the Xavier University are automatically considered. **Deadline:** May 1.

12229 ■ Xavier University ROTC Scholarships - Air Force ROTC *(Undergraduate/Scholarship)*

Purpose: To provide financial support to Xavier University students who are in need. **Focus:** Aerospace sciences. **Qualif.:** Applicants must be high school students pursuing an Air Force ROTC or college freshmen and sophomores pursuing an in-college Air Force ROTC.

Funds Avail.: No specific amount. **Duration:** Annual. **To Apply:** Applicants must submit online application.

12230 ■ Xavier University ROTC Scholarships - Army ROTC *(Undergraduate/Scholarship)*

Purpose: To provide financial support to Xavier University students who are in need. **Focus:** Military science and education. **Qualif.:** Applicants must be students pursuing military science at Xavier University.

Funds Avail.: Full-tuition, $1,200 yearly book allowance, a monthly stipend starting at $300/month. **Duration:** Annual. **To Apply:** Applicants must submit online application. **Contact:** Xavier Army ROTC Recruiting Team; Phone: 513-745-1066; Email: rotc@xavier.edu.

12231 ■ Xavier University Williams Scholarships
(Undergraduate/Scholarship)

Purpose: To financially support Xavier University business students with their education. **Focus:** Business. **Qualif.:** Applicants must be first year students enrolled in the Williams College of Business. **Criteria:** Selection will be based on merit.

Funds Avail.: $3,000. **Duration:** Annual. **Number Awarded:** 4. **To Apply:** Applicants must complete the online application. **Deadline:** December 1.

12232 ■ Yale University - Diabetes Research Center (DRC)
300 Cedar St., TAC S141
New Haven, CT 06520-8020
Ph: (203)737-5071
Fax: (203)737-5558
URL: derc.yale.edu
Social Media: twitter.com/yalemed

12233 ■ DRC Pilot and Feasibility Study Award
(Advanced Professional, Professional development/ Grant, Award)

Purpose: To provide the support that will allow an investigator to obtain preliminary data for an application for independent research support; specifically designed to foster the work of young investigators beginning a career in diabetes research. **Focus:** Medical research. **Qualif.:** Applicants must be three categories new investigators without current or past non-mentored NIH research project support

as a principal investigator; must be established investigators with no previous work in diabetes related areas who wish to apply their expertise to a problem in this area; must be established investigators in diabetes/endocrinology research who propose testing innovative ideas that represent a clear departure from ongoing research interests. **Criteria:** Priority will be given to new collaborative investigations; selection will be committee criteria; primary review criteria will be scientific excellence, innovation, diabetes relevance, and the likelihood of the project evolving into federally funded diabetes research.

Funds Avail.: $30-$35,000. **Duration:** Annual. **To Apply:** Applications can be submitted online by mail in word or PDF; proposal must be on a diabetes-related topic and be submitted using the NIH research project application (RO1) format (PHS398); applications should not exceed 7 typewritten pages, excluding: title page, abstract, budget, budget justification, most recent version of the NIH biographical sketch, other support page (list diabetes-related support first, followed by nondiabetes-related research support); please include abstract, specific aims, background and significance, research description and methods; eligible investigators must have faculty appointments at the time of the award and be independent investigators. **Deadline:** November 19. **Contact:** Department of Internal Medicine, 300 George St., Ste. 353, PO Box 208020, New Haven, CT, 06520-8020; director, Kevan Herold, MD; Phone: 203-85-7901; Email: kevan.herold@yale.edu; Kathleen Marcucio; Email: kevan.herold@yale.edu.

12234 ■ YIVO Institute for Jewish Research
15 W 16th St.
New York, NY 10011-6301
Ph: (212)246-6080
Fax: (212)294-6125
E-mail: yivomail@yivo.cjh.org
URL: www.yivo.org
Social Media: youtube.com/user/yivoinstitute

12235 ■ Abraham and Rachela Melezin Memorial Fellowship *(Doctorate, Postdoctorate/Fellowship)*

Purpose: To support doctoral or post-doctoral research on Jewish educational networks in Lithuania. **Focus:** Jewish studies. **Qualif.:** Applicants must be conducting original doctoral or post-doctoral research in the field of Lithuanian Jewish history at the YIVO Library and Archives or travel for PhD dissertation research in archives and libraries of the Baltic states.

Funds Avail.: $5,000. **Duration:** Annual. **Number Awarded:** 1. **Contact:** Dr. Eddy Portnoy, Senior Researcher & Exhibition Curator; Phone: 212-294-6139; Email: eportnoy@yivo.cjh.org.

12236 ■ Vladimir and Pearl Heifetz Memorial Fellowship *(Undergraduate, Graduate, Postgraduate/ Fellowship)*

Purpose: To assists an undergraduate, graduate or postgraduate researcher at the YIVO archives and library. **Focus:** Jewish studies. **Qualif.:** Applicant must be an undergraduate, graduate, or post-graduate researcher in Eastern European Jewish literature; there is no geographical restriction and researchers.

Funds Avail.: $3,500. **Duration:** Annual; two to three months. **Contact:** Dr. Eddy Portnoy, Senior Researcher &

Awards are arranged alphabetically below their administering organizations

Exhibition Curator; Phone: 212-294-6139; Email: eportnoy@yivo.cjh.org.

12237 ■ Aleksander and Alicja Hertz Memorial Fellowship *(Doctorate, Postdoctorate/Fellowship)*

Purpose: To support doctoral or post-doctoral research on Polish-Jewish history in the modern period. **Focus:** Jewish studies; Polish studies. **Qualif.:** Applicant must be a doctoral or post-doctoral researcher on Polish-Jewish history in the modern period, particularly Jewish-Polish relations, including the Holocaust period, and Jewish contributions to Polish literature and culture.

Funds Avail.: $4,000. **Duration:** Annual; two to three months. **Contact:** Dr. Eddy Portnoy, Senior Researcher & Exhibition Curator; Phone: 212-294-6139; Email: eportnoy@yivo.cjh.org.

12238 ■ Abram and Fannie Gottlieb Immerman and Abraham Nathan and Bertha Daskal Weinstein Memorial Fellowship *(Postdoctorate, Doctorate/Fellowship)*

Purpose: To support travel for PhD dissertation research in archives and libraries of the Baltic states. **Focus:** Art. **Qualif.:** Applicants must be a doctoral or post-doctoral researcher in the field of Lithuanian Jewish history or travel for Ph.D. dissertation research in archives and libraries of the Baltic states.

Funds Avail.: $5,000. **Duration:** Annual. **Contact:** Dr. Eddy Portnoy, Senior Researcher & Exhibition Curator; Phone: 212-294-6139; Email: eportnoy@yivo.cjh.org.

12239 ■ Natalie and Mendel Racolin Memorial Fellowship *(Postdoctorate, Doctorate/Fellowship)*

Purpose: To support doctoral or post-doctoral research in the field of East European Jewish history. **Focus:** Art. **Qualif.:** Applicant must be a doctoral or post-doctoral researcher in the field of East European Jewish studies.

Funds Avail.: $9,000. **Duration:** Annual; two to three months. **Contact:** Dr. Eddy Portnoy, Senior Researcher & Exhibition Curator; Phone: 212-294-6139; Email: eportnoy@yivo.cjh.org.

12240 ■ Maria Salit-Gitelson Tell Memorial Fellowship *(Postdoctorate, Doctorate/Fellowship)*

Purpose: To support doctoral or post-doctoral research in the field of Lithuanian Jewish history. **Focus:** Jewish studies. **Qualif.:** Applicants must be doctoral or post-doctoral research in the field of Lithuanian Jewish history or travel for Ph.D. dissertation research in archives and libraries of the Baltic states.

Funds Avail.: $5,000. **Duration:** Annual. **Contact:** Dr. Eddy Portnoy, Senior Researcher & Exhibition Curator; Phone: 212-294-6139; Email: eportnoy@yivo.cjh.org.

12241 ■ Dora and Mayer Tendler Endowed Fellowship *(Doctorate, Postdoctorate/Fellowship)*

Purpose: To support graduate research in Jewish studies. **Focus:** Jewish studies. **Qualif.:** Applicants must be doctoral or post-doctoral researcher in American Jewish history.

Funds Avail.: $5,500. **Duration:** Annual; from 2 to 3 months. **Contact:** Dr. Eddy Portnoy, Senior Researcher & Exhibition Curator; Phone: 212-294-6139; Email: eportnoy@yivo.cjh.org.

12242 ■ York Art Association (YAA)
394 York St.
York Harbor, ME 03911

Ph: (207)363-4049
URL: www.yorkartassociation.com
Social Media: www.facebook.com/YorkArtME
www.instagram.com/york_art/
twitter.com/york_art

12243 ■ Letitia Moore Charitable Trust Scholarship *(Undergraduate/Scholarship)*

Purpose: To support students majoring in art or art history. **Focus:** Art; Art history. **Qualif.:** Applicants must be enrolled in an accredited college or university; must be majoring in art or art history; must have completed their first year of study with a GPA of at least 3.0 or greater. **Criteria:** Recipients will be selected based on submitted materials.

Duration: Annual. **To Apply:** Applicants must submit a letter of application and provide proof of their eligibility; the letter should describe the applicant's educational and career goals and should identify the names and telephone numbers of two or three references familiar with their ability and aspirations; proof of eligibility must come in the form of an official transcript from the college or university which shows that the applicants is enrolled beyond the first year of study with a major in art or art history, and has attained a grade point average of at least 3.0 the prior year of study. **Deadline:** September 1. **Remarks:** To honor artist and York Art Association member Letitia Moore and her wish to provide tuition scholarships to deserving art and/or art history students. Established in 2009. **Contact:** YAA Scholarship Committee, Email: gallerymanager@yorkartassociation.com.

12244 ■ York University - Israel and Golda Koschitzky Centre for Jewish Studies (CJS)
763 Kaneff Twr.
4700 Keele St.
Toronto, ON, Canada M3J 1P3
URL: cjs.blog.yorku.ca

12245 ■ Berek and Regina Gertner OSOTF Bursary in Holocaust Studies *(Undergraduate, Graduate/Scholarship)*

Purpose: To provide scholarship to an individual who has demonstrate interest in Holocaust studies by virtue of course work or research projects. **Focus:** History. **Qualif.:** Applicant must be graduate or undergraduate student; must have demonstrated interest in Holocaust studies by virtue of course work or research projects. **Criteria:** Selection based on demonstrated financial need.

Duration: Annual.

12246 ■ York University - Schulich School of Business
111 Ian Macdonald Blvd.
Toronto, ON, Canada M3J 1P3
Ph: (416)736-2100
Free: 800-667-9380
E-mail: admissions@schulich.yorku.ca
URL: www.schulich.yorku.ca
Social Media: www.facebook.com/SchulichSchool
www.instagram.com/schulichschool
www.linkedin.com/school/schulichschool
twitter.com/SchulichSchool
www.youtube.com/user/SchulichSchool

Awards are arranged alphabetically below their administering organizations

12247 ■ Allen T. Lambert Scholarship *(Postgraduate/Scholarship)*

Purpose: To provide educational support to students who are pursuing full-time MBA degree. **Focus:** General studies/Field of study not specified. **Qualif.:** Applicants must be MBA students who are currently enrolled in the second year of study and have demonstrated academic excellence in previous studies. **Criteria:** Applicants are evaluated based on academic excellence and financial need.

Funds Avail.: $5,000.

12248 ■ Louis J. Brody Q.C. Entrance Scholarships *(Graduate/Scholarship)*

Purpose: To support students by providing educational needs. **Focus:** General studies/Field of study not specified. **Qualif.:** Applicants must be incoming MBA students who have demonstrated academic excellence in previous studies. **Criteria:** Applicants are evaluated based on academic excellence and financial need.

Funds Avail.: $2,500. **Duration:** Annual. **To Apply:** Applicants are advised to visit the organization for the application procedure.

12249 ■ Peter F. Bronfman Scholarships of Merit *(Postgraduate/Scholarship)*

Purpose: To provide educational support to students who demonstrated the highest academic standing. **Focus:** General studies/Field of study not specified. **Qualif.:** Applicants must be full-time students enrolled in the Schulich MBA program; must be active in their community; must have demonstrated leadership either in the workplace or through extracurricular activities; must have at least two years working experience; must be Canadian citizens or permanent residents of Ontario; and have demonstrated financial need. **Criteria:** Applicants are selected based on academic excellence and financial need.

Funds Avail.: $10,000. **Duration:** Annual.

12250 ■ Carol Anne Letheren Entrance Award *(Postgraduate/Award)*

Purpose: To support an incoming MBA student who has demonstrated the highest academic standing. **Focus:** General studies/Field of study not specified. **Qualif.:** Applicants must be full-time incoming MBA students who have an academic excellence in the previous studies; at least two years of full-time working experience; must be a Canadian citizens. **Criteria:** Applicants are selected based on academic excellence and financial need.

Funds Avail.: $5,000. **Duration:** Annual.

12251 ■ Marshall A. Cohen Entrance Awards *(Postgraduate/Award)*

Purpose: To provide educational support to students who are pursuing MBA, MBA/JD and Nonprofit degree. **Focus:** General studies/Field of study not specified. **Qualif.:** Applicants must be full-time MBA students who have an active participation in their community; must have demonstrated academic excellence in previous studies; must have at least two years working experience; must be Canadian citizens. **Criteria:** Applicants are selected based on community involvement and extracurricular activities which have contributed to the well-being of others, academic excellence, and financial need.

Funds Avail.: $10,000.

12252 ■ Harry Steele Entrance Award *(Postgraduate/Award)*

Purpose: To provide students the educational support they need. **Focus:** General studies/Field of study not specified.

Qualif.: Applicants must have presented an excellent academic standing (A average) from previous studies; and have shown involvement either in extra-curricular activities or community service; must be a Canadian citizen. **Criteria:** Applicants are selected based on academic excellence and financial need.

Funds Avail.: $10,000.

12253 ■ Ian Lithgow Memorial Award *(Master's/Award)*

Purpose: To support an incoming MBA student who has demonstrated the highest academic standing. **Focus:** General studies/Field of study not specified. **Qualif.:** Applicants must be full-time MBA students who have demonstrated academic excellence in the previous studies; must be Canadian citizens. **Criteria:** Applicants are selected based on academic excellence and financial need.

Funds Avail.: $5,000.

12254 ■ Irwin Allen Nadal Entrance Award *(Master's/Award)*

Purpose: To support an incoming MBA student who has demonstrated the highest academic standing. **Focus:** General studies/Field of study not specified. **Qualif.:** Applicants must be incoming MBA or IMBA students; must have a minimum cumulative grade of 6.0 (B+); must be Canadian citizens. **Criteria:** Applicants are evaluated based on academic achievements and financial need.

Funds Avail.: $2,500.

12255 ■ Kenneth Laundy Entrance Scholarship *(Graduate/Scholarship)*

Purpose: To provide educational support to those students who are entering MBA/JD degree. **Focus:** General studies/Field of study not specified. **Qualif.:** Applicants must be entering MBA/LLB student who has achieved outstanding academic performance in preparation for the joint program; must be a Canadian citizens. **Criteria:** Applicants are selected based on academic excellence and financial need.

Funds Avail.: $2,500.

12256 ■ The Bernie Kom Memorial Award *(Postgraduate/Award)*

Purpose: To help students attain financial independence. **Focus:** General studies/Field of study not specified. **Qualif.:** Applicants must be MBA students who are currently enrolled in the second year of study and have demonstrated academic excellence in previous studies; must be a Canadian citizen. **Criteria:** Applicants are evaluated based on academic excellence and financial need.

Funds Avail.: $5,000. **Duration:** Annual.

12257 ■ Lawrence Bloomberg Entrance Award *(Postgraduate/Award)*

Purpose: To financially support those students who are pursuing MBA degree. **Focus:** General studies/Field of study not specified. **Qualif.:** Applicants must have presented first class standing in previous academic work (A average); have an active participation in either extra-curricular activities or community involvement; must be a Canadian citizen. **Criteria:** Applicants are selected based on academic excellence and financial need.

Funds Avail.: $10,000. **Duration:** Annual.

12258 ■ Miles Spencer Nadal Entrance Award *(Master's/Award)*

Purpose: To support an incoming MBA student who has demonstrated the highest academic standing. **Focus:** Gen-

Awards are arranged alphabetically below their administering organizations

eral studies/Field of study not specified. **Qualif.:** Applicants must be incoming MBA or IMBA students who have demonstrated academic excellence; must have a minimum cumulative grade of 6.0 (B+); must be a Canadian citizen. **Criteria:** Applicants are evaluated based on academic achievements and financial need.

Funds Avail.: $2,500.

12259 ■ Peter F. Bronfman Entrance Award
(Postgraduate/Award)

Purpose: To provide educational support to students who demonstrated academic excellence in the previous studies. **Focus:** General studies/Field of study not specified. **Qualif.:** Applicants must be entering full-time students in the Schulich MBA program; minimum two years of full-time working experiences, leadership in either extra-curricular involvement or community involvement; must be a Canadian citizen. **Criteria:** Applicants are selected based on academic excellence and financial need.

Funds Avail.: $5,000. **Duration:** Annual. **Number Awarded:** 3.

12260 ■ Robert Krembil Scholarship of Merit
(Master's/Scholarship)

Purpose: To provide students the educational support they need. **Focus:** General studies/Field of study not specified. **Qualif.:** Applicants must be full-time MBA students who have demonstrated academic excellence; a minimum of two years working experience; must have excellent communication skills, leadership ability, and contribution within the community. scholarships are renewable in the second year of the MBA/IMBA program with achievement of a GPA of 7.0 (A-) on the first 30 credit-hours of course work. **Criteria:** Applicants are evaluated based on academic excellence and financial need.

Funds Avail.: $5,000. **Duration:** Annual. **Number Awarded:** 3.

12261 ■ Tanna H. Schulich MBA Entrance Scholarship *(Graduate/Scholarship)*

Purpose: To provide educational support to students who are pursuing their MBA degree. **Focus:** General studies/ Field of study not specified. **Qualif.:** Applicants must be incoming MBA students who have demonstrated academic excellence and at least two years working experience; must be active in their community and have demonstrated leadership qualities either in the workplace or through extra-curricular activities. **Criteria:** Applicants are selected based on academic excellence and financial need.

Funds Avail.: $27,104. **Number Awarded:** 5.

12262 ■ York Graduate Scholarship (YGS) *(Master's, Doctorate/Scholarship)*

Purpose: To provide educational support to students who are pursuing master's and doctoral levels. **Focus:** General studies/Field of study not specified.

12263 ■ York University - York Centre for Asian Research (YCAR)
Kaneff Tower., 8th Fl.
4700 Keele St.
Toronto, ON, Canada M3J 1P3
URL: ycar.apps01.yorku.ca

12264 ■ Albert C.W. Chan Foundation Award
(Graduate/Fellowship)

Purpose: To encourage and assist graduate students to carry out field research in East and/or Southeast Asia.

Focus: Asian studies. **Qualif.:** Applicants must be Canadian citizens, permanent residents or protected persons, be Ontario residents and demonstrate financial need. **Criteria:** Selection will be made by YCAR.

Funds Avail.: 1,000 Canadian Dollars. **Duration:** Annual. **To Apply:** Applicants should include CV; an unofficial copy of current York University transcript of marks (accessed through Student Web Services); two-page research proposal. **Deadline:** February 9. **Contact:** Email: ycar@yorku.ca.

12265 ■ Young Christian Leaders Scholarship Porgram
9 Broadman Pky.
Jersey City, NJ 07305
E-mail: info@yclscholarship.org
URL: www.yclscholarship.org

12266 ■ Young Christian Leaders Scholarships
(Undergraduate/Scholarship)

Purpose: To support the next generation of dedicated Christian professionals who will use their talents to impact their families, communities and the world. **Focus:** General studies/Field of study not specified. **Qualif.:** Applicants must be attending, active members of their local church; have attained at least a 3.0 grade point average on 4.0 scale in previous school semester/marking period; must be already enrolled or have plans to be enrolled full time in an undergraduate degree program; must be permanent residents of New York, New Jersey or Connecticut, but may attend school outside of these areas. **Criteria:** Selection will be based on the online votes and judges vote based on character, achievement and need.

Funds Avail.: $1,000. **Duration:** Monthly. **To Apply:** Applicants may download an application form from the website and mail it along with all the requirements. **Deadline:** 15th of every month.

12267 ■ Young Musicians Foundation (YMF)
1844 Cypress Ave.
Los Angeles, CA 90065
Ph: (323)987-0065
E-mail: info@ymf.org
URL: www.ymf.org
Social Media: www.facebook.com/
  YoungMusiciansFoundation
www.linkedin.com/company/young-musicians-foundation
twitter.com/ymf1955

12268 ■ David Weiss Scholarship Program
(Undergraduate/Scholarship)

Purpose: To provide financial assistance to young musicians for their private music instruction. **Focus:** Music. **Qualif.:** Applicants must demonstrate exceptional talent and financial need; be a resident of Southern California; instrumentalist or pianist may apply through the completion of their senior year of high school; vocalists must be between the ages of 8-26; those who are not U.S. citizens and is under age 18, parents must live in the state of California. **Criteria:** Selection is based on outstanding talent and financial need.

Duration: Annual. **Number Awarded:** Varies.

12269 ■ Young People For (YP4)
1101 15th St., NW, Ste. 600
Washington, DC 20005

Awards are arranged alphabetically below their administering organizations

Ph: (202)467-4999
URL: www.youngpeoplefor.org
Social Media: www.facebook.com/youngpeoplefor
www.instagram.com/yp4
twitter.com/yp4
www.youtube.com/user/youngpeoplefor

12270 ■ Young People For Fellowships *(Professional development/Fellowship)*

Purpose: To provide leadership development for young people committed to creating positive social change in their communities. **Focus:** General studies/Field of study not specified. **Qualif.:** Applicants must be young people to develop leadership skills and connect with a network of other progressive leaders, while creating meaningful social change in their communities. **Criteria:** Preference will be given to those who meet the criteria.

Funds Avail.: No specific amount. **Duration:** Annual. **To Apply:** Applicants must attend one mandatory regional training; must attend the regional training that aligns with the state the applicant will live; Attend YP4's 15th Annual National summit; complete a blueprint for social justice (outline, draft, and final); applications can be submitted online. **Deadline:** January 31. **Contact:** YP4 Fellowship, 1101 15th St., NW Ste. 600, Washington, DC, 20005; Phone: 202-467-4999; Fax: 202-293-2672; Email: youngpeoplefor@pfaw.org; YP4 alumnus can contact at Email: yp4alumni@pfaw.org.

12271 ■ Young Women's Alliance (YWA)

PO Box 684612
Austin, TX 78701
URL: www.youngwomensalliance.org
Social Media: www.facebook.com/youngwomensalliance
www.instagram.com/austinywa
twitter.com/austinywa

12272 ■ YWA Foundation Scholarship *(Graduate, Undergraduate/Scholarship)*

Purpose: To financially support female students with their educational pursuit. **Focus:** General studies/Field of study not specified.

Funds Avail.: No specific amount. **Duration:** Annual. **To Apply:** Applicants must submit a completed application form along with an official copy of college transcript; 2 recommendation letters; short bio; resume; community service short essay; personal essay. **Contact:** Young Leaders or Higher Education Scholarship chair; Email: scholarships@youngwomensalliance.org.

12273 ■ Youth Maritime Training Association (YMTA)

Puget Sound Maritime Historical Society
PO Box 81142
Seattle, WA 98108
URL: ymta.net
Social Media: www.facebook.com/
youthmaritimetrainingassociation

12274 ■ Norm Manly YMTA Maritime Education Scholarship *(Undergraduate/Scholarship)*

Purpose: To support students pursuing maritime training and education in community colleges, technical and vocational programs, colleges, universities, maritime academies or other educational institutions. **Focus:** Maritime studies. **Qualif.:** Applicants must currently be enrolled as seniors in a high school or affiliated high school program (including GED program) in the State of Washington; plan to pursue post-secondary training or educational program leading to a maritime or marine-related career; and, have a grade point average of at least 2.5; relatives of the PSM Board of Governors, the YMTA Committee, the executive management team, or the owners of businesses or organizations sponsoring YMTA scholarships are not eligible. **Criteria:** Selection will be based on YMTA Committee's criteria; Essays will be judged for content, organization, grammar, spelling and neatness.

Funds Avail.: $1,000 to $5,000. **Duration:** Annual. **To Apply:** Applicants must submit completed application form along with current unofficial high school transcript; essay stating course of study planned to pursue and how this scholarship will assist candidate to secure a marine-related career; letters of support from a teacher (if GPA is less than 2.5, a second letter from a teacher is required), and from a member of the maritime community (optional). **Deadline:** February 24. **Contact:** URL: http://ymta.net/ymta-scholarships; Alicia Barnes, E-mail: ymta@pugetmaritime.org; Phone: 206-812-5464.

12275 ■ Youth for Understanding (YFU)

6856 Eastern Avenue NW Suite 310
Washington, DC 20012
Ph: (202)774-5200
Fax: (202)588-7571
E-mail: info@yfu.org
URL: www.yfu-usa.org
Social Media: www.facebook.com/YFU.USA.Fan
www.instagram.com/yfuusa
www.linkedin.com/company/youth-for-understanding
www.pinterest.com/yfuusa
twitter.com/yfu_usa
www.youtube.com/c/YfuusaOrg

12276 ■ The YFU Americas Scholarship *(Undergraduate/Scholarship)*

Purpose: To provide students an opportunity to study abroad to gain intercultural understanding, learn mutual respect and develop a sense of social responsibility. **Focus:** General studies/Field of study not specified.

Funds Avail.: $1,000. **Duration:** Annual. **Deadline:** February 20.

12277 ■ Yukon Conservation Society (YCS)

302 Hawkins St.
Whitehorse, YT, Canada Y1A 1X6
Ph: (867)668-5678
E-mail: info@yukonconservation.org
URL: www.yukonconservation.org
Social Media: www.facebook.com/
yukonconservationsociety
www.instagram.com/yukonconservation/
twitter.com/YukonConservati

12278 ■ Ted Parnell Scholarship *(Undergraduate/ Scholarship)*

Purpose: To financially support students who are pursuing any aspect of environmental studies. **Focus:** Environmental

Awards are arranged alphabetically below their administering organizations

conservation; Wildlife conservation, management, and science. **Qualif.:** Applicants must be Yukon Territory residents and should be entering or currently enrolled in a post-secondary school program (excluding graduate work) in environmental studies. **Criteria:** Selection will be based on the committee's criteria.

Funds Avail.: 500 Canadian Dollars. **Duration:** Annual. **To Apply:** Applicants must submit their most recent transcripts, resume, and a cover letter which include: a description outlining environmental concerns in their locality and their ideas on how these problems can be solved, outlining both public and government responsibilities; description of their interest and involvement in the environmental field; proposed course of study and goals for that study with email subject line Ted Parnell Scholarship Application. **Deadline:** June 30. **Remarks:** The award was established to honor the life and work of Ted Parnell (1947-1981) who contributed greatly to conservation in the Yukon. **Contact:** Send applications to the Ted Parnell Scholarship Committee by email, subject line: Ted Parnell Scholarship Application. Email: outreach@yukonconservation.com.

12279 ■ The Yukon Foundation

PO Box 31622
Whitehorse, YT, Canada Y1A 6L2
Ph: (867)393-2454
E-mail: yukonfoundation@klondiker.com
URL: www.yukonfoundation.com
Social Media: www.facebook.com/YukonFoundation

12280 ■ Alano Club Scholarship (Undergraduate, College, University, Vocational/Occupational/ Scholarship)

Purpose: To help students in the Yukon pursue college degrees in fields related to social work, addiction counseling, and alcoholism. **Focus:** Counseling/Guidance; Social work. **Qualif.:** Applicants must be students enrolled at a university, college, or technical school for the forthcoming school year; must be Yukon residents for at least one year; must be studying in the fields of social work, clinical research, or counselling related to addictions or the effects of alcohol.

To Apply: Must submit transcripts along with completed application. **Deadline:** May 31. **Contact:** URL: www.yukonfoundation.com/apply.

12281 ■ Marjorie Almstrom Scholarship (Undergraduate, Master's/Scholarship)

Purpose: To provide funds for students to help them pay their college or university tuition. **Focus:** General studies/ Field of study not specified. **Qualif.:** Applicants must be 4th or 5th year post-secondary students, or Masters or equivalent, enrolled at a college or university for the forthcoming year; must be Yukon residents. **Criteria:** Selection will be based on the committee's criteria.

Funds Avail.: No specific amount. **Duration:** Annual. **To Apply:** Applicants must submit the application form for General Fund (available online), copy of their transcripts, university acceptance letters, and/or reference letters. **Deadline:** May 31.

12282 ■ Jaedyn Amann Memorial Scholarship (Undergraduate, Master's/Scholarship)

Purpose: To provide funds for students to help them pay their college or university tuition. **Focus:** General studies/

Field of study not specified. **Qualif.:** Applicants must be 4th or 5th year post-secondary students, or Masters or equivalent, enrolled at a college or university for the forthcoming year; must be Yukon residents. **Criteria:** Selection will be based on the committee's criteria.

Funds Avail.: No specific amount. **Duration:** Annual. **To Apply:** Applicants must submit the application form for the General Fund (available online), copy of their transcripts, university acceptance letters, and/or reference letters. **Deadline:** May 31.

12283 ■ Fay Anthony Scholarship (Undergraduate, College, University, Vocational/Occupational/ Scholarship)

Purpose: To help students in the Yukon pursue degrees in x-ray technology, lab technology, and sports medicine. **Focus:** Medical technology; Medicine, Sports; Radiology. **Qualif.:** Applicants must be students enrolled at a university, college, or technical school for the forthcoming school year; must be Yukon residents; must be studying in the fields of x-ray technician, lab technician, or sports medicine.

To Apply: Must submit transcripts along with completed application. **Deadline:** May 31. **Contact:** URL: www.yukonfoundation.com/apply.

12284 ■ Robert Armstrong Memorial Scholarship (Undergraduate, Master's/Scholarship)

Purpose: To provide funds for students to help them pay their college or university tuition. **Focus:** General studies/ Field of study not specified. **Qualif.:** Applicants must be 4th or 5th year post-secondary students, or Masters or equivalent, enrolled at a college or university for the forthcoming year; must be Yukon residents. **Criteria:** Selection will be based on the committee's criteria.

Funds Avail.: No specific amount. **Duration:** Annual. **To Apply:** Applicants must submit the application form for the General Fund (available online), copy of their transcripts, university acceptance letters, and/or reference letters. **Deadline:** May 31.

12285 ■ Victoria Baldwin Memorial Scholarship (Undergraduate, Master's/Scholarship)

Purpose: To provide funds for students to help them pay their college or university tuition. **Focus:** General studies/ Field of study not specified. **Qualif.:** Applicants must be 4th or 5th year post-secondary students, or Masters or equivalent, enrolled at a college or university for the forthcoming year; must be Yukon residents. **Criteria:** Selection will be based on the committee's criteria.

Funds Avail.: No specific amount. **Duration:** Annual. **To Apply:** Applicants must submit the application form for the General Fund (available online), copy of their transcripts, university acceptance letters, and/or reference letters. **Deadline:** May 31.

12286 ■ Alec Berry Scholarship (Undergraduate, College, Vocational/Occupational/Scholarship)

Purpose: To help students in the Yukon pursue degrees in mining-related fields. **Focus:** Geology; Metallurgy; Mining. **Qualif.:** Applicants must be students enrolled at a university, college, or technical school for the forthcoming school year; must be Yukon residents; must be studying in the fields of mining, geology, metallurgical sciences, or other mining-related fields.

To Apply: Submit a copy of transcripts along with the completed application form. **Deadline:** May 31. **Contact:**

Awards are arranged alphabetically below their administering organizations

URL: www.yukonfoundation.com/apply.

12287 ■ Henry Besner Memorial Scholarship
(Undergraduate, Master's/Scholarship)

Purpose: To provide funds for students to help them pay their college or university tuition. **Focus:** General studies/Field of study not specified. **Qualif.:** Applicants must be 4th or 5th year post-secondary students, or Masters or equivalent, enrolled at a college or university for the forthcoming year; must be Yukon residents. **Criteria:** Selection will be based on the committee's criteria.

Funds Avail.: No specific amount. **Duration:** Annual. **To Apply:** Applicants must submit the application form for the General Fund (available online), copy of their transcripts, university acceptance letters, and/or reference letters. **Deadline:** May 31.

12288 ■ Timothy Bierlmeier Memorial Scholarships
(Undergraduate, Master's/Scholarship)

Purpose: To provide funds for students to help them pay their college or university tuition. **Focus:** General studies/Field of study not specified. **Qualif.:** Applicants must be 4th or 5th year post-secondary students, or Masters or equivalent; must be Yukon residents. **Criteria:** Selection will be based on the committee's criteria.

Funds Avail.: No specific amount. **Duration:** Annual. **To Apply:** Submit the application form (available online), copy of their transcripts, university acceptance letters, and/or reference letters. **Deadline:** May 31.

12289 ■ Joan Bilton Scholarship *(Undergraduate, College, University, Vocational/Occupational/Scholarship)*

Purpose: To help students in the Yukon pay for college. **Focus:** General studies/Field of study not specified. **Qualif.:** Applicants must be students who have graduated from a Dawson City senior secondary school or Dawson City Campus of Yukon College and have been accepted at an accredited post-secondary college, university, or other educational institute.

To Apply: Must submit transcripts along with completed application. **Deadline:** May 31. **Contact:** URL: www.yukonfoundation.com/apply.

12290 ■ Thomas J. Black Scholarship *(Undergraduate, University, College/Scholarship)*

Purpose: To help a student from Porter Creek School pursue a college degree in environmental studies. **Focus:** Environmental science. **Qualif.:** Applicants must be Porter Creek School graduates enrolled in post-secondary education in the field of environmental studies.

To Apply: Must submit transcripts along with completed application. **Deadline:** May 31. **Contact:** URL: www.yukonfoundation.com/apply.

12291 ■ Boreal Alternate Energy Centre Scholarship *(Undergraduate, University, College, Vocational/Occupational/Scholarship)*

Purpose: To help students in the Yukon pursue college studies in alternate energy. **Focus:** Energy-related areas. **Qualif.:** Applicants must be students enrolled at a university, college, or technical school for the forthcoming school year; must be Yukon residents; must be studying in the field of alternate energy.

To Apply: Must submit transcripts along with completed application. **Deadline:** May 31. **Contact:** URL:

www.yukonfoundation.com/apply.

12292 ■ Herbie Bouwman Memorial Scholarship
(Undergraduate, Master's/Scholarship)

Purpose: To provide funds for students to help them pay their college or university tuition. **Focus:** General studies/Field of study not specified. **Qualif.:** Applicants must be 4th or 5th year post-secondary students, or Masters or equivalent, enrolled at a college or university for the forthcoming year; must be Yukon residents. **Criteria:** Selection will be based on the committee's criteria.

Funds Avail.: No specific amount. **Duration:** Annual. **To Apply:** Applicants must submit the application form for the General Fund (available online), copy of their transcripts, university acceptance letters, and/or reference letters. **Deadline:** May 31.

12293 ■ Bill Bowie Scholarship *(University, Undergraduate, College, Vocational/Occupational/Scholarship)*

Purpose: To help students in the Yukon pursue college degrees in renewable resources, especially forestry-related fields. **Focus:** Forestry; Resource management. **Qualif.:** Applicants must be students enrolled at a university, college, or technical school for the forthcoming school year; must be Yukon residents; must be pursuing studies in renewable resources. **Criteria:** Preference given to students in forestry or forest management.

To Apply: Must submit transcripts along with completed application. **Deadline:** May 31. **Contact:** URL: www.yukonfoundation.com/apply.

12294 ■ Geoffrey Bradshaw Memorial Scholarship
(Graduate/Scholarship)

Purpose: To provide funds for graduate students in geology to help them pay their college or university tuition. **Focus:** Geology. **Qualif.:** Applicants must be Canadian citizens enrolled in a Canadian university in the first or second year of a graduate geology program; must be working on a thesis that has a Yukon field component. Applicants can be awarded this scholarship more than once. **Criteria:** Selection will be based on the committee's criteria; priority given to applicants who have not previously been awarded the scholarship.

Funds Avail.: No specific amount. **Duration:** Annual. **To Apply:** Application and details available online at yukon.ca/en/bradshaw-scholarship. **Deadline:** May 31.

12295 ■ Archie Bruce Scholarship *(Undergraduate, Vocational/Occupational/Scholarship)*

Purpose: To help students in the Yukon pursue college degrees in engineering or apprenticeship trades. **Focus:** Engineering. **Qualif.:** Applicants must be 2nd to 5th year students in post-secondary studies in engineering, or Yukon government registered apprenticeship trades; must be Yukon residents.

To Apply: Must submit transcripts along with completed application. **Deadline:** May 31. **Contact:** URL: www.yukonfoundation.com/apply.

12296 ■ Gladys Bruce Scholarship *(Undergraduate/Scholarship)*

Purpose: To help students in the Yukon pursue a degree in biology or geology. **Focus:** Biological and clinical sciences; Geology. **Qualif.:** Applicants must be Yukon second-

Awards are arranged alphabetically below their administering organizations

ary school graduates pursuing college degrees in biology or geology.

To Apply: Must submit transcripts along with completed application. **Deadline:** May 31. **Contact:** URL: www.yukonfoundation.com/apply.

12297 ■ John Bunker Scholarship *(Vocational/ Occupational, College/Scholarship)*

Purpose: To help students in the Yukon pursue further education in medical technologies or apprenticeship trades. **Focus:** Education, Vocational-technical; Medical technology. **Qualif.:** Applicants must be Yukon secondary school graduates pursuing college degrees in medical technologies (such as lab tech, x-ray tech) or registered apprenticeship trades.

To Apply: Must submit transcripts along with completed application. **Deadline:** May 31. **Contact:** URL: www.yukonfoundation.com/apply.

12298 ■ G.I. and Martha Cameron Scholarship *(Undergraduate/Scholarship)*

Purpose: To assist Yukon-born students in pursuing a college degree in nursing or humanities. **Focus:** Humanities; Nursing. **Qualif.:** Applicant must be a Yukon-born resident pursuing post-secondary training in nursing or a humanities discipline.

To Apply: Must submit completed application, transcripts, and a letter detailing why the applicant has chosen their career path. **Deadline:** May 31. **Contact:** URL: www.yukonfoundation.com/apply.

12299 ■ Robert & Jean Campbell Scholarship *(Undergraduate, University, College, Vocational/ Occupational/Scholarship)*

Purpose: To help Yukon and Atlin students pursue college degrees in business management or education. **Focus:** Business administration; Education; Management. **Qualif.:** Applicants must be Yukon or Atlin students studying in the fields of business management or education.

To Apply: Must submit transcripts along with completed application. **Deadline:** May 31. **Contact:** URL: www.yukonfoundation.com/apply.

12300 ■ Brian Campion Scholarship *(Graduate, Undergraduate/Scholarship)*

Purpose: To assist Yukon students to further their studies in Law. **Focus:** Law. **Qualif.:** Applicants must be students enrolled in a college or university studying in the field of law; must be a Yukon resident. **Criteria:** Selection will be based on the committee's criteria.

Funds Avail.: No specific amount. **Duration:** Annual. **To Apply:** Applicants must submit the application form (available online), copy of their transcripts, university acceptance letters, and/or reference letters. **Deadline:** May 31. **Contact:** URL: www.yukonfoundation.com/apply.

12301 ■ Chechahko Consumers Co-Op Ltd. Scholarship *(Master's/Scholarship)*

Purpose: To provide funds for students to help them pay their college or university tuition. **Focus:** General studies/ Field of study not specified. **Qualif.:** Applicants must be 4th or 5th year post-secondary students, or Masters or equivalent; must be Yukon residents. **Criteria:** Selection will be based on the committee's criteria.

Funds Avail.: No specific amount. **Duration:** Annual. **To Apply:** Applicants must submit the application form for the

General Fund (available online), copy of their transcripts, university acceptance letters, and/or reference letters. **Deadline:** May 31.

12302 ■ Helen & Orval Couch Memorial Scholarship *(Undergraduate/Scholarship)*

Purpose: To provide funds for students to help them pay their college or university tuition. **Focus:** Agricultural sciences; Child development; Education, Vocational-technical; Nursing; Political science. **Qualif.:** Applicants must be Yukon residents for at least two years and enrolled in a college, trade school, or university in one of the following programs: heavy duty mechanics or any registered apprenticeship trade; political studies; child development; agriculture; or nursing. **Criteria:** Selection will be based on the committee's criteria.

Funds Avail.: No specific amount. **Duration:** Annual. **To Apply:** Applicants must submit the application form (available online), copy of their transcripts, university acceptance letters, and/or reference letters. **Deadline:** May 31. **Contact:** URL: www.yukonfoundation.com/apply.

12303 ■ Douglas B. Craig Scholarship *(Undergraduate, College, University, Vocational/Occupational/ Scholarship)*

Purpose: To help Yukon students pursue college degrees or projects in the fields of environmental engineering, sustainable energy, climate change, and related fields. **Focus:** Energy-related areas; Environmental conservation. **Qualif.:** Applicants must be students enrolled at a university, college, or technical school for the forthcoming school year; must be Yukon residents; must be studying in the fields of environmental engineering, sustainable energy, climate change, or related fields.

To Apply: Must submit transcripts along with completed application form. **Deadline:** May 31. **Contact:** URL: www.yukonfoundation.com/apply.

12304 ■ Marvin Crawford Scholarship *(College, Vocational/Occupational/Scholarship)*

Purpose: To help Yukon residents pursue studies in refrigeration, air conditioning, and other accredited trades. **Focus:** Education, Vocational-technical; Heating, air conditioning, and refrigeration. **Qualif.:** Applicants must be established Yukon residents studying refrigeration, air conditioning, or other accredited trades.

To Apply: Must submit transcripts along with completed application. **Deadline:** May 31. **Contact:** URL: www.yukonfoundation.com/apply.

12305 ■ Jim Davie Memorial Scholarship *(Undergraduate, Master's/Scholarship)*

Purpose: To provide funds for students to help them pay their college or university tuition. **Focus:** General studies/ Field of study not specified. **Qualif.:** Applicants must be 4th or 5th year post-secondary students, or Masters or equivalent, enrolled at a college or university for the forthcoming year; must be Yukon residents. **Criteria:** Selection will be based on the committee's criteria.

Funds Avail.: No specific amount. **Duration:** Annual. **To Apply:** Applicants must submit the application form for the General Fund (available online), copy of their transcripts, university acceptance letters, and/or reference letters. **Deadline:** May 31.

Awards are arranged alphabetically below their administering organizations

12306 ▪ Dawson District Renewable Resources Council Scholarship *(Undergraduate, College, University, Vocational/Occupational/Scholarship)*

Purpose: To help Canadian citizens from the traditional territory of the Tr'ondek Hwech'in pursue undergraduate degrees or diplomas in renewable resources. **Focus:** Resource management. **Qualif.:** Applicants must be Canadian citizens who have lived in the traditional territory of the Tr'ondek Hwech'in for at least two years; must be undergraduate students in recognized degree/diploma certificate programs in renewable resources.

To Apply: Must submit transcripts and two letters of reference along with completed application. **Contact:** URL: www.yukonfoundation.com/apply.

12307 ▪ Belle & Curly Desrosiers Scholarship *(Undergraduate, College, University, Vocational/Occupational/Scholarship)*

Purpose: To help students in the Yukon with physical disabilities attend college. **Focus:** General studies/Field of study not specified. **Qualif.:** Applicants must be students enrolled at a university, college, or technical school for the forthcoming school year; must be Yukon residents; must have a physical disability.

To Apply: Must submit transcripts along with completed application. **Deadline:** May 31. **Contact:** URL: www.yukonfoundation.com/apply.

12308 ▪ Anne & Konrad Domes Scholarship *(Undergraduate, University, College, Vocational/Occupational/Scholarship)*

Purpose: To help students in the Yukon pursue college degrees in architecture or drafting. **Focus:** Architecture; Drafting. **Qualif.:** Applicants must be post-secondary students enrolled in architecture or drafting; must have a minimum 3 years of Yukon residency.

To Apply: Must submit transcripts along with completed application. **Deadline:** May 31. **Contact:** URL: www.yukonfoundation.com/apply.

12309 ▪ Marnie & Bill Drury Scholarship *(Undergraduate, University, College, Vocational/Occupational/Scholarship)*

Purpose: To help students in the Yukon pursue college degrees in art and music. **Focus:** Art; Music. **Qualif.:** Applicants must be Yukon students attending an accredited art or music school.

To Apply: Must submit transcripts along with completed application. **Deadline:** May 31. **Contact:** URL: www.yukonfoundation.com/apply.

12310 ▪ Dr. Allan Duncan Memorial Scholarship *(Undergraduate, Master's/Scholarship)*

Purpose: To provide funds for students to help them pay their college or university tuition. **Focus:** General studies/Field of study not specified. **Qualif.:** Applicants must be 4th or 5th year post-secondary students, or Masters or equivalent, enrolled at a college or university for the forthcoming year; must be Yukon residents. **Criteria:** Selection will be based on the committee's criteria.

Funds Avail.: No specific amount. **Duration:** Annual. **To Apply:** Applicants must submit the application form for the General Fund (available online), copy of their transcripts, university acceptance letters, and/or reference letters. **Deadline:** May 31.

12311 ▪ Debra Dungey Scholarship *(Undergraduate, Graduate, University, College/Scholarship)*

Purpose: To help female Yukon students pursue college degrees in social work. **Focus:** Social work. **Qualif.:** Applicants must be female post-secondary students studying social work; must have at least one year Yukon residency.

To Apply: Must submit transcripts along with completed application. **Deadline:** May 31. **Contact:** URL: www.yukonfoundation.com/apply.

12312 ▪ David Eby Memorial Scholarship *(Undergraduate, Master's, Graduate/Scholarship)*

Purpose: To help Yukon students pay for college or university. **Focus:** General studies/Field of study not specified. **Qualif.:** Applicants must be 4th or 5th year post-secondary students, or Masters or equivalent; must be Yukon residents.

Duration: Annual. **To Apply:** Application form for the General Fund should be completed online at www.yukonfoundation.com/apply. **Deadline:** May 31.

12313 ▪ Mark & Heinz Eichhorn Scholarship *(College, Vocational/Occupational/Scholarship)*

Purpose: To help students from the Yukon and Mayo pursue education in apprenticeship trades. **Focus:** Education, Vocational-technical. **Qualif.:** Applicants must be Yukon or Mayo students registered in Government of Yukon apprenticeship trades.

To Apply: Must submit transcripts along with completed application. **Deadline:** May 31. **Contact:** URL: www.yukonfoundation.com/apply.

12314 ▪ Firth Family Scholarship *(Undergraduate, Graduate, Master's/Scholarship)*

Purpose: To help Yukon students pay for college or university. **Focus:** General studies/Field of study not specified. **Qualif.:** Applicants must be 4th or 5th year post-secondary students, or Masters or equivalent; must be Yukon residents.

Duration: Annual. **To Apply:** Applicants must complete the General Fund application online at www.yukonfoundation.com/apply. **Deadline:** May 31.

12315 ▪ Bea Firth Scholarship *(Undergraduate, Graduate/Scholarship)*

Purpose: To help students in the Yukon pursue degrees to become doctors and nurses. **Focus:** Medicine; Nursing. **Qualif.:** Applicants must be Yukon residents studying to be nurses or doctors.

To Apply: Must submit transcripts along with completed application. **Deadline:** May 31. **Contact:** URL: www.yukonfoundation.com/apply.

12316 ▪ Adrian Fisher Scholarship *(Undergraduate, College, University/Scholarship)*

Purpose: To help students in the Yukon pursue education to become teachers. **Focus:** Education; Teaching. **Qualif.:** Applicants must be Yukon school graduates pursuing teacher training.

To Apply: Must submit transcripts along with completed application. **Deadline:** May 31. **Contact:** URL: www.yukonfoundation.com/apply.

12317 ▪ Maureen & Gilles Fontaine Scholarship *(Undergraduate, College, University, Vocational/Occupational/Scholarship)*

Purpose: To help students from the Yukon who are physically challenged attend college. **Focus:** General studies/

Awards are arranged alphabetically below their administering organizations

Field of study not specified. **Qualif.:** Applicants must be students enrolled at a university, college, or technical school for the forthcoming school year; must be Yukon residents; must be physically challenged.

To Apply: Must submit transcripts along with completed application. **Deadline:** May 31. **Contact:** URL: www.yukonfoundation.com/apply.

12318 ■ Donald Frizzell Memorial Scholarship
(Undergraduate, Graduate, Master's/Scholarship)

Purpose: To help Yukon students pay for college or university. **Focus:** General studies/Field of study not specified. **Qualif.:** Applicants must be 4th or 5th year post-secondary students, or Masters or equivalent; must be Yukon residents.

Duration: Annual. **To Apply:** Applicants must complete the General Fund application at www.yukonfoundation.org/apply. **Deadline:** May 31.

12319 ■ Joe Goodeill Scholarship *(Undergraduate, University, College/Scholarship)*

Purpose: To help students from the Yukon pursue a degree in sports medicine. **Focus:** Medicine, Sports. **Qualif.:** Applicants must be Yukon high school graduates studying sports medicine.

To Apply: Applicants must submit a copy of transcripts along with the completed application. **Deadline:** May 31. **Contact:** URL: www.yukonfoundation.com/apply.

12320 ■ Tamara Guttman Memorial Scholarship
(Undergraduate, University, College, Vocational/Occupational/Scholarship)

Purpose: To help Yukon students studying dance, social work, or apprenticeship trades. **Focus:** Dance; Education, Vocational-technical; Social work. **Qualif.:** Applicants must be Yukon residents; must be studying dance, social work, or registered/accredited apprenticeship trades.

To Apply: Must submit a copy of transcripts along with the completed application. **Deadline:** May 31. **Contact:** URL: www.yukonfoundation.com/apply.

12321 ■ Bert & Karen Hadvick Scholarship
(Undergraduate, University, College, Vocational/Occupational/Scholarship)

Purpose: To help students in the Yukon pursue college degrees in business management or attend accredited trades training programs. **Focus:** Business administration; Management; Technology. **Qualif.:** Applicants must be Yukon residents; must be enrolled at a university, college, or technical school for the upcoming school year; must be studying business management or in accredited trades training programs.

To Apply: Must submit a copy of transcripts along with the completed application. **Deadline:** May 31. **Contact:** URL: www.yukonfoundation.com/apply.

12322 ■ Chuck Halliday Scholarship *(Undergraduate, University, College, Vocational/Occupational/Scholarship)*

Purpose: To help students in the Yukon pursue college studies in business or economics. **Focus:** Business; Economics. **Qualif.:** Applicants must be Yukon residents; must be attending a university, college, or technical school for the forthcoming year; must be pursuing studies in business or economics.

To Apply: Must submit a copy of transcripts along with the completed application. **Deadline:** May 31. **Contact:** URL: www.yukonfoundation.com/apply.

12323 ■ Ted & Nicky Harrison Memorial Fund
(Undergraduate, Master's/Scholarship)

Purpose: To provide funds for Yukon artists to help them pay their college or university tuition. **Focus:** Art. **Qualif.:** Applicants must be students enrolled in college, trade school, or university in an art field; must be Yukon residents. **Criteria:** Selection will be based on the committee's criteria.

Funds Avail.: No specific amount. **Duration:** Annual. **To Apply:** Applicants must submit the application form (available online), copy of their transcripts, university acceptance letters, and/or reference letters. **Deadline:** May 31. **Contact:** URL: www.yukonfoundation.com/apply.

12324 ■ Dereen Hildebrand Scholarship
(Undergraduate, College, University, Vocational/Occupational/Scholarship)

Purpose: To help students in the Yukon study art in college. **Focus:** Art. **Qualif.:** Applicants must be students enrolled in an art program at a university, college, or technical school for the forthcoming school year; must be Yukon residents.

To Apply: Must submit transcripts along with completed application. **Deadline:** May 31. **Contact:** URL: www.yukonfoundation.com/apply.

12325 ■ Nedien Hoganson Memorial Scholarship
(Undergraduate, Master's/Scholarship)

Purpose: To provide funds for students to help them pay their college or university tuition. **Focus:** General studies/Field of study not specified. **Qualif.:** Applicants must be 4th or 5th year post-secondary students, or Masters or equivalent, enrolled at a college or university for the forthcoming year; must be Yukon residents. **Criteria:** Selection will be based on the committee's criteria.

Funds Avail.: No specific amount. **Duration:** Annual. **To Apply:** Applicants must submit the application form for the General Fund (available online), copy of their transcripts, university acceptance letters, and/or reference letters. **Deadline:** May 31.

12326 ■ The Hougen Family Fund Scholarship
(Undergraduate, College, University, Vocational/Occupational/Scholarship)

Purpose: To help students attend college and aid in the scholarly study, preservation, and enhancement of the Yukon. **Focus:** Area and ethnic studies. **Qualif.:** Applicants must be students enrolled at a university, college, or technical school for the forthcoming school year; must be Yukon residents; must be enrolled in a field that leads to the study, preservation, or enhancement of historical and cultural activities related to the Yukon.

To Apply: Transcripts must be submitted along with the completed application. **Deadline:** May 31. **Contact:** URL: www.yukonfoundation.com/apply.

12327 ■ Donald Hoy Memorial Scholarship
(Undergraduate/Scholarship)

Purpose: To provide funds for music students to help them pay their college or university tuition. **Focus:** Music. **Qualif.:** Applicants must be music students enrolled in a college, trade school, or university for the forthcoming year;

Awards are arranged alphabetically below their administering organizations

must be residents of the Yukon for at least 5 years; must demonstrate financial need. **Criteria:** Selection will be based on the committee's criteria.

Funds Avail.: No specific amount. **Duration:** Annual. **To Apply:** Applicants must submit the application form (available online), copy of their transcripts, university acceptance letters, and/or reference letters. **Deadline:** May 31. **Contact:** URL: www.yukonfoundation.com/apply.

12328 ■ John Hoyt Memorial Scholarship
(Undergraduate, Master's/Scholarship)

Purpose: To provide funds for students to help them pay their college or university tuition. **Focus:** General studies/Field of study not specified. **Qualif.:** Applicants must be 4th or 5th year post-secondary students, or Masters or equivalent, enrolled at a college or university for the forthcoming year; must be Yukon residents. **Criteria:** Selection will be based on the committee's criteria.

Funds Avail.: No specific amount. **Duration:** Annual. **To Apply:** Applicants must submit the application form for the General Fund (available online), copy of their transcripts, university acceptance letters, and/or reference letters. **Deadline:** May 31.

12329 ■ Indian River Scholarship *(Undergraduate, University, College, Vocational/Occupational/ Scholarship)*

Purpose: To help students in the Yukon pursue post-secondary studies. **Focus:** General studies/Field of study not specified. **Qualif.:** Applicants must be members of the Klondike Placer Miners' Assoc. (KPMA) or their immediate family; must be enrolled at a university, college, or technical school for the forthcoming year; must be Yukon graduates.

To Apply: Must submit a copy of transcripts, a letter of recommendation, and a brief essay on placer mining and what it has done for the applicant along with the completed application form. **Deadline:** May 31. **Contact:** URL: www.yukonfoundation.com/apply.

12330 ■ Helen Janko Memorial Scholarship
(Undergraduate, Master's/Scholarship)

Purpose: To provide funds for students to help them pay their college or university tuition. **Focus:** General studies/Field of study not specified. **Qualif.:** Applicants must be 4th or 5th year post-secondary students, or Masters or equivalent, enrolled at a college or university for the forthcoming year; must be Yukon residents. **Criteria:** Selection will be based on the committee's criteria.

Funds Avail.: No specific amount. **Duration:** Annual. **To Apply:** Applicants must submit the application form for the General Fund (available online), copy of their transcripts, university acceptance letters, and/or reference letters. **Deadline:** May 31.

12331 ■ Harry Johannes Scholarship *(Undergraduate, Graduate/Scholarship)*

Purpose: To provide funds for engineering students focusing on geology to help them pay their college or university tuition. **Focus:** Geology. **Qualif.:** Applicants must be undergraduate or graduate students enrolled in engineering sciences, with an emphasis on geology; must be Yukon residents. **Criteria:** Selection will be based on the committee's criteria.

Funds Avail.: No specific amount. **Duration:** Annual. **To Apply:** Applicants must submit the application form (avail-

able online), copy of their transcripts, university acceptance letters, and/or reference letters. **Deadline:** May 31. **Contact:** URL: www.yukonfoundation.com/apply.

12332 ■ Douglas Johnson Memorial Scholarship
(Master's, Graduate, Undergraduate/Scholarship)

Purpose: To provide funds for students to help them pay their college or university tuition. **Focus:** General studies/Field of study not specified. **Qualif.:** Applicants must be 4th or 5th year post-secondary students, or Masters or equivalent, enrolled at a college or university for the forthcoming year; must be Yukon residents. **Criteria:** Selection will be based on the committee's criteria.

Funds Avail.: No specific amount. **Duration:** Annual. **To Apply:** Application for the General Fund is available online; include copy of transcripts, university acceptance letters, and/or reference letters. **Deadline:** May 31.

12333 ■ Marilyn King Scholarship *(Undergraduate, University, College, Vocational/Occupational/ Scholarship)*

Purpose: To help students in the Yukon pursue post-secondary education in business-related fields or accounting. **Focus:** Accounting; Business. **Qualif.:** Applicants must be enrolled at a university, college, or technical school for the forthcoming year; must be Yukon residents for at least 5 years; must be studying in business-related fields or accounting. **Criteria:** Financial need; good grades.

To Apply: Must submit a copy of transcripts along with the completed application. **Deadline:** May 31. **Contact:** URL: www.yukonfoundation.com/apply.

12334 ■ Flo Kitz Memorial Scholarship *(Undergraduate, Master's/Scholarship)*

Purpose: To provide funds for students to help them pay their college or university tuition. **Focus:** General studies/Field of study not specified. **Qualif.:** Applicants must be 4th or 5th year post-secondary students, or Masters or equivalent, enrolled at a college or university for the forthcoming year; must be Yukon residents. **Criteria:** Selection will be based on the committee's criteria.

Funds Avail.: No specific amount. **Duration:** Annual. **To Apply:** Applicants must submit the application form for the General Fund (available online), copy of their transcripts, university acceptance letters, and/or reference letters. **Deadline:** May 31.

12335 ■ Klondike Defence Force Grant *(Undergraduate, College, University, Vocational/Occupational/ Scholarship)*

Purpose: To help students in the Yukon research or study Yukon history. **Focus:** Area and ethnic studies; History. **Qualif.:** Applicants must be students enrolled at a university, college, or technical school for the forthcoming school year; must be Yukon residents; must be studying or researching Yukon history.

To Apply: Must submit transcripts along with completed application. **Deadline:** May 31. **Contact:** URL: www.yukonfoundation.com/apply.

12336 ■ Mariel Lacasse Scholarship *(Undergraduate, University, College, Vocational/Occupational/ Scholarship)*

Purpose: To help students in the Yukon pursue college degrees or certificates in child development, physiotherapy,

Awards are arranged alphabetically below their administering organizations

or occupational therapy. **Focus:** Child development; Occupational therapy; Physical therapy. **Qualif.:** Applicants must be enrolled in a university, college, or technical school for the forthcoming year; must be studying child development, physiotherapy, or occupational therapy; must have at least two years Yukon residency.

To Apply: Must submit a copy of transcripts along with the completed application. **Deadline:** May 31. **Contact:** URL: www.yukonfoundation.com/apply.

12337 ■ Queenie Leader Memorial Scholarship
(Undergraduate, Master's/Scholarship)

Purpose: To provide funds for students to help them pay their college or university tuition. **Focus:** General studies/ Field of study not specified. **Qualif.:** Applicants must be 4th or 5th year post-secondary students, or Masters or equivalent, enrolled at a college or university for the forthcoming year; must be Yukon residents. **Criteria:** Selection will be based on the committee's criteria.

Funds Avail.: No specific amount. **Duration:** Annual. **To Apply:** Applicants must submit the application form for the General Fund (available online), copy of their transcripts, university acceptance letters, and/or reference letters. **Deadline:** May 31.

12338 ■ Nesta Leduc Scholarship *(Undergraduate, University, College, Vocational/Occupational/ Scholarship)*

Purpose: To help students in the Yukon pursue college degrees in environmental sciences or health related fields. **Focus:** Environmental science; Health sciences. **Qualif.:** Applicants must be enrolled in a university, college, or technical school for the forthcoming year; must be Yukon residents; must be studying environmental sciences or health related studies.

To Apply: Must submit a copy of transcripts along with the completed application. **Deadline:** May 31. **Contact:** URL: www.yukonfoundation.com/apply.

12339 ■ Grant Livingston Memorial Scholarship
(Undergraduate, Master's/Scholarship)

Purpose: To provide funds for students to help them pay their college or university tuition. **Focus:** General studies/ Field of study not specified. **Qualif.:** Applicants must be 4th or 5th year post-secondary students, or Masters or equivalent, enrolled at a college or university for the forthcoming year; must be Yukon residents. **Criteria:** Selection will be based on the committee's criteria.

Funds Avail.: No specific amount. **Duration:** Annual. **To Apply:** Applicants must submit the application form for the General Fund (available online), copy of their transcripts, university acceptance letters, and/or reference letters. **Deadline:** May 31.

12340 ■ Claudia-Ann Lowry Scholarship
(Undergraduate, College, University, Vocational/ Occupational/Scholarship)

Purpose: To help students in the Yukon pursue art degrees in college and support artists in the Yukon. **Focus:** Art. **Qualif.:** Applicants must be students enrolled in an art program at a university, college, or technical school for the forthcoming school year; must be Yukon residents.

To Apply: Must submit transcripts along with completed application. **Deadline:** May 31. **Contact:** URL: www.yukonfoundation.com/apply.

12341 ■ Peter Lucas Scholarship *(Undergraduate, University, College, Vocational/Occupational/ Scholarship)*

Purpose: To help students in the Yukon pursue college degrees in renewable resources. **Focus:** Resource management. **Qualif.:** Applicants must be Canadian citizens living in the Na-cho Nyak Dun/Nothern Tutchone district with at least two years residency; must be enrolled in a university, college, or technical school for the forthcoming year; must be pursuing studies in renewable resources.

To Apply: Must submit a copy of transcripts along with the completed application. **Deadline:** May 31. **Contact:** URL: www.yukonfoundation.com/apply.

12342 ■ Ole & Mary Lunde Scholarship *(Undergraduate, University, College, Vocational/Occupational, Graduate/Scholarship)*

Purpose: To help students in the Yukon pursue degrees to become doctors or in Yukon Native studies. **Focus:** Area and ethnic studies; Medicine. **Qualif.:** Applicants must be enrolled full-time in a university, college, or technical school for the forthcoming year; must be studying to become a doctor or pursuing Yukon Native studies; must have at least two years Yukon residency.

To Apply: Must submit a copy of transcripts along with the completed application. **Deadline:** May 31. **Contact:** URL: www.yukonfoundation.com/apply.

12343 ■ Dr. Sally Macdonald Scholarship
(Undergraduate, Master's/Scholarship)

Purpose: To provide funds for students to help them pay their college or university tuition. **Focus:** General studies/ Field of study not specified. **Qualif.:** Applicants must be 4th or 5th year post-secondary students, or Masters or equivalent, enrolled at a college or university for the forthcoming year; must be Yukon residents. **Criteria:** Selection will be based on the committee's criteria.

Funds Avail.: No specific amount. **Duration:** Annual. **To Apply:** Applicants must submit the application form for the General Fund (available online), copy of their transcripts, university acceptance letters, and/or reference letters. **Deadline:** May 31.

12344 ■ Norman Matechuk Memorial Scholarship
(Undergraduate, Master's/Scholarship)

Purpose: To provide funds for students to help them pay their college or university tuition. **Focus:** General studies/ Field of study not specified. **Qualif.:** Applicants must be 4th or 5th year post-secondary students, or Masters or equivalent, enrolled at a college or university for the forthcoming year; must be Yukon residents. **Criteria:** Selection will be based on the committee's criteria.

Funds Avail.: No specific amount. **Duration:** Annual. **To Apply:** Applicants must submit the application form for the General Fund (available online), copy of their transcripts, university acceptance letters, and/or reference letters. **Deadline:** May 31.

12345 ■ James McLachlan Scholarship *(Undergraduate, University, College/Scholarship)*

Purpose: To help students in the Yukon pursue college degrees in mining or geology. **Focus:** Geology; Mining. **Qualif.:** Applicants must be enrolled in a university, college, or technical school for the forthcoming year; must be Yukon residents; must be 2nd, 3rd, or 4th year post-

Awards are arranged alphabetically below their administering organizations

secondary students studying mining or geology.

To Apply: Must submit a copy of transcripts along with the completed application. **Deadline:** May 31. **Contact:** URL: www.yukonfoundation.com/apply.

12346 ■ Les McLaughlin Scholarship *(Undergraduate, University, College, Vocational/Occupational/Scholarship)*

Purpose: To help students in the Yukon pursue college studies in journalism or Yukon history. **Focus:** Area and ethnic studies; History; Journalism. **Qualif.:** Applicants must be enrolled in a university, college, or technical school for the forthcoming year; must be Yukon high school graduates; must be studying journalism or doing research or studies in Yukon history.

To Apply: Must submit a copy of transcripts along with the completed application. **Deadline:** May 31. **Contact:** URL: www.yukonfoundation.com/apply.

12347 ■ Bea & George McLeod Scholarship *(Undergraduate, University, College, Vocational/Occupational, Other/Scholarship)*

Purpose: To help students in the Yukon pursue studies in aviation, aircraft maintenance engineering, or a commercial pilot's license. **Focus:** Aviation. **Qualif.:** Applicants must be Yukon residents enrolled in post-secondary education in the field of aviation, or working to obtain a commercial pilot's license, or working to obtain a license in aircraft maintenance engineering.

To Apply: Must submit a copy of transcripts along with the completed application. **Deadline:** May 31. **Contact:** URL: www.yukonfoundation.com/apply.

12348 ■ Pat & Donald Merrill Scholarship *(Undergraduate, University, College, Vocational/Occupational/Scholarship)*

Purpose: To help students in the Yukon pursue trades training or studies in Yukon environment natural resources. **Focus:** Natural resources; Technology. **Qualif.:** Applicants must be enrolled in a university, college, or technical school for the forthcoming year; must be Yukon high school graduates; must be studying in Yukon environment natural resources or trades training. **Criteria:** Financial need.

To Apply: Must submit a copy of transcripts along with the completed application. **Deadline:** May 31. **Contact:** URL: www.yukonfoundation.com/apply.

12349 ■ Rita & Frank Mooney Scholarship *(Undergraduate, University, College, Vocational/Occupational/Scholarship)*

Purpose: To help students in the Yukon pursue college degrees in engineering, nutrition, or teaching. **Focus:** Engineering; Nutrition; Teaching. **Qualif.:** Applicants must be enrolled in a university, college, or technical school for the forthcoming year; must be Yukon residents; must be pursuing degrees in engineering, nutrition, or teaching, or volunteering in an underdeveloped country (alternates between categories each year).

To Apply: Must submit a copy of transcripts along with the completed application. **Deadline:** May 31. **Contact:** URL: www.yukonfoundation.com/apply.

12350 ■ Brian Morris Scholarship *(Undergraduate, University, College, Vocational/Occupational/Scholarship)*

Purpose: To help students in the Yukon pursue post-secondary degrees or certificates or trades training. **Focus:**

General studies/Field of study not specified. **Qualif.:** Applicants must be enrolled in a college, university, or technical school for the forthcoming school year; must be Yukon residents who completed at least three years of high school in the Yukon.

To Apply: Must submit a copy of transcripts, two letters of reference, and completed application. **Deadline:** May 31. **Contact:** URL: www.yukonfoundation.com/apply.

12351 ■ James W. Murdoch Scholarship *(Undergraduate, University, College, Vocational/Occupational/Scholarship)*

Purpose: To help students in the Yukon pursue post-secondary studies in music, drama, or fine arts. **Focus:** Arts; Music; Theater arts. **Qualif.:** Applicants must be enrolled in a college, university, or trade school for the forthcoming school year; must be Yukon residents; must be pursuing studies in music, drama, or fine arts.

To Apply: Must submit a copy of transcripts along with the completed application. **Deadline:** May 31. **Contact:** URL: www.yukonfoundation.com/apply.

12352 ■ Gordon Newman Recreation Scholarship *(Undergraduate, University, College, Vocational/Occupational/Scholarship)*

Purpose: To help students in the Yukon pursue post-secondary degrees in recreation studies. **Focus:** Parks and recreation; Sports studies. **Qualif.:** Applicants must be enrolled in a college, university, or technical school in the field of recreation studies; must have at least one year of Yukon residency.

To Apply: Must submit a copy of transcripts along with the completed application. **Deadline:** May 31. **Contact:** URL: www.yukonfoundation.com/apply.

12353 ■ Erik Nielsen Memorial Scholarship *(Undergraduate, Master's/Scholarship)*

Purpose: To provide funds for students to help them pay their college or university tuition. **Focus:** General studies/Field of study not specified. **Qualif.:** Applicants must be 4th or 5th year post-secondary students, or Masters or equivalent, enrolled at a college or university for the forthcoming year; must be Yukon residents. **Criteria:** Selection will be based on the committee's criteria.

Funds Avail.: No specific amount. **Duration:** Annual. **To Apply:** Applicants must submit the application form for the General Fund (available online), copy of their transcripts, university acceptance letters, and/or reference letters. **Deadline:** May 31.

12354 ■ Al Oster Music Legacy Scholarship *(Other, Professional development/Scholarship)*

Purpose: To help musicians and composers in the Yukon preserve Yukon music. **Focus:** Music. **Qualif.:** Applicants must be Yukon musicians/composers featuring the preservation of Yukon history or legends, for world-wide consumption and archival storage; must be Yukon residents for at least three years.

To Apply: Application form is available online at www.yukonfoundation.com/apply. **Deadline:** May 31.

12355 ■ Patnode Family Scholarship *(Undergraduate, University, College, Vocational/Occupational/Scholarship)*

Purpose: To help students in the Yukon pursue post-secondary studies in fine arts, mining, geology, or gemol-

---

Awards are arranged alphabetically below their administering organizations

ogy. **Focus:** Arts; Gemology; Geology; Mining. **Qualif.:** Applicants must be enrolled in a college, university, or technical school for the forthcoming year; must be Yukon residents; must be pursuing studies in fine arts, mining, geology, or gemology.

To Apply: Must submit a copy of transcripts along with the completed application. **Deadline:** May 31. **Contact:** URL: www.yukonfoundation.com/apply.

12356 ■ Herman Peterson Scholarship *(Vocational/ Occupational, Undergraduate, University, College/ Scholarship)*

Purpose: To help students in the Yukon pursue training in accredited apprenticeship trades. **Focus:** Technology. **Qualif.:** Applicants must be enrolled in a college, university, or technical school for the forthcoming year; must be Yukon residents; must be in accredited apprentice trades training programs.

To Apply: Must submit transcripts along with completed application. **Deadline:** May 31. **Contact:** URL: www.yukonfoundation.com/apply.

12357 ■ J. L. Phelps Scholarship *(Undergraduate, University, College, Vocational/Occupational/ Scholarship)*

Purpose: To help students in the Yukon pursue college degrees in engineering and business management. **Focus:** Business administration; Engineering; Management. **Qualif.:** Applicants must be enrolled in a college, university, or technical school for the forthcoming year; must be Yukon residents; must be pursuing post-secondary studies in the fields of engineering or business management.

To Apply: Must submit transcripts along with completed application. **Deadline:** May 31. **Contact:** URL: www.yukonfoundation.com/apply.

12358 ■ Garry Phillips Scholarship *(Undergraduate, University, College, Vocational/Occupational/ Scholarship)*

Purpose: To help students in the Yukon pursue college studies or apprenticeship trades. **Focus:** Automotive technology; Health care services; Nursing; Technology. **Qualif.:** Applicants must be enrolled in a college, university, or technical school for the forthcoming year; must be Yukon residents; must be pursuing home care, nursing, recreational vehicle technician, or accredited apprenticeship trades training. Categories alternate from year to year.

To Apply: Must submit transcripts along with completed application. **Deadline:** May 31. **Contact:** URL: www.yukonfoundation.com/apply.

12359 ■ The Porter Creek Citizens' Assoc. Scholarship *(Undergraduate, University, College, Vocational/ Occupational/Scholarship)*

Purpose: To help students in the Yukon pursue college degrees. **Focus:** General studies/Field of study not specified. **Qualif.:** Applicants must be graduates of Porter Creek secondary who have been residents of Porter Creek for a minimum of two years; must be enrolled in a college, university, or technical school for the forthcoming year. **Criteria:** Selection will be based on the following: good citizenship - participation in school and community affairs; good character - interpersonal relationships, attitudes to fellow students an teachers, and personal traits; conduct - punctuality, attendance, behavior, work habits, and attitude.

To Apply: Must submit transcripts, proof of residency (letter from the school principal), and two letters of reference along with completed application. **Deadline:** May 31. **Contact:** URL: www.yukonfoundation.com/apply.

12360 ■ Diamond & James Quong Memorial Scholarship *(Graduate, Master's, Undergraduate/ Scholarship)*

Purpose: To provide funds for students to help them pay their college or university tuition. **Focus:** General studies/ Field of study not specified. **Qualif.:** Applicants must be 4th or 5th year post-secondary students, or Masters or equivalent, enrolled at a college or university for the forthcoming year; must be Yukon residents. **Criteria:** Selection will be based on the committee's criteria.

Funds Avail.: No specific amount. **Duration:** Annual. **To Apply:** Applicants must submit the application form for the General Fund (available online), copy of their transcripts, university acceptance letters, and/or reference letters. **Deadline:** May 31.

12361 ■ Ivan & Dianna Raketti Scholarship *(Undergraduate, Graduate, Master's/Scholarship)*

Purpose: To help Yukon students pay for college or university. **Focus:** General studies/Field of study not specified. **Qualif.:** Applicants must be 4th or 5th year post-secondary students, or Masters or equivalent; must be Yukon residents.

Duration: Annual. **To Apply:** Applicants must complete the General Fund application form at www.yukonfoundation.com/apply. **Deadline:** May 31.

12362 ■ Gary Reynolds Scholarship *(Undergraduate, University, College, Vocational/Occupational/ Scholarship)*

Purpose: To help students in the Yukon pursue college degrees. **Focus:** General studies/Field of study not specified. **Qualif.:** Applicants must be 2nd to 5th year students enrolled in a college, university, or technical school for the forthcoming year; must be Yukon residents.

To Apply: Must submit transcripts along with completed application. **Deadline:** May 31. **Contact:** URL: www.yukonfoundation.com/apply.

12363 ■ Evelyn (Babe) Richards Scholarship *(Undergraduate, University, College, Vocational/ Occupational/Scholarship)*

Purpose: To help students in the Yukon pursue college studies in child development. **Focus:** Child development. **Qualif.:** Applicants must be Yukon residents enrolled in a college, university, or technical school for the forthcoming year in the field of child development.

To Apply: Must submit transcripts along with completed application. **Deadline:** May 31. **Contact:** URL: www.yukonfoundation.com/apply.

12364 ■ Paula Joan Riehl Memorial Scholarship *(High School/Scholarship)*

Purpose: To help high school students pay for international travel. **Focus:** General studies/Field of study not specified. **Qualif.:** Applicants must be F.H. Collins 11th and 12th grade students participating in secondary school international travel.

To Apply: Application is available online at www.yukonfoundation.com/apply.

Awards are arranged alphabetically below their administering organizations

12365 ■ Red Rogers Memorial Scholarship *(Undergraduate, Master's/Scholarship)*

Purpose: To provide funds for students to help them pay their college or university tuition. **Focus:** General studies/ Field of study not specified. **Qualif.:** Applicants must be 4th or 5th year post-secondary students, or Masters or equivalent, enrolled at a college or university for the forthcoming year; must be Yukon residents. **Criteria:** Selection will be based on the committee's criteria.

Funds Avail.: No specific amount. **Duration:** Annual. **To Apply:** Applicants must submit the application form for the General Fund (available online), copy of their transcripts, university acceptance letters, and/or reference letters. **Deadline:** May 31.

12366 ■ John Rowan Scholarship *(Undergraduate, University, College, Vocational/Occupational/ Scholarship)*

Purpose: To help students in the Yukon pursue teacher training or apprenticeship trades training. **Focus:** Teaching; Technology. **Qualif.:** Applicants must be enrolled in a college, university, or technical school for the forthcoming year; must be Yukon residents; must be pursuing teacher training or registered apprenticeship trades training.

To Apply: Must submit transcripts along with completed application. **Deadline:** May 31. **Contact:** URL: www.yukonfoundation.com/apply.

12367 ■ Schmidt Family Scholarship *(Undergraduate, University, College/Scholarship)*

Purpose: To help women in the Yukon pursue college studies in law or social services. **Focus:** Law; Social work. **Qualif.:** Applicants must be women pursuing post-secondary studies in law or social services; must have a minimum of five years Yukon residency. **Criteria:** Financial need; good grades.

To Apply: Must submit transcripts along with completed application. **Deadline:** May 31. **Remarks:** Established by Ballarat Mines and the family in memory of Marion and Harold Schmidt and their son Craig Anthony. **Contact:** URL: www.yukonfoundation.com/apply.

12368 ■ Senyk Memorial Scholarship *(Undergraduate, Master's/Scholarship)*

Purpose: To provide funds for students to help them pay their college or university tuition. **Focus:** General studies/ Field of study not specified. **Qualif.:** Applicants must be 4th or 5th year post-secondary students, or Masters or equivalent, enrolled at a college or university for the forthcoming year; must be Yukon residents. **Criteria:** Selection will be based on the committee's criteria.

Funds Avail.: No specific amount. **Duration:** Annual. **To Apply:** Applicants must submit the application form for the General Fund (available online), copy of their transcripts, university acceptance letters, and/or reference letters. **Deadline:** May 31.

12369 ■ Joan Shaxon Scholarship *(Undergraduate, University, College, Vocational/Occupational/ Scholarship)*

Purpose: To help students in the Yukon pursue college studies in fine arts, art history, museum studies, or arts administration. **Focus:** Art history; Art industries and trade; Museum science. **Qualif.:** Applicants must be enrolled in a college, university, or technical school; must be Yukon

residents; must be studying in the fields of fine arts, art history, museum studies, or arts administration.

To Apply: Must submit transcripts along with completed application. **Deadline:** May 31. **Contact:** URL: www.yukonfoundation.com/apply.

12370 ■ Ben Sheardown Scholarship *(Undergraduate, University, College/Scholarship)*

Purpose: To help students in the Yukon pursue college studies in renewable resources or the environment. **Focus:** Environmental conservation; Environmental science; Resource management. **Qualif.:** Applicants must be Yukon post-secondary students pursuing college studies in renewable resources or the environment at a college or university for the forthcoming year.

To Apply: Must submit transcripts along with completed application. **Deadline:** May 31. **Contact:** URL: www.yukonfoundation.com/apply.

12371 ■ Dr. Brent Slobodin Memorial Scholarship in the Humanities *(Undergraduate, Graduate, University, College/Scholarship)*

Purpose: To help students in the Yukon pursue university studies in the humanities. **Focus:** Classical studies; English language and literature; History; Humanities; Linguistics; Philosophy; Political science. **Qualif.:** Applicants must be Yukon students in the 2nd year or up of studies at a provincial college or university; must have a demonstrated interest in, and intent to specialize in, one or more of the following humanities subjects: history, political studies, philosophy, classics, English, or languages. **Criteria:** Applications will be sent to the family who shall select the successful candidate to recommend to the Foundation.

To Apply: Must submit the following along with the completed application: transcripts; a short statement (no more than four typed, double-spaced pages) showing demonstrated interest and academic excellence with an intent to specialize in one of the noted humanities subjects as well as some experience in volunteer and community; and a resume. **Deadline:** May 31. **Contact:** URL: www.yukonfoundation.com/apply.

12372 ■ Smyth Family Scholarship *(Undergraduate, University, College, Vocational/Occupational/ Scholarship)*

Purpose: To help veterans and Cadets in the Yukon pursue college studies. **Focus:** General studies/Field of study not specified. **Qualif.:** Applicants must be veterans or former Cadets; must be enrolled in a college, university, or technical school; must have at least one year of Yukon residency.

To Apply: Must submit transcripts, proof of service, and completed application. **Deadline:** May 31. **Contact:** URL: www.yukonfoundation.com/apply.

12373 ■ Steele Family Memorial Scholarship *(Undergraduate, Master's/Scholarship)*

Purpose: To provide funds for students to help them pay their college or university tuition. **Focus:** General studies/ Field of study not specified. **Qualif.:** Applicants must be 4th or 5th year post-secondary students, or Masters or equivalent, enrolled at a college or university for the forthcoming year; must be Yukon residents. **Criteria:** Selection will be based on the committee's criteria.

Funds Avail.: No specific amount. **Duration:** Annual. **To Apply:** Applicants must submit the application form for the General Fund (available online), copy of their transcripts,

Awards are arranged alphabetically below their administering organizations

university acceptance letters, and/or reference letters. **Deadline:** May 31.

12374 ■ John & Doris Stenbraten Scholarship
(Undergraduate, University, College, Vocational/ Occupational/Scholarship)

Purpose: To help students in the Yukon attend college or do research related to the Yukon, animal welfare, or mining. **Focus:** Animal rights; Area and ethnic studies; Veterinary science and medicine. **Qualif.:** Applicants must be students enrolled at a university, college, or technical school for the forthcoming school year; must be Yukon residents; must be seeking a degree in veterinary studies, writing or publishing a book related to the Yukon, working on a project relating to mining in the Yukon, or working on a project relating to animal welfare in the Yukon.

To Apply: Must submit transcripts along with completed application. **Deadline:** May 31. **Contact:** URL: www.yukonfoundation.com/apply.

12375 ■ Stuart/SIM Northern Education Scholarship
(Undergraduate, University, College, Vocational/ Occupational/Scholarship)

Purpose: To help students in the Yukon pursue college degrees that will benefit the development of the Yukon. **Focus:** Criminal justice; Environmental science; Law. **Qualif.:** Applicants must be Yukon residents enrolled in a college, university, or technical school for the forthcoming year; must be studying in any area which would be of benefit to the development of the Yukon, including justice, environment, alternate dispute resolution, and aboriginal law.

To Apply: Must submit transcripts along with completed application. **Deadline:** May 31. **Contact:** URL: www.yukonfoundation.com/apply.

12376 ■ Rod Tait Memorial Scholarship
(Undergraduate, College, University, Vocational/ Occupational/Scholarship)

Purpose: To help students in the Yukon attend college or do research related to agriculture. **Focus:** Agricultural sciences. **Qualif.:** Applicants must be students enrolled at a university, college, or technical school for the forthcoming school year; must be Yukon residents; must be studying agriculture, working on a project involving agriculture in the Yukon, or pursuing skills that support agriculture.

To Apply: Must submit transcripts along with completed application. **Deadline:** May 31. **Contact:** URL: www.yukonfoundation.com/apply.

12377 ■ Peg & Aubrey Tanner Scholarship
(Undergraduate, College, University, Vocational/ Occupational/Scholarship)

Purpose: To help students in the Yukon pursue college studies related to environmental studies or protecting the Yukon environment. **Focus:** Environmental conservation. **Qualif.:** Applicants must be students enrolled at a university, college, or technical school for the forthcoming school year; must be Yukon residents for at least five years; must be studying environmental sciences or involved in a project for protection of the natural environment of the Yukon.

To Apply: Must submit transcripts along with completed application. **Deadline:** May 31. **Contact:** URL: www.yukonfoundation.com/apply.

12378 ■ Betty & Charles Taylor Scholarship *(Graduate, Undergraduate/Scholarship)*

Purpose: To provide funds for medical students to help them pay their college or university tuition. **Focus:** Medi-
cine. **Qualif.:** Applicants must be students enrolled in a college or university for the forthcoming year; must be studying in the field of medicine; must be Yukon residents. **Criteria:** Selection will be based on the committee's criteria.

Funds Avail.: No specific amount. **Duration:** Annual. **To Apply:** Applicants must submit the application form (available online), copy of their transcripts, university acceptance letters, and/or reference letters. **Deadline:** May 31. **Contact:** URL: www.yukonfoundation.com/apply.

12379 ■ Edith & Victor Thomas Scholarship
(Undergraduate, University, College/Scholarship)

Purpose: To help students in the Yukon pursue college studies in musical careers. **Focus:** Education, Music; Music. **Qualif.:** Applicants must be Yukon students enrolled in a college or university for the forthcoming year; must be pursuing musical career studies.

To Apply: Must submit transcripts along with completed application. **Deadline:** May 31. **Contact:** URL: www.yukonfoundation.com/apply.

12380 ■ J.J. Van Bibber Scholarship *(Undergraduate, University, College, Vocational/Occupational/ Scholarship)*

Purpose: To help students in the Yukon pursue college studies in education or training in apprenticeship trades. **Focus:** Education; Technology. **Qualif.:** Applicants must be Yukon residents enrolled in a college, university, or technical school for the forthcoming year; must have a minimum of five years Yukon residency; must be studying in the field of education or pursuing training in accredited apprenticeship trades. **Criteria:** Demonstrated financial need.

To Apply: Must submit the following along with the completed application: transcripts, a short essay describing educational goals, and a letter from a teacher or principal speaking to the applicant's attendance, commitment, hard work, and dedication. **Deadline:** May 31. **Contact:** URL: www.yukonfoundation.com/apply.

12381 ■ Vancouver Yukoners Legacy Scholarship
(Vocational/Occupational, College, Undergraduate/ Scholarship)

Purpose: To help students in the Yukon pursue studies or training in technical programs or apprenticeship trades. **Focus:** Heating, air conditioning, and refrigeration; Medical laboratory technology; Radiology; Technology. **Qualif.:** Applicants must be Yukon students pursuing post-secondary studies in technical programs (such as refrigeration, lab tech, x-ray tech) or Yukon government registered apprenticeship trades; must have a minimum five year Yukon residency.

To Apply: Must submit transcripts along with completed application. **Deadline:** May 31. **Contact:** URL: www.yukonfoundation.com/apply.

12382 ■ Joan Veinott Scholarship *(Undergraduate, University, College/Scholarship)*

Purpose: To support students in the Yukon pursuing post-secondary social work studies. **Focus:** Social work. **Qualif.:** Applicants must be Yukon students enrolled in a college or university in the field of social work.

To Apply: Must submit transcripts along with completed application. **Deadline:** May 31. **Contact:** URL: www.yukonfoundation.com/apply.

Awards are arranged alphabetically below their administering organizations

12383 ■ Village of Mayo Heritage Fund Scholarship
(Undergraduate, University, College, Vocational/Occupational/Scholarship)

Purpose: To help Mayo-area students pursue post-secondary education. **Focus:** General studies/Field of study not specified. **Qualif.:** Applicants must be Mayo-area students enrolled in a college, university, or technical school for the forthcoming year.

To Apply: Must submit the following along with the completed application: transcripts and a short essay on how applicant's education plans will benefit the future of the community. **Deadline:** May 31. **Contact:** URL: www.yukonfoundation.com/apply.

12384 ■ Dorreene & Herb Wahl Scholarship
(Undergraduate, University, College/Scholarship)

Purpose: To help students in the Yukon pursue college degrees in teaching and environmental studies. **Focus:** Environmental science; Teaching. **Qualif.:** Applicants must be Yukon residents pursuing post-secondary careers in teaching or environmental studies.

To Apply: Must submit a copy of transcripts along with the completed application. **Deadline:** May 31. **Contact:** URL: www.yukonfoundation.com/apply.

12385 ■ Matthew Watson Scholarship
(Undergraduate, University, College, Graduate/Scholarship)

Purpose: To help students in the Yukon pursue post-secondary studies in scientific research and medicine. **Focus:** Medicine; Science. **Qualif.:** Applicants must be post-secondary students enrolled at a college or university in the fields of scientific research or medicine; must be Yukon residents.

To Apply: Must submit transcripts along with completed application. **Deadline:** May 31. **Contact:** URL: www.yukonfoundation.com/apply.

12386 ■ Matthew Webster Scholarship
(Undergraduate, College, Vocational/Occupational/Scholarship)

Purpose: To help students in the Yukon pursue studies in technical fields, construction design, or apprenticeship training. **Focus:** Construction; Technology. **Qualif.:** Applicants must be pursuing post-secondary studies in technical studies, construction design, and/or apprenticeship studies; must have a minimum of two years Yukon residency.

To Apply: Must submit a copy of transcripts along with the completed application. **Deadline:** May 31. **Contact:** URL: www.yukonfoundation.com/apply.

12387 ■ Whitehorse Business & Professional Women's Club Bursary
(Undergraduate, University, College, Vocational/Occupational/Scholarship)

Purpose: To help female students in the Yukon pursue post-secondary education. **Focus:** General studies/Field of study not specified. **Qualif.:** Applicants must be female students furthering their education at any recognized educational institution; must have a minimum of two years Yukon residency. **Criteria:** Demonstrated financial need.

To Apply: Must submit a copy of transcripts along with the completed application. **Deadline:** May 31. **Contact:** URL: www.yukonfoundation.com/apply.

12388 ■ Whitehorse Copper Mines Scholarship
(Undergraduate, University, College, Vocational/Occupational/Scholarship)

Purpose: To help students in the Yukon pursue mining-related post-secondary studies. **Focus:** Mining. **Qualif.:** Applicants must be Yukon residents completing a minimum of two years in mining-related studies.

To Apply: Must submit a copy of transcripts along with the completed application. **Deadline:** May 31. **Contact:** URL: www.yukonfoundation.com/apply.

12389 ■ Whitehorse Glacier Bears Swim Club Scholarship
(Undergraduate, University, College, Vocational/Occupational/Scholarship)

Purpose: To help past and current members of the club pursue post-secondary education. **Focus:** General studies/Field of study not specified. **Qualif.:** Applicants must be current or past members of the Swim Club; must be enrolled full-time in a college, university, or technical school; must be Yukon residents.

To Apply: Must submit a copy of transcripts along with the completed application. **Deadline:** May 31. **Contact:** URL: www.yukonfoundation.com/apply.

12390 ■ Whitehorse Shotokan Karate Club Scholarship
(Undergraduate, Master's/Scholarship)

Purpose: To provide funds for students to help them pay their college or university tuition. **Focus:** General studies/Field of study not specified. **Qualif.:** Applicants must be 4th or 5th year post-secondary students, or Masters or equivalent, enrolled at a college or university for the forthcoming year; must be Yukon residents. **Criteria:** Selection will be based on the committee's criteria.

Funds Avail.: No specific amount. **Duration:** Annual. **To Apply:** Applicants must submit the application form for the General Fund (available online), copy of their transcripts, university acceptance letters, and/or reference letters. **Deadline:** May 31.

12391 ■ Flo Whyard-Holland America Line-Westours Scholarship
(Undergraduate/Scholarship)

Purpose: To help female students in the Yukon studying journalism. **Focus:** Journalism. **Qualif.:** Applicants must be woman studying journalism; must be Yukon residents.

To Apply: Must submit transcripts along with completed application. **Deadline:** May 31. **Contact:** URL: www.yukonfoundation.com/apply.

12392 ■ Dr. Anne Williams Scholarship
(Undergraduate, Graduate/Scholarship)

Purpose: To help students in the Yukon pursue degrees to become family medicine physicians. **Focus:** Medicine. **Qualif.:** Applicants must be medical students seeking to specialize in family medicine; must have a minimum of five years continuous Yukon residency; must have demonstrated financial need.

To Apply: Must submit a copy of transcripts along with the completed application. **Deadline:** May 31. **Contact:** URL: www.yukonfoundation.com/apply.

12393 ■ Shirley Williams Scholarship
(Undergraduate, University, College/Scholarship)

Purpose: To help students in the Yukon pursue teacher training studies. **Focus:** Teaching. **Qualif.:** Applicants must be enrolled in a college or university full-time for the forthcoming school year in a teacher training program; must be Yukon residents.

To Apply: Must submit a copy of transcripts along with the completed application. **Deadline:** May 31. **Contact:** URL: www.yukonfoundation.com/apply.

Awards are arranged alphabetically below their administering organizations

12394 ■ Robert Wilson Scholarship *(Undergraduate, College, Vocational/Occupational/Scholarship)*

Purpose: To help students in the Yukon pursue training in accredited technical and trades programs. **Focus:** Technology. **Qualif.:** Applicants must be Yukon students enrolled in any accredited technical or trades training programs.

To Apply: Must submit a copy of transcripts along with the completed application. **Deadline:** May 31. **Contact:** URL: www.yukonfoundation.com/apply.

12395 ■ Jeff Young Memorial Scholarship *(Undergraduate, Master's/Scholarship)*

Purpose: To provide funds for students to help them pay their college or university tuition. **Focus:** General studies/ Field of study not specified. **Qualif.:** Applicants must be 4th or 5th year post-secondary students, or Masters or equivalent, enrolled at a college or university for the forthcoming year; must be Yukon residents. **Criteria:** Selection will be based on the committee's criteria.

Funds Avail.: No specific amount. **Duration:** Annual. **To Apply:** Applicants must submit the application form for the General Fund (available online), copy of their transcripts, university acceptance letters, and/or reference letters. **Deadline:** May 31.

12396 ■ Yukon Anniversaries Commission Scholarship *(Undergraduate, University, College, Vocational/ Occupational/Scholarship)*

Purpose: To help students in the Yukon pursue post-secondary tourism-related studies. **Focus:** Hotel, institutional, and restaurant management; Travel and tourism. **Qualif.:** Applicants must be enrolled full-time in a college, university, or technical school for the forthcoming year; must be pursing tourism-related studies, including tourism management, administration, marketing, hospitality, mountain rescue, ski patrol, avalanche control, search/ rescue, and camp expediters; must have a minimum of one year Yukon residency.

To Apply: Must submit a copy of transcripts along with the completed application. **Deadline:** May 31. **Contact:** URL: www.yukonfoundation.com/apply.

12397 ■ The Yukon Foundation Medical Laboratory Scholarship *(Graduate, Master's, Undergraduate/ Scholarship)*

Purpose: To provide funds for students to help them pay their college or university tuition. **Focus:** Medical laboratory technology. **Qualif.:** Applicants must be 4th or 5th year post-secondary students, or Masters or equivalent, enrolled at a college or university for the forthcoming year; must be Yukon residents; must be studying in the field of medical laboratory. **Criteria:** Selection will be based on the committee's criteria.

Funds Avail.: No specific amount. **Duration:** Annual. **To Apply:** Applicants must submit the application for the General Fund (available online), copy of their transcripts, university acceptance letters, and/or reference letters. **Deadline:** May 31.

12398 ■ Yukon Outdoors Club Scholarship *(Undergraduate, University, College, Vocational/ Occupational/Scholarship)*

Purpose: To help students in the Yukon pursue degrees in wildlife management or to work in a National or Territorial Park or historic reserve. **Focus:** Parks and recreation; Wildlife conservation, management, and science. **Qualif.:** Applicants must be Yukon residents enrolled full-time in a college, university, or technical school for the forthcoming year; must be pursuing degrees in wildlife management or seeking to qualify to work in a National/Territorial Park or historic preserve.

To Apply: Must submit a copy of transcripts along with the completed application. **Deadline:** May 31. **Remarks:** Established by the Chilkoot Sourdough Bakery. Established in 1998. **Contact:** URL: www.yukonfoundation.com/apply.

12399 ■ Y.W.C.A. of Yukon Scholarship *(Undergraduate, University, College, Vocational/Occupational/ Scholarship)*

Purpose: To help female students in the Yukon pursue post-secondary education. **Focus:** General studies/Field of study not specified. **Qualif.:** Applicants must be women who are at least 25 years old and need assistance to further their education; must have a minimum of five years Yukon residency.

To Apply: Must submit a copy of transcripts along with the completed application. **Deadline:** May 31. **Contact:** URL: www.yukonfoundation.com/apply.

12400 ■ Yukon Law Foundation

PO Box 31789
Whitehorse, YT, Canada Y1A 6L3
Ph: (867)667-7500
Fax: (867)393-3904
E-mail: info@yukonlawfoundation.com
URL: www.yukonlawfoundation.com

12401 ■ Yukon Law Foundation Scholarship *(Undergraduate/Scholarship)*

Purpose: To provide financial assistance to qualified students who want to pursue their studies. **Focus:** Law. **Qualif.:** Applicants must be students attending law or law related studies. **Criteria:** Selection shall be based on academic achievement, residency, community involvement, and financial need.

Funds Avail.: $15,000. **Duration:** Annual. **Number Awarded:** 1. **To Apply:** Applicants must complete the application along with the original (total of 7 hard copies); must include all the required information, attachments, letters of reference. **Deadline:** August 31. **Contact:** PO Box 31789, Whitehorse, Yukon, Y1A 6L3; Phone: 867-667-7500; Fax: 867-393-3904; Email: execdir@yukonlawfoundation.com.

12402 ■ The Zebra

301 Chicon St., Ste. A
Austin, TX 78702
Free: 888-255-4364
URL: www.thezebra.com
Social Media: www.facebook.com/TheZebraCo
instagram.com/thezebraco
www.linkedin.com/company/the-zebra
twitter.com/TheZebraCo

12403 ■ The Zebra "Show Off Your Stripes" Scholarship *(Undergraduate, Graduate, Vocational/ Occupational, Community College/Scholarship)*

Purpose: To help students pay for higher education. **Focus:** General studies/Field of study not specified. **Qualif.:**

Awards are arranged alphabetically below their administering organizations

Applicants must be currently enrolled at a four-year university, graduate program, community college, trade school, or high school located in the continental United States, and must provide proof of enrollment in the form of a school transcript.

Funds Avail.: $1,000. **To Apply:** Application information available online at www.thezebra.com/insurance-news/5994/scholarship-the-zebra/. **Deadline:** May 31. **Contact:** scholarship@thezebra.com.

12404 ■ Zelle LLP

500 Washington Ave. S, Ste. 400
Minneapolis, MN 55415
Ph: (612)339-2020
Fax: (612)336-9100
Free: 800-229-5294
URL: www.zelle.com
Social Media: www.facebook.com/zellellp/
linkedin.com/company/ZelleLLP
twitter.com/zelleLLP

12405 ■ Zelle Diversity in Law Scholarship
(Undergraduate/Scholarship)

Purpose: To support minority students who are pursuing education in law. **Focus:** Law. **Qualif.:** Applicants must be law students who are either members of a diverse group that is historically underrepresented in the private practice of law, or demonstrate a long-standing commitment to diversity that will be furthered by award of the scholarship; must be first-year law students enrolled full-time at an ABA-accredited law school or be part-time or joint-degree students in their second year of law school at an ABA-accredited law school. **Criteria:** Selection will be based on the following academic performance, writing skills, demonstrated leadership skill, interest in litigation, financial need and a desire to practice in one of the cities where Zelle Hofmann maintains an office.

Funds Avail.: $15,000. **Contact:** Diversity Coordinator, Kristin Suga Heres; Email: kheres@zelle.com.

12406 ■ Zelus Recovery

1965 S Eagle Rd., Ste. 140
Meridian, ID 83642
Fax: (208)957-6506
Free: 866-365-4436
E-mail: info@zelusrecovery.com
URL: www.zelusrecovery.com
Social Media: www.facebook.com/ZelusRecovery
twitter.com/ZelusRecovery

12407 ■ Zelus Recovery College Scholarship
(Undergraduate, Graduate/Scholarship)

Purpose: To further the message that treating adolescents and young adults with substance abuse problems is a means of helping them find their way back to health and happiness so they can become contributing members of society. **Focus:** General studies/Field of study not specified. **Qualif.:** Applicants must be currently enrolled or enrolling in the upcoming semester at a college, university, or trade school in the U.S.; must be aged 18 years or older.

Funds Avail.: $1,000. **To Apply:** Write essay (500-1,000 words) on how substance abuse has affected your life. Include your full name, age, phone number, address, and the name of your school. **Deadline:** August 1. **Contact:** Email: info@zelusrecovery.com.

12408 ■ Zeta Phi Beta Sorority, Inc.

1734 New Hampshire Ave. NW
Washington, DC 20009
Ph: (202)387-3103
URL: www.zphib1920.org
Social Media: www.facebook.com/ZPHIBHQ
www.pinterest.com/officialzetapin
twitter.com/ZPHIBHQ

12409 ■ Mildred Cater Bradham Social Work Fellowships *(Graduate, Professional development/Fellowship)*

Purpose: To support students in pursuit of higher education. **Focus:** Social work. **Qualif.:** Applicant must be a Zeta Phi Beta Sorority Inc. member; pursuing a full-time graduate or professional degree in social work in an accredited college or university program. **Criteria:** Selection is based on the application and supporting documents.

Funds Avail.: $500-$1,000. **Duration:** Annual; for one academic year (Fall-Spring). **To Apply:** Applicant must submit completed application forms along with the required materials. **Deadline:** February 1.

12410 ■ Deborah Partridge Wolfe International Fellowship (Graduate) *(Graduate, Undergraduate/Fellowship)*

Purpose: To provide educational support to students who are in need. **Focus:** General studies/Field of study not specified. **Qualif.:** Applicant must be a full-time graduate or undergraduate U.S. student studying abroad or full-time graduate or undergraduate foreign student studying in the U.S. **Criteria:** Selection is based on the application and supporting documents.

Funds Avail.: $500-$1,000. **Duration:** Annual. **To Apply:** Applicants must submit a completed application form and documented proof of academic study and plan of program to the scholarship chairperson with signature of school administrator or program director. **Deadline:** February 1. **Contact:** Zeta Phi Beta Sorority, Inc., National Educational Foundation, 1734 New Hampshire Ave. NW, Washington, DC, 20009; Phone: 202-387-3103.

12411 ■ Lullelia W. Harrison Scholarships in Counseling *(Graduate, Undergraduate/Scholarship)*

Purpose: To support students who are pursuing higher education. **Focus:** Counseling/Guidance. **Qualif.:** Applicant must be a full-time graduate or undergraduate level student enrolled in a degree program in counseling. **Criteria:** Selection is based on the application and supporting documents.

Funds Avail.: $500-$1,000. **Duration:** Annual; for one academic year (Fall-Spring). **To Apply:** Applicant must submit completed application forms along with the required materials. **Deadline:** February 1.

12412 ■ Isabel M. Herson Scholarships in Education *(Graduate, Undergraduate/Scholarship)*

Purpose: To support students who are pursuing higher education. **Focus:** Education, Elementary; Education--Curricula. **Qualif.:** Applicant must be a graduate or undergraduate level student enrolled full-time in a degree program in either elementary or secondary education. **Criteria:** Selection is based on the application and supporting documents.

Awards are arranged alphabetically below their administering organizations

Funds Avail.: $500-$1,000. **Duration:** Annual; for one academic year (Fall-Spring). **To Apply:** Applicant must submit completed application forms along with the required materials.

12413 ■ Zora Neale Hurston Scholarships
(Graduate/Scholarship)

Purpose: To support students who are pursuing higher education. **Focus:** Anthropology. **Qualif.:** Applicant must be a graduate student enrolled full-time and pursuing a degree in anthropology or any related field of study. **Criteria:** Selection is based on the application and supporting documents.

Funds Avail.: $500-$1,000. **Duration:** Annual; for one academic year (Fall-Spring). **To Apply:** Applicant must submit completed application forms along with the required materials. **Deadline:** February 1.

12414 ■ S. Evelyn Lewis Memorial Scholarships in Medical Health Sciences *(Graduate, Undergraduate/Scholarship)*

Purpose: To provide educational support to students who are in need. **Focus:** Health sciences; Medicine. **Qualif.:** Applicant must be a female full-time graduate or undergraduate enrolled in a program leading to a degree in medicine or health sciences. **Criteria:** Selection is based on the application and supporting documents.

Funds Avail.: $500-$1,000. **Duration:** Annual; for one academic year (Fall-Spring). **To Apply:** Applicant must submit completed application forms along with the required materials. **Deadline:** February 1.

12415 ■ Nancy B. Woolridge McGee Graduate Fellowships *(Graduate/Fellowship)*

Purpose: To support students in pursuit of higher education. **Focus:** General studies/Field of study not specified. **Qualif.:** Applicant must be a Zeta Phi Beta Sorority Inc. member; pursuing a full-time graduate or professional degree in an accredited college or university program.

Funds Avail.: $500-$1,000. **Duration:** Annual; for one academic year (Fall-Spring).

12416 ■ Zeta Phi Beta General Undergraduate Scholarship *(Undergraduate/Scholarship)*

Purpose: To provide educational support to students who are in need. **Focus:** General studies/Field of study not specified. **Qualif.:** Applicants must be a full-time undergraduate freshman, sophomore, junior, senior or graduating high school students planning to enter college. **Criteria:** Selection is based on the application and supporting documents.

Funds Avail.: $500-$1,000. **Duration:** Annual. **Contact:** Zeta Phi Beta Sorority, Inc., National Educational Foundation, 1734 New Hampshire Ave. NW, Washington, DC, 20009; Phone: 202-387-3103.

12417 ■ Zeta Phi Beta Sorority General Graduate Fellowships *(Graduate/Fellowship)*

Purpose: To provide educational support to students who are in need. **Focus:** General studies/Field of study not specified. **Qualif.:** Applicant must be a female full-time graduate with a professional degree, masters, doctoral or enrolled in post-doctoral study. **Criteria:** Selection is based on the application.

Funds Avail.: $2,500. **Duration:** Annual. **To Apply:** Applicants must submit a completed application form along

with the required materials. **Contact:** Zeta Phi Beta Sorority, Inc., National Educational Foundation, 1734 New Hampshire Ave. NW, Washington, DC, 20009; Phone: 202-387-3103.

12418 ■ Zonta Club of Hilo (ZCH)
PO Box 1915
Hilo, HI 96721-1915
E-mail: info@zontahilo.org
URL: www.zontahilo.org

12419 ■ Amelia Earhart Fellowship *(Graduate/Fellowship)*

Purpose: To provide financial support for qualified females intending to pursue their graduate Ph.D. or doctoral degrees in aerospace-related science and aerospace-related engineering. **Focus:** Aerospace sciences; Engineering, Aerospace/Aeronautical/Astronautical. **Qualif.:** Applicants must be graduate study in aerospace-related sciences and aerospace-related engineering.

Funds Avail.: $10,000. **Duration:** Annual. **Remarks:** Established in 1938.

12420 ■ Zonta International Foundation (ZIF)
1200 Harger Rd. Ste. 330
Oak Brook, IL 60523
Ph: (630)928-1400
E-mail: zontaintl@zonta.org
URL: www.zonta.org
Social Media: www.facebook.com/ZontaInternational
www.instagram.com/Zontaintl
twitter.com/ZontaIntl
www.youtube.com/user/ZontaInternational

12421 ■ Jane M. Klausman Women in Business Scholarships *(Graduate, Undergraduate/Scholarship)*

Purpose: To support women pursuing their undergraduate degree leading to a Master's in business management. **Focus:** Business. **Criteria:** Selection will be based on the committee's criteria.

Funds Avail.: $2,000 each at the district/region level and $8,000 each at international level. **Duration:** Annual. **Number Awarded:** 32. **Deadline:** August 15. **Contact:** Email: programs@zonta.org.

12422 ■ Zuckerman Institute
510 Madison Ave., Ste. 2901
New York, NY 10022
Ph: (212)326-4014
E-mail: info@zuckermaninstitute.org
URL: zuckerman-scholars.org
Social Media: www.facebook.com/ZuckermanSTEM
www.instagram.com/zuckerman_stem_leaders
twitter.com/stem_program

12423 ■ Zuckerman STEM Leadership Program *(Postdoctorate/Scholarship)*

Purpose: To support future generations of leaders in science, technology, engineering, and math in the United States and Israel, and to foster greater collaboration between the world's most advanced scientific research centers. **Focus:** Engineering; Mathematics and mathemati-

Awards are arranged alphabetically below their administering organizations

cal sciences; Science. **Qualif.:** Applicants must be postdoctoral scholars in a STEM field from premier universities in the United States who wish to do research at one of seven Israeli universities: Bar-Ilan University, Ben-Gurion University of the Negev, Hebrew University of Jerusalem, Technion-Israel Institute of Technology, Tel Aviv University, University of Haifa, and Weizmann Institute of Science. **Criteria:** Selection is based on academic and research achievements, as well as on personal merit and leadership qualities, without regard to race, religion, gender, ethnicity, or age.

Funds Avail.: $50,000. **Duration:** Up to two years. **To Apply:** Application and details available at zuckerman-scholars.org/ourprograms/postdoc-program/. **Deadline:** January 15 (first), March 15 (second). **Contact:** Email: stem@zuckermaninstitute.org.

12424 ■ Zumper.com
49 Geary St.
San Francisco, CA 94118
URL: www.zumper.com
Social Media: www.facebook.com/zumperinc

www.instagram.com/zumper
www.pinterest.com/zumper
twitter.com/zumper

12425 ■ Zumper Apartments Scholarship *(College, High School/Scholarship)*

Purpose: To help a student gain an education. **Focus:** General studies/Field of study not specified. **Qualif.:** Applicant must be a legal U.S. resident in high school or college; must be attending an accredited university or college in the upcoming school semester. **Criteria:** Selection is based on the overall strength of the application materials.

Funds Avail.: $1,000. **Duration:** 2/year. **Number Awarded:** 2 (one each semester). **To Apply:** Applicants should fill out the form online at zumper.com/scholarship; must submit a short piece of 500 words in writing, that includes the following: How I have impacted fellow student body or community; Housing advice for students at my school: What's one piece of advice I would give first-time student renters. **Deadline:** April 1; November 15. **Contact:** Abdel ElMenshawy abdel@zumper.com.

Awards are arranged alphabetically below their administering organizations

This index classifies awards by one or more of some 400 specific subject categories. Citations are arranged alphabetically under all appropriate subject categories. Each citation is followed by the study level and award type, which appear in parentheses. The number following the parenthetical information indicates the book entry number for a particular award, not a page number.

Abortion (See Family planning)

Academic medicine (See Medicine)

Accounting

Accounting Club Scholarship *(Undergraduate/Scholarship)* [11469]

EFWA Moss Adams Foundation Scholarships *(Undergraduate/Scholarship)* [4303]

African American Network - Carolinas Scholarship Fund *(Undergraduate/Scholarship)* [4715]

AFWA Masters Scholarships *(Master's/Scholarship)* [58]

AFWA Undergraduate Scholarships *(Undergraduate/Scholarship)* [59]

AICPA Accountemps Student Scholarship Award *(Graduate/Scholarship)* [1015]

AICPA John L. Carey Scholarship Awards *(Graduate/Scholarship)* [1016]

AICPA Minority Scholarship *(Undergraduate, Graduate/Scholarship)* [1017]

AICPA Two-Year Transfer Scholarship *(Four Year College, Undergraduate/Scholarship)* [1018]

ALPFA Scholarship *(Graduate, Undergraduate, Master's/Scholarship)* [2231]

Anthony Gerharz Scholarship *(Undergraduate, Graduate/Scholarship)* [7457]

ASCPA High School Scholarships *(Graduate/Scholarship, Monetary)* [1816]

ASCPA Private University Scholarships *(Master's, Graduate/Scholarship)* [1817]

ASMC National Scholarship Program *(Graduate/Scholarship)* [1520]

Association of Government Accountants Graduate Scholarships for Community Service *(Graduate/Scholarship)* [2187]

Association of Government Accountants Graduate Scholarships for Full-time study *(Graduate/Scholarship)* [2188]

Association of Government Accountants Graduate Scholarships for Part-time study *(Graduate/Scholarship)* [2189]

Attorney-CPA Foundation Scholarships *(Postgraduate/Scholarship)* [430]

AWSCPA National Scholarships *(Graduate/Scholarship)* [1678]

BadCredit.orgs Wealth Wise Scholarship *(Undergraduate, Graduate/Scholarship)* [2401]

H. Burton Bates Jr. Scholarships *(Graduate, Undergraduate/Scholarship)* [11843]

Thomas M. Berry Jr. Scholarships *(Graduate, Undergraduate/Scholarship)* [11844]

Bill and Nell Biggs Scholarship *(Undergraduate/Scholarship)* [11508]

Candon, Todd, & Seabolt Scholarship Fund *(Undergraduate, Four Year College, University/Scholarship)* [5385]

Chet And Janett Perry Rotary Club Of Fort Myers Scholarship Fund *(Undergraduate/Scholarship)* [10674]

Community Bank - Lee Guggisberg Foundation Memorial Scholarships *(Undergraduate/Scholarship)* [9535]

Mable B. Crawford Memorial Scholarships *(Undergraduate/Scholarship)* [11444]

Crush The CPA Exam Scholarship *(Undergraduate, Professional development/Scholarship)* [3924]

CSCPA College Scholarships *(Graduate, Undergraduate/Scholarship)* [3539]

CSCPA High School Scholarships *(Undergraduate, Graduate/Scholarship)* [3540]

CSCPA Sophomore Scholarships *(Undergraduate/Scholarship)* [3541]

The Educational Foundation of KyCPA Scholarships *(Undergraduate/Scholarship)* [6539]

Eldon E. and JoAnn C. Kuhns Family Scholarship *(Undergraduate, Graduate/Scholarship)* [7458]

Ernst and Young Scholarships *(Undergraduate/Scholarship)* [1979]

FICPA Educational Foundation 1040K Race Scholarships *(Undergraduate/Scholarship, Award)* [4636]

Floyd E. Lietz Scholarship Fund *(Undergraduate/Scholarship)* [9383]

Clay Ford Florida Board of Accountancy Minority Scholarships *(Undergraduate/Scholarship)* [4627]

Frank H. Ault Scholarship *(Undergraduate/Scholarship)* [9814]

GACFE Scholarship Program *(Graduate, Undergraduate/Scholarship)* [2134]

Sam Gallant Memorial Scholarships *(Graduate, Undergraduate/Scholarship)* [1818]

George J.Waterman Memorial Scholarship *(Undergraduate/Scholarship)* [11898]

GWSCPA Scholarship Fund *(Undergraduate/Scholarship)* [5229]

Lenore and George Hedla Accounting Scholarship *(Undergraduate/Scholarship)* [11482]

HSF/Marathon Oil College Scholarship Program *(Undergraduate/Scholarship)* [5531]

Dixon Hughes Goodman Scholarships *(Undergraduate, Graduate/Scholarship)* [11845]

IAAI Scholarship Foundation Accounting Scholarships *(Undergraduate/Scholarship)* [5733]

Idaho Society of CPA's Scholarships *(Other/Scholarship)* [5678, 5685]

IMA Memorial Education Fund Scholarships (MEF) *(Graduate, Undergraduate/Scholarship)* [5848]

Institute of Management Accountants FAR Doctoral Student Grants Program *(Doctorate/Grant)* [5849]

John M. & Mary A. Shanley Memorial Scholarship *(Undergraduate, Graduate/Scholarship)* [10690]

Marilyn King Scholarship *(Undergraduate, University, College, Vocational/Occupational/Scholarship)* [12333]

KPMG Foundation Minority Accounting Doctoral Scholarships *(Doctorate/Scholarship)* [6609]

Mike and Mary Jean Kruse Scholarship Fund *(Graduate, Undergraduate/Scholarship)* [3631]

Paul J. Laninga Memorial Scholarship *(Undergraduate/Scholarship)* [5089]

MACPA Scholarships *(Undergraduate, Graduate/Scholarship)* [7114]

Maricopa County Community College District Scholarships (MCCCD) *(Undergraduate/Scholarship)* [7034]

Michele L. McDonald Scholarships *(Undergraduate/Scholarship)* [4304]

Melissa J. Wolf Accounting Scholarship *(Undergraduate/Scholarship)* [11486]

Harry Mestel Memorial Accounting Scholarship Fund *(Undergraduate/Scholarship)* [10780]

Michigan Accountancy Foundation Final Year Accounting Scholarship *(Graduate/Scholarship)* [7301]

Minnesota Association of Public Accountant Scholarship *(Undergraduate/Scholarship)* [7404]

David J. Moynihan Scholarships *(Undergraduate, Graduate/Scholarship)* [8331]

MSCPA Scholarship - Montana Tech *(Undergraduate, Graduate/Scholarship)* [7459]

MSCPA Scholarship - MSU Bozeman *(Undergraduate, Graduate/Scholarship)* [7460]

MSCPA Scholarship - University of Montana *(Undergraduate, Graduate/Scholarship)* [7461]

MSCPA Undergraduate Scholarship *(Undergraduate/Scholarship)* [7421]

NABA National Scholarship Program *(Graduate, Undergraduate/Scholarship, Award, Monetary)* [7613]

NAFA Corporate Aviation Business Scholarship *(Undergraduate, Graduate/Scholarship)* [7592]

National Scholarships *(Graduate, Undergraduate/Award, Scholarship)* [1679]

NCACPA Outstanding Minority Accounting Student Scholarships *(Undergraduate/Scholarship)* [8426]

Hubert A. Nelson Scholarship Fund *(Graduate/Scholarship)* [4216]

NESCPA Fifth-year (150 hour) scholarships *(Graduate/Scholarship)* [8198]

NESCPA General Scholarship *(Graduate, Undergraduate/Scholarship)* [8199]

NJSCPA College Scholarships *(Graduate, Undergraduate/Scholarship)* [8287]

NJSCPA High School Seniors *(Undergraduate/Scholarship)* [8288]

North Carolina CPA Foundation Scholarships *(Undergraduate/Scholarship)* [8427]

NSA Scholarship Foundation *(Undergraduate/Scholarship)* [8079]

OAIA Scholarships *(Undergraduate, Graduate/Scholarship)* [8700]

Rhonda J.B. O'Leary Memorial Scholarship *(Undergraduate, Graduate/Scholarship)* [4305]

Oregon College/University Scholarships *(Undergraduate/Scholarship)* [8721]

OSCPA Educational Foundation High School Scholarships *(Undergraduate/Scholarship)* [8722]

Ritchie-Jennings Memorial Scholarship Program *(Undergraduate, Graduate/Scholarship)* [2132]

Robert A. Kleckner Scholarship Fund *(Undergraduate, Graduate/Scholarship)* [10699]

Ross/Nickey Scholarships *(Graduate/Scholarship)* [7422]

Scott Brownlee Memorial Scholarship *(Undergraduate, Graduate/Scholarship)* [7462]

Society of Louisiana Certified Public Accountants Scholarships *(Undergraduate, Master's, Doctorate/Scholarship)* [10382]

The Stanley H. Stearman Awards *(Undergraduate/Scholarship)* [8080]

Striving for Greatness Accounting & Finance Scholarship *(Undergraduate/Scholarship)* [9214]

Stuart Cameron and Margaret McLeod Memorial Scholarship (SCMS) *(Graduate, Undergraduate/Scholarship)* [5850]

Surety and Fidelity Industry Intern and Scholarship Program *(Undergraduate, Graduate/Scholarship)* [10885]

T. Frank Booth Memorial Scholarship Endowment Fund *(Undergraduate/Scholarship)* [4756]

Talbert Family Memorial Scholarship *(Undergraduate/Scholarship)* [3490]

Public University Senior and Master's Program Scholarships *(Graduate/Scholarship)* [1819]

Virginia Tech Doctoral Scholarship *(Doctorate/Scholarship)* [11846]

VSCPA Educational Foundation Minority Accounting Scholarship *(Graduate, Undergraduate/Scholarship)* [11847]

VSCPA Educational Foundation Undergraduate Accounting Scholarships *(Undergraduate/Scholarship)* [11848]

VSCPA Graduate and PhD Accounting Scholarship *(Doctorate, Graduate/Scholarship)* [11849]

Washington CPA Foundation Scholarship *(Undergraduate/Scholarship)* [11899]

Wells Fargo American Indian Scholarship Program *(Undergraduate/Scholarship)* [996]

Wells Fargo Career Scholarship *(Undergraduate/Scholarship)* [11506]

Women In Need Scholarships *(Undergraduate/Scholarship)* [4306]

Women In Transition Scholarships *(Undergraduate/Scholarship)* [4307]

Yount, Hyde & Barbour Scholarships *(Undergraduate, Graduate/Scholarship)* [11850]

Actuarial science

Actuarial Diversity Scholarship *(Undergraduate/Scholarship)* [69]

Caribbean Actuarial Scholarship *(Undergraduate/Scholarship)* [70]

CAS Trust Scholarship Program *(Undergraduate/Scholarship, Monetary, Award)* [3183]

DW Simpson Actuarial Science Scholarship *(Undergraduate/Scholarship)* [4242]

Curtis E. Huntington Memorial Scholarship *(Undergraduate/Scholarship)* [71]

International Association of Black Actuaries Scholarships *(Undergraduate/Scholarship)* [5907]

Elizabeth M. Mauro Reimbursement Awards *(Advanced Professional/Award)* [72]

Actuary of Tomorrow - Stuart A. Robertson Memorial Scholarship *(Undergraduate/Scholarship)* [73]

Saskatchewan Government Insurance Actuarial Science Scholarship *(Graduate/Scholarship)* [9887]

Harold W. Schloss Memorial Scholarship Fund *(Undergraduate/Scholarship, Monetary)* [3184]

Adult education

NASCOE Traditional Scholarships *(Undergraduate/Scholarship)* [7649]

Larry B. Wickham Memorial Scholarship for Graduate Studies *(Graduate/Scholarship)* [7487]

Advertising (See also Public relations)

AAA Doctoral Dissertation Grant Competition *(Doctorate/Grant)* [422]

ANA Multicultural Excellence Scholarship Fund (MAIP) *(Graduate, Undergraduate/Internship)* [509]

Ann Liguori Foundation Sports Media Scholarship *(Graduate, Undergraduate/Scholarship)* [8366]

The Aweber Developing Futures Scholarship *(Undergraduate/Scholarship)* [2389]

Bill Bernbach Diversity Scholarships *(Undergraduate/Scholarship)* [510]

George H. Clinton Scholarship *(Undergraduate/Scholarship)* [8837]

Don S. Maurer Advertising Scholarship *(Undergraduate/Scholarship)* [11182]

The Harold K. Douthit Scholarship *(Undergraduate/Scholarship)* [8580]

The Lagrant Foundation - Graduate Scholarships *(Graduate/Scholarship)* [6632]

The Lagrant Foundation - Undergraduate Scholarships *(Undergraduate/Scholarship)* [6633]

Ohio Newspaper Association Minority Scholarship *(Undergraduate/Scholarship)* [8581]

ONWA Annual Scholarship *(Undergraduate/Scholarship)* [8582]

Springer - Jim Springer Memorial Scholarship *(Undergraduate/Scholarship)* [3489]

Jay A. Strassberg Memorial Scholarship *(Undergraduate/Scholarship)* [2855]

Worldstudio AIGA Scholarships *(Graduate, Undergraduate/Scholarship)* [12205]

Aeronautics (See also Aviation)

AIAA Foundation Scholarship Program *(Graduate, Undergraduate/Scholarship, Award, Monetary)* [1005]

AMA/Charles H. Grant Scholarship Program *(Undergraduate/Scholarship)* [50]

Cliff and Nancy Telford Scholarship Fund *(Undergraduate/Scholarship)* [51]

Col Mary Feik Cadet Flight Scholarship *(Undergraduate/Scholarship)* [3422]

Glendale Latino Association Scholarships *(Undergraduate/Scholarship)* [4999]

NDSGC American Indian Scholarships *(Undergraduate/Scholarship)* [8467]

NDSGC Graduate Fellowships *(Graduate, Master's, Doctorate/Scholarship, Fellowship)* [8468]

NDSGC Summer Faculty Fellowship *(Professional development/Scholarship, Fellowship)* [8469]

NDSGC Undergraduate Fellowships *(Undergraduate/Scholarship, Fellowship)* [8470]

NDSGC Undergraduate Scholarship *(Undergraduate/Scholarship)* [8471]

Pearl I. Young Scholarship *(Undergraduate/Scholarship)* [8472]

PSGC/NASA Space Grant Fellowships at the PSGC Affiliate Institutions *(Graduate/Fellowship)* [8966]

U.S. Air Force ROTC High School Scholarship - Type 1 *(High School/Scholarship)* [11282]

Aerospace sciences

A. Verville Fellowship *(Professional development/Fellowship)* [10190]

Air Force Association/Grantham Scholarships *(Undergraduate/Scholarship)* [146]

Erin J.C. Arsenault Fellowships in Space Governance *(Graduate/Fellowship)* [7188]

Charles A. Lindbergh Fellowships *(Graduate/Fellowship)* [10191]

Daedalian Foundation Matching Scholarships *(Undergraduate/Scholarship)* [3953]

Kenneth J. De Witt NASA/OSGC Scholarship at The University of Toledo *(Undergraduate/Scholarship)* [8596]

Descendants Scholarships *(Undergraduate/Scholarship)* [3954]

DOE Computational Science Graduate Fellowship (DOE CSGF) *(Doctorate, Graduate/Fellowship)* [6611]

Amelia Earhart Fellowship *(Graduate/Fellowship)* [12419]

Guggenheim Fellowships *(Doctorate/Fellowship)* [10192]

John and Alice Egan Multi-Year Mentioning Scholarship Program *(Undergraduate/Scholarship)* [3955]

Thomas R. McGetchin Memorial Scholarship Award *(Undergraduate/Scholarship)* [11423]

Michigan Space Grant Consortium Research Seed Grant Program *(Professional development/Grant)* [7330]

MSGC Internships *(Undergraduate/Internship)* [7003]

MSGC Undergraduate-Under-Represented Minority Fellowship Program *(Undergraduate/Fellowship)* [7331]

Navy, Army or Air Force ROTC Program *(Graduate/Scholarship)* [3956]

NCSGC Undergraduate Research Scholarships *(Undergraduate/Scholarship)* [8457]

NCSGC Undergraduate Scholarships *(Undergraduate/Scholarship)* [8458]

Edward A. O'Connor Founder's Scholarship *(Undergraduate/Scholarship)* [99]

OSGC Community College Scholarships *(Undergraduate/Scholarship)* [8600]

OSGC Education Scholarships *(Undergraduate/Scholarship)* [8601]

Pitsenbarger Award *(Undergraduate, Graduate/Grant, Award)* [150]

John R. Sevier Memorial Scholarship Award *(Undergraduate/Scholarship)* [11424]

Frederick A. Tarantino Memorial Scholarship Award *(Undergraduate/Scholarship)* [11425]

TSGC Graduate Fellowships *(Graduate/Fellowship)* [10994]

U.S. Air Force ROTC High School Scholarship - Type 1 *(High School/Scholarship)* [11282]

James B. Willett Educational Memorial Scholarship Award *(Undergraduate/Scholarship)* [11426]

Michael Wilson Scholarships *(Undergraduate/Scholarship)* [151]

Xavier University ROTC Scholarships - Air Force ROTC *(Undergraduate/Scholarship)* [12229]

Aesthetics

KCC-JEE Graduate Fellowships *(Graduate/Fellowship)* [6580]

African studies (See also Area and ethnic studies)

African Humanities Program *(Postdoctorate/Fellowship)* [819]

Ruth Simms Hamilton Research Fellowship *(Graduate/Fellowship)* [10927]

Learning from Peace in Sub-Saharan Africa *(Professional development/Grant)* [11377]

African-American studies (See also Area and ethnic studies)

MHS African American Studies Fellowships *(Professional development/Fellowship)* [7147]

Muddy Waters Scholarships *(Undergraduate, Graduate/Scholarship)* [2632]

Lydia Donaldson Tutt-Jones Memorial Research Grant *(Graduate, Other, Master's/Grant)* [109]

Aggression and violence (See also Sociology)

Belfer-Aptman Dissertation Research Awards *(Doctorate/Award)* [7247]

Scotiabank Undergraduate Award for Studies in Violence Against Women and Children *(Undergraduate/Award)* [11730]

Aging (See Gerontology)

Agribusiness (See also Agricultural sciences)

Louisiana Agricultural Consultants Association Scholarship *(Graduate, Undergraduate/Scholarship)* [6896]

Douglas McRorie Memorial Scholarships *(Doctorate, Master's/Scholarship, Award)* [131]

National Poultry and Food Distributors Association Scholarships *(Undergraduate/Scholarship)* [8042]

NDFU Scholarship *(Undergraduate/Scholarship)* [8462]

NPC Scholarship *(Graduate/Scholarship)* [8040]

Progressive Dairy Producer Awards *(All/Grant)* [7826]

WEDA Scholarship Program (*Professional development/Scholarship*) [11979]

Agricultural economics (See Agriculture, Economic aspects)

Agricultural sciences

Kyutaro and Yasuo Abiko Memorial Scholarship (*Undergraduate/Scholarship*) [6243]

Myron "Ted" Asplin Foundation Scholarships (*Professional development/Scholarship*) [5739]

Forrest Bassford Student Award (*Undergraduate/Award*) [6881]

The Bentley Cropping Systems Fellowship (*Graduate/Fellowship*) [3263]

Carey Family Scholarship (*Undergraduate/Scholarship*) [7086]

CME Beef Industry Scholarship (*Undergraduate/Scholarship*) [7744]

Helen & Orval Couch Memorial Scholarship (*Undergraduate/Scholarship*) [12302]

Charles Dobbins FTA Scholarships (*Undergraduate, Vocational/Occupational/Scholarship*) [4846]

Dr. Alfred E. Slinkard Scholarship (*Graduate/Scholarship*) [9921]

Don Jaques Memorial Fellowship (*Graduate/Fellowship*) [9922]

Edon Farmers Cooperative Scholarships (*Undergraduate/Scholarship*) [4297]

Elena Sanchez Memorial WSWS Outstanding Student Scholarship Program (*Graduate, Undergraduate/Scholarship*) [11993]

Eugene Boyko Memorial Scholarship (*Undergraduate/Scholarship*) [249]

Everett Family Scholarship (*Undergraduate, College, University/Scholarship*) [7101]

Florida Fertilizer and Agrichemical Association Scholarships (*Undergraduate/Scholarship*) [4634]

Carleton A. Friday Scholarship (*Undergraduate/Scholarship*) [7377]

GCSAA Student Essay Contest (*Graduate, Undergraduate/Prize*) [5033]

GFAI Industry Immersion Scholarship Program (*Undergraduate/Scholarship*) [5064]

Graduate Student Pest Management Award (*Graduate/Grant, Award*) [3108]

Ronald P. Guerrette FFA Scholarship Fund (*Undergraduate/Scholarship*) [6980]

Jim Graham Scholarship (*Undergraduate/Scholarship*) [8455]

Kenneth G. Weckel Scholarship (*Undergraduate/Scholarship*) [7378]

Kraft Foods Food Science Minority Scholarship (*Undergraduate/Scholarship*) [11739]

L. Gordon "Link" Linkous Scholarship (*Undergraduate/Scholarship*) [11103]

Dan & Pauline Lutkenhouse & Hawaii Tropical Botanical Garden Scholarship and Educational Fund (*Undergraduate, Graduate/Scholarship*) [5407]

McCloy Fellowships in Agriculture (*Professional development/Fellowship*) [810]

Monsanto Commitment To Agriculture Scholarships (*Undergraduate/Scholarship*) [7449]

Gerald O. Mott Award (*Graduate/Award*) [3916]

NAAE Upper Division Scholarship (*Undergraduate/Scholarship*) [7609]

National Poultry and Food Distributors Association Scholarships (*Undergraduate/Scholarship*) [8042]

NBIA Scholarship (*Undergraduate/Scholarship*) [8220]

NDFU Scholarship (*Undergraduate/Scholarship*) [8462]

Nebraska Farm Bureau Greater Horizon Scholarship (*Undergraduate/Scholarship*) [8187]

NGC College Scholarships (*Graduate, Undergraduate/Scholarship*) [7900]

Progressive Dairy Producer Awards (*All/Grant*) [7826]

Saskatchewan Pulse Growers Undergraduate Scholarships (*Undergraduate/Scholarship*) [9923]

Herbert M. Saylor Memorial Scholarship (*Graduate/Scholarship*) [10586]

Shear-Miles Agricultural Scholarship (*Graduate, Doctorate/Scholarship*) [11647]

Shear-Miles Agricultural Scholarship/Fellowship (*Graduate, Doctorate/Fellowship, Scholarship*) [11648]

Everett Oscar Shimp Memorial Scholarships (*Undergraduate/Scholarship*) [8878]

Stanley W. Strew Scholarship (*Undergraduate/Scholarship*) [2785]

Rod Tait Memorial Scholarship (*Undergraduate, College, University, Vocational/Occupational/Scholarship*) [12376]

USDA-NIFA-AFRI Merit Awards (*Postdoctorate/Award, Recognition, Prize*) [10534]

Women's Leadership in Agriculture Scholarship (*Undergraduate/Scholarship*) [8578]

Worcester County Conservation District Annual Scholarships Program (*Undergraduate/Scholarship*) [12186]

Work Ethic Scholarship (*Vocational/Occupational, Two Year College/Scholarship*) [7384]

Agriculture, Economic aspects

Agriculture Future of America Community Scholarships (*Undergraduate/Scholarship*) [133]

Agriculture Future of America Scholarships (*Undergraduate/Scholarship*) [134]

Alberta Holstein Association Scholarships (*Undergraduate/Scholarship*) [267]

Clackamas County Farm Bureau Agricultural Scholarships (*Undergraduate/Scholarship*) [8715]

Claude Robinson Memorial Scholarship (*Undergraduate/Scholarship*) [7969]

Don Aron Scholarship (*Undergraduate/Scholarship*) [7783]

Ellis W. Rowe Memorial Scholarship (*Graduate/Scholarship*) [5268]

Keith Gilmore Foundation - Diploma Scholarships (*Other/Scholarship*) [4970]

Keith Gilmore Foundation - Postgraduate Scholarships (*Postgraduate/Scholarship*) [4971]

Keith Gilmore Foundation - Undergraduate Scholarships (*Undergraduate/Scholarship*) [4972]

HAESF Professional Internship Program (*Doctorate/Internship*) [5645]

M.G. "Doc" Headley Scholarships (*Undergraduate/Scholarship*) [10826]

Independent Professional Seed Association Student Recognition Awards (*Undergraduate/Scholarship*) [5740]

John M. & Mary A. Shanley Memorial Scholarship (*Undergraduate, Graduate/Scholarship*) [10690]

Gregory D. Johnson Memorial Scholarships (*Doctorate, Graduate, Master's/Scholarship*) [7970]

The Maschhoffs Pork Production Scholarships (*Undergraduate/Scholarship*) [7971]

National Junior Swine Association Outstanding Member Scholarships (*Graduate/Scholarship*) [7972]

National Poultry and Food Distributors Association Scholarships (*Undergraduate/Scholarship*) [8042]

NDFU Scholarship (*Undergraduate/Scholarship*) [8462]

Nebraska Farm Bureau Greater Horizon Scholarship (*Undergraduate/Scholarship*) [8187]

New York State Association of Agricultural Fairs Scholarship (*Undergraduate/Scholarship*) [8319]

NJSA Visionary Leader Scholarships (*Graduate/Scholarship*) [7973]

NMPF National Dairy Leadership Scholarship Program (*Graduate, Master's, Doctorate/Scholarship*) [8013]

Nuffield Canada Farming Scholarships (*Undergraduate/Scholarship*) [8555]

Oregon Farm Bureau Memorial Scholarship (*Undergraduate, Graduate, High School/Scholarship*) [8716]

Dr. Robert and Anna Shaw Scholarship (*Undergraduate/Scholarship*) [309]

Pat Shimp Memorial Scholarships (*Undergraduate/Scholarship*) [8879]

Jason Shipley Memorial Scholarships (*Undergraduate/Scholarship*) [7974]

Working for Farmers' Success Scholarships (*Undergraduate/Scholarship*) [3240]

Yamhill County Farm Bureau Scholarships (*Undergraduate/Scholarship*) [8717]

Agronomy (See Agricultural sciences)

AIDS

HIV Prevention Research Advocacy Fellowships (*Professional development/Fellowship*) [2368]

Mathilde Krim Fellowships in Biomedical Research (*Doctorate/Fellowship*) [1685]

NYCT Paid Graduate Student Philanthropy Fellowships - Health and People with Special Needs (*Graduate/Fellowship*) [8308]

Air pollution

Dave Benferado Scholarship (*Graduate/Scholarship*) [159]

Milton Feldstein Memorial Scholarships (*Graduate/Scholarship*) [160]

GWS Scholarship Program (*Undergraduate, Graduate/Scholarship*) [165]

Jacqueline Shields Memorial Scholarship (*Graduate/Scholarship*) [161]

Local A&WMA Sections and Chapter Scholarships (*Graduate/Scholarship*) [162]

Richard Stessel Memorial Scholarship (*Graduate/Scholarship*) [163]

Walter A. Rosenblith New Investigator Award (*Postdoctorate/Award*) [5426]

Southern Section A&WMA Scholarships (*Graduate/Scholarship*) [10668]

Alcoholism (See Substance abuse)

Allied health (See Health sciences)

Alzheimer's disease

Firefly Foundation/ASRP Spark Award (*Postdoctorate/Grant*) [412, 4570]

NBHRF/ASRP Doctoral Training Awards (*Doctorate/Award*) [413, 8212]

New Investigator Research Grant (*Postdoctorate/Grant*) [415]

Part the Cloud: Translational Research Funding (*Postgraduate/Grant*) [416]

Sigma Kappa Foundation Alzheimer's/Gerontology Scholarship (*Graduate/Scholarship*) [10122]

Thome Foundation Awards Program in Alzheimer's Disease Drug Discovery Research (*Professional development/Grant*) [5445]

U.S.-U.K. Young Investigator Exchange Fellowship (*Postdoctorate/Fellowship*) [417]

The Zenith Fellows Award Program (Zenith) (*Postdoctorate/Fellowship*) [418]

American history (See History, American)

American Indian studies (See Native American studies)

American studies (See United States studies)

Amyotrophic lateral sclerosis

Brain Canada-ALS Canada Career Transition Awards (*Postdoctorate, Advanced Professional, Professional development/Grant*) [2672]

Brain Canada-ALS Canada Discovery Grants (*Advanced Professional, Professional development/Grant*) [2673]

Brain Canada-ALS Canada Hudson Translational Team Grants (*Advanced Professional, Professional development/Grant*) [2674]

Ancient Greece (See Classical studies)

Ancient history (See History, Ancient)

Anesthesiology

Baxter Corporation Canadian Research Awards in Anesthesia *(Other/Award, Monetary)* [2877]
CAS Research Award in Neuroanesthesia *(Other/Award)* [2879]
CAS/Vitaid-LMA Residents' Research Grant Competition *(Other/Award)* [2880]
FAER Mentored Research Training Grants *(Professional development/Grant)* [4702]
FAER Research in Education Grants *(Advanced Professional/Grant)* [4703]
FAER Research Fellowship Grants *(Postdoctorate, Postgraduate, Graduate/Grant)* [4704]
Health is a Right Not a Privilege Scholarship *(Advanced Professional, Master's, Graduate/Scholarship)* [8561]
Dale O. Heimberger CRNA Memorial Scholarship Fund *(Graduate/Scholarship)* [10764]
IARS Mentored Research Award (IMRA) *(Professional development/Award, Grant)* [5899]
Carl Koller Memorial Research Grants *(Professional development/Grant)* [1557]
SCA/IARS Starter Grant *(Graduate/Grant)* [10298]
David S. Sheridan Canadian Research Awards *(Other/Award)* [2881]
SOAP/Kybele International Outreach Grant *(Advanced Professional, Professional development/Grant)* [10448]

Animal rights

Richard E. Andrews Memorial Scholarship *(Undergraduate/Scholarship, Monetary)* [694]
PETA Foundation Law Internship *(Graduate/Internship)* [8979]
Shaw-Worth Memorial Scholarship *(Undergraduate/Scholarship)* [5638]
John & Doris Stenbraten Scholarship *(Undergraduate, University, College, Vocational/Occupational/Scholarship)* [12374]
Young Birder Scholarships *(Undergraduate/Scholarship, Monetary)* [695]

Animal science and behavior (See also Zoology)

A. Stanley Rand Fellowship Program *(Undergraduate, Doctorate, Postdoctorate/Fellowship)* [10224]
ABS Student Research Grant *(Graduate/Grant)* [1716]
Richard E. Andrews Memorial Scholarship *(Undergraduate/Scholarship, Monetary)* [694]
Angus Foundation Graduate Student Degree Scholarship Program *(Graduate/Scholarship)* [1712]
Angus/Talon Youth Educational Learning Program Endowment Fund *(Graduate, Undergraduate/Scholarship)* [1714]
Marian Breland Bailey Award *(Graduate, Undergraduate/Award)* [2063]
W.D. Farr Scholarship *(Graduate/Scholarship)* [7745]
Rob and Bessie Welder Wildlife Foundation's graduate research fellowship *(Graduate, Master's, Doctorate/Fellowship)* [11958]
ABS Amy R. Samuels Cetacean Behavior and Conservation Award *(Graduate/Grant)* [1717]
Sheep Heritage Foundation Memorial Scholarship *(Graduate, Doctorate/Scholarship)* [1383]
Smithsonian Institution Graduate Student Fellowships *(Graduate/Fellowship)* [10205]
Smithsonian Institution Postdoctoral Researcher Fellowships *(Postdoctorate/Fellowship)* [10206]
Smithsonian Institution Predoctoral Student Fellowships *(Doctorate, Postgraduate/Fellowship)* [10207]

Smithsonian Institution Senior Researcher Fellowships *(Professional development/Fellowship)* [10208]
Smithsonian Minority Awards Program - Visiting Student *(Graduate/Fellowship)* [10209]
Stark County Dairy Promoters Scholarship Fund *(Graduate/Scholarship)* [10794]
STRI Short-Term Fellowships *(Undergraduate, Graduate, Postdoctorate/Fellowship)* [10226]
Sutton Scholarship Award *(Undergraduate/Award, Scholarship)* [10891]
Earl S. Tupper Three-year Postdoctoral Fellowship *(Postdoctorate/Fellowship)* [10227]
Young Birder Scholarships *(Undergraduate/Scholarship, Monetary)* [695]

Anthropology

ARCE Funded Fellowships *(Doctorate, Postdoctorate/Fellowship)* [1336]
ARCE Research Associates Fellowship *(Doctorate, Postdoctorate, Professional development/Fellowship)* [1337]
Franklin Mosher Baldwin Memorial Fellowships *(Master's, Doctorate/Fellowship)* [6751]
Condon Prize for Best Student Essay in Psychological Anthropology *(Graduate, Undergraduate/Prize, Recognition)* [10505]
Conference and Workshop Grants *(Professional development/Grant)* [11960]
Engaged Anthropology Grant *(Doctorate, Postdoctorate/Grant)* [11961]
Fejos Postdoctoral Fellowships in Ethnographic Film *(Postdoctorate/Fellowship)* [11962]
Hunt Postdoctoral Fellowships *(Postdoctorate/Fellowship)* [11963]
Carrie Hunter-Tate Award *(Undergraduate, Graduate/Award)* [7702]
Zora Neale Hurston Scholarships *(Graduate/Scholarship)* [12413]
Leakey Foundation Research Grants *(Doctorate, Advanced Professional/Grant)* [6752]
Margaret Mead Award *(Doctorate/Award)* [10272]
Larry Matfay Cultural Heritage Scholarship *(Undergraduate, Graduate/Scholarship)* [6592]
The William P. McHugh Memorial Fund *(Doctorate, Graduate/Grant)* [1338]
National Endowment for the Humanities Fellowship *(Graduate/Fellowship)* [1339]
Pi Gamma Mu Scholarships *(Graduate/Scholarship)* [9160]
Kenneth W. Russell Memorial Fellowships *(Graduate/Fellowship)* [729]
Smithsonian Institution Graduate Student Fellowships *(Graduate/Fellowship)* [10205]
Smithsonian Institution Postdoctoral Researcher Fellowships *(Postdoctorate/Fellowship)* [10206]
Smithsonian Institution Predoctoral Student Fellowships *(Doctorate, Postgraduate/Fellowship)* [10207]
Smithsonian Institution Senior Researcher Fellowships *(Professional development/Fellowship)* [10208]
Smithsonian Minority Awards Program - Visiting Student *(Graduate/Fellowship)* [10209]
Society for Linguistic Anthropology Annual Student Essay Prize *(Graduate, Undergraduate/Monetary)* [10380]
SPA/Lemelson Fellowship Program *(Graduate/Award)* [10506]
STRI Short-Term Fellowships *(Undergraduate, Graduate, Postdoctorate/Fellowship)* [10226]
Earl S. Tupper Three-year Postdoctoral Fellowship *(Postdoctorate/Fellowship)* [10227]
The United States Department of State, Bureau of Educational & Cultural Affairs Fellowships *(Graduate/Fellowship)* [1340]
The Virtuous Prom Peace Scholarship *(Undergraduate, Graduate, Postgraduate/Scholarship)* [11852]
Wadsworth African Fellowships *(Doctorate/Fellowship)* [11964]
Wadsworth International Fellowships *(Graduate/Fellowship)* [11965]
Wenner-Gren Foundation Dissertation Fieldwork Grants *(Doctorate/Grant)* [11966]

Wenner-Gren Foundation Post-PhD Research Grants *(Doctorate, Postdoctorate/Grant)* [11967]

Applied art (See Art industries and trade)

Applied mathematics (See Mathematics and mathematical sciences)

Aquaculture

Cecelia Connelly Graduate Scholarship in Underwater Archaeology *(Graduate, Undergraduate/Scholarship)* [12135]
Lloyd Bridges Scholarship *(Graduate/Scholarship)* [3204]

Archeology

AIA Graduate Student Travel Awards *(Graduate/Grant, Award)* [1772]
Andrew W. Mellon Fellowships For Conservation Training Programs *(Graduate/Fellowship)* [10197]
ARCE Funded Fellowships *(Doctorate, Postdoctorate/Fellowship)* [1336]
ARCE Research Associates Fellowship *(Doctorate, Postdoctorate, Professional development/Fellowship)* [1337]
Archaeological Institute of America Fellowships for Study in the US *(Postdoctorate/Fellowship)* [1773]
Archaeology of Portugal Fellowship *(Professional development, Graduate/Fellowship)* [1774]
Pierre and Patricia Bikai Fellowship *(Graduate/Fellowship)* [725]
Graduate and Undergraduate Fellowship Awards *(Doctorate, Graduate, Undergraduate/Fellowship, Award)* [3195]
Cecelia Connelly Graduate Scholarship in Underwater Archaeology *(Graduate, Undergraduate/Scholarship)* [12135]
Anna C. and Oliver C. Colburn Fellowships *(Doctorate/Fellowship)* [1775]
DAI Fellowship for Study in Berlin *(Postdoctorate/Fellowship)* [1776]
Bert and Sally de Vries Fellowship *(Undergraduate, Graduate/Fellowship)* [726]
Dorothy Mountain Memorial Scholarship *(Graduate/Scholarship)* [6922]
Kenan T. Erim Fellowships for Archaeological Research at Aphrodisias *(Postdoctorate/Fellowship)* [1346]
Fieldwork Fellowship *(Undergraduate, Graduate/Award, Fellowship)* [4449]
Jennifer C. Groot Memorial Fellowship *(Undergraduate, Graduate/Fellowship)* [727]
Harrell Family Fellowship *(Graduate/Fellowship)* [728]
Harry Walts Memorial Graduate Scholarship *(Graduate/Scholarship)* [6923]
Jane C. Waldbaum Archaeological Field School Scholarship *(Undergraduate, Graduate/Scholarship, Award)* [1777]
Samuel H. Kress Grants for Research and Publication in Classical Art and Architecture *(Professional development, Graduate/Grant, Award)* [1778]
The William P. McHugh Memorial Fund *(Doctorate, Graduate/Grant)* [1338]
Minority Scholarship in Classics and Classical Archaeology *(Undergraduate/Fellowship)* [10311]
National Endowment for the Humanities Advanced Fellowships for Research in Turkey *(Postdoctorate/Fellowship)* [1349, 7871]
National Endowment for the Humanities Fellowship *(Graduate/Fellowship)* [1339]
Olivia James Traveling Fellowship *(Professional development/Fellowship)* [1779]
Harriet and Leon Pomerance Fellowships *(Graduate/Fellowship)* [1780]
Kenneth W. Russell Memorial Fellowships *(Graduate/Fellowship)* [729]
Arthur C. Parker Scholarship *(Undergraduate, Graduate/Scholarship)* [10270]

Burton MacDonald and Rosemarie Sampson Fellowship (Undergraduate, Graduate/Fellowship) [730]

James A. Sauer Memorial Fellowships (Graduate/Fellowship) [731]

Smithsonian Institution Graduate Student Fellowships (Graduate/Fellowship) [10205]

Smithsonian Institution Postdoctoral Researcher Fellowships (Postdoctorate/Fellowship) [10206]

Smithsonian Institution Predoctoral Student Fellowships (Doctorate, Postgraduate/Fellowship) [10207]

Smithsonian Institution Senior Researcher Fellowships (Professional development/Fellowship) [10208]

The United States Department of State, Bureau of Educational & Cultural Affairs Fellowships (Graduate/Fellowship) [1340]

Helen M. Woodruff Fellowships (Postdoctorate/Fellowship) [1781]

Architectural engineering (See Engineering, Architectural)

Architecture (See also Landscape architecture and design)

AAUW Selected Professions Fellowships (Graduate, Master's, Doctorate/Fellowship) [35]

ACI Foundation Scholarships (Graduate/Scholarship) [786]

ACI W.R. Grace Scholarships (Graduate/Scholarship) [789]

AIA Northeast Illinois Student Scholarships (Undergraduate, Graduate/Scholarship) [1009]

Eleanor Allwork Scholarship (Undergraduate/Scholarship) [138]

American Association of University Women Selected Professions Fellowships (Other/Fellowship) [668]

Annika Teig Fellowship (Postgraduate/Internship) [1375]

ARCE Funded Fellowships (Doctorate, Postdoctorate/Fellowship) [1336]

ARCE Research Associates Fellowship (Doctorate, Postdoctorate, Professional development/Fellowship) [1337]

Architects Association of PEI Scholarship (Master's, Doctorate, Graduate/Scholarship) [3701]

Association for Women in Architecture Scholarships (Undergraduate/Scholarship) [2309]

BK Lighting / Ron Naus Scholarship (Graduate, Undergraduate/Scholarship) [5935]

Arthur Buckwell Memorial Scholarship (Undergraduate/Scholarship) [5804]

Carpenters' Company Scholarship Program (Undergraduate/Scholarship) [3175]

CINTAS Foundation Fellowship in Architecture & Design (Professional development/Fellowship) [3417]

D&A Florida Scholarships (Undergraduate/Scholarship) [10678]

Anne & Konrad Domes Scholarship (Undergraduate, University, College, Vocational/Occupational/Scholarship) [12308]

Charles Dubose Scholarships (Undergraduate/Scholarship) [5326]

Kenan T. Erim Fellowships for Archaeological Research at Aphrodisias (Postdoctorate/Fellowship) [1346]

Galvanize the Future: A Richard L. Brooks Memorial Scholarship (Undergraduate, Graduate/Scholarship) [934]

Generation III Scholarship (Undergraduate/Scholarship) [4285]

Huber Engineered Woods Product Evaluation Scholarships (Graduate/Scholarship) [4500]

JMA Architecture Studios Scholarship (Undergraduate/Scholarship) [9405]

John M. & Mary A. Shanley Memorial Scholarship (Undergraduate, Graduate/Scholarship) [10690]

Kluge Fellowship (Doctorate, Graduate/Fellowship) [6573]

Samuel H. Kress Grants for Research and Publication in Classical Art and Architecture (Professional development, Graduate/Grant, Award) [1778]

Arnold "Les" Larsen, FAIA, Memorial Scholarships (Graduate/Scholarship) [1010]

Dolores Zohrab Liebmann Fund - Graduate School Fellowships (Graduate/Fellowship) [6845]

Malayalee Engineers Association Scholarships (Undergraduate/Scholarship) [7012]

Maryland Building Industry Association, Eastern Shore Chapter Scholarship Fund (Undergraduate, High School/Scholarship) [3574]

Katharine & Bryant Mather Scholarship (Graduate/Scholarship) [791]

The William P. McHugh Memorial Fund (Doctorate, Graduate/Grant) [1338]

Kumar Mehta Scholarship (Graduate/Scholarship) [792]

National Endowment for the Humanities Fellowship (Graduate/Fellowship) [1339]

National Federation of the Blind Scholarship Program (Undergraduate/Scholarship, Monetary) [7878]

The Deborah J. Norden Fund (Graduate/Grant) [1785]

Pardee Community Building Scholarship (Undergraduate/Scholarship) [9419]

PCH Architects LLP - Steven J. Lehnhof Memorial Architectural Scholarship (Undergraduate/Scholarship) [9571]

Plan NH's Scholarship and Fellowship Program (Community College, Four Year College, Undergraduate, Graduate, Vocational/Occupational/Scholarship) [9188]

Polaire Weissman Fund Fellowship (Graduate/Fellowship) [7279]

Resilience Action Fund Scholarship (Graduate/Scholarship) [4504]

SAH Study Tour Fellowships (Graduate/Fellowship) [10276]

Samuel H. Kress Foundation Fellowships (Doctorate/Fellowship) [10277]

Leo and Trinidad Sanchez Scholarships (Undergraduate/Scholarship) [10138]

SOM Foundation Architecture, Design and Urban Design Prize (Graduate/Prize) [10159]

SOM Foundation Travel Fellowships in Architecture, Design and Urban Design (Graduate, Undergraduate/Fellowship) [10161]

Stewardson Keefe LeBrun Travel Grant (Professional development/Grant, Award) [139]

Stuart L. Noderer Memorial Scholarship (Undergraduate/Scholarship) [9855]

Study Scholarship for Artists or Musicians (Graduate, Postdoctorate/Scholarship) [4066]

Tom Cory Scholarships (Undergraduate, Graduate/Scholarship) [1787]

Sally Kress Tompkins Fellowship (Graduate/Fellowship) [10278]

TrustedPros Scholarships (Undergraduate/Scholarship) [11131]

UC MEXUS-CONACYT Doctoral Fellowship (Doctorate/Fellowship) [11552]

The United States Department of State, Bureau of Educational & Cultural Affairs Fellowships (Graduate/Fellowship) [1340]

Vectorworks Design Scholarship (Undergraduate, Graduate/Scholarship) [11796]

Dimitri J. Ververelli Memorial Scholarship for Architecture and/or Engineering (Undergraduate/Scholarship) [5469]

Washington University Law School Olin Fellowships for Women (Advanced Professional/Fellowship) [11924]

Bertold E. Weinberg Scholarship (Graduate/Scholarship) [793]

Ernest Wilby Memorial Scholarship (Undergraduate/Scholarship) [5805]

Beverly Willis Architecture Foundation Travel Fellowship (Doctorate/Fellowship) [10279]

Worldstudio AIGA Scholarships (Graduate, Undergraduate/Scholarship) [12205]

Architecture, Naval

ASEE-NRL Postdoctoral Fellowship Program (Postdoctorate/Fellowship) [11389]

Robert N. Herbert Undergraduate Scholarships (Undergraduate/Scholarship) [10433]

Malayalee Engineers Association Scholarships (Undergraduate/Scholarship) [7012]

NDSEG Fellowship (Graduate/Fellowship) [7834]

Mandell and Lester Rosenblatt Undergraduate Scholarship (Undergraduate/Scholarship) [10434]

Archival science (See Library and archival sciences)

Area and ethnic studies

ACMS Intensive Mongolian Language Fellowship (Undergraduate/Fellowship) [720]

ACOR-CAORC Post-Doctoral Fellowships (Postdoctorate/Fellowship) [723]

ACOR-CAORC Pre-Doctoral Fellowships (Graduate, Doctorate/Fellowship) [724]

Boren Fellowships (Graduate/Fellowship) [5840]

Boren Scholarships (Undergraduate, College/Scholarship) [5841]

Ruth B. Fein Prize (Graduate/Prize) [1063]

Alan R. and Barbara D. Finberg Fellowships (Graduate/Fellowship) [5634]

Ford Foundation Dissertation Fellowship (Postdoctorate/Fellowship) [4672, 7572]

Ford Foundation Diversity Fellowships (Graduate, Doctorate, Postdoctorate, Postgraduate/Fellowship) [7573]

Ford Foundation Postdoctoral Fellowship (Postdoctorate/Fellowship) [4673, 7574]

Ford Foundation Predoctoral Fellowship (Graduate, Doctorate/Fellowship) [4674, 7575]

HIAA Graduate Student Travel Grants (Graduate/Grant) [5534]

The Hougen Family Fund Scholarship (Undergraduate, College, University, Vocational/Occupational/Scholarship) [12326]

Houtan Scholarship (Graduate/Scholarship) [5604]

Klondike Defence Force Grant (Undergraduate, College, University, Vocational/Occupational/Scholarship) [12335]

Ole & Mary Lunde Scholarship (Undergraduate, University, College, Vocational/Occupational, Graduate/Scholarship) [12342]

Mangasar M. Mangasarian Scholarship Fund (Graduate/Scholarship) [11544]

Les McLaughlin Scholarship (Undergraduate, University, College, Vocational/Occupational/Scholarship) [12346]

Pokross/Curhan Family Fund Prize (Graduate, Undergraduate/Prize) [1064]

Short-term Senior Fellowships in Iranian Studies (Graduate, Master's, Doctorate/Fellowship) [1031]

John & Doris Stenbraten Scholarship (Undergraduate, University, College, Vocational/Occupational/Scholarship) [12374]

Theodore E.D. Braun Research Travel Fellowship (Other/Fellowship) [1439]

Armenian studies (See also Area and ethnic studies)

Arthur H. Dadian Scholarship Grants (Undergraduate/Scholarship) [1870]

Parsegh and Thora Essefian Memorial Grant (Undergraduate/Scholarship) [1876]

Dolores Zohrab Liebmann Fund - Publication Grants (Graduate, Undergraduate/Grant) [6847]

Art (See also Performing arts; Visual arts)

Adrienne Zoe Fedok Art and Music Scholarship (Undergraduate/Scholarship) [4773]

American Watercolor Society Scholarship Program for Art Teachers (Undergraduate, Graduate/Scholarship) [1648]

ARCE Funded Fellowships (Doctorate, Postdoctorate/Fellowship) [1336]

ARCE Research Associates Fellowship (Doctorate, Postdoctorate, Professional development/Fellowship) [1337]

Artist-in-Residence Workspace Grant (Professional development/Grant) [3210]

Joan Auld Scholarship (Undergraduate/Scholarship) [3702]

Jenny Panitch Beckow Memorial Scholarship - Canada (Graduate/Scholarship) [6283]

Jenny Panitch Beckow Memorial Scholarship - Israel (Graduate/Scholarship) [6284]

BEF Scholarship of the Arts (Graduate, Undergraduate/Scholarship) [4440]

Beta Sigma Phi Visual Arts Scholarship (Undergraduate/Scholarship) [10049]

James M. Brahney Scholarship (Professional development/Scholarship) [5729]

Edwin Anthony and Adelaide Boudreaux Cadogan Scholarships (Graduate/Fellowship) [9870]

Karin Carton Scholarship (Graduate/Scholarship) [4850]

Emi Chance for Aspiring Artists Scholarship (Undergraduate/Scholarship) [11475]

Paul Collins Scholarship (Undergraduate/Scholarship) [5143]

Convergence Assistantship Grants (Undergraduate/Grant) [5283]

Cynthia and Alan Baran Fine Arts and Music Scholarship Fund (Undergraduate/Scholarship) [3609]

Chester Dale Fellowships (Doctorate/Fellowship) [7275]

David G. Robinson Arts Scholarship Fund (Undergraduate/Scholarship) [10679]

The Dendel Scholarship (Graduate, Undergraduate/Scholarship) [5284]

Dewey Lee Curtis Symposium Scholarships (Advanced Professional/Scholarship) [3989]

Mychajlo Dmytrenko Fine Arts Foundation Scholarships (Undergraduate/Scholarship) [11410]

Pauly D'Orlando Memorial Art Scholarship (Graduate, Undergraduate/Scholarship) [11248]

Douglass Foundation Fellowship in American Art (Doctorate/Fellowship) [10214]

The Drawn to Art Fellowship (Doctorate/Fellowship) [488]

Marnie & Bill Drury Scholarship (Undergraduate, University, College, Vocational/Occupational/Scholarship) [12309]

Fine Arts Association Minority Scholarship (Undergraduate/Scholarship) [4564]

Fine Arts Association United Way Scholarship (Undergraduate/Scholarship) [4565]

Patricia and Phillip Frost Fellowships (Doctorate, Postdoctorate/Fellowship) [10215]

GAAC Project Grants (Undergraduate, Professional development/Grant) [4995]

The Gallery Collection's Create-A-Greeting-Card Scholarship (Undergraduate/Scholarship) [4848]

George E. Judd Scholarship Fund (Undergraduate/Scholarship) [10686]

Getty Scholar Grants (Professional development/Grant) [4959]

Global Art Grant (Graduate/Grant) [2613]

The George Gurney Fellowship Endowment Fund (Doctorate, Postdoctorate/Fellowship) [10216]

Gwen Yarnell Theatre Scholarship (Undergraduate/Scholarship) [4566]

HAESF Professional Internship Program (Doctorate/Internship) [5645]

Ted & Nicky Harrison Memorial Fund (Undergraduate, Master's/Scholarship) [12323]

Dereen Hildebrand Scholarship (Undergraduate, College, University, Vocational/Occupational/Scholarship) [12324]

Abram and Fannie Gottlieb Immerman and Abraham Nathan and Bertha Daskal Weinstein Memorial Fellowship (Postdoctorate, Doctorate/Fellowship) [12238]

Indiana State University Creative and Performing Arts Awards (Undergraduate/Scholarship) [5769]

Donald Wills Jacobs Scholarships (Undergraduate/Scholarship) [11452]

Joanna Townsend Applied Arts Scholarship (All/Scholarship) [2129]

Samuel H. Kress Grants for Research and Publication in Classical Art and Architecture (Professional development, Graduate/Grant, Award) [1778]

Jay and Deborah Last Fellowships (Doctorate/Fellowship) [494]

Claudia-Ann Lowry Scholarship (Undergraduate, College, University, Vocational/Occupational/Scholarship) [12340]

Lucy Hilty Research Grant (Graduate/Grant) [1312]

Dorothy L. Maddy Academic Scholarship (Undergraduate/Scholarship) [10744]

Marion Barr Stanfield Art Scholarship (Graduate, Undergraduate/Scholarship) [11252]

Marvin R. and Pearl E. Patterson Family Scholarship (Undergraduate/Scholarship) [5095]

Mathilda & Carolyn Gallmeyer Scholarship (Undergraduate/Scholarship) [5165]

The William P. McHugh Memorial Fund (Doctorate, Graduate/Grant) [1338]

Mearl K. Gable II Memorial Grant (Other/Grant) [5285]

Mill Creek Chamber of Commerce Scholarship (Undergraduate/Scholarship) [7393]

J. Clawson Mills Scholarships (Doctorate/Fellowship) [7278]

Letitia Moore Charitable Trust Scholarship (Undergraduate/Scholarship) [12243]

Muriel Hannah Scholarship in Art (Undergraduate, Graduate/Scholarship) [11487]

The Jack K. & Gertrude Murphy Award (Graduate/Award) [9871]

National Endowment for the Humanities Advanced Fellowships for Research in Turkey (Postdoctorate/Fellowship) [1349, 7871]

National Endowment for the Humanities Fellowship (Graduate/Fellowship) [1339]

Northwest-Shoals Community College Fine Arts Scholarships - Art (Undergraduate/Scholarship) [8527]

Pennies for Art Scholarship (Undergraduate/Scholarship) [4902]

Silvio and Eugenia Petrini Grants (Other/Grant) [5286]

Phi Theta Kappa Scholarship (Undergraduate/Scholarship) [5765]

Philip F. Vineberg Travelling Fellowship in the Humanities (Undergraduate/Scholarship, Monetary) [7184]

Natalie and Mendel Racolin Memorial Fellowship (Postdoctorate, Doctorate/Fellowship) [12239]

Regina Higdon Scholarship (Undergraduate/Scholarship) [3642]

James Renwick Fellowship in American Craft (Doctorate, Postdoctorate/Fellowship) [10217]

Helen Lansdowne Resor Scholarship (Undergraduate, Graduate, Other/Scholarship) [11018]

Sara Roby Fellowship in Twentieth-Century American Realism (Doctorate, Postdoctorate/Fellowship) [10218]

Dr. Robert and Anna Shaw Scholarship (Undergraduate/Scholarship) [309]

Spring Forward Scholarship (Undergraduate/Award) [39]

Stacey Scholarship Fund (All/Scholarship) [7822]

Cecilia Steinfeldt Fellowships for Research in the Arts and Material Culture (Professional development/Fellowship) [11000]

Study Scholarship for Artists or Musicians (Graduate, Postdoctorate/Scholarship) [4066]

Joshua C. Taylor Fellowships (Doctorate, Postdoctorate/Fellowship) [10219]

The Terra Foundation Fellowships in American Art (Undergraduate, Doctorate, Postdoctorate/Fellowship) [10220]

Terra Foundation Research Travel Grants (Doctorate, Undergraduate/Grant) [10965]

The William H. Truettner Fellowship Endowment Fund (Undergraduate, Doctorate, Postdoctorate/Fellowship) [10221]

UAA Kimura Scholarship Fund for Photography (Undergraduate/Scholarship) [11504]

The United States Department of State, Bureau of Educational & Cultural Affairs Fellowships (Graduate/Fellowship) [1340]

Washington University Law School Olin Fellowships for Women (Advanced Professional/Fellowship) [11924]

J. B. C. Watkins Award (Professional development/Fellowship) [2873]

Western Governors' Association "Celebrate the West" High School Art Competition (High School/Award) [11983]

Jane and Morgan Whitney Fellowships (Graduate/Fellowship) [7284]

Worldstudio AIGA Scholarships (Graduate, Undergraduate/Scholarship) [12205]

Wyeth Foundation Predoctoral Fellowship (Postdoctorate/Fellowship) [10222]

Art, Caricatures and cartoons

Joanna Townsend Applied Arts Scholarship (All/Scholarship) [2129]

Worldstudio AIGA Scholarships (Graduate, Undergraduate/Scholarship) [12205]

Art conservation

FAIC Individual Professional Development Scholarships (Professional development/Scholarship) [4700]

Kress Conservation Fellowships (Postgraduate/Fellowship) [6614]

NGA Conservation Fellowships (Graduate/Fellowship) [7898]

Smithsonian Postgraduate/Postdoctoral Fellowships in Conservation of Museum Collections (Postgraduate, Postdoctorate/Fellowship) [10212]

Art criticism (See Criticism (Art, Drama, Literary))

Art history

The Bothmer Fellowship (Doctorate, Graduate/Fellowship) [7273]

Kenan T. Erim Fellowships for Archaeological Research at Aphrodisias (Postdoctorate/Fellowship) [1346]

Annette Kade Fellowships (Graduate/Fellowship) [7277]

Louis I. Jaffe Memorial Scholarship-ODU (Graduate/Scholarship) [5274]

Luce/ACLS Dissertation Fellowships in American Art (Graduate, Doctorate/Fellowship) [824]

Letitia Moore Charitable Trust Scholarship (Undergraduate/Scholarship) [12243]

Margaret B. Ševenko Prize in Islamic Art and Culture (Doctorate, Graduate/Prize) [5535]

Joan Shaxon Scholarship (Undergraduate, University, College, Vocational/Occupational/Scholarship) [12369]

Smithsonian Institution Graduate Student Fellowships (Graduate/Fellowship) [10205]

Smithsonian Institution Postdoctoral Researcher Fellowships (Postdoctorate/Fellowship) [10206]

Smithsonian Institution Predoctoral Student Fellowships (Doctorate, Postgraduate/Fellowship) [10207]

Smithsonian Institution Senior Researcher Fellowships (Professional development/Fellowship) [10208]

Eric E. Smoker Memorial Scholarship (Undergraduate, Two Year College, Four Year College/Scholarship) [8490]

The Hanns Swarzenski and Brigitte Horney Swarzenski Fellowship (Graduate/Fellowship) [7283]

United States Capitol Historical Society Fellowships (Graduate/Fellowship) [11299]

Virginia Museum of Fine Arts Visual Arts Fellowships (Graduate, Other, Undergraduate/Fellowship) [11839]

Art industries and trade

Paul Collins Scholarship (Undergraduate/Scholarship) [5143]

Dr. Robert and Anna Shaw Scholarship (Undergraduate/Scholarship) [309]

Joan Shaxon Scholarship (Undergraduate, University, College, Vocational/Occupational/Scholarship) [12369]

University of Toronto Nortel Institute Undergraduate Scholarships (Undergraduate/Scholarship) [11701]

Art, Performing (See Performing arts)

Art, Roman

Shohet Scholars Grant Program (SSG) (Professional development/Grant) [5962]

Art therapy

American Art Therapy Association Anniversary Scholarship (Graduate/Scholarship) [501]

Myra Levick Scholarship Fund (Graduate/Scholarship) [502]

Rawley Silver Award for Excellence (Graduate/Scholarship) [503]

Rawley Silver Research Award (Postgraduate, Postdoctorate/Award, Recognition) [504]

Art, Visual (See Visual arts)

Arthritis

Arthritis Foundation Investigator Awards (Doctorate/Award) [1971]

Arts

Aaron Copland Bogliasco Fellowships in Music (Professional development/Fellowship) [2641]

AFA Film and Video Arts Project Grants (Professional development/Grant) [257]

American-Scandinavian Foundation Grants to Study in Scandinavia (Graduate/Grant) [1374]

Andrew Gronholdt Arts Scholarship (Undergraduate, Vocational/Occupational, Graduate, Master's/Scholarship) [328]

Antonio Cirino Memorial Scholarship (Graduate/Scholarship) [9688]

Art Acquisition by Application (Professional development/Grant) [260]

Arts Foundation of Cape Cod Scholarships (Undergraduate, Vocational/Occupational/Scholarship) [1975]

Arts Graduate Scholarship (Graduate/Scholarship) [285]

William E. Barto Scholarship Fund (Undergraduate/Scholarship) [4200]

Leo Biaggi de Blasys Bogliasco Fellowships (Undergraduate/Scholarship) [2642]

Bogliasco Fellowships (Professional development/Fellowship) [2643]

John Burroughs Bogliasco Fellowships (Professional development/Fellowship) [2644]

Bush Fellowship (Professional development/Fellowship) [2756]

Cultural Relations Individual Project Funding (Professional development/Grant) [261]

Dance Individual Project Funding (Professional development/Grant) [262]

The Douglass Foundation Fellowship in American Art (Graduate/Fellowship) [7276]

EAA Members Memorial Scholarship (Undergraduate/Scholarship) [4391]

EAA Workshop Scholarships (Undergraduate/Scholarship) [4392]

Ed Haas Memorial Scholarship Fund (Graduate/Scholarship) [10824]

Edgecliff McAuley Art Scholarships (Undergraduate/Scholarship) [12221]

Albinas Elskus Scholarship (Other/Scholarship) [10743]

Bruce T. and Jackie Mahi Erickson Scholarship (Graduate, Undergraduate/Scholarship) [8924]

Florida Education Fund McKnight Doctoral Fellowship (Graduate/Fellowship) [4629]

Don Fox Memorial Scholarship (Undergraduate/Scholarship) [232]

William E. "Bill" Gallagher Scholarship (Undergraduate/Scholarship) [8847]

Mona Gray Creative Arts Scholarship (Graduate, Undergraduate/Scholarship) [6306]

Graybar Canada Award of Excellence Scholarships (Undergraduate/Scholarship) [4347]

John Simon Guggenheim Memorial Fellowships - United States & Canadian Competition (Graduate, Postgraduate, Undergraduate/Fellowship) [5250]

Guntley-Lorimer Science and Arts Scholarships (Undergraduate/Scholarship) [2594]

HACU/KIA Motors America, Inc. STEAM Scholarships (Undergraduate, Graduate/Scholarship) [5516, 6543]

Helen R. (Finley) Loescher and Stephen B. Loescher Scholarship (High School/Scholarship) [3679]

Jacob K. Javits Fellowships Program (Master's, Doctorate/Fellowship) [11310]

Jerome Robbins Bogliasco Fellowships in Dance (Professional development/Fellowship) [2645]

Jewish Federation Academic Scholarship (Graduate, Undergraduate/Scholarship) [6310]

Martha Julian Memorial Scholarship (Undergraduate/Scholarship) [233]

Henry and Chiyo Kuwahara Creative Arts Award (Graduate/Scholarship) [6248]

Ladies Literary Club Scholarship (Undergraduate/Scholarship) [5161]

Ted Lewis Memorial Scholarship (Undergraduate/Scholarship) [234]

Literary Individual Project Funding (Professional development/Grant) [264]

Dorothy L. Maddy Workshop/Seminar Scholarship (Other/Scholarship) [10745]

John H. Moss Scholarships (Undergraduate/Scholarship) [11697]

James W. Murdoch Scholarship (Undergraduate, University, College, Vocational/Occupational/Scholarship) [12351]

National PTA Reflections - Outstanding Interpretation Awards (Undergraduate/Award, Medal, Scholarship) [8055]

NCECA Graduate Student Fellowships (Graduate/Fellowship) [7787]

NHFA Scholarships (Graduate/Scholarship) [7930]

NYCT Paid Graduate Student Philanthropy Fellowships - Arts and Historic Preservation (Graduate/Fellowship) [8305]

Patnode Family Scholarship (Undergraduate, University, College, Vocational/Occupational/Scholarship) [12355]

Pembroke Center Seed Grants (Professional development/Grant) [2726]

Polaire Weissman Fund Fellowship (Graduate/Fellowship) [7279]

Prescott Fine Arts Association Scholarship Program (Undergraduate/Scholarship) [9269]

Quality Bath.com Scholarship (Community College, College, University, Undergraduate, Graduate/Scholarship) [9453]

Regina Brown Undergraduate Student Fellowship (Undergraduate/Fellowship) [7788]

Rome Prize (Postdoctorate, Graduate, Undergraduate/Prize, Award) [476]

Leo S. Rowe Pan American Fund (Graduate, Undergraduate/Loan) [8739]

Dale M. Schoettler Scholarship for Visually Impaired Students (Undergraduate, Graduate/Scholarship) [9874]

Art Competition Scholarship Program (Undergraduate/Scholarship) [9952]

Roger Sessions Memorial Bogliasco Fellowships in Music (Professional development/Fellowship) [2647]

Julia Shahan and Shahan Siran Nevshehir Memorial Grant (Undergraduate/Scholarship) [1903]

Smithsonian Minority Awards Program - Visiting Student (Graduate/Fellowship) [10209]

Eric E. Smoker Memorial Scholarship (Undergraduate, Two Year College, Four Year College/Scholarship) [8490]

Terra Foundation Fellowships at the Smithsonian American Art Museum (Postdoctorate/Fellowship) [10963]

Terra Foundation Postdoctoral Teaching Fellowships at the Institut National d'Histoire de l'Art, Paris (Postdoctorate/Fellowship) [10964]

Terra Summer Residency Fellowships (Master's, Doctorate/Fellowship) [10966]

UC MEXUS Scholars in Residence Program - Graduate (Graduate/Scholarship) [11555]

UCSD Black Alumni Scholarship for Arts and Humanities (Undergraduate/Scholarship) [9857]

Chancellor's Graduate Fellowship (Advanced Professional/Fellowship) [11923]

James P. and Joy Y. Zana Scholarship (Undergraduate/Scholarship) [5127]

Asian studies (See also Area and ethnic studies)

Albert C.W. Chan Foundation Award (Graduate/Fellowship) [12264]

Huang Hsing Chun-tu Hsueh Fellowship Fund (Graduate, Postdoctorate, Undergraduate, Professional development/Grant) [1256]

UC-Berkeley/ISEEES/CCS Postdoctoral Fellowships (Postdoctorate/Fellowship) [11535]

Astronautics

AIAA Foundation Scholarship Program (Graduate, Undergraduate/Scholarship, Award, Monetary) [1005]

Astronomy and astronomical sciences (See also Space and planetary sciences)

American Astronomical Society Small Research Grants (Doctorate/Grant) [681]

Annie Jump Cannon Award in Astronomy (Doctorate/Award, Recognition) [682]

Chrétien International Research Grants (Doctorate/Grant) [683]

DOE Computational Science Graduate Fellowship (DOE CSGF) (Doctorate, Graduate/Fellowship) [6611]

Grants-in-Aid of Research (GIAR) (Graduate, Undergraduate/Grant) [10128]

NPSC Fellowship (Graduate/Fellowship) [5056]

Rodger Doxsey Travel Prize (Graduate, Postdoctorate/Prize) [684]

Smithsonian Institution Graduate Student Fellowships (Graduate/Fellowship) [10205]

Smithsonian Institution Postdoctoral Researcher Fellowships (Postdoctorate/Fellowship) [10206]

Smithsonian Institution Predoctoral Student Fellowships (Doctorate, Postgraduate/Fellowship) [10207]

Smithsonian Institution Senior Researcher Fellowships (Professional development/Fellowship) [10208]

Athletics

Canadian Seniors' Golf Association Scholarships (Undergraduate/Scholarship) [5028]

Earl and Countess of Wessex - World Championships in Athletics Scholarship (Undergraduate/Scholarship) [289]

Founding Fathers Leadership Scholarships (Undergraduate/Scholarship) [12113]

The Gene & John Athletic Fund (Undergraduate/Scholarship) [10850]

Jeff Oliphant Memorial Post-Graduate Scholarship (Postgraduate/Scholarship) [12114]

Terry Mellor Continuing Education Grant (Undergraduate/Grant) [10735]

Mike Niemeyer Memorial Football Scholarship (Undergraduate/Scholarship) [9563]

Mueller Undergraduate Scholarship (Undergraduate/Scholarship) [12115]

Northwest-Shoals Community College Athletic Scholarships (Undergraduate/Scholarship) [8526]

Redlands High School Boy's Varsity Volleyball Scholarships (Undergraduate/Scholarship) [9584]

Atmospheric science (See also Meteorology)

CASFM-Ben Urbonas Scholarship *(Graduate/Scholarship)* [3524]

EPP/MSI Undergraduate Scholarship Program (USP) *(Undergraduate/Scholarship)* [11303]

GWS Scholarship Program *(Undergraduate, Graduate/Scholarship)* [165]

NOAA Graduate Sciences Scholarships *(Graduate/Scholarship)* [11305]

U.S. Air Force ROTC High School Scholarship - Type 1 *(High School/Scholarship)* [11282]

Audiology (See Speech and language pathology/audiology)

Australian studies (See Area and ethnic studies)

Automotive technology

AIA and the Global Automotive Aftermarket Symposium Scholarships *(Undergraduate/Scholarship)* [2357]

AmericanMuscle's Student Scholarship Program *(College, University/Scholarship)* [1681]

ISA Aerospace Industries Division - William H. Atkinson Scholarships *(Graduate, Undergraduate/Scholarship)* [6085]

Auto Body Technician Certificate Scholarship *(Graduate/Scholarship)* [9884]

Automotive Technician Scholarship Program *(Undergraduate/Scholarship)* [7160]

Automotive Women's Alliance Foundation Scholarships *(Undergraduate/Scholarship)* [2366]

Tom Babcox Memorial Scholarships *(Professional development/Scholarship)* [2351]

Bob and Dawn Hardy Automotive Scholarship *(Undergraduate/Scholarship)* [6195]

Rob Copeland Memorial Scholarship *(Undergraduate/Scholarship)* [6785]

Florida Automotive Industry Scholarships *(Undergraduate/Scholarship)* [2352]

Friends of Mary Automotive Scholarship *(Undergraduate/Scholarship)* [10052]

Hans McCorriston Grant *(Undergraduate/Grant)* [2358]

ISA Educational Foundation Scholarship *(Undergraduate, Graduate/Scholarship)* [6086]

ISA Executive Board Scholarship *(Graduate, Undergraduate/Scholarship)* [6087]

ISA Section and District Scholarships - Houston *(Graduate, Undergraduate/Scholarship)* [6088]

ISA Section and District Scholarships - Lehigh Valley *(Graduate, Undergraduate/Scholarship)* [6089]

ISA Section and District Scholarships - Richmond Hopewell *(Graduate, Undergraduate/Scholarship)* [6090]

ISA Section and District Scholarships - Southwestern Wyoming *(Graduate, Undergraduate/Scholarship)* [6091]

ISA Section and District Scholarships - Texas, Louisiana and Mississippi *(Graduate, Undergraduate/Scholarship)* [6092]

ISA Section and District Scholarships - Wilmington *(Graduate, Undergraduate/Scholarship)* [6093]

ISA Technical Division Scholarships - Analysis Division *(Graduate, Undergraduate/Scholarship)* [6094]

ISA Technical Division Scholarships - Chemical and Petroleum Industries Division *(College, University/Scholarship)* [6095]

ISA Technical Division Scholarships - Food and Pharmaceutical Industries Division *(Graduate, Undergraduate/Scholarship)* [6096]

ISA Technical Division Scholarships - Power Industry Division *(Graduate, Undergraduate/Scholarship)* [6097]

ISA Technical Division Scholarships - Process Measurement and Control Division *(Graduate, Undergraduate/Scholarship)* [6098]

ISA Technical Division Scholarships - Pulp and Paper Industry Division *(Graduate, Undergraduate/Scholarship)* [6099]

ISA Technical Division Scholarships - Test Measurement Division *(Graduate, Undergraduate/Scholarship)* [6100]

ISA Technical Division Scholarships - Water and Wastewater Industries Division *(Graduate, Undergraduate/Scholarship)* [6101]

Bob and Mary Ives Scholarship *(Graduate, Undergraduate/Scholarship)* [6102]

Kenneth Rogers Memorial Scholarship *(Undergraduate/Scholarship)* [6805]

The Medallion Fund Scholarship *(Undergraduate/Scholarship)* [8254]

Norman E. and Mary-Belle Huston Scholarship *(Graduate, Undergraduate/Scholarship)* [6103]

Arthur Paulin Automotive Aftermarket Scholarship Awards *(Postgraduate, Undergraduate/Scholarship)* [2359]

Garry Phillips Scholarship *(Undergraduate, University, College, Vocational/Occupational/Scholarship)* [12358]

Ralph Silverman Memorial Scholarship *(Undergraduate/Scholarship)* [2362]

Carl C. and Abbie Rebman Trust Scholarship *(Undergraduate/Scholarship)* [5124]

Richard C. Gauthier CADA Scholarship *(Undergraduate/Scholarship)* [3839]

SEMA Memorial Scholarship and Loan Forgiveness Award *(Graduate, Undergraduate/Loan, Scholarship)* [10720]

SEMA Memorial Scholarships *(Graduate, Undergraduate/Scholarship)* [10721]

Sloan Northwood University Heavy-Duty Scholarships *(Undergraduate/Scholarship)* [2353]

Specialty Equipment Market Association Scholarships *(Graduate, Undergraduate, Vocational/Occupational/Scholarship)* [10722]

University of the Aftermarket Foundation Scholarship *(Community College/Scholarship)* [11428]

Work Ethic Scholarship *(Vocational/Occupational, Two Year College/Scholarship)* [7384]

Aviation (See also Aeronautics)

A. Verville Fellowship *(Professional development/Fellowship)* [10190]

ADMA International Scholarship *(Undergraduate/Scholarship)* [2372]

Advanced Mountain Flight Training Scholarship *(Professional development, Vocational/Occupational/Scholarship)* [12009]

AE Flight Training Scholarship *(Other/Scholarship)* [8400]

AE Jet Type Rating Scholarships *(Other/Scholarship)* [8401]

AE Technical Training Scholarship *(Other/Scholarship)* [8402]

Air Traffic Control Association Full-time Employee Student Scholarship *(Other/Scholarship)* [155]

Air Traffic Control Association Non-employee Student Scholarships *(Undergraduate/Scholarship)* [156]

Aircraft Owners and Pilots Association Scholarships *(Undergraduate/Scholarship)* [174]

Al Conklin and Bill de Decker Business Aviation Management Scholarship *(Undergraduate/Scholarship)* [7732]

Alaska Airlines Pilot Scholarship *(All/Scholarship)* [8741]

AMACESP Student Scholarships *(Undergraduate/Scholarship)* [197]

Association of Flight Attendants Scholarship Fund *(Undergraduate/Scholarship)* [2179]

Donald A. Baldwin Sr. Business Aviation Management Scholarship *(Professional development/Scholarship)* [7733]

UAA Janice K. Barden Aviation Scholarship *(Undergraduate/Scholarship)* [7734]

CAC Gerry Bruno Scholarship *(Graduate, Undergraduate/Scholarship)* [199]

Charles A. Lindbergh Fellowships *(Graduate/Fellowship)* [10191]

Donald W. F. Ching Memorial Scholarship Fund *(Undergraduate, Two Year College, Four Year College/Scholarship)* [5392]

Chuck Peacock Memorial Scholarship *(Undergraduate/Scholarship)* [175]

Col Mary Feik Cadet Flight Scholarship *(Undergraduate/Scholarship)* [3422]

John P. Culhane Professional Pilot Scholarship *(Undergraduate, Vocational/Occupational/Scholarship)* [236]

David Arver Memorial Scholarship *(Undergraduate/Scholarship)* [176]

Johnny Davis Memorial Scholarship *(Undergraduate/Scholarship)* [177]

Arlene Davis Scholarships *(Undergraduate/Scholarship)* [4030]

Frank Der Yuen Aviation Scholarship *(Undergraduate/Scholarship)* [8804]

Distinguished Flying Cross Society Scholarship *(Undergraduate/Scholarship)* [4116]

F. Atlee Dodge Maintenance Scholarship *(Undergraduate/Scholarship)* [237]

Duncan Aviation Scholarship *(Undergraduate/Scholarship)* [178, 4238]

Dutch and Ginger Arver Scholarship *(Undergraduate/Scholarship)* [179]

Eugene S. Kropf Scholarship *(Undergraduate/Scholarship)* [11526]

Field Aviation Co. Inc. Scholarship *(Undergraduate/Scholarship)* [180]

Flight Attendants/Flight Technician Scholarship *(Other/Scholarship)* [7735]

Flight Safety International Bell 206/Bell 407 Scholarship *(Professional development, Vocational/Occupational/Scholarship)* [12010]

Lowell Gaylor Memorial Scholarships *(Undergraduate/Scholarship)* [181]

Lawrence Ginocchio Aviation Scholarships *(Undergraduate/Scholarship)* [7736]

Bud Glover Memorial Scholarships *(Undergraduate/Scholarship)* [182]

Guggenheim Fellowships *(Doctorate/Fellowship)* [10192]

Leon Harris/Les Nichols Memorial Scholarships to Spartan College of Aeronautics & Technology *(Undergraduate/Scholarship)* [183]

Don C. Hawkins Memorial Scholarships *(Undergraduate/Scholarship)* [184]

Commercial Helicopter Pilot Rating Scholarships *(Other/Scholarship)* [5456]

Helicopter Foundation International Maintenance Technician Certificate Scholarships *(Other/Scholarship)* [5457]

Honeywell Avionics Scholarships *(Undergraduate/Scholarship)* [185]

Edward Horne Scholarship *(Advanced Professional/Scholarship)* [8742]

ICAS Foundation / GAMA Scholarship *(College, Undergraduate, University/Scholarship)* [4885]

International Operators Scholarship *(Professional development/Scholarship)* [7737]

James Wisecup Memorial Flight Training Scholarship *(Vocational/Occupational, Advanced Professional/Scholarship)* [12011]

Joseph Frasca Excellence in Aviation Scholarship *(Undergraduate, Graduate/Scholarship)* [11527]

Joshua Esch Mitchell Aviation Scholarship *(Undergraduate/Scholarship)* [5160]

The ISASI Rudolf Kapustin Memorial Scholarship *(Undergraduate/Scholarship)* [6083]

L-3 Communications Avionics Systems Scholarships *(Undergraduate/Scholarship)* [186]

Leadership Conference Scholarship *(Other/Scholarship)* [7738]

Lee Tarbox Memorial Scholarship *(Undergraduate/Scholarship)* [187]

MAF Canada Scholarship Fund *(Undergraduate/Scholarship)* [7419]

Maintenance Technical Reward and Career Scholarship *(Undergraduate/Scholarship)* [7739]

NBCFAE Mamie W. Mallory National Scholarship Program *(Undergraduate/Scholarship)* [7718]

Marty Rosness Student Scholarship *(Other/Scholarship)* [1798]

Bea & George McLeod Scholarship *(Undergraduate, University, College, Vocational/Occupational, Other/Scholarship)* [12347]

Mid-Continent Instruments and Avionics Scholarship *(Undergraduate/Scholarship)* [188]

Monte Mitchell Scholarship *(Undergraduate/Scholarship)* [189]

NAFA Corporate Aviation Business Scholarship *(Undergraduate, Graduate/Scholarship)* [7592]

Michelle North Scholarships for Safety *(Other/Scholarship)* [5458]

Paul A. Whelan Aviation and Aerospace Scholarship *(Graduate, Undergraduate/Scholarship)* [11528]

Bob Reeve Aviation Management Scholarship *(Undergraduate/Scholarship)* [238]

Robinson Helicopter R22/R44 Safety Course Scholarship *(Professional development/Scholarship)* [12012]

Rockwell Collins Scholarships *(Undergraduate/Scholarship)* [190]

Bill Sanderson Aviation Maintenance Technician Scholarships *(Postgraduate/Scholarship)* [5459]

Schedulers and Dispatchers Monetary Scholarship *(Other/Scholarship)* [7740]

Thomas J. Slocum Memorial Scholarships to Redstone College *(Undergraduate/Scholarship)* [191]

Sporty's/Cincinnati Avionics Scholarships *(Undergraduate, Vocational/Occupational/Scholarship)* [192]

Edward W. Stimpson Aviation Excellence Award Scholarship *(Undergraduate, College, University/Scholarship)* [4886]

Tailhook Educational Foundation Scholarship *(Undergraduate, Postdoctorate/Scholarship)* [10907]

Kei Takemoto Memorial Scholarships *(Undergraduate/Scholarship)* [193]

Texas State Technical College Scholarships *(Undergraduate/Scholarship)* [194]

Tom Taylor Memorial Scholarship to Spartan College of Aeronautics & Technology *(Undergraduate/Scholarship)* [195]

U.S. Aircraft Insurance Group Professional Development Program (USAIG PDP) Scholarships *(Undergraduate/Scholarship)* [7741]

Vicki Cruse Memorial Emergency Maneuver Training Scholarship *(Undergraduate/Scholarship)* [8403]

Whirly-Girls Helicopter Add-On Flight Training Scholarship *(Professional development, Vocational/Occupational/Scholarship)* [12013]

Whirly-Girls Jean Tinsley Memorial HELI-EXPO Scholarship *(Professional development, Vocational/Occupational/Scholarship)* [12014]

William M. Fanning Maintenance Scholarship *(Undergraduate/Scholarship)* [7742]

Work Ethic Scholarship *(Vocational/Occupational, Two Year College/Scholarship)* [7384]

Banking (See also Accounting; Finance)

Bank of Canada Fellowship Award *(Doctorate, Other/Fellowship)* [2423]

Norm Bromberger Research Bursary *(Undergraduate, Graduate/Scholarship)* [11672]

Conference of State Bank Supervisors Graduate Schools of Banking and Trust Scholarships *(Graduate/Scholarship)* [3736]

Amy and Tim Dauphinee Scholarship *(Graduate/Scholarship)* [2912]

Alexander Fraser Laidlaw Fellowship *(Graduate/Fellowship)* [2913]

Lemaire Co-operative Studies Award *(Undergraduate, Graduate/Scholarship)* [2914]

Lloyd Houlden Fellowship *(Advanced Professional, Professional development/Fellowship)* [2897]

Wells Fargo American Indian Scholarship Program *(Undergraduate/Scholarship)* [996]

Behavioral sciences

Owen F. Aldis Scholarship Fund *(Doctorate/Scholarship)* [6109]

Applied Behavior Analysis EDU $1,000 Excellence in Practice Scholarship *(Graduate/Scholarship)* [1760]

CASBS Fellowships *(Doctorate, Other/Fellowship)* [3208]

The Christine Mirzayan Science & Technology Policy Graduate Fellowship Program *(Graduate, Postdoctorate, High School/Fellowship)* [7571]

EAPSI Fellowships *(Doctorate, Graduate/Fellowship, Award)* [8067]

Epilepsy Foundation Behavioral Sciences Post-Doctoral Fellowships *(Postdoctorate/Fellowship)* [4419]

Epilepsy Foundation Behavioral Sciences Student Fellowships *(Graduate, Undergraduate/Fellowship)* [4420]

Epilepsy Foundation Research Grants *(Doctorate/Grant)* [4424]

Eleanor Guetzloe Undergraduate Scholarship *(Undergraduate/Scholarship)* [3853]

Hope for Healing Scholarship *(Undergraduate, Graduate, Doctorate, Master's/Scholarship)* [4541]

National Institute of Health Undergraduate Scholarship Program (NIH UGSP) *(Undergraduate/Scholarship)* [11341]

NDSEG Fellowship *(Graduate/Fellowship)* [7834]

Wayne F. Placek Grants *(Graduate, Doctorate/Grant)* [1287]

Russell Sage Foundation's Visiting Scholars Program *(Postdoctorate, Doctorate/Fellowship)* [9774]

Ruth L. Kirschstein Individual Predoctoral NRSA for MD/PhD and other Dual Degree Fellowships *(Doctorate, Master's/Fellowship)* [11337]

SOPHE/ATSDR Student Fellowships in Environmental Health or Emergency Preparedness *(Graduate/Fellowship)* [10513]

SOPHE/CDC Student Fellowship in Unintentional Injury Prevention *(Doctorate, Master's/Fellowship)* [10514]

SOPHE/CDC Student Fellowships in Child, Adolescent and School Health *(Doctorate, Graduate, Master's/Fellowship)* [10515]

Louis Stokes Urban Health Policy Fellows Program *(Other/Fellowship)* [3743]

Student Researcher Award, From the Behavioral Gerontology SIG *(Undergraduate, Graduate/Award)* [2064]

Targeted Research Initiative for Health Outcomes *(Doctorate/Grant)* [4427]

Bible studies (See also Religion; Theology)

CSF Graduate Fellowship *(Graduate/Fellowship)* [3325]

Roland E. Murphy, O.Carm., Scholarship *(Undergraduate/Scholarship)* [3186]

Bilingual and cross-cultural education (See Education, Bilingual and cross-cultural)

Biochemistry (See also Chemistry)

Career Awards at the Scientific Interface (CASI) *(Undergraduate, Postdoctorate, Graduate/Grant)* [2753]

Gladys Anderson Emerson Scholarship *(Undergraduate/Award, Scholarship)* [6152]

Epilepsy Foundation Pre-doctoral Research Training Fellowships *(Graduate/Fellowship)* [4423]

Kris Knudson Memorial Scholarship *(Graduate, Undergraduate/Scholarship)* [11484]

Larson Aquatic Research Support Scholarships (LARS) *(Graduate/Scholarship, Monetary, Recognition)* [1643]

Thermo Fisher Scientific Antibody Scholarship *(Undergraduate, Graduate/Scholarship)* [11016]

Bioengineering (See Engineering, Biomedical)

Bioethics (See Ethics and bioethics)

Biological and clinical sciences (See also Biology)

Arthur and Barbara Pape Endowment *(Graduate/Grant)* [11666]

Raymond B. Bauer Research Award *(Professional development/Award, Grant)* [7322]

Gladys Bruce Scholarship *(Undergraduate/Scholarship)* [12296]

Burroughs Wellcome Travel Fellowships *(Undergraduate, Graduate/Fellowship)* [10531]

C. Lalor Burdick Scholarship *(Graduate, Master's, Doctorate/Scholarship)* [7040]

Charles A. King Trust Postdoctoral Research Fellowship *(Postdoctorate/Fellowship)* [5434]

The Christine Mirzayan Science & Technology Policy Graduate Fellowship Program *(Graduate, Postdoctorate, High School/Fellowship)* [7571]

Daland Fellowships in Clinical Investigation *(Doctorate, Postgraduate/Fellowship)* [1212]

Dr. Biljan Memorial Awards *(Advanced Professional/Award, Grant)* [2980]

EAPSI Fellowships *(Doctorate, Graduate/Fellowship, Award)* [8067]

Endowment Fund for Education Grants *(Undergraduate/Grant)* [2575]

Endowment Fund for Education Scholarships (EFFE) *(Undergraduate/Grant, Scholarship)* [2576]

FASEB MARC Travel Awards *(Undergraduate, Graduate, Postdoctorate/Award)* [10532]

FIU ForEverglades Scholarship *(Graduate, Doctorate, Master's/Scholarship)* [4455]

ForEverglades Scholarship *(Graduate, Master's, Doctorate/Scholarship)* [4456]

International Clinical Research Fellowship *(Graduate/Fellowship)* [4193]

John Marshall Everglades Internship Program *(Undergraduate/Internship)* [4457]

Lewis and Clark Fund for Exploration and Field Research *(Doctorate/Grant)* [1215]

Lola Ellis Robertson Scholarship *(Graduate, Master's, Doctorate/Scholarship)* [7050]

March of Dimes General Research Grants *(Professional development/Grant)* [7026]

Max M. Burger Endowed Scholarship in Embryology *(Graduate, Master's, Doctorate/Scholarship)* [7051]

MDI Biological Laboratory High school Student Summer Research Fellowship *(High School/Fellowship)* [7484]

MDI Biological Laboratory Undergraduate Summer Research Fellowships *(Undergraduate/Fellowship)* [7485]

MGH Department of Psychiatry Global Psychiatric Clinical Research Training Program *(Advanced Professional/Fellowship)* [7139]

National GEM Consortium - PhD Science Fellowships *(Doctorate, Graduate/Fellowship)* [7904]

Basil O'Connor Starter Scholar Research Awards (BOC) *(Professional development/Grant)* [7028]

SFP Mid-Career/Mentor Award *(Other/Grant)* [10331]

Smithsonian Institution Graduate Student Fellowships *(Graduate/Fellowship)* [10205]

Smithsonian Institution Postdoctoral Researcher Fellowships *(Postdoctorate/Fellowship)* [10206]

Smithsonian Institution Predoctoral Student Fellowships *(Doctorate, Postgraduate/Fellowship)* [10207]

Smithsonian Institution Senior Researcher Fellowships *(Professional development/Fellowship)* [10208]

Louis Stokes Urban Health Policy Fellows Program *(Other/Fellowship)* [3743]

UC MEXUS-CONACYT Doctoral Fellowship *(Doctorate/Fellowship)* [11552]

Susan C. Weiss Clinical Advancement Scholarship *(Other/Scholarship)* [10446]

Biology (See also Biological and clinical sciences)

A. Stanley Rand Fellowship Program *(Undergraduate, Doctorate, Postdoctorate/Fellowship)* [10224]

AAA Postdoctoral Fellowship *(Postdoctorate/Fellowship)* [513]

AIST Ohio Valley Member Chapter Scholarships *(Undergraduate/Scholarship)* [2217]

Catherine H. Beattie Fellowships *(Graduate/Fellowship)* [3238, 4858]

The B.O.G. Pest Control Scholarship Funds *(Undergraduate, Graduate/Scholarship)* [2639]

Burroughs Wellcome Fund Collaborative Research Travel Grants (CRTG) *(Doctorate, Postdoctorate/Grant)* [2750]

Career Awards at the Scientific Interface (CASI) *(Undergraduate, Postdoctorate, Graduate/Grant)* [2753]

Graduate and Undergraduate Fellowship Awards *(Doctorate, Graduate, Undergraduate/Fellowship, Award)* [3195]

CNS-UCSB Graduate Fellowships for Science and Engineering *(Postdoctorate/Fellowship)* [11563]

David and Deborah Clark Fellowship *(Graduate/Fellowship)* [8744]

David H. Smith Conservation Research Fellowship *(Postdoctorate/Fellowship)* [10314]

Arnold Arboretum Deland Award for Student Research *(Graduate, Undergraduate/Grant)* [5361]

Charles Dobbins FTA Scholarships *(Undergraduate, Vocational/Occupational/Scholarship)* [4846]

Dr. Edward G. Voss Memorial Scholarship *(Undergraduate/Scholarship)* [11618]

DOE Computational Science Graduate Fellowship (DOE CSGF) *(Doctorate, Graduate/Fellowship)* [6611]

Dole Food Fellowship *(Graduate/Fellowship)* [8745]

Douglas Lake Improvement Association Scholarship *(Undergraduate/Scholarship)* [11619]

Dow Chemical Company Fellowships *(Graduate/Fellowship)* [8027]

E.E. Williams Research Grant *(Master's, Doctorate/Grant)* [5498]

E.I. DuPont Graduate Fellowship *(Graduate/Fellowship)* [8028]

Emily P. Foster Fellowship *(Graduate/Fellowship)* [8746]

F. Christian and Betty Thompson Fellowship *(Graduate/Fellowship)* [8747]

Florence C. Rose and S. Meryl Rose Endowed Scholarship *(Master's, Graduate, Doctorate/Scholarship)* [7042]

Frank R. Lillie Fellowship and Scholarship *(Undergraduate, Graduate/Scholarship)* [7044]

Fred and Avery Test Scholarship *(Undergraduate/Scholarship)* [11620]

Gary and Gussie Williams Scholarship *(Undergraduate/Scholarship)* [11621]

Marian P. and David M. Gates Scholarship for Non-Residents *(Undergraduate/Scholarship)* [11622]

Frank Caleb & Margaret Thompson Gates Student Scholarships *(Undergraduate/Scholarship)* [11623]

George E. Nichols Undergraduate Scholarship *(Undergraduate/Scholarship)* [11624]

Harry Hampton Fund Scholarship *(Undergraduate/Scholarship)* [5266]

Helm Family Scholarship *(Undergraduate/Scholarship)* [9819]

Howard A. Crum Memorial Scholarship *(Undergraduate/Scholarship)* [11625]

Indspire Health Careers Bursary and Scholarships *(Graduate, Undergraduate/Scholarship)* [5774]

Investigators in the Pathogenesis of Infectious Disease *(Doctorate, Postdoctorate/Grant)* [2754]

James L. Plafkin Memorial Scholarship *(Undergraduate/Scholarship)* [11626]

Joel T. Heinen Undergraduate Support Scholarship *(Undergraduate/Scholarship)* [11629]

John and Elisabeth Buck Endowed Scholarship *(Graduate, Postdoctorate/Scholarship)* [7047]

J.P. and Madeline Trinkaus Endowed Scholarship in Embryology *(Graduate, Doctorate, Master's/Scholarship)* [7048]

Julian E. Carnes Scholarship Endowment Fund *(Undergraduate/Scholarship)* [4738]

AACT John Kitt Memorial Scholarship *(Undergraduate/Scholarship)* [538]

Jeffery P. LaFage Graduate Student Research Award *(Master's, Doctorate/Grant)* [4397]

Lakselaget Foundation Scholarship Fund *(Graduate, Undergraduate/Scholarship)* [6635]

Life Sciences Research Foundation Postdoctoral Fellowship Program *(Postdoctorate/Fellowship)* [6851]

Lillian and Murray Slatkin Fellowship *(Graduate/Fellowship)* [8748]

Lowe Family First Summer Student Scholarship *(Undergraduate/Scholarship)* [11630]

Dolphus E. Milligan Graduate Fellowships *(Graduate/Fellowship)* [8029]

MSA Graduate Fellowship *(Graduate/Fellowship)* [7532]

National Association of Biology Teachers BioClub Student Award *(Undergraduate/Scholarship)* [7611]

NDSEG Fellowship *(Graduate/Fellowship)* [7834]

NGC College Scholarships *(Graduate, Undergraduate/Scholarship)* [7900]

NOBCChE Procter and Gamble Fellowships *(Graduate/Fellowship)* [8030]

Northern Scientific Training Program *(Graduate/Scholarship)* [1791]

Research Internships in Science and Engineering (RISE) *(Undergraduate/Internship)* [4065]

Rexford Daubenmire Fellowship *(Graduate/Fellowship)* [8751]

Rob and Bessie Welder Wildlife Foundation's graduate research fellowship *(Graduate, Master's, Doctorate/Fellowship)* [11958]

Jennifer Robinson Memorial Scholarship *(Graduate/Scholarship)* [1792]

Rowe Family Fellowships *(Graduate/Fellowship)* [8752]

Herbert M. Saylor Memorial Scholarship *(Graduate/Scholarship)* [10586]

Schrank Family Scholarship *(Undergraduate/Scholarship)* [11631]

SICB Fellowship of Graduate Student Travel (FGST) *(Graduate/Fellowship)* [10374]

SICB Grants-in-Aid of Research Program (GIAR) *(Graduate/Grant)* [10375]

Eastman Kodak Dr. Theophilus Sorrell Fellowships *(Graduate/Fellowship)* [8032]

STRI Short-Term Fellowships *(Undergraduate, Graduate, Postdoctorate/Fellowship)* [10226]

Thermo Fisher Scientific Antibody Scholarship *(Undergraduate, Graduate/Scholarship)* [11016]

Earl S. Tupper Three-year Postdoctoral Fellowship *(Postdoctorate/Fellowship)* [10227]

UMBS Istock Family Scholarship *(Undergraduate/Scholarship)* [11632]

UMBS Returning Student Award *(Undergraduate/Scholarship)* [11633]

William L. Brown *(Graduate/Fellowship)* [8754]

Biology, Marine

Atlantic Salmon Federation Olin Fellowships *(Graduate/Fellowship)* [2347]

Boyd Lyon Sea Turtle Fund Scholars *(Doctorate, Graduate, Postgraduate/Scholarship)* [6952]

Caswell Grave Scholarship *(Undergraduate, Graduate/Scholarship)* [7041]

Charles H. Bussmann Graduate Scholarship *(Graduate, Undergraduate/Scholarship)* [7068]

Ellis W. Rowe Memorial Scholarship *(Graduate/Scholarship)* [5268]

Dr. Nancy Foster Scholarship Program *(Doctorate/Scholarship)* [8017]

Dr. Nancy Foster Scholarships *(Graduate/Scholarship)* [4695]

Frank Morrell Endowed Memorial Scholarship *(Graduate, Master's, Doctorate/Scholarship)* [7043]

Herbert W. Rand Fellowship and Scholarship *(Undergraduate, Graduate/Scholarship)* [7045]

Horace W. Stunkard Scholarship *(Undergraduate, Graduate/Scholarship)* [7046]

ICRS Graduate Fellowships *(Doctorate, Graduate/Fellowship)* [5976]

International Women's Fishing Association Scholarship Trust *(Graduate/Scholarship)* [6146]

Arthur Klorfein Scholarship and Fellowship Fund *(Undergraduate, Graduate/Scholarship)* [7049]

Link Foundation/Smithsonian Graduate Fellowships in Marine Science *(Graduate/Fellowship)* [10201]

Marine Technology Society ROV Scholarship (MTS ROV) *(Undergraduate, Graduate/Scholarship)* [7069]

MASNA Student Scholarships *(Undergraduate, Graduate/Scholarship)* [7036]

MBL Pioneers Fund *(Undergraduate, Graduate/Scholarship)* [7052]

Milton L. Shifman Endowed Scholarship *(Graduate, Undergraduate/Scholarship)* [7053]

The MTS Student Scholarship for Graduate Students *(Graduate/Scholarship)* [7070]

The MTS Student Scholarship for Graduating High School Seniors *(Undergraduate/Scholarship)* [7071]

The MTS Student Scholarship for Two-Year, Technical, Engineering and Community College Students *(Undergraduate/Scholarship)* [7072]

Oceanic Research Group Scholarships *(Graduate, Undergraduate/Scholarship)* [8573]

Our World Underwater Scholarship Society North American Rolex Scholarships *(Undergraduate, Graduate/Scholarship)* [8776]

The Paros-Digiquartz Scholarship *(Graduate, Undergraduate/Scholarship)* [7073]

Pfizer Scholarship Fund *(Undergraduate, Graduate/Scholarship)* [7055]

Ruth Sager Scholarship *(Undergraduate, Graduate/Scholarship)* [7056]

S. O. Mast Founders' Scholarship *(Undergraduate/Scholarship)* [7057]

Thomas B. Grave and Elizabeth F. Grave Scholarship *(Undergraduate, Graduate/Scholarship)* [7059]

William Randolph Hearst Educational Endowment *(Undergraduate, Graduate/Scholarship)* [7060]

Biology, Molecular

Sloan Research Fellowships *(Doctorate/Fellowship)* [10171]

Biomedical engineering (See Engineering, Biomedical)

Biomedical research (See also Medical research)

Biomedical Research Grants *(Postdoctorate/Grant)* [6545]

Donald A. B. Lindberg Research Fellowship *(Doctorate, Graduate/Fellowship)* [7217]

Gilliam Fellowships for Advanced Study *(Postdoctorate, Master's, Graduate/Fellowship)* [5615]

Helen Hay Whitney Foundation Postdoctoral Research Fellowship *(Postdoctorate, Master's/Fellowship)* [12020]

Henry Friesen Awards and Lecture *(Doctorate/Award)* [10265]

HHMI International Student Research Fellowships *(Doctorate/Fellowship)* [5616]

HHMI Medical Research Fellowship *(Undergraduate/Fellowship)* [5617]

Abby and Howard Milstein Innovation Award in Reproductive Medicine *(Advanced Professional, Professional development, Graduate/Grant)* [6329]

Abby and Howard Milstein Reproductive Medicine Research Award *(Advanced Professional, Professional development/Grant)* [6330]

National Institute of Health Undergraduate Scholarship Program (NIH UGSP) *(Undergraduate/Scholarship)* [11341]

NSBRI First Award Fellowships *(Postdoctorate/Fellowship)* [8121]

Pew Latin American Fellows Program in the Biomedical Sciences *(Other/Fellowship)* [9052]

SRF Post-doctoral Fellowships *(Postdoctorate/Fellowship)* [9982]

Young Investigators Achievement Award *(Advanced Professional, Professional development, Graduate/Grant)* [6331]

Biomedical sciences

BMES Graduate and Undergraduate Student Awards *(Graduate, Undergraduate/Award)* [2578]

Career Awards for Medical Scientists (CAMS) *(Postdoctorate/Grant)* [2751]

Ruth L. Kirschstein Individual Predoctoral NRSA for MD/PhD and other Dual Degree Fellowships *(Doctorate, Master's/Fellowship)* [11337]

Saul T. Wilson, Jr. Internship *(Graduate, Undergraduate/Internship)* [11301]

Biophysics (See also Physics)

Career Awards at the Scientific Interface (CASI) *(Undergraduate, Postdoctorate, Graduate/Grant)* [2753]

Grass Fellowships at the Marine Biological Laboratory *(Doctorate, Postdoctorate/Fellowship)* [5205]

Lou Hochberg Awards - University/College Essay Awards *(Undergraduate/Award, Monetary)* [8756]

Lou Hochberg Awards - Thesis and Dissertation Awards *(Graduate/Award, Monetary)* [8757]

Graduate Fellowship Program - Peter Verhofstadt Fellowships *(Graduate/Fellowship)* [10002]

Blood banking

Canadian Blood Services Graduate Fellowship Program *(Graduate/Fellowship)* [2920]

Canadian Blood Services Postdoctoral Fellowship Program *(Postdoctorate/Fellowship)* [2921]

Botany

Arkansas Green Industry Association Student Scholarships *(Undergraduate/Scholarship)* [1827]

ASPT General Graduate Student Research Grant Fund *(Master's, Doctorate/Grant)* [1538]

Mary A. Bancroft Memorial Scholarship *(Graduate/Scholarship)* [6372]

California Waterfowl Association College Scholarships *(Undergraduate/Scholarship)* [2842]

Earl Core Student Research Award *(Professional development/Grant)* [10643]

Hannah T. Croasdale Fellowships *(Graduate/Fellowship)* [9144]

CSSA Research Grants Program *(Undergraduate, Graduate, Advanced Professional, Other/Grant)* [2773]

Arnold Arboretum Deland Award for Student Research *(Graduate, Undergraduate/Grant)* [5361]

Richard Evans Schultes Research Award *(Graduate/Award)* [10320]

Garden Club of America Awards in Tropical Botany (GCA) *(Doctorate/Award)* [4859]

Louisiana Agricultural Consultants Association Scholarship *(Graduate, Undergraduate/Scholarship)* [6896]

NGC College Scholarships *(Graduate, Undergraduate/Scholarship)* [7900]

Rob and Bessie Welder Wildlife Foundation's graduate research fellowship *(Graduate, Master's, Doctorate/Fellowship)* [11958]

Tailor Made Lawns Scholarship Fund *(Undergraduate/Scholarship)* [10909]

British studies (See also Scottish studies)

Carl H. Pforzheimer, Jr., Research Grants *(Graduate, Other/Grant)* [6507]

Broadcasting (See also Media arts)

Abe Voron Award *(Graduate/Scholarship)* [2703]

Ann Liguori Foundation Sports Media Scholarship *(Graduate, Undergraduate/Scholarship)* [8366]

APSA Congressional Fellowships for Journalists *(Advanced Professional, Professional development/Fellowship)* [1247]

Atkinson Fellowships in Public Policy *(Professional development/Fellowship)* [2338]

AWSM Broadcasting Scholarship *(Undergraduate/Scholarship)* [2322]

John Bayliss Broadcast Foundation Internship Programs *(Undergraduate/Internship)* [2451]

John Bayliss Broadcast Foundation Radio Scholarships *(Undergraduate/Scholarship)* [2452]

Broadcast Education and Development Program *(Other/Scholarship)* [3526]

George H. Clinton Scholarship *(Undergraduate/Scholarship)* [8837]

APTRA-Clete Roberts/Kathryn Dettman Memorial Journalism Scholarship *(Undergraduate/Scholarship)* [2022]

Joe Durso, Jr. Memorial Scholarship *(Undergraduate/Scholarship)* [7451]

E. Lanier (Lanny) Finch Scholarship *(Undergraduate/Scholarship)* [4923]

Great Falls Broadcasters Association Scholarships *(Undergraduate/Scholarship)* [7452]

Howard L. Green Scholarships *(Undergraduate/Scholarship)* [8273]

Harold E. Ennes Scholarship *(Graduate/Scholarship)* [10285]

Indiana Broadcasters Association College Scholarship Program *(Undergraduate/Scholarship)* [5750]

ISBA Scholarship Program *(Undergraduate/Scholarship)* [5689]

Kansas Association of Broadcasters Scholarships *(Undergraduate/Scholarship)* [6359]

Anna-Maria and Stephen M. Kellen Fellowships *(Professional development/Fellowship)* [809]

Linda Simmons Memorial Scholarship *(Graduate/Scholarship)* [240]

Mary L. Brown Scholarship DMACC *(Undergraduate/Scholarship)* [6161]

Montana Broadcasters Association Broadcast Engineering Scholarships *(Undergraduate/Scholarship)* [7453]

OAB Kids Scholarships *(Undergraduate/Scholarship)* [8575]

OAB Kids Scholarship *(Undergraduate/Scholarship)* [8576]

Oregon Association of Broadcasters Scholarships *(Undergraduate/Scholarship)* [8698]

Walter S. Patterson Scholarships *(Graduate/Scholarship)* [2704]

Rick Brewer Scholarship *(Undergraduate/Scholarship)* [11207]

Robert D. Greenberg Scholarship *(Graduate, Other/Scholarship)* [10286]

SBE/Ennes Youth Scholarships *(Graduate/Scholarship)* [10287]

Helen J. Sioussat/Fay Wells Scholarships *(Graduate/Scholarship)* [2705]

Stephen Gates Memorial Scholarship *(Undergraduate/Scholarship)* [11211]

Alexander M. Tanger Scholarships *(Graduate/Scholarship)* [2706]

Two Year/Community Broadcast Education Association Scholarship Awards *(Other/Scholarship)* [2707]

Vincent T. Wasilewski Award *(Graduate/Scholarship)* [2708]

Glenn Wilson Broadcast Journalism Scholarship *(Undergraduate/Scholarship)* [8887]

Wisconsin Broadcasters Association Foundation Student Scholarships *(Graduate/Scholarship)* [12117]

Business

10x Digital Marketing Scholarship *(Undergraduate, Graduate/Scholarship)* [4]

280 Group Product Management Scholarship *(Undergraduate, Graduate/Scholarship)* [10]

The ABWA Sunrise Chapter Scholarship Fund *(Undergraduate, Vocational/Occupational/Scholarship)* [3709]

Accenture American Indian Scholarship Fund *(Graduate, Undergraduate/Scholarship)* [993]

AfterCollege Business Student Scholarship *(Undergraduate, Graduate, Doctorate/Scholarship)* [119]

AICPA Accountemps Student Scholarship Award *(Graduate/Scholarship)* [1015]

AICPA Minority Scholarship *(Undergraduate, Graduate/Scholarship)* [1017]

AICPA Two-Year Transfer Scholarship *(Four Year College, Undergraduate/Scholarship)* [1018]

Alaska Aerospace Development Corporation Scholarships *(Undergraduate/Scholarship)* [11433]

Allmand Law Scholarship Contest *(Undergraduate/Scholarship)* [372]

ALPFA Scholarship *(Graduate, Undergraduate, Master's/Scholarship)* [2231]

The Alsandor Law Firm Scholarship Contest *(Undergraduate/Scholarship)* [407]

ARA Scholarship Awards *(Undergraduate/Scholarship)* [2364]

Arkansas Green Industry Association Professional Grants *(Professional development/Grant)* [1826]

ARS Lazarian Graduate Scholarship *(Graduate, Master's, Doctorate/Scholarship)* [1854]

ASBPE Young Leaders Scholarship *(Professional development/Scholarship)* [1390]

ASEE/NSF Small Business Postdoctoral Research Diversity Fellowship (SBPRDF) *(Postdoctorate/Fellowship)* [1442, 8066]

Auto-Pets "Out-of-the-Box Thinking" Scholarships *(All/Scholarship)* [2355]

The Aweber Developing Futures Scholarship *(Undergraduate/Scholarship)* [2389]

BadCredit.orgs Wealth Wise Scholarship *(Undergraduate, Graduate/Scholarship)* [2401]

Bank of America Junior Achievement Scholarship in honor of Donna Champion Fund *(Undergraduate/Scholarship)* [4719]

Bank of Canada Governor's Awards *(Doctorate, Other/Award)* [2424]

Banner Bank Business Scholarship *(Undergraduate/Scholarship)* [6783]

The Dora J. Beattie IBEA Scholarship *(Undergraduate/Scholarship)* [5695]

Benson Law Firm Scholarship Contest *(Undergraduate/Scholarship)* [2477]

Boeing Business Scholarships *(Undergraduate/Scholarship)* [5020]

The Gloria Bousley Graduate Scholarship *(Graduate/Scholarship)* [5696]

Brylak Law Safety Scholarship Contest *(Undergraduate/Scholarship)* [2734]

Buick Achievers Scholarship Program *(Undergraduate/Scholarship)* [4905]

Business Leaders of Tomorrow *(Community College, Four Year College, Graduate/Scholarship)* [7478]

BusinessStudent.com Business Leaders Scholarship *(College, University, Undergraduate, Graduate, Doctorate/Scholarship)* [2765]

C-1 General Youth Scholarship *(Undergraduate/Scholarship)* [6940]

C200 Scholar Awards *(Graduate/Scholarship)* [3550]

Canadian Association for Studies in Co-operation Scholarships - Alexander Fraser Laidlaw Fellowship *(Graduate/Fellowship)* [2951]

Canadian Association for Studies in Co-operation Scholarships - Amy and Tim Dauphinee Scholarship *(Graduate/Scholarship)* [2952]

Canadian Association for Studies in Co-operation Scholarships Lemaire Co-operative Studies Award *(Graduate, Undergraduate/Scholarship)* [2953]

Carey Family Scholarship *(Undergraduate/Scholarship)* [7086]

Karin Carton Scholarship *(Graduate/Scholarship)* [4850]

Catrala - Hawaii Scholarship Fund *(Undergraduate, University, Two Year College, Four Year College/Scholarship)* [5388]

C.C.H.R.M.A. Scholarships *(Undergraduate/Scholarship)* [3469]

CEIBS scholarship *(Graduate/Scholarship)* [7724]

Melba Dawn Chiarenza Scholarship Fund *(Undergraduate/Scholarship)* [11946]

The Christine Mirzayan Science & Technology Policy Graduate Fellowship Program *(Graduate, Postdoctorate, High School/Fellowship)* [7571]

Citi/TELACU Scholars Mentoring Program *(Undergraduate/Scholarship)* [10940]

Clark High School Academy of Finance Scholarship *(Undergraduate/Scholarship)* [9394]

Community Bank - Lee Guggisberg Foundation Memorial Scholarships *(Undergraduate/Scholarship)* [9535]

Congressional and Business Leadership Awards *(Undergraduate/Scholarship)* [4837]

Connecticut Mortgage Bankers Social Affairs Fund *(Undergraduate/Scholarship)* [5321]

Cornell/Goodman Scholarship *(Undergraduate, College, University, Vocational/Occupational/Scholarship)* [7093]

Mable B. Crawford Memorial Scholarships *(Undergraduate/Scholarship)* [11444]

Critical Language Scholarships at Summer Institutes. (CLS) *(Graduate, Undergraduate/Scholarship)* [1345]

Francis X. Crowley Scholarship *(Undergraduate/Scholarship)* [8248]

Crush the GMAT Scholarship Program *(Undergraduate, Graduate/Scholarship)* [3926]

Crush the PMP Scholarship Program *(Undergraduate, Graduate/Scholarship)* [3930]

CustomerServ Scholarship *(University/Scholarship)* [3946]

D&A Florida Scholarships *(Undergraduate/Scholarship)* [10678]

David and Sharon Seaver Family Scholarship Fund in Memory of Timothy D. Seaver *(Undergraduate/Scholarship)* [5074]

Kenneth D. and Katherine D. Davis Scholarship *(Undergraduate/Scholarship)* [8842]

Don Debolt Franchising Scholarship Program *(Undergraduate/Scholarship)* [6011]

Delta Faucet Scholarships *(Undergraduate/Scholarship)* [9204]

Denton Scholarship *(Graduate/Scholarship)* [10081]

DeVries Law School Scholarship *(Undergraduate/Scholarship)* [4070]

Discover MBA Loans *(Graduate/Loan, Scholarship)* [4113]

Dr. Ezra Nesbeth Foundation Scholarship *(Undergraduate/Scholarship)* [6213]

Dr. F. Ross Byrd Scholarship *(Graduate/Scholarship)* [11909]

Economic Club of Grand Rapids Scholarship *(Undergraduate/Scholarship)* [5150]

EDC International Business Scholarships *(Undergraduate/Scholarship)* [2940]

Elite Entrepreneurs Scholarship Contest *(Undergraduate, Graduate, High School/Scholarship)* [4369]

Evans Warncke Robinson, LLC Scholarship Contest *(Undergraduate/Scholarship)* [4453]

Evelyn Abrams Memorial Scholarship *(Undergraduate/Scholarship)* [9399]

Harry Feldman Memorial Scholarship *(Undergraduate/Scholarship)* [6290]

Brendan Flores Alumni Leadership Circle Scholarship - Clark High School *(Undergraduate/Scholarship)* [9400]

Florida Education Fund McKnight Doctoral Fellowship *(Graduate/Fellowship)* [4629]

Floto-Peel Family Scholarship Fund *(Undergraduate, Vocational/Occupational/Scholarship)* [5076]

Michael D. Ford Memorial Scholarship *(Graduate, Undergraduate/Scholarship)* [11477]

Forté Fellowships *(Master's/Fellowship)* [4689]

Jan and Glenn Fredericks Scholarship *(Graduate, Undergraduate/Scholarship)* [11478]

Gabe Stepetin Business Scholarship *(Undergraduate, Vocational/Occupational, Graduate, Master's/Scholarship)* [329]

G.E. Lighting Canada Community Leadership Awards *(Undergraduate/Award)* [4345]

Generation III Scholarship *(Undergraduate/Scholarship)* [4285]

Doris Y. and John J. Gerber Scholarship *(Undergraduate/Scholarship)* [11910]

William R. Goldfarb Memorial Scholarships *(Undergraduate/Scholarship)* [1940]

Goldman Sachs/Matsuo Takabuki Commemorative Scholarship *(Graduate/Scholarship)* [8926]

Helen B. and Lewis E. Goldstein Scholarship *(Undergraduate, Graduate/Scholarship)* [6273]

Graybar Canada Award of Excellence Scholarships *(Undergraduate/Scholarship)* [4347]

Garabed, Zabel and Vahe Hachikian Scholarship Grant *(Undergraduate, Graduate/Scholarship)* [1881]

HAESF Professional Internship Program *(Doctorate/Internship)* [5645]

Anna E. Hall Memorial Scholarships *(Undergraduate, Graduate, Doctorate/Scholarship)* [9084]

Chuck Halliday Scholarship *(Undergraduate, University, College, Vocational/Occupational/Scholarship)* [12322]

Harvey Fellows Program *(Graduate/Fellowship)* [7519]

Hekemian Family Scholarship Grants *(Undergraduate/Scholarship)* [1884]

Raymond T. Hoge Scholarship Fund *(Undergraduate/Scholarship)* [10765]

IAAP Wings Chapter Scholarships *(Undergraduate/Scholarship)* [5901]

ICI Business Leadership Scholarship *(Undergraduate, Graduate, Professional development/Scholarship)* [5959]

INKAS Rising Star Scholarship *(University/Scholarship)* [5789]

International Dairy-Deli-Bakery Association's Scholarship for Growing the Future *(Graduate, Undergraduate/Scholarship)* [5988]

International Management Council Scholarship (IMC) *(Undergraduate/Scholarship)* [3681]

Dwight P. Jacobus Scholarships *(Undergraduate/Scholarship)* [2277]

Jet Business Scholarship *(Graduate/Scholarship)* [6267]

Josephine P. White Eagle Scholar *(Undergraduate, Graduate/Scholarship)* [5537]

Kaia Lynn Markwalter Endowed Scholarship *(Undergraduate/Scholarship)* [6804]

Kerrwil's J.W. Kerr Continuing Education Scholarship Awards *(Undergraduate/Scholarship)* [4351]

Marilyn King Scholarship *(Undergraduate, University, College, Vocational/Occupational/Scholarship)* [12333]

Jane M. Klausman Women in Business Scholarships *(Graduate, Undergraduate/Scholarship)* [12421]

Lance Surety College Scholarships *(Undergraduate, Graduate/Scholarship)* [6644]

Paul J. Laninga Memorial Scholarship *(Undergraduate/Scholarship)* [5089]

Las Vegas Chinatown Scholarship *(Undergraduate/Scholarship)* [9409]

League of Latin American Citizens General Electric Scholarships *(Undergraduate/Scholarship)* [6747]

Doreen Legg Memorial Scholarships *(Undergraduate/Scholarship)* [9556]

David C. Lizárraga Fellowship *(Graduate/Fellowship)* [10941]

Logojoy Student Entrepreneur Scholarship *(Undergraduate, Graduate/Scholarship)* [6888]

Margaret G. Johnson and Marge J. Stout Scholarship *(Undergraduate/Scholarship)* [6817]

Martin Walmsley Award for Entrepreneurship *(Graduate/Award)* [8636]

Mas Family Scholarship *(Graduate, Undergraduate/Scholarship)* [7120]

Mill Creek Chamber of Commerce Scholarship *(Undergraduate/Scholarship)* [7393]

Robert E. and Judy More Scholarship Fund *(Undergraduate/Scholarship)* [4599]

Morgan Stanley Tribal Scholars Program *(Undergraduate/Scholarship)* [982]

MPI-WI Founders Grant Program *(Professional development/Grant)* [7241]

NAB Dollars for Scholars $1,000 College Scholarship *(Undergraduate, Graduate/Scholarship)* [8418]

NABA National Scholarship Program *(Graduate, Undergraduate/Scholarship, Award, Monetary)* [7613]

NAFA Corporate Aviation Business Scholarship *(Undergraduate, Graduate/Scholarship)* [7592]

NAIFA West Michigan Scholarship *(Undergraduate/Scholarship)* [5170]

NASE Future Entrepreneur *(Undergraduate/Scholarship)* [7692]

National Technical Honor Society Scholarships *(Professional development/Scholarship)* [2763]

NCAIED American Indian Business Scholarship Program *(Graduate, Master's, Undergraduate/Scholarship)* [7747]

Paul and Ruth Neidhold Business Scholarship *(Undergraduate/Scholarship)* [3689]

Hubert A. Nelson Scholarship Fund *(Graduate/Scholarship)* [4216]

New York Financial Writers' Associations Scholarships *(Graduate, Undergraduate/Scholarship)* [8311]

North American Van Lines Military Scholarship Competition *(Undergraduate/Scholarship)* [8424]

Novak Awards *(Doctorate/Monetary, Award)* [67]

NYFWA Scholarships *(Undergraduate, Graduate/Scholarship)* [8312]

Seth Okin Good Deeds Scholarships *(Undergraduate, Graduate, Community College/Scholarship)* [9283]

Open Society Presidential Fellowship *(Graduate/Fellowship)* [8665]

Pardee Community Building Scholarship *(Undergraduate/Scholarship)* [9419]

Pathways College Scholarship *(Undergraduate/Scholarship)* [8917]

Patriot Education Scholarship Fund *(Undergraduate/Scholarship)* [6994]

Peggy (Kommer) Novosad Scholarship *(Graduate, Postgraduate/Scholarship)* [5173]

Pepperdine University School of Law JD/MBA Endowed Scholarship *(Undergraduate/Scholarship)* [9023]

PHI Research Fund Grant *(Other/Grant)* [9254]

The Thomas R. Pickering Foreign Affairs Fellowship *(Graduate, Undergraduate/Fellowship)* [11346, 12050]

Pignalberi Public Policy Scholarship *(Graduate/Scholarship)* [11489]

Julia T. Pingree Student Scholarship *(Undergraduate/Scholarship)* [8252]

PlasticPlace Young Entrepreneurs Scholarship Award *(Undergraduate/Scholarship)* [9192]

Plumbing-Heating-Cooling Contractors Association Educational Foundation Massachusetts Auxiliary Scholarships *(Undergraduate/Scholarship)* [9205]

Plumbing-Heating-Cooling Contractors Association Educational Foundation Need-Based Scholarships *(Undergraduate/Scholarship)* [9206]

PHCC of Texas Auxiliary and PHCC Educational Foundation funds *(Undergraduate/Scholarship)* [9207]

Progressive Dairy Producer Awards *(All/Grant)* [7826]

Prospanica Scholarship *(Graduate, Undergraduate/Scholarship)* [9360]

Quincy Brown Memorial Scholarship *(Undergraduate/Scholarship)* [9573]

Resilience Action Fund Scholarship *(Graduate/Scholarship)* [4504]

RFDF-MBA Fellowship *(Graduate/Fellowship)* [9707]

RFDF MBA Preparation Fellowships *(Graduate/Fellowship)* [9708]

Richard C. Gauthier CADA Scholarship *(Undergraduate/Scholarship)* [3839]

Rick and Beverly Lattin Education Scholarship *(Undergraduate/Scholarship)* [5103]

Dorothy Worden Ronken Scholarships *(Graduate/Scholarship)* [4042]

Ruth Messmer Scholarship Fund *(Undergraduate/Scholarship)* [10702]

Dale M. Schoettler Scholarship for Visually Impaired Students *(Undergraduate, Graduate/Scholarship)* [9874]

Scotiabank Scholarship *(Undergraduate/Scholarship)* [2426, 2601]

Senator James Gladstone Memorial Scholarship *(Graduate, Undergraduate/Scholarship)* [270]

Senior Leaders & Scholars Fellowship *(Other, Professional development/Fellowship)* [5646]

SGI Business Insurance Diploma Scholarships *(Undergraduate/Scholarship)* [9890]

Pat Shimp Memorial Scholarships *(Undergraduate/Scholarship)* [8879]

A.O. Smith Scholarships *(Undergraduate/Scholarship)* [9208]

Helen D. Snow Memorial Scholarship *(Undergraduate, Graduate, Doctorate/Scholarship)* [9085]

The Frank H. Sobey Awards for Excellence in Business Studies *(Undergraduate/Award)* [10238]

Sodowsky Law Firm Scholarship *(College, University, Undergraduate/Scholarship)* [10570]

The Solano Law Firm Scholarship Contest *(College, University, Undergraduate/Scholarship)* [10576]

Student Entrepreneur Scholarship *(Undergraduate, Graduate/Scholarship)* [5355]

Edward P. Suchecki Family Scholarship *(Undergraduate/Scholarship)* [5109]

Surety and Fidelity Industry Intern and Scholarship Program *(Undergraduate, Graduate/Scholarship)* [10885]

TaskEasy Scholarships for Future Entrepreneurs *(Undergraduate/Scholarship)* [10923]

TechChecks Business Leadership Scholarships *(Undergraduate/Scholarship)* [10931]

Toyota/TELACU Scholarships *(Undergraduate/Scholarship)* [10942]

Jacki Tuckfield Memorial Graduate Business Scholarship Fund *(Doctorate, Graduate, Master's/Scholarship)* [7299]

UAA College of Business and Public Policy Scholarships - American Marketing Association & F.X. Dale Tran Memorial Scholarship *(Graduate, Undergraduate/Scholarship)* [11499]

Undergraduate/Graduate Scholarships *(Undergraduate, Graduate/Scholarship)* [5989]

Vivian M. Kommer Scholarship *(Undergraduate/Scholarship)* [5190]

WASBO Safety, Security and Wellness Grant *(Other/Grant)* [12111]

WASBO Scholarship Program *(Undergraduate/Scholarship)* [11883]

Chancellor's Graduate Fellowship *(Advanced Professional/Fellowship)* [11923]

Washington University Law School Olin Fellowships for Women *(Advanced Professional/Fellowship)* [11924]

Wayne G. Failor Scholarship Fund *(Undergraduate/Scholarship)* [8969]

Wells Fargo Career Scholarship *(Undergraduate/Scholarship)* [11506]

Jerry Wheeler Scholarships *(Undergraduate/Scholarship)* [10625]

Bradford White Corporation Scholarships *(Undergraduate/Scholarship)* [9209]

Wilkinson and Company LLP Scholarships *(Undergraduate/Scholarship)* [12033]

Women In Defense HORIZONS Scholarship *(Graduate, Undergraduate/Scholarship)* [12133]

Xavier University Williams Scholarships *(Undergraduate/Scholarship)* [12231]

Business administration

AACE International Competitive Scholarships *(Undergraduate/Scholarship)* [22]

AAUW Selected Professions Fellowships *(Graduate, Master's, Doctorate/Fellowship)* [35]

African American Network - Carolinas Scholarship Fund *(Undergraduate/Scholarship)* [4715]

American Association of University Women Selected Professions Fellowships *(Other/Fellowship)* [668]

ARS Lazarian Graduate Scholarship *(Graduate, Master's, Doctorate/Scholarship)* [1854]

ASAC-CJAS PhD Research Grant Award *(Doctorate/Grant, Award)* [79]

ASMC National Scholarship Program *(Graduate/Scholarship)* [1520]

Lawrence Bayer Business Administration Scholarships *(Undergraduate/Scholarship)* [11437]

Mark A. Beltz Scholarship *(Graduate, Undergraduate/Scholarship)* [11473]

Bill and Nell Biggs Scholarship *(Undergraduate/Scholarship)* [11508]

Robert & Jean Campbell Scholarship *(Undergraduate, University, College, Vocational/Occupational/Scholarship)* [12299]

Rick Crane Group Real Estate Scholarship Fund *(Undergraduate/Scholarship)* [6786]

Crush the GMAT Scholarship Program *(Undergraduate, Graduate/Scholarship)* [3926]

CTRF Scholarships for Graduate Study in Transportation *(Graduate/Scholarship)* [3134]

Dan M. Reichard, Jr. Scholarship *(Undergraduate, Graduate/Scholarship)* [1299]

Bert & Karen Hadvick Scholarship *(Undergraduate, University, College, Vocational/Occupational/Scholarship)* [12321]

Geordie Hilton Academic Scholarships *(Undergraduate/Scholarship)* [5030]

Conrad N. Hilton Scholarships *(Undergraduate/Scholarship)* [4962]

Graduate Study Fellowship *(Professional development/Fellowship)* [6065]

ISU Networks Scholarship *(Undergraduate/Scholarship)* [5763]

JDBNOW Scholarship *(Two Year College, Undergraduate, Graduate/Scholarship)* [6259]

Ron LaFreniere Business Administration Scholarship *(Undergraduate/Scholarship)* [10057]

Mary Elizabeth Lockwood Beneventi MBA Scholarship *(Graduate/Scholarship, Award, Monetary)* [8098]

Minorities in Government Finance Scholarship *(Graduate, Undergraduate/Scholarship)* [5054]

Native Hawaiian Chamber of Commerce Scholarship *(Graduate, Undergraduate/Scholarship)* [8932]

Osram Sylvania Scholastic Achievement Awards *(Undergraduate/Scholarship)* [4352]

J. L. Phelps Scholarship *(Undergraduate, University, College, Vocational/Occupational/Scholarship)* [12357]

Philips Lighting Continuing Education Awards *(Undergraduate/Scholarship)* [4353]

Ritchie-Jennings Memorial Scholarship Program *(Undergraduate, Graduate/Scholarship)* [2132]

Royal Bank Scholarships *(Undergraduate, Master's, Graduate/Scholarship)* [2600]

Schneider Electric Student Merit Awards *(Undergraduate/Scholarship)* [4355]

Wes Burton Memorial Scholarship *(Undergraduate/Scholarship)* [12097]

The WESCO Student Achievement Award *(Undergraduate/Scholarship)* [4361, 11969]

Urashi Zen Scholarships *(Undergraduate/Scholarship)* [9320]

Business Communications

McAllister Fellowship *(Professional development/Fellowship)* [2072]

Byzantine studies (See also Area and ethnic studies)

Dumbarton Oaks Fellowship *(Doctorate, Graduate/Fellowship)* [4222]

Dumbarton Oaks Junior Fellowship *(Graduate/Fellowship)* [4223]

Dumbarton Oaks Research Library and Collection Bliss Symposium Award *(Undergraduate, Graduate/Award)* [4224]

Dumbarton Oaks Research Library and Collection Graduate Research Workshops *(Undergraduate, Graduate/Fellowship)* [4225]

Dumbarton Oaks Research Library and Collection One-Month Research Stipends *(Doctorate/Monetary)* [4226]

Dumbarton Oaks Research Library and Collection Post-Baccalaureate Media Fellowships *(Professional development/Fellowship)* [4227]

Dumbarton Oaks Research Library and Collection Project Grants *(Doctorate/Grant)* [4228]

Dumbarton Oaks Research Library and Collection Short-Term Predoctoral Residencies Grants *(Undergraduate/Grant)* [4229]

Dumbarton Oaks Research Library and Collection Summer Fellowship *(Graduate/Fellowship)* [4230]

Dumbarton Oaks Research Library and Collection Summer Internships for Harvard Students *(Undergraduate, Graduate/Internship)* [4231]

Dumbarton Oaks Research Library and Collection Post-Doctoral Teaching Fellowships *(Postdoctorate/Fellowship)* [4232]

William R. Tyler Fellowships *(Graduate/Fellowship)* [4234]

Canadian studies (See also Area and ethnic studies)

ALIS Fellowships for Full-time Studies in French *(Undergraduate/Fellowship)* [282]

Canadian Studies Postdoctoral Fellowships *(Postdoctorate/Fellowship)* [3800]

International Council for Canadian Studies Graduate Student Scholarships *(Graduate/Scholarship)* [3801]

Jane Glassco Northern Fellowship *(Professional development/Fellowship)* [5050]

Shastri Scholar Travel Subsidy Grants (SSTSG) *(Graduate, Professional development/Grant)* [10037]

The Kennett Y. Spencer Memorial Scholarship *(Graduate/Scholarship)* [11524]

W. Kaye Lamb Award for the Best Student works *(Undergraduate/Scholarship)* [2701]

Weston Family Awards in Northern Research *(Doctorate, Master's/Award)* [11999]

Cancer (See Oncology)

Cardiology (See Medicine, Cardiology)

Caricature (See Art, Caricatures and cartoons)

Cartography/Surveying

CALS Memorial Scholarship *(Undergraduate/Scholarship)* [3751]

Deed of Award *(Undergraduate/Scholarship, Award)* [2944]

The Arthur and Janet Holzheimer Fellowship in the History of Cartography *(Postdoctorate, Doctorate/Fellowship)* [8373]

MALSCE Memorial Scholarship *(Undergraduate/Scholarship)* [7122]

Nawrot Marek Memorial Scholarship *(Undergraduate/Scholarship)* [9673]

NSPS and AAGS Scholarships *(Undergraduate/Scholarship)* [8119]

Pennsylvania Land Surveyors' Foundation Scholarship *(Undergraduate/Scholarship)* [8962]

Cartooning (See Art, Caricatures and cartoons)

Cave studies

Graduate and Undergraduate Fellowship Awards *(Doctorate, Graduate, Undergraduate/Fellowship, Award)* [3195]

CCF Academic Fellowships in Karst Studies - Graduate *(Master's, Doctorate/Fellowship)* [3192]

CCF Academic Fellowships in Karst Studies - Undergraduate *(Undergraduate/Fellowship)* [3193]

NSS Sara Corrie Memorial Grants *(Professional development/Grant)* [8125]

NSS Conservation Grants *(Advanced Professional/Grant)* [8126]

NSS Education Grants *(Undergraduate/Grant)* [8127]

Ralph W. Stone Graduate Fellowships *(Graduate/Fellowship)* [8129]

Central European studies (See European studies)

Chemical engineering (See Engineering, Chemical)

Chemistry (See also Biochemistry; Electrochemistry)

AACC International Travel Grants *(Advanced Professional, Professional development/Grant)* [540]

AACC Van Slyke Foundation Research Grants *(Professional development/Grant)* [541]

ACS Award for Research at an Undergraduate Institution *(Postdoctorate/Award, Recognition, Grant, Monetary)* [735]

ACS Rubber Division Undergraduate Scholarship *(Undergraduate/Scholarship)* [738]

AESF Foundation Scholarships *(Undergraduate, Graduate/Scholarship)* [7704]

AIST Ohio Valley Member Chapter Scholarships *(Undergraduate/Scholarship)* [2217]

SETAC/EA Jeff Black Fellowship Award *(Postgraduate/Fellowship)* [10324]

The B.O.G. Pest Control Scholarship Funds *(Undergraduate, Graduate, Graduate/Scholarship)* [2639]

Burroughs Wellcome Fund Collaborative Research Travel Grants (CRTG) *(Doctorate, Postdoctorate/Grant)* [2750]

Career Awards at the Scientific Interface (CASI) *(Undergraduate, Postdoctorate, Graduate/Grant)* [2753]

CHF Travel Grants *(Professional development/Grant)* [9971]

CNS-UCSB Graduate Fellowships for Science and Engineering *(Postdoctorate/Fellowship)* [11563]

Arthur C. Cope Award *(Advanced Professional/Monetary, Medal, Grant, Award, Recognition)* [736]

D&A Florida Scholarships *(Undergraduate/Scholarship)* [10678]

DEPS Graduate Scholarship *(Graduate/Scholarship)* [4099]

The William Donald Dixon Research Grant *(Graduate, Undergraduate, Advanced Professional/Grant)* [3011]

DOE Computational Science Graduate Fellowship (DOE CSGF) *(Doctorate, Graduate/Fellowship)* [6611]

Dow Chemical Company Fellowships *(Graduate/Fellowship)* [8027]

Camille Dreyfus Teacher-Scholar Awards *(Professional development/Grant)* [4181]

E.I. DuPont Graduate Fellowship *(Graduate/Fellowship)* [8028]

Gladys Anderson Emerson Scholarship *(Undergraduate/Award, Scholarship)* [6152]

William Robert Findley Graduate Chemistry Scholarship *(Graduate/Scholarship, Award, Monetary)* [8097]

Getty Postdoctoral Fellowship in Conservation Science *(Postdoctorate/Fellowship)* [4956]

Garabed, Zabel and Vahe Hachikian Scholarship Grant *(Undergraduate/Scholarship)* [1881]

Helm Family Scholarship *(Undergraduate/Scholarship)* [9819]

Indspire Health Careers Bursary and Scholarships *(Graduate, Undergraduate/Scholarship)* [5774]

The James Davidson Innovative Student Scholarship *(Graduate/Scholarship)* [10739]

Julian E. Carnes Scholarship Endowment Fund *(Undergraduate/Scholarship)* [4738]

AACT John Kitt Memorial Scholarship *(Undergraduate/Scholarship)* [538]

Larson Aquatic Research Support Scholarships (LARS) *(Graduate/Scholarship, Monetary, Recognition)* [1643]

Imelda *(Graduate, High School/Scholarship)* [3722]

Dolphus E. Milligan Graduate Fellowships *(Graduate/Fellowship)* [8029]

National GEM Consortium - PhD Science Fellowships *(Doctorate, Graduate/Fellowship)* [7904]

NDSEG Fellowship *(Graduate/Fellowship)* [7834]

NOBCChE Procter and Gamble Fellowships *(Graduate/Fellowship)* [8030]

NPSC Fellowship *(Graduate/Fellowship)* [5056]

Ralph H. Potts Memorial Fellowship Award *(Graduate/Award, Fellowship)* [1184]

Lendon N. Pridgen, GlaxoSmithKline - NOBCChE Fellowships *(Graduate/Fellowship)* [8031]

Research Internships in Science and Engineering (RISE) *(Undergraduate/Internship)* [4065]

Science History Institute Travel Grants *(All/Grant)* [9972]

Sloan Research Fellowships *(Doctorate/Fellowship)* [10171]

Eastman Kodak Dr. Theophilus Sorrell Fellowships *(Graduate/Fellowship)* [8032]

Thermo Fisher Scientific Antibody Scholarship *(Undergraduate, Graduate/Scholarship)* [11016]

UAA Ardell French Memorial Scholarship *(Undergraduate/Scholarship)* [11498]

Graduate Fellowship Program - Peter Verhofstadt Fellowships *(Graduate/Fellowship)* [10002]

Child care

Alberta Child Care Association Professional Development Grants *(Professional development/Grant)* [253]

IODE 100th Anniversary Grant *(Other/Grant)* [7758]

Pilot Project Grant *(Professional development/Award, Grant)* [10456]

Child development

AACPDM Student Travel Scholarship *(Professional development/Scholarship)* [438]

ADHD Fellowship *(Postdoctorate/Fellowship)* [6568]

Helen & Orval Couch Memorial Scholarship *(Undergraduate/Scholarship)* [12302]

Huenefeld/Denton Scholarships *(Undergraduate/Scholarship)* [4038]

Mariel Lacasse Scholarship *(Undergraduate, University, College, Vocational/Occupational/Scholarship)* [12336]

Irene Brand Lieberman Memorial Scholarship *(Graduate/Scholarship)* [6298]

Evelyn (Babe) Richards Scholarship *(Undergraduate, University, College, Vocational/Occupational/Scholarship)* [12363]

Children's literature (See Literature, Children's)

Chinese studies (See also Area and ethnic studies)

Comparative Perspectives on Chinese Culture and Society Grantees *(Doctorate/Grant)* [823]

Louise Wallace Hackney Fellowships for the Study of Chinese Art *(Doctorate/Fellowship)* [1191]

Chiropractic medicine (See Medicine, Chiropractic)

Choreography (See also Dance)

Jerome Robbins Bogliasco Fellowships in Dance *(Professional development/Fellowship)* [2645]

Christian education

Beatitudes Fellowships *(Professional development/Fellowship)* [2458]

Chester H. Bruce Memorial Scholarship *(Undergraduate/Scholarship)* [8836]

Doris W. Frey Memorial Scholarship Fund *(Graduate/Scholarship)* [10681]

FCSLA Seminary or Diaconate or Religious Life Scholarships *(Graduate/Scholarship)* [4577]

Lewis B. Barber Memorial Scholarship Fund *(Undergraduate/Scholarship)* [10695]

Louisville Institute Dissertation Fellowships (DF) *(Doctorate/Fellowship)* [6912]

Louisville Institute Project Grant for Researchers (PGR) *(Doctorate/Grant)* [6913]

Louisville Institute Sabbatical Grants for Researchers (SGR) *(Doctorate/Grant)* [6914]

Louisville Institute's First Book Grant Program for Minority Scholars (FBM) *(Doctorate/Grant)* [6915]

Trinity Education Foundation Seminary Scholarship *(Graduate/Scholarship)* [11112]

Church occupations (See Religion)

Cinema

William A. Fraker Student Heritage Awards *(Graduate, Undergraduate/Award)* [1396]

Gerald Pratley Award *(Doctorate, Graduate/Scholarship)* [2089]

Civil engineering (See Engineering, Civil)

Civil rights

CCLA Summer Legal Volunteer Opportunities for Law Students and Law Graduates *(Graduate, Undergraduate/Internship)* [2948]

Bernard Chernos Essay Contest *(High School/Prize)* [2949]

Christiane Cook Memorial Scholarship *(Undergraduate/Scholarship)* [749]

Kalmen Kaplansky Scholarships in Economic and Social Rights *(Graduate/Scholarship)* [4138]

MALDEF Dream Act Student Activist Scholarships *(Undergraduate, Graduate/Scholarship)* [7290]

The Robert Masur Fellowship in Civil Liberties *(Undergraduate/Fellowship)* [11160]

NARAL Pro-Choice America Development Internships *(Undergraduate, Graduate, Professional development/Internship)* [7551]

NARAL Summer Intership Program *(Undergraduate, Graduate, Professional development/Internship)* [7552]

Reverend H. John and Asako Yamashita Memorial Scholarship *(Graduate/Scholarship)* [6254]

Minoru Yasui Memorial Scholarship *(Graduate/Scholarship)* [6255]

Classical music (See Music, Classical)

Classical studies (See also Area and ethnic studies)

Arthur Patch McKinlay Scholarship *(Graduate, Undergraduate/Scholarship)* [753]

Desmond Conacher Scholarship *(Graduate/Scholarship)* [10259]

Glenn Knudsvig Memorial Scholarships *(Graduate, Undergraduate/Scholarship)* [754]

Minority Scholarship in Classics and Classical Archaeology *(Undergraduate/Fellowship)* [10311]

Ed Phinney Commemorative Scholarships *(Graduate, Undergraduate/Scholarship)* [755]

Clair Shirey Scholarships *(Undergraduate/Scholarship)* [11464]

Dr. Brent Slobodin Memorial Scholarship in the Humanities *(Undergraduate, Graduate, University, College/Scholarship)* [12371]

Clinical laboratory sciences

AACPDM Transformative Practice Grant Award *(Professional development/Grant)* [439]

Alpha Mu Tau Undergraduate Scholarships *(Undergraduate/Scholarship, Monetary)* [1398]

Luis W. Alvarez Postdoctoral Fellowships in Computational Science *(Doctorate/Fellowship)* [6735]

Lawrence Fellowship *(Doctorate/Fellowship)* [11321]

Dorothy Morrison Undergraduate Scholarships *(Undergraduate/Scholarship, Monetary)* [1400]

Clinical sciences (See Biological and clinical sciences)

Commercial design (See Design)

Communications

AFCEA War Veterans Scholarships (Undergraduate/ Scholarship) [105]

Ameel J. Fisher Scholarship (Undergraduate/Scholarship) [11174]

American Speech Language Hearing Foundation Clinical Research Grant (Doctorate/Grant) [1595]

American Speech Language Hearing Foundation Endowed Scholarships (Graduate, Master's, Doctorate/Scholarship) [1596]

American Speech Language Hearing Foundation General Scholarships (Graduate, Master's, Doctorate/Scholarship) [1597]

American Speech Language Hearing Foundation International Student Scholarship (Graduate, Master's, Doctorate/Scholarship) [1598]

American Speech Language Hearing Foundation Minority Student Scholarship (Graduate, Master's, Doctorate/Scholarship) [1599]

American Speech Language Hearing Foundation Scholarship for Student with A Disability (Graduate, Master's, Doctorate/Scholarship) [1600]

Ann Liguori Foundation Sports Media Scholarship (Graduate, Undergraduate/Scholarship) [8366]

APC High School Scholarship (Graduate/Scholarship) [84]

Applied Urban Communication Research Grants (Professional development/Grant) [4270]

APSA-MCI Communications Congressional Fellowship (Advanced Professional, Professional development, Postdoctorate/Fellowship) [1250]

Ardis Kipp Cohoon Scholarship (Undergraduate/ Scholarship) [11175]

ASHFoundation New Century Scholars Doctoral Scholarship (Doctorate/Scholarship) [1601]

ASHFoundation New Century Scholars Research Grant (Doctorate/Grant) [1602]

ASHFoundation Speech Science Research Grant (Doctorate/Grant) [1605]

ASHFoundation Student Research Grant in Audiology (Doctorate/Grant) [1606]

ASHFoundation Student Research Grant in Early Childhood Language Development (Doctorate, Master's/Grant) [1607]

The Aweber Developing Futures Scholarship (Undergraduate/Scholarship) [2389]

Francis Warren Baker Memorial Scholarships (Undergraduate/Scholarship) [10094]

Jim Batten Community Newspaper Internship (Undergraduate/Internship) [11177]

Beaverbrook Media at McGill Student Paper Prize (Undergraduate/Prize) [2955]

The Bert Saperstein Communication Scholarship Fund (Undergraduate/Scholarship) [2490]

Bob Quincy Scholarship (Undergraduate/Scholarship) [11178]

James M. Brahney Scholarship (Professional development/Scholarship) [5729]

Lieutenant General Douglas D. Buchholz Memorial Scholarship (Undergraduate/Scholarship) [106]

CCAE Ontario Regional Chapter Scholarship (Advanced Professional, Professional development/Scholarship) [6742]

CEJIL Communications Internships (Professional development, Graduate/Internship) [3230]

Charles McCorkle Hauser Scholarship (Undergraduate/Scholarship) [11179]

Chuck Pezzano Scholarship (College, Graduate/ Scholarship) [5955]

George H. Clinton Scholarship (Undergraduate/ Scholarship) [8837]

The Irving W. Cook WA0CGS Scholarship (Undergraduate/Scholarship) [1936]

The Charles Clarke Cordle Memorial Scholarship (Undergraduate/Scholarship) [1937]

CUPRAP Communications Internship Award for Students of Color (Undergraduate/Award) [3518]

David Julian Whichard Scholarship (Undergraduate/ Scholarship) [11180]

Don and Barbara Curtis Excellence Fund for Extra-curricular Activities (Undergraduate/Scholarship) [11181]

The Harold K. Douthit Scholarship (Undergraduate/ Scholarship) [8580]

ECA Centennial Scholarships (Master's, Doctorate/ Scholarship) [4271]

Edward Heywood Megson Scholarship (Undergraduate/Scholarship) [11183]

Edward Jackson International Travel Award (Undergraduate/Award) [11184]

Elton Casey Scholarship (Undergraduate/Scholarship) [11185]

Erwin Potts Scholarship (Undergraduate/Scholarship) [11186]

Reese Felts Scholarships (Undergraduate/Scholarship) [11187]

The Charles N. Fisher Memorial Scholarship (Undergraduate/Scholarship) [1939]

Florida Outdoor Writers Association Scholarships (FOWA) (Undergraduate/Scholarship) [4644]

Joy Gibson MATC Cohort Award (Undergraduate/ Scholarship) [11188]

Keith Gilmore Foundation - Diploma Scholarships (Other/Scholarship) [4970]

Keith Gilmore Foundation - Postgraduate Scholarships (Postgraduate/Scholarship) [4971]

Keith Gilmore Foundation - Undergraduate Scholarships (Undergraduate/Scholarship) [4972]

GLAAD Communications/PR Internships - New York (Undergraduate, Graduate/Internship) [4983]

GLAAD Spanish-Language and Latino Media Internships - Los Angeles (Undergraduate, Graduate/ Internship) [4984]

GLAAD Youth Issues Internships - New York (Undergraduate, Graduate/Internship) [4985]

Glenn Keever Scholarship (Undergraduate/Scholarship) [11189]

The Paul and Helen L. Grauer Scholarships (Undergraduate/Scholarship) [1941]

Howard L. Green Scholarships (Undergraduate/ Scholarship) [8273]

HAESF Professional Internship Program (Doctorate/ Internship) [5645]

Harriet Irsay Scholarship (Graduate, Undergraduate/ Scholarship) [1045]

International Foodservice Editorial Council Scholarship (Graduate/Scholarship) [6007]

Iowa Journalism Institute Scholarships (Graduate, Undergraduate/Scholarship) [6167]

James Davis Scholarship (Undergraduate/Scholarship) [11190]

James F. Hurley III Bicentennial Merit Scholarship (Undergraduate/Scholarship) [11191]

Kathryn M. Cronin Scholarship (Undergraduate, Graduate/Scholarship) [11192]

Kays Gary Scholarship (Undergraduate/Scholarship) [11193]

The Dr. James L. Lawson Memorial Scholarship (Undergraduate/Scholarship) [1947]

Mackey-Byars Scholarship for Communication Excellence (Undergraduate/Scholarship) [11195]

Margaret A. Blanchard Scholarship (Graduate/ Scholarship) [11196]

Marjorie Usher Ragan Scholarship (Undergraduate/ Scholarship) [11197]

Mas Family Scholarship (Graduate, Undergraduate/ Scholarship) [7120]

The Fred R. McDaniel Memorial Scholarship (Undergraduate/Scholarship) [1948]

The Mississippi Scholarship (Undergraduate/Scholarship) [1950]

NHFA Scholarships (Graduate/Scholarship) [7930]

OAB Kids Scholarship (Undergraduate/Scholarship) [8576]

Ohio Newspaper Association Minority Scholarship (Undergraduate/Scholarship) [8581]

ONWA Annual Scholarship (Undergraduate/Scholarship) [8582]

Palmer Farley Memorial Scholarship (Graduate/ Scholarship) [5277]

Paul B. & Aline Flynn Scholarship Fund (Undergraduate/Scholarship) [10698]

Paul Green Houston Scholarship (Undergraduate/ Scholarship) [11201]

Peter DeWitt Pruden and Phyllis Harrill Pruden Scholarship (Undergraduate/Scholarship) [11202]

Philip Alston Scholarship (Undergraduate/Scholarship) [11203]

Stephen D. Pisinski Memorial Scholarship (Undergraduate/Scholarship) [9436]

Robert Pittman Scholarships-Internships (Undergraduate/Scholarship, Internship) [11204]

Print and Graphics Scholarship Foundation Awards (Graduate, Undergraduate/Award) [9330]

PRSA Diversity Multicultural Scholarships (Undergraduate/Scholarship) [9438]

Quincy Sharpe Mills Memorial Scholarship (Undergraduate/Scholarship) [11205]

Raleigh Mann Scholarship (Undergraduate/Scholarship) [11206]

Richard J. Roth Journalism Fellowship (Graduate/ Fellowship) [8328]

Robert Winchester Dodson Scholarship (Undergraduate/Scholarship) [11208]

Gertrude J. Robinson Book Prize (Professional development/Prize, Award) [2956]

William C. Rogers Scholarship (Undergraduate/ Scholarship) [4937]

Soros Justice Media Fellowships - Track I (Professional development/Fellowship) [8668]

Soros Justice Media Fellowships - Track II (Professional development/Fellowship) [8669]

Sports Internships - Los Angeles (Undergraduate, Graduate/Internship) [4989]

Stephen Gates Memorial Scholarship (Undergraduate/Scholarship) [11211]

Steve Mason Sports Media Scholarship (Graduate, Undergraduate/Scholarship) [7991]

Sutton Scholarship Award (Undergraduate/Award, Scholarship) [10891]

TCAdvance Scholarship (Undergraduate/Scholarship) [11144]

Jim and Pat Thacker Sports Communication Internship (Undergraduate/Internship) [11212]

Tom Bost Scholarship (Undergraduate/Scholarship) [11213]

Trans Issues Internships - New York (Undergraduate, Graduate/Internship) [4990]

Tucker Family Scholarship (Undergraduate/Scholarship) [11214]

Turf and Ornamental Communicators Association Scholarship Program (Undergraduate/Scholarship) [11139]

USGLC Internships - Communications (Undergraduate, Doctorate/Internship) [11368]

The L. Phil and Alice J. Wicker Scholarship (Undergraduate/Scholarship) [1966]

Tom Wicker Award (Graduate/Award) [11216]

Glenn Wilson Broadcast Journalism Scholarship (Undergraduate/Scholarship) [8887]

WTVD Scholarship (Undergraduate/Scholarship) [11217]

Communications technologies

Nortel Institute for Telecommunications Graduate Scholarship (Graduate, Master's/Scholarship) [11706]

Nortel Scholarship (Undergraduate/Scholarship) [11707]

OAS Scholarships for Professional Development - Disaster Communications Management (Professional development/Scholarship) [8732]

OAS Scholarships for Professional Development - Satellite Communications (Professional development/Scholarship) [8734]

Community leadership (See Leadership, Institutional and community)

Computer and information sciences

AAUW Selected Professions Fellowships (Graduate, Master's, Doctorate/Fellowship) [35]

AFCEA Cyber Security Scholarship *(Undergraduate, Graduate/Scholarship)* [103]

African American Network - Carolinas Scholarship Fund *(Undergraduate/Scholarship)* [4715]

AfterCollege Engineering & Technology Student Scholarship *(Undergraduate, Graduate, Doctorate, Master's/Scholarship)* [120]

Air Products and Chemicals, Inc. Scholarships *(Undergraduate/Scholarship)* [2191]

AISES Intel Growing The Legacy Scholarship Program *(Graduate, Undergraduate/Scholarship)* [1001]

AISES Oracle Academy Scholarship *(Graduate, Undergraduate/Scholarship)* [1002, 5044]

AIST Ohio Valley Member Chapter Scholarships *(Undergraduate/Scholarship)* [2217]

Stephanie Ali Memorial Scholarships *(Undergraduate/Scholarship)* [11682]

American Association of University Women Selected Professions Fellowships *(Other/Fellowship)* [668]

The Dora J. Beattie IBEA Scholarship *(Undergraduate/Scholarship)* [5695]

William (Billbo) Boston/Harold Knopp Scholarship *(Undergraduate/Scholarship)* [8833]

Kathi Bowles Scholarships for Women in Technology *(Undergraduate, Graduate/Scholarship)* [2311]

Buck Bragunier Leadership Scholarship *(Four Year College, University/Scholarship)* [1840]

Richard A. Brown Student Scholarship *(Undergraduate/Scholarship)* [10977]

Burroughs Wellcome Fund Collaborative Research Travel Grants (CRTG) *(Doctorate, Postdoctorate/Grant)* [2750]

Career Awards at the Scientific Interface (CASI) *(Undergraduate, Postdoctorate, Graduate/Grant)* [2753]

China and East Asia Google PhD Fellowships *(Doctorate/Fellowship)* [5045]

Cyber Security Scholarship *(College, University, Undergraduate, Vocational/Occupational/Scholarship)* [4315]

CyberCorps (R): Scholarship For Service *(Undergraduate, Graduate, Doctorate/Scholarship)* [11393]

D&A Florida Scholarships *(Undergraduate/Scholarship)* [10678]

Dr. Ezra Nesbeth Foundation Scholarship *(Undergraduate/Scholarship)* [6213]

DOE Computational Science Graduate Fellowship (DOE CSGF) *(Doctorate, Graduate/Fellowship)* [6611]

Dotcom-Monitor Women in Computing Scholarship *(Undergraduate/Scholarship)* [4134]   •

EAPSI Fellowships *(Doctorate, Graduate/Fellowship, Award)* [8067]

Edwin F. Wiegand Science & Technology Scholarship *(Undergraduate/Scholarship)* [9397]

ESA Foundation Scholarship *(Undergraduate/Scholarship)* [4394]

Facebook Fellowship Program *(Doctorate/Fellowship)* [4476]

Faye Lynn Roberts Education Scholarship Fund *(Undergraduate, Graduate/Scholarship)* [10684]

Frank Fong Scholarships *(Undergraduate/Scholarship)* [10267]

Future Digital Marketers Scholarship *(College, University/Scholarship)* [2657]

William R. Goldfarb Memorial Scholarships *(Undergraduate/Scholarship)* [1940]

Google European Doctoral Fellowships *(Doctorate/Fellowship)* [5046]

Google US/Canada PhD Fellowships *(Graduate, Doctorate/Fellowship)* [5047]

Helm Family Scholarship *(Undergraduate/Scholarship)* [9819]

Jeri Hodges Leadership Scholarship *(Professional development/Scholarship)* [10978]

HostingAdvice.com Future Web Developers Annual Scholarship *(Undergraduate/Scholarship)* [5590]

ICS Scholarship *(Undergraduate/Scholarship)* [8518]

Influenster Code Like a Girl Scholarships *(Undergraduate, Graduate/Scholarship)* [5782]

Internet Society Fellowships to the IETF *(Master's, Postdoctorate/Fellowship)* [6150]

(ISC)2 Foundation Information Security Undergraduate Scholarships *(Undergraduate/Scholarship)* [6024]

Jimmy Guild Memorial Scholarship *(Undergraduate/Scholarship)* [6802]

John M. & Mary A. Shanley Memorial Scholarship *(Undergraduate, Graduate/Scholarship)* [10690]

Julian E. Carnes Scholarship Endowment Fund *(Undergraduate/Scholarship)* [4738]

Robert E. Knight Professional Scholarship *(Graduate/Scholarship)* [10979]

Malayalee Engineers Association Scholarships *(Undergraduate/Scholarship)* [7012]

John Mazurek Memorial-Morgex Insurance Scholarship *(Other/Scholarship)* [314]

Microsoft Research Graduate Women's Scholarships *(Graduate/Scholarship)* [7356]

Microsoft Research PhD Fellowships *(Doctorate/Fellowship)* [7357]

MIE Solutions Scholarship Opportunity *(Undergraduate/Scholarship)* [7382]

Morphisec's Women in Cybersecurity Scholarships *(Undergraduate, Graduate/Scholarship)* [7470]

NANOG Scholarship Program *(Undergraduate, Graduate/Scholarship)* [9943]

National GEM Consortium - PhD Science Fellowships *(Doctorate, Graduate/Fellowship)* [7904]

NDSEG Fellowship *(Graduate/Fellowship)* [7834]

Edsel Newman Scholarships *(Undergraduate/Scholarship)* [6830]

Northrop Grumman Engineering Scholars Program *(Undergraduate/Scholarship)* [8498]

NPSC Fellowship *(Graduate/Fellowship)* [5056]

NVIDIA Graduate Fellowships *(Postdoctorate/Fellowship)* [8567]

Paul and Ellen Ruckes Scholarship *(Graduate, Undergraduate/Scholarship)* [917]

PGM Undergraduate Scholarship *(Undergraduate/Scholarship)* [9153]

The PHD Scholarship *(Undergraduate/Scholarship)* [1954]

Public Health Informatics Fellowship Program (PHIFP) *(Professional development, Master's, Graduate/Fellowship)* [11332]

The Ray, NØRP, & Katie, WØKTE, Pautz Scholarship *(Undergraduate/Scholarship)* [1956]

John Riddick Student Grant *(Graduate/Grant)* [7559]

Everett Oscar Shimp Memorial Scholarships *(Undergraduate/Scholarship)* [8878]

Ralph W. Shrader Diversity Scholarship *(Graduate/Scholarship)* [107]

Sloan Research Fellowships *(Doctorate/Fellowship)* [10171]

Henry D. and Ruth G. Swartz Family Scholarship *(Undergraduate/Scholarship)* [5110]

Syncrude/Athabasca University Aboriginal Scholarships *(Undergraduate/Scholarship)* [10902]

Tech Mastery Scholarships *(Undergraduate, Graduate/Scholarship)* [9635]

University of Toronto Accenture Scholarships *(Undergraduate/Scholarship)* [11700]

UPE Scholarship Awards *(Graduate, Undergraduate/Scholarship)* [11765]

VIP Women in Technology Scholarship *(Two Year College, Undergraduate, Graduate/Scholarship)* [11856]

Vision Tech Camps Scholarship *(Community College, Four Year College/Scholarship)* [11854]

Web Design Scholarship *(Undergraduate/Scholarship)* [2665]

Wes Burton Memorial Scholarship *(Undergraduate/Scholarship)* [12097]

Women In Defense HORIZONS Scholarship *(Graduate, Undergraduate/Scholarship)* [12133]

Women Techmakers Udacity Scholarship *(Graduate, Undergraduate/Scholarship)* [5048]

The Frank & Betty Woodhams Memorial Scholarship *(Undergraduate/Scholarship)* [7260]

Ralph Yetka Memorial Scholarships *(Undergraduate/Scholarship)* [11466]

Urashi Zen Scholarships *(Undergraduate/Scholarship)* [9320]

Conservation of natural resources

ABS Student Research Grant *(Graduate/Grant)* [1716]

American Society of Mining and Reclamation Memorial Scholarship Award *(Undergraduate, Community College, College, University/Scholarship, Recognition)* [1522]

Gloria Barron Wilderness Society Scholarship *(Graduate, Undergraduate/Scholarship)* [12031]

CCF Academic Fellowships in Karst Studies - Undergraduate *(Undergraduate/Fellowship)* [3193]

Doris Duke Conservation Fellows Program *(Master's/Fellowship)* [12046]

Kathryn Fuller Science for Nature Fund *(Graduate, Postdoctorate/Fellowship)* [12203]

Getty Conservation Guest Scholars *(Professional development/Grant)* [4953]

Getty Postdoctoral Fellowship in Conservation Science *(Postdoctorate/Fellowship)* [4956]

Kent S. Butler Memorial Groundwater Stewardship Scholarship Essay Contest *(Undergraduate/Scholarship, Award)* [2443]

The Kleinhans Fellowship *(Professional development/Fellowship)* [9495]

Latin American Student Field Research Award *(Graduate/Fellowship)* [1505]

National Geographic Young Explorers Grants *(Advanced Professional/Grant)* [7909]

NCEA Postdoctoral Research Program *(Postdoctorate/Fellowship)* [11360]

Rob and Bessie Welder Wildlife Foundation's graduate research fellowship *(Graduate, Master's, Doctorate/Fellowship)* [11958]

Paul W. Rodgers Scholarship *(Undergraduate/Scholarship)* [5925]

Kenneth W. Russell Memorial Fellowships *(Graduate/Fellowship)* [729]

WDHOF Undergraduate Scholarships in Marine Conservation *(Undergraduate/Scholarship)* [12137]

Worcester County Conservation District Annual Scholarships Program *(Undergraduate/Scholarship)* [12186]

Construction

AACE International Competitive Scholarships *(Undergraduate/Scholarship)* [22]

ACI BASF Construction Chemicals Student Fellowship *(Graduate, Undergraduate/Fellowship)* [782]

ACI Charles Pankow Student Fellowship *(Graduate, Undergraduate/Fellowship)* [784]

ACI Elmer Baker Student Fellowship *(Undergraduate/Fellowship)* [785]

ACI President's Fellowships *(Doctorate, Master's/Fellowship)* [787]

AGC Foundation Outstanding Educator Awards *(Other/Award, Monetary)* [2016]

ASA Graduate Scholarships *(Graduate/Scholarship)* [1385]

Associated General Contractors of Connecticut Scholarships (AGC/CT Scholarship) *(Undergraduate/Scholarship)* [3759]

ACI Baker Student Fellowships *(Undergraduate/Fellowship)* [790]

Beck – O.J. Beck, Jr. Memorial Scholarship *(Undergraduate/Scholarship)* [3464]

Carpenters' Company Scholarship Program *(Undergraduate/Scholarship)* [3175]

Darooge Family Scholarship *(Undergraduate/Scholarship)* [5145]

Lee S. Evans/National Housing Endowment Scholarships *(Undergraduate, Graduate/Scholarship)* [7934]

Herb Adrian Memorial Scholarship Endowment *(Undergraduate/Scholarship)* [4735]

Horch Roofing Trade School Scholarship *(Vocational/Occupational/Scholarship)* [5584]

Saul Horowitz Jr. Memorial Graduate Award *(Graduate/Scholarship, Award)* [126]

Huber Engineered Woods Product Evaluation Scholarships *(Graduate/Scholarship)* [4500]

International Code Council Scholarship *(Graduate/Scholarship)* [4501]

Maryland Building Industry Association, Eastern Shore Chapter Scholarship Fund (Undergraduate, High School/Scholarship) [3574]

National Association of Women in Construction Construction Trades Scholarship (Undergraduate/Scholarship) [7708]

National Association of Women in Construction Founders Undergraduate Scholarship (Undergraduate/Scholarship) [7709]

Nixon Family Scholarship Fund (Undergraduate, High School/Scholarship) [11950]

Pardee Community Building Scholarship (Undergraduate/Scholarship) [9419]

PLCAC Student Award Program (Postgraduate/Award) [9182]

Plan NH's Scholarship and Fellowship Program (Community College, Four Year College, Undergraduate, Graduate, Vocational/Occupational/Scholarship) [9188]

Portland Cement Association Scholarship (Graduate/Scholarship) [4503]

Resilience Action Fund Scholarship (Graduate/Scholarship) [4504]

Herman J. Smith Scholarship (Undergraduate, Graduate/Scholarship) [7935]

Betty Spalton Scholarships (Undergraduate/Scholarship) [2454]

TrustedPros Scholarships (Undergraduate/Scholarship) [11131]

United States Society on Dams Scholarships (Graduate, Undergraduate/Scholarship) [11399]

Vectorworks Design Scholarship (Undergraduate, Graduate/Scholarship) [11796]

Matthew Webster Scholarship (Undergraduate, College, Vocational/Occupational/Scholarship) [12386]

Ted G. Wilson Memorial Scholarships (Undergraduate/Scholarship) [9338]

Work Ethic Scholarship (Vocational/Occupational, Two Year College/Scholarship) [7384]

Consulting

PON Graduate Student Grants (Graduate/Grant) [5368]

PON Next Generation Grants (Doctorate, Postdoctorate/Grant) [5369]

PON Summer Fellowships (Graduate/Fellowship) [5370]

Consumer affairs

Geraldine Clewell Fellowships - Doctoral Student (Graduate/Fellowship) [9107]

Geraldine Clewell Fellowships - Masteral (Graduate/Fellowship) [9108]

Closs/Parnitzke/Clarke Scholarship (Undergraduate/Scholarship) [9109]

Margaret Drew Alpha Scholarship (Graduate/Scholarship) [9110]

Lydia Fohn-Hansen/Lola Hill Memorial Scholarships (Undergraduate, Graduate/Scholarship) [11447]

Genevieve Forthun Scholarships (Undergraduate/Scholarship) [9111]

Mary Weiking Franken Scholarships (Undergraduate/Scholarship) [9112]

Geraldine Clewell Scholarship (Undergraduate/Scholarship) [9113]

Jackman Scholarships (Undergraduate/Scholarship) [9114]

Jean Dearth Dickerscheid Fellowship (Graduate/Fellowship) [9115]

Treva C. Kintner Scholarships (Undergraduate/Scholarship) [9116]

Martha Combs Jenkins Scholarship (Undergraduate/Scholarship) [9117]

Nell Bryant Robinson Scholarship (Undergraduate/Scholarship) [9118]

Phi Upsilon Omicron Candle Fellowships (Graduate, Postgraduate/Fellowship) [9119]

Phi Upsilon Omicron Challenge Scholarships (Undergraduate/Scholarship) [9120]

Phi Upsilon Omicron Diamond Anniversary Fellowships (Graduate/Fellowship) [9121]

Phi Upsilon Omicron Founders Fellowship (Graduate/Fellowship) [9122]

Phi Upsilon Omicron Golden Anniversary Scholarships (Undergraduate/Scholarship) [9123]

Phi Upsilon Omicron Past Presidents Scholarships (Undergraduate/Scholarship) [9124]

Phi Upsilon Omicron Presidents Research Fellowship (Graduate, Master's, Doctorate, Postdoctorate/Fellowship) [9125]

Lucile Rust Scholarships (Undergraduate/Scholarship) [9126]

Margaret Jerome Sampson Scholarships (Undergraduate/Scholarship) [9128]

Lillian P. Schoephoerster Scholarships (Undergraduate/Scholarship) [9129]

Tommie J. Hamner Scholarship (Undergraduate/Scholarship) [9131]

Cooley's anemia

Vern Parish Award (Graduate, Postgraduate, Doctorate/Scholarship) [1088]

Cosmetology

AiryHair Cosmetology Scholarship (Undergraduate, Graduate/Scholarship) [201]

Cosmetic Laser Technician Scholarship (Vocational/Occupational, Professional development/Scholarship) [7980]

Melissa Eleanor Ernest Scholarship (Undergraduate/Scholarship) [6200]

H. Wayne VanAgtmael Cosmetology Scholarship (Undergraduate/Scholarship) [5081]

Joe Francis Haircare Scholarship (Undergraduate/Scholarship) [4811]

Helen F. "Jerri" Rand Memorial Scholarships (Undergraduate, Vocational/Occupational/Scholarship) [3715]

Sally Beauty Scholarships for High School Graduates (High School/Scholarship) [9336]

Salon Supply Store Cosmetology Scholarships (Undergraduate/Scholarship) [9789]

Sue Fleming Memorial Scholarship for Allied Health (Undergraduate/Scholarship) [2787]

Counseling/Guidance

Alano Club Scholarship (Undergraduate, College, University, Vocational/Occupational/Scholarship) [12280]

Dottie Martin Teacher Scholarship (Graduate, Undergraduate/Scholarship) [8437]

Jane Engelberg Memorial Fellowship (JEMF) (Professional development/Fellowship) [8100]

Lullelia W. Harrison Scholarships in Counseling (Graduate, Undergraduate/Scholarship) [12411]

NAJA Scholarship (Graduate/Scholarship) [7664]

OSCA Graduate Student Scholarship Program (Graduate/Scholarship) [8594]

Ross Trust Future School Counselors Essay Competition (Undergraduate/Award, Prize) [834]

TCA Outstanding Graduate Student Award (Graduate/Award) [10981]

Colin Wasacase Scholarship (Undergraduate/Scholarship) [8661]

Crafts

Joan Auld Scholarship (Undergraduate/Scholarship) [3702]

Craft Research Fund Grants (Other/Grant) [3212]

EAIA Research Grants (Other/Grant) [4248]

Piscataqua Region Artist Advancement Grant (Professional development/Grant) [8259]

Worldstudio AIGA Scholarships (Graduate, Undergraduate/Scholarship) [12205]

Creative arts (See Arts)

Creative writing

Arts Foundation of Cape Cod Scholarships (Undergraduate, Vocational/Occupational/Scholarship) [1975]

Jack Kent Cooke Graduate Arts Awards (Graduate/Award) [3819]

Dr. Julianne Malveaux Scholarship (Undergraduate/Scholarship) [7668]

Milton Postgraduate Fellowship (Postgraduate/Fellowship) [3214]

The Reedsy National Creative Writing Scholarship (Undergraduate/Scholarship) [9607]

Eleanor M. Wolfson Memorial Scholarship Fund (Undergraduate/Scholarship) [4607]

Criminal justice

ACJA/LAE Student Paper Competition (Undergraduate, Graduate/Scholarship) [836]

ACJA/LAE Student Scholarship Program (Undergraduate/Scholarship) [837]

ACJA/LAE Student Scholarship Program - Graduate Level (Graduate, Master's, Doctorate/Scholarship) [838]

Affirmative Action Student Scholarship Mini-Grant Travel Awards (Undergraduate, Master's/Grant) [41]

Richard E. Arnason Court Scholarship Program (Undergraduate/Scholarship) [3816]

Brian A. Aselton Memorial Scholarship (Undergraduate/Scholarship) [5316]

Brian Jimenez Memorial Scholarship (Undergraduate/Scholarship) [9533]

Carli Edwards Memorial Scholarship (Undergraduate/Scholarship) [10051]

Robert C. Carson Memorial Bursary (Undergraduate/Scholarship) [287]

Gene Carte Student Paper Competition Awards (Undergraduate, Graduate/Prize) [1419]

Jorge Espejel Contreras IALEIA Scholarship (Undergraduate/Scholarship) [5930]

Correctional Education Association Scholarships (Graduate, Undergraduate/Scholarship) [3841]

Colonel Richard M. Dawson Highway Patrol Scholarship Fund (Undergraduate/Scholarship) [3610]

Libby Deschenes Prize for Applied Research (Undergraduate/Prize) [11989]

Emmett H. Turner Scholarship Fund (Undergraduate/Scholarship) [3617]

Niqui McCown Honor and Memorial Scholarship Fund (Undergraduate/Scholarship) [11949]

Michael Oykhman Criminal Law and Evidence Scholarship (Juris Doctorate, Advanced Professional/Scholarship) [8800]

Minnesota Association County Probation Officers Scholarships (Undergraduate/Scholarship) [7402]

June Morrison Scholarship Fund (Undergraduate/Scholarship) [11990]

NIJ Visiting Fellows Program (Other/Fellowship) [7943]

Ruth D. Peterson Fellowship for Racial and Ethnic Diversity (Doctorate/Fellowship) [1420]

Pi Gamma Mu Scholarships (Graduate/Scholarship) [9160]

Richard McGrath Memorial Fund Award (Undergraduate/Award) [839]

Ritchie-Jennings Memorial Scholarship Program (Undergraduate, Graduate/Scholarship) [2132]

Soros Justice Advocacy Fellowships - Track I (Professional development/Fellowship) [8666]

Soros Justice Advocacy Fellowships - Track II (Professional development/Fellowship) [8667]

Soros Justice Media Fellowships - Track I (Professional development/Fellowship) [8668]

Soros Justice Media Fellowships - Track II (Professional development/Fellowship) [8669]

Stuart/SIM Northern Education Scholarship (Undergraduate, University, College, Vocational/Occupational/Scholarship) [12375]

Tiftickjian Law Firm, P.C. Juvenile Justice Law School Scholarships (Graduate/Scholarship) [11030]

Triple Crown Award (Other/Recognition, Award) [8075]

Miki Vohryzek-Bolden Student Paper Competition (Undergraduate/Prize) [11991]

W.E.B. Du Bois Program (Doctorate/Fellowship) [7944]

Criminology

Canadian Identification Society Essay/Scholarship Awards *(Advanced Professional, Professional development/Award)* [3010]

Robert C. Carson Memorial Bursary *(Undergraduate/Scholarship)* [287]

Gene Carte Student Paper Competition Awards *(Undergraduate, Graduate/Prize)* [1419]

CICC Postdoctoral Fellowship *(Postdoctorate/Fellowship)* [3255]

Libby Deschenes Prize for Applied Research *(Undergraduate/Prize)* [11989]

Edward Foster Award *(Advanced Professional/Award)* [3012]

FSF Student Travel Grant *(Undergraduate, Graduate/Grant)* [4678]

June Morrison Scholarship Fund *(Undergraduate/Scholarship)* [11990]

Ruth D. Peterson Fellowship for Racial and Ethnic Diversity *(Doctorate/Fellowship)* [1420]

Miki Vohryzek-Bolden Student Paper Competition *(Undergraduate/Prize)* [11991]

Criticism (Art, Drama, Literary)

Melba Dawn Chiarenza Scholarship Fund *(Undergraduate/Scholarship)* [11946]

Northwest-Shoals Community College Fine Arts Scholarships - Drama *(Undergraduate/Scholarship)* [8528]

Wendy Y. Wolfson Memorial Scholarship Fund *(Undergraduate/Scholarship)* [4608]

Cross-cultural studies

Edith and Arnold N. Bodtker Grants *(Undergraduate, Graduate/Grant, Internship)* [3968]

IAESTE United States Internships *(Undergraduate/Internship)* [3937]

Culinary arts

The AIWF Scholarship Program *(Graduate, Undergraduate/Scholarship)* [1056]

Alliance of Black Culinarians Scholarships *(Undergraduate/Scholarship)* [9389]

Balestreri/Cutino Scholarship *(Undergraduate/Scholarship)* [841]

James Beard Foundation Scholarship Program *(College, Community College, Undergraduate, Professional development/Scholarship)* [9939]

CANFIT Nutrition, Physical Education and Culinary Arts Scholarships *(Graduate, Undergraduate/Scholarship)* [3561]

Letitia B. Carter Scholarships *(Undergraduate, Advanced Professional/Scholarship)* [9649]

Chaîne des Rôtisseurs Scholarships *(Undergraduate/Scholarship)* [842]

Vickie Clark-Flaherty Scholarships *(Undergraduate/Scholarship)* [8444]

CTC Culinary Arts Scholarship Endowment *(Undergraduate, Vocational/Occupational/Scholarship)* [11162]

Culinary Scholarship (2-year Program) *(Undergraduate/Scholarship)* [3005]

Linda Cullen Memorial Scholarship *(Undergraduate/Scholarship)* [843]

Davidson and Jones Hotel Corporation Scholarship *(Undergraduate/Scholarship)* [8445]

Elizabeth Shafer Memorial Scholarship *(Undergraduate/Scholarship)* [9398]

For the Love of Chocolate Foundation Scholarships *(Undergraduate, Graduate, Professional development/Scholarship)* [4670]

Geri Coccodrilli Culinary Scholarship *(Undergraduate/Scholarship)* [5079]

Marcia S. Harris Legacy Fund Scholarships *(Undergraduate, Advanced Professional/Scholarship)* [9650]

International Dairy-Deli-Bakery Association's Scholarship for Growing the Future *(Graduate, Undergraduate/Scholarship)* [5988]

International Foodservice Editorial Council Scholarship *(Graduate/Scholarship)* [6007]

Stanley "Doc" Jensen Scholarships *(Undergraduate/Scholarship)* [844]

Karl Mehlmann Scholarship *(Undergraduate/Scholarship)* [3530]

Andrew Macrina Scholarships *(Undergraduate/Scholarship)* [845]

Ray and Gertrude Marshall Scholarships *(Undergraduate/Scholarship)* [846]

North Carolina Hospitality Education Foundation Scholarship *(Undergraduate/Scholarship)* [8446]

NC Hospitality Education Foundation Scholarships - Graduate *(Graduate/Scholarship)* [8447]

NC Hospitality Education Foundation Scholarships - High School *(Undergraduate/Scholarship)* [8448]

NC Hospitality Education Foundation Scholarships - Two Year Community or Junior College *(Undergraduate/Scholarship)* [8449]

NCRLA Golden Corral Scholarship *(Undergraduate/Scholarship)* [8450]

NRAEF Scholarship *(Undergraduate/Scholarship)* [9651]

Oklahoma Restaurant Association Scholarships *(Other/Scholarship)* [8612]

Hermann G. Rusch Scholarship *(Other/Scholarship)* [847]

South Carolina Undergraduate Scholarships *(Undergraduate/Scholarship)* [10615]

Spice Box Grants *(Advanced Professional/Grant)* [848]

Charlie Trotters's Culinary Education Foundation Scholarships *(Other, Undergraduate/Scholarship)* [849]

Culture

Andrew W. Mellon Fellowships For Conservation Training Programs *(Graduate/Fellowship)* [10197]

Audrey Lumsden-Kouvel Fellowship *(Postdoctorate/Fellowship)* [8369]

Jenny Panitch Beckow Memorial Scholarship - Canada *(Graduate/Scholarship)* [6283]

Jenny Panitch Beckow Memorial Scholarship - Israel *(Graduate/Scholarship)* [6284]

Stephen Botein Fellowships *(Doctorate/Fellowship)* [485]

Shirley Cheshire Memorial Scholarship Awards *(Undergraduate/Scholarship)* [7756]

Cultural Relations Individual Project Funding *(Professional development/Grant)* [261]

Jenny d'Héricourt Fellowship *(Doctorate/Fellowship)* [487]

Fellowships for Creative and Performing Artists and Writers *(Professional development/Fellowship)* [490]

Fieldwork Fellowship *(Undergraduate, Graduate/Award, Fellowship)* [4449]

Gabriel Dumont College Graduate Student Bursary *(Postgraduate, Master's, Doctorate/Scholarship)* [4236]

IAF Fellowships *(Doctorate/Fellowship)* [5883]

IASC Associate Fellowships *(Doctorate/Fellowship)* [11719]

IASC Doctoral Fellowships - Dissertation *(Doctorate/Fellowship)* [11720]

IASC Doctoral Fellowships - Pre-Dissertation *(Doctorate/Fellowship)* [11721]

IASC Postdoctoral Fellowships *(Postdoctorate/Fellowship)* [11722]

IASC Visiting Fellowships *(Professional development/Fellowship)* [11723]

Indigenous Arts Individual Project Funding *(Professional development/Grant)* [263]

Justin G. Schiller Fellowship *(Doctorate, Postdoctorate/Fellowship)* [492]

Lapides Fellowships in Pre-1865 Juvenile Literature and Ephemera *(Graduate, Postdoctorate/Fellowship)* [493]

Jay and Deborah Last Fellowships *(Doctorate/Fellowship)* [494]

NMNH American Indian Program Fellowships *(Graduate/Fellowship)* [10203]

The Barbara L. Packer Fellowship *(Doctorate, Postdoctorate/Fellowship)* [496]

Kate B. and Hall J. Peterson Fellowships *(Doctorate/Fellowship)* [497]

Margaret B. Ševenko Prize in Islamic Art and Culture *(Doctorate, Graduate/Prize)* [5535]

Smithsonian Minority Awards Program - Visiting Student *(Graduate/Fellowship)* [10209]

U.V.A. Faculty Fellowships *(Professional development/Fellowship)* [11724]

Cystic fibrosis

CCFF Clinical Fellowships *(Doctorate, Graduate/Fellowship)* [4543]

CCFF Fellowships *(Doctorate, Graduate/Fellowship)* [4544]

CCFF Scholarships *(Doctorate, Graduate/Scholarship)* [4545]

Dairy science

DFA Cares Foundation Scholarship Program *(Undergraduate/Scholarship)* [3958]

NMPF National Dairy Leadership Scholarship Program *(Graduate, Master's, Doctorate/Scholarship)* [8013]

Progressive Dairy Producer Awards *(All/Grant)* [7826]

South Dakota Division Scholarships *(Undergraduate/Scholarship)* [7375]

Stark County Dairy Promoters Scholarship Fund *(Graduate/Scholarship)* [10794]

Dance (See also Choreography; Performing arts)

Arts Foundation of Cape Cod Scholarships *(Undergraduate, Vocational/Occupational/Scholarship)* [1975]

Dance Individual Project Funding *(Professional development/Grant)* [262]

Deloris Carter Hampton Scholarship *(Undergraduate/Scholarship)* [9296]

DFA Production Grant *(Professional development/Grant)* [3966]

Peter Dwyer Scholarships *(Undergraduate/Scholarship)* [2872]

James Echols Scholarship Award *(Undergraduate/Recognition, Award, Scholarship)* [2781]

Flamenco Student Scholarship *(Undergraduate, Professional development/Scholarship)* [4614]

Geeta Rastogi Memorial Scholarship *(Undergraduate/Scholarship)* [11757]

Graduate Student Travel Grants *(Graduate, Other/Grant)* [10318]

Grants to Artists *(Advanced Professional/Grant)* [4769]

Mona Gray Creative Arts Scholarship *(Graduate, Undergraduate/Scholarship)* [6306]

Tamara Guttman Memorial Scholarship *(Undergraduate, University, College, Vocational/Occupational/Scholarship)* [12320]

IDTA Freestyle Scholarships *(Other/Scholarship)* [5991]

In-course Scholarships - Chinese Dance Workshop Scholarships *(Undergraduate/Scholarship)* [11693]

Indiana State University Creative and Performing Arts Awards *(Undergraduate/Scholarship)* [5769]

Joanna Townsend Applied Arts Scholarship *(All/Scholarship)* [2129]

John F. Kennedy Scholarship Award *(Undergraduate/Recognition, Award, Scholarship)* [2782]

Caroline H. Newhouse Scholarship Fund *(Professional development/Scholarship, Grant)* [3163]

Study Scholarship for Artists or Musicians *(Graduate, Postdoctorate/Scholarship)* [4066]

Winifred Van Hagen/Rosalind Cassidy Scholarship Award *(Undergraduate, Graduate/Recognition, Award)* [2783]

Data processing (See Computer and information sciences)

Dental hygiene

American Dental Hygienists' Association Institute for Oral Health Research Grants *(Master's/Grant)* [859]

Bailey/Hollister Scholarship (Graduate, Professional development/Scholarship) [8956]
Colgate-Palmolive/HDA Foundation Scholarships (Master's, Postgraduate/Scholarship) [5518]
Dr. Lancelot Brown Dental Scholarships (Undergraduate/Scholarship) [6214]
Dr. Sidney Rafal Memorial Scholarship (Undergraduate/Scholarship) [5324]
Irene Woodall Graduate Scholarship (Graduate/Scholarship) [860]
Ken LaFountaine First Nations Scholarship (Undergraduate/Scholarship) [10056]
National Dental Hygienists' Association Scholarships (Undergraduate/Scholarship) [7839]
Procter & Gamble Professional Oral Health/HDA Foundation Scholarships (Undergraduate/Scholarship) [5519]
IADR David B. Scott Fellowship (Professional development/Fellowship, Award) [5917]
Sigma Phi Alpha Graduate Scholarship (Graduate/Scholarship) [861]
Sycamore Hills Dentistry Scholarship (College, University/Scholarship) [10900]
Dr. Juan D. Villarreal/HDA Foundation Scholarships (Undergraduate/Scholarship) [5520]
Alice Hinchcliffe Williams, RDH, MS Merit Scholarship (Graduate/Scholarship) [11833]
Wilma Motley Memorial California Merit Scholarship (Undergraduate/Scholarship) [862]

Dental laboratory technology

CAMS Summer Research Fellowship (Undergraduate/Fellowship) [3307]
Paul W. Clopper Scholarship Grant for Junior Dental Students (Undergraduate/Scholarship) [5709]
Dr. Lancelot Brown Dental Scholarships (Undergraduate/Scholarship) [6214]
Esther Lim Memorial Scholarships (Undergraduate/Scholarship) [3308]
Procter & Gamble Professional Oral Health/HDA Foundation Scholarships (Undergraduate/Scholarship) [5519]
Ruth Liu Memorial Scholarship (Undergraduate/Scholarship) [3309]
Sycamore Hills Dentistry Scholarship (College, University/Scholarship) [10900]

Dentistry

AACD Dentist Fellowships (Professional development/Fellowship) [446]
AADA Student Spouse Scholarship (Professional development/Scholarship) [357]
AAP Educator Scholarship (Postdoctorate/Scholarship) [472]
AAWD Colgate Research Award (Undergraduate/Scholarship, Award, Monetary) [674]
Henry and Maria Ahrens Charitable Trust Scholarship (Undergraduate, Graduate/Scholarship) [5117]
Allied Dental Student Scholarship Program (Undergraduate/Scholarship) [853]
American Dental Association Dental Assisting Scholarship Program (Undergraduate/Scholarship) [854]
American Dental Association Dental Hygiene Scholarship Program (Undergraduate/Scholarship) [855]
American Dental Association Dental Laboratory Technology Scholarship Program (Undergraduate/Scholarship) [856]
American Dental Association Minority Dental Student Scholarships (Undergraduate/Scholarship) [857]
Army Health Professions Scholarship Program (HPSP) (Professional development/Scholarship) [11288]
AvaCare Medical Scholarship (Undergraduate/Scholarship) [2370]
Bud and Linda Tarrson Fellowship (Professional development/Fellowship) [473]
IADR John Clarkson Fellowship (Postdoctorate/Fellowship) [5913]

American Academy of Periodontology Dr. D. Walter Cohen Teaching Fellowships (Professional development/Fellowship) [474]
Colgate-Palmolive/HDA Foundation Scholarships (Master's, Postgraduate/Scholarship) [5518]
Competitive Research Grants (Graduate/Grant) [555]
DAAD Study Scholarship Awards (Graduate, Undergraduate/Scholarship) [4059]
Deana Kendrick Foundation Scholarship (Undergraduate/Scholarship) [6522]
Discover Health Professions Loans (Graduate/Loan, Scholarship) [4111]
Discover Residency Loans (Graduate/Loan, Scholarship) [4114]
Dr. Lancelot Brown Dental Scholarships (Undergraduate/Scholarship) [6214]
Dr. Mac Scholarship Fund (Undergraduate/Scholarship) [3612]
Dr. Nicholas J. Piergrossi Memorial Scholarship (Undergraduate/Scholarship) [5323]
Dr. Sidney Rafal Memorial Scholarship (Undergraduate/Scholarship) [5324]
Endodontic Educator Fellowship Award (Graduate, Undergraduate/Fellowship) [556]
IADR John Gray Fellowship (Other/Fellowship) [5914]
Hall County Medical Society Scholarship (Undergraduate, Graduate/Scholarship) [5122]
Nicholas S. Hetos, DDS, Memorial Graduate Scholarship (Graduate, Doctorate/Scholarship) [5466]
Howard B. Higgins South Carolina Dental Scholarships (Undergraduate/Scholarship) [4736]
Indspire Health Careers Bursary and Scholarships (Graduate, Undergraduate/Scholarship) [5774]
IOKDS Health Careers Scholarship (College, University, Undergraduate, Graduate, Doctorate/Scholarship) [6050]
Jason Lang Scholarship (Undergraduate/Scholarship) [292]
John M. & Mary A. Shanley Memorial Scholarship (Undergraduate, Graduate/Scholarship) [10690]
Kansas Dental Education Opportunities Program (Graduate/Scholarship) [6362]
Kenhub Scholarship Program (Undergraduate, Postgraduate/Scholarship) [6524]
Murse World Scholarship (Undergraduate, Graduate, Postdoctorate/Scholarship) [7507]
NAAMA Scholarships (Undergraduate/Scholarship) [7598]
IADR Toshio Nakao Fellowship (Other/Fellowship) [5915]
OMSF Clinical Surgery Fellowship (Professional development/Fellowship) [8682]
Procter & Gamble Professional Oral Health/HDA Foundation Scholarships (Undergraduate/Scholarship) [5519]
Resident Research Summit Scholarship (Professional development, Advanced Professional/Scholarship) [8683]
IADR Norton Ross Fellowship (Postgraduate/Fellowship) [5916]
Jeptha Wade Schureman Scholarship Program (Undergraduate/Scholarship) [3724]
Dr. Eugene M. Seidner Student Scholarship Program (Undergraduate, Graduate/Scholarship) [46]
Smile Marketing Dental Scholarship (Doctorate/Scholarship) [10177]
Dr. Kiyoshi Sonoda Memorial Scholarship (Graduate, Master's/Scholarship) [6253]
Sycamore Hills Dentistry Scholarship (College, University/Scholarship) [10900]
Dr. Juan D. Villarreal/HDA Foundation Scholarships (Undergraduate/Scholarship) [5520]
Webb Family Grant (Postdoctorate/Scholarship) [3200]

Dermatology

American Acne and Rosacea Society Mentorship Grant (Professional development/Grant) [480]
International Society Travel Grant (Professional development/Grant) [450]
Maibach Travel Grant (Professional development/Grant) [799]

William Weston Research Award (Postgraduate/Grant) [10457]

Design

ACI Cagley Student Fellowship (Graduate, Master's, Undergraduate/Fellowship) [783]
ACI President's Fellowships (Doctorate, Master's/Fellowship) [787]
Joan Auld Scholarship (Undergraduate/Scholarship) [3702]
Stella Blum Research Grant (Graduate, Undergraduate/Grant) [3843]
Buick Achievers Scholarship Program (Undergraduate/Scholarship) [4905]
CSA College and University Collection Care Grant (Other/Grant) [3844]
CSA Travel Research Grants (Advanced Professional/Grant) [3845]
Adele Filene Student Presenter Grant (Graduate, Undergraduate/Grant) [3846]
ITAA Graduate Student Best Paper Award (Graduate/Award, Monetary) [6129]
Logojoy Student Entrepreneur Scholarship (Undergraduate, Graduate/Scholarship) [6888]
Dorothy L. Maddy Workshop/Seminar Scholarship (Other/Scholarship) [10745]
MJSA Education Foundation Scholarship (Undergraduate/Scholarship) [7024]
Polaire Weissman Fund Fellowship (Graduate/Fellowship) [7279]
Quality Bath.com Scholarship (Community College, College, University, Undergraduate, Graduate/Scholarship) [9453]
Helen Lansdowne Resor Scholarship (Undergraduate, Graduate, Other/Scholarship) [11018]
SOM Foundation Architecture, Design and Urban Design Prize (Graduate/Prize) [10159]
SOM Foundation Travel Fellowships in Architecture, Design and Urban Design (Graduate, Undergraduate/Fellowship) [10161]
Vectorworks Design Scholarship (Undergraduate, Graduate/Scholarship) [11796]
Websauce Web Design Scholarship (Undergraduate/Scholarship) [11954]
Women's Jewelry Association Member Grants (Professional development/Grant) [12163]

Diabetes

Early-Career Patient-Oriented Diabetes Research Awards (Professional development/Award) [6347]
Eli Lilly Graduate Scholarship (Graduate, Postgraduate/Scholarship) [2091]
Innovative Grants-Pilot and Research Tool Grants (Postdoctorate/Grant) [6348]
Advanced Postdoctoral Fellowships (Postdoctorate, Master's/Fellowship) [6349]
Career Development Awards (Professional development, Postdoctorate/Grant, Award) [6350]
JDRF Postdoctoral Fellowships (Postdoctorate/Fellowship) [6351]
The Youth Scholarship Program (Undergraduate/Scholarship) [5725]

Dietetics (See Nutrition)

Disabilities

AACPDM Student Travel Scholarship (Professional development/Scholarship) [438]
AAHD Scholarships (Graduate, Undergraduate/Scholarship) [568]
AAIDD Fellowship (Advanced Professional, Professional development/Fellowship) [577]
American Speech Language Hearing Foundation Clinical Research Grant (Doctorate/Grant) [1595]
American Speech Language Hearing Foundation Endowed Scholarships (Graduate, Master's, Doctorate/Scholarship) [1596]
American Speech Language Hearing Foundation General Scholarships (Graduate, Master's, Doctorate/Scholarship) [1597]
American Speech Language Hearing Foundation Scholarship for Student with A Disability (Graduate, Master's, Doctorate/Scholarship) [1600]

Ethel Louise Armstrong Foundation Scholarships *(Graduate, Master's/Scholarship, Monetary)* [1267]

ASHFoundation New Century Scholars Doctoral Scholarship *(Doctorate/Scholarship)* [1601]

ASHFoundation New Century Scholars Research Grant *(Doctorate/Grant)* [1602]

ASHFoundation Student Research Grant in Audiology *(Doctorate/Grant)* [1606]

BMO Capital Markets Lime Connect Equity through Education Scholarships *(Undergraduate, Graduate/Scholarship)* [6860]

BMO Financial Group Lime Connect Canada Scholarship Program for Students with Disablilities *(Undergraduate, Graduate/Scholarship)* [6861]

BSF Research Grants *(Professional development/Grant)* [2441]

ChairScholars Florida Scholarship Program *(Undergraduate/Scholarship)* [3274]

Deborah Munroe Noonan Memorial Research Fund *(Professional development/Grant)* [5436]

Google Lime Scholarship *(Undergraduate, Graduate, Doctorate/Scholarship)* [6862]

P. Johnson and C. Kolb Memorial Scholarships *(Undergraduate, Graduate, Master's, Doctorate/Scholarship)* [9873]

Katie MacDonald Memorial Scholarships *(Graduate, Undergraduate/Scholarship)* [11273]

Mary Switzer Research Fellowships - Distinguished Fellowships *(Doctorate/Fellowship)* [11312]

NBCUniversal Tony Coelho Media Scholarship *(Undergraduate, Graduate/Scholarship)* [618]

NYCT Paid Graduate Student Philanthropy Fellowships - Health and People with Special Needs *(Graduate/Fellowship)* [8308]

Parkinson Canada Clinical Movement Disorder Fellowship *(Advanced Professional, Professional development/Fellowship)* [8892]

Siobhan Isabella Reid Memorial Scholarships *(Graduate, Undergraduate/Scholarship)* [6754]

Small Grants for Community Projects and Educational Programs *(Other/Grant)* [8262]

Mary Switzer Research Fellowships - Merit Fellowships *(Professional development/Fellowship)* [11313]

Whitaker-Minard Memorial Scholarship *(Undergraduate/Scholarship)* [8886]

Drafting

Anne & Konrad Domes Scholarship *(Undergraduate, University, College, Vocational/Occupational/Scholarship)* [12308]

Drama criticism (See Criticism (Art, Drama, Literary))

Drawing (See also Art; Visual arts)

Yvonne L. Bombardier Visual Arts Scholarship Program *(Master's, Doctorate/Scholarship)* [2651]

Drug abuse (See Substance abuse)

Early childhood education (See Education, Early childhood)

Earth sciences

W.L. Calvert Memorial Scholarships *(Graduate/Scholarship)* [5596]

EERI/FEMA NEHRP Graduate Fellowship in Earthquake Hazard Reduction *(Graduate/Fellowship)* [4250, 11362]

El Dorado County Mineral and Gem Society Scholarship *(Graduate/Scholarship)* [4328]

FIU ForEverglades Scholarship *(Graduate, Doctorate, Master's/Scholarship)* [4455]

ForEverglades Scholarship *(Graduate, Master's, Doctorate/Scholarship)* [4456]

John Marshall Everglades Internship Program *(Undergraduate/Internship)* [4457]

National GEM Consortium - PhD Science Fellowships *(Doctorate, Graduate/Fellowship)* [7904]

NWF Campus Ecology Fellowships *(Graduate, Undergraduate/Fellowship)* [8161]

Paleontological Society Student Research Award *(Graduate, Undergraduate/Grant)* [29]

Research Internships in Science and Engineering (RISE) *(Undergraduate/Internship)* [4065]

Smithsonian Institution Graduate Student Fellowships *(Graduate/Fellowship)* [10205]

Smithsonian Institution Postdoctoral Researcher Fellowships *(Postdoctorate/Fellowship)* [10206]

Smithsonian Institution Predoctoral Student Fellowships *(Doctorate, Postgraduate/Fellowship)* [10207]

Smithsonian Institution Senior Researcher Fellowships *(Professional development/Fellowship)* [10208]

Smithsonian Minority Awards Program - Visiting Student *(Graduate/Fellowship)* [10209]

Student travel awards *(Graduate/Award)* [30]

UC MEXUS-CONACYT Doctoral Fellowship *(Doctorate/Fellowship)* [11552]

East European studies (See European studies)

Ecology (See also Environmental science)

A. Stanley Rand Fellowship Program *(Undergraduate, Doctorate, Postdoctorate/Fellowship)* [10224]

Arthur and Barbara Pape Endowment *(Graduate/Grant)* [11666]

The B. Harper Bull Scholarship Awards *(Graduate, Doctorate, Postgraduate/Award)* [11060]

California Waterfowl Association College Scholarships *(Undergraduate/Scholarship)* [2842]

CTEC Internships *(Undergraduate/Internship)* [1727]

CTEC Scholarships *(Graduate/Scholarship)* [1728]

Abby Marlatt Scholarship *(Undergraduate/Scholarship)* [11740]

Mary and Elliot Wood Foundation Graduate Scholarship *(Graduate/Scholarship)* [4744]

Maude Keisling / Cumberland County Extension Homemakers Scholarship Fund *(Undergraduate/Scholarship)* [3634]

Andrew W. Mellon Foundation Fellowships *(Graduate/Fellowship)* [8749]

NERL Postdoctoral Research Program *(Postdoctorate, Advanced Professional, Professional development/Fellowship)* [11352]

NERRS Graduate Research Fellowship *(Graduate/Fellowship)* [7875]

NGC College Scholarships *(Graduate, Undergraduate/Scholarship)* [7900]

Rob and Bessie Welder Wildlife Foundation's graduate research fellowship *(Graduate, Master's, Doctorate/Fellowship)* [11958]

STRI Short-Term Fellowships *(Undergraduate, Graduate, Postdoctorate/Fellowship)* [10226]

Earl S. Tupper Three-year Postdoctoral Fellowship *(Postdoctorate/Fellowship)* [10227]

Economic history (See History, Economic)

Economics

280 Group Product Management Scholarship *(Undergraduate, Graduate/Scholarship)* [10]

American Enterprise Institute National Research Initiative Fellowships (NRI) *(Professional development/Fellowship)* [872]

American Institute for Economic Research Student Summer Fellowship *(Graduate, Undergraduate/Fellowship)* [1028]

ANSER Graduate Student Awards for Research on Nonprofits and the Social Economy *(Graduate/Award)* [2252]

ARCE Funded Fellowships *(Doctorate, Postdoctorate/Fellowship)* [1336]

ARCE Research Associates Fellowship *(Doctorate, Postdoctorate, Professional development/Fellowship)* [1337]

ARS Lazarian Graduate Scholarship *(Graduate, Master's, Doctorate/Scholarship)* [1854]

ASEE/NSF Small Business Postdoctoral Research Diversity Fellowship (SBPRDF) *(Postdoctorate/Fellowship)* [1442, 8066]

ASMC National Scholarship Program *(Graduate/Scholarship)* [1520]

Association of Government Accountants Graduate Scholarships for Community Service *(Graduate/Scholarship)* [2187]

Association of Government Accountants Graduate Scholarships for Full-time study *(Graduate/Scholarship)* [2188]

Association of Government Accountants Graduate Scholarships for Part-time study *(Graduate/Scholarship)* [2189]

Baltimore Community Fellowships *(Advanced Professional/Fellowship)* [8663]

Bank of Canada Fellowship Award *(Doctorate, Other/Fellowship)* [2423]

Bank of Canada Governor's Awards *(Doctorate, Other/Award)* [2424]

Mark A. Beltz Scholarship *(Graduate, Undergraduate/Scholarship)* [11473]

Business Leaders of Tomorrow *(Community College, Four Year College, Graduate/Scholarship)* [7478]

Calihan Academic Grants *(Graduate, Professional development/Fellowship, Grant)* [65]

Calihan Travel Grants *(Other, Graduate/Grant)* [66]

CDC Steven M. Teutsch Prevention Effectiveness (PE) *(Doctorate/Fellowship)* [11328]

Chopivsky Fellowships *(Graduate/Fellowship)* [11889]

Clark High School Academy of Finance Scholarship *(Undergraduate/Scholarship)* [9394]

Mable B. Crawford Memorial Scholarships *(Undergraduate/Scholarship)* [11444]

CTRF Scholarships for Graduate Study in Transportation *(Graduate/Scholarship)* [3134]

Dan Stewart Scholarship *(Other/Scholarship)* [8433]

Denton Scholarship *(Graduate/Scholarship)* [10081]

Dr. Julianne Malveaux Scholarship *(Undergraduate/Scholarship)* [7668]

Enid Hall Griswold Memorial Scholarship *(Undergraduate/Scholarship, Award, Monetary)* [8096]

FIU ForEverglades Scholarship *(Graduate, Doctorate, Master's/Scholarship)* [4455]

Brendan Flores Alumni Leadership Circle Scholarship - Clark High School *(Undergraduate/Scholarship)* [9400]

ForEverglades Scholarship *(Graduate, Master's, Doctorate/Scholarship)* [4456]

Governor James E. Holshouser Professional Development Scholarship *(Other/Scholarship)* [8434]

Anna E. Hall Memorial Scholarships *(Undergraduate, Graduate, Doctorate/Scholarship)* [9084]

Chuck Halliday Scholarship *(Undergraduate, University, College, Vocational/Occupational/Scholarship)* [12322]

Harkness Fellowships in Health Care Policy and Practice *(Doctorate, Graduate/Fellowship)* [3555]

Harvey Fellows Program *(Graduate/Fellowship)* [7519]

Conrad N. Hilton Scholarships *(Undergraduate/Scholarship)* [4962]

Jack Ervin Economic Development Institute Scholarship *(Other/Scholarship)* [8435]

John Marshall Everglades Internship Program *(Undergraduate/Internship)* [4457]

Kalmen Kaplansky Scholarships in Economic and Social Rights *(Graduate/Scholarship)* [4138]

Lloyd Houlden Fellowship *(Advanced Professional, Professional development/Fellowship)* [2897]

Maricopa County Community College District Scholarships (MCCCD) *(Undergraduate/Scholarship)* [7034]

Mary and Elliot Wood Foundation Graduate Scholarship *(Graduate/Scholarship)* [4744]

Mas Family Scholarship *(Graduate, Undergraduate/ Scholarship)* [7120]

The William P. McHugh Memorial Fund *(Doctorate, Graduate/Grant)* [1338]

Douglas McRorie Memorial Scholarships *(Doctorate, Master's/Scholarship, Award)* [131]

Minorities in Government Finance Scholarship *(Graduate, Undergraduate/Scholarship)* [5054]

MPAC-DC Graduate Policy Fellowships *(Graduate/ Fellowship)* [7517]

NAFA Corporate Aviation Business Scholarship *(Undergraduate, Graduate/Scholarship)* [7592]

National Endowment for the Humanities Fellowship *(Graduate/Fellowship)* [1339]

National Iranian American Council Fellowships *(Graduate, Undergraduate/Fellowship)* [7956]

NGC College Scholarships *(Graduate, Undergraduate/Scholarship)* [7900]

NMPF National Dairy Leadership Scholarship Program *(Graduate, Master's, Doctorate/Scholarship)* [8013]

Novak Awards *(Doctorate/Monetary, Award)* [67]

Diane Olsen Memorial Scholarship *(Undergraduate/ Scholarship)* [11488]

Pi Gamma Mu Scholarships *(Graduate/Scholarship)* [9160]

The Thomas R. Pickering Foreign Affairs Fellowship *(Graduate, Undergraduate/Fellowship)* [11346, 12050]

PlasticPlace Young Entrepreneurs Scholarship Award *(Undergraduate/Scholarship)* [9192]

Doug Purvis Prize *(Other/Prize)* [2885]

Betty Rendel Scholarships *(Undergraduate/Scholarship)* [7886]

Resilience Action Fund Scholarship *(Graduate/ Scholarship)* [4504]

Royal Bank Scholarships *(Undergraduate, Master's, Graduate/Scholarship)* [2600]

Senator James Gladstone Memorial Scholarship *(Graduate, Undergraduate/Scholarship)* [270]

Sloan Research Fellowships *(Doctorate/Fellowship)* [10171]

Helen D. Snow Memorial Scholarship *(Undergraduate, Graduate, Doctorate/Scholarship)* [9085]

The United States Department of State, Bureau of Educational & Cultural Affairs Fellowships *(Graduate/Fellowship)* [1340]

Wells Fargo Career Scholarship *(Undergraduate/ Scholarship)* [11506]

Women In Defense HORIZONS Scholarship *(Graduate, Undergraduate/Scholarship)* [12133]

Editors and editing

Aubespin Scholarships *(Undergraduate/Scholarship)* [801]

Kaiser Media Fellowships in Health Reporting *(Advanced Professional, Professional development/ Fellowship)* [6355]

Eugene C. Pulliam Fellowships for Editorial Writing *(Other/Fellowship)* [10086]

Claudette Upton Scholarships *(Undergraduate/ Scholarship)* [4289]

Education

3M Fellowship Award *(Postdoctorate/Fellowship)* [12214]

Academic Education Scholarship *(Professional development/Scholarship)* [8940]

AECT Foundation Mentor Endowment Scholarship *(Doctorate, Graduate/Scholarship)* [2155]

AECT McJulien Graduate Student Scholarship Award *(Graduate, Doctorate/Scholarship)* [2157]

AERA Fellows Program *(Postdoctorate/Fellowship)* [869]

AERA Minority Dissertation Fellowship in Education Research *(Doctorate/Fellowship)* [870]

AFCEA STEM Teacher Graduate Scholarships *(Graduate/Scholarship)* [104, 7022]

AIEA Presidential Fellows Program *(Undergraduate/ Fellowship)* [2201]

Alberta Teachers Association Doctoral Fellowships in Education *(Doctorate/Fellowship)* [312]

Alberta Teachers Association Educational Research Award *(Other/Scholarship)* [313]

The William Tasse Alexander Scholarship *(Undergraduate/Scholarship)* [4716]

American Quarter Horse Foundation Scholarships *(Undergraduate, Graduate/Scholarship)* [1310]

AMS Teacher Education Scholarships *(Undergraduate/Scholarship)* [1129]

Mike Ardaw Scholarships *(Undergraduate/Scholarship)* [11436]

Art and Dannie Weber Scholarship *(Undergraduate/ Scholarship)* [12061]

ASM Science Teaching Fellowships - Student *(Undergraduate/Fellowship)* [1518]

Barbara Jordan Memorial Scholarships *(Undergraduate, Graduate/Scholarship)* [2300]

The Dora J. Beattie IBEA Scholarship *(Undergraduate/Scholarship)* [5695]

Bertha M. Fase Memorial Scholarship *(Undergraduate/Scholarship)* [5069]

Beta Province Project 2000 Scholarship *(Undergraduate/Scholarship)* [6407]

Thomas M. Blake Memorial Scholarships *(Undergraduate/Scholarship)* [3753]

Richard A. Brown Student Scholarship *(Undergraduate/Scholarship)* [10977]

Gösta Bruce Scholarship Fund *(Other/Scholarship)* [6059]

Burney – Cecil E. Burney Scholarship *(Undergraduate/Scholarship)* [3468]

CAEYC Presidents Education Award *(Graduate/ Award, Scholarship)* [2779]

Robert & Jean Campbell Scholarship *(Undergraduate, University, College, Vocational/Occupational/ Scholarship)* [12299]

Carey Family Scholarship *(Undergraduate/Scholarship)* [7086]

Ben and Vicky Cayetano Scholarship Fund *(Undergraduate, College, University, Two Year College/ Scholarship)* [5389]

CEE Cultural Diversity Grant *(Professional development/Grant)* [7798]

Cengage Travel Award for Teachers of Reading at a Community College *(Professional development/ Monetary)* [3512]

Charles Lee Anderson Memorial Scholarship *(Undergraduate/Scholarship)* [3674]

CHCI Graduate Fellowship Program *(Graduate, Professional development/Fellowship)* [3746]

Maridell Braham Condon Scholarships *(Undergraduate/Scholarship)* [10098]

Bill & Joan Cones Scholarship *(Undergraduate, College, University/Scholarship)* [7090]

Christiane Cook Memorial Scholarship *(Undergraduate/Scholarship)* [749]

Judy Crocker Memorial Scholarship Fund *(Undergraduate/Scholarship)* [4730]

CSSE New Scholar Fellowship (CSSE) *(Professional development/Fellowship)* [10262]

CSSHE Masters Thesis/Project Awards *(Master's/ Award)* [3124]

CSSHE Research and Scholarship Award *(Professional development/Award)* [3125]

Deloris Carter Hampton Scholarship *(Undergraduate/Scholarship)* [9296]

Delta Gamma Foundation Florence Margaret Harvey Memorial Scholarship *(Graduate, Undergraduate/Scholarship)* [914]

Disability Care Center Special Education Scholarships *(Undergraduate/Scholarship)* [4105]

Dr. Stephen J. Fortgang / University of Northern Iowa Chapter Scholarship *(Undergraduate/Scholarship)* [6379]

Donna Gail Scholarship for Chapter Service *(Undergraduate, Graduate, Doctorate/Scholarship)* [6380]

Marusia and Michael Dorosh Fellowship *(Master's, Graduate/Fellowship)* [3027]

Dottie Martin Teacher Scholarship *(Graduate, Undergraduate/Scholarship)* [8437]

EAPSI Fellowships *(Doctorate, Graduate/Fellowship, Award)* [8067]

Ecolab Scholarship *(Undergraduate/Scholarship)* [971]

Erickson Education Scholarship *(Undergraduate/ Scholarship)* [5075]

Helen E. Evans Scholarship *(Undergraduate, College, University/Scholarship)* [7100]

Evelyn Abrams Memorial Scholarship *(Undergraduate/Scholarship)* [9399]

FASSE-International Assembly International Understanding Grants *(Professional development/ Grant)* [7795]

Lee K. Feino Scholarship *(Undergraduate, Graduate/Scholarship)* [7790]

Adrian Fisher Scholarship *(Undergraduate, College, University/Scholarship)* [12316]

Marjorie Gosselin Fitzgerald, Upsilon, Permanently Restricted Scholarship Fund *(Undergraduate/ Scholarship)* [6427]

FREA Scholarship *(Undergraduate/Scholarship)* [4651]

Future Educators Scholarship *(College, University/ Scholarship)* [7491]

William E. "Bill" Gallagher Scholarship *(Undergraduate/Scholarship)* [8847]

The Gates Millennium Scholars *(Undergraduate/ Scholarship)* [5529]

George C. Balch Scholarship *(Graduate/Scholarship)* [11383]

Laverne L. Gibson Memorial Scholarship *(Undergraduate/Scholarship)* [8848]

FAMU Presidential Scholarship - George W. Gore Assistantship Scholarship *(Undergraduate/Scholarship)* [4621]

Graduate Award *(Graduate/Award, Scholarship)* [6854]

Graduate Student Scholar Award *(Graduate/Scholarship)* [9164]

Martha and Oliver Hansen Memorial Scholarships *(Undergraduate/Scholarship)* [6202]

Harriet Irsay Scholarship *(Graduate, Undergraduate/ Scholarship)* [1045]

Eileen Harrison Education Scholarships *(Graduate, Undergraduate/Scholarship)* [5083]

HECUA Scholarship for Social Justice *(Undergraduate, Graduate/Scholarship)* [5506]

Jeri Hodges Leadership Scholarship *(Professional development/Scholarship)* [10978]

Raymond T. Hoge Scholarship Fund *(Undergraduate/Scholarship)* [10765]

Cathy Hopper Memorial Scholarship *(Undergraduate/Scholarship)* [9821]

Huenefeld/Denton Scholarships *(Undergraduate/ Scholarship)* [4038]

IARSLCE Graduate Student Scholarships *(Graduate/Scholarship)* [5937]

IASP Visiting Professor Grant *(Professional development/Grant)* [5943]

IDEC Special Project Grant *(Professional development/Grant)* [5888]

IPPR North Events Internship *(Undergraduate/Internship)* [5854]

Jack Kent Cooke Foundation College Scholarship Program *(Undergraduate/Scholarship)* [3820]

Dwight P. Jacobus Scholarships *(Undergraduate/ Scholarship)* [2277]

JEA Action Research Initiative *(Postgraduate/Grant)* [6303]

Jewish Federation Academic Scholarship *(Graduate, Undergraduate/Scholarship)* [6310]

John Alexander McLean Scholarship *(Undergraduate/Scholarship)* [11022]

Josephine P. White Eagle Scholar *(Undergraduate, Graduate/Scholarship)* [5537]

June Danby and Pat Pearse Education Scholarship *(Undergraduate/Scholarship)* [6203]

Armenag and Armenhooi Kalustian Memorial Grant *(Undergraduate/Scholarship)* [1887]

Gladys Kamakakokalani 'Ainoa Brandt Scholarships *(Graduate, Undergraduate/Scholarship)* [8929]

KDP Huntington Bank Scholarship *(Undergraduate/ Scholarship)* [6384]

KDP International Scholarship Program - President Scholarship *(Undergraduate, Graduate, Doctorate/ Scholarship)* [6385]

Robert E. Knight Professional Scholarship *(Graduate/Scholarship)* [10979]

Kovaluk Scholarship Fund *(Undergraduate/Scholarship)* [11412]

Liela Klinger Kurztman Memorial Scholarship *(Undergraduate/Scholarship)* [6296]

Lee Womack Scholarship (Undergraduate/Scholarship) [7431]

Lex T. Eckenrode Scholarship for PELS (Professional development/Scholarship) [11831]

Lila Fahlman Scholarship (Undergraduate, Graduate/Scholarship) [2960]

Richard Lim Professional Development Scholarship (Advanced Professional, Professional development/Scholarship, Recognition) [6743]

Louise Wachter Wickham Scholarship (Undergraduate/Scholarship) [5092]

Lula Faye Clegg Memorial Scholarship Endowment Fund (Undergraduate/Scholarship) [4743]

James Madison Foundation - Junior Fellowships (Advanced Professional, Graduate/Fellowship) [6227]

James Madison Foundation - Senior Fellowships (Advanced Professional/Fellowship) [6228]

Margaret McFarlane Alkek Undergraduate Scholarship (Undergraduate/Scholarship) [4006]

Maricopa County Community College District Scholarships (MCCCD) (Undergraduate/Scholarship) [7034]

Marion A. and Ruth K. Sherwood Business Scholarship (Undergraduate/Scholarship) [5093]

Marsh Writing/Research Scholarship Awards (Undergraduate, Graduate, Doctorate/Scholarship) [6389]

Edna L. Martin Scholarship Fund (Undergraduate/Scholarship) [3633]

Mary and Elliot Wood Foundation Graduate Scholarship (Graduate/Scholarship) [4744]

Bill Mason Memorial Scholarship Fund (Undergraduate/Scholarship) [8810]

Maude Keisling / Cumberland County Extension Homemakers Scholarship Fund (Undergraduate/Scholarship) [3634]

ARTC Glenn Moon Scholarships (Undergraduate/Scholarship) [5340]

NAAE Upper Division Scholarship (Undergraduate/Scholarship) [7609]

Nadene M Thomas Graduate Research Bursary (Graduate/Scholarship) [315]

NAED/Spencer Dissertation Fellowship Program (Graduate, Doctorate/Fellowship) [7577]

NEA Foundation Learning and Leadership Grants (Professional development/Grant) [8185]

Craig D. Newman Memorial Scholarship (Undergraduate/Scholarship) [5409]

North Dakota Division Scholarships (Undergraduate, Graduate/Scholarship) [7373]

North Mecklenburg Teachers' Memorial Scholarship Fund (Undergraduate/Scholarship) [4749]

Nicholas H. Noyes, Jr. Scholarship (Undergraduate/Scholarship) [6391]

NYCT Paid Graduate Student Philanthropy Fellowships - Children, Youth, Families, Education, Human Justice and Workforce (Graduate/Fellowship) [8306]

O'Brien Foundation Fellowships (Professional development/Fellowship) [8571]

Overflow Scholarships (Undergraduate/Scholarship) [1803]

Peter T. Steinwedell Scholarship (Graduate/Scholarship) [5341]

Philip F. Vineberg Travelling Fellowship in the Humanities (Undergraduate/Scholarship, Monetary) [7184]

Pi Lambda Theta Scholarship (Undergraduate/Scholarship) [11743]

PLP Scholarships (Undergraduate/Scholarship, Award, Monetary) [8985]

A. H. Pollard Travelling PhD Scholarships (Postdoctorate/Scholarship) [5810]

Poundmaker Memorial Scholarships (Undergraduate/Scholarship) [11675]

Presidential Scholarship (Master's/Scholarship) [1534]

Caroline Previdi of Sandy Hook Elementary Memorial Scholarship (Undergraduate, Graduate/Scholarship) [2548]

PSAC National Member Scholarship (Postgraduate/Scholarship, Monetary) [9446]

Rosa Quezada Memorial Education Scholarships (Undergraduate/Scholarship) [3755]

R&E Foundation Education Scholar Grant (Graduate, Other/Scholarship) [9482]

Richard and Patricia Hazel Minority Scholarship Award (Undergraduate/Scholarship) [3577]

Robert W. and Bernice Ingalls Staton Scholarships (Undergraduate/Scholarship) [11654]

Charles and Ruth Ronin Memorial Scholarships (Undergraduate/Scholarship) [9600]

Dorothy Worden Ronken Scholarships (Graduate/Scholarship) [4042]

Rosemary Cook Education Scholarship (Undergraduate/Scholarship) [5179]

Rudolph Dillman Memorial Scholarship (Graduate, Undergraduate/Scholarship) [919]

Save a Life Scholarship (College, University, Vocational/Occupational, Undergraduate, Graduate/Scholarship) [448]

Everett Oscar Shimp Memorial Scholarships (Undergraduate/Scholarship) [8878]

Skooblie Scholarships (Undergraduate/Scholarship) [10163]

Lillian Smith Scholarship for Teaching Students (Graduate, Undergraduate/Scholarship) [11493]

Sons of Scotland Past Grand Chiefs Scholarship (Undergraduate/Scholarship) [10593]

John Soto Scholarships (Undergraduate/Scholarship) [3756]

Sheri Stears Education Scholarship (Undergraduate/Scholarship) [11494]

Sturgulewski Family Scholarship (Graduate, Undergraduate/Scholarship) [11495]

John A. and Jean Quinn Sullivan Scholarship Funds (Undergraduate/Scholarship) [4220]

Hatton W. Sumners Endowed Undergraduate School Scholarships (Undergraduate/Scholarship) [10878]

Hatton W. Sumners Non-Endowed Undergraduate and Graduate Scholarships (Undergraduate, Graduate/Scholarship) [10879]

Susan Brager Occupational Education Scholarship (Undergraduate/Scholarship) [9424]

Tarkanian Teacher Education Academy at Clark High School Scholarship (Undergraduate/Scholarship) [9426]

Teacher.org's Inspire Our Future Scholarship (All/Scholarship) [10925]

Alan and Grace Tenn Scholarship Fund (Undergraduate, Graduate/Scholarship) [5414]

Charles A. Townsend Scholarship (Undergraduate/Scholarship) [8883]

Unifor Scholarship (Professional development, Undergraduate/Scholarship) [11223]

UW-Madison School of Education Minority Scholarship (Undergraduate/Scholarship) [11751]

Marta Vallin Memorial Scholarship (Undergraduate/Scholarship) [3757]

J.J. Van Bibber Scholarship (Undergraduate, University, College, Vocational/Occupational/Scholarship) [12380]

Vivian Drenckhahn Student Scholarship (Undergraduate, Graduate/Scholarship) [10516]

Marjorie Rose Warren Scholarship (Undergraduate/Scholarship) [9863]

Wayne-Meador-Elliott Scholarship (Undergraduate/Scholarship) [8884]

Richard M. Weaver Fellowships (Graduate/Fellowship) [5886]

Webb – Faye and Rendell C Webb JR Scholarship (Undergraduate/Scholarship) [3491]

Alma White - Delta Chapter, Delta Kappa Gamma Scholarship (Undergraduate, University, College, Two Year College/Scholarship) [5415]

Fred Wiesner Educational Excellence Scholarships (Undergraduate, Graduate/Scholarship) [2301]

Williams – Dr. Dana Williams Scholarship (Undergraduate/Scholarship) [3492]

The Winston-Salem Foundation Scholarship (Undergraduate/Scholarship) [12099]

Wisconsin Minority Teacher Loan (Undergraduate/Loan) [10812]

Wisconsin Teacher of the Visually Impaired Loan (Undergraduate, Graduate/Loan) [10814]

Paul R. Wolf Memorial Scholarships (Graduate/Scholarship) [2012]

Reverend H. John and Asako Yamashita Memorial Scholarship (Graduate/Scholarship) [6254]

Minoru Yasui Memorial Scholarship (Graduate/Scholarship) [6255]

Clarence and Virginia Young Trust Scholarship (Undergraduate/Scholarship) [5416]

Amelia Zollner IPPR/UCL Internship Award (Undergraduate/Internship) [5855]

Education, Bilingual and cross-cultural

AECT Legacy Graduate Scholarship (Master's, Graduate, Professional development/Scholarship) [2156]

Mead Leadership Fellowships (Professional development/Fellowship) [8482]

New Mexico Association for Bilingual Education Scholarships (NMABE) (Undergraduate/Scholarship) [8295]

Robert Roy Award (Advanced Professional/Award, Recognition) [2099]

H.H. Stern Award (Advanced Professional/Award) [2100]

Education, Early childhood

Early Childhood Educators Scholarship Program (Undergraduate/Scholarship) [7158]

Patty Hamilton Early Childhood Development Scholarships (Undergraduate/Scholarship) [11450]

Carol Hoy Scholarship Fund (Undergraduate/Scholarship) [4778]

JCC Association Graduate Education Scholarships (Graduate/Scholarship) [6257]

Katharine Whiteside Taylor Grant (Professional development/Scholarship) [8826]

Molly Ann Mishler Memorial Scholarships (College/Scholarship) [11457]

Morgan Stanley Pediatrics Fellowships (Postgraduate, Graduate/Fellowship) [686]

NKA Dr. Violet B. Robinson Memorial Graduate Scholarship (Advanced Professional/Scholarship) [7978]

Education, Elementary

AECT Legacy Graduate Scholarship (Master's, Graduate, Professional development/Scholarship) [2156]

Albert Einstein Distinguished Educator Fellowships (AEF) (Graduate, Other/Fellowship) [11108]

Gina L. Barnhart Memorial Scholarship Fund (Undergraduate/Scholarship) [4585]

Carrie and George Lyter Scholarship (Undergraduate/Scholarship) [4775]

Marion Jones Donaldson Scholarship Fund (Undergraduate/Scholarship) [4589]

Harold D. Drummond Scholarships (Undergraduate, Graduate/Scholarship) [6381]

Norma Gotwalt Scholarship Fund (Undergraduate/Scholarship) [4777]

Isabel M. Herson Scholarships in Education (Graduate, Undergraduate/Scholarship) [12412]

Carol Hoy Scholarship Fund (Undergraduate/Scholarship) [4778]

John P. and Tashia F. Morgridge Scholarship (Undergraduate, Graduate/Scholarship) [11736]

Dr. Eva Kleinpeter Scholarship (Undergraduate/Scholarship) [6387]

Lindsay M. Entz Memorial Scholarship Fund (Undergraduate/Scholarship) [4595]

Linda and Vincent McGrath Scholarship (Undergraduate/Scholarship) [6390]

The Ruth Cook Pfautz Memorial Scholarship Fund (Undergraduate/Scholarship) [4782]

Rose Marie Princ Memorial Scholarship (Undergraduate/Scholarship) [9421]

Jack Rosen Scholarship (Undergraduate/Scholarship) [6393]

Regie Routman Teacher Recognition Grant (Advanced Professional/Grant, Recognition) [6038]

Mary Kean White Memorial Scholarship Fund (Undergraduate, Doctorate/Scholarship) [10802]

Ralph Yetka Memorial Scholarships (Undergraduate/Scholarship) [11466]

Education, English as a second language

Douglas-Coldwell Foundation Scholarships in Social Affairs *(Graduate/Scholarship)* [4137]
Sarah Jane Houston Scholarships *(Undergraduate/Scholarship)* [4037]
Arlene Kuhner Memorial Scholarship *(Undergraduate/Scholarship)* [11485]
William R. Pfalzgraf Memorial Scholarship *(Undergraduate/Scholarship)* [8867]

Education, Industrial

ARA Region 10/Dorothy Wellnitz Scholarship – Canada *(Undergraduate, Vocational/Occupational/Scholarship)* [1332]
ARA Region Two/Ron Marshall Scholarship *(Undergraduate/Scholarship)* [1333]
Gary L. Buffington Memorial Scholarships *(Undergraduate/Scholarship)* [5780]
FPA Summer Internships Program *(Undergraduate/Internship)* [4616]
Daniel Lasky Scholarship Fund *(Undergraduate/Scholarship, Award)* [8023]
Leonard Hawk Founders Scholarship *(Graduate, Undergraduate, Vocational/Occupational/Scholarship)* [1334]
Material Handling Education Foundation Scholarships *(Doctorate, Graduate, Undergraduate/Scholarship)* [7293]

Education, Medical

AAMA Houston Chapter Health Training Scholarships *(Other/Scholarship)* [1770]
ABA Doctoral Traveling Fellowship *(Advanced Professional, Professional development/Fellowship)* [704]
Jonathan Alan Scholarship Fund *(Undergraduate/Scholarship)* [11941]
Alice Newell Joslyn Medical Scholarship *(Undergraduate, Doctorate, Master's/Scholarship)* [2460]
Canadian Pain Society Post-Doctoral Fellowship Awards *(Postdoctorate/Fellowship)* [3086]
CPS Clinical Pain Management Fellowship Awards *(Postgraduate/Fellowship)* [3087]
CPS Excellence in Interprofessional Pain Education Awards *(Other/Award)* [3088]
CPS Interprofessional Nursing Project Awards *(Other/Award)* [3089]
CPS Knowledge Translation Research Awards *(Other/Grant)* [3090]
CPS Nursing Excellence in Pain Management Awards *(Professional development/Award)* [3091]
CPS Nursing Research and Education Awards *(Other/Grant)* [3092]
CPS Outstanding Pain Mentorship Award *(Other/Award)* [3093]
CPS Trainee Research Awards *(Doctorate/Grant, Award)* [3094]
The Davis Educational Fund *(Undergraduate, Vocational/Occupational/Scholarship)* [3711]
Donald B. Doty Educational Award *(Advanced Professional/Award, Grant)* [11995]
Dulemba Aleksander & Stefania Scholarship *(Undergraduate/Scholarship)* [9662]
Florence L. Smith Medical Scholarship *(Graduate/Scholarship)* [5270]
Lapeer County Medical Fund *(Undergraduate/Scholarship)* [6666]
Lewis K. Martin II, M.D. and Cheryl Rose Martin Scholarship Fund *(Graduate/Scholarship)* [5275]
Albert and Eloise Midyette Memorial Scholarship Fund *(Undergraduate/Scholarship)* [4746]
Mingenback Family Scholarship Fund *(Undergraduate, Graduate/Scholarship)* [5016]
Herbert W. Nickens Medical Student Scholarships *(Advanced Professional/Scholarship)* [2044]
Gilberto and Lennetta Pesquera Medical School Scholarships *(Graduate/Scholarship)* [5001]
Drs. Kirkland Ruffin & Willcox Ruffin Scholarships *(Graduate/Scholarship)* [5279]
Victor and Ruth N. Goodman Memorial Scholarship *(Graduate/Scholarship)* [5281]

Victoria M. Gardner Scholarship *(Undergraduate/Scholarship)* [11215]
Alan D. Waggoner Sonographer Student Scholarship Award *(Undergraduate/Scholarship)* [1423]
Zelma Gray Medical School Scholarship *(Graduate, Doctorate/Scholarship)* [4709]

Education, Music

AOSA Research Grant *(Professional development/Grant)* [1186]
Bach Organ Scholarship *(Undergraduate/Scholarship)* [9689]
TCDA Carroll Barnes Student Scholarships *(Undergraduate/Scholarship)* [740]
TCDA Jim and Glenda Casey Professional Scholarships *(Other/Scholarship)* [741]
Brent R. Churchill Memorial Scholarship *(Undergraduate/Scholarship)* [6977]
Constant Memorial Scholarship *(Undergraduate/Scholarship)* [9691]
Dalcroze Society of America Memorial Scholarships *(Graduate/Scholarship)* [3962]
William R. Gard Memorial Scholarships *(Graduate/Scholarship)* [7666]
The Sharon Holmes ASTA/NJ Scholarship *(Undergraduate/Scholarship)* [1614]
Muddy Waters Scholarships *(Undergraduate, Graduate/Scholarship)* [2632]
Nickels for Notes Music Scholarship *(Undergraduate/Scholarship)* [4901]
Jerry Robbins Scholarship *(Undergraduate/Scholarship)* [6392]
TCDA Abbott IPCO Professional Scholarships *(Other/Scholarship)* [742]
TCDA Bill Gorham Student Scholarship *(Undergraduate/Scholarship)* [743]
TCDA Cloys Webb Student Scholarship *(Undergraduate/Scholarship)* [744]
TCDA Gandy Ink Professional Scholarship *(Professional development/Scholarship)* [745]
TCDA General Fund Scholarships *(Undergraduate/Scholarship)* [746]
TCDA Past Presidents Student Scholarship *(Undergraduate/Scholarship)* [747]
Edith & Victor Thomas Scholarship *(Undergraduate, University, College/Scholarship)* [12379]
Williams Chorale Bacardi Fallon Scholarships *(High School/Award, Scholarship)* [12037]

Education, Physical

Ruth Abernathy Presidential Undergraduate Scholarship *(Undergraduate/Scholarship, Fellowship, Award, Monetary)* [10347]
American Sokol Merit Award *(Undergraduate/Scholarship, Recognition)* [1593]
Dr. Andy Anderson Young Professional Awards *(Professional development/Award)* [9146]
Bonnie Sorenson Scudder Memorial Scholarship *(Undergraduate/Scholarship)* [3669]
CANFIT Nutrition, Physical Education and Culinary Arts Scholarships *(Graduate, Undergraduate/Scholarship)* [3561]
James Echols Scholarship Award *(Undergraduate/Recognition, Award, Scholarship)* [2781]
William E. "Bill" Gallagher Scholarship *(Undergraduate/Scholarship)* [8847]
Gretchen Hauff Memorial Scholarship *(Undergraduate/Scholarship)* [9404]
Indiana State University Creative and Performing Arts Awards *(Undergraduate/Scholarship)* [5769]
JCC Association Graduate Education Scholarships *(Graduate/Scholarship)* [6257]
John F. Kennedy Scholarship Award *(Undergraduate/Recognition, Award, Scholarship)* [2782]
Michael Moody Fitness Scholarship *(Undergraduate, Graduate/Scholarship)* [7464]
North American Society Fellowship Award (NAS Fellowship) *(Professional development/Fellowship)* [9147]
PHE Canada National Award for Teaching Excellence in Physical Education *(Professional development/Recognition)* [9148]
PHE Canada Student Awards *(Undergraduate/Award)* [9149]

R. Tait Mckenzie Award *(Professional development/Award)* [9150]
Taylor Statten Memorial Fellowships *(Graduate/Scholarship)* [11698]
Winifred Van Hagen/Rosalind Cassidy Scholarship Award *(Undergraduate, Graduate/Recognition, Award)* [2783]
Veronica Gantt Memorial Scholarship *(Undergraduate/Scholarship)* [9429]

Education, Religious

Cecilia Rowan Memorial Fellowship *(Postgraduate/Fellowship)* [8638]
International Scholarship Programs for Community Service *(Undergraduate/Scholarship)* [7249]
MACC Scholarships *(Other/Scholarship)* [7288]
Margaret Lynch Memorial Fellowship *(Postgraduate/Fellowship)* [8642]
The Mary E. Bivins Ministry Scholarship Program *(Graduate, Undergraduate/Scholarship)* [2584]
The William P. McHugh Memorial Fund *(Doctorate, Graduate/Grant)* [1338]
National Endowment for the Humanities Fellowship *(Graduate/Fellowship)* [1339]
Philip F. Vineberg Travelling Fellowship in the Humanities *(Undergraduate/Scholarship, Monetary)* [7184]
The United States Department of State, Bureau of Educational & Cultural Affairs Fellowships *(Graduate/Fellowship)* [1340]

Education, Secondary

Albert Einstein Distinguished Educator Fellowships (AEF) *(Graduate, Other/Fellowship)* [11108]
Leonore Annenberg Teaching Fellowships *(Graduate/Fellowship)* [12045]
Mary Ann Brichta Scholarships *(Undergraduate/Scholarship)* [11735]
Tese Caldarelli Memorial Scholarship *(Graduate, Undergraduate/Scholarship)* [7622]
Marion Jones Donaldson Scholarship Fund *(Undergraduate/Scholarship)* [4589]
George Koeppel Scholarship/All School *(Undergraduate/Scholarship)* [11738]
La Voz Latina Scholarship *(Undergraduate/Scholarship)* [3684]
NACA Foundation Graduate Scholarships *(Graduate, Master's, Doctorate/Scholarship)* [7624]
NACA Mid Atlantic Higher Education Research Scholarships *(Master's/Scholarship)* [7625]
NACA Multicultural Professional Development Grant *(Undergraduate, Graduate, Professional development/Grant)* [7627]
NACA Scholarship for Student Leaders in the Central & Northern Plains Regions *(Undergraduate/Scholarship)* [7628]
NACA Scholarship for Student Leaders in the Mid America & Central Regions *(Undergraduate/Scholarship)* [7629]
NACA Silver Anniversary Scholarship for Student Leaders *(Undergraduate/Scholarship)* [7630]
NACA South Student Leadership Scholarships *(Undergraduate/Scholarship)* [7631]
Noyce Scholarships for Secondary Math and Science Education *(Undergraduate/Scholarship)* [5764]
Patricia Buchanan Memorial Scholarship *(Undergraduate/Scholarship)* [11742]
Rose Marie Princ Memorial Scholarship *(Undergraduate/Scholarship)* [9421]
Carl M. Rose Memorial Scholarship *(Undergraduate/Scholarship)* [8874]
Woodrow Wilson-Rockefeller Brothers Fund Fellowships for Aspiring Teachers of Color *(Undergraduate/Fellowship)* [12052]
Ralph Yetka Memorial Scholarships *(Undergraduate/Scholarship)* [11466]
Zagunis Student Leader Scholarship *(Graduate, Undergraduate/Scholarship)* [7633]

Education, Special

AECT Legacy Graduate Scholarship *(Master's, Graduate, Professional development/Scholarship)* [2156]

Antonia Dellas Memorial Scholarship (Undergraduate/Scholarship) [6192]

Disability Care Center Special Education Scholarships (Undergraduate/Scholarship) [4105]

J. Everett and Louise Light Scholarships (Undergraduate, Graduate/Scholarship) [6382]

Laverne L. Gibson Memorial Scholarship (Undergraduate/Scholarship) [8848]

Illinois Special Education Teacher Tuition Waiver Scholarship (SETTW) (Undergraduate/Scholarship) [5712]

KDP MBNA Scholarships (Undergraduate, Graduate/Scholarship) [6386]

Military Order of the Purple Heart (Undergraduate/Scholarship) [6813]

Mollie Lukken Memorial Scholarship (Graduate, Other/Scholarship) [6345]

NAJA Scholarship (Graduate/Scholarship) [7664]

Siobhan Isabella Reid Memorial Scholarships (Graduate, Undergraduate/Scholarship) [6754]

UCT Scholarship (Other/Scholarship) [8693]

William B. Martin East Carolina University Scholarship (Undergraduate/Scholarship) [6395]

Workshops, Inc. and Stark MRDD Fostering Diversity Through Special Needs Scholarship Fund (Undergraduate/Scholarship) [10803]

Education, Vocational-technical

ALOA Scholarship Foundation (Undergraduate/Scholarship) [374]

ARA Scholarship Awards (Undergraduate/Scholarship) [2364]

John Bunker Scholarship (Vocational/Occupational, College/Scholarship) [12297]

Chester H. Bruce Memorial Scholarship (Undergraduate/Scholarship) [8836]

Helen & Orval Couch Memorial Scholarship (Undergraduate/Scholarship) [12302]

Marvin Crawford Scholarship (College, Vocational/Occupational/Scholarship) [12304]

Mark & Heinz Eichhorn Scholarship (College, Vocational/Occupational/Scholarship) [12313]

Faye Lynn Roberts Education Scholarship Fund (Undergraduate, Graduate/Scholarship) [10684]

Tamara Guttman Memorial Scholarship (Undergraduate, University, College, Vocational/Occupational/Scholarship) [12320]

Harrisville Lion's Club Scholarship (Undergraduate, Vocational/Occupational/Scholarship) [8854]

Horch Roofing Trade School Scholarship (Vocational/Occupational/Scholarship) [5584]

IOIA Organic Community Initiative Scholarships (Other/Scholarship) [6054]

Lake Dollars for Scholars Endowment Fund (Undergraduate/Scholarship) [10774]

Laura M. Fleming Scholarship (Undergraduate, Vocational/Occupational/Scholarship) [4740]

The Leaders of Tomorrow Award (/Award) [4267]

Margaret G. Johnson and Marge J. Stout Scholarship (Undergraduate/Scholarship) [6817]

Maricopa County Community College District Scholarships (MCCCD) (Undergraduate/Scholarship) [7034]

Lt. Colonel Robert G. Moreland Vocational/Technical Fund (Undergraduate/Scholarship) [10783]

National Dairy Herd Information Association Scholarship Program (Undergraduate/Scholarship) [7824]

Northwest-Shoals Community College Applied Technology Scholarship (Undergraduate/Scholarship) [8525]

William R. Reaser Scholarship (Vocational/Occupational, Undergraduate/Scholarship) [8869]

Mary K. Smith Rector Scholarship (Undergraduate, Vocational/Occupational/Scholarship) [8870]

IOIA Andrew Rutherford Scholarships (Other/Scholarship) [6055]

Bill Sawyer Memorial Scholarship (Undergraduate/Scholarship) [6820]

Senior Scholarships (Undergraduate, Vocational/Occupational/Scholarship) [8077]

Shinn Family Scholarship (Undergraduate/Scholarship) [6821]

Beatrice Drinnan Spence Scholarship (Undergraduate, Vocational/Occupational/Scholarship) [4268]

Texas Mutual Scholarship Program (Undergraduate, Vocational/Occupational/Scholarship) [10990]

Turner Family Scholarships (Undergraduate, Vocational/Occupational/Scholarship) [4760]

Virginia C. Jack and Ralph L. Jack Scholarship Fund (Undergraduate/Scholarship) [10800]

The Wilbert L. and Zora F. Holmes Scholarship (Undergraduate/Scholarship) [4764]

The Harriet Glen Wilmore Scholarship (Undergraduate, Vocational/Occupational/Scholarship) [4765]

Work Ethic Scholarship (Vocational/Occupational, Two Year College/Scholarship) [7384]

Education--Curricula

Audrey L. Wright Scholarship (Undergraduate/Scholarship) [5135]

Louise Berman Fellows Award (Graduate, Master's, Doctorate/Fellowship) [6378]

Ed Haas Memorial Scholarship Fund (Graduate/Scholarship) [10824]

Isabel M. Herson Scholarships in Education (Graduate, Undergraduate/Scholarship) [12412]

Louisa Anne Oriente Scholarship (Graduate, Doctorate/Scholarship) [6388]

Educational administration

AASA Educational Administration Scholarship (Postgraduate/Scholarship) [635]

William J. Brennan Graduate Assistant Fellowships (Graduate/Fellowship) [8685]

Tese Caldarelli Memorial Scholarship (Graduate, Undergraduate/Scholarship) [7622]

Cindy Andrews Educational Scholarship (Undergraduate/Scholarship) [9534]

CSSHE Masters Thesis/Project Awards (Master's/Award) [3124]

CSSHE Research and Scholarship Award (Professional development/Award) [3125]

ETS/CGS Award for Innovation in Promoting Success in Graduate Education (Graduate/Award) [3868]

Jacque Placette Chapman Master's Fellowships (Graduate, Master's/Fellowship) [8686]

NACA Foundation Graduate Scholarships (Graduate, Master's, Doctorate/Scholarship) [7624]

NACA Mid Atlantic Higher Education Research Scholarships (Master's/Scholarship) [7625]

NACA Multicultural Professional Development Grant (Undergraduate, Graduate, Professional development/Grant) [7627]

NACA Scholarship for Student Leaders in the Central & Northern Plains Regions (Undergraduate/Scholarship) [7628]

NACA Scholarship for Student Leaders in the Mid America & Central Regions (Undergraduate/Scholarship) [7629]

NACA Silver Anniversary Scholarship for Student Leaders (Undergraduate/Scholarship) [7630]

NACA South Student Leadership Scholarships (Undergraduate/Scholarship) [7631]

Order of Omega Doctoral Fellowships (Doctorate, Graduate/Fellowship) [8687]

Region I Travel Grants (Professional development/Grant) [7814]

Zagunis Student Leader Scholarship (Graduate, Undergraduate/Scholarship) [7633]

Electrical engineering (See Engineering, Electrical)

Electrochemistry (See also Chemistry)

Oronzio de Nora Industrial Electrochemistry Fellowships (Postdoctorate/Fellowship) [4363]

Electronics

Convectair Sustainable Development Scholarship Awards (Undergraduate/Scholarship) [4339]

The Irving W. Cook WA0CGS Scholarship (Undergraduate/Scholarship) [1936]

The Charles Clarke Cordle Memorial Scholarship (Undergraduate/Scholarship) [1937]

SRC NRI Hans J. Coufal Fellowships (Graduate/Fellowship) [10004]

Bob Dyer/OEL Apprenticeship Scholarships (Undergraduate/Scholarship) [4340]

Eaton Awards of Academic Achievement (Undergraduate/Scholarship) [4341]

EFC Atlantic Region Scholarships (Undergraduate/Scholarship) [4342]

EFC University and College Scholarships (Undergraduate/Scholarship) [4343]

The Charles N. Fisher Memorial Scholarship (Undergraduate/Scholarship) [1939]

The Paul and Helen L. Grauer Scholarships (Undergraduate/Scholarship) [1941]

Graybar Canada Award of Excellence Scholarships (Undergraduate/Scholarship) [4347]

Hammond Power Solutions Inc. Outstanding Electrical Scholar Awards (HPS) (Undergraduate/Award) [4348]

Hubbell Canada LP "Electrical Industry Leadership" Scholarship Awards (Undergraduate/Scholarship) [4350, 5610]

Charles Hutchins Educational Grant (Graduate/Grant) [10889]

IEEE - Photonics Society Graduate Student Fellowship (Graduate/Fellowship) [5691]

IRARC Memorial, Joseph P. Rubino, WA4MMD, Scholarship (Undergraduate/Scholarship) [1946]

Johnny Lineberry Memorial Scholarship (Undergraduate, Vocational/Occupational/Scholarship) [12080]

Kerrwil's J.W. Kerr Continuing Education Scholarship Awards (Undergraduate/Scholarship) [4351]

The Dr. James L. Lawson Memorial Scholarship (Undergraduate/Scholarship) [1947]

Charles LeGeyt Fortescue Scholarship (Graduate/Scholarship, Award, Monetary) [5817]

The Fred R. McDaniel Memorial Scholarship (Undergraduate/Scholarship) [1948]

The Mississippi Scholarship (Undergraduate/Scholarship) [1950]

NanoSTAR Seed Fund Program (Advanced Professional/Grant) [11726]

The PHD Scholarship (Undergraduate/Scholarship) [1954]

RAB Design Lighting Award of Excellence (Undergraduate/Scholarship) [4354]

The Ray, NØRP, & Katie, WØKTE, Pautz Scholarship (Undergraduate/Scholarship) [1956]

Sonepar Canada Scholarship Awards (Undergraduate/Scholarship) [4357]

The Standard Recognition of Excellence Awards (Undergraduate/Scholarship) [4358]

Stelpro Scholarship 360: Energizing Potential (Undergraduate/Scholarship) [4359]

The WESCO Student Achievement Award (Undergraduate/Scholarship) [4361, 11969]

The L. Phil and Alice J. Wicker Scholarship (Undergraduate/Scholarship) [1966]

Work Ethic Scholarship (Vocational/Occupational, Two Year College/Scholarship) [7384]

Emergency and disaster services

Harry J. Morris, Jr. Emergency Services (Undergraduate/Scholarship) [5157]

Gail L. Hartshorn Memorial Fund (Other/Scholarship) [8856]

Johns Hopkins Department of Emergency Medicine Administration Fellowships (Advanced Professional, Professional development/Fellowship) [6316]

IAEM Scholarship Program (Undergraduate, Graduate/Scholarship) [5919]

John I. & Madeleine R. Taeni Scholarship Fund (Undergraduate/Scholarship) [10689]

Johns Hopkins Medicine Disaster Fellowships (Professional development/Fellowship) [6317]

Johns Hopkins Medicine Emergency Medical Services Fellowship (Professional development/Fellowship) [6318]

Johns Hopkins Medicine International Emergency and Public Health Fellowships (Graduate, Professional development/Fellowship) [6319]

Johns Hopkins Medicine Medical Education Fellowships (Professional development/Fellowship) [6320]

Johns Hopkins Medicine Research Fellowships (Professional development/Fellowship) [6322]

Johns Hopkins Medicine Ultrasound Fellowships (Professional development/Fellowship) [6323]

William C. Leary Memorial Emergency Services Scholarship (Undergraduate, Vocational/Occupational/Scholarship) [11163]

Mary Fran Myers Scholarship (Professional development, Undergraduate, Graduate, Doctorate/Scholarship) [11565]

Employment

NEEBC Scholarship Award (Undergraduate, Graduate/Scholarship) [8244]

Upjohn Institute Early Career Research Awards (ECRA) (Professional development/Grant, Award) [11759]

Endocrinology

Dr. Biljan Memorial Awards (Advanced Professional/Award, Grant) [2980]

Endocrine Society Summer Research Fellowships (Graduate, Undergraduate/Fellowship) [4383]

Energy-related areas

AIPN Student Scholarships (Graduate, Undergraduate/Scholarship) [2203]

Alberta Innovates Graduate Student Scholarships (Graduate/Scholarship) [275]

American Association of Blacks in Energy Scholarships (Undergraduate/Scholarship) [517]

American Planning Association ENRE Student Fellowship Program (Graduate/Fellowship) [1242]

Association of Energy Engineers Foundation Scholarship Program (Graduate, Undergraduate/Scholarship) [2159]

Boreal Alternate Energy Centre Scholarship (Undergraduate, University, College, Vocational/Occupational/Scholarship) [12291]

Douglas B. Craig Scholarship (Undergraduate, College, University, Vocational/Occupational/Scholarship) [12303]

DEED Student Research Grant/Internships (Undergraduate, Graduate/Grant, Internship) [1297]

e8 Sustainable Energy Development Post-Doctoral Scholarship Programme (Master's/Scholarship) [5008]

EMLF Law Student Scholarships (Undergraduate/Scholarship) [4387]

Joseph L. Fisher Doctoral Dissertation Fellowships (Graduate/Fellowship) [9645]

Purdue University Ray W. Herrick Laboratories Research Fellowship (Graduate/Fellowship) [9451]

Frances C. Hidell Scholarship (Undergraduate/Scholarship) [2144]

Iowa Association for Energy Efficiency Scholarship (Undergraduate/Scholarship) [6154]

Kurz Industrial Solutions Wind Energy Scholarship Fund (Graduate/Scholarship) [6618]

Louisan Mamer Fellowship (Postgraduate/Fellowship) [12161]

NanoSTAR Seed Fund Program (Advanced Professional/Grant) [11726]

Dennis J. O'Brien USAEE Best Student Paper Award (Undergraduate/Award) [11296]

Rocky Mountain Coal Mining Institute Technical Scholarships (Two Year College/Scholarship) [9728]

Schatz Energy Fellowships for Graduate Studies (Graduate/Fellowship, Recognition) [5640]

USAEE/IAEE North American Conference Registration Fee Scholarships (Undergraduate/Scholarship) [11297]

Engineering

AAAS Mass Media Science & Engineering Fellows Program (Undergraduate, Graduate, Postdoctorate/Fellowship) [506]

AAAS Science and Technology Policy Fellowships (Professional development/Fellowship) [507]

AAUW Selected Professions Fellowships (Graduate, Master's, Doctorate/Fellowship) [35]

Accenture American Indian Scholarship Fund (Graduate, Undergraduate/Scholarship) [993]

ACI Foundation Scholarships (Graduate/Scholarship) [786]

ACI W.R. Grace Scholarships (Graduate/Scholarship) [789]

Advanced Light Source Collaborative Postdoctoral Fellowship Program (Postdoctorate/Fellowship) [6734]

AES Graduate Studies Grants (Graduate/Grant, Award) [2349]

AFCEA Cyber Security Scholarship (Undergraduate, Graduate/Scholarship) [103]

AFCEA STEM Teacher Graduate Scholarships (Graduate/Scholarship) [104, 7022]

AFCEA War Veterans Scholarships (Undergraduate/Scholarship) [105]

African American Network - Carolinas Scholarship Fund (Undergraduate/Scholarship) [4715]

AfterCollege Engineering & Technology Student Scholarship (Undergraduate, Graduate, Doctorate, Master's/Scholarship) [120]

AfterCollege STEM Inclusion Scholarship (Undergraduate, Graduate/Scholarship) [122]

AHETEMS General Scholarships (Undergraduate, Graduate/Scholarship) [10068]

AHETEMS Professional Scholarships (Graduate/Scholarship) [10069]

Ahlswede, Norman & Marie Endowed Engineering Scholarship (Undergraduate/Scholarship) [11732]

Aises A. T. Anderson Memorial Scholarship (Graduate, Undergraduate/Scholarship) [1000]

AIST Midwest Member Chapter - Betty McKern Scholarship (Undergraduate/Scholarship) [2208]

AIST Midwest Member Chapter - Don Nelson Scholarship (Undergraduate/Scholarship) [2209]

AIST Midwest Member Chapter - Engineering Scholarships (Undergraduate/Scholarship) [2210]

AIST Midwest Member Chapter - Jack Gill Scholarship (Undergraduate/Scholarship) [2211]

AIST Midwest Member Chapter - Mel Nickel Scholarship (Undergraduate/Scholarship) [2212]

AIST Midwest Member Chapter - Western States Award (Undergraduate/Scholarship) [2213]

AIST Northeastern Ohio Member Chapter - Alfred B. Glossbrenner Scholarship (Undergraduate/Scholarship) [2214]

AIST Northeastern Ohio Member Chapter - John Klusch Scholarships (Undergraduate/Scholarship) [2215]

AIST Southeast Member Chapter - Gene Suave Scholarship (Undergraduate/Scholarship) [2218]

Alaska Aerospace Development Corporation Scholarships (Undergraduate/Scholarship) [11433]

Alberta Innovates - Technology Futures Graduate Student Scholarships in Nanotechnology (Doctorate, Graduate/Scholarship) [277]

Alberta Innovates - Technology Futures Graduate Student Scholarships in Omics (Doctorate, Master's, Professional development/Scholarship) [278]

Stephanie Ali Memorial Scholarships (Undergraduate/Scholarship) [11682]

Alwin B. Newton Scholarship (Undergraduate/Scholarship) [1468]

American Association of University Women Selected Professions Fellowships (Other/Fellowship) [668]

American Council of Engineering Companies of Illinois Scholarships (Undergraduate, Postdoctorate/Scholarship) [805]

American Society of Heating, Refrigerating, and Air-Conditioning Memorial Scholarships (Undergraduate/Scholarship) [1469]

Anil and Neema Thakrar Family Fund #1 (Undergraduate/Scholarship) [4774]

Marvin Anmuth Scholarship (Undergraduate, Graduate/Scholarship) [6269]

Mike Ardaw Scholarships (Undergraduate/Scholarship) [11436]

AREMA Committee 12 - Rail Transit Scholarships (Undergraduate/Scholarship) [1316]

AREMA Committee 18 - Light Density and Short Line Railways Scholarships (Undergraduate/Scholarship) [1317]

AREMA Committee 24 - Education and Training Scholarships (Undergraduate/Scholarship) [1318]

AREMA Committee 27 - Maintenance-of-Way Work Equipment Scholarships (Undergraduate/Scholarship) [1319]

AREMA Committee 33 - Electric Energy Utilization Scholarships (Undergraduate/Scholarship) [1320]

AREMA Michigan Tech Alumni Scholarships (Graduate, Undergraduate/Scholarship) [1321]

AREMA Presidential Spouse Scholarship (Undergraduate/Scholarship) [1322]

AREMA Women's Engineering Scholarship (Undergraduate/Scholarship) [1323]

ASGP Graduate Research Fellowships (Graduate/Fellowship) [244]

ASHARE Undergraduate Engineering Scholarships (Undergraduate/Scholarship) [1470]

ASNT Fellowship Award (Graduate/Fellowship, Award) [1531]

Astronaut Scholarship Foundation Scholarship (Undergraduate/Scholarship) [2332]

Athena San Diego Pinnacle Scholarship (Undergraduate/Scholarship) [9799]

Auto-Pets "Out-of-the-Box Thinking" Scholarships (All/Scholarship) [2355]

AWMA Louisiana Section Scholarship (Undergraduate, Graduate/Scholarship) [167]

B&W Y-12 Scholarship Fund (Undergraduate/Scholarship) [4254]

Barry M. Goldwater Scholarship (Undergraduate/Scholarship) [11733]

Bechtel Engineering and Science Scholarship (Undergraduate/Scholarship) [7075]

Charles E. Behlke Engineering Memorial Scholarships (Undergraduate/Scholarship) [11438]

Bernard Michel Scholarship (Undergraduate/Scholarship) [2862]

Bill and Nell Biggs Scholarship (Undergraduate/Scholarship) [11508]

Bluepay Stem Scholarship (Graduate, Undergraduate/Scholarship) [2630]

Boeing Company Scholarship (Undergraduate/Scholarship) [10050]

Buck Bragunier Leadership Scholarship (Four Year College, University/Scholarship) [1840]

Breast Cancer Car Donations Annual College Scholarship (Undergraduate/Scholarship) [2685]

The Henry Broughton, K2AE, Memorial Scholarship (Undergraduate/Scholarship) [1930]

Archie Bruce Scholarship (Undergraduate, Vocational/Occupational/Scholarship) [12295]

Lieutenant General Douglas D. Buchholz Memorial Scholarship (Undergraduate/Scholarship) [106]

Buick Achievers Scholarship Program (Undergraduate/Scholarship) [4905]

Graduate Fellowship Program - Robert M. Burger Fellowships (Doctorate, Graduate/Fellowship) [9999]

Burroughs Wellcome Fund Collaborative Research Travel Grants (CRTG) (Doctorate, Postdoctorate/Grant) [2750]

Career Awards at the Scientific Interface (CASI) (Undergraduate, Postdoctorate, Graduate/Grant) [2753]

Willis H. Carrier Scholarships (Undergraduate/Scholarship) [1471]

Castle & Cooke Mililani Technology Park Scholarship Fund (Undergraduate, University, Four Year College/Scholarship) [5387]

Ben and Vicky Cayetano Scholarship Fund (Undergraduate, College, University, Two Year College/Scholarship) [5389]

CEMF Engineering Ambassador Awards (Undergraduate/Award) [2964]

CEMF Rona Hatt Chemical Engineering Ambassador Award (Graduate, Undergraduate/Award) [2965]

Center for Engineering in Medicine Predoctoral Fellows Program (Postdoctorate/Fellowship) [7132]

CH2M/AEESP Outstanding Doctoral Dissertation Award *(Doctorate/Award)* [2164, 3271]

Channabasappa Memorial Scholarships *(Graduate, Doctorate/Scholarship)* [5993]

Chapter 1 - Detroit Associate Scholarship *(Graduate, Undergraduate, Vocational/Occupational, Two Year College, Four Year College/Award)* [10386]

Chapter 79/198/311 Scholarship *(Graduate, Undergraduate, Vocational/Occupational, Community College/Scholarship)* [10398]

CHCI Graduate Fellowship Program *(Graduate, Professional development/Fellowship)* [3746]

The Christine Mirzayan Science & Technology Policy Graduate Fellowship Program *(Graduate, Postdoctorate, High School/Fellowship)* [7571]

The Churchill Scholarships *(Postgraduate/Scholarship)* [3331]

CIMON Inc Scholarship *(College, University/Scholarship)* [3333]

CitizenshipTests.org Engineering and Science Scholarship *(Undergraduate/Scholarship)* [3991]

Claude B. Hart Memorial Scholarship *(Undergraduate/Scholarship)* [12066]

Frank M. Coda Scholarships *(Undergraduate/Scholarship)* [1472]

College of Engineering and Physical Sciences Industry Scholarship *(Undergraduate/Scholarship)* [11650]

Critical Language Scholarships at Summer Institutes. (CLS) *(Graduate, Undergraduate/Scholarship)* [1345]

CSX Scholarships *(Undergraduate/Scholarship)* [1324]

John J. Cunningham Memorial Scholarships *(Undergraduate/Scholarship)* [1325]

D&A Florida Scholarships *(Undergraduate/Scholarship)* [10678]

Frank L. Dautriel Memorial Scholarships for Graduates *(Graduate/Scholarship)* [6900]

Frank L. Dautriel Memorial Scholarships for Undergraduates *(Undergraduate/Scholarship)* [6901]

Dave Caldwell Scholarship *(Graduate/Scholarship, Monetary)* [1640]

Decommissioning, and Environmental Science Division Graduate Scholarship *(Undergraduate/Scholarship)* [1164]

Dorothy and Dick Burgess Scholarship *(Undergraduate/Scholarship)* [6197]

Duane Hanson Scholarship *(Undergraduate/Scholarship)* [1473]

EAPSI Fellowships *(Doctorate, Graduate/Fellowship, Award)* [8067]

Eidson - John R. Eidson Jr.,'38 Scholarship *(Undergraduate/Scholarship)* [3474]

Bruce T. and Jackie Mahi Erickson Scholarship *(Graduate, Undergraduate/Scholarship)* [8924]

Larry L. Etherton Scholarships *(Graduate, Undergraduate/Scholarship)* [1326]

Facebook Fellowship Program *(Doctorate/Fellowship)* [4476]

AIST Benjamin F. Fairless Scholarship *(Undergraduate/Scholarship)* [2220]

Fermilab Science Undergraduate Laboratory Internship *(Undergraduate/Internship)* [11316]

Fermilab Summer Internships in Science & Technology (SIST) *(Undergraduate/Internship)* [11317]

FIU ForEverglades Scholarship *(Graduate, Doctorate, Master's/Scholarship)* [4455]

FLASH Social Science Scholarships *(Graduate/Scholarship)* [4499]

Florida Education Fund McKnight Doctoral Fellowship *(Graduate/Fellowship)* [4629]

Frank Fong Scholarships *(Undergraduate/Scholarship)* [10267]

Ford Motor Company Undergraduate Scholarship Award *(Undergraduate/Scholarship)* [11548]

ForEverglades Scholarship *(Graduate, Master's, Doctorate/Scholarship)* [4456]

Michael W. and Jean D. Franke Family Foundation Scholarships *(Graduate, Undergraduate/Scholarship)* [1327]

Michael and Gina Garcia Rail Engineering Scholarships *(Undergraduate, Graduate/Scholarship)* [1328]

The Gates Millennium Scholars *(Undergraduate/Scholarship)* [5529]

Gauthier Family Scholarship Fund *(Undergraduate/Scholarship)* [5078]

Generation III Scholarship *(Undergraduate/Scholarship)* [4285]

Georgia Engineering Foundation Scholarships *(Graduate/Scholarship)* [4928]

Benjamin A. Gilman International Scholarship *(Undergraduate/Scholarship)* [11479]

Girls in Stem (GIS) Scholarship *(Undergraduate/Scholarship)* [9716]

GIST - Orben F. Gist Memorial Scholarship Endowment *(Undergraduate, Community College/Scholarship)* [8511]

Glendale Latino Association Scholarships *(Undergraduate/Scholarship)* [4999]

The Dr. Robert H. Goddard Memorial Scholarship *(Graduate, Undergraduate/Scholarship)* [8123]

William R. Goldfarb Memorial Scholarships *(Undergraduate/Scholarship)* [1940]

Gorrondona & Associates, Inc. / WTS High School Scholarships *(Two Year College, Four Year College/Scholarship)* [12174]

Graduating Texas High School Seniors Scholarship *(Undergraduate/Scholarship)* [10992]

Grant H. Flint International Scholarship Program - Category II *(Undergraduate/Scholarship)* [10581]

Grants-in-Aid of Research (GIAR) *(Graduate, Undergraduate/Grant)* [10128]

GREAT MINDS Collegiate Scholarship Program *(Undergraduate/Scholarship)* [368]

HACU/KIA Motors America, Inc. STEAM Scholarships *(Undergraduate, Graduate/Scholarship)* [5516, 6543]

Harold E. Ennes Scholarship *(Graduate/Scholarship)* [10285]

Helm Family Scholarship *(Undergraduate/Scholarship)* [9819]

Henry Adams Scholarship *(Undergraduate/Scholarship)* [1474]

Herb And Ann Fincher Scholarship Fund *(Undergraduate/Scholarship)* [3571]

Purdue University Ray W. Herrick Laboratories Research Fellowship *(Graduate/Fellowship)* [9451]

Herschede Engineering Scholarship *(Graduate/Scholarship)* [10082]

Hertz Foundation Graduate Fellowship Award *(Graduate/Fellowship)* [5502]

Hertz Doctoral Thesis Prize *(Graduate/Prize)* [5503]

The Hertz Graduate Fellowship Award *(Graduate, Master's, Doctorate/Fellowship)* [7645]

Huber Engineered Woods Product Evaluation Scholarships *(Graduate/Scholarship)* [4500]

IDA Fellowship/Scholarship Programs *(Other/Fellowship)* [5994]

Industrial R&D Fellowships *(Postdoctorate/Fellowship)* [3805]

Influenster Code Like a Girl Scholarships *(Undergraduate, Graduate/Scholarship)* [5782]

INKAS Rising Star Scholarship *(University/Scholarship)* [5789]

International Code Council Scholarship *(Graduate/Scholarship)* [4501]

ISPE Foundation Scholarship *(Undergraduate/Scholarship)* [5707]

ITEEA Greer/FTE Grants *(Other/Grant)* [6124]

JMJ Phillip Group College Scholarships *(Graduate, University, Four Year College, Two Year College/Scholarship)* [6312]

John M. & Mary A. Shanley Memorial Scholarship *(Undergraduate, Graduate/Scholarship)* [10690]

John Marshall Everglades Internship Program *(Undergraduate/Internship)* [4457]

Joseph C. Johnson Memorial Grant *(Undergraduate/Grant)* [1392]

Josef Princ Memorial Scholarship *(Undergraduate/Scholarship)* [9407]

Julian E. Carnes Scholarship Endowment Fund *(Undergraduate/Scholarship)* [4738]

Graduate Fellowship Program - Mahboob Khan/Advanced Micro Devices Fellowships *(Doctorate, Graduate/Fellowship)* [10000]

AIST Willy Korf Memorial Fund *(Undergraduate, Graduate/Scholarship)* [2221]

Kurt H. and Donna M. Schuler Cash Grant *(Undergraduate/Scholarship, Grant)* [1393]

Lamar University College of Engineering Scholarships *(Undergraduate/Scholarship)* [7852]

Laser Technology, Engineering and Applications Scholarship *(Graduate, Undergraduate/Scholarship)* [10727]

Claudette Mackay Lassonde Ambassador Award *(Doctorate, Undergraduate/Award)* [2966]

Latinos in Technology Scholarship *(Undergraduate/Scholarship)* [10136]

Dolores Zohrab Liebmann Fund - Graduate School Fellowships *(Graduate/Fellowship)* [6845]

AIST Ronald E. Lincoln Memorial Scholarship *(Undergraduate/Scholarship)* [2222]

David C. Lizárraga Fellowship *(Graduate/Fellowship)* [10941]

Lt Col Romeo - Josephine Bass Ferretti Scholarship *(Undergraduate/Scholarship)* [148]

Robert Mack Scholarships *(Graduate, Undergraduate/Scholarship)* [6956]

MAES Founders Scholarship *(Graduate, Undergraduate/Scholarship)* [6964]

MAES General Scholarships *(Graduate, Undergraduate/Scholarship)* [6965]

MAES Padrino/Madrina Scholarships *(Graduate, Undergraduate/Scholarship)* [6966]

MAES Pipeline Scholarship *(Graduate, Undergraduate/Scholarship)* [6967]

MAES Presidential Scholarship *(Graduate, Undergraduate/Scholarship)* [6968]

MAES Scholarships *(Graduate/Scholarship)* [6969]

Malayalee Engineers Association Scholarships *(Undergraduate/Scholarship)* [7012]

Maley/FTE Scholarships *(Graduate/Scholarship)* [6126]

Manulife Financial Scholarship *(Undergraduate/Scholarship)* [3793]

Marvin Arnold and Irene Jaquetta Heye Scholarship *(Undergraduate/Scholarship)* [9833]

Maryland Building Industry Association, Eastern Shore Chapter Scholarship Fund *(Undergraduate, High School/Scholarship)* [3574]

Mas Family Scholarship *(Graduate, Undergraduate/Scholarship)* [7120]

Katharine & Bryant Mather Scholarship *(Graduate/Scholarship)* [791]

MCEA Financial Assistance Award *(Undergraduate/Scholarship)* [7062]

Thomas R. McGetchin Memorial Scholarship Award *(Undergraduate/Scholarship)* [11423]

MediaMister $1000 Student Scholarship *(Undergraduate, Graduate/Scholarship)* [7211]

Kumar Mehta Scholarship *(Graduate/Scholarship)* [792]

Michigan Society of Professional Engineers Scholarships *(Undergraduate/Scholarship)* [7328]

John G. and Betty J. Mick Scholarship Fund *(Undergraduate/Scholarship)* [10781]

Raymond W. Miller, PE Scholarships *(Undergraduate/Scholarship)* [4631]

Molded Dimensions, LLC Scholarship *(College, University/Scholarship)* [7428]

Montana Broadcasters Association Broadcast Engineering Scholarships *(Undergraduate/Scholarship)* [7453]

Salvatore J. Monte Thermoplastic Materials & Foams Division Scholarship *(Undergraduate/Scholarship)* [10491]

Rita & Frank Mooney Scholarship *(Undergraduate, University, College, Vocational/Occupational/Scholarship)* [12349]

Robert E. and Judy More Scholarship Fund *(Undergraduate/Scholarship)* [4599]

Murrietta Circuits Scholarship Opportunity *(Undergraduate, College, University/Scholarship)* [7505]

Nancy Lorraine Jensen Memorial Scholarship Fund *(Undergraduate/Scholarship)* [10590]

National Board Technical Scholarship *(College, Four Year College, University/Scholarship)* [7730]

National Co-op Scholarship Program *(Undergraduate/Scholarship)* [12190]

National Debt Relief Scholarship *(University, Four Year College, Undergraduate/Scholarship)* [7828]

National GEM Consortium - MS Engineering Fellowships *(Master's/Fellowship)* [7902]

National GEM Consortium - PhD Engineering Fellowships *(Master's, Graduate/Fellowship)* [7903]

National Science Foundation Graduate Research Fellowship Program (GRFP) *(Graduate/Fellowship)* [8068]

National Security Technologies Engineering and Science Scholarships *(Undergraduate/Scholarship)* [9414]

NBT Trade School, Community/Technical College, or University Scholarships *(Undergraduate/Scholarship)* [8563]

Edsel Newman Scholarships *(Undergraduate/Scholarship)* [6830]

Donald E. Nichols Scholarships *(Undergraduate/Scholarship)* [1475]

Nixon Family Scholarship Fund *(Undergraduate, High School/Scholarship)* [11950]

Norfolk Southern Foundation Scholarships *(Undergraduate/Scholarship)* [1329]

Northrop Grumman Engineering Scholars Program *(Undergraduate/Scholarship)* [8498]

Ocean Industry Student Research Awards *(Undergraduate, Graduate, Postdoctorate/Award)* [9641]

Ohio Space Grant Consortium Graduate Fellowships *(Graduate, Doctorate, Master's/Fellowship)* [8598]

Ohio Space Grant Consortium Special Minority Fellowships *(Doctorate, Graduate, Master's/Fellowship)* [8599]

Oslo International Summer School Scholarship *(Undergraduate/Scholarship)* [10591]

Out to Innovate Scholarship *(Graduate, Undergraduate, Community College/Scholarship)* [8019]

Packard Fellowships for Science and Engineering *(Professional development/Fellowship)* [8808]

Joseph M. Parish Memorial Grants *(Undergraduate/Grant)* [1394]

Patricia & Armen Oumedian Scholarship *(Undergraduate/Scholarship)* [5172]

Paul and Ellen Ruckes Scholarship *(Graduate, Undergraduate/Scholarship)* [917]

Pennsylvania Engineering Foundation (PEF) Grants: Undergraduate *(Undergraduate/Scholarship)* [8964]

J. L. Phelps Scholarship *(Undergraduate, University, College, Vocational/Occupational/Scholarship)* [12357]

Helen Edwards Summer Internship *(Undergraduate/Internship)* [11319]

Polymer Modifiers and Additives Division (PMAD) Scholarship (PMAD) *(Undergraduate, Graduate/Scholarship)* [10493]

Postdoctoral Fellowship *(Postdoctorate, Doctorate/Fellowship)* [11419]

Eric Primavera Memorial Scholarships *(Undergraduate/Scholarship)* [4632]

AIST Judith A. Quinn Detroit Member Chapter Scholarship *(Undergraduate/Scholarship)* [2223]

Ralph Modjeski Scholarship *(Graduate, Undergraduate/Scholarship)* [9240]

Red Olive Women in STEM Scholarship *(Undergraduate, Graduate/Scholarship)* [9516]

REMSA Scholarships *(Undergraduate/Scholarship)* [1330]

Research Internships in Science and Engineering (RISE) *(Undergraduate/Internship)* [4065]

Reuben H. Fleet Memorial Scholarship *(Undergraduate/Scholarship)* [9845]

Richard P. Covert, Ph.D., LFHIMSS Scholarships for Management Systems *(Graduate, Postgraduate, Undergraduate/Scholarship)* [5450]

RA Consulting Service/Maria Riley Scholarships *(Graduate, Undergraduate/Scholarship)* [7893]

Robert D. Greenberg Scholarship *(Graduate, Other/Scholarship)* [10286]

Paul V. Roberts/AEESP Outstanding Doctoral Dissertation Award *(Doctorate/Prize, Monetary)* [2165]

Rocky Mountain Coal Mining Institute Engineering/Geology Scholarships *(Four Year College/Scholarship)* [9727]

Barnes W. Rose, Jr. and Eva Rose Nichol Scholarship Fund *(Graduate/Scholarship)* [322]

Roy Cooper Memorial Scholarship *(Undergraduate/Scholarship)* [6758]

AIST David H. Samson Canadian Scholarship *(Undergraduate/Scholarship)* [2224]

Saskatchewan Pulse Growers Undergraduate Scholarships *(Undergraduate/Scholarship)* [9923]

AIST William E. Schwabe Memorial Scholarship *(Undergraduate/Scholarship)* [2225]

Science and Engineering Apprenticeship Program (SEAP) *(High School/Internship)* [1444]

Science, Mathematics And Research for Transformation Scholarship for Service Program (SMART) *(Undergraduate, Graduate/Scholarship)* [1445, 9974]

John R. Sevier Memorial Scholarship Award *(Undergraduate/Scholarship)* [11424]

SGI Graduate Research Grant *(Graduate/Grant)* [9891]

Dr. Robert and Anna Shaw Scholarship *(Undergraduate/Scholarship)* [309]

Shell Incentive Fund Scholarship *(Undergraduate/Scholarship)* [10041]

Shell Oil Company Technical Scholarship *(Undergraduate/Scholarship)* [10042]

Shell Process Technology Scholarships *(Undergraduate/Scholarship)* [10043]

Marion A. and Ruth K. Sherwood Engineering Scholarship *(Undergraduate/Scholarship)* [5108]

SHPE Dissertation Scholarship *(Doctorate/Scholarship)* [10351]

SHPE Professional Scholarship *(Master's, Doctorate/Scholarship)* [10352]

Alfred P. Sloan Foundation Graduate Scholarships - Sloan Indigenous Graduate Partnership (SIGP) *(Master's, Doctorate/Scholarship)* [7581]

Alfred P. Sloan Foundation Graduate Scholarships - Sloan Minority Ph.D. Program (MPHD) *(Doctorate/Scholarship)* [7582]

SME Education Foundation Family Scholarships *(Undergraduate/Scholarship)* [10415]

SME Future Leaders of Manufacturing Scholarship *(Graduate, Undergraduate/Scholarship)* [10416]

William Brewster Snow Award *(Master's/Award, Monetary)* [2166]

SPEATBC Entrance Scholarship *(Graduate, High School/Scholarship)* [10518]

SRC Master's Scholarships Program *(Graduate, Master's/Scholarship)* [10001]

SREB-State Doctoral Scholars Program - Doctoral Award *(Doctorate, Graduate/Scholarship)* [10664]

The Robert P. Stearns/SCS Engineers Scholarship Award *(Graduate/Scholarship)* [10582]

Stuart L. Noderer Memorial Scholarship *(Undergraduate/Scholarship)* [9855]

Sturgulewski Family Scholarship *(Graduate, Undergraduate/Scholarship)* [11495]

SWE Scholarships *(Undergraduate, Graduate/Scholarship)* [10564]

Frederick A. Tarantino Memorial Scholarship Award *(Undergraduate/Scholarship)* [11425]

Thompson Scholarship for Women in Safety *(Doctorate/Scholarship)* [1573]

Toronto Rehabilitation Institute Graduate Student Scholarships - Ontario Student Opportunities Trust Fund (OSOTF) *(Graduate/Scholarship)* [11065]

Toyota/TELACU Scholarships *(Undergraduate/Scholarship)* [10942]

Reuben Trane Scholarships *(Undergraduate/Scholarship)* [1476]

Truthfinder Scholarship for Women in STEM *(Undergraduate, Graduate, Two Year College/Scholarship)* [11133]

UAA Quanterra Scholarship *(Master's, Doctorate/Scholarship)* [11505]

UC MEXUS-CONACYT Doctoral Fellowship *(Doctorate/Fellowship)* [11552]

UCSD Black Alumni Scholarships for Engineering, Mathematics and Science *(Undergraduate/Scholarship)* [9858]

UNCF Merck Graduate Science Research Dissertation Fellowships *(Graduate/Fellowship)* [7268, 11270]

UNCF/Merck Postdoctoral Science Research Fellowships *(Postdoctorate/Scholarship)* [7269, 11271]

United Engineering Foundation Grants *(All/Grant)* [11259]

U.S. Air Force ROTC High School Scholarship - Type 1 *(High School/Scholarship)* [11282]

University of Toronto Accenture Scholarships *(Undergraduate/Scholarship)* [11700]

University of Toronto Nortel Institute Undergraduate Scholarships *(Undergraduate/Scholarship)* [11701]

USA Cargo Trailer Scholarship *(Undergraduate, Graduate/Scholarship)* [11776]

USGA/Chevron STEM Scholarship Program *(Undergraduate/Scholarship)* [11373]

UW-Madison Engineering Diversity Scholarship *(Undergraduate/Scholarship)* [11748]

Vale Master's Engineering Ambassador Award *(Master's/Award)* [2967]

Vectorworks Design Scholarship *(Undergraduate, Graduate/Scholarship)* [11796]

Dimitri J. Ververelli Memorial Scholarship for Architecture and/or Engineering *(Undergraduate/Scholarship)* [5469]

Virginia Tech Student Travel Award *(Undergraduate, Graduate/Award)* [2167]

Vision Tech Camps Scholarship *(Community College, Four Year College/Scholarship)* [11854]

W. Wesley Eckenfelder Graduate Research Award *(Master's, Doctorate/Award)* [2168]

The Gary Wagner, K3OMI, Scholarship *(Undergraduate/Scholarship)* [1965]

Chancellor's Graduate Fellowship *(Advanced Professional/Fellowship)* [11923]

Washington University Law School Olin Fellowships for Women *(Advanced Professional/Fellowship)* [11924]

Bertold E. Weinberg Scholarship *(Graduate/Scholarship)* [793]

William E. Weisel Scholarship *(Undergraduate/Scholarship)* [10418]

Wes Burton Memorial Scholarship *(Undergraduate/Scholarship)* [12097]

James B. Willett Educational Memorial Scholarship Award *(Undergraduate/Scholarship)* [11426]

William Pigott Memorial Scholarship *(Undergraduate/Scholarship)* [3694]

Ted G. Wilson Memorial Scholarships *(Undergraduate/Scholarship)* [9338]

Women In Defense HORIZONS Scholarship *(Graduate, Undergraduate/Scholarship)* [12133]

WSGC Community College Transfer Scholarships *(Undergraduate/Scholarship)* [11901]

The YASME Foundation Scholarship *(Undergraduate/Scholarship)* [1968]

Ralph Yetka Memorial Scholarships *(Undergraduate/Scholarship)* [11466]

Zuckerman STEM Leadership Program *(Postdoctorate/Scholarship)* [12423]

Engineering, Aerospace/Aeronautical/Astronautical

DEPS Graduate Scholarship *(Graduate/Scholarship)* [4099]

Amelia Earhart Fellowship *(Graduate/Fellowship)* [12419]

NDSEG Fellowship *(Graduate/Fellowship)* [7834]

Graduate Research Fellows (GRF) *(Graduate/Fellowship)* [9969]

Engineering, Agricultural

AACE International Competitive Scholarships *(Undergraduate/Scholarship)* [22]

NPC Scholarship *(Graduate/Scholarship)* [8040]

Engineering, Architectural

AACE International Competitive Scholarships *(Undergraduate/Scholarship)* [22]

AISC/Great Lakes Fabricators and Erectors Association Scholarships *(Graduate/Scholarship)* [1051]

AISC/Ohio Structural Steel Association Scholarships *(Undergraduate, Master's/Scholarship)* [1052]

AISC/Rocky Mountain Steel Construction Association Scholarships *(Undergraduate, Master's/Scholarship)* [1053]

AISC/Southern Association of Steel Fabricators Scholarships *(Undergraduate, Master's/Scholarship)* [1054]

Michael Baker Corp. Scholarship for Diversity in Engineering (Undergraduate/Scholarship) [2192]
Carpenters' Company Scholarship Program (Undergraduate/Scholarship) [3175]
Edilia and François Auguste de Montêquin Fellowships (Doctorate/Fellowship) [10274]
Drzymala Janusz & Roma Scholarship (Undergraduate/Scholarship) [9661]
J.W. "Bill" Neese Scholarship (Undergraduate/Scholarship, Monetary, Award) [5972]
PCH Architects LLP - Steven J. Lehnhof Memorial Architectural Scholarship (Undergraduate/Scholarship) [9571]
SOM Foundation Structural Engineering Travel Fellowships (Doctorate, Graduate, Master's, Undergraduate/Fellowship) [10160]
William J. Tangye Scholarship (Undergraduate/Scholarship, Monetary, Award) [5974]

Engineering, Automotive

AmericanMuscle's Student Scholarship Program (College, University/Scholarship) [1681]
University of the Aftermarket Foundation Scholarship (Community College/Scholarship) [11428]

Engineering, Biomedical

BMES Graduate and Undergraduate Student Awards (Graduate, Undergraduate/Award) [2578]
Robert G. Dailey SPE Detroit Section Scholarship (Undergraduate/Scholarship) [10484]
DOE Computational Science Graduate Fellowship (DOE CSGF) (Doctorate, Graduate/Fellowship) [6611]

Engineering, Chemical

AACE International Competitive Scholarships (Undergraduate/Scholarship) [22]
ACI BASF Construction Chemicals Student Fellowship (Graduate, Undergraduate/Fellowship) [782]
ACS Rubber Division Undergraduate Scholarship (Undergraduate/Scholarship) [738]
AESF Foundation Scholarships (Undergraduate, Graduate/Scholarship) [7704]
AIChE Minority Scholarship Awards for College Students (Undergraduate/Scholarship) [1020]
AIChE Minority Scholarship Awards for Incoming College Freshmen (Undergraduate/Scholarship) [1021]
Air Products and Chemicals, Inc. Scholarships (Undergraduate/Scholarship) [2191]
AISES Intel Growing The Legacy Scholarship Program (Graduate, Undergraduate/Scholarship) [1001]
The B.O.G. Pest Control Scholarship Funds (Undergraduate, Graduate/Scholarship) [2639]
Canadian Technical Asphalt Association Scholarships (Undergraduate/Scholarship) [3130]
Robert E. Cramer Product Design & Development Scholarship (Undergraduate/Scholarship) [10483]
DEPS Graduate Scholarship (Graduate/Scholarship) [4099]
Donald F. & Mildred Topp Othmer Scholarship Awards (Undergraduate/Scholarship) [1022]
Dow Chemical Company Fellowships (Graduate/Fellowship) [8027]
E.I. DuPont Graduate Fellowship (Graduate/Fellowship) [8028]
Lew Erwin Extrusion Division Scholarship (Master's, Postgraduate, Doctorate/Scholarship) [10485]
Fleming/Blaszcak Scholarships (Undergraduate, Graduate/Scholarship) [10486]
Composites Division/Harold Giles Scholarship (Undergraduate, Graduate/Scholarship) [10487]
Gulf Coast Hurricane Scholarship (Undergraduate/Scholarship) [10488]
HSF/Marathon Oil College Scholarship Program (Undergraduate/Scholarship) [5531]
Injection Molding Division Scholarship (Undergraduate, Graduate/Scholarship) [10489]
John J. McKetta Undergraduate Scholarship (Undergraduate/Scholarship) [1023]
Thermoset Division/James I. Mackenzie and James H. Cunningham Scholarships (Undergraduate, Graduate/Scholarship) [10490]

Maricopa County Community College District Scholarships (MCCCD) (Undergraduate/Scholarship) [7034]
Dolphus E. Milligan Graduate Fellowships (Graduate/Fellowship) [8029]
NDSEG Fellowship (Graduate/Fellowship) [7834]
Ted and Ruth Neward Scholarships (Undergraduate, Graduate/Scholarship) [10492]
NOBCChE Procter and Gamble Fellowships (Graduate/Fellowship) [8030]
NPSC Fellowship (Graduate/Fellowship) [5056]
SEE Education Foundation Scholarship (Undergraduate, Graduate, Doctorate/Scholarship) [6107]
Ralph W. Shrader Diversity Scholarship (Graduate/Scholarship) [107]
Carrie Fox Solin Blow Molding Division Memorial Scholarships (Undergraduate/Scholarship) [10494]
Eastman Kodak Dr. Theophilus Sorrell Fellowships (Graduate/Fellowship) [8032]
SPE Foundation General Scholarships (Undergraduate, Graduate/Scholarship) [10495]
SPE Vinyl Plastics Division Educational Grants (Undergraduate/Grant) [10496]
Thermoforming Division Scholarship (Undergraduate, Graduate/Scholarship) [10497]
Thermoplastic Elastomers Special Interest Group Scholarship (Undergraduate, Graduate/Scholarship) [10498]
Evald Torokvei Foundation Scholarships (Graduate/Scholarship) [11699]

Engineering, Civil

AACE International Competitive Scholarships (Undergraduate/Scholarship) [22]
AGC NYS Scholarship Program (Undergraduate, Graduate/Scholarship) [2018]
AHETEMS/ExxonMobil Scholarships (Undergraduate/Scholarship) [10067]
AISC/Ohio Structural Steel Association Scholarships (Undergraduate, Master's/Scholarship) [1052]
AISC/Rocky Mountain Steel Construction Association Scholarships (Undergraduate, Master's/Scholarship) [1053]
AISC/Southern Association of Steel Fabricators Scholarships (Undergraduate, Master's/Scholarship) [1054]
American Council of Independent Laboratories Academic Scholarships (Undergraduate/Scholarship, Award) [815]
Arsham Amirikian Engineering Scholarship (Undergraduate/Scholarship) [1655]
ASCE Freeman Fellowship (Graduate/Fellowship, Award) [1783]
ASDSO Undergraduate Scholarship (Undergraduate/Scholarship) [2295]
Associated General Contractors of Connecticut Scholarships (AGC/CT Scholarship) (Undergraduate/Scholarship) [3759]
Association of State Dam Safety Officials memorial Undergraduate Scholarship (Undergraduate/Scholarship) [2296]
Michael Baker Corp. Scholarship for Diversity in Engineering (Undergraduate/Scholarship) [2192]
ACI Baker Student Fellowships (Undergraduate/Fellowship) [790]
Canadian Technical Asphalt Association Scholarships (Undergraduate/Scholarship) [3130]
CFUW Memorial Fellowship (Master's/Fellowship) [2971]
The Warren E. "Whitey" Cole A.S.H.E. Scholarship Fund (Undergraduate/Scholarship) [4588]
Francis X. Crowley Scholarship (Undergraduate/Scholarship) [8248]
Galvanize the Future: A Richard L. Brooks Memorial Scholarship (Undergraduate, Graduate/Scholarship) [934]
Saul Horowitz Jr. Memorial Graduate Award (Graduate/Scholarship, Award) [126]
HSF/Marathon Oil College Scholarship Program (Undergraduate/Scholarship) [5531]
International Association of Foundation Drilling Scholarships for Civil Engineering Students (Graduate/Scholarship) [81]

International Association of Foundation Drilling Scholarships for Part-time Civil Engineering Graduate School Students (Graduate/Scholarship) [82]
Donald Jamieson Fellowship (Graduate/Fellowship) [3112]
Elson T. Killam Memorial Scholarship (Undergraduate, Graduate/Scholarship) [8249]
MALSCE Memorial Scholarship (Undergraduate/Scholarship) [7122]
Maricopa County Community College District Scholarships (MCCCD) (Undergraduate/Scholarship) [7034]
National Federation of the Blind Scholarship Program (Undergraduate/Scholarship, Monetary) [7878]
NDSEG Fellowship (Graduate/Fellowship) [7834]
NSPS Berntsen International Scholarship in Surveying Technology (Undergraduate/Scholarship) [8118]
Pardee Community Building Scholarship (Undergraduate/Scholarship) [9419]
SOM Foundation Structural Engineering Travel Fellowships (Doctorate, Graduate, Master's, Undergraduate/Fellowship) [10160]
WRI Education Foundation Scholarships - Graduate (Graduate/Scholarship) [12103]
WRI Education Foundation Scholarships - High School Seniors (Undergraduate/Scholarship) [12104]
WRI Education Foundation Scholarships - Undergraduate (Undergraduate/Scholarship) [12105]

Engineering, Computer

AISES Intel Growing The Legacy Scholarship Program (Graduate, Undergraduate/Scholarship) [1001]
AISES Oracle Academy Scholarship (Graduate, Undergraduate/Scholarship) [1002, 5044]
Barriger - Zachary Barriger Memorial Scholarship Fund (Undergraduate/Scholarship) [3463]
NANOG Scholarship Program (Undergraduate, Graduate/Scholarship) [9943]
NVIDIA Graduate Fellowships (Postdoctorate/Fellowship) [8567]
Women Techmakers Udacity Scholarship (Graduate, Undergraduate/Scholarship) [5048]

Engineering, Electrical

AACE International Competitive Scholarships (Undergraduate/Scholarship) [22]
Affiliated Distributors Electrical Industry Scholarship Awards (Undergraduate/Scholarship) [4337]
AHETEMS/ExxonMobil Scholarships (Undergraduate/Scholarship) [10067]
AISES Intel Growing The Legacy Scholarship Program (Graduate, Undergraduate/Scholarship) [1001]
AIST Ohio Valley Member Chapter Scholarships (Undergraduate/Scholarship) [2217]
Barriger - Zachary Barriger Memorial Scholarship Fund (Undergraduate/Scholarship) [3463]
Burndy Canada Inc. Academic Achievement Awards (Undergraduate/Scholarship) [4338]
Convectair Sustainable Development Scholarship Awards (Undergraduate/Scholarship) [4339]
DEPS Graduate Scholarship (Graduate/Scholarship) [4099]
DOE Computational Science Graduate Fellowship (DOE CSGF) (Doctorate, Graduate/Fellowship) [6611]
Bob Dyer/OEL Apprenticeship Scholarships (Undergraduate/Scholarship) [4340]
Eaton Awards of Academic Achievement (Undergraduate/Scholarship) [4341]
EFC Atlantic Region Scholarships (Undergraduate/Scholarship) [4342]
EFC University and College Scholarships (Undergraduate/Scholarship) [4343]
Franklin Empire Scholarship Awards (Undergraduate/Scholarship) [4344]
G.E. Lighting Canada Community Leadership Awards (Undergraduate/Award) [4345]

Gerrie Electric Memorial Scholarship Awards (Undergraduate/Scholarship) [4346]

Graybar Canada Award of Excellence Scholarships (Undergraduate/Scholarship) [4347]

Perry F. Hadlock Memorial Scholarships (Undergraduate/Scholarship) [1943]

Hammond Power Solutions Inc. Outstanding Electrical Scholar Awards (HPS) (Undergraduate/Award) [4348]

E.B. Horsman & Son Scholarships (Undergraduate/Scholarship) [4349]

HSF/Marathon Oil College Scholarship Program (Undergraduate/Scholarship) [5531]

Hubbell Canada LP "Electrical Industry Leadership" Scholarship Awards (Undergraduate/Scholarship) [4350, 5610]

Kerrwil's J.W. Kerr Continuing Education Scholarship Awards (Undergraduate/Scholarship) [4351]

Julia Kiene Fellowships in Electrical Energy (Graduate/Fellowship) [12159]

League of Latin American Citizens General Electric Scholarships (Undergraduate/Scholarship) [6747]

Imelda (Graduate, High School/Scholarship) [3722]

Louis T. Klauder Scholarship (Undergraduate, Graduate/Scholarship) [1303]

Lyle Mamer Fellowship (Graduate/Fellowship) [12160]

Maricopa County Community College District Scholarships (MCCCD) (Undergraduate/Scholarship) [7034]

The Edmond A. Metzger Scholarship (Undergraduate/Scholarship) [1949]

Microsoft Research Graduate Women's Scholarships (Graduate/Scholarship) [7356]

Microsoft Research PhD Fellowships (Doctorate/Fellowship) [7357]

NANOG Scholarship Program (Undergraduate, Graduate/Scholarship) [9943]

NDSEG Fellowship (Graduate/Fellowship) [7834]

NPSC Fellowship (Graduate/Fellowship) [5056]

NVIDIA Graduate Fellowships (Postdoctorate/Fellowship) [8567]

Osram Sylvania Scholastic Achievement Awards (Undergraduate/Scholarship) [4352]

Philips Lighting Continuing Education Awards (Undergraduate/Scholarship) [4353]

RAB Design Lighting Award of Excellence (Undergraduate/Scholarship) [4354]

Schneider Electric Student Merit Awards (Undergraduate/Scholarship) [4355]

Ralph W. Shrader Diversity Scholarship (Graduate/Scholarship) [107]

Siemens Canada Academic Awards (Undergraduate/Scholarship) [4356, 10079]

Sonepar Canada Scholarship Awards (Undergraduate/Scholarship) [4357]

The Standard Recognition of Excellence Awards (Undergraduate/Scholarship) [4358]

Stelpro Scholarship 360: Energizing Potential (Undergraduate/Scholarship) [4359]

The WESCO Student Achievement Award (Undergraduate/Scholarship) [4361, 11969]

Engineering, Geological

Graduate and Undergraduate Fellowship Awards (Doctorate, Graduate, Undergraduate/Fellowship, Award) [3195]

Marliave Scholarship Fund (Graduate/Scholarship) [2161]

Rocky Mountain Coal Mining Institute Engineering/Geology Scholarships (Four Year College/Scholarship) [9727]

Martin L. Stout Scholarships (Graduate, Undergraduate/Scholarship) [2162]

Engineering, Hydraulic

Channabasappa Memorial Scholarships (Graduate, Doctorate/Scholarship) [5993]

IDA Fellowship/Scholarship Programs (Other/Fellowship) [5994]

Engineering, Industrial

AACE International Competitive Scholarships (Undergraduate/Scholarship) [22]

A.O. Putnam Memorial Scholarship (Undergraduate/Scholarship) [5826]

CDC Steven M. Teutsch Prevention Effectiveness (PE) (Doctorate/Fellowship) [11328]

Chapter 4 - Lawrence A. Wacker Memorial Scholarship (Undergraduate/Scholarship) [10391]

Chapter 17 - St. Louis Scholarship (Undergraduate/Scholarship) [10388]

Chapter 23 - Quad Cities Scholarship (Undergraduate/Scholarship) [10389]

Chapter 31 - Peoria Scholarship (Undergraduate/Scholarship) [10390]

Chapter 52 - Wichita Scholarship (Graduate, Undergraduate, Vocational/Occupational, Community College/Scholarship) [10392]

Chapter 56 - Ft. Wayne Scholarship (Graduate, Undergraduate, Vocational/Occupational, Community College/Scholarship) [10393]

Chapter 67 - Phoenix Scholarship (Undergraduate/Scholarship) [10397]

Robert E. Cramer Product Design & Development Scholarship (Undergraduate/Scholarship) [10483]

Robert G. Dailey SPE Detroit Section Scholarship (Undergraduate/Scholarship) [10484]

Lew Erwin Extrusion Division Scholarship (Master's, Postgraduate, Doctorate/Scholarship) [10485]

John S.W. Fargher, Jr. Scholarship (Graduate/Scholarship) [5827]

Fleming/Blaszcak Scholarships (Undergraduate, Graduate/Scholarship) [10486]

Dwight D. Gardner Scholarship (Undergraduate/Scholarship) [5828]

Gilbreth Memorial Fellowship (Graduate/Fellowship) [5829]

Composites Division/Harold Giles Scholarship (Undergraduate, Graduate/Scholarship) [10487]

Gulf Coast Hurricane Scholarship (Undergraduate/Scholarship) [10488]

IISE Council of Fellows Undergraduate Scholarship (Undergraduate/Scholarship) [5830]

IISE Presidents Scholarship (Undergraduate/Scholarship) [5831]

John L. Imhoff Scholarship (Graduate, Undergraduate/Scholarship) [5832]

Injection Molding Division Scholarship (Undergraduate, Graduate/Scholarship) [10489]

E. Wayne Kay Graduate Scholarships (Graduate, Doctorate/Scholarship) [10406]

Thermoset Division/James I. Mackenzie and James H. Cunningham Scholarships (Undergraduate, Graduate/Scholarship) [10490]

Harold and Inge Marcus Scholarship (Undergraduate/Scholarship) [5833]

McMurray Stern - Scholarship Opportunity (Undergraduate, College, University/Scholarship) [7197]

Marvin Mundel Memorial Scholarship (Undergraduate/Scholarship) [5834]

Clarence & Josephine Myers Undergraduate Scholarships (Graduate, Undergraduate, Vocational/Occupational, Community College/Scholarship) [10409]

Ted and Ruth Neward Scholarships (Undergraduate, Graduate/Scholarship) [10492]

North Central Region 9 Scholarship (Undergraduate/Scholarship) [10410]

Schneider/Bingle PLTW Scholarship (Undergraduate/Scholarship) [10412]

SME Future Leaders of Manufacturing Scholarship (Graduate, Undergraduate/Scholarship) [10416]

Carrie Fox Solin Blow Molding Division Memorial Scholarships (Undergraduate/Scholarship) [10494]

SPE Foundation General Scholarships (Undergraduate, Graduate/Scholarship) [10495]

SPE Vinyl Plastics Division Educational Grants (Undergraduate/Grant) [10496]

Thermoforming Division Scholarship (Undergraduate, Graduate/Scholarship) [10497]

Thermoplastic Elastomers Special Interest Group Scholarship (Undergraduate, Graduate/Scholarship) [10498]

UPS Scholarship for Female Students (Undergraduate/Scholarship) [5836]

UPS Scholarship for Minority Students (Undergraduate/Scholarship) [5837]

Lisa Zaken Award For Excellence (Graduate, Undergraduate/Award, Monetary) [5838]

Engineering, Marine

Charles H. Bussmann Graduate Scholarship (Graduate, Undergraduate/Scholarship) [7068]

Robert N. Herbert Undergraduate Scholarships (Undergraduate/Scholarship) [10433]

Marine Technology Society ROV Scholarship (MTS ROV) (Undergraduate, Graduate/Scholarship) [7069]

The MTS Student Scholarship for Two-Year, Technical, Engineering and Community College Students (Undergraduate/Scholarship) [7072]

Mandell and Lester Rosenblatt Undergraduate Scholarship (Undergraduate/Scholarship) [10434]

SUT Houston Graduate Scholarships (Graduate/Scholarship) [10547]

SUT Houston Undergraduate Scholarships (Undergraduate/Scholarship) [10548]

John V. Wehausen Graduate Scholarships for Advanced Study in Ship Hydrodynamics and Wave Theory (Graduate/Scholarship) [10435]

Engineering, Materials

ACI Richard N. White Student Fellowship (Graduate, Undergraduate/Fellowship) [788]

AISES Intel Growing The Legacy Scholarship Program (Graduate, Undergraduate/Scholarship) [1001]

Robert E. Cramer Product Design & Development Scholarship (Undergraduate/Scholarship) [10483]

Robert G. Dailey SPE Detroit Section Scholarship (Undergraduate/Scholarship) [10484]

Electronics Division: Lewis C. Hoffman Scholarship (Undergraduate/Scholarship) [733]

Lew Erwin Extrusion Division Scholarship (Master's, Postgraduate, Doctorate/Scholarship) [10485]

Fleming/Blaszcak Scholarships (Undergraduate, Graduate/Scholarship) [10486]

Galvanize the Future: A Richard L. Brooks Memorial Scholarship (Undergraduate, Graduate/Scholarship) [934]

Composites Division/Harold Giles Scholarship (Undergraduate, Graduate/Scholarship) [10487]

Gulf Coast Hurricane Scholarship (Undergraduate/Scholarship) [10488]

Injection Molding Division Scholarship (Undergraduate, Graduate/Scholarship) [10489]

Thermoset Division/James I. Mackenzie and James H. Cunningham Scholarships (Undergraduate, Graduate/Scholarship) [10490]

NDSEG Fellowship (Graduate/Fellowship) [7834]

Ted and Ruth Neward Scholarships (Undergraduate, Graduate/Scholarship) [10492]

Carrie Fox Solin Blow Molding Division Memorial Scholarships (Undergraduate/Scholarship) [10494]

SPE Vinyl Plastics Division Educational Grants (Undergraduate/Grant) [10496]

Thermoforming Division Scholarship (Undergraduate, Graduate/Scholarship) [10497]

Thermoplastic Elastomers Special Interest Group Scholarship (Undergraduate, Graduate/Scholarship) [10498]

Engineering, Mechanical

AACE International Competitive Scholarships (Undergraduate/Scholarship) [22]

ACS Rubber Division Undergraduate Scholarship (Undergraduate/Scholarship) [738]

AESF Foundation Scholarships (Undergraduate, Graduate/Scholarship) [7704]

AHETEMS/ExxonMobil Scholarships (Undergraduate/Scholarship) [10067]

Air Products and Chemicals, Inc. Scholarships (Undergraduate/Scholarship) [2191]

AIST Ohio Valley Member Chapter Scholarships (Undergraduate/Scholarship) [2217]

Auxiliary Undergraduate Scholarships (Undergraduate/Scholarship) [1998]

Chapter 4 - Lawrence A. Wacker Memorial Scholarship (Undergraduate/Scholarship) [10391]

Chapter 52 - Wichita Scholarship *(Graduate, Undergraduate, Vocational/Occupational, Community College/Scholarship)* [10392]

Chapter 56 - Ft. Wayne Scholarship *(Graduate, Undergraduate, Vocational/Occupational, Community College/Scholarship)* [10393]

Convectair Sustainable Development Scholarship Awards *(Undergraduate/Scholarship)* [4339]

DOE Computational Science Graduate Fellowship (DOE CSGF) *(Doctorate, Graduate/Fellowship)* [6611]

Elisabeth M. and Winchell M. Parsons Scholarship *(Doctorate/Scholarship)* [1999]

Frances C. Hidell Scholarship *(Undergraduate/ Scholarship)* [2144]

HSF/Marathon Oil College Scholarship Program *(Undergraduate/Scholarship)* [5531]

Paul C. K. Lam Memorial Scholarship at The University of Akron *(Undergraduate/Scholarship)* [8597]

Imelda *(Graduate, High School/Scholarship)* [3722]

Louis T. Klauder Scholarship *(Undergraduate, Graduate/Scholarship)* [1303]

Lucy and Charles W.E. Clarke Scholarship *(Undergraduate/Scholarship, Award)* [2000]

Maricopa County Community College District Scholarships (MCCCD) *(Undergraduate/Scholarship)* [7034]

Clarence & Josephine Myers Undergraduate Scholarships *(Graduate, Undergraduate, Vocational/ Occupational, Community College/Scholarship)* [10409]

North Central Region 9 Scholarship *(Undergraduate/Scholarship)* [10410]

NPSC Fellowship *(Graduate/Fellowship)* [5056]

Osram Sylvania Scholastic Achievement Awards *(Undergraduate/Scholarship)* [4352]

Philips Lighting Continuing Education Awards *(Undergraduate/Scholarship)* [4353]

RAB Design Lighting Award of Excellence *(Undergraduate/Scholarship)* [4354]

Rice-Cullimore Scholarship *(Graduate/Scholarship)* [2001]

Marjorie Roy Rothermel Scholarship *(Master's/ Scholarship)* [2002]

Siemens Canada Academic Awards *(Undergraduate/Scholarship)* [4356, 10079]

Albert E. Wischmeyer Scholarship *(Undergraduate/ Scholarship)* [10419]

Engineering, Metallurgical

AESF Foundation Scholarships *(Undergraduate, Graduate/Scholarship)* [7704]

AIST Ohio Valley Member Chapter Scholarships *(Undergraduate/Scholarship)* [2217]

Engineering, Mining and Mineral

American Society of Mining and Reclamation Memorial Scholarship Award *(Undergraduate, Community College, University/Scholarship, Recognition)* [1522]

SME Coal & Energy Division Scholarship *(Undergraduate/Scholarship)* [10429]

SME Environmental Division Scholarship *(Undergraduate, Graduate/Scholarship)* [10430]

Engineering, Naval

ASNE Scholarship *(Graduate, Undergraduate/Scholarship)* [1524]

Engineering, Nuclear

American Nuclear Society Incoming Freshman Scholarships *(Undergraduate/Scholarship)* [1160]

American Nuclear Society Nevada Section Scholarship *(Undergraduate/Scholarship)* [1161, 9390]

American Nuclear Society Undergraduates Scholarships *(Undergraduate/Scholarship)* [1162]

DOE Computational Science Graduate Fellowship (DOE CSGF) *(Doctorate, Graduate/Fellowship)* [6611]

Frances C. Hidell Scholarship *(Undergraduate/ Scholarship)* [2144]

SEE Education Foundation Scholarship *(Undergraduate, Graduate, Doctorate/Scholarship)* [6107]

Engineering, Ocean

Canadian Hydrographic Association Student Award *(Undergraduate/Award)* [3008]

Robert N. Herbert Undergraduate Scholarships *(Undergraduate/Scholarship)* [10433]

NDSEG Fellowship *(Graduate/Fellowship)* [7834]

Mandell and Lester Rosenblatt Undergraduate Scholarship *(Undergraduate/Scholarship)* [10434]

Engineering, Optical

BACUS Scholarship *(Graduate, Undergraduate/ Scholarship)* [10724]

Raymond Davis Scholarships *(Undergraduate, Graduate/Scholarship)* [10371]

DEPS Graduate Scholarship *(Graduate/Scholarship)* [4099]

D.J. Lovell Scholarship *(Graduate, Undergraduate/ Scholarship)* [10725]

Robert S. Hilbert Memorial Student Travel Grants *(Graduate, Undergraduate/Grant)* [8677]

Michael Kidger Memorial Scholarship in Optical Design *(Undergraduate/Scholarship)* [10726]

Optical Design and Engineering Scholarship *(Graduate, Undergraduate/Scholarship)* [10728]

SPIE Student Author Travel Grants *(Graduate, Undergraduate/Grant)* [10729]

Engineering, Petroleum

AHETEMS/ExxonMobil Scholarships *(Undergraduate/Scholarship)* [10067]

Frances C. Hidell Scholarship *(Undergraduate/ Scholarship)* [2144]

HSF/Marathon Oil College Scholarship Program *(Undergraduate/Scholarship)* [5531]

Petroleum Engineering Scholarships *(Undergraduate/Scholarship)* [10473]

Wayne-Meador-Elliott Scholarship *(Undergraduate/ Scholarship)* [8884]

English language and literature (See also Linguistics; Literature)

Avery Award *(Undergraduate, High School/Award)* [11668]

CEE Cultural Diversity Grant *(Professional development/Grant)* [7798]

Edwyna Wheadon Postgraduate Training Scholarship *(Postgraduate/Scholarship)* [7799]

Evoke Strategy Writing Scholarship *(Undergraduate/ Scholarship)* [4459]

Wilhelmina Gordon Foundation Scholarships *(Undergraduate/Scholarship)* [7757]

Indiana State University Creative and Performing Arts Awards *(Undergraduate/Scholarship)* [5769]

Langfitt-Ambrose Scholarship *(Undergraduate/ Scholarship)* [8863]

NCTE Research Foundation Grants *(Other/Grant)* [7800]

William R. Pfalzgraf Memorial Scholarship *(Undergraduate/Scholarship)* [8867]

Dr. Brent Slobodin Memorial Scholarship in the Humanities *(Undergraduate, Graduate, University, College/Scholarship)* [12371]

Susan P. Schroeder Memorial Scholarship *(Undergraduate/Scholarship)* [6822]

Swensrud Teacher Fellowships at MHS (Massachusetts Historical Society) *(Professional development/Fellowship)* [7154]

Enology

American Wine Society Educational Foundation Scholarships (AWSEF) *(Graduate/Scholarship)* [1676]

Nancy Johnston Memorial Scholarships *(Graduate, Undergraduate/Scholarship)* [10956]

Entomology

AAPA Student Research Scholarship *(Graduate, Undergraduate/Scholarship)* [631]

Ed Becker Conference Travel Awards *(Undergraduate, Graduate/Award)* [4403]

Biological Survey of Canada Scholarship *(Postgraduate/Scholarship)* [4404]

John H. Borden Scholarship *(Postgraduate/Scholarship)* [4405]

Brooks Scholarship *(Graduate/Scholarship)* [4411]

Coleopterists Society - Youth Incentive Award *(High School/Award, Grant)* [3502]

Dr. Lloyd M. Dosdall Memorial Scholarships *(Postgraduate/Scholarship)* [4406]

Entomological Society of Canada Danks Scholarship *(Postgraduate/Scholarship)* [4407]

Entomological Society of Saskatchewan Student Presentation Award *(Undergraduate/Award)* [4412]

Entomological Society of Saskatchewan Travel Awards *(Professional development/Award)* [4413]

Graduate Research Travel Scholarships *(Graduate/ Scholarship)* [4408]

Nancy Johnston Memorial Scholarships *(Graduate, Undergraduate/Scholarship)* [10956]

Kenneth and Barbara Starks Plant Resistance to Insects Graduate Student Award *(Graduate/ Award)* [4396]

Keith Kevan Scholarship *(Postgraduate/Scholarship)* [4409]

Jeffery P. LaFage Graduate Student Research Award *(Master's, Doctorate/Grant)* [4397]

Lillian and Alex Feir Graduate Student Travel Award in Insect Physiology, Biochemistry, or Molecular Biology *(Master's, Doctorate/Award)* [4398]

Louisiana Agricultural Consultants Association Scholarship *(Graduate, Undergraduate/Scholarship)* [6896]

Henry and Sylvia Richardson Research Grant *(Postdoctorate/Grant)* [4401]

Rove Pest Control Scholarships *(Undergraduate/ Scholarship)* [9747]

Shripat Kamble Urban Entomology Graduate Student Award for Innovative Research *(Doctorate/ Award)* [4399]

Environmental conservation

CCF Academic Fellowships in Karst Studies - Graduate *(Master's, Doctorate/Fellowship)* [3192]

Douglas B. Craig Scholarship *(Undergraduate, College, University, Vocational/Occupational/Scholarship)* [12303]

CTEC Internships *(Undergraduate/Internship)* [1727]

Antenore C. "Butch" Davanzo Scholarships *(Graduate, Undergraduate/Scholarship)* [7348]

Ellen Eberhardt Memorial Scholarship Fund *(Undergraduate/Scholarship)* [10825]

Joseph L. Fisher Doctoral Dissertation Fellowships *(Graduate/Fellowship)* [9645]

Grand Canyon Historical Society Scholarships *(Graduate/Scholarship)* [5066]

John P. Hennessey Scholarship *(Graduate, Undergraduate/Scholarship)* [7349]

Kurz Industrial Solutions Wind Energy Scholarship Fund *(Graduate/Scholarship)* [6618]

Lindbergh Grants *(Professional development/Grant)* [6869]

L. Gordon "Link" Linkous Scholarship *(Undergraduate/Scholarship)* [11103]

Bill Mason Memorial Scholarship Fund *(Undergraduate/Scholarship)* [8810]

National Geographic Conservation Trust Grants *(Doctorate, Advanced Professional/Grant)* [7906]

National Geographic Expedition Council Grants *(Advanced Professional/Grant)* [7907]

National Geographic Society/Waitt Grants *(Advanced Professional/Grant, Award)* [7908]

National Geographic Young Explorers Grants *(Advanced Professional/Grant)* [7909]

NGC College Scholarships *(Graduate, Undergraduate/Scholarship)* [7900]

NYCT Paid Graduate Student Philanthropy Fellowships - Community Development and the Environment *(Graduate/Fellowship)* [8307]

OPIRG McMaster Public Interest Research Grant (PIG) *(Undergraduate, Graduate/Grant)* [7195]

Ted Parnell Scholarship *(Undergraduate/Scholarship)* [12278]

Ted Rollins Eco Scholarship *(Undergraduate/Scholarship)* [11158]

ABS Amy R. Samuels Cetacean Behavior and Conservation Award *(Graduate/Grant)* [1717]

Ben Sheardown Scholarship *(Undergraduate, University, College/Scholarship)* [12370]

Shred Nations Scholarship *(Undergraduate, Graduate/Scholarship)* [10071]

Switzer Environmental Fellowship *(Graduate/Fellowship)* [9721]

Peg & Aubrey Tanner Scholarship *(Undergraduate, College, University, Vocational/Occupational/Scholarship)* [12377]

VASWCD College Scholarship *(College, Four Year College, Two Year College, Undergraduate/Scholarship)* [11104]

VPPPA June Brothers Scholarship *(Graduate, Undergraduate/Scholarship)* [11862]

VPPPA Stephen Brown Scholarship *(Graduate, Undergraduate/Scholarship)* [11863]

Jack H. Wagner Scholarship *(Graduate, Undergraduate/Scholarship)* [7350]

Frederick K. Weyerhaeuser Forest History Fellowship *(Graduate/Fellowship)* [4682]

William "Sully" Sullivan Scholarship *(Graduate, Undergraduate/Scholarship)* [11864]

Worcester County Conservation District Annual Scholarships Program *(Undergraduate/Scholarship)* [12186]

Environmental design

Plan NH's Scholarship and Fellowship Program *(Community College, Four Year College, Undergraduate, Graduate, Vocational/Occupational/Scholarship)* [9188]

Vectorworks Design Scholarship *(Undergraduate, Graduate/Scholarship)* [11796]

Worldstudio AIGA Scholarships *(Graduate, Undergraduate/Scholarship)* [12205]

Environmental law

EMLF Law Student Scholarships *(Undergraduate/Scholarship)* [4387]

Local A&WMA Sections and Chapter Scholarships *(Graduate/Scholarship)* [162]

McCloy Fellowships in Environmental Policy *(Professional development/Fellowship)* [811]

Property and Environment Research Center Graduate Fellowships *(Graduate/Fellowship)* [9351]

Southern Section A&WMA Scholarships *(Graduate/Scholarship)* [10668]

Switzer Environmental Fellowship *(Graduate/Fellowship)* [9721]

Environmental science (See also Ecology)

A. Stanley Rand Fellowship Program *(Undergraduate, Doctorate, Postdoctorate/Fellowship)* [10224]

American Society of Mining and Reclamation Memorial Scholarship Award *(Undergraduate, Community College, College, University/Scholarship, Recognition)* [1522]

Max Bell Senior Fellow Grants *(Advanced Professional/Grant)* [2469]

Thomas J. Black Scholarship *(Undergraduate, University, College/Scholarship)* [12290]

The B.O.G. Pest Control Scholarship Funds *(Undergraduate, Graduate/Scholarship)* [2639]

Stephen Bronfman Scholarship *(Graduate/Scholarship)* [6286]

Carol Bond Fund Community College Students Scholarship *(Undergraduate/Scholarship)* [8452]

Carol Bond Scholarship *(Undergraduate/Scholarship)* [8453]

Rachel Carson Prize *(Other/Prize)* [1450]

CH2M/AEESP Outstanding Doctoral Dissertation Award *(Doctorate/Award)* [2164, 3271]

Chopivsky Fellowships *(Graduate/Fellowship)* [11889]

Convectair Sustainable Development Scholarship Awards *(Undergraduate/Scholarship)* [4339]

Frank L. Dautriel Memorial Scholarships for Graduates *(Graduate/Scholarship)* [6900]

Frank L. Dautriel Memorial Scholarships for Undergraduates *(Undergraduate/Scholarship)* [6901]

Dave Lamb Scholarship *(Graduate/Scholarship)* [11912]

DOE Computational Science Graduate Fellowship (DOE CSGF) *(Doctorate, Graduate/Fellowship)* [6611]

EMLF Law Student Scholarships *(Undergraduate/Scholarship)* [4387]

EPA Science to Achieve Results Fellowships (STAR) *(Graduate/Fellowship)* [11350]

FAMU Presidential Scholarship - Florida Community College Scholarships *(Undergraduate/Scholarship)* [4620]

ForestGEO Research Grants *(Graduate, Postdoctorate, Professional development/Grant)* [10225]

GFLC AWMA Scholarship Program *(Undergraduate, Graduate/Scholarship)* [4907]

Grant H. Flint International Scholarship Program - Category II *(Undergraduate/Scholarship)* [10581]

GWS Scholarship Program *(Undergraduate, Graduate/Scholarship)* [165]

Harry Hampton Fund Scholarship *(Undergraduate/Scholarship)* [5266]

IAGLR Scholarship *(Doctorate/Scholarship)* [5924]

J.B. and Marilyn McKenzie Graduate Student Fellowship *(Graduate/Fellowship)* [11627]

Jim Anderson Memorial Scholarship *(Undergraduate/Scholarship)* [8363]

Joel T. Heinen Student Research Fellowship *(Undergraduate, Graduate/Fellowship)* [11628]

Nesta Leduc Scholarship *(Undergraduate, University, College, Vocational/Occupational/Scholarship)* [12338]

Legacy Inc. College Undergraduate and Graduate Scholarships *(Other/Scholarship)* [6766]

Marjorie M. Hendricks Environmental Education Scholarship *(Undergraduate/Scholarship)* [5094]

George Perkins Marsh Prize *(Other/Prize)* [1455]

Mary and Elliot Wood Foundation Graduate Scholarship *(Graduate/Scholarship)* [4744]

Randall Mathis Scholarship for Environmental Studies Fund *(Undergraduate/Scholarship)* [1824]

Ben Meadows Natural Resource Scholarships - Academic Achievement Scholarships *(Undergraduate/Scholarship)* [4684]

Ben Meadows Natural Resource Scholarships - Leadership Scholarships *(Undergraduate/Scholarship)* [4685]

MHS/Cushing Academy Fellowships on Environmental History *(Professional development/Fellowship)* [7148]

Miller G. Sherwood Family Scholarship *(Undergraduate/Scholarship)* [5097]

NCNJ-AWMA Undergraduate Scholarship *(Undergraduate/Scholarship)* [172]

NEHA/AAS Scholarship *(Graduate, Undergraduate/Scholarship)* [478, 7873]

N.G. Kaul Memorial Scholarship *(Doctorate, Graduate/Scholarship)* [8364]

Eric Niemitalo Scholarship in Earth and Environmental Science *(Undergraduate/Scholarship)* [10060]

NMPF National Dairy Leadership Scholarship Program *(Graduate, Master's, Doctorate/Scholarship)* [8013]

Postdoctoral Fellowship *(Postdoctorate, Doctorate/Fellowship)* [11419]

Hal Rothman Dissertation Fellowship *(Doctorate, Graduate/Fellowship)* [1458]

SAEMS Environmental Scholarships *(Undergraduate, Graduate/Scholarship)* [10645]

Samuel P. Hays Research Fellowship *(Other/Fellowship)* [1459]

Ben Sheardown Scholarship *(Undergraduate, University, College/Scholarship)* [12370]

William Brewster Snow Award *(Master's/Award, Monetary)* [2166]

The Robert P. Stearns/SCS Engineers Scholarship Award *(Graduate/Scholarship)* [10582]

Stuart/SIM Northern Education Scholarship *(Undergraduate, University, College, Vocational/Occupational/Scholarship)* [12375]

Switzer Environmental Fellowship *(Graduate/Fellowship)* [9721]

Tailor Made Lawns Scholarship Fund *(Undergraduate/Scholarship)* [10909]

UC MEXUS-CONACYT Doctoral Fellowship *(Doctorate/Fellowship)* [11552]

Udall Scholarship *(Undergraduate/Scholarship)* [11533]

Virginia Tech Student Travel Award *(Undergraduate, Graduate/Award)* [2167]

W. Wesley Eckenfelder Graduate Research Award *(Master's, Doctorate/Award)* [2168]

Dorreene & Herb Wahl Scholarship *(Undergraduate, University, College/Scholarship)* [12384]

Environmental technology

AESF Foundation Scholarships *(Undergraduate, Graduate/Scholarship)* [7704]

Alberta Innovates Graduate Student Scholarships *(Graduate/Scholarship)* [275]

Jim Bourque Scholarship *(Undergraduate/Scholarship)* [1790]

Frank L. Dautriel Memorial Scholarships for Graduates *(Graduate/Scholarship)* [6900]

Frank L. Dautriel Memorial Scholarships for Undergraduates *(Undergraduate/Scholarship)* [6901]

Tara Welch Gallagher Environmental Scholarship *(Graduate/Scholarship)* [5272]

NCNJ-AWMA Undergraduate Scholarship *(Undergraduate/Scholarship)* [172]

Shred Nations Scholarship *(Undergraduate, Graduate/Scholarship)* [10071]

Switzer Environmental Fellowship *(Graduate/Fellowship)* [9721]

Thompson Scholarship for Women in Safety *(Doctorate/Scholarship)* [1573]

Udall Undergraduate Scholarship *(Undergraduate/Scholarship)* [11165]

Epidemiology (See also Infectious diseases)

Alex's Lemonade Stand Foundation Epidemiology Grants *(Doctorate, Master's, Professional development/Grant)* [336]

Raymond B. Bauer Research Award *(Professional development/Award, Grant)* [7322]

Epilepsy

Epilepsy Foundation Behavioral Sciences Post-Doctoral Fellowships *(Postdoctorate/Fellowship)* [4419]

Epilepsy Foundation Behavioral Sciences Student Fellowships *(Graduate, Undergraduate/Fellowship)* [4420]

Epilepsy Foundation Health Sciences Student Fellowships *(Doctorate, Graduate/Fellowship)* [4421]

Epilepsy Foundation Post-doctoral Research and Training Fellowships *(Postdoctorate/Fellowship)* [4422]

Epilepsy Foundation Pre-doctoral Research Training Fellowships *(Graduate/Fellowship)* [4423]

Epilepsy Foundation Research Grants *(Doctorate/Grant)* [4424]

Epilepsy Foundation Research and Training Fellowships for Clinicians *(Doctorate, Other/Grant)* [4425]

Partnership for Pediatric Epilepsy Research *(Doctorate/Grant)* [4426]

Savoy Foundation Postdoctoral and Clinical Research Fellowships *(Postdoctorate/Fellowship)* [4658]

Targeted Research Initiative for Health Outcomes *(Doctorate/Grant)* [4427]

Equine studies

AEF Educational Scholarship *(Undergraduate/Scholarship)* [255]

Alabama Horse Council Scholarships *(Undergraduate/Scholarship)* [224]

Neil Clark Memorial Scholarship *(Undergraduate/Scholarship)* [8156]

Ethics and bioethics

Charlotte W. Newcombe Doctoral Dissertation Fellowship *(Graduate/Fellowship)* [8387, 12049]

Ethnography

Andrew W. Mellon Fellowships For Conservation Training Programs *(Graduate/Fellowship)* [10197]
Fejos Postdoctoral Fellowships in Ethnographic Film *(Postdoctorate/Fellowship)* [11962]

European studies

Alliance-CES Pre-Dissertation Research Fellowship *(Graduate/Fellowship)* [3855]
CES Conference Travel Grants *(Graduate, Professional development/Grant)* [3856]
CJH-NEH Fellowships for Senior Scholars *(Doctorate/Fellowship)* [3222]
CJH-Prins Foundation Fellowships for Senior Scholars *(Doctorate/Fellowship)* [3223]
CJH-Prins Foundation Post-Doctoral and Early Career Fellowship for Emigrating Scholars *(Professional development, Postdoctorate/Fellowship)* [3224]
Educational and Cultural Affairs Alumni Small Grants Program (ECA) *(Other/Grant)* [6069]
European Studies First Article Prize *(Professional development/Prize)* [3857]
Dr. Guido Goldman Fellowships *(Postdoctorate/Fellowship)* [807]
History of Art: Institutional Fellowships *(Graduate/Fellowship)* [6613]
Individual Advanced Research Opportunities Program For Master's Students *(Graduate, Master's/Fellowship)* [6070]
IREX Individual Advanced Research Opportunities Program For Postdoctoral Scholars *(Postdoctorate/Fellowship)* [6071]
IREX Individual Advanced Research Opportunities Program For Pre-doctoral Students *(Doctorate/Fellowship)* [6072]
IREX Individual Advanced Research Opportunities Program For Professionals *(Other/Fellowship)* [6073]
Mellon-CES Dissertation Completion Fellowships in European Studies. *(Graduate/Fellowship)* [3858]
The RSA-Centre for Reformation and Renaissance Studies (CRRS) Grant (CRRS) *(Doctorate/Grant)* [11818]

Family planning

Geraldine Clewell Fellowships - Doctoral Student *(Graduate/Fellowship)* [9107]
Geraldine Clewell Fellowships - Masteral *(Graduate/Fellowship)* [9108]
Closs/Parnitzke/Clarke Scholarship *(Undergraduate/Scholarship)* [9109]
Margaret Drew Alpha Scholarship *(Graduate/Scholarship)* [9110]
Lydia Fohn-Hansen/Lola Hill Memorial Scholarships *(Undergraduate, Graduate/Scholarship)* [11447]
Genevieve Forthun Scholarships *(Undergraduate/Scholarship)* [9111]
Mary Weiking Franken Scholarships *(Undergraduate/Scholarship)* [9112]
Geraldine Clewell Scholarship *(Undergraduate/Scholarship)* [9113]
Jackman Scholarships *(Undergraduate/Scholarship)* [9114]
Jean Dearth Dickerscheid Fellowship *(Graduate/Fellowship)* [9115]
Treva C. Kintner Scholarships *(Undergraduate/Scholarship)* [9116]
Martha Combs Jenkins Scholarship *(Undergraduate/Scholarship)* [9117]
Nell Bryant Robinson Scholarship *(Undergraduate/Scholarship)* [9118]
NYCT Paid Graduate Student Philanthropy Fellowships - Children, Youth, Families, Education, Human Justice and Workforce *(Graduate/Fellowship)* [8306]

Phi Upsilon Omicron Candle Fellowships *(Graduate, Postgraduate/Fellowship)* [9119]
Phi Upsilon Omicron Challenge Scholarships *(Undergraduate/Scholarship)* [9120]
Phi Upsilon Omicron Diamond Anniversary Fellowships *(Graduate/Fellowship)* [9121]
Phi Upsilon Omicron Founders Fellowship *(Graduate/Fellowship)* [9122]
Phi Upsilon Omicron Golden Anniversary Scholarships *(Undergraduate/Scholarship)* [9123]
Phi Upsilon Omicron Past Presidents Scholarships *(Undergraduate/Scholarship)* [9124]
Phi Upsilon Omicron Presidents Research Fellowship *(Graduate, Master's, Doctorate, Postdoctorate/Fellowship)* [9125]
Lucile Rust Scholarships *(Undergraduate/Scholarship)* [9126]
Margaret Jerome Sampson Scholarships *(Undergraduate/Scholarship)* [9128]
Lillian P. Schoephoerster Scholarships *(Undergraduate/Scholarship)* [9129]
SFP Junior Investigator's Career Development Awards *(Other/Grant)* [10330]
SFP Mid-Career/Mentor Award *(Other/Grant)* [10331]
SFP Student Research Grants *(Graduate/Grant)* [10332]
Tommie J. Hamner Scholarship *(Undergraduate/Scholarship)* [9131]

Family/Marital therapy (See also Rehabilitation, Physical/Psychological)

AAMFT Minority Fellowship Program (MFP) *(Doctorate, Graduate/Fellowship)* [602]
Dissertation Completion Fellowship (DCF) *(Doctorate/Fellowship)* [603]

Fashion design

Paul Arnold Memorial Scholarships *(Other/Scholarship)* [9288]
Arts Foundation of Cape Cod Scholarships *(Undergraduate, Vocational/Occupational/Scholarship)* [1975]
California Association of Family and Consumer Sciences - San Diego Chapter Scholarship *(Undergraduate, Graduate/Scholarship)* [9805]
Hadar J. Chemtob Memorial Scholarship *(Undergraduate/Scholarship)* [6288]
Edith Head Undergraduate Scholarships *(Undergraduate/Scholarship)* [4032]
S. Penny Chappell Scholarship *(Undergraduate/Scholarship)* [9127]
Sutherland/Purdy Scholarship *(Undergraduate/Scholarship)* [9130]
Women's Jewelry Association Member Grants *(Professional development/Grant)* [12163]
Worldstudio AIGA Scholarships *(Graduate, Undergraduate/Scholarship)* [12205]

Filmmaking (See also Media arts)

AFA Film and Video Arts Project Grants *(Professional development/Grant)* [257]
Anne Friedberg Innovative Scholarship Award *(Other/Scholarship)* [10309]
Betty Rose Scholarship *(Undergraduate/Scholarship)* [1407]
Canadian Picture Pioneers Scholarship *(Undergraduate/Scholarship)* [3100]
Documentary Film Grants *(Professional development/Grant)* [409]
Fellowships for Creative and Performing Artists and Writers *(Professional development/Fellowship)* [490]
Carole Fielding Student Grant *(Undergraduate, Graduate/Grant)* [11567]
Mona Gray Creative Arts Scholarship *(Graduate, Undergraduate/Scholarship)* [6306]
Harvey Fellows Program *(Graduate/Fellowship)* [7519]

Hedy Lamarr Achievement Award for Emerging Leaders in Entertainment Technology *(Undergraduate/Award)* [4086]
The Scott Pearlman Field Awards *(Professional development/Award)* [4470]
Helen Lansdowne Resor Scholarship *(Undergraduate, Graduate, Other/Scholarship)* [11018]
Steve Kaplan TV & Film Studies Award *(Other/Award)* [1412]
TFOS Fellowship Awards *(Graduate, Postdoctorate/Fellowship)* [10929]
Truer Than Fiction Award *(Professional development/Award)* [4556]
Worldstudio AIGA Scholarships *(Graduate, Undergraduate/Scholarship)* [12205]

Finance (See also Accounting; Banking)

African American Network - Carolinas Scholarship Fund *(Undergraduate/Scholarship)* [4715]
AFWA Masters Scholarships *(Master's/Scholarship)* [58]
AFWA Undergraduate Scholarships *(Undergraduate/Scholarship)* [59]
Allmand Law Scholarship Contest *(Undergraduate/Scholarship)* [372]
ALPFA Scholarship *(Graduate, Undergraduate, Master's/Scholarship)* [2231]
The Alsandor Law Firm Scholarship Contest *(Undergraduate/Scholarship)* [407]
ASMC National Scholarship Program *(Graduate/Scholarship)* [1520]
BadCredit.orgs Wealth Wise Scholarship *(Undergraduate, Graduate/Scholarship)* [2401]
Bank of Canada Fellowship Award *(Doctorate, Other/Fellowship)* [2423]
Bank of Canada Governor's Awards *(Doctorate, Other/Award)* [2424]
Benson Law Firm Scholarship Contest *(Undergraduate/Scholarship)* [2477]
Brylak Law Safety Scholarship Contest *(Undergraduate/Scholarship)* [2734]
Business Leaders of Tomorrow *(Community College, Four Year College, Graduate/Scholarship)* [7478]
Canadian Derivatives Scholarship *(Postgraduate/Scholarship)* [2663]
Candon, Todd, & Seabolt Scholarship Fund *(Undergraduate, Four Year College, University/Scholarship)* [5385]
Clark High School Academy of Finance Scholarship *(Undergraduate/Scholarship)* [9394]
Amy and Tim Dauphinee Scholarship *(Graduate/Scholarship)* [2912]
DeVries Law School Scholarship *(Undergraduate/Scholarship)* [4070]
Elite Entrepreneurs Scholarship Contest *(Undergraduate, Graduate, High School/Scholarship)* [4369]
Ernst and Young Scholarships *(Undergraduate/Scholarship)* [1979]
Evans Warncke Robinson, LLC Scholarship Contest *(Undergraduate/Scholarship)* [4453]
FINCAD Women in Finance Scholarships *(Graduate/Scholarship)* [4562]
Brendan Flores Alumni Leadership Circle Scholarship - Clark High School *(Undergraduate/Scholarship)* [9400]
Daniel B. Goldberg Scholarship *(Graduate/Scholarship, Recognition)* [5052]
Goldman Sachs/Matsuo Takabuki Commemorative Scholarship *(Graduate/Scholarship)* [8926]
Frank L. Greathouse Government Accounting Scholarship *(Graduate, Undergraduate/Award, Scholarship)* [5053]
Harvey Fellows Program *(Graduate/Fellowship)* [7519]
Helene M. Overly Memorial Graduate Scholarship *(Graduate/Scholarship)* [12170]
Herb Adrian Memorial Scholarship Endowment *(Undergraduate/Scholarship)* [4735]
IMA Memorial Education Fund Scholarships (MEF) *(Graduate, Undergraduate/Scholarship)* [5848]
ISU Networks Scholarship *(Undergraduate/Scholarship)* [5763]

Alexander Fraser Laidlaw Fellowship *(Graduate/Fellowship)* [2913]

Lemaire Co-operative Studies Award *(Undergraduate, Graduate/Scholarship)* [2914]

Maricopa County Community College District Scholarships (MCCCD) *(Undergraduate/Scholarship)* [7034]

Douglas McRorie Memorial Scholarships *(Doctorate, Master's/Scholarship, Award)* [131]

Minorities in Government Finance Scholarship *(Graduate, Undergraduate/Scholarship)* [5054]

Robert E. and Judy More Scholarship Fund *(Undergraduate/Scholarship)* [4599]

NABA National Scholarship Program *(Graduate, Undergraduate/Scholarship, Award, Monetary)* [7613]

NAFA Corporate Aviation Business Scholarship *(Undergraduate, Graduate/Scholarship)* [7592]

NAIFA West Michigan Scholarship *(Undergraduate/Scholarship)* [5170]

New York Financial Writers' Associations Scholarships *(Graduate, Undergraduate/Scholarship)* [8311]

NYFWA Scholarships *(Undergraduate, Graduate/Scholarship)* [8312]

Ritchie-Jennings Memorial Scholarship Program *(Undergraduate, Graduate/Scholarship)* [2132]

Robert A. Kleckner Scholarship Fund *(Undergraduate, Graduate/Scholarship)* [10699]

Robert Toigo Foundation Fellowship *(Master's/Fellowship)* [11048]

Royal Bank Scholarships *(Undergraduate, Master's, Graduate/Scholarship)* [2600]

Senator James Gladstone Memorial Scholarship *(Graduate, Undergraduate/Scholarship)* [270]

Sharon D. Banks Memorial Undergraduate Scholarship *(Undergraduate/Scholarship)* [12171]

South Carolina Association for Financial Professionals Certified Treasury Professional Scholarships *(Other/Scholarship)* [10606]

South Carolina Association for Financial Professionals College Education Scholarships *(Undergraduate/Scholarship)* [10607]

Striving for Greatness Accounting & Finance Scholarship *(Undergraduate/Scholarship)* [9214]

Stuart Cameron and Margaret McLeod Memorial Scholarship (SCMS) *(Graduate, Undergraduate/Scholarship)* [5850]

Surety and Fidelity Industry Intern and Scholarship Program *(Undergraduate, Graduate/Scholarship)* [10885]

The Turnkey Lender's Scholarship Program *(Undergraduate/Scholarship)* [11154]

Wells Fargo American Indian Scholarship Program *(Undergraduate/Scholarship)* [996]

Wells Fargo Career Scholarship *(Undergraduate/Scholarship)* [11506]

Financial aid

ACB Foundation Grants for Pro Bono Projects *(Other/Grant)* [757]

Fine arts (See Art)

Finnish studies (See Area and ethnic studies)

Fires and fire prevention

CFSA Randal Brown & Associates Awards *(Undergraduate/Award)* [2114]

CFSA Aon Fire Protection Engineering Award *(Undergraduate/Scholarship)* [2115]

CFSA City of Markham, Buildings Standards Department Award *(Undergraduate/Scholarship)* [2116]

CFSA Fire Safety Awards *(Postgraduate/Scholarship)* [2117]

CFSA Founders Award for Leadership & Excellence *(Graduate, Postgraduate/Scholarship)* [2118]

CFSA Leber Rubes Inc. Awards *(Postgraduate/Award, Monetary)* [2119]

CFSA LRI Engineering Award *(Undergraduate/Scholarship)* [2120]

CFSA Nadine International Awards *(Undergraduate/Scholarship)* [2121]

CFSA Siemens Canada Award *(Undergraduate/Scholarship)* [2122]

CFSA Underwriters' Laboratories of Canada Awards *(Undergraduate/Scholarship)* [2123]

Friends and Family of Christopher J. Kohlmeier Scholarship *(Undergraduate/Scholarship)* [9547]

Harry J. Morris, Jr. Emergency Services *(Undergraduate/Scholarship)* [5157]

International Association of Wildland Fire Graduate-Level Scholarships *(Graduate/Scholarship)* [5947]

John Charles Wilson and Robert Doran Sr. Scholarship *(Undergraduate/Scholarship)* [5903]

Joseph C. Menezes Scholarship Fund *(Undergraduate/Scholarship)* [5905]

The Junior Firefighter of the Year Award *(Undergraduate/Scholarship)* [8154]

Thompson Scholarship for Women in Safety *(Doctorate/Scholarship)* [1573]

Work Ethic Scholarship *(Vocational/Occupational, Two Year College/Scholarship)* [7384]

Fisheries sciences/management

J Frances Allen Scholarship Award *(Doctorate/Scholarship)* [887]

The B. Harper Bull Scholarship Awards *(Graduate, Doctorate, Postgraduate/Award)* [11060]

Norman S. Baldwin Fishery Science Scholarship *(Doctorate, Master's/Scholarship)* [5923]

Jack B. Fisher Scholarship Fund *(Graduate/Scholarship)* [10758]

Harry Hampton Fund Scholarship *(Undergraduate/Scholarship)* [5266]

ICAFS Idaho Graduate Student Scholarship *(Graduate/Scholarship)* [889]

ICAFS Idaho High School Student Scholarship *(Undergraduate/Scholarship)* [890]

ICAFS Idaho Undergraduate Student Scholarship *(Undergraduate/Scholarship)* [891]

Susan B. Martin Scholarship *(Graduate/Scholarship)* [892]

Ben Meadows Natural Resource Scholarships - Academic Achievement Scholarships *(Undergraduate/Scholarship)* [4684]

Ben Meadows Natural Resource Scholarships - Leadership Scholarships *(Undergraduate/Scholarship)* [4685]

Ronald L. Schmied Scholarship *(Other, Undergraduate/Scholarship)* [5253]

Vern Parish Award *(Graduate, Postgraduate, Doctorate/Scholarship)* [1088]

Floriculture

NGC College Scholarships *(Graduate, Undergraduate/Scholarship)* [7900]

Joseph Shinoda Memorial Scholarship *(Undergraduate/Scholarship)* [10047]

Folklore

Muddy Waters Scholarships *(Undergraduate, Graduate/Scholarship)* [2632]

Smithsonian Institution Graduate Student Fellowships *(Graduate/Fellowship)* [10205]

Smithsonian Institution Postdoctoral Researcher Fellowships *(Postdoctorate/Fellowship)* [10206]

Smithsonian Institution Predoctoral Student Fellowships *(Doctorate, Postgraduate/Fellowship)* [10207]

Smithsonian Institution Senior Researcher Fellowships *(Professional development/Fellowship)* [10208]

Food science and technology

All Star Purchasing *(Undergraduate/Scholarship)* [344]

Allen Allured Fellowship *(Graduate/Fellowship)* [9345]

American Association of Cereal Chemists Graduate Fellowship Program *(Graduate/Fellowship)* [3266]

ASBC Foundation Graduate Scholarships *(Graduate/Scholarship)* [1387]

ASBC Foundation Undergraduate Scholarships *(Undergraduate/Scholarship)* [1388]

Clifford L. Bedford Scholarship Award *(Undergraduate/Scholarship)* [5220]

The Bentley Cropping Systems Fellowship *(Graduate/Fellowship)* [3263]

California Association of Family and Consumer Sciences - San Diego Chapter Scholarship *(Undergraduate, Graduate/Scholarship)* [9805]

Career Development Scholarships *(Postgraduate/Scholarship)* [4666]

Letitia B. Carter Scholarships *(Undergraduate, Advanced Professional/Scholarship)* [9649]

E. H. Marth Food Protection And Food Sciences Scholarship *(Undergraduate/Scholarship)* [12109]

Feeding Tomorrow Scholarships *(Graduate, Undergraduate/Scholarship)* [5819]

Carleton A. Friday Scholarship *(Undergraduate/Scholarship)* [7377]

Great Lakes Section Diversity Scholarship *(Graduate, Undergraduate/Scholarship)* [5221]

Marcia S. Harris Legacy Fund Scholarships *(Undergraduate, Advanced Professional/Scholarship)* [9650]

International Association for Food Protection - Student Travel Scholarship Program *(Undergraduate, Graduate/Scholarship)* [5921]

International Foodservice Editorial Council Scholarship *(Graduate/Scholarship)* [6007]

Kenneth G. Weckel Scholarship *(Undergraduate/Scholarship)* [7378]

AACT John Kitt Memorial Scholarship *(Undergraduate/Scholarship)* [538]

LionsDeal.com Scholarships *(Undergraduate/Scholarship)* [6875]

Maine Nutrition Council Scholarships *(Undergraduate/Scholarship)* [7001]

Margaret J. Andrew Memorial Scholarship *(Undergraduate, Graduate/Scholarship)* [10116]

National Poultry and Food Distributors Association Scholarships *(Undergraduate/Scholarship)* [8042]

NMPF National Dairy Leadership Scholarship Program *(Graduate, Master's, Doctorate/Scholarship)* [8013]

NRAEF Scholarship *(Undergraduate/Scholarship)* [9651]

Stark County Dairy Promoters Scholarship Fund *(Graduate/Scholarship)* [10794]

Raymond J. Tarleton Graduate Fellowships *(Graduate/Fellowship)* [3267]

Undergraduate/Graduate Scholarships *(Undergraduate, Graduate/Scholarship)* [5989]

Food service careers

Al Schuman/Ecolab Undergraduate Entrepreneurial Scholarship *(Undergraduate/Scholarship)* [8061]

California Association of Family and Consumer Sciences - San Diego Chapter Scholarship *(Undergraduate, Graduate/Scholarship)* [9805]

Career Development Scholarships *(Postgraduate/Scholarship)* [4666]

Letitia B. Carter Scholarships *(Undergraduate, Advanced Professional/Scholarship)* [9649]

David Meador Foundation - Hospitality-Food Service Scholarships *(Undergraduate/Scholarship)* [8241]

GED Jump Start Scholarships *(Professional development/Scholarship)* [9959]

Marcia S. Harris Legacy Fund Scholarships *(Undergraduate, Advanced Professional/Scholarship)* [9650]

IFSEA Worthy Goal Scholarships *(Two Year College, Undergraduate, Vocational/Occupational, Four Year College/Scholarship)* [6005]

International Dairy-Deli-Bakery Association's Scholarship for Growing the Future *(Graduate, Undergraduate/Scholarship)* [5988]

International Foodservice Editorial Council Scholarship *(Graduate/Scholarship)* [6007]

Les Dames D'Escoffier New York Corporate Scholarship *(Undergraduate/Scholarship)* [6777]

Nancy Curry Scholarship *(Vocational/Occupational, Undergraduate, Graduate, Postgraduate/Scholarship, Award)* [9960]

NRAEF Scholarship (Undergraduate/Scholarship) [9651]

Oklahoma Restaurant Association Scholarships (Other/Scholarship) [8612]

Richardson-Applebaum Award (Doctorate, Master's, Graduate/Scholarship) [4662]

Schwan's Food Service Scholarship (Vocational/ Occupational, Professional development/Scholarship, Award) [9961]

Jeff Siegel Memorial Scholarships (Undergraduate/ Scholarship) [8317]

SNF Professional Growth Scholarship (Graduate, Undergraduate, Vocational/Occupational, Postgraduate/Scholarship, Award) [9962]

Winston Build Your Future Scholarship (Graduate, Undergraduate, Vocational/Occupational/Scholarship) [9963]

Foreign languages

AISLS Grants for Language Instruction (Graduate/ Grant) [1049]

ARIT Summer Fellowships for Intensive Advanced Turkish Language Study (Graduate, Undergraduate/Fellowship) [655, 1344, 4914, 11307, 11309]

Audrey L. Wright Scholarship (Undergraduate/Scholarship) [5135]

Pete and Ellen Bensley Memorial Scholarship Fund (Undergraduate/Scholarship) [4721]

Blakemore Freeman Fellowships (Undergraduate, Advanced Professional/Fellowship) [2622]

FLAS Academic Year Fellowships (Graduate, Undergraduate/Fellowship) [11569]

German Society Scholarships (Undergraduate/ Scholarship) [4951]

The Michael J. Hogan Foreign Language Fellowship (Graduate/Fellowship) [10356]

ISCALC International Scholarship Fund (Undergraduate/Scholarship) [4594]

Italian Language Scholarship (Undergraduate/Scholarship) [8690]

Kor Memorial Scholarship (Undergraduate, Graduate/Scholarship) [6570]

Language Teacher Bursary Program (Other/Award) [294]

Languages In Teacher Education Scholarship (Undergraduate/Scholarship) [295]

MACC Scholarships (Other/Scholarship) [7288]

Mead Leadership Fellowships (Professional development/Fellowship) [8482]

Palo Verde High School Barbara Edwards Memorial Scholarship (Undergraduate/Scholarship) [9416]

The Thomas R. Pickering Foreign Affairs Fellowship (Graduate, Undergraduate/Fellowship) [11346, 12050]

Richard J. Schmeelk Fellowship (Graduate/Fellowship) [9934]

Susanna Stover Root Memorial Scholarship (Undergraduate/Scholarship) [6470]

UF Center for Latin American Studies FLAS Summer Fellowships (Master's, Graduate, Undergraduate/Award, Fellowship) [11570]

Forestry

The B. Harper Bull Scholarship Awards (Graduate, Doctorate, Postgraduate/Award) [11060]

Bill Bowie Scholarship (University, Undergraduate, College, Vocational/Occupational/Scholarship) [12293]

Chopivsky Fellowships (Graduate/Fellowship) [11889]

Cecil Earl Clapp, Sr. Memorial Scholarship (Undergraduate/Scholarship) [8505]

Harry Hampton Fund Scholarship (Undergraduate/ Scholarship) [5266]

James L. and Genevieve H. Goodwin Scholarship (Undergraduate/Scholarship) [5334]

L. Gordon "Link" Linkous Scholarship (Undergraduate/Scholarship) [11103]

Ben Meadows Natural Resource Scholarships - Academic Achievement Scholarships (Undergraduate/Scholarship) [4684]

Ben Meadows Natural Resource Scholarships - Leadership Scholarships (Undergraduate/Scholarship) [4685]

NGC College Scholarships (Graduate, Undergraduate/Scholarship) [7900]

NTHA Forest Resources Scholarships for College Students (Undergraduate/Scholarship) [8496]

Frederick K. Weyerhaeuser Forest History Fellowship (Graduate/Fellowship) [4682]

The World Forest Institute International Fellowship (Undergraduate/Fellowship) [12198]

French studies (See also Area and ethnic studies)

ALIS Fellowships for Full-time Studies in French (Undergraduate/Fellowship) [282]

Alliance Francaise of Hartford Harpin/Rohinsky Scholarships (Undergraduate/Scholarship) [5313]

Walter J. Jensen Fellowships (Other/Fellowship) [9081]

Mary Isabel Sibley Fellowship (Doctorate/Fellowship) [9082]

Funeral services (See also Mortuary science)

ABFSE National Scholarship Program (Undergraduate/Scholarship) [697]

NFDA Professional Women's Conference Scholarship (Undergraduate/Scholarship) [4844]

Gaming industry

Wells Fargo American Indian Scholarship Program (Undergraduate/Scholarship) [996]

Gastroenterology

The Crohn's and Colitis Canada Grants-in-Aid of Research program (Advanced Professional, Professional development/Grant) [3908]

Crohn's and Colitis Canada Innovations in IBD Research (Advanced Professional, Professional development/Grant) [3909]

International GI Training Grant (Professional development/Grant) [761]

Gemology

Color Masters Scholarship (Undergraduate/Scholarship) [4875]

George W. Juno Scholarship (Graduate/Scholarship) [4877]

GIA Scholarship - Distance Education eLearning (Graduate/Scholarship) [4878]

Goldia.com Jewelry Scholarships (Undergraduate, Graduate/Scholarship) [5025]

Mikimoto Scholarship (Graduate/Scholarship) [4880]

Patnode Family Scholarship (Undergraduate, University, College, Vocational/Occupational/Scholarship) [12355]

Richard T. Liddicoat Scholarship (Graduate/Scholarship) [4882]

William Goldberg Scholarship (Undergraduate/ Scholarship) [4883]

Worthy Gemological Scholarships (Undergraduate/ Scholarship) [12211]

Genealogy

The ASG Scholar Award (Professional development/ Award) [1463]

General studies/Field of study not specified

1-800-Pain-Free Scholarship (Two Year College, Undergraduate, Graduate/Scholarship) [141]

1Dental Scholarship (Undergraduate, Graduate/ Scholarship) [8]

4-H Youth in Action Awards (Graduate, Undergraduate, Vocational/Occupational, High School, College, University/Scholarship) [7564]

The "21" Endowed Scholarships (Undergraduate/ Scholarship) [6781]

100th Infantry Battalion Veterans Memorial Scholarship Fund (Undergraduate, University, College, Vocational/Occupational/Scholarship) [5374]

$600 Scholarship Opportunity by Pound Coffee (All/ Scholarship) [9260]

$1,000 Scholarship for Veterans (Undergraduate/ Scholarship) [9042]

$1000 uPONICS Hydroponics/Aquaponics Scholarship (Undergraduate/Scholarship) [11761]

$1,500 Annual Video Contest Scholarship for Students (High School, College, University/Scholarship) [6186]

$1500 College Monk Short Essay Scholarship (Undergraduate, Graduate/Scholarship) [3508]

$1,500 Video Contest Scholarship for Students Who Enjoy Writing (High School, College, University/ Scholarship) [3824]

$2,000 College Scholarship for the Business Leaders of Tomorrow (Undergraduate/Scholarship) [2759]

$2,000 Nitro College Scholarship (Community College, University, Undergraduate, Graduate/Scholarship) [8407]

2020 The Nuclear Family Scholarship (College, University, Undergraduate/Scholarship) [6689]

$2,500 College Raptor Scholarship (College, University, Undergraduate, Graduate, Community College/Scholarship) [3510]

$5000 Imagine Scholarship (College, University/ Scholarship) [9755]

The 86211 Scholarship (Undergraduate/Scholarship) [9643]

A-1 Auto Transport Scholarship (Two Year College, Four Year College, Graduate, High School, Vocational/Occupational/Scholarship) [20]

A-2 Joaquim Pereira Memorial Scholarship (Undergraduate/Scholarship) [6935]

A-4 António Mattos Memorial Scholarship (Undergraduate/Scholarship) [6936]

"A Better World" Spirituality and Technology Advancement Scholarship (Undergraduate, Graduate/Scholarship) [3305]

AAAA Scholarship Program (Undergraduate, Graduate/Scholarship) [1911]

AAFSW "Twice Exceptional" Merit Scholarship for High School Seniors, Gap Year, and College Students (Undergraduate/Scholarship) [2024]

AAFSW Merit Scholarship for College Students (College, Undergraduate/Scholarship) [2025]

AAIB Scholarships (Undergraduate/Scholarship) [575]

AAJUW Scholarship (Graduate, Undergraduate/ Scholarship) [579]

A&B Ohana Scholarship Fund (Undergraduate, College, Two Year College, Vocational/Occupational/ Scholarship) [5375]

Aaron Edward Arnoldsen Memorial Scholarship (Undergraduate/Scholarship) [1922]

AAS-American Society for Eighteenth-Century Studies Fellowships (Doctorate/Fellowship) [482]

AAS CIAC Small Grants (Graduate/Grant) [2060]

AAS Korean Studies Scholarship Program (Graduate/Scholarship) [2061]

The AASSC Gurli Aagaard Woods Undergraduate Publication Award (Undergraduate/Award) [2032]

The AASSC Marna Feldt Graduate Publication Award (Graduate/Award) [2033]

AASSC Norwegian Travel Grant (Undergraduate, College, University/Grant) [2034]

AAUW American Fellowships (Doctorate, Postdoctorate/Fellowship) [32]

AAUW Career Development Grants (Graduate, Advanced Professional, Professional development/ Grant) [33]

AAUW Honolulu Branch Education Funds (Undergraduate, Graduate, Master's/Scholarship) [5376]

AAUW International Fellowships (Master's, Doctorate, Postdoctorate/Fellowship) [34]

Anthony Abbene Scholarship Fund (Undergraduate/ Scholarship) [5663]

Clifford V. Abbott Memorial Scholarships (Undergraduate/Scholarship) [10820]

AbbVie Immunology Scholarship (Community College, Undergraduate, Graduate, Vocational/Occupational, Doctorate/Scholarship) [9938]

Alois and Marie Goldmann Scholarship *(Graduate/ Scholarship)* [5675]

Alpha Chi Omega Love and Loyalty Grants *(Professional development/Grant)* [382]

Alpha Chi Sigma Scholarship Awards *(Graduate, Undergraduate/Scholarship)* [384]

Alpha Delta Gamma Educational Foundation Scholarship *(Undergraduate, Graduate/Scholarship)* [386]

Alpha Kappa Alpha - Educational Advancement Foundation Undergraduate Financial Need-Based Scholarships *(Undergraduate/Scholarship)* [388]

Alpha Kappa Alpha - Educational Advancement Foundation Undergraduate Merit Scholarships *(Undergraduate/Scholarship)* [389]

Alpha Kappa Trust Scholarship-Beta Omega *(Undergraduate/Scholarship)* [10091]

Alpha Tau Omega Graduate Scholarship *(Graduate/ Scholarship)* [401]

Alpha Tau Omega Undergraduate Scholarships *(Undergraduate/Scholarship)* [402]

Martin K. Alsup and Frank Schroeder Memorial Music Scholarship *(Undergraduate/Scholarship)* [8830]

Altrusa International of Grand Rapids Scholarship *(Undergraduate/Scholarship)* [5133]

Alumni Endowed Scholarship *(Undergraduate/ Scholarship)* [2840]

Jaedyn Amann Memorial Scholarship *(Undergraduate, Master's/Scholarship)* [12282]

The Amato Sanita Brighter Future Scholarship *(Undergraduate, Graduate, Advanced Professional/ Scholarship)* [9876]

Amelia and Emanuel Nessell Family Scholarship Fund *(Undergraduate/Scholarship)* [4197]

Americal Legacy Foundation Scholarship *(Undergraduate/Scholarship)* [420]

American Association of University Women Career Development Grants *(Postgraduate/Grant)* [665]

American Association of University Women International Fellowships *(Graduate, Postgraduate, Master's/Fellowship)* [666]

American Association of University Women(AAUW) Sue Gottcent Memorial Scholarship Fund *(Undergraduate, Graduate/Scholarship)* [10670]

American Association for Women in Community Colleges Doctoral Scholarship *(Undergraduate/Scholarship)* [671]

American Association for Women in Community Colleges LEADERS Institute Scholarship *(Other/ Scholarship)* [672]

American Council of the Blind Scholarships *(Graduate, Undergraduate/Scholarship)* [803]

American Darts Organization Memorial Youth National Scholarship *(Undergraduate/Scholarship)* [851]

American Dissertation Fellowships *(Doctorate, Postdoctorate/Fellowship)* [669]

American Foreign Service Association Scholarship Fund Program *(Undergraduate/Scholarship)* [912]

American Indian Endowed Scholarship *(Graduate, Undergraduate/Scholarship)* [11916]

American Legion Boys/Girls State Scholarship *(High School/Scholarship)* [6782]

American Legion Department of Vermont Scholarship *(Undergraduate/Scholarship)* [1075]

American Legion Eagle Scout of the Year *(Undergraduate/Scholarship)* [7843]

American Legion Florence/Lauderdale Post 11 Scholarship *(Undergraduate, Community College/ Scholarship)* [8501]

The American Legion Legacy Scholarship *(Undergraduate/Scholarship)* [1070]

The American Life Fund Scholarship *(Undergraduate, Graduate/Scholarship)* [1086]

American Lung Association Biomedical Research Grants (RG) *(Doctorate/Grant)* [1094]

American Patriot Scholarship *(Undergraduate/Scholarship, Monetary)* [7388]

American-Scandinavian Foundation Fellowships/ Grants in the United States *(Graduate, Professional development/Fellowship, Grant)* [1372]

American-Scandinavian Foundation Fellowships to Study in Scandinavia *(Graduate/Fellowship)* [1373]

American Water Ski Educational Foundation Scholarships *(Undergraduate/Scholarship)* [11778]

T. Thomas Amirian Memorial Grant *(Undergraduate/ Scholarship)* [1860]

AMLN Scholarships for Arab American Students *(Graduate, Undergraduate/Scholarship)* [1127]

AMVETS National Scholarships - Entering College Freshmen *(Undergraduate/Scholarship)* [1696]

AMVETS National Scholarships - For Veterans *(Undergraduate/Scholarship)* [1697]

AMVETS National Scholarships - JROTC *(Undergraduate, College/Medal)* [1698]

Anaheim Police Survivors and Scholarship Fund *(Undergraduate/Scholarship)* [1703]

Anchor Scholarship Foundation Scholarships *(Undergraduate, Four Year College, Two Year College/Scholarship)* [1705]

Andersen Nontraditional Scholarships for Women's Education and Retraining (ANSWER) *(Undergraduate/Scholarship)* [4717]

Anderson Cummings AC Scholarship for Higher Education *(Undergraduate/Scholarship)* [1707]

Anderson Niskanen Scholarship Fund *(Graduate/ Scholarship)* [4198]

Andrea Will Memorial Scholarship *(Undergraduate/ Scholarship)* [10093]

Andrew Foster Scholarship *(Undergraduate/Scholarship)* [7720]

Androscoggin County Chamber of Commerce Adult Scholarships *(Professional development/Scholarship)* [6825]

Angus Foundation Scholarships *(Undergraduate, Graduate/Scholarship)* [7965]

Angus Foundation Undergraduate Student Scholarships *(Undergraduate/Scholarship)* [1713]

Annabel Lambeth Jones Brevard College Merit Scholarship Fund *(Undergraduate/Scholarship)* [4718]

Anne L. "Annie" Alexander and Blaise Robert "B R" Alexander *(Undergraduate/Scholarship)* [4583]

Anne Lowe Scholarship *(Undergraduate/Scholarship, Award)* [3323]

Anne M. Fassett Scholarship Fund *(Undergraduate, Graduate/Scholarship)* [10671]

Annette and Ernest Keith Memorial Scholarship *(Undergraduate/Scholarship)* [9520]

Annie Wagner Memorial Scholarship Fund *(Undergraduate/Scholarship)* [3336]

Annual Bloom Legal Scholarship for Students Affected by Cerebral Palsy *(Community College, Undergraduate/Scholarship)* [2628]

Annual CGTrader Scholarship *(High School, Undergraduate, Graduate/Scholarship)* [3269]

Annual Educational Scholarships *(Undergraduate/ Scholarship)* [7566]

Annual Pool Cleaner Scholarship *(Undergraduate, Postgraduate/Scholarship)* [7523]

Anthony Munoz Scholarship Fund *(Undergraduate/ Scholarship)* [7501]

APHF Academic Scholarship *(Undergraduate/Scholarship)* [1204]

APIASF Scholarships *(Undergraduate/Scholarship)* [1994]

APLA Merit Award *(Professional development/Scholarship)* [2344]

APT US&C Scholarships *(Advanced Professional/ Scholarship)* [2271]

ARAFCS Doctoral Scholarship *(Doctorate, Graduate/Scholarship)* [1821]

ARAFCS Masters Scholarship *(Graduate, Master's/ Scholarship)* [1822]

Ararat Association Scholarship Grant *(Undergraduate/Scholarship)* [1861]

Archie Hartwell Nash Memorial Scholarship Fund *(Graduate, Undergraduate/Scholarship)* [3601]

Arctic Physical Therapy Scholarship *(Undergraduate/Scholarship)* [1794]

A.R.F.O.R.A. Undergraduate Scholarships for Women *(Undergraduate/Scholarship)* [1366]

ARIT Summer Fellowships for Intensive Advanced Turkish Language Study *(Graduate, Undergraduate/Fellowship)* [655, 1344, 4914, 11307, 11309]

Arkansas Single Parent Scholarship *(Undergraduate, Graduate/Scholarship)* [1836]

Connie "Chelo" Armendariz Memorial Scholarships *(Undergraduate/Scholarship)* [9521]

Armenian American Veterans' Association of Worcester Scholarship *(Undergraduate/Scholarship)* [1862]

Armenian Professional Society Graduate Student Scholarship *(Graduate/Scholarship)* [1852]

Robert Armstrong Memorial Scholarship *(Undergraduate, Master's/Scholarship)* [12284]

ARS Undergraduate Scholarship *(Undergraduate/ Scholarship)* [1855]

Ardemis, Armenoohy, and Arpi Arsenian Memorial Grant *(Undergraduate/Scholarship)* [1863]

Arthritis Champions Scholarship *(Undergraduate, Graduate/Scholarship, Monetary)* [1970]

Arthur H. Daniels Memorial Scholarship *(Undergraduate/Scholarship)* [9522]

Arthur and Juna Fisher Memorial Track Scholarship *(Undergraduate/Scholarship)* [9523]

Arthur M. & Berdena King Eagle Scout Scholarship *(Undergraduate/Scholarship)* [7844]

Artificial Intelligence & Ethics *(Graduate, Undergraduate/Scholarship)* [12]

ASBA College Scholarship Grant Program *(Professional development/Scholarship)* [1381]

ASECS Graduate Student Research Paper Award *(Graduate/Prize)* [1426]

ASECS Innovative Course Design Competition *(Undergraduate/Award)* [1427]

ASEH Minority Travel Grants *(Graduate, Other/ Grant)* [1449]

Diana Ashe-Clayton Memorial Scholarship *(Undergraduate/Scholarship)* [8502]

Ashley E. Ketcher Memorial Scholarship *(Undergraduate/Scholarship)* [3667]

Asia Pacific Foundation of Canada Junior Research Fellowships *(Undergraduate, Master's/Fellowship)* [4711]

Asia Pacific Foundation of Canada Post-Graduate Research Fellowships *(Master's, Doctorate/Fellowship)* [4713]

Asian Development Bank - Japan Scholarship Program *(Graduate, Master's/Scholarship)* [4261]

Asian and Pacific Islander Queer Sisters Scholarship (APIQS) *(Undergraduate/Scholarship)* [9289]

ASIS Foundation Chapter Matching Scholarship *(Undergraduate/Scholarship)* [1996]

ASIST Scholarship (ASIST) *(Professional development/Scholarship)* [4463]

Darrell and Palchie Asselin Scholarship Fund *(Undergraduate/Scholarship)* [4199]

Association for the Advancement of Baltic Studies Dissertation Grants for Graduate Students *(Doctorate/Grant)* [2030]

Association for Compensatory Educators of Texas Paraprofessionals Scholarships *(Other/Scholarship)* [2141]

Association for Compensatory Educators of Texas Students *(Graduate/Scholarship)* [2142]

Association of Donor Recruitment Professionals Hughes Scholarships *(Other/Scholarship)* [2150]

Association of Donor Recruitment Professionals Presidential Scholarships *(Other/Scholarship)* [2151]

Association of the United States Navy Scholarships *(Undergraduate/Scholarship)* [2303]

Marguerite Chapootian Atamian Memorial Grant *(Undergraduate/Scholarship)* [1865]

Atlanta Alumnae Chapter Achievement Scholarship *(Undergraduate/Scholarship)* [3999]

Atlas Shrugged Essay Contest *(Graduate, Undergraduate, High School/Prize)* [2395]

Audrey Loftus Memorial Scholarship *(University/ Scholarship)* [11516]

A. B. and Hazel Augenstein Scholarship *(Undergraduate/Scholarship)* [7078]

Austin Alumnae Association Beta Xi Scholarship in Memory of Katherine Peeres Woolridge *(Undergraduate/Scholarship)* [6400]

Autism/ASD Scholarship *(Community College, Four Year College, Graduate, Vocational/Occupational, Professional development/Scholarship)* [6518]

Autism Scholarship *(Community College, Four Year College, Vocational/Occupational/Scholarship)* [4537]

Autism Scholarship *(High School, Two Year College, Four Year College, Graduate, Vocational/Occupational, Professional development/Scholarship)* [2617, 4051]

Autism Scholarship *(Two Year College, Four Year College, Vocational/Occupational/Scholarship)* [9712]

Auto Accident Law Firm Survivor Scholarships *(Graduate/Scholarship)* [1758]

Ava's Grace Scholarship Program *(Graduate, Undergraduate/Scholarship)* [9949]

AWMA Niagara Frontier Section College Scholarship *(Graduate, Undergraduate/Scholarship)* [169]

AX Control, Inc. Academic Scholarship *(College/Scholarship)* [2391]

AXA Achievement Scholarship *(Undergraduate/Scholarship)* [2393]

Susan Ayers Memorial Scholarships *(Undergraduate/Scholarship)* [9391]

Ayn Rand Institute Anthem Essay Contest *(High School, Undergraduate/Prize)* [2396]

Ayn Rand Institute Fountainhead Essay Contest *(High School, Undergraduate/Prize)* [2397]

John M. Azarian Memorial Armenian Youth Scholarship Fund *(Undergraduate/Scholarship)* [2399]

B-2 LAFF 20-30's Financial Aid Scholarship *(Postgraduate/Scholarship)* [6937]

B-3 LAFF 20-30's Financial Aid Scholarship *(Professional development/Scholarship)* [6938]

B-4 Albert S. Vieira Memorial Scholarship *(Professional development/Scholarship)* [6939]

B-Brave McMahon/Stratton Scholarship Fund *(Undergraduate/Scholarship)* [4584]

B. J. Runnels Dean Scholarship Fund *(Undergraduate/Scholarship)* [3602]

Back to School Scholarship *(All/Scholarship)* [7437]

BAFTX Early Starters Award *(Undergraduate/Award)* [2696]

BAFTX Graduate Award *(Graduate/Award)* [2697]

BAFTX Junior Achievers Award *(Undergraduate/Award)* [2698]

BAFTX Undergraduate Award *(Undergraduate/Award)* [2699]

Baha'i Faith Scholarship for Racial Harmony *(Undergraduate/Scholarship)* [9524]

The Bailey Family Foundation College Scholarship Program *(Undergraduate/Scholarship)* [2403]

The Bailey Family Foundation High School Scholarships Program *(Undergraduate/Scholarship)* [2404]

Esther Tuttle Bailey Memorial Scholarship *(Undergraduate/Scholarship)* [6401]

Lincoln C. Bailey Memorial Scholarship Fund *(Undergraduate/Scholarship)* [6079]

Barbara Bailey Scholarship *(Undergraduate/Scholarship)* [9291]

Mark B. Bain Graduate Fellowship *(Doctorate, Master's, Graduate/Fellowship)* [5612]

Marian Wood Baird Scholarship *(Undergraduate/Scholarship)* [11401]

Baker Scholarship *(Doctorate, Professional development/Scholarship)* [4888]

Victoria Baldwin Memorial Scholarship *(Undergraduate, Master's/Scholarship)* [12285]

Balfour Scholarship *(Graduate/Scholarship)* [9087]

Ballard Family Foundation Scholarships *(Undergraduate/Scholarship)* [9800]

Irene Ballinger Memorial Scholarship *(Undergraduate/Scholarship)* [7079]

Bambi Bailey Scholarship Fund *(Undergraduate/Scholarship)* [3589]

Brenda S. Bank Educational Workshop Scholarship *(Undergraduate/Scholarship)* [10341]

Bank of Hawaii Foundation Scholarship Fund *(Undergraduate, University, College, Two Year College/Scholarship)* [5382]

Banting Postdoctoral Fellowships Program *(Postdoctorate/Fellowship)* [3804]

Barakat Trust and Barakat Foundation Scholarships *(Graduate, Postdoctorate/Scholarship)* [1767]

Barbara Bonnema Memorial Scholarship *(Undergraduate/Scholarship)* [9525]

Barbara Hagan Richards Scholarship Fund *(Undergraduate/Scholarship)* [3603]

Barbara and Nicole Heacox Foreign Study & Travel Scholarship *(Undergraduate/Scholarship)* [5068]

Joe Barbarow Memorial Scholarship *(Undergraduate/Scholarship)* [8832]

Barber-Owen-Thomas Scholarship *(Undergraduate/Scholarship)* [10095]

Edgar Barge Memorial Scholarship *(Undergraduate/Scholarship)* [5118]

Baron and Budd Attorneys Mesothelioma Cancer Victims Memorial Scholarships *(College, University/Scholarship)* [2437]

Barr Foundation Scholarship *(Undergraduate/Scholarship)* [3337]

Barrett Family Scholarship Fund *(Undergraduate/Scholarship)* [3338]

Barry "Tyler" Rhea Memorial Scholarship *(Undergraduate/Scholarship)* [8503]

The Jean Bartel Military Scholarship *(Undergraduate/Scholarship)* [7415]

The Bascom Hill Society Scholarship *(Undergraduate/Scholarship)* [11734]

W. H. (Bert) Bates Oxford Cup Scholarship *(Undergraduate, Graduate/Scholarship)* [2503]

Marian Sims Baughn Scholarship *(Undergraduate/Scholarship)* [6402]

Hazel Reed Baumeister Scholarship Program *(Undergraduate/Scholarship)* [10130]

Timothy Baylink Good Fellowship Awards *(Undergraduate/Fellowship)* [9526]

Bayly-Tiffany Scholarships *(Undergraduate/Scholarship)* [11712]

BBPA First Generation Scholarships *(College, University, Undergraduate/Scholarship)* [2587]

BCCC Foundation General Scholarship Fund *(Undergraduate/Scholarship)* [2414]

BCCC Workforce Creation Scholarship *(Undergraduate/Scholarship)* [2415]

BCPF Bursaries *(Undergraduate/Scholarship)* [10731]

BCSF Scholarships *(Undergraduate/Scholarship)* [2604]

BDC Visiting Fellowship *(Advanced Professional, Professional development/Fellowship)* [2715]

Suzanne Beauregard Scholarships *(Undergraduate, Graduate/Scholarship)* [5027]

Beaver Medical Clinic Foundation - Dr. Glenn Adams Memorial Award *(Undergraduate/Scholarship)* [9527]

Beaver Medical Clinic Foundation - H.E.A.R.T. Academy Award *(Undergraduate/Scholarship)* [9528]

Beaver Medical Clinic Foundation - Premedical Award *(Undergraduate/Scholarship)* [9529]

BECA General Scholarship *(Undergraduate/Scholarship)* [2461]

Becas Univision Scholarship Program *(Undergraduate, Graduate/Scholarship)* [5528]

Stephen D. Bechtel, Jr. Oxford Cup Scholarship *(Undergraduate, Graduate/Scholarship)* [2504]

Dennis J. Beck Memorial Scholarship *(Undergraduate/Scholarship)* [6193]

Garvin L. Beck Scholarships *(Undergraduate/Scholarship)* [9530]

BEF General Academic Scholarships *(Undergraduate, Graduate/Scholarship)* [4438]

BEF Sacks For CF Scholarship *(Graduate, Undergraduate/Scholarship)* [4439]

Notah Begay III Scholarship Program *(Undergraduate/Scholarship)* [317]

Alfred D. Bell, Jr. Travel Grants *(Graduate/Grant)* [4681]

John Bell and Lawrence Thornton Scholarship Fund *(Undergraduate/Scholarship)* [5315]

The Betty Bell Scholarship Fund *(Undergraduate/Scholarship)* [5548]

Bellevue PFLAG Scholarships *(Graduate, High School/Scholarship)* [9292]

Ben Robinette Scholarship Fund *(Undergraduate/Scholarship)* [4720]

Benbrook Scholarship *(Graduate/Scholarship)* [1838]

Benchwarmers Club of Redlands Scholarship- Jess Mercado Memorial *(Undergraduate/Scholarship)* [9531]

H. Y. Benedict Fellowships *(Graduate/Fellowship)* [376]

George Benes, MD & Michael Mallee, EdD Point Scholarships *(Undergraduate, Graduate, Doctorate/Scholarship)* [9218]

Benjamin Riggs Scholarship *(Undergraduate/Scholarship)* [4916]

Bertram W. Bennett Memorial Scholarship *(Undergraduate, Graduate/Scholarship)* [2505]

Bennett – Reverend E.F. Bennett Scholarship *(Undergraduate/Scholarship)* [3465]

Bergman Scholarship *(Undergraduate/Scholarship)* [8460]

Bergmann Family Scholarship *(Undergraduate/Scholarship)* [7080]

The Joseph Berkman, and Michael and Sarah Chipkin Holocaust/Genocide Studies Award *(Graduate/Scholarship)* [10842]

Bernard Amtmann Fellowship *(Postgraduate, Other/Fellowship)* [2569]

Bernard B. and Mary L. Brusin Scholarship Fund *(Undergraduate/Scholarship)* [4201]

Richard L. Bernardi Memorial Scholarship *(Undergraduate/Scholarship)* [3668]

Jean Clark Berry Scholarship *(Undergraduate, Graduate/Scholarship)* [6403]

James R. and Geraldine F. Bertelsen Scholarship *(Undergraduate/Scholarship)* [9802]

Henry Besner Memorial Scholarship *(Undergraduate, Master's/Scholarship)* [12287]

Best Foot Forward Scholarship *(Undergraduate, College, University/Scholarship)* [5203]

The Best Hoverboard Scholarship Era *(College, University/Scholarship)* [2492]

Booksrun Scholarship Financial Aid *(Undergraduate, Graduate/Scholarship)* [2653]

Beta Foundation Merit Scholarships *(Graduate, Undergraduate/Scholarship)* [2506]

Beta Gamma Memorial Scholarship *(Undergraduate/Scholarship)* [4000]

Beta Lambda Project 2000 Scholarship *(Undergraduate/Scholarship)* [6404]

Beta Mu Project 2000 Scholarship *(Undergraduate/Scholarship)* [6405]

Beta Pi Project 2000 Scholarship in Memory of Kristy LeMond *(Undergraduate/Scholarship)* [6406]

Beta Pi Sigma Sorority Local Chapter Scholarship (BPSSS) *(Undergraduate/Scholarship)* [2501]

Beta Sigma Scholarship *(Undergraduate/Scholarship)* [10096]

Beta Tau Scholarship Fund *(Undergraduate/Scholarship)* [6408]

Beta Theta Memorial Scholarship *(Graduate, Undergraduate/Scholarship)* [6409]

Beta Xi Project 2000 Scholarship *(Undergraduate/Scholarship)* [6410]

Beta Zeta Project 2000 Scholarship *(Undergraduate/Scholarship)* [6411]

Beth Carew Memorial Scholarship Program *(Undergraduate/Scholarship)* [7920]

Beth K. Fields Scholarship *(University/Scholarship)* [11574]

Bethune-Cookman University Excelsior Level 1 Scholarship *(Undergraduate/Scholarship)* [2564]

Bethune-Cookman University Presidential Scholarship *(Undergraduate/Scholarship)* [2565]

Beverley Mascoll Scholarship *(Undergraduate/Scholarship)* [2588]

Beyond the Cure Ambassador Scholarship Program *(Community College, College, Undergraduate, Graduate, Vocational/Occupational/Scholarship)* [7767]

Timothy Bierlmeier Memorial Scholarships *(Undergraduate, Master's/Scholarship)* [12288]

Bill Dickey Scholarship Association Scholarship *(Undergraduate, High School/Scholarship)* [4082]

Bill McCarthy Boy Scout Scholarship Fund *(Undergraduate/Scholarship)* [10752]

Joan Bilton Scholarship *(Undergraduate, College, University, Vocational/Occupational/Scholarship)* [12289]

Helen & Bob Bintz Scholarship *(Undergraduate/Scholarship)* [7081]

Birmingham-Southern College Eagle Scout Scholarships *(Undergraduate/Scholarship)* [7845]

Birmingham Student Scholarships *(Undergraduate/Scholarship)* [2580]

Dr. Richard E. Bjork Memorial Graduate Study Award *(Graduate/Scholarship)* [10843]

Law Offices of David A. Black Annual Hearing Impaired Scholarships *(All/Scholarship)* [6701]

Black Men Building Resources Scholarship *(Undergraduate/Scholarship)* [5137]

NICSA/William T. Blackwell Scholarship Fund *(Undergraduate/Scholarship)* [7952]

Kyle R. Blanco Memorial Scholarship *(Undergraduate, Graduate/Scholarship)* [2507]

Blaski Alex Memorial Scholarship *(Undergraduate/Scholarship)* [9657]

Bob and Linda Kohlhepp Scholarship Fund *(Undergraduate/Scholarship)* [3339]

Sandra Bobbitt Continuing Education Scholarship *(Undergraduate/Scholarship)* [2254]

BOCA Scholarship *(Undergraduate/Scholarship)* [8796]

Gerald J. and Helen Bogen Fund *(Undergraduate/Scholarship)* [5225]

Sarkis Bogosian Memorial Grant *(Undergraduate/Scholarship)* [1866]

Therese and David Bohbot Scholarship *(Undergraduate/Scholarship)* [6285]

Bolick Foreign Student Scholarships *(Undergraduate/Scholarship)* [11439]

Brian Bolton Graduate/Mature Student Essay Awards *(Graduate/Award)* [4823]

BOMA/NY Scholarship *(Undergraduate/Scholarship)* [2741]

Boomer Benefits Scholarship *(Undergraduate, Graduate/Scholarship)* [2655]

Booz Allen Hawaii Scholarship Fund *(Undergraduate, Four Year College, University/Scholarship)* [5384]

Borden Inc. Scholarship Fund *(Undergraduate/Scholarship)* [3340]

Borek Maria and Czeslaw Scholarship *(Undergraduate/Scholarship)* [9658]

David L. Boren Undergraduate Scholarships *(Graduate, Undergraduate/Scholarship)* [2184]

Boston City Federation "Return to School" Scholarships *(Undergraduate, Graduate/Scholarship)* [4897]

Boston Intercollegiate Alumnae Association Adelphe Scholarship *(Undergraduate/Scholarship)* [6412]

The Dr. George T. Bottomley Scholarship *(Undergraduate/Scholarship)* [4835, 7166]

Herbie Bouwman Memorial Scholarship *(Undergraduate, Master's/Scholarship)* [12292]

Dr. Howard L. Bowen Scholarship *(Undergraduate/Scholarship)* [7005]

Billy Bowling Memorial Scholarship *(Undergraduate/Scholarship)* [8504]

Bowties and Books Scholarship *(Undergraduate, College, University/Scholarship)* [2661]

Boy Scouts of America Troop 3 Art Till/Nathan E. Smith Memorial Scholarship *(Undergraduate, Vocational/Occupational/Scholarship)* [9532]

Dr. Betty J. Boyd-Beu and Edwin G. Beu, Jr. Scholarships *(Undergraduate/Scholarship)* [11440]

W. Scott Boyd Group Grant *(Advanced Professional/Grant)* [5951]

BPW Foundation Career Advancement Scholarships *(Undergraduate/Scholarship)* [2761]

Charles Bradley Memorial Scholarships *(Undergraduate/Scholarship)* [5300]

Byard Braley Scholarship *(Undergraduate/Scholarship)* [6156]

The Helen and Edward Brancati Teacher Development Scholarship *(Professional development, Postgraduate/Scholarship)* [3148]

The Branch Out Scholarship *(Undergraduate, College, University/Scholarship)* [2582]

The Brandenburg Education Scholarship *(College, University, Undergraduate/Scholarship)* [6270]

Brandon Magalassi Memorial Scholarship Foundation Scholarship Awards *(Undergraduate/Scholarship)* [6971]

Brem - Marion Luna Brem/Pat McNeil Health and Education Endowment *(Undergraduate/Scholarship)* [3466]

Breslauer Family Scholarships *(Undergraduate/Scholarship)* [9803]

Hilda E. Bretzlaff Foundation Scholarships *(Undergraduate/Scholarship, Grant)* [2687]

Brian Cummins Memorial Scholarship *(Undergraduate/Scholarship)* [5317]

The Tommy Bright Scholarship Fund *(Undergraduate/Scholarship)* [5549]

Margaret Brine Graduate Scholarships For Women *(Graduate, Master's, Doctorate/Scholarship)* [2978]

Bristol-Myers Squibb Scholarship for Cancer Survivors *(Community College, Four Year College, Vocational/Occupational, Undergraduate/Scholarship)* [9940]

Louise A. Broderick San Diego County Scholarship *(Undergraduate/Scholarship)* [9804]

Louis J. Brody Q.C. Entrance Scholarships *(Graduate/Scholarship)* [12248]

Peter F. Bronfman Scholarships of Merit *(Postgraduate/Scholarship)* [12249]

Seth R. and Corinne H. Brooks Memorial Scholarships *(Undergraduate/Scholarship)* [2508]

Dorothy B. Brothers Executive Scholarship Program *(Undergraduate/Scholarship)* [12155]

William G. Broughton Fellowship for Outstanding Achievement *(Undergraduate, Graduate, Vocational/Occupational, Other/Fellowship)* [4975]

Fred and Mary Jane Brower Scholarship *(Undergraduate, Graduate/Scholarship)* [2509]

D.C. and Virginia Brown Scholarship *(Undergraduate/Scholarship)* [3467]

Long-term Fellowship *(Graduate, Doctorate/Fellowship)* [2719]

John Carter Brown Library Short-Term Fellowships *(Doctorate, Postdoctorate/Fellowship)* [2720]

Catherine Amelia Thew Brown Memorial Scholarship *(Undergraduate/Scholarship)* [7082]

Ronald H. Brown Memorial Scholarship *(Undergraduate/Scholarship)* [11408]

Jesse Brown Memorial Youth Scholarship Program *(Advanced Professional/Scholarship)* [4107]

Edward M. Brown Oxford Cup Scholarship *(Undergraduate, Graduate/Scholarship)* [2510]

Bernice & Gordon Brown Scholarship *(Undergraduate/Scholarship)* [6287]

Harry and Lucille Brown Scholarship *(Undergraduate/Scholarship)* [5138]

Ron Brown Scholarship *(Undergraduate/Scholarship)* [2722]

Murray L. Brown Scholarships *(Undergraduate/Scholarship)* [7006]

Bruce and Marjorie Sundlun Scholarship *(Undergraduate/Scholarship)* [9690]

Bruce Shelton Scholarship *(Undergraduate, High School/Scholarship)* [12064]

The Robert W. Brunsman Memorial Scholarship *(Professional development/Scholarship)* [6041]

Bryant Essay Scholarships *(Undergraduate, Graduate/Scholarship)* [2731]

Bryant Visual Content Scholarships *(Undergraduate, Graduate/Scholarship)* [2732]

Bryce/Lietzke/Martin Scholarship *(Undergraduate/Scholarship)* [8834]

Hermine Buchakian Scholarship Grant *(Undergraduate/Scholarship)* [1868]

Frederick S. Bucholz Scholarship *(Undergraduate, Graduate/Scholarship)* [2511]

Peter Buck Fellowships Program - Graduate *(Graduate/Fellowship)* [10199]

Peter Buck Fellowships Program - Postdoctoral *(Postdoctorate/Fellowship)* [10200]

William & Martha Buckingham Scholarship *(Undergraduate/Scholarship)* [7083]

Bunnell Scholarships *(Undergraduate/Scholarship)* [11441]

George M. Burditt Scholarships *(Undergraduate/Scholarship)* [2181]

Adam S. Burford Memorial Scholarship *(Undergraduate, Graduate/Scholarship)* [2512]

Freda Burge Scholarship *(Undergraduate/Scholarship)* [8835]

Burger King Employee Scholars Program *(Undergraduate/Scholarship)* [2747]

Burger King Scholars Program *(Undergraduate/Scholarship)* [2748]

Loyal D. Burkett Memorial Scholarships *(Undergraduate/Scholarship)* [11442]

Business, Education and Technology Scholarships *(Graduate, Undergraduate/Scholarship)* [362]

Buster Lindsay Memorial Scholarship *(Undergraduate, High School/Scholarship)* [3670]

Buster Pool Memorial Scholarship Fund *(Undergraduate/Scholarship)* [3605]

Buzzell, Welsh & Hill College Scholarship Program *(Graduate/Scholarship)* [2769]

BWI Scholarship *(Undergraduate, Community College, University/Scholarship)* [2771]

Leon C. Bynoe Memorial Scholarships *(Undergraduate/Scholarship)* [11683]

Thad Byrne Memorial Scholarship *(Undergraduate, Graduate/Scholarship)* [2513]

George J. Bysiewicz Scholarship Fund *(Other/Scholarship)* [3590]

C. Rodney Demarest Memorial Scholarship *(Undergraduate/Scholarship)* [5318]

CAG Health and Health Care Study Group Awards *(Graduate/Award)* [2085]

Calamus Foundation Point Scholarship *(Undergraduate, Graduate, Doctorate/Scholarship)* [9219]

Caledonia Alumni Association Scholarship *(Graduate/Scholarship)* [7085]

Charlotte Calfian Scholarship Grant *(Undergraduate/Scholarship)* [1869]

Calhoun Valedictorian, Salutatorian/Top 5 Scholarships *(Other/Scholarship)* [2777]

California Council of the Blind Scholarships *(Undergraduate, Graduate, Vocational/Occupational/Scholarship)* [2794]

Harry D. Callahan Educational Trust *(Undergraduate/Scholarship)* [10754]

John L. Calvert Memorial Scholarship *(Undergraduate, Graduate/Scholarship)* [2514]

Calvin Alumni Association-Washington, D.C. Scholarships *(Undergraduate/Scholarship)* [2844]

Camden County College Foundation Scholarships *(Undergraduate/Scholarship, Award)* [2860]

Camilla C. Johnson Scholarship *(Undergraduate/Scholarship)* [5139]

Camp Network Counselor Appreciation Scholarships *(Undergraduate/Scholarship)* [2866]

Lucille Campbell Scholarship Fund *(Undergraduate, High School/Scholarship)* [11943]

Theodore R. Campbell Scholarship *(Undergraduate/Scholarship)* [286]

Canada-Ukraine Parliamentary Program Internship Scholarships (CUPP) *(Undergraduate/Scholarship, Internship)* [11888]

Canadian Federation of Independent Grocers National Scholarship *(Undergraduate/Scholarship)* [4531]

Canadian Federation of University Women Etobicoke Bursary *(Undergraduate/Scholarship)* [11684]

Canadian Hard of Hearing Association Scholarship Program *(Undergraduate/Scholarship)* [2997]

Canadian Iranian Foundation Scholarship *(Undergraduate/Scholarship)* [3035]

The Canadian Parking Association Scholarship (CPA) *(Undergraduate/Scholarship)* [2125]

Canadian Seniors' Golf Association Scholarships *(Undergraduate/Scholarship)* [5028]

Cancer for College Scholarship *(Graduate, Undergraduate/Scholarship)* [3138]

Cancer Survivors' Fund Scholarship *(Undergraduate/Scholarship)* [3146]

Commander Ronald J. Cantin Scholarships *(Undergraduate/Scholarship)* [3454]

CAP Student Leadership Award *(Undergraduate/Scholarship)* [2910]

Kasie Ford Capling Memorial Scholarship Endowment Fund *(Undergraduate/Scholarship)* [4723]

The Lester J. Cappon Fellowship in Documentary Editing *(Postdoctorate/Fellowship)* [8370]

CAPT Winifred Quick Collins, USN (Ret.) Scholarship *(Undergraduate/Scholarship)* [8172]

Captain Jodi Callahan Memorial Scholarship *(Graduate, Master's/Scholarship)* [147]

The CarBrain.com Scholarship *(Two Year College, Undergraduate, Graduate, High School/Scholarship)* [3155]

Daniel Cardillo Charitable Fund *(Professional development/Scholarship)* [6975]

CardRates.com Financial Futures Scholarship *(Community College/Scholarship)* [3161]

Career Enhancement Grant *(Professional development/Grant)* [4432]

CareerFitter Online Scholarship *(Undergraduate, Graduate/Scholarship)* [3165]

Carl E. Brooks Scholarship Fund *(Undergraduate/Scholarship)* [10673]

Carl H. Lindner Family Fund *(Undergraduate/Scholarship)* [3341]

Carl & Lucille Jarrett Scholarship Fund *(Undergraduate/Scholarship)* [4587]

William F. Carl Scholarships *(Undergraduate/Scholarship)* [8443]

Gladys Ross Carlson Adelphe Scholarship Fund *(Undergraduate, Graduate/Scholarship)* [6413]

Carnegie Observatories Graduate Research Fellowships *(Graduate, Doctorate/Fellowship)* [3173]

Herb Carnegie Scholarship *(Undergraduate/Scholarship)* [2590]

Carol Anne Letheren Entrance Award *(Postgraduate/Award)* [12250]

The Carolina Panthers Players Sam Mills Memorial Scholarship *(Undergraduate/Scholarship)* [4724]

Carolinas-Virginias Hardware Scholarship *(Undergraduate/Scholarship)* [4725]

Carolyn Gallmeyer Scholarship *(Undergraduate/Scholarship)* [5140]

Carolyn Wones Recruitment Grant *(Undergraduate/Grant)* [3671]

Karin Carton Scholarship *(Graduate/Scholarship)* [4850]

Orin Carver Scholarship *(Undergraduate/Scholarship)* [3703]

Cascara Vacation Rentals Hospitality Matters Scholarships *(Undergraduate, Graduate/Scholarship)* [3181]

Joe & Peggy Casey Memorial Scholarship *(Undergraduate/Scholarship)* [7087]

George H. and Anna Casper Fund *(Undergraduate, Graduate/Scholarship, Loan)* [10755]

Thomas D. and Karen H. Cassady Scholarship *(Undergraduate, Graduate/Scholarship)* [2515]

Castellini Foundation Scholarship *(Undergraduate/Scholarship)* [3342]

Kerri Castellini Women's Leadership Scholarship *(Undergraduate, Graduate, Community College/Scholarship)* [9280]

Castle & Cooke George W.Y. Yim Scholarship Fund *(Undergraduate, Graduate, Two Year College, Four Year College, University/Scholarship)* [5386]

Castle & Cooke Mililani Technology Park Scholarship Fund *(Undergraduate, University, Four Year College/Scholarship)* [5387]

Catholic Relief Services Summer Internship *(Undergraduate, Graduate/Internship)* [3188]

Catrala - Hawaii Scholarship Fund *(Undergraduate, University, Two Year College, Four Year College/Scholarship)* [5388]

Ben and Vicky Cayetano Scholarship Fund *(Undergraduate, College, University, Two Year College/Scholarship)* [5389]

CBC Spouses Education Scholarship *(Graduate, Undergraduate/Scholarship)* [3738]

CCGSE Mentorship Award *(Graduate/Award)* [10261]

CCU Endowed Scholarships *(Undergraduate/Scholarship)* [3528]

C.D. Howard Scholarship *(Undergraduate/Scholarship, Monetary, Award)* [5970]

Betty J. Cecere Memorial Scholarship Endowment Fund *(Graduate/Scholarship)* [11944]

Cedarcrest Farms Scholarships *(Graduate, Undergraduate/Scholarship)* [1058]

Celler Legal P.A. Employment Skills Scholarship Program *(Undergraduate/Scholarship)* [3206]

Center for the Education of Women Scholarships *(Graduate, Undergraduate/Scholarship)* [11635]

Centerville-Abington Dollars for Scholars *(Undergraduate/Scholarship)* [11945]

Central Pacific Bank Scholarship Fund *(Undergraduate/Scholarship)* [5390]

CESEF Postgraduate Scholarship Program *(Postdoctorate/Scholarship)* [4660]

CFCC Foundation Merit Scholarship *(Undergraduate/Scholarship)* [3151]

CFNIL Senior Memorial Scholarship *(Undergraduate/Scholarship)* [3672]

CFT/ACPSOP Scholarship Fund *(Undergraduate/Scholarship)* [3343]

CGA Scholarships *(Undergraduate/Scholarship)* [2812]

CGPF Endowments Conference Scholarships *(Undergraduate/Scholarship)* [2994]

CGSA Student Scholarship Awards *(Undergraduate/Award, Scholarship)* [2992]

ChairScholars National Scholarship Program *(Undergraduate/Scholarship)* [3275]

Logan S. Chambers Individual Scholarship *(Other/Scholarship)* [5952]

Harry H. and Floy B. Chapin Scholarships *(Undergraduate/Scholarship)* [3673]

Oscar Chapman Memorial Scholarship *(Undergraduate, Graduate/Scholarship)* [2516]

Nancy J. Chapman Scholarships *(Other/Scholarship)* [2152]

Chappie Hall Scholarship *(Undergraduate/Scholarship)* [2]

Charles (Charlie) A. Bassett Endowed Scholarship *(Undergraduate/Scholarship)* [5070]

Charles and Claire Phillips Scholarship Fund *(Undergraduate/Scholarship)* [3344]

Charles E. Peterson Fellowships *(Other/Fellowship)* [2334]

Charles and Eleanor Rycenga Education Scholarship *(Undergraduate/Scholarship)* [5071]

Charles Fred Wonson Scholarship *(Graduate/Scholarship)* [11713]

Charles Shafae Scholarship *(Undergraduate, Four Year College/Scholarship)* [8818]

Charlotte Housing Authority Scholarship Fund (CHASF) *(Undergraduate/Scholarship)* [4726]

Charlotte-Mecklenburg Schools Scholarship Incentive Fund *(Undergraduate/Scholarship)* [3277, 4727]

Charlotte Pride Scholarship *(Community College, Two Year College, Undergraduate, Four Year College/Scholarship)* [3279]

Charlotte R. SchmidLapp Scholarship Fund *(Undergraduate/Scholarship)* [3345]

Chartway Federal Credit Union Director's Memorial Scholarship *(Undergraduate, Graduate/Scholarship)* [3281]

CHEA Undergraduate Scholarship Program for Students with Disabilities *(Undergraduate/Scholarship)* [2814]

CHEA Vocational Grants *(Vocational/Occupational, Two Year College/Grant)* [2815]

The Cheatham County Scholarship Fund *(Undergraduate/Scholarship)* [3607]

Chechahko Consumers Co-Op Ltd. Scholarship *(Master's/Scholarship)* [12301]

Chereddi NarayanaRao & Radhamanohari Scholarships *(Graduate/Scholarship)* [10948]

Cherokee Nation Graduate Scholarship *(Graduate/Scholarship)* [3283]

Cherokee Nation Pell Scholarships *(Undergraduate/Scholarship)* [3284]

Sgt. Cherven Scholarship *(Undergraduate/Scholarship)* [7128]

Chester Arzell and Helen Miller Montgomery Scholarship *(Undergraduate/Scholarship)* [12065]

Chevalier Award Scholarship *(Undergraduate/Scholarship)* [2958]

Cheyenne High School Desert Shields Scholarship *(Undergraduate/Scholarship)* [9392]

Chicana / Latina Foundation Scholarship Program *(Graduate, Undergraduate/Scholarship)* [3289]

Camille C. Chidiac Fund Scholarship *(Undergraduate, Four Year College, Two Year College, Vocational/Occupational/Scholarship)* [5391]

Kevin Child Scholarship *(Undergraduate/Scholarship)* [7921]

Childhood Cancer Survivor Scholarship *(Undergraduate, College, University, Vocational/Occupational/Scholarship)* [3291]

Children of Evangeline Section Scholarships *(Graduate, Undergraduate/Scholarship)* [10472]

Children of Fallen Patriots Scholarships *(Community College, Undergraduate, Graduate, Vocational/Occupational/Scholarship)* [3294]

Children of Unitarian Universalist Religious Professionals Grant *(Undergraduate/Grant)* [11246]

Childrens Scholarship Fund-Charlotte *(Undergraduate/Scholarship)* [4728]

Chinese Professionals Association of Canada Professional Achievement Awards (PAA) *(Professional development/Award)* [3311]

Dolly Ching Scholarship *(Undergraduate, Two Year College, Four Year College/Scholarship)* [5393]

Chip Johnson Memorial Scholarship Fund *(Undergraduate/Scholarship)* [10675]

Choose Your Future Scholarship Fund *(Undergraduate/Scholarship)* [3608]

Chris M. Kurzweil Scholarship *(Undergraduate/Scholarship)* [3717]

Christine Kerr Cawthorne Scholarship *(Undergraduate/Scholarship)* [10097]

Christine Soper Scholarship *(Undergraduate/Scholarship)* [5142]

Christopher Todd Grant Memorial Fund *(Undergraduate/Scholarship)* [3346]

Commander Daniel J. Christovich Scholarship *(Undergraduate/Scholarship)* [3455]

Chrysler Technical Scholarship Fund *(Undergraduate/Scholarship)* [3996]

CHS - Bursary Program Scholarships *(Undergraduate/Scholarship)* [3001]

CHS - Mature Student Bursary Program Scholarships *(Undergraduate/Scholarship)* [3002]

The Church, Langdon, Lopp, Banet Law Scholarships *(Undergraduate, Four Year College/Scholarship)* [3329]

CIA Undergraduate Scholarships *(Undergraduate/Scholarship)* [2185, 3244]

C.I.B.C Scholarship *(Undergraduate, Graduate/Scholarship)* [2591, 3014]

CIFAR Azrieli Global Scholars program *(Professional development/Scholarship)* [3020]

Cimarron-Memorial Spartan Staff Scholarships *(Undergraduate/Scholarship)* [9393]

Cincinnati Bell Foundation Scholarship *(Undergraduate/Scholarship)* [3347]

Cincinnati Financial Corporation Fund *(Undergraduate/Scholarship)* [3348]

Citi Foundation Scholarship Program *(Undergraduate/Scholarship)* [978]

City of Boston Disability Scholarship Contest *(Undergraduate/Scholarship)* [4535]

City Of Sanibel Employee Dependent Scholarship Fund *(Undergraduate/Scholarship)* [10676]

Civitan Shropshire Scholarship *(Undergraduate, Vocational/Occupational/Scholarship)* [3424]

Claes Nobel Academic Scholarships for Members *(High School, College/Scholarship)* [8103]

Neil Clark Memorial Scholarship *(Undergraduate/Scholarship)* [8156]

Clarke Adams Memorial Fund *(Undergraduate/Scholarship)* [6662]

Classic Wines of California Scholarships *(Undergraduate/Scholarship)* [2797]

Clay Maitland CGF Scholarship *(Undergraduate/Scholarship)* [3456]

Clement T. Hanson Scholarship *(Undergraduate/Scholarship)* [7430]

Cleve Holloway Memorial Scholarship *(Undergraduate/Scholarship)* [3652]

Cleveland Alumni Association Scholarship *(Undergraduate, Graduate/Scholarship)* [2517]

James L. Clifford Prize *(Other/Prize, Monetary)* [1430]

Bryan Cline Memorial Soccer Scholarship Program *(Undergraduate/Scholarship)* [318]

L. Robert Clough Memorial Scholarship *(Undergraduate, Graduate/Scholarship)* [2518]

The Club at Morningside Scholarship *(Undergraduate, Graduate/Scholarship)* [9806]

Clubs of America Scholarship Program *(Undergraduate/Scholarship)* [3446]

CMC/MMC Scholarships (CMC) *(Other/Scholarship)* [6026]

CMSF Scholarship *(Graduate/Scholarship)* [3319]

CNIB Master's Scholarships *(Master's/Scholarship)* [3047]

CNST Scholarship *(Doctorate, Graduate/Scholarship)* [2146]

Coast Guard Foundation Enlisted Education Scholarship *(Advanced Professional/Scholarship)* [3457]

Coca-Cola First Generation Scholarships (Undergraduate/Scholarship) [979]

Coca-Cola Scholars Program Scholarship (Undergraduate/Scholarship) [3494]

Code Play LEARN Scholarship (Two Year College, Undergraduate, Graduate/Scholarship) [3496]

Coeur d'Alene Alumni Scholarship (Undergraduate/Scholarship) [6784]

COF Dependent Scholarship Program (Undergraduate, Graduate/Scholarship) [9142]

COHEAO Scholarship (Undergraduate/Scholarship) [3450]

Marshall A. Cohen Entrance Awards (Postgraduate/Award) [12251]

The COIT Clean GIF Scholarship Contest (Undergraduate, Graduate/Scholarship) [3498]

Cole Family Scholarships (All/Scholarship) [9294]

College-Bound Award (High School/Award, Scholarship) [6853]

The College Bound Scholarship (Undergraduate/Scholarship) [11917]

The College Club of Hartford Scholarships (Undergraduate/Scholarship) [5319]

College of Fellows Travel Scholarship (Undergraduate/Scholarship) [3024]

College Success Foundation Chateau Ste. Michelle Scholarship Fund (Undergraduate/Scholarship) [3514]

College Success Foundation Leadership 1000 Scholarship (Undergraduate/Scholarship) [3515]

College Success Foundation Washington State Governors' Scholarship for Foster Youth (Undergraduate/Scholarship) [3516]

Collier Scholarship (Undergraduate, College, University/Scholarship) [7088]

Lloyd E. and Rachel S. Collins Scholarship (Undergraduate, Graduate, High School/Scholarship) [12067]

Columbus Citizens Foundation College Scholarships (Undergraduate/Scholarship) [3543]

Columbus Citizens Foundation High School Scholarships (Undergraduate/Scholarship) [3544]

Colwell Law Group Single Parent Scholarship (Community College, University, Undergraduate/Scholarship) [3548]

The Commonwealth Fund Mongan Fellowship in Minority Health Policy (Other/Fellowship) [3554]

Commonwealth "Good Citizen" Scholarships (Undergraduate/Scholarship) [2193]

Communal Studies Association Research Fellowships (Graduate/Fellowship) [3557]

The Communities in Schools Jack Tate ThinkCollege Scholarship (Undergraduate/Scholarship) [4729]

Community Foundation of the Fox River Valley Scholarship (Undergraduate, Graduate, High School/Scholarship) [3584]

Community Foundation of Northern Illinois Scholarship (Undergraduate/Scholarship) [3675]

Community Service Scholarship - GreenMatch (Undergraduate, Graduate/Scholarship) [5239]

Community's Memorial Scholarship (Undergraduate, College, University/Scholarship) [7089]

Bill & Joan Cones Scholarship (Undergraduate, College, University/Scholarship) [7090]

Congressional Fellowship (Other/Fellowship) [3741]

Connaught Fellowship (Graduate/Fellowship) [11704]

Connecticut Association of Latinos in Higher Education Scholarships (Undergraduate/Scholarship) [3754, 5320]

Karen A. Connick Memorial Scholarship (Undergraduate/Scholarship) [5119]

Dwight O. Connor/Ellen Conner Lepp/Danhart Scholarship (Undergraduate/Scholarship) [8838]

The Connor Group Kids & Community Partners Scholarship (Two Year College, Undergraduate, Graduate/Scholarship) [3765]

Consumers Credit Union Scholarship (Undergraduate, College, Vocational/Occupational, Two Year College, University/Scholarship) [3814]

Jack Kent Cooke Dissertation Fellowship Award (Doctorate/Fellowship) [3818]

Alex Cooper Memorial Scholarship (Undergraduate, College, University/Scholarship) [7092]

Madison and Edith Cooper Scholarships (Undergraduate/Scholarship) [9807]

COPA Scholarship Fund (Undergraduate/Scholarship) [3084]

Cope Middle School PTSA Scholarship (Undergraduate/Scholarship) [9537]

Arthur E. Copeland Scholarship (Four Year College, Two Year College/Scholarship) [11293]

Helen Copeland Scholarship (Professional development, Undergraduate, Vocational/Occupational/Scholarship) [11294]

Copper and Brass Servicenter Association Scholarship Program (Undergraduate/Scholarship) [3833]

Corinne and Fred Capuder Memorial Scholarship (Undergraduate/Scholarship) [3349]

Cornell/Goodman Scholarship (Undergraduate, College, University, Vocational/Occupational/Scholarship) [7093]

Coronado High School Counselors' Scholarship (Undergraduate/Scholarship) [9395]

Corporal Joseph Martinez U.S. Army/Durango High School AFJROTC Scholarship (Undergraduate/Scholarship) [9396]

Corwin Nixon Scholarship Fund (Undergraduate/Scholarship) [3350]

Coupons for Save Scholarship (All/Scholarship) [3882]

Courage to Grow Scholarships (Undergraduate/Scholarship) [3884]

Pfizer Soozie Courter Hemophilia Scholarship Program (Undergraduate/Scholarship) [7922]

COUSE-Gram Scholarship Fund (Undergraduate/Scholarship) [10677]

The Cover Guy Annual Scholarship (Undergraduate, Graduate/Scholarship) [3890]

CoverWallet Small Business Scholarship (Two Year College, Four Year College, Graduate/Scholarship) [3892]

Covington Award (Doctorate, Graduate/Award) [7781]

Covington-Cincinnati/Northern Kentucky Alumni Chapter - Dane Wagge Scholarships (University/Scholarship) [11575]

Steve Cowan Memorial Scholarships (Undergraduate/Scholarship) [3906]

Justin Forrest Cox "Beat the Odds" Memorial Scholarships (Undergraduate/Scholarship) [3470]

CPYC/CNOA Youth Leadership Scholarship (Undergraduate/Scholarship) [2820, 2822]

Crafton Elementary School PTA Scholarship (Undergraduate/Scholarship) [9538]

Crafton Hills College Foundation Scholarship (Undergraduate/Scholarship) [9539]

Craig Scholarship (Undergraduate, College, University/Scholarship) [7094]

Crain Scholarship Program (Undergraduate/Scholarship) [10131]

Crawford Scholarship (Undergraduate/Scholarship) [9808]

Creative Glass Fellowship Program (Advanced Professional/Fellowship) [3898]

Credible $2,500 Scholarship (Graduate/Scholarship) [3902]

Crescent Electric Sustainability Scholarship (Undergraduate/Scholarship) [3904]

CRMA Scholarship (Graduate, Undergraduate/Scholarship) [3287]

Crosley Law Firm Distracted Driving Scholarship (Four Year College/Scholarship) [3918]

Crosset Family Foundation Scholarship (Undergraduate/Scholarship) [3351]

CrossLites Scholarship (Undergraduate, Graduate/Scholarship) [3922]

Crowder Scholarship (Undergraduate/Scholarship) [4731]

Crush the GRE Scholarship Program (Undergraduate, Graduate/Scholarship) [3927]

Lydia Cruz and Sandra Maria Ramos Scholarships (Graduate/Scholarship) [4026]

CSA Fraternal Life Scholarships (Undergraduate/Scholarship) [3933]

CSLA Leaders of Distinction Award (Professional development/Recognition) [3127]

CSLA Leadership Scholarship (Undergraduate/Scholarship) [3128]

CSM Virgil R. Williams Scholarship (Undergraduate/Scholarship) [101, 4389, 11276]

Curry Awards for Girls and Young Women (Undergraduate/Scholarship) [10132]

Cindy Curry Memorial Scholarship (Undergraduate/Scholarship) [8841]

Stormy Ray Cushing Scholarship (Undergraduate, College, University/Scholarship) [7095]

D. Glenn Hilts Scholarship (Graduate, Undergraduate/Scholarship) [2288]

DAAD Undergraduate Scholarship Program (Undergraduate/Scholarship) [4060]

Arthur H. Dadian Scholarship Grants (Undergraduate/Scholarship) [1870]

Thomas Richard Dadourian Memorial Grant (Undergraduate/Scholarship) [1871]

Alexander A. Dadourian Scholarship (Undergraduate/Scholarship) [1872]

Dadour Dadourian Scholarship Fund (Undergraduate/Scholarship) [1873]

Dale Hughes Jr Memorial Scholarship (Undergraduate/Scholarship) [10821]

George Dale Scholarship Fund (Undergraduate/Scholarship) [1973]

Dallas Alumnae Association Adelphe Scholarship in Memory of Janet Jones Buford (Undergraduate/Scholarship) [6414]

Dallas Alumnae Association Gamma Phi Chapter Scholarship (Undergraduate/Scholarship) [6415]

Marvin E. Daly Memorial Scholarship (Undergraduate/Scholarship) [8506]

The DamagedCars.com Summer Scholarship (Two Year College, Undergraduate, Graduate, High School/Scholarship) [3156]

Damon Runyon Physician-Scientist Training Awards (Postdoctorate, Professional development/Award) [9758]

Dan and Rachel Mahi Educational Scholarship (Graduate, Undergraduate/Scholarship) [8921]

D&R Sobey Scholarships (Undergraduate/Scholarship) [10237]

Daniel Gerber, Sr. Medallion Scholarship (Undergraduate/Scholarship) [4939]

Daniel Kahikina and Millie Akaka Scholarship (Graduate, Undergraduate/Scholarship) [8922]

Daniel L. Reiss Memorial Scholarship (Undergraduate/Scholarship) [5073]

Bal Dasa Scholarship Fund (Undergraduate, University, College, Two Year College, Vocational/Occupational/Scholarship) [5394]

Dater Foundation Scholarship (Undergraduate/Scholarship) [3352]

George A. Davala Scholarship (Undergraduate, Vocational/Occupational/Scholarship) [7007]

Dave Sauer Memorial College Scholarship (Undergraduate/Scholarship) [170]

David J. Joseph Company Scholarship Fund (Undergraduate/Scholarship) [3353]

David Library Fellowships (Doctorate, Postdoctorate/Fellowship) [3973]

Ruth and Victor David Scholarship (Undergraduate, Graduate/Scholarship) [6289]

David W. Schacht Native American Student Scholarship (Undergraduate/Scholarship) [2479]

Lucile Caswell Davids Memorial Adelphe Scholarship (Undergraduate, Graduate/Scholarship) [6416]

Jim Davie Memorial Scholarship (Undergraduate, Master's/Scholarship) [12305]

Davis Family Scholarship (Undergraduate/Scholarship) [9809]

Davis Memorial Foundation Scholarship (Graduate, Undergraduate/Scholarship) [3977]

Dwight F. Davis Memorial Scholarship (Undergraduate/Scholarship) [11402]

The Davis-Putter Scholarship Fund (Undergraduate, Graduate/Scholarship) [9770]

Lawrence E. and Jean L. Davis Scholarship (Undergraduate/Scholarship) [8843]

William W. Dawson Memorial Scholarship (Undergraduate, Graduate/Scholarship) [2519]

Brian M. Day Scholarships (Undergraduate, Graduate/Scholarship) [9295]

DBI Scholarship Fund (Undergraduate/Scholarship) [3611]

D.C. Cornelius Memorial Scholarship (Undergraduate, Graduate/Scholarship) [12068]

Dealsshutter.com Scholarship (College, University/Scholarship) [3983]

Dean A. Froehlich Endowed Scholarship (Undergraduate/Scholarship) [6787]

The Dean Prim Scholarship (Undergraduate/Scholarship) [12069]

Dean – Derek Lee Dean Soccer Scholarships (Undergraduate/Scholarship) [3471]

Deborah Jean Rydberg Memorial Scholarship (Undergraduate/Scholarship) [3676]

Deborah Partridge Wolfe International Fellowship (Graduate) (Graduate, Undergraduate/Fellowship) [12410]

Debt.com Scholarship (All/Scholarship) [3987]

Julia B. DeCapua Fund (Undergraduate/Scholarship) [5226]

Walter M. Decker Point Scholarship (Graduate, Undergraduate/Scholarship) [9220]

Laurence Decore Awards for Student Leadership (Undergraduate/Scholarship) [288]

Dee Wacksman Scholarship Fund (Undergraduate/Scholarship) [3354]

Anthony R. Dees Educational Workshop Scholarship (Graduate/Scholarship) [10342]

Defensive Driving scholarship (Undergraduate/Scholarship) [3994]

Deja Vu Surf Hawaii Scholarship Fund (Undergraduate, Two Year College, Four Year College/Scholarship) [5395]

Edward Delaney Scholarship (Professional development/Scholarship) [2198]

Delta Chi Alumnae Memorial Scholarship (Undergraduate/Scholarship) [10099]

Delta Epsilon Sigma Graduate Fellowship (Graduate/Fellowship) [4017]

Delta Epsilon Sigma Undergraduate Scholarships (Undergraduate/Scholarship) [4018]

Delta Iota Alumni Scholarship (Undergraduate/Scholarship) [10146]

Delta Kappa Gamma Society International World Fellowship (Graduate/Fellowship) [4022]

Delta Kappa Project 2000 Scholarship (Undergraduate/Scholarship) [6417]

Delta Nu Project 2000 Scholarship (Undergraduate/Scholarship) [6418]

Delta Phi Epsilon Educational Foundation Scholarships (Graduate/Scholarship) [4024]

Delta Project 2000 Scholarship (Undergraduate/Scholarship) [6419]

Delta Tau Project 2000 Scholarship (Undergraduate/Scholarship) [6420]

Delta Tau Scholarship (Undergraduate, Graduate/Scholarship) [2520]

Delta Upsilon Project 2000 Nowell Memorial Scholarship (Undergraduate/Scholarship) [6421]

Gail Patrick Undergraduate Scholarships (Undergraduate/Scholarship) [4031]

Law Offices of Michael A. DeMayo Scholarships (Undergraduate/Scholarship) [6708]

Democrats for Life of America Scholarship Essay (College, Community College, High School, Undergraduate, Graduate, Vocational/Occupational/Scholarship) [4047]

Bobby Michael Denton Memorial Scholarship (High School/Scholarship) [8508]

Denver Scholarship Foundation General Scholarship Fund (Graduate/Scholarship) [4053]

Dick Depaolis Memorial Scholarship (Undergraduate/Scholarship) [3718]

Garabed and Almast Der Megrditchian Scholarship Grants (Undergraduate/Scholarship) [1874]

Belle & Curly Desrosiers Scholarship (Undergraduate, College, University, Vocational/Occupational/Scholarship) [12307]

Detroit Economic Club Scholarship (Undergraduate/Scholarship) [3719]

Helen L. Dewar Scholarship (Undergraduate/Scholarship) [11020]

Beta Nu/Caryl Cordis D'hondt Scholarship (Undergraduate/Scholarship) [10100]

Theta/Caryl Cordis D'hondt Scholarship (Undergraduate/Scholarship) [10101]

Diabetes Hope Scholarship Program (Undergraduate/Scholarship) [4072]

The Lilly Diabetes Tomorrow's Leaders Scholarship (Undergraduate/Scholarship) [4074]

Diamond Resort Scholarship Fund (Undergraduate, Two Year College, Four Year College/Scholarship) [5396]

Diana Brown Endowed Scholarship (Undergraduate/Scholarship) [6788]

Robert Martz DiGiacomo Memorial Scholarship Fund (Undergraduate/Scholarship) [10756]

Digital Marketing Scholarship Program (Undergraduate/Scholarship) [3177]

The Direct Energy Live Brighter Scholarship (Undergraduate/Scholarship) [4095]

DirectTextbook.com Scholarship Essay Contest (College, Undergraduate, University/Scholarship) [4097]

Disability Care Center Disabled Student Scholarships (Undergraduate/Scholarship) [4104]

Disabled Veteran Scholarship (College, Vocational/Occupational/Scholarship) [9713]

Disabled Veteran Student Scholarship (Two Year College, Four Year College/Scholarship) [12018]

Disabled Veterans Scholarship (Community College, College, Vocational/Occupational/Scholarship) [4538]

Disabled Veterans Scholarship (Vocational/Occupational, Community College, Four Year College, Graduate, Professional development/Scholarship) [6519]

Discover Graduate Loans (Graduate, Master's, Doctorate/Loan, Scholarship) [4110]

Distinguished Young Women - Cash Scholarships (High School/Scholarship) [4118]

Distracted Driving Scholarship (High School, Two Year College, University/Scholarship) [6188]

Dr. Kathy Dixon Memorial Scholarship (Undergraduate, University, College/Scholarship) [7097]

Dr. Allan A. Dixon Memorial Scholarships (Postgraduate/Scholarship) [3106]

DLF Graduate Scholarship Program (Graduate/Scholarship) [3960]

DMSF Scholarship (High School/Scholarship) [7503]

Do-Over Scholarship (Undergraduate, High School/Scholarship) [11226]

DO Supply Academic Scholarship (Undergraduate/Scholarship) [4122]

Dobranowski Julian Memorial Scholarship (Undergraduate/Scholarship) [9659]

Doc Keen Memorial Scholarship Fund (Undergraduate/Scholarship) [10680]

Dr. Ali Jarrahi Merit Scholarship (Undergraduate/Scholarship) [6172]

Dr. George and Isabelle Elanjian Scholarship (Undergraduate/Scholarship) [11638]

Dr. Gunnar B. Stickler Scholarship (Undergraduate, Vocational/Occupational/Scholarship) [10839]

Dr. J Glenn Radcliffe Scholarship Fund (Undergraduate/Scholarship) [10822]

Dr. Mark Rathke Family Scholarship Fund (Graduate/Scholarship) [4202]

Dr. Mary Anne Chambers Scholarship (Undergraduate/Scholarship) [6215]

Dr. Nancy Smith Midgette Scholarship (Undergraduate/Scholarship) [10102]

Dr. William A. and Marceleine J. Sautter Hanover-Horton Youth of Promise Scholarship (Graduate/Scholarship) [6196]

Doctoral Dissertation Grants (Doctorate/Grant) [6075]

Doddridge County High School Promise Scholarship in Memory of Hattie Leggett (Undergraduate/Scholarship) [8844]

Jim Dodson Law Scholarship for Brain Injury Victims & Their Caregivers (Undergraduate/Scholarship) [4124]

Dody Boyd Scholarship Fund (Undergraduate/Scholarship) [3613]

Hans and Margaret Doe Charitable Trust Scholarship (Community College, Vocational/Occupational, College, University, Undergraduate, Graduate/Scholarship) [9810]

Emmett J. Doerr Memorial Distinguished Scout Scholarship (High School/Scholarship) [7846]

Dofflemyer Scholarship (Undergraduate/Scholarship) [7847]

Dollar-A-Day Academic Scholarships (Graduate, Undergraduate/Scholarship) [4126]

DOLPHIN SCHOLARSHIPS (Undergraduate/Scholarship) [4128]

Don C. Beaver Memorial Scholarship (Undergraduate/Scholarship) [2798]

Don and Madalyn Sickafoose Educational Trust Fund (Undergraduate/Scholarship, Loan) [10757]

Don and Norine Lowry Awards for Women of Excellence (Undergraduate, Graduate, Advanced Professional/Scholarship) [4291]

Donald and Florence Hunting Scholarship (Undergraduate/Scholarship) [5146]

Donald J. DeYoung Scholarship (Undergraduate/Scholarship) [5147]

Donald O. Coffman Scholarship (Graduate, Undergraduate/Scholarship) [9300]

Donald Worster Travel Grant (Graduate, Other/Grant) [1451]

Doniphan Community Foundation Scholarships (Undergraduate, Community College, Vocational/Occupational/Scholarship) [5120]

Don't Wait to Reach Your Potential (High School/Scholarship) [9258]

DontPayFull $500 Annual Student Scholarship (High School, College, University, Undergraduate/Scholarship) [4132]

Doraine "Pursuit of Educational Excellence" Scholarship (Undergraduate/Scholarship) [3472]

Doreen Brady Memorial Scholarship (Postgraduate/Scholarship) [8639]

Dorothy B. & Charles E. Thomas Scholarship (Undergraduate/Scholarship) [5148]

Dorothy E. Hofmann Pembroke Scholarship (Undergraduate/Scholarship) [5325]

Dorothy M. Bolyard Memorial Scholarship (Undergraduate/Scholarship) [9812]

Dorothy Mitchell Memorial Scholarship (Undergraduate/Scholarship) [9541]

The Father Connie Dougherty Scholarship Fund (Undergraduate, Vocational/Occupational/Scholarship) [3712]

The Douglas Psychotherapy Do Good General Education Scholarship (Undergraduate, Graduate/Scholarship) [4140]

Downeast Energy Scholarships (Undergraduate/Scholarship) [4142]

Downes - Jay and Rheba Downes Memorial Scholarship (Undergraduate/Scholarship) [3473]

Tim Downing Memorial Scholarship Program (Professional development/Scholarship) [2906]

Helen Cashatt Drais Memorial Adelphe Scholarship (Undergraduate/Scholarship) [6422]

The Dream is Inclusive Scholarship (Two Year College, Undergraduate, Graduate, Professional development, Vocational/Occupational/Scholarship) [8624]

Charles Drew Scholarships (Other/Scholarship) [2153]

DriversEdHub.com Scholarship (Undergraduate/Scholarship) [3992]

Drone Technology College Scholarshi p (High School, Undergraduate/Scholarship) [4183]

Drummond Law Firm Scholarship (Graduate, College/Scholarship) [4189]

DSACF Modern Woodmen of America Scholarship Fund (Undergraduate/Scholarship) [4203]

Henry Belin du Pont Dissertation Fellowships (Doctorate, Graduate/Fellowship) [5257]

Duane V. Puerde Memorial Scholarship Fund (Undergraduate/Scholarship) [3564]

Steve Duckett Local Conservation Scholarship (Undergraduate, Postgraduate, Community College, Graduate/Scholarship) [9281]

Julia M. Duckwall Scholarship (Professional development/Scholarship) [2199]

A. O. Duer Scholarship Award (Undergraduate/Scholarship) [7661]

Doris Duke Conservation Fellows Program (Master's/Fellowship) [12046]

Duluth Central High School Alumni Scholarship Fund (Graduate/Scholarship) [4205]

Dunbar Heritage Scholarship Fund (Undergraduate/Scholarship) [10683]

Dr. Allan Duncan Memorial Scholarship (Undergraduate, Master's/Scholarship) [12310]

John Holt Duncan Memorial Scholarship *(Undergraduate, Graduate/Scholarship)* [2521]

Wade and Marcelene Duncan Scholarship *(Undergraduate/Scholarship)* [12070]

Dunkin' Donuts Philadelphia Regional Scholarship Program *(Undergraduate/Scholarship)* [9941]

Durning Sisters Scholarships *(Graduate/Scholarship)* [4001]

Dwight Hibbard Scholarship Fund *(Undergraduate/Scholarship)* [3355]

Dwight Mosley Scholarship Award *(Undergraduate/Scholarship)* [11403]

Dwight Teed Scholarship Fund *(Undergraduate/Scholarship)* [10881]

Brenda Dye Music Boosters Scholarship *(Undergraduate, University, College/Scholarship)* [7098]

Joshua Dyke Family Scholarship *(Undergraduate/Scholarship)* [11021]

E-Waste Scholarship *(High School, Undergraduate, Graduate/Scholarship)* [4090]

Howard and Gladys Eakes Memorial Scholarship *(Undergraduate/Scholarship)* [5121]

East Carolina Scholarship *(Undergraduate, Graduate/Scholarship)* [2522]

East-West Center Graduate Degree Fellowship *(Master's, Doctorate, Graduate/Fellowship)* [4262]

Easter Scholarship *(All/Scholarship)* [7438]

Eastern Orthodox Scouting Scholarships *(Undergraduate/Scholarship)* [7848]

David Eby Memorial Scholarship *(Undergraduate, Master's, Graduate/Scholarship)* [12312]

The École Nationale des Chartes Exchange Fellowship *(Postdoctorate/Fellowship)* [8371]

École Polytechnique Commemorative Awards *(Master's, Doctorate, Graduate/Fellowship)* [2972]

Economic Club Business Study Abroad Scholarships *(Undergraduate/Scholarship)* [5149]

Edith Macias Vann Southern California *(Undergraduate/Scholarship)* [12151]

Edmonton Epilepsy Association Scholarship *(Undergraduate/Scholarship)* [4294]

Edmonton Epilepsy Continuing Education Scholarships *(Undergraduate/Scholarship)* [4295]

Education Factor Scholarships *(Graduate, Undergraduate/Scholarship)* [7207]

Education Matters Scholarship *(Undergraduate, High School/Scholarship)* [11227]

"Education is Power" Scholarships *(Undergraduate/Scholarship)* [7923]

Educational Excellence Award *(Graduate/Award)* [3120]

Educational Loan Program for Gay and Lesbian Students *(Undergraduate/Loan)* [3615]

Edward Kent Welch Memorial Scholarship *(Undergraduate/Scholarship)* [12071]

Edward Leon Duhamel Freemasons Scholarship *(Undergraduate/Scholarship)* [9692]

The Edwards Annual College Scholarships *(Undergraduate/Scholarship)* [4320]

Esther Edwards Graduate Scholarships *(Doctorate, Professional development/Scholarship)* [4890]

Edwin H. and Louise N. Williamson Endowed Scholarship *(Undergraduate/Scholarship)* [12072]

Hillel Einhorn New Investigator Award *(Doctorate/Award)* [10377]

Eisbrouch & Marsh Scholarship Awards *(Undergraduate, Graduate/Scholarship)* [4326]

The Dwight D. Eisenhower/Ann Cook Whitman Washington, D.C. Scholarship Program *(Undergraduate/Scholarship)* [4961]

El Pomar Fellowship *(Graduate/Fellowship)* [4330]

The Eleanor A. Ernest Scholarship *(Graduate/Scholarship)* [6199]

Eleanor Perry Memorial Endowed Scholarship *(Undergraduate/Scholarship)* [6789]

eLearners Online College Scholarship *(Undergraduate/Scholarship)* [4332]

The eLearners Scholarship for Military Personnel, Veterans, and Spouses *(College, Vocational/Occupational/Scholarship)* [4333]

Elements Behavioral Health Scholarship *(College, University, Undergraduate/Scholarship)* [4365]

Elena Sanchez Memorial WSWS Outstanding Student Scholarship Program *(Graduate, Undergraduate/Scholarship)* [11993]

Elgin Alumni Association Scholarship *(Undergraduate, University, College/Scholarship)* [7099]

W. Todd Elias Memorial Scholarship *(Undergraduate, Graduate/Scholarship)* [2523]

Elin J. Stene/Xi Scholarship *(Undergraduate/Scholarship)* [10103]

Elise Reed Jenkins Memorial Scholarship *(Undergraduate/Scholarship)* [10104]

Elizabeth Brittingham Pusey Scholarship *(Graduate/Scholarship)* [3565]

Elizabeth McKissick Memorial Scholarship *(Undergraduate/Scholarship)* [6790]

Elizabeth Nash Foundation Scholarship *(Undergraduate, Graduate/Scholarship)* [7554]

Elizabeth T. Williams Memorial Scholarship *(Undergraduate/Scholarship)* [12074]

Elks National Foundation Most Valuable Student Scholarship Contest *(Undergraduate/Scholarship)* [2816, 4371]

Ella Wilson Johnson Scholarship Fund *(Undergraduate/Scholarship)* [3356]

Ellen Swallow Richards Travel Grant *(Graduate, Other/Grant)* [1452]

The Dr. Robert Elliott Memorial Scholarship *(Undergraduate/Scholarship)* [7167, 8264]

The Pauline Elliott Scholarship *(Undergraduate/Scholarship)* [7168, 8265]

Elmer Cooke Young-Ethel Taylor Young Scholarship Fund *(Undergraduate/Scholarship)* [5327]

Elmer and Rosa Lee Collins Scholarship *(Undergraduate/Scholarship)* [12075]

Elsa Ludeke Scholarship *(Graduate/Scholarship)* [4034]

Emerald Creek Capital Scholarship *(Undergraduate/Scholarship)* [4374]

Emerging Entrepreneur Scholarship Grant *(Other/Scholarship, Grant)* [6771]

Emoji Scholarship *(All/Scholarship)* [7439]

Employment Boost College Scholarship *(College, University/Scholarship)* [4381]

Enders Student Fellowship *(Graduate/Fellowship)* [2081]

Most Valuable Student scholarships *(Undergraduate/Scholarship)* [4372]

Enhanced Insurance Scholarships Program *(Undergraduate/Scholarship)* [11763]

Epsilon Delta Project 2000 Scholarship *(Undergraduate/Scholarship)* [6423]

Epsilon Epsilon Scholarship *(Undergraduate/Scholarship)* [10105]

Epsilon Mu Scholarship *(Graduate, Undergraduate/Scholarship)* [6424]

Epsilon Tau Pi's Soaring Eagle Scholarship *(Undergraduate/Scholarship)* [7849]

Epsilon Tau Scholarship *(Undergraduate/Scholarship)* [10106]

Alan R. Epstein "Reach for the Stars" Scholarships *(College/Scholarship)* [7297]

E.R. and Lillian B. Dimmette Scholarship *(Undergraduate/Scholarship)* [4732]

The Robert C. Erb Sr. Scholarship *(Undergraduate/Scholarship)* [7169]

Eric L. Jacobson Memorial Scholarship *(Undergraduate/Scholarship)* [9542]

Erin L. Jenkins Memorial Scholarship *(Undergraduate/Scholarship)* [4776]

Ernest and Charlene Stachowiak Memorial Scholarship *(Undergraduate/Scholarship)* [3677]

Ernest Hemingway Research Grants *(Other/Grant)* [5475, 6528]

Escondido High School (EHS) Class of '56 Scholarship *(Community College, Vocational/Occupational/Scholarship)* [9813]

Steven Esposito Memorial Scholarship *(Undergraduate, Graduate, Doctorate/Scholarship)* [9221]

Essay Service Writer's Encouragement Scholarship *(Undergraduate/Scholarship)* [4445]

Essay Writing Contest *(Undergraduate, Graduate/Scholarship)* [4447]

Esther M. Smith Scholarship Fund *(Undergraduate/Scholarship)* [3566]

Eugene Northrup Scholarship *(Undergraduate/Scholarship)* [6791]

Eunice Miles Scholarship *(Graduate/Scholarship)* [4876]

European College of Liberal Arts Scholarships (ECLA) *(Undergraduate/Scholarship)* [11411]

Chick Evans Caddie Scholarships *(Undergraduate/Scholarship)* [11981]

Blossom Kalama Evans Memorial Scholarship Fund *(Undergraduate, University, Four Year College, Two Year College/Scholarship)* [5398]

Eve Kraft Education & College Scholarship *(Undergraduate/Scholarship)* [11404]

Evelyn S. Nish Scholarship *(Undergraduate/Scholarship)* [10107]

E.W. Scripps Foundation Scholarship *(Undergraduate/Scholarship)* [3357]

Exabeam Cyber Security Scholarship *(Undergraduate, Graduate/Scholarship)* [4461]

Excel Staffing Companies Scholarships for Excellence in Continuing Education *(Undergraduate/Scholarship)* [319]

Executive Women International Scholarship Program (EWISP) *(Undergraduate/Scholarship)* [4464]

Exercise For Life Athletic Scholarship *(Undergraduate/Scholarship)* [4441]

Express Medical Supply Scholarship Program *(Undergraduate/Scholarship)* [4472]

F.A. and Charlotte Blount Scholarship *(Undergraduate/Scholarship)* [12076]

Facebook Journalism Project Scholarship *(Graduate, Undergraduate/Scholarship)* [7989]

FACT "Second Chance" Scholarship Program *(Undergraduate/Scholarship)* [4527]

Faculty Research Visit Grants *(Doctorate/Grant)* [4061]

Fairbanks Chapter Legacy Scholarship *(Undergraduate/Scholarship)* [11517]

Faith Speckhard Scholarship *(Graduate/Scholarship)* [6201]

Ambassador Minerva Jean Falcon Hawaii Scholarship *(Undergraduate, Graduate, Two Year College, College, University/Scholarship)* [5399]

The Fallen Heroes Scholarship *(Undergraduate/Scholarship)* [3458]

James Mackenzie Fallows Scholarships Honoring Gertrude Baccus *(Undergraduate/Scholarship)* [9543]

Families of Freedom Scholarship Fund - Scholarship America *(Undergraduate, Vocational/Occupational/Scholarship)* [4482]

The Fantasy Sports Daily Scholarship Program - General Scholarship for Advanced Education *(Undergraduate, Graduate, Master's/Scholarship)* [4493]

Fargo Supplier Diversity Scholarship *(Undergraduate/Scholarship)* [9301]

Farmer Family Scholarship Fund *(Undergraduate/Scholarship)* [3358]

Farmington UNICO Scholarship Fund *(Undergraduate/Scholarship)* [5328]

David Edward Farson Scholarships *(Undergraduate/Scholarship)* [8845]

Father J. Harold Conway Memorial Scholarship *(Postgraduate/Scholarship)* [8640]

Father's Day Scholarship *(All/Scholarship)* [7440]

James R. Favor Risk Management Scholarship Fund *(Undergraduate/Scholarship)* [6425]

FCBA Foundation College Scholarship Program *(Undergraduate/Scholarship)* [4511]

FCSLA Graduate Scholarships *(Graduate/Scholarship)* [4575]

FCSLA High School Scholarships *(High School, College, Graduate/Scholarship)* [4576]

FCSLA Undergraduate College Scholarships *(Undergraduate, Two Year College, Four Year College/Scholarship)* [4578]

FCSLA Vocational/Technical/Trade Scholarships *(Vocational/Occupational/Scholarship)* [4579]

Federal Student Loans for Graduate Students *(Graduate/Loan)* [4318]

Federalsburg Rotary Club Scholarship *(Undergraduate/Scholarship)* [3567]

FEEA-NTEU Scholarships *(Graduate, Postgraduate, Undergraduate/Scholarship)* [4515]

Nolan W. Feeser Scholarship Fund *(Undergraduate/Scholarship)* [4590]

FEF Scholarship *(Undergraduate/Scholarship)* [4478]

Fellowship in the PMAC-AGPC *(Professional development/Fellowship)* [9349]

The Judy Felt Memorial Volunteerism Scholarship *(College, Undergraduate/Scholarship)* [2026]

Diane Ross Fennekohl Endowment Fund for Education *(Undergraduate/Scholarship)* [6426]

Edward Fennel Mauldin Endowed Scholarship *(Undergraduate, Community College/Scholarship)* [8509]

Fifth Month Scholarship *(Undergraduate, High School/Scholarship)* [11228]

Fifth Third Bank Scholarship Fund *(Undergraduate/Scholarship)* [3359]

Find Your Path Scholarship *(Graduate, College/Scholarship)* [10837]

Firth Family Scholarship *(Undergraduate, Graduate, Master's/Scholarship)* [12314]

Fish Finder Guides Scholarship *(Undergraduate, Graduate/Scholarship)* [4610]

The Fisher-Clark Memorial Endowed Scholarship *(Undergraduate/Scholarship)* [6792]

Sergeant Paul Fisher Scholarship *(Undergraduate/Scholarship)* [7830]

Gloria Flaherty Scholarship *(Graduate/Scholarship)* [5014]

Flavor of the Month Scholarship *(Undergraduate, High School/Scholarship)* [11229]

The FLEOA Foundation Scholastic Program *(Undergraduate/Scholarship)* [4519]

Fletemeyer Family Scholarship Fund *(Undergraduate/Scholarship)* [3360]

Flis Walter & Anna Memorial Scholarship *(Undergraduate/Scholarship)* [9663]

Florette B. Hoffheimer Scholarship Fund *(Undergraduate/Scholarship)* [3361]

Flow Feet Foot the Bill Scholarship *(Two Year College, University/Award)* [4653]

Flynn - Barney Flynn Memorial Scholarship *(Undergraduate/Scholarship)* [3475]

FMA-FEEA Scholarship Program *(Graduate/Scholarship)* [4516, 4521]

Judge Daniel F. Foley Memorial Scholarship *(Undergraduate/Scholarship)* [1913]

Maureen & Gilles Fontaine Scholarship *(Undergraduate, College, University, Vocational/Occupational/Scholarship)* [12317]

Foot Locker Scholar Athletes *(Undergraduate/Scholarship)* [4668]

Anne Ford Scholarships *(High School/Scholarship)* [7753]

Foresters Competitive Scholarship *(Undergraduate, Vocational/Occupational, Four Year College, Two Year College/Scholarship)* [5737]

FormsBirds Scholarship *(Undergraduate/Scholarship)* [4687]

Fostering Hope Scholarship *(Undergraduate/Scholarship)* [8846]

Foundation for the Advancement of Aboriginal Youth Bursary Program *(Undergraduate/Scholarship)* [3788]

Foundation for the Advancement of Aboriginal Youth Scholarships *(Undergraduate/Scholarship)* [3789]

Foundation for the Carolinas Rotary Scholarship Fund *(Undergraduate/Scholarship)* [4733]

Foundation Public Service Scholarship Award *(Undergraduate/Scholarship)* [4786]

Foundation Scholarships *(Graduate/Scholarship)* [8619]

Foundation Transfer Scholarship *(Undergraduate/Scholarship)* [6793]

Foundation for Your Future Scholarship *(College/Scholarship)* [12058]

Mary Metzger Fouse Memorial Scholarship Fund *(Undergraduate/Scholarship)* [6428]

Terry Fox Memorial Scholarship *(Undergraduate/Scholarship)* [8147]

Captain Ernest W. Fox Perpetual Scholarship *(Advanced Professional/Scholarship)* [3459]

Frame My Future Scholarship Contest *(Undergraduate, Graduate/Scholarship, Prize)* [3327]

Francis Harris Gresham Scholarship Fund *(Undergraduate/Scholarship)* [10685]

The Joe Francomano Scholarship *(Undergraduate/Scholarship)* [6343]

Frank and Charlene Harris Scholarship Fund *(Undergraduate/Scholarship)* [3618]

Frank Foster Skillman Fund *(Undergraduate/Scholarship)* [3362]

Frank G. Araujo Memorial Scholarship *(Undergraduate/Scholarship)* [9545]

Frank L. Weil Memorial Eagle Scout Scholarship *(Undergraduate/Scholarship)* [7850]

Frank S. Land Scholarship *(Undergraduate/Scholarship)* [4049]

Johnny & Sarah Frank Scholarships *(Undergraduate/Scholarship)* [11448]

Frankfort/Capital Region Alumni Chapter *(University/Scholarship)* [11576]

John Hope Franklin Dissertation Fellowship *(Doctorate/Fellowship)* [1213]

James Franklin and Dorothy J. Warnell Scholarship Fund *(Undergraduate, Vocational/Occupational/Scholarship)* [3713]

Franklin Elementary School PTA Scholarship *(Undergraduate/Scholarship)* [9546]

Franklin Research Grants *(Doctorate/Grant)* [1214]

Benjamin Franklin Trust Fund *(Undergraduate, Vocational/Occupational/Scholarship)* [4591]

John L. and Victory E. Frantz Scholarship *(Undergraduate/Scholarship)* [5077]

Fraser Family Scholarships *(Undergraduate/Scholarship)* [9401]

FRAXA Fellowships *(Postdoctorate, Master's/Fellowship, Recognition, Monetary)* [4819]

Freedom Alliance Scholarship Fund *(Undergraduate/Scholarship)* [4821]

Dale E. Fridell Memorial Scholarships *(Undergraduate, Vocational/Occupational/Scholarship)* [10858]

The Nathan J. and Virginia H. Friedman College Scholarship *(Undergraduate, Four Year College, University/Scholarship)* [6271]

The Phil Friel Scholarship *(Undergraduate/Scholarship)* [7170]

Friends of Coal Scholarships *(Undergraduate/Scholarship)* [11971]

Donald Frizzell Memorial Scholarship *(Undergraduate, Graduate, Master's/Scholarship)* [12318]

Mary Alice Fry Memorial Scholarship *(Undergraduate, Graduate/Scholarship)* [6429]

Daniel G. and Helen I. Fultz Scholarship Fund *(Undergraduate/Scholarship)* [4592]

#thefutureisfemale scholarship *(Undergraduate, Graduate, Four Year College, Two Year College/Scholarship)* [11127]

Future of School Scholarship Program *(Undergraduate/Award)* [9942]

Gadde Sitaramamma & Tirupataiah Scholarship *(Graduate/Scholarship)* [10949]

Joe E. Gaddy, Jr. and Margaret W. Gaddy Scholarship *(Undergraduate/Scholarship)* [12078]

Gaebe Eagle Scout Award *(Undergraduate/Scholarship)* [7851]

Gail Garner Memorial R.I.S.E. Scholarship *(Undergraduate/Scholarship)* [9548]

Harry Gairey Scholarship *(Undergraduate/Scholarship)* [2592]

GALAS Scholarship *(Undergraduate, Graduate/Scholarship)* [4868]

Farley Moody Galbraith Scholarship *(Graduate/Scholarship)* [3653]

Whitney Laine Gallahar Memorial Scholarship Fund *(Undergraduate/Scholarship)* [3654]

Gallo Blue Chip Scholarships *(Undergraduate/Scholarship)* [5301]

Lionel Galstaun Memorial Grant *(Undergraduate/Scholarship)* [1877]

Gamma Chi Project 2000 Scholarship *(Undergraduate/Scholarship)* [6430]

Gamma Iota Scholarship *(Undergraduate/Scholarship)* [10108]

Gamma Iota Scholarships - Gamma Tau *(Undergraduate/Scholarship)* [10109]

Gamma Iota Scholarships - Zeta Kappa *(Undergraduate/Scholarship)* [10110]

Gamma Iota Scholarships - Zeta Nu *(Undergraduate/Scholarship)* [10111]

Gamma Lambda Scholarship *(Undergraduate/Scholarship)* [10112]

Gamma Mu Project 2000 Scholarship *(Undergraduate/Scholarship)* [6431]

The Gamma Mu Scholarships Program *(Vocational/Occupational, Professional development, Undergraduate, Graduate, Postgraduate/Scholarship)* [4854]

Gamma Pi Project 2000 Scholarship *(Undergraduate/Scholarship)* [6432]

Gamma Sigma Alpha Graduate Scholarship *(Graduate/Scholarship)* [4856]

Gamma Theta Project 2000 Scholarship *(Undergraduate/Scholarship)* [6433]

Gamma Zeta Project 2000 Scholarship *(Undergraduate/Scholarship)* [6434]

Gardner Foundation Scholarship *(Undergraduate/Scholarship)* [3363]

Peter M. Gargano Scholarship Fund *(Undergraduate/Scholarship)* [4206]

Edwin W. Gaston Scholarships *(Undergraduate/Scholarship)* [377]

David A. and Pamela A. Gault Charitable Fund *(Undergraduate/Scholarship)* [10759]

James L. Gavin Memorial Scholarship *(Undergraduate, Graduate/Scholarship)* [2524]

A.R.F.O.R.A. Martha Gavrila Scholarships for Women *(Postgraduate/Scholarship)* [1368]

GAWP Graduate Scholarships *(Graduate/Scholarship)* [4925]

GE Aviation Scholarship Fund *(Undergraduate/Scholarship)* [3364]

Gehring Memorial Foundation Scholarships *(Graduate, Undergraduate/Scholarship)* [5742]

GEICO Life Scholarship *(Undergraduate/Scholarship)* [5021]

Victoria S. and Bradley L. Geist Scholarships *(Undergraduate, University, College, Vocational/Occupational/Scholarship)* [5400, 5437]

Geraldine Geistert Boss Scholarship *(Undergraduate/Scholarship)* [5151]

Irma Gelhausen Scholarship Fund *(Graduate/Scholarship)* [6663]

General Falcon Scholarships *(Undergraduate/Scholarship)* [9243]

General John Paul Ratay Educational Fund Grants *(Undergraduate/Grant)* [7389]

General Mills Foundation Scholarships *(Undergraduate/Scholarship)* [981]

George J. Mitchell Scholarship *(Postgraduate/Scholarship)* [11774]

George and Pearl Strickland Scholarship Fund *(Graduate, Undergraduate/Scholarship)* [3586]

Georgetown Working League Scholarship *(Undergraduate/Scholarship)* [4917]

Gerard Swartz Fudge Memorial Scholarship *(Postgraduate/Scholarship)* [5664]

Gerber Foundation Merit Scholarship *(Graduate/Scholarship)* [4940]

German Historical Institute Fellowships at the Horner Library *(Postdoctorate, Master's/Fellowship)* [4943]

Bunny Kline Gerner & Robin Gerner Doty Memorial Adelphe Scholarship *(Undergraduate/Scholarship)* [6435]

Elizabeth Tucker Gessley Scholarship *(Undergraduate/Scholarship)* [6436]

Get A Boost $2,000 Scholarship *(All/Scholarship)* [2608]

Get Ahead Scholarship *(Undergraduate, Graduate/Scholarship)* [4474]

Getty GRI-NEH Postdoctoral Fellowships *(Postdoctorate/Fellowship)* [4955]

Getty Postdoctoral Fellowships *(Postdoctorate/Fellowship)* [4957]

Getty Predoctoral Fellowships *(Doctorate/Fellowship)* [4958]

Getty Research Exchange Fellowship Program for Cultural Heritage Preservation *(Doctorate/Fellowship)* [1347]

GFWC Women's Club of South County scholarship program *(Undergraduate/Scholarship)* [9693]

The Elaine and Barry Gilbert College Scholarship *(Undergraduate/Scholarship)* [6272]

Shane Gilbert Memorial Scholarship *(Undergraduate/Scholarship)* [8849]

William Harrison Gill Education Fund *(Undergraduate/Scholarship)* [2480]

Benjamin A. Gilman International Scholarship *(Undergraduate/Scholarship)* [11479]

Susan Kay Munson Gilmore Memorial Scholarship *(Undergraduate, Vocational/Occupational, Graduate/Scholarship)* [3678]

The Alex Gissler Memorial Scholarship *(Undergraduate/Scholarship)* [7171]

GLATA Living Memorial Doctorate Scholarship *(Doctorate/Scholarship)* [5215]

GLATA Living Memorial Graduate Scholarship *(Graduate/Fellowship, Scholarship)* [5216]

Herman and Bess Glazer Scholarship Fund *(Undergraduate/Scholarship)* [5227]

Glazing Industry Scholarship *(Advanced Professional/Scholarship)* [9402]

Gleaner Life Insurance Society Scholarship *(Graduate/Scholarship)* [4997]

Glen and Babs Carlson Endowed Scholarship *(Undergraduate/Scholarship)* [6794]

Glenn B. Anderson Scholarship *(Graduate, Undergraduate/Scholarship)* [7721]

Global Entrepreneur's Award *(High School, College/Award)* [6314]

Glogowski Franciszek Memorial Scholarship *(Undergraduate/Scholarship)* [9665]

Glenn Godfrey Sr. Memorial Scholarship *(Undergraduate, Graduate/Scholarship)* [6589]

Godparents for Tanzania Scholarship *(Undergraduate/Scholarship)* [5012]

Shirley J. Gold Scholarship *(Undergraduate, Vocational/Occupational/Scholarship)* [883]

Golden Door Scholarship *(Graduate/Scholarship)* [5018]

Golden Key Advisor Professional Development Grant *(Professional development/Grant)* [5022]

Golden Key Graduate Scholar Award *(Graduate/Scholarship)* [5023]

Goldman, Sachs and Company Fund *(Undergraduate/Scholarship)* [3365]

Helen B. and Lewis E. Goldstein Scholarship *(Undergraduate, Graduate/Scholarship)* [6273]

Joshua Gomes Memorial Scholarship Fund *(Graduate/Scholarship)* [7924]

Diane G. Lowe and John Gomez, IV Scholarship Fund *(Undergraduate/Scholarship)* [3620]

Arthur H. Goodman Memorial Scholarship *(Undergraduate, University/Scholarship)* [9815]

Lucille May Gopie Scholarships *(Undergraduate, Graduate/Scholarship)* [2593]

Thomas Boston Gordon Memorial Scholarship *(Undergraduate, Graduate, University/Scholarship)* [2526]

Barnett D. Gordon Scholarships *(Graduate, Undergraduate/Scholarship)* [5743]

Gordy Fink Memorial Scholarship *(Undergraduate/Scholarship)* [9403]

Sarah "Sally" Ives Gore Gamma Kappa Sapphire Scholarships *(Graduate, Undergraduate/Scholarship)* [6437]

Richard C. Gorecki Scholarships *(Graduate/Scholarship)* [9244]

Charles F. Gould Endowment Scholarships *(Undergraduate/Scholarship)* [11449]

Anna K. Gower and Annabelle K. Gower Scholarship Fund *(Undergraduate, University, College, Two Year College, Vocational/Occupational/Scholarship)* [5402]

Graduate Student Fellowships *(Graduate/Fellowship)* [4547]

Grand Rapids Scholarship Association *(Undergraduate/Scholarship)* [5152]

Grand Rapids Trans Foundation Academic Scholarship *(Undergraduate, Two Year College, Vocational/Occupational/Scholarship)* [5197]

Grand Rapids University Prep Founders' Scholarship *(Undergraduate/Scholarship)* [5153]

Grande Prairie 4-H District Scholarship *(Undergraduate/Scholarship)* [14]

Granger Business Association College Scholarship *(Graduate/Scholarship)* [5199]

Grant H. Flint International Scholarship Program - Category I *(Undergraduate/Scholarship)* [10580]

Russ Grant Memorial Scholarship for Tennis *(Undergraduate/Scholarship)* [8851]

Ella T. Grasso Literary Scholarship *(Undergraduate/Scholarship)* [11221]

Grays Harbor Community Foundation Scholarships *(Undergraduate, Graduate, Scholarship)* [5213]

Greater Seattle Business Association Scholarships (GSBA Scholarships) *(Undergraduate, Graduate/Scholarship)* [5223]

Bishop Charles P. Greco Graduate Fellowships *(Graduate, Master's/Fellowship)* [6578]

Greek Orthodox Archdiocese of America Paleologos Graduate Scholarships *(Graduate/Scholarship)* [5231]

Green Hill Yacht and Country Club Scholarship *(Undergraduate, High School/Scholarship)* [3568]

Green Knight Economic Development Corporation Scholarships *(Undergraduate/Scholarship)* [5235]

Crystal Green Memorial Scholarship *(Graduate/Scholarship)* [2626]

Joshua "Josh" Green Memorial Scholarship Endowment *(Undergraduate, Community College/Scholarship)* [8512]

James H. and Shirley L. Green Scholarship Fund *(Undergraduate/Scholarship)* [10761]

Curt Greene Memorial Scholarships *(Undergraduate/Scholarship)* [5302]

Greenwich Scholarship Association Scholarships (GSA) *(Undergraduate/Scholarship)* [5241]

Anna Munger Greenwood Memorial Adelphe Scholarship *(Undergraduate/Scholarship)* [6438]

Griffin Foundation Scholarships *(Undergraduate/Scholarship)* [5243]

Homajean Grisham Memorial Scholarship *(Undergraduate/Scholarship)* [8513]

Shelby Grissom Memorial Scholarship *(Undergraduate, Community College/Scholarship)* [8514]

Reginald K. Groome Memorial Scholarships *(Undergraduate/Scholarship)* [9986]

Kathern F. Gruber Scholarship Program *(Undergraduate, Graduate/Scholarship)* [2624]

Gruwell Scholarship *(Undergraduate/Scholarship)* [3569]

Guerra - Melissa Ann (Missy) Guerra Scholarship *(Undergraduate/Scholarship)* [3476]

Bobette Bibo Gugliotta Memorial Scholarships for Creative Writing *(Undergraduate/Scholarship)* [10133]

GuildScholar Awards *(Undergraduate/Scholarship)* [6855]

Hai Guin Scholarships *(Undergraduate, Graduate/Scholarship)* [5260]

Guin-Stanford Scholarship *(Advanced Professional/Scholarship)* [3655]

Larry Gulley Scholarship *(Undergraduate/Scholarship)* [10343]

George Gurdjian Memorial Grant *(Undergraduate/Scholarship)* [1879]

Antranik and Alice Gurdjian Scholarship Grant *(Undergraduate/Scholarship)* [1880]

Patricia S. Gustafson '56 Memorial Scholarship Fund *(Graduate/Scholarship)* [4207]

Guthikonda BasavapunnaRao & Umadevi Scholarship *(Graduate/Scholarship)* [10950]

Guthikonda Ramabrahmam & Balamani Scholarship *(Graduate/Scholarship)* [10951]

Mary Ewing Guthrey/Mary Keller Moyer Memorial Scholarship *(Undergraduate, Graduate/Scholarship)* [6439]

Gwin J. and Ruth Kolb Research Travel Fellowship *(Doctorate, Other/Fellowship)* [1433]

Gwynedd Mercy University Presidential Scholarship *(Undergraduate/Scholarship)* [5255]

H. Kruger Kaprielian Scholarship *(Undergraduate/Scholarship)* [11714]

Garabed, Zabel and Vahe Hachikian Scholarship Grant *(Undergraduate/Scholarship)* [1881]

Hackett Family Scholarship *(Undergraduate/Scholarship)* [5155]

HACU/Denny's Hungry for Education Scholarships *(Undergraduate, Graduate/Scholarship)* [5515]

Suzanne Lovell Hadsell Memorial Scholarship *(Undergraduate, Graduate/Scholarship)* [6440]

HAESF Graduate Scholarships *(Graduate/Scholarship)* [5644]

Leslie Jane Hahn Memorial Scholarships *(Undergraduate/Scholarship)* [9816]

Michael Hakeem Memorial Essay Contest for Ongoing College Students *(Undergraduate/Scholarship)* [4824]

Ralph Hale and Martha L. Ruppert Educational Scholarship *(Undergraduate/Grant)* [10134]

Hall of Achievement Scholarship *(Undergraduate/Scholarship)* [2799]

Guy D. & Mary Edith Halladay Graduate Scholarship *(Undergraduate/Scholarship)* [5156]

Halloween Costume Scholarship *(All/Scholarship)* [7441]

Harold B. Halter Memorial Scholarship *(Undergraduate/Scholarship)* [4497]

Alice Hamilton Prize *(Other/Prize)* [1453]

Al Hamilton Scholarship *(Undergraduate/Scholarship)* [2595]

Stan Hamilton Scholarship *(Graduate/Scholarship)* [9885]

George and Mary Josephine Hamman Foundation Scholarships *(Undergraduate/Scholarship)* [5264]

The Caitlin Hammaren Memorial Scholarship *(Undergraduate/Scholarship)* [6441]

HANA Scholars *(Undergraduate, Graduate, Doctorate/Scholarship)* [4891]

Hancock Family Snow Hill High School Scholarship *(Graduate/Scholarship)* [3570]

Byron Hanke Fellowships *(Doctorate, Graduate, Undergraduate/Fellowship)* [4767]

Clayburn J. Sr. & Garnet R. Hanna Scholarship *(Undergraduate/Scholarship)* [8852]

Haraldson Foundation Scholarships *(Undergraduate, Graduate/Scholarship)* [5288]

Isaac and Mary Harbottle Scholarship *(Graduate, Undergraduate/Scholarship)* [8927]

Charles Henry Hardin Memorial Scholarship *(Undergraduate, Graduate, Scholarship)* [2527]

Harness Tracks of America Scholarship Fund *(Undergraduate/Scholarship)* [5304]

Margaret Shumavonian Harnischfeger Scholarship *(Undergraduate/Scholarship)* [1883]

Harold and Eleanor Ringelberg Scholarship *(Undergraduate/Scholarship)* [5082]

Harriet Erich Graduate Fellowship *(Graduate/Fellowship)* [4002]

Morton and Beatrice Harrison Scholarship Fund *(Undergraduate/Scholarship)* [4593]

Harry A. Donn Scholarship *(Undergraduate/Scholarship)* [5329]

Harry Munoz Memorial Scholarship *(Undergraduate/Scholarship)* [9550]

Harry Steele Entrance Award *(Postgraduate/Award)* [12252]

Dave Hart Graduate Scholarship *(Graduate/Scholarship)* [10654]

Carroll Hart Scholarship *(Graduate/Scholarship)* [10344]

Hartford Grammar School Scholarship Fund *(Undergraduate/Scholarship)* [5331]

Hartford Whalers Booster Club Scholarship *(Undergraduate/Scholarship)* [5353]

Harry C. Hartleben III/Gordon Page Corbitt Scholarship *(Undergraduate/Scholarship)* [8855]

Gregory Linn Haught Citizenship Award *(Undergraduate/Scholarship)* [8857]

Dorcas Edmonson Haught Scholarship *(Undergraduate/Scholarship)* [8858]

Celeste Hayo Memorial Scholarship Fund *(Undergraduate, College, University/Scholarship)* [5403]

Hazel D. Isbell Foundation Fellowships *(Graduate/Fellowship)* [4003]

H.C. Schott Foundation Scholarship *(Undergraduate/Scholarship)* [3366]

HCF Community Scholarships Fund *(Undergraduate, Graduate/Scholarship)* [5404]

HCRTA/Glen O. & Wyllabeth Scholarship Fund *(Undergraduate/Scholarship)* [3367]

The Healthline & NORD Stronger Scholarship *(Undergraduate/Scholarship)* [5452]

Healthy Communities Scholarship *(Undergraduate, Graduate, Community College/Scholarship)* [9282]

Dr. James H. Heckman Memorial Scholarship Fund *(Undergraduate/Scholarship)* [10763]

Howell Heflin Memorial Scholarship *(Undergraduate/Scholarship)* [8515]

Heghinian Scholarships *(Undergraduate/Scholarship)* [4035]

Heidelberg Distributing Scholarship Fund *(Undergraduate/Scholarship)* [3368]

Heinz Pet Products Scholarship Fund *(Undergraduate/Scholarship)* [3369]

Helen and George Kilik Scholarship (Undergraduate/Scholarship) [290]

Helen J. & Harold Gilman Smith Scholarship (Graduate, Undergraduate/Scholarship) [2481]

Helen Steiner Rice Scholarship Fund (Undergraduate/Scholarship) [3370]

Helena B. Cobb Higher Education (four Year) Scholarship (Undergraduate, Vocational/Occupational/Scholarship) [12165]

The Helena B. Cobb Scholarships (Undergraduate, Vocational/Occupational/Scholarship) [12166]

Hellenic Times Scholarships (Undergraduate, Graduate/Scholarship) [5461]

Hellenic University Club of Philadelphia Founders Scholarship (Undergraduate/Scholarship) [5465]

Ronald, Randall and Roger Helman Scholarship (Undergraduate, Graduate/Scholarship) [2528]

Heloise Werthan Kuhn Scholarship Fund (Undergraduate/Scholarship) [3621]

"Help to Save" Scholarship (College, University/Scholarship) [3880]

Hemlow Prize in Burney Studies (Graduate/Prize) [1434]

Jeanne H. Hemmingway Scholarship Fund (Undergraduate/Scholarship) [4208]

John Henderson Endowment Scholarships (Undergraduate/Scholarship) [11451]

Henderson Memorial Endowed Scholarship (Undergraduate/Scholarship) [6796]

Dr. E. Bruce Hendrick Scholarship Program (All/Scholarship) [5669]

Thomas J. Henry Leadership Scholarship Program (Undergraduate, Graduate/Scholarship) [5483]

Henry L.P. Schmelzer College Transitions Scholarship Fund (Undergraduate/Scholarship) [6982]

Henry S. and Carolyn Adams Scholarship (Undergraduate/Scholarship) [4734]

Henry Salvatori Scholarship (Undergraduate/Scholarship) [8689]

Gene Henson Scholarship (Undergraduate/Scholarship) [2340]

Herb Kohl Educational Foundation Student Excellence Scholarship (Undergraduate/Scholarship) [6582]

Herb Kohl Educational Foundation Student Initiative Scholarship (Undergraduate/Scholarship) [6583]

Herbert Hoover Uncommon Student Award (Undergraduate/Scholarship) [5557]

Herman H. Derksen Scholarship (Undergraduate/Scholarship) [9820]

Herman P. Kopplemann Fund (Undergraduate/Scholarship) [5332]

Hernandez – Manuel Hernandez, Jr. Memoral Scholarship (Undergraduate/Scholarship) [3477]

George L. and June L. Herpel Memorial Scholarship (Graduate/Scholarship) [2529]

Jessica M. Herron, Epsilon Nu, Memorial Scholarship (Undergraduate, Graduate/Scholarship) [6443]

Ella Beren Hersch Scholarship (Undergraduate/Scholarship) [8859]

Herzog August Bibliothek Wolfenbüttel Fellowships (Postdoctorate/Fellowship) [8372]

Wayne E. Hesch Memorial Scholarship (Undergraduate, Graduate/Scholarship) [1691]

Walston and Jewel Hester Memorial Scholarship Endowment (Undergraduate, Community College/Scholarship) [8516]

HFA Educational Scholarship (Undergraduate/Scholarship) [5479]

Dorothy Hicks Graduate Scholarship (Graduate/Scholarship) [10655]

Jim Hierlihy Memorial Scholarship (Undergraduate/Scholarship) [4429]

High School Academic Scholarship (Undergraduate/Scholarship) [10053]

Highlands Ranch Dental Group Scholarship (Undergraduate, High School/Scholarship) [5508]

HII Scholarship Fund (Community College, Two Year College, Four Year College, Undergraduate, University/Scholarship) [5655]

Douglas W. Hill, Jr. Scholarship (Undergraduate, Graduate/Scholarship) [2530]

John A. Hill Memorial Scholarship (Undergraduate, Graduate/Scholarship) [2531]

Gus and Henrietta Hill Scholarship Fund (Graduate/Scholarship) [4209]

Oregon Latino Scholarship Fund (Graduate, Undergraduate/Scholarship) [5526]

Hispanic Scholarship Fund General College Scholarship Program (HSF) (Undergraduate/Scholarship) [5530]

Hispanic Serving Institution Scholarships (HSIS) (Undergraduate/Scholarship) [11280]

Historically Black College or University Scholarships (HBCUS) (Undergraduate/Scholarship) [11281]

C.H.(Chuck) Hodgson Scholarships (Undergraduate/Scholarship) [12005]

The George W. and Ethel B. Hoefler Fund (Undergraduate/Scholarship) [3714]

Hoffman Family Scholarship (Undergraduate/Scholarship) [5085]

Henry Hoffman Memorial Scholarship (Undergraduate/Scholarship) [7641]

Irving J. Hoffman Memorial Scholarships (Undergraduate/Scholarship) [11691]

Nedien Hoganson Memorial Scholarship (Undergraduate, Master's/Scholarship) [12325]

The Thelma S. Hoge Memorial Scholarship (Graduate/Scholarship) [3596]

Holiday Celebration Scholarship (All/Scholarship) [7442]

Dr. Marshall E. Hollis Scholarship (Undergraduate, Graduate/Scholarship) [2532]

Robert Holmes Scholarship (Undergraduate/Scholarship) [3720]

George Holopigian Memorial Grants (Undergraduate/Scholarship) [1885]

Home Improvement Scholarship (High School, Undergraduate, Graduate, Vocational/Occupational/Scholarship) [7521]

Homus E-Commerce Research Scholarship (College, University, Undergraduate, Graduate, Community College, Vocational/Occupational, Professional development/Scholarship) [5553]

Honest. Wild. Beautiful. Scholarship Program (Undergraduate, Graduate/Scholarship) [1721]

Hope Through Learning Award (Undergraduate/Award) [5551]

Frank and Gladys Hopkins Endowed Scholarships (Undergraduate/Scholarship) [6798]

Harry Hopmeyer Memorial Scholarship (Undergraduate/Scholarship) [6292]

Detroit Tigers Willie Horton Scholarship (Undergraduate/Scholarship) [3721]

Hosinec Family Scholarships (Graduate, Undergraduate/Grant) [11692]

HostGator Technology Scholarship (Community College, Undergraduate, Graduate/Scholarship) [5588]

Max and Julia Houghton Duluth Central Scholarships (Undergraduate/Scholarship) [4210]

Houston Alumnae Association Doris Krikham Brokaw Memorial Adelphe Scholarship (Undergraduate, Graduate/Scholarship) [6444]

Houston Alumnae Association, Eunice "Scotty" Scott Siverson Memorial Adelphe Scholarship (Undergraduate, Graduate/Scholarship) [6445]

Houston Alumnae Chapter Graduate Fellowship (Graduate/Fellowship) [4004]

The HoustonMovers.com Scholarship (Undergraduate/Scholarship) [5602]

The Hirair and Anna Hovnanian Foundation Presidential Scholarship (Undergraduate/Scholarship) [5512]

Hirair and Anna Hovnanian Foundation Scholarship (Undergraduate/Scholarship) [5513]

Soldotna Chamber of Commerce/Vera Howarth Memorial Scholarship (Undergraduate/Scholarship) [10578]

John Hoyt Memorial Scholarship (Undergraduate, Master's/Scholarship) [12328]

HSF/Wells Fargo Scholarship Program (Undergraduate, Graduate, High School/Scholarship) [5532]

Albert W. and Mildred Hubbard Scholarships (Undergraduate/Scholarship) [9822]

Amber Huber Memorial Scholarship (Undergraduate/Scholarship) [3680]

Hubert K. and JoAnn Seymour Scholarship (Undergraduate/Scholarship) [8461]

David Hudak Memorial Essay Contest for Freethinking Students of Color (Undergraduate/Scholarship) [4825]

A. Joseph Huerta "Puedo" Scholarships (Undergraduate/Scholarship) [3478]

Hugh and Elizabeth Montgomery Scholarship Fund (Undergraduate/Scholarship) [6983]

Hugh & Helen Wood Nepalese Scholarship (Undergraduate/Scholarship) [2482]

Hughes Memorial Foundatio n (Other/Scholarship) [5619]

Paul A. Hughes Memorial Scholarships (Undergraduate/Scholarship) [2800]

Humane Studies Fellowship (Graduate/Fellowship) [5824]

Anna C. Hume Scholarship (Undergraduate/Scholarship) [4976]

Kevin Hummer Point Scholarship (Graduate, Undergraduate, Doctorate/Scholarship) [9223]

Betty Jo Creighton Hunkele Adelphe Scholarship (Undergraduate/Scholarship) [6446]

The Husband and Wife Law Team Scholarship (Undergraduate/Scholarship) [2689]

The Husenig Foundation Scholarship Grant (Undergraduate/Scholarship) [1886]

Hushy Lipton Memorial Scholarship Fund (Undergraduate, Graduate, Postgraduate/Scholarship) [2985]

Hylan Family Scholarship (Two Year College, Four Year College/Scholarship) [5671]

I Have a Dream Scholarship (Graduate, High School/Scholarship) [11230]

I Have a Dream Scholarships (Undergraduate/Scholarship) [6218]

IAHCSMM-Purdue University Scholarship (Professional development/Scholarship) [5927]

Ian Lithgow Memorial Award (Master's/Award) [12253]

Iberdrola USA Scholarships (Undergraduate/Scholarship) [6984]

ICC General Scholarship Fund (Undergraduate/Scholarship, Monetary, Award) [5971]

ICDA Graduate Scholarships (Graduate/Scholarship) [6158]

ICDA Research Grants (Graduate/Grant) [6159]

Ice Skating Institute of America Education Foundation Scholarships (Undergraduate/Scholarship) [5673]

ICI Military Scholarship (Undergraduate, Vocational/Occupational/Scholarship) [5960]

Idaho Opportunity Scholarship (Undergraduate/Scholarship) [10805]

IDRC Research Awards (Master's, Doctorate/Award) [3264]

IEHA Education/Scholarship Foundation Award (Undergraduate/Scholarship) [5998]

Ella R. Ifill Fund (Undergraduate/Scholarship) [6985]

Illinois Association of Chamber of Commerce Executives Scholarships (Professional development/Scholarship) [5693]

Illinois Division of Midwest Dairy Educational Award (Undergraduate/Scholarship) [7369]

Illuminator Educational Foundation Scholarships (Undergraduate, Graduate/Scholarship) [2801]

ILMA foundation Scholarship Program (Undergraduate/Scholarship) [5735]

Ilse B. Hanfmann, George Hanfmann and Machteld J. Mellink Burslari Fellowship. (Doctorate/Fellowship) [1348]

Imagine America College Scholarships for High School Students (Undergraduate/Scholarship) [5717]

Imagine America Military Awards Program (Undergraduate/Scholarship) [5718]

Imagine America Scholarships for Adults (Undergraduate/Scholarship) [5719]

Immerse Education University Scholarship (Undergraduate, University, College/Scholarship) [5721]

Imprex Scholarship (College, University/Scholarship) [5727]

Ina Knutsen Scholarship (Undergraduate/Scholarship) [10054]

Independent University Alumni Association Scholarships (Graduate, Undergraduate/Scholarship) [5744]

Indian River Scholarship (Undergraduate, University, College, Vocational/Occupational/Scholarship) [12329]

Indiana FFA Association State Fair Scholarship (Undergraduate/Scholarship) [5752]

Indiana State University Academic Excellence Scholarship (Undergraduate/Scholarship) [5757]

Indiana State University Academic Promise Scholarships (Undergraduate/Scholarship) [5768]

Indiana State University Incentive Scholarship (Undergraduate/Scholarship) [5758]

Indiana State University President's Scholarships (Undergraduate/Scholarship) [5759]

Indiana State University Transfer Student Scholarships (Undergraduate/Scholarship) [5761]

Indonesian Directorate General of Higher Education Scholarships (DIKTI) (Graduate/Scholarship) [4263]

Indspire Post-Secondary Education Scholarships (PSE) (Graduate, Undergraduate, Vocational/Occupational, Two Year College, Four Year College/Scholarship) [5775]

Informatics Post Doctoral Fellowships (Doctorate/Fellowship) [9056]

Informatics Pre Doctoral Fellowships (Doctorate/Fellowship) [9057]

Informatics Sabbatical Fellowships (Doctorate, Postdoctorate, Master's/Fellowship) [9058]

Information Age Publishing HMJ Scholarship award (Doctorate, Graduate/Scholarship) [5784]

Jennifer Ingrum Scholarship Fund (Undergraduate/Scholarship) [3623]

INIA Scholarship Program (Undergraduate/Scholarship) [6044]

Injury to Opportunity Scholarship (Vocational/Occupational/Scholarship) [4252]

Injury Scholarship (Undergraduate/Scholarship) [5308, 7164]

Inland Northwest Business Alliance Scholarships (INBA) (Undergraduate/Scholarship) [9302]

Institute for the International Education of Students Faculty Fellowships (Postdoctorate/Fellowship) [5843, 8374]

Instructional Design & Learning Technologies Scholarships (Undergraduate, Graduate/Scholarship) [4335]

Insurify Safe Driving Scholarship (Undergraduate/Scholarship) [5881]

International Door Association Scholarship Foundation Program (Undergraduate/Scholarship) [5996]

International Executive Housekeepers Association Spartan Scholarship Award (Undergraduate/Scholarship) [5999]

International Grenfell Association Bursary (Undergraduate, Postgraduate/Scholarship) [6017]

International Grenfell Association High School Bursaries (Undergraduate/Scholarship) [6018]

International Grenfell Association Post-Secondary Bursaries (Undergraduate/Scholarship) [6019]

International Order of the King's Daughters and Sons North American Indian Scholarship Program (Undergraduate/Scholarship) [989]

International Peace Scholarship Fund (IPS) (Graduate, Master's, Doctorate/Scholarship) [8975]

International Radio and Television Society Foundation Summer Fellowships Program (Undergraduate, Graduate/Fellowship) [6067]

International Sanitary Supply Association Foundation Scholarships (Undergraduate/Scholarship) [6081]

The Interracial Scholarship Fund of Greater Hartford (Undergraduate/Scholarship) [5333]

IODE Labrador Bursary (Undergraduate/Scholarship) [7759]

IOKDS Native American Scholarships (Undergraduate, University, College, Vocational/Occupational/Scholarship) [6051]

Iowa Division of Midwest Dairy Educational Award (Undergraduate/Scholarship) [7370]

Ira G. Turpin Scholar Program Fund (Undergraduate/Scholarship) [10767]

Iranian-American Scholarship Fund (Undergraduate, Graduate/Scholarship) [7954]

Irene Carlson Gnaedinger Memorial Scholarship (Undergraduate/Scholarship) [6800]

Iris Scholarship (Undergraduate/Scholarship) [6447]

Irma E. Voigt Memorial Scholarship (Undergraduate/Scholarship) [10113]

Greg Irons Award Fund (Undergraduate/Award) [4211]

David L. Irons Memorial Scholarship Fund (Undergraduate, Two Year College, Four Year College/Scholarship) [5405]

Irwin Allen Nadal Entrance Award (Master's/Award) [12254]

Irwin S. Lerner Student Scholarship (Undergraduate/Scholarship) [8108]

Isabel Mayer Kirkpatrick Scholarship Fund (Undergraduate/Scholarship) [10687]

ISDS Graduate Student Scholarships (Doctorate, Graduate/Scholarship) [6105]

ISF Excellence in Community Service Scholarship (Undergraduate/Scholarship) [6173]

ISF Undergraduate Scholarship (Undergraduate/Scholarship) [6174]

Patricia and Gail Ishimoto Memorial Scholarship (Undergraduate/Scholarship) [6247]

Islamic Scholarship Fund Scholarship (ISF) (Graduate, Undergraduate/Scholarship) [6178]

Broughton Isom Memorial Scholarship (Undergraduate/Scholarship) [8519]

ISU Child of Alumni Book Voucher Awards (Undergraduate/Scholarship) [5770]

ITMS Shannon Fellowships (Graduate, Undergraduate/Fellowship) [6132]

IWSH Essay Scholarship Contest (Undergraduate, College, University, Vocational/Occupational/Scholarship) [6144]

J. Ward Sleichter and Frances F. Sleichter Memorial Fund (Undergraduate/Scholarship) [4779]

Jack Family Scholarship (Undergraduate/Scholarship) [5158]

Jack H. Brown Future Leaders Scholarships (Undergraduate/Scholarship) [2802]

The Jack and Jill of America Foundation's National Scholarship Program (Undergraduate/Scholarship) [6190]

Jack Kent Cooke Foundation Undergraduate Transfer Scholarship (Undergraduate/Scholarship) [3821]

Jack Kent Cooke Foundation Young Scholars Program (Undergraduate/Scholarship) [3822]

Jack M. & Mary Lou Gruber Scholarship (Undergraduate/Scholarship) [6801]

Jack M. Nagasaka Memorial Scholarship (Undergraduate/Scholarship) [9551]

Jackie Robinson Scholarship Award (Undergraduate/Scholarship) [9723]

Jackson Club Scholarship Fund (Undergraduate/Scholarship) [4212]

Jackson High School Alumni Scholarship Fund (Graduate/Scholarship) [10768]

Holly Jackson-Wuller Memorial Scholarship (Undergraduate/Scholarship) [8860]

Jacob R. & Mary M. VanLoo & Lenore K. VanLoo Scholarship (Undergraduate/Scholarship) [5159]

Freddy L. Jacobs Individual Scholarship (Undergraduate/Scholarship) [5953]

Cory Jam Memorial Award (Undergraduate/Scholarship) [4213]

Jamaican Canadian Association Alberta Scholarship Program (Undergraduate/Scholarship) [6225]

Jamail/Long Challenge Grant Scholarships (Undergraduate, Graduate/Scholarship) [5522]

James Bilder Scholarship Fund (Undergraduate/Scholarship) [10688]

James E. Hoff, S.J. Scholar (Undergraduate/Scholarship) [12223]

James H. Patrenos Memorial Scholarship (Undergraduate/Scholarship) [10147]

James L. Biggane Fellowship in Finance (Graduate/Fellowship) [8325]

James and Marilyn Rockefeller Scholarship Fund (Undergraduate/Scholarship) [6986]

James V. Johnson Scholarship Endowment Fund (Undergraduate/Scholarship) [4737]

James W. Junior and Jane T. Brown Scholarship (Undergraduate, Vocational/Occupational/Scholarship) [5086]

Jan DiMartino Delany Memorial Scholarship (Undergraduate/Scholarship) [4780]

Jane Beattie Memorial Scholarship (Graduate/Scholarship) [10378]

Helen Janko Memorial Scholarship (Undergraduate, Master's/Scholarship) [12330]

Janssen Infectious Disease Point Scholarships (Undergraduate, Graduate, Doctorate/Scholarship) [9224]

Jason Chaney Memorial Scholarship (High School/Scholarship) [11948]

Jay C. and B. Nadine Leggett Charitable Fund (Undergraduate/Scholarship) [10769]

Jay Hammond Memorial Scholarship (Graduate/Scholarship) [11518]

Hon. Michaelle Jean Scholarship (Undergraduate/Scholarship) [2596]

The Jeffcoat Firm Annual Scholarship Essay & Video Competition (College, University, Graduate/Scholarship) [6261]

Jefferson Graduate Fellowship (Doctorate, Graduate/Fellowship) [6263]

Jeffrey D. Ralston Memorial Scholarship (Undergraduate/Scholarship) [7562]

Kenneth Jernigan Scholarships (Undergraduate/Scholarship, Monetary) [7877]

Harry Jerome Legacy Scholarship (Undergraduate, Graduate/Scholarship) [2597]

Jerome Peters Family Fund (Undergraduate/Scholarship) [6987]

Jerry Newson Scholarship Fund (Undergraduate/Scholarship) [3624]

Jim Doogan Memorial Scholarship (Undergraduate/Scholarship) [11519]

Jim & Nancy Hinkle Travel Grants (Graduate/Grant) [5476]

Jimmy Edwards Scholarship Fund (Undergraduate/Scholarship) [3625]

Joan Rogers Kamps Bursary (Undergraduate, Postgraduate, Professional development/Scholarship) [8641]

Joel R. Friend Scholarship (Undergraduate/Scholarship) [2483]

John Caoile Memorial Scholarship (Other/Scholarship) [9406]

John D. Wirth Travel Grant (Graduate, Other/Grant) [1454]

John E. Mayfield ABLE Scholarship Fund (Graduate/Scholarship) [3626]

John Flynn Memorial Scholarship (Undergraduate/Scholarship) [3682]

John G. Brokaw Scholarship (Undergraduate/Scholarship) [8173]

John G. Williams Scholarship Foundation (Undergraduate/Scholarship) [12039]

John & Ruth Childe Scholarship Fund (Undergraduate/Scholarship) [10691]

John S. and Marjoria R. Cunningham Camp Scholarship (Other/Scholarship) [6988]

Johnny Bench Scholarship Fund (Undergraduate/Scholarship) [3371]

The Robert L. Johns Vocational Scholarship (Vocational/Occupational/Scholarship) [4871]

Wilma Winberg Johnson Adelphe Scholarship for Chapter Consultants (Undergraduate/Scholarship) [6448]

Douglas Johnson Memorial Scholarship (Master's, Graduate, Undergraduate/Scholarship) [12332]

Joint Japan/World Bank Graduate Scholarship Program for Developing Country National (JJ/WBGSP) (Graduate/Scholarship) [12192]

Joint Japan/World Bank Graduate Scholarship Program for Japanese National (JJ/WBGSP) (Graduate, Master's, Doctorate/Scholarship) [12193]

George E. Jonas Scholarships (Graduate, Undergraduate/Scholarship) [6894]

NASSP/Herff Jones Principal's Leadership Award (Undergraduate/Scholarship) [7690]

Jordan Abdo Memorial Scholarship Fund (Undergraduate/Scholarship) [10692]

Joseph and Amelia Saks Scholarship (Undergraduate/Scholarship) [3656]

Joseph S. Stern Scholarship Fund (Undergraduate/Scholarship) [3372]

Joseph Sumner Smith Scholarship (Undergraduate/Scholarship) [11250]

Joseph W. Mayo ALS Scholarship Fund (Graduate/Scholarship) [6989]

Josephine Hooker Shain Scholarship (Undergraduate/Scholarship) [4918]

Josephine de Karman Fellowship (Doctorate/Fellowship) [6503]

Joyce C. Hall College Scholarship (Undergraduate/Scholarship) [8981]

JPGtoPDF College Scholarship (Undergraduate, Graduate/Scholarship) [6339]

J.R. (Joe) Power National Scholarship (Postgraduate/Scholarship, Monetary) [9443]

Juchniewicz Kazimiera Memorial Scholarship (Undergraduate/Scholarship) [9666]

Judge Benjamin Schwartz Memorial Fund (Undergraduate/Scholarship) [3373]

Judge Isaac Anderson, Jr. Scholarship Fund (Undergraduate/Scholarship) [10693]

Judge Sidney M. Aronovitz Memorial Scholarship Fund (Undergraduate/Scholarship) [7298]

Judge William J. Nelson Scholarship Fund (Undergraduate/Scholarship) [10694]

Judith Keller Marx Krumholz Scholarship (Graduate/Scholarship) [9824]

Judith Warner Memorial Scholarship (Undergraduate/Scholarship) [9408]

JuicingBeasts Staying Healthy Scholarship (Undergraduate, Graduate/Scholarship) [6341]

Juilfs Foundation Scholarship (Undergraduate/Scholarship) [3374]

Juliann and Joe Maxwell Scholarship Fund for Employees of Tractor Supply (Undergraduate/Scholarship) [3627]

Juliann King Maxwell Scholarship Fund for Riverview High School (Undergraduate, Vocational/Occupational/Scholarship) [3628]

Julio C. Diaz Academic Scholarship Fund (Undergraduate/Scholarship) [10770]

The Junior Achievement of East Central Ohio, Inc. Scholarship Fund (Undergraduate, High School/Scholarship) [10771]

Justin Scot Alston Memorial Scholarship (Undergraduate/Scholarship) [5665]

JW Surety Bonds Scholarships (Undergraduate, Graduate/Scholarship) [6353]

Kacperski Stefan & Weronika Memorial Scholarship (Undergraduate/Scholarship) [9667]

David A. Kaiser Memorial Scholarship Fund (Undergraduate/Scholarship) [10772]

Armenag and Armenhooi Kalustian Memorial Grant (Undergraduate/Scholarship) [1887]

Kamehameha Schools Class of 1968 "Ka Poli O Kaiona" Scholarships (Graduate, Undergraduate/Scholarship) [8930]

Kamehameha Schools Class of 1972 Scholarship (Graduate, Undergraduate/Scholarship) [8931]

Aram and Adrine Kamparosyan Memorial Grant (Undergraduate/Scholarship) [1888]

Martin S. Kane Memorial Community Service Award Scholarships (Undergraduate/Scholarship) [3572]

Kansas Distinguished Scholarship Program (Graduate/Scholarship) [6363]

The Walter S. Kapala Scholarship Trust (Undergraduate/Scholarship) [5335]

Joseph Kaplan Fund (Graduate, Undergraduate/Scholarship) [5745]

Don Kaplan Legacy Scholarships (Undergraduate/Scholarship) [2803]

Kappa Kappa Gamma Foundation of Canada Graduate Scholarship (Graduate, Doctorate/Scholarship) [6486]

Kappa Kappa Gamma Foundation - Mary Maxwell Gates Scholarship (Undergraduate, Graduate/Scholarship) [6449]

Kappa Kappa Gamma Foundation Project 2000 Scholarship (Undergraduate/Scholarship) [6450]

Kappa Project 2000 Scholarship (Undergraduate/Scholarship) [6451]

Karen D. Carsel Memorial Scholarship (Undergraduate/Scholarship) [916]

Mitchell Karper Memorial Scholarship (Undergraduate/Scholarship) [6293]

Philip R. Karr, III Scholarship Fund (Graduate/Scholarship) [4926]

K.A.S.A. Memorial Scholarship (Undergraduate/Scholarship) [8861]

KASF scholarships (Graduate, Undergraduate/Scholarship) [6597]

KASF Designated Scholarships (Graduate, Undergraduate/Scholarship) [6598]

KASF General Scholarships (Undergraduate, Graduate, Professional development/Scholarship) [6599]

Kathy D. and Stephen J. Anderson Scholarship Fund (Undergraduate/Scholarship) [3629]

Joseph Katz Memorial Scholarship (Undergraduate/Scholarship) [6294]

Ka'u Chamber of Commerce Scholarship (Undergraduate/Scholarship) [6505]

Kawano Family Scholarships (Undergraduate/Scholarship) [9825]

KCC Foundation Gold Key Scholarship (Undergraduate/Scholarship) [6513]

KCC Foundation Scholarship (Undergraduate/Scholarship) [6514]

KCC Trustee Scholarship (Undergraduate/Scholarship) [6515]

Keepers Preservation Education Fund (Undergraduate/Award) [6990]

KEF General Scholarships (Undergraduate, Graduate/Scholarship) [6590]

KEF Vocational Award (Undergraduate/Award) [6591]

Keiko Fukuda Scholarship (Undergraduate, Postgraduate/Scholarship) [11385]

Keith Maffioli Scholarship (Undergraduate/Scholarship) [3683]

Dr. Charles Kelly Memorial Scholarships (Undergraduate/Scholarship) [8862]

Kelsey's Law Distracted Driving Awareness Scholarship (High School, Undergraduate/Scholarship) [7305]

Kemper K. Knapp Scholarship (Undergraduate/Scholarship) [11737]

Southwest Ohio Environmental Horticulture Association (SOEHA) Lloyd W. Kennedy Scholarship (Graduate/Scholarship) [8587]

Kennedy T. Friend Scholarship Fund (Graduate, Undergraduate/Scholarship) [348]

Kenneth H. Breeden Scholarship (Undergraduate/Scholarship) [6658]

Kenneth Laundy Entrance Scholarship (Graduate/Scholarship) [12255]

Kentucky Alumni Club Scholarships - Lexington/Central Kentucky Alumni Chapter (Graduate, High School/Scholarship) [11577]

Kentucky Alumni Club Scholarships - Somerset/Lake Cumberland Area Alumni Chapter (University/Scholarship) [11578]

Kentucky Educational Excellence Scholarship (Undergraduate/Scholarship) [2572]

Edgar Kerstan Memorial Scholarship (Undergraduate/Scholarship) [7258]

Key to a Bright Future Scholarship (Graduate, College/Scholarship) [6714]

KGP Cornaro Scholarship (Graduate/Scholarship) [6397]

Khaki University and Y.M.C.A. Memorial Scholarships (Undergraduate/Scholarship) [11694]

The Kids' Chance of Florida Scholarship Program (All/Scholarship) [6550]

Kids and Community Scholarship Program (College, University/Scholarship) [6552]

The Mary and Millard Kiker Scholarship (Undergraduate/Scholarship) [4739]

Kilbuck Family Native American Scholarship (Undergraduate/Scholarship) [2484]

Killam Fellowships (Undergraduate/Fellowship) [4771]

Kimberly Elementary School PTA Scholarship (Undergraduate/Scholarship) [9552]

King Ice Scholarship (Undergraduate, Graduate/Scholarship) [6556]

King of Maids Scholarship (Undergraduate, Graduate/Scholarship) [6560]

Kingsbury Elementary School PTA Scholarship (Undergraduate/Scholarship) [9553]

Kip Dental and Orthodontics Scholarship (Undergraduate/Scholarship) [6562]

James P. Kirkgasser Memorial Scholarship (Undergraduate, Graduate/Scholarship) [2533]

Dr. Elemer and Eva Kiss Scholarship Fund (Undergraduate/Scholarship) [5642]

Tamo Kitaura Scholarships (Other/Scholarship) [11386]

Flo Kitz Memorial Scholarship (Undergraduate, Master's/Scholarship) [12334]

Kiwanis Club of Escondido Scholarship (Undergraduate/Scholarship) [9826]

Kiwanis Club of Redlands Foundation Academic Excellence Scholarship (Undergraduate/Scholarship) [9554]

Kiwanis Club of Redlands Foundation - Martin and Dorothy Munz Scholarship (Undergraduate/Scholarship) [9555]

Gerda and Kurt Klein Scholarships (Undergraduate/Scholarship) [5592]

Klimt Stefan & Janina Scholarship (Undergraduate/Scholarship) [9668]

J. Merrill Knapp Research Fellowship (Graduate/Fellowship) [952]

Iver and Cora Knapstad Scholarships (Undergraduate/Scholarship) [11453]

David Knight Graduate Scholarship (Graduate/Scholarship) [10656]

John G. F. Knight Memorial Scholarship (Undergraduate, Graduate/Scholarship) [2534]

Knox Hume Scholarship Fund (Undergraduate/Scholarship) [3630]

Steven Kobrynsky Memorial Scholarship (Undergraduate/Scholarship) [3029]

Kodali Veeraiah & Sarojini Scholarship (Graduate/Scholarship) [10952]

George Kokociski Memorial Scholarships (Undergraduate/Scholarship) [9669]

Anna and John Kolesar Memorial Scholarship (Undergraduate/Scholarship) [293]

The Bernie Kom Memorial Award (Postgraduate/Award) [12256]

Susan G. Komen for the Cure College Scholarship Awards (Two Year College/Award, Scholarship) [6586]

KON/GEICO LeaderShape Undergraduate Scholarship (Undergraduate/Scholarship) [6490]

Henriette & Marcel Korner Scholarship (Undergraduate/Scholarship) [6295]

Kosciuszko Foundation Graduate Study and Research in Poland Scholarships (Graduate, Postgraduate/Scholarship) [6601]

Kosciuszko Foundation Tuition Scholarships (Graduate/Scholarship) [6602]

Haig Koumjian Memorial Grant (Undergraduate/Scholarship) [1892]

Eileen Kraus Scholarship (Two Year College, Four Year College/Scholarship) [3763]

Sharon Kreikemeier Memorial Scholarships (Undergraduate/Scholarship) [8189]

CHS James Kreppner Memorial Scholarship and Bursary Program (Undergraduate/Scholarship) [3003]

Carl A. Kroch Oxford Cup Memorial Scholarship (Undergraduate, Graduate/Scholarship) [2535]

Kroger Cincinnati/Dayton Scholarship Fund (Undergraduate/Scholarship) [3375]

Doreen Kronick Scholarships (Graduate/Scholarship) [2130]

Kristin Bjurstrom Krueger Student Scholarship Program (Undergraduate/Scholarship) [7240]

KTA Chapter Adviser Research Grant Award (Professional development/Grant) [6501]

Kuropas Jan Memorial Scholarship (Undergraduate/Scholarship) [9670]

Sam and Florice Kuwahara Memorial Scholarship (Undergraduate/Scholarship) [6249]

Kyle R. Moreland Memorial Scholarship (Undergraduate/Scholarship) [5088]

L. Gordon, Jr. and June D. Pfefferkorn Scholarship (Undergraduate/Scholarship) [12082]

L. & T. Woolfolk Memorial Scholarship Fund (Undergraduate/Scholarship) [3376]

LA Tutors 123 Innovation in Education Scholarship (All/Scholarship) [6626]

Gretchen Laatsch Scholarships (Graduate/Scholarship) [2139]

LAFS - Cal State University San Marcos General Scholarships (Undergraduate/Scholarship) [2462]

Laine - Casey Laine Armed Services Scholarship (Undergraduate/Scholarship) [3479]

Lalor Foundation Post-Doctoral Fellowships (Post-doctorate/Fellowship) [6637]

Lambda Project 2000 Scholarship (Undergraduate/Scholarship) [6453]

Otho E. Lane Memorial Scholarship (Undergraduate, Graduate/Scholarship) [2536]

Lanford Family Highway Worker Memorial Scholarship Program (High School/Scholarship) [1362]

Katherine Roberts LaPorte Memorial Adelphe Scholarship (Undergraduate/Scholarship) [6455]

Larry Dean Davis Scholarship (Undergraduate/Scholarship) [8938]

The LasikPlus My Vision Essay Scholarship (Undergraduate, Graduate/Scholarship) [6669]

Austin E. Lathrop Scholarships (Undergraduate/Scholarship) [11454]

Laura Moore Cunningham Foundation General Scholarship (Undergraduate/Scholarship) [6807]

Lavina Laible Scholarship (Undergraduate/Scholarship) [5162]

Law Office of David P. Shapiro Annual Leukemia Scholarships (Vocational/Occupational, Community College, University, Undergraduate, College/Scholarship) [6691]

Law Offices of Mark E. Salomone Scholarship for Road Safety (Undergraduate/Scholarship) [6706]

The Law Offices of Sean M. Cleary Scholarship (Undergraduate/Scholarship) [6712]

LAWCHA Graduate Student Travel Grants (Graduate/Grant) [6628]

Lawrence Bloomberg Entrance Award (Postgraduate/Award) [12257]

Lawrence E. and Mabel Jackson Rudberg Scholarship Fund (Undergraduate/Scholarship) [4214]

Lawrence and Louise Robbins Scholarship Fund (Undergraduate/Scholarship) [6991]

Lawrence Madeiros Scholarship (Undergraduate/Scholarship) [7925]

Lay – Sue Kay Lay Memorial Scholarship (Undergraduate/Scholarship) [3480]

LCSC Presidential Out-of-State Tuition Scholarships (Undergraduate/Scholarship) [6808]

L.D. and Elsie Long Memorial Scholarship (Graduate/Scholarship) [12083]

LDAS Scholarship (Undergraduate/Scholarship) [6760]

Danny T. Le Memorial Scholarship (Undergraduate/Scholarship) [11822]

Franklin M. Leach Scholarships (Undergraduate/Scholarship) [11455]

Queenie Leader Memorial Scholarship (Undergraduate, Master's/Scholarship) [12337]

League Foundation Scholarships (Undergraduate/Scholarship) [6745]

Jack W. Leatherman Family Scholarship (Undergraduate, Vocational/Occupational/Scholarship) [5090]

Lebbeus F. Bissell Scholarship Fund (Undergraduate/Scholarship) [5336]

Patrick Ledden Honorary Scholarships (Undergraduate/Scholarship) [9827]

Leesa Social Impact Scholarship (College, University, Undergraduate/Scholarship) [6764]

The Herbert Lehman Education Fund Scholarship (Undergraduate/Scholarship) [7540]

Lehman Family Scholarship (Undergraduate/Scholarship) [9828]

Lemelson Center Fellowships (Doctorate, Postdoctorate, Professional development/Fellowship) [10194]

Lemelson Center Travel to Collections Awards (Graduate, Professional development/Award) [10195]

Lemon Grove Education Foundation Scholarship (Undergraduate, Graduate/Scholarship) [9829]

Rebecca Christine Lenci Thespian Memorial Scholarship (Undergraduate/Scholarship) [9830]

The Stan Lencki Scholarship (Undergraduate/Scholarship) [7172]

Franklin A. Lenfesty Memorial Scholarship (Undergraduate/Scholarship) [8520]

Leo Gilmartin Scholarship (Undergraduate/Scholarship) [9211]

Leopold Education Project Scholarship (Undergraduate/Scholarship) [3685]

Leopold Schepp Foundation Scholarship (Undergraduate, Graduate/Scholarship) [9932]

Leslie and Mary Ella Scales Scholarship (Undergraduate/Scholarship) [3657]

Lester and Eleanor Webster Foundation Fund (Undergraduate/Scholarship) [10775]

LeverEdge Scholarship (College, Undergraduate, Graduate/Scholarship) [6779]

Jack A. and Louise S. Levine Memorial Scholarships (Undergraduate/Scholarship) [9557]

William J. Levy Point Scholarship (Undergraduate, Graduate, Doctorate/Scholarship) [9226]

Lewis-Clark Coin Club Endowed Scholarship (Undergraduate/Scholarship) [6810]

Lewis-Clark State College Foundation Scholars (Undergraduate/Scholarship) [6811]

Lewis-Clark State College In-State Non-Traditional Student Scholarship (Undergraduate/Scholarship) [6812]

Lewis-Clark State College Provost Scholarship (Undergraduate/Scholarship) [6814]

George T. Lewis, Jr. Academic Scholarship Fund (Undergraduate/Scholarship) [4742]

Lewis-Reynolds-Smith Founders Fellowship (Graduate/Fellowship) [5477]

Lewiston Service League Memorial Scholarship (Undergraduate/Scholarship) [6815]

Lexington Alumni Scholarships (Undergraduate/Scholarship) [6827]

Lexington Community Foundation Annual Scholarships (Undergraduate/Scholarship) [6828]

Lexington Community Foundation/CCC Scholarships (Undergraduate/Scholarship) [6829]

Dolores Zohrab Liebmann Fund - Independent Research/Study Grants (Graduate, Undergraduate/Grant) [6846]

LIFE Lessons Scholarship Program (Undergraduate/Scholarship) [6849]

Lighthouse International Scholarships - College-bound Awards (High School, Undergraduate/Scholarship) [6856]

Lighthouse International Scholarships - Graduate Awards (Graduate, Postgraduate/Scholarship) [6857]

Lighthouse International Scholarships - Undergraduate Awards (Undergraduate/Scholarship) [6858]

Lily and Catello Sorrentino Memorial Scholarship (Undergraduate/Scholarship) [9694]

Lime Connect Pathways Scholarship for High School Seniors with Disabilities (Undergraduate/Scholarship) [6863]

Lindenwood University Scouting Scholarships (Undergraduate/Scholarship) [7853]

Obrzut Ling Scholarships (Graduate/Scholarship) [9303]

Linsley Scholarship Fund (Undergraduate, Vocational/Occupational/Scholarship) [3301]

David Linton Memorial Scholarship (Undergraduate, Graduate/Scholarship) [2537]

The Lawrence Lipking Fellowship (Postdoctorate/Fellowship) [8376]

Emil S. Liston Award (Other/Scholarship) [7662]

Litner + Deganian College Scholarship Program (College, University/Scholarship) [6879]

Grant Livingston Memorial Scholarship (Undergraduate, Master's/Scholarship) [12339]

LLN Student Scholarships (Undergraduate/Scholarship) [6677]

E.C. Lloyd and J.C.U. Johnson Scholarship Fund (Undergraduate/Scholarship) [3658]

Loan for Service for Graduates (Graduate/Loan) [995]

Local 564 Scholarship Fund (Undergraduate, Vocational/Occupational/Scholarship) [6142]

Local 827 Peter J. Casey Scholarship (Undergraduate/Scholarship) [5957]

Miriam "Doc" Locke Memorial Adelphe Scholarships (Graduate/Scholarship) [6456]

Lockheed Martin Scholarship (Undergraduate/Scholarship) [8521]

Stephen Logan Memorial Scholarship (Undergraduate/Scholarship) [4872]

London Goodenough Association of Canada Scholarships (Graduate/Scholarship) [6886]

Lone Star GIA Associate and Alumni Scholarships (Undergraduate/Scholarship) [4879]

Lawrence A. Long Memorial Law Scholarship (Graduate/Scholarship) [404]

Bart Longo Memorial Scholarship Program (Undergraduate, Graduate/Scholarship) [7762]

Megan Nicole Longwell Scholarship (Undergraduate/Scholarship) [8864]

Louise Loomis Memorial Adelphe Scholarships (Undergraduate/Scholarship) [6457]

Michael Lorenzen Foundation Scholarship (Undergraduate, Graduate/Scholarship) [6890]

Lorne and Ruby Bonnell Scholarship (Master's, Graduate/Scholarship) [3704]

Lorraine E. Swain Scholarship (Undergraduate/Scholarship) [10114]

Lou & Dorie Amen Legacy Scholarship (Undergraduate/Scholarship) [2804]

Sir James Lougheed Award of Distinction (Doctorate, Graduate, Master's/Award) [297]

Louis B. Zapoleon Memorial Fund (Undergraduate/Scholarship) [3377]

Louis I. Jaffe Memorial Scholarship-NSU Alumni (Graduate/Scholarship) [5273]

Louise Bales Gallagher Scholarship (Undergraduate/Scholarship) [4005]

Louise Tillotson Teaching Fellowship (Professional development/Fellowship) [8257]

Louise Tillotson Teaching Professional Development Scholarship (Professional development/Scholarship) [8258]

Love Of Bonita Empowerment Scholarship Fund (Undergraduate/Scholarship) [10696]

Lowe Simpson Scholarship Fund (Undergraduate/Scholarship) [3378]

Horace G. Lozier Memorial Scholarship (Undergraduate, Graduate/Scholarship) [2538]

Lt. Holly Adams Memorial Scholarship Fund (Undergraduate/Scholarship) [3632]

Bill Lucas Memorial Scholarship Endowment (Undergraduate, Community College/Scholarship) [8522]

Lucidchart Scholarship (Undergraduate, Graduate/Scholarship) [6927]

Lucidpress Scholarship (Undergraduate, Graduate/Scholarship) [6928]

Lucile Cheever Graubart/Lambda Scholarship (Undergraduate/Scholarship) [10115]

Lucille E. McGee Scholarship Endowment Fund (Undergraduate/Scholarship) [6204]

Lucy Hsu Ho Scholarship (Undergraduate/Scholarship) [2485]

Lugonia Alumni/Harrison Lightfoot Scholarship (Undergraduate/Scholarship) [9558]

Luis Arreola Memorial Scholarship (Undergraduate/Scholarship) [9831]

Charles Luttman Scholarship (Undergraduate/Scholarship) [2875]

Lyle Everingham Scholarship Fund (Undergraduate/Scholarship) [3379]

Lyle and Rlene Everingham Family Fund (Undergraduate/Scholarship) [3380]

M. William and Frances J. Tilghman Scholarship (Undergraduate/Scholarship) [3573]

John Mabry Forestry Scholarships (Undergraduate/Scholarship) [9489]

MAC Emeritus Membership Award (Professional development/Award) [7366]

Bill MacAloney Legacy Scholarships (Undergraduate/Scholarship) [2805]

MacArthur Fellows Program (Professional development/Fellowship) [6954]

Dr. Sally Macdonald Scholarship (Undergraduate, Master's/Scholarship) [12343]

Mackenzie King Open Scholarship (Graduate, Postgraduate, Undergraduate/Scholarship) [7182]

Carol E. Macpherson Memorial Scholarship (Graduate, Undergraduate/Scholarship) [11645]

James Madison Graduate Fellowships (Graduate/Fellowship) [6229]

Madson Graduate Scholarship (Graduate/Scholarship) [10083]

John T. & Frances J. Maghielse Scholarship (Undergraduate/Scholarship) [5163]

The Rick Mahoney Scholarship (Undergraduate/Scholarship) [7173]

Mailcheck Scholarship $1,500 (College, University, Undergraduate/Scholarship) [8770]

Maine Community College Scholarships (MCCS) (Undergraduate, Vocational/Occupational/Scholarship) [7008]

Maine Community Foundation - Rice Scholarships (Undergraduate/Scholarship) [6992]

Maine Vietnam Veterans Scholarship (Advanced Professional/Scholarship) [6993]

Alexander M. and June L. Maisin Foundation Scholarship (Undergraduate/Scholarship) [6275]

The Make It Move Scholarships (Undergraduate/Scholarship) [1762]

Make Me Laugh Scholarship (Undergraduate, High School/Scholarship) [11231]

Make Us Proud Scholarships (Undergraduate/Scholarship) [5372]

Make Your Mark Scholarship (Graduate, College/Scholarship) [5294]

Malini E. Sathyadev Memorial Scholarship (Undergraduate/Scholarship) [9832]

Joseph J. Malone Fellowship in Arab and Islamic Studies (Professional development/Fellowship) [7812]

Mamie Adams Memorial Award (Undergraduate, Four Year College, Two Year College/Scholarship) [6816]

Manasel Manasselian Memorial Grant (Undergraduate/Scholarship) [1894]

Cora Aguda Manayan Fund Scholarship (Undergraduate/Scholarship) [5408]

Manchester Scholarship Foundation - Adult Learners Scholarship (Undergraduate/Scholarship) [5337]

Manhattan Street Capital National Scholarship (Undergraduate/Scholarship) [7016]

Manning & Zimmerman Distracted Driving Scholarship (College, University, Undergraduate, Vocational/Occupational/Scholarship) [6697]

Mansfield Soccer Association Scholarship (Undergraduate/Scholarship) [7020]

Margaret E. Waldron Memorial Fund (Undergraduate/Scholarship) [4596]

Margaret T. Craig Community Service Scholarship (Undergraduate/Scholarship) [3686]

Margarian Scholarship (Undergraduate, Graduate/Scholarship) [7032]

Margery J. Seeger Scholarship (Undergraduate/Scholarship) [5164]

Marian Johnson Frutiger Sisterhood Scholarship (Undergraduate/Scholarship) [10117]

Aurelia Varallo Mariani Scholarship Program (Graduate/Scholarship) [7556]

Marie Tremaine Fellowship (Postgraduate, Other/Fellowship) [2570]

Marine Corp Scholarship Foundation Scholarship (Vocational/Occupational, Community College, Undergraduate/Scholarship) [7066]

Marine Corps League National Scholarship (Undergraduate/Scholarship) [7064]

Shirley Stone Marinkovich Memorial Scholarships (Undergraduate/Scholarship) [6458]

Mario Pedrozzi Scholarship (Undergraduate, Graduate/Scholarship) [8950]

Mariposa Elementary School PTA Scholarship (Undergraduate/Scholarship) [9559]

Marisol Scholarship (Undergraduate/Scholarship) [6459]

Marjorie Kovler Research Fellowship (Professional development/Fellowship) [6532]

Markley Family Scholarship Fund (Undergraduate/Scholarship) [10778]

Markley Scholarship (Undergraduate, Graduate/Scholarship) [7623]

Marshall Foundation Scholars Program (Undergraduate/Scholarship) [7112]

Thomas Marshall Graduate Student Awards (Postgraduate/Grant, Award) [1579]

Marshall Memorial Fellowship (Other/Fellowship) [4946]

Marshall Phelps Athletic Memorial Scholarship (Undergraduate/Scholarship) [9560]

Samuel Taylor Marshall Scholarship (Graduate, Undergraduate/Scholarship) [2539]

Martha W. Tanner Memorial Fund (Undergraduate/Scholarship) [3381]

Martin Fischer Training Award (Undergraduate/Award) [2995]

Martin Sisters Scholarship (Undergraduate/Scholarship) [4007]

John S. Martinez and Family Scholarship Fund (Undergraduate/Scholarship) [3591]

Eric Martinez Memorial Scholarships (Graduate, Undergraduate/Scholarship) [11274]

The Anthony A. Martino Memorial Scholarship (Undergraduate/Scholarship) [5010]

A. Lucchetti Martino Scholarship (Undergraduate/Scholarship) [7961]

Marvin Rammelsberg Scholarship Fund (Undergraduate/Scholarship) [3382]

The Mary and Elliott Wood Foundation Undergraduate Scholarship (Undergraduate/Scholarship) [4745]

Mary Main Memorial Scholarship (Undergraduate/Scholarship) [5339]

Mary Mouzon Darby Undergraduate Scholarship (Undergraduate/Scholarship) [5622]

Mary Roberts Scholarship Fund (Undergraduate/Scholarship) [3383]

Mary Stuart Rogers Scholarship (Undergraduate/Scholarship) [12035]

Mary Turnbull Schacht Memorial Scholarship (Undergraduate/Scholarship) [10118]

Margaret Edwards Mason Adelphe Scholarship (Undergraduate/Scholarship) [6460]

Massachusetts Federation of Polish Women's Clubs Scholarships (Undergraduate/Scholarship) [6604]

Norman Matechuk Memorial Scholarship (Undergraduate, Master's/Scholarship) [12344]

Matt Harmon Memorial Scholarship Fund (Undergraduate/Scholarship) [10697]

Matt Stager Memorial Scholarship (Undergraduate/Scholarship) [11929]

Mature Student Scholarship (Undergraduate/Scholarship) [4430]

Edmund F. Maxwell Scholarships (Undergraduate/Scholarship) [7162]

May-Cassioppi Scholarship (Undergraduate/Scholarship) [3688]

John E. Mayfield Scholarship Fund for Cheatham County Central High School (Undergraduate/Scholarship) [3635]

John E. Mayfield Scholarship Fund for Harpeth High School (Undergraduate/Scholarship) [3636]

John E. Mayfield Scholarship Fund for Pleasant View Christian High School (Undergraduate/Scholarship) [3637]

John E. Mayfield Scholarship Fund for Sycamore High School (Undergraduate/Scholarship) [3638]

Maziarz Tadeusz Scholarship (Undergraduate/Scholarship) [9671]

Charles "Chuck" McAdams Memorial Scholarships (Graduate, Undergraduate/Scholarship) [10921]

McBurney Disability Resource Center General Scholarships (Undergraduate/Scholarship) [11741]

McCall Educational Fund (Undergraduate/Scholarship) [3384]

The First Lieutenant Scott McClean Love Memorial Scholarship - Children of Soldiers (Undergraduate, Vocational/Occupational/Scholarship) [1917]

The First Lieutenant Scott McClean Love Memorial Scholarship - Spouses of Soldiers (Undergraduate, Vocational/Occupational/Scholarship) [1918]

Dave McCloud Aviation Memorial Scholarships (Undergraduate/Scholarship) [11456]

McDaniel College Eagle Scout Scholarship (Undergraduate/Scholarship) [7854]

McDonald's Inspiration Celebration Scholarship (Undergraduate, Graduate/Scholarship) [11026]

Richard J. McDonough Scholarship (Undergraduate/Scholarship) [7009]

McFarffels Scholarships (Undergraduate/Scholarship) [9304]

Nancy B. Woolridge McGee Graduate Fellowships (Graduate/Fellowship) [12415]

Mary Bowles McInnis Adelphe Scholarship (Undergraduate/Scholarship) [6461]

The McKelvey Scholarship (Undergraduate/Scholarship) [7193]

McKinley Elementary School PTA Scholarship (Undergraduate/Scholarship) [9561]

John L. and Eleanore I. Mckinley Scholarships (Undergraduate/Scholarship) [4039]

McKinney Sisters Scholarship (Undergraduate/Scholarship) [4008]

Joan Reagin McNeill Scholarships - Alpha Theta (Undergraduate/Scholarship) [10119]

Joan Reagin McNeill Scholarships - Theta Phi (Undergraduate/Scholarship) [10120]

MCRTA Book Scholarships (Undergraduate/Scholarship) [7295]

David Meador Foundation - Club Management Student Scholarships (Undergraduate/Scholarship) [8242]

The Medalist Club Post Graduate Scholarship (Postgraduate/Scholarship) [7203]

Medford Rogue Rotary Scholarship (Undergraduate/Scholarship) [7209]

Medicus Student Exchange Scholarship (Graduate, Undergraduate/Scholarship) [10895]

The MEDIGO Scholarship Program (Undergraduate, Graduate/Scholarship) [7234]

Medina County Retired Teachers Association Scholarship (Graduate/Scholarship) [7236]

MEFA Graduate Loans (Graduate/Loan) [7130]

Carl J. Megel Scholarship (Undergraduate/Scholarship) [884]

Dr. Ernest and Minnie Mehl Scholarships (Undergraduate/Scholarship) [298]

Megan Meier Memorial Scholarships (Undergraduate/Scholarship) [7243]

Fred & Lena Meijer Scholarships (Undergraduate/Scholarship) [5166]

Melanie and Todd Edmondson Memorial Scholarship (Undergraduate/Scholarship) [3660]

Melbourne & Alice E. Frontjes Scholarship (Undergraduate/Scholarship) [5167]

K. Cyrus Melikian Memorial Grant (Undergraduate/Scholarship) [1895]

E.V. and Nancy Melosi Travel Grants (Graduate, Other/Grant) [1456]

Melvin Kruger Endowed Scholarship Program (Graduate, Undergraduate/Scholarship) [8063, 9739]

Memorial Fund Scholarship (Undergraduate/Scholarship) [7785]

Men of Principle Scholarship (Undergraduate, Graduate/Scholarship) [2540]

Menominee Tribal Scholarships (Undergraduate, Graduate, High School/Scholarship) [7256]

Mensa Canada Scholarship Programme (Undergraduate/Scholarship) [7259]

Mensa Education and Research Foundation U.S. Scholarship (Undergraduate/Scholarship) [7262]

Al Mercury Scholarships (Undergraduate/Scholarship) [11696]

John K. Merrell Scholarship (Undergraduate, Graduate/Scholarship) [2541]

Steven Craig Merrill Memorial Scholarship (Undergraduate, Graduate/Scholarship) [2542]

Mesothelioma Memorial Scholarships (Undergraduate, Vocational/Occupational/Scholarship) [10859]

Mesquite Club Evening Chapter Inc. Scholarship (Undergraduate/Scholarship) [9410]

Meyer D. and Dorothy C. Silverman Scholarship Fund (Undergraduate/Scholarship) [3639]

MICA Scholarships (Undergraduate/Scholarship) [7386]

Michael Bany Memorial Scholarship Fund (Undergraduate/Scholarship) [3385]

Michael D. Curtin Renaissance Student Memorial Scholarship (Graduate/Scholarship) [4257]

Michael Herman Scholarship (Undergraduate, Vocational/Occupational/Scholarship) [5096]

Michael J. Hoggard Memorial Scholarship (Undergraduate/Scholarship) [9411]

Michael J. Wolf Scholarship (Undergraduate/Scholarship) [5168]

Michigan Education Association Scholarships (Undergraduate/Scholarship) [7313]

Michigan Sugar Queen Scholarship (Undergraduate/Scholarship) [7342]

Michno Bronislaw Memorial Scholarship (Undergraduate/Scholarship) [9672]

Mickey Donnelly Memorial Scholarship (Undergraduate/Scholarship) [9412]

Micklin Law Group Scholarship (College, University/Scholarship) [7352]

Beth Middleton Memorial Scholarships (Undergraduate/Scholarship) [4486]

Midland Company Scholarship Fund (Undergraduate/Scholarship) [3386]

Midlothian Rotary Club "Service Above Self" Scholarships (Undergraduate/Scholarship) [7363]

Midwest Modern Language Association Fellowship (Doctorate, Postdoctorate/Fellowship) [7380, 8377]

Mihaly Russin Scholarship Awards (Graduate/Scholarship) [9765]

Mike and Gail Donley Spouse Scholarship (Undergraduate, Graduate, Postgraduate/Scholarship) [149]

Mike Hylton Memorial Scholarship (Undergraduate/Scholarship) [5480]

Mike Niemeyer Memorial Football Scholarship (Undergraduate/Scholarship) [9563]

Milacron Geier Scholarship Fund (Undergraduate/Scholarship) [3387]

Milan Getting Scholarship (Undergraduate/Scholarship) [10574]

Mildred E. Troske Music Scholarship (Undergraduate/Scholarship) [5169]

Miles Spencer Nadal Entrance Award (Master's/Award) [12258]

Military Service Scholarship (Graduate, Undergraduate/Scholarship) [10084]

The MILK Scholarship (University/Scholarship) [7391]

Miller – Brian and Colleen Miller Math and Science Scholarship (Undergraduate/Scholarship) [3482]

Millicent Mary Schaffner Endowed Memorial Scholarship (Undergraduate/Scholarship) [5098]

Millie Gonzalez Memorial Scholarship (Undergraduate/Scholarship) [5481]

Carolina Panthers Players Sam Mills Memorial Scholarships (Undergraduate/Scholarship) [4747]

Milton and Edith Brown Memorial Scholarship Fund (Undergraduate/Scholarship) [3388]

Minerva Scholarships (Undergraduate/Scholarship) [2598]

Minneapolis Jewish Federation Camp Scholarships (Undergraduate, Other/Scholarship) [7400]

Minnesota Division Scholarships (Undergraduate/Scholarship) [7371]

Minnesota Power Community Involvement Scholarship Fund (Undergraduate/Scholarship) [4215]

Minnie Hopkins Scholarship Fund (Graduate/Scholarship) [10782]

Minority Scholarship Award (Undergraduate/Scholarship) [3575]

Minton-Spidell-Jackowski Point Scholarship (Undergraduate, Graduate, Doctorate/Scholarship) [9227]

Miss America Social Impact Initiative Scholarship (Undergraduate/Scholarship) [7417]

Missigman Scholarship Fund (Undergraduate/Scholarship) [4598]

Dikran Missirlian Scholarship Grant (Undergraduate/Scholarship) [1896]

George J. Mitchell Postgraduate Scholarships (Postgraduate/Scholarship) [7646]

MKC/Preuss Scholarship (Undergraduate, Community College, University/Scholarship) [9835]

MMC Scholarships (Other/Scholarship) [6027]

MMUF Dissertation Grants (Graduate/Grant) [12047]

MMUF Travel and Research Grants (Graduate, Undergraduate/Grant) [12048]

MoKan Division of Midwest Dairy Educational Award (Undergraduate/Scholarship) [7372]

Momeni Foundation Scholastic Achievement Scholarships (Undergraduate/Scholarship) [7955]

Money Metals Exchange & Sound Money Defense League Scholarship (Undergraduate, Graduate/Scholarship) [7435]

Murray Montague Memorial Scholarship (Undergraduate/Scholarship) [5129]

The Montana Advocates Scholarship (All/Scholarship) [90]

Montesi Scholarship (Undergraduate/Scholarship) [4866]

M. Steve Moore Memorial Scholarship (Undergraduate, Graduate/Award) [2544]

Moore Middle School PTA Scholarship (Undergraduate/Scholarship) [9564]

Annabelle Moore Scholarship (Undergraduate/Scholarship) [2745]

The Dr. Blanca Moore-Velez Woman of Substance Scholarship (Undergraduate/Scholarship) [7669]

Morgan and Jeanie Sherwood Travel Grant (Graduate, Other/Grant) [1457]

Robert L. Morlan Redlands Area Interfaith Council Scholarships (Undergraduate/Scholarship) [9565]

Morris L. and Rebecca Ziskind Memorial Scholarship (Undergraduate/Scholarship) [5666]

Morris M. Pulver Scholarship Fund (Undergraduate, Graduate, Postgraduate/Scholarship) [2986]

Brian Morris Scholarship (Undergraduate, University, College, Vocational/Occupational/Scholarship) [12350]

James B. Morris Scholarship (Undergraduate/Scholarship) [7474]

Mortar Board National Foundation Fellowship (Postdoctorate/Fellowship, Award) [7476]

Morton Bahr Scholarship (Undergraduate/Scholarship) [3559]

Mother's Day Scholarship (All/Scholarship) [7443]

John R. Mott Scholarships (Undergraduate, Graduate/Scholarship) [7482]

MPI CRV Membership Scholarships (Other/Scholarship) [7238]

MPOWER Financing's Global Citizen Scholarship (College, University, Undergraduate/Scholarship) [7489]

MSAA Scholarship Program (Graduate/Scholarship) [7410]

MSEA/SEIU Part-time Student Members Scholarships (Undergraduate/Scholarship) [7010]

Dudley Mullins/Cabot Corporation Scholarship (Undergraduate/Scholarship) [8865]

Muncy Rotary Club Scholarship Fund (Undergraduate/Scholarship) [4600]

Muncy Scholars Awards Fund (Undergraduate/Scholarship) [4601]

Murtha Cullina LLP Scholarship Fund (Undergraduate/Scholarship) [3592]

Muscle Shoals Kiwanis Club/Wal-mart (Undergraduate/Scholarship) [8523]

MyApartmentMap Housing Fall Scholarship (Undergraduate/Scholarship) [7527]

NACA Mid Atlantic Undergraduate Scholarship (Undergraduate/Scholarship) [7626]

NACADA Scholarships (Graduate, Postdoctorate/Scholarship) [7568]

The Nadia Christensen Prize (All/Prize) [1377]

NAFA Scholarship Program (Undergraduate/Scholarship) [7590]

NANBPWC National Scholarship (Graduate/Scholarship) [7670]

Robyn Nance Memorial Scholarships (Undergraduate/Scholarship) [9566]

Napoleon A. Jones, III Memorial Scholarship (Undergraduate/Scholarship) [9837]

NARFE-FEEA Scholarship Awards Program (Undergraduate/Scholarship) [4517, 7584]

Kermit B. Nash Academic Scholarships (Graduate/Scholarship) [10073]

JoAhn Brown Nash Memorial Scholarship Fund (Undergraduate/Scholarship) [3640]

Nate Mack/Cindi Turner Scholarship (Undergraduate/Scholarship) [9413]

National AAHAM Scholarship (Undergraduate/Scholarship) [570]

National Association for the Self-Employed Scholarships (Undergraduate, High School/Scholarship) [7693]

National Beta Club Scholarships (Undergraduate/Scholarship, Monetary) [7714]

The National Center for Health Statistics Postdoctoral Research Program (NCHS) (Postdoctorate/Fellowship) [11329]

National Collegiate Athletic Association Postgraduate Scholarships (Postgraduate/Scholarship) [7771]

National Court Reporters Association Student Intern Scholarship (Undergraduate/Scholarship) [7818]

National Federation of the Blind Scholarship Program (Undergraduate/Scholarship, Monetary) [7878]

National Guard Association of Rhode Island Scholarship (Undergraduate/Scholarship) [7913]

National High School Oratorical Contest Scholarship (Undergraduate/Scholarship) [1072]

National Huguenot Society College and Postgraduate Student Scholarships (Undergraduate, Postgraduate/Scholarship) [7937]

National Merit Harris Corporation Scholarship Program (Undergraduate/Scholarship) [5306]

National Merit Scholarship Program (Undergraduate/Scholarship) [8003]

National MS Society New Jersey Metro Chapter Scholarship Program (Undergraduate/Scholarship) [8015]

National Organization of Italian-American Women Scholarships (Undergraduate, Graduate/Scholarship) [8025]

National Pathfinder Scholarship (Graduate, Master's, Undergraduate/Scholarship) [7885]

National Preservation Institute Scholarships (Undergraduate/Scholarship) [8044]

National Technical Honor Society Scholarships (NTHS) (Undergraduate/Scholarship) [4487]

Native American Education Grants (Graduate, Undergraduate/Grant) [990]

Naval Helicopter Association Scholarship (Graduate, Undergraduate/Scholarship) [8170]

The Nazareth Scholarships - Sr. Kevin Whelan Scholarship (Undergraduate/Scholarship) [8183]

NBCUniversal Point Scholarship (Undergraduate, Graduate, Doctorate/Scholarship) [9228]

NCBWL Scholarships (Graduate/Scholarship) [7557]

NCCF Survivor Scholarship (Undergraduate/Scholarship) [7773]

NCRF New Professional Reporter Grant (Other/Grant) [7819]

Need-Based Scholarships (Undergraduate/Scholarship) [9100]

Douglas J. Neeley Memorial Scholarship (Undergraduate, Graduate/Scholarship) [2546]

Nell and Spencer Waggoner Scholarship (Undergraduate/Scholarship) [12084]

Carol Nelson Scholarship (Undergraduate/Scholarship) [6462]

Bill Nelson Scholarship Endowment (BNSE) (Undergraduate, Graduate/Scholarship) [8780]

Nelson Schwab Jr. Scholarship Fund (Undergraduate/Scholarship) [3389]

NEMLA Summer Fellowships (Graduate/Fellowship) [8484]

NEMRA Educational Scholarship Foundation (Undergraduate, Vocational/Occupational/Scholarship) [7866]

Andrew Nerland Scholarships (Undergraduate/Scholarship) [11458]

Netfloor USA Access Flooring College Scholarships (Undergraduate/Scholarship) [8208]

Nethercott Family Scholarship Fund (Undergraduate/Scholarship) [3390]

Nettie and Edward Shelah Scholarship Fund (Undergraduate/Scholarship) [10830]

Nettie and Jesse Gorov Scholarship (Undergraduate/Scholarship) [3690]

Reverend John S. Nettles Scholarships (Undergraduate/Scholarship) [3661]

Alan H. Neville Memorial Scholarships (Graduate/Scholarship) [363]

New Hampshire Snowmobile Association Book Scholarships (Undergraduate/Scholarship) [8269]

New Heights Scholarship (Undergraduate/Scholarship) [2767]

New Mexico Manufactured Housing Association Scholarship Fund (Undergraduate/Scholarship) [320]

New Orleans Ghost Tours Scholarships (Undergraduate/Scholarship) [8297]

New York State Senate - Legislative Fellowship (Graduate, Postgraduate/Fellowship) [8326]

The New York Times College Scholarship (Undergraduate/Scholarship, Internship) [8354]

The Newberry Consortium in American Indian Studies Graduate Student Fellowships *(Graduate/Fellowship)* [8379]

Newberry Library ACM/GLCA Faculty Fellowships *(Other/Fellowship)* [2014, 8380]

The Newberry Library Short-Term Residential Fellowships for Individual Research *(Postdoctorate, Doctorate/Fellowship)* [8382]

Newcomer Supply Student Scholarship *(Undergraduate/Scholarship)* [8110]

Newfangled Networks $1,000 Scholarship *(Undergraduate, Graduate/Scholarship)* [8389]

Newman Civic Fellowship *(Undergraduate/Fellowship)* [2868]

Craig D. Newman Memorial Scholarship *(Undergraduate/Scholarship)* [5409]

Newman University Scouting Scholarships *(Undergraduate/Scholarship)* [7855]

NFPA Youth Scholarships *(Undergraduate/Scholarship)* [7896]

NGAT Educational Foundation Scholarship *(Graduate, Undergraduate/Scholarship)* [7915]

Le Hoang Nguyen College Scholarships (LHN) *(Undergraduate/Scholarship)* [11823]

The Thuy Nguyen Scholarships *(High School/Scholarship)* [11824]

NHAEOP Member Scholarships *(Undergraduate/Scholarship)* [8251]

NHEERL Postdoctoral Research Program *(Postdoctorate, Advanced Professional, Professional development/Fellowship)* [11354]

The NHPGA Apprentice Scholarship *(Undergraduate/Scholarship)* [7174]

NHS Scholarships *(Undergraduate/Scholarship)* [7932]

NIBA Presidential Scholarships *(Undergraduate/Scholarship)* [7941]

Erik Nielsen Memorial Scholarship *(Undergraduate, Master's/Scholarship)* [12353]

Nikko Cosmetic Surgery Center Annual Breast Cancer Survivor Scholarships *(All/Scholarship)* [8398]

NING Scholarship *(Undergraduate, Graduate/Scholarship)* [8405]

Nissan North America, Inc. Scholarships *(Undergraduate/Scholarship)* [983]

Louise McKinney Post-secondary Scholarship *(Undergraduate/Scholarship)* [299]

NLBRA Age-Out Scholarship *(Undergraduate/Scholarship)* [7993]

NLBRA National Royalty Scholarship *(Other/Scholarship)* [7994]

NLBRA Rainwater Scholarships *(Undergraduate/Scholarship)* [7995]

NLBRA World All Around Scholarships *(Undergraduate/Scholarship)* [7996]

NLBRA World Event Scholarships *(Undergraduate/Scholarship)* [7997]

NLBRA/Wrangler Academic Scholarships *(Undergraduate/Scholarship)* [7998]

NLBRA Youth Board Officer Scholarships *(Undergraduate/Scholarship)* [7999]

NMCRS Gold Star Scholarship Program *(Undergraduate/Scholarship)* [8180]

NMSC College and University Sponsorship of Merit Scholarship Awards *(Undergraduate/Scholarship)* [8004]

NMSC Corporate-Sponsored merit Scholarship Awards *(Undergraduate/Scholarship)* [8005]

NMSC National Achievement Scholarship Program *(Undergraduate/Scholarship)* [8006]

NMSC Special Scholarships *(Undergraduate/Scholarship)* [8007]

Charles S. Noble Scholarships for Study at Harvard *(Undergraduate/Scholarship)* [300]

The Edna A. Noblin Scholarship *(Undergraduate/Scholarship)* [6659]

Alfred H. Nolle Scholarship *(Undergraduate/Scholarship)* [378]

Non Commissioned Officers Association Scholarships *(Undergraduate/Scholarship)* [8409]

Noplag Scholarship Essay Contest *(High School, Undergraduate, Graduate/Scholarship)* [8416]

Nor' Easters Scholarship *(Undergraduate/Scholarship)* [5541]

Nor' Easters Scholarships - Two-year Program *(Undergraduate/Scholarship)* [5542]

Norall Scholarship Trust *(Undergraduate, Postdoctorate/Scholarship)* [6831]

Nordic Skiing Association of Anchorage Scholarship *(Graduate/Scholarship)* [242]

Norman J. Tschantz, Walter C. Deuble and Dominic J. Bagnoli, Jr. Caddie Scholarship Fund *(Undergraduate/Scholarship)* [10784]

Norman K. Russell Scholarship *(Graduate, Doctorate/Scholarship)* [8034]

Norman W. Kramer Outstanding Scholar Award *(Undergraduate/Scholarship)* [7345]

North Carolina Heroes Financial Hardship Grant *(Other/Grant)* [8439]

North Dakota Farmers Union Co-op House Scholarship *(Undergraduate/Scholarship)* [8463]

North Las Vegas Firefighters William J. Harnedy Memorial Scholarship *(Undergraduate/Scholarship)* [9415]

North Texas GIA Alumni Association Scholarship *(Undergraduate/Scholarship)* [4881]

North Texas Relocation Professionals Scholarship *(Undergraduate/Scholarship)* [8478]

Northern Alberta Development Council Bursaries Program *(Undergraduate/Scholarship)* [301]

Northern Alberta Development Council Bursary *(Undergraduate/Scholarship)* [302]

Northern Virginia Alumnae Chapter Scholarship *(Undergraduate/Scholarship)* [4009]

Northwest Community Center Scholarship *(Undergraduate/Scholarship)* [3691]

Northwest-Shoals Community College Academic Scholarship *(Undergraduate/Scholarship)* [8524]

Northwest-Shoals Community College High School Academic Scholarships *(Undergraduate/Scholarship)* [8530]

Northwest-Shoals Community College Independent Computer Scholarships *(Undergraduate/Scholarship)* [8531]

Northwest-Shoals Community College Student Activities Scholarships *(Undergraduate/Scholarship)* [8532]

NotMP3 Scholarship Program *(College, University, Undergraduate/Scholarship)* [8549]

Notre Dame Club of Canton, Ohio Scholarship Fund *(Undergraduate/Scholarship)* [10785]

NSHSS Academic Paper Awards *(High School/Scholarship)* [8104]

NSHSS National Scholar Awards *(High School, College/Scholarship)* [8105]

NSSA/NSCA Collegiate High School Senior Scholarships *(Undergraduate/Scholarship)* [8131]

Number 1 Auto Transport Annual Scholarship *(Undergraduate, Graduate/Scholarship)* [8557]

NW-SCC Faculty and Staff Scholarship *(Undergraduate/Scholarship)* [8533]

NW-SCC General Foundation Scholarship *(Undergraduate/Scholarship)* [8534]

NWAG Georgia Students Scholarship *(Undergraduate/Scholarship)* [8395]

NWAG Nigeria Scholarships *(Undergraduate/Scholarship)* [8396]

NWSA Graduate Scholarship *(Master's, Doctorate/Scholarship)* [8166]

The NYCTutoring.com Scholarship *(Undergraduate/Scholarship)* [8569]

AEBC Rick Oakes Scholarships for the Arts *(Undergraduate/Scholarship)* [364]

OAS Academic Scholarship for Undergraduate Studies *(Undergraduate/Scholarship)* [8731]

WillEtta "Willie" Long Oates, Gamma Nu, Memorial Scholarship *(Undergraduate, Graduate/Scholarship)* [6463]

Obuchi Student Scholarship *(Graduate/Scholarship)* [4264]

Odd Fellows Lodge #8 Endowed Scholarship *(Undergraduate/Scholarship)* [6818]

The Captain Jennifer Shafer Odom Memorial Scholarship - Children of Soldiers *(Undergraduate, Vocational/Occupational/Scholarship)* [1919]

The Captain Jennifer Shafer Odom Memorial Scholarship - Spouses of Soldiers *(Undergraduate, Vocational/Occupational/Scholarship)* [1920]

Don and Jan O'Dowd/SAA Statewide Scholarships *(Undergraduate/Scholarship)* [11460]

Ohio National Foundation Scholarship *(Undergraduate/Scholarship)* [3391]

O'Jay's Scholarship Fund *(Undergraduate/Scholarship)* [10786]

Seth Okin Good Deeds Scholarships *(Undergraduate, Graduate, Community College/Scholarship)* [9283]

Oliver Rosenberg Educational Trust *(Undergraduate/Scholarship)* [4781]

Roy C. and Dorothy Jean Olson Memorial Scholarship *(Graduate/Scholarship)* [6042]

Olympia Tumwater Foundation Traditional Scholarships *(Undergraduate, High School/Scholarship)* [8616]

Olympia Tumwater Foundation Transitional (non-traditional) Scholarships *(Undergraduate/Scholarship)* [8617]

Charlie O'Meilia Scholarship *(Undergraduate/Scholarship, Monetary, Award)* [5973]

ONECA Four Directions Scholarship *(Undergraduate/Scholarship)* [8660]

OOBS Student Leadership Scholarships *(Undergraduate/Scholarship)* [8778]

OOIDA Mary Johnston Scholarship Program *(Undergraduate/Scholarship)* [8798]

Open Society Fellowship *(Other/Fellowship)* [8664]

OppU Achievers Scholarship *(Undergraduate/Scholarship)* [8673]

Optimist Club of Redlands Scholarship- Ralph Maloof *(Undergraduate/Scholarship)* [9568]

Optimist Club of Redlands Scholarship- Virgina Elliott *(Undergraduate/Scholarship)* [9569]

Order Sons of Italy Foundation General Scholarships *(Graduate, Undergraduate/Scholarship)* [8691]

Organization of American States AOS-Placed Scholarships *(Graduate, Undergraduate/Scholarship)* [8736]

Organization of American States Graduate Scholarships *(Doctorate, Graduate/Scholarship)* [8737]

Organization of American States Self-Placed Scholarships *(Doctorate, Graduate/Scholarship)* [8738]

Organization of Chinese Americans Scholarships *(Undergraduate/Scholarship)* [1986]

The Gail Karp Orgell Scholarship *(Four Year College, University, Undergraduate/Scholarship)* [6276]

Original Tax Credit Scholarship *(Master's, Doctorate/Scholarship)* [1802]

Orrie & Dorothy Cassada Scholarship *(Undergraduate/Scholarship)* [5171]

Charles & Mitch Ota Foundation Scholarship *(Undergraduate, Two Year College, Four Year College/Scholarship)* [5410]

The Otis and Florence Lapham Memorial Scholarship *(Graduate/Scholarship)* [6205]

Alvin G. Ott Fish & Wildlife Scholarship *(Undergraduate/Scholarship)* [11461]

Satenik & Adom Ourian Education Foundation Scholarship *(Undergraduate/Scholarship)* [1897]

Outlaw Student's Minority Scholarships *(Undergraduate/Scholarship)* [10861]

Charles and Melva T. Owen Memorial Scholarships *(Undergraduate/Scholarship, Monetary)* [7879]

Elvina Jane Owen Scholarship *(Graduate, Undergraduate/Scholarship)* [4894]

Ozarks Division of Midwest Dairy Educational Award *(Undergraduate/Scholarship)* [7374]

The Pac-12 Postgraduate Scholarships *(Graduate/Scholarship)* [8802]

Pacific Beacon Scholarship *(Community College, University, Undergraduate, Vocational/Occupational/Scholarship)* [9838]

Dr. Nicholas Padis Memorial Graduate Scholarship *(Graduate/Scholarship)* [5467]

Casilda Pagan Educational/Vocational Scholarships *(Graduate, Undergraduate, Postgraduate/Scholarship)* [5594]

Ben Palacio Scholarships *(Undergraduate/Scholarship)* [11387]

PALCUS National Scholarship Program *(Undergraduate/Scholarship)* [9250]

E. William Palmer Memorial Scholarship *(Undergraduate, Graduate/Scholarship)* [2547]

Palo Verde High School Faculty Follies Scholarship *(Undergraduate/Scholarship)* [9417]

PAM General Conference Scholarships *(Other/Scholarship)* [9264]

The PanHellenic Scholarship (Undergraduate/Scholarship) [8816]

Panther Cafe Scholarships (Undergraduate/Scholarship) [9418]

Cissy McDaniel Parker Scholarships (Undergraduate/Scholarship) [4010]

E.U. and Gene Parker Scholarships (Undergraduate/Scholarship, Monetary) [7880]

Parking Industry Institute Scholarship Program (Undergraduate/Scholarship) [8036]

Carl Parsell Scholarship Fund (Undergraduate/Scholarship) [7303]

Participation-Based Scholarships (Undergraduate/Scholarship) [9101]

Pasteur Foundation Postdoctoral Fellowship (Postdoctorate/Fellowship) [8913]

Pat and Cliff Rogers Nursing Scholarship (Undergraduate/Scholarship) [11509]

Pat Dermargosian Memorial Scholarship (Undergraduate/Scholarship) [9570]

PATCH Early Childhood Education Scholarships (Graduate/Scholarship) [8915]

Gail Patrick Charitable Trust Scholarships (Graduate/Scholarship) [4041]

Q. O. (Quint) Patrick Scholarships (Undergraduate/Scholarship) [12006]

Joanne Holbrook Patton Military Spouse Scholarships (Graduate, Undergraduate/Scholarship) [8009]

Paul & Inger Friend 4-H Scholarship Fund (Undergraduate/Scholarship) [10831]

Paula Backscheider Archival Fellowship (Other/Fellowship) [1437]

Pauline Hand Memorial Scholarship (Other/Scholarship) [10832]

Pauline LaFon Gore Scholarship Fund (Undergraduate/Scholarship) [3641]

PDFelement Scholarship (Undergraduate, Graduate/Scholarship) [12181]

PEA Bursaries (Undergraduate/Scholarship) [9340]

PEA Scholarships (Undergraduate/Scholarship) [9341]

Pearman Family Scholarship (Undergraduate/Scholarship) [9839]

Peg Hart Harrison Memorial Scholarship (Undergraduate/Scholarship) [4011]

Full Pellegrini Scholarship (Undergraduate, Graduate/Scholarship) [10896]

Pembroke Center's Faculty Research Fellowships (Professional development/Fellowship) [2724]

Pembroke Center Graduate Student Fellowships (Graduate, Postdoctorate/Fellowship) [2725]

Pembroke Center for Teaching and Research on Women Postdoctoral Research Associateships (Postdoctorate/Fellowship) [2727]

Pennsboro High School Alumni Scholarship (Undergraduate/Scholarship) [8866]

PennyGeeks.com Car Insurance Essay Scholarship (Undergraduate/Scholarship) [8971]

P.E.O. Chapter DS Scholarship (Undergraduate, Vocational/Occupational/Scholarship) [5101]

The P.E.O. Educational Loan Fund (ELF) (Undergraduate, Master's, Doctorate/Loan) [8976]

P.E.O. Scholar Awards (PSA) (Doctorate/Award, Scholarship) [8977]

Pepper Family Scholarship Fund (Undergraduate/Scholarship) [3392]

Nalini Perera Little Lotus Bud Master's Scholarships (Master's/Scholarship) [3048]

Perry Township School Memorial Scholarship Fund (Undergraduate/Scholarship) [10787]

The Persons in or Affected by Recovery Scholarship (Undergraduate, Graduate/Scholarship) [5233]

Persons Case Scholarship (Undergraduate, Graduate/Scholarship) [303]

Peter F. Bronfman Entrance Award (Postgraduate/Award) [12259]

Peter and Jody Larkin Legacy Scholarship (Undergraduate/Scholarship) [2806]

Larry A. Peters Endowment Fund Scholarship (Undergraduate/Scholarship) [1898]

Captain James H. Peterson Memorial Scholarships (Undergraduate/Scholarship) [5290]

William H. and Lena M. Petree Scholarship (Graduate/Scholarship) [12087]

Pfafftown Jaycees/Lynn Canada Memorial Scholarship (Undergraduate/Scholarship, Award) [12088]

PFLAG Howard County Scholarship (Undergraduate/Scholarship) [9054]

Phi Delta Gamma Academic Achievement Awards (Undergraduate/Scholarship) [9095]

Phi Eta Sigma Graduate Scholarships (Graduate, Other/Scholarship) [9089]

Phi Eta Sigma Undergraduate Scholarship Awards (Undergraduate/Scholarship) [9090]

Phi Eta Sigma Undergraduate Scholarships (Undergraduate/Scholarship) [9091]

Phi Kappa Phi DissertationFellowships (Doctorate/Fellowship) [9097]

Phi Kappa Phi Fellowship (Graduate, Undergraduate/Fellowship) [9098]

Phi Kappa Sigma Foundation Scholarship (Undergraduate/Scholarship) [9102]

Phil Shykes Memorial Scholarship Fund (Graduate/Scholarship) [4217]

The Walter T. Philippy Scholarship (Undergraduate/Scholarship) [7175]

Phillip Guy Richardson Memorial Scholarship (Undergraduate/Scholarship) [6207]

Jean L. Phillips Auburn Scholarship Fund (Undergraduate/Scholarship) [3662]

Lowell Phillips Scholarship (Undergraduate/Scholarship) [3705]

Phoenix Pride Scholarship (Undergraduate/Scholarship) [9137]

PhRMA Foundation Informatics Research Starter Grants (Doctorate/Grant) [9066]

Pi Kapp Scholars Award (Undergraduate/Scholarship) [9162]

Pi Project 2000 Tali James Memorial Scholarship (Undergraduate/Scholarship) [6465]

Pichler Family Scholarship Fund (Undergraduate/Scholarship) [3393]

Pidperyhora Eleonora Scholarship (Undergraduate/Scholarship) [9674]

Herschel H. Pifer Scholarship (Undergraduate/Scholarship) [8868]

Pinnacol Foundation Scholarship (Undergraduate, Community College, Vocational/Occupational/Scholarship) [9176]

The PinProsPlus Scholarship (College, University, Graduate/Scholarship) [9178]

The Pinto Ranch Western Achievement Scholarship (Graduate/Scholarship) [9180]

Platt Excavation Fellowships (Other, Undergraduate/Fellowship) [1379]

PLUS Foundation Financial Aid Scholarship (Undergraduate/Scholarship) [9212]

The Henry Dewitt Plyler Scholarship (Undergraduate/Scholarship) [4750]

PNC Scholarship Fund (Undergraduate/Scholarship) [3394]

Point Community College Scholarship Program (Undergraduate, Community College/Scholarship) [9229]

POLAR Northern Resident Scholarship (Doctorate, Master's/Scholarship) [2147]

Polar Scholarship (Doctorate, Graduate/Scholarship) [2148]

PolicyPak Scholarship (Undergraduate, Graduate/Scholarship) [9238]

Polish American Club of North Jersey Scholarships (Undergraduate/Scholarship) [6605]

Polish National Alliance of Brooklyn, USA Scholarships (Undergraduate/Scholarship) [6606]

Pollard-Bailey Scholarship (Undergraduate/Scholarship) [9840]

The David J. Pollini Scholarship (Undergraduate/Scholarship) [7176]

Francis Poloshian Memorial Grant (Undergraduate/Scholarship) [1899]

James Poloshian Memorial Grant (Undergraduate/Scholarship) [1900]

The Pope Scholarship Award (Undergraduate/Scholarship) [7177]

The Porter Creek Citizens' Assoc. Scholarship (Undergraduate, University, College, Vocational/Occupational/Scholarship) [12359]

AFT Robert G. Porter Scholars Program (Undergraduate/Scholarship) [881]

Post-High School Tuition Scholarship Program (Undergraduate/Scholarship) [3190]

Poteet Strawberry Festival Association Scholarships (Graduate, Undergraduate/Scholarship) [9256]

Gerald Powell Scholarships (Undergraduate/Scholarship) [3663]

Powers-Knapp Scholarship Program (Undergraduate/Scholarship) [11744]

Prairie Baseball Academy Scholarship (Undergraduate/Scholarship) [304]

Catherine Prelinger Award (Postdoctorate/Scholarship) [3830]

Pretty Photoshop Actions Bi-Annual Scholarship (Undergraduate, Graduate/Scholarship) [9273]

Price Benowitz Social Justice Scholarships (Undergraduate, Graduate, Community College/Scholarship) [9285]

Jim and Dee Price Family Scholarship (Undergraduate, Community College, College, University/Scholarship) [5123]

Pride Foundation Regional Scholarships (Undergraduate/Scholarship) [9307]

Pride Foundation Scholarships (Undergraduate/Scholarship) [9771]

Pride of the Rose Scholarship (Undergraduate/Scholarship) [9309]

Prince Henry Society Scholarships (Undergraduate/Scholarship) [9326]

Priscilla Gamble Scholarship Fund (Undergraduate/Scholarship) [3395]

Miguel Pro Scholarships (Undergraduate/Scholarship) [12224]

Procter and Gamble Foundation Scholarship (Undergraduate/Scholarship) [3396]

Professional Woman's Magazine Scholarship Opportunity (Undergraduate/Scholarship) [9347]

Professional Women of Redlands, PoWeR to Continue Learning Scholarships (Undergraduate/Scholarship) [9572]

Progress Lane Scholarship Fund (Undergraduate/Scholarship) [3576]

Provincial and Regional 4-H Scholarship (Undergraduate/Scholarship) [15]

Joseph E. Pryor Graduate Fellowships (Graduate/Fellowship) [379]

Cheryl White Pryor Memorial Scholarship (Undergraduate/Scholarship) [4012]

Phillis Brinton Pryor Panhellenic Scholarship (Undergraduate/Scholarship) [6466]

PSAC-AGR National Scholarship (Postgraduate/Scholarship, Monetary) [9444]

PSAC - Coughlin National Scholarships (Postgraduate/Scholarship, Monetary) [9445]

PSAC Regional Scholarships (Postgraduate/Scholarship, Monetary) [9447]

PSHF Good Idea Grant (Other/Grant) [9441]

Pt. Lay Memorial Scholarships (Undergraduate/Scholarship) [11462]

Public Service Fellows Internship Program - Center for Government Leadership (Undergraduate, Graduate/Internship) [8904]

Public Service Fellows Internship Program - Education and Outreach (Undergraduate, Graduate, Professional development/Internship) [8905]

Public Service Fellows Internship Program - Government Transformation and Agency Partnerships (Undergraduate, Graduate, Professional development/Internship) [8906]

Public Service Fellows Internship Program - Human Resources (Professional development, Other/Internship) [8907]

Public Service Internship Program - Communications (Undergraduate, Graduate, Professional development/Internship) [8908]

Public Service Internship Program - Development (Undergraduate, Graduate, Professional development/Internship) [8909]

Public Service Internship Program - Government Affairs (Undergraduate, Graduate, Professional development/Internship) [8910]

Public Service Internship Program - Research and Program Evaluation Focus (Undergraduate, Graduate, Professional development/Internship) [8911]

Pulaski Scholarships for Advanced Studies (Graduate, Master's/Scholarship) [827]

Harry B. Pulver Scholarships (Undergraduate/Scholarship) [5002]

Qualcomm San Diego Science, Technology, Engineering and Mathematics Scholarship (Undergraduate/Scholarship) [9841]

Quality Company Formations Scholarship (College, University, Undergraduate/Scholarship) [9455]

Queen Elizabeth II Graduate Scholarship (Doctorate, Graduate, Master's/Scholarship) [305]

Rosemary Quigley Memorial Scholarship (Undergraduate, Graduate/Scholarship) [4442]

The Michael J. Quill Scholarship (Undergraduate/Scholarship) [11075]

Diamond & James Quong Memorial Scholarship (Graduate, Master's, Undergraduate/Scholarship) [12360]

R. Garn Haycock Memorial Scholarship (Undergraduate/Scholarship) [9574]

Rachel Graham Memorial Scholarship (Undergraduate/Scholarship) [9575]

RADM William A. Sullivan, USN (Ret.) Scholarship (Undergraduate/Scholarship) [8174]

The Raffin-Gathercole Scholarship (Undergraduate/Scholarship) [4873]

Railroad and Mine Workers Memorial Scholarship (Graduate/Scholarship) [6250]

Rains - J.J. Rains Memorial Scholarship (Undergraduate/Scholarship) [3483]

Ivan & Dianna Raketti Scholarship (Undergraduate, Graduate, Master's/Scholarship) [12361]

Ralph and Josephine Smith Fund (Undergraduate/Scholarship) [4602]

Rancho Bernardo/Smith Scholarship (Undergraduate/Scholarship) [9842]

Randy Williams Scholarship (Undergraduate/Scholarship) [9843]

Jeannette Rankin Scholarships (Undergraduate, Vocational/Occupational/Scholarship) [9501]

Marie Mathew Rask-Gamma Omicron Educational Endowment (Undergraduate/Scholarship) [6467]

Ratingle Scholarship Program (College, University, Community College, Undergraduate, Graduate/Scholarship) [9506]

Mary C. Rawlins Scholarships (Graduate/Scholarship) [5342]

Ray And Mary Bell Scholarship (Undergraduate/Scholarship) [9844]

W.B. Ray High School Class of '56 Averill Johnson Scholarship (Undergraduate/Scholarship) [3484]

Ray and Pearl Sams Scholarship (Undergraduate/Scholarship) [12089]

The Shirley and Robert Raymer College Scholarship (Four Year College, University, Undergraduate/Scholarship) [6277]

Raymond A. Kent-Navy V-12/ROTC (Undergraduate/Scholarship) [11579]

Raymond and Augusta Klink Scholarship Fund (Undergraduate/Scholarship) [3397]

Raymond and Donald Beeler Memorial Scholarship (Undergraduate/Scholarship) [9576]

Raytheon Scholars (Undergraduate/Scholarship) [9508]

Reach for Your Goal Scholarship (Undergraduate/Scholarship) [5174]

Read Carlock Memorial Scholarship Fund (Other/Scholarship) [1800]

Real Estate Elevated Scholarship (Community College, Undergraduate, Graduate/Scholarship) [9510]

RealtyHop Scholarship (Undergraduate, Two Year College/Scholarship) [9512]

Mary K. Smith Rector Scholarship (Undergraduate, Vocational/Occupational/Scholarship) [8870]

Redlands Baseball/Softball for Youth Scholarship (Undergraduate/Scholarship) [9577]

Redlands Community Scholarship Foundation Awards (Undergraduate/Scholarship) [9578]

Redlands Council PTA - Dorathy Jolley Memorial Scholarship (Undergraduate/Scholarship) [9579]

Redlands Evening Lions Club - Barbara Westen Memorial Scholarship (Undergraduate/Scholarship) [9580]

Redlands High School Academic Decathlon Scholarship (Undergraduate/Scholarship) [9582]

Redlands High School Aquatics Booster Club Scholarship (Undergraduate/Scholarship) [9583]

Redlands High School Boy's Varsity Volleyball Scholarships (Undergraduate/Scholarship) [9584]

Redlands High School Girls' Volleyball Boosters Scholarship Awards (Undergraduate/Scholarship) [9585]

Redlands High School Mock Trial Scholarship (Undergraduate/Scholarship) [9586]

Redlands High School-PTSA Scholarship (Undergraduate/Scholarship) [9587]

Redlands High School Softball Booster Scholarship (Undergraduate/Scholarship) [9588]

Redlands High School Spiritleaders Scholarship (Undergraduate/Scholarship) [9589]

Redlands Morning Kiwanis Club Foundation Scholarships (Graduate/Scholarship) [9592]

Redlands Rotary Club Foundation Discretionary Scholarship (Undergraduate/Scholarship) [9593]

Redlands Rotary Club Scholarship - Donald C. Anderson (Undergraduate/Scholarship) [9594]

Redlands Rotary Club Scholarship - Ernest L. Cronemeyer (Undergraduate/Scholarship) [9595]

Regina B. Shearn Scholarship (Graduate, Undergraduate/Scholarship) [398]

Regions Riding Forward Scholarship Essay Contest (Undergraduate, High School/Scholarship) [9618]

Registered Apprenticeship Program/CTS Scholarships (RAP) (Undergraduate/Scholarship) [306]

J.H. Stewart Reid Memorial Fellowship Trust (Doctorate/Fellowship) [9629]

Jacob L. Reinecke Memorial Scholarship (Undergraduate/Scholarship) [5102]

Renardo A. Matteucci Family Scholarship (Undergraduate/Scholarship) [3597]

Rene Matos Memorial Scholarship Program (Undergraduate, Vocational/Occupational/Scholarship) [7928]

RentHop Scholarship (Undergraduate, Two Year College/Scholarship) [9637]

The Responsify Empowering Others Scholarship (Undergraduate/Scholarship) [9647]

Restoring Self Scholarship (Undergraduate/Scholarship) [5559]

Resume Template Design Scholarships (Undergraduate, Graduate/Scholarship) [11800]

Retired League Postmasters Scholarship Program (Undergraduate/Scholarship) [9655]

Returning Adult and Single-Parent Scholarships (Undergraduate/Scholarship) [11745]

Reuben R. Cowles Youth Educational Award (Undergraduate, Graduate/Award) [1059]

W. Reymont Scholarships (Undergraduate/Scholarship) [9675]

Gary Reynolds Scholarship (Undergraduate, University, College, Vocational/Occupational/Scholarship) [12362]

Reynoldsburg-Pickerington Rotary Club High School Scholarship (Undergraduate/Scholarship) [9681]

R.G. and Ruth Crossno Scholarship (Undergraduate/Scholarship) [4258]

Barry "Tyler" Rhea Memorial Scholarship (Undergraduate, Community College/Scholarship) [8535]

Lori Rhett Memorial Scholarships (Graduate, Undergraduate/Scholarship) [7632]

Rhode Island Association of Former Legislators Scholarship (Graduate/Scholarship) [9696]

Rhode Island Commission on Women/Freda H. Goldman Education Award (Undergraduate/Award) [9697]

John J. and Elizabeth Rhodes Scholarship (Undergraduate, Graduate/Scholarship) [2549]

Rich Abjian Leadership Scholarship (Undergraduate/Scholarship) [9420]

Ben C. Rich Memorial Scholarship (Undergraduate, Graduate/Scholarship) [2550]

Richard Cecil Todd and Clauda Pennock Todd Tripod Scholarship (Graduate, Undergraduate/Scholarship) [9104]

Richard Goolsby Scholarship - Created by William and Martha Debrule (Graduate, Undergraduate/Scholarship) [4751]

Richard Heekin Scholarship Fund (Undergraduate/Scholarship) [3398]

Richard J. Schnell Memorial Scholarship (Postdoctorate/Scholarship) [3692]

Richard L. Baker Memorial Scholarship Fund (Undergraduate/Scholarship) [10833]

Richard R. Tufenkian Scholarships (Undergraduate/Scholarship) [1848]

James Edward "Bill" Richards Scholarships (Undergraduate/Scholarship) [3643]

Rick Arkans Eagle Scout Scholarship (Undergraduate/Scholarship) [7856]

Rick Munoz Memorial Scholarship (Undergraduate/Scholarship) [9597]

Rider Family Scholarship (Undergraduate/Scholarship, Award) [12090]

The Jasper Ridge Restoration Fellowship (Graduate, Undergraduate/Fellowship) [4279]

Riding Into the Future (Undergraduate, College, University/Scholarship) [6775]

Paula Joan Riehl Memorial Scholarship (High School/Scholarship) [12364]

Riggs Cove Foundation Scholarship (Undergraduate/Scholarship) [4919]

Rim-Freeman Point Scholarship (Undergraduate/Scholarship) [9230]

Rimington Trophy Scholarship (Undergraduate, Graduate/Scholarship) [4443]

Lois McDonald Rinehart Adelphe Scholarship (Undergraduate, Graduate/Scholarship) [6468]

Lana K. Rinehart Scholarships (Undergraduate/Scholarship) [3578]

Josephine Ringold Scholarship (Undergraduate/Scholarship) [5175]

Ripley Rotary Scholarship/The Judge Oliver Kessel Scholarship (Undergraduate, Vocational/Occupational/Scholarship) [8871]

Rise to Shine Scholarship (Undergraduate/Scholarship) [353]

RISLA Student Loans (Undergraduate, Graduate/Loan) [9701]

Riverside Sheriffs Association Member Scholarship Program (Graduate, Undergraduate/Scholarship) [9710]

RMACRAO Professional Development Scholarship (Professional development/Scholarship) [9725]

RMHC African American Future Achievers Scholarship (Undergraduate/Scholarship) [9734]

RMHC Asia Scholarship (Undergraduate/Scholarship) [9735]

RMHC HACER Scholarship (Undergraduate/Scholarship) [9736]

RMNP Research Fellowship (Graduate/Fellowship) [9730]

Road to Success Scholarship (Undergraduate/Scholarship) [8551]

Robbie Miller Memorial Endowed Scholarship (Undergraduate/Scholarship) [6819]

Robby Baker Memorial Scholarship (Graduate/Scholarship) [321]

Robert B. And Dorothy Pence Scholarship Fund (Undergraduate/Scholarship) [10700]

Robert B. and Sophia Whiteside Scholarship Fund (Graduate/Scholarship) [4218]

Robert C. & Margaret A. Schikora Scholarship Fund (Undergraduate/Scholarship) [10701]

Robert G. Campbell Scholarship (Undergraduate/Scholarship) [9598]

Robert H. Reakirt Scholarship Fund (Undergraduate/Scholarship) [3399]

Robert Krembil Scholarship of Merit (Master's/Scholarship) [12260]

Robert L. & Hilda Treasure Mitchell Scholarship (Undergraduate/Scholarship) [5176]

Robert P. Ernest Scholarship (Undergraduate/Scholarship) [6208]

Robert R. Palmer Research Travel Fellowship (Other/Fellowship) [1438]

Robert S. McNamara Fellowships Program (RSMFP) (Doctorate/Fellowship, Monetary) [12194]

Robert Sutherland/Harry Jerome Entrance Award (Undergraduate/Scholarship) [2599, 9461]

James H. Roberts Athletic Scholarship (Undergraduate/Scholarship) [8872]

Thomas Warren Roberts Memorial Scholarship (Undergraduate/Scholarship) [8873]

Marion Roberts Memorial Scholarships (Undergraduate/Scholarship) [2360]

A.D. Al and Maxine Robertson Memorial Scholarship (Undergraduate/Scholarship) [11463]

Robinhood Marine Center Scholarship (Undergraduate/Scholarship) [4920]

Robinson G. Allen Athletic Memorial Scholarship (Undergraduate/Scholarship) [9599]

August M. Rocco Scholarship Fund (Undergraduate/Scholarship) [10788]

Rockford Area Habitat for Humanity College Scholarship (Undergraduate/Scholarship) [3693]

Rodney Williams Legacy Scholarship (Graduate/Scholarship) [11580]

Rodziny Krawczyk-Krane Family Scholarship (Undergraduate/Scholarship) [9676]

R.O.E.A. Dumitru Golea Goldy-Gemu Scholarships (Undergraduate, High School/Scholarship) [1369]

ROFL Scholarship (Undergraduate, College, University/Scholarship) [9236]

Roger and Jacquelyn Vander Laan Family Scholarship (Undergraduate/Scholarship) [5177]

Roger and Joyce Howe Scholarship Fund (Undergraduate/Scholarship) [3400]

Roger K. Hughes Legacy Scholarship (Undergraduate/Scholarship) [2807]

Kimberly Marie Rogers Memorial Scholarship Fund (Undergraduate, Vocational/Occupational/Scholarship) [4603]

Red Rogers Memorial Scholarship (Undergraduate, Master's/Scholarship) [12365]

Roy Seymour Rogers and Geraldine Ruth Rogers Scholarship (Undergraduate/Scholarship) [11023]

Sandra Journey Rolf Scholarship Fund (Undergraduate, Graduate/Scholarship) [6469]

Ronald McDonald House Charities Scholarship (Undergraduate/Scholarship) [9737]

Ronald T. Smith Family Scholarship (Undergraduate, Graduate/Scholarship) [5178]

Doris Hardinger Roome Scholarship Fund (Undergraduate, Graduate, Two Year College, Four Year College/Scholarship) [5411]

Roothbert Fund Scholarships (Undergraduate, Graduate/Scholarship) [9741]

Rose Cassin Memorial Scholarship (Postgraduate/Scholarship) [8644]

Dr. Wayne F. Rose Scholarship Fund (Undergraduate/Scholarship) [4604]

Rosenberg-Ibarra Scholarships (Graduate/Scholarship) [9312]

Jean and Tom Rosenthal Scholarship Program (Undergraduate/Scholarship) [3723]

Ross P. Broesamle Education Fund (Undergraduate/Scholarship) [6667]

The Bea and Harry Ross Scholarship Endowment (Graduate/Scholarship) [10847]

Rotary Club of Annapolis Scholarship (Graduate/Scholarship) [1719]

The Rotary Club of Cape Coral Goldcoast Scholarship (Undergraduate/Scholarship) [3149]

Rotary Club of Corpus Christi Scholarship (Undergraduate/Scholarship) [3485]

The Rotary Club of Rancho Bernardo Sunrise Community Service Scholarships (Undergraduate/Scholarship) [9846]

Rotary Foundation Global Grant Scholarships Supplement (Graduate/Scholarship, Grant) [9745]

Rothberg International School Graduate Merit Scholarship (Graduate, Master's/Scholarship) [2987]

Royal Canadian Regiment Association Bursaries (Undergraduate/Scholarship) [9751]

R.S. Williamson & Eliford Mott Memorial Scholarships (Undergraduate/Scholarship) [12007]

Ruppert Scholarship (Undergraduate/Scholarship) [2831]

Russell Athletics Scholarship (Undergraduate/Scholarship) [2336]

Dave & Laurie Russell Family Scholarships for Habitat for Humanity of Kent County Families (Undergraduate/Scholarship) [5180]

Ruth Adams Memorial Scholarship (Undergraduate/Scholarship) [9601]

Ruth E. Jenkins Scholarship (Undergraduate/Scholarship) [9847]

Ruth and Sherman Zudekoff Scholarship Fund (Undergraduate/Scholarship) [3593]

Alexander Rutherford High School Achievement Scholarship (Undergraduate/Scholarship) [307]

Rutherford Scholars (Undergraduate/Scholarship) [308]

The Ryan Law Group Scholarship (Undergraduate/Scholarship) [9768]

Michael Clarkson Ryan Memorial Scholarship (Undergraduate, Graduate/Scholarship) [2551]

Ryerson Scholarships (Undergraduate/Scholarship) [6219]

S. David Shor Scholarship Fund (Undergraduate/Scholarship) [3401]

Safe Teen Driver Scholarship (Undergraduate, Vocational/Occupational, College/Scholarship) [4978]

Saint Andrews Scholarships (Undergraduate/Scholarship) [9776]

St. Francis Xavier Scholarship (Undergraduate/Scholarship) [12225]

St. James Armenian Apostolic Church Scholarships (Undergraduate, Vocational/Occupational/Scholarship) [9780]

St. Patrick's Day Scholarship (All/Scholarship) [7444]

Saint Paul University Financial Aid Bursaries (Undergraduate, Graduate/Scholarship) [9785]

St. Petersburg Personal Injury Attorneys McQuaid & Douglas $2,000 Scholarship Contest (College, Undergraduate, Vocational/Occupational, Professional development/Scholarship) [9787]

Saints Cyril and Methodius Scholarships (Undergraduate/Scholarship) [9766]

Sakura Finetek Student Scholarship (Undergraduate/Scholarship) [8113]

Sam J. Hord Memorial Scholarship (Undergraduate/Scholarship) [10629]

Samfund grants (Other/Grant) [9793]

Samsung American Legion Scholarship (Undergraduate/Scholarship) [1073]

San Angelo Area Foundation Scholarship (All/Scholarship) [9795]

The San Diego Foundation Community Scholarship I (Undergraduate/Scholarship) [9848]

The San Diego Foundation Community Scholarship II (Undergraduate/Scholarship) [9849]

San Pasqual Academy Scholarship (Undergraduate/Scholarship) [9850]

Sand Plains & Lewis A. and Gurry F. Batten Education Scholarship (Undergraduate/Scholarship) [8877]

Sandra Jo Hornick Scholarship (Undergraduate/Scholarship) [6394]

Sandra Sebrell Bailey Scholarship (Undergraduate/Scholarship) [4043]

Sarah Shinn Marshall Scholarship (Undergraduate, Graduate/Scholarship) [4013]

Frank Sarli Memorial Scholarship (Undergraduate/Scholarship) [7820]

SARP Professional Development Grant (Professional development/Grant) [9882]

Saskatchewan Government Insurance Anniversary Scholarships (Undergraduate/Scholarship) [9888]

Saskatchewan Government Insurance Corporate Scholarships (Undergraduate/Scholarship) [9889]

Saskatchewan School Boards Association Graduate Student Award (Graduate/Award) [9926]

Saskatchewan Trucking Association Scholarships (Undergraduate/Scholarship) [9928]

Roger C. Sathre Memorial Scholarship Fund (Graduate/Scholarship) [5680]

Saunders – Kevin Saunders Wheelchair Success Scholarship (Undergraduate/Scholarship) [3486]

Save Mart Legacy Scholarships (Undergraduate/Scholarship) [2808]

John A. Savoy Scholarship Fund (Undergraduate/Scholarship) [4605]

S.C. Johnson, A Family Company Scholarship Fund (Undergraduate/Scholarship) [3402]

SCC Full-Time Continuing Student Scholarship (Undergraduate/Scholarship) [10062]

SCC Part-Time Continuing Student Scholarship (Undergraduate/Scholarship) [10063]

Schmidt Kramer Annual Scholarship For Academic Excellence (Undergraduate/Scholarship) [9936]

Scholarship Award of the Bell Aliant Pioneer Volunteers (Graduate/Scholarship) [3050]

Scholarship Contest from Dealroom (College, University/Scholarship) [3981]

Scholarship for Disabled Veterans (High School, Community College, Four Year College, Graduate, Professional development, Vocational/Occupational/Scholarship) [6702]

Scholarship Foundation of Santa Barbara General Scholarship Program (Undergraduate, Graduate/Scholarship) [9951]

The Scholarship Foundation of Wakefield Scholarships (All/Scholarship) [9955]

Scholarship for Indigenous Students (Undergraduate/Scholarship) [8148]

Scholarship-Leadership Awards (Undergraduate/Scholarship) [6499]

Scholarship Program By My Weather Analyser (Postgraduate, Undergraduate/Scholarship) [7525]

Scholarship for Students of Colour (Undergraduate/Scholarship) [8149]

School Nutrition Association of Kansas Education Scholarship (Undergraduate/Scholarship) [9965]

Schools first Federal Credit Union Scholarship (Undergraduate/Scholarship) [9602]

Alice Southworth Schulman, Class of 1954, Simmons Scholarships for Unitarian Universalist Women (Undergraduate/Scholarship) [11255]

David and Jinny Schultz Family Scholarship (Undergraduate/Scholarship) [5104]

Evalee C. Schwarz Educational Loans (Undergraduate, Graduate/Loan) [9967]

Science Environment Scholarship by Drones Globe (Undergraduate, Graduate, Postgraduate/Scholarship) [4185]

ScienceSoft Scholarship (Graduate, Undergraduate/Scholarship) [9976]

SCLEOA Scholarships (Undergraduate, Professional development/Scholarship) [10609]

A.J. and Lynda Hare Scribante Scholarship Fund (Undergraduate/Scholarship) [6471]

The SE Rankings Scholarship Program (Undergraduate, Graduate, Professional development/Scholarship) [9992]

Seabee Memorial Scholarship Association Scholarships (Undergraduate/Scholarship) [10231]

Seaman Family Scholarship (Undergraduate/Scholarship) [3487]

Seameo-Vietnam Scholarship Program (Graduate/Scholarship) [4265]

Fred A. Seaton Memorial Scholarship (Undergraduate, Graduate/Scholarship) [2552]

Aaron Seesan Memorial Scholarship Fund (Undergraduate/Scholarship) [10790]

Seldovia Native Association Achievement Scholarships (Undergraduate, Graduate/Scholarship) [9996]

Seldovia Native Association General Scholarships (Undergraduate, Graduate/Scholarship) [9997]

D. Mitchell Self Memorial Scholarship (Undergraduate/Scholarship) [8536]

David W. Self Scholarship (Undergraduate/Scholarship) [11263]

Semple Foundation Scholarship (Undergraduate/Scholarship) [3403]

The Seneca Scholarship (High School, College/Scholarship) [10006]

Archak and Meroum Senekjian Memorial Grant (Undergraduate/Scholarship) [1902]

Senior Master Sergeant William Sowers Memorial Scholarship (Undergraduate/Grant) [114]

Senior Scholar Scholarship Presented by 65Medicare.org (Two Year College, Four Year College/Scholarship) [18]

SeniorAdvice Caregiver Scholarships (Undergraduate/Scholarship) [10008]

SeniorAdvice Volunteer Scholarships (Undergraduate/Scholarship) [10009]

Sentinels of Freedom Scholarship (Advanced Professional/Scholarship) [10011]

Senyk Memorial Scholarship (Undergraduate, Master's/Scholarship) [12368]

SEO Optimizers Scholarships (All/Scholarship) [10015]

Sequoyah Graduate Scholarship (Master's/Scholarship) [2040]

Serena D. Dalton Scholarship (Undergraduate/Scholarship) [12091]

Sertoma Hard of Hearing and Deaf Scholarship *(Undergraduate/Scholarship)* [10020]

ServiceMaster By Glenns Preparation Scholarship *(University, Undergraduate, Vocational/Occupational/Scholarship)* [10022]

ServiceScape Scholarship *(College, University/Scholarship)* [10024]

Servus Credit Union 4-H Scholarship *(College, University, Undergraduate/Scholarship)* [16]

Frank B. Sessa Scholarship *(Professional development/Scholarship)* [2499]

Seth Koehler Central High School *(Undergraduate, Vocational/Occupational/Scholarship)* [5106]

The S.F. Humanities, Inc: Leo Hills Scholarship *(Undergraduate, Graduate/Scholarship)* [6278]

SFP Scholarships *(Undergraduate/Scholarship)* [9947]

Shamsie – Judge Terry Shamsie Scholarship *(Undergraduate/Scholarship)* [3488]

Albert F. Shanker Scholarship *(Undergraduate/Scholarship)* [885]

Ken and Sandy Sharkey Family Scholarship *(Undergraduate/Scholarship)* [5107]

Sharp Criminal Lawyers Autism Scholarship *(College, Undergraduate, Vocational/Occupational/Scholarship)* [10035]

Josephine Kerbey Shaw Memorial Undergraduate Scholarship *(Undergraduate/Scholarship)* [6472]

The Jim Sheerin Scholarship *(Undergraduate/Scholarship)* [7178]

William C. Scheetz Memorial Scholarship *(Undergraduate, Graduate/Scholarship)* [2553]

Susan Goldsmith Shelley Scholarship *(Undergraduate/Scholarship)* [6473]

Robert P. Sheppard Leadership Awards *(High School, College/Scholarship)* [8106]

Sherman L. & Mabel C. Lepard Scholarship *(Undergraduate/Scholarship)* [5181]

Albert and Dorothy Shigekuni Scholarship Fund *(Undergraduate/Scholarship)* [5412]

Lynn Brower Shonk Memorial Scholarship *(Undergraduate/Scholarship)* [6474]

Col. Richard R. (Misty) and Sally Shoop Scholarship *(Undergraduate, Graduate/Scholarship)* [2554]

Shoreline and Lake Forest Park scholarship *(Undergraduate/Scholarship)* [10064]

Shout It Out Scholarship *(Undergraduate, High School/Scholarship)* [11232]

Sigma Diagnostics Student Scholarships *(Undergraduate/Scholarship)* [8114]

Sigma Kappa Foundation Alumnae Continuing Education Scholarship *(Graduate, Undergraduate/Scholarship)* [10121]

Sigma Kappa Foundation Founders' Scholarships *(Undergraduate/Scholarship)* [10123]

Sigma Kappa Foundation Michigan Scholarship *(Undergraduate/Scholarship)* [10124]

Harvey L. Simmons Memorial Scholarships *(Undergraduate/Scholarship)* [9851]

Simms Scholarship *(Undergraduate, Community College/Scholarship)* [8537]

Simon Youth Community Scholarship Program *(Undergraduate/Scholarship)* [10140]

Simonton Windows Scholarship *(Undergraduate/Scholarship)* [8880]

Col. John R. Simpson Memorial Scholarship *(Undergraduate, Graduate/Scholarship)* [2555]

Single Mother Scholarship *(Undergraduate, Graduate, College, University/Scholarship)* [9743]

Aaron B. Singleton Memorial Scholarship *(Undergraduate/Scholarship)* [8538]

Bill Six Memorial Scholarship *(Undergraduate/Scholarship)* [8881]

Sixt Rent a Car Scholarships *(Undergraduate/Scholarship)* [10152]

Skalny Scholarship for Polish Studies *(Undergraduate/Scholarship)* [828]

Ruth Skeeles Memorial Scholarship Fund *(Undergraduate/Scholarship)* [10792]

Francelene Skinner Memorial Scholarships *(Undergraduate/Scholarship)* [6832]

Rand Skolnick Point Scholarship *(Undergraduate, Graduate, Doctorate/Scholarship)* [9231]

Skubiak & Rivas - Justice in Action Scholarship *(College, University, Vocational/Occupational, Undergraduate/Scholarship)* [10165]

The Skylight Effect Scholarship Contest *(Undergraduate, Graduate/Scholarship)* [10167]

SLEAMC Scholarships *(Graduate, Undergraduate/Scholarship)* [10045]

Robert W. Sledge Fellowships *(Graduate/Fellowship)* [380]

Sleeping Angels Co. Scholarships *(College, University/Scholarship)* [10169]

SMA Alumni Foundation Legacy Scholarship Program *(Other/Scholarship)* [10816]

SMA Foundation Scholarship Fund *(Undergraduate/Scholarship)* [10707]

SmartMeasurement's Dream for a Better Future: Student Scholarship *(High School, Vocational/Occupational, College, University, Undergraduate/Scholarship)* [10173]

Smartways Marketing Scholarship *(Undergraduate, Postdoctorate/Scholarship)* [10175]

Smiley Elementary School PTA Scholarship - Beverly Roberts Memorial *(Undergraduate/Scholarship)* [9603]

Eva Smith Bursary *(Postgraduate/Scholarship)* [6220]

Ryan and Jamie Smith Essay Contest *(Graduate, Postgraduate/Scholarship)* [10179]

Gladys Ann Smith Greater Los Angeles Women's Council Scholarship *(Undergraduate/Scholarship)* [8175]

James George Smith Memorial Scholarship *(Undergraduate, Graduate/Scholarship)* [2556]

Brian Smith Memorial Scholarships *(Undergraduate/Scholarship)* [2669]

J. Craig and Page T. Smith Scholarship *(Undergraduate/Scholarship)* [10186]

Richard S. Smith Scholarships *(Undergraduate/Scholarship)* [11264]

Smith's Personal Best Scholarships *(Undergraduate/Scholarship)* [9423]

The SMPE NY Scholarship Loan Program *(Undergraduate/Scholarship, Loan)* [10421]

SMUD Powering Futures Scholarship *(Undergraduate, Two Year College, University/Scholarship)* [10233]

Smyth Family Scholarship *(Undergraduate, University, College, Vocational/Occupational/Scholarship)* [12372]

Gladys Snauble Scholarship *(Undergraduate/Scholarship)* [5182]

SNMMI-TS Bachelor's Degree Completion Scholarships *(Undergraduate/Scholarship)* [10442]

Boleslaw & Irena Sobczak Scholarships *(Undergraduate/Scholarship)* [9678]

Sobeys & Empire Work Experience & Scholarship Program - Future Leaders Awards *(Other/Scholarship)* [10239]

Society of Allied Weight Engineers Scholarships *(Undergraduate/Scholarship)* [10268]

Softer H2O Scholarship Program *(Undergraduate, Graduate/Scholarship)* [10572]

Dale and Betty George Sola Scholarships *(Undergraduate/Scholarship)* [4219]

Solvable.com Debt-Free Scholarship *(Two Year College, College, University, Undergraduate/Scholarship)* [10584]

David C. Sommerville Memorial Scholarship *(Undergraduate, Graduate/Scholarship)* [9852]

Sonja S. Maguire Outstanding Scholastic Achievement Awards *(Graduate, Undergraduate/Scholarship)* [10897]

Soroptimist International of Chambersburg Fund *(Undergraduate/Scholarship)* [4783]

Soroptimist International of Redlands Scholarship *(Undergraduate/Scholarship)* [9604]

Paul & Daisy Soros Fellowships *(Graduate/Fellowship)* [10597]

SORP Student Conference Scholarship *(Graduate, Undergraduate/Scholarship)* [10454]

South Central Modern Language Association Fellowships *(Doctorate, Postdoctorate/Fellowship)* [8383]

South Coast High School Senior Honors Scholarship Program *(Graduate/Scholarship)* [9953]

South Jersey Golf Association Scholarships *(Undergraduate/Scholarship)* [10627]

South Kentucky RECC High School Senior Scholarship Program *(Undergraduate/Scholarship)* [10630]

Southern Scholarship Foundation Scholarships *(Undergraduate, Graduate, Postgraduate/Scholarship)* [10666]

Southwest Florida Community Foundation College Assistance Scholarships *(Undergraduate/Scholarship)* [10703]

Southwest Florida Deputy Sheriffs Association Fund *(Undergraduate/Scholarship)* [10704]

Southwest Native-American Foundation Scholarships *(Undergraduate, University, Four Year College/Scholarship)* [10709]

SouthWest Sun Solar $500 Scholarship *(Undergraduate/Scholarship)* [10711]

Sovereign Nations Scholarships *(Undergraduate/Scholarship)* [984]

Kathy Spadoni Memorial Scholarships *(Graduate/Scholarship)* [9313]

Nathan Sparks Memorial Scholarship *(Undergraduate/Scholarship)* [3664]

Phillip A. Spiegel IASP Congress Trainee Scholarship *(Graduate, Undergraduate/Scholarship)* [5945]

The Lawrence Alan Spiegel Remembrance Scholarship *(Undergraduate/Scholarship)* [5546]

The Spirit Square Center for Arts and Education Scholarship Fund *(Undergraduate/Scholarship)* [4754]

Spokeo Connections Scholarships *(Undergraduate/Scholarship)* [10733]

Spouse Tuition Aid Loan Program (STAP) *(Undergraduate, Graduate/Loan)* [8181]

SPROWT Scholarship for Women *(Undergraduate/Scholarship)* [5201]

The Square Up Scholarship Program *(Two Year College, Undergraduate, Vocational/Occupational, Four Year College/Scholarship)* [6616]

SREB-State Doctoral Scholars Program - Dissertation Award *(Doctorate/Scholarship, Award)* [10663]

SSOC Scholarship *(Undergraduate/Scholarship)* [9930]

The Charles B. Staat Memorial Scholarship *(Graduate/Scholarship)* [10741]

Stand Watie Scholarship *(Undergraduate/Scholarship)* [10588]

Alexander Standish Memorial Scholarship *(Professional development/Scholarship)* [3749]

Lasek Stanisław and Aniela Scholarship *(Undergraduate/Scholarship)* [9679]

A.R.O.Y. Stanitz Scholarships *(Undergraduate/Scholarship)* [1370]

Stanley Moore FUI Foundation Regional Scholarships *(Four Year College, High School, Two Year College/Scholarship)* [8464]

Stanley Moore National Scholarships *(Undergraduate/Scholarship)* [8465]

Minnie Patton Stayman Scholarships *(Undergraduate/Scholarship)* [8968]

Steele Family Memorial Scholarship *(Undergraduate, Master's/Scholarship)* [12373]

Stella B. Johnson Scholarship *(Undergraduate/Scholarship)* [12092]

Stephen J. Brady Stop Hunger Scholarships *(Undergraduate/Scholarship)* [636]

Stephen Lankester Scholarship *(Undergraduate/Scholarship)* [5184]

Stephen T. Marchello Scholarship *(Graduate/Scholarship)* [7030]

H. H. Stephenson, Jr. Oxford Cup Scholarship *(Undergraduate, Graduate/Scholarship)* [2557]

Hugh E. Stephenson, Jr. Oxford Cup Scholarship *(Undergraduate, Graduate/Scholarship)* [2558]

Elizabeth Coulter Stephenson Scholarships *(Undergraduate/Scholarship)* [4044]

Sterbenz-Ryan Scholarship *(Undergraduate, Vocational/Occupational/Scholarship)* [9778]

Steven L. Coffey Memorial Scholarship *(Undergraduate/Scholarship)* [4259]

Richie Stevenson Scholarship Fund *(Undergraduate/Scholarship)* [3645]

Mary Stewart and William T. Covington, Jr. Scholarship Fund *(Undergraduate/Scholarship)* [4755]

Dell Chenoweth Stifel Scholarship *(Graduate/Scholarship)* [6476]

The Richard Stockton College of New Jersey Foundation Alumni Association Graduate Awards *(Graduate/Scholarship)* [10848]

Glenna Stone Memorial Scholarship *(Undergraduate/Scholarship)* [2999]

Stop-Painting.com Scholarships *(Undergraduate/Scholarship)* [5791]

Stout Law Firm Family Matters Scholarship *(College, University, Vocational/Occupational, Undergraduate/Scholarship)* [10854]

Mark and Karla Stuart Family Scholarship *(Undergraduate/Scholarship)* [9854]

Student Essay Contest *(High School/Prize)* [1683]

Student Loan Relief Scholarship *(All/Scholarship)* [7445]

Student Research Foundation Personal Achievement Scholarship *(Undergraduate/Scholarship)* [4309]

Student Travel Grant *(Undergraduate/Grant)* [7361]

Students of History Scholarship *(Undergraduate/Scholarship)* [10869]

Study.com CLEP Scholarship *(Other/Scholarship)* [10871]

Study.com Scholarship Florida Students *(Undergraduate, College/Scholarship)* [10872]

Study.com Scholarship Texas Students *(Undergraduate, College/Scholarship)* [10873]

Stultz Scholarship *(Undergraduate/Scholarship)* [12093]

Subic Bay-Cubi Point Scholarships *(Undergraduate/Scholarship)* [8176]

Substance Abuse and Mental Health Awareness in Veterans Scholarship *(Undergraduate, Graduate/Scholarship)* [4187]

Sugar Spun Scholarship *(Undergraduate, Graduate/Scholarship)* [10875]

Phil Sullivan Scholarships *(Undergraduate/Scholarship)* [9314]

Summer Scholarship *(All/Scholarship)* [7446]

Summer Scholarships in Epidemiology *(Undergraduate/Scholarship)* [3951]

Summerside-Natick International Friendship Hockey Fund *(Undergraduate/Scholarship)* [3706]

Superpower Scholarship *(Undergraduate, High School/Scholarship)* [11233]

The Sure Oak Scholarship *(College, University/Scholarship)* [10883]

SuretyBonds.com Small Business Scholarship *(Undergraduate/Scholarship)* [10887]

The Susan Kelly Power and Helen Hornbeck Tanner Fellowship *(Doctorate, Postdoctorate/Fellowship)* [8384]

Susan Thompson Buffett Foundation Scholarship *(Undergraduate, Two Year College/Scholarship)* [2739]

Sussman-Miller Educational Assistance Award Program *(Undergraduate/Scholarship)* [323]

SUVCW Scholarships *(Undergraduate/Scholarship)* [10595]

Sweep All Scholarship *(College, University/Scholarship)* [10893]

Sweet and Simple Scholarship *(Undergraduate, High School/Scholarship)* [11234]

Jeffrery Tyler Sweitzer Wrestling Memorial Scholarship Fund *(Undergraduate/Scholarship)* [10795]

Timothy S. Sweterlitsch Memorial Scholarship Fund *(Undergraduate/Scholarship)* [10796]

Symee Ruth Feinberg Memorial Scholarship Fund *(Undergraduate/Scholarship)* [5345]

Hazaros Tabakoglu Scholarship Fund *(Undergraduate/Scholarship)* [8309]

TACL-LA Taiwanese American Community Scholarship (TACS) *(Undergraduate/Scholarship)* [10911]

TACS/A. Bragas and Associates Student Scholarships *(Undergraduate/Scholarship)* [10972]

TACS/Texas Tech University K-12 *(Undergraduate/Scholarship)* [10973]

Tacy Anna Smith Memorial Scholarship Endowment Fund *(Undergraduate/Scholarship)* [4757]

The Donald H. Bernstein and John B. Talbert Jr. Scholarship *(Undergraduate/Scholarship)* [4758]

Tall Awareness Scholarships *(Graduate/Scholarship)* [9425]

Tall Clubs International Student Scholarships *(Undergraduate/Scholarship)* [10915]

TANA Foundation Graduate Scholarships *(Graduate/Scholarship)* [10953]

Tanna H. Schulich MBA Entrance Scholarship *(Graduate/Scholarship)* [12261]

Ryan "Munchie" Taylor Memorial Scholarships *(Undergraduate/Scholarship)* [6944]

TCA-ACBH Scholarship to Turkey Program *(Undergraduate/Scholarship)* [86, 11142]

TCA Scholarship Fund *(Undergraduate/Scholarship)* [11121]

TCA-UMD Scholarship to Turkey Program *(Undergraduate/Scholarship)* [11143]

TCATA College Scholarship Fund *(Undergraduate/Scholarship)* [11004]

TeamMates Mentoring Program Scholarship *(Undergraduate/Scholarship)* [5125]

Technical, vocational or associate's degree programs *(Undergraduate/Scholarship)* [10621]

Technical Scholarship *(Undergraduate/Scholarship)* [8592]

Technical Women's Organization Education Scholarship *(Advanced Professional, Graduate/Scholarship)* [10933]

Technology - Students Scholarship Program *(College, University/Scholarship)* [4246]

Ted Ousley Scholarship Endowment Fund *(Undergraduate/Scholarship)* [4759]

Teddy Wilburn Scholarship Fund *(Undergraduate/Scholarship)* [3646]

Telecommunications Association of Michigan - Category II - IV Scholarship *(Undergraduate/Scholarship)* [10944]

Telluride Association Summer Program Scholarships *(Undergraduate/Scholarship)* [10946]

Tennessee Learner's Scholarship *(College, High School/Scholarship)* [3888]

Tennessee Trucking Foundation Scholarship Fund *(Undergraduate/Scholarship)* [3647]

Texas Scholarship of Academic Excellence *(Undergraduate, Graduate/Scholarship)* [1708]

Texas Telephone Association Foundation Scholarships *(Undergraduate/Scholarship)* [11002]

Text=Wrecks Scholarship *(Graduate, College/Scholarship)* [4968]

TFC Edward A. Plank, Jr. Memorial Scholarship *(Undergraduate/Scholarship)* [3579]

ThanksUSA Scholarship *(Undergraduate, Vocational/Occupational/Scholarship)* [11006]

Elizabeth R. Thomas Alumni Nursing Scholarship *(Undergraduate/Scholarship)* [10065]

Thomas Arkle Clark Scholar-Leader of the Year *(Graduate, Undergraduate/Scholarship)* [9092]

Barbara Thomas Bursary *(Undergraduate/Award)* [6221]

Thomas D. Coffield Scholarship *(Undergraduate/Scholarship)* [5185]

Thomas E. Shown, M.D. Memorial Scholarship *(Undergraduate/Scholarship)* [12094]

Thomas J. Emery Memorial Fund Scholarship *(Undergraduate/Scholarship)* [3404]

Thomas J. Watson Fellowship *(Undergraduate/Fellowship)* [11939]

C.R. Thomas Scholarship *(Undergraduate/Scholarship)* [8882]

Karen Thompson Memorial Scholarship *(Undergraduate, Community College/Scholarship)* [8539]

Katrina Thompson Scholarship *(Community College, College, University, Undergraduate, Vocational/Occupational/Scholarship)* [9856]

Matilda B. Thompson Scholarship *(Undergraduate/Scholarship)* [5555]

Thornberg/Havens Scholarship *(Undergraduate/Scholarship)* [4045]

Arthur A. Thovmasian, Jr. Memorial Grant *(Undergraduate/Scholarship)* [1904]

The Thurgood Marshall College Fund *(Undergraduate/Scholarship)* [10856]

Dorothy J. Thurston Graduate Scholarship *(Undergraduate/Scholarship)* [5186]

Tibor T. Polgar Fellowship *(Graduate, Undergraduate/Scholarship)* [5613]

Tien Bui Memorial Scholarship *(Undergraduate/Scholarship)* [12095]

Tillman Scholars Program *(Undergraduate, Graduate/Scholarship)* [11036]

The Tingen & Williams Undergraduate Scholarship *(Undergraduate/Scholarship)* [11040]

Titan Web Agency Bi-Annual Scholarship Program *(Community College, Four Year College, Two Year College/Scholarship)* [11042]

T.L. Conlan Scholarship Fund *(Undergraduate/Scholarship)* [3405]

Tobi's Scholarship *(Undergraduate/Scholarship)* [11044]

Mario J. Tocco Hydrocephalus Foundation Scholarships *(Undergraduate/Scholarship)* [5667]

Michael W. Toennis Scholarship *(Undergraduate, Graduate/Scholarship)* [2559]

Tom Gifford Scholarship *(Undergraduate/Scholarship)* [5112]

Tommy Douglas Scholarship *(Undergraduate/Scholarship)* [8150]

TonaLaw Veteran's Scholarship *(Undergraduate, Graduate, Professional development, Vocational/Occupational/Scholarship)* [11050]

Took Trust Point Scholarship *(Undergraduate, Graduate/Scholarship)* [9232]

The Toolsy Scholarship: The Importance of Craftship *(All/Scholarship)* [11052]

Top Ten List Scholarship *(Undergraduate, High School/Scholarship)* [11235]

Top10bestbudget Annual Scholarship Award *(Undergraduate, Postgraduate/Scholarship)* [10013]

Toptal Scholarships for Women *(All/Scholarship)* [11054]

TopTechGiant $1,000 Scholarship *(Two Year College, Community College, Undergraduate, Graduate/Scholarship)* [11056]

Ferdinand Torres Scholarships *(Graduate, Undergraduate/Scholarship)* [920]

Dr. Harry Jeffrey Tourigian Memorial Grant *(Undergraduate/Scholarship)* [1905]

The Town and County Club Scholarship *(Undergraduate/Scholarship)* [5346]

Toyota Point Scholarship *(Undergraduate, Graduate, Doctorate/Scholarship)* [9233]

TRALA Industry Scholarship Awards *(Undergraduate/Scholarship)* [11119]

Vera Tran Memorial Scholarships *(Undergraduate/Scholarship)* [11825]

Transatlantic Fellows Program *(Other/Fellowship)* [4947]

The TranscriptionServices.com Scholarship *(Undergraduate/Scholarship)* [11073]

Traub-Dicker Rainbow Scholarships (TDRS) *(Undergraduate/Scholarship)* [10851]

Travis Dunning Memorial Scholarship *(Undergraduate/Scholarship)* [9427]

Trelut Family Legacy Scholarship *(Undergraduate/Scholarship)* [2809]

Tri Delta Alpha Eta Scholarships *(Undergraduate/Scholarship)* [4014]

Tri Delta Alpha Rho Leadership Scholarships *(Undergraduate/Scholarship)* [4015]

Triadex Scholarship *(Undergraduate/Scholarship)* [11106]

Tim Triner Letter Carriers Scholarship Fund *(Undergraduate/Scholarship)* [10798]

Trinity Scholars Program *(Undergraduate/Scholarship)* [11113]

Tristin Memorial Scholarships *(Undergraduate, Vocational/Occupational/Scholarship)* [6756]

Trolling Battery Scholarship *(Undergraduate, Graduate/Scholarship)* [11117]

Jo Anne J. Trow Undergraduate Scholarships *(Undergraduate/Scholarship)* [393]

Truckload Carriers Association Scholarships *(Undergraduate/Scholarship)* [11122]

Trudeau Fellowships - Regular *(Advanced Professional, Professional development/Fellowship)* [11125]

Tschudy Family Scholarship *(Undergraduate/Scholarship)* [5687]

Tsutako Curo Scholarship *(Undergraduate/Scholarship)* [9428]

Hans Turley Prize in Queer Eighteenth-Century Studies *(Graduate, Other/Prize)* [1440]

Jeff Turner-Forsyth Audubon Society Scholarship *(Undergraduate/Scholarship)* [12096]

Mark and Vera Turner Memorial Scholarships (Undergraduate/Scholarship) [6833]

Scott Alan Turner Personal Finance Scholarship (High School, Undergraduate/Scholarship) [11152]

Tuscumbia Kiwanis Club Scholarship (Undergraduate/Scholarship) [8540]

U-M Alumnae Club (University of Michigan) Scholarships (Undergraduate/Scholarship) [5187]

UAA Alumni Association Scholarship (Undergraduate/Scholarship) [11497]

UAF Alumni Association Scholarship (Undergraduate/Scholarship) [11520]

UC MEXUS - CICESE Graduate Student Short-Term Research and Non-degree Training (Graduate/Grant) [11550]

UC MEXUS-CONACYT Collaborative Grants (Professional development/Grant) [11551]

UC MEXUS-CONACYT Postdoctoral Research Fellowships (Postdoctorate/Fellowship) [11553]

UC MEXUS Scholars in Residence Program - Recent University Graduates (Postgraduate, Graduate/Scholarship) [11556]

UC MEXUS Scholars in Residence Program - Visiting Faculty (Professional development/Scholarship) [11557]

UFCW Local Union Scholarships (All/Scholarship) [11261]

Ugly Sweater Scholarship (High School, College, University, Graduate, Undergraduate/Scholarship) [9957]

UNC-CGI C.V. Starr Scholarship (Undergraduate, Graduate/Scholarship) [3217]

Undergraduate Scholarship (Undergraduate/Scholarship) [3285]

The UNH Alumni Association Legacy Scholarship (Undergraduate/Scholarship) [11651]

UNH Parents Association Endowed Scholarship (Undergraduate/Scholarship) [11652]

UNICO Merrimack Valley Scholarships (Graduate/Scholarship) [11219]

Unigo $10K Scholarship (Undergraduate, High School/Scholarship) [11236]

Union of Marash Armenian Student Funds (Undergraduate, Graduate/Scholarship) [11241]

Union Plus Scholarship Program (Undergraduate, Graduate/Scholarship) [11243]

Union Plus Scholarship Program (Undergraduate/Scholarship) [6139]

United Methodist General Scholarships (Undergraduate, Graduate/Scholarship) [4895]

U.S. Air Force ROTC High School Scholarship - Type 2 (High School/Scholarship) [11283]

U.S. Air Force ROTC In-College Scholarships - Type 2 (High School/Scholarship) [11284]

U.S. Bank Scholarships (Undergraduate/Scholarship) [9859]

U.S. Bates Scholarship (Undergraduate/Scholarship) [6140]

U.S. BIA Indian Higher Education Grants (Undergraduate/Grant) [991]

U.S. News Path to College Scholarship (Undergraduate/Scholarship) [11391]

United Way Of Forsyth County Scholarship (Other/Scholarship) [6660]

UnitedAg Scholarship Program (Undergraduate/Scholarship) [11415]

University of Alaska Regents' Scholarship (Undergraduate/Scholarship) [11512]

University Club Lamp of Learning Scholarship (Undergraduate, University/Scholarship) [9860]

University of Louisville Eagle Scout Scholarships (Undergraduate/Scholarship, Award) [7857]

University of Oregon Dean's Scholarships (Undergraduate/Scholarship) [11655]

University of Oregon Diversity Excellence Scholarship (Undergraduate/Scholarship) [11656]

University of Oregon General University Scholarship (Undergraduate, Graduate/Scholarship) [11657]

University of Oregon Presidential Scholarship (Undergraduate/Scholarship) [11658]

University of Puget Sound LGBT Leadership Scholarship (Undergraduate/Scholarship) [9772]

University of Southern Mississippi Eagle Scout Scholarship (Undergraduate/Scholarship) [7858]

University of Toronto Student Union (UTSU) Undergraduate Grant (Undergraduate/Grant) [11702]

University of Wisconsin-Madison Chancellor's Scholarship Program (Undergraduate/Scholarship) [11746]

University of Wisconsin-Madison National Merit Scholarship (Undergraduate/Scholarship) [11747]

Unpakt College Scholarship (Undergraduate, Graduate/Scholarship) [11755]

Urban and Regional Policy Fellowship (Other/Fellowship) [4948]

The Urban Scholarship Fund (Graduate/Scholarship) [10975]

Urgent.ly Driving Transportation Innovation Scholarship (Undergraduate, Graduate, Vocational/Occupational/Scholarship) [11769]

US Bank NA Scholarship Fund (Undergraduate/Scholarship) [3406]

USA/USA-Ukramerazha Scholarships (Undergraduate/Scholarship) [11413]

USAttorneys.com Immigration Scholarships Essay Contest (Undergraduate/Scholarship) [11780]

USAttorneys.com National Scholarships Essay Contest (Undergraduate/Scholarship) [11781]

USAWOASF/Grantham University On-Line Scholarship (Graduate/Scholarship) [11290]

USAWOASF Regular Scholarship (Graduate/Scholarship) [11291]

USC Latino Alumni Association Scholarships (Graduate, Undergraduate/Scholarship) [11783]

USET Scholarship Fund (Undergraduate/Scholarship) [11278]

USHJA Foundation Hamel Scholarship for Further Education (Undergraduate/Scholarship) [11375]

USPAACC Ampcus Hallmark Scholarship (Undergraduate/Scholarship) [11395]

USPAACC College Hallmark Scholarships (Undergraduate/Scholarship) [11396]

USPAACC Denny's Hungry for Education Scholarship (Undergraduate/Scholarship) [11397]

USS Coral Sea - Scholarship Program (Undergraduate/Scholarship) [11785]

USTA Serves College Education Scholarship (Undergraduate/Scholarship) [11405]

USTA Serves College Textbook Scholarship (Undergraduate/Scholarship) [11406]

The Utah Advocates Scholarship (College, University/Scholarship) [88]

Utah Chiefs of Police Scholarship Program (College, Undergraduate, University/Scholarship) [11787]

Utah ROLF Scholarship (Community College/Award) [4367]

Utility Workers Union of America Scholarship Program (Undergraduate/Scholarship) [11789]

UW-Madison GLBT Alumni Council Scholarships (Undergraduate, Graduate/Scholarship) [11749]

V. Thomas Forehand, Jr. Scholarship (Undergraduate/Scholarship) [11717]

V.A. Leonard Scholarship (Graduate, Undergraduate/Scholarship) [399]

Vale Manitoba Operations Post-secondary Scholarship (Undergraduate/Scholarship, Internship) [11421]

Valentine's Day Scholarship (All/Scholarship) [7447]

Vallabhaneni Sukundamma & Lakshmaiah Scholarship (Graduate/Scholarship) [10954]

ValuePenguin Scholarships (Undergraduate/Scholarship) [11791]

Roy Vander Putten (Advanced Professional/Scholarship) [3460]

Keith C. Vanderhyde Scholarship (Undergraduate/Scholarship) [5188]

Vegetarian Resource Group College Scholarship (Undergraduate, High School/Scholarship, Monetary, Award) [11798]

Diana Venable Scholarship (Undergraduate, Community College/Scholarship) [9861]

Helen Veress-Mitchell Scholarship Fund (Undergraduate/Scholarship) [3153]

Chester M. Vernon Memorial Eagle Scout Scholarships (Undergraduate/Scholarship) [7859]

Veteran Benefits Scholarship (Community College, Four Year College, Graduate/Scholarship) [11807]

Veterans of Foreign Wars Scout of the Year (Undergraduate/Scholarship) [7860]

VFW Post 5140/Paul W. Shockley Sr. Memorial Scholarship (Undergraduate/Scholarship) [8541]

Viber Mobile Technology Scholarship (Graduate/Scholarship) [11816]

Victoria Ovis Memorial Scholarship (Undergraduate/Scholarship) [7982]

Village of Mayo Heritage Fund Scholarship (Undergraduate, University, College, Vocational/Occupational/Scholarship) [12383]

Vine Deloria Jr. Memorial Scholarship (Graduate, Professional development/Scholarship) [985]

Virgil K. Lobring Scholarship Program (Undergraduate/Scholarship) [3725]

Virginia Valk Fehsenfeld Scholarship (Undergraduate/Scholarship) [5189]

Gupton A. Vogt Oxford Cup Memorial Scholarship (Undergraduate, Graduate/Scholarship) [2560]

Voice Talent Online Scholarship (College, University, Undergraduate/Scholarship) [11860]

Chad Vollmer Scholarships (Undergraduate/Scholarship) [5191]

W. Eldridge and Emily Lowe Scholarship (Undergraduate, Graduate/Scholarship) [10148]

W. Philip Braender and Nancy Coleman Braender Scholarship Fund (Undergraduate/Scholarship) [5347]

Jane and Gregg Waddill Memorial Adelphe Scholarship (Undergraduate/Scholarship) [6477]

Joseph W. Wade Memorial Scholarship Endowment (Undergraduate, Community College/Scholarship) [8542]

Robert & Barbara Wade Scholarships (Undergraduate/Scholarship) [6834]

WAEPA Scholarship Program (Undergraduate, Vocational/Occupational/Scholarship) [12207]

Wakeford Gelini Driver Safety Scholarship (Undergraduate, Graduate, Vocational/Occupational, College/Scholarship) [11866]

Laramie Walden Memorial Fund (Undergraduate/Scholarship) [4762]

Helen Zick Walker Adelphe Scholarship (Undergraduate/Scholarship) [6478]

Walmart Associate Scholarship (Undergraduate/Scholarship) [11868]

Walta Wilkinson Carmichael Scholarship (Graduate/Scholarship) [10125]

Walter C. Winchester Scholarship (Undergraduate/Scholarship) [5192]

Walter "Doc" Hurley Scholarship Fund of Greater Hartfort (Undergraduate/Scholarship) [5348]

Walter & Elsie Carr Endowed Scholarship (Undergraduate/Scholarship) [6823]

Walter and Lucille Harper Transfer Scholarship (Graduate/Scholarship) [6516]

Walter and Marilyn Bartlett Scholarship Fund (Undergraduate/Scholarship) [3407]

Robert E. Walter Memorial Scholarship (Undergraduate/Scholarship) [6958]

Walter Samek III Memorial Scholarship (Graduate/Scholarship) [3598]

Lynn McNabb Walton Adelphe Scholarhship (Undergraduate/Scholarship) [6479]

War Memorial Doctoral Scholarships (Postgraduate/Scholarship) [7760]

Warren M. Anderson Scholarship (Undergraduate/Scholarship) [5766]

Washington College Grant (SNG) (Undergraduate/Grant) [11919]

Watson-Brown Scholarship (Undergraduate/Scholarship) [11936]

Wayne County Bank Scholarship (Undergraduate/Scholarship) [8543]

Web Design Scholarship (College, University, Undergraduate, Vocational/Occupational, Graduate/Scholarship, Award) [6917]

The Arthur and Lila Weinberg Fellowship for Independent Researchers (Other, Graduate/Fellowship) [8385]

The Bee Winkler Weinstein Scholarship Fund (Undergraduate, Vocational/Occupational/Scholarship) [10852]

Weiss & Paarz Annual Rising Star Scholarship (Undergraduate/Scholarship) [11956]

Weissbuch Family Scholarship (Undergraduate/ Scholarship) [9864]

Wells Fargo Point Scholarship (Undergraduate, Graduate/Scholarship) [9234]

Wells Fargo Scholarship Program for People with Disabilities (Undergraduate/Scholarship) [9944]

Wells Fargo Veterans Scholarship Program (Undergraduate, Graduate, Two Year College, Four Year College/Scholarship) [9945]

Ida B. Wells Graduate Student Fellowship (Graduate/Fellowship) [3831]

Jean Hess Wells Memorial Adelphe Graduate Scholarship (Graduate/Scholarship) [6480]

Jean Hess Wells Memorial Adelphe Scholarship (Undergraduate/Scholarship) [6481]

Donald M. Wells Scholarships (Undergraduate/ Scholarship) [5193]

Peter R. Weitz Prize (Other/Prize) [4949]

Judy Kay Wendland-Young Scholarship (Undergraduate/Scholarship) [6279]

Francis X. Weninger Scholarships (Undergraduate/ Scholarship) [12226]

John R. and Joan F. Werren Scholarships Fund (Undergraduate/Scholarship) [10801]

Wesley C. Cameron Scholarship (Undergraduate/ Scholarship) [8177]

Wesley R. Habley Summer Institute Scholarships (Professional development/Scholarship) [7569]

West Virginia PTA Scholarship (Undergraduate/ Scholarship) [11973]

Western-Southern Foundation Scholarship (Undergraduate/Scholarship) [3408]

Mary Elizabeth Westpheling - Long Beach (Calif.) Alumnae Association Memorial Scholarhip (Undergraduate/Scholarship) [6482]

WFMC Ride for the Fallen Memorial Scholarship (Two Year College, Four Year College, Vocational/ Occupational/Scholarship) [11872]

Whidbey Island Giving Circle Scholarships (Undergraduate/Scholarship) [9317]

WHIMA Established Professional Development Scholarship (Graduate/Scholarship) [12119]

Law Office of David D. White Annual Traumatic Brain Injury Scholarships (College, Community College, University, Vocational/Occupational/ Scholarship) [6687]

White Collar Defense Diversity Scholarships (Undergraduate, Graduate/Scholarship) [9286]

White Gloves Scholarship (Undergraduate/Scholarship) [12016]

White House Fellows (Other/Fellowship) [9271]

Bob Evans And Wayne White Scholarship (Graduate, High School/Scholarship) [4708]

Whitehorse Business & Professional Women's Club Bursary (Undergraduate, University, College, Vocational/Occupational/Scholarship) [12387]

Whitehorse Glacier Bears Swim Club Scholarship (Undergraduate, University, College, Vocational/ Occupational/Scholarship) [12389]

Whitehorse Shotokan Karate Club Scholarship (Undergraduate, Master's/Scholarship) [12390]

Ann Cook Whitman Scholarships for Perry High School (Undergraduate/Scholarship) [4964]

Why Decor Matters Scholarship (Undergraduate/ Scholarship) [10713]

Why Get Your Blue On? Video Scholarships (Graduate, Undergraduate/Award, Scholarship) [11997]

Wicomico High School Class of '55 Schloarship (Undergraduate/Scholarship) [3580]

WIEA Scholarships (Doctorate, Graduate, Undergraduate, Vocational/Occupational, Master's, Doctorate/Scholarship) [12121]

Elmo Wierenga Alumni Scholarship (Undergraduate/ Scholarship) [5194]

Elie Wiesel Prize in Ethics (Undergraduate/Prize, Award) [12022]

WIGA College Scholarships (Postgraduate, Graduate, Undergraduate/Scholarship) [11894]

Hair Loss Scholarship (College, University, Undergraduate, Graduate, Two Year College, Vocational/Occupational/Scholarship) [12024]

The Fred C. Wikoff Jr. Scholarship (Undergraduate, Vocational/Occupational/Scholarship) [4763]

William A. Friedlander Scholarship Fund (Undergraduate/Scholarship) [3409]

William and Beatrice Kavanaugh Memorial Scholarship (Graduate/Scholarship) [6211]

William "Buddy" Sentner Scholarship Award (Undergraduate, High School/Scholarship) [629]

William and Clara Bryan Scholarship Fund (Undergraduate/Scholarship) [3648]

William F. Vilas Merit Scholarship (Undergraduate/ Scholarship) [11752]

William H. Andrews/HAWS Scholarship (Undergraduate/Scholarship) [12098]

William H. Davis, Jr. Scholarship (Undergraduate/ Scholarship) [3599]

William J. Rielly/MCURC Scholarship Fund (Undergraduate/Scholarship) [3410]

William J. Yankee Memorial Scholarship (Undergraduate/Scholarship, Monetary, Recognition) [1263]

William R. Bowen Scholarship (Undergraduate/ Scholarship) [3581]

William T. Burbage Family Memorial Scholarship (Undergraduate/Scholarship) [3582]

William T. Hartzell Memorial Scholarship (Undergraduate/Scholarship) [9605]

Mary Katherine "Kathy" Williamson Scholarship Fund (Undergraduate/Scholarship) [3665]

Wilma Sackett Dressel Scholarship (Undergraduate/ Scholarship) [10126]

The Ronald P. Wilmot Scholarship (Undergraduate, Graduate/Scholarship) [6280]

Dr. Alice E. Wilson Awards (Master's, Doctorate/ Fellowship) [2976]

Bob Wilson Legacy Scholarships (Undergraduate/ Scholarship) [2810]

Wirefly.com Scholarhip: Wireless Technology and Society (Undergraduate, Graduate/Scholarship) [12107]

Wisconsin Lawton Minority Retention Grants (Undergraduate/Grant) [11753]

W. L. Shattuck Scholarship (Undergraduate, Graduate, High School/Scholarship) [5681]

Woksape Oyate: "Wisdom of the People" Distinguished Scholars Awards (Undergraduate/Grant) [986]

Nona Hobbs Wolfe Memorial Scholarship (Undergraduate/Scholarship) [6483]

Woman's Club of Nashville Scholarship Endowment Fund (Undergraduate/Scholarship) [3649]

Women in Coaching National Coaching Institute Scholarships (Undergraduate/Scholarship) [3448]

Women In Rural Electrification Scholarships (W.I.R. E.) (Undergraduate/Scholarship) [10631]

Women's Army Corps Veterans Association Scholarships (Undergraduate/Scholarship) [12153]

Women's Club of Grand Haven Scholarship (Undergraduate/Scholarship) [5114]

Women's Overseas and Service League Scholarships for Women (Undergraduate/Scholarship) [12168]

Wood County Technical/Caperton Center Scholarship (Undergraduate/Scholarship) [8889]

Rolla F. Wood Graduate Scholarships (Graduate, Undergraduate/Scholarship) [9105]

Woodex Bearing Company Scholarship (Undergraduate/Scholarship) [4921]

Woodrow Wilson International Center for Scholars Fellowships (Doctorate, Postdoctorate/Fellowship) [12043]

Betsy B. Woodward Scholarships (Undergraduate/ Scholarship) [2182]

Woodward Trustees Foundation Scholarship (Undergraduate/Scholarship) [3411]

Wyman and Cleo Woodyard Family Scholarship (Undergraduate, University, College/Scholarship) [5126]

Worthy Women's Professional Studies Scholarship (Vocational/Occupational/Scholarship) [12212]

Wozumi Family Scholarships (Undergraduate/Scholarship) [9318]

Wpromote Digital Marketing Scholarship (Undergraduate, Graduate/Scholarship) [12219]

Writing the Future (Undergraduate, College, University/Scholarship) [4078]

WSAJ American Justice Essay Scholarships (Undergraduate/Scholarship) [11905]

WSAJ Presidents' Scholarships (Undergraduate/ Scholarship) [11907]

WSSA Student Paper Competition (Undergraduate, Graduate/Award, Monetary) [11987]

WYCUP Scholarship Program (Other/Scholarship) [12196]

Margaret Wyeth Scholarships (Undergraduate/ Scholarship) [3698]

Wynne Family Memorial Fund (Undergraduate/ Scholarship) [3412]

Xavier Community-Engaged Fellowships (Undergraduate/Fellowship) [12227]

Xavier University Presidential Scholarships (Undergraduate/Scholarship) [12228]

The YFU Americas Scholarship (Undergraduate/ Scholarship) [12276]

York Graduate Scholarship (YGS) (Master's, Doctorate/Scholarship) [12262]

York Regional Police Scholarships (Undergraduate/ Scholarship) [6222]

You Go Girl! Scholarships (Undergraduate/Scholarship) [9319]

Young Christian Leaders Scholarships (Undergraduate/Scholarship) [12266]

Alma H. Young Emerging Scholar Award (Doctorate/ Award) [11767]

Jeff Young Memorial Scholarship (Undergraduate, Master's/Scholarship) [12395]

Young People For Fellowships (Professional development/Fellowship) [12270]

Donnell B. Young Scholarships (Undergraduate/ Scholarship) [326]

Your Skin Is In College Ambassador Scholarships (Undergraduate/Scholarship) [7245]

Your Time to Climb Scholarship (Undergraduate/ Scholarship) [10958]

Youth Affairs Committee Rising Star Scholarships (Undergraduate/Scholarship) [6223]

Youth Empowerment Summit Scholarships (Undergraduate/Scholarship) [7722]

Youth Forward Scholarship Opportunity (High School, College, University/Scholarship) [7841]

Youth Partners Accessing Capital (YPAC) (Undergraduate/Scholarship) [390]

YWA Foundation Scholarship (Graduate, Undergraduate/Scholarship) [12272]

Y.W.C.A. of Yukon Scholarship (Undergraduate, University, College, Vocational/Occupational/Scholarship) [12399]

Aram Zakian Memorial Fund Scholarship (Undergraduate/Scholarship) [1906]

Araxie Zakian Memorial Grant (Undergraduate/ Scholarship) [1907]

Pedro Zamora Young Leaders Scholarship (Undergraduate, Graduate/Scholarship) [7588]

Charles Zarigian, Esq. Memorial Award (Undergraduate/Scholarship) [1908]

George Zartarian Memorial Grant (Undergraduate/ Scholarship) [1909]

The Zebra "Show Off Your Stripes" Scholarship (Undergraduate, Graduate, Vocational/Occupational, Community College/Scholarship) [12403]

Zelus Recovery College Scholarship (Undergraduate, Graduate/Scholarship) [12407]

Zenko Family Scholarship (Undergraduate/Scholarship) [5115]

Zenon C. R. Hansen Leadership Scholarship (Undergraduate/Scholarship) [7861]

Zeta Chapter Memorial Award (Undergraduate/ Award) [3699]

Zeta Phi Beta General Undergraduate Scholarship (Undergraduate/Scholarship) [12416]

Zeta Phi Beta Sorority General Graduate Fellowships (Graduate/Fellowship) [12417]

Zeta Sigma Project 2000 Scholarship (Undergraduate/Scholarship) [6484]

Zimmermann Scholarship (Graduate/Scholarship) [10898]

Jacob Ziskind Memorial Fund for Upperclassmen (Graduate, Undergraduate/Scholarship) [5746]

Zombie Apocalypse Scholarship (Undergraduate, High School/Scholarship) [11237]

Zumper Apartments Scholarship (College, High School/Scholarship) [12425]

Genetics

BSF Research Grants (Professional development/ Grant) [2441]

Jane Engelberg Memorial Fellowship (JEMF) (Professional development/Fellowship) [8100]

Epilepsy Foundation Pre-doctoral Research Training Fellowships (Graduate/Fellowship) [4423]

Rob and Bessie Welder Wildlife Foundation's graduate research fellowship (Graduate, Master's, Doctorate/Fellowship) [11958]

Geography (See also Cartography/Surveying)

AAG Dissertation Research Grants (Doctorate/ Grant) [563]

Canadian Historical Geography Award (Master's, Graduate, Undergraduate/Prize) [2086]

Graduate and Undergraduate Fellowship Awards (Doctorate, Graduate, Undergraduate/Fellowship, Award) [3195]

CTRF Scholarships for Graduate Study in Transportation (Graduate/Scholarship) [3134]

Darrel Hess Community College Geography Scholarship (Undergraduate/Scholarship) [564]

Excellence in Geographic Information Systems Scholarships (Graduate/Scholarship) [11446]

FIU ForEverglades Scholarship (Graduate, Doctorate, Master's/Scholarship) [4455]

ForEverglades Scholarship (Graduate, Master's, Doctorate/Scholarship) [4456]

Ivan Franko School of Ukrainian Studies Ukraine Travel Award (Undergraduate/Grant) [3028]

John Marshall Everglades Internship Program (Undergraduate/Internship) [4457]

Hans Klinkenberg Memorial Scholarship (Undergraduate/Scholarship) [3022]

NCSS Grant for Geographic Literacy (Other/Grant) [7796]

Eric Niemitalo Scholarship in Earth and Environmental Science (Undergraduate/Scholarship) [10060]

Pi Gamma Mu Scholarships (Graduate/Scholarship) [9160]

Robin P. Armstrong Memorial Prize for Excellence in Indigenous Studies (Graduate/Award, Monetary) [2087]

Geology

Alec Berry Scholarship (Undergraduate, College, Vocational/Occupational/Scholarship) [12286]

Geoffrey Bradshaw Memorial Scholarship (Graduate/Scholarship) [12294]

Gladys Bruce Scholarship (Undergraduate/Scholarship) [12296]

Cameco Corporation Scholarships in the Geological Sciences - Continuing Students (Undergraduate/ Scholarship) [2863]

Cameco Corporation Scholarships in the Geological Sciences - Entering Students (Undergraduate/ Scholarship) [2864]

Graduate and Undergraduate Fellowship Awards (Doctorate, Graduate, Undergraduate/Fellowship, Award) [3195]

Dan Rigel Memorial Educational Grant (Professional development, Advanced Professional/Grant) [2046]

Farouk El-Baz Student Research Grants (Graduate, Undergraduate, Doctorate, Master's/Grant) [4909]

Geological Society of America Graduate Student Research Grants (Doctorate, Graduate/Grant) [4910]

A. Allen Graffham Research Grant (Advanced Professional, Professional development/Grant) [2047]

Frances C. Hidell Scholarship (Undergraduate/ Scholarship) [2144]

HSF/Marathon Oil College Scholarship Program (Undergraduate/Scholarship) [5531]

Harry Johannes Scholarship (Undergraduate, Graduate/Scholarship) [12331]

James McLachlan Scholarship (Undergraduate, University, College/Scholarship) [12345]

Eric Niemitalo Scholarship in Earth and Environmental Science (Undergraduate/Scholarship) [10060]

NPSC Fellowship (Graduate/Fellowship) [5056]

Paleontological Society Student Research Award (Graduate, Undergraduate/Grant) [29]

Patnode Family Scholarship (Undergraduate, University, College, Vocational/Occupational/Scholarship) [12355]

Ralph W. Stone Graduate Fellowship in Cave and Karst Studies (Graduate/Fellowship) [8128]

Student travel awards (Graduate/Award) [30]

René M. Vandervelde Research Grants (Professional development/Grant) [2049]

Wayne-Meador-Elliott Scholarship (Undergraduate/ Scholarship) [8884]

Geophysics (See also Physics)

CfA Postdoctoral Fellowship (Postdoctorate/Fellowship) [5357]

Clay Postdoctoral Fellowship (Postdoctorate/Fellowship) [5358]

CSEG Scholarship Trust Fund (Graduate, Undergraduate/Scholarship) [3116]

Frances C. Hidell Scholarship (Undergraduate/ Scholarship) [2144]

HSF/Marathon Oil College Scholarship Program (Undergraduate/Scholarship) [5531]

SAO Predoctoral Fellowship (Graduate/Fellowship) [5359]

Geosciences

AWG Minority Scholarship (Undergraduate/Scholarship) [2313]

Chrysalis Scholarship (Graduate/Scholarship) [2314]

AWG Maria Luisa Crawford Field Camp Scholarships (Undergraduate/Scholarship) [2315]

EAPSI Fellowships (Doctorate, Graduate/Fellowship, Award) [8067]

HGS Foundation Undergraduate Scholarships (Undergraduate/Scholarship) [5597]

Janet Cullen Tanaka Geosciences Undergraduate Scholarship (Undergraduate/Scholarship) [2316]

NDSEG Fellowship (Graduate/Fellowship) [7834]

NMHM Global Volcanism Program for Visiting Scientist/Postdoctoral Fellowships (Postdoctorate, Advanced Professional/Fellowship) [10202]

Glen Ruby Memorial Scholarships (Undergraduate/ Scholarship) [3122]

Shell Incentive Fund Scholarship (Undergraduate/ Scholarship) [10041]

Shell Oil Company Technical Scholarship (Undergraduate/Scholarship) [10042]

Shell Process Technology Scholarships (Undergraduate/Scholarship) [10043]

Society of Exploration Geophysicists Scholarships (Graduate, Undergraduate/Scholarship, Monetary, Award) [10328]

United States Geospatial Intelligence Foundation Graduate Scholarships (Graduate/Scholarship) [11364]

United States Geospatial Intelligence Foundation High School Scholarships (Undergraduate, Doctorate, Graduate, High School/Scholarship) [11365]

United States Geospatial Intelligence Foundation Undergraduate Scholarships (Undergraduate/ Scholarship) [11366]

Geriatric medicine (See Medicine, Geriatric)

German studies (See also Area and ethnic studies)

Leo Baeck Institute - DAAD Fellowships (Doctorate/ Fellowship) [4057]

CJH-NEH Fellowships for Senior Scholars (Doctorate/Fellowship) [3222]

CJH-Prins Foundation Fellowships for Senior Scholars (Doctorate/Fellowship) [3223]

CJH-Prins Foundation Post-Doctoral and Early Career Fellowship for Emigrating Scholars (Professional development, Postdoctorate/Fellowship) [3224]

DAAD Learn German in Germany Grants (Doctorate/Grant) [4058]

German Historical Institute Doctoral and Postdoctoral Fellowships (Doctorate, Postgraduate/Fellowship) [4942]

German Society Scholarships (Undergraduate/ Scholarship) [4951]

German Studies Research Grants (Undergraduate/ Grant) [4062]

Dr. Guido Goldman Fellowships (Postdoctorate/Fellowship) [807]

Hochschulsommerkurse (Undergraduate/Award) [4063]

Dr. Richard M. Hunt Fellowships (Doctorate, Postdoctorate/Fellowship) [808]

Intensive Language Course Grant (Graduate, Undergraduate/Grant) [4064]

Gerontology

AAG Provincial Student Award (Graduate/Award) [246]

AFAR Scholarships for Research in the Biology of Aging (Graduate, Doctorate/Scholarship) [874]

AGS Clinical Student Research Award (Undergraduate/Award) [946]

Alzheimer's/Gerontology Scholarship (Graduate/ Scholarship) [10092]

Ann C. Beckingham Scholarship (Graduate, Other/ Scholarship) [2989]

Annie Kirshenblatt Memorial Scholarship (Graduate, Undergraduate/Scholarship) [11062]

The Paul B. Beeson Emerging Leaders Career Development Award in Aging(K76) (Professional development/Grant) [875, 5310]

Margery Boyce Bursary Award (Graduate/Award, Scholarship) [2893]

The Brookdale Leadership in Aging Fellowship Program (Other/Fellowship) [2713]

CFN Interdisciplinary Fellowships Program (Graduate, Postdoctorate, Advanced Professional/Fellowship) [2982]

CGNA Memorial Scholarship (Graduate, Other/ Scholarship) [2990]

Helene and George Coward Award in Gerontology (Graduate/Award) [11709]

Edmonton Chapter Student Award (Graduate/ Award) [247]

Extendicare Scholarships in Gerontology (Master's/ Scholarship) [3059]

Glenn/AFAR Breakthroughs in Gerontology Awards (Postgraduate/Grant) [876]

Glenn Foundation for Medical Research and AFAR Grants for Junior Faculty (Professional development/Grant) [877]

Centre on Aging Betty Havens Memorial Graduate Fellowship (Graduate, Doctorate, Master's/Fellowship) [11584]

Health and Aging Policy Fellows Program (Advanced Professional, Professional development/ Fellowship) [1255]

Hpgs Graduate Scholarships (Graduate/Scholarship) [5421]

HPGS Undergraduate Scholarships (Undergraduate/ Scholarship) [5422]

Jack MacDonell Scholarship for Research in Aging (Graduate, Doctorate, Master's/Scholarship) [11585]

Donald Menzies Bursary Award (Postgraduate/ Scholarship, Award) [2894]

Esther and Samuel Milmot Scholarship (Graduate, Undergraduate/Scholarship) [11586]

Partners HealthCare Geriatric Psychiatry Fellowship (Professional development/Fellowship) [7140]

Shoshana Philipp (Kirshenblatt) R.N. Memorial Scholarships (Graduate, Undergraduate/Scholarship) [11063]

Schlegel-UW RIA Scholarship (Doctorate/Scholarship) [2895]

Wilfred George Scott Fellowship in Gerontology (Graduate/Fellowship) [11710]

Sigma Kappa Foundation Alzheimer's/Gerontology Scholarship *(Graduate/Scholarship)* [10122]

Student Researcher Award, From the Behavioral Gerontology SIG *(Undergraduate, Graduate/Award)* [2064]

University of Manitoba Centre on Aging Research Fellowship *(Advanced Professional/Fellowship)* [11587]

Virginia M. Smyth Scholarship *(Graduate/Scholarship)* [4930]

Government (See also Political science)

ARS Lazarian Graduate Scholarship *(Graduate, Master's, Doctorate/Scholarship)* [1854]

ASA/NSF/BLS Fellowships *(Graduate/Fellowship, Recognition, Grant)* [1609, 8065, 11343]

Bryce Harlow Fellowship *(Graduate/Fellowship)* [5298]

Congressional Research Grants *(Graduate/Grant)* [4101]

Enid Hall Griswold Memorial Scholarship *(Undergraduate/Scholarship, Award, Monetary)* [8096]

Fellowship on Women & Public Policy *(Graduate/Fellowship)* [11522]

The Judge Ralph Fisch Police Explorer Scholarship Program *(Undergraduate/Scholarship)* [4646]

Gary Merrill Memorial Scholarship Fund *(Undergraduate/Scholarship)* [6979]

George Oliver Benton Memorial Scholarship Fund *(Undergraduate/Scholarship)* [3619]

Conrad N. Hilton Scholarships *(Undergraduate/Scholarship)* [4962]

IAF Fellowships *(Doctorate/Fellowship)* [5883]

John Allen Love Scholarship *(Graduate, Undergraduate/Scholarship)* [11715]

Ray and Kathy LaHood Scholarships for the Study of American Government *(Undergraduate/Scholarship)* [4102]

Mary and Elliot Wood Foundation Graduate Scholarship *(Graduate/Scholarship)* [4744]

MAT Scholarship *(Undergraduate, Vocational/Occupational/Scholarship)* [7406]

Betty Rendel Scholarships *(Undergraduate/Scholarship)* [7886]

USGLC Internships - Government Relations *(Undergraduate, Graduate/Internship)* [11369]

USGLC Internships - Policy *(Undergraduate, Graduate/Internship)* [11371]

Paul A. Volcker Fund *(Undergraduate, Graduate, Doctorate, Professional development/Grant)* [1260]

Women In Defense HORIZONS Scholarship *(Graduate, Undergraduate/Scholarship)* [12133]

Graphic art and design (See also Art)

APC High School Scholarship *(Graduate/Scholarship)* [84]

Paul Arnold Memorial Scholarships *(Other/Scholarship)* [9288]

Cadmus Communications Corporation Graphics Scholarship Endowment Fund *(Undergraduate/Scholarship)* [4722]

ESA Foundation Scholarship *(Undergraduate/Scholarship)* [4394]

The Gallery Collection's Create-A-Greeting-Card Scholarship *(Undergraduate/Scholarship)* [4848]

Graphic Design Scholarships *(Undergraduate, Graduate/Scholarship)* [8411]

Elizabeth Greenhalgh Memorial Scholarships in Journalism, Graphic Arts, or Photography *(Undergraduate/Scholarship)* [12136]

International Foodservice Editorial Council Scholarship *(Graduate/Scholarship)* [6007]

Joanna Townsend Applied Arts Scholarship *(All/Scholarship)* [2129]

Maine Graphic Arts Association Scholarships *(Undergraduate/Scholarship)* [6997]

MHS Andrew Oliver Research Fellowships *(Professional development/Fellowship)* [7152]

PGSF Scholarship *(Undergraduate/Scholarship)* [9332]

Print and Graphics Scholarship Foundation Awards *(Graduate, Undergraduate/Award)* [9330]

Harry V. Quadracci Memorial Scholarship *(Undergraduate, Graduate/Scholarship)* [5209]

Society of Graphic Designers of Canada Adobe Scholarships *(Undergraduate/Scholarship)* [10255]

Society of Graphic Designers of Canada Applied Arts Scholarships *(Undergraduate/Scholarship)* [10256]

Society of Graphic Designers of Canada Veer Scholarships *(Undergraduate/Scholarship)* [10257]

The Jane Suganuma Memorial Scholarship Fund *(Undergraduate, Graduate, University, College, Two Year College/Scholarship)* [5413]

Tag and Label Manufacturers Institute Scholarships - Four-Year Colleges *(Undergraduate/Scholarship)* [10904]

Vectorworks Design Scholarship *(Undergraduate, Graduate/Scholarship)* [11796]

Vision Tech Camps Scholarship *(Community College, Four Year College/Scholarship)* [11854]

Web Design Scholarship *(Undergraduate/Scholarship)* [2665]

Worldstudio AIGA Scholarships *(Graduate, Undergraduate/Scholarship)* [12205]

Greek studies (See also Area and ethnic studies)

Christopher Demetris Memorial Scholarships *(Undergraduate/Scholarship)* [5463]

Dr. Michael Dorizas Memorial Scholarships *(Undergraduate/Scholarship)* [5464]

Hellenic University Club of Philadelphia Founders Scholarship *(Undergraduate/Scholarship)* [5465]

Mary Isabel Sibley Fellowship *(Doctorate/Fellowship)* [9082]

Handicapped

American Speech Language Hearing Foundation General Scholarships *(Graduate, Master's, Doctorate/Scholarship)* [1597]

ASHFoundation Student Research Grant in Audiology *(Doctorate/Grant)* [1606]

Health care services

ABA President's Continuing Education Grant *(Advanced Professional, Professional development/Grant)* [705]

ACMPE Scholarship Fund Program (SFI) *(Graduate, Undergraduate/Scholarship)* [7213]

AHCJ Reporting Fellowships on Health Care Performance *(Other/Fellowship)* [3552]

AHRQ Mentored Clinical Scientist Research Career Development Award *(Doctorate, Master's/Award)* [11325]

Albert W. Dent Graduate Student Scholarship *(Undergraduate/Scholarship)* [763]

American Cancer Society - Postdoctoral Fellowships *(Doctorate/Fellowship)* [715]

Australian-American Health Policy Fellowships *(Doctorate, Graduate/Fellowship)* [3553]

The Ellis Bonner Award *(Graduate/Scholarship)* [7653]

Corris Boyd Scholarship *(Graduate/Scholarship)* [2305]

Dvora Brodie Scholarships *(Graduate, Postgraduate, Undergraduate/Scholarship)* [5447]

Cardiac Health Foundation of Canada Scholarship *(Graduate/Scholarship)* [3158]

Leigh Carter Scholarship Fund *(Undergraduate/Scholarship)* [3606]

Casey Family Services Alumni Scholarship *(Undergraduate, Master's, Vocational/Occupational/Scholarship)* [4693]

CentraState Associated Auxiliaries Scholarship *(Undergraduate/Scholarship)* [3248]

CentraState Healthcare Foundation Health Professions Scholarships *(Undergraduate/Scholarship)* [3250]

CHCI Graduate Fellowship Program *(Graduate, Professional development/Fellowship)* [3746]

CHOIR MD Post-Residency Fellowship in Health Services Research *(Postdoctorate/Fellowship)* [11811]

CTSI Collaborative Translational Pilot Project Program *(Professional development/Grant)* [8356]

David A. Kronick Travelling Fellowship *(Doctorate, Graduate/Fellowship)* [7216]

Deana Kendrick Foundation Scholarship *(Undergraduate/Scholarship)* [6522]

Dr. Kathy Dixon Memorial Scholarship *(Undergraduate, University, College/Scholarship)* [7097]

Donald A. B. Lindberg Research Fellowship *(Doctorate, Graduate/Fellowship)* [7217]

Duluth Building and Construction Trades Council Scholarship Fund *(Graduate/Scholarship)* [4204]

Edwina Foye Award for Outstanding Graduate Student *(Undergraduate, Professional, Graduate/Scholarship)* [4805]

The Eileen J. Smith, R.N. Memorial Scholarship *(Undergraduate/Scholarship)* [6198]

Lee K. Feine Scholarship *(Undergraduate, Graduate/Scholarship)* [7790]

Foster G. McGaw Graduate Student Scholarship *(Graduate/Scholarship)* [764]

Gardner Foundation Education Scholarship *(Professional development/Scholarship)* [5786]

The Florence Gaynor Award *(Graduate/Scholarship)* [7654]

John Glaser Scholarships *(Graduate/Scholarship)* [3506]

Harkness Fellowships in Health Care Policy and Practice *(Doctorate, Graduate/Fellowship)* [3555]

Health and Aging Policy Fellows Program *(Advanced Professional, Professional development/Fellowship)* [1255]

Health Services Research Dissertation Awards *(Doctorate/Award)* [11326]

Healthcare Information Management Systems Scholarships *(Graduate, Postgraduate, Undergraduate/Scholarship)* [5448]

HQF New Quality Professional Grant *(Professional development/Award, Grant)* [7657]

HRET Health Career Scholarships *(Postgraduate, Undergraduate/Scholarship)* [8275]

Gaynold Jensen Education Stipends *(Postdoctorate, Other/Scholarship)* [4084]

Kaiser Permanente Northern California Delivery Science Fellowship Program *(Postgraduate/Fellowship)* [6357]

The Dr. Terry Kavanagh Fellowship *(Graduate/Fellowship)* [3159]

Leslie Baranowski Scholarship for Professional Excellence *(Professional development/Scholarship)* [5787]

Lillie Hope-McGarvey Health Scholarship *(Undergraduate, Vocational/Occupational, Graduate, Master's/Scholarship)* [330]

Robert Mack Scholarships *(Graduate, Undergraduate/Scholarship)* [6956]

Maria Gonzalez Borrero Scholarship Fund *(Undergraduate/Scholarship)* [5338]

Maricopa County Community College District Scholarships (MCCCD) *(Undergraduate/Scholarship)* [7034]

MediaMister $1000 Student Scholarship *(Undergraduate, Graduate/Scholarship)* [7211]

MedicalFieldCareers.com Healthcare Scholarship *(Professional development/Scholarship)* [7227]

NOHIMSS Student Scholarship Program *(Undergraduate, Master's, Doctorate/Scholarship)* [8494]

North Carolina Association of Health Care Recruiters Scholarship *(Undergraduate/Scholarship)* [8429]

Northern California Chapter of HIMSS Scholarships *(Graduate, Postgraduate, Undergraduate/Scholarship)* [5449]

NTHS/HOSA Scholarships *(Undergraduate/Scholarship)* [8140]

NYCT Paid Graduate Student Philanthropy Fellowships - Health and People with Special Needs *(Graduate/Fellowship)* [8308]

Oliver Joel and Ellen Pell Denny Healthcare Scholarship *(Undergraduate/Scholarship)* [12085]

Outlaw Student's Medical Professions Scholarships *(Undergraduate/Scholarship)* [10860]

Paul Tejada Memorial Scholarship (Undergraduate/Scholarship) [6206]

Garry Phillips Scholarship (Undergraduate, University, College, Vocational/Occupational/Scholarship) [12358]

Portuguese American Police Association Scholarships (Undergraduate/Scholarship) [9252]

Reid Hospital Graduate Student Scholarships (Graduate/Scholarship) [11951]

Research-in-Training Grant (Doctorate/Grant) [12029]

Rhea Sourifman Caplin Memorial Scholarship (Undergraduate/Scholarship) [5343]

The Haynes Rice Award (Graduate/Scholarship) [7655]

Robert Wood Johnson Foundation Health Policy Fellows (Advanced Professional, Professional development/Fellowship) [6326]

Robert Wood Johnson Health Policy Fellowships (Advanced Professional, Professional development/Fellowship) [6327]

SALEF Health Career Scholarships (Undergraduate, Graduate/Scholarship) [9791]

Service League Volunteer Scholarships (Undergraduate/Scholarship) [11891]

Pat Shimp Memorial Scholarships (Undergraduate/Scholarship) [8879]

Society for the Arts in Healthcare Student Scholarships (Doctorate, Graduate, Undergraduate/Scholarship) [10281]

Louis Stokes Health Scholars Program (Undergraduate/Scholarship) [3742]

S. Leonard Syme Training Fellowship (Master's, Doctorate/Fellowship) [5877]

Udall Scholarship (Undergraduate/Scholarship) [11533]

Vincent Trotter Health Care Scholarship (Undergraduate/Scholarship) [9862]

The Leon And Margaret Williams Scholarship (Undergraduate/Scholarship) [9866]

David A. Winston Health Policy Scholarship (Graduate/Scholarship) [2307]

Violet Wondergem Health Science Scholarships (Undergraduate/Scholarship) [5195]

Health education

AAHD Scholarships (Graduate, Undergraduate/Scholarship) [568]

Ruth Abernathy Presidential Undergraduate Scholarship (Undergraduate/Scholarship, Fellowship, Award, Monetary) [10347]

ACS/ASA Health Policy and Management Scholarships (Professional development/Scholarship) [1616]

Dr. Andy Anderson Young Professional Awards (Professional development/Award) [9146]

Jane B. Aron Doctoral Fellowship (Doctorate/Fellowship) [7695]

Astra Zeneca Medical Scholarship (Advanced Professional/Scholarship) [8222]

Barbara A. Cooley Master's Scholarship (Master's/Scholarship, Award, Monetary) [10348]

Max Bell Senior Fellow Grants (Advanced Professional/Grant) [2469]

Berton W. Huestis Memorial Scholarship (Advanced Professional/Scholarship) [8224]

BMO Medical Education Scholarship (Advanced Professional/Scholarship) [8225]

Cathy L. Brock Memorial Scholarships (Graduate/Scholarship) [5814]

CIBC Medical Education Scholarships (Advanced Professional/Scholarship) [8226]

Evelyn L. Cockrell Memorial Scholarship (Undergraduate/Scholarship) [10983]

Dr. Frank and Audrey Wanamaker Medical Scholarship (Advanced Professional/Scholarship) [8227]

Dr. Henrik and Wanda Tonning Memorial Scholarship (Advanced Professional/Scholarship) [8228]

Dr. Isaac Keillor Farrer, Advanced Medical Education Scholarship (Advanced Professional/Scholarship) [8229]

Dr. Paul and Gayle Sohi Medical Education Scholarship (Advanced Professional/Scholarship) [8230]

Edwina Foye Award for Outstanding Graduate Student (Undergraduate, Graduate/Scholarship) [4805]

NSPF Ray B. Essick Scholarship Awards (Other/Scholarship) [8135]

Friends of the Christofor Foundation Scholarship (Advanced Professional/Scholarship) [8231]

Full Circle Scholarship (Graduate, Undergraduate/Scholarship) [980, 2042]

Health and Aging Policy Fellows Program (Advanced Professional, Professional development/Fellowship) [1255]

Horizon Health Network Scholarship (Advanced Professional/Scholarship) [8232]

Steven Huesing Scholarships (Graduate, Undergraduate/Scholarship) [4088]

JCC Association Graduate Education Scholarships (Graduate/Scholarship) [6257]

Kaiser Media Fellowships in Health Reporting (Advanced Professional, Professional development/Fellowship) [6355]

Bill Kane Undergraduate Scholarship (Undergraduate/Scholarship, Award, Monetary) [10349]

Karen Schuvie Scholarship (Undergraduate/Scholarship, Loan) [6368]

KHIMA Graduate Scholarship (Graduate/Scholarship) [6369]

David B. Larson Fellowships in Health and Spirituality (Postdoctorate/Fellowship) [6574]

Randall Mathis Scholarship for Environmental Studies Fund (Undergraduate/Scholarship) [1824]

G. William McQuade Memorial Scholarships (Advanced Professional/Scholarship) [8233]

Migrant Health Scholarships (Other/Scholarship) [7749]

Minnesota Health Information Management Association Scholarships (Undergraduate/Scholarship) [7408]

National Swimming Pool Foundation Scholarship Award (Other/Scholarship) [8136]

NB College of Physicians and Surgeons Medical Education Scholarship (Advanced Professional/Scholarship) [8234]

North American Society Fellowship Award (NAS Fellowship) (Professional development/Fellowship) [9147]

PHE Canada Student Awards (Undergraduate/Award) [9149]

R. Tait Mckenzie Award (Professional development/Award) [9150]

RBC Medical Education Scholarship (Advanced Professional/Scholarship) [8235]

The Recovery Village Health Care Scholarship (Undergraduate/Scholarship) [9514]

Regional Development Corporation Scholarship (Advanced Professional/Scholarship) [8236]

Resident Research Grant (Postgraduate, Professional development/Grant) [9158]

Robert R. McCain Memorial Scholarship (Advanced Professional/Scholarship) [8237]

Elliott C. Roberts Scholarships (Graduate/Scholarship) [5815]

SALEF Health Career Scholarships (Undergraduate, Graduate/Scholarship) [9791]

Scotiabank Medical Education Scholarship (Advanced Professional/Scholarship) [8238]

SOPHE/ATSDR Student Fellowships in Environmental Health or Emergency Preparedness (Graduate/Fellowship) [10513]

SOPHE/CDC Student Fellowship in Unintentional Injury Prevention (Doctorate, Master's/Fellowship) [10514]

SOPHE/CDC Student Fellowships in Child, Adolescent and School Health (Doctorate, Graduate, Master's/Fellowship) [10515]

Louis Stokes Health Scholars Program (Undergraduate/Scholarship) [3742]

Sue A. Malone Scholarship (Doctorate, Graduate, Professional development/Scholarship) [6370]

TD Bank Medical Education Scholarship (Advanced Professional/Scholarship) [8239]

Terry Linda Potter Scholarship (Undergraduate/Scholarship) [5111]

TxHIMA HIA-HIT Scholarship (Undergraduate/Scholarship) [10984]

TxHIMA Outstanding Student Scholarship (Undergraduate/Scholarship) [10985]

US Acute Care Solutions Health Information Management Scholarship Fund (Undergraduate/Scholarship) [10799]

Health sciences

AASLD Advanced/Transplant Hepatology Award (Professional development/Award) [644]

AASLD Autoimmune Liver Diseases Pilot Research Award (Graduate, Doctorate, Postdoctorate, Professional development/Award, Grant) [645]

AASLD Clinical, Translational and Outcomes Research Awards (Professional development/Grant) [646]

AASLD NP/PA Clinical Hepatology Fellowship (Professional development/Fellowship) [647]

AASLD Pinnacle Research Award in Liver Disease (Professional development/Award) [648]

AATS Cardiothoracic Surgery Resident Poster Competition (Other/Award) [659]

AATS Perioperative/Team-Based Care Poster Competition (Professional development/Award) [660]

AATS Resident Critical Care Scholarships (Professional development/Scholarship) [661]

AATS/STS Cardiothoracic Ethics Forum Scholarships (Professional development/Scholarship) [662, 10543]

Dr. Anderson Abbott Awards (Undergraduate/Scholarship) [11681]

Afdhal / McHutchison LIFER Award (Postdoctorate, Professional development/Award) [649]

Aiea General Hospital Association Scholarship (Undergraduate, College, Two Year College, University/Scholarship) [5378]

AIHS Graduate Studentships (Master's, Doctorate/Fellowship) [272]

AIHS Postgraduate Fellowships (Postgraduate, Advanced Professional/Fellowship) [273]

ALA Allergic Respiratory Diseases Research Award (Doctorate/Award) [1093]

Alberta Innovates Graduate Student Scholarships (Graduate/Scholarship) [275]

Allied Health Care Professional Scholarship (Undergraduate/Scholarship) [5711]

American Lung Association Biomedical Research Grants (RG) (Doctorate/Grant) [1094]

American Lung Association Clinical Patient Care Research Grants (CG) (Doctorate/Grant) [1095]

American Lung Association Dalsemer Research Grants (DA) (Doctorate/Grant) [1096]

American Lung Association DeSousa Awards (Postgraduate/Award) [1097]

American Lung Association Senior Research Training Fellowships (RT) (Doctorate/Fellowship) [1098]

American Lung Association Social-Behavioral Research Grants (SB) (Doctorate/Grant) [1099]

American Society of Electroneurodiagnostic Technologists Student Education Grants (Undergraduate/Grant) [1981]

ATS Abstract Scholarships (Undergraduate, Graduate, Doctorate/Scholarship) [1621]

Bill Bendiner and Doug Morgenson Scholarship (Undergraduate/Scholarship) [9293]

Body of Young Adult Advisors Scholarship (BOYAA) (Graduate, Master's, Doctorate/Scholarship) [11167]

Burton J. Moyer Memorial Fellowship (Graduate, Undergraduate/Fellowship) [5428]

Joseph R. Calder, Jr., MD Scholarship Fund (Undergraduate/Scholarship) [4586]

Canadian Cancer Society Travel Awards (Doctorate, Master's, Postdoctorate/Award) [2942]

Vyaire Fellowship for Neonatal and Pediatric Therapists (Professional development/Fellowship) [1352]

CDC Steven M. Teutsch Prevention Effectiveness (PE) (Doctorate/Fellowship) [11328]

CentraState Band Aid Open Committee Scholarship (Undergraduate/Scholarship) [3249]

Charles A. King Trust Postdoctoral Research Fellowship (Postdoctorate/Fellowship) [5434]

Clarivate Analytics/MLA Doctoral Fellowship (Doctorate, Graduate/Fellowship) [7215]

Davis Foundation Postdoctoral Fellowships (Doctorate, Master's/Fellowship) [5435]

DCH Freehold Toyota Scholarship (Undergraduate/Scholarship) [3251]

Dr. Ezra Nesbeth Foundation Scholarship (Undergraduate/Scholarship) [6213]

The Eating Recovery Center Foundation Early Career Investigator Grants (Professional development/Grant) [7863]

James Echols Scholarship Award (Undergraduate/Recognition, Award, Scholarship) [2781]

Jeri Eiserman, RRT Professional Education Research Fellowship (Professional development/Fellowship) [1353]

Epilepsy Foundation Health Sciences Student Fellowships (Doctorate, Graduate/Fellowship) [4421]

Fanconi Anemia Research Grants (Postdoctorate, Doctorate/Grant) [4491]

Feeding Hope Fund for Clinical Research Grants (Professional development/Grant) [7864]

Florida Education Fund McKnight Doctoral Fellowship (Graduate/Fellowship) [4629]

George Hi'ilani Mills Scholarship (Graduate/Scholarship) [8925]

Gordon W. and Agnes P. Cobb Scholarship (Undergraduate/Scholarship) [4256]

HLS/MLA Professional Development Grants (Other/Grant) [7218]

Houston/Nancy Holliman Scholarship (Undergraduate/Scholarship) [4036]

HRET Health Career Scholarships (Postgraduate, Undergraduate/Scholarship) [8275]

HRSA Scholarships for Disadvantaged Students (Undergraduate/Scholarship) [11334]

Indian Health Service Professionals Program (Undergraduate/Scholarship) [988]

International Trainee Scholarships (ITS) (Doctorate/Scholarship) [1622]

J. Newell Stannard Fellowship (Graduate, Undergraduate/Fellowship) [5429]

Jerome M. Sullivan Research Fund (Professional development/Fellowship) [1354]

Josephine P. White Eagle Scholar (Undergraduate, Graduate/Scholarship) [5537]

Kenhub Scholarship Program (Undergraduate, Postgraduate/Scholarship) [6524]

John F. Kennedy Scholarship Award (Undergraduate/Recognition, Award, Scholarship) [2782]

KFOC Allied Health Doctoral Fellowships (Doctorate/Fellowship) [6546]

KFOC Allied Health Scholarships (Graduate/Scholarship) [6547]

Robert S. Landauer, Sr. Memorial Fellowship (Graduate, Undergraduate/Fellowship) [5430]

Nesta Leduc Scholarship (Undergraduate, University, College, Vocational/Occupational/Scholarship) [12338]

S. Evelyn Lewis Memorial Scholarships in Medical Health Sciences (Graduate, Undergraduate/Scholarship) [12414]

Lung Cancer Discovery Award (LCD) (Doctorate/Award) [1100]

Lung Health Dissertation Grants (LH) (Doctorate/Grant) [1101]

Marilyn Yetso Memorial Scholarship (Graduate, Master's, Doctorate/Scholarship) [11168]

Olivia M. Marquart Scholarships (Graduate, Master's, Doctorate/Scholarship) [11169]

Medical Scrubs Collection Scholarship (Undergraduate, Graduate/Scholarship) [7225]

Mentored Research Fellowship (Postdoctorate/Fellowship) [7534]

Michael Moody Fitness Scholarship (Undergraduate, Graduate/Scholarship) [7464]

MLA/NLM Spectrum Scholarship (Undergraduate/Scholarship) [7220]

MLA Research, Development, and Demonstration Project Grant (Graduate/Grant) [7221]

MLA Scholarship for Minority Students (Graduate/Scholarship) [7223]

Monaghan/Trudell Fellowships for Aerosol Technique Development (Professional development/Fellowship) [1355]

National Biosafety and Biocontainment Training Program Fellowships (Graduate, Postgraduate/Fellowship) [7716]

NBHRF Bridge Grants (Professional development/Grant) [8213]

NBHRF Establishment Grants (Professional development/Grant) [8215]

NBHRF Health Research Strategic Initiative Grants (Professional development/Grant) [8216]

NLM Associate Fellowship (Postgraduate/Fellowship) [11339]

Helen Woodruff Nolop Scholarships in Audiology and Allied Fields (Graduate/Scholarship) [4040]

Pembroke Center Seed Grants (Professional development/Grant) [2726]

Philips Respironics Fellowships in Mechanical Ventilation (Professional development/Fellowship) [1358]

Philips Respironics Fellowships in Non-Invasive Respiratory Care (Professional development/Fellowship) [1359]

PhRMA Foundation Health Outcomes Pre Doctoral Fellowships (Doctorate/Fellowship) [9063]

PhRMA Foundation Health Outcomes Research Starter Grants (Doctorate/Grant) [9064]

PhRMA Foundation Health Outcomes Sabbatical Fellowships (Postdoctorate, Master's/Fellowship) [9065]

PhRMA Foundation Post Doctoral Health Outcomes Fellowships (Postdoctorate/Fellowship) [9071]

Rehabmart.com $25,000 Scholarship Fund (Undergraduate/Scholarship) [9627]

Richard J. Burk, Jr., Fellowship (Graduate, Undergraduate/Fellowship) [5431]

Robert Browning Scholarships (Undergraduate/Scholarship) [9311]

Robert Gardner Memorial Fellowship (Graduate, Undergraduate/Fellowship) [5432]

Robert Wood Johnson Foundation Health Policy Fellows (Advanced Professional, Professional development/Fellowship) [6326]

Save a Life Scholarship (College, University, Vocational/Occupational, Undergraduate, Graduate/Scholarship) [448]

Charles W. Serby COPD Research Fellowship (Professional development/Fellowship) [1360]

Dr. Robert Norman Shaw Scholarship (Undergraduate/Scholarship) [310]

Louis Stokes Health Scholars Program (Undergraduate/Scholarship) [3742]

Louis Stokes Urban Health Policy Fellows Program (Other/Fellowship) [3743]

Sue A. Malone Scholarship (Doctorate, Graduate, Professional development/Scholarship) [6370]

Sue Fleming Memorial Scholarship for Allied Health (Undergraduate/Scholarship) [2787]

TEVA Canada Survivor Scholarship (Undergraduate, University/Scholarship) [3292]

UMDF Clinical Research Fellowship Training Awards (Professional development/Fellowship) [11266]

Winifred Van Hagen/Rosalind Cassidy Scholarship Award (Undergraduate, Graduate/Recognition, Award) [2783]

Vanier Canada Graduate Scholarships Program (Graduate/Scholarship) [3808]

Washington Hospital Employee Association Scholarship (Undergraduate/Scholarship) [11892]

Health services administration

The Ellis Bonner Award (Graduate/Scholarship) [7653]

Cathy L. Brock Memorial Scholarships (Graduate/Scholarship) [5814]

CDC Steven M. Teutsch Prevention Effectiveness (PE) (Doctorate/Fellowship) [11328]

City of Toronto Scholarships for Aboriginal Health (Graduate, Undergraduate/Scholarship) [11688]

The Florence Gaynor Award (Graduate/Scholarship) [7654]

Foster G. McGaw Scholarship (Undergraduate, Graduate/Scholarship) [2306]

The Haynes Rice Award (Graduate/Scholarship) [7655]

Elliott C. Roberts Scholarships (Graduate/Scholarship) [5815]

Louis Stokes Health Scholars Program (Undergraduate/Scholarship) [3742]

Toronto Rehabilitation Institute Graduate Student Scholarships - Ontario Student Opportunities Trust Fund (OSOTF) (Graduate/Scholarship) [11065]

TxHIMA Outstanding Student Scholarship (Undergraduate/Scholarship) [10985]

UAB Health Policy Fellowship (Graduate, Master's, Doctorate/Scholarship) [11430]

Hearing and deafness

A.G. Bell College Scholarship Program (Undergraduate, Graduate/Scholarship, Award) [332]

A.G. Bell School Age Financial Aid Program (High School/Scholarship, Monetary) [333]

American Speech Language Hearing Foundation Clinical Research Grant (Doctorate/Grant) [1595]

American Speech Language Hearing Foundation Endowed Scholarships (Graduate, Master's, Doctorate/Scholarship) [1596]

American Speech Language Hearing Foundation General Scholarships (Graduate, Master's, Doctorate/Scholarship) [1597]

American Speech Language Hearing Foundation International Student Scholarship (Graduate, Master's, Doctorate/Scholarship) [1598]

American Speech Language Hearing Foundation Minority Student Scholarship (Graduate, Master's, Doctorate/Scholarship) [1599]

American Speech Language Hearing Foundation Scholarship for Student with A Disability (Graduate, Master's, Doctorate/Scholarship) [1600]

ANS Research Grant Award (Professional development/Grant) [1158]

ASHFoundation New Century Scholars Research Grant (Doctorate/Grant) [1602]

ASHFoundation Student Research Grant in Audiology (Doctorate/Grant) [1606]

ASHFoundation Student Research Grant in Early Childhood Language Development (Doctorate, Master's/Grant) [1607]

Daniel H. Pokorny Memorial Scholarship Award (Undergraduate/Scholarship) [9624]

Elizabeth Benson Scholarship Award (Undergraduate/Scholarship) [9625]

Houston/Nancy Holliman Scholarship (Undergraduate/Scholarship) [4036]

NAJA Scholarship (Graduate/Scholarship) [7664]

Sertoma Communicative Disorders Scholarship (Undergraduate/Scholarship) [10019]

THFC Medical Research Grants (Professional development/Grant) [5454]

Heating, air conditioning, and refrigeration

Marvin Crawford Scholarship (College, Vocational/Occupational/Scholarship) [12304]

EGIA Foundation Scholarship Program (Vocational/Occupational, Two Year College/Scholarship) [4322]

Donald L. Frendberg Program (Undergraduate, Vocational/Occupational/Scholarship) [9609]

Horch Roofing Trade School Scholarship (Vocational/Occupational/Scholarship) [5584]

Dave Nelsen Scholarships (Undergraduate/Scholarship) [7672]

PTAC Crew Scholarship for HVAC Students (Vocational/Occupational/Scholarship) [9381]

Rees Scholarship Foundation - HVACR and Water Heating Technician Program (Community College, Undergraduate, Vocational/Occupational/Scholarship) [9610]

Rees Scholarship Foundation - Veterans Program (Vocational/Occupational, Undergraduate/Scholarship) [9611]

TrustedPros Scholarships (Undergraduate/Scholarship) [11131]

Vancouver Yukoners Legacy Scholarship (Vocational/Occupational, College, Undergraduate/Scholarship) [12381]

Work Ethic Scholarship (Vocational/Occupational, Two Year College/Scholarship) [7384]

Hematology

Adolescent/Young Adult Lymphoma Correlative Studies Grant *(Advanced Professional/Grant)* [6946]

Aplastic Anemia and Myelodysplasia Association of Canada Scholarships *(Graduate, Master's/Scholarship)* [3054]

Chronic Lymphocytic Leukemia Grant *(Advanced Professional/Grant)* [6947]

Diffuse Large B-Cell Lymphoma Grant *(Advanced Professional/Grant)* [6948]

Follicular Lymphoma Pathways Grant *(Advanced Professional/Grant)* [6949]

Mantle Cell Lymphoma Therapeutic Studies Grant *(Advanced Professional/Grant)* [6950]

Hemophilia

Doreen McMullan McCarthy Memorial Academic Scholarship for Women with Bleeding Disorders *(Undergraduate/Scholarship)* [7926]

Gail Posluns Fellowships in Hematology *(Postdoctorate/Fellowship)* [6931]

Herpetology

E.E. Williams Research Grant *(Master's, Doctorate/Grant)* [5498]

The Herpetologists' League Graduate Research Award *(Graduate/Award)* [5499]

Jones-Lovich Grants in Southwestern Herpetology *(Master's, Doctorate/Grant)* [5500]

Peace Frogs Fellowships *(Graduate/Fellowship)* [8750]

Hispanic American studies

LAEF Scholarships *(Undergraduate/Scholarship)* [6675]

LULAC GM Scholarship *(/Award)* [6748]

LULAC National Scholarship Fund (LNSF) *(Graduate, Undergraduate/Scholarship)* [6749]

Histology

Leonard Noble Educational Scholarships *(Professional development/Scholarship)* [8111]

Robert A. Clark Memorial Educational Scholarship *(Professional development/Scholarship)* [8112]

Thermo Scientific Educational Scholarships *(Professional development/Scholarship)* [8115]

Ventana Medical Systems In Situ Hybridization Awards *(Other/Award)* [8116]

Historic preservation

Association for Preservation Technology International Student Scholarships *(Graduate, Undergraduate/Scholarship)* [2262]

DAR Centennial Scholarship *(Undergraduate/Scholarship, Award, Monetary)* [8094]

Death Valley '49ers Scholarships *(Undergraduate/Scholarship)* [3985]

Grand Canyon Historical Society Scholarships *(Graduate/Scholarship)* [5066]

Keepers Preservation Education Fund Fellowship *(Graduate/Fellowship)* [10275]

Mildred Colodny Diversity Scholarships for Graduate Program in Historic Preservation *(Graduate/Scholarship, Award, Monetary)* [8145]

NAPC Forum Student Scholarships *(Undergraduate, Graduate/Scholarship)* [7594]

NYCT Paid Graduate Student Philanthropy Fellowships - Arts and Historic Preservation *(Graduate/Fellowship)* [8305]

Plan NH's Scholarship and Fellowship Program *(Community College, Four Year College, Undergraduate, Graduate, Vocational/Occupational/Scholarship)* [9188]

The Aaron and Rita Slom Scholarships *(Undergraduate/Scholarship)* [11069]

Herb Stovel Scholarship - National Trust Conference Bursaries *(Undergraduate, Graduate, Professional development/Scholarship)* [8142]

Herb Stovel Scholarship - Project Research Bursaries *(Undergraduate, Graduate, Professional development/Scholarship)* [8143]

History

A. Stanley Rand Fellowship Program *(Undergraduate, Doctorate, Postdoctorate/Fellowship)* [10224]

A.F. Zimmerman Scholarship *(Graduate, Master's/Scholarship)* [9073]

Dr. Feroz Ahmed Memorial Educational Post-Graduate Scholarships *(Doctorate, Postgraduate/Scholarship)* [10144]

American Historical Association Fellowships in Aerospace History *(Doctorate/Fellowship)* [958]

ARCE Funded Fellowships *(Doctorate, Postdoctorate/Fellowship)* [1336]

ARCE Research Associates Fellowship *(Doctorate, Postdoctorate, Professional development/Fellowship)* [1337]

ARS Lazarian Graduate Scholarship *(Graduate, Master's, Doctorate/Scholarship)* [1854]

Albert J. Beveridge Grant for Research in the History of the Western Hemisphere *(Doctorate/Grant)* [959]

Blanche Raper Zimmerman Scholarship *(Other/Scholarship)* [12062]

Burney – Cecil E. Burney Scholarship *(Undergraduate/Scholarship)* [3468]

Rachel Carson Prize *(Other/Prize)* [1450]

CCWH / Berks Graduate Student Fellowship *(Graduate/Fellowship)* [3828]

CCWH Nupur Chaudhuri Article Prize *(Professional development/Prize)* [3829]

CHF Travel Grants *(Professional development/Grant)* [9971]

D.F. Plett Graduate Fellowship *(Graduate/Fellowship)* [9202]

Jenny d'Héricourt Fellowship *(Doctorate/Fellowship)* [487]

Marusia and Michael Dorosh Fellowship *(Master's, Graduate/Fellowship)* [3027]

Douglas-Coldwell Foundation Scholarships in Social Affairs *(Graduate/Scholarship)* [4137]

Enid Hall Griswold Memorial Scholarship *(Undergraduate/Scholarship, Award, Monetary)* [8096]

Enkababian Family and Sarian Family Memorial Grant *(Undergraduate/Scholarship)* [1875]

Ivan Franko School of Ukrainian Studies Ukraine Travel Award *(Undergraduate/Grant)* [3028]

Gadzala Franciszek Memorial Scholarship *(Undergraduate/Scholarship)* [9664]

William E. "Bill" Gallagher Scholarship *(Undergraduate/Scholarship)* [8847]

Berek and Regina Gertner OSOTF Bursary in Holocaust Studies *(Undergraduate, Graduate/Scholarship)* [12245]

Margaret S. Gilbert Scholarship Fund *(Graduate/Scholarship)* [10760]

Gilder Lehrman Short-Term research Fellowships *(Graduate, Postdoctorate/Fellowship)* [6773]

Louis Gottschalk Prize *(Other/Prize)* [1432]

Governor William A. Egan Award *(Undergraduate/Award)* [11480]

Grand Canyon Historical Society Scholarships *(Graduate/Scholarship)* [5066]

Graydon A. Tunstall Undergraduate Student Scholarship *(Undergraduate/Scholarship)* [9074]

Velma Shotwell Griffin Memorial Scholarship Fund *(Undergraduate/Scholarship)* [10762]

Harriet Irsay Scholarship *(Graduate, Undergraduate/Scholarship)* [1045]

Hench Post-Dissertation Fellowship *(Postdoctorate/Fellowship)* [491]

Conrad N. Hilton Scholarships *(Undergraduate/Scholarship)* [4962]

Brooke Hindle Postdoctoral Fellowships *(Postdoctorate, Doctorate/Fellowship)* [10363]

Huggins-Quarles Award *(Doctorate, Graduate/Award)* [8726]

Mary M. Hughes Research Fellowships in Texas History *(Professional development/Fellowship)* [10997]

Huguenot Society of South Carolina Graduate Scholarship *(Graduate/Scholarship)* [5621]

J. Franklin Jameson Fellowship in American History *(Doctorate/Fellowship)* [960]

John H. Jenkins Research Fellowships in Texas History *(Professional development/Fellowship)* [10998]

Mary Jon and J. P. Bryan Leadership in Education Awards *(Advanced Professional/Award)* [10999]

Justin G. Schiller Fellowship *(Doctorate, Postdoctorate/Fellowship)* [492]

Klondike Defence Force Grant *(Undergraduate, College, University, Vocational/Occupational/Scholarship)* [12335]

Melvin Kranzberg Dissertation Fellowships *(Doctorate/Fellowship)* [10364]

Michael Kraus Research Grants *(Doctorate/Grant)* [961]

Lapides Fellowships in Pre-1865 Juvenile Literature and Ephemera *(Graduate, Postdoctorate/Fellowship)* [493]

LAWCHA Graduate Student Travel Grants *(Graduate/Grant)* [6628]

Lerner-Scott Prize *(Doctorate/Prize)* [8728]

Littleton-Griswold Research Grant *(Doctorate/Grant)* [962]

Louis Pelzer Memorial Award *(Graduate/Award)* [8729]

George Perkins Marsh Prize *(Other/Prize)* [1455]

Larry Matfay Cultural Heritage Scholarship *(Undergraduate, Graduate/Scholarship)* [6592]

The William P. McHugh Memorial Fund *(Doctorate, Graduate/Grant)* [1338]

Les McLaughlin Scholarship *(Undergraduate, University, College, Vocational/Occupational/Scholarship)* [12346]

Thomas S. Morgan Memorial Scholarship *(Graduate, Master's/Scholarship)* [9075]

NACBS Dissertation Fellowship *(Graduate, Doctorate/Fellowship)* [8420]

NACBS-Dissertation Year Fellowship *(Postdoctorate/Fellowship)* [8421]

NACBS-Huntington Library Fellowship *(Doctorate, Postdoctorate/Fellowship)* [8422]

National Council on Public History Graduate Student Travel Awards *(Doctorate, Graduate, Master's/Grant)* [7792]

National Council on Public History Student Project Awards *(Undergraduate/Grant)* [7793]

National Endowment for the Humanities Advanced Fellowships for Research in Turkey *(Postdoctorate/Fellowship)* [1349, 7871]

National Endowment for the Humanities Fellowship *(Graduate/Fellowship)* [1339]

National Federation of the Blind Scholarship Program *(Undergraduate/Scholarship, Monetary)* [7878]

NMNH American Indian Program Fellowships *(Graduate/Fellowship)* [10203]

The Barbara L. Packer Fellowship *(Doctorate, Postdoctorate/Fellowship)* [496]

Petroleum History Society Graduate Scholarships *(Graduate/Scholarship)* [9048]

Phi Alpha Theta Doctoral Scholarship *(Doctorate/Scholarship)* [9076]

Phi Alpha Theta Faculty Advisor Research Grant *(Other/Grant)* [9077]

Pi Gamma Mu Scholarships *(Graduate/Scholarship)* [9160]

The John Pine Memorial Award *(Doctorate, Graduate, Undergraduate/Scholarship)* [9078]

Catherine Prelinger Award *(Postdoctorate/Scholarship)* [3830]

Charles and Ruth Ronin Memorial Scholarships *(Undergraduate/Scholarship)* [9600]

Hal Rothman Dissertation Fellowship *(Doctorate, Graduate/Fellowship)* [1458]

Samuel P. Hays Research Fellowship *(Other/Fellowship)* [1459]

Bernadotte E. Schmitt Grant *(Doctorate/Grant)* [963]

Everett Oscar Shimp Memorial Scholarships *(Undergraduate/Scholarship)* [8878]

Dr. Brent Slobodin Memorial Scholarship in the Humanities *(Undergraduate, Graduate, University, College/Scholarship)* [12371]

Smithsonian Institution Graduate Student Fellowships *(Graduate/Fellowship)* [10205]

Smithsonian Institution Postdoctoral Researcher Fellowships *(Postdoctorate/Fellowship)* [10206]

Smithsonian Institution Predoctoral Student Fellowships *(Doctorate, Postgraduate/Fellowship)* [10207]

Smithsonian Institution Senior Researcher Fellowships *(Professional development/Fellowship)* [10208]

Hatton W. Sumners Endowed Undergraduate School Scholarships *(Undergraduate/Scholarship)* [10878]

Hatton W. Sumners Non-Endowed Undergraduate and Graduate Scholarships *(Undergraduate, Graduate/Scholarship)* [10879]

Terra Foundation Fellowships at the Smithsonian American Art Museum *(Postdoctorate/Fellowship)* [10963]

Terra Foundation Postdoctoral Teaching Fellowships at the Institut National d'Histoire de l'Art, Paris *(Postdoctorate/Fellowship)* [10964]

Terra Summer Residency Fellowships *(Master's, Doctorate/Fellowship)* [10966]

Barbara and Howard Thompson Scholarships *(Undergraduate/Scholarship)* [6209]

The United States Department of State, Bureau of Educational & Cultural Affairs Fellowships *(Graduate/Fellowship)* [1340]

Ida B. Wells Graduate Student Fellowship *(Graduate/Fellowship)* [3831]

Frederick K. Weyerhaeuser Forest History Fellowship *(Graduate/Fellowship)* [4682]

William E. Parrish Scholarship *(Graduate, Master's/Scholarship)* [9079]

History, American

Arthur M. Schlesinger Jr. Research Fellowship *(Professional development/Fellowship)* [6531]

Ballard Breaux Visiting Fellowships *(Postdoctorate/Fellowship)* [4558]

Stephen Botein Fellowships *(Doctorate/Fellowship)* [485]

Betty Sams Christian Fellowships *(Doctorate/Fellowship)* [11835]

Cromwell Fellowships *(Graduate/Fellowship)* [1461]

Dr. Aura-Lee A. and James Hobbs Pittenger American History Scholarship *(Undergraduate/Scholarship, Award, Monetary)* [8095]

W.B.H. Dowse Fellowships *(Graduate/Fellowship)* [7142]

Fellowships for Creative and Performing Artists and Writers *(Professional development/Fellowship)* [490]

Filson Fellowships *(Postdoctorate, Doctorate/Fellowship)* [4559]

Filson Historical Society Master's Thesis Fellowship *(Master's/Fellowship)* [4560]

MHS Marc Friedlaender Fellowships *(Professional development/Fellowship)* [7144]

German Historical Institute Doctoral and Postdoctoral Fellowships *(Doctorate, Postgraduate/Fellowship)* [4942]

ICJS Short-Term Fellowships *(Doctorate, Postdoctorate, Advanced Professional/Fellowship)* [10184]

John Higham Research Fellowship *(Postdoctorate/Fellowship)* [5723, 8727]

The Legacy Fellowship *(Doctorate/Fellowship)* [495]

Lloyd Lewis Fellowships in American History *(Postdoctorate/Fellowship)* [8375]

Suzanne and Caleb Loring Research Fellowships *(Professional development/Fellowship)* [7145]

James Madison Foundation - Junior Fellowships *(Advanced Professional, Graduate/Fellowship)* [6227]

James Madison Foundation - Senior Fellowships *(Advanced Professional/Fellowship)* [6228]

MHS Andrew W. Mellon Fellowships *(Professional development, Doctorate/Fellowship)* [7146]

MHS Long-Term Research Fellowships *(Professional development/Fellowship)* [7149]

MHS/Massachusetts Society of the Cincinnati Fellowships *(Professional development/Fellowship)* [7150]

NeMLA-University at Buffalo Special Collections Fellowship *(Undergraduate, Graduate/Fellowship)* [8485]

Kate B. and Hall J. Peterson Fellowships *(Doctorate/Fellowship)* [497]

Platt Family Scholarship Prize Essay Contest *(Undergraduate/Scholarship, Monetary)* [6867]

Presidency Research Fund *(Graduate, Postdoctorate, Undergraduate, Professional development/Grant)* [1259]

Benjamin F. Stevens Fellowships *(Professional development/Fellowship)* [7153]

Swensrud Teacher Fellowships at MHS (Massachusetts Historical Society) *(Professional development/Fellowship)* [7154]

The Joyce Tracy Fellowship *(Doctorate/Fellowship)* [499]

United States Capitol Historical Society Fellowships *(Graduate/Fellowship)* [11299]

Woody Guthrie Fellowship *(Professional development/Fellowship)* [2637]

Wyeth Foundation For American Art Publication Grant *(Other/Grant)* [3504]

History, Ancient

ARIT Fellowships in the Humanities and Social Sciences in Turkey *(Postdoctorate, Graduate/Fellowship)* [1342, 3850, 11345, 11348]

History, Art (See Art history)

History, Economic

Arthur H. Cole Grants in Aid *(Doctorate/Grant)* [4281]

EHA Exploratory Travel and Data Grants *(Doctorate/Grant)* [4282]

EHA Graduate Dissertation Fellowships *(Graduate/Fellowship)* [4283]

History, Military

ABC-Clio Research Grants *(Graduate/Grant)* [10425]

CMH Dissertation Fellowships *(Graduate/Fellowship)* [11286]

J.L. Granatstein Post-Doctoral Fellowship *(Postdoctorate/Fellowship)* [11530]

Marshall-Baruch Fellowships *(Doctorate/Fellowship)* [7111]

The Wilson Fellowship *(Postdoctorate/Fellowship)* [11677]

Women In Defense HORIZONS Scholarship *(Graduate, Undergraduate/Scholarship)* [12133]

History of printing (See Printing--History)

History of science (See Science--History)

History, United States (See History, American)

Home Economics

California Association of Family and Consumer Sciences - San Diego Chapter Scholarship *(Undergraduate, Graduate/Scholarship)* [9805]

Canadian Home Economics Association Fellowship (CHEA) *(Postgraduate/Fellowship)* [2969]

FACS Graduate Fellowships *(Graduate, Undergraduate/Fellowship)* [7706]

Dolores Ruth Heady Hardy Memorial Scholarship *(Undergraduate/Scholarship)* [6442]

Kappa Omicron Nu National Alumni Fellowships *(Graduate/Fellowship)* [6489]

Eileen C. Maddex Fellowships *(Graduate/Fellowship)* [6493]

Homosexuality

The Duberman-Zal Fellowship *(Graduate/Scholarship)* [3234]

GAPA Foundation Scholarship *(Undergraduate, Graduate, High School, Vocational/Occupational/Scholarship)* [9334]

The Robert Giard Fellowship *(Graduate/Fellowship)* [3235]

Joan Heller-Diane Bernard Fellowships *(Graduate, Undergraduate/Fellowship)* [3236]

Horticulture

ACS Scholarship *(Undergraduate/Scholarship)* [795]

American Society for Horticultural Science Travel Grants *(Graduate, Undergraduate/Grant)* [1478]

Arizona Nursery Association Scholarships *(Undergraduate, Graduate, College, University/Scholarship)* [1812]

Arkansas Green Industry Association Professional Grants *(Professional development/Grant)* [1826]

Arkansas Green Industry Association Student Scholarships *(Undergraduate/Scholarship)* [1827]

The Artist in Landscape Design Scholarship *(Undergraduate/Scholarship)* [8585]

ASHS Industry Division Student Travel Grant *(Graduate, Undergraduate/Grant)* [1479]

ASHS Scholars Award *(Undergraduate/Scholarship)* [1480]

Ball Horticultural Company Scholarship *(Undergraduate/Scholarship)* [894]

Vic and Margaret Ball Student Intern Scholarships *(Undergraduate/Internship)* [895]

Catherine H. Beattie Fellowships *(Graduate/Fellowship)* [3238, 4858]

Harold Bettinger Scholarship *(Undergraduate, Graduate/Scholarship)* [896]

Leonard Bettinger Vocational Scholarship *(Undergraduate, Vocational/Occupational/Scholarship)* [897]

Bill Egan Memorial Award *(Undergraduate/Scholarship)* [8702]

James Bridenbaugh Memorial Scholarship *(Undergraduate/Scholarship)* [898]

John Carew Memorial Scholarship *(Graduate/Scholarship)* [899]

Bryan A. Champion Memorial Scholarship *(Undergraduate/Scholarship)* [5586]

Christmas Tree Chapter Scholarship Awards *(Undergraduate/Scholarship)* [8703]

Clackamas Chapter Ed Wood Memorial Award *(Undergraduate/Scholarship)* [8704]

Clackamas Chapter Scholarship Awards *(Undergraduate/Scholarship)* [8705]

The James H. Davis Memorial Scholarship *(Undergraduate, Postgraduate/Scholarship)* [4638]

Earl Dedman Memorial Scholarship *(Undergraduate/Scholarship)* [900]

Emerald Empire Chapter Scholarship Awards *(Undergraduate/Scholarship)* [8706]

FFA Scholarship *(Undergraduate/Scholarship)* [8586]

Fruits and Vegetable Industries Scholarships *(Undergraduate/Scholarship)* [7333]

The Garden Club Council of Winston-Salem and Forsyth County Scholarship *(Undergraduate/Scholarship)* [12079]

Gardeners of America/Men's Garden Clubs of America Scholarship *(Undergraduate/Scholarship)* [4864]

Herb Society of America Research Grant *(Professional development/Grant)* [5485]

Hill Country Master Gardeners Horticulture Scholarship *(Undergraduate, Graduate/Scholarship)* [5510]

Horticulture Scholarship from Frances Sylvia Zverina *(Undergraduate/Scholarship)* [5486]

Horticulture Scholarship of the Western Reserve Herb Society *(Undergraduate/Scholarship)* [5487]

Howard A. Clark Horticulture Scholarship Fund *(Undergraduate/Scholarship)* [3622]

Idaho Nursery and Landscape Association Scholarships *(Undergraduate/Scholarship)* [5683]

Illinois Landscape Contractors Association Scholarships *(Undergraduate/Scholarship)* [5703]

Jordan B. Tatter Scholarship *(Undergraduate, Graduate/Scholarship)* [7334]

Katherine M. Grosscup Scholarships in Horticulture *(Undergraduate, Graduate/Scholarship)* [4860]

Joseph H. Klupenger Scholarship Awards *(Undergraduate/Scholarship, Award)* [8707]

Phil Kozel Memorial Scholarship *(Undergraduate/Scholarship)* [8588]

Louisiana Agricultural Consultants Association Scholarship *(Graduate, Undergraduate/Scholarship)* [6896]

Markham-Colegrave International Scholarships *(Undergraduate/Scholarship)* [901]

Ann Lane Mavromatis Scholarship *(Undergraduate/Scholarship)* [967]

MELNA Scholarship *(Undergraduate, Graduate/Scholarship)* [6999]

Miklos Faust International Travel Award *(Doctorate/Grant)* [1481]

Mt. Hood Chapter Scholarship Awards *(Undergraduate/Scholarship)* [8708]

Nashville Unit Scholarships *(Undergraduate/Scholarship, Grant)* [5488]

National Greenhouse Manufacturers Association (NGMA) Scholarships *(Undergraduate/Scholarship)* [902]

NGC College Scholarships *(Graduate, Undergraduate/Scholarship)* [7900]

Stan and Mary Stark Alumni Scholarship *(Other/Scholarship)* [7967]

North Carolina Nursery and Landscape Association Horticulture Scholarships *(Undergraduate/Scholarship)* [8441]

Mike and Flo Novovesky Scholarship *(Undergraduate/Scholarship)* [903]

Nurseries Foundation Scholarship Awards *(Undergraduate/Scholarship)* [8709]

Nurseries Memorial Award *(Graduate/Scholarship)* [8710]

Lawrence "Bud" Ohlman Memorial Scholarships *(Undergraduate/Scholarship)* [904]

ONLA President's Scholarship *(Undergraduate/Scholarship)* [8589]

ONLA Scholarships *(Undergraduate, Two Year College, College/Scholarship)* [8590]

Oregon Association of Nurseries Scholarship Program *(Graduate/Scholarship)* [8711]

Pennsylvania Heartland Unit Scholarship *(Undergraduate/Scholarship)* [5489]

Perfect Plants Scholarship *(Community College/Scholarship)* [9036]

Rain Bird Intelligent Use of Water Scholarship *(Undergraduate/Scholarship)* [6652, 9491]

James K. Rathmell Jr. Memorial Scholarship *(Undergraduate, Graduate/Scholarship)* [905]

Retail Chapter Scholarship Awards *(Undergraduate/Scholarship)* [8712]

Stanley Smith Horticultural Fellowships *(Graduate, Undergraduate/Fellowship)* [8753]

South Texas Unit Scholarship *(Undergraduate/Scholarship)* [5490]

John L. Tomasovic, Sr. Scholarship *(Undergraduate/Scholarship)* [906]

Edward Tuinier Memorial Scholarship *(Undergraduate/Scholarship)* [907]

Jacob and Rita Van Namen Marketing Scholarship *(Undergraduate/Scholarship)* [908]

Vocational (Bettinger, Holden & Perry) scholarship *(Undergraduate, Vocational/Occupational/Scholarship)* [909]

West Michigan Nursery and Landscape Association Scholarship *(Undergraduate/Scholarship)* [5113]

Willamette Chapter Scholarship Awards *(Undergraduate/Scholarship)* [8713]

Violet Wondergem Health Science Scholarship *(Undergraduate, Graduate/Scholarship)* [910]

Hotel, institutional, and restaurant management

AH&LEF American Express Scholarship *(Undergraduate/Scholarship)* [969]

American Express Professional Development Scholarship *(Other/Scholarship)* [970]

Caribbean Hotel and Tourism Association Scholarship *(Graduate, Undergraduate/Scholarship)* [3167]

Letitia B. Carter Scholarships *(Undergraduate, Advanced Professional/Scholarship)* [9649]

Vickie Clark-Flaherty Scholarships *(Undergraduate/Scholarship)* [8444]

Clem Judd Jr. Memorial Scholarship *(Undergraduate/Scholarship)* [5418]

Davidson and Jones Hotel Corporation Scholarship *(Undergraduate/Scholarship)* [8445]

Marcia S. Harris Legacy Fund Scholarships *(Undergraduate, Advanced Professional/Scholarship)* [9650]

R.W. "Bob" Holden Memorial Scholarships *(Undergraduate/Scholarship)* [5419]

Hospitality Career Scholarship *(Undergraduate/Scholarship)* [11038]

HSMAI Foundation Scholarship *(Graduate/Scholarship)* [5608]

The Hyatt Hotels Fund For Minority Lodging Management Students *(Undergraduate/Scholarship)* [972]

International Foodservice Editorial Council Scholarship *(Graduate/Scholarship)* [6007]

John A. Rothschild Bachelor Degree in Hospitality Scholarship *(Undergraduate, Community College/Scholarship)* [3006]

Les Dames D'Escoffier New York Corporate Scholarship *(Undergraduate/Scholarship)* [6777]

Michigan Sugar Company Hotel Restaurant/Resort Management Scholarship *(Undergraduate/Scholarship)* [7341]

North Carolina Hospitality Education Foundation Scholarship *(Undergraduate/Scholarship)* [8446]

NC Hospitality Education Foundation Scholarships - Graduate *(Graduate/Scholarship)* [8447]

NC Hospitality Education Foundation Scholarships - High School *(Undergraduate/Scholarship)* [8448]

NC Hospitality Education Foundation Scholarships - Two Year Community or Junior College *(Undergraduate/Scholarship)* [8449]

NCRLA Golden Corral Scholarship *(Undergraduate/Scholarship)* [8450]

NRAEF Scholarship *(Undergraduate/Scholarship)* [9651]

Oklahoma Restaurant Association Scholarships *(Other/Scholarship)* [8612]

Ontario Women's Institute Scholarships *(Undergraduate/Scholarship)* [4525]

The Arthur J. Packard Memorial Scholarship *(Undergraduate/Scholarship)* [973]

PepsiCo Foundation Scholarships *(Undergraduate/Scholarship)* [974, 9034]

Rama Scholarships for the American Dream *(Graduate, Undergraduate/Scholarship)* [975]

Steve Hymans Extended Stay Scholarship Program *(Undergraduate/Scholarship)* [976]

Twenty Four Seven Hotels Scholarship Opportunity *(Undergraduate, College, University/Scholarship)* [11156]

Yukon Anniversaries Commission Scholarship *(Undergraduate, University, College, Vocational/Occupational/Scholarship)* [12396]

Housing

California Association of Family and Consumer Sciences - San Diego Chapter Scholarship *(Undergraduate, Graduate/Scholarship)* [9805]

CHCI Graduate Fellowship Program *(Graduate, Professional development/Fellowship)* [3746]

NACCED Annual John C. Murphy Scholarships *(Graduate, Undergraduate/Scholarship)* [7643]

Human relations

Bill Bendiner and Doug Morgenson Scholarship *(Undergraduate/Scholarship)* [9293]

David C. Maloney Scholarship *(Undergraduate/Scholarship)* [8021]

Derivative Duo Scholarships *(Undergraduate/Scholarship)* [9299]

April Relyea Scholarship *(Graduate, Undergraduate/Scholarship)* [11490]

Human rights

Alberta Award for the Study of Canadian Human Rights and Multiculturalism *(Doctorate, Graduate, Master's/Award)* [280]

Beverlee Bell Scholarships in Human Rights and Democracy *(Graduate/Scholarship)* [4136]

Robert L. Bernstein Fellowships in International Human Rights *(Graduate/Fellowship)* [5630]

Canadian Japanese-Mennonite Scholarship *(Undergraduate/Scholarship)* [7254]

CEJIL Communications Internships *(Professional development, Graduate/Internship)* [3230]

CEJIL Legal Internships *(Graduate, Professional development/Internship)* [3231]

CHRGJ Emerging Human Rights Scholarship Conference *(Graduate/Scholarship)* [8358]

CHRGJ International Human Rights Fellowships *(Doctorate, Professional development/Fellowship)* [8359]

CHRGJ Students Human Rights Scholars Program *(Graduate, Advanced Professional, Professional development/Scholarship)* [8360]

Arthur C. Helton Fellowship Program *(Undergraduate, Graduate/Fellowship)* [1489]

Arthur Helton Global Rights Fellowships *(Graduate/Fellowship)* [8361]

Henigson Human Rights Fellowship *(Graduate, Master's, Juris Doctorate/Fellowship)* [5365]

Kovaluk Scholarship Fund *(Undergraduate/Scholarship)* [11412]

NYCT Paid Graduate Student Philanthropy Fellowships - Children, Youth, Families, Education, Human Justice and Workforce *(Graduate/Fellowship)* [8306]

OPIRG McMaster Public Interest Research Grant (PIG) *(Undergraduate, Graduate/Grant)* [7195]

Satter Human Rights Fellowship *(Graduate, Master's, Juris Doctorate/Fellowship)* [5366]

Spirit of Anne Frank Scholarship Award *(Undergraduate/Scholarship)* [4813]

Upper Midwest Human Rights Fellowship Program *(Graduate/Scholarship, Fellowship)* [5632]

George Watt Prize *(Undergraduate, Graduate/Prize)* [6865]

Minoru Yasui Memorial Scholarship *(Graduate/Scholarship)* [6255]

Humanities

AAS National Endowment for the Humanities Long-Term Fellowships *(Postdoctorate/Fellowship)* [483]

ACLS Collaborative Research Fellowships *(Doctorate/Fellowship)* [817]

ACLS Fellowships *(Advanced Professional, Professional development/Fellowship)* [818]

ACOR-CAORC Post-Doctoral Fellowships *(Postdoctorate/Fellowship)* [723]

African Humanities Program *(Postdoctorate/Fellowship)* [819]

Dr. Feroz Ahmed Memorial Educational Post-Graduate Scholarships *(Doctorate, Postgraduate/Scholarship)* [10144]

AISLS Dissertation Planning Grants *(Graduate/Grant)* [1047]

AISLS Fellowships Program *(Doctorate/Fellowship)* [1048]

American Research in the Humanities in China Fellowships *(Doctorate/Fellowship)* [820]

ARCE Funded Fellowships *(Doctorate, Postdoctorate/Fellowship)* [1336]

ARCE Research Associates Fellowship *(Doctorate, Postdoctorate, Professional development/Fellowship)* [1337]

ARIT Fellowships in the Humanities and Social Sciences in Turkey *(Postdoctorate, Graduate/Fellowship)* [1342, 3850, 11345, 11348]

ARIT/NEH Fellowships *(Postgraduate/Fellowship)* [1343]

Leo Biaggi de Blasys Bogliasco Fellowships *(Undergraduate/Scholarship)* [2642]

Bogliasco Fellowships *(Professional development/Fellowship)* [2643]

Ara S. Boyan Scholarship Grant *(Undergraduate/Scholarship)* [1867]

ACLS Frederick Burkhardt Residential Fellowships *(Other/Fellowship)* [486, 821]

Frederick Burkhardt Residential Fellowships for Recently Tenured Scholars *(Advanced Professional, Professional development/Fellowship)* [822]

G.I. and Martha Cameron Scholarship *(Undergraduate/Scholarship)* [12298]

Carter G. Woodson Institute Post-doctoral Residential Research & Teaching Fellowship *(Postdoctorate/Fellowship)* [12183]

Carter G. Woodson Institute Pre-doctoral Fellowship *(Doctorate/Fellowship)* [12184]

CJH-NEH Fellowships for Senior Scholars *(Doctorate/Fellowship)* [3222]

CJH-Prins Foundation Fellowships for Senior Scholars *(Doctorate/Fellowship)* [3223]

CJH-Prins Foundation Post-Doctoral and Early Career Fellowship for Emigrating Scholars *(Professional development, Postdoctorate/Fellowship)* [3224]

Critical Language Scholarships at Summer Institutes. (CLS) *(Graduate, Undergraduate/Scholarship)* [1345]

David C. Maloney Scholarship *(Undergraduate/Scholarship)* [8021]

Dissertation Proposal Development Fellowship *(Doctorate/Fellowship)* [10243]

Ed Haas Memorial Scholarship Fund *(Graduate/Scholarship)* [10824]

Ellis W. Rowe Memorial Scholarship *(Graduate/Scholarship)* [5268]

Eurasia Program Fellowships - Dissertation Development Awards *(Doctorate/Fellowship)* [10244]

Eurasia Program Fellowships - Pre-Dissertation Awards *(Doctorate/Fellowship)* [10245]

European Studies First Article Prize *(Professional development/Prize)* [3857]

Maro Ajemian Galstaun Memorial Grant *(Undergraduate/Scholarship)* [1878]

Getty Scholar Grants *(Professional development/Grant)* [4959]

Harry Frank Guggenheim Dissertation Fellowships *(Doctorate/Fellowship)* [5247]

Harry Frank Guggenheim Foundation Research Grants *(Professional development/Grant)* [5248]

John Simon Guggenheim Memorial Fellowships - United States & Canadian Competition *(Graduate, Postgraduate, Undergraduate/Fellowship)* [5250]

International Dissertation Research Fellowship (IDRF) *(Graduate, Doctorate/Fellowship)* [10246]

International Society for Humor Studies Graduate Student Awards (GSA) *(Graduate/Award, Scholarship)* [6111]

International Society for Humor Studies Scholarly Contribution Awards (SCA) *(Other/Award)* [6112]

Japan Society for the Promotion of Science Fellowship (JSPS) *(Doctorate/Fellowship)* [10247]

Jacob K. Javits Fellowships Program *(Master's, Doctorate/Fellowship)* [11310]

Robert E. Kelsey Annual Scholarship *(Undergraduate/Scholarship)* [8954]

Kluge Fellowship *(Doctorate, Graduate/Fellowship)* [6573]

Korean Studies Dissertation Workshop *(Graduate/Fellowship)* [10248]

Short-Term Library Resident Research Fellowships *(Doctorate/Fellowship)* [1216]

Dolores Zohrab Liebmann Fund - Graduate School Fellowships *(Graduate/Fellowship)* [6845]

Lois Hole Humanities and Social Sciences Scholarship *(Undergraduate/Scholarship)* [296]

Louis I. Jaffe Memorial Scholarship-ODU *(Graduate/Scholarship)* [5274]

Mary and Elliot Wood Foundation Graduate Scholarship *(Graduate/Scholarship)* [4744]

O. Ruth McQuown Scholarship - Graduate Award for Current Students *(Graduate/Scholarship)* [11572]

Mellon/ACLS Dissertation Completion Fellowships *(Graduate, Doctorate/Fellowship)* [825]

Mellon Fellowships for Dissertation Research in Original Sources *(Doctorate/Fellowship)* [3870]

Multi-Country Research Fellowship *(Doctorate, Postdoctorate/Fellowship)* [3851]

NAFA International Dissertation Research Fellowships *(Graduate, Doctorate/Fellowship)* [7647]

National Endowment for the Humanities Advanced Fellowships for Research in Turkey *(Postdoctorate/Fellowship)* [1349, 7871]

National Humanities Center Fellowships *(Doctorate, Postdoctorate/Fellowship)* [7939]

Newberry Library National Endowment for the Humanities Fellowships *(Postdoctorate/Fellowship)* [8381]

Pembroke Center Seed Grants *(Professional development/Grant)* [2726]

Pierre Elliott Trudeau Foundation octoral Scholarships *(Doctorate/Scholarship)* [11124]

Post-Doctoral Summer Travel-Research Grants *(Postdoctorate/Grant)* [5871]

Robert W. and Bernice Ingalls Staton Scholarships *(Undergraduate/Scholarship)* [11654]

Rome Prize *(Postdoctorate, Graduate, Undergraduate/Prize, Award)* [476]

Rovelstad Scholarship *(Undergraduate, Graduate/Scholarship)* [3871]

Dale M. Schoettler Scholarship for Visually Impaired Students *(Undergraduate, Graduate/Scholarship)* [9874]

Musia & Leon Schwartz Scholarship *(Graduate/Scholarship)* [6299]

SHAFR Dissertation Completion Fellowship *(Doctorate/Fellowship)* [10359]

Dr. Brent Slobodin Memorial Scholarship in the Humanities *(Undergraduate, Graduate, University, College/Scholarship)* [12371]

SSHRC Doctoral Fellowship Program *(Doctorate/Fellowship, Scholarship)* [3797]

Summer Language Study Grants in Turkey *(Graduate/Grant)* [5872]

UC MEXUS-CONACYT Doctoral Fellowship *(Doctorate/Fellowship)* [11552]

UCSD Black Alumni Scholarship for Arts and Humanities *(Undergraduate/Scholarship)* [9857]

Vanier Canada Graduate Scholarships Program *(Graduate/Scholarship)* [3808]

Winterthur Research Fellowships *(Graduate/Fellowship)* [12101]

Woody Guthrie Fellowship *(Professional development/Fellowship)* [2637]

Huntington's disease

HDSA Research Grants *(Graduate/Grant)* [5657]

Hereditary Disease Foundation Basic Research Grants Program *(Advanced Professional/Grant)* [5494]

The Donald A. King Summer Research Fellowship *(Undergraduate/Fellowship)* [5658]

Don King Student Fellowships *(Undergraduate/Fellowship)* [5659]

Hydrology

Arizona Hydrological Society Academic Scholarships *(Graduate, Undergraduate/Scholarship)* [1808]

The B. Harper Bull Scholarship Awards *(Graduate, Doctorate, Postgraduate/Award)* [11060]

Canadian Hydrographic Association Student Award *(Undergraduate/Award)* [3008]

CASFM-Ben Urbonas Scholarship *(Graduate/Scholarship)* [3524]

Hydro Research Foundation Fellowships *(Advanced Professional/Fellowship)* [5661]

L. Gordon "Link" Linkous Scholarship *(Undergraduate/Scholarship)* [11103]

Illustrators and illustrations

Inez Demonet Scholarship *(Graduate/Scholarship)* [11804]

Joanna Townsend Applied Arts Scholarship *(All/Scholarship)* [2129]

UAA Kimura Scholarship Fund for Illustration *(Undergraduate/Scholarship)* [11503]

Vesalius Trust Student Research Scholarship Program *(Graduate, Undergraduate/Scholarship)* [11805]

Worldstudio AIGA Scholarships *(Graduate, Undergraduate/Scholarship)* [12205]

Immigration

Abba P. Schwartz Research Fellowship *(Professional development/Fellowship)* [6530]

John Higham Research Fellowship *(Postdoctorate/Fellowship)* [5723, 8727]

Immunology

AAI Careers in Immunology Fellowship Program *(Graduate, Doctorate, Postdoctorate/Fellowship)* [572]

AAI Public Policy Fellows Program (PPFP) *(Doctorate, Postdoctorate/Fellowship)* [573]

Clinic & Laboratory Integration Program (CLIP) *(Professional development/Grant)* [3140]

CRI Irvington Postdoctoral Fellowships *(Postdoctorate/Fellowship)* [3141]

Kris Knudson Memorial Scholarship *(Graduate, Undergraduate/Scholarship)* [11484]

Student Training and Research in Tumor Immunology Grants *(Graduate/Grant)* [3142]

Dr. Steven S. Zalcman Memorial Scholarship *(Graduate, Postgraduate/Scholarship)* [6301]

Indian studies (Asia)

Shastri Scholar Travel Subsidy Grants (SSTSG) *(Graduate, Professional development/Grant)* [10037]

SHOT-NASA Fellowship *(Doctorate/Fellowship)* [10365]

Industrial and labor relations

Mackenzie King Travelling Scholarship *(Graduate/Scholarship, Monetary)* [7183]

Mary C. Babcock Fellowship *(Postgraduate/Fellowship)* [8643]

NPELRA Foundation - Anthony C. Russo Scholarships *(Graduate/Scholarship)* [8057]

Industrial design

FPA Summer Internships Program *(Undergraduate/Internship)* [4616]

Gianninoto Industrial Design Graduate Scholarship *(Graduate, Undergraduate/Scholarship)* [5778]

Tom D. Ralls Memorial Scholarship *(Professional development/Scholarship)* [4807]

Tag and Label Manufacturers Institute Scholarships - Two-Year Colleges *(Undergraduate/Scholarship)* [10905]

Vectorworks Design Scholarship *(Undergraduate, Graduate/Scholarship)* [11796]

Worldstudio AIGA Scholarships *(Graduate, Undergraduate/Scholarship)* [12205]

Industrial education (See Education, Industrial)

Industrial hygiene

Thompson Scholarship for Women in Safety *(Doctorate/Scholarship)* [1573]

Industry and trade

The Bruce Clement Post-Secondary Education Scholarship *(Undergraduate/Scholarship)* [8267]

EAIA Research Grants *(Other/Grant)* [4248]

Oil & Gas, Trades & Technology (OGTT) Bursary and Scholarship Awards (OGTT) *(Undergraduate/Scholarship)* [5776]

Syncrude/Athabasca University Aboriginal Scholarships *(Undergraduate/Scholarship)* [10902]

WEDA Scholarship Program *(Professional development/Scholarship)* [11979]

Infectious diseases (See also Epidemiology)

Dr. James A. Ferguson Emerging Infectious Diseases Research Initiatives for Student Enhancement Fellowship (RISE) *(Graduate/Fellowship)* [6526]

Investigators in the Pathogenesis of Infectious Disease *(Doctorate, Postdoctorate/Grant)* [2754]

ISID Small Grants *(Postdoctorate, Professional development/Grant)* [6114]

Information science and technology

AFCEA Cyber Security Scholarship *(Undergraduate, Graduate/Scholarship)* [103]

AFCEA War Veterans Scholarships *(Undergraduate/ Scholarship)* [105]

Affirm Scholarship Program *(Undergraduate/Scholarship)* [2175]

Alberta Innovates Graduate Student Scholarships *(Graduate/Scholarship)* [275]

Alberta Innovates - Technology Futures Graduate Student Scholarships in ICT *(Doctorate, Graduate, Master's/Scholarship)* [276]

APALA Scholarship *(Doctorate, Master's/Scholarship)* [1990]

Boeing Company Scholarship *(Undergraduate/ Scholarship)* [10050]

Kathi Bowles Scholarships for Women in Technology *(Undergraduate, Graduate/Scholarship)* [2311]

Christian Larew Memorial Scholarship *(Graduate/ Scholarship, Monetary)* [6838]

Clarivate Analytics/MLA Doctoral Fellowship *(Doctorate, Graduate/Fellowship)* [7215]

Edwin F. Wiegand Science & Technology Scholarship *(Undergraduate/Scholarship)* [9397]

Eli Lilly And Company/BDPA Scholarship *(Undergraduate, Graduate, Master's/Scholarship)* [2456]

Eugene Garfield Doctoral Dissertation Fellowship *(Doctorate/Fellowship)* [2497]

Graybar Canada Award of Excellence Scholarships *(Undergraduate/Scholarship)* [4347]

HostingAdvice.com Future Web Developers Annual Scholarship *(Undergraduate/Scholarship)* [5590]

Iowa Library Association Foundation Scholarships *(Graduate/Scholarship)* [6163]

(ISC)2 Foundation Information Security Undergraduate Scholarships *(Undergraduate/Scholarship)* [6024]

Maricopa County Community College District Scholarships (MCCCD) *(Undergraduate/Scholarship)* [7034]

Arthur L. Norberg Travel Fund *(Advanced Professional/Grant)* [11640]

Paul Evan Peters Fellowship *(Master's, Doctorate, Graduate/Fellowship)* [3452]

Symantec Research Labs Graduate Fellowships *(Doctorate, Graduate/Fellowship)* [8547]

Syncrude/Athabasca University Aboriginal Scholarships *(Undergraduate/Scholarship)* [10902]

Technology First / ROBERT V. MCKENNA SCHOLARSHIP *(Undergraduate/Scholarship)* [10935]

The Jack Tillson Scholarship Fund *(Graduate/Scholarship)* [6164]

The Adelle and Erwin Tomash Fellowship in the History of Information Technology *(Doctorate, Graduate/Fellowship)* [11641]

VIP Women in Technology Scholarship *(Two Year College, Undergraduate, Graduate/Scholarship)* [11856]

Wells Fargo American Indian Scholarship Program *(Undergraduate/Scholarship)* [996]

Insurance and insurance-related fields

Randy Henry Memorial Scholarship *(Undergraduate/ Scholarship)* [9343]

Intermediaries and Reinsurance Underwriters Association Summer Intern Scholarships Program *(Undergraduate/Scholarship)* [5890]

ISU Gongaware Scholarship *(Undergraduate/Scholarship)* [5762]

William H. McGannon Foundation Scholarships *(Graduate, Undergraduate/Scholarship)* [7180]

Patriot Education Scholarship Fund *(Undergraduate/ Scholarship)* [6994]

Risk Management and Insurance Scholarship *(Graduate/Scholarship)* [9886]

Surety and Fidelity Industry Intern and Scholarship Program *(Undergraduate, Graduate/Scholarship)* [10885]

Intelligence service

AFCEA War Veterans Scholarships *(Undergraduate/ Scholarship)* [105]

CFR National Intelligence Fellowships *(Professional development/Fellowship)* [3861]

Jorge Espejel Contreras IALEIA Scholarship *(Undergraduate/Scholarship)* [5930]

Henley-Putnam University Scholarships *(Other/ Scholarship)* [5931]

Interdisciplinary studies

BSF General Scholarship Awards *(College, University/Scholarship)* [2439]

Ford Foundation Dissertation Fellowship *(Postdoctorate/Fellowship)* [4672, 7572]

Ford Foundation Diversity Fellowships *(Graduate, Doctorate, Postdoctorate, Postgraduate/Fellowship)* [7573]

Ford Foundation Postdoctoral Fellowship *(Postdoctorate/Fellowship)* [4673, 7574]

Ford Foundation Predoctoral Fellowship *(Graduate, Doctorate/Fellowship)* [4674, 7575]

Heather McCallum Scholarship *(Professional development/Scholarship, Award)* [2104]

O. Ruth McQuown Scholarship - Graduate Award for Current Students *(Graduate/Scholarship)* [11572]

Interior design

Paul Arnold Memorial Scholarships *(Other/Scholarship)* [9288]

ASID Foundation Legacy Scholarships for Graduate Students *(Graduate/Scholarship)* [1486]

Eloise Pitts O'More Scholarship Fund *(Undergraduate/Scholarship)* [3616]

IDEC Special Project Grant *(Professional development/Grant)* [5888]

IFDA Student Member Scholarship *(Undergraduate/ Scholarship)* [6014]

International Furnishings and Design Association Part-time Student Scholarship *(Undergraduate/ Scholarship)* [6015]

Irene Winifred Eno Grant *(Professional development/Grant)* [1487]

Plan NH's Scholarship and Fellowship Program *(Community College, Four Year College, Undergraduate, Graduate, Vocational/Occupational/ Scholarship)* [9188]

Vectorworks Design Scholarship *(Undergraduate, Graduate/Scholarship)* [11796]

Worldstudio AIGA Scholarships *(Graduate, Undergraduate/Scholarship)* [12205]

Internal medicine (See Medicine, Internal)

International affairs and relations

Americans for Informed Democracy Global Scholar Program *(Undergraduate/Scholarship)* [1687]

ARS Lazarian Graduate Scholarship *(Graduate, Master's, Doctorate/Scholarship)* [1854]

Samuel Flagg Bemis Dissertation Research Grants *(Graduate/Grant)* [10354]

Boren Fellowships *(Graduate/Fellowship)* [5840]

Boren Scholarships *(Undergraduate, College/Scholarship)* [5841]

Burkle Center Funding for Faculty Research Working Group Projects *(Graduate/Grant)* [11546]

CFR Military Fellowships *(Professional development/Fellowship)* [3860]

CFR National Intelligence Fellowships *(Professional development/Fellowship)* [3861]

CFR Stanton Nuclear Security Fellowship *(Doctorate, Postdoctorate, Advanced Professional/Fellowship)* [3862]

CFR Volunteer Internships *(Undergraduate, Graduate/Internship)* [3863]

Donald W. F. Ching Memorial Scholarship Fund *(Undergraduate, Two Year College, Four Year College/Scholarship)* [5392]

D&A Florida Scholarships *(Undergraduate/Scholarship)* [10678]

Denton Scholarship *(Graduate/Scholarship)* [10081]

Robert A. and Barbara Divine Graduate Student Travel Fund *(Graduate/Grant)* [10355]

Alan R. and Barbara D. Finberg Fellowships *(Graduate/Fellowship)* [5634]

Mayme and Herb Frank Scholarship Program *(Graduate/Scholarship)* [1984]

Burton L. Gerber Scholarship *(Undergraduate/ Scholarship)* [2525]

Graduate Fellowships for Study of International Affairs *(Graduate, Master's/Fellowship)* [4093]

Harriet Irsay Scholarship *(Graduate, Undergraduate/ Scholarship)* [1045]

Arthur C. Helton Fellowship Program *(Undergraduate, Graduate/Fellowship)* [1489]

Conrad N. Hilton Scholarships *(Undergraduate/ Scholarship)* [4962]

International Affairs Fellowships in Japan (IAF) *(Professional development/Fellowship)* [3864]

International Affairs Fellowships in Nuclear Security (IAF-NS) *(Professional development/Fellowship)* [3865]

ISCALC International Scholarship Fund *(Undergraduate/Scholarship)* [4594]

James B. Pearson Fellowship *(Graduate/Scholarship)* [6361]

John Allen Love Scholarship *(Graduate, Undergraduate/Scholarship)* [11715]

Koren and Alice Odian Kasparian Memorial Grant *(Undergraduate/Scholarship)* [1889]

Lawrence Gelfand - Armin Rappaport - Walter LaFeber Dissertation Fellowship *(Graduate/Fellowship)* [10357]

Mackenzie King Travelling Scholarship *(Graduate/ Scholarship, Monetary)* [7183]

Mas Family Scholarship *(Graduate, Undergraduate/ Scholarship)* [7120]

MPAC-DC Graduate Policy Fellowships *(Graduate/ Fellowship)* [7517]

Myrna F. Bernath Fellowship *(Doctorate, Graduate/ Fellowship)* [10358]

National Iranian American Council Fellowships *(Graduate, Undergraduate/Fellowship)* [7956]

Pi Gamma Mu Scholarships *(Graduate/Scholarship)* [9160]

The Thomas R. Pickering Foreign Affairs Fellowship *(Graduate, Undergraduate/Fellowship)* [11346, 12050]

Rangel Graduate Fellowship *(Graduate/Fellowship)* [9499]

Herbert Roback Scholarship *(Graduate, Master's/ Scholarship)* [7579]

Harold W. Rosenthal Fellowship in International Relations *(Professional development/Fellowship)* [2264]

SHAFR Dissertation Completion Fellowship *(Doctorate/Fellowship)* [10359]

Stuart L. Bernath Dissertation Research Grant *(Graduate/Grant)* [10360]

TCAdvance Scholarship *(Undergraduate/Scholarship)* [11144]

USGLC Internships - Communications *(Undergraduate, Doctorate/Internship)* [11368]

USGLC Internships - Government Relations *(Undergraduate, Graduate/Internship)* [11369]

USGLC Internships - Outreach *(Undergraduate, Graduate/Internship)* [11370]

USGLC Internships - Policy *(Undergraduate, Graduate/Internship)* [11371]

W. Stull Holt Dissertation Fellowship *(Graduate/Fellowship)* [10361]

Women In Defense HORIZONS Scholarship *(Graduate, Undergraduate/Scholarship)* [12133]

International trade

Merchants Exchange Scholarship *(Undergraduate, Vocational/Occupational, Graduate, Professional development/Scholarship)* [7266]

Italian studies (See also Area and ethnic studies)

Agnes E. Vaghi Scholarship (Undergraduate/Scholarship) [7960]

Japanese studies (See also Area and ethnic studies)

Mary Jane Hendrie Memorial Scholarships (Graduate, Undergraduate/Scholarship) [11690]

Japan Foundation, New York Doctoral Candidates (Doctorate/Fellowship) [6233]

Japan Foundation, New York Scholars and Researchers (Long-Term) (Professional development/Fellowship) [6234]

Japan Foundation, New York Scholars and Researchers (Short-Term) (Professional development/Fellowship) [6235]

KCC-JEE Graduate Fellowships (Graduate/Fellowship) [6580]

The Shincho Graduate Fellowship for Study in Japan (Graduate/Fellowship) [6509]

Jazz (See Music, Jazz)

Jewish studies (See also Area and ethnic studies)

Abraham and Rachela Melezin Memorial Fellowship (Doctorate, Postdoctorate/Fellowship) [12235]

AJL Scholarship for Library School Students (Graduate/Scholarship) [2229]

Berkowitz Fellowship (Professional development/Fellowship) [11032]

CJH Graduate Research Fellowships (Doctorate/Fellowship) [3221]

CJH-NEH Fellowships for Senior Scholars (Doctorate/Fellowship) [3222]

CJH-Prins Foundation Fellowships for Senior Scholars (Doctorate/Fellowship) [3223]

CJH-Prins Foundation Post-Doctoral and Early Career Fellowship for Emigrating Scholars (Professional development, Postdoctorate/Fellowship) [3224]

CJH Visiting Scholars Program (Doctorate/Fellowship) [3225]

Mark & Dorothy Danzker Scholarship (Postgraduate/Scholarship) [6305]

Lee K. Feine Scholarship (Undergraduate, Graduate/Scholarship) [7790]

Jack Gitlitz Memorial Scholarship - Israel (Graduate, Undergraduate/Scholarship) [6291]

HBI Gilda Slifka Internship Program (Graduate, Undergraduate/Internship) [2680]

HBI Scholar-in-Residence Program (Undergraduate, Graduate, Postgraduate/Scholarship) [2681]

Vladimir and Pearl Heifetz Memorial Fellowship (Undergraduate, Graduate, Postgraduate/Fellowship) [12236]

Aleksander and Alicja Hertz Memorial Fellowship (Doctorate, Postdoctorate/Fellowship) [12237]

International Scholarship Programs for Community Service (Undergraduate/Scholarship) [7249]

JEA Action Research Initiative (Postgraduate/Grant) [6303]

Joseph S. Steinberg Emerging Jewish Filmmaker Fellowship (Undergraduate, Graduate/Fellowship) [3226]

Judaic Studies and/or Studies in Israel (Undergraduate, Postgraduate/Scholarship) [6307]

The Loewenstein-Wiener Fellowship (Professional development, Doctorate, Postdoctorate/Fellowship) [1061]

MFJC Doctoral Scholarships (Doctorate/Scholarship) [7250]

MFJC Fellowship Grants (Professional development/Fellowship) [7251]

Musia & Leon Schwartz Scholarship (Graduate/Scholarship) [6299]

Bernard Michael Tarshis Memorial Scholarship (Undergraduate/Scholarship) [6300]

Maria Salit-Gitelson Tell Memorial Fellowship (Postdoctorate, Doctorate/Fellowship) [12240]

Dora and Mayer Tendler Endowed Fellowship (Doctorate, Postdoctorate/Fellowship) [12241]

The Tikvah Fellowship (Undergraduate/Fellowship) [11034]

Ephraim E. Urbach Post-Doctoral Fellowship (Postdoctorate/Fellowship) [7252]

Joel A. Weinstein Memorial Scholarship (Postgraduate, Undergraduate/Scholarship) [6308]

Wexner Graduate Fellowship / Davidson Scholars Program (Graduate/Fellowship) [12003]

Journalism

Leroy F. Aarons Scholarship Award (Graduate, Undergraduate/Scholarship) [7988]

Abe Fellowships for Journalists (Professional development/Fellowship) [10242]

Kyutaro and Yasuo Abiko Memorial Scholarship (Undergraduate/Scholarship) [6243]

Al Muammar Scholarships for Journalism (Undergraduate/Scholarship) [1766]

Alaska Press Club Scholarships (Undergraduate/Scholarship) [11435]

Floyd S. Alford Jr. Scholarships (Undergraduate/Scholarship) [11173]

Allison E. Fisher Scholarship (Undergraduate, Graduate/Scholarship) [7615]

Ameel J. Fisher Scholarship (Undergraduate/Scholarship) [11174]

American Quarter Horse Foundation Scholarships (Undergraduate, Graduate/Scholarship) [1310]

Ann Liguori Foundation Sports Media Scholarship (Graduate, Undergraduate/Scholarship) [8366]

APSA Congressional Fellowships for Journalists (Advanced Professional, Professional development/Fellowship) [1247]

APSA-MCI Communications Congressional Fellowship (Advanced Professional, Professional development, Postdoctorate/Fellowship) [1250]

Ardis Kipp Cohoon Scholarship (Undergraduate/Scholarship) [11175]

ARS Lazarian Graduate Scholarship (Graduate, Master's, Doctorate/Scholarship) [1854]

ASA Inc. Journalism Internship Program (Undergraduate/Internship) [1864]

Asia Pacific Foundation of Canada Media Fellowships (Professional development/Fellowship) [4712]

AT&T Business Internship Awards (Undergraduate, Graduate/Internship) [11176]

Atkinson Fellowships in Public Policy (Professional development/Fellowship) [2338]

Elaine Atwood Scholarship (Undergraduate, Graduate/Scholarship) [11470]

Francis Warren Baker Memorial Scholarships (Undergraduate/Scholarship) [10094]

Jim Batten Community Newspaper Internship (Undergraduate/Internship) [11177]

N.S. Beinstock Fellowships (Other/Fellowship) [9469]

Pete and Ellen Bensley Memorial Scholarship Fund (Undergraduate/Scholarship) [4721]

Bernard Kilgore Memorial Scholarship (Undergraduate/Scholarship) [8282]

Bob Baxter Scholarship (Graduate, Undergraduate/Scholarship) [8046]

Bob East Scholarship (Graduate, Undergraduate/Scholarship) [8047]

Bob Quincy Scholarship (Undergraduate/Scholarship) [11178]

William (Billbo) Boston/Harold Knopp Scholarship (Undergraduate/Scholarship) [8833]

Ed Bradley Scholarships (Undergraduate/Scholarship) [9470]

Carlos M. Castaneda Journalism Scholarship (Graduate/Scholarship) [4840]

Charles McCorkle Hauser Scholarship (Undergraduate/Scholarship) [11179]

CJF Canadian Journalism Fellowships (Graduate, Other, Undergraduate/Fellowship) [6620]

Michele Clark Fellowships (Undergraduate/Fellowship) [9471]

George H. Clinton Scholarship (Undergraduate/Scholarship) [8837]

D&A Florida Scholarships (Undergraduate/Scholarship) [10678]

David Julian Whichard Scholarship (Undergraduate/Scholarship) [11180]

Frank del Olmo Memorial Scholarships (Undergraduate/Scholarship) [3197]

Dr. Julianne Malveaux Scholarship (Undergraduate/Scholarship) [7668]

The Harold K. Douthit Scholarship (Undergraduate/Scholarship) [8580]

Drue Smith / Society of Professional Journalists' Scholarship Fund (Undergraduate/Scholarship) [3614]

Richard Drukker Memorial Scholarships (Undergraduate/Scholarship) [8283]

Edward Heywood Megson Scholarship (Undergraduate/Scholarship) [11183]

Edward Jackson International Travel Award (Undergraduate/Award) [11184]

Elizabeth Neuffer Fellowship (Other/Fellowship) [6148]

Erwin Potts Scholarship (Undergraduate/Scholarship) [11186]

Faith Initiatives Internships - New York (Undergraduate, Graduate/Internship) [4981]

Fellowships for Creative and Performing Artists and Writers (Professional development/Fellowship) [490]

Reese Felts Scholarships (Undergraduate/Scholarship) [11187]

Alan R. and Barbara D. Finberg Fellowships (Graduate/Fellowship) [5634]

Flora Lewis Fellowship (Graduate, Undergraduate/Scholarship) [8784]

Florida Outdoor Writers Association Scholarships (FOWA) (Undergraduate/Scholarship) [4644]

Emanuel R. Freedman Scholarship (Graduate, Undergraduate/Scholarship) [8785]

Joel Garcia Memorial Scholarship (Undergraduate/Scholarship) [3198]

George Foreman Tribute to Lyndon B. Johnson (Undergraduate/Scholarship) [9472]

Joy Gibson MATC Cohort Award (Undergraduate/Scholarship) [11188]

Keith Gilmore Foundation - Diploma Scholarships (Other/Scholarship) [4970]

Keith Gilmore Foundation - Postgraduate Scholarships (Postgraduate/Scholarship) [4971]

Keith Gilmore Foundation - Undergraduate Scholarships (Undergraduate/Scholarship) [4972]

GLAAD Spanish-Language and Latino Media Internships - Los Angeles (Undergraduate, Graduate/Internship) [4984]

GLAAD Youth Issues Internships - New York (Undergraduate, Graduate/Internship) [4985]

Glenn Keever Scholarship (Undergraduate/Scholarship) [11189]

Howard L. Green Scholarships (Undergraduate/Scholarship) [8273]

Elizabeth Greenhalgh Memorial Scholarships in Journalism, Graphic Arts, or Photography (Undergraduate/Scholarship) [12136]

Greg Clerk Award (Advanced Professional, Professional development/Award) [6621]

Guy P. Gannett Scholarship Fund (Undergraduate/Scholarship) [6981]

The Alison Hardy Tea and Bursary (Undergraduate/Recognition) [7816]

Harper's Magazine Scholarships (Graduate, Undergraduate/Scholarship) [8786]

Harriet Irsay Scholarship (Graduate, Undergraduate/Scholarship) [1045]

Harvey Fellows Program (Graduate/Fellowship) [7519]

INF Scholarships (Undergraduate/Scholarship) [6166]

Inter American Press Association Scholarships (Undergraduate/Scholarship) [10253]

International Foodservice Editorial Council Scholarship (Graduate/Scholarship) [6007]

Iowa Journalism Institute Scholarships (Graduate, Undergraduate/Scholarship) [6167]

Irene Corbally Kuhn Scholarship (Graduate, Undergraduate/Scholarship) [8787]

James Davis Scholarship (Undergraduate/Scholarship) [11190]

James F. Hurley III Bicentennial Merit Scholarship (Undergraduate/Scholarship) [11191]

JCCF Equal Voice Journalism Scholarship *(Professional development/Scholarship)* [11591]

JEA Future Journalism Teacher Scholarships *(Undergraduate, Master's/Scholarship)* [6336]

Journalist of the Year Scholarships *(Undergraduate, Monetary, Scholarship)* [6337]

Kaiser Media Fellowships in Health Reporting *(Advanced Professional, Professional development/Fellowship)* [6355]

Kathryn M. Cronin Scholarship *(Undergraduate, Graduate/Scholarship)* [11192]

Kays Gary Scholarship *(Undergraduate/Scholarship)* [11193]

Anna-Maria and Stephen M. Kellen Fellowships *(Professional development/Fellowship)* [809]

Kit C. King Graduate Scholarships *(Graduate/Scholarship)* [8048]

Kiplinger Fellowship *(Professional development/Fellowship)* [8605]

John S. Knight Journalism Fellowships *(Other/Fellowship)* [6576]

Knight-Wallace Reporting Fellowships *(Professional development/Fellowship)* [11870]

William D. Krahling Excellence in Journalism Scholarship *(Undergraduate/Scholarship)* [403]

Elaine Johnson Lampert Journalism Memorial Adelphe Scholarship *(Undergraduate/Award)* [6454]

Lester G. Benz Memorial Scholarship for College Journalism Study *(Other/Scholarship)* [9463]

Lilly Scholarships in Religion for Journalists *(Other/Scholarship)* [9633]

Kay Longcope Scholarship Award *(Graduate, Undergraduate/Scholarship)* [7990]

Warren Mack Scholarship *(Undergraduate/Scholarship)* [6333]

Art Margosian Scholarship *(Undergraduate/Scholarship)* [6334]

Marjorie Usher Ragan Scholarship *(Undergraduate/Scholarship)* [11197]

Mas Family Scholarship *(Graduate, Undergraduate/Scholarship)* [7120]

The Maxwell Scholarship in Graduate Medical Journalism *(Graduate/Scholarship)* [11198]

Durwood McAlister Scholarship *(Undergraduate/Scholarship)* [4935]

McClatchy Minority Scholarship and Fellowship *(Undergraduate/Scholarship)* [10617]

McCloy Fellowships in Environmental Policy *(Professional development/Fellowship)* [811]

McCloy Fellowships in Journalism *(Professional development/Fellowship)* [812]

Anne O'Hare McCormick Memorial Scholarship *(Graduate/Scholarship)* [8393]

C.A. "Pete" McKnight Scholarships *(High School/Scholarship)* [11199]

Les McLaughlin Scholarship *(Undergraduate, University, College, Vocational/Occupational/Scholarship)* [12346]

The Michener-Deacon Fellowship for Investigative Journalism *(Professional development/Fellowship)* [4655]

The Michener-Deacon Fellowship for Journalism Education *(Professional development/Fellowship)* [4656]

Mike Reynolds Scholarship *(Undergraduate/Scholarship)* [9473]

Jacque I. Minnotte Health Reporting Fellowship *(Other/Fellowship)* [9474]

Morris Newspaper Corporation Scholarship *(Undergraduate/Scholarship)* [4936]

Muddy Waters Scholarships *(Undergraduate, Graduate/Scholarship)* [2632]

Edward R. Murrow Press Fellowships *(Professional development/Fellowship)* [3866]

National Iranian American Council Fellowships *(Graduate, Undergraduate/Fellowship)* [7956]

Edward J. Nell Memorial Scholarships in Journalism *(Undergraduate/Scholarship)* [9464]

New York Financial Writers' Associations Scholarships *(Graduate, Undergraduate/Scholarship)* [8311]

NPPF Still & Multimedia Scholarship *(Undergraduate/Scholarship)* [8049]

NPPF TV News Scholarship *(Undergraduate/Scholarship)* [8050]

NYFWA Scholarships *(Undergraduate, Graduate/Scholarship)* [8312]

Ohio Newspaper Association Minority Scholarship *(Undergraduate/Scholarship)* [8581]

ONWA Annual Scholarship *(Undergraduate/Scholarship)* [8582]

Paul B. & Aline Flynn Scholarship Fund *(Undergraduate/Scholarship)* [10698]

Paul Green Houston Scholarship *(Undergraduate/Scholarship)* [11201]

The Scott Pearlman Field Awards *(Professional development/Award)* [4470]

Peter DeWitt Pruden and Phyllis Harrill Pruden Scholarship *(Undergraduate/Scholarship)* [11202]

The PHD Scholarship *(Undergraduate/Scholarship)* [1954]

Philip Alston Scholarship *(Undergraduate/Scholarship)* [11203]

Stephen D. Pisinski Memorial Scholarship *(Undergraduate/Scholarship)* [9436]

Robert Pittman Scholarships-Internships *(Undergraduate/Scholarship, Internship)* [11204]

Carter Pitts Scholarships *(Undergraduate/Scholarship)* [6168]

Lou and Carole Prato Sports Reporting Scholarship *(Undergraduate/Scholarship)* [9475]

Presidents Scholarship *(Undergraduate/Scholarship)* [9476]

Pulliam/Kilgore Freedom of Information Internships *(Undergraduate/Internship)* [10503]

Quincy Sharpe Mills Memorial Scholarship *(Undergraduate/Scholarship)* [11205]

Raleigh Mann Scholarship *(Undergraduate/Scholarship)* [11206]

Reid Blackburn Scholarship *(Undergraduate/Scholarship)* [8051]

Reuters Fellowship *(Graduate, Undergraduate/Fellowship)* [8788]

Reuters Institute Visiting Fellowships *(Professional development/Fellowship)* [11660]

Richard J. Roth Journalism Fellowship *(Graduate/Fellowship)* [8328]

Rick Brewer Scholarship *(Undergraduate/Scholarship)* [11207]

Robert Winchester Dodson Scholarship *(Undergraduate/Scholarship)* [11208]

Eugene L. Roberts, Jr. Prize *(Undergraduate/Prize)* [11209]

William C. Rogers Scholarship *(Undergraduate/Scholarship)* [4937]

Roy Rowan Scholarship *(Graduate, Undergraduate/Scholarship)* [8789]

SAJA Student Scholarship *(Undergraduate, Graduate/Scholarship)* [10604]

David R. Schweisberg Memorial Scholarship *(Graduate, Undergraduate/Scholarship)* [8790]

SCSPA Scholarship *(Graduate/Scholarship)* [10618]

SCSPA Yearbook Scholarship *(Undergraduate/Scholarship)* [10619]

Carole Simpson Scholarship *(Undergraduate/Scholarship)* [9477]

A.C. Snow and Katherine Snow Smith Scholarship *(High School/Scholarship)* [11210]

Sports Internships - Los Angeles *(Undergraduate, Graduate/Internship)* [4989]

Standard and Poor's Award for Economic and Business Reporting - S&P Scholarships *(Graduate, Undergraduate/Scholarship)* [8791]

Steve Mason Sports Media Scholarship *(Graduate, Undergraduate/Scholarship)* [7991]

Steve Petix Journalism Scholarship *(Undergraduate/Scholarship)* [9853]

H.L. Stevenson Fellowship *(Graduate, Undergraduate/Fellowship)* [8792]

Jay A. Strassberg Memorial Scholarship *(Undergraduate/Scholarship)* [2855]

Sturgulewski Family Scholarship *(Graduate, Undergraduate/Scholarship)* [11495]

Hatton W. Sumners Endowed Undergraduate School Scholarships *(Undergraduate/Scholarship)* [10878]

Hatton W. Sumners Non-Endowed Undergraduate and Graduate Scholarships *(Undergraduate, Graduate/Scholarship)* [10879]

Stan Swinton Fellowship *(Graduate, Undergraduate/Fellowship)* [8793]

Taylor/Blakeslee University Fellowships *(Graduate/Award)* [3848]

THEO WILSON SCHOLARSHIP *(Graduate, Undergraduate/Scholarship)* [8794]

Tom Bost Scholarship *(Undergraduate/Scholarship)* [11213]

Trans Issues Internships - New York *(Undergraduate, Graduate/Internship)* [4990]

Tucker Family Scholarship *(Undergraduate/Scholarship)* [11214]

UAA GCI Scholarship *(Undergraduate/Scholarship)* [11502]

UAA Kimura Scholarship Fund for Photography *(Undergraduate/Scholarship)* [11504]

UAF College of Liberal Arts - Anchorage Daily News Journalism Awards *(Undergraduate/Scholarship)* [11514]

University Journalism Scholarships *(Undergraduate/Scholarship)* [8583]

Flo Whyard-Holland America Line-Westours Scholarship *(Undergraduate/Scholarship)* [12391]

Tom Wicker Award *(Graduate/Award)* [11216]

Glenn Wilson Broadcast Journalism Scholarship *(Undergraduate/Scholarship)* [8887]

Pete Wilson Journalism Scholarship *(Graduate, Undergraduate/Scholarship)* [9478]

WTVD Scholarship *(Undergraduate/Scholarship)* [11217]

Korean studies

Fall Fellowships in Korean Studies *(Other/Fellowship)* [6594]

Korean Language Study Awards *(Graduate, Professional development/Scholarship)* [6595]

Labor

LAWCHA Graduate Student Travel Grants *(Graduate/Grant)* [6628]

Upjohn Institute Early Career Research Awards (ECRA) *(Professional development/Grant, Award)* [11759]

Labor relations (See Industrial and labor relations)

Laboratory technology (See Medical laboratory technology)

Land economics (See Land management)

Land management

AIERF Undergraduate Scholarship *(Undergraduate/Scholarship)* [1764]

HSF/Marathon Oil College Scholarship Program *(Undergraduate/Scholarship)* [5531]

Ivanhoe Foundation Fellowship *(Master's/Fellowship)* [6184]

NASLR Mined Land Reclamation Educational Grant *(Undergraduate/Grant)* [7700]

NGC College Scholarships *(Graduate, Undergraduate/Scholarship)* [7900]

Landscape architecture and design

AIA Alaska College Scholarship Program *(Graduate, Undergraduate/Scholarship)* [1007]

ASLA Council of Fellows *(Undergraduate/Scholarship)* [1491]

ASLA Council of Fellows Scholarships *(Undergraduate/Scholarship)* [6646]

CLCA Landscape Educational Advancement Foundation Scholarship *(Undergraduate/Scholarship)* [2818]

Enid W. and Bernard B. Spigel Architectural Scholarship *(Graduate/Scholarship)* [5269]

The Garden Club Council of Winston-Salem and Forsyth County Scholarship *(Undergraduate/Scholarship)* [12079]

Hawaii Chapter/David T. Woolsey Scholarship (Undergraduate, Graduate, Professional development/Scholarship) [6647]

Steven G. King Play Environments Scholarship (Undergraduate, Master's/Scholarship) [6648]

Landscape Forms Design for People Scholarship (Undergraduate/Scholarship) [6649]

Mellon Fellowships in Urban Landscape Studies (Graduate, Master's, Doctorate/Fellowship) [4233]

MNLA Academic Scholarship (Undergraduate/Scholarship) [7317]

NGC College Scholarships (Graduate, Undergraduate/Scholarship) [7900]

Courtland P. Paul Scholarships (Undergraduate/Scholarship) [6650]

Plan NH's Scholarship and Fellowship Program (Community College, Four Year College, Undergraduate, Graduate, Vocational/Occupational/Scholarship) [9188]

Peridian International, Inc./Rae L. Price, FASLA Scholarship (Undergraduate/Scholarship) [1492]

Peridian International, Inc./Rae L. Price, FASLA Scholarships (Undergraduate/Scholarship) [6651]

Rain Bird Intelligent Use of Water Scholarship (Undergraduate/Scholarship) [6652, 9491]

Vectorworks Design Scholarship (Undergraduate, Graduate/Scholarship) [11796]

Worldstudio AIGA Scholarships (Graduate, Undergraduate/Scholarship) [12205]

Languages (See Foreign languages)

Latin American studies (See also Area and ethnic studies)

Arthur M. Schlesinger Jr. Research Fellowship (Professional development/Fellowship) [6531]

FAIC Latin American and Caribbean Scholars Program (Other/Scholarship) [1025]

Foundation of American Institute for Conservation Lecture Grants (Other/Grant) [1026]

Catarino and Evangelina Hernández Research Fellowships in Latino History (Advanced Professional/Fellowship) [10996]

IAF Fellowships (Doctorate/Fellowship) [5883]

Leo S. Rowe Pan American Fund (Graduate, Undergraduate/Loan) [8739]

Thesaurus Linguae Latinae Fellowship (TTL) (Doctorate/Fellowship) [10312]

UC MEXUS-CICESE Graduate Student Short-Term Research and Training Program (Master's, Doctorate, Postdoctorate/Grant) [11539]

UC MEXUS Dissertation Research Grants (Graduate/Grant) [11554]

UC MEXUS Small Grants for UC Postdocs (Postdoctorate/Grant) [11558]

UC MEXUS Small Grants for UC Students (Graduate, Postdoctorate/Grant) [11559]

UF Center for Latin American Studies FLAS Summer Fellowships (Master's, Graduate, Undergraduate/Award, Fellowship) [11570]

Law

1L and 2L Diversity Fellowship Programs (Undergraduate/Fellowship) [5042]

1L Diversity Fellowships (Graduate/Fellowship) [4827]

1L SUMMER INTERNSHIP PROGRAM Prudential Financial, Inc. (Postgraduate/Internship) [7600]

AAJ Trial Advocacy Scholarship (Undergraduate/Scholarship) [581]

AALL Leadership Academy Grant (Professional development/Grant) [585]

AALL Minority Leadership Development Award (Graduate/Award) [586]

AALL Research Fund (Professional development/Grant) [587]

AALL Technical Services SIS Active Member Grant (Professional development/Grant) [588]

AALL Technical Services SIS Experienced Member General Grant (Professional development/Grant) [589]

AALL Technical Services SIS Leadership Academy Grant (Professional development/Grant) [590]

AALL Technical Services SIS Management Institute Grant (Professional development/Grant) [591]

AALL Technical Services SIS New Member General Grant (Professional development/Grant) [592]

AALL/Wolters Kluwer Law & Business Grants (Professional development/Grant) [593]

AAUW Selected Professions Fellowships (Graduate, Master's, Doctorate/Fellowship) [35]

The Abas Law Foundation Scholarship (Graduate, Postgraduate/Scholarship) [1992]

ABF Law and Social Science Dissertation Fellowship and Mentoring Program (Graduate/Fellowship) [690]

ABF Montgomery Summer Research Diversity Fellowships in Law and Social Science (Undergraduate/Fellowship) [691]

ABF/NSF Doctoral Fellowships Program in Law & Inequality (Doctorate/Fellowship, Award) [692]

Abram D. and Maxine H. Londa Scholarship (Undergraduate/Scholarship) [8290]

Accenture American Indian Scholarship Fund (Graduate, Undergraduate/Scholarship) [993]

ACJA/LAE Student Scholarship Program - Graduate Level (Graduate, Master's, Doctorate/Scholarship) [838]

Adler Pollock & Sheehan Diversity Scholarships (Undergraduate/Fellowship) [77]

Affirmative Action Student Scholarship Mini-Grant Travel Awards (Undergraduate, Master's/Grant) [41]

Aiello Harris Legal Scholarships (Undergraduate, Graduate/Scholarship) [144]

Justice John F. Aiso Scholarship (Undergraduate/Scholarship) [6237]

Akron Bar Association Foundation Scholarships (Undergraduate/Scholarship) [203]

Alan Holoch Memorial Grant (Professional development/Grant) [594]

Albert J. and Mae Lee Memorial Scholarship (Undergraduate/Scholarship) [8987]

Alexander D. Pringle Memorial Scholarship (Advanced Professional/Scholarship) [9328]

Alexander G. Gray, Jr., Scholarship Award (Graduate/Scholarship) [7156]

Neil Alexander Scholarships (Undergraduate/Scholarship) [7586]

ALL-SIS Conference of Newer Law Librarians Grants (Professional development/Grant) [595]

Alliance Defending Freedom - Blackstone Legal Fellowships (Undergraduate/Fellowship) [359]

Allmand Law Scholarship Contest (Undergraduate/Scholarship) [372]

Almeric L. Christian Memorial Scholarship (Graduate/Scholarship) [11829]

Tillie B. Alperin Scholarship (Graduate/Scholarship) [11595]

The Alsandor Law Firm Scholarship Contest (Undergraduate/Scholarship) [407]

American Association of University Women Selected Professions Fellowships (Other/Fellowship) [668]

American Counsel Association Scholarships (Undergraduate/Scholarship) [832]

American Enterprise Institute National Research Initiative Fellowships (NRI) (Professional development/Fellowship) [872]

American Judges Association Law Student Essay Competition (Undergraduate/Prize) [1066]

American Psychology-Law Society Dissertation Awards (Graduate/Award) [1291]

American Psychology-Law Society Student Grants-In-Aid (Graduate/Grant) [1292]

Grace Andow Memorial Scholarship (Undergraduate, Graduate/Scholarship) [6244]

Anheuser-Busch NAPABA Law Foundation Presidential Scholarships (Undergraduate/Scholarship) [7601]

Ann Marie Bredefeld Scholarship (Undergraduate/Scholarship) [8988]

Annual Eichholz Scholarship (Graduate/Scholarship) [4324]

Annual Young, Marr & Associates Scholarship (Undergraduate/Scholarship) [1723]

APABA Silicon Valley Achievement Scholarship (Advanced Professional/Scholarship) [1988]

Appalachian School of Law Merit Scholarship Program (Undergraduate/Scholarship) [1756]

Armenian Bar Association Scholarships (Graduate/Scholarship) [1846]

Kush Arora Federal Criminal Justice Reform Scholarships (Undergraduate, Graduate/Scholarship) [9279]

ARS Lazarian Graduate Scholarship (Graduate, Master's, Doctorate/Scholarship) [1854]

Arthur Lockwood Beneventi Law Scholarship (Undergraduate/Scholarship, Award, Monetary) [8093]

Benjamin Asbell Memorial Awards (Graduate, Undergraduate/Scholarship) [2846]

Athalie Clarke Endowed Scholarship (Undergraduate/Scholarship) [8989]

Attorney-CPA Foundation Scholarships (Postgraduate/Scholarship) [430]

H. Thomas Austern Memorial Writing Competition (Doctorate/Award, Prize) [4664]

William Stone Ayres Scholarship (Graduate/Scholarship) [4146]

Baker Donelson Diversity Scholarship (Undergraduate/Scholarship) [2406]

Baker McKenzie Diversity Fellowship (Postgraduate, Professional development/Fellowship) [2411]

Baker McKenzie Graduate Legal Studies Scholarships (Graduate, Professional development/Scholarship) [2412]

BakerHostetler Diversity Fellowship Program (Undergraduate/Fellowship) [2408]

Balfour Scholarship (Graduate/Scholarship) [9087]

Mark T. Banner Scholarships for Law Students (Postdoctorate/Scholarship) [6873]

Bar President's Scholarship (Undergraduate/Scholarship) [11931]

Barbara A. Shacochis Scholarship (Undergraduate/Scholarship) [8990]

Eivind H. Barth, Jr. Memorial Award (Undergraduate, Graduate/Scholarship) [2847]

Bay Area Minority Law Student Scholarship (Graduate, Undergraduate/Scholarship) [2433]

Beck-Pfann Memorial Scholarship (Undergraduate/Scholarship) [8991]

Harvey Bell Memorial Prize (Graduate/Prize, Scholarship) [11674]

Benjamin G. Shatz Scholarship (Undergraduate/Scholarship) [8992]

Viscount Bennett Fellowship (Graduate/Fellowship) [2918]

Benson & Bingham First Annual Scholarship (Graduate/Scholarship) [2475]

Benson Law Firm Scholarship Contest (Undergraduate/Scholarship) [2477]

Berkowitz Fellowship (Professional development/Fellowship) [11032]

Robert L. Bernstein Fellowships in International Human Rights (Graduate/Fellowship) [5630]

Beverly Estate Scholarship (Undergraduate/Scholarship) [4147]

Bick Bickson Scholarship Fund (Undergraduate, Graduate/Award) [5383]

Bohemian Lawyers Association of Chicago Scholarships (Graduate/Scholarship) [2649]

Aaron J. Boria, PLLC, Scholarship (Undergraduate, Graduate/Scholarship) [2659]

George and Mary Brammer Scholarship (Undergraduate/Scholarship) [4148]

Brian Dane Cleary Memorial Scholarship (Undergraduate/Scholarship) [8993]

The Phyllis Lister-Brown Memorial Scholarship (Undergraduate/Scholarship) [11146]

Angela Faye Brown Video Essay Contest (Graduate/Scholarship) [2717]

Peggy Browning Fund - Chicago School-Year Fellowships (Graduate, Undergraduate/Fellowship) [2729]

Brylak Law Safety Scholarship Contest (Undergraduate/Scholarship) [2734]

Buckfire & Buckfire, P.C. Law School Diversity Scholarships (Graduate/Scholarship) [2736]

Buder Scholarships for American Indian Law Students (Undergraduate/Scholarship) [11921]

William S. Bullinger Scholarships (Doctorate/Scholarship) [4506]

C. Bainbridge Smith Scholarship *(Undergraduate/ Scholarship)* [8299]

Johnston Cabaniss Scholarships *(Graduate/Scholarship)* [226]

California Bar Foundation 3L Diversity Scholarship *(Undergraduate/Scholarship)* [2789, 3812, 10602]

California ChangeLawyers 1L scholarship *(Graduate/Scholarship)* [2790]

California Consumer Attorney P.C.s Annual Consumer Advocacy Scholarship *(Undergraduate, Graduate/Scholarship)* [2792]

CALL/ACBD Education Reserve Fund Grant *(Professional development/Grant)* [2899]

CALL/ACBD Research Grants *(Graduate/Grant)* [2900]

CALT Prize for Academic Excellence *(Other/Prize)* [2904]

Camille F. Gravel, Jr. Scholarship *(Professional development/Scholarship)* [6898]

Brian Campion Scholarship *(Graduate, Undergraduate/Scholarship)* [12300]

Canadian Energy Law Foundation Graduate Scholarship in Law *(Advanced Professional/Scholarship)* [2962]

Canadian Institute for Advanced Legal Studies French Language Scholarships *(Graduate, Advanced Professional/Scholarship)* [5793]

Canadian IT Law Association Student Writing Contest *(Undergraduate/Prize)* [3132]

CAPSLE Bursary. *(Graduate/Fellowship)* [2908]

Robert C. Carson Memorial Bursary *(Undergraduate/Scholarship)* [287]

Catzman Award for Professionalism and Civility *(Advanced Professional, Professional development/ Award)* [96]

Ben and Vicky Cayetano Scholarship Fund *(Undergraduate, College, University, Two Year College/ Scholarship)* [5389]

CCLA Summer Legal Volunteer Opportunities for Law Students and Law Graduates *(Graduate, Undergraduate/Internship)* [2948]

CEJIL Legal Internships *(Graduate, Professional development/Internship)* [3231]

CHCI Graduate Fellowship Program *(Graduate, Professional development/Fellowship)* [3746]

CHRGJ Emerging Human Rights Scholarship Conference *(Graduate/Scholarship)* [8358]

CHRGJ International Human Rights Fellowships *(Doctorate, Professional development/Fellowship)* [8359]

CHRGJ Students Human Rights Scholars Program *(Graduate, Advanced Professional, Professional development/Scholarship)* [8360]

The Christine Mirzayan Science & Technology Policy Graduate Fellowship Program *(Graduate, Postdoctorate, High School/Fellowship)* [7571]

CISDL Global Research Fellowship - Associate Fellows *(Graduate/Fellowship)* [3257]

CISDL Global Research Fellowship - Legal Research Fellows *(Graduate/Fellowship)* [3258]

CISDL Global Research Fellowships - Senior Research Fellows *(Other/Fellowship)* [3259]

City Bar Diversity Fellowship Program *(Undergraduate/Fellowship)* [8300]

Claude T Coffman Scholarship *(Graduate/Scholarship)* [11596]

John Colvin Law Award *(Graduate/Scholarship)* [3546]

Community Legal Services of Philadelphia Fellowships *(Postgraduate, Graduate/Fellowship)* [3729]

Cooley Diversity Fellowship *(Graduate, Undergraduate/Fellowship)* [3826]

Cores & Associates Scholarship Contest *(Undergraduate/Scholarship)* [3835]

Hon. Joseph W. Cowgill Memorial Award *(Undergraduate, Graduate/Scholarship)* [2848]

Craig Lensch Memorial Scholarship *(Undergraduate/Scholarship)* [2710]

Mable B. Crawford Memorial Scholarships *(Undergraduate/Scholarship)* [11444]

Cross & Smith Annual $1,000 College Scholarship *(Two Year College, Undergraduate, Graduate/ Scholarship)* [3920]

Crush the LSAT Scholarship Program *(Undergraduate, Graduate/Scholarship)* [3928]

CTRF Scholarships for Graduate Study in Transportation *(Graduate/Scholarship)* [3134]

Cuban American Bar Association Scholarships *(Professional development/Scholarship)* [3935]

John J. Curtin, Jr. Fellowships *(Undergraduate/Fellowship)* [688]

D&A Florida Scholarships *(Undergraduate/Scholarship)* [10678]

The Hugh and Hazel Darling Dean's Scholarship *(Undergraduate/Scholarship)* [8994]

Darling Foundation Endowed School of Law Scholarship *(Undergraduate/Scholarship)* [8995]

David and Camille Boatwright Endowed Scholarship *(Undergraduate/Scholarship)* [8996]

Davis Wright Tremaine 1L Diversity Scholarship *(Undergraduate/Scholarship)* [3979]

DBA Scholarships *(Undergraduate/Scholarship)* [4130]

DeVries Law School Scholarship *(Undergraduate/ Scholarship)* [4070]

Dezao Legal Awards *(Advanced Professional/Scholarship)* [6704]

Diagnosis Delayed Scholarship *(Graduate/Scholarship)* [4076]

Diana M. Priestly Memorial Scholarship *(Undergraduate/Scholarship)* [2901]

Carol DiMaiti Scholarship *(Undergraduate/Scholarship)* [7124]

Raymond DiPaglia Endowment Scholarship *(Undergraduate/Scholarship)* [4149]

Discover Bar Exam Loans *(Graduate/Loan, Scholarship)* [4109]

Discover Law Loans *(Graduate/Loan, Scholarship)* [4112]

Diversity Fellowship Program (DFP) *(Undergraduate/Fellowship)* [7466]

Diversity in Psychology and Law Research Award *(Undergraduate, Graduate/Grant, Award)* [1293]

Diversity Scholars Awards *(Undergraduate/Award, Recognition)* [3810]

Diversity Scholarship *(Graduate/Scholarship, Award)* [1796]

Daniel B. Dixon Scholarship Fund *(Undergraduate/ Scholarship)* [346]

Grace O. Doane Scholarship *(Undergraduate/Scholarship)* [4150]

Donald W. Banner Diversity Fellowship for Law Students *(Graduate/Fellowship)* [2428]

Hon. Ralph W.E. Donges Memorial Award *(Undergraduate, Graduate/Scholarship)* [2849]

Joseph M. Dorgan Scholarship *(Undergraduate/ Scholarship)* [4151]

Marusia and Michael Dorosh Fellowship *(Master's, Graduate/Fellowship)* [3027]

Drake University Law School Law Opportunity Scholarship - Disadvantage *(Undergraduate/ Scholarship)* [4152]

Drake University Law School Law Opportunity Scholarship - Diversity *(Undergraduate/Scholarship)* [4153]

Drake University Law School Public Service Scholarships *(Undergraduate/Scholarship)* [4154]

C. Cleveland Drennon, Jr. Memorial Scholarship *(Graduate/Scholarship)* [11597]

DuBois Brothers Award *(Undergraduate, Graduate/ Scholarship)* [2850]

A DUI Defense Scholarship *(Graduate/Scholarship)* [8761]

Earl Warren Civil Rights Training Scholarships *(Graduate/Scholarship)* [7538]

Earl Warren Scholarship *(Graduate/Scholarship)* [7539]

Robert E. Early Memorial Scholarship *(Undergraduate/Scholarship)* [4155]

Edward D. Di Loreto-Odell S. McConnell Scholarship *(Undergraduate/Scholarship)* [8997]

Edward Traurig Scholarship *(Undergraduate/Scholarship)* [11932]

Mike Eidson Scholarship *(Graduate, Undergraduate/ Scholarship)* [582]

Herman E. Elgar Memorial Scholarship *(Undergraduate/Scholarship)* [4156]

Elite Entrepreneurs Scholarship Contest *(Undergraduate, Graduate, High School/Scholarship)* [4369]

Equal Justice Works Fellowships *(Graduate, Undergraduate/Fellowship)* [4436]

Ervin Fellowship *(Graduate/Fellowship)* [6768]

Evans and Petree Law Firm Scholarship *(Graduate/ Scholarship)* [11598]

Evans Warncke Robinson, LLC Scholarship Contest *(Undergraduate/Scholarship)* [4453]

Everett Fellowship *(Graduate/Fellowship)* [6769]

The Exoneration Education Initiative *(Undergraduate/Scholarship)* [11028]

The Expert Institute Legal Blog Post Writing Contest *(Graduate/Scholarship)* [4468]

Faegre Baker Daniels Diversity & Inclusion Fellowships *(Graduate/Fellowship)* [4480]

D.J. Fairgrave Education Trust *(Undergraduate/ Scholarship)* [4157]

Farella Braun + Martel LLP 1L Diversity Scholarship Program *(Undergraduate/Scholarship)* [4495]

Judge McIntyre Faries Scholarship *(Undergraduate/ Scholarship)* [8998]

Walter Moran Farmer Scholarships *(Juris Doctorate/ Scholarship)* [11922]

FBANC Foundation NAPABA Convention Scholarship *(Advanced Professional/Scholarship)* [4554]

F.C. Grote Fund *(Graduate, Undergraduate/Scholarship)* [347]

FCBA Foundation Law School Scholarship Programs *(Postgraduate/Scholarship)* [4512]

FCBA Foundation Law School Summer Internship Stipend Program *(Professional development/Internship)* [4513]

FCIL Schaffer Grants for Foreign Law Librarians *(Professional development/Grant)* [596]

Federal Court Bench and Bar Scholarships *(Graduate/Scholarship)* [11599]

Fielding Law Group Scholarship Contest *(Undergraduate/Scholarship)* [4549]

Alan R. and Barbara D. Finberg Fellowships *(Graduate/Fellowship)* [5634]

The Fred Finch Scholarship *(Undergraduate/Scholarship)* [11147]

Finnegan Diversity Scholarship *(Juris Doctorate/ Scholarship)* [4568]

Fish & Richardson 1L Diversity Fellowship Program *(Undergraduate/Fellowship)* [4612]

Florence Young Memorial Scholarships *(Master's/ Scholarship)* [2039]

Leland Stanford Forrest Scholarship *(Undergraduate/Scholarship)* [4158]

Franchise Law Diversity Scholarship Awards *(Undergraduate/Scholarship)* [6012]

John Hope Franklin Prize *(Other/Prize)* [6723]

Fraser Stryker Diversity Scholarship Program *(Undergraduate/Scholarship)* [4817]

Froberg-Suess JD/MBA Scholarship *(Undergraduate/Scholarship)* [8999]

NWT Law Foundation/Graeme Garson Scholarships *(Advanced Professional/Scholarship)* [8545]

George N. Lindsay Fellowship *(Graduate/Fellowship)* [6740]

Georgelis Injury Law Firm, P.C. Scholarship Award *(Graduate/Scholarship)* [4912]

Gerald Garner Memorial Scholarship *(Undergraduate/Scholarship)* [9000]

John J. Gibbons Fellowship in Public Interest & Constitutional Law *(Professional development/ Fellowship)* [4966]

Terry M. Giles Honor Scholar Program *(Undergraduate/Scholarship)* [9001]

The Marie Trahan/Susman Godfrey Scholarship *(Undergraduate/Scholarship)* [11148]

Keren Goldenberg Public Defender Scholarship *(College/Scholarship)* [6695]

Helen B. and Lewis E. Goldstein Scholarship *(Undergraduate, Graduate/Scholarship)* [6273]

Goodman Acker Scholarships *(Graduate/Scholarship)* [5040]

Government Documents Special Interest Section - Veronica Maclay Travel Grant *(Professional development/Grant)* [597]

Wilford Hayes Gowen Scholarship Fund *(Undergraduate/Scholarship)* [11600]

Graduate Research Awards for Disarmament, Arms Control and Non-Proliferation *(Master's, Doctorate/Award)* [10142]

Grants in Aid for Early Career Professionals *(Graduate/Grant)* [1294]

Priscilla Green Scholarships *(Undergraduate/Scholarship)* [3894]

Michael Greenberg Student Writing Competition *(Graduate/Monetary, Scholarship)* [7986]

Greg Matthews Memorial Scholarship *(Undergraduate/Scholarship)* [9002]

Guajardo & Marks Law School Scholarship *(Graduate/Scholarship)* [5245]

Gunnar Nicholson Endowed Scholarship *(Undergraduate/Scholarship)* [9003]

Guy P. Greenwald Jr. Endowed Scholarship Fund *(Undergraduate/Scholarship)* [9004]

Hans H. and Margaret B. Doe Scholarship *(Graduate, Undergraduate/Scholarship)* [9817]

Lex and Scott Hawkins Endowed Scholarship *(Undergraduate/Scholarship)* [4159]

Thomas T. Hayashi Memorial Scholarship *(Graduate, Undergraduate/Scholarship)* [6246]

Edward and Cora Hayes Scholarship *(Undergraduate/Scholarship)* [4160]

Annamae Heaps Law Scholarship *(Undergraduate/Scholarship)* [4161]

Joseph T. Helling Scholarship Fund *(Undergraduate/Scholarship)* [5748]

Helmer, Conley & Kasselman Annual College Scholarship *(Undergraduate/Scholarship)* [5471]

John M. Helmick Law Scholarship *(Undergraduate/Scholarship)* [4162]

Arthur C. Helton Fellowship Program *(Undergraduate, Graduate/Fellowship)* [1489]

Arthur Helton Global Rights Fellowships *(Graduate/Fellowship)* [8361]

Henigson Human Rights Fellowship *(Graduate, Master's, Juris Doctorate/Fellowship)* [5365]

Herbert Law Office Scholarship Contest *(Undergraduate/Scholarship)* [5492]

Herbert Herff Presidential Law Scholarships *(Graduate/Scholarship)* [11601]

Hermann Law Group, PLLC Safety Scholarship Contest *(Undergraduate/Scholarship)* [5496]

Hierholzer-Fojtik Scholarship *(Undergraduate/Scholarship)* [5084]

HIPLA Fellowship *(Undergraduate/Fellowship)* [5599]

HIPLA Scholarships for University of Houston Law Center Students *(Graduate, Undergraduate/Scholarship)* [5600]

Robert and Elaine Hoffman Memorial Scholarships *(Graduate/Scholarship)* [11602]

Hon. Peggy Bernheim Memorial Scholarship *(Undergraduate/Scholarship)* [2711]

Kathryn Hookanson Law Fellowship *(Graduate/Fellowship)* [11603]

John C. "Jack" Hough Memorial Law Scholarship *(Graduate/Scholarship)* [11604]

Howard A. White Endowed Scholarship *(Undergraduate/Scholarship)* [9005]

Howard Fox Memorial Law Scholarship Fund *(Graduate/Scholarship)* [2488]

John Peters Humphrey Student Fellowships *(Graduate/Fellowship)* [3877]

Cecil C. Humphreys Law Fellowships *(Graduate/Fellowship, Internship)* [11605]

IABA Scholarship *(Graduate/Scholarship)* [6170]

IALL Regular Bursaries *(Other/Scholarship)* [5933]

ICNL Research Fellowships *(Advanced Professional, Professional development/Fellowship)* [5964]

The Idaho Advocates Scholarship *(University, Graduate/Scholarship)* [92]

IILJ Scholarships *(Doctorate/Scholarship)* [5845]

IILJ Visiting Fellowships and Research *(Postdoctorate/Fellowship)* [5846]

ILSA Internships *(Undergraduate/Internship)* [6029]

Indigenous Bar Association Law Student Scholarship *(Undergraduate/Scholarship)* [5772]

International Law Research Program's Graduate Scholarship Competition (CIGI ILRP) *(Advanced Professional, Professional development/Scholarship)* [3261]

Iowa Association of Electric Cooperatives - Electric Cooperative Pioneer Trust Fund Scholarship *(Undergraduate/Scholarship)* [4163]

Graduate Study Fellowship *(Professional development/Fellowship)* [6065]

James P. Irish Scholarship *(Undergraduate/Scholarship)* [4164]

J. McDonald and Judy Williams School of Law Scholarship *(Undergraduate/Scholarship)* [9006]

Jamie Phillips Endowed Scholarship Fund *(Undergraduate/Scholarship)* [9007]

Jan Jancin Award *(Undergraduate/Award)* [4697]

Jane S. Glenn Memorial Endowed Scholarship *(Undergraduate/Scholarship)* [9718]

Jason Lang Scholarship *(Undergraduate/Scholarship)* [292]

Jewish Federation Academic Scholarship *(Graduate, Undergraduate/Scholarship)* [6310]

J.L. Weigand, Jr. Legal Education Trust Scholarship *(Undergraduate/Scholarship)* [11876]

Financial Need Minority Scholarships *(Undergraduate/Scholarship)* [11149]

John M. & Mary A. Shanley Memorial Scholarship *(Undergraduate, Graduate/Scholarship)* [10690]

John Purfield Endowed Scholarship *(Undergraduate/Scholarship)* [9008]

MCCA Lloyd M. Johnson, Jr. Scholarships *(Graduate/Scholarship)* [7412]

Bernadine Johnson-Marshall and Martha Bell Williams Scholarships *(Undergraduate/Scholarship)* [2068]

The Barbara Jordan Scholarship *(Undergraduate/Scholarship)* [11150]

Joseph H. Gellert Scholarship *(Graduate/Scholarship)* [4240]

Josephine P. White Eagle Scholar *(Undergraduate, Graduate/Scholarship)* [5537]

JSR Foundation Endowed School of Law Scholarship *(Undergraduate/Scholarship)* [9009]

Judge Delmas C. Hill Scholarship *(Undergraduate/Scholarship)* [11877]

Judge Edward Y. Kakita Memorial Scholarship *(Undergraduate/Scholarship)* [6238]

Julia Kwan Endowed Scholarship *(Graduate/Scholarship)* [9010]

Justice Janie L. Shores Scholarship *(Undergraduate/Scholarship)* [227]

Kae and Kay Brockermeyer Endowed Scholarship Fund *(Undergraduate/Scholarship)* [9011]

WLALA Fran Kandel Public Interest Grants *(Postgraduate/Grant)* [12143]

Kaplan Lawyers PC Legal Scholarships *(Graduate/Scholarship)* [6376]

Kaplan Scholarships *(Undergraduate/Scholarship)* [5524]

Koren and Alice Odian Kasparian Memorial Grant *(Undergraduate/Scholarship)* [1889]

Kegler Brown Diversity Scholarship *(Undergraduate/Scholarship)* [6511]

Martha W. Keister Memorial Travel Grant *(Professional development/Grant)* [3522]

Kerrigan Scholarship Foundation *(Undergraduate/Scholarship)* [9012]

James N. Kincanon Scholarship *(Undergraduate/Scholarship)* [9719]

Martin Luther King Law Scholarship *(Undergraduate/Scholarship)* [4165]

Forest A. King Scholarship *(Undergraduate/Scholarship)* [4166]

Kluge Fellowship *(Doctorate, Graduate/Fellowship)* [6573]

Koch Scholars Program *(Undergraduate/Scholarship)* [11878]

Marcia J. Koslov Scholarship *(Professional development/Scholarship)* [598]

Krist-Reavley Minority Scholarship *(Undergraduate/Scholarship)* [9013]

George F. Kugler, Jr. Award *(Undergraduate, Graduate/Scholarship)* [2851]

Ladah Law Firm, PLLC Injury Scholarships *(Undergraduate, Graduate/Scholarship)* [6630]

The Ladas Memorial Award - Student Category *(Undergraduate/Award)* [6135]

Attorney Raymond Lahoud Scholar Program *(Undergraduate, Graduate/Scholarship)* [2449]

James D. Lang Memorial Scholarship *(Graduate/Scholarship)* [2902]

Frank H. Lang Merit Scholarships *(Undergraduate/Scholarship)* [6656]

Latham Diversity Scholars - 2L Diversity Scholars *(Undergraduate/Scholarship)* [6673]

The Law Alumni Honor Student Scholarship *(Graduate/Scholarship)* [11606]

Law Fellows Program *(Undergraduate/Fellowship)* [7607]

Graduate Fellowships *(Graduate/Fellowship)* [6679]

Law Foundation of Newfoundland and Labrador Law School Scholarships *(Advanced Professional/Scholarship)* [6681]

Community Leadership in Justice Fellowship - The Law Foundation of Ontario *(Other/Fellowship)* [6683]

Law Office of A. Sam Jubran Scholarship Contest *(University, College, Undergraduate/Scholarship)* [6685]

The Law Offices of Scott Henry Scholarship Contest *(Undergraduate/Scholarship)* [6710]

Law School Scholarship *(Graduate/Scholarship)* [2618, 9714]

Law and Society Association Article Prize *(Other/Prize, Award)* [6724]

Law and Society Association Dissertation Prize *(Other/Prize)* [6725]

Law and Society Association International Prize *(Other/Award, Recognition)* [6726]

Law and Society Association Undergraduate Student Paper Prize *(Undergraduate/Prize)* [6727]

Law Society Scholarship *(Graduate/Scholarship)* [6730]

Law Student Scholarship *(Graduate/Scholarship)* [4539, 6520, 9878]

Verne Lawyer Scholarship *(Undergraduate/Scholarship)* [4167]

LeClairRyan 1L Diversity Scholarship *(Undergraduate/Scholarship)* [6762]

Leesfield/AAJ Scholarship *(Undergraduate/Scholarship)* [583]

Judge William B. Leffler Scholarship *(Graduate/Scholarship)* [11607]

Legal Internships *(Professional development/Internship)* [3228]

Leslie C. Green Veterans Scholarship *(Juris Doctorate, Advanced Professional/Scholarship)* [3878]

Frederick D. Lewis Jr. Scholarships *(Undergraduate/Scholarship)* [4168]

Jack G. Lezman Scholarship Contest *(College, University, Undergraduate/Scholarship)* [6836]

Dolores Zohrab Liebmann Fund - Graduate School Fellowships *(Graduate/Fellowship)* [6845]

Lim, Ruger & Kim Scholarships *(Undergraduate/Scholarship)* [7602]

LimNexus Foundation Scholarship *(Undergraduate/Scholarship)* [6239]

Linda J. Murphy Scholarship *(Undergraduate/Scholarship)* [12141]

Davis Levin Livingston Public Interest Law Scholarships *(Postgraduate/Scholarship)* [3975]

Lloyd Houlden Fellowship *(Advanced Professional, Professional development/Fellowship)* [2897]

Los Abogados LSAT Pipeline Fellowship *(Graduate/Fellowship)* [6892]

Louthian Law School Scholarships *(Advanced Professional/Scholarship)* [6919]

The Lozano Law Firm Scholarship Contest *(College, University, Undergraduate/Scholarship)* [6925]

LSAC Diversity Matters Grants *(Graduate/Grant)* [6718]

LSAC Outreach Grants *(Professional development/Grant)* [6719]

Lucie and Thornton Blackburn Scholarship (CABL) *(Graduate, Juris Doctorate/Scholarship)* [2883]

The C. Lyons Fellowship Program *(Advanced Professional/Fellowship)* [7984]

MABF Scholarships *(Professional development/Scholarship)* [7286]

Gordon and Delores Madson Scholarship *(Undergraduate/Scholarship)* [4169]

MALDEF Dream Act Student Activist Scholarships *(Undergraduate, Graduate/Scholarship)* [7290]

MALDEF Law School Scholarship Program *(Undergraduate, Graduate/Scholarship)* [7291]

Mangum & Associates PC Scholarship Contest *(Undergraduate/Scholarship)* [7014]

Mann Law Firm Scholarships *(Advanced Professional/Scholarship)* [7018]

Honorable Carol Los Mansmann Memorial Fund (*Graduate, Undergraduate/Scholarship*) [349]

Margaret Martin Brock Scholarship in Law (*Undergraduate, Juris Doctorate/Scholarship*) [9014]

Marilynne Graboys Wool Scholarship (*Graduate/Scholarship*) [9695]

Mark and Michelle Hiepler Endowed Scholarship Fund (*Undergraduate/Scholarship*) [9015]

Howard T. Markey Memorial Scholarship (*Undergraduate/Scholarship*) [4507]

Marla Schwartz Education Grant (*Professional development, Graduate/Grant*) [599]

Martha Delman and Milton Arthur Krug Endowed Law Scholarship (*Undergraduate/Scholarship*) [9016]

Right Honourable Paul Martin Sr. Scholarships (*Graduate/Scholarship*) [5794]

Massachusetts Bar Foundation Legal Intern Fellowship Program (LIFP) (*Graduate/Fellowship*) [7126]

McCleary Law Fellows Program (*Graduate, Undergraduate/Fellowship*) [5628]

Niqui McCown Honor and Memorial Scholarship Fund (*Undergraduate/Scholarship*) [11949]

H. H. McKnight Memorial Scholarship (*Graduate/Scholarship*) [11608]

Memphis Access and Diversity Scholarships (*Graduate/Scholarship*) [11609]

John Merrick Law Scholarship (*Undergraduate/Scholarship*) [9017]

Sanders J. Mestel Legal Scholarship Fund (*Undergraduate/Scholarship*) [10779]

Michael Oykhman Criminal Law and Evidence Scholarship (*Juris Doctorate, Advanced Professional/Scholarship*) [8800]

Michigan Auto Law Student Diversity Scholarships (*Undergraduate/Scholarship*) [7306]

Mila Boyd Law Offices Scholarship Contest (*Undergraduate/Scholarship*) [2667]

Jake S. More Scholarship (*Undergraduate/Scholarship*) [4170]

My Life As A Lawyer Scholarship (*Graduate/Scholarship*) [3837]

Sam A. Myar, Jr. Law Scholarship (*Graduate/Scholarship*) [11610]

NALS of Detroit Scholarships (*Undergraduate/Scholarship*) [7544]

NALS of Michigan Scholarship (*Undergraduate/Scholarship*) [7546]

National Federation of the Blind Scholarship Program (*Undergraduate/Scholarship, Monetary*) [7878]

National Judges Association Scholarships (*Other/Scholarship*) [7963]

NCLEJ Law School Graduate Fellows and Volunteers (*Graduate, Advanced Professional/Fellowship*) [7751]

Nebraska Paralegal Association Student Scholarships (*Undergraduate/Scholarship*) [8194]

Need-Based Scholarships (*Doctorate/Scholarship*) [4508]

Aryeh Neier Fellowships (*Graduate/Fellowship*) [5635]

Charles I. Nelson Endowed Scholarship Fund (*Undergraduate/Scholarship*) [9018]

Tad Nelson Law Firm Scholarships (*Undergraduate/Scholarship*) [6716]

NIABA/NIAF Scholarships (*Graduate/Scholarship*) [7958]

Helen W. Nies Memorial Scholarship (*Postgraduate/Scholarship*) [4509]

NJSBF Labor Law Scholarship (*Undergraduate/Scholarship*) [8291]

NLF Scholarships (*Undergraduate/Scholarship*) [7603]

George H. Nofer Scholarship for Law and Public Policy (*Graduate/Scholarship, Monetary*) [334]

NWAC Helen Bassett Commemorative Student Award (*Undergraduate, Graduate/Scholarship*) [8168]

Seth Okin Good Deeds Scholarships (*Undergraduate, Graduate, Community College/Scholarship*) [9283]

Oklahoma City University Full-Time Merit Scholarships (*Undergraduate/Scholarship*) [8609]

Olin-Searle-Smith-Darling Fellows in Law (*Other/Fellowship*) [4523]

Omatsu FACL Scholarships (*Juris Doctorate, Advanced Professional/Scholarship*) [4529]

One Source Process Inc. Scholarship (*Undergraduate, Graduate/Scholarship*) [8634]

Faith E. O'Neal Scholarship (*Graduate/Scholarship*) [9459]

Open Society Presidential Fellowship (*Graduate/Fellowship*) [8665]

Dwight D. Opperman Scholarships (*Undergraduate/Scholarship*) [4171]

M. Dick Osumi Civil Rights and Public Interest Scholarship (*Graduate, Undergraduate/Scholarship*) [6240]

Otto M. Stanfield Law Scholarship (*Graduate/Scholarship*) [11253]

Patterson Belknap Webb & Tyler LLP Diversity Fellowships (*Doctorate/Fellowship*) [8919]

PCBA Diversity Scholarship (*Undergraduate/Scholarship*) [8983]

Peggy (Kommer) Novosad Scholarship (*Graduate, Postgraduate/Scholarship*) [5173]

Pepperdine University Diversity Scholarships (*Doctorate, Graduate/Scholarship*) [9019]

Pepperdine University School of Law Armenian Student Scholarship (*Undergraduate/Scholarship*) [9020]

Pepperdine University School of Law Dean's Merit Scholarship (*Doctorate, Undergraduate/Scholarship*) [9021]

Pepperdine University School of Law Faculty Scholars Award (*Doctorate, Graduate/Award*) [9022]

Pepperdine University School of Law JD/MBA Endowed Scholarship (*Undergraduate/Scholarship*) [9023]

Pepperdine University School of Law Special Law School Scholarship (*Undergraduate/Scholarship*) [9024]

Perkins Coie 1L Diversity Fellowship (*Undergraduate/Fellowship*) [9038]

Perkins Coie 1L Patent Litigation and Patent Fellowships (*Undergraduate/Fellowship*) [9039]

Perkins Coie 1L Political Law Diversity Fellowships (*Undergraduate/Fellowship*) [9040]

The Vincent S. Haneman - Joseph B. Perskie Scholarship (*Graduate, Undergraduate/Fellowship*) [2342]

PETA Foundation Law Internship (*Graduate/Internship*) [8979]

Petro Law Firm Scholarship Contest (*Graduate, College/Scholarship*) [9046]

William R. Pfalzgraf Memorial Scholarship (*Undergraduate/Scholarship*) [8867]

The Philadelphia Public Interest Fellowship Program (*Undergraduate/Fellowship*) [9133]

Philip F. Greco Memorial Scholarship (*Undergraduate/Scholarship*) [6960]

Philip F. Vineberg Travelling Fellowship in the Humanities (*Undergraduate/Scholarship, Monetary*) [7184]

Pi Gamma Mu Scholarships (*Graduate/Scholarship*) [9160]

PLP Scholarships (*Undergraduate/Scholarship, Award, Monetary*) [8985]

Harold and Harriet Plum Memorial Award (*Undergraduate, Graduate/Scholarship*) [2852]

Donald and Susie Polden Dean's Scholarships (*Graduate/Scholarship*) [11611]

PON Graduate Student Grants (*Graduate/Grant*) [5368]

PON Next Generation Grants (*Doctorate, Postdoctorate/Grant*) [5369]

PON Summer Fellowships (*Graduate/Fellowship*) [5370]

Louis C. Portella Memorial Award (*Undergraduate, Graduate/Scholarship*) [2853]

Karin Riley Porter Good Works Scholarships (*Undergraduate, Graduate/Scholarship*) [9284]

George V. Powell Diversity Scholarships (*Graduate/Scholarship*) [6654]

Practising Law Institute Scholarships (*Advanced Professional, Professional development/Scholarship*) [9262]

Pride Foundation Political Leadership Scholarships (*Undergraduate/Scholarship*) [9306]

Prince Edward Island Law Student Scholarships (*Undergraduate/Scholarship*) [6732]

Promoting the Rule of Law and Access to Justice (*Other/Grant*) [11379]

Public Interest Environmental Law Fellowships (*Graduate/Fellowship*) [4415]

Public Interest Fellowship (*Undergraduate/Fellowship*) [797]

R. Roy McMurtry Fellowship in Legal History (*Doctorate, Graduate/Fellowship*) [8772]

R. Wayne Estes Endowed Scholarship Fund (*Undergraduate/Scholarship*) [9025]

Frederick Rakestraw Law Scholarship (*Graduate/Scholarship*) [8489]

Ratner and Sugarmon Scholarship (*Graduate/Scholarship*) [11612]

Reiff & Bily Legal Scholarship (*Graduate, Undergraduate/Scholarship*) [9631]

Janet Reynoldson Memorial Scholarship (*Other/Scholarship*) [4172]

Richard S. White Fellowship (*Undergraduate/Fellowship*) [5473]

The Honorable Joseph H. Ridge Memorial Scholarship Fund (*Undergraduate/Scholarship*) [350]

Hon. Rudolph J. Rossetti Memorial Award (*Undergraduate, Graduate/Scholarship*) [2854]

Joe Rudd Scholarships (*Graduate/Scholarship*) [9732]

Russell & Lazarus Safety Scholarship Contest (*Undergraduate, College, University/Scholarship*) [9763]

SABA NC - Public Interest Post-Bar Fellowships (*Professional development/Fellowship*) [10599]

SABA NC - Public Interest Summer Fellowships (*Undergraduate/Fellowship*) [10600]

Sam Bull Memorial Scholarship (*Undergraduate/Scholarship*) [269]

Leonard H. Sandler Fellowships (*Graduate/Fellowship*) [5636]

Saratoga County Bar Association Law Student Scholarship (*Undergraduate/Scholarship*) [9880]

Sho Sato Memorial Scholarship (*Undergraduate, Graduate/Scholarship*) [6251]

Satter Human Rights Fellowship (*Graduate, Master's, Juris Doctorate/Fellowship*) [5366]

SCCLA Fellowships (*Graduate/Fellowship*) [10647]

SCCLA Scholarships (*Graduate/Scholarship*) [10648]

Schmidt Family Scholarship (*Undergraduate, University, College/Scholarship*) [12367]

Scholarship from Law Office of Yuriy Moshes, P.C. (*Undergraduate/Award, Scholarship*) [6699]

Scholarships for a Higher Education in Law (*Graduate/Scholarship*) [2683]

Jeptha Wade Schureman Scholarship Program (*Undergraduate/Scholarship*) [3724]

Scott A. Flahive Memorial Scholarship (*Undergraduate/Scholarship*) [5105]

Walter and Rita Selvy Scholarship (*Undergraduate/Scholarship*) [4173]

Senator Carl O. Koella, Jr. Memorial Scholarship Fund (*Undergraduate/Scholarship*) [3644]

Serbian Bar Association of America Scholarships (*Graduate/Scholarship*) [10017]

Seton Hall Law Merit Scholarships (*Graduate/Scholarship*) [10031]

SGM Law Group $1,000 Bi-Annual Scholarship (*Undergraduate, Graduate/Scholarship*) [10033]

Saleem Shah Early Career Award (*Doctorate/Recognition*) [1295]

Shamberg Scholars Program (*Undergraduate/Scholarship*) [11879]

Joseph Henry Shepherd Scholarship (*Graduate/Scholarship*) [11613]

Shirley J. Brooke Endowed Scholarship (*Undergraduate/Scholarship*) [9026]

Sidley Diversity and Inclusion Scholarships (*Undergraduate/Scholarship*) [10076]

Sidley Prelaw Scholars Program (*Undergraduate/Scholarship*) [10077]

Single Mother Scholarship (*Undergraduate, Graduate, College, University/Scholarship*) [9743]

Skadden Fellowship (*Graduate/Fellowship*) [10157]

Ann Kelsay Small Scholarship (*Undergraduate/Scholarship*) [6475]

James I. Smith, III Notre Dame Law School Scholarship Fund *(Graduate, Undergraduate/Scholarship)* [351]

Sodowsky Law Firm Scholarship *(College, University, Undergraduate/Scholarship)* [10570]

Louis B. Sohn Fellowships in Human Rights and Environment *(Graduate/Fellowship)* [3219]

The Solano Law Firm Scholarship Contest *(College, University, Undergraduate/Scholarship)* [10576]

Sonia Morgan Scholarship *(Undergraduate/Scholarship)* [8292]

Amy E. Spain Memorial Scholarships *(Graduate/Scholarship)* [11614]

Spangenberg Shibley & Liber Video PSA Scholarship Awards *(Undergraduate/Scholarship)* [10715]

Springfield Family Scholarship *(Graduate/Scholarship)* [11615]

Stark County Bar Association Scholarship Fund *(Undergraduate/Scholarship)* [10793]

Tom Steel Post-Graduate Fellowships *(Postgraduate, Professional development/Fellowship)* [9322]

Mike Stephenson Legal Scholarships *(Graduate/Scholarship)* [7199]

The David Stockwood Memorial Prize *(Advanced Professional, Professional development/Prize)* [97]

Jay A. Strassberg Memorial Scholarship *(Undergraduate/Scholarship)* [2855]

Robby Strong Cancer Survivor Scholarships *(Graduate/Scholarship)* [7472]

Stuart Silverman Scholarship *(Undergraduate/Scholarship)* [9027]

Stuart/SIM Northern Education Scholarship *(Undergraduate, University, College, Vocational/Occupational/Scholarship)* [12375]

Hatton W. Sumners Endowed Law Schools Scholarships *(Undergraduate, Graduate/Scholarship)* [10877]

Hatton W. Sumners Endowed Undergraduate School Scholarships *(Undergraduate/Scholarship)* [10878]

Hatton W. Sumners Non-Endowed Undergraduate and Graduate Scholarships *(Undergraduate, Graduate/Scholarship)* [10879]

Hatton W. Sumners Scholarships *(Undergraduate/Scholarship)* [8610]

Robert M. Takasugi Public Interest Fellowships *(Postgraduate/Fellowship)* [10913]

Justice Stephen K. Tamura Scholarship *(Undergraduate/Scholarship)* [6241]

Charles "Buck" and Dora Taylor Scholarship *(Undergraduate/Scholarship)* [4174]

Thomas F. Black Jr. Memorial Scholarship *(Undergraduate/Scholarship)* [9686]

Thomas and Glenna Trimble Endowed Scholarship *(Graduate/Scholarship)* [9028]

Thomas More Scholarship *(Undergraduate/Scholarship)* [5038]

The Honorable Raymond Thompson Endowed Scholarship *(Undergraduate/Scholarship)* [9029]

Thomas P. Thornton Scholarship *(Undergraduate, Graduate/Scholarship)* [5731]

Thurgood Marshall Fellowships Program *(Undergraduate/Fellowship)* [8301]

Tiftickjian Law Firm, P.C. Juvenile Justice Law School Scholarships *(Graduate/Scholarship)* [11030]

Daniel B. Toll Memorial Award *(Undergraduate, Graduate/Scholarship)* [2856]

William Tomar Memorial Award *(Undergraduate, Graduate/Scholarship)* [2857]

Triple Crown Award *(Other/Recognition, Award)* [8075]

Trustees College Scholarships *(Undergraduate/Scholarship)* [6961]

Trustees Law School Scholarship *(Undergraduate/Scholarship)* [6962]

Turco Munoz Domestic Violence Survivor Scholarship *(Undergraduate, Graduate/Scholarship)* [11137]

UC MEXUS-CONACYT Doctoral Fellowship *(Doctorate/Fellowship)* [11552]

VABANC Scholarships *(Graduate, Undergraduate/Scholarship)* [11820]

Viscount Bennett Scholarship *(Graduate/Scholarship)* [6721]

Vision Zero Auto Accident Prevention Scholarships *(Postgraduate/Scholarship)* [6693]

John D. Voelker Foundation Native American Scholarships *(Undergraduate/Scholarship)* [11858]

Bruce A. Wallace Memorial Award *(Undergraduate, Graduate/Scholarship)* [2858]

Wallace Vail Scholarship *(Undergraduate/Scholarship)* [8293]

Warner Norcross & Judd Minority Scholarships *(Undergraduate/Scholarship)* [11874]

Warren and Rosalie Gummow Endowed Scholarship *(Undergraduate/Scholarship)* [9030]

Washburn University School of Law Business and Transactional Law Center Scholarships *(Undergraduate/Scholarship)* [11880]

Washburn University School of Law Child and Family Advocacy Fellowships *(Undergraduate/Fellowship)* [11881]

Chancellor's Graduate Fellowship *(Advanced Professional/Fellowship)* [11923]

Washington University Law School Olin Fellowships for Women *(Advanced Professional/Fellowship)* [11924]

Waterbury Bar Association Scholarship *(Undergraduate/Scholarship)* [11933]

Webster Society Scholarships *(Juris Doctorate, Undergraduate/Scholarship)* [11925]

Haemer Wheatcraft Scholarship *(Undergraduate/Scholarship)* [4175]

Stan Wheeler Mentorship Awards *(Other/Award)* [6728]

The Whistleblower Lawyer-Louthian Law Legal Scholarship Award *(Graduate/Scholarship)* [6920]

The Brian J. White Endowed Law Scholarship *(Undergraduate/Scholarship)* [9031]

Paul D. White Scholarship Program *(Undergraduate/Scholarship)* [2409]

William L. Graddy Law School Scholarship Fund *(Graduate/Scholarship)* [10705]

William S. Richardson Commemorative Scholarship *(Graduate/Scholarship)* [8934]

William Verbon Black Scholarship *(Undergraduate/Scholarship)* [228]

Sidney B. Williams, Jr. Scholarships *(Undergraduate/Scholarship)* [4698]

Wilshire Law Firm Scholarship *(Undergraduate, Graduate/Scholarship)* [12041]

WLALA Scholarships *(Postgraduate/Scholarship)* [12144]

Women In Defense HORIZONS Scholarship *(Graduate, Undergraduate/Scholarship)* [12133]

Women of WSAJ Bar Preparation Scholarship *(Undergraduate/Scholarship)* [11904]

Wood County Bar Association Memorial Scholarship *(Graduate/Scholarship)* [8888]

Woodrow Judkins Endowed Scholarship *(Undergraduate/Scholarship)* [9032]

WSAJ Diversity Bar Preparation Scholarship *(Undergraduate/Scholarship)* [11906]

Wyatt, Tarrant & Combs, LLP, Dr. Benjamin L. Hooks Scholarship *(Graduate/Scholarship)* [11616]

Minoru Yasui Memorial Scholarship *(Graduate/Scholarship)* [6255]

Yukon Law Foundation Scholarship *(Undergraduate/Scholarship)* [12401]

Charles Zarigian, Esq. Memorial Award *(Undergraduate/Scholarship)* [1908]

Zarley, McKee, Thomte, Voorhees, Sease Law Scholarship *(Undergraduate/Scholarship)* [4176]

Zelle Diversity in Law Scholarship *(Undergraduate/Scholarship)* [12405]

Law enforcement

Jack Ackroyd Scholarships *(Other/Scholarship)* [2083]

Alphonso Deal Scholarship Award *(Undergraduate/Scholarship)* [7728]

American Association of State Troopers Scholarship Foundation First Scholarships *(Undergraduate/Scholarship)* [640]

American Association of State Troopers Scholarship Foundation Second Scholarships *(Undergraduate/Scholarship)* [641]

American Federation of Police and Concerned Citizen Educational Scholarship *(Undergraduate/Scholarship)* [879]

Benjamin Asbell Memorial Awards *(Graduate, Undergraduate/Scholarship)* [2846]

Jan S. Bashinski Criminalistics Graduate Thesis Assistance Grant *(Graduate/Grant)* [4676]

Canadian Identification Society Essay/Scholarship Awards *(Advanced Professional, Professional development/Award)* [3010]

The William Donald Dixon Research Grant *(Graduate, Undergraduate, Advanced Professional/Grant)* [3011]

Friends and Family of Christopher J. Kohlmeier Scholarship *(Undergraduate/Scholarship)* [9547]

Hardy, Wolf & Downing Scholarships *(Undergraduate, Graduate/Scholarship)* [5296]

Wayne Hildebrant Police Scholarship Fund *(Undergraduate/Scholarship)* [6665]

IACP University and College Police Section Scholarship *(Undergraduate/Scholarship)* [5909]

IAWP International Scholarship *(Other/Scholarship)* [5949]

John W. Kelley Memorial Scholarship Fund *(Undergraduate/Scholarship)* [10828]

V.J. Johnson Memorial Scholarships *(Undergraduate/Scholarship)* [642]

Law Enforcement Memorial Scholarship Endowment Fund *(Undergraduate/Scholarship)* [4741]

Lex T. Eckenrode Scholarship for PELS *(Professional development/Scholarship)* [11831]

NASSLEO Scholarships - Region I *(Undergraduate/Scholarship)* [7688]

Pan Pacific Law Enforcement Scholarships *(Undergraduate/Scholarship)* [9868]

Portuguese American Police Association Scholarships *(Undergraduate/Scholarship)* [9252]

Commander Newell S. Rand Jr. Scholarship Program *(Undergraduate/Scholarship)* [8828]

Sheriff W. Bruce Umpleby Law Enforcement Memorial Scholarship Fund *(Undergraduate/Scholarship)* [10791]

WIFLE Regular Scholarship Program *(Graduate, Postdoctorate, Undergraduate/Scholarship)* [12139]

Leadership, Institutional and community

Alliance Pipeline Scholarships *(Other/Scholarship)* [2417]

Americans for Informed Democracy Global Scholar Program *(Undergraduate/Scholarship)* [1687]

Bush Fellowship Program *(Professional development/Fellowship)* [2757]

Campus Pride Summer Fellows *(Undergraduate, Graduate, Postgraduate/Fellowship)* [2870]

Fraser Milner Casgrain Scholarships *(Other/Scholarship)* [2418]

CMC-KLI Leadership Research Fellowship *(Undergraduate/Fellowship)* [3428]

CMC-KLI Leadership Thesis Fellowship *(Undergraduate/Fellowship)* [3429]

CMC-KLI Social Sector Internship Program *(Undergraduate/Internship)* [3430]

Margaret A. Dankworth Management Scholarship *(Professional development/Scholarship)* [2327]

Diversity Executive Leadership Program Scholarship (DELP) *(Other/Scholarship)* [1977]

Echoing Green Global Fellowships *(Professional development/Fellowship)* [4277]

Founding Mothers Student Scholarships - Graduate *(Graduate/Scholarship)* [2233]

Greenlining Institute Policy Fellowship *(Undergraduate/Fellowship)* [5237]

Humber College Institute of Technology and Advanced Learning Scholarships *(Postgraduate/Scholarship)* [6217]

Investors Group Scholarship *(Other/Scholarship)* [2419]

Judge Ross Leadership Scholarship *(Professional development/Scholarship)* [7764]

Kathryn Huget Leadership Award *(Master's, Doctorate/Award)* [2775]

KDP International Scholarship Program - President Scholarship (Undergraduate, Graduate, Doctorate/Scholarship) [6385]

KON/GEICO LeaderShape Undergraduate Scholarship (Undergraduate/Scholarship) [6490]

Lafarge Community Leaders Scholarships (Other/Scholarship) [2420]

NCSEA New Leader Scholarship (Professional development/Scholarship) [7765]

Small Grants for Community Projects and Educational Programs (Other/Grant) [8262]

USGLC Internships - Outreach (Undergraduate, Graduate/Internship) [11370]

Youth or the Environment Scholarships (Other/Scholarship) [2421]

Liberal arts

Bernard Michel Scholarship (Undergraduate/Scholarship) [2862]

Burney – Cecil E. Burney Scholarship (Undergraduate/Scholarship) [3468]

Denis Wong & Associates Scholarship (Graduate, Undergraduate/Scholarship) [8923]

Dr. Stephen J. Fortgang / University of Northern Iowa Chapter Scholarship (Undergraduate/Scholarship) [6379]

Doris Hendren Memorial Scholarship (Undergraduate/Scholarship) [9811]

Elizabeth M. Gruber Scholarship (Graduate/Scholarship) [4033]

Harriet Irsay Scholarship (Graduate, Undergraduate/Scholarship) [1045]

Jeannette K. Watson Fellowship (Undergraduate/Fellowship) [11938]

Pathways College Scholarship (Undergraduate/Scholarship) [8917]

Library and archival sciences

AALL Leadership Academy Grant (Professional development/Grant) [585]

AALL Minority Leadership Development Award (Graduate/Award) [586]

Above and Beyond Scholarship (Graduate/Scholarship) [2826]

ACMS Library Fellowship (Graduate, Professional development, Postgraduate/Fellowship) [721]

ACRL/DVC Student Stipend (Undergraduate/Scholarship) [2136]

AECT Legacy Graduate Scholarship (Master's, Graduate, Professional development/Scholarship) [2156]

AJL Scholarship Fund (Graduate/Scholarship) [2228]

AJL Scholarship for Library School Students (Graduate/Scholarship) [2229]

ALA Century Scholarship (Master's, Doctorate/Scholarship) [2293]

Alan Holoch Memorial Grant (Professional development/Grant) [594]

ALL-SIS Conference of Newer Law Librarians Grants (Professional development/Grant) [595]

ALSC Bound to Stay Bound Books Scholarship (Graduate/Scholarship) [2237]

ALSC Summer Reading Program Grant (Other/Grant) [2238]

APALA Scholarship (Doctorate, Master's/Scholarship) [1990]

APLA Merit Award (Professional development/Scholarship) [2344]

ArLA Scholarship (Graduate/Scholarship) [1829]

Carroll Preston Baber Research Grant (Professional development/Grant) [1081]

Baker and Taylor Entertainment Audio Music/Video Product Award (Other/Award) [9431]

Baker & Taylor/YALSA Collection Development Grant (Professional development/Grant) [1083]

Louise Seaman Bechtel Fellowship (Professional development/Fellowship) [2239]

Beinecke Rare Book and Manuscript Library Visiting Postdoctoral Scholar Fellowships (Postdoctorate/Fellowship) [2464]

Blanche E. Woolls Scholarship (Graduate/Scholarship) [2496]

Diana V. Braddom FRFDS Scholarship (Professional development/Scholarship) [6843]

Carol June Bradley Award for Historical Research in Music Librarianship (Professional development/Grant, Award) [7512]

Carin Alma E. Somers Scholarship (Undergraduate/Scholarship) [2345]

Caroline M. Hewins Scholarship (Graduate, Undergraduate/Scholarship) [5351]

Rick Chace Foundation Scholarships (Graduate/Scholarship) [2246]

Christian Larew Memorial Scholarship (Graduate/Scholarship, Monetary) [6838]

Clarivate Analytics/MLA Doctoral Fellowship (Doctorate, Graduate/Fellowship) [7215]

D. Glenn Hilts Scholarship (Graduate, Undergraduate/Scholarship) [2288]

Dafoe Scholarship (Undergraduate, Master's/Scholarship) [3037]

David H. Clift Scholarship (Graduate/Scholarship, Monetary) [1077]

DEMCO New Leaders Travel Grants (Professional development/Grant) [9432]

Dena Epstein Award for Archival and Library Research in American Music (Professional development/Award) [7513]

Marusia and Michael Dorosh Fellowship (Master's, Graduate/Fellowship) [3027]

Tom and Roberta Drewes Scholarship (Graduate/Scholarship, Monetary) [6839]

Henry Belin du Pont Research Grants (Graduate/Grant) [5258]

E.J. Josey Scholarship (Graduate/Scholarship) [2606]

FCIL Schaffer Grants for Foreign Law Librarians (Professional development/Grant) [596]

Ruth Fine Memorial Student Loans (Undergraduate/Grant, Loan) [4120]

First Step Award - Wiley Professional Development Grant (Professional development/Grant, Award) [2235]

Frances Henne/YALSA Grant (Undergraduate, Professional development/Grant) [1084]

Kevin Freeman Travel Grant (Graduate, Other/Grant) [7514]

Friends of the Oro Valley Public Library Support Staff Scholarship Award (Undergraduate/Scholarship, Monetary, Award) [1810]

Loleta D. Fyan Public Library Research Grant (Professional development/Grant) [6840]

Eugene Garfield Doctoral Dissertation Fellowship (Doctorate/Fellowship) [2497]

The Gates Millennium Scholars (Undergraduate/Scholarship) [5529]

Mary V. Gaver Scholarship (Master's/Scholarship, Monetary) [6841]

Walter Gerboth Award (Other/Award, Monetary) [7515]

Getty Foundation Library Research Grants (Professional development/Grant) [4954]

GLA Beard Scholarship (Master's/Scholarship) [4932]

GLA Hubbard Scholarships (Master's/Scholarship) [4933]

Helen B. and Lewis E. Goldstein Scholarship (Undergraduate, Graduate/Scholarship) [6273]

Government Documents Special Interest Section - Veronica Maclay Travel Grant (Professional development/Grant) [597]

HLS/MLA Professional Development Grants (Other/Grant) [7218]

The Stephanie G. Hoffman Scholarship (Graduate, Undergraduate/Scholarship) [6274]

Christopher Hoy/ERT Scholarship (Graduate/Scholarship, Monetary) [1078]

Huenefeld/Denton Scholarships (Undergraduate/Scholarship) [4038]

Iowa Library Association Foundation Scholarships (Graduate/Scholarship) [6163]

Jewell Gardiner Scholarship (Undergraduate/Scholarship) [2827]

Martha W. Keister Memorial Travel Grant (Professional development/Grant) [3522]

Kodak Fellowships in Film Preservation (Graduate/Fellowship) [2247]

Marcia J. Koslov Scholarship (Professional development/Scholarship) [598]

Harold Lancour Scholarship for Foreign Study (Professional development/Scholarship) [2498]

Leadership for Diversity Paraprofessional Scholarship (Advanced Professional/Scholarship) [2828]

Leadership for Diversity TL Scholarship (Master's/Scholarship) [2829]

LLA Scholarships (LLA) (Graduate/Scholarship) [6903]

Louisa Bowen Memorial Scholarship for Graduate Students in Archival Administration (Graduate/Scholarship) [7365]

Lillian Grace Mahan Scholarship Fund (Graduate/Scholarship) [10776]

Marla Schwartz Education Grant (Professional development, Graduate/Grant) [599]

Marshall Cavendish Scholarships (Graduate/Scholarship, Monetary) [1079]

Mary Moore Mitchell Scholarship (Graduate/Scholarship) [6904]

Frederic G. Melcher Scholarships (Graduate/Scholarship) [2240]

MLA Continuing Education Grants (CE) (Graduate/Grant) [7219]

MLA Research, Development, and Demonstration Project Grant (Graduate/Grant) [7221]

MLA Scholarship (Graduate, Master's/Scholarship) [7222]

MLA Scholarship for Minority Students (Graduate/Scholarship) [7223]

Archie Motley Memorial Scholarships for Minority Students (Graduate/Scholarship) [7367]

NELA Conference Scholarships (All/Scholarship) [8246]

Louise A. Nixon Scholarship (Graduate/Scholarship) [8192]

NJLA Scholarships (Graduate, Postgraduate/Scholarship) [8277]

NLLN Continuing Education Scholarship (Professional development/Scholarship) [8492]

NYLA-Dewey Fellowship Award (Graduate/Award, Fellowship) [8314]

NYLA-Dewey Scholarship (Master's, Undergraduate/Award, Scholarship) [8315]

The Katharine Pantzer Fellowship in the British Book Trades (Other/Fellowship) [2567]

Penguin Random House Young Readers Group Award (Professional development/Grant, Award) [2241]

Pennsylvania Library Association MLS Scholarships (Graduate/Scholarship) [8958]

Paul Evan Peters Fellowship (Master's, Doctorate, Graduate/Fellowship) [3452]

Philip F. Vineberg Travelling Fellowship in the Humanities (Undergraduate/Scholarship, Monetary) [7184]

Mary Pickford Scholarships (Graduate/Scholarship) [2248]

REFORMA Scholarship (Undergraduate, Graduate/Scholarship) [9615]

REFORMA Scholarship Program (Undergraduate/Scholarship) [9616]

Research Fellowships for Yale Graduate & Professional School Students (Graduate, Professional development/Fellowship) [2465]

Roger K. Summit Scholarship (Graduate/Scholarship) [9356]

Rovelstad Scholarship (Undergraduate, Graduate/Scholarship) [3871]

Esther Schlundt Memorial Scholarship Fund (Graduate, Undergraduate/Scholarship) [5754]

Fritz Schwartz Serials Education Scholarship (Graduate/Scholarship) [7560]

Sherman Fairchild Post-Graduate Fellowship in Conservation (Graduate/Fellowship) [7468]

Sony Pictures Scholarship (Graduate/Scholarship) [2249]

George A. Strait Minority Scholarship (Graduate/Scholarship) [600]

Sue Marsh Weller Memorial Scholarship Fund (Graduate/Scholarship) [5755]

The Jack Tillson Scholarship Fund (Graduate/Scholarship) [6164]

Universal Studios Preservation Scholarships (Graduate/Scholarship) [2250]

Virginia Mathews Memorial Scholarship *(Graduate/ Scholarship)* [998]

WLA Conference Attendance Grants *(Undergraduate, Professional development/Grant)* [11896]

World Book Graduate Scholarships in Library and Information Science *(Graduate/Scholarship)* [3038]

Life sciences

antibodies-online Annual University Scholarship *(Undergraduate, Graduate/Scholarship)* [1725]

C. Lalor Burdick Scholarship *(Graduate, Master's, Doctorate/Scholarship)* [7040]

Dow Chemical Company Fellowships *(Graduate/ Fellowship)* [8027]

E.I. DuPont Graduate Fellowship *(Graduate/Fellowship)* [8028]

Florence C. Rose and S. Meryl Rose Endowed Scholarship *(Master's, Graduate, Doctorate/Scholarship)* [7042]

Foundation for the Preservation of Honey Bees Scholarship *(Graduate/Scholarship)* [4803]

J.P. and Madeline Trinkaus Endowed Scholarship in Embryology *(Graduate, Doctorate, Master's/Scholarship)* [7048]

Kraft Foods Food Science Minority Scholarship *(Undergraduate/Scholarship)* [11739]

L'Oréal-UNESCO For Women in Science International Rising Talents *(Doctorate, Postdoctorate/ Fellowship)* [8695, 11268]

Life Sciences Research Foundation Postdoctoral Fellowship Program *(Postdoctorate/Fellowship)* [6851]

Lola Ellis Robertson Scholarship *(Graduate, Master's, Doctorate/Scholarship)* [7050]

Max M. Burger Endowed Scholarship in Embryology *(Graduate, Master's, Doctorate/Scholarship)* [7051]

Michigan Society of Fellows Three-Year Fellowships *(Postdoctorate/Fellowship)* [7326]

Dolphus E. Milligan Graduate Fellowships *(Graduate/Fellowship)* [8029]

NOBCChE Procter and Gamble Fellowships *(Graduate/Fellowship)* [8030]

Paul and Ellen Ruckes Scholarship *(Graduate, Undergraduate/Scholarship)* [917]

Selman A. Waksman Endowed Scholarship in Microbial Diversity *(Graduate, Master's, Doctorate/ Scholarship)* [7058]

Everett Oscar Shimp Memorial Scholarships *(Undergraduate/Scholarship)* [8878]

Sino-American Pharmaceutical Professionals Association Scholarships *(Undergraduate/Scholarship)* [10150]

Eastman Kodak Dr. Theophilus Sorrell Fellowships *(Graduate/Fellowship)* [8032]

Thermo Fisher Scientific Antibody Scholarship *(Undergraduate, Graduate/Scholarship)* [11016]

UNCF Merck Graduate Science Research Dissertation Fellowships *(Graduate/Fellowship)* [7268, 11270]

UNCF/Merck Postdoctoral Science Research Fellowships *(Postdoctorate/Scholarship)* [7269, 11271]

Linguistics

AIIrS Persian Language Study in Tehran Fellowship *(Graduate, Master's, Doctorate/Fellowship)* [1030]

American Councils for International Education Critical Language Scholarship Program *(Undergraduate, Graduate/Scholarship)* [830]

Jenny Panitch Beckow Memorial Scholarship - Canada *(Graduate/Scholarship)* [6283]

The Ruth Crymes TESOL Fellowship for Graduate Study *(Graduate/Fellowship, Monetary, Award)* [10968]

ETS Postdoctoral Fellowships *(Postdoctorate/Fellowship)* [4311]

James Fonseca Scholarship *(Undergraduate, Graduate/Scholarship)* [395]

Ivan Franko School of Ukrainian Studies Ukraine Travel Award *(Undergraduate/Grant)* [3028]

Goddard, Indovina & Krakowski Scholarship *(Undergraduate, Graduate/Scholarship)* [396]

Graduate Student Award *(Doctorate, Master's, Graduate/Award)* [515]

Harold Gulliksen Psychometric Research Fellowship *(Doctorate, Graduate/Fellowship)* [4312]

Koren and Alice Odian Kasparian Memorial Grant *(Undergraduate/Scholarship)* [1889]

The Albert H. Marckwardt Travel Grants *(Graduate, Doctorate/Grant)* [10969]

National Endowment for the Humanities Advanced Fellowships for Research in Turkey *(Postdoctorate/Fellowship)* [1349, 7871]

NIU-CSEAS Foreign Language and Area Studies (FLAS) Graduate Fellowship *(Undergraduate, Graduate/Fellowship)* [8487]

Robert Roy Award *(Advanced Professional/Award, Recognition)* [2099]

Mary Isabel Sibley Fellowship *(Doctorate/Fellowship)* [9082]

Dr. Brent Slobodin Memorial Scholarship in the Humanities *(Undergraduate, Graduate, University, College/Scholarship)* [12371]

Sylvia Taylor Johnson Minority Fellowships in Educational Measurement *(Doctorate/Fellowship)* [4313]

The TESOL/TEFL Travel Grant *(Advanced Professional/Grant, Monetary)* [10970]

Literary criticism (See Criticism (Art, Drama, Literary))

Literature

ARCE Funded Fellowships *(Doctorate, Postdoctorate/Fellowship)* [1336]

ARCE Research Associates Fellowship *(Doctorate, Postdoctorate, Professional development/Fellowship)* [1337]

Aubrey L. Williams Research Travel Fellowship *(Doctorate/Fellowship)* [1429]

Jenny Panitch Beckow Memorial Scholarship - Canada *(Graduate/Scholarship)* [6283]

Jenny Panitch Beckow Memorial Scholarship - Israel *(Graduate/Scholarship)* [6284]

John Burroughs Bogliasco Fellowships *(Professional development/Fellowship)* [2644]

CAA National Capital Region Writing Contest *(All/ Award, Prize, Monetary)* [2916]

D&A Florida Scholarships *(Undergraduate/Scholarship)* [10678]

Jenny d'Héricourt Fellowship *(Doctorate/Fellowship)* [487]

Ivan Franko School of Ukrainian Studies Ukraine Travel Award *(Undergraduate/Grant)* [3028]

Louis Gottschalk Prize *(Other/Prize)* [1432]

The Stephanie G. Hoffman Scholarship *(Graduate, Undergraduate/Scholarship)* [6274]

Oscar Kenshur Book Prize *(Other/Prize)* [1435]

Lapides Fellowships in Pre-1865 Juvenile Literature and Ephemera *(Graduate, Postdoctorate/Fellowship)* [493]

Leif and Inger Sjöberg Award *(Advanced Professional, Professional development/Award)* [1376]

Literary Individual Project Funding *(Professional development/Grant)* [264]

Walter Rumsey Marvin Grant *(Professional development/Grant)* [8607]

The William P. McHugh Memorial Fund *(Doctorate, Graduate/Grant)* [1338]

National Endowment for the Humanities Advanced Fellowships for Research in Turkey *(Postdoctorate/Fellowship)* [1349, 7871]

National Endowment for the Humanities Fellowship *(Graduate/Fellowship)* [1339]

Oregon Literary Fellowships *(Advanced Professional/Fellowship)* [6877]

The Barbara L. Packer Fellowship *(Doctorate, Postdoctorate/Fellowship)* [496]

The Remeza Family Research and Publications Grant *(Professional development/Grant)* [3031]

Ameen Rihani Scholarship Program *(Undergraduate/Scholarship)* [1768]

R.L. Gillette Scholarship *(Undergraduate/Scholarship)* [918]

Luci Shaw Fellowship *(Undergraduate/Fellowship)* [3215]

The United States Department of State, Bureau of Educational & Cultural Affairs Fellowships *(Graduate/Fellowship)* [1340]

The William B. Wisdom Grants in Aid of Research *(Undergraduate, Graduate/Grant)* [12130]

The Thomas Wolfe Student Travel Grants in Honor of Richard S. Kennedy *(Graduate, Undergraduate/ Grant)* [12131]

Literature, Children's

Hannah Beiter Graduate Student Research Grants *(Master's, Graduate/Grant, Recognition)* [3296]

ChLA Faculty Research Grants *(Professional development/Grant)* [3297]

Don Freeman Illustrator Grants *(Advanced Professional/Grant)* [10300]

Ezra Jack Keats/Kerlan Memorial Fellowship *(Professional development/Fellowship)* [11643]

Martha Weston Grant *(Advanced Professional/ Grant)* [10301]

Multicultural Work-in-Progress Grant *(Advanced Professional/Grant)* [10302]

PEN/Phyllis Naylor Grant for Children's and Young Adult Novelists *(Other/Grant)* [8952]

SCBWI Work-in-Progress Awards (WIP) *(Advanced Professional/Award)* [10303]

Student Illustrator Scholarship *(Undergraduate, Graduate/Scholarship)* [10304]

Student Writer Scholarship *(Graduate, Doctorate, Undergraduate/Scholarship)* [10305]

Tribute Fund Community Grant *(Professional development/Grant)* [10306]

Jane Yolen Mid-List Author Grant *(Professional development/Grant)* [10307]

Local government

Congressional and Business Leadership Awards *(Undergraduate/Scholarship)* [4837]

ICMA Local Government Management Fellowship *(Master's/Fellowship)* [5968]

Logistics

Allied Van Lines Military Scholarship *(Undergraduate/Scholarship)* [370]

Helene M. Overly Memorial Graduate Scholarship *(Graduate/Scholarship)* [12170]

HSF/Marathon Oil College Scholarship Program *(Undergraduate/Scholarship)* [5531]

NDTA Academic Scholarship Program A *(Undergraduate/Scholarship)* [7836]

NDTA Academic Scholarship Program B *(Undergraduate/Scholarship)* [7837]

North American Van Lines Military Scholarship Competition *(Undergraduate/Scholarship)* [8424]

Sharon D. Banks Memorial Undergraduate Scholarship *(Undergraduate/Scholarship)* [12171]

Lou Gehrig's disease (See Amyotrophic lateral sclerosis)

Management

AACE International Competitive Scholarships *(Undergraduate/Scholarship)* [22]

Allmand Law Scholarship Contest *(Undergraduate/ Scholarship)* [372]

The Alsandor Law Firm Scholarship Contest *(Undergraduate/Scholarship)* [407]

Ben C. Francis Risk Management Education Fund *(Undergraduate/Scholarship)* [9385]

Benson Law Firm Scholarship Contest *(Undergraduate/Scholarship)* [2477]

Seth Bonder Scholarship for Applied Operations Research in Military Applications *(Doctorate/Scholarship, Monetary, Recognition, Award)* [5852]

George M. Brooker, CPM Diversity Collegiate Scholarship *(Graduate, Undergraduate/Scholarship)* [5861]

Brylak Law Safety Scholarship Contest *(Undergraduate/Scholarship)* [2734]

California Association of Family and Consumer Sciences - San Diego Chapter Scholarship (Undergraduate, Graduate/Scholarship) [9805]

Robert & Jean Campbell Scholarship (Undergraduate, University, College, Vocational/Occupational/Scholarship) [12299]

CMAA Student Conference Travel Grants (Undergraduate/Grant, Award) [3442]

Crush the PMP Scholarship Program (Undergraduate, Graduate/Scholarship) [3930]

CTP Scholarship Program (Other/Scholarship) [8053]

David A. Kronick Travelling Fellowship (Doctorate, Graduate/Fellowship) [7216]

DeVries Law School Scholarship (Undergraduate/Scholarship) [4070]

Diversity Executive Leadership Program Scholarship (DELP) (Other/Scholarship) [1977]

Elite Entrepreneurs Scholarship Contest (Undergraduate, Graduate, High School/Scholarship) [4369]

Evans Warncke Robinson, LLC Scholarship Contest (Undergraduate/Scholarship) [4453]

Donald M. Furbush Professional Development Grants (Other/Grant) [5862]

Bert & Karen Hadvick Scholarship (Undergraduate, University, College, Vocational/Occupational/Scholarship) [12321]

The Harold E. Eisenberg Foundation Scholarship (Other/Scholarship) [5979]

Herb Adrian Memorial Scholarship Endowment (Undergraduate/Scholarship) [4735]

HRH Prince Alwaleed Bin Talal ISNA Fellowships (Graduate/Fellowship) [6180]

IFMA Foundation Scholarship (Undergraduate, Graduate/Scholarship) [6001]

IMA Memorial Education Fund Scholarships (MEF) (Graduate, Undergraduate/Scholarship) [5848]

Joe Perdue Scholarship (Undergraduate/Scholarship, Award) [3443]

Willmoore H. Kendall Scholarships (Professional development/Scholarship) [3444]

Kenyon T. Payne Outstanding Student Award (Undergraduate/Award, Monetary) [7344]

Jessica King Scholarships (Other/Scholarship) [3938]

Maricopa County Community College District Scholarships (MCCCD) (Undergraduate/Scholarship) [7034]

NAGAP Graduate Student Enrollment Management Research Grants (Graduate/Grant) [7651]

North American Van Lines Military Scholarship Competition (Undergraduate/Scholarship) [8424]

Ontario Women's Institute Scholarships (Undergraduate/Scholarship) [4525]

J. L. Phelps Scholarship (Undergraduate, University, College, Vocational/Occupational/Scholarship) [12357]

Presidential Management Fellows (PMF) (Graduate, Master's/Fellowship) [11330]

John T. Riordan Professional Education Scholarships (Professional development/Fellowship) [5981]

Paul H. Rittle Sr. Professional Development Grants (Other/Grant) [5863]

Robert Hancock Memorial Scholarship Award (Undergraduate/Scholarship) [7346]

Russell Ackoff Doctoral Student Fellowship (Doctorate/Fellowship) [11662]

Stanley M. Schoenfeld Memorial Scholarship (Postgraduate/Scholarship) [8321]

Sigma Iota Epsilon Undergraduate National Scholar Awards (Undergraduate/Scholarship) [10088]

Stuart Cameron and Margaret McLeod Memorial Scholarship (SCMS) (Graduate, Undergraduate/Scholarship) [5850]

Surety and Fidelity Industry Intern and Scholarship Program (Undergraduate, Graduate/Scholarship) [10885]

Syncrude/Athabasca University Aboriginal Scholarships (Undergraduate/Scholarship) [10902]

Tag and Label Manufacturers Institute Scholarships - Four-Year Colleges (Undergraduate/Scholarship) [10904]

Val Mason Scholarship (Graduate, Professional development/Scholarship, Award) [3114]

Wells Fargo American Indian Scholarship Program (Undergraduate/Scholarship) [996]

Wells Fargo Career Scholarship (Undergraduate/Scholarship) [11506]

Manufacturing

AACE International Competitive Scholarships (Undergraduate/Scholarship) [22]

Walt Bartram Memorial Education Scholarship (Undergraduate/Scholarship) [10384]

Boeing Company Scholarship (Undergraduate/Scholarship) [10050]

Arthur and Gladys Cervenka Scholarship (Undergraduate/Scholarship) [10385]

Chapter 1 - Detroit Associate Scholarship (Graduate, Undergraduate, Vocational/Occupational, Two Year College, Four Year College/Award) [10386]

Chapter 1 – Detroit Undergraduate Scholarship (Undergraduate, Vocational/Occupational, Two Year College, Four Year College/Scholarship) [10387]

Chapter 4 - Lawrence A. Wacker Memorial Scholarship (Undergraduate/Scholarship) [10391]

Chapter 6 - Fairfield County Scholarship (Undergraduate/Scholarship) [10394]

Chapter 17 - St. Louis Scholarship (Undergraduate/Scholarship) [10388]

Chapter 23 - Quad Cities Scholarship (Undergraduate/Scholarship) [10389]

Chapter 31 - Peoria Scholarship (Undergraduate/Scholarship) [10390]

Chapter 52 - Wichita Scholarship (Graduate, Undergraduate, Vocational/Occupational, Community College/Scholarship) [10392]

Chapter 56 - Ft. Wayne Scholarship (Graduate, Undergraduate, Vocational/Occupational, Community College/Scholarship) [10393]

Chapter 63 - Morrow Scholarship (Undergraduate/Scholarship) [10395]

Chapter 63 - Smith Memorial Scholarship (Undergraduate/Scholarship) [10396]

Chapter 67 - Phoenix Scholarship (Undergraduate/Scholarship) [10397]

Chapter 79/198/311 Scholarship (Graduate, Undergraduate, Vocational/Occupational, Community College/Scholarship) [10398]

Chapter 93 - Albuquerque Scholarship (Undergraduate/Scholarship) [10399]

Dake Community Manufacturing Scholarship (Undergraduate/Scholarship) [5072]

Chapter 116 - Roscoe Douglas Scholarship (Undergraduate/Scholarship) [10400]

Connie and Robert T. Gunter Scholarship (Undergraduate/Scholarship) [10401]

Clinton J. Helton Manufacturing Scholarship (Undergraduate/Scholarship) [10402]

Lucile B. Kaufman Women's Scholarship (Undergraduate/Scholarship) [10403]

E. Wayne Kay Co-op Scholarship (Undergraduate/Scholarship) [10404]

E. Wayne Kay Community College Scholarship (Undergraduate, Community College/Scholarship) [10405]

E. Wayne Kay Graduate Scholarships (Graduate, Doctorate/Scholarship) [10406]

E. Wayne Kay High School Scholarship (Undergraduate/Scholarship) [10407]

Giuliano Mazzetti Scholarship (Undergraduate/Scholarship) [10408]

Clarence & Josephine Myers Undergraduate Scholarships (Graduate, Undergraduate, Vocational/Occupational, Community College/Scholarship) [10409]

NBT Trade School, Community/Technical College, or University Scholarships (Undergraduate/Scholarship) [8563]

North Central Region 9 Scholarship (Undergraduate/Scholarship) [10410]

Edward S. Roth Scholarship (Graduate, Undergraduate/Scholarship) [10411]

Schneider/Bingle PLTW Scholarship (Undergraduate/Scholarship) [10412]

Prof. George Schneider Scholarship (Undergraduate/Scholarship) [10413]

SME Directors Scholarships (Undergraduate/Scholarship) [10414]

SME Education Foundation Family Scholarships (Undergraduate/Scholarship) [10415]

SME Future Leaders of Manufacturing Scholarship (Graduate, Undergraduate/Scholarship) [10416]

Myrtle & Earl Walker Scholarships (Undergraduate/Scholarship) [10417]

Albert E. Wischmeyer Scholarship (Undergraduate/Scholarship) [10419]

Women of Today's Manufacturing Scholarship (Undergraduate/Scholarship) [3697]

Marine biology (See Biology, Marine)

Marine engineering (See Engineering, Marine)

Maritime studies

The Agnes Sopcak Memorial Scholarship (Undergraduate/Scholarship) [12146]

Ethyl and Armin Wiebke Memorial Scholarship (Undergraduate/Scholarship) [12147]

Dr. Nancy Foster Scholarship Program (Doctorate/Scholarship) [8017]

Dr. Nancy Foster Scholarships (Graduate/Scholarship) [4695]

LaRue A. Ditmore Music Scholarship (Undergraduate/Scholarship) [12148]

Lily H. Gridley Memorial Scholarship (Undergraduate/Scholarship) [12149]

Merchants Exchange Scholarship (Undergraduate, Vocational/Occupational, Graduate, Professional development/Scholarship) [7266]

Craig D. Newman Memorial Scholarship (Undergraduate/Scholarship) [5409]

Norm Manly YMTA Maritime Education Scholarship (Undergraduate/Scholarship) [4691, 12274]

Marketing and distribution

10x Digital Marketing Scholarship (Undergraduate, Graduate/Scholarship) [4]

All-American Vector Marketing Scholarship Program (Undergraduate/Scholarship) [11793]

American Marketing Association-Connecticut Chapter, Anna C. Klune Memorial Scholarship (Graduate/Scholarship) [5314]

Anchor Plastics Scholarships (Graduate, Undergraduate/Scholarship) [9166]

Ann Liguori Foundation Sports Media Scholarship (Graduate, Undergraduate/Scholarship) [8366]

Auto-Pets "Out-of-the-Box Thinking" Scholarships (All/Scholarship) [2355]

The Aweber Developing Futures Scholarship (Undergraduate/Scholarship) [2389]

Bank of Canada Fellowship Award (Doctorate, Other/Fellowship) [2423]

The Dora J. Beattie IBEA Scholarship (Undergraduate/Scholarship) [5695]

Bick Bickson Scholarship Fund (Undergraduate, Graduate/Award) [5383]

Mike Buoncristiano Memorial Scholarship Fund (Undergraduate/Scholarship) [7103]

Catrala - Hawaii Scholarship Fund (Undergraduate, University, Two Year College, Four Year College/Scholarship) [5388]

CCAE Ontario Regional Chapter Scholarship (Advanced Professional, Professional development/Scholarship) [6742]

Colonial Ghosts Scholarships for History & Marketing Students (Undergraduate/Scholarship) [3520]

Custom Creatives Digital Marketing Scholarship Program (Community College, Four Year College/Scholarship) [3944]

Debbie Khalil Memorial Scholarship (Graduate, Undergraduate/Scholarship) [9167]

The Harold K. Douthit Scholarship (Undergraduate/Scholarship) [8580]

Mark Duda Scholarship Fund (Graduate, Undergraduate/Scholarship) [7104]

Enterprise Schlorship (Graduate, Undergraduate/Scholarship) [9168]

Evoke Strategy Writing Scholarship (Undergraduate/Scholarship) [4459]

Federated Insurance Scholarship (Graduate, Undergraduate/Scholarship) [9169]

Dave Florence Scholarship Fund (Undergraduate/Scholarship) [7105]

Future Digital Marketers Scholarship (College, University/Scholarship) [2657]

Richard A. Hammill Scholarship Fund (Undergraduate/Scholarship) [1103]

The Harold E. Eisenberg Foundation Scholarship (Other/Scholarship) [5979]

William H. Harris Memorial Scholarships (Graduate, Undergraduate/Scholarship) [9170]

HSF/Marathon Oil College Scholarship Program (Undergraduate/Scholarship) [5531]

Kerrwil's J.W. Kerr Continuing Education Scholarship Awards (Undergraduate/Scholarship) [4351]

Don Kuhn Memorial Scholarship Fund (Graduate/Scholarship) [7106]

The Lagrant Foundation - Graduate Scholarships (Graduate/Scholarship) [6632]

The Lagrant Foundation - Undergraduate Scholarships (Undergraduate/Scholarship) [6633]

Robert J. Lavidge Global Marketing Research Award (Professional development/Award) [1104]

The Lead Roster B2B Sales & Marketing Scholarship (Undergraduate, High School/Scholarship) [1693]

Lee Epstein Fund Scholarship (Graduate, Undergraduate/Scholarship) [7107]

Maricopa County Community College District Scholarships (MCCCD) (Undergraduate/Scholarship) [7034]

Northwestern Mutual Scholarship (Graduate, Undergraduate/Scholarship) [9171]

Ohio Newspaper Association Minority Scholarship (Undergraduate/Scholarship) [8581]

ONWA Annual Scholarship (Undergraduate/Scholarship) [8582]

Phi Sigma Epsilon Past National President Scholarships (Graduate, Undergraduate/Scholarship) [9172]

The Publicity.ai SEO & Content Marketing Scholarship (Undergraduate, High School/Scholarship) [1694]

Reba Malone Scholarship (Undergraduate, Graduate/Scholarship) [1305]

John T. Riordan Professional Education Scholarships (Professional development/Fellowship) [5981]

Springer - Jim Springer Memorial Scholarship (Undergraduate/Scholarship) [3489]

Tag and Label Manufacturers Institute Scholarships - Four-Year Colleges (Undergraduate/Scholarship) [10904]

Undergraduate/Graduate Scholarships (Undergraduate, Graduate/Scholarship) [5989]

Valuing Diversity PhD Scholarship (Doctorate/Scholarship) [1105]

Vector Marketing Canadian Scholarship Award (Undergraduate/Scholarship) [11794]

Vector Marketing Scholarship (Graduate, Undergraduate/Scholarship) [9173]

Websauce Web Design Scholarship (Undergraduate/Scholarship) [11954]

Whan Memorial Scholarships (Graduate, Undergraduate/Scholarship) [9174]

Glenn Wilson Broadcast Journalism Scholarship (Undergraduate/Scholarship) [8887]

Willa Yeck Memorial Scholarship Fund (Undergraduate/Scholarship) [7108]

Lorraine Zitone Memorial Scholarship Fund (Undergraduate/Scholarship) [7109]

Material and process engineering (See Engineering, Materials)

Materials handling

IFMA Foundation Scholarship (Undergraduate, Graduate/Scholarship) [6001]

Materials research/science

ACI Foundation Scholarships (Graduate/Scholarship) [786]

ACI W.R. Grace Scholarships (Graduate/Scholarship) [789]

AESF Foundation Scholarships (Undergraduate, Graduate/Scholarship) [7704]

ASNT Fellowship Award (Graduate/Fellowship, Award) [1531]

DEPS Graduate Scholarship (Graduate/Scholarship) [4099]

DOE Computational Science Graduate Fellowship (DOE CSGF) (Doctorate, Graduate/Fellowship) [6611]

Electronics Division: Lewis C. Hoffman Scholarship (Undergraduate/Scholarship) [733]

Huber Engineered Woods Product Evaluation Scholarships (Graduate/Scholarship) [4500]

Katharine & Bryant Mather Scholarship (Graduate/Scholarship) [791]

Kumar Mehta Scholarship (Graduate/Scholarship) [792]

NPSC Fellowship (Graduate/Fellowship) [5056]

Robert B. Oliver ASNT Scholarship (Undergraduate/Scholarship) [1532]

Stanford Advanced Materials $1,000 College Scholarship (College/Scholarship) [10747]

Bertold E. Weinberg Scholarship (Graduate/Scholarship) [793]

Mathematics and mathematical sciences

AAUW Selected Professions Fellowships (Graduate, Master's, Doctorate/Fellowship) [35]

Actuarial Diversity Scholarship (Undergraduate/Scholarship) [69]

AFCEA STEM Teacher Graduate Scholarships (Graduate/Scholarship) [104, 7022]

AFCEA War Veterans Scholarships (Undergraduate/Scholarship) [105]

African American Network - Carolinas Scholarship Fund (Undergraduate/Scholarship) [4715]

AfterCollege Engineering & Technology Student Scholarship (Undergraduate, Graduate, Doctorate, Master's/Scholarship) [120]

AfterCollege STEM Inclusion Scholarship (Undergraduate, Graduate/Scholarship) [122]

AHETEMS General Scholarships (Undergraduate, Graduate/Scholarship) [10068]

AHETEMS Professional Scholarships (Graduate/Scholarship) [10069]

Aises A. T. Anderson Memorial Scholarship (Graduate, Undergraduate/Scholarship) [1000]

Alaska Aerospace Development Corporation Scholarships (Undergraduate/Scholarship) [11433]

AMS Centennial Fellowships (Postdoctorate/Fellowship, Monetary) [1107]

Anil and Neema Thakrar Family Fund #1 (Undergraduate/Scholarship) [4774]

ASGP Graduate Research Fellowships (Graduate/Fellowship) [244]

Astronaut Scholarship Foundation Scholarship (Undergraduate/Scholarship) [2332]

Athena San Diego Pinnacle Scholarship (Undergraduate/Scholarship) [9799]

AWM Mathematics Travel Grants (Doctorate/Grant) [2318]

BadCredit.orgs Wealth Wise Scholarship (Undergraduate, Graduate/Scholarship) [2401]

B&W Y-12 Scholarship Fund (Undergraduate/Scholarship) [4254]

Barry M. Goldwater Scholarship (Undergraduate/Scholarship) [11733]

Bill and Nell Biggs Scholarship (Undergraduate/Scholarship) [11508]

Bluepay Stem Scholarship (Graduate, Undergraduate/Scholarship) [2630]

Sam L. Booke, Sr. Scholarship (Undergraduate/Scholarship) [12063]

Buck Bragunier Leadership Scholarship (Four Year College, University/Scholarship) [1840]

Breast Cancer Car Donations Annual College Scholarship (Undergraduate/Scholarship) [2685]

Lieutenant General Douglas D. Buchholz Memorial Scholarship (Undergraduate/Scholarship) [106]

Buick Achievers Scholarship Program (Undergraduate/Scholarship) [4905]

Burroughs Wellcome Fund Collaborative Research Travel Grants (CRTG) (Doctorate, Postdoctorate/Grant) [2750]

Career Awards for Science and Mathematics Teachers (Other/Award) [2752]

Career Awards at the Scientific Interface (CASI) (Undergraduate, Postdoctorate, Graduate/Grant) [2753]

Caribbean Actuarial Scholarship (Undergraduate/Scholarship) [70]

Carrie and George Lyter Scholarship (Undergraduate/Scholarship) [4775]

Chapter 79/198/311 Scholarship (Graduate, Undergraduate, Vocational/Occupational, Community College/Scholarship) [10398]

CHCI Graduate Fellowship Program (Graduate, Professional development/Fellowship) [3746]

The Churchill Scholarships (Postgraduate/Scholarship) [3331]

CIMON Inc Scholarship (College, University/Scholarship) [3333]

City of Toronto Graduate Scholarships for Women in Mathematics (Master's, Doctorate/Scholarship) [11685]

Clarence Olander School In-Service Training Grants for Grades Prek-5 (High School/Grant) [7802]

Claude B. Hart Memorial Scholarship (Undergraduate/Scholarship) [12066]

Mike Crapo Math and Science Scholarship Fund (Undergraduate/Scholarship) [5676]

CRM-ISM Postdoctoral Fellowship (Postdoctorate/Fellowship) [5807, 11417]

DOE Computational Science Graduate Fellowship (DOE CSGF) (Doctorate, Graduate/Fellowship) [6611]

EAPSI Fellowships (Doctorate, Graduate/Fellowship, Award) [8067]

Bruce T. and Jackie Mahi Erickson Scholarship (Graduate, Undergraduate/Scholarship) [8924]

Fields Research Fellowship (Postdoctorate/Fellowship) [4551]

Frank Fong Scholarships (Undergraduate/Scholarship) [10267]

Future Leader Initial NCTM Annual Meeting Attendance Awards (Advanced Professional/Award, Monetary) [7804]

The Gates Millennium Scholars (Undergraduate/Scholarship) [5529]

Margaret S. Gilbert Scholarship Fund (Graduate/Scholarship) [10760]

Girls in Stem (GIS) Scholarship (Undergraduate/Scholarship) [9716]

Glendale Latino Association Scholarships (Undergraduate/Scholarship) [4999]

Gorrondona & Associates, Inc. / WTS High School Scholarships (Two Year College, Four Year College/Scholarship) [12174]

GREAT MINDS Collegiate Scholarship Program (Undergraduate/Scholarship) [368]

HACU/KIA Motors America, Inc. STEAM Scholarships (Undergraduate, Graduate/Scholarship) [5516, 6543]

H.G. Hardbarger Science - Mathematics Award (Undergraduate, Vocational/Occupational/Award) [8853]

Dolores Ruth Heady Hardy Memorial Scholarship (Undergraduate/Scholarship) [6442]

Herb And Ann Fincher Scholarship Fund (Undergraduate/Scholarship) [3571]

Curtis E. Huntington Memorial Scholarship (Undergraduate/Scholarship) [71]

ISM Scholarships for Graduate Studies (Graduate/Scholarship) [5808]

Jimmy Guild Memorial Scholarship (Undergraduate/Scholarship) [6802]

JMJ Phillip Group College Scholarships (Graduate, University, Four Year College, Two Year College/Scholarship) [6312]

Josef Princ Memorial Scholarship (Undergraduate/Scholarship) [9407]

Joseph Wood Rogers Memorial Scholarship in Mathematics *(Undergraduate/Scholarship)* [10055]

Kevin Ernst Memorial Scholarship *(Undergraduate/Scholarship)* [5087]

Lakselaget Foundation Scholarship Fund *(Graduate, Undergraduate/Scholarship)* [6635]

Langfitt-Ambrose Scholarship *(Undergraduate/Scholarship)* [8863]

Latinos in Technology Scholarship *(Undergraduate/Scholarship)* [10136]

Laura Ann Peck Memorial Endowed Scholarship *(Undergraduate/Scholarship)* [6806]

Leo Zupin Memorial Scholarship *(Undergraduate, Vocational/Occupational/Scholarship)* [5091]

Lt Col Romeo - Josephine Bass Ferretti Scholarship *(Undergraduate/Scholarship)* [148]

MAES Founders Scholarship *(Graduate, Undergraduate/Scholarship)* [6964]

MAES General Scholarships *(Graduate, Undergraduate/Scholarship)* [6965]

MAES Padrino/Madrina Scholarships *(Graduate, Undergraduate/Scholarship)* [6966]

MAES Pipeline Scholarship *(Graduate, Undergraduate/Scholarship)* [6967]

MAES Presidential Scholarship *(Graduate, Undergraduate/Scholarship)* [6968]

MAES Scholarships *(Graduate/Scholarship)* [6969]

Margaret Svec Scholarship *(Undergraduate/Scholarship)* [10059]

Mathematics Mentoring Travel Grants *(Doctorate/Grant)* [2319]

Microsoft Research Graduate Women's Scholarships *(Graduate/Scholarship)* [7356]

Microsoft Research PhD Fellowships *(Doctorate/Fellowship)* [7357]

Molded Dimensions, LLC Scholarship *(College, University/Scholarship)* [7428]

Mu Alpha Theta Summer Grants *(Undergraduate, Graduate/Grant)* [7493]

Murrietta Circuits Scholarship Opportunity *(Undergraduate, College, University/Scholarship)* [7505]

National Co-op Scholarship Program *(Undergraduate/Scholarship)* [12190]

National Debt Relief Scholarship *(University, Four Year College, Undergraduate/Scholarship)* [7828]

National GEM Consortium - PhD Science Fellowships *(Doctorate, Graduate/Fellowship)* [7904]

NCTM Emerging Teacher-Leaders in Elementary School Mathematics Grants for Grades PreK-5 *(Other/Grant)* [7806]

NCTM Prospective 7-12 Secondary Teacher Course Work Scholarships *(Professional development/Scholarship)* [7807]

NCTM School In-Service Training Grants for Grades 6-8 *(Undergraduate/Grant)* [7808]

NCTM School In-Service Training Grants for Grades 9-12 *(Undergraduate/Grant)* [7809]

NCTM School In-Service Training Grants for Grades PreK-5 *(Undergraduate/Grant)* [7810]

Northrop Grumman Engineering Scholars Program *(Undergraduate/Scholarship)* [8498]

Noyce Scholarships for Secondary Math and Science Education *(Undergraduate/Scholarship)* [5764]

Ohio Space Grant Consortium Graduate Fellowships *(Graduate, Doctorate, Master's/Fellowship)* [8598]

Ohio Space Grant Consortium Special Minority Fellowships *(Doctorate, Graduate, Master's/Fellowship)* [8599]

Out to Innovate Scholarship *(Graduate, Undergraduate, Community College/Scholarship)* [8019]

PIMS Postdoctoral Fellowship *(Doctorate, Postdoctorate/Fellowship)* [8806]

Fields Postdoctoral Fellowships (FPDF) *(Postdoctorate/Fellowship)* [4552]

Professor Emeritus Dr. Bill Johnson Memorial Scholarship *(Undergraduate/Scholarship)* [10061]

Red Olive Women in STEM Scholarship *(Undergraduate, Graduate/Scholarship)* [9516]

Reuben H. Fleet Memorial Scholarship *(Undergraduate/Scholarship)* [9845]

Actuary of Tomorrow - Stuart A. Robertson Memorial Scholarship *(Undergraduate/Scholarship)* [73]

Carl M. Rose Memorial Scholarship *(Undergraduate/Scholarship)* [8874]

Jack Rosen Scholarship *(Undergraduate/Scholarship)* [6393]

Science, Mathematics And Research for Transformation Scholarship for Service Program (SMART) *(Undergraduate, Graduate/Scholarship)* [1445, 9974]

Everett Oscar Shimp Memorial Scholarships *(Undergraduate/Scholarship)* [8878]

SHPE Dissertation Scholarship *(Doctorate/Scholarship)* [10351]

SHPE Professional Scholarship *(Master's, Doctorate/Scholarship)* [10352]

Ralph W. Shrader Diversity Scholarship *(Graduate/Scholarship)* [107]

Alfred P. Sloan Foundation Graduate Scholarships - Sloan Indigenous Graduate Partnership (SIGP) *(Master's, Doctorate/Scholarship)* [7581]

Alfred P. Sloan Foundation Graduate Scholarships - Sloan Minority Ph.D. Program (MPHD) *(Doctorate/Scholarship)* [7582]

Sloan Research Fellowships *(Doctorate/Fellowship)* [10171]

SREB-State Doctoral Scholars Program - Doctoral Award *(Doctorate, Graduate/Scholarship)* [10664]

Summer Undergraduate Fellowship Program *(Undergraduate/Fellowship)* [623]

Truthfinder Scholarship for Women in STEM *(Undergraduate, Graduate, Two Year College/Scholarship)* [11133]

UCSD Black Alumni Scholarships for Engineering, Mathematics and Science *(Undergraduate/Scholarship)* [9858]

USGA/Chevron STEM Scholarship Program *(Undergraduate/Scholarship)* [11373]

Graduate Fellowship Program - Peter Verhofstadt Fellowships *(Graduate/Fellowship)* [10002]

Wes Burton Memorial Scholarship *(Undergraduate/Scholarship)* [12097]

Women In Defense HORIZONS Scholarship *(Graduate, Undergraduate/Scholarship)* [12133]

Woodcock Family Education Scholarship Program *(Undergraduate/Scholarship)* [324]

The Frank & Betty Woodhams Memorial Scholarship *(Undergraduate/Scholarship)* [7260]

WSGC Community College Transfer Scholarships *(Undergraduate/Scholarship)* [11901]

Zuckerman STEM Leadership Program *(Postdoctorate/Scholarship)* [12423]

Mechanical engineering (See Engineering, Mechanical)

Mechanics and repairs

AmericanMuscle's Student Scholarship Program *(College, University/Scholarship)* [1681]

ISOPE Offshore Mechanics Scholarships for Outstanding Students *(Graduate/Scholarship)* [6116]

Media arts

AAAS Mass Media Science & Engineering Fellows Program *(Undergraduate, Graduate, Postdoctorate/Fellowship)* [506]

Academy of Motion Picture Arts and Sciences Student Academy Awards *(Undergraduate/Award)* [53]

Ann Liguori Foundation Sports Media Scholarship *(Graduate, Undergraduate/Scholarship)* [8366]

Anne Friedberg Innovative Scholarship Award *(Other/Scholarship)* [10309]

Association for Women in Sports Media Internship Program *(Undergraduate/Scholarship, Internship)* [2321]

Dalton Camp Awards *(Professional development/Award, Monetary)* [4829]

Canadian Picture Pioneers Scholarship *(Undergraduate/Scholarship)* [3100]

Design and Multimedia Internships - New York *(Undergraduate, Graduate/Internship)* [4980]

Entertainment Media Internships - Los Angeles *(Undergraduate, Graduate/Internship)* [5029]

Faith Initiatives Internships - New York *(Undergraduate, Graduate/Internship)* [4981]

Foundation Relations Internships - Los Angeles *(Undergraduate, Graduate/Internship)* [4982]

Greg Clerk Award *(Advanced Professional, Professional development/Award)* [6621]

HAESF Professional Internship Program *(Doctorate/Internship)* [5645]

Harriet Irsay Scholarship *(Graduate, Undergraduate/Scholarship)* [1045]

HBO Point Scholarship *(Graduate, Undergraduate, Doctorate/Scholarship)* [9222]

Indigenous Arts Individual Project Funding *(Professional development/Grant)* [263]

Hedy Lamarr Achievement Award for Emerging Leaders in Entertainment Technology *(Undergraduate/Award)* [4086]

News and Rapid Response Internship *(Undergraduate, Graduate/Internship)* [4986]

NHFA Scholarships *(Graduate/Scholarship)* [7930]

William C. Rogers Scholarship *(Undergraduate/Scholarship)* [4937]

Special Events Internship- New York *(Undergraduate, Graduate/Internship)* [4987]

Special Events Internships - Los Angeles *(Undergraduate, Graduate/Internship)* [4988]

TFI Latin America Media Arts Fund *(Professional development/Grant)* [11110]

Sandy Ulm Scholarships *(Undergraduate, Master's/Scholarship)* [4625]

Visual Arts and New Media Individual Project Funding *(Professional development/Grant)* [265]

Medical assisting

AASLD NP/PA Clinical Hepatology Fellowship *(Professional development/Fellowship)* [647]

Buckfire & Buckfire, P.C. Medical Diversity Scholarships *(Advanced Professional/Scholarship)* [2737]

Discover Health Professions Loans *(Graduate/Loan, Scholarship)* [4111]

Discover Residency Loans *(Graduate/Loan, Scholarship)* [4114]

Mentored Research Fellowship *(Postdoctorate/Fellowship)* [7534]

Northampton County Medical Society Alliance Scholarships *(Undergraduate/Scholarship)* [8480]

Susan Vincent Memorial Scholarship *(Undergraduate/Scholarship)* [6973]

Maxine Williams Scholarship *(Undergraduate/Scholarship)* [605]

Medical education (See Education, Medical)

Medical laboratory technology

CSMLS Student Scholarship *(Postgraduate/Scholarship, Monetary, Award)* [3118]

Indspire Health Careers Bursary and Scholarships *(Graduate, Undergraduate/Scholarship)* [5774]

Johns Hopkins Medicine Ultrasound Fellowships *(Professional development/Fellowship)* [6323]

Vancouver Yukoners Legacy Scholarship *(Vocational/Occupational, College, Undergraduate/Scholarship)* [12381]

The Yukon Foundation Medical Laboratory Scholarship *(Graduate, Master's, Undergraduate/Scholarship)* [12397]

Medical library science (See Library and archival sciences)

Medical research (See also Biomedical research)

AACC International Travel Grants *(Advanced Professional, Professional development/Grant)* [540]

AACR Basic Cancer Research Fellowships *(Postdoctorate/Fellowship, Award, Recognition)* [529]

AACR Scholar-in-Training Awards: Other Conferences and Meetings *(Graduate, Postdoctorate/Grant, Award)* [531]

AAS/AAS Trainee Research Fellowship Awards (Professional development/Fellowship) [2028]
ABTA Discovery Grant (Professional development/Grant) [700]
ABTA Medical Student Summer Fellowship Program (Undergraduate/Fellowship) [701]
ADA Junior Faculty Award (Other/Grant, Award, Monetary) [864]
ADR Postdoctoral Fellowship Awards (Advanced Professional, Professional development/Fellowship) [2691]
AF Junior Research Grant (Professional development/Grant) [1700]
AF Senior Research Grant (Advanced Professional/Grant) [1701]
AGA-Elsevier Pilot Research Award (Professional development/Award) [936]
AGA-R. Robert & Sally Funderburg Research Award in Gastric Cancer (Postdoctorate/Grant) [937]
AGA Research Scholar Award (AGA RSA) (Advanced Professional/Grant) [939]
AGA Student Research Fellowship Award (Undergraduate, Graduate/Fellowship) [941]
AHNS/AAO-HNS Young Investigator combined Award (Other/Award) [470, 954]
AHNS Pilot Grant (Other, Doctorate/Grant) [955]
AIHS Graduate Studentships (Master's, Doctorate/Fellowship) [272]
AIHS Postgraduate Fellowships (Postgraduate, Advanced Professional/Fellowship) [273]
ALF Postdoctoral Research Fellowship Award (Postdoctorate, Professional development/Fellowship) [1090]
Alzheimer's Disease Research Standard Award (Doctorate/Award) [2692]
American Cancer Society - Research Scholar Grants (Doctorate, Professional development/Grant) [716]
American Diabetes Association and Boehringer Ingelheim Research Award: Chronic Kidney Disease and Renal Insufficiency in the Setting of Diabetes (Doctorate, Professional development/Award) [7976]
American Liver Foundation Liver Scholar Award (Doctorate/Award) [1091]
American Lung Association Biomedical Research Grants (RG) (Doctorate/Grant) [1094]
Annual Research Doctoral and Postgraduate Fellowship Grant Program (Doctorate, Postdoctorate, Postgraduate, Advanced Professional/Fellowship, Grant) [2923]
APDA Research Grants (Postgraduate, Professional development/Grant) [1207]
ASC Research Grant (University/Grant) [411]
Asia-Pacific Biomedical Research Foundation Merit Awards (Postdoctorate/Award, Recognition, Prize) [10530]
ATA Research Grants (Professional development/Grant) [1624]
Ballantyne Resident Research Grant (Other, Graduate/Grant) [956]
Raymond B. Bauer Research Award (Professional development/Award, Grant) [7322]
William B. Bean Student Research Award (Undergraduate/Grant) [1196]
Bradley Stuart Beller Special Merit Award (Doctorate, Postdoctorate/Award) [3768]
Leslie Bernstein Grant (Professional development/Grant) [452]
Career Awards for Medical Scientists (CAMS) (Postdoctorate/Grant) [2751]
Vyaire Fellowship for Neonatal and Pediatric Therapists (Professional development/Fellowship) [1352]
CAS/GE Healthcare Canada Inc. Research Awards (Other/Award) [2878]
CCTS services, resources, and pilot awards (Postdoctorate, Professional development/Grant) [8603]
CFF Grants (Other/Grant) [3948]
CFF/NIH-Unfunded Award (Professional development/Grant) [3949]
CFF Pilot and Feasibility Awards (Professional development/Grant) [3950]
Charles S. Houston Grant (Advanced Professional/Grant) [12028]

CHOPR Fellowship Program (Postdoctorate/Fellowship) [11664]
Clinician Research Awards (Postgraduate, Professional development, Other/Fellowship) [8898]
Crohn's and Colitis Canada Innovations in IBD Research (Advanced Professional, Professional development/Grant) [3909]
CSCI Distinguished Scientist Lectures and Awards (Advanced Professional/Award) [10264]
CTSI Collaborative Translational Pilot Project Program (Professional development/Grant) [8356]
Damon Runyon Cancer Research Foundation Fellowships (Graduate, Postdoctorate/Fellowship) [9757]
Damon Runyon-Rachleff Innovation Awards (Postdoctorate/Award) [9759]
Damon Runyon-Sohn Pediatric Cancer Fellowship Award (Master's, Doctorate/Fellowship) [9760]
Deborah Munroe Noonan Memorial Research Fund (Professional development/Grant) [5436]
DRC Pilot and Feasibility Study Award (Advanced Professional, Professional development/Grant, Award) [12233]
Drug Development Research Professorship (Professional development/Internship) [3773]
Educational Fellowship For Practicing Physicians (Advanced Professional, Professional development/Fellowship) [9155]
AACR Gertrude B. Elion Cancer Research Award (Professional development, Graduate/Award, Recognition) [534]
Carl W. Gottschalk Research Scholar Grants (Professional development/Grant) [1526]
Hannah Post-doctoral Fellowship (Postdoctorate/Fellowship) [2020]
Health, Leisure and Human Performance Research Institute Graduate Student Travel Award (Graduate/Grant, Award) [11589]
Charles H. Hood Foundation Child Health Research Awards Program (Doctorate/Award) [5438]
IASP Collaborative Research Grants (Professional development/Grant) [5939]
IASP Developed-Developing Countries Collaborative Research Grants (Advanced Professional/Grant) [5940]
IASP Developing Countries Project: Initiative for Improving Pain Education (Advanced Professional/Grant) [5941]
IASP Research Symposium (Advanced Professional/Grant) [5942]
International GI Training Grant (Professional development/Grant) [761]
ITNS Research Grants (Other/Grant) [6137]
IWH Mustard Fellowship in Work and Health (Postgraduate/Fellowship) [5876]
Kansas State University Cancer Research Award Program (Undergraduate/Grant) [6374]
Klarman Family Foundation Grants Program in Eating Disorders Research (Professional development/Grant) [5439]
Susan G. Komen for the Cure Post-doctoral Fellowships - Clinical Research Grants (Postdoctorate/Grant, Fellowship) [6587]
Lalor Foundation Merit Awards (Postdoctorate/Award, Recognition, Prize) [10533]
LAM Pilot Project Awards (Master's, Postdoctorate/Grant) [6639]
LCRF Grant (Advanced Professional, Professional development/Grant) [6933]
Thomas R. Lee Career Development Award (Professional development/Grant, Award) [865]
Lymphatic Research Foundation Additional Support for NIH-funded F32 Postdoctoral Fellows Awards (Postdoctorate/Award) [5440]
Lymphatic Research Foundation Postdoctoral Fellowship Awards Program (Postdoctorate/Fellowship) [5441]
Macular Degeneration Research Program Grant (Doctorate/Grant) [2693]
Mentor-Based Minority Postdoctoral Fellowship (Postdoctorate/Fellowship, Monetary) [866]
Mentored Research Scholar Grant (Doctorate, Professional development/Grant) [717]
Metcalf Innovation Fellowship program (Advanced Professional, Professional development/Fellowship) [7271]

Abby and Howard Milstein Innovation Award in Reproductive Medicine (Advanced Professional, Professional development, Graduate/Grant) [6329]
Abby and Howard Milstein Reproductive Medicine Research Award (Advanced Professional, Professional development/Grant) [6330]
MMRF Research Fellow Awards (Postdoctorate, Professional development/Grant) [7495]
Monaghan/Trudell Fellowships for Aerosol Technique Development (Professional development/Fellowship) [1355]
Movember Clinical Trials (Advanced Professional/Grant) [9362]
Movember Discovery Grants (Advanced Professional, Professional development/Grant) [9363]
Movember Rising Star in Prostate Cancer Research Awards (Advanced Professional, Professional development/Grant) [9364]
Movember Team Grants (Advanced Professional, Professional development/Grant) [9365]
MSFHR Research Trainee Award (Postdoctorate, Professional development/Grant) [10181]
MSFHR Scholar Awards (Advanced Professional, Professional development/Grant) [10182]
National Glaucoma Research Program Grant (Professional development/Grant) [2694]
NBHRF/ASRP Doctoral Training Awards (Doctorate/Award) [413, 8212]
NBHRF Doctoral Studentship (Doctorate/Grant) [8214]
NBHRF Master's Studentship (Master's/Grant) [8217]
NBHRF Postdoctoral Fellowships (Postdoctorate/Fellowship) [8218]
NCCT Postdoctoral Research Program (Postdoctorate, Advanced Professional, Professional development/Fellowship) [11358]
New Investigator Grant (Postdoctorate/Grant) [9978]
NIMH Postbaccalaureate Intramural Research Awards (Graduate/Award) [7946]
NINR Mentored Patient-Oriented Research Career Development Award (Doctorate/Award) [7948]
NINR Midcareer Investigator Award in Patient-Oriented Research (Doctorate/Award) [7949]
NINR Pathway to Independence Award (Doctorate, Postdoctorate/Award) [7950]
Pancreatic Cancer Action Network-AACR Career Development Awards (Doctorate/Grant, Award) [535]
Parker B. Francis Respiratory Research Grant (Advanced Professional, Professional development/Grant) [1357]
Parkinson Canada Basic Research Fellowship (Advanced Professional/Fellowship) [8891]
Parkinson Canada New Investigator Award (Professional development/Grant) [8895]
Parkinson Canada Pilot Project Grant (Advanced Professional/Grant) [8896]
Patient Advocate Scholarship Program (Professional development/Scholarship) [3782]
PHA Research Fellowships (Professional development/Fellowship) [9449]
Philips Respironics Fellowships in Non-Invasive Respiratory Care (Professional development/Fellowship) [1359]
Postdoctoral Fellowships (Postdoctorate/Fellowship) [4809]
Postdoctoral Fellowships for Basic Scientists Program (Postdoctorate/Fellowship) [8900]
Prostate Cancer Canada Clinical Research Fellowships (Advanced Professional/Fellowship) [9366]
Prostate Cancer Canada Graduate Studentships (Graduate, Doctorate/Grant) [9367]
Prostate Cancer Canada Postdoctoral Research Fellowships (Postdoctorate, Advanced Professional/Fellowship) [9368]
PSF Research Fellowship Grants (Master's, Doctorate/Grant, Fellowship) [9190]
PSI Graham Farquharson Knowledge Translation Fellowship (Advanced Professional, Professional development/Fellowship) [9156]
PSI Healthcare Research by Community Physicians Grants (Advanced Professional, Professional development/Grant) [9157]

Ross C. Purse Doctoral Fellowship *(Graduate/Award, Fellowship)* [3049]

Resident Research Grant *(Postgraduate, Professional development/Grant)* [9158]

Resident Research Summit Scholarship *(Professional development, Advanced Professional/Scholarship)* [8683]

Robert E. Leet and Clara Guthrie Patterson Trust Mentored Research Award: Clinical, Health Services *(Doctorate, Postdoctorate/Grant)* [5442]

Clinical Scholars *(Professional development/Scholarship)* [6325]

Damon Runyon Clinical Investigator Awards *(Postgraduate/Award)* [9761]

Scholarships for the Next Generation of Scientists *(Postdoctorate/Scholarship)* [3144]

Smith Family Awards Program for Excellence in Biomedical Research *(Advanced Professional, Professional development/Award)* [5443]

SSF Research Grants *(Other/Grant)* [10154]

SSF Student Fellowships *(Doctorate, Undergraduate/Fellowship)* [10155]

Lee Summer Student Fellowship *(Undergraduate, Master's/Fellowship)* [10652]

S. Leonard Syme Training Fellowship *(Master's, Doctorate/Fellowship)* [5877]

THFC Medical Research Grants *(Professional development/Grant)* [5454]

Toronto Rehab Scholarships in Rehabilitation-Related Research *(Graduate/Scholarship)* [11064]

Translational Research Professorship *(Professional development/Internship)* [3784]

UAB Lister Hill Center Intramural Grant Program *(Professional development, Postdoctorate/Grant)* [11431]

USDA-NIFA-AFRI Merit Awards *(Postdoctorate/Award, Recognition, Prize)* [10534]

William Weston Research Award *(Postgraduate/Grant)* [10457]

Young Investigators Achievement Award *(Advanced Professional, Professional development, Graduate/Grant)* [6331]

Medical technology

Henry and Maria Ahrens Charitable Trust Scholarship *(Undergraduate, Graduate/Scholarship)* [5117]

Fay Anthony Scholarship *(Undergraduate, College, University, Vocational/Occupational/Scholarship)* [12283]

ASCP Foundation Garza & Becan-McBride Endowed Scholarship *(Undergraduate/Scholarship, Monetary)* [1402]

John Bunker Scholarship *(Vocational/Occupational, College/Scholarship)* [12297]

CAMS Summer Research Fellowship *(Undergraduate/Fellowship)* [3307]

Hall County Medical Society Scholarship *(Undergraduate, Graduate/Scholarship)* [5122]

Illinois Student Assistance Commission Medical Student Scholarship *(Undergraduate/Scholarship)* [5713]

IOKDS Health Careers Scholarship *(College, University, Undergraduate, Graduate, Doctorate/Scholarship)* [6050]

Esther Lim Memorial Scholarships *(Undergraduate/Scholarship)* [3308]

Lee G. Luna Foreign Travel Scholarship *(Professional development/Scholarship)* [8109]

Margaret Dowell-Gravatt, M.D. Scholarship *(Undergraduate/Scholarship)* [2486]

Ruth Liu Memorial Scholarship *(Undergraduate/Scholarship)* [3309]

SPSmedical CS Scholarships *(Other/Scholarship)* [5928]

Medicine (See also specific diseases)

AABB-Fenwal Specialist in Blood Bank Scholarship Awards *(Professional development/Scholarship)* [519]

AABB-Fenwal Transfusion Medicine Fellows Scholarship Awards *(Doctorate/Scholarship)* [520]

AAFP Minority Scholarships Program for Residents and Returning Students *(Professional development/Scholarship)* [454]

AAFP Resident Community Outreach Award *(Professional development/Scholarship)* [455]

AAFP Tomorrow's Leader Award *(Professional development/Scholarship)* [456]

AAMA Houston Chapter Health Training Scholarships *(Other/Scholarship)* [1770]

AASLD Advanced/Transplant Hepatology Award *(Professional development/Award)* [644]

AASLD Autoimmune Liver Diseases Pilot Research Award *(Graduate, Doctorate, Postdoctorate, Professional development/Award, Grant)* [645]

AASLD Clinical, Translational and Outcomes Research Awards *(Professional development/Grant)* [646]

AASLD Pinnacle Research Award in Liver Disease *(Professional development/Award)* [648]

AAUW Selected Professions Fellowships *(Graduate, Master's, Doctorate/Fellowship)* [35]

Dr. Anderson Abbott Awards *(Undergraduate/Scholarship)* [11681]

Accenture American Indian Scholarship Fund *(Graduate, Undergraduate/Scholarship)* [993]

Afdhal / McHutchison LIFER Award *(Postdoctorate, Professional development/Award)* [649]

AGA Research Foundation Fellowship to Faculty Transition Award *(Professional development/Fellowship)* [938]

AGA Research Scholar Award (AGA RSA) *(Advanced Professional/Grant)* [939]

Henry and Maria Ahrens Charitable Trust Scholarship *(Undergraduate, Graduate/Scholarship)* [5117]

Aises A. T. Anderson Memorial Scholarship *(Graduate, Undergraduate/Scholarship)* [1000]

AKF Clinical Scientist in Nephrology Fellowship (CSN) *(Postgraduate/Fellowship)* [1068]

Allegheny County Medical Society Medical Student Scholarship *(Advanced Professional/Scholarship)* [4796]

Alliance Medical Education Scholarship (AMES) *(Undergraduate, Graduate/Scholarship)* [4797]

Dr. and Mrs. David B. Allman Medical Scholarship *(Undergraduate/Scholarship)* [7414]

AMA Foundation Physicians of Tomorrow Scholarships *(Graduate/Scholarship)* [1111]

American Association of University Women Selected Professions Fellowships *(Other/Fellowship)* [668]

AMSN Career Mobility Scholarship *(Undergraduate, Doctorate/Scholarship)* [48]

AMTF Graduate Scholarships *(Graduate/Scholarship, Monetary)* [1399]

Annual Research Doctoral and Postgraduate Fellowship Grant Program *(Doctorate, Postdoctorate, Postgraduate, Advanced Professional/Fellowship, Grant)* [2923]

ANPA Young Investigator Awards *(Postdoctorate/Grant)* [1155]

Armenian American Medical Association Scholarship Program *(Undergraduate, Graduate/Scholarship)* [1842]

Army Health Professions Scholarship Program (HPSP) *(Professional development/Scholarship)* [11288]

ARS Lazarian Graduate Scholarship *(Graduate, Master's, Doctorate/Scholarship)* [1854]

ASA Minority Fellowship Program (ASA MFP) *(Doctorate/Fellowship)* [1590]

ASLMS Educational Grants *(Undergraduate, Graduate, Professional development/Grant)* [1494]

ASLMS Research Grant *(Postdoctorate/Grant, Monetary)* [1495]

AvaCare Medical Scholarship *(Undergraduate/Scholarship)* [2370]

Dr. Noyes L. Avery, Jr. & Ann E. Avery Scholarship *(Undergraduate, Graduate/Scholarship)* [5136]

Jenny Panitch Beckow Memorial Scholarship - Canada *(Graduate/Scholarship)* [6283]

Jenny Panitch Beckow Memorial Scholarship - Israel *(Graduate/Scholarship)* [6284]

Benign Essential Blepharospasm Research Foundation Research Grants *(Doctorate/Grant)* [2473]

Linn-Benton County Scholarships *(Undergraduate/Scholarship)* [8719]

Body of Young Adult Advisors Scholarship (BOYAA) *(Graduate, Master's, Doctorate/Scholarship)* [11167]

Linda Brandt Research Award *(Postgraduate/Award)* [2260]

Burlington Medical Student Bursary *(Undergraduate/Grant)* [8646]

Joseph R. Calder, Jr., MD Scholarship Fund *(Undergraduate/Scholarship)* [4586]

Career Awards at the Scientific Interface (CASI) *(Undergraduate, Postdoctorate, Graduate/Grant)* [2753]

Ben and Vicky Cayetano Scholarship Fund *(Undergraduate, College, University, Two Year College/Scholarship)* [5389]

CCFA Career Development Awards *(Doctorate/Grant, Award)* [3911]

CCFA Research Fellowship Awards *(Doctorate, Graduate/Fellowship, Award)* [3912]

CCFA Student Research Fellowship Awards *(Graduate, Undergraduate/Grant, Fellowship, Award)* [3913]

Center for Engineering in Medicine Predoctoral Fellows Program *(Postdoctorate/Fellowship)* [7132]

Chronic Pain Medicine Research Grant *(Professional development/Grant)* [1556]

COTF Mental Health Research Grant *(Undergraduate/Award, Grant)* [3079]

Crohn's and Colitis Foundation of America Senior Research Awards *(Doctorate, Graduate/Grant, Award)* [3914]

Crush the USMLE Scholarship Program *(Undergraduate, Graduate/Scholarship)* [3931]

The Cure Starts Now Foundation Grants *(Graduate, Doctorate/Grant)* [3940]

DAAD Study Scholarship Awards *(Graduate, Undergraduate/Scholarship)* [4059]

D&A Florida Scholarships *(Undergraduate/Scholarship)* [10678]

Deana Kendrick Foundation Scholarship *(Undergraduate/Scholarship)* [6522]

Diagnosis Delayed Scholarship *(Graduate/Scholarship)* [4076]

Dr. Frank and Florence Marino Scholarship *(Undergraduate/Scholarship)* [5322]

Dr. Horace Furumoto Innovations Professional Development - Young Investigator Award *(Professional development/Award)* [1496]

Doris W. Frey Memorial Scholarship Fund *(Graduate/Scholarship)* [10681]

Donald B. Doty Educational Award *(Advanced Professional/Award, Grant)* [11995]

Lee K. Feine Scholarship *(Undergraduate, Graduate/Scholarship)* [7790]

Bea Firth Scholarship *(Undergraduate, Graduate/Scholarship)* [12315]

A. Ward Ford Memorial Research Grant *(Postdoctorate, Professional development/Grant)* [1497]

The William and Francis Fry Honorary Fellowship for Contributions to Therapeutic Ultrasound *(Professional development/Fellowship)* [6118]

The Future of Bariatric Surgery Scholarship *(Undergraduate, Graduate, Vocational/Occupational/Scholarship)* [2435]

Gantenbein Medical Fund Fellowship *(Graduate/Fellowship)* [4092]

George Hi'ilani Mills Scholarship *(Graduate/Scholarship)* [8925]

S. William & Martha R. Goff Educational Scholarship *(Undergraduate/Scholarship)* [8850]

William R. Goldfarb Memorial Scholarships *(Undergraduate/Scholarship)* [1940]

Scott A. Gunder, MD, DCMS Presidential Scholarship *(Undergraduate, Graduate/Scholarship)* [4798]

HAESF Professional Internship Program *(Doctorate/Internship)* [5645]

Jack Hajinian Memorial Grant *(Undergraduate/Scholarship)* [1882]

Hall County Medical Society Scholarship *(Undergraduate, Graduate/Scholarship)* [5122]

Hans H. and Margaret B. Doe Scholarship *(Graduate, Undergraduate/Scholarship)* [9817]

George L. and June L. Herpel Memorial Scholarship *(Graduate/Scholarship)* [2529]

Johns Hopkins Department of Emergency Medicine Administration Fellowships *(Advanced Professional, Professional development/Fellowship)* [6316]

Dr. Gilbert Hopson Medical Student Bursary *(Undergraduate/Grant)* [8647]

HRSA Scholarships for Disadvantaged Students *(Undergraduate/Scholarship)* [11334]

Dr. James L. Hutchinson and Evelyn Ribbs Hutchinson Medical School Scholarship *(Undergraduate/Scholarship)* [10135]

IAASM Aviation Medicine Scholarship *(Professional development/Scholarship)* [5897]

Indiana State University Rural Health Scholarship *(Undergraduate/Scholarship)* [5760]

Indspire Health Careers Bursary and Scholarships *(Graduate, Undergraduate/Scholarship)* [5774]

Intermountain Medical Imaging Scholarship *(Undergraduate, Community College/Scholarship)* [5892]

International Scholars Program for Young Vascular Surgeons *(Graduate/Scholarship)* [10555]

IOKDS Health Careers Scholarship *(College, University, Undergraduate, Graduate, Doctorate/Scholarship)* [6050]

ISTU Student Prizes *(Undergraduate/Prize)* [6119]

Jason Lang Scholarship *(Undergraduate/Scholarship)* [292]

Jewish Federation Academic Scholarship *(Graduate, Undergraduate/Scholarship)* [6310]

John J. Bonica Trainee Fellowship *(Professional development/Fellowship)* [5944]

John M. & Mary A. Shanley Memorial Scholarship *(Undergraduate, Graduate/Scholarship)* [10690]

Johns Hopkins Medicine Emergency Medical Services Fellowship *(Professional development/Fellowship)* [6318]

Johns Hopkins Medicine Medical Education Fellowships *(Professional development/Fellowship)* [6320]

Johns Hopkins Medicine Observation Medicine Fellowships *(Professional development/Fellowship)* [6321]

Johns Hopkins Medicine Research Fellowships *(Professional development/Fellowship)* [6322]

Joseph J. Fitzsimmons Scholarship Fund *(Doctorate/Scholarship)* [11384]

Araxy Kechejian Memorial Grant *(Undergraduate/Scholarship)* [1890]

Kenhub Scholarship Program *(Undergraduate, Postgraduate/Scholarship)* [6524]

Lamaze Childbirth Educator Program Scholarship *(Professional development/Scholarship)* [6642]

Karen E. Latt Memorial Scholarship *(Graduate/Scholarship)* [6297]

S. Evelyn Lewis Memorial Scholarships in Medical Health Sciences *(Graduate, Undergraduate/Scholarship)* [12414]

Dolores Zohrab Liebmann Fund - Graduate School Fellowships *(Graduate/Fellowship)* [6845]

Lillie Hope-McGarvey Health Scholarship *(Undergraduate, Vocational/Occupational, Graduate, Master's/Scholarship)* [330]

Lawrence S. Linn Research Grant *(Undergraduate, Graduate, Advanced Professional/Grant)* [10338]

Ole & Mary Lunde Scholarship *(Undergraduate, University, College, Vocational/Occupational, Graduate/Scholarship)* [12342]

Dan & Pauline Lutkenhouse & Hawaii Tropical Botanical Garden Scholarship and Educational Fund *(Undergraduate, Graduate/Scholarship)* [5407]

Lycoming County Medical Society Scholarship *(Undergraduate, Graduate/Scholarship)* [4799]

Dr. Arlene MacIntyre Medical Student Bursary *(Undergraduate/Grant, Recognition)* [8648]

Dr. Edward May Magruder Medical Scholarships *(Undergraduate/Scholarship)* [751]

Margaret Dowell-Gravatt, M.D. Scholarship *(Undergraduate/Scholarship)* [2486]

Marilyn Yetso Memorial Scholarship *(Graduate, Master's, Doctorate/Scholarship)* [11168]

Olivia M. Marquart Scholarships *(Graduate, Master's, Doctorate/Scholarship)* [11169]

Marvin H. and Kathleen G. Teget Leadership Scholarship *(Undergraduate/Scholarship)* [10866]

Medical Scrubs Collection Scholarship *(Undergraduate, Graduate/Scholarship)* [7225]

Michael A. Russo Memorial Scholarship *(Undergraduate/Scholarship)* [9562]

Abby and Howard Milstein Innovation Award in Reproductive Medicine *(Advanced Professional, Professional development, Graduate/Grant)* [6329]

Abby and Howard Milstein Reproductive Medicine Research Award *(Advanced Professional, Professional development/Grant)* [6330]

Mission Bay Hospital Auxiliary Scholarship *(Undergraduate/Scholarship)* [9834]

Montgomery County Medical Society – William W. Lander, MD, Medical Student Scholarship *(Undergraduate/Scholarship)* [4800]

MSHQ Premed Scholarship *(Undergraduate, Graduate, Postgraduate/Scholarship)* [7205]

Murse World Scholarship *(Undergraduate, Graduate, Postdoctorate/Scholarship)* [7507]

Nadine Barrie Smith Student Award *(Undergraduate/Award)* [6120]

National Ataxia Foundation Postdoctoral Fellowship Award *(Postdoctorate/Fellowship, Award)* [7711]

National Ataxia Foundation Research Grants *(Other/Grant)* [7712]

National Biosafety and Biocontainment Training Program Fellowships *(Graduate, Postgraduate/Fellowship)* [7716]

National Federation of the Blind Scholarship Program *(Undergraduate/Scholarship, Monetary)* [7878]

National Medical Fellowships Need-Based Scholarships *(Undergraduate/Scholarship)* [8001]

OMSBF District Four - Physician Care Bursary *(Undergraduate/Grant)* [8649]

Pappaioanou Veterinary Public Health and Applied Epidemiology Fellowships *(Undergraduate/Fellowship)* [3202]

Paul S. Robinson Award *(Postgraduate/Award)* [10322]

Gilberto and Lennetta Pesquera Medical School Scholarships *(Graduate/Scholarship)* [5001]

PGM Graduate Scholarship *(Graduate/Scholarship)* [9152]

PKD Foundation Fellowships *(Doctorate, Graduate/Fellowship)* [9184]

Preventive Medicine Residency and Fellowship (PMR) *(Other/Fellowship)* [11331]

Rebecca Lee Crumpler, M.D. Scholarship *(Advanced Professional/Scholarship)* [2070]

The Recovery Village Health Care Scholarship *(Undergraduate/Scholarship)* [9514]

Research-in-Training Grant *(Doctorate/Grant)* [12029]

RSDSA Research Grants *(Other/Grant)* [9613]

Moti L. & Kamla Rustgi International Travel Awards *(Professional development/Grant)* [942]

Save a Life Scholarship *(College, University, Vocational/Occupational, Undergraduate, Graduate/Scholarship)* [448]

Scholarship in Medical Education Award *(Advanced Professional, Professional development/Scholarship)* [10339]

Jeptha Wade Schureman Scholarship Program *(Undergraduate/Scholarship)* [3724]

Dr. Henry Seneca Charitable Trust Scholarship *(Undergraduate/Scholarship)* [1901]

Chiyoko and Thomas Shimazaki Scholarship *(Graduate/Scholarship)* [6252]

Norma J. Shoemaker Award for Critical Care Nursing Excellence *(Professional development/Award)* [10316]

SOHN Allied Health to BSN Degree Scholarship *(Undergraduate/Scholarship)* [10450]

Southern California Lambda Medical Student Scholarships *(Undergraduate, Graduate/Scholarship)* [10650]

Dr. William E. & Norma Sprague Scholarship *(Undergraduate, Graduate/Scholarship)* [5183]

Steve Dearduff Scholarship Fund *(Graduate, Undergraduate/Scholarship)* [3587]

Summer Intern Scholarships In Cardiothoracic Surgery *(Undergraduate/Scholarship, Internship)* [663]

Sun Life Financial Medical Student Bursary *(Undergraduate/Grant)* [8650]

SVS Vascular Surgery Trainee Advocacy Travel Scholarship *(Advanced Professional, Professional development/Scholarship, Grant)* [10556]

Sylvia Parkinson Fund *(Undergraduate/Scholarship)* [5344]

Betty & Charles Taylor Scholarship *(Graduate, Undergraduate/Scholarship)* [12378]

TEVA Canada Survivor Scholarship *(Undergraduate, University/Scholarship)* [3292]

Dr. Peter A. Theodos Memorial Graduate Scholarship *(Graduate/Scholarship)* [5468]

Thompson Scholarship for Women in Safety *(Doctorate/Scholarship)* [1573]

Dr. Harry Jeffrey Tourigian Memorial Grant *(Undergraduate/Scholarship)* [1905]

Sam Tughan Scholarships *(Undergraduate/Scholarship)* [6182]

Underrepresented in Medicine award *(Graduate/Scholarship)* [1112]

Myrtle Siegfried, MD, and Michael Vigilante, MD Scholarship *(Undergraduate/Scholarship)* [4801]

The Sybil Jennings Vorheis Memorial Undergraduate Scholarships *(Undergraduate/Scholarship)* [4761]

Percy W. Wadman, M.D. Scholarship *(Postgraduate/Scholarship)* [4815]

Washington University Law School Olin Fellowships for Women *(Advanced Professional/Fellowship)* [11924]

Matthew Watson Scholarship *(Undergraduate, University, College, Graduate/Scholarship)* [12385]

Dr. Anne Williams Scholarship *(Undergraduate, Graduate/Scholarship)* [12392]

Arthur N. Wilson, MD, Scholarships *(Undergraduate/Scholarship)* [1113]

Women's Leadership Training Grant *(Advanced Professional, Professional development/Grant)* [10557]

Worcester District Medical Society Scholarship Fund *(Undergraduate/Scholarship)* [12188]

Young Investigators Achievement Award *(Advanced Professional, Professional development, Graduate/Grant)* [6331]

Medicine, Cardiology

ASE Career Development Award *(Advanced Professional/Grant)* [1422]

Canadian Association of Cardiac Rehabilitation Graduate Scholarship Awards *(Graduate/Scholarship)* [2887]

CCCN Research Grant Program *(Professional development/Grant)* [3791]

The Dr. Richard Allen Williams and Genita Evangelista Johnson Scholarship, AMA Foundation Scholarship *(Undergraduate/Scholarship)* [2066]

Wagner-Torizuka Fellowship *(Professional development/Fellowship)* [10445]

Medicine, Cardiovascular (See also Medicine, Cardiology)

International Scholars Program for Young Vascular Surgeons *(Graduate/Scholarship)* [10555]

SVS Vascular Surgery Trainee Advocacy Travel Scholarship *(Advanced Professional, Professional development/Scholarship, Grant)* [10556]

Women's Leadership Training Grant *(Advanced Professional, Professional development/Grant)* [10557]

Medicine, Cerebrovascular

International Scholars Program for Young Vascular Surgeons *(Graduate/Scholarship)* [10555]

SVS Vascular Surgery Trainee Advocacy Travel Scholarship *(Advanced Professional, Professional development/Scholarship, Grant)* [10556]

Women's Leadership Training Grant *(Advanced Professional, Professional development/Grant)* [10557]

Medicine, Chiropractic

Beatrice K. Blair Scholarships *(Undergraduate/Scholarship)* [2620]

ChiroHealthUSA Foxworth Family Scholarship (Doctorate/Scholarship) [3313]

F. Maynard Lipe Scholarship Award (Master's, Postgraduate/Scholarship) [759]

Medicine, Geriatric

APDA Post-Doctoral Research Fellowship (Postdoctorate/Fellowship) [1206]

Claire M. Fagin Fellow Award (Doctorate/Scholarship) [7917]

Hpgs Graduate Scholarships (Graduate/Scholarship) [5421]

HPGS Undergraduate Scholarships (Undergraduate/Scholarship) [5422]

NHCGNE Patricia G. Archbold Scholar Award (Doctorate/Scholarship) [7918]

Medicine, Gynecological and obstetrical

SMFM/AAOGF Scholarship Awards (Graduate/Scholarship) [10423]

Medicine, Internal

Epilepsy Foundation Research and Training Fellowships for Clinicians (Doctorate, Other/Grant) [4425]

Medicine, Nuclear

Mitzi & William Blahd, MD, Pilot Research Grant (Professional development/Grant) [10437]

Paul Cole Student Technologist Scholarship (Undergraduate/Scholarship) [10438]

SNMMI Robert E. Henkin, MD, Government Relations Fellowship (Professional development/Fellowship) [10439]

PDEF Professional Development Scholarship (Professional development/Scholarship) [10440]

R&E Foundation Education Scholar Grant (Graduate, Other/Scholarship) [9482]

SNMMI-TS Advanced Practitioner Program Scholarship (Professional development/Scholarship) [10441]

SNNMI Predoctoral Molecular Imaging Scholar Program (Doctorate/Scholarship) [10443]

Marc Tetalman, MD, Memorial Award (Professional development, Doctorate/Recognition) [10444]

Medicine, Orthopedic

AOFAS Research Grants Program (Graduate/Grant) [1193]

J. Robert Gladden Orthopaedic Society PGY5 ABOS Board Preparation Scholarship (Professional development/Scholarship) [4992]

J. Robert Gladden Orthopaedic Society Traveling Fellowship Support (Professional development/Fellowship) [4993]

Arthur H. Huene Memorial Award (Doctorate/Grant) [8947]

F. Maynard Lipe Scholarship Award (Master's, Postgraduate/Scholarship) [759]

Orthopaedic Foot and Ankle Fellowships (Graduate, Professional development/Fellowship) [1194]

OTA Member Full Research Grant (Other/Grant) [8763]

St. Giles Young Investigator Award (Doctorate/Grant) [8948]

Medicine, Osteopathic

AACOM Scholar in Residence Program (Professional development/Scholarship) [545]

William G. Anderson, DO, Minority Scholarships (Undergraduate/Scholarship) [1198]

Discover Health Professions Loans (Graduate/Loan, Scholarship) [4111]

Discover Residency Loans (Graduate/Loan, Scholarship) [4114]

Humanism in Medicine Scholarships (Undergraduate/Scholarship) [10865]

Illinois Student Assistance Commission Medical Student Scholarship (Undergraduate/Scholarship) [5713]

Kansas Osteopathic Medical Service Scholarship (Graduate, Other/Scholarship) [6366]

Marvin H. and Kathleen G. Teget Leadership Scholarship (Undergraduate/Scholarship) [10866]

Morgan Stanley Pediatrics Fellowships (Postgraduate, Graduate/Fellowship) [686]

NAAMA Scholarships (Undergraduate/Scholarship) [7598]

Osteopathic Medical School Scholarship (Undergraduate/Scholarship) [8271]

Osteopathic Medical Student Research Fellowship Program (Undergraduate/Fellowship) [10867]

Russell C. McCaughan Heritage Scholarship (Undergraduate/Scholarship, Award) [1199]

Scleroderma Foundation Established Investigator Grants (Doctorate/Grant) [9979]

Scleroderma Foundation New Investigator Grants (Doctorate/Grant) [9980]

Welch Scholars Grants (Undergraduate/Grant) [1200]

Medicine, Pediatric

American Pediatric Surgical Nurses Association Educational Grant (Other/Grant) [1210]

Antimicrobial Stewardship Fellowship Award (Professional development/Fellowship) [8945]

Daland Fellowships in Clinical Investigation (Doctorate, Postgraduate/Fellowship) [1212]

John W. Duckett Jr., AFUD Pediatric Research Scholarships (Undergraduate/Scholarship) [10469]

Heidi Patriquin Award for International Education (Advanced Professional, Professional development/Fellowship) [10465]

Lizette Peterson Homer Injury Prevention Grant (Other, Undergraduate, Graduate/Grant) [1739]

Marion and Donald Routh Student Research Grant (Graduate/Grant) [1740]

A. James McAdams Short-Term Study Stipend (Professional development/Grant) [10461]

National Association of Pediatric Nurse Practitioners McNeil Rural and Underserved Scholarships (Graduate/Scholarship) [7680]

Morgan Stanley Pediatrics Fellowships (Postgraduate, Graduate/Fellowship) [686]

Norman Siegel Research Scholar Grants in Pediatrics (Doctorate/Grant) [1527]

SPU Research Grant (Undergraduate/Grant) [10470]

SPP Young Investigator Research Grant (Postdoctorate, Master's/Grant) [10462]

William Weston Research Award (Postgraduate/Grant) [10457]

Medicine, Pulmonary

PHA Research Fellowships (Professional development/Fellowship) [9449]

Medicine, Sports

AMSSM-ACSM Clinical Research Grants (Professional development/Grant) [1115]

Fay Anthony Scholarship (Undergraduate, College, University, Vocational/Occupational/Scholarship) [12283]

Larry Ashley Memorial Scholarship Award (Other/Award, Scholarship) [2127]

Joe Goodeill Scholarship (Undergraduate, University, College/Scholarship) [12319]

Swede Swanson Memorial Scholarships (Undergraduate/Scholarship) [8190]

Medicine, Veterinary (See Veterinary science and medicine)

Medieval studies

ARIT Fellowships in the Humanities and Social Sciences in Turkey (Postdoctorate, Graduate/Fellowship) [1342, 3850, 11345, 11348]

Birgit Baldwin Fellowship (Graduate/Fellowship) [7229]

Medieval Academy Dissertation Grants (Graduate/Grant) [7230]

Post-Doctoral Mellon Fellowships (Postdoctorate/Fellowship) [9246]

Schallek Award (Graduate/Award) [7231]

Schallek Fellowship (Graduate/Fellowship) [7232]

Meniere's disease

AOS Research Training Fellowships (Graduate/Fellowship) [1202]

Mental health

AACPDM Student Travel Scholarship (Professional development/Scholarship) [438]

AED Student/Early Career Investigator Travel Fellowship Program (Postgraduate/Fellowship) [43]

AED Student Research Grants (Undergraduate, Graduate, Postgraduate/Grant) [44]

Azrieli Neurodevelopmental Research Program (Advanced Professional/Grant) [2671]

Bell Aliant Medical Education Scholarship (Advanced Professional/Scholarship) [8223]

Brain Canada-ALS Canada Discovery Grants (Advanced Professional, Professional development/Grant) [2673]

Brain Canada-ALS Canada Hudson Translational Team Grants (Advanced Professional, Professional development/Grant) [2674]

Brain Canada/CQDM (Advanced Professional/Grant) [2675]

Brain Canada/NeuroDevNet Developmental Neurosciences Research Training Awards (Postdoctorate, Advanced Professional, Professional development/Grant) [2676]

Brain Canada/RBC Research Partnership in Mental Health Services for Children and Youth Funds (Advanced Professional/Grant) [2677]

Catharine Wilder Guiles Scholarship (Graduate/Scholarship) [6976]

Council on Social Work Education Minority Fellowship Program for Doctoral Students (Postdoctorate/Fellowship) [3874]

Derivative Duo Scholarships (Undergraduate/Scholarship) [9299]

Grant Assistance Program for Autism Professionals - College Programs (Undergraduate/Grant) [8652]

Grant Assistance Program for Autism Professionals - Doctoral Programs (Doctorate/Grant) [8653]

Grant Assistance Program for Autism Professionals - Institutional Standards (Undergraduate, Graduate/Grant) [8654]

Grant Assistance Program for Autism Professionals - Masters Programs (Master's/Grant) [8655]

Grant Assistance Program for Autism Professionals - Professional Certification Programs (Undergraduate, Professional development/Grant) [8656]

Grant Assistance Program for Autism Professionals - Retroactive Assistance (Advanced Professional, Professional development/Grant) [8657]

Grant Assistance Program for Autism Professionals - Undergraduate Programs (Undergraduate/Grant) [8658]

Hope for Healing Scholarship (Undergraduate, Graduate, Doctorate, Master's/Scholarship) [4541]

HRSA Scholarships for Disadvantaged Students (Undergraduate/Scholarship) [11334]

Lutheran Student Scholastic and Service Scholarships - College and University Students (Undergraduate/Scholarship) [2562]

MGH Department of Psychiatry Behavioral Neurology and Neuropsychiatry Fellowship Program (Advanced Professional, Professional development/Fellowship) [7136]

NAJA Scholarship (Graduate/Scholarship) [7664]

OMHF Postdoctoral Fellowships (Postdoctorate/Fellowship) [7264]

Platform Support Grants (Advanced Professional/Grant) [2678]

Don Renschler Scholarships (Graduate/Scholarship) [9310]

Seasons in Malibu Annual Scholarship *(Undergraduate, Graduate/Scholarship)* [9994]

Mental retardation

AAIDD Fellowship *(Advanced Professional, Professional development/Fellowship)* [577]

NYCT Paid Graduate Student Philanthropy Fellowships - Health and People with Special Needs *(Graduate/Fellowship)* [8308]

Metallurgy

AIST Foundation Engineering Scholarship *(Undergraduate/Scholarship)* [2205]

AIST Midwest Member Chapter - Betty McKern Scholarship *(Undergraduate/Scholarship)* [2208]

AIST Midwest Member Chapter - Don Nelson Scholarship *(Undergraduate/Scholarship)* [2209]

AIST Midwest Member Chapter - Engineering Scholarships *(Undergraduate/Scholarship)* [2210]

AIST Midwest Member Chapter - Jack Gill Scholarship *(Undergraduate/Scholarship)* [2211]

AIST Midwest Member Chapter - Mel Nickel Scholarship *(Undergraduate/Scholarship)* [2212]

AIST Midwest Member Chapter - Western States Award *(Undergraduate/Scholarship)* [2213]

AIST Northeastern Ohio Member Chapter - Alfred B. Glossbrenner Scholarship *(Undergraduate/Scholarship)* [2214]

AIST Northeastern Ohio Member Chapter - John Klusch Scholarships *(Undergraduate/Scholarship)* [2215]

AIST Southeast Member Chapter - Gene Suave Scholarship *(Undergraduate/Scholarship)* [2218]

Alec Berry Scholarship *(Undergraduate, College, Vocational/Occupational/Scholarship)* [12286]

AIST Benjamin F. Fairless Scholarship *(Undergraduate/Scholarship)* [2220]

Gerald V. Henderson Memorial Scholarship *(Undergraduate, Graduate/Scholarship)* [10427]

H.H. Harris Foundation Scholarship *(Professional development, Undergraduate/Scholarship, Monetary)* [932]

AIST Willy Korf Memorial Fund *(Undergraduate, Graduate/Scholarship)* [2221]

AIST Ronald E. Lincoln Memorial Scholarship *(Undergraduate/Scholarship)* [2222]

Mineral & Metallurgical Processing Division Scholarships and Richard Klimpel Memorial Scholarships (MPD) *(Undergraduate, Graduate/Scholarship)* [10428]

AIST Judith A. Quinn Detroit Member Chapter Scholarship *(Undergraduate/Scholarship)* [2223]

IPMI Richard Rubin Memorial Scholarship Award *(Graduate/Scholarship)* [6063]

AIST William E. Schwabe Memorial Scholarship *(Undergraduate/Scholarship)* [2225]

Sheet Metal And Air Conditioning Contractors' National Association College of Fellows Scholarship Program *(Undergraduate/Scholarship)* [10039]

SME Coal & Energy Division Scholarship *(Undergraduate/Scholarship)* [10429]

SME Environmental Division Scholarship *(Undergraduate, Graduate/Scholarship)* [10430]

Henry DeWitt Smith Graduate Scholarship *(Graduate/Scholarship)* [10431]

Meteorology (See also Atmospheric science)

AMS Freshman Undergraduate Scholarship *(Undergraduate/Scholarship)* [1119]

AMS Graduate Fellowships *(Graduate/Fellowship)* [1121]

AMS/Industry/Government Graduate Fellowships *(Graduate/Fellowship)* [1122]

AMS Minority Scholarships *(Undergraduate/Scholarship)* [1123]

AMS Senior Named Scholarships *(Undergraduate/Scholarship)* [1124]

Andrew Thomson Prize in Applied Meteorology *(Professional development/Award, Prize)* [3040]

CASFM-Ben Urbonas Scholarship *(Graduate/Scholarship)* [3524]

CMOS-SCMO President's Prize *(Professional development/Prize)* [3041]

CMOS Undergraduate Scholarships *(Undergraduate/Scholarship)* [3042]

Roger Daley Postdoctoral Publication Awards *(Postdoctorate/Monetary, Award)* [3043]

Tertia M.C. Hughes Memorial Graduate Student Prize *(Graduate/Award, Prize)* [3044]

John Jeffries Meteorology Scholarship *(Graduate/Scholarship)* [4502]

The Naval Weather Service Association Scholarship *(Undergraduate/Scholarship)* [1125]

François J. Saucier Prize in Applied Oceanography *(Professional development/Award, Prize)* [3045]

Microbiology (See also Biology)

AIST Ohio Valley Member Chapter Scholarships *(Undergraduate/Scholarship)* [2217]

American Society for Microbiology International Fellowships for Africa *(Postdoctorate/Fellowship)* [1510]

American Society for Microbiology International Fellowships for Asia *(Postdoctorate/Fellowship)* [1511]

American Society for Microbiology International Fellowships for Latin America and the Caribbean *(Postdoctorate/Fellowship)* [1512]

American Society for Microbiology Undergraduate Research Fellowship *(Undergraduate/Fellowship, Award, Monetary)* [1513]

ASM/CDC Program in Infectious Disease and Public Health Microbiology *(Postdoctorate/Fellowship)* [1514]

ASM Research Capstone Fellowship *(Undergraduate/Fellowship, Award, Monetary)* [1516]

ASM Robert D. Watkins Graduate Research Fellowship *(Postdoctorate/Fellowship, Monetary)* [1517]

CHPI Travel Fellowships *(Undergraduate/Fellowship)* [7186]

International Association for Food Protection - Student Travel Scholarship Program *(Undergraduate, Graduate/Scholarship)* [5921]

Kris Knudson Memorial Scholarship *(Graduate, Undergraduate/Scholarship)* [11484]

Margaret Dowell-Gravatt, M.D. Scholarship *(Undergraduate/Scholarship)* [2486]

National Biosafety and Biocontainment Training Program Fellowships *(Graduate, Postgraduate/Fellowship)* [7716]

Selman A. Waksman Endowed Scholarship in Microbial Diversity *(Graduate, Master's, Doctorate/Scholarship)* [7058]

Midwifery

A.C.N.M. Foundation, Inc. Fellowship for Graduate Education *(Doctorate, Postdoctorate/Fellowship)* [768]

ACNM Foundation Midwives of Color-Watson Midwifery Student Scholarship *(Undergraduate/Scholarship)* [769]

Allied Health Care Professional Scholarship *(Undergraduate/Scholarship)* [5711]

Kenhub Scholarship Program *(Undergraduate, Postgraduate/Scholarship)* [6524]

Military history (See History, Military)

Military science and education

Burton L. Gerber Scholarship *(Undergraduate/Scholarship)* [2525]

National Military Intelligence Foundation Scholarship *(Undergraduate, Graduate/Scholarship)* [8011]

Colonel Nate Smith Scholarship *(Graduate, Undergraduate/Scholarship)* [7201]

UW-Madison Reserve Officers Training Corps Scholarships (ROTC) *(Undergraduate/Scholarship)* [11750]

Xavier University ROTC Scholarships - Army ROTC *(Undergraduate/Scholarship)* [12230]

Mineralogy

EMLF Law Student Scholarships *(Undergraduate/Scholarship)* [4387]

The Ludo Frevel Crystallography Scholarship *(Graduate/Scholarship)* [5966]

MAC Foundation Scholarship *(Graduate, Postdoctorate/Scholarship)* [2243]

Mineral & Metallurgical Processing Division Scholarships and Richard Klimpel Memorial Scholarships (MPD) *(Undergraduate, Graduate/Scholarship)* [10428]

Mineralogical Association of Canada Scholarships *(Doctorate, Graduate/Scholarship)* [2244]

MSA Grant for Research in Crystallography *(Professional development/Grant)* [7397]

MSA Grant for Student Research in Mineralogy and Petrology *(Undergraduate, Graduate/Grant)* [7398]

SME Coal & Energy Division Scholarship *(Undergraduate/Scholarship)* [10429]

SME Environmental Division Scholarship *(Undergraduate, Graduate/Scholarship)* [10430]

Mining (See also Engineering, Mining and Mineral)

American Society of Mining and Reclamation Memorial Scholarship Award *(Undergraduate, Community College, College, University/Scholarship, Recognition)* [1522]

Alec Berry Scholarship *(Undergraduate, College, Vocational/Occupational/Scholarship)* [12286]

Gerald V. Henderson Memorial Scholarship *(Undergraduate, Graduate/Scholarship)* [10427]

Joseph A. Holmes Safety Association Scholarship *(High School/Scholarship)* [5544]

James McLachlan Scholarship *(Undergraduate, University, College/Scholarship)* [12345]

National Association of Abandoned Mine Land Programs Scholarship *(Undergraduate/Scholarship)* [7605]

Mary R. Norton Memorial Scholarship Award for Women *(Graduate/Award, Scholarship, Monetary, Recognition)* [2330]

Patnode Family Scholarship *(Undergraduate, University, College, Vocational/Occupational/Scholarship)* [12355]

SME Coal & Energy Division Scholarship *(Undergraduate/Scholarship)* [10429]

SME Environmental Division Scholarship *(Undergraduate, Graduate/Scholarship)* [10430]

Henry DeWitt Smith Graduate Scholarship *(Graduate/Scholarship)* [10431]

Whitehorse Copper Mines Scholarship *(Undergraduate, University, College, Vocational/Occupational/Scholarship)* [12388]

Ministry (See Religion)

Minorities

Actuarial Diversity Scholarship *(Undergraduate/Scholarship)* [69]

American Speech Language Hearing Foundation Endowed Scholarships *(Graduate, Master's, Doctorate/Scholarship)* [1596]

American Speech Language Hearing Foundation Minority Student Scholarship *(Graduate, Master's, Doctorate/Scholarship)* [1599]

Baker McKenzie Diversity Fellowship *(Postgraduate, Professional development/Fellowship)* [2411]

Marcus Mosiah Garvey Scholarships *(Undergraduate/Scholarship)* [6216]

Modern languages

ARIT Fellowships in the Humanities and Social Sciences in Turkey *(Postdoctorate, Graduate/Fellowship)* [1342, 3850, 11345, 11348]

MLA Financial Assistance *(Graduate, Advanced Professional/Grant)* [7426]

Molecular biology (See Biology, Molecular)

Mortuary science (See also Funeral services)

ABFSE National Scholarship Program *(Undergraduate/Scholarship)* [697]
Brenda Renee Horn and Steve Mack Memorial Scholarships *(Undergraduate/Scholarship)* [4842]
Joseph E. Hagan Memorial Scholarship *(Graduate/Scholarship)* [4843]
NFDA Professional Women's Conference Scholarship *(Undergraduate/Scholarship)* [4844]
OGR Award of Excellence Scholarships *(Undergraduate/Scholarship)* [6048]

Motherhood

Childbirth Educator Program Scholarships *(Other/Scholarship)* [6641]

Multiple sclerosis

endMS Doctoral Studentship Awards *(Doctorate/Internship)* [7497]
endMS Master's Studentship Awards *(Master's/Internship)* [7498]
endMS Postdoctoral Fellowships *(Postdoctorate/Fellowship)* [7499]

Muscular dystrophy

Dystonia Medical Research Foundation Clinical Fellowships *(Postdoctorate/Fellowship)* [4244]
MDA Development Grants *(Doctorate/Grant)* [7509]
MDA Research Grants *(Advanced Professional/Grant)* [7510]
MDF Postdoctoral Fellowship *(Postdoctorate/Fellowship)* [7536]
RSDSA Research Grants *(Other/Grant)* [9613]

Museum science

AAMC Foundation Engagement Program for International Curators Grants *(Advanced Professional, Professional development/Grant)* [2057]
Betsy B. and Garold A. Leach Scholarship *(Undergraduate/Scholarship)* [4028]
Rick Chace Foundation Scholarships *(Graduate/Scholarship)* [2246]
Conservation and Scientific Research Fellowships *(Graduate/Fellowship)* [7274]
Douglass Foundation Fellowship in American Art *(Doctorate/Fellowship)* [10214]
Patricia and Phillip Frost Fellowships *(Doctorate, Postdoctorate/Fellowship)* [10215]
The George Gurney Fellowship Endowment Fund *(Doctorate, Postdoctorate/Fellowship)* [10216]
Kodak Fellowships in Film Preservation *(Graduate/Fellowship)* [2247]
Kress/AAR Fellowships *(Professional development/Fellowship)* [2058]
Lee Kimche McGrath Worldwide Fellowship *(Other/Fellowship)* [2286]
Mary Pickford Scholarships *(Graduate/Scholarship)* [2248]
James Renwick Fellowship in American Craft *(Doctorate, Postdoctorate/Fellowship)* [10217]
Research Scholarship in Photograph Conservation *(Graduate/Scholarship)* [7280]
Sara Roby Fellowship in Twentieth-Century American Realism *(Doctorate, Postdoctorate/Fellowship)* [10218]
Joan Shaxon Scholarship *(Undergraduate, University, College, Vocational/Occupational/Scholarship)* [12369]
Smithsonian Fellowships in Museum Practice *(Professional development, Graduate/Fellowship)* [10188]
Smithsonian Postgraduate/Postdoctoral Fellowships in Conservation of Museum Collections *(Postgraduate, Postdoctorate/Fellowship)* [10212]
Sony Pictures Scholarship *(Graduate/Scholarship)* [2249]

Joshua C. Taylor Fellowships *(Doctorate, Postdoctorate/Fellowship)* [10219]
The Terra Foundation Fellowships in American Art *(Undergraduate, Doctorate, Postdoctorate/Fellowship)* [10220]
The William H. Truettner Fellowship Endowment Fund *(Undergraduate, Doctorate, Postdoctorate/Fellowship)* [10221]
United States Capitol Historical Society Fellowships *(Graduate/Fellowship)* [11299]
Universal Studios Preservation Scholarships *(Graduate/Scholarship)* [2250]
Wyeth Foundation Predoctoral Fellowship *(Postdoctorate/Fellowship)* [10222]

Music

Aaron Copland Bogliasco Fellowships in Music *(Professional development/Fellowship)* [2641]
RPMDA/Ed Adams Memorial Scholarships *(Other/Scholarship)* [9653]
Adrienne Zoe Fedok Art and Music Scholarship *(Undergraduate/Scholarship)* [4773]
Music Individual Project Funding *(Professional development/Grant)* [258]
Albert and Alice Nacinovich Music Scholarship Fund *(Undergraduate/Scholarship)* [4582]
Martin K. Alsup and Frank Schroeder Memorial Music Scholarship *(Undergraduate/Scholarship)* [8830]
American Guild of Organists, Canton Chapter Charitable Fund *(Undergraduate/Scholarship)* [10751]
The Anderson Group Summer Institute Scholarships *(Other/Scholarship)* [1710]
Mary Anderson Memorial Intermediate Woodwind Scholarship *(Other/Scholarship)* [9895]
AOSA Research Grant *(Professional development/Grant)* [1186]
AOSA Research Partnership Grant *(Professional development/Grant)* [1187]
Arts Foundation of Cape Cod Scholarships *(Undergraduate, Vocational/Occupational/Scholarship)* [1975]
Bernt Balchen, Jr. and Olav Jorgen Hegge Hardingfele Scholarships *(Other/Scholarship)* [5292]
Barta-Lehman Musical Scholarship *(Undergraduate/Scholarship)* [9801]
Jenny Panitch Beckow Memorial Scholarship - Canada *(Graduate/Scholarship)* [6283]
Jenny Panitch Beckow Memorial Scholarship - Israel *(Graduate/Scholarship)* [6284]
Belmont University Commercial Music Showcase Scholarship Fund *(Undergraduate/Scholarship)* [2471, 3604]
Betty Rose Scholarship *(Undergraduate/Scholarship)* [1407]
Carol June Bradley Award for Historical Research in Music Librarianship *(Professional development/Grant, Award)* [7512]
Brandon Fradd Fellowship in Music Composition *(Professional development/Fellowship)* [3416]
Ralph Burkhardt Scholarship Fund *(Undergraduate, High School/Scholarship)* [11942]
Burney – Cecil E. Burney Scholarship *(Undergraduate/Scholarship)* [3468]
Llewellyn L. Cayvan String Instrument Scholarship *(Undergraduate, Graduate/Scholarship)* [5141]
Charlotte V. Bergen Scholarship *(Undergraduate/Scholarship)* [1408]
Irene R. Christman Scholarship *(Undergraduate/Scholarship)* [8960]
CIRMMT Student Awards *(Graduate, Master's, Doctorate/Award)* [3253]
CMA Private Lesson Program: Instrumental Scholarships for Elementary and Middle School Students *(Undergraduate/Scholarship)* [3420]
Contemporary Club Scholarship *(Undergraduate/Scholarship)* [9536]
Bill Cormack Scholarships *(Undergraduate/Scholarship)* [10987]
Gerald M. Crane Music Award Scholarship *(Undergraduate/Scholarship)* [5144]
Creative Soul Music School Scholarship *(Graduate/Scholarship)* [3900]
Cynthia and Alan Baran Fine Arts and Music Scholarship Fund *(Undergraduate/Scholarship)* [3609]

Daryl Cooper Intermediate Piano Beethoven Scholarship *(Other/Scholarship)* [9898]
David Weiss Scholarship Program *(Undergraduate/Scholarship)* [12268]
Dena Epstein Award for Archival and Library Research in American Music *(Professional development/Award)* [7513]
Dennis Coleman Scholarship *(Undergraduate/Scholarship)* [9297]
Dennis Coleman Scholarships *(Undergraduate/Scholarship)* [9298]
Marnie & Bill Drury Scholarship *(Undergraduate, University, College, Vocational/Occupational/Scholarship)* [12309]
Edgecliff McAuley Music Scholarship *(Undergraduate/Scholarship)* [12222]
Edward Rollin Clinton Memorial for Music Scholarship *(Undergraduate/Scholarship)* [11476]
Erika A. and George E. Brattain, Sr. Donor Advised Scholarship Fund *(Undergraduate, High School/Scholarship)* [11947]
Fran Morgenstern Davis Scholarship *(Undergraduate/Scholarship)* [1409]
Frances England & Hugheen Ferguson Memorial Intermediate Piano Haydn & Mozart Scholarship *(Other/Scholarship)* [9899]
Kevin Freeman Travel Grant *(Graduate, Other/Grant)* [7514]
Maro Ajemian Galstaun Memorial Grant *(Undergraduate/Scholarship)* [1878]
William R. Gard Memorial Scholarships *(Graduate/Scholarship)* [7666]
Geeta Rastogi Memorial Scholarship *(Undergraduate/Scholarship)* [11757]
Walter Gerboth Award *(Other/Award, Monetary)* [7515]
Doris and Clarence Glick Classical Music Scholarship Fund *(Undergraduate, Graduate, Two Year College, Four Year College, University/Scholarship)* [5401]
Goodfellow Memorial Oratorio Scholarship *(Other/Scholarship)* [9902]
Grants to Artists *(Advanced Professional/Grant)* [4769]
Mona Gray Creative Arts Scholarship *(Graduate, Undergraduate/Scholarship)* [6306]
Velma Shotwell Griffin Memorial Scholarship Fund *(Undergraduate/Scholarship)* [10762]
Gunild Keetman Scholarship *(Other, Undergraduate/Scholarship)* [8724]
Guy D. & Mary Edith Halladay Music Scholarship *(Graduate, Undergraduate/Scholarship)* [5154]
Miriam Hoffman Scholarship *(Undergraduate, Graduate/Scholarship)* [4892]
Donald Hoy Memorial Scholarship *(Undergraduate/Scholarship)* [12327]
Indiana State University Creative and Performing Arts Awards *(Undergraduate/Scholarship)* [5769]
Jackson Memorial Intermediate Piano Recital Scholarship *(Graduate/Scholarship)* [9905]
Jeffrey Carollo Music Scholarship *(Undergraduate/Scholarship)* [8279]
Joanna Townsend Applied Arts Scholarship *(All/Scholarship)* [2129]
Johanna Mitchell Memorial Intermediate Viola/Cello/ Double Bass Scholarship *(Graduate, Undergraduate/Scholarship)* [9906]
Alvin H. Johnson AMS 50 Dissertation Fellowships *(Doctorate/Fellowship)* [1143]
Douglas Gray Kimel Scholarship *(Undergraduate/Scholarship)* [12081]
Kiwanis of Wascana Senior Cello/Viola/Double Bass Scholarship *(Graduate/Scholarship)* [9908]
Emily Day Koppell Memorial Adelphe Scholarship *(Undergraduate, Graduate/Scholarship)* [6452]
Hedy Lamarr Achievement Award for Emerging Leaders in Entertainment Technology *(Undergraduate/Award)* [4086]
Leiber and Stoller Music Scholarship *(Undergraduate/Scholarship)* [1410]
Louis Armstrong Award Honoring W.C. Handy *(Undergraduate/Scholarship)* [1411]
Arif Mardin Music Fellowship *(Other/Fellowship)* [11141]
Margaret McFarlane Alkek Undergraduate Scholarship *(Undergraduate/Scholarship)* [4006]

Mark A. Reid Memorial Scholarship (Undergraduate/Scholarship) [3687]

Martin " Marty" Allen Scholarship (Undergraduate/Scholarship) [3481]

Mary Anderson Memorial (Sacred) Choral Scholarship (Undergraduate/Scholarship) [9910]

Howard Mayer Brown Fellowship (Graduate/Fellowship) [1146]

MCBA Scholarship (MCBA) (Undergraduate/Scholarship) [7308]

Christopher Mesi Memorial Music Scholarships (Undergraduate/Scholarship) [3179]

Glenn Miller Scholarship (Undergraduate/Scholarship) [7395]

Shelby L. Molter Music Education Scholarship (Undergraduate, Graduate/Scholarship) [2543]

Muddy Waters Scholarships (Undergraduate, Graduate/Scholarship) [2632]

James W. Murdoch Scholarship (Undergraduate, University, College, Vocational/Occupational/Scholarship) [12351]

Music Teachers' Association of California Goodlin Scholarship (High School/Scholarship) [9836]

Music for Young Children Saskatchewan Teachers' Association Senior Chopin Scholarship (Other/Scholarship) [9912]

Music for Young Children Saskatchewan Teachers' Association Senior Piano Chopin Scholarship (Other/Scholarship) [9913]

Need-based and Merit Scholarships (Undergraduate/Scholarship) [4273]

Northwest-Shoals Community College Fine Arts Scholarships - Music (Undergraduate/Scholarship) [8529]

NPM Academic Scholarship (Graduate, Undergraduate/Scholarship) [7674]

NPM Program Scholarship (Graduate, Undergraduate/Scholarship) [7675]

Orford String Quartet Scholarship (Professional development/Scholarship) [3786]

Al Oster Music Legacy Scholarship (Other, Professional development/Scholarship) [12354]

PAM Scholarship for Montreat (All/Scholarship) [9265]

Paul Mansur Award (Undergraduate/Scholarship) [6021]

William R. Pfalzgraf Memorial Scholarship (Undergraduate/Scholarship) [8867]

Philip F. Vineberg Travelling Fellowship in the Humanities (Undergraduate/Scholarship, Monetary) [7184]

Barbara Potter Scholarship Fund (Professional development/Scholarship) [1188]

Redlands High School Terrier Band Boosters Club Scholarship (Undergraduate/Scholarship) [9590]

Redlands High School Vocal Music Boosters Scholarship (Undergraduate/Scholarship) [9591]

R.L. Gillette Scholarship (Undergraduate/Scholarship) [918]

Robert W. and Bernice Ingalls Staton Scholarships (Undergraduate/Scholarship) [11654]

S. Byrl Ross Memorial Scholarship (Undergraduate/Scholarship) [8875]

Ruth K. Jacobs Memorial Scholarship (Graduate/Scholarship) [3317]

Ruth M. Cogan Foundation Trust (Undergraduate/Scholarship) [10789]

Saskatchewan Registered Music Teachers' Association Senior Romantic Music Scholarship (Other/Scholarship) [9916]

Curtis M. Saulsbury Scholarship Fund (Undergraduate/Scholarship) [3594]

Brown Schoenheit Memorial Scholarship (Undergraduate/Scholarship) [11492]

Roger Sessions Memorial Bogliasco Fellowships in Music (Professional development/Fellowship) [2647]

Shields-Gillespie Scholarship (Other/Scholarship) [1189]

Blanche Squires Memorial Senior Brass Scholarship (Undergraduate/Scholarship) [9917]

Steve Kaplan TV & Film Studies Award (Other/Award) [1412]

Study Scholarship for Artists or Musicians (Graduate, Postdoctorate/Scholarship) [4066]

Texas Music Educators Association Past-Presidents Memorial Scholarships (Undergraduate/Scholarship) [10988]

Edith & Victor Thomas Scholarship (Undergraduate, University, College/Scholarship) [12379]

Johnny Trombly Memorial Scholarship (Undergraduate/Scholarship) [7433]

Barry Tuckwell Award (All/Scholarship) [6022]

Violin Society of America Scholarships (Undergraduate/Scholarship) [11827]

Gordon C. Wallis Memorial Senior Piano Beethoven Scholarship (Other/Scholarship) [9919]

Louis Dreyfus Warner-Chappell City College Scholarship (Undergraduate/Scholarship) [1413]

Wayne County College Fund (Graduate/Scholarship) [11952]

Wayne-Meador-Elliott Scholarship (Undergraduate/Scholarship) [8884]

Portia White Scholarship (Undergraduate/Scholarship) [2602]

Willa Beach-Porter CTBA Music Scholarship Fund (Undergraduate/Scholarship) [3246]

Gary S. Wilmer/RAMI Music Scholarship (Undergraduate/Scholarship) [3696]

Wendy Y. Wolfson Memorial Scholarship Fund (Undergraduate/Scholarship) [4608]

Women's Italian Club of Boston Scholarships (Undergraduate/Scholarship) [4903]

John W. Work III Memorial Foundation Scholarship Fund (Undergraduate/Scholarship) [3650]

Music, Classical

Gladys C. Anderson Memorial Scholarship (Undergraduate/Scholarship) [915]

Doris and Clarence Glick Classical Music Scholarship Fund (Undergraduate, Graduate, Two Year College, Four Year College, University/Scholarship) [5401]

Music composition

Pete Carpenter Fellowship (Professional development/Fellowship) [2634]

John Lennon Scholarships (Undergraduate/Scholarship) [2635]

Peermusic Latin Scholarship (Undergraduate/Scholarship) [2636]

Music education (See Education, Music)

Music, Jazz

Central Florida Jazz Society Scholarships (Undergraduate/Scholarship) [3242]

Music, Opera (See Opera)

Music, Piano

Chopin Foundation Scholarship (Other/Scholarship) [3315]

Kipling and District Music Festival Intermediate Chopin Scholarship (Other/Scholarship) [9907]

Nickels for Notes Music Scholarship (Undergraduate/Scholarship) [4901]

Music therapy

AMTA Past Presidents' Conference Scholar (Professional development/Scholarship) [1132]

AMTA Student Conference Scholar (Undergraduate, Graduate/Scholarship) [1133]

Edwina Eustis Dick Scholarship for Music Therapy Interns (Graduate/Scholarship) [1134]

Arthur Flagler Fultz Research Award (Professional development/Grant) [1135]

Anne Emery Kyllo Professional Scholarship (Professional development/Scholarship) [1136]

Theodore Meyer Scholarship (Undergraduate, Graduate/Scholarship) [1137]

Nickels for Notes Music Scholarship (Undergraduate/Scholarship) [4901]

Brian and Cathy Smith Memorial Fund (Graduate/Scholarship) [1138]

Christine K. Stevens Development Scholarship (Undergraduate, Graduate/Scholarship) [1139]

Florence Tyson Grant to Study Music Psychotherapy (Professional development/Grant) [1140]

Music, Violin

Mrs. Clare K. Mendel Memorial Senior Violin Recital Scholarship (Graduate/Scholarship) [9911]

Music, Vocal

Covey Intermediate Female Voice Scholarship (Graduate/Scholarship) [9897]

Goodfellow Memorial Canadian Vocal Music Scholarship (Other/Scholarship) [9900]

Goodfellow Memorial Grade A Female Voice Scholarship (Undergraduate/Scholarship) [9901]

Goodfellow Memorial Senior Grade A Male Voice Scholarship (Other/Scholarship) [9903]

Goodfellow Memorial Senior Operatic Scholarship (Graduate/Scholarship) [9904]

Viginia & Susan Hawk Scholarship (Other/Scholarship) [9818]

Heather Laxdal Memorial Grade B Female Voice Scholarship (Undergraduate/Scholarship) [9909]

Music Scholarship for Undergraduate in Voice (Undergraduate/Scholarship) [4900]

Nickels for Notes Music Scholarship (Undergraduate/Scholarship) [4901]

Regan Grant Memorial Intermediate Musical Theatre Ballad Scholarship (Other/Scholarship) [9914]

S. Byrl Ross Memorial Scholarship (Undergraduate/Scholarship) [8875]

Saskatchewan Choral Federation Open Choral Scholarship (Graduate/Award, Scholarship) [9915]

Thomas and Don Hatton Memorial Senior Grade B Male Voice Scholarship (Graduate/Scholarship) [9918]

Musicology

Martin K. Alsup and Frank Schroeder Memorial Music Scholarship (Undergraduate/Scholarship) [8830]

M. Elizabeth C. Bartlet Fund (Graduate, Doctorate/Grant) [1142]

Ida Halpern Fellowship and Award (Doctorate/Fellowship) [10326]

Jan LaRue Travel Fund (Doctorate, Postdoctorate/Grant) [1144]

Janet Levy Fund (Doctorate/Grant) [1145]

Howard Mayer Brown Fellowship (Graduate/Fellowship) [1146]

Harold Powers World Travel Fund (Doctorate, Postdoctorate/Grant) [1147]

Woody Guthrie Fellowship (Professional development/Fellowship) [2637]

Myasthenia Gravis

Myasthenia Gravis Foundation of America Nursing Research Fellowships (Undergraduate/Fellowship) [7529]

Student Fellowship (Graduate, Undergraduate/Fellowship) [7530]

National security

AFCEA Cyber Security Scholarship (Undergraduate, Graduate/Scholarship) [103]

CFR Stanton Nuclear Security Fellowship (Doctorate, Postdoctorate, Advanced Professional/Fellowship) [3862]

(ISC)2 Foundation Information Security Undergraduate Scholarships (Undergraduate/Scholarship) [6024]

Rieser Fellowships (Undergraduate/Fellowship) [2743]

Samuel S. Wilks Memorial Award (Advanced Professional/Award, Monetary) [1612]

Women In Defense HORIZONS Scholarship (Graduate, Undergraduate/Scholarship) [12133]

Native American studies

AAIA Allogan Slagle Memorial Scholarship *(Undergraduate, Graduate/Scholarship)* [2036]

Adolf Van Pelt Scholarship *(Undergraduate/Scholarship)* [2037]

Larry Matfay Cultural Heritage Scholarship *(Undergraduate, Graduate/Scholarship)* [6592]

Newberry Consortium on American Indian Studies Faculty Fellowships *(Professional development/Fellowship)* [8378]

Phillips Fund for Native American Research *(Doctorate, Master's/Grant)* [1217]

Smithsonian Native American Awards Program - Community Scholars *(Graduate, Doctorate, Postdoctorate, Professional development/Fellowship)* [10210]

Smithsonian Native American Awards Program - Visiting Student *(Graduate/Fellowship)* [10211]

Udall Undergraduate Scholarship *(Undergraduate/Scholarship)* [11165]

Natural resources

Aises A. T. Anderson Memorial Scholarship *(Graduate, Undergraduate/Scholarship)* [1000]

American Planning Association ENRE Student Fellowship Program *(Graduate/Fellowship)* [1242]

EMLF Law Student Scholarships *(Undergraduate/Scholarship)* [4387]

Grand Haven Offshore Challenge Scholarship *(Undergraduate/Scholarship)* [5080]

Great Lakes Commission Sea Grant Fellowship *(Graduate/Grant, Fellowship)* [5218]

Randall Mathis Scholarship for Environmental Studies Fund *(Undergraduate/Scholarship)* [1824]

Ben Meadows Natural Resource Scholarships - Academic Achievement Scholarships *(Undergraduate/Scholarship)* [4684]

Ben Meadows Natural Resource Scholarships - Leadership Scholarships *(Undergraduate/Scholarship)* [4685]

Pat & Donald Merrill Scholarship *(Undergraduate, University, College, Vocational/Occupational/Scholarship)* [12348]

Property and Environment Research Center Graduate Fellowships *(Graduate/Fellowship)* [9351]

Property and Environment Research Center Lone Mountain Fellowships *(Other/Fellowship)* [9352]

Property and Environment Research Center Media Fellowships *(Other/Fellowship)* [9353]

Julian Simon Fellowships *(Postgraduate/Fellowship)* [9354]

Guy A. Woodings Scholarships *(Undergraduate/Scholarship)* [11465]

Natural sciences

ACOR-CAORC Post-Doctoral Fellowships *(Postdoctorate/Fellowship)* [723]

Alexander Graham Bell Canada Graduate Scholarships-Doctoral Program *(Doctorate, Master's/Scholarship)* [3803]

Lorraine Allison Scholarship *(Graduate/Scholarship)* [1789]

Ora E. Anderson Scholarship *(Undergraduate, High School/Scholarship)* [4706]

AWMA Louisiana Section Scholarship *(Undergraduate, Graduate/Scholarship)* [167]

Buck Bragunier Leadership Scholarship *(Four Year College, University/Scholarship)* [1840]

CTFS-ForestGEO Research Grants Program *(Graduate, Postdoctorate, Advanced Professional/Grant)* [10229]

ForestGEO Research Grants *(Graduate, Postdoctorate, Professional development/Grant)* [10225]

Margaret S. Gilbert Scholarship Fund *(Graduate/Scholarship)* [10760]

John Simon Guggenheim Memorial Fellowships - United States & Canadian Competition *(Graduate, Postgraduate, Undergraduate/Fellowship)* [5250]

J.B. and Marilyn McKenzie Graduate Student Fellowship *(Graduate/Fellowship)* [11627]

Joel T. Heinen Student Research Fellowship *(Undergraduate, Graduate/Fellowship)* [11628]

Laura Ann Peck Memorial Endowed Scholarship *(Undergraduate/Scholarship)* [6806]

Dolores Zohrab Liebmann Fund - Graduate School Fellowships *(Graduate/Fellowship)* [6845]

Multi-Country Research Fellowship *(Doctorate, Postdoctorate/Fellowship)* [3851]

Newkirk Graduate Student Fellow Awards *(Doctorate, Graduate/Fellowship)* [8391]

NSERC Postgraduate Scholarships-Doctoral Program *(Doctorate/Scholarship)* [3806]

Saskatchewan Pulse Growers Undergraduate Scholarships *(Undergraduate/Scholarship)* [9923]

Alfred P. Sloan Foundation Graduate Scholarships - Sloan Indigenous Graduate Partnership (SIGP) *(Master's, Doctorate/Scholarship)* [7581]

Alfred P. Sloan Foundation Graduate Scholarships - Sloan Minority Ph.D. Program (MPHD) *(Doctorate/Scholarship)* [7582]

Susan P. Schroeder Memorial Scholarship *(Undergraduate/Scholarship)* [6822]

Vanier Canada Graduate Scholarships Program *(Graduate/Scholarship)* [3808]

Naval architecture (See Architecture, Naval)

Naval art and science

ASEE-NRL Postdoctoral Fellowship Program *(Postdoctorate/Fellowship)* [11389]

Naval Research Enterprise Internship Program (NREIP) *(Graduate, Undergraduate/Internship)* [1443]

Naval engineering (See Engineering, Naval)

Nephrology

American Nephrology Nurses' Association Evidence-Based Research Grants *(Other/Grant)* [1151]

KFOC Allied Health Doctoral Fellowships *(Doctorate/Fellowship)* [6546]

KFOC Allied Health Scholarships *(Graduate/Scholarship)* [6547]

KFOC Biomedical Scholarships *(Doctorate/Scholarship)* [6548]

Nephrology Nurse Researcher Awards *(Doctorate/Award)* [1152]

Barbara F. Prowant Nursing Research Grants *(Graduate/Grant)* [1153]

Neurology

AAN Clinical Research Training Fellowship *(Other/Scholarship)* [458]

AAN International Scholarship Award *(Professional development/Scholarship, Award)* [459]

AAN Medical Student Summer Research Scholarship *(Graduate/Scholarship)* [460]

AANS Medical Student Summer Research Fellowships (MSSRF) *(Undergraduate/Fellowship)* [607]

ANPA Young Investigator Awards *(Postdoctorate/Grant)* [1155]

ANS Neurotology Fellowship Award *(Other/Fellowship)* [1157]

ARRS/ASNR Scholarship in Neuroradiology *(Advanced Professional/Scholarship)* [1364, 1529]

Brain Canada-ALS Canada Career Transition Awards *(Postdoctorate, Advanced Professional, Professional development/Grant)* [2672]

Brain Canada-ALS Canada Discovery Grants *(Advanced Professional, Professional development/Grant)* [2673]

Brain Canada-ALS Canada Hudson Translational Team Grants *(Advanced Professional, Professional development/Grant)* [2674]

Jeanne Timmins Costello Fellowships (JTC) *(Professional development/Fellowship)* [7190]

Dr. George C. Cotzias Memorial Fellowship *(Other, Professional development/Fellowship)* [1208]

Daland Fellowships in Clinical Investigation *(Doctorate, Postgraduate/Fellowship)* [1212]

Epilepsy Foundation Research and Training Fellowships for Clinicians *(Doctorate, Other/Grant)* [4425]

Grass Fellowships at the Marine Biological Laboratory *(Doctorate, Postdoctorate/Fellowship)* [5205]

Clinical Translational Fellowship at Pfizer *(Advanced Professional/Fellowship)* [7134]

MGH Department of Psychiatry Behavioral Neurology and Neuropsychiatry Fellowship Program *(Advanced Professional, Professional development/Fellowship)* [7136]

MGH Department of Psychiatry Global Psychiatric Clinical Research Training Program *(Advanced Professional/Fellowship)* [7139]

NJCBIR Individual Research Grants *(Graduate, Professional development, Postdoctorate, Doctorate/Grant)* [10807]

NJCBIR Pilot Research Grants *(Other/Grant)* [10808]

NJCBIR Postdoctoral and Graduate Student Fellowships *(Graduate, Postdoctorate, Professional development, Doctorate/Fellowship)* [10809]

NJCBIR Programmatic Multi-Investigator Project Grants *(Other/Grant)* [10810]

Postdoctoral Fellowships for Clinical Neurologists *(Postdoctorate/Fellowship)* [8901]

The Preston Robb Fellowship *(Professional development, College, Master's/Fellowship)* [7191]

Wagner-Torizuka Fellowship *(Professional development/Fellowship)* [10445]

William P. Van Wagenen Fellowship *(Undergraduate/Fellowship)* [608]

Dr. Steven S. Zalcman Memorial Scholarship *(Graduate, Postgraduate/Scholarship)* [6301]

Neurophysiology

Grass Fellowships at the Marine Biological Laboratory *(Doctorate, Postdoctorate/Fellowship)* [5205]

Neuroscience

ASET Scholarships *(Other/Scholarship)* [1982]

Azrieli Neurodevelopmental Research Program *(Advanced Professional/Grant)* [2671]

Lynn Ann Baldwin Scholarships *(Master's/Scholarship)* [2093]

Brain Canada-ALS Canada Discovery Grants *(Advanced Professional, Professional development/Grant)* [2673]

Brain Canada-ALS Canada Hudson Translational Team Grants *(Advanced Professional, Professional development/Grant)* [2674]

Brain Canada/CQDM *(Advanced Professional/Grant)* [2675]

Brain Canada/NeuroDevNet Developmental Neurosciences Research Training Awards *(Postdoctorate, Advanced Professional, Professional development/Grant)* [2676]

Certified Neuroscience Registered Nurse Recertification Grant Program *(Other/Grant)* [610]

CTF Young Investigator Award (YIA) *(Graduate, Postdoctorate, Doctorate/Award)* [3299]

Epilepsy Foundation Post-doctoral Research and Training Fellowships *(Postdoctorate/Fellowship)* [4422]

Epilepsy Foundation Pre-doctoral Research Training Fellowships *(Graduate/Fellowship)* [4423]

Grass Fellowships at the Marine Biological Laboratory *(Doctorate, Postdoctorate/Fellowship)* [5205]

Integra Foundation NNF Research Grant Awards *(Professional development/Grant)* [611]

IRSF Mentored Training Fellowships *(Advanced Professional/Fellowship)* [6077]

Jessie Young Certification Bursary *(Other/Award)* [2094]

Klingenstein Fellowships in the Neurosciences *(Doctorate, Master's/Fellowship)* [6566]

Clinical Translational Fellowship at Pfizer *(Advanced Professional/Fellowship)* [7134]

Neuroscience Certification Bursary Awards *(Other/Award)* [2095]

Platform Support Grants *(Advanced Professional/Grant)* [2678]

Sloan Research Fellowships *(Doctorate/Fellowship)* [10171]

STRI Short-Term Fellowships *(Undergraduate, Graduate, Postdoctorate/Fellowship)* [10226]
Earl S. Tupper Three-year Postdoctoral Fellowship *(Postdoctorate/Fellowship)* [10227]
Undergraduate Scholars Program *(Graduate/Scholarship)* [5606]
Weston Brain Institute International Fellowships in Neuroscience *(Graduate/Fellowship)* [12000]
Weston Brain Institute Rapid Response Program *(Postdoctorate, Advanced Professional, Professional development/Grant)* [12001]
Dr. Steven S. Zalcman Memorial Scholarship *(Graduate, Postgraduate/Scholarship)* [6301]

Nonprofit sector

ANSER Graduate Student Awards for Research on Nonprofits and the Social Economy *(Graduate/Award)* [2252]
Campus Pride Summer Fellows *(Undergraduate, Graduate, Postgraduate/Fellowship)* [2870]
EJI Justice Fellowship *(Graduate, Postgraduate, Professional development/Fellowship)* [4434]
Emerging Scholars Award *(Graduate/Award)* [2275]

Nuclear medicine (See Medicine, Nuclear)

Nuclear science

American Nuclear Society Nevada Section Scholarship *(Undergraduate/Scholarship)* [1161, 9390]
American Nuclear Society Undergraduates Scholarships *(Undergraduate/Scholarship)* [1162]
Everitt P. Blizard Memorial Scholarship *(Graduate/Scholarship)* [1163]
Glenn T. Seaborg Congressional Science and Engineering Fellowship *(Professional development/Fellowship)* [1165]
Allan F. Henry/Paul A. Greebler Scholarship *(Graduate/Scholarship)* [1166]
Saul Levine Memorial Scholarship *(Graduate/Scholarship)* [1167]
Nuclear Criticality Safety Pioneers Scholarship *(Graduate/Scholarship)* [1168]
James F. Schumar Scholarship *(Graduate/Scholarship)* [1169]

Numismatics

Frances M. Schwartz Fellowship *(Other/Fellowship)* [1171, 10026]

Nursing

AAACN Conference Scholarship for Nursing Students *(Undergraduate/Scholarship)* [424]
AAACN Education Scholarship *(Undergraduate/Scholarship)* [425]
AAACN Research/Evidence Based Practice Project Awards *(Undergraduate/Grant, Scholarship)* [426]
AACN Continuing Professional Development Scholarships *(Advanced Professional/Scholarship)* [553]
AANP Education Advancement Scholarships *(Graduate/Scholarship, Grant)* [12209]
AASLD NP/PA Clinical Hepatology Fellowship *(Professional development/Fellowship)* [647]
Academic Education Scholarship *(Professional development/Scholarship)* [8940]
ACNM Foundation Midwives of Color-Watson Midwifery Student Scholarship *(Undergraduate/Scholarship)* [769]
ACS Doctoral Degree Scholarships in Cancer Nursing *(Doctorate, Graduate/Scholarship)* [713]
ACS Graduate Scholarships in Cancer Nursing Practice *(Graduate, Master's, Doctorate/Scholarship)* [714]
AfterCollege/AACN Nursing Scholarship *(Undergraduate, Master's, Doctorate/Scholarship)* [118]
Dr. Feroz Ahmed Memorial Educational Post-Graduate Scholarships *(Doctorate, Postgraduate/Scholarship)* [10144]

Henry and Maria Ahrens Charitable Trust Scholarship *(Undergraduate, Graduate/Scholarship)* [5117]
AKCNL Nightingale Scholarship *(Graduate, Undergraduate/Scholarship)* [2074]
Allied Health Care Professional Scholarship *(Undergraduate/Scholarship)* [5711]
American Pediatric Surgical Nurses Association Educational Grant *(Other/Grant)* [1210]
American Quarter Horse Foundation Scholarships *(Undergraduate, Graduate/Scholarship)* [1310]
AMSN Career Mobility Scholarship *(Undergraduate, Doctorate/Scholarship)* [48]
ANCA Scholarships *(Undergraduate/Scholarship)* [1915]
ANF/ENRS Nursing Research Society *(Professional development/Grant)* [1174]
Sigma Theta Tau, International Nursing Research Grants (STTI) *(Master's, Doctorate/Grant)* [1175]
Ann C. Beckingham Scholarship *(Graduate, Other/Scholarship)* [2989]
Anne Sturrock Nursing Scholarship Fund *(Undergraduate, Graduate/Scholarship)* [10672]
AORN Academic Scholarships *(Undergraduate, Master's, Doctorate/Scholarship, Monetary)* [2257]
AORN Foundation Scholarship Program *(Undergraduate, Doctorate, Master's/Scholarship, Monetary)* [2258]
Arizona Nurses Foundation Scholarships *(Graduate/Scholarship)* [1814]
AstraZeneca Award *(Doctorate/Award)* [3055]
AvaCare Medical Scholarship *(Undergraduate/Scholarship)* [2370]
Bachelor of Science in Nursing Academic Scholarships *(Graduate/Scholarship)* [7548]
Dr. Johnella Banks Memorial Scholarships *(Undergraduate/Scholarship)* [2610]
Raymond B. Bauer Research Award *(Professional development/Award, Grant)* [7322]
Dr. Ann C. Beckingham Scholarships *(Doctorate/Scholarship)* [3056]
Reckitt Benckiser Student Scholarships *(Graduate/Scholarship)* [7677]
Linn-Benton County Scholarships *(Undergraduate/Scholarship)* [8719]
Dr. Noorali and Sabiya Bharwani Endowment *(Undergraduate/Scholarship)* [8413]
Hussein Jina Bharwani Memorial Endowment *(Undergraduate/Scholarship)* [8414]
Jan Bingle Scholarships *(Master's, Doctorate/Scholarship)* [3438]
Joan Blend Scholarship Fund *(Undergraduate, Graduate/Scholarship)* [10753]
Board of Certification for Emergency Nursing (BCEN) Undergraduate Scholarship *(Undergraduate/Scholarship)* [4376]
Breakthrough to Nursing Scholarships *(Undergraduate/Scholarship)* [4790]
Ruby A. Brown Memorial Scholarships *(Undergraduate/Scholarship)* [4255]
Katie Brush Memorial Scholarships *(Master's, Doctorate/Scholarship)* [7637]
Joan Butler Award in Perinatal Intensive Care Nursing *(Advanced Professional/Award)* [7755]
The byourself Scholarship Fund *(Undergraduate, Vocational/Occupational/Scholarship)* [3710]
Stephen J. Byrnes & Mary "Sally" Byrnes Scholarship *(Undergraduate, Two Year College, Four Year College/Scholarship)* [7084]
CACCN/Baxter Corporation Guardian Scholarship *(Professional development/Scholarship)* [2889]
CACCN Educational Awards *(Professional development/Grant)* [2890]
CACCN Research Grant *(Professional development/Grant)* [2891]
Joseph R. Calder, Jr., MD Scholarship Fund *(Undergraduate/Scholarship)* [4586]
G.I. and Martha Cameron Scholarship *(Undergraduate/Scholarship)* [12298]
Canadian Nurses Foundation Northern Award *(Undergraduate/Scholarship)* [3057]
Canadian Nurses Foundation Scholarships *(Undergraduate, Master's, Doctorate/Scholarship)* [3058]
CANS/SNRS Dissertation Research Grant *(Doctorate/Grant)* [10658]

Career Mobility Scholarships *(Graduate, Undergraduate, Vocational/Occupational/Scholarship)* [4791]
CCCN Research Grant Program *(Professional development/Grant)* [3791]
Certified in Care Coordination and Transition Management (CCCTM) Certification Grant *(Undergraduate/Scholarship)* [427]
Certified Neuroscience Registered Nurse Recertification Grant Program *(Other/Grant)* [610]
CGNA Memorial Scholarship *(Graduate, Other/Scholarship)* [2990]
Melba Dawn Chiarenza Scholarship Fund *(Undergraduate/Scholarship)* [11946]
Children's National Health System Pediatric Nursing Student Scholarships *(Undergraduate/Scholarship)* [124]
CHOPR Fellowship Program *(Postdoctorate/Fellowship)* [11664]
Frances N. Christian Memorial Endowment Nursing Scholarship *(Graduate, Undergraduate/Scholarship)* [10844]
City of Toronto Queen Elizabeth II Sesquicentennial Scholarships in Community Health Nursing for Graduates *(Graduate/Scholarship)* [11686]
City of Toronto Queen Elizabeth II Sesquicentennial Scholarships in Community Health Nursing for Undergraduates *(Undergraduate/Scholarship)* [11687]
Colorado Nurses Association: Virginia Paulson Memorial Scholarship *(Graduate, Undergraduate/Scholarship)* [3532]
Colorado Nurses Foundation Nightingale Named Scholarship *(Graduate, Undergraduate/Scholarship)* [3533]
Conduct and Utilization of Research in Nursing (CURN) Awards *(Professional development, Doctorate, Master's/Prize)* [7319]
Helen & Orval Couch Memorial Scholarship *(Undergraduate/Scholarship)* [12302]
Crush the NCLEX Scholarship Program *(Four Year College, Graduate/Scholarship)* [3929]
Dan Mordecai Educational Scholarship Award *(Graduate, Undergraduate/Scholarship)* [8210]
Ashley Darby Memorial Scholarship *(Community College, Undergraduate/Scholarship)* [8507]
Marge Sorreles Davies Memorial Scholarship *(Undergraduate, College, University/Scholarship)* [7096]
Deana Kendrick Foundation Scholarship *(Undergraduate/Scholarship)* [6522]
Jane Delano Student Nurse Scholarships *(Undergraduate, Graduate/Scholarship)* [1149]
Discover Health Professions Loans *(Graduate/Loan, Scholarship)* [4111]
Discover Residency Loans *(Graduate/Loan, Scholarship)* [4114]
Don and Eileen Fulton Nursing Scholarship Fund *(Undergraduate/Scholarship)* [10823]
Donald E. Pizzini Memorial Nurse Scholarship *(Undergraduate, Professional development/Scholarship)* [7455]
Doris W. Frey Memorial Scholarship Fund *(Graduate/Scholarship)* [10681]
Drs. Ira and Udaya Dash Nursing Scholarship Fund *(Undergraduate, Graduate/Scholarship)* [10682]
Elaine Gelman Scholarship *(Undergraduate/Scholarship)* [7678]
Elevating Healthcare Scholarship *(Undergraduate/Scholarship)* [24]
Virginia Elizabeth and Alma Vane Taylor Nursing Scholarship *(Undergraduate/Scholarship)* [12073]
Ellis W. Rowe Memorial Scholarship *(Graduate/Scholarship)* [5268]
ENA Foundation Annual Conference Scholarships *(Professional development, Advanced Professional/Scholarship)* [4377]
ENA Foundation Seed Grants *(Master's, Advanced Professional/Grant)* [4378]
ENA Foundation Undergraduate State Challenge Scholarship *(Undergraduate/Scholarship)* [4379]
ExceptionalNurse.com Scholarships *(Undergraduate/Scholarship)* [4466]
Faye Lynn Roberts Education Scholarship Fund *(Undergraduate, Graduate/Scholarship)* [10684]

Lola Fehr: Nightingale Scholarships (Graduate, Undergraduate/Scholarship) [3534]

Christine Filipovich Scholarships (Master's, Doctorate/Scholarship) [3439]

Bea Firth Scholarship (Undergraduate, Graduate/Scholarship) [12315]

Florida Education Fund McKnight Doctoral Fellowship (Graduate/Fellowship) [4629]

Florida Nurses Foundation Scholarships (Undergraduate, Master's, Doctorate/Scholarship) [4640]

Floto-Peel Family Scholarship Fund (Undergraduate, Vocational/Occupational/Scholarship) [5076]

Forsyth County Nursing Scholarship (Undergraduate/Scholarship) [12077]

Arkansas Nursing Foundation - Dorothea Fund Scholarships (Other/Scholarship) [1831]

Gardner Foundation Education Scholarship (Professional development/Scholarship) [5786]

GIST - Mattie Lou Gist Memoral Scholarship Endowment (Undergraduate, Community College/Scholarship) [8510]

Dr. Helen Preston Glass Fellowships (Master's/Fellowship) [3060]

William R. Goldfarb Memorial Scholarships (Undergraduate/Scholarship) [1940]

GradSchools.com Minority Graduate Nursing Scholarship (Graduate/Scholarship) [4316]

Arkansas Nursing Foundation - Mary Gray Scholarships (Other/Scholarship) [1832]

Gretchen Dimico Memorial Scholarship (Undergraduate/Scholarship) [6795]

GSA Scholarships for International Nurses (Undergraduate, Master's/Scholarship) [5006]

Hall County Medical Society Scholarship (Undergraduate, Graduate/Scholarship) [5122]

Hazel Simms Nursing Scholarship (Other/Scholarship) [6664]

Health Professional Nursing Student Loans (Undergraduate, Graduate, Community College, Doctorate/Loan) [7424]

Health is a Right Not a Privilege Scholarship (Advanced Professional, Master's, Graduate/Scholarship) [8561]

Helen R Greenamyer Memorial Fund (Undergraduate/Scholarship) [10827]

Judy Hill Memorial Scholarships (Undergraduate/Scholarship) [3061]

H.M. Muffly Memorial Scholarship (Graduate, Undergraduate/Scholarship) [3535]

Hope for Healing Scholarship (Undergraduate, Graduate, Doctorate, Master's/Scholarship) [4541]

HRET Health Career Scholarships (Postgraduate, Undergraduate/Scholarship) [8275]

HRSA Scholarships for Disadvantaged Students (Undergraduate/Scholarship) [11334]

Esther McAfee Flippo Hunt Memorial Scholarship (Undergraduate/Scholarship) [8517]

Idaho Nursing and Health Professions Scholarship Fund (Undergraduate/Scholarship) [5677]

Illinois Student Assistance Commission Nursing Education Scholarship (Undergraduate, Graduate, College/Scholarship) [5714]

The Imogene Ward Nursing Scholarship (Undergraduate/Scholarship) [4623]

Indspire Health Careers Bursary and Scholarships (Graduate, Undergraduate/Scholarship) [5774]

Integra Foundation NNF Research Grant Awards (Professional development/Grant) [611]

Intermountain Medical Imaging Scholarship (Undergraduate, Community College/Scholarship) [5892]

IOKDS Health Careers Scholarship (College, University, Undergraduate, Graduate, Doctorate/Scholarship) [6050]

Susan K. Ipacs Nursing Legacy Scholarship (Undergraduate, High School/Scholarship) [4707]

Jean Goodwill Scholarship (Graduate/Scholarship) [3016]

Jean Wright-Elson Scholarship (Doctorate, Graduate, Undergraduate/Scholarship) [9823]

John I. & Madeleine R. Taeni Scholarship Fund (Undergraduate/Scholarship) [10689]

Johnson and Johnson/AACN Minority Nurse Faculty Scholars (Graduate/Scholarship) [543]

Johnson & Johnson Scholarships (Undergraduate/Scholarship) [3062]

Kansas Nurse Educator Service Scholarship (Graduate/Scholarship) [6364]

Kenhub Scholarship Program (Undergraduate, Postgraduate/Scholarship) [6524]

Dr. Dorothy J. Kergin Fellowships (Doctorate, Master's/Fellowship) [3063]

Lake Dollars for Scholars Endowment Fund (Undergraduate/Scholarship) [10774]

Candia Baker Laughlin Certification Scholarship (Undergraduate/Scholarship) [428]

Lawsuit Legal American Nursing Support Scholarships (Undergraduate, Graduate/Scholarship) [6738]

Leslie Baranowski Scholarship for Professional Excellence (Professional development/Scholarship) [5787]

Lighting the Way for Nursing Scholarship (Doctorate/Scholarship) [25]

Tecla Lin & Nelia Laroza Memorial Scholarships (Undergraduate/Scholarship) [3064]

Lois Widly Student Scholarships (Graduate, Undergraduate/Scholarship) [6046]

Gertie S. Lowe Nursing Scholarship Awards (Undergraduate/Scholarship) [3659]

Dan & Pauline Lutkenhouse & Hawaii Tropical Botanical Garden Scholarship and Educational Fund (Undergraduate, Graduate/Scholarship) [5407]

Margaret Mallett Nursing Scholarship (Undergraduate/Scholarship) [10058]

Mandel and Lauretta Abrahamer Scholarship Fund (Undergraduate/Scholarship) [10829]

March of Dimes Graduate Nursing Scholarships (Graduate/Scholarship) [7027]

Margaret Dowell-Gravatt, M.D. Scholarship (Undergraduate/Scholarship) [2486]

Marianne M. Stenvig Scholarship (Master's, Doctorate/Scholarship) [10623]

Eleanor Jean Martin Award (Master's/Scholarship) [3065]

Mary Ann Mikulic Scholarship (Other/Scholarship) [2273]

Master's Degree with a Major in Nursing Academic Scholarships (Graduate/Scholarship) [7549]

John Mazurek Memorial-Morgex Insurance Scholarship (Other/Scholarship) [314]

The McLean Scholarship for Nursing and Physician Assistant Majors (Undergraduate/Scholarship) [2194]

National Association of Pediatric Nurse Practitioners McNeil Annual Scholarships (Undergraduate/Scholarship) [7679]

National Association of Pediatric Nurse Practitioners McNeil Rural and Underserved Scholarships (Graduate/Scholarship) [7680]

Medical Scrubs Collection Scholarship (Undergraduate, Graduate/Scholarship) [7225]

Michigan League for Nursing Student Scholarships (Undergraduate/Scholarship) [7315]

Albert and Eloise Midyette Memorial Scholarship Fund (Undergraduate/Scholarship) [4746]

Military Nurses Association Scholarships (Master's/Scholarship) [3066]

Joseph and Catherine Missigman Memorial Nursing Scholarships (Undergraduate/Scholarship) [4597]

MNF Scholarships (Undergraduate, Graduate/Scholarship) [7320]

MODNA Nursing Education Scholarship (Doctorate, Graduate/Scholarship) [7359]

Margaret Munro Award (Undergraduate/Scholarship) [3067]

Murse World Scholarship (Undergraduate, Graduate, Postdoctorate/Scholarship) [7507]

Dr. Helen K. Mussallem Fellowships (Master's/Fellowship) [3068]

National American Arab Nurses Association Scholarships for Nursing Study (Undergraduate, Master's/Scholarship) [7596]

National Black Nurses Association Scholarships (Undergraduate/Scholarship) [7726]

New Brunswick Nurses Association Scholarships (Master's/Scholarship) [3069]

Sharon Nield Memorial Scholarships (Undergraduate/Scholarship) [3070]

The North Carolina League For Nursing Academic Scholarship (Graduate, Master's/Scholarship) [4748]

North Ottawa Hospital Auxiliary Scholarship (Undergraduate/Scholarship) [5099]

Northampton County Medical Society Alliance Scholarships (Undergraduate/Scholarship) [8480]

NOVA Foundation Scholarships (Doctorate, Master's/Scholarship) [8559]

NURSE Corps Scholarship Program (Professional development/Scholarship) [11335]

Orthopaedic Specialists of the Carolinas Nursing Scholarship (Undergraduate/Scholarship) [12086]

Outlaw Student's Nursing School Scholarships (Undergraduate/Scholarship) [10862]

Senator Norman Paterson Fellowships (TBC) (Doctorate/Scholarship) [3071]

Paul Tejada Memorial Scholarship (Undergraduate/Scholarship) [6206]

Margaret Pemberton Scholarships (Undergraduate/Scholarship) [2611]

Shoshana Philipp (Kirshenblatt) R.N. Memorial Scholarships (Graduate, Undergraduate/Scholarship) [11063]

Garry Phillips Scholarship (Undergraduate, University, College, Vocational/Occupational/Scholarship) [12358]

PNAA Nursing Scholarship Award (Master's, Doctorate/Scholarship) [9135]

Carl C. and Abbie Rebman Trust Scholarship (Undergraduate/Scholarship) [5124]

Rhea Sourifman Caplin Memorial Scholarship (Undergraduate/Scholarship) [5343]

Roy Anderson Memorial Scholarship (Graduate, Undergraduate/Scholarship) [3536]

Lucille and Edward R. Roybal Foundation Public Health Scholarships (Graduate, Undergraduate/Scholarship) [9753]

RRANN Program Scholarship (Undergraduate/Scholarship) [11491]

Kathleen and Winnifred Ruane Graduate Student Research Grant for Nurses (Undergraduate/Grant) [11582]

Ruth Milan-Altrusa Scholarship Fund (Undergraduate/Scholarship) [6995]

Saint Elizabeth Health Care Scholarship for Community Health Nursing (Undergraduate/Scholarship) [2170]

St. Joseph's Hospital School of Nursing Alumnae Scholarship (Undergraduate/Scholarship) [8876]

Sanofi Pasteur Scholarships (Master's/Scholarship) [3072]

Save a Life Scholarship (College, University, Vocational/Occupational, Undergraduate, Graduate/Scholarship) [448]

Jeptha Wade Schureman Scholarship Program (Undergraduate/Scholarship) [3724]

Senator Patricia K. McGee Nursing Faculty Scholarship (Doctorate, Graduate/Scholarship) [8323]

Senior Scholarships (Undergraduate, Vocational/Occupational/Scholarship) [8077]

Senior Wisdom Scholarship (Undergraduate, Graduate/Scholarship, Award) [9186]

Pat Shimp Memorial Scholarships (Undergraduate/Scholarship) [8879]

Sigma Theta Tau International Scholarships (Doctorate/Scholarship) [3073]

Ann Kelsay Small Scholarship (Undergraduate/Scholarship) [6475]

SNRS Dissertation Research Grants (Doctorate/Grant) [10659]

SNRS Research Grants (Professional development/Grant) [10660]

SNRS/STTI Research Grants (Professional development/Grant) [10661]

Society of Pediatric Nurses Academic Educational Scholarship (Undergraduate, Graduate/Scholarship) [10459]

SOHN Allied Health to BSN Degree Scholarship (Undergraduate/Scholarship) [10450]

SOHN Graduate Degree Scholarship (Undergraduate/Scholarship) [10451]

SOHN RN to BSN Degree Scholarship (Undergraduate/Scholarship) [10452]

Sparking the Future in Healthcare Scholarship (Doctorate/Scholarship) [26]

Specialty Nursing Scholarships (Undergraduate/Scholarship) [4792]

Sue Fleming Memorial Scholarship for Allied Health *(Undergraduate/Scholarship)* [2787]

Syncrude/Athabasca University Aboriginal Scholarships *(Undergraduate/Scholarship)* [10902]

TD Meloche Monnex Centennial Doctoral Scholarship *(Doctorate/Scholarship)* [3074]

Cheryl M. Thomas Scholarship *(Undergraduate, Graduate, Postdoctorate/Scholarship)* [27]

UAA Alaska Kidney Foundation Scholarship *(Graduate, Undergraduate/Scholarship)* [11496]

United Health Foundation National Association of Hispanic Nurses Scholarships *(High School/Scholarship)* [7659]

John Vanderlee Award *(Undergraduate/Scholarship)* [3075]

Virginia C. Jack and Ralph L. Jack Scholarship Fund *(Undergraduate/Scholarship)* [10800]

The Sybil Jennings Vorheis Memorial Undergraduate Scholarships *(Undergraduate/Scholarship)* [4761]

Sue Walicki Nursing Scholarships *(Undergraduate/Scholarship)* [6210]

Patty Walter Memorial Scholarships *(Graduate, Undergraduate/Scholarship)* [3537]

Washington State Nurses Association Foundation Scholarships (WSNF) *(Graduate, Undergraduate/Scholarship)* [11914]

West Virginia Nurses Association District No. 3 Professional Nursing Scholarships *(Undergraduate/Scholarship)* [8885]

William G. and Mayme J. Green Fund *(Undergraduate/Scholarship)* [5349]

Lippincott Williams and Wilkins Scholarships (LWW Scholarship) *(Master's, Doctorate/Scholarship)* [3440]

Wisconsin Nursing Student Loan *(Graduate, Undergraduate, Doctorate/Loan)* [10813]

WOCN Society Accredited Educational Scholarship *(Graduate, Undergraduate/Scholarship)* [12216]

WOCN Society Advanced Educational Scholarship *(Graduate/Scholarship)* [12217]

Joan C. Yoder Memorial Nursing Scholarships *(Undergraduate/Scholarship)* [11467]

Nursing administration

CHOPR Fellowship Program *(Postdoctorate/Fellowship)* [11664]

Nursing, Cardiovascular and cerebrovascular

Epilepsy Foundation Pre-doctoral Research Training Fellowships *(Graduate/Fellowship)* [4423]

Nursing, Neonatal

Academy of Neonatal Nursing Conference Scholarships *(Professional development/Scholarship)* [55]

ANF/ANN-FNRE Nursing Research Grants *(Professional development/Grant)* [1173]

Foundation for Neonatal Research and Education Scholarship *(Doctorate, Graduate, Postgraduate, Undergraduate/Scholarship)* [4794]

ANN Ingrid Josefin Ridky Academic Scholarships *(Undergraduate, Graduate/Scholarship)* [56]

Nursing, Oncological

Bachelor's in Nursing Degree Scholarship *(Undergraduate/Scholarship)* [8626]

CBCF - Ontario Nurse and Allied Health Professional Fellowships *(Advanced Professional, Professional development/Fellowship)* [2929]

Clinical Project Funding for Advanced Practice Oncology Nurses *(Advanced Professional, Professional development/Grant)* [8627]

Oncology Nursing Society Foundation - Doctoral Scholarships *(Doctorate/Scholarship)* [8628]

Oncology Nursing Society Foundation - Master's Scholarships *(Graduate, Master's/Scholarship)* [8629]

ONS Foundation Congress Scholarships *(Professional development/Scholarship)* [8630]

Research Career Development Award *(Professional development/Grant)* [8631]

Research Grant Funding (RE01) *(Advanced Professional/Grant)* [8632]

Nursing, Pediatric

Eight and Forty Lung and Respiratory Disease Nursing Scholarships *(Other/Scholarship)* [1071]

Pediatric Endocrinology Nursing Society Academic Education Scholarships *(Undergraduate/Scholarship)* [8941]

PENS Conference Reimbursement Scholarship *(Undergraduate/Scholarship)* [8942]

PENS Research Grants *(Professional development/Grant)* [8943]

Nursing, Psychiatric

Associates in Behavioral Health Scholarships *(Graduate/Scholarship)* [9290]

RPNAS Baccalaureate Level Program Scholarship *(Undergraduate/Scholarship)* [9620]

RPNAS Doctorate Level Program Scholarship *(Doctorate/Scholarship)* [9621]

RPNAS Master's Level Program Scholarship *(Master's/Scholarship)* [9622]

Nutrition

ASBC Foundation Undergraduate Scholarships *(Undergraduate/Scholarship)* [1388]

AvaCare Medical Scholarship *(Undergraduate/Scholarship)* [2370]

Birmingham District Alabama Dietetic Association Scholarships *(Graduate, Undergraduate/Scholarship)* [217]

California Association of Family and Consumer Sciences - San Diego Chapter Scholarship *(Undergraduate, Graduate/Scholarship)* [9805]

CANFIT Nutrition, Physical Education and Culinary Arts Scholarships *(Graduate, Undergraduate/Scholarship)* [3561]

Margaret Drew Alpha Scholarship *(Graduate/Scholarship)* [9110]

ILSI North America Future Leader Award *(Professional development/Grant)* [6031]

International Foodservice Editorial Council Scholarship *(Graduate/Scholarship)* [6007]

Les Dames D'Escoffier New York Corporate Scholarship *(Undergraduate/Scholarship)* [6777]

Maine Nutrition Council Scholarships *(Undergraduate/Scholarship)* [7001]

Mary and Elliot Wood Foundation Graduate Scholarship *(Graduate/Scholarship)* [4744]

Rita & Frank Mooney Scholarship *(Undergraduate, University, College, Vocational/Occupational/Scholarship)* [12349]

Murse World Scholarship *(Undergraduate, Graduate, Postdoctorate/Scholarship)* [7507]

Nell Bryant Robinson Scholarship *(Undergraduate/Scholarship)* [9118]

NMPF National Dairy Leadership Scholarship Program *(Graduate, Master's, Doctorate/Scholarship)* [8013]

North Alabama Dietetic Association Scholarships *(Undergraduate, Graduate/Scholarship)* [218]

North Dakota Division Scholarships *(Undergraduate, Graduate/Scholarship)* [7373]

Northeast Alabama District Dietetic Association Scholarships *(Graduate, Undergraduate/Scholarship)* [219]

Margaret Jerome Sampson Scholarships *(Undergraduate/Scholarship)* [9128]

Saskatchewan Pulse Growers Undergraduate Scholarships *(Undergraduate/Scholarship)* [9923]

William E. Smith Scholarships *(Graduate/Scholarship)* [220]

Southeast Alabama Dietetic Association Scholarships *(Graduate, Undergraduate/Scholarship)* [221]

Stark County Dairy Promoters Scholarship Fund *(Graduate/Scholarship)* [10794]

Wood Fruitticher Grocery Company, Inc. Scholarships *(Graduate, Undergraduate/Scholarship)* [222]

Occupational safety and health

AAOHN Professional Development Scholarships - Academic Study *(Graduate/Scholarship)* [613]

AAOHN Professional Development Scholarships - Continuing Education *(Professional development/Scholarship)* [614]

ASSP Diversity Committee Scholarship *(Doctorate/Scholarship)* [1559]

ASSP Foundation Academic Scholarship Program *(Undergraduate, Graduate, Doctorate, Vocational/Occupational/Scholarship)* [1560]

ASSP Foundation Professional Education Grant Program *(Professional development/Grant)* [1561]

Warren K. Brown Scholarship *(Undergraduate/Scholarship)* [1562]

Central Indiana Jim Kriner Memorial Scholarship *(Undergraduate/Scholarship)* [1563]

Doctoral Scholarship Outside Québec *(Doctorate/Scholarship)* [5796]

Scott Dominguez - Craters of the Moon Chapter Scholarship *(Graduate, Undergraduate/Scholarship)* [1564]

David Iden Memorial Safety Scholarships *(Undergraduate/Scholarship)* [1565]

IRSST Doctoral Scholarship *(Doctorate/Scholarship)* [5797]

IRSST Doctoral Scholarships Supplement *(Doctorate/Scholarship)* [5798]

IRSST Master's Scholarships *(Master's/Scholarship)* [5799]

IRSST Master's Scholarships Supplement *(Master's/Scholarship)* [5800]

IRSST postdoctoral fellowship *(Postdoctorate/Fellowship)* [5801]

Southwest Chapter Roy Kinslow Scholarship *(Undergraduate/Scholarship)* [1566]

James P. Kohn Memorial Scholarship *(Doctorate/Scholarship)* [1567]

Liberty Mutual Scholarships *(Undergraduate/Scholarship)* [1568]

Marsh Risk Consulting Scholarships *(Undergraduate/Scholarship)* [1569]

Dick Martin Scholarships *(Postgraduate/Scholarship, Award)* [2946]

North Florida Chapter Safety Education Scholarships *(Undergraduate/Scholarship)* [1570]

Harold F. Polston Scholarships *(Graduate, Undergraduate/Scholarship)* [1571]

Postdoctoral Fellowship in Québec *(Postdoctorate/Fellowship)* [5802]

Isobel Robinson Historical Research Grant *(Professional development/Grant)* [3081]

Julie Schmid Research Scholarship *(Advanced Professional/Scholarship)* [2255]

Louis Stokes Health Scholars Program *(Undergraduate/Scholarship)* [3742]

Harry Taback 9/11 Memorial Scholarships *(Undergraduate/Scholarship)* [1572]

Thompson Scholarship for Women in Safety *(Doctorate/Scholarship)* [1573]

UPS Diversity Scholarship *(Undergraduate/Scholarship)* [1574]

VPPPA June Brothers Scholarship *(Graduate, Undergraduate/Scholarship)* [11862]

VPPPA Stephen Brown Scholarship *(Graduate, Undergraduate/Scholarship)* [11863]

William C. Ray, CIH, CSP Arizona Scholarship *(Doctorate/Scholarship)* [1575]

William "Sully" Sullivan Scholarship *(Graduate, Undergraduate/Scholarship)* [11864]

Occupational therapy

COTA Scholarship for Occupational Therapy Assistants *(Undergraduate/Scholarship)* [8774]

COTF Graduate Scholarships *(Doctorate, Master's/Scholarship)* [3077]

COTF/Invacare Master's Scholarship *(Master's/Scholarship)* [3078]

David A. Couch Memorial Scholarship *(Undergraduate/Scholarship)* [8839]

Discover Health Professions Loans *(Graduate/Loan, Scholarship)* [4111]

Discover Residency Loans *(Graduate/Loan, Scholarship)* [4114]

Edith Weingarten Scholarship *(Postgraduate/Scholarship)* [1177]

Frank Oppenheimer Scholarship *(Postgraduate/Scholarship)* [1178]

Goldwin Howland Scholarship *(Master's, Doctorate/Scholarship)* [3080]

IOKDS Health Careers Scholarship *(College, University, Undergraduate, Graduate, Doctorate/Scholarship)* [6050]

Kappa Delta Phi Scholarship *(Postgraduate/Scholarship)* [1179]

Mariel Lacasse Scholarship *(Undergraduate, University, College, Vocational/Occupational/Scholarship)* [12336]

Margaret Dowell-Gravatt, M.D. Scholarship *(Undergraduate/Scholarship)* [2486]

Mary Minglen Scholarship *(Postgraduate/Scholarship)* [1180]

NorthCoast Medical Scholarship *(Postgraduate/Scholarship)* [1181]

Thelma Cardwell Scholarship *(Master's, Doctorate/Scholarship)* [3082]

Willard & Spackman Scholarship Program *(Postgraduate/Scholarship)* [1182]

Ocean engineering (See Engineering, Ocean)

Oceanography

Andrew Thomson Prize in Applied Meteorology *(Professional development/Award, Prize)* [3040]

Boyd Lyon Sea Turtle Fund Scholars *(Doctorate, Graduate, Postgraduate/Scholarship)* [6952]

Canadian Hydrographic Association Student Award *(Undergraduate/Award)* [3008]

CMOS-SCMO President's Prize *(Professional development/Prize)* [3041]

Roger Daley Postdoctoral Publication Awards *(Postdoctorate/Monetary, Award)* [3043]

DOE Computational Science Graduate Fellowship (DOE CSGF) *(Doctorate, Graduate/Fellowship)* [6611]

EPP/MSI Undergraduate Scholarship Program (USP) *(Undergraduate/Scholarship)* [11303]

Dr. Nancy Foster Scholarship Program *(Doctorate/Scholarship)* [8017]

Dr. Nancy Foster Scholarships *(Graduate/Scholarship)* [4695]

Tertia M.C. Hughes Memorial Graduate Student Prize *(Graduate/Award, Prize)* [3044]

ISMER Student Financial Assistance *(Master's, Doctorate/Monetary, Grant)* [11670]

Merchants Exchange Scholarship *(Undergraduate, Vocational/Occupational, Graduate, Professional development/Scholarship)* [7266]

The Naval Weather Service Association Scholarship *(Undergraduate/Scholarship)* [1125]

NDSEG Fellowship *(Graduate/Fellowship)* [7834]

NOAA Graduate Sciences Scholarships *(Graduate/Scholarship)* [11305]

François J. Saucier Prize in Applied Oceanography *(Professional development/Award, Prize)* [3045]

Robert L. Wiegel Scholarship for Coastal Studies *(Graduate/Scholarship)* [9865]

Oncology

AACR Basic Cancer Research Fellowships *(Postdoctorate/Fellowship, Award, Recognition)* [529]

AACR Minority and Minority-Serving Institution Faculty Scholar Awards *(Doctorate, Postdoctorate/Award)* [530]

ABTA Basic Research Fellowships *(Postdoctorate/Fellowship)* [699]

ABTA Translational Grant Program *(Postdoctorate/Grant)* [702]

Adolescent/Young Adult Lymphoma Correlative Studies Grant *(Advanced Professional/Grant)* [6946]

Alex's Lemonade Stand Foundation Epidemiology Grants *(Doctorate, Master's, Professional development/Grant)* [336]

Alex's Lemonade Stand Foundation Innovation Grants *(Other/Grant)* [337]

Alex's Lemonade Stand Foundation Young Investigator Grants *(Doctorate, Master's, Professional development/Grant)* [338]

American Association for Cancer Research Minority Scholar in Cancer Research Awards *(Graduate/Award)* [533]

Annual Research Doctoral and Postgraduate Fellowship Grant Program *(Doctorate, Postdoctorate, Postgraduate, Advanced Professional/Fellowship, Grant)* [2923]

Aplastic Anemia and Myelodysplasia Association of Canada Scholarships *(Graduate, Master's/Scholarship)* [3054]

ARS Young Oncologist Travel Grants *(Professional development/Grant)* [1314]

ASCO/CCF Young Investigator Awards *(Professional development, Advanced Professional/Grant)* [3767]

ASTRO Junior Faculty Career Research Training Award *(Advanced Professional, Professional development/Award)* [1545]

ASTRO Minority Summer Fellowship Award *(Postgraduate, Professional development/Fellowship, Award)* [1546]

ASTRO Residents/Fellows in Radiation Oncology Research Seed Grant *(Advanced Professional, Professional development/Grant)* [1547]

ASTRO/ROI Comparative Effectiveness Research Awards *(Professional development/Award)* [1548]

Bradley Stuart Beller Special Merit Award *(Doctorate, Postdoctorate/Award)* [3768]

BHCRI Bridge Funds *(Advanced Professional, Professional development/Grant)* [5648]

BHCRI Cancer Research Training Program (CRTP) Awards *(Graduate, Postdoctorate, Advanced Professional, Professional development/Grant)* [5649]

BHCRI Matching Funds *(Advanced Professional, Professional development/Grant)* [5650]

BHCRI Miscellaneous Funds *(Advanced Professional, Professional development/Grant)* [5651]

BHCRI Seed Funds *(Advanced Professional, Professional development/Grant)* [5652]

BHCRI Studentship Awards *(Undergraduate, Graduate, Advanced Professional/Grant)* [5653]

Career Development Grant in molecular genetics *(Advanced Professional, Professional development/Grant)* [11071]

CARO-ELEKTA Research Fellowship Program *(Professional development/Fellowship)* [2102]

CBCF - BC/Yukon Region Breast Cancer Research Grants Competition *(Advanced Professional/Grant)* [2924]

CBCF - BC/Yukon Region Breast Cancer Survivor Dragon Boat Grants *(Professional development/Grant)* [2925]

CBCF - BC/Yukon Region Community Health Grants *(Professional development/Grant)* [2926]

CBCF - BC/Yukon Region Small Initiative Funds *(Professional development/Grant)* [2927]

CBCF - Ontario Nurse and Allied Health Professional Fellowships *(Advanced Professional, Professional development/Fellowship)* [2929]

CBCF - Ontario Physician Fellowships *(Doctorate, Professional development/Fellowship)* [2930]

CBCF - Ontario Research Fellowships *(Doctorate, Postdoctorate, Professional development/Fellowship)* [2931]

CBCF - Ontario Research Project Grants *(Advanced Professional, Professional development/Grant)* [2932]

CBCF - Prairies/NWT Grants in Basic Biomedical Research *(Advanced Professional, Professional development/Grant)* [2934]

CBCF - Prairies/NWT Grants in Clinical Research *(Advanced Professional, Professional development/Grant)* [2935]

CBCF - Prairies/NWT Grants in Health Services and Policy Research *(Advanced Professional, Professional development/Grant)* [2936]

CBCF - Prairies/NWT Postdoctoral Fellowships *(Postdoctorate, Professional development/Fellowship)* [2937]

CBCF - Prairies/NWT Research Grants in Psychosocial, Cultural and Environmental Determinants of Health *(Advanced Professional, Professional development/Grant)* [2938]

CCF Career Development Award *(Professional development/Grant)* [3769]

CCF Improving Cancer Care Grants *(Professional development, Doctorate/Grant)* [3770]

CCF Merit Award *(Professional development, Doctorate/Award)* [3771]

Chronic Lymphocytic Leukemia Grant *(Advanced Professional/Grant)* [6947]

Comparative Effectiveness Research Professorship (CERP) *(Professional development, Doctorate/Grant)* [3772]

The Cure Starts Now Foundation Grants *(Graduate, Doctorate/Grant)* [3940]

Diffuse Large B-Cell Lymphoma Grant *(Advanced Professional/Grant)* [6948]

AACR Gertrude B. Elion Cancer Research Award *(Professional development, Graduate/Award, Recognition)* [534]

Follicular Lymphoma Pathways Grant *(Advanced Professional/Grant)* [6949]

Norm Hollend Fellowships in Oncology *(Postdoctorate/Fellowship)* [6930]

IHSPR Institute Community Support (ICS) Program *(Undergraduate, Graduate, Postgraduate, Postdoctorate/Prize)* [5879]

International Development and Education Award in Palliative Care *(Professional development/Award)* [3774]

International Development and Education Awards *(Professional development, Doctorate/Grant)* [3775]

International Innovation Grants *(Professional development/Grant)* [3776]

Jane Coffin Childs Memorial Fund - Medical Research Postdoctoral Fellowship *(Postdoctorate, Doctorate/Fellowship)* [3303]

Kansas State University Cancer Research Award Program *(Undergraduate/Grant)* [6374]

Kimmel Scholar Award *(Doctorate/Grant)* [6554]

LCRF Grant *(Advanced Professional, Professional development/Grant)* [6933]

Brigid Leventhal Special Merit Award *(Postdoctorate, Professional development/Award)* [3777]

Long-term International Fellowships *(Professional development/Fellowship)* [3778]

Mantle Cell Lymphoma Therapeutic Studies Grant *(Advanced Professional/Grant)* [6950]

Medical Student Rotation for Underrepresented Populations *(Graduate, Master's/Grant)* [3779]

Morgan Stanley Pediatrics Fellowships *(Postgraduate, Graduate/Fellowship)* [686]

Movember Clinical Trials *(Advanced Professional/Grant)* [9362]

Movember Discovery Grants *(Advanced Professional, Professional development/Grant)* [9363]

Movember Rising Star in Prostate Cancer Research Awards *(Advanced Professional, Professional development/Grant)* [9364]

Movember Team Grants *(Advanced Professional, Professional development/Grant)* [9365]

James B. Nachman Endowed ASCO Junior Faculty Award in Pediatric Oncology *(Doctorate, Professional development/Grant, Monetary)* [3780]

Pain and Symptom Management Special Merit Award *(Postdoctorate, Professional development/Award)* [3781]

Pancreatic Cancer Action Network-AACR Career Development Awards *(Doctorate/Grant, Award)* [535]

Patient Advocate Scholarship Program *(Professional development/Scholarship)* [3782]

PCF Challenge Awards *(Professional development/Award)* [9370]

PCF Young Investigator Award *(Professional development, Postdoctorate/Award)* [9371]

Prevent Cancer Foundation Fellowships *(Postdoctorate/Fellowship)* [9277]

Prostate Cancer Canada Clinical Research Fellowships *(Advanced Professional/Fellowship)* [9366]

Prostate Cancer Canada Graduate Studentships *(Graduate, Doctorate/Grant)* [9367]

Prostate Cancer Canada Postdoctoral Research Fellowships (Postdoctorate, Advanced Professional/Fellowship) [9368]

Resident Travel Award for Underrepresented Populations (Professional development/Award) [3783]

SWS Barbara Rosenblum Scholarship (Doctorate/Fellowship, Scholarship) [10568]

Wagner-Torizuka Fellowship (Professional development/Fellowship) [10445]

Women in Cancer Research Scholar Awards (Graduate, Postdoctorate/Award, Monetary) [536]

Opera

Bel Canto Vocal Scholarship Foundation (Graduate/Scholarship) [2467]

Viginia & Susan Hawk Scholarship (Other/Scholarship) [9818]

Opera Foundation Scholarship (Other/Scholarship) [8671]

Operations research

CDC Steven M. Teutsch Prevention Effectiveness (PE) (Doctorate/Fellowship) [11328]

University of Texas at Austin Special Research Grants (Professional development/Grant) [11679]

Anna Valicek Award (Graduate, Master's, Doctorate/Medal, Scholarship) [6003]

Ophthalmology

Army Health Professions Scholarship Program (HPSP) (Professional development/Scholarship) [11288]

LSU Eye Center Clinical Retina Fellowships (Undergraduate/Fellowship) [6910]

Optical engineering (See Engineering, Optical)

Optics

BACUS Scholarship (Graduate, Undergraduate/Scholarship) [10724]

Corning Outstanding Student Paper Competition (Graduate, Undergraduate/Award) [8675]

D.J. Lovell Scholarship (Graduate, Undergraduate/Scholarship) [10725]

Harvey M. Pollicove Memorial Scholarship (Undergraduate, Graduate/Scholarship) [8676]

Jean Bennett Memorial Student Travel Grant (Graduate, Undergraduate/Grant) [8678]

Michael Kidger Memorial Scholarship in Optical Design (Undergraduate/Scholarship) [10726]

Maiman Student Paper Competition (Graduate, Undergraduate/Award) [8679]

Optical Design and Engineering Scholarship (Graduate, Undergraduate/Scholarship) [10728]

SPIE Student Author Travel Grants (Graduate, Undergraduate/Grant) [10729]

Emil Wolf Outstanding Student Paper Competition (Graduate, Undergraduate/Award) [8680]

Optometry

ACVO Best Resident Manuscript Awards (Undergraduate/Recognition) [780]

AOF/Johnson & Johnson Vision Care - Innovation in Education Grants (Advanced Professional, Professional development/Grant) [462]

Army Health Professions Scholarship Program (HPSP) (Professional development/Scholarship) [11288]

Discover Health Professions Loans (Graduate/Loan, Scholarship) [4111]

Discover Residency Loans (Graduate/Loan, Scholarship) [4114]

William C. Ezell Fellowship (Graduate, Master's/Fellowship) [466]

FFB-C Postdoctoral Fellowships (Postdoctorate/Fellowship) [4788]

Terrance N. Ingraham Pediatric Optometry Residency Award (Graduate/Award) [463]

Kansas Optometry Service Scholarship (Graduate, Undergraduate/Scholarship) [6365]

Kenhub Scholarship Program (Undergraduate, Postgraduate/Scholarship) [6524]

Antoinette M. Molinari Memorial Scholarships (Doctorate/Scholarship) [467]

Lucille and Edward R. Roybal Foundation Public Health Scholarships (Graduate, Undergraduate/Scholarship) [9753]

Vincent Salierno Memorial Scholarship (Doctorate/Award, Scholarship) [468]

Sheldon Wechsler and George Mertz Contact Lens Residency Award (Professional development, Advanced Professional/Award) [464]

Ornithology

James L. Baillie Memorial Fund - Student Award for Field Research (Graduate/Grant) [4451]

The E. Alexander Bergstrom Memorial Research Award (Undergraduate, Master's/Award) [2177]

Blake-Nuttall Fund Grants (Other/Grant) [8565]

Fred Cooke Student Award (Undergraduate/Grant) [10294]

George A. Hall / Harold F. Mayfield Grant (Undergraduate, Professional development/Grant) [12054]

Helen G. and Allan D. Cruickshank Education Award (Undergraduate, Doctorate, Postdoctorate/Grant) [4642]

James L. Baillie Student Research Award (Undergraduate/Grant) [10295]

Louis Agassiz Fuertes Grant (Professional development/Grant) [12055]

Rob and Bessie Welder Wildlife Foundation's graduate research fellowship (Graduate, Master's, Doctorate/Fellowship) [11958]

Paul A. Stewart Grant (Professional development/Grant) [12056]

Taverner Awards (Undergraduate/Grant) [10296]

Orthotics prosthetics technology

OPERF/ABC Resident Travel Award (Professional development/Grant) [8765]

OPERF Student Awards (Professional development/Grant) [8766]

OPERF Fellowships (Graduate, Master's/Fellowship) [8767]

OPERF Small Grants (Doctorate/Grant) [8768]

Osteopathic medicine (See Medicine, Osteopathic)

Otolaryngology

ANS Research Grant Award (Professional development/Grant) [1158]

Otology

ANS Research Grant Award (Professional development/Grant) [1158]

AOS Research Training Fellowships (Graduate/Fellowship) [1202]

Otosclerosis

AOS Research Training Fellowships (Graduate/Fellowship) [1202]

Packaging

Member Student Scholarships (Undergraduate/Scholarship) [9050]

Painting (See also Art)

American Watercolor Society Scholarship Program for Art Teachers (Undergraduate, Graduate/Scholarship) [1648]

Yvonne L. Bombardier Visual Arts Scholarship Program (Master's, Doctorate/Scholarship) [2651]

Albinas Elskus Scholarship (Other/Scholarship) [10743]

Theodore Rousseau Fellowships (Graduate/Fellowship) [7281]

The Slifka Foundation Interdisciplinary Fellowship (Doctorate, Master's/Fellowship) [7282]

Pakistani studies

AIPS Long Term Fellowships (Doctorate, Postdoctorate/Fellowship) [1036]

AIPS Post-Doctoral Fellowship (Postdoctorate/Fellowship) [1037]

AIPS Pre-Doctoral Fellowship (Doctorate, Postdoctorate/Fellowship) [1038]

AIPS Short Term Fellowships (Doctorate, Postdoctorate/Fellowship) [1039]

Paleontology

Dan Rigel Memorial Educational Grant (Professional development, Advanced Professional/Grant) [2046]

Estes Memorial (Graduate/Grant) [10559]

A. Allen Graffham Research Grant (Advanced Professional, Professional development/Grant) [2047]

Loeblich and Tappan Student Research Award (Graduate, Undergraduate/Grant) [3942]

Paleontological Society International Research Program Sepkoski Grants (Advanced Professional, Graduate/Grant) [8814]

Charles Sternberg Scholarship (Graduate/Scholarship) [2048]

STRI Short-Term Fellowships (Undergraduate, Graduate, Postdoctorate/Fellowship) [10226]

Earl S. Tupper Three-year Postdoctoral Fellowship (Postdoctorate/Fellowship) [10227]

René M. Vandervelde Research Grants (Professional development/Grant) [2049]

James R. Welch Scholarship (Graduate/Scholarship) [2050]

Paralegal studies

AAFPE LEX Scholarship (Undergraduate/Scholarship) [616]

AALL Research Fund (Professional development/Grant) [587]

AALL/Wolters Kluwer Law & Business Grants (Professional development/Grant) [593]

ACJA/LAE Student Paper Competition (Undergraduate, Graduate/Scholarship) [836]

Aiello Harris Legal Scholarships (Undergraduate, Graduate/Scholarship) [144]

Bar President's Scholarship (Undergraduate/Scholarship) [11931]

Therese A. "Teri" Cannon Educational Scholarship (Other/Scholarship) [6061]

Gene Carte Student Paper Competition Awards (Undergraduate, Graduate/Prize) [1419]

CLA/CP Scholarship (Other/Scholarship) [9782]

Community Legal Services of Philadelphia Fellowships (Postgraduate, Graduate/Fellowship) [3729]

DAPA Student Member Scholarships (Undergraduate, Postgraduate/Scholarship) [3964]

Lise M. Duchesneau Scholarship (Undergraduate/Scholarship) [2097]

Edward Traurig Scholarship (Undergraduate/Scholarship) [11932]

Gail Goodell Folsom Memorial Scholarships (Undergraduate/Scholarship) [7542]

Judge and Mrs. Robert D. Horowitz Legal Scholarship Fund (Graduate, Undergraduate/Scholarship) [10766]

Kentucky Paralegal Association Paralegal Student Scholarships (Undergraduate/Scholarship) [6535]

Samuel Krugliak Legal Scholarship Fund (Undergraduate/Scholarship) [10773]

NALS of Detroit Scholarships (Undergraduate/Scholarship) [7544]

NALS of Michigan Scholarship (Undergraduate/Scholarship) [7546]

NFPA PCCE Scholarship (Other, Professional development/Scholarship) [7882]

NFPA/Thomson Reuters Scholarships (Undergraduate, Two Year College/Scholarship) [7883]

Professional Certification Exam Scholarship *(Undergraduate, Professional development/Scholarship)* [9797]

Richard McGrath Memorial Fund Award *(Undergraduate/Award)* [839]

Rochelle Scholarship *(College/Scholarship)* [6908]

St. Louis Paralegal Student Scholarships *(Undergraduate/Scholarship)* [9783]

Vermont Paralegal Organization Paralegal Certification Scholarship *(Undergraduate/Scholarship)* [11802]

John D. Voelker Foundation Native American Scholarships *(Undergraduate/Scholarship)* [11858]

Warner Norcross & Judd Minority Scholarships *(Undergraduate/Scholarship)* [11874]

Waterbury Bar Association Scholarship *(Undergraduate/Scholarship)* [11933]

WBA Paralegal/Legal Assistant Scholarship *(Undergraduate/Scholarship)* [11934]

Paramedics

Harry J. Morris, Jr. Emergency Services *(Undergraduate/Scholarship)* [5157]

Gail L. Hartshorn Memorial Fund *(Other/Scholarship)* [8856]

John I. & Madeleine R. Taeni Scholarship Fund *(Undergraduate/Scholarship)* [10689]

Platinum Educational Groups Annual Scholarships Program *(All/Scholarship)* [9194]

Parapsychology

Eileen J. Garrett Scholarship *(Undergraduate, Postgraduate/Scholarship)* [8824]

Parapsychological Association Research Endowment *(Undergraduate/Recognition, Grant)* [8822]

Alex Tanous Scholarship Award *(Undergraduate/Scholarship)* [10919]

Parkinson's disease

APDA Post-Doctoral Research Fellowship *(Postdoctorate/Fellowship)* [1206]

APDA Research Grants *(Postgraduate, Professional development/Grant)* [1207]

Clinician Research Awards *(Postgraduate, Professional development, Other/Fellowship)* [8898]

Dr. George C. Cotzias Memorial Fellowship *(Other, Professional development/Fellowship)* [1208]

Parkinson Canada Basic Research Fellowship *(Advanced Professional/Fellowship)* [8891]

Parkinson Canada Clinical Movement Disorder Fellowship *(Advanced Professional, Professional development/Fellowship)* [8892]

Parkinson Canada Clinical Research Fellowship *(Professional development/Fellowship)* [8893]

Parkinson Canada Graduate Student Award *(Graduate, Advanced Professional/Award)* [8894]

Parkinson Canada New Investigator Award *(Professional development/Grant)* [8895]

Parkinson Canada Pilot Project Grant *(Advanced Professional/Grant)* [8896]

Parkinson's Disease Foundation International Research Grants Program (IRGP) *(Postdoctorate/Grant)* [8899]

Postdoctoral Fellowships for Basic Scientists Program *(Postdoctorate/Fellowship)* [8900]

Postdoctoral Fellowships for Clinical Neurologists *(Postdoctorate/Fellowship)* [8901]

Summer Student Fellowships *(Undergraduate, Graduate/Fellowship)* [8902]

Parks and recreation

George Torkildsen Literary Award *(Professional development/Award, Trophy)* [12200]

National Recreation and Park Association Diversity Scholarships *(Undergraduate/Scholarship)* [8059]

Gordon Newman Recreation Scholarship *(Undergraduate, University, College, Vocational/Occupational/Scholarship)* [12352]

Thomas and Ruth River International Scholarship *(Undergraduate, Graduate/Scholarship)* [12201]

Yukon Outdoors Club Scholarship *(Undergraduate, University, College, Vocational/Occupational/Scholarship)* [12398]

Pathology

Investigators in the Pathogenesis of Infectious Disease *(Doctorate, Postdoctorate/Grant)* [2754]

SPP Young Investigator Research Grant *(Postdoctorate, Master's/Grant)* [10462]

Gordon F. Vawter Pathologist-in-Training Award *(Graduate, Postgraduate/Grant)* [10463]

Peace studies

Ford Foundation Dissertation Fellowship *(Postdoctorate/Fellowship)* [4672, 7572]

Ford Foundation Diversity Fellowships *(Graduate, Doctorate, Postdoctorate, Postgraduate/Fellowship)* [7573]

Ford Foundation Postdoctoral Fellowship *(Postdoctorate/Fellowship)* [4673, 7574]

Ford Foundation Predoctoral Fellowship *(Graduate, Doctorate/Fellowship)* [4674, 7575]

Herbert Scoville Jr. Peace Fellowship *(Graduate/Fellowship)* [9988]

Learning from Peace in Sub-Saharan Africa *(Professional development/Grant)* [11377]

Mary and Elliot Wood Foundation Graduate Scholarship *(Graduate/Scholarship)* [4744]

Peace Dissertation Prize Grant *(Postgraduate/Grant)* [11378]

Promoting the Rule of Law and Access to Justice *(Other/Grant)* [11379]

Jennings Randolph Peace Scholarship Dissertation Program *(Doctorate/Scholarship, Fellowship)* [11380]

United States Institute of Peace Jennings Randolph Senior Fellowship Program *(Advanced Professional/Fellowship)* [11381]

Rieser Fellowships *(Undergraduate/Fellowship)* [2743]

Rotary Peace Fellowship Program *(Graduate, Master's/Fellowship)* [4195]

Pediatric medicine (See Medicine, Pediatric)

Performing arts

ACHE Junior and Community College Performing Arts Scholarship Program *(Undergraduate/Scholarship)* [207]

AFA Theatre & Performance Art Project Grants *(Professional development/Grant)* [259]

Arts Council of Greater Grand Rapids Minority Scholarship *(Undergraduate/Scholarship)* [5134]

ASTR Research Fellowships *(Doctorate/Fellowship)* [1577]

CBC Spouses Performing Arts Scholarship *(Undergraduate/Scholarship)* [3739]

Jack Kent Cooke Graduate Arts Awards *(Graduate/Award)* [3819]

Clare Cooke Performing Arts Scholarship *(Undergraduate, College, University/Scholarship)* [7091]

John L. Dales Standard Scholarship *(Undergraduate/Scholarship)* [9990]

Fellowships for Creative and Performing Artists and Writers *(Professional development/Fellowship)* [490]

Eugenia Vellner Fischer Award for the Performing Arts *(Undergraduate/Scholarship)* [7416]

Florida Education Fund McKnight Doctoral Fellowship *(Graduate/Fellowship)* [4629]

George E. Judd Scholarship Fund *(Undergraduate/Scholarship)* [10686]

Grants to Artists *(Advanced Professional/Grant)* [4769]

Ken Gray Scholarship *(Undergraduate/Scholarship)* [11481]

Joanna Townsend Applied Arts Scholarship *(All/Scholarship)* [2129]

Muddy Waters Scholarships *(Undergraduate, Graduate/Scholarship)* [2632]

PWC Core Apprentice Program *(Other/Internship)* [9200]

Star-Ledger Scholarships for the Performing Arts *(Undergraduate/Scholarship)* [8280]

Theatre Guild Scholarship *(Undergraduate/Scholarship)* [11012]

UAA Friends of the Performing Arts Scholarship *(Undergraduate/Scholarship)* [11501]

The Wolf Trap Accounting Internship Program *(Graduate, Other, Undergraduate/Internship)* [12127]

Wolf Trap's Grants for High School Performing Arts Teachers *(Other/Grant)* [12128]

Personnel administration/human resources

C.C.H.R.M.A. Scholarships *(Undergraduate/Scholarship)* [3469]

Susan R. Meisinger Fellowship for Graduate Study in HR *(Graduate, Master's, Advanced Professional/Fellowship)* [10367]

Michael R. Losey Excellence In HR Research Award *(Graduate, Undergraduate/Award, Recognition)* [10368]

NPELRA Foundation - Anthony C. Russo Scholarships *(Graduate/Scholarship)* [8057]

SHRM Certification Scholarships - Individual *(Professional development/Scholarship)* [10369]

Pesticide science

PWIPM Professional Empowerment Grant *(Graduate/Grant)* [8038]

Petroleum engineering (See Engineering, Petroleum)

Pharmaceutical sciences

AFPE Gateway Research Scholarships *(Doctorate/Scholarship)* [922]

AFPE Pre-Doctoral Fellowships in Pharmaceutical Sciences *(Doctorate/Fellowship)* [923]

AFPE Pre-Doctoral Fellowships in Pharmaceutical Sciences for Underrepresented Minorities *(Doctorate, Graduate/Fellowship)* [924]

Dr. Feroz Ahmed Memorial Educational Post-Graduate Scholarships *(Doctorate, Postgraduate/Scholarship)* [10144]

IOKDS Health Careers Scholarship *(College, University, Undergraduate, Graduate, Doctorate/Scholarship)* [6050]

NACDS Foundation Merit-Based Scholarship Awards *(All/Scholarship, Award)* [7635]

Pharmacology

Canadian Society for Pharmacology and Therapeutics Clinical Fellowship Award *(Advanced Professional/Fellowship)* [6624]

Epilepsy Foundation Pre-doctoral Research Training Fellowships *(Graduate/Fellowship)* [4423]

Merck Frosst Canada Inc. Postgraduate Pharmacy Fellowship Award *(Postgraduate, Graduate, Doctorate/Fellowship)* [2172]

Pharmacology/Toxicology Pre Doctoral Fellowships *(Doctorate/Fellowship)* [9062]

PhRMA Foundation Pharmacology/Toxicology Post Doctoral Fellowships *(Postdoctorate/Fellowship)* [9068]

PhRMA Foundation Pharmacology/Toxicology Research Starter Grants *(Doctorate/Grant)* [9069]

PhRMA Foundation Pharmacology/Toxicology Sabbatical Fellowships *(Postdoctorate, Master's/Fellowship)* [9070]

Paul M. Vanhoutte Distinguished Lectureship in Vascular Pharmacology *(Professional development, Postgraduate/Award)* [1536]

Pharmacy

Mary Louise Andersen Scholarship *(Undergraduate/Scholarship)* [1742]

APhA Foundation Scholarship *(Undergraduate/Scholarship)* [1743]

George F. Archambault Scholarship *(Undergraduate/Scholarship)* [1744]

Armenian American Pharmacists' Association Scholarship *(Graduate/Scholarship)* [1844]

ASHP Student Research Awards *(Doctorate/Award)* [1465]

Boyle Family Scholarship *(Undergraduate/Scholarship)* [1745]

Joseph R. Calder, Jr., MD Scholarship Fund *(Undergraduate/Scholarship)* [4586]

Christian Pharmacists Fellowship International (CPFI) *(Advanced Professional/Scholarship)* [3321]

J.C. and Rheba Cobb Memorial Scholarships *(Undergraduate/Scholarship)* [7775]

DAAD Study Scholarship Awards *(Graduate, Undergraduate/Scholarship)* [4059]

Discover Health Professions Loans *(Graduate/Loan, Scholarship)* [4111]

Discover Residency Loans *(Graduate/Loan, Scholarship)* [4114]

Marvin and Joanell Dyrstad Scholarship *(Undergraduate/Scholarship)* [1746]

Epilepsy Foundation Pre-doctoral Research Training Fellowships *(Graduate/Fellowship)* [4423]

Gloria Francke Scholarship *(Undergraduate/Scholarship)* [1747]

John A. Gans Scholarship *(Undergraduate/Scholarship)* [1748]

Robert D. Gibson Scholarship *(Undergraduate/Scholarship)* [1749]

Indspire Health Careers Bursary and Scholarships *(Graduate, Undergraduate/Scholarship)* [5774]

Jason Lang Scholarship *(Undergraduate/Scholarship)* [292]

John W. Webb Lecture Award *(Other/Award, Recognition, Monetary)* [1466]

Sam Kalman Scholarship *(Undergraduate/Scholarship)* [1750]

Juan and Esperanza Luna Scholarship *(Undergraduate/Scholarship)* [1751]

Maryland Poison Center Clinical Toxicology Fellowship *(Doctorate, Graduate/Fellowship)* [7116]

Merck Frosst Canada Ltd. Postgraduate Pharmacy Fellowships *(Graduate, Postgraduate, Doctorate/Fellowship)* [2173]

NACDS Foundation Merit-Based Scholarship Awards *(All/Scholarship, Award)* [7635]

NCPA Foundation Presidential Scholarships *(Undergraduate/Scholarship)* [7776]

NCPA Summer Internship Program *(Undergraduate/Internship)* [7777]

Pharmaceutics Post Doctoral Fellowships *(Doctorate/Fellowship)* [9059]

Pharmaceutics Research Starter Grants *(Doctorate/Grant)* [9060]

Pharmaceutics Sabbatical Fellowships *(Master's, Doctorate/Fellowship)* [9061]

PhRMA Foundation Pharmaceutics Pre Doctoral Fellowships *(Postdoctorate/Fellowship)* [9067]

Neil Pruitt, Sr. Memorial Scholarships *(Undergraduate/Scholarship)* [7778]

Paul Pumpian Scholarship *(Undergraduate/Scholarship)* [1752]

Rho Chi, AFPE First Year Graduate Fellowships *(Graduate/Fellowship)* [9683]

Rho Chi Society Clinical Research Scholarships *(Postdoctorate/Scholarship)* [9684]

Colonel Jerry W. Ross Scholarship *(Undergraduate/Scholarship)* [1753]

Lucille and Edward R. Roybal Foundation Public Health Scholarships *(Graduate, Undergraduate/Scholarship)* [9753]

Willard B. Simmons Sr. Memorial Scholarships *(Undergraduate/Scholarship)* [7779]

Ann Kelsay Small Scholarship *(Undergraduate/Scholarship)* [6475]

TEVA Canada Survivor Scholarship *(Undergraduate, University/Scholarship)* [3292]

Charles C. Thomas Scholarship *(Undergraduate/Scholarship)* [1754]

Thomas W. Gallagher Scholarship Fund *(Undergraduate/Scholarship)* [10797]

TSHP R&E Foundation Scholarship Program *(Undergraduate, Graduate/Scholarship)* [11135]

WMSHP Scholarship *(Graduate/Scholarship)* [11985]

Philology

Thesaurus Linguae Latinae Fellowship (TTL) *(Doctorate/Fellowship)* [10312]

Philosophy

Calihan Academic Grants *(Graduate, Professional development/Fellowship, Grant)* [65]

Calihan Travel Grants *(Other, Graduate/Grant)* [66]

Marcus Mosiah Garvey Scholarships *(Undergraduate/Scholarship)* [6216]

Novak Awards *(Doctorate/Monetary, Award)* [67]

Ameen Rihani Scholarship Program *(Undergraduate/Scholarship)* [1768]

Dr. Brent Slobodin Memorial Scholarship in the Humanities *(Undergraduate, Graduate, University, College/Scholarship)* [12371]

Photogrammetry

Robert E. Altenhofen Memorial Scholarships *(Graduate, Undergraduate/Scholarship)* [2004]

ERDAS Internship *(Graduate/Internship)* [2005]

Francis H. Moffitt Scholarship *(Graduate, Undergraduate/Scholarship)* [2006]

Kenneth J. Osborn Scholarship *(Undergraduate/Scholarship)* [2007]

Leica Scholarship *(Graduate/Scholarship)* [2008]

Paul R. Wolf Memorial Scholarships *(Graduate/Scholarship)* [2012]

Photography

Allison E. Fisher Scholarship *(Undergraduate, Graduate/Scholarship)* [7615]

Bob Baxter Scholarship *(Graduate, Undergraduate/Scholarship)* [8046]

Bob East Scholarship *(Graduate, Undergraduate/Scholarship)* [8047]

Yvonne L. Bombardier Visual Arts Scholarship Program *(Master's, Doctorate/Scholarship)* [2651]

Raymond Davis Scholarships *(Undergraduate, Graduate/Scholarship)* [10371]

The Gallery Collection's Create-A-Greeting-Card Scholarship *(Undergraduate/Scholarship)* [4848]

Glendale Latino Association Scholarships *(Undergraduate/Scholarship)* [4999]

Elizabeth Greenhalgh Memorial Scholarships in Journalism, Graphic Arts, or Photography *(Undergraduate/Scholarship)* [12136]

International Foodservice Editorial Council Scholarship *(Graduate/Scholarship)* [6007]

Kit C. King Graduate Scholarships *(Graduate/Scholarship)* [8048]

Manzer-Keener-Wefler Scholarship Fund *(Undergraduate/Scholarship)* [10777]

NPPF Still & Multimedia Scholarship *(Undergraduate/Scholarship)* [8049]

NPPF TV News Scholarship *(Undergraduate/Scholarship)* [8050]

The Scott Pearlman Field Awards *(Professional development/Award)* [4470]

Reid Blackburn Scholarship *(Undergraduate/Scholarship)* [8051]

SPE Student Awards for Innovations in Imaging *(Undergraduate, Graduate/Scholarship)* [10475]

UAA Kimura Scholarship Fund for Photography *(Undergraduate/Scholarship)* [11504]

Worldstudio AIGA Scholarships *(Graduate, Undergraduate/Scholarship)* [12205]

Photography, Journalistic

Tom Hanson Photojournalism Award *(All/Internship)* [6622]

Physical education (See Education, Physical)

Physical rehabilitation (See Rehabilitation, Physical/Psychological)

Physical sciences

AIST Ohio Valley Member Chapter Scholarships *(Undergraduate/Scholarship)* [2217]

American Council of Independent Laboratories Academic Scholarships *(Undergraduate/Scholarship, Award)* [815]

American Sokol Merit Award *(Undergraduate/Scholarship, Recognition)* [1593]

AWMA Louisiana Section Scholarship *(Undergraduate, Graduate/Scholarship)* [167]

The Christine Mirzayan Science & Technology Policy Graduate Fellowship Program *(Graduate, Postdoctorate, High School/Fellowship)* [7571]

College of Engineering and Physical Sciences Industry Scholarship *(Undergraduate/Scholarship)* [11650]

Discover Residency Loans *(Graduate/Loan, Scholarship)* [4114]

Getty Postdoctoral Fellowship in Conservation Science *(Postdoctorate/Fellowship)* [4956]

IAF Fellowships *(Doctorate/Fellowship)* [5883]

Michigan Society of Fellows Three-Year Fellowships *(Postdoctorate/Fellowship)* [7326]

Paul and Ellen Ruckes Scholarship *(Graduate, Undergraduate/Scholarship)* [917]

Roy Cooper Memorial Scholarship *(Undergraduate/Scholarship)* [6758]

Alfred P. Sloan Foundation Graduate Scholarships - Sloan Minority Ph.D. Program (MPHD) *(Doctorate/Scholarship)* [7582]

UC MEXUS-CONACYT Doctoral Fellowship *(Doctorate/Fellowship)* [11552]

UNCF Merck Graduate Science Research Dissertation Fellowships *(Graduate/Fellowship)* [7268, 11270]

UNCF/Merck Postdoctoral Science Research Fellowships *(Postdoctorate/Fellowship)* [7269, 11271]

Graduate Fellowship Program - Peter Verhofstadt Fellowships *(Graduate/Fellowship)* [10002]

Physical therapy

The Achieve Physical Therapy & Fitness Scholarship *(Doctorate/Scholarship)* [10841]

APTA Minority Scholarships - Faculty Development Scholarships *(Postdoctorate/Scholarship, Award, Recognition)* [1232]

APTA Minority Scholarships - Physical Therapist Assistant Students *(Undergraduate/Scholarship, Award, Recognition)* [1233]

APTA Minority Scholarships - Physical Therapist Students *(Undergraduate/Scholarship, Award, Recognition)* [1234]

Larry Ashley Memorial Scholarship Award *(Other/Award, Scholarship)* [2127]

David A. Couch Memorial Scholarship *(Undergraduate/Scholarship)* [8839]

Discover Health Professions Loans *(Graduate/Loan, Scholarship)* [4111]

IOKDS Health Careers Scholarship *(College, University, Undergraduate, Graduate, Doctorate/Scholarship)* [6050]

Mariel Lacasse Scholarship *(Undergraduate, University, College, Vocational/Occupational/Scholarship)* [12336]

Margaret Dowell-Gravatt, M.D. Scholarship *(Undergraduate/Scholarship)* [2486]

Michael Moody Fitness Scholarship *(Undergraduate, Graduate/Scholarship)* [7464]

The Shanon Newberry Physical Therapy Scholarship Endowment *(Doctorate/Scholarship)* [10845]

The Physical Therapy Faculty Scholarship Endowment *(Graduate/Scholarship)* [10846]

Everett Oscar Shimp Memorial Scholarships *(Undergraduate/Scholarship)* [8878]

The Sybil Jennings Vorheis Memorial Undergraduate Scholarships (Undergraduate/Scholarship) [4761]

Monica M. Weaver Memorial Fund (Undergraduate/Scholarship) [4606]

Physics

AAPM Graduate Fellowship (Graduate/Fellowship) [620]

Andreas Acrivos Dissertation Award in Fluid Dynamics (Graduate, Doctorate/Award, Recognition, Monetary) [1219]

ACS Rubber Division Undergraduate Scholarship (Undergraduate/Scholarship) [738]

AFCEA War Veterans Scholarships (Undergraduate/Scholarship) [105]

Alaska Aerospace Development Corporation Scholarships (Undergraduate/Scholarship) [11433]

American Institute of Physics Congressional Science Fellowship (Doctorate/Fellowship) [1042]

American Institute of Physics State Department Science Fellowship (Doctorate/Fellowship) [1043]

American Physical Society Minority Undergraduate Scholarships (Undergraduate/Scholarship) [1220]

Michael P. Anderson Scholarships in Space Science (Undergraduate/Scholarship) [8082]

APS Scholarships for Minority Undergraduate Physics Majors (Undergraduate/Scholarship) [1221]

Arthur B.C. Walker II Scholarship (Undergraduate/Scholarship) [8083]

Award for Outstanding Doctoral Dissertation in Laser Science (Doctorate, Postdoctorate/Award) [1222]

Award for Outstanding Doctoral Thesis Research in Biological Physics (Doctorate, Postdoctorate/Award, Recognition, Monetary) [1223]

Charles S. Brown Scholarships in Physics (Graduate, Undergraduate/Scholarship) [8084]

Lieutenant General Douglas D. Buchholz Memorial Scholarship (Undergraduate/Scholarship) [106]

Burroughs Wellcome Fund Collaborative Research Travel Grants (CRTG) (Doctorate, Postdoctorate/Grant) [2750]

Career Awards at the Scientific Interface (CASI) (Undergraduate, Postdoctorate, Graduate/Grant) [2753]

CfA Postdoctoral Fellowship (Postdoctorate/Fellowship) [5357]

Clay Postdoctoral Fellowship (Postdoctorate/Fellowship) [5358]

CNS-UCSB Graduate Fellowships for Science and Engineering (Postdoctorate/Fellowship) [11563]

SRC NRI Hans J. Coufal Fellowships (Graduate/Fellowship) [10004]

D&A Florida Scholarships (Undergraduate/Scholarship) [10678]

DEPS Graduate Scholarship (Graduate/Scholarship) [4099]

Dissertation Award in Hadronic Physics (Doctorate, Postdoctorate/Award, Recognition, Monetary) [1224]

Peggy Dixon Two-Year Scholarships (Undergraduate/Scholarship) [10477]

DOE Computational Science Graduate Fellowship (DOE CSGF) (Doctorate, Graduate/Fellowship) [6611]

DREAM - Diversity Recruitment Recruitment through Education and Mentoring Program (Undergraduate/Fellowship) [621]

Robert A. Ellis Scholarships in Physics (Undergraduate/Scholarship) [8085]

Fermilab Internships for Physics Majors (Undergraduate/Internship) [11315]

Fermilab Science Undergraduate Laboratory Internship (Undergraduate/Internship) [11316]

Fermilab Summer Internships in Science & Technology (SIST) (Undergraduate/Internship) [11317]

Frank Fong Scholarships (Undergraduate/Scholarship) [10267]

Glendale Latino Association Scholarships (Undergraduate/Scholarship) [4999]

Harvey Washington Banks Scholarship in Astronomy (Undergraduate/Scholarship) [8086]

Helm Family Scholarship (Undergraduate/Scholarship) [9819]

Elmer S. Imes Scholarships in Physics (Undergraduate/Scholarship) [8087]

Julian E. Carnes Scholarship Endowment Fund (Undergraduate/Scholarship) [4738]

Leadership Scholarships (Undergraduate/Scholarship) [10478]

Lee Teng Undergraduate Fellowship in Accelerator Science and Engineering (Undergraduate/Fellowship) [11318]

Imelda (Graduate, High School/Scholarship) [3722]

Herbert Levy Memorial Scholarship (Undergraduate/Scholarship) [10479]

Barbara Lotze Scholarships for Future Teachers (Undergraduate/Scholarship) [625]

M. Hildred Blewett Fellowship (Postdoctorate/Fellowship, Award, Monetary) [1225]

Walter Samuel McAfee Scholarships in Space Physics (Undergraduate/Scholarship) [8088]

Ronald E. McNair Scholarships in Space and Optical Physics (Undergraduate/Scholarship) [8089]

Nicholas Metropolis Award for Outstanding Doctoral Thesis Work in Computational Physics (Doctorate, Postdoctorate/Award, Recognition, Monetary) [1226]

Willie Hobbs Moore Scholarships (Undergraduate/Scholarship) [8090]

Harry L. Morrison Scholarships (Undergraduate/Scholarship) [8091]

National GEM Consortium - PhD Science Fellowships (Doctorate, Graduate/Fellowship) [7904]

NDSEG Fellowship (Graduate/Fellowship) [7834]

Northampton County Medical Society Alliance Scholarships (Undergraduate/Scholarship) [8480]

Northrop Grumman Engineering Scholars Program (Undergraduate/Scholarship) [8498]

NPSC Fellowship (Graduate/Fellowship) [5056]

Cecilia Payne-Gaposchkin Doctoral Dissertation Award in Astrophysics (Doctorate, Postdoctorate/Award, Recognition, Monetary) [1227]

Helen Edwards Summer Internship (Undergraduate/Internship) [11319]

Research Internships in Science and Engineering (RISE) (Undergraduate/Internship) [4065]

Richard L. Greene Dissertation Award in Experimental Condensed Matter or Materials Physics (Doctorate, Postdoctorate/Award, Recognition, Monetary) [1228]

Marshall N. Rosenbluth Outstanding Doctoral Thesis Award (Doctorate, Postdoctorate/Award, Recognition, Monetary) [1229]

RSNA/AAPM Graduate Fellowship (Graduate/Fellowship) [622]

SAO Predoctoral Fellowship (Graduate/Fellowship) [5359]

Ralph W. Shrader Diversity Scholarship (Graduate/Scholarship) [107]

Sloan Research Fellowships (Doctorate/Fellowship) [10171]

SPS Future Teacher Scholarships (Undergraduate/Scholarship) [10480]

SPS Leadership Scholarships (Undergraduate/Scholarship) [10481]

Summer Undergraduate Fellowship Program (Undergraduate/Fellowship) [623]

Mitsuyoshi Tanaka Dissertation Award in Experimental Particle Physics (Doctorate, Postdoctorate/Award, Recognition, Monetary) [1230]

TRIUMF Summer Research Award (Undergraduate/Award, Scholarship) [11115]

Graduate Fellowship Program - Peter Verhofstadt Fellowships (Graduate/Fellowship) [10002]

Women In Defense HORIZONS Scholarship (Graduate, Undergraduate/Scholarship) [12133]

Physiology

Benjamin Kaminer Endowed Scholarship in Physiology (Graduate, Doctorate, Master's/Scholarship) [7038]

Bruce and Betty Alberts Endowed Scholarship in Physiology (Undergraduate/Scholarship) [7039]

Dominion of Canada General Insurance Company Graduate Scholarship in Actuarial Science (Graduate, Master's, Doctorate/Scholarship) [11728]

Epilepsy Foundation Pre-doctoral Research Training Fellowships (Graduate/Fellowship) [4423]

Lazaro J. Mandel Young Investigator Award (Advanced Professional/Monetary, Award) [1236]

Martin Frank Diversity Travel Award (Undergraduate, Postdoctorate/Fellowship, Award, Monetary) [1237]

Mountain Memorial Fund (Undergraduate/Award) [7054]

Physiotherapy Foundation of Canada Research Grant (Other/Grant) [3096]

Porter Physiology Development Fellowship (Doctorate/Fellowship, Award, Monetary) [1238]

B.E. Schnurr Memorial Fund Research Grants (Other/Grant) [3097]

STRI Short-Term Fellowships (Undergraduate, Graduate, Postdoctorate/Fellowship) [10226]

Caroline tum Suden/Frances Hellebrandt Professional Opportunity Awards (Postdoctorate, Graduate/Award, Monetary) [1239]

Earl S. Tupper Three-year Postdoctoral Fellowship (Postdoctorate/Fellowship) [10227]

Shih-Chun Wang Young Investigator Award (Advanced Professional/Monetary, Award) [1240]

Ann Collins Whitmore Memorial Scholarship (ACWMS) (Graduate/Scholarship) [3098]

Piano music (See Music, Piano)

Planetary sciences (See Space and planetary sciences)

Plastic surgery

American Association of Plastic Surgeons Academic Scholar Program (Professional development/Scholarship) [627]

Podiatry

Discover Health Professions Loans (Graduate/Loan, Scholarship) [4111]

Discover Residency Loans (Graduate/Loan, Scholarship) [4114]

Zelda Walling Vicha Memorial Scholarship (Undergraduate/Scholarship) [1540]

Poetry

Grants to Artists (Advanced Professional/Grant) [4769]

Ruth Lilly and Dorothy Sargent Rosenberg Poetry Fellowships (Professional development/Fellowship, Prize) [9216]

Polish studies (See also Area and ethnic studies)

Falcon Achievement Scholarships (Undergraduate/Scholarship) [9242]

Harriet Irsay Scholarship (Graduate, Undergraduate/Scholarship) [1045]

Aleksander and Alicja Hertz Memorial Fellowship (Doctorate, Postdoctorate/Fellowship) [12237]

Kosciuszko Foundation Graduate Study and Research in Poland Scholarships (Graduate, Postgraduate/Scholarship) [6601]

Kosciuszko Foundation Year Abroad Scholarships (Graduate, Undergraduate/Scholarship) [6603]

Massachusetts Federation of Polish Women's Clubs Scholarships (Undergraduate/Scholarship) [6604]

Polish American Club of North Jersey Scholarships (Undergraduate/Scholarship) [6605]

Polish National Alliance of Brooklyn, USA Scholarships (Undergraduate/Scholarship) [6606]

Skalny Scholarship for Polish Studies (Undergraduate/Scholarship) [828]

Dr. Marie E. Zakrzewski Medical Scholarships (Doctorate/Scholarship) [6607]

Political science

Harry E. Adrian Memorial Grant (Undergraduate/Scholarship) [1857]

American Enterprise Institute National Research Initiative Fellowships (NRI) *(Professional development/Fellowship)* [872]

American Institute for Economic Research Student Summer Fellowship *(Graduate, Undergraduate/Fellowship)* [1028]

APSA Congressional Fellowships *(Other/Fellowship)* [4945]

APSA Congressional Fellowships for Journalists *(Advanced Professional, Professional development/Fellowship)* [1247]

APSA Congressional Fellowships for Political Scientists *(Advanced Professional, Professional development, Postdoctorate/Fellowship)* [1248]

APSA Fund for Latino Scholarship *(Undergraduate, Graduate/Scholarship)* [1249]

APSA-MCI Communications Congressional Fellowship *(Advanced Professional, Professional development, Postdoctorate/Fellowship)* [1250]

APSA Minority Fellowship Program *(Doctorate/Fellowship)* [1251]

APSA Small Research Grant Program *(Professional development/Grant)* [1252]

APSA U.S. Federal Executives Fellowships *(Advanced Professional, Professional development/Fellowship)* [1253]

ARCE Funded Fellowships *(Doctorate, Postdoctorate/Fellowship)* [1336]

ARCE Research Associates Fellowship *(Doctorate, Postdoctorate, Professional development/Fellowship)* [1337]

ARS Lazarian Graduate Scholarship *(Graduate, Master's, Doctorate/Scholarship)* [1854]

Marguerite Ross Barnett Fund *(Graduate, Postdoctorate, Undergraduate/Grant)* [1254]

Mark A. Beltz Scholarship *(Graduate, Undergraduate/Scholarship)* [11473]

Pat Brakke Political Science Scholarship *(Undergraduate/Scholarship)* [11474]

Burney – Cecil E. Burney Scholarship *(Undergraduate/Scholarship)* [3468]

Ben and Vicky Cayetano Scholarship Fund *(Undergraduate, College, University, Two Year College/Scholarship)* [5389]

CHCI Congressional Internship Program *(Undergraduate/Internship)* [3745]

CIGNA Healthcare Graduate Scholarships *(Graduate/Scholarship)* [7888]

CIGNA Undergraduate Scholarships *(Undergraduate/Scholarship)* [7889]

Helen & Orval Couch Memorial Scholarship *(Undergraduate/Scholarship)* [12302]

D&A Florida Scholarships *(Undergraduate/Scholarship)* [10678]

Denton Scholarship *(Graduate/Scholarship)* [10081]

Douglas-Coldwell Foundation Scholarships in Social Affairs *(Graduate/Scholarship)* [4137]

Enid Hall Griswold Memorial Scholarship *(Undergraduate/Scholarship, Award, Monetary)* [8096]

Enkababian Family and Sarian Family Memorial Grant *(Undergraduate/Scholarship)* [1875]

Governor William A. Egan Award *(Undergraduate/Award)* [11480]

Guzkowski Family Scholarships *(Undergraduate/Scholarship)* [9549]

Harkness Fellowships in Health Care Policy and Practice *(Doctorate, Graduate/Fellowship)* [3555]

Huang Hsing Chun-tu Hsueh Fellowship Fund *(Graduate, Postdoctorate, Undergraduate, Professional development/Grant)* [1256]

John Peters Humphrey Student Fellowships *(Graduate/Fellowship)* [3877]

John Streiff Memorial Scholarship *(Undergraduate/Scholarship)* [6803]

Rita Mae Kelly Fund *(Graduate, Doctorate, Undergraduate, Professional development/Grant)* [1257]

George Keverian Public Service Scholarship *(Undergraduate/Scholarship)* [1891]

The William P. McHugh Memorial Fund *(Doctorate, Graduate/Grant)* [1338]

Warren E. Miller Fund in Electoral Politics *(Advanced Professional, Graduate, Postdoctorate, Undergraduate/Grant)* [1258]

Minorities in Government Finance Scholarship *(Graduate, Undergraduate/Scholarship)* [5054]

MPAC-DC Graduate Policy Fellowships *(Graduate/Fellowship)* [7517]

NARAL Summer Internship Program *(Undergraduate, Graduate, Professional development/Internship)* [7552]

National Endowment for the Humanities Fellowship *(Graduate/Fellowship)* [1339]

National Iranian American Council Fellowships *(Graduate, Undergraduate/Fellowship)* [7956]

Perkins Coie 1L Political Law Diversity Fellowships *(Undergraduate/Fellowship)* [9040]

Pi Gamma Mu Scholarships *(Graduate/Scholarship)* [9160]

The Thomas R. Pickering Foreign Affairs Fellowship *(Graduate, Undergraduate/Fellowship)* [11346, 12050]

Presidency Research Fund *(Graduate, Postdoctorate, Undergraduate, Professional development/Grant)* [1259]

Pride Foundation Political Leadership Scholarships *(Undergraduate/Scholarship)* [9306]

Betty Rendel Scholarships *(Undergraduate/Scholarship)* [7886]

Ameen Rihani Scholarship Program *(Undergraduate/Scholarship)* [1768]

Fauneil J. Rinn Scholarships *(Undergraduate/Scholarship)* [10137]

Charles and Ruth Ronin Memorial Scholarships *(Undergraduate/Scholarship)* [9600]

Sam Bull Memorial Scholarship *(Undergraduate/Scholarship)* [269]

Dr. Brent Slobodin Memorial Scholarship in the Humanities *(Undergraduate, Graduate, University, College/Scholarship)* [12371]

Donald Smiley Prize *(Advanced Professional/Prize, Award, Recognition)* [2111]

Hatton W. Sumners Endowed Undergraduate School Scholarships *(Undergraduate/Scholarship)* [10878]

Hatton W. Sumners Non-Endowed Undergraduate and Graduate Scholarships *(Undergraduate, Graduate/Scholarship)* [10879]

TCAdvance Scholarship *(Undergraduate/Scholarship)* [11144]

Barbara and Howard Thompson Scholarships *(Undergraduate/Scholarship)* [6209]

The United States Department of State, Bureau of Educational & Cultural Affairs Fellowships *(Graduate/Fellowship)* [1340]

Jill Vickers Prize *(Other/Award)* [2112]

Women In Defense HORIZONS Scholarship *(Graduate, Undergraduate/Scholarship)* [12133]

Women & Politics Fund *(Graduate, Postdoctorate, Undergraduate, Professional development/Grant)* [1261]

Urashi Zen Scholarships *(Undergraduate/Scholarship)* [9320]

Portuguese studies (See also Area and ethnic studies)

G-1 Research Project Grants *(Undergraduate/Grant)* [6941]

G-2 Summer Portuguese Language Program *(Undergraduate/Grant)* [6942]

G-3 Summer Program in Portugal *(Postgraduate/Grant)* [6943]

Poultry science

The Canadian Poultry Research Council Postgraduate Scholarship *(Postgraduate/Scholarship)* [3102]

National Poultry and Food Distributors Association Scholarships *(Undergraduate/Scholarship)* [8042]

Practical nursing (See Nursing)

Pre-Columbian studies

Alexander Graham Bell Canada Graduate Scholarships-Doctoral Program *(Doctorate, Master's/Scholarship)* [3803]

Dumbarton Oaks Fellowship *(Doctorate, Graduate/Fellowship)* [4222]

Dumbarton Oaks Junior Fellowship *(Graduate/Fellowship)* [4223]

Dumbarton Oaks Research Library and Collection Post-Doctoral Teaching Fellowships *(Postdoctorate/Fellowship)* [4232]

NSERC Postgraduate Scholarships-Doctoral Program *(Doctorate/Scholarship)* [3806]

Preservation

Smithsonian Postgraduate/Postdoctoral Fellowships in Conservation of Museum Collections *(Postgraduate, Postdoctorate/Fellowship)* [10212]

SPOOM Research Grants *(Graduate/Grant)* [10500]

Printing trades and industries

Alcoa Scholarship *(Undergraduate, Graduate/Scholarship)* [5207]

The Cerutti Group Scholarship *(Undergraduate/Scholarship)* [5208]

FIRST Operator Certification Awards *(Professional development/Internship)* [4618]

Robert "Bob" Strahan Memorial Scholarship *(Undergraduate, Graduate/Scholarship)* [5210]

TCAdvance Scholarship *(Undergraduate/Scholarship)* [11144]

Werner B. Thiele Memorial Scholarship *(Graduate, Undergraduate/Scholarship)* [5211]

Printing--History

The Katharine Pantzer Fellowship in the British Book Trades *(Other/Fellowship)* [2567]

Printmaking

Harry V. Quadracci Memorial Scholarship *(Undergraduate, Graduate/Scholarship)* [5209]

Psychiatry

ADHD Fellowship *(Postdoctorate/Fellowship)* [6568]

Associates in Behavioral Health Scholarships *(Graduate/Scholarship)* [9290]

Daland Fellowships in Clinical Investigation *(Doctorate, Postgraduate/Fellowship)* [1212]

Epilepsy Foundation Research and Training Fellowships for Clinicians *(Doctorate, Other/Grant)* [4425]

Clinical Translational Fellowship at Pfizer *(Advanced Professional/Fellowship)* [7134]

MGH Department of Psychiatry Behavioral Neurology and Neuropsychiatry Fellowship Program *(Advanced Professional, Professional development/Fellowship)* [7136]

Eating Disorders Summer Research Fellowship *(Advanced Professional, Professional development/Fellowship)* [7137]

MGH Department of Psychiatry Forensic Psychiatry Fellowship *(Professional development/Fellowship)* [7138]

MGH Department of Psychiatry Global Psychiatric Clinical Research Training Program *(Advanced Professional/Fellowship)* [7139]

Partners HealthCare Geriatric Psychiatry Fellowship *(Professional development/Fellowship)* [7140]

SOBP Travel Fellowship Award-Early Career Investigator-International *(Postdoctorate/Fellowship)* [10283]

Psychology

AED Student/Early Career Investigator Travel Fellowship Program *(Postgraduate/Fellowship)* [43]

AED Student Research Grants *(Undergraduate, Graduate, Postgraduate/Grant)* [44]

American Psychology-Law Society Dissertation Awards *(Graduate/Award)* [1291]

American Psychology-Law Society Student Grants-In-Aid *(Graduate/Grant)* [1292]

Annette Urso Rickel Foundation Dissertation Award for Public Policy *(Graduate/Scholarship)* [1273]

APA Division 39 Scholars Program *(Graduate/Scholarship)* [1734]

APA Society Convention Research Awards (Undergraduate, Graduate/Award) [9375]

APA 125th Anniversary Scholarship (Doctorate, Graduate/Scholarship) [1274]

APF High School Psychology Outreach Grants (Advanced Professional, Professional development/Grant) [1275]

APF Professional Development Awards for High School Psychology Teachers (Advanced Professional, Professional development/Grant) [1276]

APF Visionary Grants (Graduate/Grant) [1277]

Applied Behavior Analysis EDU $1,000 Excellence in Practice Scholarship (Graduate/Scholarship) [1760]

Applied Social Issues Internship Program (Undergraduate, Graduate, Doctorate/Internship) [10508]

APS Convention Society Research Awards (Undergraduate, Graduate/Award) [9376]

APS Student Research Award (APS) (Undergraduate, Graduate/Award) [2266]

APsaA Fellowship (Doctorate, Postdoctorate/Fellowship) [1265]

Army Health Professions Scholarship Program (HPSP) (Professional development/Scholarship) [11288]

ASA Minority Fellowship Program (ASA MFP) (Doctorate/Fellowship) [1590]

Associates in Behavioral Health Scholarships (Graduate/Scholarship) [9290]

Association for Psychological Science Student Grants (APS) (Graduate, Undergraduate/Grant) [2267]

Dr. Jon Baker Memorial Scholarship (Other/Scholarship) [11471]

Jan S. Bashinski Criminalistics Graduate Thesis Assistance Grant (Graduate/Grant) [4676]

Raymond B. Bauer Research Award (Professional development/Award, Grant) [7322]

Benton-Meier Scholarships (Graduate/Scholarship) [1278]

William and Dorothy Bevan Scholarship (Graduate, Master's, Doctorate/Scholarship) [1279]

Bisexual Foundation Scholarships (Graduate/Scholarship, Award) [1736]

Ellin Bloch and Pierre Ritchie Diversity Dissertation Grant (Graduate/Grant) [1269]

Charles and Carol Spielberger Scholarship (Graduate, Master's, Doctorate/Scholarship) [1280]

Child Welfare and Development (CWD) Scholarship (Undergraduate/Scholarship) [4489]

CPA-F Scholarship (Graduate/Scholarship) [2824]

Diversity in Psychology and Law Research Award (Undergraduate, Graduate/Grant, Award) [1293]

Early Childhood Educators Scholarship Program (Undergraduate/Scholarship) [7158]

Elizabeth Munsterberg Koppitz Child Psychology Graduate Student Fellowship (Graduate/Fellowship) [1281]

Epilepsy Foundation Pre-doctoral Research Training Fellowships (Graduate/Fellowship) [4423]

ETS Postdoctoral Fellowships (Postdoctorate/Fellowship) [4311]

Nancy B. Forest and L. Michael Honaker Master's Grant for Research in Psychology (Graduate/Grant) [1270]

Violet and Cyril Franks Scholarship (Graduate/Scholarship) [1282]

The Gordon Allport Intergroup Relations Prize (Professional development/Monetary, Prize) [10509]

Grant Assistance Program for Autism Professionals - College Programs (Undergraduate/Grant) [8652]

Grant Assistance Program for Autism Professionals - Doctoral Programs (Doctorate/Grant) [8653]

Grant Assistance Program for Autism Professionals - Institutional Standards (Undergraduate, Graduate/Grant) [8654]

Grant Assistance Program for Autism Professionals - Masters Programs (Master's/Grant) [8655]

Grant Assistance Program for Autism Professionals - Professional Certification Programs (Undergraduate, Professional development/Grant) [8656]

Grant Assistance Program for Autism Professionals - Retroactive Assistance (Advanced Professional, Professional development/Grant) [8657]

Grant Assistance Program for Autism Professionals - Undergraduate Programs (Undergraduate/Grant) [8658]

Grants in Aid for Early Career Professionals (Graduate/Grant) [1294]

Lee Hakel Graduate Student Scholarship (Graduate/Scholarship) [10334]

Harold Gulliksen Psychometric Research Fellowship (Doctorate, Graduate/Fellowship) [4312]

Paul E. Henkin School Psychology Travel Grant (Doctorate/Grant) [1730]

William C. Howell Scholarship (Graduate, Master's, Doctorate/Scholarship) [1283]

Janet Hyde Graduate Student Research Grant (Doctorate, Graduate/Grant) [1732]

Leslie W. Joyce and Paul W. Thayer Graduate Fellowship in I-O Psychology (Graduate/Fellowship) [10335]

Chris L. Kleinke Scholarship (Graduate/Scholarship) [11483]

Harry and Miriam Levinson Scholarship (Graduate, Master's, Doctorate/Scholarship) [1284]

Malyon Smith Scholarship Research Award (Graduate/Scholarship) [1737]

Massachusetts General Hospital/Harvard Medical School Internship (Doctorate/Internship) [7135]

Ruth G. and Joseph D. Matarazzo Scholarship (Graduate, Master's, Doctorate/Scholarship) [1285]

The Clara Mayo Grants (Graduate/Grant) [10510]

Meredith P. Crawford Fellowship in I-O Psychology (Doctorate/Fellowship) [5626]

NAJA Scholarship (Graduate/Scholarship) [7664]

NASP-ERT Minority Scholarship Program (Graduate/Scholarship) [7686]

NJPA Foundation Scholarship for Research on Diversity Issues (Graduate/Scholarship) [8285]

Peter and Malina James and Dr. Louis P. James Legacy Scholarship (Graduate, Master's, Doctorate/Scholarship) [1286]

Pi Gamma Mu Scholarships (Graduate/Scholarship) [9160]

David Pilon Scholarships for Training in Professional Psychology (Graduate/Scholarship) [1271]

Wayne F. Placek Grants (Graduate, Doctorate/Grant) [1287]

PLP Scholarships (Undergraduate/Scholarship, Award, Monetary) [8985]

Psychology Association of Saskatchewan Student Scholarships - Academic Achievement (Master's, Doctorate/Scholarship) [9378]

Psychology Association of Saskatchewan Student Scholarships - Research Based (Master's, Doctorate/Scholarship) [9379]

Clarence J. Rosecrans Scholarship (Graduate, Master's, Doctorate/Scholarship) [1288]

Esther Katz Rosen Fund Grants (Graduate/Grant) [1289]

Saleem Shah Early Career Award (Doctorate/Recognition) [1295]

SPA/Lemelson Fellowship Program (Graduate/Award) [10506]

SPSSI Grants-In-Aid Program (Graduate, Postdoctorate/Grant) [10511]

SSCP Dissertation Grant Award (Graduate/Grant) [10524]

Taylor Statten Memorial Fellowships (Graduate/Scholarship) [11698]

Sylvia Taylor Johnson Minority Fellowships in Educational Measurement (Doctorate/Fellowship) [4313]

Tara Lynne Arnold Scholarship Fund (Undergraduate/Scholarship) [10834]

Mary L. Tenopyr Graduate Student Scholarship (Graduate/Scholarship) [10336]

Harry and Pola Triandis Doctoral Thesis Award (Doctorate/Grant) [5911]

The Virtuous Prom Peace Scholarship (Undergraduate, Graduate, Postgraduate/Scholarship) [11852]

Public administration

Marvin A. Andrews Scholarships/Internships (Graduate, Undergraduate/Internship, Scholarship) [1805]

APSA-MCI Communications Congressional Fellowship (Advanced Professional, Professional development, Postdoctorate/Fellowship) [1250]

Erin J.C. Arsenault Fellowships in Space Governance (Graduate/Fellowship) [7188]

Association of Government Accountants Graduate Scholarships for Community Service (Graduate/Scholarship) [2187]

Association of Government Accountants Graduate Scholarships for Full-time study (Graduate/Scholarship) [2188]

Association of Government Accountants Graduate Scholarships for Part-time study (Graduate/Scholarship) [2189]

James M. Banovetz Illinois Local Government Fellowships (Graduate, Undergraduate/Fellowship) [5698]

Marguerite Ross Barnett Fund (Graduate, Postdoctorate, Undergraduate/Grant) [1254]

CHCI Graduate Fellowship Program (Graduate, Professional development/Fellowship) [3746]

CHCI Public Policy Fellowships (Professional development/Fellowship) [3747]

The Christine Mirzayan Science & Technology Policy Graduate Fellowship Program (Graduate, Postdoctorate, High School/Fellowship) [7571]

CIGNA Healthcare Graduate Scholarships (Graduate/Scholarship) [7888]

CIGNA Undergraduate Scholarships (Undergraduate/Scholarship) [7889]

Dr. Julianne Malveaux Scholarship (Undergraduate/Scholarship) [7668]

Charles A. Esser Memorial Scholarships (Graduate/Scholarship) [1806]

Fellowship on Women & Public Policy (Graduate/Fellowship) [11522]

GLAAD Communications/PR Internships - New York (Undergraduate, Graduate/Internship) [4983]

Jane R. Glaser Scholarship (Undergraduate/Scholarship) [1626]

Goya Scholarships (Graduate/Scholarship) [10028]

Guzkowski Family Scholarships (Undergraduate/Scholarship) [9549]

HAESF Professional Internship Program (Doctorate/Internship) [5645]

Graduate Study Fellowship (Professional development/Fellowship) [6065]

Kathleen Kelly Undergraduate Scholarship (Undergraduate/Scholarship) [9434]

Michael Koizumi APWA Internship Scholarship (Undergraduate/Scholarship, Internship) [1308]

Minorities in Government Finance Scholarship (Graduate, Undergraduate/Scholarship) [5054]

George H. Nofer Scholarship for Law and Public Policy (Graduate/Scholarship, Monetary) [334]

Pi Gamma Mu Scholarships (Graduate/Scholarship) [9160]

The Thomas R. Pickering Foreign Affairs Fellowship (Graduate, Undergraduate/Fellowship) [11346, 12050]

Stephen D. Pisinski Memorial Scholarship (Undergraduate/Scholarship) [9436]

Pride Foundation Political Leadership Scholarships (Undergraduate/Scholarship) [9306]

Fauneil J. Rinn Scholarships (Undergraduate/Scholarship) [10137]

Herbert Roback Scholarship (Graduate, Master's/Scholarship) [7579]

Senior Leaders & Scholars Fellowship (Other, Professional development/Fellowship) [5646]

Thomas J. Stanton, Jr. Scholarships (Graduate/Scholarship) [10029]

Paul A. Volcker Fund (Undergraduate, Graduate, Doctorate, Professional development/Grant) [1260]

Washington City/County Management Association Scholarships (Graduate/Scholarship) [11885]

Gary Yoshimura Scholarship (Undergraduate/Scholarship) [9439]

Public affairs

Americans for Informed Democracy Global Scholar Program (Undergraduate/Scholarship) [1687]

Atkinson Fellowships in Public Policy (Professional development/Fellowship) [2338]

Elaine Atwood Scholarship *(Undergraduate, Graduate/Scholarship)* [11470]

Bryce Harlow Fellowship *(Graduate/Fellowship)* [5298]

Cleveland Executive Fellowships (CEF) *(Other/Fellowship)* [3434]

Jennifer Curtis Byler Scholarship *(Undergraduate/Scholarship)* [8133]

MPAC-DC Graduate Policy Fellowships *(Graduate/Fellowship)* [7517]

Open Society Presidential Fellowship *(Graduate/Fellowship)* [8665]

Clifford Roberts Graduate Fellowships *(Doctorate/Fellowship)* [4963]

William C. Rogers Scholarship *(Undergraduate/Scholarship)* [4937]

Stanley M. Schoenfeld Memorial Scholarship *(Postgraduate/Scholarship)* [8321]

TCAdvance Scholarship *(Undergraduate/Scholarship)* [11144]

Theodore C. Sorensen Research Fellowship *(Other/Fellowship)* [6533]

UAA GCI Scholarship *(Undergraduate/Scholarship)* [11502]

Public health

AAHD Scholarships *(Graduate, Undergraduate/Scholarship)* [568]

AAI Public Policy Fellows Program (PPFP) *(Doctorate, Postdoctorate/Fellowship)* [573]

ALA Allergic Respiratory Diseases Research Award *(Doctorate/Award)* [1093]

American Lung Association Clinical Patient Care Research Grants (CG) *(Doctorate/Grant)* [1095]

American Lung Association Dalsemer Research Grants (DA) *(Doctorate/Grant)* [1096]

American Lung Association DeSousa Awards *(Postgraduate/Award)* [1097]

American Lung Association Senior Research Training Fellowships (RT) *(Doctorate/Fellowship)* [1098]

American Lung Association Social-Behavioral Research Grants (SB) *(Doctorate/Grant)* [1099]

APHA Student Scholarship *(Undergraduate, Graduate/Scholarship)* [1834]

APHL-CDC Infectious Diseases Laboratory Fellowship *(Doctorate/Fellowship)* [2269]

ASPPH/CDC Public Health Fellowship Program *(Doctorate, Graduate/Fellowship)* [2279]

ASPPH/EPA Environmental Health Fellowship Program *(Doctorate, Postdoctorate/Fellowship)* [2280]

ASPPH/NHTSA Public Health Fellowship Program *(Doctorate, Master's/Fellowship)* [2281]

ASPPH Public Health Fellowship Program *(Doctorate, Postdoctorate/Fellowship)* [2282]

ASPPH Public Health Preparedness Fellowship Program *(Postdoctorate/Fellowship)* [2283]

AWMA Louisiana Section Scholarship *(Undergraduate, Graduate/Scholarship)* [167]

Max Bell Senior Fellow Grants *(Advanced Professional/Grant)* [2469]

CANFIT Nutrition, Physical Education and Culinary Arts Scholarships *(Graduate, Undergraduate/Scholarship)* [3561]

Catherine E. Philbin Scholarship *(Undergraduate, Graduate/Scholarship)* [4898]

Malcolm U. Dantzler Scholarships *(Graduate/Scholarship)* [10611]

Frank L. Dautriel Memorial Scholarships for Graduates *(Graduate/Scholarship)* [6900]

Frank L. Dautriel Memorial Scholarships for Undergraduates *(Undergraduate/Scholarship)* [6901]

Elizabeth and Sherman Asche Memorial Scholarship *(Graduate, Undergraduate/Scholarship)* [2038]

Fahs-Beck Fund for Research and Experimentation - Doctoral Dissertation Grants *(Doctorate/Grant)* [8303]

Fahs-Beck Fund for Research and Experimentation - Postdoctoral Grants *(Postdoctorate/Grant)* [8304]

Florida Public Health Association Public Health Graduate Scholarships *(Graduate, Undergraduate/Scholarship)* [4648]

Florida Public Health Association Public Health Undergraduate Scholarships *(Undergraduate/Scholarship)* [4649]

The Gates Millennium Scholars *(Undergraduate/Scholarship)* [5529]

Great Lakes Commission Sea Grant Fellowship *(Graduate/Grant, Fellowship)* [5218]

GWS Scholarship Program *(Undergraduate, Graduate/Scholarship)* [165]

HAESF Professional Internship Program *(Doctorate/Internship)* [5645]

HRSA Scholarships for Disadvantaged Students *(Undergraduate/Scholarship)* [11334]

Institute for Health Metrics and Evaluation Post Bachelor Fellowship (PBF) *(Graduate/Fellowship)* [5821]

Institute for Health Metrics and Evaluation Post Graduate Fellowships (PGF) *(Doctorate, Postdoctorate/Fellowship)* [5822]

Jewish Federation Academic Scholarship *(Graduate, Undergraduate/Scholarship)* [6310]

Johns Hopkins Medicine International Emergency and Public Health Fellowships *(Graduate, Professional development/Fellowship)* [6319]

LPHA Scholarships *(Graduate, Undergraduate/Scholarship)* [6906]

Lung Cancer Discovery Award (LCD) *(Doctorate/Award)* [1100]

Lung Health Dissertation Grants (LH) *(Doctorate/Grant)* [1101]

National Biosafety and Biocontainment Training Program Fellowships *(Graduate, Postgraduate/Fellowship)* [7716]

PhRMA Foundation Health Outcomes Pre Doctoral Fellowships *(Doctorate/Fellowship)* [9063]

PhRMA Foundation Health Outcomes Research Starter Grants *(Doctorate/Grant)* [9064]

PhRMA Foundation Health Outcomes Sabbatical Fellowships *(Postdoctorate, Master's/Fellowship)* [9065]

PhRMA Foundation Post Doctoral Health Outcomes Fellowships *(Postdoctorate/Fellowship)* [9071]

ASPPH/CDC Allan Rosenfield Global Health Fellowship Program *(Postdoctorate, Postgraduate/Fellowship)* [2284]

Lucille and Edward R. Roybal Foundation Public Health Scholarships *(Graduate, Undergraduate/Scholarship)* [9753]

South Carolina Public Health Association Scholarships *(Professional development/Scholarship, Monetary)* [10612]

Louis Stokes Health Scholars Program *(Undergraduate/Scholarship)* [3742]

UAB Health Policy Fellowship *(Graduate, Master's, Doctorate/Scholarship)* [11430]

UAB Lister Hill Center Intramural Grant Program *(Professional development, Postdoctorate/Grant)* [11431]

Vivian Drenckhahn Student Scholarship *(Undergraduate, Graduate/Scholarship)* [10516]

Public relations (See also Advertising)

Ann Liguori Foundation Sports Media Scholarship *(Graduate, Undergraduate/Scholarship)* [8366]

AWSM Public Relations Scholarship/Internships *(/Scholarship, Internship)* [2323]

CCAE Ontario Regional Chapter Scholarship *(Advanced Professional, Professional development/Scholarship)* [6742]

Evoke Strategy Writing Scholarship *(Undergraduate/Scholarship)* [4459]

GLAAD Spanish-Language and Latino Media Internships - Los Angeles *(Undergraduate, Graduate/Internship)* [4984]

Harriet Irsay Scholarship *(Graduate, Undergraduate/Scholarship)* [1045]

International Foodservice Editorial Council Scholarship *(Graduate/Scholarship)* [6007]

IPR Pathfinder Award *(Postgraduate/Recognition)* [5857]

Ketchum Excellence in Public Relations Research Award *(Graduate/Fellowship, Internship)* [5858]

Jessica King Scholarships *(Other/Scholarship)* [3938]

The Lagrant Foundation - Graduate Scholarships *(Graduate/Scholarship)* [6632]

The Lagrant Foundation - Undergraduate Scholarships *(Undergraduate/Scholarship)* [6633]

Louis M. Connor, Jr. Scholarship *(Undergraduate/Scholarship)* [11194]

Makovsky Best Master's Thesis of the Year Award *(Master's/Award)* [5859]

Stephen D. Pisinski Memorial Scholarship *(Undergraduate/Scholarship)* [9436]

Betsy Plank/PRSSA Scholarships *(Undergraduate/Scholarship)* [9437]

PRSA Diversity Multicultural Scholarships *(Undergraduate/Scholarship)* [9438]

Richard J. Roth Journalism Fellowship *(Graduate/Fellowship)* [8328]

Rick Brewer Scholarship *(Undergraduate/Scholarship)* [11207]

William C. Rogers Scholarship *(Undergraduate/Scholarship)* [4937]

Springer - Jim Springer Memorial Scholarship *(Undergraduate/Scholarship)* [3489]

Jay A. Strassberg Memorial Scholarship *(Undergraduate/Scholarship)* [2855]

TCAdvance Scholarship *(Undergraduate/Scholarship)* [11144]

Torchia Scholarship in Public Relations *(Undergraduate/Scholarship)* [3104]

Gary Yoshimura Scholarship *(Undergraduate/Scholarship)* [9439]

Public service

ARS Lazarian Graduate Scholarship *(Graduate, Master's, Doctorate/Scholarship)* [1854]

CAPAL Public Service Scholarships *(Graduate, Undergraduate/Scholarship)* [3734]

CHCI Graduate Fellowship Program *(Graduate, Professional development/Fellowship)* [3746]

CHCI Public Policy Fellowships *(Professional development/Fellowship)* [3747]

Johnnie L. Cochran, Jr./MWH Scholarships *(Graduate, Undergraduate/Scholarship)* [7890]

Community Project Grants *(Other/Grant)* [8261]

Alice Yuriko Endo Memorial Scholarship *(Undergraduate/Scholarship)* [6245]

James Mackenzie Fallows Scholarships Honoring William Cunningham *(Undergraduate/Scholarship)* [9544]

Walter Moran Farmer Scholarships *(Juris Doctorate/Scholarship)* [11922]

IGS John Gardner Fellowship *(Undergraduate/Fellowship)* [11537]

Caroline and Martin Gross Fellowship *(Professional development/Fellowship)* [8256]

Harry S. Truman Scholarships *(Undergraduate, Graduate/Scholarship)* [11129]

Idaho Governor's Cup Scholarship *(Undergraduate/Scholarship)* [6799]

WLALA Fran Kandel Public Interest Grants *(Postgraduate/Grant)* [12143]

George Keverian Public Service Scholarship *(Undergraduate/Scholarship)* [1891]

Master of Public Administratation Fellowship *(Graduate, Postgraduate, Other/Fellowship)* [8152]

Al Maurer Awards *(Undergraduate, Graduate, Advanced Professional/Scholarship)* [4292]

NFBPA Future Colleagues Scholarships *(Undergraduate/Scholarship)* [7891]

NFBPA Land-Use Planning Scholarships *(Master's, Doctorate/Scholarship)* [7892]

Pignalberi Public Policy Scholarship *(Graduate/Scholarship)* [11489]

PSAC National Member Scholarship *(Postgraduate/Scholarship, Monetary)* [9446]

Richard A. Wiebe Public Service Fellowship *(Graduate/Fellowship)* [8327]

The Rotary Club of Charlotte Public Safety Scholarship Fund *(Undergraduate/Scholarship)* [4752]

Sheila Tarr-Smith Memorial Scholarship *(Undergraduate/Scholarship)* [9422]

The Donald A. Strauss Scholarship *(Undergraduate/Scholarship)* [11532]

UAA College of Business and Public Policy Scholarships - American Marketing Association & F.X. Dale Tran Memorial Scholarship (Graduate, Undergraduate/Scholarship) [11499]

Undergraduate Session Assistants Program (Undergraduate/Other) [8329]

Webster Society Scholarships (Juris Doctorate, Undergraduate/Scholarship) [11925]

Willie T. Loud scholarship (Undergraduate, Graduate/Scholarship) [7894]

Willis W. and Ethel M. Clark Foundation Investment in Community Fellowship (Graduate/Fellowship) [3432]

Publishing

Alcoa Scholarship (Undergraduate, Graduate/Scholarship) [5207]

The Cerutti Group Scholarship (Undergraduate/Scholarship) [5208]

Malcolm and Mildred Freiberg Fellowships (Professional development/Fellowship) [7143]

Durwood McAlister Scholarship (Undergraduate/Scholarship) [4935]

Morris Newspaper Corporation Scholarship (Undergraduate/Scholarship) [4936]

PHSC Publication Grant (Professional development/Grant) [9139]

PHSC Research Grant (Professional development/Grant) [9140]

Harry V. Quadracci Memorial Scholarship (Undergraduate, Graduate/Scholarship) [5209]

Robert "Bob" Strahan Memorial Scholarship (Undergraduate, Graduate/Scholarship) [5210]

Werner B. Thiele Memorial Scholarship (Graduate, Undergraduate/Scholarship) [5211]

Wyeth Foundation For American Art Publication Grant (Other/Grant) [3504]

Pulmonary medicine (See Medicine, Pulmonary)

Puppetry

UNIMA-USA Scholarship (Professional development/Scholarship) [11239]

Quality assurance and control

Richard A. Freund International Scholarships (Graduate/Scholarship, Award, Monetary) [1542]

Ellis R. Ott Scholarships (Graduate, Master's/Scholarship) [1543]

Radio and television

Allison E. Fisher Scholarship (Undergraduate, Graduate/Scholarship) [7615]

American Radio Relay League Louisiana Memorial Scholarships (Undergraduate/Scholarship) [1924]

Earl I. Anderson Scholarships (Undergraduate/Scholarship) [1925]

The ARRL General Fund Scholarship (Undergraduate/Scholarship) [1926]

The Ernest L. Baulch, W2TX, and Marcia E. Baulch, WA2AKJ, Scholarship (Undergraduate/Scholarship) [1927]

The Richard W. Bendicksen, N7ZL, Memorial Scholarship (Undergraduate/Scholarship) [1928]

The William Bennett, W7PHO, Memorial Scholarship (Undergraduate/Scholarship) [1929]

The Henry Broughton, K2AE, Memorial Scholarship (Undergraduate/Scholarship) [1930]

The Mary Lou Brown Scholarship (Undergraduate/Scholarship) [1931]

Ben and Vicky Cayetano Scholarship Fund (Undergraduate, College, University, Two Year College/Scholarship) [5389]

The Central Arizona DX Association Scholarship (Undergraduate/Scholarship) [1932]

The Challenge Met Scholarship (Undergraduate/Scholarship) [1933]

The Chicago FM Club Scholarship (Undergraduate/Scholarship) [1934]

The Tom and Judith Comstock Scholarship (Undergraduate/Scholarship) [1935]

The Irving W. Cook WA0CGS Scholarship (Undergraduate/Scholarship) [1936]

The Charles Clarke Cordle Memorial Scholarship (Undergraduate/Scholarship) [1937]

The Dayton Amateur Radio Association Scholarship (Undergraduate/Scholarship) [1938]

The Charles N. Fisher Memorial Scholarship (Undergraduate/Scholarship) [1939]

William R. Goldfarb Memorial Scholarships (Undergraduate/Scholarship) [1940]

The Paul and Helen L. Grauer Scholarships (Undergraduate/Scholarship) [1941]

The K2TEO Martin J. Green, Sr. Memorial Scholarship (Undergraduate/Scholarship) [1942]

Greg Clerk Award (Advanced Professional, Professional development/Award) [6621]

Perry F. Hadlock Memorial Scholarships (Undergraduate/Scholarship) [1943]

The Albert H. Hix, W8AH, Memorial Scholarship (Undergraduate/Scholarship) [1944]

Seth Horen, K1LOM Memorial Scholarships (Undergraduate/Scholarship) [1945]

IRARC Memorial, Joseph P. Rubino, WA4MMD, Scholarship (Undergraduate/Scholarship) [1946]

Ken Kashiwahara Scholarships (Undergraduate/Scholarship) [9466]

The Dr. James L. Lawson Memorial Scholarship (Undergraduate/Scholarship) [1947]

The Fred R. McDaniel Memorial Scholarship (Undergraduate/Scholarship) [1948]

The Edmond A. Metzger Scholarship (Undergraduate/Scholarship) [1949]

The Mississippi Scholarship (Undergraduate/Scholarship) [1950]

Muddy Waters Scholarships (Undergraduate, Graduate/Scholarship) [2632]

The New England FEMARA Scholarship (Undergraduate/Scholarship) [1951]

Northern California DX Foundation Scholarships (Undergraduate/Scholarship) [1952]

OAS Scholarships for Professional Development - Radio Spectrum Monitoring Techniques and Procedures (Professional development/Scholarship) [8733]

The Peoria Area Amateur Radio Club Scholarship (Undergraduate/Scholarship) [1953]

The PHD Scholarship (Undergraduate/Scholarship) [1954]

The Thomas W. Porter, W8KYZ, Scholarship Honoring Michael Daugherty, W8LSE (Undergraduate/Scholarship) [1955]

Quarter Century Wireless Association Scholarship Program (Undergraduate/Scholarship) [9457]

The Ray, NØRP, & Katie, WØKTE, Pautz Scholarship (Undergraduate/Scholarship) [1956]

The Don Riebhoff Memorial Scholarship (Undergraduate/Scholarship) [1957]

RTDNF Scholarships (Undergraduate/Scholarship) [9480]

The Bill, W2ONV, and Ann Salerno Memorial Scholarship (Undergraduate/Scholarship) [1958]

The Eugene "Gene" Sallee, W4YFR, Memorial Scholarship (Undergraduate, Graduate/Scholarship) [1959]

Abe Schechter Graduate Scholarships (Graduate/Scholarship) [9467]

The Scholarship of the Morris Radio Club of New Jersey (Undergraduate/Scholarship) [1960]

The Six Meter Club of Chicago Scholarship (Undergraduate/Scholarship) [1961]

The Zachary Taylor Stevens Scholarship (Undergraduate/Scholarship) [1962]

The Carole J. Streeter, KB9JBR, Scholarship (Undergraduate/Scholarship) [1963]

The Norman E. Strohmeier, W2VRS, Memorial Scholarship (Undergraduate/Scholarship) [1964]

The Gary Wagner, K3OMI, Scholarship (Undergraduate/Scholarship) [1965]

The L. Phil and Alice J. Wicker Scholarship (Undergraduate/Scholarship) [1966]

Yankee Clipper Contest Club Youth Scholarship (Undergraduate/Scholarship) [1967]

The YASME Foundation Scholarship (Undergraduate/Scholarship) [1968]

Radiology

Anna B. Ames Clinical Excellence Student Grant (Undergraduate/Grant) [2835]

Fay Anthony Scholarship (Undergraduate, College, University, Vocational/Occupational/Scholarship) [12283]

ARRS/ASNR Scholarship in Neuroradiology (Advanced Professional/Scholarship) [1364, 1529]

ARS Young Oncologist Travel Grants (Professional development/Grant) [1314]

ASRT Research Grants (Professional development/Grant) [1550]

Burton J. Moyer Memorial Fellowship (Graduate, Undergraduate/Fellowship) [5428]

Heidi Patriquin Award for International Education (Advanced Professional, Professional development/Fellowship) [10465]

Intermountain Medical Imaging Scholarship (Undergraduate, Community College/Scholarship) [5892]

J. Newell Stannard Fellowship (Graduate, Undergraduate/Fellowship) [5429]

Jerman-Cahoon Student Scholarship (Undergraduate/Scholarship) [1551]

Robert S. Landauer, Sr. Memorial Fellowship (Graduate, Undergraduate/Fellowship) [5430]

Royce Osborn Minority Scholarship (Undergraduate/Scholarship) [1552]

R&E Foundation Education Scholar Grant (Graduate, Other/Scholarship) [9482]

Research Resident/Fellow Grant (Professional development/Grant) [9483]

Richard J. Burk, Jr., Fellowship (Graduate, Undergraduate/Fellowship) [5431]

Robert Gardner Memorial Fellowship (Graduate, Undergraduate/Fellowship) [5432]

RSNA/AUR/APDR/SCARD Radiology Education Research Development Grant (Professional development/Grant) [9484]

RSNA Education Scholar Grant (Professional development/Grant) [9485]

Research Scholar Grant (Professional development/Grant) [9486]

RSNA Research Seed Grant (Professional development/Grant) [9487]

Ruth McMillan Academic Excellence Student Scholarship (Undergraduate, Four Year College, Two Year College/Grant) [2836]

Siemens Clinical Advancement Scholarship (Master's, Doctorate, Professional development/Scholarship) [1553]

Society for Pediatric Radiology Research Fellows (Graduate, Other/Fellowship) [10466]

Society for Pediatric Radiology Seed Grants (Graduate, Other/Grant) [10467]

Superior District Legislative Mentoring Student Grants (Undergraduate/Grant) [2837]

Superior District Legislative Mentoring Student Grants RT to DC (Undergraduate/Grant) [2838]

Ultrsound Schools Info Student Scholarship (Two Year College, Undergraduate/Scholarship) [11171]

Vancouver Yukoners Legacy Scholarship (Vocational/Occupational, College, Undergraduate/Scholarship) [12381]

Varian Radiation Therapy Advancement Scholarship (Master's, Doctorate, Professional development/Scholarship) [1554]

Reading

Cengage Travel Award for Teachers of Reading at a Community College (Professional development/Monetary) [3512]

Jeanne S. Chall Research Fellowship (Doctorate, Graduate/Fellowship, Grant) [6033]

Elva Knight Research Grant (Professional development, Graduate/Grant, Award) [6034]

Malcolm and Mildred Freiberg Fellowships (Professional development/Fellowship) [7143]

ILA Teacher as Researcher Grant (Professional development/Grant) [6035]

Nila Banton Smith Research Dissemination Support Grant (Professional development/Grant) [6036]

Helen M. Robinson Grants (Doctorate/Grant) [6037]

Steven A. Stahl Research Grant (Graduate/Grant, Award) [6039]

Real estate

AIERF Undergraduate Scholarship *(Undergraduate/ Scholarship)* [1764]

George M. Brooker, CPM Diversity Collegiate Scholarship *(Graduate, Undergraduate/Scholarship)* [5861]

Charles Grossman Graduate Scholarship *(Graduate/Scholarship)* [5978]

Connecticut Mortgage Bankers Social Affairs Fund *(Undergraduate/Scholarship)* [5321]

Rick Crane Group Real Estate Scholarship Fund *(Undergraduate/Scholarship)* [6786]

Downtown Apartment Companys Scholarship Program *(Undergraduate/Scholarship)* [4144]

Donald M. Furbush Professional Development Grants *(Other/Grant)* [5862]

Graduate Realtor Institute Scholarships *(Graduate/ Scholarship)* [6537]

Mary Lou Fiala Fellowship *(Graduate/Fellowship)* [5980]

Michigan Realtors Scholarship Trust *(Graduate, Undergraduate/Scholarship)* [7324]

PREA Scholarship *(Undergraduate, Graduate, Scholarship)* [8973]

Paul H. Rittle Sr. Professional Development Grants *(Other/Grant)* [5863]

Schurgin Family Foundation Scholarship *(Undergraduate/Scholarship)* [5982]

Recreational therapy

Ed Dunkelblau Scholarship *(All/Scholarship)* [2052]

The Margie Klein "Paper Plate" Scholarships *(All/ Scholarship)* [2053]

Lenny Ravich "Shalom" Scholarships *(Advanced Professional/Scholarship)* [2054]

Patty Wooten Scholarships *(Professional development/Scholarship, Award, Recognition)* [2055]

Rehabilitation, Physical/Psychological

Raymond B. Bauer Research Award *(Professional development/Award, Grant)* [7322]

Delta Gamma Foundation Florence Margaret Harvey Memorial Scholarship *(Graduate, Undergraduate/Scholarship)* [914]

Mary Switzer Research Fellowships - Distinguished Fellowships *(Doctorate/Fellowship)* [11312]

Rudolph Dillman Memorial Scholarship *(Graduate, Undergraduate/Scholarship)* [919]

Seasons in Malibu Annual Scholarship *(Undergraduate, Graduate/Scholarship)* [9994]

Mary Switzer Research Fellowships - Merit Fellowships *(Professional development/Fellowship)* [11313]

Religion

The Ambrose-Ramsey Trust *(Undergraduate/Scholarship)* [8831]

ARCE Funded Fellowships *(Doctorate, Postdoctorate/Fellowship)* [1336]

ARCE Research Associates Fellowship *(Doctorate, Postdoctorate, Professional development/Fellowship)* [1337]

Martha and Robert Atherton Ministerial Scholarship *(Master's/Scholarship)* [11245]

TCDA Carroll Barnes Student Scholarships *(Undergraduate/Scholarship)* [740]

Rosalie Bentzinger Scholarships *(Doctorate/Scholarship)* [4889]

Pamfil and Maria Bujea Family Orthodox Christian Seminarian Scholarships *(Undergraduate/Scholarship)* [1367]

Calihan Academic Grants *(Graduate, Professional development/Fellowship, Grant)* [65]

Calihan Travel Grants *(Other, Graduate/Grant)* [66]

CSBS Annual Student Prize Competition *(Graduate/ Prize)* [3110]

CSF Graduate Fellowship *(Graduate/Fellowship)* [3325]

CTRF Scholarships for Graduate Study in Transportation *(Graduate/Scholarship)* [3134]

David Pohl Scholarship *(Master's/Scholarship)* [11247]

Dr. Mubin Syed And Mrs. Afshan Syed Scholarship Program *(Undergraduate/Scholarship)* [6176]

Doris W. Frey Memorial Scholarship Fund *(Graduate/Scholarship)* [10681]

David Eaton Scholarship *(Master's/Scholarship)* [11249]

FCSLA Seminary or Diaconate or Religious Life Scholarships *(Graduate/Scholarship)* [4577]

IOKDS Student Ministry Scholarships *(Master's/ Scholarship)* [6052]

Iwalani Carpenter Sowa Scholarship *(Graduate/ Scholarship)* [8928]

Jack Shand Research Grants. *(Advanced Professional/Grant)* [10526]

John M. & Mary A. Shanley Memorial Scholarship *(Undergraduate, Graduate/Scholarship)* [10690]

Joseph H. Fichter Research Grant *(Postdoctorate/ Grant)* [2290]

Journey Toward Ordained Ministry Scholarships *(Undergraduate, Graduate/Scholarship)* [4893]

The Olympia Brown and Max Kapp Award *(Master's/Scholarship)* [11251]

KCC-JEE Graduate Fellowships *(Graduate/Fellowship)* [6580]

David B. Larson Fellowships in Health and Spirituality *(Postdoctorate/Fellowship)* [6574]

Lewis B. Barber Memorial Scholarship Fund *(Undergraduate/Scholarship)* [10695]

Margaret E. Phillips Scholarship *(Undergraduate/ Scholarship)* [11716]

William F. Miles Scholarships *(Graduate/Scholarship)* [5276]

Molly McKay Scholarship *(Undergraduate/Scholarship)* [11200]

National Federation of the Blind Scholarship Program *(Undergraduate/Scholarship, Monetary)* [7878]

Charlotte W. Newcombe Doctoral Dissertation Fellowship *(Graduate/Fellowship)* [8387, 12049]

Novak Awards *(Doctorate/Monetary, Award)* [67]

Peale Scholarship Grant *(Professional development/ Scholarship)* [9094]

Richard D. and Sheppard R. Cooke Memorial Scholarship *(Graduate/Scholarship)* [5278]

Robert J. McNamara Student Paper Award *(Graduate/Award, Monetary)* [2291]

Roy H. Pollack Scholarship *(Graduate, Master's/ Scholarship)* [11254]

Samuel Robinson Award *(Undergraduate/Award)* [9267]

Shannon Fellowships *(Professional development/ Fellowship)* [6133]

Hy Smith Endowment Fund *(Undergraduate/Scholarship)* [5280]

Tabat Scholarship Award *(Graduate/Scholarship)* [4533]

TCDA Bill Gorham Student Scholarship *(Undergraduate/Scholarship)* [743]

TCDA Cloys Webb Student Scholarship *(Undergraduate/Scholarship)* [744]

TCDA Gandy Ink Professional Scholarship *(Professional development/Scholarship)* [745]

TCDA General Fund Scholarships *(Undergraduate/ Scholarship)* [746]

TCDA Past Presidents Student Scholarship *(Undergraduate/Scholarship)* [747]

The Rev. Chuck and Nancy Thomas Scholarship *(Professional development/Scholarship)* [11256]

Trinity Education Foundation Seminary Scholarship *(Graduate/Scholarship)* [11112]

Von Ogden Vogt Scholarship *(Master's/Scholarship)* [11257]

Wexner Graduate Fellowship / Davidson Scholars Program *(Graduate/Fellowship)* [12003]

Charles Zarigian, Esq. Memorial Award *(Undergraduate/Scholarship)* [1908]

Religious education (See Education, Religious)

Remote sensing

ERDAS Internship *(Graduate/Internship)* [2005]

Francis H. Moffitt Scholarship *(Graduate, Undergraduate/Scholarship)* [2006]

NERL Postdoctoral Research Program *(Postdoctorate, Advanced Professional, Professional development/Fellowship)* [11352]

Robert N. Colwell Fellowship *(Doctorate/Fellowship)* [2009]

Ta Liang Award *(Graduate/Award)* [2010]

William A. Fischer Scholarship *(Graduate/Scholarship)* [2011]

Renaissance studies

Dante Prize *(Undergraduate/Prize, Monetary)* [3970]

Charles Hall Grandgent Award *(Graduate/Award, Monetary)* [3971]

Resource management

ASMC National Scholarship Program *(Graduate/ Scholarship)* [1520]

Bill Bowie Scholarship *(University, Undergraduate, College, Vocational/Occupational/Scholarship)* [12293]

Dawson District Renewable Resources Council Scholarship *(Undergraduate, College, University, Vocational/Occupational/Scholarship)* [12306]

FIU ForEverglades Scholarship *(Graduate, Doctorate, Master's/Scholarship)* [4455]

ForEverglades Scholarship *(Graduate, Master's, Doctorate/Scholarship)* [4456]

John Marshall Everglades Internship Program *(Undergraduate/Internship)* [4457]

Peter Lucas Scholarship *(Undergraduate, University, College, Vocational/Occupational/Scholarship)* [12341]

Susan R. Meisinger Fellowship for Graduate Study in HR *(Graduate, Master's, Advanced Professional/Fellowship)* [10367]

Ben Sheardown Scholarship *(Undergraduate, University, College/Scholarship)* [12370]

Respiratory therapy

Advance Degree and Clinical Research Training Grants in Alpha-1 Antitrypsin Deficiency *(Master's/ Grant)* [1351]

NBRC Frederic Helmholz, Jr., MD Educational Research Fund *(Master's, Doctorate/Grant)* [1356]

Parker B. Francis Respiratory Research Grant *(Advanced Professional, Professional development/ Grant)* [1357]

Rheumatology (See Arthritis)

Risk management

FLASH Social Science Scholarships *(Graduate/ Scholarship)* [4499]

ISU Gongaware Scholarship *(Undergraduate/Scholarship)* [5762]

William H. McGannon Foundation Scholarships *(Graduate, Undergraduate/Scholarship)* [7180]

NCEA Postdoctoral Research Program *(Postdoctorate/Fellowship)* [11360]

NRMRL Postdoctoral Research Program *(Postdoctorate, Advanced Professional, Professional development/Fellowship)* [11356]

Risk Management and Insurance Scholarship *(Graduate/Scholarship)* [9886]

Russell Ackoff Doctoral Student Fellowship *(Doctorate/Fellowship)* [11662]

Thompson Scholarship for Women in Safety *(Doctorate/Scholarship)* [1573]

Roman art (See Art, Roman)

Romanian studies (See Area and ethnic studies)

Russian studies

CJH-NEH Fellowships for Senior Scholars *(Doctorate/Fellowship)* [3222]

CJH-Prins Foundation Fellowships for Senior Scholars *(Doctorate/Fellowship)* [3223]

CJH-Prins Foundation Post-Doctoral and Early Career Fellowship for Emigrating Scholars *(Professional development, Postdoctorate/Fellowship)* [3224]

Science

AAA Education Research Scholarship *(Graduate, Postdoctorate/Scholarship)* [512]

AAAS Science and Technology Policy Fellowships *(Professional development/Fellowship)* [507]

AACC International Travel Grants *(Advanced Professional, Professional development/Grant)* [540]

AACC Van Slyke Foundation Research Grants *(Professional development/Grant)* [541]

AACR-Undergraduate Scholar Awards *(Undergraduate/Award)* [532]

Advanced Light Source Collaborative Postdoctoral Fellowship Program *(Postdoctorate/Fellowship)* [6734]

AFCEA STEM Teacher Graduate Scholarships *(Graduate/Scholarship)* [104, 7022]

African American Network - Carolinas Scholarship Fund *(Undergraduate/Scholarship)* [4715]

AfterCollege Science Student Scholarship *(Undergraduate, Graduate, Doctorate/Scholarship)* [121]

AfterCollege STEM Inclusion Scholarship *(Undergraduate, Graduate/Scholarship)* [122]

AHETEMS General Scholarships *(Undergraduate, Graduate/Scholarship)* [10068]

AHETEMS Professional Scholarships *(Graduate/Scholarship)* [10069]

AIP State Department Fellowship *(Postdoctorate/Fellowship, Recognition)* [1041]

Aises A. T. Anderson Memorial Scholarship *(Graduate, Undergraduate/Scholarship)* [1000]

AIST Southeast Member Chapter - Gene Suave Scholarship *(Undergraduate/Scholarship)* [2218]

Alberta Innovates - Technology Futures Graduate Student Scholarships in Nanotechnology *(Doctorate, Graduate/Scholarship)* [277]

Alberta Innovates - Technology Futures Graduate Student Scholarships in Omics *(Doctorate, Master's, Professional development/Scholarship)* [278]

American Association of Family and Consumer Sciences Undergraduate Scholarships *(Undergraduate/Scholarship)* [561]

American Council of Independent Laboratories Academic Scholarships *(Undergraduate/Scholarship, Award)* [815]

AMSA Graduate Student Research Poster Competition *(Graduate, Doctorate, Master's/Award)* [1109]

Anil and Neema Thakrar Family Fund #1 *(Undergraduate/Scholarship)* [4774]

Hettie M. Anthony Fellowship *(Doctorate/Fellowship)* [6495]

Mike Ardaw Scholarships *(Undergraduate/Scholarship)* [11436]

ASC Ph.D. Research Scholarship Award *(Doctorate, Postdoctorate/Scholarship)* [1415]

ASCLD Scholarship Program *(Graduate, Undergraduate, Master's, Doctorate/Scholarship, Award, Monetary)* [1417]

ASGP Graduate Research Fellowships *(Graduate/Fellowship)* [244]

Asia-Pacific Biomedical Research Foundation Merit Awards *(Postdoctorate/Award, Recognition, Prize)* [10530]

ASM Congressional Science Fellowship *(Postdoctorate/Fellowship)* [1515]

ASMS Research Awards *(Other/Award)* [1508]

Astronaut Scholarship Foundation Scholarship *(Undergraduate/Scholarship)* [2332]

Athena San Diego Pinnacle Scholarship *(Undergraduate/Scholarship)* [9799]

B&W Y-12 Scholarship Fund *(Undergraduate/Scholarship)* [4254]

Barry M. Goldwater Scholarship *(Undergraduate/Scholarship)* [11733]

Bechtel Engineering and Science Scholarship *(Undergraduate/Scholarship)* [7075]

Jenny Panitch Beckow Memorial Scholarship - Canada *(Graduate/Scholarship)* [6283]

Jenny Panitch Beckow Memorial Scholarship - Israel *(Graduate/Scholarship)* [6284]

Bill and Nell Biggs Scholarship *(Undergraduate/Scholarship)* [11508]

Bluepay Stem Scholarship *(Graduate, Undergraduate/Scholarship)* [2630]

Buck Bragunier Leadership Scholarship *(Four Year College, University/Scholarship)* [1840]

Breast Cancer Car Donations Annual College Scholarship *(Undergraduate/Scholarship)* [2685]

The Henry Broughton, K2AE, Memorial Scholarship *(Undergraduate/Scholarship)* [1930]

Marjorie M. Brown Dissertation Fellowship *(Doctorate/Fellowship)* [6488]

Marjorie M. Brown Fellowship Program *(Postdoctorate/Fellowship)* [6496]

Buick Achievers Scholarship Program *(Undergraduate/Scholarship)* [4905]

Graduate Fellowship Program - Robert M. Burger Fellowships *(Doctorate, Graduate/Fellowship)* [9999]

Canadian Identification Society Essay/Scholarship Awards *(Advanced Professional, Professional development/Award)* [3010]

Career Awards for Science and Mathematics Teachers *(Other/Award)* [2752]

Carrie and George Lyter Scholarship *(Undergraduate/Scholarship)* [4775]

Castle & Cooke Mililani Technology Park Scholarship Fund *(Undergraduate, University, Four Year College/Scholarship)* [5387]

CFUW Memorial Fellowship *(Master's/Fellowship)* [2971]

Channabasappa Memorial Scholarships *(Graduate, Doctorate/Scholarship)* [5993]

CHCI Graduate Fellowship Program *(Graduate, Professional development/Fellowship)* [3746]

Charline Chilson Scholarships *(Undergraduate/Scholarship)* [4029]

CIMON Inc Scholarship *(College, University/Scholarship)* [3333]

CitizenshipTests.org Engineering and Science Scholarship *(Undergraduate/Scholarship)* [3991]

Jeffrey Cook Student Travel Scholarships to PLEA *(Postgraduate/Scholarship)* [10289]

Cottrell Scholar Award (CSA) *(Graduate, Advanced Professional, Professional development/Award)* [9639]

Robert E. Cramer Product Design & Development Scholarship *(Undergraduate/Scholarship)* [10483]

Creative Diagnostics Fall Scholarship Program *(Undergraduate, Graduate/Scholarship)* [3896]

Critical Language Scholarships at Summer Institutes. (CLS) *(Graduate, Undergraduate/Scholarship)* [1345]

Robert G. Dailey SPE Detroit Section Scholarship *(Undergraduate/Scholarship)* [10484]

Ashley Darby Memorial Scholarship *(Community College, Undergraduate/Scholarship)* [8507]

Decommissioning, and Environmental Science Division Graduate Scholarship *(Undergraduate/Scholarship)* [1164]

Delta Gamma Undergraduate Merit-Based Scholarships *(Undergraduate/Scholarship)* [4020]

Denis Wong & Associates Scholarship *(Graduate, Undergraduate/Scholarship)* [8923]

Development Fund for Black Students in Science and Technology Scholarship *(Undergraduate/Scholarship)* [4068]

Dr. Kathy Dixon Memorial Scholarship *(Undergraduate, University, College/Scholarship)* [7097]

The William Donald Dixon Research Grant *(Graduate, Undergraduate, Advanced Professional/Grant)* [3011]

Office of Science Graduate Student Research (SCGSR) Program *(Graduate, Master's, Postdoctorate/Fellowship)* [11323]

Camille and Henry Dreyfus Foundation - Senior Scientist Mentor Program *(Professional development/Grant)* [4180]

Drzymala Janusz & Roma Scholarship *(Undergraduate/Scholarship)* [9661]

Edward Foster Award *(Advanced Professional/Award)* [3012]

Bruce T. and Jackie Mahi Erickson Scholarship *(Graduate, Undergraduate/Scholarship)* [8924]

Lew Erwin Extrusion Division Scholarship *(Master's, Postgraduate, Doctorate/Scholarship)* [10485]

Fleming/Blaszcak Scholarships *(Undergraduate, Graduate/Scholarship)* [10486]

Florida Education Fund McKnight Doctoral Fellowship *(Graduate/Fellowship)* [4629]

The Ginny Frankenthaler Memorial Scholarships *(Undergraduate/Scholarship)* [10633]

FSF Field Grant *(Professional development/Grant)* [4677]

The Gates Millennium Scholars *(Undergraduate/Scholarship)* [5529]

Eloise Gerry Fellowships *(Graduate/Fellowship)* [5058]

Composites Division/Harold Giles Scholarship *(Undergraduate, Graduate/Scholarship)* [10487]

Benjamin A. Gilman International Scholarship *(Undergraduate/Scholarship)* [11479]

Girls in Stem (GIS) Scholarship *(Undergraduate/Scholarship)* [9716]

Glendale Latino Association Scholarships *(Undergraduate/Scholarship)* [4999]

The Dr. Robert H. Goddard Memorial Scholarship *(Graduate, Undergraduate/Scholarship)* [8123]

William R. Goldfarb Memorial Scholarships *(Undergraduate/Scholarship)* [1940]

Gorrondona & Associates, Inc. / WTS High School Scholarships *(Two Year College, Four Year College/Scholarship)* [12174]

Grants-in-Aid of Research (GIAR) *(Graduate, Undergraduate/Grant)* [10128]

GREAT MINDS Collegiate Scholarship Program *(Undergraduate/Scholarship)* [368]

Gulf Coast Hurricane Scholarship *(Undergraduate/Scholarship)* [10488]

Guntley-Lorimer Science and Arts Scholarships *(Undergraduate/Scholarship)* [2594]

HACU/KIA Motors America, Inc. STEAM Scholarships *(Undergraduate, Graduate/Scholarship)* [5516, 6543]

H.G. Hardbarger Science - Mathematics Award *(Undergraduate, Vocational/Occupational/Award)* [8853]

Dolores Ruth Heady Hardy Memorial Scholarship *(Undergraduate/Scholarship)* [6442]

Hertz Foundation Graduate Fellowship Award *(Graduate/Fellowship)* [5502]

Hertz Doctoral Thesis Prize *(Graduate/Prize)* [5503]

The Hertz Graduate Fellowship Award *(Graduate, Master's, Doctorate/Fellowship)* [7645]

Hinman-Jensen Endowed Scholarship *(Undergraduate/Scholarship)* [6797]

IDA Fellowship/Scholarship Programs *(Other/Fellowship)* [5994]

Injection Molding Division Scholarship *(Undergraduate, Graduate/Scholarship)* [10489]

John D. Isaacs Marine Undergraduate Research Assistant Program *(Undergraduate/Grant)* [11561]

Janet and Horace Allen Science Scholarship *(Undergraduate/Scholarship)* [291]

Jeffrey Cook Memorial Faculty Retreat Scholarship *(Professional development/Scholarship)* [10290]

JMJ Phillip Group College Scholarships *(Graduate, University, Four Year College, Two Year College/Scholarship)* [6312]

JSA/Jefferson Lab Graduate Fellowship *(Doctorate, Graduate/Scholarship)* [6265]

Dr. Arthur A. Kezian DDS Science Scholarship *(Undergraduate, Graduate, College, University/Scholarship)* [6541]

Graduate Fellowship Program - Mahboob Khan/Advanced Micro Devices Fellowships *(Doctorate, Graduate/Fellowship)* [10000]

KON National Alumni Chapter Grant *(Professional development/Grant)* [6491]

KON New Initiatives Grant *(Professional development/Grant)* [6492]

L'Oréal USA For Women in Science Fellowship *(Postdoctorate/Fellowship)* [8696]

Lakselaget Foundation Scholarship Fund *(Graduate, Undergraduate/Scholarship)* [6635]

Lalor Foundation Merit Awards *(Postdoctorate/Award, Recognition, Prize)* [10533]

Latinos in Technology Scholarship *(Undergraduate/Scholarship)* [10136]

Short-Term Library Resident Research Fellowships *(Doctorate/Fellowship)* [1216]

Lt Col Romeo - Josephine Bass Ferretti Scholarship *(Undergraduate/Scholarship)* [148]

Lucas Grant *(Professional development/Grant)* [4679]

Dan & Pauline Lutkenhouse & Hawaii Tropical Botanical Garden Scholarship and Educational Fund *(Undergraduate, Graduate/Scholarship)* [5407]

Thermoset Division/James I. Mackenzie and James H. Cunningham Scholarships *(Undergraduate, Graduate/Scholarship)* [10490]

MAES Founders Scholarship *(Graduate, Undergraduate/Scholarship)* [6964]

MAES General Scholarships *(Graduate, Undergraduate/Scholarship)* [6965]

MAES Padrino/Madrina Scholarships *(Graduate, Undergraduate/Scholarship)* [6966]

MAES Pipeline Scholarship *(Graduate, Undergraduate/Scholarship)* [6967]

MAES Presidential Scholarship *(Graduate, Undergraduate/Scholarship)* [6968]

MAES Scholarships *(Graduate/Scholarship)* [6969]

Lazaro J. Mandel Young Investigator Award *(Advanced Professional/Monetary, Award)* [1236]

Masonic-Range Science Scholarship *(Undergraduate/Scholarship)* [10520]

Thomas R. McGetchin Memorial Scholarship Award *(Undergraduate/Scholarship)* [11423]

Molded Dimensions, LLC Scholarship *(College, University/Scholarship)* [7428]

Nell I. Mondy Fellowships *(Graduate/Fellowship)* [5059]

Salvatore J. Monte Thermoplastic Materials & Foams Division Scholarship *(Undergraduate/Scholarship)* [10491]

Robert E. and Judy More Scholarship Fund *(Undergraduate/Scholarship)* [4599]

John H. Moss Scholarships *(Undergraduate/Scholarship)* [11697]

MSA Presidential Student Awards (PSA) *(Graduate, Undergraduate/Scholarship)* [7354]

Murrietta Circuits Scholarship Opportunity *(Undergraduate, College, University/Scholarship)* [7505]

Nancy Lorraine Jensen Memorial Scholarship Fund *(Undergraduate/Scholarship)* [10590]

National Co-op Scholarship Program *(Undergraduate/Scholarship)* [12190]

National Debt Relief Scholarship *(University, Four Year College, Undergraduate/Scholarship)* [7828]

National Federation of the Blind Scholarship Program *(Undergraduate/Scholarship, Monetary)* [7878]

National GEM Consortium - MS Engineering Fellowships *(Master's/Scholarship)* [7902]

National Science Foundation Graduate Research Fellowship Program (GRFP) *(Graduate/Fellowship)* [8068]

National Security Technologies Engineering and Science Scholarships *(Undergraduate/Scholarship)* [9414]

Ted and Ruth Neward Scholarships *(Undergraduate, Graduate/Scholarship)* [10492]

Maureen E. Nolan-Cahill Memorial Scholarship *(Undergraduate/Scholarship)* [11459]

Northern Scientific Training Program *(Graduate/Scholarship)* [1791]

Novus Biologicals Scholarship Program *(All/Scholarship)* [8553]

Noyce Scholarships for Secondary Math and Science Education *(Undergraduate/Scholarship)* [5764]

NSERC's E.W.R Steacie Memorial Fellowships *(Professional development/Fellowship)* [3807]

Ocean Industry Student Research Awards *(Undergraduate, Graduate, Postdoctorate/Award)* [9641]

Ohio Space Grant Consortium Graduate Fellowships *(Graduate, Doctorate, Master's/Fellowship)* [8598]

Ohio Space Grant Consortium Special Minority Fellowships *(Doctorate, Graduate, Master's/Fellowship)* [8599]

Omicron Nu Research Fellowship *(Postdoctorate, Graduate/Fellowship)* [6497]

Oslo International Summer School Scholarship *(Undergraduate/Scholarship)* [10591]

Out to Innovate Scholarship *(Graduate, Undergraduate, Community College/Scholarship)* [8019]

Packard Fellowships for Science and Engineering *(Professional development/Fellowship)* [8808]

Pat and John MacTavish Scholarship *(Undergraduate/Scholarship)* [5100]

Martha Mitchell Pearson Memorial Scholarship *(Undergraduate, Graduate/Scholarship)* [6464]

Phi Theta Kappa Scholarship *(Undergraduate/Scholarship)* [5765]

Polymer Modifiers and Additives Division (PMAD) Scholarship (PMAD) *(Undergraduate, Graduate/Scholarship)* [10493]

Ralph H. Potts Memorial Fellowship Award *(Graduate/Award, Fellowship)* [1184]

R&D Systems Scholarship *(All/Scholarship)* [9497]

Red Olive Women in STEM Scholarship *(Undergraduate, Graduate/Scholarship)* [9516]

Reuben H. Fleet Memorial Scholarship *(Undergraduate/Scholarship)* [9845]

Carl M. Rose Memorial Scholarship *(Undergraduate/Scholarship)* [8874]

Jack Rosen Scholarship *(Undergraduate/Scholarship)* [6393]

Ross A. Wilson Science Scholarship *(Undergraduate/Scholarship)* [11024]

Leo S. Rowe Pan American Fund *(Graduate, Undergraduate/Loan)* [8739]

Chester & Maria Sadowski Memorial Scholarships *(Undergraduate/Scholarship)* [9677]

SBSE Ases Student Travel Scholarship *(Graduate/Scholarship)* [10291]

SBSE Student Retreat Scholarship *(Master's, Doctorate/Scholarship)* [10292]

Dale M. Schoettler Scholarship for Visually Impaired Students *(Undergraduate, Graduate/Scholarship)* [9874]

Science and Engineering Apprenticeship Program (SEAP) *(High School/Internship)* [1444]

Science, Mathematics And Research for Transformation Scholarship for Service Program (SMART) *(Undergraduate, Graduate/Scholarship)* [1445, 9974]

SDE Fellowship *(Graduate, Postgraduate/Fellowship)* [5060]

John R. Sevier Memorial Scholarship Award *(Undergraduate/Scholarship)* [11424]

Everett Oscar Shimp Memorial Scholarships *(Undergraduate/Scholarship)* [8878]

SHPE Dissertation Scholarship *(Doctorate/Scholarship)* [10351]

SHPE Professional Scholarship *(Master's, Doctorate/Scholarship)* [10352]

Sigma Delta Epsilon Fellowship (SDEF) *(Graduate/Fellowship)* [5061]

Carrie Fox Solin Blow Molding Division Memorial Scholarships *(Undergraduate/Scholarship)* [10494]

SPE Foundation General Scholarships *(Undergraduate, Graduate/Scholarship)* [10495]

SPE Vinyl Plastics Division Educational Grants *(Undergraduate/Grant)* [10496]

SRC Master's Scholarships Program *(Graduate, Master's/Scholarship)* [10001]

SREB-State Doctoral Scholars Program - Doctoral Award *(Doctorate, Graduate/Scholarship)* [10664]

Stuart L. Noderer Memorial Scholarship *(Undergraduate/Scholarship)* [9855]

SWS Student Scholarships *(Undergraduate/Scholarship)* [10562]

Frederick A. Tarantino Memorial Scholarship Award *(Undergraduate/Scholarship)* [11425]

Thermoforming Division Scholarship *(Undergraduate, Graduate/Scholarship)* [10497]

Thermoplastic Elastomers Special Interest Group Scholarship *(Undergraduate, Graduate/Scholarship)* [10498]

Tocris Scholarship Program *(All/Scholarship)* [11046]

Toyota Tapestry Grants for Science Teachers *(Other/Grant)* [8070]

TriBeta Research Grant Awards *(Undergraduate/Grant)* [2494]

Truthfinder Scholarship for Women in STEM *(Undergraduate, Graduate, Two Year College/Scholarship)* [11133]

UAA Quanterra Scholarship *(Master's, Doctorate/Scholarship)* [11505]

UCSD Black Alumni Scholarships for Engineering, Mathematics and Science *(Undergraduate/Scholarship)* [9858]

USGA/Chevron STEM Scholarship Program *(Undergraduate/Scholarship)* [11373]

Vessa Notchev Fellowship (VNF) *(Graduate/Fellowship)* [5062]

Vision Tech Camps Scholarship *(Community College, Four Year College/Scholarship)* [11854]

Shih-Chun Wang Young Investigator Award *(Advanced Professional/Monetary, Award)* [1240]

Matthew Watson Scholarship *(Undergraduate, University, College, Graduate/Scholarship)* [12385]

James B. Willett Educational Memorial Scholarship Award *(Undergraduate/Scholarship)* [11426]

Woodcock Family Education Scholarship Program *(Undergraduate/Scholarship)* [324]

WSGC Community College Transfer Scholarships *(Undergraduate/Scholarship)* [11901]

WSGC Scholarships for Incoming Freshmen *(Undergraduate/Scholarship)* [11902]

The YASME Foundation Scholarship *(Undergraduate/Scholarship)* [1968]

Zuckerman STEM Leadership Program *(Postdoctorate/Scholarship)* [12423]

Science technologies

AAAS Mass Media Science & Engineering Fellows Program *(Undergraduate, Graduate, Postdoctorate/Fellowship)* [506]

AAAS Science and Technology Policy Fellowships *(Professional development/Fellowship)* [507]

AVS Applied Surface Science Division *(Graduate/Award)* [2374]

AVS Biomaterial Interfaces Division - Early Career Researchers Awards (BID-ECR) *(Graduate/Monetary)* [2375]

AVS Electronic Materials and Photonic Division Postdoctoral Award *(Postdoctorate/Award)* [2376]

AVS Manufacturing Science and Technology Group *(Graduate/Award)* [2377]

AVS MEMS and NEMS Technical Group Best Paper Award *(Undergraduate, Graduate/Monetary)* [2378]

AVS Nanometer-Scale Science and Technology Division Graduate Award *(Graduate/Monetary)* [2379]

AVS Spectroscopic Ellipsometry Focus Topic Graduate Student Awards *(Graduate/Award)* [2380]

AVS Thin Film Division James Harper Awards *(Graduate/Monetary)* [2381]

Mark A. Beltz Scholarship *(Graduate, Undergraduate/Scholarship)* [11473]

John Coburn and Harold Winters Student Award in Plasma Science and Technology *(Graduate/Award)* [2382]

Graduate Student Fellowships for Alternatives to the Use of Animals in Science *(Graduate, Doctorate/Fellowship)* [6009]

Dorothy M. and Earl S. Hoffman Award *(Graduate/Award)* [2383]

Magnetic Interfaces & Nanostructures Division - Leo M. Falicov Student Award *(Graduate/Grant)* [2384]

Manulife Financial Scholarship *(Undergraduate/Scholarship)* [3793]

Morton M. Traum Surface Science Student Award *(Graduate, Doctorate/Prize)* [2385]

Martha Mitchell Pearson Memorial Scholarship *(Undergraduate, Graduate/Scholarship)* [6464]

Pembroke Center Seed Grants *(Professional development/Grant)* [2726]

Russell & Sigurd Varian Award *(Graduate/Recognition)* [2386]

Saskatchewan School Boards Association Education Scholarships *(Graduate/Scholarship)* [9925]

Nellie Yeoh Whetten Award *(Graduate/Recognition)* [2387]

Science--History

AMS Graduate Fellowship in the History of Science *(Graduate/Fellowship)* [1120]

Scottish studies (See also British studies)

Clan Ross Foundation Scholarships (Undergraduate/Scholarship) [3426]

Screenwriting

CineStory Feature Fellowship (Professional development/Fellowship) [3414]

Sculpture

Yvonne L. Bombardier Visual Arts Scholarship Program (Master's, Doctorate/Scholarship) [2651]
Alex J. Ettl Grants (Other/Grant) [8072]
Ken Gray Scholarship (Undergraduate/Scholarship) [11481]
National Sculpture Society Participation Scholarships (Undergraduate/Scholarship) [8073]
Helen Lansdowne Resor Scholarship (Undergraduate, Graduate, Other/Scholarship) [11018]

Security

Cyber Security Scholarship (College, University, Undergraduate, Vocational/Occupational/Scholarship) [4315]
IOBSE Scholarships (Undergraduate/Scholarship) [6057]
Morphisec's Women in Cybersecurity Scholarships (Undergraduate, Graduate/Scholarship) [7470]

Sexuality

CLAGS Fellowship Award (Graduate, Advanced Professional/Award, Fellowship) [3233]
Loren Frankel Memorial Scholarship (Undergraduate, Graduate/Scholarship) [1117]
Friends of Project 10 Models of Excellence Scholarship (Undergraduate/Scholarship) [4831]
GJEC Dissertation Completion Fellowship (Postdoctorate/Fellowship) [7336]
Larry King/Jeffrey Fashion Cares Point Scholarship (Undergraduate, Graduate, Doctorate/Scholarship) [9225]
RBPA Scholarship (Undergraduate, Graduate, Doctorate/Scholarship) [9493]
Society for the Scientific Study of Sexuality Student Research Grant (Undergraduate/Grant) [10528]
UCLA-CSW Travel Grants (Graduate, Undergraduate/Grant) [11542]

Social sciences

Abe Fellowship (Professional development/Fellowship) [10241]
ABF Law and Social Science Dissertation Fellowship and Mentoring Program (Graduate/Fellowship) [690]
ABF Montgomery Summer Research Diversity Fellowships in Law and Social Science (Undergraduate/Fellowship) [691]
ACLS Collaborative Research Fellowships (Doctorate/Fellowship) [817]
ACLS Fellowships (Advanced Professional, Professional development/Fellowship) [818]
ACOR-CAORC Post-Doctoral Fellowships (Postdoctorate/Fellowship) [723]
Dr. Feroz Ahmed Memorial Educational Post-Graduate Scholarships (Doctorate, Postgraduate/Scholarship) [10144]
AISLS Dissertation Planning Grants (Graduate/Grant) [1047]
AISLS Fellowships Program (Doctorate/Fellowship) [1048]
Lorraine Allison Scholarship (Graduate/Scholarship) [1789]
American Enterprise Institute National Research Initiative Fellowships (NRI) (Professional development/Fellowship) [872]
American Research in the Humanities in China Fellowships (Doctorate/Fellowship) [820]
Applied Social Issues Internship Program (Undergraduate, Graduate, Doctorate/Internship) [10508]

ARIT Fellowships in the Humanities and Social Sciences in Turkey (Postdoctorate, Graduate/Fellowship) [1342, 3850, 11345, 11348]
Baltimore Community Fellowships (Advanced Professional/Fellowship) [8663]
UAA Michael Baring-Gould Memorial Scholarship (Graduate, Undergraduate/Scholarship) [11472]
Raymond B. Bauer Research Award (Professional development/Award, Grant) [7322]
Jeanne Humphrey Block Dissertation Award (Postdoctorate/Award) [5363]
ACLS Frederick Burkhardt Residential Fellowships (Other/Fellowship) [486, 821]
Frederick Burkhardt Residential Fellowships for Recently Tenured Scholars (Advanced Professional, Professional development/Fellowship) [822]
Carter G. Woodson Institute Post-doctoral Residential Research & Teaching Fellowship (Postdoctorate/Fellowship) [12183]
Carter G. Woodson Institute Pre-doctoral Fellowship (Doctorate/Fellowship) [12184]
Graduate and Undergraduate Fellowship Awards (Doctorate, Graduate, Undergraduate/Fellowship, Award) [3195]
Mariam K. Chamberlain Fellowship in Women and Public Policy (Graduate/Fellowship) [5874]
The Christine Mirzayan Science & Technology Policy Graduate Fellowship Program (Graduate, Postdoctorate, High School/Fellowship) [7571]
Critical Language Scholarships at Summer Institutes. (CLS) (Graduate, Undergraduate/Scholarship) [1345]
CTFS-ForestGEO Research Grants Program (Graduate, Postdoctorate, Advanced Professional/Grant) [10229]
Dissertation Proposal Development Fellowship (Doctorate/Fellowship) [10243]
Marusia and Michael Dorosh Fellowship (Master's, Graduate/Fellowship) [3027]
Lee Dubin Memorial Scholarship (Undergraduate/Scholarship) [3500]
EAPSI Fellowships (Doctorate, Graduate/Fellowship, Award) [8067]
Epilepsy Foundation Behavioral Sciences Post-Doctoral Fellowships (Postdoctorate/Fellowship) [4419]
Eurasia Program Fellowships - Dissertation Development Awards (Doctorate/Fellowship) [10244]
Eurasia Program Fellowships - Pre-Dissertation Awards (Doctorate/Fellowship) [10245]
European Studies First Article Prize (Professional development/Prize) [3857]
FASSE-International Assembly International Understanding Grants (Professional development/Grant) [7795]
FLASH Social Science Scholarships (Graduate/Scholarship) [4499]
Getty Scholar Grants (Professional development/Grant) [4959]
Charles D. Gonthier Research Fellowship (Graduate, Advanced Professional/Fellowship) [3018]
The Gordon Allport Intergroup Relations Prize (Professional development/Monetary, Prize) [10509]
Harry Frank Guggenheim Dissertation Fellowships (Doctorate/Fellowship) [5247]
Harry Frank Guggenheim Foundation Research Grants (Professional development/Grant) [5248]
John Simon Guggenheim Memorial Fellowships - United States & Canadian Competition (Graduate, Postgraduate, Undergraduate/Fellowship) [5250]
HAESF Professional Internship Program (Doctorate/Internship) [5645]
Ruth Simms Hamilton Research Fellowship (Graduate/Fellowship) [10927]
IAF Fellowships (Doctorate/Fellowship) [5883]
International Dissertation Research Fellowship (IDRF) (Graduate, Doctorate/Fellowship) [10246]
Japan Society for the Promotion of Science Fellowship (JSPS) (Doctorate/Fellowship) [10247]
Jacob K. Javits Fellowships Program (Master's, Doctorate/Fellowship) [11310]
John Streiff Memorial Scholarship (Undergraduate/Scholarship) [6803]
Rita Mae Kelly Fund (Graduate, Doctorate, Undergraduate, Professional development/Grant) [1257]

Robert E. Kelsey Annual Scholarship (Undergraduate/Scholarship) [8954]
Martin Luther King Jr. Scholarships (Graduate/Scholarship) [6558]
Kluge Fellowship (Doctorate, Graduate/Fellowship) [6573]
Korean Studies Dissertation Workshop (Graduate/Fellowship) [10248]
Dolores Zohrab Liebmann Fund - Graduate School Fellowships (Graduate/Fellowship) [6845]
Lois Hole Humanities and Social Sciences Scholarship (Undergraduate/Scholarship) [296]
The Clara Mayo Grants (Graduate/Grant) [10510]
O. Ruth McQuown Scholarship - Graduate Award for Current Students (Graduate/Scholarship) [11572]
Mellon/ACLS Dissertation Completion Fellowships (Graduate, Doctorate/Fellowship) [825]
Mellon Fellowships for Dissertation Research in Original Sources (Doctorate/Fellowship) [3870]
Michigan Society of Fellows Three-Year Fellowships (Postdoctorate/Fellowship) [7326]
Multi-Country Research Fellowship (Doctorate, Postdoctorate/Fellowship) [3851]
NAFA International Dissertation Research Fellowships (Graduate, Doctorate/Fellowship) [7647]
NAPRHSW Scholarships (Undergraduate, Graduate/Scholarship) [7682]
National Endowment for the Humanities Advanced Fellowships for Research in Turkey (Postdoctorate/Fellowship) [1349, 7871]
National Institute of Health Undergraduate Scholarship Program (NIH UGSP) (Undergraduate/Scholarship) [11341]
NCSS Grant for Geographic Literacy (Other/Grant) [7796]
Newkirk Graduate Student Fellow Awards (Doctorate, Graduate/Fellowship) [8391]
Next Generation Social Sciences in Africa: Doctoral Dissertation Completion Fellowship (Doctorate/Fellowship) [3169, 10249]
Next Generation Social Sciences in Africa: Doctoral Dissertation Proposal Fellowship (Doctorate/Fellowship) [3170, 10250]
Next Generation Social Sciences in Africa: Doctoral Dissertation Research Fellowship (Doctorate/Fellowship) [3171, 10251]
Pembroke Center Seed Grants (Professional development/Grant) [2726]
Philip H. Melanson Memorial Scholarship (Undergraduate, Graduate/Scholarship) [11593]
Pierre Elliott Trudeau Foundation octoral Scholarships (Doctorate/Scholarship) [11124]
Post-Doctoral Summer Travel-Research Grants (Postdoctorate/Grant) [5871]
Postdoctoral Fellowship (Postdoctorate, Doctorate/Fellowship) [11419]
Russell Sage Foundation's Visiting Scholars Program (Postdoctorate, Doctorate/Fellowship) [9774]
SFP Mid-Career/Mentor Award (Other/Grant) [10331]
SGI Graduate Research Grant (Graduate/Grant) [9891]
SHAFR Dissertation Completion Fellowship (Doctorate/Fellowship) [10359]
Smithsonian Minority Awards Program - Visiting Student (Graduate/Fellowship) [10209]
Spirit of Anne Frank Scholarship Award (Undergraduate/Scholarship) [4813]
SSHRC Doctoral Fellowship Program (Doctorate/Fellowship, Scholarship) [3797]
SSHRC Postdoctoral Fellowships (Postdoctorate/Fellowship) [3798]
SSSP Racial/Ethnic Minority Graduate Fellowship (Graduate/Fellowship, Award, Monetary) [10537]
Louis Stokes Urban Health Policy Fellows Program (Other/Fellowship) [3743]
Summer Language Study Grants in Turkey (Graduate/Grant) [5872]
UC MEXUS-CONACYT Doctoral Fellowship (Doctorate/Fellowship) [11552]
Vanier Canada Graduate Scholarships Program (Graduate/Scholarship) [3808]
Woody Guthrie Fellowship (Professional development/Fellowship) [2637]

Social work

Alano Club Scholarship *(Undergraduate, College, University, Vocational/Occupational/Scholarship)* [12280]

Associates in Behavioral Health Scholarships *(Graduate/Scholarship)* [9290]

Eileen Blackey Doctoral Fellowship *(Doctorate/Fellowship)* [7696]

Mildred Cater Bradham Social Work Fellowships *(Graduate, Professional development/Fellowship)* [12409]

Robert K. Brown Scholarships *(Undergraduate, Master's/Scholarship)* [2589]

Carl A. Scott Book Scholarship *(Undergraduate/Scholarship)* [3873]

Cenie Jomo Williams Tuition Scholarship *(Graduate, Undergraduate/Scholarship)* [7617]

Child Welfare and Development (CWD) Scholarship *(Undergraduate/Scholarship)* [4489]

Consuelo W. Gosnell Memorial MSW Scholarship *(Graduate/Fellowship)* [7697]

Council on Social Work Education Minority Fellowship Program for Doctoral Students *(Postdoctorate/Fellowship)* [3874]

Council on Social Work Education Scholars Program *(Doctorate/Scholarship)* [3875]

Dr. Joyce Beckett Scholarship *(Graduate, Undergraduate/Scholarship)* [7618]

Douglas-Coldwell Foundation Scholarships in Social Affairs *(Graduate/Scholarship)* [4137]

Debra Dungey Scholarship *(Undergraduate, Graduate, University, College/Scholarship)* [12311]

Echoing Green Black Male Achievement Fellowships *(Professional development/Fellowship)* [4275]

Echoing Green Climate Fellowships *(Professional development/Fellowship)* [4276]

EJI Justice Fellowship *(Graduate, Postgraduate, Professional development/Fellowship)* [4434]

Emma and Meloid Algood Tuition Scholarship *(Graduate, Undergraduate/Scholarship)* [7619]

Alice Yuriko Endo Memorial Scholarship *(Undergraduate/Scholarship)* [6245]

Lee K. Feine Scholarship *(Undergraduate, Graduate/Scholarship)* [7790]

Tamara Guttman Memorial Scholarship *(Undergraduate, University, College, Vocational/Occupational/Scholarship)* [12320]

Hampton Roads Association of Social Workers Scholarship *(Graduate/Scholarship)* [5271]

Health and Aging Policy Fellows Program *(Advanced Professional, Professional development/Fellowship)* [1255]

HFMH Bilingual Scholarships for Mental Health Workforce Diversity *(Graduate/Scholarship)* [5539]

International Scholarship Programs for Community Service *(Undergraduate/Scholarship)* [7249]

Jewish Federation Academic Scholarship *(Graduate, Undergraduate/Scholarship)* [6310]

Verne LaMarr Lyons Memorial MSW Scholarship *(Graduate, Master's/Fellowship)* [7698]

Irene Brand Lieberman Memorial Scholarship *(Graduate/Scholarship)* [6298]

Maude Keisling / Cumberland County Extension Homemakers Scholarship Fund *(Undergraduate/Scholarship)* [3634]

Joseph McCulley Educational Trust Fund *(Graduate, Undergraduate/Grant)* [11695]

NYCT Paid Graduate Student Philanthropy Fellowships - Community Development and the Environment *(Graduate/Fellowship)* [8307]

OPIRG McMaster Public Interest Research Grant (PIG) *(Undergraduate, Graduate/Grant)* [7195]

Philip F. Vineberg Travelling Fellowship in the Humanities *(Undergraduate/Scholarship, Monetary)* [7184]

Pi Gamma Mu Scholarships *(Graduate/Scholarship)* [9160]

Portuguese American Police Association Scholarships *(Undergraduate/Scholarship)* [9252]

Pride Foundation Social Work Scholarships *(Undergraduate/Scholarship)* [9308]

Schmidt Family Scholarship *(Undergraduate, University, College/Scholarship)* [12367]

Selena Danette Brown Book Scholarship *(Graduate, Undergraduate/Scholarship)* [7620]

Taylor Statten Memorial Fellowships *(Graduate/Scholarship)* [11698]

Steve Dearduff Scholarship Fund *(Graduate, Undergraduate/Scholarship)* [3587]

Turco Munoz Domestic Violence Survivor Scholarship *(Undergraduate, Graduate/Scholarship)* [11137]

Joan Veinott Scholarship *(Undergraduate, University, College/Scholarship)* [12382]

Chancellor's Graduate Fellowship *(Advanced Professional/Fellowship)* [11923]

Washington University Law School Olin Fellowships for Women *(Advanced Professional/Fellowship)* [11924]

Wellstone Fellowships for Social Justice *(Graduate/Fellowship)* [4484]

Reverend H. John and Asako Yamashita Memorial Scholarship *(Graduate/Scholarship)* [6254]

Sociology (See also Aggression and violence)

Dr. Feroz Ahmed Memorial Educational Post-Graduate Scholarships *(Doctorate, Postgraduate/Scholarship)* [10144]

ASA Minority Fellowship Program (ASA MFP) *(Doctorate/Fellowship)* [1590]

ASA Student Forum Travel Awards *(Undergraduate, Graduate/Award)* [1591]

UAA Michael Baring-Gould Memorial Scholarship *(Graduate, Undergraduate/Scholarship)* [11472]

Child Welfare and Development (CWD) Scholarship *(Undergraduate/Scholarship)* [4489]

Douglas-Coldwell Foundation Scholarships in Social Affairs *(Graduate/Scholarship)* [4137]

Early Childhood Educators Scholarship Program *(Undergraduate/Scholarship)* [7158]

Marcus Mosiah Garvey Scholarships *(Undergraduate/Scholarship)* [6216]

Beth B. Hess Memorial Scholarship *(Doctorate, Graduate/Fellowship, Award)* [10566]

IARSLCE Graduate Student Scholarships *(Graduate/Scholarship)* [5937]

Lee Student Support Fund *(Undergraduate, Graduate/Award, Monetary, Recognition)* [10536]

The Cheryl Allyn Miller Award *(Doctorate, Graduate/Award)* [10567]

National Women's Studies Association Lesbian Caucus Award *(Master's, Doctorate/Award, Grant)* [8165]

Pi Gamma Mu Scholarships *(Graduate/Scholarship)* [9160]

The Thomas R. Pickering Foreign Affairs Fellowship *(Graduate, Undergraduate/Fellowship)* [11346, 12050]

UAA Eveline Schuster Memorial Award/Scholarship *(Graduate, Undergraduate/Scholarship)* [11500]

The Virtuous Prom Peace Scholarship *(Undergraduate, Graduate, Postgraduate/Scholarship)* [11852]

Minoru Yasui Memorial Scholarship *(Graduate/Scholarship)* [6255]

Soil science

Karl C. Ivarson Scholarship for Students in Soil Science and Related Studies *(Master's, Doctorate/Scholarship, Award)* [130]

STRI Short-Term Fellowships *(Undergraduate, Graduate, Postdoctorate/Fellowship)* [10226]

Earl S. Tupper Three-year Postdoctoral Fellowship *(Postdoctorate/Fellowship)* [10227]

South Asian studies

NIU-CSEAS Foreign Language and Area Studies (FLAS) Graduate Fellowship *(Undergraduate, Graduate/Fellowship)* [8487]

Space and planetary sciences (See also Astronomy and astronomical sciences)

ASGP Graduate Research Fellowships *(Graduate/Fellowship)* [244]

Connecticut Space Grant College Consortium Undergraduate Research Fellowships *(Undergraduate/Fellowship)* [3761]

Thomas R. McGetchin Memorial Scholarship Award *(Undergraduate/Scholarship)* [11423]

NASA RISGC Graduate Fellowships *(Master's, Postdoctorate, Graduate/Fellowship)* [9699]

NASA WVSGC Undergraduate Research Fellowship *(Undergraduate/Fellowship)* [11975]

PSGC/NASA Space Grant Fellowships at the PSGC Affiliate Institutions *(Graduate/Fellowship)* [8966]

John R. Sevier Memorial Scholarship Award *(Undergraduate/Scholarship)* [11424]

Frederick A. Tarantino Memorial Scholarship Award *(Undergraduate/Scholarship)* [11425]

James B. Willett Educational Memorial Scholarship Award *(Undergraduate/Scholarship)* [11426]

Spanish studies (See Area and ethnic studies)

Special education (See Education, Special)

specific diseases

SCDAA Post-Doctoral Research Fellowships *(Postdoctorate/Fellowship)* [10074]

Speech and language pathology/Audiology

American Speech Language Hearing Foundation Clinical Research Grant *(Doctorate/Grant)* [1595]

American Speech Language Hearing Foundation Endowed Scholarships *(Graduate, Master's, Doctorate/Scholarship)* [1596]

American Speech Language Hearing Foundation General Scholarships *(Graduate, Master's, Doctorate/Scholarship)* [1597]

American Speech Language Hearing Foundation International Student Scholarship *(Graduate, Master's, Doctorate/Scholarship)* [1598]

American Speech Language Hearing Foundation Minority Student Scholarship *(Graduate, Master's, Doctorate/Scholarship)* [1599]

American Speech Language Hearing Foundation Scholarship for Student with A Disability *(Graduate, Master's, Doctorate/Scholarship)* [1600]

ASHFoundation New Century Scholars Doctoral Scholarship *(Doctorate/Scholarship)* [1601]

ASHFoundation New Century Scholars Research Grant *(Doctorate/Grant)* [1602]

ASHFoundation New Investigators Research Grant *(Doctorate/Grant)* [1603]

ASHFoundation NSSLHA Scholarship *(Graduate/Scholarship)* [1604]

ASHFoundation Speech Science Research Grant *(Doctorate/Grant)* [1605]

ASHFoundation Student Research Grant in Audiology *(Doctorate/Grant)* [1606]

ASHFoundation Student Research Grant in Early Childhood Language Development *(Doctorate, Master's/Grant)* [1607]

Fred Berg Awards *(Undergraduate/Award)* [4299]

L.I. Bryson Memorial Senior Speech Arts Scholarship *(Other/Scholarship)* [9896]

Communication Disorder/Speech Therapy Scholarship *(Graduate/Scholarship)* [4899]

Dwight A. Hamilton Scottish Rite Foundation of Colorado Graduate Scholarship in Speech-Language Pathology *(Graduate/Scholarship)* [9984]

Educational Audiology Association Doctoral Scholarship *(Doctorate/Scholarship)* [4300]

ETS Postdoctoral Fellowships *(Postdoctorate/Fellowship)* [4311]

Frederick V. Hunt Postdoctoral Research Fellowship in Acoustics *(Postdoctorate/Fellowship)* [61]

Harold Gulliksen Psychometric Research Fellowship *(Doctorate, Graduate/Fellowship)* [4312]

Houston/Nancy Holliman Scholarship *(Undergraduate/Scholarship)* [4036]

IOKDS Health Careers Scholarship *(College, University, Undergraduate, Graduate, Doctorate/Scholarship)* [6050]

James E. West Fellowship *(Graduate/Fellowship)* [62]

Maryland Speech Language Hearing Association Graduate Scholarships *(Graduate/Scholarship)* [7118]

Noel D. Matkin Awards *(Undergraduate/Award)* [4301]

NAJA Scholarship *(Graduate/Scholarship)* [7664]

New Investigator Research Grant *(Doctorate/Grant)* [432]

Helen Woodruff Nolop Scholarships in Audiology and Allied Fields *(Graduate/Scholarship)* [4040]

OSHA Graduate Scholarship *(Doctorate, Master's/Scholarship)* [8614]

Sertoma Communicative Disorders Scholarship *(Undergraduate/Scholarship)* [10019]

Raymond H. Stetson Scholarship in Phonetics and Speech Science *(Graduate/Scholarship)* [63]

Student Investigator Research Grant - General Audiology/Hearing Science *(Graduate, Doctorate/Grant)* [433]

Student Investigator Research Grant - Hearing Aids, Clinical Protocols and Patient Outcomes *(Graduate, Doctorate/Grant)* [434]

Student Investigator Research Grant - Vestibular *(Graduate, Doctorate/Grant)* [435]

Student Summer Research Fellowship *(Undergraduate, Graduate/Fellowship)* [436]

Sylvia Taylor Johnson Minority Fellowships in Educational Measurement *(Doctorate/Fellowship)* [4313]

Speech, Debate, and Forensics

William R. Pfalzgraf Memorial Scholarship *(Undergraduate/Scholarship)* [8867]

Spinal cord injuries and research

180 Medical College Scholarship Program *(Undergraduate, Graduate, Professional development/Scholarship)* [6]

Individual K-Grants *(All/Grant)* [6564]

Morton Cure Paralysis Fund Research Grants *(Professional development, Postdoctorate/Grant)* [7480]

Psychosocial Research Pilot Grants *(Professional development/Grant)* [8201]

Psychosocial Research - Postdoctoral Psychosocial Fellowships *(Postdoctorate/Fellowship)* [8202]

Psychosocial Research Studies and Demonstration Projects *(Professional development/Grant)* [8203]

PVA Research Foundation Fellowships *(Postdoctorate/Fellowship)* [8820]

Bryon Riesch Paralysis Foundation Research Grants *(Professional development/Grant)* [9703]

Travis Roy Foundation Individual Grants *(All/Grant)* [9749]

SCIRTS (Spinal Cord Injury Research on the Translational Spectrum) Pilot Research Grants *(Professional development/Grant)* [8204]

SCIRTS (Spinal Cord Injury Research on the Translational Spectrum) Postdoctoral Fellowships *(Postdoctorate/Fellowship)* [8205]

SCIRTS (Spinal Cord Injury Research on the Translational Spectrum) Senior Research Grants *(Professional development/Grant)* [8206]

Sports medicine (See Medicine, Sports)

Sports studies

Henry H. Anderson, Jr. Sail Training Scholarship *(Professional development/Scholarship, Recognition, Award)* [10917]

Annual Golf Scholarship *(Graduate, Postgraduate/Scholarship)* [5036]

Bat and Ball Game Womens Sports Scholarship *(Undergraduate/Scholarship)* [2445]

Bernice Barabash Sports Scholarship *(Graduate/Scholarship)* [6194]

Walter Byers Postgraduate Scholarships *(Graduate, Postgraduate/Scholarship)* [7769]

Ethnic Minority and Women's Enhancement Postgraduate Scholarships *(Graduate, Postgraduate/Scholarship)* [7770]

Geordie Hilton Academic Scholarships *(Undergraduate/Scholarship)* [5030]

John McLendon Minority Postgraduate Scholarship *(Postdoctorate/Scholarship)* [7639]

Lineups.com Future of Sports Scholarship Program *(Undergraduate, Graduate/Scholarship)* [6871]

Michael Moody Fitness Scholarship *(Undergraduate, Graduate/Scholarship)* [7464]

Gordon Newman Recreation Scholarship *(Undergraduate, University, College, Vocational/Occupational/Scholarship)* [12352]

Northside Booster Club - Felix R. Sepulveda Memorial Scholarship *(Undergraduate/Scholarship)* [9567]

Saskatchewan Hockey Association Scholarships *(Undergraduate/Scholarship)* [9893]

Gary Vanden Berg Internship Grant *(Undergraduate/Grant)* [10737]

Veronica Gantt Memorial Scholarship *(Undergraduate/Scholarship)* [9429]

Sports writing

Association for Women in Sports Media Internship Program *(Undergraduate/Scholarship, Internship)* [2321]

Chuck Pezzano Scholarship *(College, Graduate/Scholarship)* [5955]

Statistics

AAUW Selected Professions Fellowships *(Graduate, Master's, Doctorate/Fellowship)* [35]

ASA/NSF/BLS Fellowships *(Graduate/Fellowship, Recognition, Grant)* [1609, 8065, 11343]

Edward C. Bryant Scholarship for an Outstanding Graduate Student in Survey Statistics *(Graduate/Scholarship)* [1610]

Burroughs Wellcome Fund Collaborative Research Travel Grants (CRTG) *(Doctorate, Postdoctorate/Grant)* [2750]

Career Awards at the Scientific Interface (CASI) *(Undergraduate, Postdoctorate, Graduate/Grant)* [2753]

Mariam K. Chamberlain Fellowship in Women and Public Policy *(Graduate/Fellowship)* [5874]

Jorge Espejel Contreras IALEIA Scholarship *(Undergraduate/Scholarship)* [5930]

ETS Postdoctoral Fellowships *(Postdoctorate/Fellowship)* [4311]

Gertrude M. Cox Scholarship *(Master's, Doctorate/Scholarship)* [1611]

Harold Gulliksen Psychometric Research Fellowship *(Doctorate, Graduate/Fellowship)* [4312]

Ellis R. Ott Scholarships *(Graduate, Master's/Scholarship)* [1543]

Samuel S. Wilks Memorial Award *(Advanced Professional/Award, Monetary)* [1612]

Sylvia Taylor Johnson Minority Fellowships in Educational Measurement *(Doctorate/Fellowship)* [4313]

Substance abuse

Addiction Treatment Scholarship *(Undergraduate/Scholarship)* [5424]

The Recovery Village Health Care Scholarship *(Undergraduate/Scholarship)* [9514]

Suicide

AFSP Distinguished Investigator Grants *(Postgraduate/Grant)* [926]

AFSP Pilot Innovation Grants *(Postgraduate/Grant)* [927]

AFSP Postdoctoral Research Fellowships Innovation Grants *(Postgraduate/Fellowship)* [928]

AFSP Standard Research Innovation Grants *(Postgraduate/Grant)* [929]

AFSP Young Investigator Innovation Grants *(Postgraduate/Grant)* [930]

Surgery

AAS/AAS Trainee Research Fellowship Awards *(Professional development/Fellowship)* [2028]

AAST/ETHICON Research Grants in Local Wound Haemostatics and Hemorrhage Control Scholarships *(Graduate, Postgraduate/Grant)* [651]

AAST/KCI Research Grant *(Doctorate/Grant)* [652]

AAST Medical Student, Resident and In-Training Fellow Scholarships *(Advanced Professional/Scholarship)* [653]

AATS Cardiothoracic Surgery Resident Poster Competition *(Other/Award)* [659]

AATS Perioperative/Team-Based Care Poster Competition *(Professional development/Award)* [660]

AATS/STS Cardiothoracic Ethics Forum Scholarships *(Professional development/Scholarship)* [662, 10543]

ACS Faculty Research Fellowships *(Professional development/Fellowship)* [773]

ACS Resident Research Scholarships *(Advanced Professional/Scholarship)* [774]

American Association for Hand Surgery Annual Research Awards *(Professional development/Grant)* [566]

American College of Surgeons Australia/New Zealand Traveling Fellowship *(Undergraduate/Fellowship)* [775]

American College of Surgeons International Guest Scholarship *(Professional development/Scholarship)* [776]

American Pediatric Surgical Nurses Association Educational Grant *(Other/Grant)* [1210]

American Society of Colon and Rectal Surgeons International Fellowships *(Other/Fellowship)* [1404]

American Society of Colon and Rectal Surgeons International Travel Scholarships *(Other/Scholarship)* [1405]

AMSN Career Mobility Scholarship *(Undergraduate, Doctorate/Scholarship)* [48]

ANPA Young Investigator Awards *(Postdoctorate/Grant)* [1155]

ARS Young Oncologist Travel Grants *(Professional development/Grant)* [1314]

Leslie Bernstein Grant *(Professional development/Grant)* [452]

Daland Fellowships in Clinical Investigation *(Doctorate, Postgraduate/Fellowship)* [1212]

Donald B. Doty Educational Award *(Advanced Professional/Award, Grant)* [11995]

Foundation for Surgical Technology Scholarships *(Graduate/Scholarship)* [2298]

George H. A. Clowes, Jr. MD, FACS, Memorial Research Career Development Award *(Professional development/Fellowship)* [777]

Health Policy Scholarship for General Surgeons *(Professional development/Scholarship)* [778]

OMSF Clinical Surgery Fellowship *(Professional development/Fellowship)* [8682]

PSF Research Fellowship Grants *(Master's, Doctorate/Grant, Fellowship)* [9190]

Resident Research Summit Scholarship *(Professional development, Advanced Professional/Scholarship)* [8683]

SUS Foundation Junior Faculty Research Scholar Award *(Other/Scholarship)* [10550]

Wyeth-SUS Clinical Scholar Awards *(Postgraduate, Professional development/Award)* [10551]

Surveying (See Cartography/ Surveying)

Swedish studies

Lilly Lorenzen Scholarships *(Undergraduate/Scholarship)* [1618]

Malmberg Scholarships *(Undergraduate/Scholarship)* [1619]

Systems engineering

ISA Aerospace Industries Division - William H. Atkinson Scholarships *(Graduate, Undergraduate/Scholarship)* [6085]

ISA Educational Foundation Scholarship *(Undergraduate, Graduate/Scholarship)* [6086]

ISA Executive Board Scholarship *(Graduate, Undergraduate/Scholarship)* [6087]

ISA Section and District Scholarships - Houston *(Graduate, Undergraduate/Scholarship)* [6088]

ISA Section and District Scholarships - Lehigh Valley *(Graduate, Undergraduate/Scholarship)* [6089]

ISA Section and District Scholarships - Richmond Hopewell *(Graduate, Undergraduate/Scholarship)* [6090]

ISA Section and District Scholarships - Southwestern Wyoming *(Graduate, Undergraduate/Scholarship)* [6091]

ISA Section and District Scholarships - Texas, Louisiana and Mississippi *(Graduate, Undergraduate/Scholarship)* [6092]

ISA Section and District Scholarships - Wilmington *(Graduate, Undergraduate/Scholarship)* [6093]

ISA Technical Division Scholarships - Analysis Division *(Graduate, Undergraduate/Scholarship)* [6094]

ISA Technical Division Scholarships - Chemical and Petroleum Industries Division *(College, University/Scholarship)* [6095]

ISA Technical Division Scholarships - Food and Pharmaceutical Industries Division *(Graduate, Undergraduate/Scholarship)* [6096]

ISA Technical Division Scholarships - Power Industry Division *(Graduate, Undergraduate/Scholarship)* [6097]

ISA Technical Division Scholarships - Process Measurement and Control Division *(Graduate, Undergraduate/Scholarship)* [6098]

ISA Technical Division Scholarships - Pulp and Paper Industry Division *(Graduate, Undergraduate/Scholarship)* [6099]

ISA Technical Division Scholarships - Test Measurement Division *(Graduate, Undergraduate/Scholarship)* [6100]

ISA Technical Division Scholarships - Water and Wastewater Industries Division *(Graduate, Undergraduate/Scholarship)* [6101]

Bob and Mary Ives Scholarship *(Graduate, Undergraduate/Scholarship)* [6102]

James E. Long Memorial Post Doctoral Fellowship *(Postdoctorate/Fellowship)* [5984]

Johns Hopkins University/Applied Physics Laboratory Alexander Kossiakoff Scholarship *(Doctorate, Graduate, Master's/Scholarship)* [5985]

Norman E. and Mary-Belle Huston Scholarship *(Graduate, Undergraduate/Scholarship)* [6103]

Stevens Doctoral Award *(Doctorate/Award)* [5986]

Taxonomy

Charlie Fleming Scholarship Fund (CFEF) *(Undergraduate/Scholarship)* [8138]

Teaching

AACTE Outstanding Book Awards *(Other/Award, Recognition)* [547]

AACTE Outstanding Dissertation Awards *(Doctorate/Award)* [548]

AMS Teacher Education Scholarships *(Undergraduate/Scholarship)* [1129]

APF High School Psychology Outreach Grants *(Advanced Professional, Professional development/Grant)* [1275]

Leon Bradley Scholarship Program *(Undergraduate/Scholarship)* [638]

Canadian Zionist Federation - Dr. Leon Aryeh Kronitz Scholarship *(Undergraduate, Graduate/Scholarship)* [9534]

Cindy Andrews Educational Scholarship *(Undergraduate/Scholarship)* [9534]

Clarence Olander School In-Service Training Grants for Grades Prek-5 *(High School/Grant)* [7802]

Jennifer D. Coulter Memorial Scholarship *(Undergraduate/Scholarship)* [8840]

David G. Imig Award for Distinguished Achievement in Teacher Education *(Other/Award, Recognition)* [549]

Donna Gail Scholarship for Chapter Service *(Undergraduate, Graduate, Doctorate/Scholarship)* [6380]

Ernest Duncan - Pre-K-8 Preservice Teacher Action Research Grants *(Professional development/Grant)* [7803]

Patricia Hughes Eastaugh Teaching Scholarship *(Undergraduate/Scholarship)* [11445]

Edward C. Pomeroy Award for Outstanding Contributions to Teacher Education *(Other/Award, Recognition)* [550]

Edwyna Wheadon Postgraduate Training Scholarship *(Postgraduate/Scholarship)* [7799]

ETS Postdoctoral Fellowships *(Postdoctorate/Fellowship)* [4311]

Adrian Fisher Scholarship *(Undergraduate, College, University/Scholarship)* [12316]

Future Leader Initial NCTM Annual Meeting Attendance Awards *(Advanced Professional/Award, Monetary)* [7804]

Educator Conditional Scholarship And Repayment Programs *(Other, Undergraduate/Loan, Scholarship)* [11918]

Harold Gulliksen Psychometric Research Fellowship *(Doctorate, Graduate/Fellowship)* [4312]

Ida L. Hartenberg Charitable Scholarships *(Undergraduate/Scholarship)* [5330]

Harvey Fellows Program *(Graduate/Fellowship)* [7519]

Herb Kohl Educational Foundation Teacher Fellowship Program *(Professional development/Fellowship)* [6584]

Cathy Hopper Memorial Scholarship *(Undergraduate/Scholarship)* [9821]

ITEEA Greer/FTE Grants *(Other/Grant)* [6124]

J. Jay Hostetler Scholarship *(Undergraduate/Scholarship)* [6383]

John I. & Madeleine R. Taeni Scholarship Fund *(Undergraduate/Scholarship)* [10689]

John M. & Mary A. Shanley Memorial Scholarship *(Undergraduate, Graduate/Scholarship)* [10690]

Mary Jon and J. P. Bryan Leadership in Education Awards *(Advanced Professional/Award)* [10999]

June Danby and Pat Pearse Education Scholarship *(Undergraduate/Scholarship)* [6203]

KHEAA Teacher Scholarship *(Undergraduate/Scholarship)* [2573]

Doreen Legg Memorial Scholarships *(Undergraduate/Scholarship)* [9556]

Margaret B. Lindsey Award for Distinguished Research in Teacher Education *(Other/Award, Recognition)* [551]

Louisa Anne Oriente Scholarship *(Graduate, Doctorate/Scholarship)* [6388]

James Madison Foundation - Junior Fellowships *(Advanced Professional, Graduate/Fellowship)* [6227]

James Madison Foundation - Senior Fellowships *(Advanced Professional/Fellowship)* [6228]

Maley/FTE Scholarships *(Graduate/Scholarship)* [6126]

The Albert H. Marckwardt Travel Grants *(Graduate, Doctorate/Grant)* [10969]

Mathematics Graduate Course Work Scholarships for Grades 6-8 Teachers *(Graduate/Scholarship)* [7805]

Minority Teachers of Illinois Scholarship (MTI) *(Undergraduate/Scholarship)* [5715]

Rita & Frank Mooney Scholarship *(Undergraduate, University, College, Vocational/Occupational/Scholarship)* [12349]

Edith Cantor Morrison Memorial Scholarship *(Undergraduate, Graduate/Scholarship)* [2545]

North Carolina Council of Epsilon Sigma Alpha Scholarships *(Graduate/Scholarship)* [8431]

Outlaw Student's Teacher Scholarship *(Undergraduate/Scholarship)* [10863]

Poundmaker Memorial Scholarships *(Undergraduate/Scholarship)* [11675]

Quincy Brown Memorial Scholarship *(Undergraduate/Scholarship)* [9573]

Redlands Teachers Association Scholarship *(Undergraduate/Scholarship)* [9596]

Rev. Alfred E. Monson Scholarship *(Other/Fellowship)* [4862]

John Rowan Scholarship *(Undergraduate, University, College, Vocational/Occupational/Scholarship)* [12366]

Don Sahli-Kathy Woodall Graduate Scholarships *(Graduate/Scholarship)* [10960]

Sons and Daughters Don Sahli-Kathy Woodall Scholarships *(Graduate, Undergraduate/Scholarship)* [10961]

Save a Life Scholarship *(College, University, Vocational/Occupational, Undergraduate, Graduate/Scholarship)* [448]

Judith Gold Stitzel Endowment for Excellence in Women's Studies Teaching and Learning *(Professional development/Grant)* [11977]

Sylvia Taylor Johnson Minority Fellowships in Educational Measurement *(Doctorate/Fellowship)* [4313]

Teacher Education Scholarship *(Advanced Professional/Scholarship)* [1130]

Teacher.org's Inspire Our Future Scholarship *(All/Scholarship)* [10925]

Alan and Grace Tenn Scholarship Fund *(Undergraduate, Graduate/Scholarship)* [5414]

The TESOL/TEFL Travel Grant *(Advanced Professional/Grant, Monetary)* [10970]

Verna Curry Boyer Scholarship Fund *(Undergraduate/Scholarship)* [10835]

Dorreene & Herb Wahl Scholarship *(Undergraduate, University, College/Scholarship)* [12384]

Marjorie Rose Warren Scholarship *(Undergraduate/Scholarship)* [9863]

Shirley Williams Scholarship *(Undergraduate, University, College/Scholarship)* [12393]

Wisconsin Minority Teacher Loan *(Undergraduate/Loan)* [10812]

Wisconsin Teacher of the Visually Impaired Loan *(Undergraduate, Graduate/Loan)* [10814]

Charles Zarigian, Esq. Memorial Award *(Undergraduate/Scholarship)* [1908]

Technical communications

Alaska Aerospace Development Corporation Scholarships *(Undergraduate/Scholarship)* [11433]

Julia Broderick Scholarships *(Undergraduate/Scholarship)* [10818]

Marian Norby Scholarships *(Other/Scholarship)* [6883]

The Melissa Pellegrin Memorial Scholarship Fund *(Undergraduate, Graduate/Scholarship)* [8759]

SBE/Ennes Youth Scholarships *(Graduate/Scholarship)* [10287]

STC-Lone Star Chapter Traditional Education Scholarships *(Graduate, Undergraduate/Scholarship)* [10539]

STC-PSC Scholarships *(Undergraduate, Graduate/Scholarship)* [10541]

STC Scholarships *(Graduate, Undergraduate/Scholarship)* [6884]

Technical training (See Education, Vocational-technical)

Technology

Accenture American Indian Scholarship Fund *(Graduate, Undergraduate/Scholarship)* [993]

AFCEA STEM Teacher Graduate Scholarships *(Graduate/Scholarship)* [104, 7022]

Affirm Scholarship Program *(Undergraduate/Scholarship)* [2175]

AfterCollege STEM Inclusion Scholarship *(Undergraduate, Graduate/Scholarship)* [122]

AGE-WELL Graduate Student and Postdoctoral Awards in Technology and Aging *(Master's, Doctorate, Postdoctorate/Award)* [128]

AHETEMS General Scholarships *(Undergraduate, Graduate/Scholarship)* [10068]

AHETEMS Professional Scholarships *(Graduate/Scholarship)* [10069]

AIP State Department Fellowship *(Postdoctorate/Fellowship, Recognition)* [1041]

Aises A. T. Anderson Memorial Scholarship *(Graduate, Undergraduate/Scholarship)* [1000]

ASGP Graduate Research Fellowships *(Graduate/Fellowship)* [244]

Bank of America Junior Achievement Scholarship in honor of Donna Champion Fund *(Undergraduate/Scholarship)* [4719]

Bluepay Stem Scholarship *(Graduate, Undergraduate/Scholarship)* [2630]

Kathi Bowles Scholarships for Women in Technology *(Undergraduate, Graduate/Scholarship)* [2311]

Buick Achievers Scholarship Program *(Undergraduate/Scholarship)* [4905]

Graduate Fellowship Program - Robert M. Burger Fellowships *(Doctorate, Graduate/Fellowship)* [9999]

Arthur and Gladys Cervenka Scholarship *(Undergraduate/Scholarship)* [10385]

Chapter 6 - Fairfield County Scholarship *(Undergraduate/Scholarship)* [10394]

CHCI Graduate Fellowship Program *(Graduate, Professional development/Fellowship)* [3746]

CIRMMT Student Awards *(Graduate, Master's, Doctorate/Award)* [3253]

CN Scholarships for Women *(Undergraduate/Scholarship)* [3052]

CNS-UCSB Graduate Fellowships for Science and Engineering *(Postdoctorate/Fellowship)* [11563]

Development Fund for Black Students in Science and Technology Scholarship *(Undergraduate/Scholarship)* [4068]

Dr. Ezra Nesbeth Foundation Scholarship *(Undergraduate/Scholarship)* [6213]

Eben Tisdale Fellowship *(Undergraduate/Fellowship, Monetary)* [4838]

Bruce T. and Jackie Mahi Erickson Scholarship *(Graduate, Undergraduate/Scholarship)* [8924]

Full Stack Student Scholarship *(Graduate/Scholarship)* [4833]

Future STEM Teacher Scholarship *(Undergraduate/Scholarship)* [10937]

Girls in Stem (GIS) Scholarship *(Undergraduate/Scholarship)* [9716]

GIST - Orben F. Gist Memorial Scholarship Endowment *(Undergraduate, Community College/Scholarship)* [8511]

Gorrondona & Associates, Inc. / WTS High School Scholarships *(Two Year College, Four Year College/Scholarship)* [12174]

GREAT MINDS Collegiate Scholarship Program *(Undergraduate/Scholarship)* [368]

Perry F. Hadlock Memorial Scholarships *(Undergraduate/Scholarship)* [1943]

Bert & Karen Hadvick Scholarship *(Undergraduate, University, College, Vocational/Occupational/Scholarship)* [12321]

Half Chrome Drones Scholarship *(Other/Scholarship)* [5262]

Helm Family Scholarship *(Undergraduate/Scholarship)* [9819]

Hinman-Jensen Endowed Scholarship *(Undergraduate/Scholarship)* [6797]

ITEEA Greer/FTE Grants *(Other/Grant)* [6124]

Arthur Jackman Scholarship *(Community College, Vocational/Occupational/Scholarship)* [5406]

JMJ Phillip Group College Scholarships *(Graduate, University, Four Year College, Two Year College/Scholarship)* [6312]

Lucile B. Kaufman Women's Scholarship *(Undergraduate/Scholarship)* [10403]

Graduate Fellowship Program - Mahboob Khan/Advanced Micro Devices Fellowships *(Doctorate, Graduate/Fellowship)* [10000]

Laser Technology, Engineering and Applications Scholarship *(Graduate, Undergraduate/Scholarship)* [10727]

Latinos in Technology Scholarship *(Undergraduate/Scholarship)* [10136]

Lindbergh Grants *(Professional development/Grant)* [6869]

Litherland/FTEE Undergraduate Scholarships *(Undergraduate/Scholarship)* [6125]

Lt Col Romeo - Josephine Bass Ferretti Scholarship *(Undergraduate/Scholarship)* [148]

MAES Founders Scholarship *(Graduate, Undergraduate/Scholarship)* [6964]

MAES General Scholarships *(Graduate, Undergraduate/Scholarship)* [6965]

MAES Padrino/Madrina Scholarships *(Graduate, Undergraduate/Scholarship)* [6966]

MAES Pipeline Scholarship *(Graduate, Undergraduate/Scholarship)* [6967]

MAES Presidential Scholarship *(Graduate, Undergraduate/Scholarship)* [6968]

MAES Scholarships *(Graduate/Scholarship)* [6969]

Malayalee Engineers Association Scholarships *(Undergraduate/Scholarship)* [7012]

Maley/FTE Scholarships *(Graduate/Scholarship)* [6126]

Maley/FTEE Teacher Professional Development Scholarships *(Professional development/Scholarship)* [6127]

Giuliano Mazzetti Scholarship *(Undergraduate/Scholarship)* [10408]

Pat & Donald Merrill Scholarship *(Undergraduate, University, College, Vocational/Occupational/Scholarship)* [12348]

Michigan Council of Women in Technology High School Scholarship Program *(High School/Scholarship)* [7310]

Michigan Council of Women in Technology Undergraduate Scholarship Program *(Undergraduate, Graduate/Scholarship)* [7311]

Murrietta Circuits Scholarship Opportunity *(Undergraduate, College, University/Scholarship)* [7505]

National Debt Relief Scholarship *(University, Four Year College, Undergraduate/Scholarship)* [7828]

National Science Foundation Graduate Research Fellowship Program (GRFP) *(Graduate/Fellowship)* [8068]

NDIA Picatinny Chapter Scholarships *(Undergraduate/Scholarship)* [7832]

Nixon Family Scholarship Fund *(Undergraduate, High School/Scholarship)* [11950]

Ocean Industry Student Research Awards *(Undergraduate, Graduate, Postdoctorate/Award)* [9641]

Ohio Space Grant Consortium Graduate Fellowships *(Graduate, Doctorate, Master's/Fellowship)* [8598]

Ohio Space Grant Consortium Special Minority Fellowships *(Doctorate, Graduate, Master's/Fellowship)* [8599]

Out to Innovate Scholarship *(Graduate, Undergraduate, Community College/Scholarship)* [8019]

Martha Mitchell Pearson Memorial Scholarship *(Undergraduate, Graduate/Scholarship)* [6464]

Herman Peterson Scholarship *(Vocational/Occupational, Undergraduate, University, College/Scholarship)* [12356]

Garry Phillips Scholarship *(Undergraduate, University, College, Vocational/Occupational/Scholarship)* [12358]

Proven Data Recovery Technology Scholarships *(All/Scholarship)* [9373]

PSAI Scholarship Fund *(Undergraduate/Scholarship)* [9248]

Red Olive Women in STEM Scholarship *(Undergraduate, Graduate/Scholarship)* [9516]

Jack Rosen Scholarship *(Undergraduate/Scholarship)* [6393]

John Rowan Scholarship *(Undergraduate, University, College, Vocational/Occupational/Scholarship)* [12366]

Samuel S. Wilks Memorial Award *(Advanced Professional/Award, Monetary)* [1612]

Prof. George Schneider Scholarship *(Undergraduate/Scholarship)* [10413]

Science, Mathematics And Research for Transformation Scholarship for Service Program (SMART) *(Undergraduate, Graduate/Scholarship)* [1445, 9974]

SHPE Dissertation Scholarship *(Doctorate/Scholarship)* [10351]

SHPE Professional Scholarship *(Master's, Doctorate/Scholarship)* [10352]

SPEATBC Entrance Scholarship *(Graduate, High School/Scholarship)* [10518]

SRC Master's Scholarships Program *(Graduate, Master's/Scholarship)* [10001]

SREB-State Doctoral Scholars Program - Doctoral Award *(Doctorate, Graduate/Scholarship)* [10664]

Truthfinder Scholarship for Women in STEM *(Undergraduate, Graduate, Two Year College/Scholarship)* [11133]

Undergraduate Scholars Program *(Graduate/Scholarship)* [5606]

USGA/Chevron STEM Scholarship Program *(Undergraduate/Scholarship)* [11373]

J.J. Van Bibber Scholarship *(Undergraduate, University, College, Vocational/Occupational/Scholarship)* [12380]

Vancouver Yukoners Legacy Scholarship *(Vocational/Occupational, College, Undergraduate/Scholarship)* [12381]

Myrtle & Earl Walker Scholarships *(Undergraduate/Scholarship)* [10417]

Websauce Web Design Scholarship *(Undergraduate/Scholarship)* [11954]

Matthew Webster Scholarship *(Undergraduate, College, Vocational/Occupational/Scholarship)* [12386]

William E. Weisel Scholarship *(Undergraduate/Scholarship)* [10418]

William P. Elrod Memorial Scholarship *(Undergraduate/Scholarship)* [10938]

Robert Wilson Scholarship *(Undergraduate, College, Vocational/Occupational/Scholarship)* [12394]

Wisconsin Laboratory Association Graduate Student Scholarships *(Graduate/Scholarship)* [12123]

WLA Scholarships *(Undergraduate, Graduate/Scholarship)* [12124]

Wisconsin Laboratory Association Undergraduate University Student Scholarships *(Undergraduate/Scholarship)* [12125]

WSGC Community College Transfer Scholarships *(Undergraduate/Scholarship)* [11901]

Telecommunications systems

Jim Bourque Scholarship *(Undergraduate/Scholarship)* [1790]

Dickey Rural Networks Scholarship *(Undergraduate, Vocational/Occupational/Scholarship)* [4080]

William Taylor in Radiocommunications Scholarships *(Undergraduate/Scholarship)* [3795]

NANOG Scholarship Program *(Undergraduate, Graduate/Scholarship)* [9943]

OAS Scholarships for Professional Development - Disaster Communications Management *(Professional development/Scholarship)* [8732]

OAS Scholarships for Professional Development - Radio Spectrum Monitoring Techniques and Procedures *(Professional development/Scholarship)* [8733]

OAS Scholarships for Professional Development - Satellite Communications *(Professional development/Scholarship)* [8734]

OAS Scholarships for Professional Development - The ABC of Telecommunications *(Professional development/Scholarship)* [8735]

The SSPI Mid-Atlantic Chapter Scholarship *(Graduate, Undergraduate/Scholarship)* [10522]

RABC William Taylor Scholarships *(Undergraduate/Scholarship)* [4360]

Television (See Radio and television)

Testing, educational/psychological

AERA-ETS Fellowship Program in Measurement and Education Research *(Doctorate/Fellowship)* [868]

ASNT Fellowship Award *(Graduate/Fellowship, Award)* [1531]

Robert B. Oliver ASNT Scholarship *(Undergraduate/ Scholarship)* [1532]

Textile science

California Association of Family and Consumer Sciences - San Diego Chapter Scholarship *(Undergraduate, Graduate/Scholarship)* [9805]

Charles H. Stone-Piedmont Scholarship *(Undergraduate, Graduate/Scholarship, Monetary)* [657]

ITAA Graduate Student Best Paper Award *(Graduate/Award, Monetary)* [6129]

S. Penny Chappell Scholarship *(Undergraduate/ Scholarship)* [9127]

Sutherland/Purdy Scholarship *(Undergraduate/ Scholarship)* [9130]

Theater arts

AFA Theatre & Performance Art Project Grants *(Professional development/Grant)* [259]

ASTR Research Fellowships *(Doctorate/Fellowship)* [1577]

David Beltran Memorial Scholarship *(Undergraduate/Scholarship)* [9540]

Peter Dwyer Scholarships *(Undergraduate/Scholarship)* [2872]

S. Randolph Edmonds Young Scholars Competition *(Graduate, Undergraduate/Scholarship)* [2615]

Fund for Small Theatres *(Other/Grant)* [366]

Mona Gray Creative Arts Scholarship *(Graduate, Undergraduate/Scholarship)* [6306]

Gwen Yarnell Theatre Scholarship *(Undergraduate/ Scholarship)* [4566]

Helen Krich Chinoy Dissertation Fellowship *(Doctorate/Fellowship)* [1578]

Indiana State University Creative and Performing Arts Awards *(Undergraduate/Scholarship)* [5769]

Jerome Fellowships *(Other/Fellowship)* [9196]

Hedy Lamarr Achievement Award for Emerging Leaders in Entertainment Technology *(Undergraduate/Award)* [4086]

Robert G. Lawrence Prize *(Doctorate, Graduate/ Prize, Award)* [2105]

Leighton M. Ballew Directing Scholarship *(Undergraduate/Scholarship)* [10635]

Many Voices Fellowships *(Other/Fellowship)* [9197]

Margaret McFarlane Alkek Undergraduate Scholarship *(Undergraduate/Scholarship)* [4006]

Marian A. Smith Costume Scholarship Award *(Graduate/Scholarship)* [10636]

Thomas Marshall Graduate Student Awards *(Postgraduate/Grant, Award)* [1579]

McKnight Fellowships *(Other/Fellowship)* [9198]

McKnight Theater Artist Fellowships *(Other/Fellowship)* [9199]

James W. Murdoch Scholarship *(Undergraduate, University, College, Vocational/Occupational/ Scholarship)* [12351]

NEA/TCG Career Development Program for Designers *(Professional development/Grant)* [7868, 11008]

NEA/TCG Career Development Program *(Professional development/Grant)* [7869, 11009]

Polly Holliday Scholarship Award *(Undergraduate/ Scholarship, Monetary)* [10637]

Robert Porterfield Graduate Scholarship *(Graduate/ Scholarship)* [10638]

Robert Porterfield Scholarship *(Graduate/Scholarship)* [10639]

PWC Core Apprentice Program *(Other/Internship)* [9200]

Redlands Footlighters, Inc. - Merle and Peggy Williams Scholarship *(Undergraduate/Scholarship)* [9581]

Alan Schneider Director Award *(Professional development/Award, Grant)* [11010]

The Ann Shaw International TYA Fellowship *(Professional development/Fellowship)* [11014]

Southeastern Theatre Conference Secondary School Scholarship *(Undergraduate/Scholarship)* [10640]

Stephen Schwartz Musical Theatre Scholarship *(Undergraduate/Scholarship)* [5624]

Theatre Guild Scholarship *(Undergraduate/Scholarship)* [11012]

Patricia Van Kirk Scholarship *(Undergraduate/Scholarship)* [9316]

Wilder Dimension Scholarships for Advanced Study in Theatre Arts *(Graduate/Scholarship)* [4178]

William E. Wilson Scholarship *(Graduate/Scholarship)* [10641]

William R. Durham Drama and Theater Scholarship *(Undergraduate/Scholarship)* [3695]

Theology (See also Religion)

Ellen Blodgett Memorial Scholarship *(Master's/ Scholarship)* [8333]

William L. Bradley Memorial Scholarship *(Master's/ Scholarship)* [8334]

Paul W. Bradley Scholarship *(Master's/Scholarship)* [8335]

Calihan Academic Grants *(Graduate, Professional development/Fellowship, Grant)* [65]

Calihan Travel Grants *(Other, Graduate/Grant)* [66]

CSF Graduate Fellowship *(Graduate/Fellowship)* [3325]

Esther Cummings Memorial Scholarship *(Master's/ Scholarship)* [8336]

Margaret Eddy Scholarship *(Graduate, Master's/ Scholarship)* [8337]

Ethel Mae Gaston Memorial Scholarship *(Master's/ Scholarship)* [8338]

Emily V. Gibbes Scholarship *(Master's/Scholarship)* [8339]

The William Randolph Hearst Endowed Scholarship *(Master's/Scholarship)* [8340]

George L. and June L. Herpel Memorial Scholarship *(Graduate/Scholarship)* [2529]

The Melvyn F. Hester Scholarship *(Master's/Scholarship)* [8341]

The Barbara J. and M. William Howard Jr. Scholarship *(Master's/Scholarship)* [8342]

The Sang Ok Hur Scholarships *(Master's/Scholarship)* [8343]

Harry A. Kuljian Memorial Grant *(Undergraduate/ Scholarship)* [1893]

The Hwain Chang Lee scholarship *(Master's/Scholarship)* [8344]

The William K. Lee Scholarship *(Master's/Scholarship)* [8345]

The Margaret Smith Maase Scholarships *(Master's/ Scholarship)* [8346]

The Ann M. Mallouk Scholarships *(Master's/Scholarship)* [8347]

The Rev. Richard S. McCarroll and Mrs. E. Allison McCarroll Scholarship *(Master's/Scholarship)* [8348]

The Ella and Harold Midtbo Scholarship *(Master's/ Scholarship)* [8349]

The William Howard Morton Scholarship *(Master's/ Scholarship)* [8350]

Novak Awards *(Doctorate/Monetary, Award)* [67]

Abraham A. Oyedeji Scholarship *(Master's/Scholarship)* [8351]

J. Milton Richardson Theological Fellowship *(Graduate/Fellowship)* [405]

Tabat Scholarship Award *(Graduate/Scholarship)* [4533]

The Virtuous Prom Peace Scholarship *(Undergraduate, Graduate, Postgraduate/Scholarship)* [11852]

The George D. Younger Scholarship *(Graduate/ Scholarship)* [8352]

Tourette syndrome

Tourette Association of America Research Grant Awards *(Master's, Doctorate/Grant)* [11067]

Toxicology

AACT Junior Investigator Research Grants *(Professional development/Grant)* [441]

AACT Research Award *(Professional development/ Grant)* [442]

AACT Toxicology Trainee Research Grants *(Professional development/Grant)* [443]

Colgate-Palmolive PostDoctoral Fellowship Award in In Vitro Toxicology *(Postdoctorate/Fellowship)* [10545]

GWS Scholarship Program *(Undergraduate, Graduate/Scholarship)* [165]

International Association for Food Protection - Student Travel Scholarship Program *(Undergraduate, Graduate/Scholarship)* [5921]

Lampe-Kunkel Memorial Award *(Professional development/Grant)* [444]

Michael P. Spadafora Medical Toxicology Travel Award *(Professional development/Grant)* [766]

NCCT Postdoctoral Research Program *(Postdoctorate, Advanced Professional, Professional development/Fellowship)* [11358]

Pharmacology/Toxicology Pre Doctoral Fellowships *(Doctorate/Fellowship)* [9062]

PhRMA Foundation Pharmacology/Toxicology Post Doctoral Fellowships *(Postdoctorate/Fellowship)* [9068]

PhRMA Foundation Pharmacology/Toxicology Research Starter Grants *(Doctorate/Grant)* [9069]

PhRMA Foundation Pharmacology/Toxicology Sabbatical Fellowships *(Postdoctorate, Master's/Fellowship)* [9070]

Trades training (See Education, Vocational-technical)

Traffic management (See Transportation)

Translating

Institute for Anarchist Studies Grants for Radical Writers and Translators *(Professional development/Grant)* [5812]

Leif and Inger Sjöberg Award *(Advanced Professional, Professional development/Award)* [1376]

Transportation

ABA Diversity Scholarships *(Graduate/Scholarship)* [707]

ABA Members Scholarships *(Undergraduate, Graduate/Scholarship)* [708]

Air Traffic Control Association Full-time Employee Student Scholarship *(Other/Scholarship)* [155]

Allied Van Lines Military Scholarship *(Undergraduate/Scholarship)* [370]

American Bus Association Academic Merit Scholarships *(Undergraduate, Graduate/Scholarship)* [709]

Bus & Tour Operator Scholarships *(Undergraduate, Graduate/Scholarship)* [710]

CTP Scholarship Program *(Other/Scholarship)* [8053]

Dallas/Fort Worth Chapter WTS Undergraduate Scholarship *(Undergraduate/Scholarship)* [12173]

Dan M. Reichard, Jr. Scholarship *(Undergraduate, Graduate/Scholarship)* [1299]

Dr. George M. Smerk Scholarship *(Undergraduate, Graduate/Scholarship)* [1300]

Florida Public Transportation Association Scholarships (FPTA) *(Undergraduate, Graduate/Scholarship)* [1301]

Gabrial A. Hartl Scholarship *(Undergraduate/Scholarship)* [157]

Greater DFW WTS Undergraduate Leadership Scholarship *(Undergraduate/Scholarship)* [12175]

HSF/Marathon Oil College Scholarship Program *(Undergraduate/Scholarship)* [5531]

Institute of Transportation Engineers - Texas District Fellowships *(Graduate/Fellowship)* [5865]

Western District fellowship *(Graduate/Fellowship)* [5866]

Jack R. Gilstrap Scholarship *(Undergraduate, Graduate/Scholarship)* [1302]

Louis T. Klauder Scholarship *(Undergraduate, Graduate/Scholarship)* [1303]

NAPT Continuing Education Award *(Undergraduate/Award)* [7684]

NDTA Academic Scholarship Program A *(Undergraduate/Scholarship)* [7836]

NDTA Academic Scholarship Program B *(Undergraduate/Scholarship)* [7837]

Parsons Brinckerhoff / Jim Lammie Scholarship *(Undergraduate, Graduate/Scholarship)* [1304]

Greater DFW WTS Monique Pegues Graduate Leadership Scholarship *(Graduate/Scholarship)* [12176]

Peter L. Picknelly Honorary Scholarships *(Graduate/Scholarship)* [711]

Reba Malone Scholarship *(Undergraduate, Graduate/Scholarship)* [1305]

Richard J. Bouchard - AECOM Scholarship *(Undergraduate, Graduate/Scholarship)* [1306]

Frank J. Richter Scholarship *(Graduate, Undergraduate/Scholarship)* [633]

SC&R Foundation Grant Program *(Undergraduate/Grant)* [10717]

SC&R Foundation Scholarship *(Undergraduate/Scholarship)* [10718]

Wanda J. Schafer Graduate Scholarship *(Graduate/Scholarship)* [12177]

Sharon D. Banks Memorial Undergraduate Scholarship *(Undergraduate/Scholarship)* [12171]

E.J. Sierleja Memorial Fellowship *(Graduate/Fellowship)* [5835]

Snowmobile Association of Massachusetts Awards / Scholarships *(Undergraduate/Scholarship)* [10235]

TAC Foundation – 3M Canada "Bob Margison Memorial" Scholarship *(Graduate, Undergraduate/Scholarship)* [11077]

TAC Foundation-407 ETR Scholarships *(Undergraduate, Graduate/Scholarship)* [11078]

TAC Foundation-Amec Foster Wheeler Scholarships *(Undergraduate, Graduate/Scholarship)* [11079]

TAC Foundation-ATS Traffic Scholarships *(Undergraduate, Graduate/Scholarship)* [11080]

TAC Foundation-Canadian Council of Independent Laboratories Graduate Student Scholarship (CCIL) *(Graduate/Scholarship)* [11081]

TAC Foundation-CCMTA Road Safety Scholarships *(Undergraduate, Graduate/Scholarship)* [11082]

TAC Foundation-Cement Association of Canada Scholarships *(Graduate, Undergraduate/Scholarship)* [11083]

TAC Foundation-Dillon Consulting Scholarships *(Undergraduate, Graduate/Scholarship)* [11084]

TAC Foundation-Dr. Ralph Haas Graduate Student Scholarships *(Graduate/Scholarship)* [11085]

TAC Foundation-EllisDon Community College/CEGEP Scholarships *(Undergraduate/Scholarship)* [11086]

TAC Foundation-exp Scholarships *(Undergraduate, Graduate/Scholarship)* [11087]

TAC Foundation-Golder Associates Ltd. Scholarships *(Undergraduate, Graduate/Scholarship)* [11088]

TAC Foundation-HDR Corporation Graduate Student Scholarships *(Graduate/Scholarship)* [11089]

TAC Foundation-IBI Group Scholarships *(Undergraduate, Graduate/Scholarship)* [11090]

TAC Foundation-ISL Engineering Scholarships *(Undergraduate, Graduate/Scholarship)* [11091]

TAC Foundation-LEA Consulting Ltd. Scholarships *(Undergraduate, Graduate/Scholarship)* [11092]

TAC Foundation-MMM Group Limited Scholarships *(Undergraduate, Graduate/Scholarship)* [11093]

TAC Foundation-Municipalities Scholarships *(Undergraduate, Graduate/Scholarship)* [11094]

TAC Foundation-Parsons Scholarships *(Undergraduate, Graduate/Scholarship)* [11095]

TAC Foundation-Peto MacCallum Undergraduate & College Scholarships *(Undergraduate/Scholarship)* [11096]

TAC Foundation-Provinces and Territories Scholarships *(Undergraduate, Graduate/Scholarship)* [11097]

TAC Foundation-SNC Lavalin Scholarships *(Undergraduate, Graduate/Scholarship)* [11098]

TAC Foundation-Stantec Consulting Dr. Ralph Haas Scholarships *(Graduate, Undergraduate/Scholarship)* [11099]

TAC Foundation-Tetra Tech EBA Inc. Scholarships *(Undergraduate, Graduate/Scholarship)* [11100]

Transoft Solutions, Inc. Ahead of the Curve Scholarship (AOTC) *(Graduate, Undergraduate/Scholarship)* [5867]

Transportation Association of Canada Foundation Scholarships *(Graduate, Undergraduate/Scholarship)* [11101]

Transportation YOU High School Scholarship *(High School/Scholarship)* [12178]

Urgent.ly Driving Transportation Innovation Scholarship *(Undergraduate, Graduate, Vocational/Occupational/Scholarship)* [11769]

WTS Community College/Technical/Trade School Scholarship *(Two Year College, Vocational/Occupational/Scholarship)* [12179]

Travel and tourism

ABA Diversity Scholarships *(Graduate/Scholarship)* [707]

ABA Members Scholarships *(Undergraduate, Graduate/Scholarship)* [708]

America Express Travel Scholarships *(Undergraduate/Scholarship)* [1581]

American Bus Association Academic Merit Scholarships *(Undergraduate, Graduate/Scholarship)* [709]

ASTA Alaska Airlines Scholarships *(Undergraduate/Scholarship)* [1582]

ASTA Holland America Line Graduate Research Scholarships *(Graduate/Scholarship)* [1583]

ASTA Rigby, Healy, Simmons Scholarships *(Graduate, Undergraduate/Scholarship)* [1584]

Avis Budget Group Scholarships *(Graduate/Scholarship)* [1585]

Bick Bickson Scholarship Fund *(Undergraduate, Graduate/Award)* [5383]

Bus & Tour Operator Scholarships *(Undergraduate, Graduate/Scholarship)* [710]

Catrala - Hawaii Scholarship Fund *(Undergraduate, University, Two Year College, Four Year College/Scholarship)* [5388]

Donald W. F. Ching Memorial Scholarship Fund *(Undergraduate, Two Year College, Four Year College/Scholarship)* [5392]

Graduate Student Award *(Doctorate, Master's, Graduate/Award)* [515]

David J. Hallissey Memorial Internships *(Graduate, Undergraduate/Internship)* [1586]

ISTTE Scholarship *(Graduate, Undergraduate/Scholarship)* [6122]

John A. Rothschild Bachelor Degree in Hospitality Scholarship *(Undergraduate, Community College/Scholarship)* [3006]

Mike Kabo Global Scholarships *(Professional development/Scholarship)* [5004]

North Carolina Hospitality Education Foundation Scholarship *(Undergraduate/Scholarship)* [8446]

NC Hospitality Education Foundation Scholarships - High School *(Undergraduate/Scholarship)* [8448]

NC Hospitality Education Foundation Scholarships - Two Year Community or Junior College *(Undergraduate/Scholarship)* [8449]

Craig D. Newman Memorial Scholarship *(Undergraduate/Scholarship)* [5409]

Peter L. Picknelly Honorary Scholarships *(Graduate/Scholarship)* [711]

George Reinke Scholarships *(Other/Scholarship)* [1587]

South Carolina Tourism and Hospitality Educational Foundation Scholarships *(Undergraduate/Scholarship)* [10614]

Allegheny Branch of Mid-America Chapter - Nancy Stewart Professional Development Scholarships *(Professional development/Scholarship)* [1588]

Sue & Ken Dyer Foundation Travel Scholarship *(Other/Scholarship)* [4784]

Thomas and Ruth River International Scholarship *(Undergraduate, Graduate/Scholarship)* [12201]

Yukon Anniversaries Commission Scholarship *(Undergraduate, University, College, Vocational/Occupational/Scholarship)* [12396]

Tuberculosis

Graduate Pulmonary Nursing Fellowship *(Professional development/Fellowship, Scholarship)* [4572]

Northrop-Park Fellowship *(Professional development/Fellowship)* [4573]

Turfgrass management

Drew Smith Memorial Scholarship *(Undergraduate/Scholarship)* [3563]

GCSAA Scholars Competition *(Undergraduate/Scholarship)* [5032]

GCSAA Student Essay Contest *(Graduate, Undergraduate/Prize)* [5033]

Safer Athletic Field Environments Scholarships (SAFE) *(Graduate, Undergraduate, Two Year College/Scholarship)* [10736]

Dr. James Watson Fellowship Program *(Doctorate, Graduate/Fellowship)* [5034, 11058]

Turkish studies

Dissertation Writing Grants *(Graduate/Grant)* [5869]

Institute of Turkish Studies Sabbatical Research Grants *(Other/Grant)* [5870]

Post-Doctoral Summer Travel-Research Grants *(Postdoctorate/Grant)* [5871]

Summer Language Study Grants in Turkey *(Graduate/Grant)* [5872]

Ukrainian studies

Helen Darcovich Memorial Doctoral Fellowship *(Doctorate/Fellowship)* [3026]

Leo J. Krysa Family Undergraduate Scholarships *(Undergraduate/Scholarship)* [3030]

Stasiuk Master's Research Fellowship *(Master's/Fellowship)* [3032]

Ukrainian Canadian Professional and Business Club Scholarships in Education *(Undergraduate/Scholarship)* [3033]

United States studies

American Historical Print Collectors Society Fellowship *(Doctorate/Fellowship)* [484, 965]

The Christoph Daniel Ebeling Fellowship *(Postdoctorate, Doctorate/Fellowship)* [489, 4055]

Henry Salvatori Fellowships *(Graduate/Fellowship)* [5885]

Kislak Fellowship for the Study of the History and Cultures of the Early Americas *(Undergraduate, Graduate/Fellowship)* [6572]

Marshall-Baruch Fellowships *(Doctorate/Fellowship)* [7111]

Institute Andrew W. Mellon Postdoctoral Research Fellowships *(Graduate/Fellowship)* [8621]

Omohundro Institute-NEH Postdoctoral Fellowships *(Graduate/Fellowship)* [8622]

The Reese Fellowship *(Doctorate/Fellowship)* [498]

Smithsonian Institution Graduate Student Fellowships *(Graduate/Fellowship)* [10205]

Smithsonian Institution Postdoctoral Researcher Fellowships *(Postdoctorate/Fellowship)* [10206]

Smithsonian Institution Predoctoral Student Fellowships *(Doctorate, Postgraduate/Fellowship)* [10207]

Smithsonian Institution Senior Researcher Fellowships *(Professional development/Fellowship)* [10208]

United States Capitol Historical Society Fellowships *(Graduate/Fellowship)* [11299]

Urban affairs/design/planning

American Planning Association ENRE Student Fellowship Program *(Graduate/Fellowship)* [1242]

CIGNA Healthcare Graduate Scholarships *(Graduate/Scholarship)* [7888]

CIGNA Undergraduate Scholarships *(Undergraduate/Scholarship)* [7889]

HECUA Scholarship for Community Engagement *(Undergraduate/Scholarship)* [5505]

Holzheimer Memorial Student Scholarship *(Graduate, Master's/Scholarship)* [1243]

Jewish Federation Academic Scholarship *(Graduate, Undergraduate/Scholarship)* [6310]

The Robert A. Catlin/David W. Long Scholarship *(Graduate/Scholarship)* [1244]

McCloy Fellowships in Urban Affairs *(Professional development/Fellowship)* [813]

Judith McManus Price Scholarship *(Undergraduate, Graduate/Scholarship)* [1245]

Resilience Action Fund Scholarship *(Graduate/Scholarship)* [4504]

UC MEXUS-CONACYT Doctoral Fellowship *(Doctorate/Fellowship)* [11552]

Vectorworks Design Scholarship *(Undergraduate, Graduate/Scholarship)* [11796]

Worldstudio AIGA Scholarships *(Graduate, Undergraduate/Scholarship)* [12205]

Urology

AUA Foundation Urology Research Bridge Awards *(Postgraduate/Award)* [11771]

KFOC Allied Health Scholarships *(Graduate/Scholarship)* [6547]

KFOC Biomedical Scholarships *(Doctorate/Scholarship)* [6548]

Urology Care Foundation/Astellas Rising Star in Urology Research Awards *(Postdoctorate, Other/Award)* [11772]

Western University - Endourology Fellowship *(Professional development/Fellowship)* [4385]

Vacuum science and technology

Society of Vacuum Coaters Foundation Scholarship *(Undergraduate, Graduate/Scholarship)* [10553]

Vegetarianism

Vegetarian Resource Group College Scholarship *(Undergraduate, High School/Scholarship, Monetary, Award)* [11798]

Veterinary science and medicine

AABP Amstutz Scholarship *(Undergraduate/Scholarship)* [522]

AABP Bovine Veterinary Student Recognition Award *(Undergraduate/Scholarship, Award)* [523]

AABP Education Grants *(Graduate, Postgraduate, Master's/Grant)* [524]

AABP Student Externship Program *(Undergraduate/Scholarship)* [525]

AAEP/ALSIC Scholarships *(Undergraduate/Scholarship)* [558]

AAEP Foundation Past Presidents' Research Fellow *(Graduate, Professional development/Scholarship)* [559]

ACVO Best Resident Manuscript Awards *(Undergraduate/Recognition)* [780]

American Quarter Horse Foundation Scholarships *(Undergraduate, Graduate/Scholarship)* [1310]

Animal Compassion Undergraduate Scholarships *(Undergraduate/Scholarship)* [9044]

Army Health Professions Scholarship Program (HPSP) *(Professional development/Scholarship)* [11288]

AVMA Fellowship Program *(Professional development/Fellowship)* [1628]

AZVT Laurie Page-Peck Scholarship *(Graduate/Scholarship)* [2325]

Wade O. Brinker Resident Research Award *(Postgraduate, Professional development/Grant)* [11813]

DAAD Study Scholarship Awards *(Graduate, Undergraduate/Scholarship)* [4059]

Discover Health Professions Loans *(Graduate/Loan, Scholarship)* [4111]

Discover Residency Loans *(Graduate/Loan, Scholarship)* [4114]

Downeast Feline Fund *(Graduate/Scholarship)* [6978]

Allan Eldin & Agnes Sutorik Geiger Scholarship Fund *(Undergraduate, Graduate/Scholarship)* [5397]

Keith Gilmore Foundation - Postgraduate Scholarships *(Postgraduate/Scholarship)* [4971]

Keith Gilmore Foundation - Undergraduate Scholarships *(Undergraduate/Scholarship)* [4972]

M.G. "Doc" Headley Scholarships *(Undergraduate/Scholarship)* [10826]

Hohn-Johnson Research Award *(Professional development/Grant)* [11814]

Investigators in the Pathogenesis of Infectious Disease *(Doctorate, Postdoctorate/Grant)* [2754]

Dr. Roger E. Meisner Veterinary Medicine Educational Scholarship Fund *(Undergraduate, Graduate/Scholarship)* [8474]

Merial Excellence in Preventive Medicine in Beef Award *(Other/Grant)* [526]

Merial Excellence in Preventive Medicine in Dairy Award *(Other/Grant)* [527]

North Dakota Veterinary Medical Association Scholarships *(Undergraduate/Scholarship)* [8475]

Pappaioanou Veterinary Public Health and Applied Epidemiology Fellowships *(Undergraduate/Fellowship)* [3202]

Rob and Bessie Welder Wildlife Foundation's graduate research fellowship *(Graduate, Master's, Doctorate/Fellowship)* [11958]

Stark County Dairy Promoters Scholarship Fund *(Graduate/Scholarship)* [10794]

John & Doris Stenbraten Scholarship *(Undergraduate, University, College, Vocational/Occupational/Scholarship)* [12374]

Dr. William "Tim" Whalen Memorial Scholarships *(Undergraduate/Scholarship)* [8476]

Saul T. Wilson, Jr. Internship *(Graduate, Undergraduate/Internship)* [11301]

Video

AFA Film and Video Arts Project Grants *(Professional development/Grant)* [257]

Carole Fielding Student Grant *(Undergraduate, Graduate/Grant)* [11567]

Vietnamese studies

Gamewardens Scholarship Program *(High School/Scholarship)* [4852]

BM1 James Elliott Williams Memorial Scholarship Fund *(Undergraduate/Scholarship)* [8936]

Violence (See Aggression and violence)

Violin (See Music, Violin)

Visual arts

Arts Council of Greater Grand Rapids Minority Scholarship *(Undergraduate/Scholarship)* [5134]

Arts Foundation of Cape Cod Scholarships *(Undergraduate, Vocational/Occupational/Scholarship)* [1975]

William E. Barto Scholarship Fund *(Undergraduate/Scholarship)* [4200]

Bill Bendiner and Doug Morgenson Scholarship *(Undergraduate/Scholarship)* [9293]

CBC Spouses Visual Arts Scholarship *(Undergraduate/Scholarship)* [3740]

CINTAS-Knight Fellowship inthe Visual Arts *(Professional development/Fellowship)* [3418]

Constant Memorial Scholarship *(Undergraduate/Scholarship)* [9691]

Jack Kent Cooke Graduate Arts Awards *(Graduate/Award)* [3819]

Dr Piotrowski Adolph Memorial Art Scholarship *(Undergraduate/Scholarship)* [9660]

Florida Education Fund McKnight Doctoral Fellowship *(Graduate/Fellowship)* [4629]

Grants to Artists *(Advanced Professional/Grant)* [4769]

Manzer-Keener-Wefler Scholarship Fund *(Undergraduate/Scholarship)* [10777]

Elizabeth Massey Award *(Postgraduate/Award)* [2974]

Jack D. Motteler Scholarship *(Undergraduate/Scholarship)* [9305]

Native Hawaiian Visual Arts Scholarship *(Graduate, Undergraduate/Scholarship)* [8933]

New Museum Bogliasco Fellowship in Visual Art *(Professional development/Fellowship)* [2646]

Piscataqua Region Artist Advancement Grant *(Professional development/Grant)* [8259]

Robert W. and Bernice Ingalls Staton Scholarships *(Undergraduate/Scholarship)* [11654]

The Sally Cole Visual Arts Scholarship Program *(Undergraduate/Scholarship)* [4753]

Ric Ulrich and Chuck Pischke Scholarships *(Undergraduate/Scholarship)* [9315]

Patricia Van Kirk Scholarship *(Undergraduate/Scholarship)* [9316]

Virginia Museum of Fine Arts Visual Arts Fellowships *(Graduate, Other, Undergraduate/Fellowship)* [11839]

Visual Arts and New Media Individual Project Funding *(Professional development/Grant)* [265]

Wyeth Foundation For American Art Publication Grant *(Other/Grant)* [3504]

Visual impairment

Joanne Angle Investigator Award *(Professional development/Award, Grant)* [9275]

National Federation of the Blind Scholarship Program *(Undergraduate/Scholarship, Monetary)* [7878]

Ross C. Purse Doctoral Fellowship *(Graduate/Award, Fellowship)* [3049]

Thome Foundation Awards Program in Age-Related Macular Degeneration Research *(Professional development/Grant)* [5444]

Wisconsin Teacher of the Visually Impaired Loan *(Undergraduate, Graduate/Loan)* [10814]

Viticulture

American Wine Society Educational Foundation Scholarships (AWSEF) *(Graduate/Scholarship)* [1676]

ASEV Traditional Scholarship *(Graduate, Undergraduate/Scholarship)* [1447]

Nancy Johnston Memorial Scholarships *(Graduate, Undergraduate/Scholarship)* [10956]

Vocational-technical education (See Education, Vocational-technical)

Waste management

Dave Benferado Scholarship *(Graduate/Scholarship)* [159]

EREF Doctoral Scholarship *(Doctorate/Scholarship)* [4417]

Milton Feldstein Memorial Scholarships *(Graduate/Scholarship)* [160]

GWS Scholarship Program *(Undergraduate, Graduate/Scholarship)* [165]

Ivanhoe Foundation Fellowship *(Master's/Fellowship)* [6184]

Jacqueline Shields Memorial Scholarship *(Graduate/Scholarship)* [161]

Local A&WMA Sections and Chapter Scholarships *(Graduate/Scholarship)* [162]

Richard Stessel Memorial Scholarship *(Graduate/Scholarship)* [163]

Southern Section A&WMA Scholarships *(Graduate/Scholarship)* [10668]

Water resources

Abel Wolman Fellowship *(Doctorate/Fellowship, Award, Monetary)* [1634]

AGWT Baroid Scholarships *(Undergraduate/Scholarship)* [948]

AGWT Thomas M. Stetson Scholarships *(Undergraduate/Scholarship)* [949]

Amtrol Scholarship *(High School/Scholarship)* [950, 1689]

ARCADIS Scholarship *(Master's, Doctorate/Scholarship, Monetary)* [1635]

Association of California Water Agencies Scholarship *(Undergraduate/Scholarship)* [2076]

AWWA American Water Scholarship *(Master's, Doctorate/Scholarship, Monetary)* [1636]

The B. Harper Bull Scholarship Awards *(Graduate, Doctorate, Postgraduate/Award)* [11060]

HDR/Henry "Bud" Benjes Scholarships *(Master's/Scholarship, Monetary)* [1637]

Steve Bonk Scholarship *(Undergraduate, Graduate/Scholarship)* [3136]

Leo Bourassa Scholarship *(Undergraduate, Graduate/Scholarship)* [11837]

Bryant L. Bench Scholarship *(Master's/Scholarship, Monetary)* [1638]

California Sea Grant State Fellowship *(Graduate/Fellowship)* [2833]

Thomas R. Camp Scholarships *(Graduate/Scholarship, Monetary)* [1639]

Canadian Water Resources Association Harker/Cameron Women in Water Scholarship *(Graduate/Scholarship)* [2107]

Canham Graduate Studies Scholarship *(Graduate/Scholarship)* [11927]

Channabasappa Memorial Scholarships *(Graduate, Doctorate/Scholarship)* [5993]

Clair A. Hill Scholarship *(Undergraduate/Scholarship)* [2077]

Colonel Theodore A. Leisen Memorial and Training Endowment Fund *(Graduate/Grant)* [8196]

Francis X. Crowley Scholarship *(Undergraduate/Scholarship)* [8248]

Dave Caldwell Scholarship *(Graduate/Scholarship, Monetary)* [1640]

Dillon Consulting Scholarship *(Graduate/Scholarship)* [2108]

Eva Nieminski Honorary Graduate Science and Engineering Scholarship *(Graduate/Scholarship)* [5894]

GCFI Student Travel Awards *(Undergraduate/Award)* [5252]

GWS Scholarship Program *(Undergraduate, Graduate/Scholarship)* [165]

Hazen and Sawyer Scholarship *(Master's/Scholarship, Monetary)* [1641]

Rich Herbert Memorial Scholarship *(Undergraduate, Master's, Doctorate/Scholarship)* [1630]

Holly A. Cornell Scholarship *(Master's/Scholarship, Monetary)* [1642, 3272]

IDA Fellowship/Scholarship Programs *(Other/Fellowship)* [5994]

Illinois Lake Management Association Undergraduate/Graduate Scholarships *(Graduate, Undergraduate/Scholarship)* [5700]

IMS AWWA Graduate Science and Engineering Scholarships *(Graduate/Scholarship)* [5895]

Ivanhoe Foundation Fellowship *(Master's/Fellowship)* [6184]

JDRF Outreach Scholarship *(Undergraduate, Master's, Doctorate/Scholarship)* [5705]

Elson T. Killam Memorial Scholarship *(Undergraduate, Graduate/Scholarship)* [8249]

John A. Knauss Marine Policy Fellowship *(Graduate/Fellowship)* [11304]

DSRSD James B. Kohnen Scholarships *(Undergraduate, High School/Scholarship)* [4191]

Larson Aquatic Research Support Scholarships (LARS) *(Graduate/Scholarship, Monetary, Recognition)* [1643]

NWRI Fellowship *(Graduate, Doctorate/Fellowship)* [8158]

Robert Esser Student Achievement Scholarship *(Graduate, Undergraduate/Scholarship)* [5701]

Ronald B. Linsky Fellowship for Outstanding Water Research *(Graduate, Master's, Doctorate/Fellowship)* [8159]

Roy W. Likins Scholarship *(Undergraduate, Graduate/Scholarship)* [1646]

Stantec Scholarship *(Master's, Doctorate/Scholarship, Monetary)* [1644]

Stephen K. Hall ACWA Water Law and Policy Scholarship *(Undergraduate/Scholarship)* [2078]

William V. Storch Student Award *(Undergraduate, Graduate/Award)* [1632]

Ken Thomson Scholarship *(Graduate/Scholarship)* [2109]

VA AWWA Graduate Student Scholarships *(Graduate/Scholarship)* [11841]

Water supply industry

Abel Wolman Fellowship *(Doctorate/Fellowship, Award, Monetary)* [1634]

ARCADIS Scholarship *(Master's, Doctorate/Scholarship, Monetary)* [1635]

Len Assante Scholarship Program *(Undergraduate/Scholarship)* [7911]

AWWA American Water Scholarship *(Master's, Doctorate/Scholarship, Monetary)* [1636]

HDR/Henry "Bud" Benjes Scholarships *(Master's/Scholarship, Monetary)* [1637]

Bryant L. Bench Scholarship *(Master's/Scholarship, Monetary)* [1638]

Thomas R. Camp Scholarships *(Graduate/Scholarship, Monetary)* [1639]

Colonel Theodore A. Leisen Memorial and Training Endowment Fund *(Graduate/Grant)* [8196]

Dave Caldwell Scholarship *(Graduate/Scholarship, Monetary)* [1640]

Eva Nieminski Honorary Graduate Science and Engineering Scholarship *(Graduate/Scholarship)* [5894]

Hazen and Sawyer Scholarship *(Master's/Scholarship, Monetary)* [1641]

Holly A. Cornell Scholarship *(Master's/Scholarship, Monetary)* [1642, 3272]

IMS AWWA Graduate Science and Engineering Scholarships *(Graduate/Scholarship)* [5895]

JDRF Outreach Scholarship *(Undergraduate, Master's, Doctorate/Scholarship)* [5705]

Larson Aquatic Research Support Scholarships (LARS) *(Graduate/Scholarship, Monetary, Recognition)* [1643]

Michigan Stormwater-Floodplain Association Scholarships *(Graduate, Undergraduate/Scholarship)* [7338]

Roy W. Likins Scholarship *(Undergraduate, Graduate/Scholarship)* [1646]

Stantec Scholarship *(Master's, Doctorate/Scholarship, Monetary)* [1644]

VA AWWA Graduate Student Scholarships *(Graduate/Scholarship)* [11841]

Welding

Aim High Jerry Clay Scholarship *(Undergraduate/Scholarship)* [5132]

Airgas - Terry Jarvis Memorial Scholarship *(Undergraduate/Scholarship)* [1650]

American Welding Society District Scholarships *(Undergraduate/Scholarship)* [1651]

American Welding Society Graduate Research Fellowships *(Graduate/Fellowship)* [1652]

American Welding Society National Scholarships *(Undergraduate/Scholarship)* [1653]

American Welding Society Past Presidents Scholarships *(Undergraduate, Graduate, Master's, Doctorate/Scholarship)* [1654]

Arsham Amirikian Engineering Scholarship *(Undergraduate/Scholarship)* [1655]

Amos and Marilyn Winsand - Detroit Section Named Scholarship *(Undergraduate/Scholarship)* [1656]

AWS International Scholarship Program *(Undergraduate, Graduate/Scholarship)* [1657]

Airgas - Jerry Baker Scholarship *(Undergraduate/Scholarship)* [1658]

Edward J. Brady Memorial Scholarship *(Undergraduate/Scholarship)* [1659]

Donald and Shirley Hastings Scholarship *(Undergraduate/Scholarship)* [1660]

Donald F. Hastings Scholarship *(Undergraduate/Scholarship)* [1661]

Horch Roofing Trade School Scholarship *(Vocational/Occupational/Scholarship)* [5584]

Howard E. and Wilma J. Adkins Memorial Scholarship *(Undergraduate/Scholarship)* [1662]

Hypertherm International HyTech Leadership Scholarships *(Graduate/Scholarship)* [1663]

ITW Welding Companies Scholarships *(Undergraduate/Scholarship)* [1664]

Jack R. Barckhoff Welding Management Scholarship *(Undergraduate/Scholarship)* [1665]

John C. Lincoln Memorial Scholarship *(Undergraduate/Scholarship)* [1666]

LCSC Welding Club Scholarship *(Undergraduate/Scholarship)* [6809]

Miller Electric International WorldSkills Competition Scholarship *(Undergraduate/Scholarship)* [1667]

Nixon Family Scholarship Fund *(Undergraduate, High School/Scholarship)* [11950]

Ronald C. and Joyce Pierce - Mobile Section Named Scholarships *(Undergraduate/Scholarship)* [1668]

Praxair International Scholarship *(Undergraduate/Scholarship)* [1669]

Resistance Welding Manufacturers Alliance Scholarship *(Undergraduate/Scholarship)* [1670]

Robert L. Peaslee Brazing Scholarship *(Undergraduate/Scholarship)* [1671]

James A. Turner, Jr. Memorial Scholarship *(Undergraduate/Scholarship)* [1672]

William A. and Ann M. Brothers Scholarship *(Undergraduate/Scholarship)* [1673]

William B. Howell Memorial Scholarship *(Undergraduate/Scholarship)* [1674]

Work Ethic Scholarship *(Vocational/Occupational, Two Year College/Scholarship)* [7384]

Wildlife conservation, management, and science

The B. Harper Bull Scholarship Awards *(Graduate, Doctorate, Postgraduate/Award)* [11060]

Bat Conservation International Granting Programs *(Graduate, Undergraduate/Scholarship)* [2447]

Leslie Brown Memorial Grant *(Advanced Professional/Grant)* [9503]

California Waterfowl Association College Scholarships *(Undergraduate/Scholarship)* [2842]

Lyle Carlson Wildlife Management Scholarships *(Undergraduate/Scholarship)* [11443]

Charles Dobbins FTA Scholarships *(Undergraduate, Vocational/Occupational/Scholarship)* [4846]

Wildlife and Conservation Medicine Internship *(All/Fellowship)* [3436]

Harry Hampton Fund Scholarship *(Undergraduate/Scholarship)* [5266]

L. Gordon "Link" Linkous Scholarship *(Undergraduate/Scholarship)* [11103]

Ben Meadows Natural Resource Scholarships - Academic Achievement Scholarships *(Undergraduate/Scholarship)* [4684]

Ben Meadows Natural Resource Scholarships - Leadership Scholarships *(Undergraduate/Scholarship)* [4685]

NGC College Scholarships *(Graduate, Undergraduate/Scholarship)* [7900]

NWRA Research Grants *(Professional development/Grant)* [8163]

Ted Parnell Scholarship *(Undergraduate/Scholarship)* [12278]

Rob and Bessie Welder Wildlife Foundation's graduate research fellowship *(Graduate, Master's, Doctorate/Fellowship)* [11958]

Dr. Orrin Rongstad Wildlife Scholarship *(Undergraduate/Scholarship)* [11510]

Russian Student Scholarship *(Undergraduate/Scholarship)* [11511]

Sutton Scholarship Award *(Undergraduate/Award, Scholarship)* [10891]

Stephen R. Tully Memorial Grant *(Advanced Professional/Grant)* [9504]

Wild Felid Legacy Scholarship *(Graduate/Scholarship)* [12026]

Yukon Outdoors Club Scholarship *(Undergraduate, University, College, Vocational/Occupational/Scholarship)* [12398]

Women's studies

J Frances Allen Scholarship Award *(Doctorate/ Scholarship)* [887]

American Association of University Women Master's and First Professional Awards *(Professional development/Award)* [667]

ASECS Women's Caucus Editing and Translation Fellowship *(Doctorate/Fellowship)* [1428]

Center for the Education of Women Student Research Grants *(Graduate, Undergraduate/Grant)* [11636]

CFUW Aboriginal Women's Award *(Postgraduate/ Fellowship)* [2970]

CFUW Memorial Fellowship *(Master's/Fellowship)* [2971]

Mariam K. Chamberlain Fellowship in Women and Public Policy *(Graduate/Fellowship)* [5874]

City of Toronto Women's Studies Scholarships *(Graduate, Undergraduate/Scholarship)* [11689]

Marusia and Michael Dorosh Fellowship *(Master's, Graduate/Fellowship)* [3027]

Emilie Du Chatelet Award *(Doctorate/Award)* [1431]

Fellowship on Women & Public Policy *(Graduate/ Fellowship)* [11522]

Elizabeth Fry Memorial Bursary *(Undergraduate, Graduate/Scholarship)* [6671]

HBI Gilda Slifka Internship Program *(Graduate, Undergraduate/Internship)* [2680]

HBI Scholar-in-Residence Program *(Undergraduate, Graduate, Postgraduate/Scholarship)* [2681]

Janet Hyde Graduate Student Research Grant *(Doctorate, Graduate/Grant)* [1732]

Joseph H. Fichter Research Grant *(Postdoctorate/ Grant)* [2290]

Penny Kanner Dissertation Research Fellowship *(Doctorate/Fellowship)* [11541]

Bourse Georgette LeMoyne *(Graduate/Fellowship)* [2973]

Lila Fahlman Scholarship *(Undergraduate, Graduate/Scholarship)* [2960]

Catherine Macaulay Prize *(Graduate/Prize)* [1436]

O. Ruth McQuown Scholarship - Graduate Award for Current Students *(Graduate/Scholarship)* [11572]

Dr. Margaret McWilliams Pre-Doctoral Fellowship *(Doctorate/Fellowship)* [2975]

Ruth R. and Alyson R. Miller Fellowships *(Professional development/Fellowship)* [7151]

National Women's Studies Association Lesbian Caucus Award *(Master's, Doctorate/Award, Grant)* [8165]

Catherine Prelinger Award *(Postdoctorate/Scholarship)* [3830]

Provost Entrance Scholarship *(Undergraduate/ Scholarship)* [3731]

Scotiabank Undergraduate Award for Studies in Violence Against Women and Children *(Undergraduate/Award)* [11730]

Judith Gold Stitzel Endowment for Excellence in Women's Studies Teaching and Learning *(Professional development/Grant)* [11977]

Tara Lynne Arnold Scholarship Fund *(Undergraduate/Scholarship)* [10834]

UCLA-CSW Travel Grants *(Graduate, Undergraduate/Grant)* [11542]

Mair Verthuy Scholarship *(Undergraduate/Scholarship)* [3732]

Ida B. Wells Graduate Student Fellowship *(Graduate/Fellowship)* [3831]

Whirly-Girls Helicopter Add-On Flight Training Scholarship *(Professional development, Vocational/Occupational/Scholarship)* [12013]

Woodrow Wilson Dissertation Fellowship in Women's Studies *(Doctorate/Fellowship)* [12051]

WLALA Scholarships *(Postgraduate/Scholarship)* [12144]

Women & Politics Fund *(Graduate, Postdoctorate, Undergraduate, Professional development/Grant)* [1261]

Women's Health Research Foundation of Canada Scholarship Program *(Graduate/Scholarship)* [12157]

Writing

Bodie McDowell Scholarship *(Graduate, Undergraduate/Scholarship)* [8782]

CAA National Capital Region Writing Contest *(All/ Award, Prize, Monetary)* [2916]

The Edit My Paper Proofreading Scholarships *(Undergraduate/Scholarship)* [4287]

Evoke Strategy Writing Scholarship *(Undergraduate/ Scholarship)* [4459]

Fellowships for Creative and Performing Artists and Writers *(Professional development/Fellowship)* [490]

Mona Gray Creative Arts Scholarship *(Graduate, Undergraduate/Scholarship)* [6306]

Velma Shotwell Griffin Memorial Scholarship Fund *(Undergraduate/Scholarship)* [10762]

Institute for Anarchist Studies Grants for Radical Writers and Translators *(Professional development/Grant)* [5812]

Jim Poore Memorial Scholarship Fund *(Undergraduate/Scholarship)* [5679]

The Melissa Pellegrin Memorial Scholarship Fund *(Undergraduate, Graduate/Scholarship)* [8759]

PEN/Phyllis Naylor Grant for Children's and Young Adult Novelists *(Other/Grant)* [8952]

Eugene C. Pulliam Fellowship for Editorial Writing *(Other/Fellowship)* [10502]

Stasiuk Master's Research Fellowship *(Master's/ Fellowship)* [3032]

W. Kaye Lamb Award for the Best Student works *(Undergraduate/Scholarship)* [2701]

Youth

IODE 100th Anniversary Grant *(Other/Grant)* [7758]

NYCT Paid Graduate Student Philanthropy Fellowships - Children, Youth, Families, Education, Human Justice and Workforce *(Graduate/Fellowship)* [8306]

Tiftickjian Law Firm, P.C. Juvenile Justice Law School Scholarships *(Graduate/Scholarship)* [11030]

VFW Voice of Democracy *(Undergraduate/Scholarship)* [11809]

WLALA Scholarships *(Postgraduate/Scholarship)* [12144]

Zoology

AAZK/AZA Advances in Animal Keeping Course Grants *(Professional development/Grant)* [676]

AAZK Conservation, Preservation and Restoration Grants *(Professional development/Grant)* [677]

AAZK Professional Development Grants *(Professional development/Grant)* [678]

AAZK Research Grants *(Professional development/ Grant)* [679]

Albert R. and Alma Shadle Fellowship *(Graduate/ Fellowship)* [1499]

American Society of Mammalogists Grants-in-Aid of Research *(Graduate, Undergraduate/Grant)* [1500]

American Society Of Mammalogists Fellowship In Mammalogy *(Graduate/Fellowship)* [1501]

California Waterfowl Association College Scholarships *(Undergraduate/Scholarship)* [2842]

Margaret A. Dankworth Management Scholarship *(Professional development/Scholarship)* [2327]

Frederick and Helen Gaige Award *(Professional development/Grant)* [1483]

Graduate Student Honoraria - A. Brazier Howell Award *(Master's, Doctorate/Award)* [1502]

Graduate Student Honoraria - Elmer C. Birney Award *(Master's, Doctorate/Award)* [1503]

Harry Hampton Fund Scholarship *(Undergraduate/ Scholarship)* [5266]

Libbie H. Hyman Memorial Scholarship *(Graduate, Undergraduate/Scholarship)* [10373]

Graduate Student Honoraria - Anna M. Jackson Awards *(Master's, Doctorate/Award)* [1504]

Latin American Student Field Research Award *(Graduate/Fellowship)* [1505]

Margaret Dowell-Gravatt, M.D. Scholarship *(Undergraduate/Scholarship)* [2486]

Oliver P. Pearson Award *(Doctorate/Fellowship)* [1506]

Primate Conservation Grants *(Graduate, Professional development/Grant)* [9324]

Edward C. Raney Fund Award *(Professional development/Grant)* [1484]

Robert O. Wagner Professional Development Scholarship *(Professional development/Scholarship)* [2328]

This index lists awards that are restricted by the applicant's residence of legal record. Award citations are arranged alphabetically under the following geographic headings: United States, United States (by region), United States (by state), Canada, Canada (by province), International, International (by region), and International (by country). Each citation is followed by the study level and award type, which appear in parentheses. Numbers following the parenthetical information indicate book entry numbers for particular awards, not page numbers.

UNITED STATES

1-800-Pain-Free Scholarship *(Two Year College, Undergraduate, Graduate/Scholarship)* [141]

$1,000 Scholarship for Veterans *(Undergraduate/Scholarship)* [9042]

$1000 uPONICS Hydroponics/Aquaponics Scholarship *(Undergraduate/Scholarship)* [11761]

$1500 College Monk Short Essay Scholarship *(Undergraduate, Graduate/Scholarship)* [3508]

180 Medical College Scholarship Program *(Undergraduate, Graduate, Professional development/Scholarship)* [6]

1Dental Scholarship *(Undergraduate, Graduate/Scholarship)* [8]

1L and 2L Diversity Fellowship Programs *(Undergraduate/Fellowship)* [5042]

1L Diversity Fellowships *(Graduate/Fellowship)* [4827]

1L SUMMER INTERNSHIP PROGRAM Prudential Financial, Inc. *(Postgraduate/Internship)* [7600]

$2,000 Nitro College Scholarship *(Community College, University, Undergraduate, Graduate/Scholarship)* [8407]

2020 The Nuclear Family Scholarship *(College, University, Undergraduate/Scholarship)* [6689]

$2,500 College Raptor Scholarship *(College, University, Undergraduate, Graduate, Community College/Scholarship)* [3510]

3M Fellowship Award *(Postdoctorate/Fellowship)* [12214]

4-H Youth in Action Awards *(Graduate, Undergraduate, Vocational/Occupational, High School, College, University/Scholarship)* [7564]

$5000 Imagine Scholarship *(College, University/Scholarship)* [9755]

The 86211 Scholarship *(Undergraduate/Scholarship)* [9643]

A-2 Joaquim Pereira Memorial Scholarship *(Undergraduate/Scholarship)* [6935]

A-4 António Mattos Memorial Scholarship *(Undergraduate/Scholarship)* [6936]

A. Stanley Rand Fellowship Program *(Undergraduate, Doctorate, Postdoctorate/Fellowship)* [10224]

A. Verville Fellowship *(Professional development/Fellowship)* [10190]

AAA Education Research Scholarship *(Graduate, Postdoctorate/Scholarship)* [512]

AAA Postdoctoral Fellowship *(Postdoctorate/Fellowship)* [513]

AAAA Scholarship Program *(Undergraduate, Graduate/Scholarship)* [1911]

AAACN Conference Scholarship for Nursing Students *(Undergraduate/Scholarship)* [424]

AAACN Education Scholarship *(Undergraduate/Scholarship)* [425]

AAACN Research/Evidence Based Practice Project Awards *(Undergraduate/Grant, Scholarship)* [426]

AAAS Mass Media Science & Engineering Fellows Program *(Undergraduate, Graduate, Postdoctorate/Fellowship)* [506]

AABB-Fenwal Specialist in Blood Bank Scholarship Awards *(Professional development/Scholarship)* [519]

AABB-Fenwal Transfusion Medicine Fellows Scholarship Awards *(Doctorate/Scholarship)* [520]

AABP Amstutz Scholarship *(Undergraduate/Scholarship)* [522]

AABP Bovine Veterinary Student Recognition Award *(Undergraduate/Scholarship, Award)* [523]

AABP Education Grants *(Graduate, Postgraduate, Master's/Grant)* [524]

AABP Student Externship Program *(Undergraduate/Scholarship)* [525]

AACOM Scholar in Residence Program *(Professional development/Scholarship)* [545]

AACPDM Student Travel Scholarship *(Professional development/Scholarship)* [438]

AACPDM Transformative Practice Grant Award *(Professional development/Grant)* [439]

AACR Minority and Minority-Serving Institution Faculty Scholar Awards *(Doctorate, Postdoctorate/Award)* [530]

AACR-Undergraduate Scholar Awards *(Undergraduate/Award)* [532]

AACT Junior Investigator Research Grants *(Professional development/Grant)* [441]

AACT Toxicology Trainee Research Grants *(Professional development/Grant)* [443]

AACTE Outstanding Book Awards *(Other/Award, Recognition)* [547]

AACTE Outstanding Dissertation Awards *(Doctorate/Award)* [548]

AAEP/ALSIC Scholarships *(Undergraduate/Scholarship)* [558]

AAEP Foundation Past Presidents' Research Fellow *(Graduate, Professional development/Scholarship)* [559]

AAFPE LEX Scholarship *(Undergraduate/Scholarship)* [616]

AAFSW "Twice Exceptional" Merit Scholarship for High School Seniors, Gap Year, and College Students *(Undergraduate/Scholarship)* [2024]

AAG Dissertation Research Grants *(Doctorate/Grant)* [563]

AAHD Scholarships *(Graduate, Undergraduate/Scholarship)* [568]

AAI Careers in Immunology Fellowship Program *(Graduate, Doctorate, Postdoctorate/Fellowship)* [572]

AAI Public Policy Fellows Program (PPFP) *(Doctorate, Postdoctorate/Fellowship)* [573]

AAIA Allogan Slagle Memorial Scholarship *(Undergraduate, Graduate/Scholarship)* [2036]

AAIB Scholarships *(Undergraduate/Scholarship)* [575]

AAIDD Fellowship *(Advanced Professional, Professional development/Fellowship)* [577]

AAJ Trial Advocacy Scholarship *(Undergraduate/Scholarship)* [581]

AALL Leadership Academy Grant *(Professional development/Grant)* [585]

AALL Minority Leadership Development Award *(Graduate/Award)* [586]

AALL Research Fund *(Professional development/Grant)* [587]

AALL Technical Services SIS New Member General Grant *(Professional development/Grant)* [592]

AALL/Wolters Kluwer Law & Business Grants *(Professional development/Grant)* [593]

AAMA Houston Chapter Health Training Scholarships *(Other/Scholarship)* [1770]

AAMC Foundation Engagement Program for International Curators Grants *(Advanced Professional, Professional development/Grant)* [2057]

AAMFT Minority Fellowship Program (MFP) *(Doctorate, Graduate/Fellowship)* [602]

AAN Clinical Research Training Fellowship *(Other/Scholarship)* [458]

AAN Medical Student Summer Research Scholarship *(Graduate/Scholarship)* [460]

AANS Medical Student Summer Research Fellowships (MSSRF) *(Undergraduate/Fellowship)* [607]

AAP Educator Scholarship *(Postdoctorate/Scholarship)* [472]

Aaron Copland Bogliasco Fellowships in Music *(Professional development/Fellowship)* [2641]

Leroy F. Aarons Scholarship Award *(Graduate, Undergraduate/Scholarship)* [7988]

AAS/AAS Trainee Research Fellowship Awards *(Professional development/Fellowship)* [2028]

AAS-American Society for Eighteenth-Century Studies Fellowships *(Doctorate/Fellowship)* [482]

AAS Korean Studies Scholarship Program *(Graduate/Scholarship)* [2061]

AAS National Endowment for the Humanities Long-Term Fellowships *(Postdoctorate/Fellowship)* [483]

AASA Educational Administration Scholarship *(Postgraduate/Scholarship)* [635]

AASLD Autoimmune Liver Diseases Pilot Research Award *(Graduate, Doctorate, Postdoctorate, Professional development/Award, Grant)* [645]

AASLD Clinical, Translational and Outcomes Research Awards *(Professional development/Grant)* [646]

AASLD NP/PA Clinical Hepatology Fellowship *(Professional development/Fellowship)* [647]

AAST/ETHICON Research Grants in Local Wound Haemostatics and Hemorrhage Control Scholarships *(Graduate, Postgraduate/Grant)* [651]

AAST/KCI Research Grant *(Doctorate/Grant)* [652]

AATS Perioperative/Team-Based Care Poster Competition *(Professional development/Award)* [660]

AATS Resident Critical Care Scholarships *(Professional development/Scholarship)* [661]

AATS/STS Cardiothoracic Ethics Forum Scholarships *(Professional development/Scholarship)* [662, 10543]

AAUW American Fellowships *(Doctorate, Postdoctorate/Fellowship)* [32]

AAUW Career Development Grants *(Graduate, Advanced Professional, Professional development/Grant)* [33]

AAUW International Fellowships *(Master's, Doctorate, Postdoctorate/Fellowship)* [34]

AAUW Selected Professions Fellowships *(Graduate, Master's, Doctorate/Fellowship)* [35]

ABA Diversity Scholarships *(Graduate/Scholarship)* [707]

ABA Members Scholarships *(Undergraduate, Graduate/Scholarship)* [708]

Abba P. Schwartz Research Fellowship *(Professional development/Fellowship)* [6530]

Anthony Abbene Scholarship Fund *(Undergraduate/Scholarship)* [5663]

AbbVie Immunology Scholarship *(Community College, Undergraduate, Graduate, Vocational/Occupational, Doctorate/Scholarship)* [9938]

ABC-Clio Research Grants *(Graduate/Grant)* [10425]

Abe Fellowship *(Professional development/Fellowship)* [10241]

Abe Fellowships for Journalists *(Professional development/Fellowship)* [10242]

Abe Voron Award *(Graduate/Scholarship)* [2703]

Alejandro "Alex" Abecia Reaching High Scholarships *(Undergraduate/Scholarship)* [3462]

Abel Wolman Fellowship *(Doctorate/Fellowship, Award, Monetary)* [1634]

Abercrombie and Fitch Global Diversity and Leadership Scholar Awards *(Undergraduate/Scholarship)* [8102]

Ruth Abernathy Presidential Undergraduate Scholarship *(Undergraduate/Scholarship, Fellowship, Award, Monetary)* [10347]

ABF Law and Social Science Dissertation Fellowship and Mentoring Program *(Graduate/Fellowship)* [690]

ABF Montgomery Summer Research Diversity Fellowships in Law and Social Science *(Undergraduate/Fellowship)* [691]

ABF/NSF Doctoral Fellowships Program in Law & Inequality *(Doctorate/Fellowship, Award)* [692]

ABFSE National Scholarship Program *(Undergraduate/Scholarship)* [697]

Kyutaro and Yasuo Abiko Memorial Scholarship *(Undergraduate/Scholarship)* [6243]

Abraham and Rachela Melezin Memorial Fellowship *(Doctorate, Postdoctorate/Fellowship)* [12235]

Abram D. and Maxine H. Londa Scholarship *(Undergraduate/Scholarship)* [8290]

ABTA Basic Research Fellowships *(Postdoctorate/Fellowship)* [699]

The ABWA Sunrise Chapter Scholarship Fund *(Undergraduate, Vocational/Occupational/Scholarship)* [3709]

Academic Education Scholarship *(Professional development/Scholarship)* [8940]

Academy of Motion Picture Arts and Sciences Student Academy Awards *(Undergraduate/Award)* [53]

Academy of Neonatal Nursing Conference Scholarships *(Professional development/Scholarship)* [55]

Accenture American Indian Scholarship Fund *(Graduate, Undergraduate/Scholarship)* [993]

ACHE Junior and Community College Athletic Scholarship Program *(Undergraduate/Scholarship)* [206]

ACHE Junior and Community College Performing Arts Scholarship Program *(Undergraduate/Scholarship)* [207]

ACHE Two-Year College Academic Scholarship Program *(Undergraduate/Scholarship)* [210]

ACI Elmer Baker Student Fellowship *(Undergraduate/Fellowship)* [785]

ACI Foundation Scholarships *(Graduate/Scholarship)* [786]

ACJA/LAE Student Paper Competition *(Undergraduate, Graduate/Scholarship)* [836]

ACJA/LAE Student Scholarship Program *(Undergraduate/Scholarship)* [837]

ACJA/LAE Student Scholarship Program - Graduate Level *(Graduate, Master's, Doctorate/Scholarship)* [838]

Wayne D. Ackerman Family Scholarship Fund *(Undergraduate/Scholarship)* [10749]

ACLS Collaborative Research Fellowships *(Doctorate/Fellowship)* [817]

ACLS Fellowships *(Advanced Professional, Professional development/Fellowship)* [818]

ACMPE Scholarship Fund Program (SFI) *(Graduate, Undergraduate/Scholarship)* [7213]

ACMS Field Research Fellowship Program *(Postdoctorate/Fellowship)* [719]

ACMS Library Fellowship *(Graduate, Professional development, Postgraduate/Fellowship)* [721]

A.C.N.M. Foundation, Inc. Fellowship for Graduate Education *(Doctorate, Postdoctorate/Fellowship)* [768]

ACOR-CAORC Post-Doctoral Fellowships *(Postdoctorate/Fellowship)* [723]

ACOR-CAORC Pre-Doctoral Fellowships *(Graduate, Doctorate/Fellowship)* [724]

ACPA Foundation Annual Fund *(Professional development/Grant)* [771]

Andreas Acrivos Dissertation Award in Fluid Dynamics *(Graduate, Doctorate/Award, Recognition, Monetary)* [1219]

ACRL/DVC Student Stipend *(Undergraduate/Scholarship)* [2136]

ACS/ASA Health Policy and Management Scholarships *(Professional development/Scholarship)* [1616]

ACS Award for Research at an Undergraduate Institution *(Postdoctorate/Award, Recognition, Grant, Monetary)* [735]

ACS Doctoral Degree Scholarships in Cancer Nursing *(Doctorate, Graduate/Scholarship)* [713]

ACS Faculty Research Fellowships *(Professional development/Fellowship)* [773]

ACS Graduate Scholarships in Cancer Nursing Practice *(Graduate, Master's, Doctorate/Scholarship)* [714]

ACS Resident Research Scholarships *(Advanced Professional/Scholarship)* [774]

ACS Rubber Division Undergraduate Scholarship *(Undergraduate/Scholarship)* [738]

ACS Scholarship *(Undergraduate/Scholarship)* [795]

ACSUS Distinguished Dissertation Award *(Doctorate/Award)* [2080]

ACUI Research and Education Grant *(Undergraduate, Graduate, Professional development/Grant)* [2138]

ACVO Best Resident Manuscript Awards *(Undergraduate/Recognition)* [780]

EFWA Moss Adams Foundation Scholarships *(Undergraduate/Scholarship)* [4303]

Ruth D. Adams Fund *(Undergraduate/Scholarship)* [4581]

RPMDA/Ed Adams Memorial Scholarships *(Other/Scholarship)* [9653]

Carl Joseph Adelhardt Memorial Scholarship *(Undergraduate/Scholarship)* [4870]

Adelson Scholarship *(Undergraduate/Scholarship)* [9387]

ADMA International Scholarship *(Undergraduate/Scholarship)* [2372]

Admiral Mike Boorda Loan Program *(Undergraduate/Loan)* [8179]

Adolescent/Young Adult Lymphoma Correlative Studies Grant *(Advanced Professional/Grant)* [6946]

Adolf Van Pelt Scholarship *(Undergraduate/Scholarship)* [2037]

Harry E. Adrian Memorial Grant *(Undergraduate/Scholarship)* [1857]

Adrienne Zoe Fedok Art and Music Scholarship *(Undergraduate/Scholarship)* [4773]

Advance Degree and Clinical Research Training Grants in Alpha-1 Antitrypsin Deficiency *(Master's/Grant)* [1351]

Advance Prevention Lawsuit Legal Scholarships *(Undergraduate, Graduate/Scholarship)* [6737]

Advanced Light Source Collaborative Postdoctoral Fellowship Program *(Postdoctorate/Fellowship)* [6734]

Advanced Mountain Flight Training Scholarship *(Professional development, Vocational/Occupational/Scholarship)* [12009]

AE Flight Training Scholarship *(Other/Scholarship)* [8400]

AE Jet Type Rating Scholarships *(Other/Scholarship)* [8401]

A.E. Robert Friedman Scholarship *(Undergraduate, High School/Scholarship)* [8812]

AE Technical Training Scholarship *(Other/Scholarship)* [8402]

AECT Foundation Mentor Endowment Scholarship *(Doctorate, Graduate/Scholarship)* [2155]

AECT Legacy Graduate Scholarship *(Master's, Graduate, Professional development/Scholarship)* [2156]

AED Student/Early Career Investigator Travel Fellowship Program *(Postgraduate/Fellowship)* [43]

AED Student Research Grants *(Undergraduate, Graduate, Postgraduate/Grant)* [44]

AERA-ETS Fellowship Program in Measurement and Education Research *(Doctorate/Fellowship)* [868]

AERA Fellows Program *(Postdoctorate/Fellowship)* [869]

AERA Minority Dissertation Fellowship in Education Research *(Doctorate/Fellowship)* [870]

AES Graduate Studies Grants *(Graduate/Grant, Award)* [2349]

AESF Foundation Scholarships *(Undergraduate, Graduate/Scholarship)* [7704]

A.F. Zimmerman Scholarship *(Graduate, Master's/Scholarship)* [9073]

AFAR Scholarships for Research in the Biology of Aging *(Graduate, Doctorate/Scholarship)* [874]

AFCEA Cyber Security Scholarship *(Undergraduate, Graduate/Scholarship)* [103]

AFCEA STEM Teacher Graduate Scholarships *(Graduate/Scholarship)* [104, 7022]

AFCEA War Veterans Scholarships *(Undergraduate/Scholarship)* [105]

Afdhal / McHutchison LIFER Award *(Postdoctorate, Professional development/Award)* [649]

Affirm Scholarship Program *(Undergraduate/Scholarship)* [2175]

Affirmative Action Student Scholarship Mini-Grant Travel Awards *(Undergraduate, Master's/Grant)* [41]

AFPE Gateway Research Scholarships *(Doctorate/Scholarship)* [922]

AFPE Pre-Doctoral Fellowships in Pharmaceutical Sciences *(Doctorate/Fellowship)* [923]

AFPE Pre-Doctoral Fellowships in Pharmaceutical Sciences for Underrepresented Minorities *(Doctorate, Graduate/Fellowship)* [924]

AFSA Scholarship Program *(Undergraduate/Scholarship)* [153]

AFSP Distinguished Investigator Grants *(Postgraduate/Grant)* [926]

AFSP Pilot Innovation Grants *(Postgraduate/Grant)* [927]

AFSP Postdoctoral Research Fellowships Innovation Grants *(Postgraduate/Fellowship)* [928]

AFSP Standard Research Innovation Grants *(Postgraduate/Grant)* [929]

AFSP Young Investigator Innovation Grants *(Postgraduate/Grant)* [930]

AfterCollege STEM Inclusion Scholarship *(Undergraduate, Graduate/Scholarship)* [122]

AfterCollege Succurro Scholarship *(Undergraduate, Graduate, Doctorate/Scholarship)* [123]

A.G. Bell School Age Financial Aid Program *(High School/Scholarship, Monetary)* [333]

Samuel Agabian Memorial Grant *(Undergraduate/Scholarship)* [1858]

AGBU Heritage Scholar Grant *(Undergraduate/Scholarship, Grant)* [1850]

AGC Foundation Outstanding Educator Awards *(Other/Award, Monetary)* [2016]

AGC NYS Scholarship Program *(Undergraduate, Graduate/Scholarship)* [2018]

Agnes E. Vaghi Scholarship *(Undergraduate/Scholarship)* [7960]

The Agnes Sopcak Memorial Scholarship *(Undergraduate/Scholarship)* [12146]

Agriculture Future of America Community Scholarships *(Undergraduate/Scholarship)* [133]

Agriculture Future of America Scholarships *(Undergraduate/Scholarship)* [134]

AGWT Baroid Scholarships *(Undergraduate/Scholarship)* [948]

AGWT Thomas M. Stetson Scholarships *(Undergraduate/Scholarship)* [949]

AHCJ Reporting Fellowships on Health Care Performance *(Other/Fellowship)* [3552]

The Patty Ahearn-Victoria Elementary School Scholarship *(Undergraduate/Scholarship)* [9518]

AHETEMS/ExxonMobil Scholarships *(Undergraduate/Scholarship)* [10067]

ALPFA Scholarship (Graduate, Undergraduate, Master's/Scholarship) [2231]

Alpha Chi Sigma Scholarship Awards (Graduate, Undergraduate/Scholarship) [384]

Alpha Delta Gamma Educational Foundation Scholarship (Undergraduate, Graduate/Scholarship) [386]

Alpha Kappa Alpha - Educational Advancement Foundation Undergraduate Financial Need-Based Scholarships (Undergraduate/Scholarship) [388]

Alpha Kappa Alpha - Educational Advancement Foundation Undergraduate Merit Scholarships (Undergraduate/Scholarship) [389]

Alpha Kappa Trust Scholarship-Beta Omega (Undergraduate/Scholarship) [10091]

Alpha Mu Tau Undergraduate Scholarships (Undergraduate/Scholarship, Monetary) [1398]

Alpha Tau Omega Graduate Scholarship (Graduate/Scholarship) [401]

Alpha Tau Omega Undergraduate Scholarships (Undergraduate/Scholarship) [402]

Alphonso Deal Scholarship Award (Undergraduate/Scholarship) [7728]

The Alsandor Law Firm Scholarship Contest (Undergraduate/Scholarship) [407]

ALSC Bound to Stay Bound Books Scholarship (Graduate/Scholarship) [2237]

Robert E. Altenhofen Memorial Scholarships (Graduate, Undergraduate/Scholarship) [2004]

Alumni Endowed Scholarship (Undergraduate/Scholarship) [2840]

Luis W. Alvarez Postdoctoral Fellowships in Computational Science (Doctorate/Fellowship) [6735]

Alwin B. Newton Scholarship (Undergraduate/Scholarship) [1468]

Alzheimer's/Gerontology Scholarship (Graduate/Scholarship) [10092]

Alzheimer's Disease Research Standard Award (Doctorate/Award) [2692]

AMACESP Student Scholarships (Undergraduate/Scholarship) [197]

The Amato Sanita Brighter Future Scholarship (Undergraduate, Graduate, Advanced Professional/Scholarship) [9876]

Ameel J. Fisher Scholarship (Undergraduate/Scholarship) [11174]

America Express Travel Scholarships (Undergraduate/Scholarship) [1581]

Americal Legacy Foundation Scholarship (Undergraduate/Scholarship) [420]

American Acne and Rosacea Society Mentorship Grant (Professional development/Grant) [480]

American Association of Blacks in Energy Scholarships (Undergraduate/Scholarship) [517]

American Association for Cancer Research Minority Scholar in Cancer Research Awards (Graduate/Award) [533]

American Association of Cereal Chemists Graduate Fellowship Program (Graduate/Fellowship) [3266]

American Association of Family and Consumer Sciences Undergraduate Scholarships (Undergraduate/Scholarship) [561]

American Association for Hand Surgery Annual Research Awards (Professional development/Grant) [566]

American Association of Plastic Surgeons Academic Scholar Program (Professional development/Scholarship) [627]

American Association of State Troopers Scholarship Foundation First Scholarships (Undergraduate/Scholarship) [640]

American Association of State Troopers Scholarship Foundation Second Scholarships (Undergraduate/Scholarship) [641]

American Association of University Women Career Development Grants (Postgraduate/Grant) [665]

American Association of University Women Master's and First Professional Awards (Professional development/Award) [667]

American Association of University Women Selected Professions Fellowships (Other/Fellowship) [668]

American Association for Women in Community Colleges Doctoral Scholarship (Undergraduate/Scholarship) [671]

American Association for Women in Community Colleges LEADERS Institute Scholarship (Other/Scholarship) [672]

American Astronomical Society Small Research Grants (Doctorate/Grant) [681]

American Bus Association Academic Merit Scholarships (Undergraduate, Graduate/Scholarship) [709]

American Cancer Society - Postdoctoral Fellowships (Doctorate/Fellowship) [715]

American Cancer Society - Research Scholar Grants (Doctorate, Professional development/Grant) [716]

American Council of Engineering Companies of Illinois Scholarships (Undergraduate, Postdoctorate/Scholarship) [805]

American Council of Independent Laboratories Academic Scholarships (Undergraduate/Scholarship, Award) [815]

American Councils for International Education Critical Language Scholarship Program (Undergraduate, Graduate/Scholarship) [830]

American Counsel Association Scholarships (Undergraduate/Scholarship) [832]

American Darts Organization Memorial Youth National Scholarship (Undergraduate/Scholarship) [851]

American Dental Association Dental Assisting Scholarship Program (Undergraduate/Scholarship) [854]

American Dental Association Dental Hygiene Scholarship Program (Undergraduate/Scholarship) [855]

American Dental Association Dental Laboratory Technology Scholarship Program (Undergraduate/Scholarship) [856]

American Dental Association Minority Dental Student Scholarships (Undergraduate/Scholarship) [857]

American Dental Hygienists' Association Institute for Oral Health Research Grants (Master's/Grant) [859]

American Diabetes Association and Boehringer Ingelheim Research Award: Chronic Kidney Disease and Renal Insufficiency in the Setting of Diabetes (Doctorate, Professional development/Award) [7976]

American Dissertation Fellowships (Doctorate, Postdoctorate/Fellowship) [669]

American Enterprise Institute National Research Initiative Fellowships (NRI) (Professional development/Fellowship) [872]

American Federation of Police and Concerned Citizen Educational Scholarship (Undergraduate/Scholarship) [879]

American Foreign Service Association Scholarship Fund Program (Undergraduate/Scholarship) [912]

American Historical Association Fellowships in Aerospace History (Doctorate/Fellowship) [958]

American Historical Print Collectors Society Fellowship (Doctorate/Fellowship) [484, 965]

American Institute for Economic Research Student Summer Fellowship (Graduate, Undergraduate/Fellowship) [1028]

American Institute of Physics Congressional Science Fellowship (Doctorate/Fellowship) [1042]

American Institute of Physics State Department Science Fellowship (Doctorate/Fellowship) [1043]

American Legion Eagle Scout of the Year (Undergraduate/Scholarship) [7843]

The American Legion Legacy Scholarship (Undergraduate/Scholarship) [1070]

American Liver Foundation Liver Scholar Award (Doctorate/Award) [1091]

American Lung Association Biomedical Research Grants (RG) (Doctorate/Grant) [1094]

American Lung Association Clinical Patient Care Research Grants (CG) (Doctorate/Grant) [1095]

American Lung Association Dalsemer Research Grants (DA) (Doctorate/Grant) [1096]

American Lung Association Senior Research Training Fellowships (RT) (Doctorate/Fellowship) [1098]

American Lung Association Social-Behavioral Research Grants (SB) (Doctorate/Grant) [1099]

American Marketing Association-Connecticut Chapter, Anna C. Klune Memorial Scholarship (Graduate/Scholarship) [5314]

American Nuclear Society Incoming Freshman Scholarships (Undergraduate/Scholarship) [1160]

American Nuclear Society Undergraduates Scholarships (Undergraduate/Scholarship) [1162]

American Patriot Scholarship (Undergraduate/Scholarship, Monetary) [7388]

American Pediatric Surgical Nurses Association Educational Grant (Other/Grant) [1210]

American Physical Society Minority Undergraduate Scholarships (Undergraduate/Scholarship) [1220]

American Planning Association ENRE Student Fellowship Program (Graduate/Fellowship) [1242]

American Psychology-Law Society Dissertation Awards (Graduate/Award) [1291]

American Quarter Horse Foundation Scholarships (Undergraduate, Graduate/Scholarship) [1310]

American-Scandinavian Foundation Fellowships to Study in Scandinavia (Graduate/Fellowship) [1373]

American-Scandinavian Foundation Grants to Study in Scandinavia (Graduate/Grant) [1374]

American Society of Colon and Rectal Surgeons International Fellowships (Other/Fellowship) [1404]

American Society of Colon and Rectal Surgeons International Travel Scholarships (Other/Scholarship) [1405]

American Society of Heating, Refrigerating, and Air-Conditioning Memorial Scholarships (Undergraduate/Scholarship) [1469]

American Society for Horticultural Science Travel Grants (Graduate, Undergraduate/Grant) [1478]

American Society of Mammalogists Grants-in-Aid of Research (Graduate, Undergraduate/Grant) [1500]

American Society for Microbiology Undergraduate Research Fellowship (Undergraduate/Fellowship, Award, Monetary) [1513]

American Society of Mining and Reclamation Memorial Scholarship Award (Undergraduate, Community College, College, University/Scholarship, Recognition) [1522]

American Society Of Mammalogists Fellowship In Mammalogy (Graduate/Fellowship) [1501]

American Sokol Merit Award (Undergraduate/Scholarship, Recognition) [1593]

American Speech Language Hearing Foundation Clinical Research Grant (Doctorate/Grant) [1595]

American Speech Language Hearing Foundation Endowed Scholarships (Graduate, Master's, Doctorate/Scholarship) [1596]

American Speech Language Hearing Foundation General Scholarships (Graduate, Master's, Doctorate/Scholarship) [1597]

American Speech Language Hearing Foundation International Student Scholarship (Graduate, Master's, Doctorate/Scholarship) [1598]

American Speech Language Hearing Foundation Minority Student Scholarship (Graduate, Master's, Doctorate/Scholarship) [1599]

American Speech Language Hearing Foundation Scholarship for Student with A Disability (Graduate, Master's, Doctorate/Scholarship) [1600]

American Water Ski Educational Foundation Scholarships (Undergraduate/Scholarship) [11778]

American Watercolor Society Scholarship Program for Art Teachers (Undergraduate, Graduate/Scholarship) [1648]

American Welding Society District Scholarships (Undergraduate/Scholarship) [1651]

American Welding Society National Scholarships (Undergraduate/Scholarship) [1653]

American Welding Society Past Presidents Scholarships (Undergraduate, Graduate, Master's, Doctorate/Scholarship) [1654]

Americans for Informed Democracy Global Scholar Program (Undergraduate/Scholarship) [1687]

T. Thomas Amirian Memorial Grant (Undergraduate/Scholarship) [1860]

Arsham Amirikian Engineering Scholarship (Undergraduate/Scholarship) [1655]

AMLN Scholarships for Arab American Students (Graduate, Undergraduate/Scholarship) [1127]

AMS Centennial Fellowships (Postdoctorate/Fellowship, Monetary) [1107]
AMS Freshman Undergraduate Scholarship (Undergraduate/Scholarship) [1119]
AMS Graduate Fellowship in the History of Science (Graduate/Fellowship) [1120]
AMS Graduate Fellowships (Graduate/Fellowship) [1121]
AMS Minority Scholarships (Undergraduate/Scholarship) [1123]
AMS Senior Named Scholarships (Undergraduate/Scholarship) [1124]
AMS Teacher Education Scholarships (Undergraduate/Scholarship) [1129]
AMSA Graduate Student Research Poster Competition (Graduate, Doctorate, Master's/Award) [1109]
AMSN Career Mobility Scholarship (Undergraduate, Doctorate/Scholarship) [48]
AMSSM-ACSM Clinical Research Grants (Professional development/Grant) [1115]
AMTA Past Presidents' Conference Scholar (Professional development/Scholarship) [1132]
AMTA Student Conference Scholar (Undergraduate, Graduate/Scholarship) [1133]
AMTF Graduate Scholarships (Graduate/Scholarship, Monetary) [1399]
Amtrol Scholarship (High School/Scholarship) [950, 1689]
AMVETS National Scholarships - Entering College Freshmen (Undergraduate/Scholarship) [1696]
AMVETS National Scholarships - For Veterans (Undergraduate/Scholarship) [1697]
AMVETS National Scholarships - JROTC (Undergraduate, College/Medal) [1698]
Anaheim Police Survivors and Scholarship Fund (Undergraduate/Scholarship) [1703]
ANCA Scholarships (Undergraduate/Scholarship) [1915]
Anchor Scholarship Foundation Scholarships (Undergraduate, Four Year College, Two Year College/Scholarship) [1705]
Andersen Nontraditional Scholarships for Women's Education and Retraining (ANSWER) (Undergraduate/Scholarship) [4717]
William G. Anderson, DO, Minority Scholarships (Undergraduate/Scholarship) [1198]
The Anderson Group Summer Institute Scholarships (Other/Scholarship) [1710]
Henry H. Anderson, Jr. Sail Training Scholarship (Professional development/Scholarship, Recognition, Award) [10917]
Michael P. Anderson Scholarships in Space Science (Undergraduate/Scholarship) [8082]
Grace Andow Memorial Scholarship (Undergraduate, Graduate/Scholarship) [6244]
Andrew Gronholdt Arts Scholarship (Undergraduate, Vocational/Occupational, Graduate, Master's/Scholarship) [328]
Andrew W. Mellon Fellowships For Conservation Training Programs (Graduate/Fellowship) [10197]
Richard E. Andrews Memorial Scholarship (Undergraduate/Scholarship, Monetary) [694]
Androscoggin County Chamber of Commerce Adult Scholarships (Professional development/Scholarship) [6825]
ANF/ANN-FNRE Nursing Research Grants (Professional development/Grant) [1173]
ANF/ENRS Nursing Research Society (Professional development/Grant) [1174]
Angus Foundation Graduate Student Degree Scholarship Program (Graduate/Scholarship) [1712]
Angus Foundation Scholarships (Undergraduate, Graduate/Scholarship) [7965]
Angus Foundation Undergraduate Student Scholarships (Undergraduate/Scholarship) [1713]
Angus/Talon Youth Educational Learning Program Endowment Fund (Graduate, Undergraduate/Scholarship) [1714]
Anheuser-Busch NAPABA Law Foundation Presidential Scholarships (Undergraduate/Scholarship) [7601]
Anil and Neema Thakrar Family Fund #1 (Undergraduate/Scholarship) [4774]
Anna B. Ames Clinical Excellence Student Grant (Undergraduate/Grant) [2835]

Annabel Lambeth Jones Brevard College Merit Scholarship Fund (Undergraduate/Scholarship) [4718]
Anne L. "Annie" Alexander and Blaise Robert "B R" Alexander (Undergraduate/Scholarship) [4583]
Anne Lowe Scholarship (Undergraduate/Scholarship, Award) [3323]
Anne M. Fassett Scholarship Fund (Undergraduate, Graduate/Scholarship) [10671]
Leonore Annenberg Teaching Fellowships (Graduate/Fellowship) [12045]
Annette and Ernest Keith Memorial Scholarship (Undergraduate/Scholarship) [9520]
Annette Urso Rickel Foundation Dissertation Award for Public Policy (Graduate/Scholarship) [1273]
Annie Jump Cannon Award in Astronomy (Doctorate/Award, Recognition) [682]
Annie Wagner Memorial Scholarship Fund (Undergraduate/Scholarship) [3336]
Annual Bloom Legal Scholarship for Students Affected by Cerebral Palsy (Community College, Undergraduate/Scholarship) [2628]
Annual Educational Scholarships (Undergraduate/Scholarship) [7566]
Annual Research Doctoral and Postgraduate Fellowship Grant Program (Doctorate, Postdoctorate, Postgraduate, Advanced Professional/Fellowship, Grant) [2923]
Annual Young, Marr & Associates Scholarship (Undergraduate/Scholarship) [1723]
ANS Neurotology Fellowship Award (Other/Fellowship) [1157]
ANS Research Grant Award (Professional development/Grant) [1158]
Hettie M. Anthony Fellowship (Doctorate/Fellowship) [6495]
antibodies-online Annual University Scholarship (Undergraduate, Graduate/Scholarship) [1725]
Antimicrobial Stewardship Fellowship Award (Professional development/Fellowship) [8945]
A.O. Putnam Memorial Scholarship (Undergraduate/Scholarship) [5826]
AOF/Johnson & Johnson Vision Care - Innovation in Education Grants (Advanced Professional, Professional development/Grant) [462]
AOFAS Research Grants Program (Graduate/Grant) [1193]
AORN Academic Scholarships (Undergraduate, Master's, Doctorate/Scholarship, Monetary) [2257]
AORN Foundation Scholarship Program (Undergraduate, Doctorate, Master's/Scholarship, Monetary) [2258]
AOSA Research Grant (Professional development/Grant) [1186]
AOSA Research Partnership Grant (Professional development/Grant) [1187]
APA Division 39 Scholars Program (Graduate/Scholarship) [1734]
APA Society Convention Research Awards (Undergraduate, Graduate/Award) [9375]
APABA Silicon Valley Achievement Scholarship (Advanced Professional/Scholarship) [1988]
APALA Scholarship (Doctorate, Master's/Scholarship) [1990]
APC High School Scholarship (Graduate/Scholarship) [84]
APDA Post-Doctoral Research Fellowship (Postdoctorate/Fellowship) [1206]
APDA Research Grants (Postgraduate, Professional development/Grant) [1207]
APF High School Psychology Outreach Grants (Advanced Professional, Professional development/Grant) [1275]
APF Professional Development Awards for High School Psychology Teachers (Advanced Professional, Professional development/Grant) [1276]
APF Visionary Grants (Graduate/Grant) [1277]
APHF Academic Scholarship (Undergraduate/Scholarship) [1204]
APHL-CDC Infectious Diseases Laboratory Fellowship (Doctorate/Fellowship) [2269]
Appalachian School of Law Merit Scholarship Program (Undergraduate/Scholarship) [1756]
Applied Urban Communication Research Grants (Professional development/Grant) [4270]

APS Convention Society Research Awards (Undergraduate, Graduate/Award) [9376]
APS Scholarships for Minority Undergraduate Physics Majors (Undergraduate/Scholarship) [1221]
APS Student Research Award (APS) (Undergraduate, Graduate/Award) [2266]
APSA Congressional Fellowships for Journalists (Advanced Professional, Professional development/Fellowship) [1247]
APSA Congressional Fellowships for Political Scientists (Advanced Professional, Professional development, Postdoctorate/Fellowship) [1248]
APSA Fund for Latino Scholarship (Undergraduate, Graduate/Scholarship) [1249]
APSA-MCI Communications Congressional Fellowship (Advanced Professional, Professional development, Postdoctorate/Fellowship) [1250]
APSA Minority Fellowship Program (Doctorate/Fellowship) [1251]
APSA Small Research Grant Program (Professional development/Grant) [1252]
APSA U.S. Federal Executives Fellowships (Advanced Professional, Professional development/Fellowship) [1253]
APsaA Fellowship (Doctorate, Postdoctorate/Fellowship) [1265]
APTA Minority Scholarships - Faculty Development Scholarships (Postdoctorate/Scholarship, Award, Recognition) [1232]
APTA Minority Scholarships - Physical Therapist Assistant Students (Undergraduate/Scholarship, Award, Recognition) [1233]
APTA Minority Scholarships - Physical Therapist Students (Undergraduate/Scholarship, Award, Recognition) [1234]
ARA Region Two/Ron Marshall Scholarship (Undergraduate/Scholarship) [1333]
ARA Scholarship Awards (Undergraduate/Scholarship) [2364]
Ararat Association Scholarship Grant (Undergraduate/Scholarship) [1861]
ARCADIS Scholarship (Master's, Doctorate/Scholarship, Monetary) [1635]
ARCE Funded Fellowships (Doctorate, Postdoctorate/Fellowship) [1336]
ARCE Research Associates Fellowship (Doctorate, Postdoctorate, Professional development/Fellowship) [1337]
Archaeological Institute of America Fellowships for Study in the US (Postdoctorate/Fellowship) [1773]
Archaeology of Portugal Fellowship (Professional development, Graduate/Fellowship) [1774]
Archie Hartwell Nash Memorial Scholarship Fund (Graduate, Undergraduate/Scholarship) [3601]
Arctic Physical Therapy Scholarship (Undergraduate/Scholarship) [1794]
Ardis Kipp Cohoon Scholarship (Undergraduate/Scholarship) [11175]
AREMA Committee 12 - Rail Transit Scholarships (Undergraduate/Scholarship) [1316]
AREMA Committee 18 - Light Density and Short Line Railways Scholarships (Undergraduate/Scholarship) [1317]
AREMA Committee 24 - Education and Training Scholarships (Undergraduate/Scholarship) [1318]
AREMA Committee 27 - Maintenance-of-Way Work Equipment Scholarships (Undergraduate/Scholarship) [1319]
AREMA Committee 33 - Electric Energy Utilization Scholarships (Undergraduate/Scholarship) [1320]
AREMA Michigan Tech Alumni Scholarships (Graduate, Undergraduate/Scholarship) [1321]
AREMA Presidential Spouse Scholarship (Undergraduate/Scholarship) [1322]
AREMA Women's Engineering Scholarship (Undergraduate/Scholarship) [1323]
A.R.F.O.R.A. Undergraduate Scholarships for Women (Undergraduate/Scholarship) [1366]
ARIT Fellowships in the Humanities and Social Sciences in Turkey (Postdoctorate, Graduate/Fellowship) [1342, 3850, 11345, 11348]
ARIT/NEH Fellowships (Postgraduate/Fellowship) [1343]

ARIT Summer Fellowships for Intensive Advanced Turkish Language Study *(Graduate, Undergraduate/Fellowship)* [655, 1344, 4914, 11307, 11309]

Arizona Hydrological Society Academic Scholarships *(Graduate, Undergraduate/Scholarship)* [1808]

Armenian American Medical Association Scholarship Program *(Undergraduate, Graduate/Scholarship)* [1842]

Armenian American Pharmacists' Association Scholarship *(Graduate/Scholarship)* [1844]

Armenian American Veterans' Association of Worcester Scholarship *(Undergraduate/Scholarship)* [1862]

Armenian Bar Association Scholarships *(Graduate/Scholarship)* [1846]

Armenian Professional Society Graduate Student Scholarship *(Graduate/Scholarship)* [1852]

Ethel Louise Armstrong Foundation Scholarships *(Graduate, Master's/Scholarship, Monetary)* [1267]

Army Health Professions Scholarship Program (HPSP) *(Professional development/Scholarship)* [11288]

Jane B. Aron Doctoral Fellowship *(Doctorate/Fellowship)* [7695]

The ARRL General Fund Scholarship *(Undergraduate/Scholarship)* [1926]

ARS Lazarian Graduate Scholarship *(Graduate, Master's, Doctorate/Scholarship)* [1854]

ARS Undergraduate Scholarship *(Undergraduate/Scholarship)* [1855]

Ardemis, Armenoohy, and Arpi Arsenian Memorial Grant *(Undergraduate/Scholarship)* [1863]

Arthritis Champions Scholarship *(Undergraduate, Graduate/Scholarship, Monetary)* [1970]

Arthritis Foundation Investigator Awards *(Doctorate/Award)* [1971]

Arthur and Barbara Pape Endowment *(Graduate/Grant)* [11666]

Arthur B.C. Walker II Scholarship *(Undergraduate/Scholarship)* [8083]

Arthur H. Daniels Memorial Scholarship *(Undergraduate/Scholarship)* [9522]

Arthur and Juna Fisher Memorial Track Scholarship *(Undergraduate/Scholarship)* [9523]

Arthur Lockwood Beneventi Law Scholarship *(Undergraduate/Scholarship, Award, Monetary)* [8093]

Arthur M. & Berdena King Eagle Scout Scholarship *(Undergraduate/Scholarship)* [7844]

Arthur M. Schlesinger Jr. Research Fellowship *(Professional development/Fellowship)* [6531]

Arthur Patch McKinlay Scholarship *(Graduate, Undergraduate/Scholarship)* [753]

Artist-in-Residence Workspace Grant *(Professional development/Grant)* [3210]

The Artist in Landscape Design Scholarship *(Undergraduate/Scholarship)* [8585]

ASA Graduate Scholarships *(Graduate/Scholarship)* [1385]

ASA Inc. Journalism Internship Program *(Undergraduate/Internship)* [1864]

ASA Minority Fellowship Program (ASA MFP) *(Doctorate/Fellowship)* [1590]

ASA/NSF/BLS Fellowships *(Graduate/Fellowship, Recognition, Grant)* [1609, 8065, 11343]

ASA Student Forum Travel Awards *(Undergraduate, Graduate/Award)* [1591]

ASBA College Scholarship Grant Program *(Professional development/Scholarship)* [1381]

ASBC Foundation Graduate Scholarships *(Graduate/Scholarship)* [1387]

ASC Ph.D. Research Scholarship Award *(Doctorate, Postdoctorate/Scholarship)* [1415]

ASCE Freeman Fellowship *(Graduate/Fellowship, Award)* [1783]

ASCLD Scholarship Program *(Graduate, Undergraduate, Master's, Doctorate/Scholarship, Award, Monetary)* [1417]

ASCP Foundation Garza & Becan-McBride Endowed Scholarship *(Undergraduate/Scholarship, Monetary)* [1402]

ASDSO Undergraduate Scholarship *(Undergraduate/Scholarship)* [2295]

ASECS Graduate Student Research Paper Award *(Graduate/Prize)* [1426]

ASECS Innovative Course Design Competition *(Undergraduate/Award)* [1427]

ASECS Women's Caucus Editing and Translation Fellowship *(Doctorate/Fellowship)* [1428]

ASEE-NRL Postdoctoral Fellowship Program *(Postdoctorate/Fellowship)* [11389]

ASEE/NSF Small Business Postdoctoral Research Diversity Fellowship (SBPRDF) *(Postdoctorate/Fellowship)* [1442, 8066]

ASEH Minority Travel Grants *(Graduate, Other/Grant)* [1449]

ASEV Traditional Scholarship *(Graduate, Undergraduate/Scholarship)* [1447]

The ASG Scholar Award *(Professional development/Award)* [1463]

ASGP Graduate Research Fellowships *(Graduate/Fellowship)* [244]

ASHARE Undergraduate Engineering Scholarships *(Undergraduate/Scholarship)* [1470]

ASHFoundation New Century Scholars Doctoral Scholarship *(Doctorate/Scholarship)* [1601]

ASHFoundation New Century Scholars Research Grant *(Doctorate/Grant)* [1602]

ASHFoundation New Investigators Research Grant *(Doctorate/Grant)* [1603]

ASHFoundation NSSLHA Scholarship *(Graduate/Scholarship)* [1604]

ASHFoundation Speech Science Research Grant *(Doctorate/Grant)* [1605]

ASHFoundation Student Research Grant in Audiology *(Doctorate/Grant)* [1606]

ASHFoundation Student Research Grant in Early Childhood Language Development *(Doctorate, Master's/Grant)* [1607]

Ashley E. Ketcher Memorial Scholarship *(Undergraduate/Scholarship)* [3667]

ASHP Student Research Awards *(Doctorate/Award)* [1465]

ASHS Industry Division Student Travel Grant *(Graduate, Undergraduate/Grant)* [1479]

ASHS Scholars Award *(Undergraduate/Scholarship)* [1480]

Asia-Pacific Biomedical Research Foundation Merit Awards *(Postdoctorate/Award, Recognition, Prize)* [10530]

Asian Development Bank - Japan Scholarship Program *(Graduate, Master's/Scholarship)* [4261]

ASID Foundation Legacy Scholarships for Graduate Students *(Graduate/Scholarship)* [1486]

ASIS Foundation Chapter Matching Scholarship *(Undergraduate/Scholarship)* [1996]

ASIST Scholarship (ASIST) *(Professional development/Scholarship)* [4463]

ASLA Council of Fellows *(Undergraduate/Scholarship)* [1491]

ASLA Council of Fellows Scholarships *(Undergraduate/Scholarship)* [6646]

ASLMS Research Grant *(Postdoctorate/Grant, Monetary)* [1495]

ASM/CDC Program in Infectious Disease and Public Health Microbiology *(Postdoctorate/Fellowship)* [1514]

ASM Congressional Science Fellowship *(Postdoctorate/Fellowship)* [1515]

ASM Robert D. Watkins Graduate Research Fellowship *(Postdoctorate/Fellowship, Monetary)* [1517]

ASM Science Teaching Fellowships - Student *(Undergraduate/Fellowship)* [1518]

ASMC National Scholarship Program *(Graduate/Scholarship)* [1520]

ASMS Research Awards *(Other/Award)* [1508]

ASNE Scholarship *(Graduate, Undergraduate/Scholarship)* [1524]

ASNT Fellowship Award *(Graduate/Fellowship, Award)* [1531]

Myron "Ted" Asplin Foundation Scholarships *(Professional development/Scholarship)* [5739]

ASPPH/CDC Public Health Fellowship Program *(Doctorate, Graduate/Fellowship)* [2279]

ASPPH/EPA Environmental Health Fellowship Program *(Doctorate, Postdoctorate/Fellowship)* [2280]

ASPPH/NHTSA Public Health Fellowship Program *(Doctorate, Master's/Fellowship)* [2281]

ASPPH Public Health Fellowship Program *(Doctorate, Postdoctorate/Fellowship)* [2282]

ASPPH Public Health Preparedness Fellowship Program *(Postdoctorate/Fellowship)* [2283]

ASPT General Graduate Student Research Grant Fund *(Master's, Doctorate/Grant)* [1538]

ASRT Research Grants *(Professional development/Grant)* [1550]

Len Assante Scholarship Program *(Undergraduate/Scholarship)* [7911]

Association for the Advancement of Baltic Studies Dissertation Grants for Graduate Students *(Doctorate/Grant)* [2030]

Association for Compensatory Educators of Texas Paraprofessionals Scholarships *(Other/Scholarship)* [2141]

Association for Compensatory Educators of Texas Students *(Graduate/Scholarship)* [2142]

Association of Donor Recruitment Professionals Hughes Scholarships *(Other/Scholarship)* [2150]

Association of Donor Recruitment Professionals Presidential Scholarships *(Other/Scholarship)* [2151]

Association of Energy Engineers Foundation Scholarship Program *(Graduate, Undergraduate/Scholarship)* [2159]

Association of Flight Attendants Scholarship Fund *(Undergraduate/Scholarship)* [2179]

Association of Government Accountants Graduate Scholarships for Community Service *(Graduate/Scholarship)* [2187]

Association of Government Accountants Graduate Scholarships for Full-time study *(Graduate/Scholarship)* [2188]

Association of Government Accountants Graduate Scholarships for Part-time study *(Graduate/Scholarship)* [2189]

Association for Preservation Technology International Student Scholarships *(Graduate, Undergraduate/Scholarship)* [2262]

Association for Psychological Science Student Grants (APS) *(Graduate, Undergraduate/Grant)* [2267]

Association of State Dam Safety Officials memorial Undergraduate Scholarship *(Undergraduate/Scholarship)* [2296]

Association of the United States Navy Scholarships *(Undergraduate/Scholarship)* [2303]

Association for Women in Sports Media Internship Program *(Undergraduate/Scholarship, Internship)* [2321]

ASSP Diversity Committee Scholarship *(Doctorate/Scholarship)* [1559]

ASSP Foundation Academic Scholarship Program *(Undergraduate, Graduate, Doctorate, Vocational/Occupational/Scholarship)* [1560]

ASSP Foundation Professional Education Grant Program *(Professional development/Grant)* [1561]

ASTA Alaska Airlines Scholarships *(Undergraduate/Scholarship)* [1582]

ASTA Holland America Line Graduate Research Scholarships *(Graduate/Scholarship)* [1583]

ASTA Rigby, Healy, Simmons Scholarships *(Graduate, Undergraduate/Scholarship)* [1584]

ASTR Research Fellowships *(Doctorate/Fellowship)* [1577]

ASTRO Junior Faculty Career Research Training Award *(Advanced Professional, Professional development/Award)* [1545]

ASTRO Minority Summer Fellowship Award *(Postgraduate, Professional development/Fellowship, Award)* [1546]

ASTRO Residents/Fellows in Radiation Oncology Research Seed Grant *(Advanced Professional, Professional development/Grant)* [1547]

ASTRO/ROI Comparative Effectiveness Research Awards *(Professional development/Award)* [1548]

Astronaut Scholarship Foundation Scholarship *(Undergraduate/Scholarship)* [2332]

Marguerite Chapootian Atamian Memorial Grant *(Undergraduate/Scholarship)* [1865]

AT&T Business Internship Awards *(Undergraduate, Graduate/Internship)* [11176]

Martha and Robert Atherton Ministerial Scholarship *(Master's/Scholarship)* [11245]

Atlantic Salmon Federation Olin Fellowships *(Graduate/Fellowship)* [2347]

ATS Abstract Scholarships *(Undergraduate, Graduate, Doctorate/Scholarship)* [1621]

Attorney-CPA Foundation Scholarships *(Postgraduate/Scholarship)* [430]

AUA Foundation Urology Research Bridge Awards *(Postgraduate/Award)* [11771]

Aubespin Scholarships *(Undergraduate/Scholarship)* [801]

Audrey Loftus Memorial Scholarship *(University/Scholarship)* [11516]

Audrey Lumsden-Kouvel Fellowship *(Postdoctorate/Fellowship)* [8369]

H. Thomas Austern Memorial Writing Competition *(Doctorate/Award, Prize)* [4664]

Austin Alumnae Association Beta Xi Scholarship in Memory of Katherine Peeres Woolridge *(Undergraduate/Scholarship)* [6400]

Australian-American Health Policy Fellowships *(Doctorate, Graduate/Fellowship)* [3553]

Autism/ASD Scholarship *(Community College, Four Year College, Graduate, Vocational/Occupational, Professional development/Scholarship)* [6518]

Autism Scholarship *(High School, Two Year College, Four Year College, Graduate, Vocational/Occupational, Professional development/Scholarship)* [2617, 4051]

Autism Scholarship *(Two Year College, Four Year College, Vocational/Occupational/Scholarship)* [9712]

Auto Accident Law Firm Survivor Scholarships *(Graduate/Scholarship)* [1758]

Auto-Pets "Out-of-the-Box Thinking" Scholarships *(All/Scholarship)* [2355]

Automotive Technician Scholarship Program *(Undergraduate/Scholarship)* [7160]

Automotive Women's Alliance Foundation Scholarships *(Undergraduate/Scholarship)* [2366]

Auxiliary Undergraduate Scholarships *(Undergraduate/Scholarship)* [1998]

AvaCare Medical Scholarship *(Undergraduate/Scholarship)* [2370]

Avis Budget Group Scholarships *(Graduate/Scholarship)* [1585]

AVMA Fellowship Program *(Professional development/Fellowship)* [1628]

AVS Applied Surface Science Division *(Graduate/Award)* [2374]

AVS Biomaterial Interfaces Division - Early Career Researchers Awards (BID-ECR) *(Graduate/Monetary)* [2375]

AVS Electronic Materials and Photonic Division Postdoctoral Award *(Postdoctorate/Award)* [2376]

AVS Manufacturing Science and Technology Group *(Graduate/Award)* [2377]

AVS MEMS and NEMS Technical Group Best Paper Award *(Undergraduate, Graduate/Monetary)* [2378]

AVS Nanometer-Scale Science and Technology Division Graduate Award *(Graduate/Monetary)* [2379]

AVS Spectroscopic Ellipsometry Focus Topic Graduate Student Awards *(Graduate/Award)* [2380]

AVS Thin Film Division James Harper Awards *(Graduate/Monetary)* [2381]

Award for Outstanding Doctoral Dissertation in Laser Science *(Doctorate, Postdoctorate/Award)* [1222]

Award for Outstanding Doctoral Thesis Research in Biological Physics *(Doctorate, Postdoctorate/Award, Recognition, Monetary)* [1223]

AWG Minority Scholarship *(Undergraduate/Scholarship)* [2313]

AWM Mathematics Travel Grants *(Doctorate/Grant)* [2318]

AWMA Niagara Frontier Section College Scholarship *(Graduate, Undergraduate/Scholarship)* [169]

AWSCPA National Scholarships *(Graduate/Scholarship)* [1678]

AWWA American Water Scholarship *(Master's, Doctorate/Scholarship, Monetary)* [1636]

AX Control, Inc. Academic Scholarship *(College/Scholarship)* [2391]

AXA Achievement Scholarship *(Undergraduate/Scholarship)* [2393]

Susan Ayers Memorial Scholarships *(Undergraduate/Scholarship)* [9391]

John M. Azarian Memorial Armenian Youth Scholarship Fund *(Undergraduate/Scholarship)* [2399]

AZVT Laurie Page-Peck Scholarship *(Graduate/Scholarship)* [2325]

B-2 LAFF 20-30's Financial Aid Scholarship *(Postgraduate/Scholarship)* [6937]

B-3 LAFF 20-30's Financial Aid Scholarship *(Professional development/Scholarship)* [6938]

B-4 Albert S. Vieira Memorial Scholarship *(Professional development/Scholarship)* [6939]

B-Brave McMahon/Stratton Scholarship Fund *(Undergraduate/Scholarship)* [4584]

Tom Babcox Memorial Scholarships *(Professional development/Scholarship)* [2351]

Carroll Preston Baber Research Grant *(Professional development/Grant)* [1081]

Bachelor of Science in Nursing Academic Scholarships *(Graduate/Scholarship)* [7548]

Bachelor's in Nursing Degree Scholarship *(Undergraduate/Scholarship)* [8626]

Back to School Scholarship *(All/Scholarship)* [7437]

BACUS Scholarship *(Graduate, Undergraduate/Scholarship)* [10724]

BadCredit.orgs Wealth Wise Scholarship *(Undergraduate, Graduate/Scholarship)* [2401]

Leo Baeck Institute - DAAD Fellowships *(Doctorate/Fellowship)* [4057]

Marian Breland Bailey Award *(Graduate, Undergraduate/Award)* [2063]

Esther Tuttle Bailey Memorial Scholarship *(Undergraduate/Scholarship)* [6401]

Lincoln C. Bailey Memorial Scholarship Fund *(Undergraduate/Scholarship)* [6079]

Mark B. Bain Graduate Fellowship *(Doctorate, Master's, Graduate/Fellowship)* [5612]

Michael Baker Corp. Scholarship for Diversity in Engineering *(Undergraduate/Scholarship)* [2192]

Francis Warren Baker Memorial Scholarships *(Undergraduate/Scholarship)* [10094]

Baker Scholarship *(Doctorate, Professional development/Scholarship)* [4888]

Airgas - Jerry Baker Scholarship *(Undergraduate/Scholarship)* [1658]

ACI Baker Student Fellowships *(Undergraduate/Fellowship)* [790]

BakerHostetler Diversity Fellowship Program *(Undergraduate/Fellowship)* [2408]

Bernt Balchen, Jr. and Olav Jorgen Hegge Hardingfele Scholarships *(Other/Scholarship)* [5292]

Norman S. Baldwin Fishery Science Scholarship *(Doctorate, Master's/Scholarship)* [5923]

Donald A. Baldwin Sr. Business Aviation Management Scholarship *(Professional development/Scholarship)* [7733]

Balfour Scholarship *(Graduate/Scholarship)* [9087]

Vic and Margaret Ball Student Intern Scholarships *(Undergraduate/Internship)* [895]

Ballantyne Resident Research Grant *(Other, Graduate/Grant)* [956]

Ballard Breaux Visiting Fellowships *(Postdoctorate/Fellowship)* [4558]

Mary A. Bancroft Memorial Scholarship *(Graduate/Scholarship)* [6372]

B&W Y-12 Scholarship Fund *(Undergraduate/Scholarship)* [4254]

Brenda S. Bank Educational Workshop Scholarship *(Undergraduate/Scholarship)* [10341]

Banner Bank Business Scholarship *(Undergraduate/Scholarship)* [6783]

Mark T. Banner Scholarships for Law Students *(Postdoctorate/Scholarship)* [6873]

Barakat Trust and Barakat Foundation Scholarships *(Graduate, Postdoctorate/Scholarship)* [1767]

Barbara A. Cooley Master's Scholarship *(Master's/Scholarship, Award, Monetary)* [10348]

Barbara Bonnema Memorial Scholarship *(Undergraduate/Scholarship)* [9525]

Barbara Hagan Richards Scholarship Fund *(Undergraduate/Scholarship)* [3603]

Barber-Owen-Thomas Scholarship *(Undergraduate/Scholarship)* [10095]

UAA Janice K. Barden Aviation Scholarship *(Undergraduate/Scholarship)* [7734]

Edgar Barge Memorial Scholarship *(Undergraduate/Scholarship)* [5118]

Gina L. Barnhart Memorial Scholarship Fund *(Undergraduate/Scholarship)* [4585]

Gloria Barron Wilderness Society Scholarship *(Graduate, Undergraduate/Scholarship)* [12031]

Barry "Tyler" Rhea Memorial Scholarship *(Undergraduate/Scholarship)* [8503]

Barry M. Goldwater Scholarship *(Undergraduate/Scholarship)* [11733]

The Jean Bartel Military Scholarship *(Undergraduate/Scholarship)* [7415]

The Bascom Hill Society Scholarship *(Undergraduate/Scholarship)* [11734]

Forrest Bassford Student Award *(Undergraduate/Award)* [6881]

H. Burton Bates Jr. Scholarships *(Graduate, Undergraduate/Scholarship)* [11843]

Jim Batten Community Newspaper Internship *(Undergraduate/Internship)* [11177]

Raymond B. Bauer Research Award *(Professional development/Award, Grant)* [7322]

Marian Sims Baughn Scholarship *(Undergraduate/Scholarship)* [6402]

The Ernest L. Baulch, W2TX, and Marcia E. Baulch, WA2AKJ, Scholarship *(Undergraduate/Scholarship)* [1927]

Timothy Baylink Good Fellowship Awards *(Undergraduate/Fellowship)* [9526]

John Bayliss Broadcast Foundation Internship Programs *(Undergraduate/Internship)* [2451]

John Bayliss Broadcast Foundation Radio Scholarships *(Undergraduate/Scholarship)* [2452]

William B. Bean Student Research Award *(Undergraduate/Grant)* [1196]

Beatitudes Fellowships *(Professional development/Fellowship)* [2458]

Catherine H. Beattie Fellowships *(Graduate/Fellowship)* [3238, 4858]

The Dora J. Beattie IBEA Scholarship *(Undergraduate/Scholarship)* [5695]

Beaver Medical Clinic Foundation - Dr. Glenn Adams Memorial Award *(Undergraduate/Scholarship)* [9527]

Beaver Medical Clinic Foundation - H.E.A.R.T. Academy Award *(Undergraduate/Scholarship)* [9528]

Beaver Medical Clinic Foundation - Premedical Award *(Undergraduate/Scholarship)* [9529]

Becas Univision Scholarship Program *(Undergraduate, Graduate/Scholarship)* [5528]

Bechtel Engineering and Science Scholarship *(Undergraduate/Scholarship)* [7075]

Louise Seaman Bechtel Fellowship *(Professional development/Fellowship)* [2239]

Garvin L. Beck Scholarships *(Undergraduate/Scholarship)* [9530]

Clifford L. Bedford Scholarship Award *(Undergraduate/Scholarship)* [5220]

Hannah Beiter Graduate Student Research Grants *(Master's, Graduate/Grant, Recognition)* [3296]

Bel Canto Vocal Scholarship Foundation *(Graduate/Scholarship)* [2467]

Belfer-Aptman Dissertation Research Awards *(Doctorate/Award)* [7247]

Alfred D. Bell, Jr. Travel Grants *(Graduate/Grant)* [4681]

John Bell and Lawrence Thornton Scholarship Fund *(Undergraduate/Scholarship)* [5315]

Belmont University Commercial Music Showcase Scholarship Fund *(Undergraduate/Scholarship)* [2471, 3604]

Samuel Flagg Bemis Dissertation Research Grants *(Graduate/Grant)* [10354]

Ben C. Francis Risk Management Education Fund *(Undergraduate/Scholarship)* [9385]

Benchwarmers Club of Redlands Scholarship- Jess Mercado Memorial *(Undergraduate/Scholarship)* [9531]

Reckitt Benckiser Student Scholarships *(Graduate/Scholarship)* [7677]

The Richard W. Bendicksen, N7ZL, Memorial Scholarship *(Undergraduate/Scholarship)* [1928]

H. Y. Benedict Fellowships *(Graduate/Fellowship)* [376]

Benign Essential Blepharospasm Research Foundation Research Grants *(Doctorate/Grant)* [2473]

HDR/Henry "Bud" Benjes Scholarships *(Master's/Scholarship, Monetary)* [1637]

Benson & Bingham First Annual Scholarship *(Graduate/Scholarship)* [2475]

Benson Law Firm Scholarship Contest *(Undergraduate/Scholarship)* [2477]

Benton-Meier Scholarships *(Graduate/Scholarship)* [1278]

Linn-Benton County Scholarships *(Undergraduate/Scholarship)* [8719]

Fred Berg Awards *(Undergraduate/Award)* [4299]

Bergman Scholarship *(Undergraduate/Scholarship)* [8460]

The E. Alexander Bergstrom Memorial Research Award *(Undergraduate, Master's/Award)* [2177]

The Joseph Berkman, and Michael and Sarah Chipkin Holocaust/Genocide Studies Award *(Graduate/Scholarship)* [10842]

Berkowitz Fellowship *(Professional development/Fellowship)* [11032]

Bernard Kilgore Memorial Scholarship *(Undergraduate/Scholarship)* [8282]

Richard L. Bernardi Memorial Scholarship *(Undergraduate/Scholarship)* [3668]

Bill Bernbach Diversity Scholarships *(Undergraduate/Scholarship)* [510]

Thomas M. Berry Jr. Scholarships *(Graduate, Undergraduate/Scholarship)* [11844]

Jean Clark Berry Scholarship *(Undergraduate, Graduate/Scholarship)* [6403]

Beta Foundation Merit Scholarships *(Graduate, Undergraduate/Scholarship)* [2506]

Beta Mu Project 2000 Scholarship *(Undergraduate/Scholarship)* [6405]

Beta Pi Project 2000 Scholarship in Memory of Kristy LeMond *(Undergraduate/Scholarship)* [6406]

Beta Pi Sigma Sorority Local Chapter Scholarship (BPSSS) *(Undergraduate/Scholarship)* [2501]

Beta Province Project 2000 Scholarship *(Undergraduate/Scholarship)* [6407]

Beta Sigma Scholarship *(Undergraduate/Scholarship)* [10096]

Beta Tau Scholarship Fund *(Undergraduate/Scholarship)* [6408]

Beta Theta Memorial Scholarship *(Graduate, Undergraduate/Scholarship)* [6409]

Beta Xi Project 2000 Scholarship *(Undergraduate/Scholarship)* [6410]

Beta Zeta Project 2000 Scholarship *(Undergraduate/Scholarship)* [6411]

Beth Carew Memorial Scholarship Program *(Undergraduate/Scholarship)* [7920]

Beth K. Fields Scholarship *(University/Scholarship)* [11574]

Betty Rose Scholarship *(Undergraduate/Scholarship)* [1407]

William and Dorothy Bevan Scholarship *(Graduate, Master's, Doctorate/Scholarship)* [1279]

Albert J. Beveridge Grant for Research in the History of the Western Hemisphere *(Doctorate/Grant)* [959]

Beyond the Cure Ambassador Scholarship Program *(Community College, College, Undergraduate, Graduate, Vocational/Occupational/Scholarship)* [7767]

Leo Biaggi de Blasys Bogliasco Fellowships *(Undergraduate/Scholarship)* [2642]

Bill Dickey Scholarship Association Scholarship *(Undergraduate, High School/Scholarship)* [4082]

Bill McCarthy Boy Scout Scholarship Fund *(Undergraduate/Scholarship)* [10752]

Jan Bingle Scholarships *(Master's, Doctorate/Scholarship)* [3438]

Birmingham-Southern College Eagle Scout Scholarships *(Undergraduate/Scholarship)* [7845]

Bisexual Foundation Scholarships *(Graduate/Scholarship, Award)* [1736]

Dr. Richard E. Bjork Memorial Graduate Study Award *(Graduate/Scholarship)* [10843]

Law Offices of David A. Black Annual Hearing Impaired Scholarships *(All/Scholarship)* [6701]

SETAC/EA Jeff Black Fellowship Award *(Postgraduate/Fellowship)* [10324]

Eileen Blackey Doctoral Fellowship *(Doctorate/Fellowship)* [7696]

NICSA/William T. Blackwell Scholarship Fund *(Undergraduate/Scholarship)* [7952]

Mitzi & William Blahd, MD, Pilot Research Grant *(Professional development/Grant)* [10437]

Beatrice K. Blair Scholarships *(Undergraduate/Scholarship)* [2620]

Blake-Nuttall Fund Grants *(Other/Grant)* [8565]

Blakemore Freeman Fellowships *(Undergraduate, Advanced Professional/Fellowship)* [2622]

Blanche E. Woolls Scholarship *(Graduate/Scholarship)* [2496]

Joan Blend Scholarship Fund *(Undergraduate, Graduate/Scholarship)* [10753]

Ellin Bloch and Pierre Ritchie Diversity Dissertation Grant *(Graduate/Grant)* [1269]

Jeanne Humphrey Block Dissertation Award *(Postdoctorate/Award)* [5363]

BMES Graduate and Undergraduate Student Awards *(Graduate, Undergraduate/Award)* [2578]

BMO Capital Markets Lime Connect Equity through Education Scholarships *(Undergraduate, Graduate/Scholarship)* [6860]

Board of Certification for Emergency Nursing (BCEN) Undergraduate Scholarship *(Undergraduate/Scholarship)* [4376]

Bob Baxter Scholarship *(Graduate, Undergraduate/Scholarship)* [8046]

Bob East Scholarship *(Graduate, Undergraduate/Scholarship)* [8047]

Bob Quincy Scholarship *(Undergraduate/Scholarship)* [11178]

Sandra Bobbitt Continuing Education Scholarship *(Undergraduate/Scholarship)* [2254]

Bodie McDowell Scholarship *(Graduate, Undergraduate/Scholarship)* [8782]

Edith and Arnold N. Bodtker Grants *(Undergraduate, Graduate/Grant, Internship)* [3968]

The B.O.G. Pest Control Scholarship Funds *(Undergraduate, Graduate/Scholarship)* [2639]

Sarkis Bogosian Memorial Grant *(Undergraduate/Scholarship)* [1866]

Bohemian Lawyers Association of Chicago Scholarships *(Graduate/Scholarship)* [2649]

BOMA/NY Scholarship *(Undergraduate/Scholarship)* [2741]

Seth Bonder Scholarship for Applied Operations Research in Military Applications *(Graduate/Scholarship, Monetary, Recognition, Award)* [5852]

Bonnie Sorenson Scudder Memorial Scholarship *(Undergraduate/Scholarship)* [3669]

Sam L. Booke, Sr. Scholarship *(Undergraduate/Scholarship)* [12063]

Boomer Benefits Scholarship *(Undergraduate, Graduate/Scholarship)* [2655]

Boren Fellowships *(Graduate/Fellowship)* [5840]

Boren Scholarships *(Undergraduate, College/Scholarship)* [5841]

David L. Boren Undergraduate Scholarships *(Graduate, Undergraduate/Scholarship)* [2184]

Boston Intercollegiate Alumnae Association Adelphe Scholarship *(Undergraduate/Scholarship)* [6412]

Stephen Botein Fellowships *(Doctorate/Fellowship)* [485]

The Bothmer Fellowship *(Doctorate, Graduate/Fellowship)* [7273]

The Dr. George T. Bottomley Scholarship *(Undergraduate/Scholarship)* [4835, 7166]

Dr. Howard L. Bowen Scholarship *(Undergraduate/Scholarship)* [7005]

Bowties and Books Scholarship *(Undergraduate, College, University/Scholarship)* [2661]

Boy Scouts of America Troop 3 Art Till/Nathan E. Smith Memorial Scholarship *(Undergraduate, Vocational/Occupational/Scholarship)* [9532]

Ara S. Boyan Scholarship Grant *(Undergraduate/Scholarship)* [1867]

Dr. Betty J. Boyd-Beu and Edwin G. Beu, Jr. Scholarships *(Undergraduate/Scholarship)* [11440]

Boyd Lyon Sea Turtle Fund Scholars *(Doctorate, Graduate, Postgraduate/Scholarship)* [6952]

Corris Boyd Scholarship *(Graduate/Scholarship)* [2305]

BPW Foundation Career Advancement Scholarships *(Undergraduate/Scholarship)* [2761]

Mildred Cater Bradham Social Work Fellowships *(Graduate, Professional development/Fellowship)* [12409]

Carol June Bradley Award for Historical Research in Music Librarianship *(Professional development/Grant, Award)* [7512]

Ed Bradley Scholarships *(Undergraduate/Scholarship)* [9470]

Edward J. Brady Memorial Scholarship *(Undergraduate/Scholarship)* [1659]

James M. Brahney Scholarship *(Professional development/Scholarship)* [5729]

Byard Braley Scholarship *(Undergraduate/Scholarship)* [6156]

The Helen and Edward Brancati Teacher Development Scholarship *(Professional development, Postgraduate/Scholarship)* [3148]

The Branch Out Scholarship *(Undergraduate, College, University/Scholarship)* [2582]

Brenda Renee Horn and Steve Mack Memorial Scholarships *(Undergraduate/Scholarship)* [4842]

William J. Brennan Graduate Assistant Fellowships *(Graduate/Fellowship)* [8685]

Hilda E. Bretzlaff Foundation Scholarships *(Undergraduate/Scholarship, Grant)* [2687]

Brian A. Aselton Memorial Scholarship *(Undergraduate/Scholarship)* [5316]

Brian Jimenez Memorial Scholarship *(Undergraduate/Scholarship)* [9533]

Wade O. Brinker Resident Research Award *(Postgraduate, Professional development/Grant)* [11813]

Cathy L. Brock Memorial Scholarships *(Graduate/Scholarship)* [5814]

Julia Broderick Scholarships *(Undergraduate/Scholarship)* [10818]

The Brookdale Leadership in Aging Fellowship Program *(Other/Fellowship)* [2713]

George M. Brooker, CPM Diversity Collegiate Scholarship *(Graduate, Undergraduate/Scholarship)* [5861]

Seth R. and Corinne H. Brooks Memorial Scholarships *(Undergraduate/Scholarship)* [2508]

D.C. and Virginia Brown Scholarship *(Undergraduate/Scholarship)* [3467]

Marjorie M. Brown Dissertation Fellowship *(Doctorate/Fellowship)* [6488]

Marjorie M. Brown Fellowship Program *(Postdoctorate/Fellowship)* [6496]

Long-term Fellowship *(Graduate, Doctorate/Fellowship)* [2719]

John Carter Brown Library Short-Term Fellowships *(Doctorate, Postdoctorate/Fellowship)* [2720]

The Phyllis Lister-Brown Memorial Scholarship *(Undergraduate/Scholarship)* [11146]

Jesse Brown Memorial Youth Scholarship Program *(Advanced Professional/Scholarship)* [4107]

Ron Brown Scholarship *(Undergraduate/Scholarship)* [2722]

Warren K. Brown Scholarship *(Undergraduate/Scholarship)* [1562]

Charles S. Brown Scholarships in Physics *(Graduate, Undergraduate/Scholarship)* [8084]

Richard A. Brown Student Scholarship *(Undergraduate/Scholarship)* [10977]

Peggy Browning Fund - Chicago School-Year Fellowships *(Graduate, Undergraduate/Fellowship)* [2729]

Bruce Shelton Scholarship *(Undergraduate, High School/Scholarship)* [12064]

The Robert W. Brunsman Memorial Scholarship *(Professional development/Scholarship)* [6041]

Katie Brush Memorial Scholarships *(Master's, Doctorate/Scholarship)* [7637]

Bryant Essay Scholarships *(Undergraduate, Graduate/Scholarship)* [2731]

Bryant L. Bench Scholarship *(Master's/Scholarship, Monetary)* [1638]

Bryant Visual Content Scholarships *(Undergraduate, Graduate/Scholarship)* [2732]

Bryce Harlow Fellowship *(Graduate/Fellowship)* [5298]

Brylak Law Safety Scholarship Contest *(Undergraduate/Scholarship)* [2734]

CFCC Foundation Merit Scholarship *(Undergraduate/Scholarship)* [3151]

CFNIL Senior Memorial Scholarship *(Undergraduate/Scholarship)* [3672]

CFR National Intelligence Fellowships *(Professional development/Fellowship)* [3861]

CFR Stanton Nuclear Security Fellowship *(Doctorate, Postdoctorate, Advanced Professional/Fellowship)* [3862]

CFR Volunteer Internships *(Undergraduate, Graduate/Internship)* [3863]

Rick Chace Foundation Scholarships *(Graduate/Scholarship)* [2246]

Chaîne des Rôtisseurs Scholarships *(Undergraduate/Scholarship)* [842]

ChairScholars National Scholarship Program *(Undergraduate/Scholarship)* [3275]

Jeanne S. Chall Research Fellowship *(Doctorate, Graduate/Fellowship, Grant)* [6033]

The Challenge Met Scholarship *(Undergraduate/Scholarship)* [1933]

Mariam K. Chamberlain Fellowship in Women and Public Policy *(Graduate/Fellowship)* [5874]

Bryan A. Champion Memorial Scholarship *(Undergraduate/Scholarship)* [5586]

Channabasappa Memorial Scholarships *(Graduate, Doctorate/Scholarship)* [5993]

Harry H. and Floy B. Chapin Scholarships *(Undergraduate/Scholarship)* [3673]

Nancy J. Chapman Scholarships *(Other/Scholarship)* [2152]

Chappie Hall Scholarship *(Undergraduate/Scholarship)* [2]

Chapter 1 - Detroit Associate Scholarship *(Graduate, Undergraduate, Vocational/Occupational, Two Year College, Four Year College/Award)* [10386]

Chapter 1 Detroit Undergraduate Scholarship *(Undergraduate, Vocational/Occupational, Two Year College, Four Year College/Scholarship)* [10387]

Chapter 31 - Peoria Scholarship *(Undergraduate/Scholarship)* [10390]

Chapter 52 - Wichita Scholarship *(Graduate, Undergraduate, Vocational/Occupational, Community College/Scholarship)* [10392]

Chapter 56 - Ft. Wayne Scholarship *(Graduate, Undergraduate, Vocational/Occupational, Community College/Scholarship)* [10393]

Chapter 6 - Fairfield County Scholarship *(Undergraduate/Scholarship)* [10394]

Chapter 67 - Phoenix Scholarship *(Undergraduate/Scholarship)* [10397]

Charles A. King Trust Postdoctoral Research Fellowship *(Postdoctorate/Fellowship)* [5434]

Charles A. Lindbergh Fellowships *(Graduate/Fellowship)* [10191]

Charles and Carol Spielberger Scholarship *(Graduate, Master's, Doctorate/Scholarship)* [1280]

Charles E. Peterson Fellowships *(Other/Fellowship)* [2334]

Charles Grossman Graduate Scholarship *(Graduate/Scholarship)* [5978]

Charles H. Bussmann Graduate Scholarship *(Graduate, Undergraduate/Scholarship)* [7068]

Charles Lee Anderson Memorial Scholarship *(Undergraduate/Scholarship)* [3674]

Charles McCorkle Hauser Scholarship *(Undergraduate/Scholarship)* [11179]

Charles S. Houston Grant *(Advanced Professional/Grant)* [12028]

Charles Shafae Scholarship *(Undergraduate, Four Year College/Scholarship)* [8818]

Charlotte Housing Authority Scholarship Fund (CHASF) *(Undergraduate/Scholarship)* [4726]

Charlotte-Mecklenburg Schools Scholarship Incentive Fund *(Undergraduate/Scholarship)* [3277, 4727]

Charlotte V. Bergen Scholarship *(Undergraduate/Scholarship)* [1408]

CCWH Nupur Chaudhuri Article Prize *(Professional development/Prize)* [3829]

CHCI Congressional Internship Program *(Undergraduate/Internship)* [3745]

CHCI Graduate Fellowship Program *(Graduate, Professional development/Fellowship)* [3746]

CHCI Public Policy Fellowships *(Professional development/Fellowship)* [3747]

CHEA Vocational Grants *(Vocational/Occupational, Two Year College/Grant)* [2815]

Cherokee Nation Pell Scholarships *(Undergraduate/Scholarship)* [3284]

Chester Arzell and Helen Miller Montgomery Scholarship *(Undergraduate/Scholarship)* [12065]

Chet And Janett Perry Rotary Club Of Fort Myers Scholarship Fund *(Undergraduate/Scholarship)* [10674]

Kevin Child Scholarship *(Undergraduate/Scholarship)* [7921]

Childbirth Educator Program Scholarships *(Other/Scholarship)* [6641]

Children of Evangeline Section Scholarships *(Graduate, Undergraduate/Scholarship)* [10472]

Children of Unitarian Universalist Religious Professionals Grant *(Undergraduate/Grant)* [11246]

Children's National Health System Pediatric Nursing Student Scholarships *(Undergraduate/Scholarship)* [124]

China and East Asia Google PhD Fellowships *(Doctorate/Fellowship)* [5045]

CHOIR MD Post-Residency Fellowship in Health Services Research *(Postdoctorate/Fellowship)* [11811]

Choose Your Future Scholarship Fund *(Undergraduate/Scholarship)* [3608]

Chopin Foundation Scholarship *(Other/Scholarship)* [3315]

CHOPR Fellowship Program *(Postdoctorate/Fellowship)* [11664]

CHPI Travel Fellowships *(Undergraduate/Fellowship)* [7186]

Chrétien International Research Grants *(Doctorate/Grant)* [683]

Betty Sams Christian Fellowships *(Doctorate/Fellowship)* [11835]

Christian Larew Memorial Scholarship *(Graduate/Scholarship, Monetary)* [6838]

Frances N. Christian Memorial Endowment Nursing Scholarship *(Graduate, Undergraduate/Scholarship)* [10844]

Christian Pharmacists Fellowship International (CPFI) *(Advanced Professional/Scholarship)* [3321]

Christine Kerr Cawthorne Scholarship *(Undergraduate/Scholarship)* [10097]

The Christine Mirzayan Science & Technology Policy Graduate Fellowship Program *(Graduate, Postdoctorate, High School/Fellowship)* [7571]

Commander Daniel J. Christovich Scholarship *(Undergraduate/Scholarship)* [3455]

Chronic Lymphocytic Leukemia Grant *(Advanced Professional/Grant)* [6947]

Chrysalis Scholarship *(Graduate/Scholarship)* [2314]

Chuck Peacock Memorial Scholarship *(Undergraduate/Scholarship)* [175]

Chuck Pezzano Scholarship *(College, Graduate/Scholarship)* [5955]

The Churchill Scholarships *(Postgraduate/Scholarship)* [3331]

CIA Undergraduate Scholarships *(Undergraduate/Scholarship)* [2185, 3244]

CIGNA Healthcare Graduate Scholarships *(Graduate/Scholarship)* [7888]

CIGNA Undergraduate Scholarships *(Undergraduate/Scholarship)* [7889]

CIMON Inc Scholarship *(College, University/Scholarship)* [3333]

Cindy Andrews Educational Scholarship *(Undergraduate/Scholarship)* [9534]

CISDL Global Research Fellowship - Associate Fellows *(Graduate/Fellowship)* [3257]

CISDL Global Research Fellowship - Legal Research Fellows *(Graduate/Fellowship)* [3258]

CISDL Global Research Fellowships - Senior Research Fellows *(Other/Fellowship)* [3259]

Citi Foundation Scholarship Program *(Undergraduate/Scholarship)* [978]

Citi/TELACU Scholars Mentoring Program *(Undergraduate/Scholarship)* [10940]

CitizenshipTests.org Engineering and Science Scholarship *(Undergraduate/Scholarship)* [3991]

City Bar Diversity Fellowship Program *(Undergraduate/Fellowship)* [8300]

City of Boston Disability Scholarship Contest *(Undergraduate/Scholarship)* [4535]

City Of Sanibel Employee Dependent Scholarship Fund *(Undergraduate/Scholarship)* [10676]

Civitan Shropshire Scholarship *(Undergraduate, Vocational/Occupational/Scholarship)* [3424]

CJH Graduate Research Fellowships *(Doctorate/Fellowship)* [3221]

CJH-NEH Fellowships for Senior Scholars *(Doctorate/Fellowship)* [3222]

CJH Visiting Scholars Program *(Doctorate/Fellowship)* [3225]

Claes Nobel Academic Scholarships for Members *(High School, College/Scholarship)* [8103]

Clan Ross Foundation Scholarships *(Undergraduate/Scholarship)* [3426]

Clarivate Analytics/MLA Doctoral Fellowship *(Doctorate, Graduate/Fellowship)* [7215]

Vickie Clark-Flaherty Scholarships *(Undergraduate/Scholarship)* [8444]

Classic Wines of California Scholarships *(Undergraduate/Scholarship)* [2797]

Claude B. Hart Memorial Scholarship *(Undergraduate/Scholarship)* [12066]

Claude Robinson Memorial Scholarship *(Undergraduate/Scholarship)* [7969]

Clay Maitland CGF Scholarship *(Undergraduate/Scholarship)* [3456]

Clay Postdoctoral Fellowship *(Postdoctorate/Fellowship)* [5358]

Cleve Holloway Memorial Scholarship *(Undergraduate/Scholarship)* [3652]

Geraldine Clewell Fellowships - Doctoral Student *(Graduate/Fellowship)* [9107]

Geraldine Clewell Fellowships - Masteral *(Graduate/Fellowship)* [9108]

James L. Clifford Prize *(Other/Prize, Monetary)* [1430]

Bryan Cline Memorial Soccer Scholarship Program *(Undergraduate/Scholarship)* [318]

Clinic & Laboratory Integration Program (CLIP) *(Professional development/Grant)* [3140]

Clinical Project Funding for Advanced Practice Oncology Nurses *(Advanced Professional, Professional development/Grant)* [8627]

Clinician Research Awards *(Postgraduate, Professional development, Other/Fellowship)* [8898]

Paul W. Clopper Scholarship Grant for Junior Dental Students *(Undergraduate/Scholarship)* [5709]

Closs/Parnitzke/Clarke Scholarship *(Undergraduate/Scholarship)* [9109]

Clubs of America Scholarship Program *(Undergraduate/Scholarship)* [3446]

CMAA Student Conference Travel Grants *(Undergraduate/Grant, Award)* [3442]

CMC-KLI Leadership Research Fellowship *(Undergraduate/Fellowship)* [3428]

CMC-KLI Leadership Thesis Fellowship *(Undergraduate/Fellowship)* [3429]

CMC-KLI Social Sector Internship Program *(Undergraduate/Internship)* [3430]

CMC/MMC Scholarships (CMC) *(Other/Scholarship)* [6026]

CME Beef Industry Scholarship *(Undergraduate/Scholarship)* [7744]

CMH Dissertation Fellowships *(Graduate/Fellowship)* [11286]

CMSF Scholarship *(Graduate/Scholarship)* [3319]

Coast Guard Foundation Enlisted Education Scholarship *(Advanced Professional/Scholarship)* [3457]

J.C. and Rheba Cobb Memorial Scholarships *(Undergraduate/Scholarship)* [7775]

John Coburn and Harold Winters Student Award in Plasma Science and Technology *(Graduate/Award)* [2382]

Coca-Cola First Generation Scholarships *(Undergraduate/Scholarship)* [979]

Coca-Cola Scholars Program Scholarship *(Undergraduate/Scholarship)* [3494]

Johnnie L. Cochran, Jr./MWH Scholarships *(Graduate, Undergraduate/Scholarship)* [7890]

Code Play LEARN Scholarship *(Two Year College, Undergraduate, Graduate/Scholarship)* [3496]

Coeur d'Alene Alumni Scholarship *(Undergraduate/Scholarship)* [6784]

Legal Residence Index

Damon Runyon-Rachleff Innovation Awards *(Postdoctorate/Award)* [9759]

Damon Runyon-Sohn Pediatric Cancer Fellowship Award *(Master's, Doctorate/Fellowship)* [9760]

Dan M. Reichard, Jr. Scholarship *(Undergraduate, Graduate/Scholarship)* [1299]

Dan and Rachel Mahi Educational Scholarship *(Graduate, Undergraduate/Scholarship)* [8921]

Daniel H. Pokorny Memorial Scholarship Award *(Undergraduate/Scholarship)* [9624]

Daniel Kahikina and Millie Akaka Scholarship *(Graduate, Undergraduate/Scholarship)* [8922]

Margaret A. Dankworth Management Scholarship *(Professional development/Scholarship)* [2327]

Dante Prize *(Undergraduate/Prize, Monetary)* [3970]

Darrel Hess Community College Geography Scholarship *(Undergraduate/Scholarship)* [564]

Dave Benferado Scholarship *(Graduate/Scholarship)* [159]

Dave Caldwell Scholarship *(Graduate/Scholarship, Monetary)* [1640]

Dave Sauer Memorial College Scholarship *(Undergraduate/Scholarship)* [170]

David A. Kronick Travelling Fellowship *(Doctorate, Graduate/Fellowship)* [7216]

David Arver Memorial Scholarship *(Undergraduate/Scholarship)* [176]

David Beltran Memorial Scholarship *(Undergraduate/Scholarship)* [9540]

David C. Maloney Scholarship *(Undergraduate/Scholarship)* [8021]

David G. Imig Award for Distinguished Achievement in Teacher Education *(Other/Award, Recognition)* [549]

David H. Clift Scholarship *(Graduate/Scholarship, Monetary)* [1077]

David H. Smith Conservation Research Fellowship *(Postdoctorate/Fellowship)* [10314]

David Library Fellowships *(Doctorate, Postdoctorate/Fellowship)* [3973]

David Meador Foundation - Hospitality-Food Service Scholarships *(Undergraduate/Scholarship)* [8241]

David Pohl Scholarship *(Master's/Scholarship)* [11247]

David W. Schacht Native American Student Scholarship *(Undergraduate/Scholarship)* [2479]

Lucile Caswell Davids Memorial Adelphe Scholarship *(Undergraduate, Graduate/Scholarship)* [6416]

Davis Foundation Postdoctoral Fellowships *(Doctorate, Master's/Fellowship)* [5435]

Davis Memorial Foundation Scholarship *(Graduate, Undergraduate/Scholarship)* [3977]

The James H. Davis Memorial Scholarship *(Undergraduate, Postgraduate/Scholarship)* [4638]

Johnny Davis Memorial Scholarship *(Undergraduate/Scholarship)* [177]

The Davis-Putter Scholarship Fund *(Undergraduate, Graduate/Scholarship)* [9770]

Arlene Davis Scholarships *(Undergraduate/Scholarship)* [4030]

Raymond Davis Scholarships *(Undergraduate, Graduate/Scholarship)* [10371]

Davis Wright Tremaine 1L Diversity Scholarship *(Undergraduate/Scholarship)* [3979]

Colonel Richard M. Dawson Highway Patrol Scholarship Fund *(Undergraduate/Scholarship)* [3610]

The Dayton Amateur Radio Association Scholarship *(Undergraduate/Scholarship)* [1938]

DBA Scholarships *(Undergraduate/Scholarship)* [4130]

DBI Scholarship Fund *(Undergraduate/Scholarship)* [3611]

D.C. Cornelius Memorial Scholarship *(Undergraduate, Graduate/Scholarship)* [12068]

DCH Freehold Toyota Scholarship *(Undergraduate/Scholarship)* [3251]

Edilia and François Auguste de Montêquin Fellowships *(Doctorate/Fellowship)* [10274]

Kenneth J. De Witt NASA/OSGC Scholarship at The University of Toledo *(Undergraduate/Scholarship)* [8596]

Dean A. Froehlich Endowed Scholarship *(Undergraduate/Scholarship)* [6787]

The Dean Prim Scholarship *(Undergraduate/Scholarship)* [12069]

Dean – Derek Lee Dean Soccer Scholarships *(Undergraduate/Scholarship)* [3471]

Don Debolt Franchising Scholarship Program *(Undergraduate/Scholarship)* [6011]

Deborah Jean Rydberg Memorial Scholarship *(Undergraduate/Scholarship)* [3676]

Deborah Munroe Noonan Memorial Research Fund *(Professional development/Grant)* [5436]

Deborah Partridge Wolfe International Fellowship (Graduate) *(Graduate, Undergraduate/Fellowship)* [12410]

Debt.com Scholarship *(All/Scholarship)* [3987]

Decommissioning, and Environmental Science Division Graduate Scholarship *(Undergraduate/Scholarship)* [1164]

DEED Student Research Grant/Internships *(Undergraduate, Graduate/Grant, Internship)* [1297]

Anthony R. Dees Educational Workshop Scholarship *(Graduate/Scholarship)* [10342]

Defensive Driving scholarship *(Undergraduate/Scholarship)* [3994]

Jane Delano Student Nurse Scholarships *(Undergraduate, Graduate/Scholarship)* [1149]

Delta Chi Alumnae Memorial Scholarship *(Undergraduate/Scholarship)* [10099]

Delta Faucet Scholarships *(Undergraduate/Scholarship)* [9204]

Delta Gamma Foundation Florence Margaret Harvey Memorial Scholarship *(Graduate, Undergraduate/Scholarship)* [914]

Delta Kappa Gamma Society International World Fellowship *(Graduate/Fellowship)* [4022]

Delta Kappa Project 2000 Scholarship *(Undergraduate/Scholarship)* [6417]

Delta Nu Project 2000 Scholarship *(Undergraduate/Scholarship)* [6418]

Delta Project 2000 Scholarship *(Undergraduate/Scholarship)* [6419]

Delta Tau Project 2000 Scholarship *(Undergraduate/Scholarship)* [6420]

Delta Upsilon Project 2000 Nowell Memorial Scholarship *(Undergraduate/Scholarship)* [6421]

Law Offices of Michael A. DeMayo Scholarships *(Undergraduate/Scholarship)* [6708]

DEMCO New Leaders Travel Grants *(Professional development/Grant)* [9432]

Christopher Demetris Memorial Scholarships *(Undergraduate/Scholarship)* [5463]

Democrats for Life of America Scholarship Essay *(College, Community College, High School, Undergraduate, Graduate, Vocational/Occupational/Scholarship)* [4047]

Inez Demonet Scholarship *(Graduate/Scholarship)* [11804]

Dena Epstein Award for Archival and Library Research in American Music *(Professional development/Award)* [7513]

The Dendel Scholarship *(Graduate, Undergraduate/Scholarship)* [5284]

Denis Wong & Associates Scholarship *(Graduate, Undergraduate/Scholarship)* [8923]

Denton Scholarship *(Graduate/Scholarship)* [10081]

Bobby Michael Denton Memorial Scholarship *(High School/Scholarship)* [8508]

Denver Scholarship Foundation General Scholarship Fund *(Graduate/Scholarship)* [4053]

Dick Depaolis Memorial Scholarship *(Undergraduate/Scholarship)* [3718]

DEPS Graduate Scholarship *(Graduate/Scholarship)* [4099]

Garabed and Almast Der Megrditchian Scholarship Grants *(Undergraduate/Scholarship)* [1874]

Descendants Scholarships *(Undergraduate/Scholarship)* [3954]

Libby Deschenes Prize for Applied Research *(Undergraduate/Prize)* [11989]

Design and Multimedia Internships - New York *(Undergraduate, Graduate/Internship)* [4980]

APTRA-Clete Roberts/Kathryn Dettman Memorial Journalism Scholarship *(Undergraduate/Scholarship)* [2022]

Development Fund for Black Students in Science and Technology Scholarship *(Undergraduate/Scholarship)* [4068]

DeVries Law School Scholarship *(Undergraduate/Scholarship)* [4070]

Dewey Lee Curtis Symposium Scholarships *(Advanced Professional/Scholarship)* [3989]

Dezao Legal Awards *(Advanced Professional/Scholarship)* [6704]

DFA Cares Foundation Scholarship Program *(Undergraduate/Scholarship)* [3958]

Beta Nu/Caryl Cordis D'hondt Scholarship *(Undergraduate/Scholarship)* [10100]

Theta/Caryl Cordis D'hondt Scholarship *(Undergraduate/Scholarship)* [10101]

The Lilly Diabetes Tomorrow's Leaders Scholarship *(Undergraduate/Scholarship)* [4074]

Diagnosis Delayed Scholarship *(Graduate/Scholarship)* [4076]

Diana Brown Endowed Scholarship *(Undergraduate/Scholarship)* [6788]

Edwina Eustis Dick Scholarship for Music Therapy Interns *(Graduate/Scholarship)* [1134]

Dickey Rural Networks Scholarship *(Undergraduate, Vocational/Occupational/Scholarship)* [4080]

Diffuse Large B-Cell Lymphoma Grant *(Advanced Professional/Grant)* [6948]

Carol DiMaiti Scholarship *(Undergraduate/Scholarship)* [7124]

DirectTextbook.com Scholarship Essay Contest *(College, Undergraduate, University/Scholarship)* [4097]

Disability Care Center Disabled Student Scholarships *(Undergraduate/Scholarship)* [4104]

Disability Care Center Special Education Scholarships *(Undergraduate/Scholarship)* [4105]

Disabled Veteran Scholarship *(College, Vocational/Occupational/Scholarship)* [9713]

Disabled Veteran Student Scholarship *(Two Year College, Four Year College/Scholarship)* [12018]

Disabled Veterans Scholarship *(Vocational/Occupational, Community College, Four Year College, Graduate, Professional development/Scholarship)* [6519]

Discover Bar Exam Loans *(Graduate/Loan, Scholarship)* [4109]

Discover Graduate Loans *(Graduate, Master's, Doctorate/Loan, Scholarship)* [4110]

Discover Health Professions Loans *(Graduate/Loan, Scholarship)* [4111]

Discover Law Loans *(Graduate/Loan, Scholarship)* [4112]

Discover MBA Loans *(Graduate/Loan, Scholarship)* [4113]

Discover Residency Loans *(Graduate/Loan, Scholarship)* [4114]

Dissertation Award in Hadronic Physics *(Doctorate, Postdoctorate/Award, Recognition, Monetary)* [1224]

Dissertation Completion Fellowship (DCF) *(Doctorate/Fellowship)* [603]

Dissertation Proposal Development Fellowship *(Doctorate/Fellowship)* [10243]

Dissertation Writing Grants *(Graduate/Grant)* [5869]

Distinguished Flying Cross Society Scholarship *(Undergraduate/Scholarship)* [4116]

Distinguished Young Women - Cash Scholarships *(High School/Scholarship)* [4118]

Diversity Executive Leadership Program Scholarship (DELP) *(Other/Scholarship)* [1977]

Diversity Scholarship *(Graduate/Scholarship, Award)* [1796]

Robert A. and Barbara Divine Graduate Student Travel Fund *(Graduate/Grant)* [10355]

Daniel B. Dixon Scholarship Fund *(Undergraduate/Scholarship)* [346]

Peggy Dixon Two-Year Scholarships *(Undergraduate/Scholarship)* [10477]

D.J. Lovell Scholarship *(Graduate, Undergraduate/Scholarship)* [10725]

DLF Graduate Scholarship Program *(Graduate/Scholarship)* [3960]

Mychajlo Dmytrenko Fine Arts Foundation Scholarships *(Undergraduate/Scholarship)* [11410]

Do-Over Scholarship *(Undergraduate, High School/Scholarship)* [11226]

DO Supply Academic Scholarship *(Undergraduate/Scholarship)* [4122]

Charles Dobbins FTA Scholarships *(Undergraduate, Vocational/Occupational/Scholarship)* [4846]

Dr. Ali Jarrahi Merlt Scholarship *(Undergraduate/Scholarship)* [6172]

Dr. Aura-Lee A. and James Hobbs Pittenger American History Scholarship *(Undergraduate/Scholarship, Award, Monetary)* [8095]

Dr. Edward G. Voss Memorial Scholarship *(Undergraduate/Scholarship)* [11618]

Dr. F. Ross Byrd Scholarship *(Graduate/Scholarship)* [11909]

Dr. Frank and Florence Marino Scholarship *(Undergraduate/Scholarship)* [5322]

Dr. George and Isabelle Elanjian Scholarship *(Undergraduate/Scholarship)* [11638]

Dr. George M. Smerk Scholarship *(Undergraduate, Graduate/Scholarship)* [1300]

Dr. Gunnar B. Stickler Scholarship *(Undergraduate, Vocational/Occupational/Scholarship)* [10839]

Dr. James A. Ferguson Emerging Infectious Diseases Research Initiatives for Student Enhancement Fellowship (RISE) *(Graduate/Fellowship)* [6526]

Dr. Joyce Beckett Scholarship *(Graduate, Undergraduate/Scholarship)* [7618]

Dr. Julianne Malveaux Scholarship *(Undergraduate/Scholarship)* [7668]

Dr. Mac Scholarship Fund *(Undergraduate/Scholarship)* [3612]

Dr. Nancy Smith Midgette Scholarship *(Undergraduate/Scholarship)* [10102]

Dr. Nicholas J. Piergrossi Memorial Scholarship *(Undergraduate/Scholarship)* [5323]

Doctoral Dissertation Grants *(Doctorate/Grant)* [6075]

F. Atlee Dodge Maintenance Scholarship *(Undergraduate/Scholarship)* [237]

Jim Dodson Law Scholarship for Brain Injury Victims & Their Caregivers *(Undergraduate/Scholarship)* [4124]

Dody Boyd Scholarship Fund *(Undergraduate/Scholarship)* [3613]

DOE Computational Science Graduate Fellowship (DOE CSGF) *(Doctorate, Graduate/Fellowship)* [6611]

Office of Science Graduate Student Research (SCGSR) Program *(Graduate, Master's, Postdoctorate/Fellowship)* [11323]

Emmett J. Doerr Memorial Distinguished Scout Scholarship *(High School/Scholarship)* [7846]

Dofflemyer Scholarship *(Undergraduate/Scholarship)* [7847]

Dollar-A-Day Academic Scholarships *(Graduate, Undergraduate/Scholarship)* [4126]

Scott Dominguez - Craters of the Moon Chapter Scholarship *(Graduate, Undergraduate/Scholarship)* [1564]

Don Aron Scholarship *(Undergraduate/Scholarship)* [7783]

Don and Barbara Curtis Excellence Fund for Extracurricular Activities *(Undergraduate/Scholarship)* [11181]

Don C. Beaver Memorial Scholarship *(Undergraduate/Scholarship)* [2798]

Don Freeman Illustrator Grants *(Advanced Professional/Grant)* [10300]

Don S. Maurer Advertising Scholarship *(Undergraduate/Scholarship)* [11182]

Donald A. B. Lindberg Research Fellowship *(Doctorate, Graduate/Fellowship)* [7217]

Donald and Shirley Hastings Scholarship *(Undergraduate/Scholarship)* [1660]

Donald W. Banner Diversity Fellowship for Law Students *(Graduate/Fellowship)* [2428]

Marion Jones Donaldson Scholarship Fund *(Undergraduate/Scholarship)* [4589]

Doniphan Community Foundation Scholarships *(Undergraduate, Community College, Vocational/Occupational/Scholarship)* [5120]

Donna Gail Scholarship for Chapter Service *(Undergraduate, Graduate, Doctorate/Scholarship)* [6380]

Doris Hendren Memorial Scholarship *(Undergraduate/Scholarship)* [9811]

Pauly D'Orlando Memorial Art Scholarship *(Graduate, Undergraduate/Scholarship)* [11248]

Dorothy Mitchell Memorial Scholarship *(Undergraduate/Scholarship)* [9541]

Dorothy Mountain Memorial Scholarship *(Graduate/Scholarship)* [6922]

Dottie Martin Teacher Scholarship *(Graduate, Undergraduate/Scholarship)* [8437]

The Father Connie Dougherty Scholarship Fund *(Undergraduate, Vocational/Occupational/Scholarship)* [3712]

Douglas Lake Improvement Association Scholarship *(Undergraduate/Scholarship)* [11619]

The Douglas Psychotherapy Do Good General Education Scholarship *(Undergraduate, Graduate/Scholarship)* [4140]

Douglass Foundation Fellowship in American Art *(Doctorate/Fellowship)* [10214]

The Douglass Foundation Fellowship in American Art *(Graduate/Fellowship)* [7276]

Dow Chemical Company Fellowships *(Graduate/Fellowship)* [8027]

Downes - Jay and Rheba Downes Memorial Scholarship *(Undergraduate/Scholarship)* [3473]

Tim Downing Memorial Scholarship Program *(Professional development/Scholarship)* [2906]

Downtown Apartment Companys Scholarship Program *(Undergraduate/Scholarship)* [4144]

W.B.H. Dowse Fellowships *(Graduate/Fellowship)* [7142]

The Drawn to Art Fellowship *(Doctorate/Fellowship)* [488]

DRC Pilot and Feasibility Study Award *(Advanced Professional, Professional development/Grant, Award)* [12233]

DREAM - Diversity Recruitment Recruitment through Education and Mentoring Program *(Undergraduate/Fellowship)* [621]

The Dream is Inclusive Scholarship *(Two Year College, Undergraduate, Graduate, Professional development, Vocational/Occupational/Scholarship)* [8624]

Margaret Drew Alpha Scholarship *(Graduate/Scholarship)* [9110]

Charles Drew Scholarships *(Other/Scholarship)* [2153]

Camille and Henry Dreyfus Foundation - Senior Scientist Mentor Program *(Professional development/Grant)* [4180]

DriversEdHub.com Scholarship *(Undergraduate/Scholarship)* [3992]

Drug Development Research Professorship *(Professional development/Internship)* [3773]

Richard Drukker Memorial Scholarships *(Undergraduate/Scholarship)* [8283]

Emilie Du Chatelet Award *(Doctorate/Award)* [1431]

Henry Belin du Pont Dissertation Fellowships *(Doctorate, Graduate/Fellowship)* [5257]

Henry Belin du Pont Research Grants *(Graduate/Grant)* [5258]

Duane Hanson Scholarship *(Undergraduate/Scholarship)* [1473]

The Duberman-Zal Fellowship *(Graduate/Scholarship)* [3234]

Lee Dubin Memorial Scholarship *(Undergraduate/Scholarship)* [3500]

Mark Duda Scholarship Fund *(Graduate, Undergraduate/Scholarship)* [7104]

Doris Duke Conservation Fellows Program *(Master's/Fellowship)* [12046]

Duluth Building and Construction Trades Council Scholarship Fund *(Graduate/Scholarship)* [4204]

Dumbarton Oaks Fellowship *(Doctorate, Graduate/Fellowship)* [4222]

Dumbarton Oaks Junior Fellowship *(Graduate/Fellowship)* [4223]

Dumbarton Oaks Research Library and Collection Bliss Symposium Award *(Undergraduate, Graduate/Award)* [4224]

Dumbarton Oaks Research Library and Collection Graduate Research Workshops *(Undergraduate, Graduate/Fellowship)* [4225]

Dumbarton Oaks Research Library and Collection One-Month Research Stipends *(Doctorate/Monetary)* [4226]

Dumbarton Oaks Research Library and Collection Post-Baccalaureate Media Fellowships *(Professional development/Fellowship)* [4227]

Dumbarton Oaks Research Library and Collection Short-Term Predoctoral Residencies Grants *(Undergraduate/Grant)* [4229]

Dumbarton Oaks Research Library and Collection Summer Fellowship *(Graduate/Fellowship)* [4230]

Dumbarton Oaks Research Library and Collection Summer Internships for Harvard Students *(Undergraduate, Graduate/Internship)* [4231]

Dumbarton Oaks Research Library and Collection Post-Doctoral Teaching Fellowships *(Postdoctorate/Fellowship)* [4232]

Duncan Aviation Scholarship *(Undergraduate/Scholarship)* [178, 4238]

Wade and Marcelene Duncan Scholarship *(Undergraduate/Scholarship)* [12070]

Ed Dunkelblau Scholarship *(All/Scholarship)* [2052]

Joe Durso, Jr. Memorial Scholarship *(Undergraduate/Scholarship)* [7451]

Dutch and Ginger Arver Scholarship *(Undergraduate/Scholarship)* [179]

Dwight Teed Scholarship Fund *(Undergraduate/Scholarship)* [10881]

Dystonia Medical Research Foundation Clinical Fellowships *(Postdoctorate/Fellowship)* [4244]

E-Waste Scholarship *(High School, Undergraduate, Graduate/Scholarship)* [4090]

EAIA Research Grants *(Other/Grant)* [4248]

Howard and Gladys Eakes Memorial Scholarship *(Undergraduate/Scholarship)* [5121]

EAPSI Fellowships *(Doctorate, Graduate/Fellowship, Award)* [8067]

Earl Warren Civil Rights Training Scholarships *(Graduate/Scholarship)* [7538]

Earl Warren Scholarship *(Graduate/Scholarship)* [7539]

Early-Career Patient-Oriented Diabetes Research Awards *(Professional development/Award)* [6347]

Easter Scholarship *(All/Scholarship)* [7438]

Eastern Orthodox Scouting Scholarships *(Undergraduate/Scholarship)* [7848]

The Eating Recovery Center Foundation Early Career Investigator Grants *(Professional development/Grant)* [7863]

David Eaton Scholarship *(Master's/Scholarship)* [11249]

Eben Tisdale Fellowship *(Undergraduate/Fellowship, Monetary)* [4838]

ECA Centennial Scholarships *(Master's, Doctorate/Scholarship)* [4271]

Echoing Green Black Male Achievement Fellowships *(Professional development/Fellowship)* [4275]

Echoing Green Climate Fellowships *(Professional development/Fellowship)* [4276]

Echoing Green Global Fellowships *(Professional development/Fellowship)* [4277]

Ecolab Scholarship *(Undergraduate/Scholarship)* [971]

The École Nationale des Chartes Exchange Fellowship *(Postdoctorate/Fellowship)* [8371]

Edgecliff McAuley Art Scholarships *(Undergraduate/Scholarship)* [12221]

Edgecliff McAuley Music Scholarship *(Undergraduate/Scholarship)* [12222]

Edith Weingarten Scholarship *(Postgraduate/Scholarship)* [1177]

S. Randolph Edmonds Young Scholars Competition *(Graduate, Undergraduate/Scholarship)* [2615]

Education Factor Scholarships *(Graduate, Undergraduate/Scholarship)* [7207]

Education Matters Scholarship *(Undergraduate, High School/Scholarship)* [11227]

"Education is Power" Scholarships *(Undergraduate/Scholarship)* [7923]

Educational Audiology Association Doctoral Scholarship *(Doctorate/Scholarship)* [4300]

Educational and Cultural Affairs Alumni Small Grants Program (ECA) *(Other/Grant)* [6069]

The Educational Foundation of KyCPA Scholarships *(Undergraduate/Scholarship)* [6539]

Educational Loan Program for Gay and Lesbian Students *(Undergraduate/Loan)* [3615]

Edward C. Pomeroy Award for Outstanding Contributions to Teacher Education *(Other/Award, Recognition)* [550]

Faculty Research Visit Grants *(Doctorate/Grant)* [4061]

Faegre Baker Daniels Diversity & Inclusion Fellowships *(Graduate/Fellowship)* [4480]

FAER Mentored Research Training Grants *(Professional development/Grant)* [4702]

FAER Research in Education Grants *(Advanced Professional/Grant)* [4703]

FAER Research Fellowship Grants *(Postdoctorate, Postgraduate, Graduate/Grant)* [4704]

Fahs-Beck Fund for Research and Experimentation - Doctoral Dissertation Grants *(Doctorate/Grant)* [8303]

Fahs-Beck Fund for Research and Experimentation - Postdoctoral Grants *(Postdoctorate/Grant)* [8304]

FAIC Individual Professional Development Scholarships *(Professional development/Scholarship)* [4700]

FAIC Latin American and Caribbean Scholars Program *(Other/Scholarship)* [1025]

Fairbanks Chapter Legacy Scholarship *(Undergraduate/Scholarship)* [11517]

AIST Benjamin F. Fairless Scholarship *(Undergraduate/Scholarship)* [2220]

Faith Initiatives Internships - New York *(Undergraduate, Graduate/Internship)* [4981]

Falcon Achievement Scholarships *(Undergraduate/Scholarship)* [9242]

Fall Fellowships in Korean Studies *(Other/Fellowship)* [6594]

The Fallen Heroes Scholarship *(Undergraduate/Scholarship)* [3458]

Families of Freedom Scholarship Fund - Scholarship America *(Undergraduate, Vocational/Occupational/Scholarship)* [4482]

FAMU Presidential Scholarship - Florida Community College Scholarships *(Undergraduate/Scholarship)* [4620]

Fanconi Anemia Research Grants *(Postdoctorate, Doctorate/Grant)* [4491]

The Fantasy Sports Daily Scholarship Program - General Scholarship for Advanced Education *(Undergraduate, Graduate, Master's/Scholarship)* [4493]

Farella Braun + Martel LLP 1L Diversity Scholarship Program *(Undergraduate/Scholarship)* [4495]

John S.W. Fargher, Jr. Scholarship *(Graduate/Scholarship)* [5827]

Walter Moran Farmer Scholarships *(Juris Doctorate/Scholarship)* [11922]

Farmington UNICO Scholarship Fund *(Undergraduate/Scholarship)* [5328]

FASEB MARC Travel Awards *(Undergraduate, Graduate, Postdoctorate/Award)* [10532]

FASSE-International Assembly International Understanding Grants *(Professional development/Grant)* [7795]

Father's Day Scholarship *(All/Scholarship)* [7440]

James R. Favor Risk Management Scholarship Fund *(Undergraduate/Scholarship)* [6425]

FBANC Foundation NAPABA Convention Scholarship *(Advanced Professional/Scholarship)* [4554]

F.C. Grote Fund *(Graduate, Undergraduate/Scholarship)* [347]

FCBA Foundation Law School Scholarship Programs *(Postgraduate/Scholarship)* [4512]

FCBA Foundation Law School Summer Internship Stipend Program *(Professional development/Internship)* [4513]

FCIL Schaffer Grants for Foreign Law Librarians *(Professional development/Grant)* [596]

Federal Student Loans for Graduate Students *(Graduate/Loan)* [4318]

FEEA-NTEU Scholarships *(Graduate, Postgraduate, Undergraduate/Scholarship)* [4515]

Feeding Hope Fund for Clinical Research Grants *(Professional development/Grant)* [7864]

Feeding Tomorrow Scholarships *(Graduate, Undergraduate/Scholarship)* [5819]

Nolan W. Feeser Scholarship Fund *(Undergraduate/Scholarship)* [4590]

Ruth B. Fein Prize *(Graduate/Prize)* [1063]

Fejos Postdoctoral Fellowships in Ethnographic Film *(Postdoctorate/Fellowship)* [11962]

Milton Feldstein Memorial Scholarships *(Graduate/Scholarship)* [160]

Wildlife and Conservation Medicine Internship *(All/Fellowship)* [3436]

Fellowships for Creative and Performing Artists and Writers *(Professional development/Fellowship)* [490]

Reese Felts Scholarships *(Undergraduate/Scholarship)* [11187]

Diane Ross Fennekohl Endowment Fund for Education *(Undergraduate/Scholarship)* [6426]

Fermilab Science Undergraduate Laboratory Internship *(Undergraduate/Internship)* [11316]

Fermilab Summer Internships in Science & Technology (SIST) *(Undergraduate/Internship)* [11317]

FFA Scholarship *(Undergraduate/Scholarship)* [8586]

Field Aviation Co. Inc. Scholarship *(Undergraduate/Scholarship)* [180]

Fielding Law Group Scholarship Contest *(Undergraduate/Scholarship)* [4549]

Carole Fielding Student Grant *(Undergraduate, Graduate/Grant)* [11567]

Fieldwork Fellowship *(Undergraduate, Graduate/Award, Fellowship)* [4449]

Fifth Month Scholarship *(Undergraduate, High School/Scholarship)* [11228]

Adele Filene Student Presenter Grant *(Graduate, Undergraduate/Grant)* [3846]

Christine Filipovich Scholarships *(Master's, Doctorate/Scholarship)* [3439]

Filson Fellowships *(Postdoctorate, Doctorate/Fellowship)* [4559]

Filson Historical Society Master's Thesis Fellowship *(Master's/Fellowship)* [4560]

Alan R. and Barbara D. Finberg Fellowships *(Graduate/Fellowship)* [5634]

The Fred Finch Scholarship *(Undergraduate/Scholarship)* [11447]

William Robert Findley Graduate Chemistry Scholarship *(Graduate/Scholarship, Award, Monetary)* [8097]

Ruth Fine Memorial Student Loans *(Undergraduate/Grant, Loan)* [4120]

FIRST Operator Certification Awards *(Professional development/Internship)* [4618]

The Judge Ralph Fisch Police Explorer Scholarship Program *(Undergraduate/Scholarship)* [4646]

Eugenia Vellner Fischer Award for the Performing Arts *(Undergraduate/Scholarship)* [7416]

Fish & Richardson 1L Diversity Fellowship Program *(Undergraduate/Fellowship)* [4612]

The Fisher-Clark Memorial Endowed Scholarship *(Undergraduate/Scholarship)* [6792]

Joseph L. Fisher Doctoral Dissertation Fellowships *(Graduate/Fellowship)* [9645]

Jack B. Fisher Scholarship Fund *(Graduate/Scholarship)* [10758]

Marjorie Gosselin Fitzgerald, Upsilon, Permanently Restricted Scholarship Fund *(Undergraduate/Scholarship)* [6427]

FIU ForEverglades Scholarship *(Graduate, Doctorate, Master's/Scholarship)* [4455]

Gloria Flaherty Scholarship *(Graduate/Scholarship)* [5014]

FLAS Academic Year Fellowships *(Graduate, Undergraduate/Fellowship)* [11569]

FLASH Social Science Scholarships *(Graduate/Scholarship)* [4499]

Flavor of the Month Scholarship *(Undergraduate, High School/Scholarship)* [11229]

Fleming/Blaszcak Scholarships *(Undergraduate, Graduate/Scholarship)* [10486]

The FLEOA Foundation Scholastic Program *(Undergraduate/Scholarship)* [4519]

Flight Attendants/Flight Technician Scholarship *(Other/Scholarship)* [7735]

Flight Safety International Bell 206/Bell 407 Scholarship *(Professional development, Vocational/Occupational/Scholarship)* [12010]

Flora Lewis Fellowship *(Graduate, Undergraduate/Scholarship)* [8784]

Dave Florence Scholarship Fund *(Undergraduate/Scholarship)* [7105]

Florence Young Memorial Scholarships *(Master's/Scholarship)* [2039]

Florida Automotive Industry Scholarships *(Undergraduate/Scholarship)* [2352]

Florida Fertilizer and Agrichemical Association Scholarships *(Undergraduate/Scholarship)* [4634]

Florida Outdoor Writers Association Scholarships (FOWA) *(Undergraduate/Scholarship)* [4644]

Flow Feet Foot the Bill Scholarship *(Two Year College, University/Award)* [11187]

Flynn - Barney Flynn Memorial Scholarship *(Undergraduate/Scholarship)* [3475]

Follicular Lymphoma Pathways Grant *(Advanced Professional/Grant)* [6949]

Frank Fong Scholarships *(Undergraduate/Scholarship)* [10267]

James Fonseca Scholarship *(Undergraduate, Graduate/Scholarship)* [395]

For the Love of Chocolate Foundation Scholarships *(Undergraduate, Graduate, Professional development/Scholarship)* [4670]

Ford Foundation Dissertation Fellowship *(Postdoctorate/Fellowship)* [4672, 7572]

Ford Foundation Diversity Fellowships *(Graduate, Doctorate, Postdoctorate, Postgraduate/Fellowship)* [7573]

Ford Foundation Postdoctoral Fellowship *(Postdoctorate/Fellowship)* [4673, 7574]

Ford Foundation Predoctoral Fellowship *(Graduate, Doctorate/Fellowship)* [4674, 7575]

A. Ward Ford Memorial Research Grant *(Postdoctorate, Professional development/Grant)* [1497]

Anne Ford Scholarships *(High School/Scholarship)* [7753]

Nancy B. Forest and L. Michael Honaker Master's Grant for Research in Psychology *(Graduate/Grant)* [1270]

Foresters Competitive Scholarship *(Undergraduate, Vocational/Occupational, Four Year College, Two Year College/Scholarship)* [5737]

ForEverglades Scholarship *(Graduate, Master's, Doctorate/Scholarship)* [4456]

Forté Fellowships *(Master's/Fellowship)* [4689]

Genevieve Forthun Scholarships *(Undergraduate/Scholarship)* [9111]

Foster G. McGaw Graduate Student Scholarship *(Graduate/Scholarship)* [764]

Dr. Nancy Foster Scholarship Program *(Doctorate/Scholarship)* [8017]

Dr. Nancy Foster Scholarships *(Graduate/Scholarship)* [4695]

Foundation for Neonatal Research and Education Scholarship *(Doctorate, Graduate, Postgraduate, Undergraduate/Scholarship)* [4794]

Foundation Public Service Scholarship Award *(Undergraduate/Scholarship)* [4786]

Foundation Relations Internships - Los Angeles *(Undergraduate, Graduate/Internship)* [4982]

Foundation Scholarships *(Graduate/Scholarship)* [8619]

Foundation for Surgical Technology Scholarships *(Graduate/Scholarship)* [2298]

Foundation Transfer Scholarship *(Undergraduate/Scholarship)* [6793]

Foundation for Your Future Scholarship *(College/Scholarship)* [12058]

Founding Fathers Leadership Scholarships *(Undergraduate/Scholarship)* [12113]

Founding Mothers Student Scholarships - Graduate *(Graduate/Scholarship)* [2233]

Mary Metzger Fouse Memorial Scholarship Fund *(Undergraduate/Scholarship)* [6428]

Captain Ernest W. Fox Perpetual Scholarship *(Advanced Professional/Scholarship)* [3459]

FPA Summer Internships Program *(Undergraduate/Internship)* [4616]

William A. Fraker Student Heritage Awards *(Graduate, Undergraduate/Award)* [1396]

Frame My Future Scholarship Contest *(Undergraduate, Graduate/Scholarship, Prize)* [3327]

Fran Morgenstern Davis Scholarship *(Undergraduate/Scholarship)* [1409]

Franchise Law Diversity Scholarship Awards *(Undergraduate/Scholarship)* [6012]

Francis H. Moffitt Scholarship *(Graduate, Undergraduate/Scholarship)* [2006]

Frank and Charlene Harris Scholarship Fund *(Undergraduate/Scholarship)* [3618]

Frank G. Araujo Memorial Scholarship (Undergraduate/Scholarship) [9545]

Frank L. Weil Memorial Eagle Scout Scholarship (Undergraduate/Scholarship) [7850]

Frank Oppenheimer Scholarship (Postgraduate/Scholarship) [1178]

Frank S. Land Scholarship (Undergraduate/Scholarship) [4049]

Mayme and Herb Frank Scholarship Program (Graduate/Scholarship) [1984]

Michael W. and Jean D. Franke Family Foundation Scholarships (Graduate, Undergraduate/Scholarship) [1327]

Loren Frankel Memorial Scholarship (Undergraduate, Graduate/Scholarship) [1117]

Mary Weiking Franken Scholarships (Undergraduate/Scholarship) [9112]

The Ginny Frankenthaler Memorial Scholarships (Undergraduate/Scholarship) [10633]

Franklin Elementary School PTA Scholarship (Undergraduate/Scholarship) [9546]

John Hope Franklin Prize (Other/Prize) [6723]

Franklin Research Grants (Doctorate/Grant) [1214]

Benjamin Franklin Trust Fund (Undergraduate, Vocational/Occupational/Scholarship) [4591]

Violet and Cyril Franks Scholarship (Graduate/Scholarship) [1282]

Fraser Stryker Diversity Scholarship Program (Undergraduate/Scholarship) [4817]

FREA Scholarship (Undergraduate/Scholarship) [4651]

Fred and Avery Test Scholarship (Undergraduate/Scholarship) [11620]

Emanuel R. Freedman Scholarship (Graduate, Undergraduate/Scholarship) [8785]

Freedom Alliance Scholarship Fund (Undergraduate/Scholarship) [4821]

Kevin Freeman Travel Grant (Graduate, Other/Grant) [7514]

Malcolm and Mildred Freiberg Fellowships (Professional development/Fellowship) [7143]

The Ludo Frevel Crystallography Scholarship (Graduate/Scholarship) [5966]

Carleton A. Friday Scholarship (Undergraduate/Scholarship) [7377]

Dale E. Fridell Memorial Scholarships (Undergraduate, Vocational/Occupational/Scholarship) [10858]

MHS Marc Friedlaender Fellowships (Professional development/Fellowship) [7144]

The Phil Friel Scholarship (Undergraduate/Scholarship) [7170]

Friends of Mary Automotive Scholarship (Undergraduate/Scholarship) [10052]

Friends of the Oro Valley Public Library Support Staff Scholarship Award (Undergraduate/Scholarship, Monetary, Award) [1810]

Friends of Project 10 Models of Excellence Scholarship (Undergraduate/Scholarship) [4831]

Patricia and Phillip Frost Fellowships (Doctorate, Postdoctorate/Fellowship) [10215]

The William and Francis Fry Honorary Fellowship for Contributions to Therapeutic Ultrasound (Professional development/Fellowship) [6118]

FSF Student Travel Grant (Undergraduate, Graduate/Grant) [4678]

Full Circle Scholarship (Graduate, Undergraduate/Scholarship) [980, 2042]

Full Stack Student Scholarship (Graduate/Scholarship) [4833]

Kathryn Fuller Science for Nature Fund (Graduate, Postdoctorate/Fellowship) [12203]

Arthur Flagler Fultz Research Award (Professional development/Grant) [1135]

Daniel G. and Helen I. Fultz Scholarship Fund (Undergraduate/Scholarship) [4592]

Donald M. Furbush Professional Development Grants (Other/Grant) [5862]

Future Digital Marketers Scholarship (College, University/Scholarship) [2657]

Future Educators Scholarship (College, University/Scholarship) [7491]

#thefutureisfemale scholarship (Undergraduate, Graduate, Four Year College, Two Year College/Scholarship) [11127]

Future Leader Initial NCTM Annual Meeting Attendance Awards (Advanced Professional/Award, Monetary) [7804]

Future STEM Teacher Scholarship (Undergraduate/Scholarship) [10937]

Gabe Stepetin Business Scholarship (Undergraduate, Vocational/Occupational, Graduate, Master's/Scholarship) [329]

Joe E. Gaddy, Jr. and Margaret W. Gaddy Scholarship (Undergraduate/Scholarship) [12078]

Gaebe Eagle Scout Award (Undergraduate/Scholarship) [7851]

Frederick and Helen Gaige Award (Professional development/Grant) [1483]

Gail Garner Memorial R.I.S.E. Scholarship (Undergraduate/Scholarship) [9548]

Farley Moody Galbraith Scholarship (Graduate/Scholarship) [3653]

Whitney Laine Gallahar Memorial Scholarship Fund (Undergraduate/Scholarship) [3654]

Sam Gallant Memorial Scholarships (Graduate, Undergraduate/Scholarship) [1818]

The Gallery Collection's Create-A-Greeting-Card Scholarship (Undergraduate/Scholarship) [4848]

Lionel Galstaun Memorial Grant (Undergraduate/Scholarship) [1877]

Maro Ajemian Galstaun Memorial Grant (Undergraduate/Scholarship) [1878]

Gamewardens Scholarship Program (High School/Scholarship) [4852]

Gamma Chi Project 2000 Scholarship (Undergraduate/Scholarship) [6430]

Gamma Iota Scholarship (Undergraduate/Scholarship) [10108]

Gamma Iota Scholarships - Gamma Tau (Undergraduate/Scholarship) [10109]

Gamma Iota Scholarships - Zeta Kappa (Undergraduate/Scholarship) [10110]

Gamma Iota Scholarships - Zeta Nu (Undergraduate/Scholarship) [10111]

Gamma Lambda Scholarship (Undergraduate/Scholarship) [10112]

Gamma Mu Project 2000 Scholarship (Undergraduate/Scholarship) [6431]

The Gamma Mu Scholarships Program (Vocational/Occupational, Professional development, Undergraduate, Graduate, Postgraduate/Scholarship) [4854]

Gamma Pi Project 2000 Scholarship (Undergraduate/Scholarship) [6432]

Gamma Sigma Alpha Graduate Scholarship (Graduate/Scholarship) [4856]

Gamma Theta Project 2000 Scholarship (Undergraduate/Scholarship) [6433]

Gamma Zeta Project 2000 Scholarship (Undergraduate/Scholarship) [6434]

Gantenbein Medical Fund Fellowship (Graduate/Fellowship) [4092]

GAPA Foundation Scholarship (Undergraduate, Graduate, High School, Vocational/Occupational/Scholarship) [9334]

Michael and Gina Garcia Rail Engineering Scholarships (Undergraduate, Graduate/Scholarship) [1328]

William R. Gard Memorial Scholarships (Graduate/Scholarship) [7666]

Garden Club of America Awards in Tropical Botany (GCA) (Doctorate/Award) [4859]

Gardeners of America/Men's Garden Clubs of America Scholarship (Undergraduate/Scholarship) [4864]

IGS John Gardner Fellowship (Undergraduate/Fellowship) [11537]

Dwight D. Gardner Scholarship (Undergraduate/Scholarship) [5828]

Eugene Garfield Doctoral Dissertation Fellowship (Doctorate/Fellowship) [2497]

Peter M. Gargano Scholarship Fund (Undergraduate/Scholarship) [4206]

Gary and Gussie Williams Scholarship (Undergraduate/Scholarship) [11621]

Edwin W. Gaston Scholarships (Undergraduate/Scholarship) [377]

The Gates Millennium Scholars (Undergraduate/Scholarship) [5529]

Marian P. and David M. Gates Scholarship for Non-Residents (Undergraduate/Scholarship) [11622]

A.R.F.O.R.A. Martha Gavrila Scholarships for Women (Postgraduate/Scholarship) [1368]

GAWP Graduate Scholarships (Graduate/Scholarship) [4925]

Lowell Gaylor Memorial Scholarships (Undergraduate/Scholarship) [181]

GCFI Student Travel Awards (Undergraduate/Award) [5252]

GCSAA Scholars Competition (Undergraduate/Scholarship) [5032]

GCSAA Student Essay Contest (Graduate, Undergraduate/Prize) [5033]

GED Jump Start Scholarships (Professional development/Scholarship) [9959]

Geeta Rastogi Memorial Scholarship (Undergraduate/Scholarship) [11757]

The Gene & John Athletic Fund (Undergraduate/Scholarship) [10850]

General Falcon Scholarships (Undergraduate/Scholarship) [9243]

General John Paul Ratay Educational Fund Grants (Undergraduate/Grant) [7389]

General Mills Foundation Scholarships (Undergraduate/Scholarship) [981]

Geological Society of America Graduate Student Research Grants (Doctorate, Graduate/Grant) [4910]

George C. Balch Scholarship (Graduate/Scholarship) [11383]

George E. Judd Scholarship Fund (Undergraduate/Scholarship) [10686]

George E. Nichols Undergraduate Scholarship (Undergraduate/Scholarship) [11624]

George Foreman Tribute to Lyndon B. Johnson (Undergraduate/Scholarship) [9472]

George H. A. Clowes, Jr. MD, FACS, Memorial Research Career Development Award (Professional development/Fellowship) [777]

George Hi'ilani Mills Scholarship (Graduate/Scholarship) [8925]

George J. Mitchell Scholarship (Postgraduate/Scholarship) [11774]

George N. Lindsay Fellowship (Graduate/Fellowship) [6740]

George Torkildsen Literary Award (Professional development/Award, Trophy) [12200]

George W. Juno Scholarship (Graduate/Scholarship) [4877]

Georgelis Injury Law Firm, P.C. Scholarship Award (Graduate/Scholarship) [4912]

Gerald V. Henderson Memorial Scholarship (Undergraduate, Graduate/Scholarship) [10427]

Geraldine Clewell Scholarship (Undergraduate/Scholarship) [9113]

Gerard Swartz Fudge Memorial Scholarship (Postgraduate/Scholarship) [5664]

Doris Y. and John J. Gerber Scholarship (Undergraduate/Scholarship) [11910]

Walter Gerboth Award (Other/Award, Monetary) [7515]

German Historical Institute Doctoral and Postdoctoral Fellowships (Doctorate, Postgraduate/Fellowship) [4942]

German Historical Institute Fellowships at the Horner Library (Postdoctorate, Master's/Fellowship) [4943]

German Studies Research Grants (Undergraduate/Grant) [4062]

Berek and Regina Gertner OSOTF Bursary in Holocaust Studies (Undergraduate, Graduate/Scholarship) [12245]

Gertrude M. Cox Scholarship (Master's, Doctorate/Scholarship) [1611]

Elizabeth Tucker Gessley Scholarship (Undergraduate/Scholarship) [6436]

Get A Boost $2,000 Scholarship (All/Scholarship) [2608]

Getty Conservation Guest Scholars (Professional development/Grant) [4953]

Getty GRI-NEH Postdoctoral Fellowships (Postdoctorate/Fellowship) [4955]

Getty Postdoctoral Fellowship in Conservation Science (Postdoctorate/Fellowship) [4956]

Harness Tracks of America Scholarship Fund *(Undergraduate/Scholarship)* [5304]

Margaret Shumavonian Harnischfeger Scholarship *(Undergraduate/Scholarship)* [1883]

Harold E. Ennes Scholarship *(Graduate/Scholarship)* [10285]

Harold Gulliksen Psychometric Research Fellowship *(Doctorate, Graduate/Fellowship)* [4312]

Harper's Magazine Scholarships *(Graduate, Undergraduate/Scholarship)* [8786]

Harriet Irsay Scholarship *(Graduate, Undergraduate/Scholarship)* [1045]

Leon Harris/Les Nichols Memorial Scholarships to Spartan College of Aeronautics & Technology *(Undergraduate/Scholarship)* [183]

Morton and Beatrice Harrison Scholarship Fund *(Undergraduate/Scholarship)* [4593]

Lullelia W. Harrison Scholarships in Counseling *(Graduate, Undergraduate/Scholarship)* [12411]

Harry A. Donn Scholarship *(Undergraduate/Scholarship)* [5329]

Harry S. Truman Scholarships *(Undergraduate, Graduate/Scholarship)* [11129]

Harry Walts Memorial Graduate Scholarship *(Graduate/Scholarship)* [6923]

Dave Hart Graduate Scholarship *(Graduate/Scholarship)* [10654]

Carroll Hart Scholarship *(Graduate/Scholarship)* [10344]

Ida L. Hartenberg Charitable Scholarships *(Undergraduate/Scholarship)* [5330]

Hartford Grammar School Scholarship Fund *(Undergraduate/Scholarship)* [5331]

Harvey Fellows Program *(Graduate/Fellowship)* [7519]

Harvey M. Pollicove Memorial Scholarship *(Undergraduate, Graduate/Scholarship)* [8676]

Harvey Washington Banks Scholarship in Astronomy *(Undergraduate/Scholarship)* [8086]

Donald F. Hastings Scholarship *(Undergraduate/Scholarship)* [1661]

Don C. Hawkins Memorial Scholarships *(Undergraduate/Scholarship)* [184]

Thomas T. Hayashi Memorial Scholarship *(Graduate, Undergraduate/Scholarship)* [6246]

Hazen and Sawyer Scholarship *(Master's/Scholarship, Monetary)* [1641]

HDSA Research Grants *(Graduate/Grant)* [5657]

Health and Aging Policy Fellows Program *(Advanced Professional, Professional development/Fellowship)* [1255]

Health is a Right Not a Privilege Scholarship *(Advanced Professional, Master's, Graduate/Scholarship)* [8561]

Health Services Research Dissertation Awards *(Doctorate/Award)* [11326]

Healthcare Information Management Systems Scholarships *(Graduate, Postgraduate, Undergraduate/Scholarship)* [5448]

Healthy Communities Scholarship *(Undergraduate, Graduate, Community College/Scholarship)* [9282]

HECUA Scholarship for Community Engagement *(Undergraduate/Scholarship)* [5505]

HECUA Scholarship for Social Justice *(Undergraduate, Graduate/Scholarship)* [5506]

Heidi Patriquin Award for International Education *(Advanced Professional, Professional development/Fellowship)* [10465]

Dale O. Heimberger CRNA Memorial Scholarship Fund *(Graduate/Scholarship)* [10764]

Hekemian Family Scholarship Grants *(Undergraduate/Scholarship)* [1884]

Helen Hay Whitney Foundation Postdoctoral Research Fellowship *(Postdoctorate, Master's/Fellowship)* [12020]

Helen J. & Harold Gilman Smith Scholarship *(Graduate, Undergraduate/Scholarship)* [2481]

Helen Krich Chinoy Dissertation Fellowship *(Doctorate/Fellowship)* [1578]

Helen R. (Finley) Loescher and Stephen B. Loescher Scholarship *(High School/Scholarship)* [3679]

Helena B. Cobb Higher Education (four Year) Scholarship *(Undergraduate, Vocational/Occupational/Scholarship)* [12165]

The Helena B. Cobb Scholarships *(Undergraduate, Vocational/Occupational/Scholarship)* [12166]

Helene M. Overly Memorial Graduate Scholarship *(Graduate/Scholarship)* [12170]

Commercial Helicopter Pilot Rating Scholarships *(Other/Scholarship)* [5456]

Helicopter Foundation International Maintenance Technician Certificate Scholarships *(Other/Scholarship)* [5457]

Hellenic Times Scholarships *(Undergraduate, Graduate/Scholarship)* [5461]

Joan Heller-Diane Bernard Fellowships *(Graduate, Undergraduate/Fellowship)* [3236]

Joseph T. Helling Scholarship Fund *(Undergraduate/Scholarship)* [5748]

Helm Family Scholarship *(Undergraduate/Scholarship)* [9819]

Helmer, Conley & Kasselman Annual College Scholarship *(Undergraduate/Scholarship)* [5471]

Clinton J. Helton Manufacturing Scholarship *(Undergraduate/Scholarship)* [10402]

Hemlow Prize in Burney Studies *(Graduate/Prize)* [1434]

Hench Post-Dissertation Fellowship *(Postdoctorate/Fellowship)* [491]

Henderson Memorial Endowed Scholarship *(Undergraduate/Scholarship)* [6796]

Henigson Human Rights Fellowship *(Graduate, Master's, Juris Doctorate/Fellowship)* [5365]

SNMMI Robert E. Henkin, MD, Government Relations Fellowship *(Professional development/Fellowship)* [10439]

Henley-Putnam University Scholarships *(Other/Scholarship)* [5931]

Henry Adams Scholarship *(Undergraduate/Scholarship)* [1474]

Thomas J. Henry Leadership Scholarship Program *(Undergraduate, Graduate/Scholarship)* [5483]

Henry Salvatori Fellowships *(Graduate/Fellowship)* [5885]

Henry Salvatori Scholarship *(Undergraduate/Scholarship)* [8689]

Herb Adrian Memorial Scholarship Endowment *(Undergraduate/Scholarship)* [4735]

Herb And Ann Fincher Scholarship Fund *(Undergraduate/Scholarship)* [3571]

Herb Kohl Educational Foundation Student Excellence Scholarship *(Undergraduate/Scholarship)* [6582]

Herb Kohl Educational Foundation Student Initiative Scholarship *(Undergraduate/Scholarship)* [6583]

Herbert Law Office Scholarship Contest *(Undergraduate/Scholarship)* [5492]

Rich Herbert Memorial Scholarship *(Undergraduate, Master's, Doctorate/Scholarship)* [1630]

Herbert Scoville Jr. Peace Fellowship *(Graduate/Fellowship)* [9988]

Hermann Law Group, PLLC Safety Scholarship Contest *(Undergraduate/Scholarship)* [5496]

Hernandez – Manuel Hernandez, Jr. Memoral Scholarship *(Undergraduate/Scholarship)* [3477]

Catarino and Evangelina Hernández Research Fellowships in Latino History *(Advanced Professional/Fellowship)* [10996]

The Herpetologists' League Graduate Research Award *(Graduate/Award)* [5499]

Purdue University Ray W. Herrick Laboratories Research Fellowship *(Graduate/Fellowship)* [9451]

Jessica M. Herron, Epsilon Nu, Memorial Scholarship *(Undergraduate, Graduate/Scholarship)* [6443]

Herschede Engineering Scholarship *(Graduate/Scholarship)* [10082]

Isabel M. Herson Scholarships in Education *(Graduate, Undergraduate/Scholarship)* [12412]

Hertz Foundation Graduate Fellowship Award *(Graduate/Fellowship)* [5502]

The Hertz Graduate Fellowship Award *(Graduate, Master's, Doctorate/Fellowship)* [7645]

Aleksander and Alicja Hertz Memorial Fellowship *(Doctorate, Postdoctorate/Fellowship)* [12237]

Herzog August Bibliothek Wolfenbüttel Fellowships *(Postdoctorate/Fellowship)* [8372]

Wayne E. Hesch Memorial Scholarship *(Undergraduate, Graduate/Scholarship)* [1691]

Beth B. Hess Memorial Scholarship *(Doctorate, Graduate/Fellowship, Award)* [10566]

HFA Educational Scholarship *(Undergraduate/Scholarship)* [5479]

HFMH Bilingual Scholarships for Mental Health Workforce Diversity *(Graduate/Scholarship)* [5539]

HGS Foundation Undergraduate Scholarships *(Undergraduate/Scholarship)* [5597]

H.H. Harris Foundation Scholarship *(Professional development, Undergraduate/Scholarship, Monetary)* [932]

HHMI Medical Research Fellowship *(Undergraduate/Fellowship)* [5617]

HIAA Graduate Student Travel Grants *(Graduate/Grant)* [5534]

Dorothy Hicks Graduate Scholarship *(Graduate/Scholarship)* [10655]

Frances C. Hidell Scholarship *(Undergraduate/Scholarship)* [2144]

HII Scholarship Fund *(Community College, Two Year College, Four Year College, Undergraduate, University/Scholarship)* [5655]

Robert S. Hilbert Memorial Student Travel Grants *(Graduate, Undergraduate/Grant)* [8677]

Conrad N. Hilton Scholarships *(Undergraduate/Scholarship)* [4962]

Hinman-Jensen Endowed Scholarship *(Undergraduate/Scholarship)* [6797]

HIPLA Fellowship *(Undergraduate/Fellowship)* [5599]

HIPLA Scholarships for University of Houston Law Center Students *(Graduate, Undergraduate/Scholarship)* [5600]

Hispanic Scholarship Fund General College Scholarship Program (HSF) *(Undergraduate/Scholarship)* [5530]

Hispanic Serving Institution Scholarships (HSIS) *(Undergraduate/Scholarship)* [11280]

Historically Black College or University Scholarships (HBCUS) *(Undergraduate/Scholarship)* [11281]

History of Art: Institutional Fellowships *(Graduate/Fellowship)* [6613]

HIV Prevention Research Advocacy Fellowships *(Professional development/Fellowship)* [2368]

The Albert H. Hix, W8AH, Memorial Scholarship *(Undergraduate/Scholarship)* [1944]

HLS/MLA Professional Development Grants *(Other/Grant)* [7218]

Hochschulsommerkurse *(Undergraduate/Award)* [4063]

Jeri Hodges Leadership Scholarship *(Professional development/Scholarship)* [10978]

The George W. and Ethel B. Hoefler Fund *(Undergraduate/Scholarship)* [3714]

Dorothy M. and Earl S. Hoffman Award *(Graduate/Award)* [2383]

Henry Hoffman Memorial Scholarship *(Undergraduate/Scholarship)* [7641]

Miriam Hoffman Scholarship *(Undergraduate, Graduate/Scholarship)* [4892]

The Michael J. Hogan Foreign Language Fellowship *(Graduate/Fellowship)* [10356]

The Thelma S. Hoge Memorial Scholarship *(Graduate/Scholarship)* [3596]

Holiday Celebration Scholarship *(All/Scholarship)* [7442]

George Holopigian Memorial Grants *(Undergraduate/Scholarship)* [1885]

The Arthur and Janet Holzheimer Fellowship in the History of Cartography *(Postdoctorate, Doctorate/Fellowship)* [8373]

Holzheimer Memorial Student Scholarship *(Graduate, Master's/Scholarship)* [1243]

Hon. Peggy Bernheim Memorial Scholarship *(Undergraduate/Scholarship)* [2711]

Honeywell Avionics Scholarships *(Undergraduate/Scholarship)* [185]

Johns Hopkins Department of Emergency Medicine Administration Fellowships *(Advanced Professional, Professional development/Fellowship)* [6316]

Edward Horne Scholarship *(Advanced Professional/Scholarship)* [8742]

Saul Horowitz Jr. Memorial Graduate Award *(Graduate/Scholarship, Award)* [126]

International Clinical Research Fellowship (Graduate/Fellowship) [4193]

International Code Council Scholarship (Graduate/Scholarship) [4501]

International Dairy-Deli-Bakery Association's Scholarship for Growing the Future (Graduate, Undergraduate/Scholarship) [5988]

International Dissertation Research Fellowship (IDRF) (Graduate, Doctorate/Fellowship) [10246]

International Door Association Scholarship Foundation Program (Undergraduate/Scholarship) [5996]

International Executive Housekeepers Association Spartan Scholarship Award (Undergraduate/Scholarship) [5999]

International Foodservice Editorial Council Scholarship (Graduate/Scholarship) [6007]

International Furnishings and Design Association Part-time Student Scholarship (Undergraduate/Scholarship) [6015]

International Operators Scholarship (Professional development/Scholarship) [7737]

International Order of the King's Daughters and Sons North American Indian Scholarship Program (Undergraduate/Scholarship) [989]

International Radio and Television Society Foundation Summer Fellowships Program (Undergraduate, Graduate/Fellowship) [6067]

International Sanitary Supply Association Foundation Scholarships (Undergraduate/Scholarship) [6081]

International Scholarship Programs for Community Service (Undergraduate/Scholarship) [7249]

International Society Travel Grant (Professional development/Grant) [450]

International Women's Fishing Association Scholarship Trust (Graduate/Scholarship) [6146]

Internet Society Fellowships to the IETF (Master's, Postdoctorate/Fellowship) [6150]

The Interracial Scholarship Fund of Greater Hartford (Undergraduate/Scholarship) [5333]

Investigators in the Pathogenesis of Infectious Disease (Doctorate, Postdoctorate/Grant) [2754]

IOKDS Health Careers Scholarship (College, University, Undergraduate, Graduate, Doctorate/Scholarship) [6050]

IOKDS Student Ministry Scholarships (Master's/Scholarship) [6052]

Iowa Association of Electric Cooperatives - Electric Cooperative Pioneer Trust Fund Scholarship (Undergraduate/Scholarship) [4163]

Iowa Journalism Institute Scholarships (Graduate, Undergraduate/Scholarship) [6167]

Iowa Library Association Foundation Scholarships (Graduate/Scholarship) [6163]

Susan K. Ipacs Nursing Legacy Scholarship (Undergraduate, High School/Scholarship) [4707]

Graduate Study Fellowship (Professional development/Fellowship) [6065]

IPPR North Events Internship (Undergraduate/Internship) [5854]

Ira G. Turpin Scholar Program Fund (Undergraduate/Scholarship) [10767]

Iranian-American Scholarship Fund (Undergraduate, Graduate/Scholarship) [7954]

Irene Carlson Gnaedinger Memorial Scholarship (Undergraduate/Scholarship) [6800]

Irene Corbally Kuhn Scholarship (Graduate, Undergraduate/Scholarship) [8787]

Irene Winifred Eno Grant (Professional development/Grant) [1487]

Irene Woodall Graduate Scholarship (Graduate/Scholarship) [860]

IREX Individual Advanced Research Opportunities Program For Postdoctoral Scholars (Postdoctorate/Fellowship) [6071]

IREX Individual Advanced Research Opportunities Program For Pre-doctoral Students (Doctorate/Fellowship) [6072]

IREX Individual Advanced Research Opportunities Program For Professionals (Other/Fellowship) [6073]

Irma E. Voigt Memorial Scholarship (Undergraduate/Scholarship) [10113]

Irwin S. Lerner Student Scholarship (Undergraduate/Scholarship) [8108]

ISA Section and District Scholarships - Southwestern Wyoming (Graduate, Undergraduate/Scholarship) [6091]

ISA Section and District Scholarships - Texas, Louisiana and Mississippi (Graduate, Undergraduate/Scholarship) [6092]

ISA Section and District Scholarships - Wilmington (Graduate, Undergraduate/Scholarship) [6093]

ISBA Scholarship Program (Undergraduate/Scholarship) [5689]

ISCALC International Scholarship Fund (Undergraduate/Scholarship) [4594]

ISDS Graduate Student Scholarships (Doctorate, Graduate/Scholarship) [6105]

ISF Excellence in Community Service Scholarship (Undergraduate/Scholarship) [6173]

ISF Undergraduate Scholarship (Undergraduate/Scholarship) [6174]

Patricia and Gail Ishimoto Memorial Scholarship (Undergraduate/Scholarship) [6247]

ISID Small Grants (Postdoctorate, Professional development/Grant) [6114]

Islamic Scholarship Fund Scholarship (ISF) (Graduate, Undergraduate/Scholarship) [6178]

Broughton Isom Memorial Scholarship (Undergraduate/Scholarship) [8519]

ISOPE Offshore Mechanics Scholarships for Outstanding Students (Graduate/Scholarship) [6116]

ISTTE Scholarship (Graduate, Undergraduate/Scholarship) [6122]

ISTU Student Prizes (Undergraduate/Prize) [6119]

ISU Child of Alumni Book Voucher Awards (Undergraduate/Scholarship) [5770]

ISU Gongaware Scholarship (Undergraduate/Scholarship) [5762]

ISU Networks Scholarship (Undergraduate/Scholarship) [5763]

Italian Language Scholarship (Undergraduate/Scholarship) [8690]

ITMS Shannon Fellowships (Graduate, Undergraduate/Fellowship) [6132]

ITNS Research Grants (Other/Grant) [6137]

ITW Welding Companies Scholarships (Undergraduate/Scholarship) [1664]

Ivanhoe Foundation Fellowship (Master's/Fellowship) [6184]

Iwalani Carpenter Sowa Scholarship (Graduate/Scholarship) [8928]

J. Newell Stannard Fellowship (Graduate, Undergraduate/Fellowship) [5429]

The Jack and Jill of America Foundation's National Scholarship Program (Undergraduate/Scholarship) [6190]

Jack Kent Cooke Foundation Young Scholars Program (Undergraduate/Scholarship) [3822]

Jack M. & Mary Lou Gruber Scholarship (Undergraduate/Scholarship) [6801]

Jack M. Nagasaka Memorial Scholarship (Undergraduate/Scholarship) [9551]

Jack R. Barckhoff Welding Management Scholarship (Undergraduate/Scholarship) [1665]

Jack R. Gilstrap Scholarship (Undergraduate, Graduate/Scholarship) [1302]

Jackie Robinson Scholarship Award (Undergraduate/Scholarship) [9723]

Jackman Scholarships (Undergraduate/Scholarship) [9114]

Graduate Student Honoraria - Anna M. Jackson Awards (Master's, Doctorate/Award) [1504]

Jacque Placette Chapman Master's Fellowships (Graduate, Master's/Fellowship) [8686]

Jacqueline Shields Memorial Scholarship (Graduate/Scholarship) [161]

Jamail/Long Challenge Grant Scholarships (Undergraduate, Graduate/Scholarship) [5522]

The James Davidson Innovative Student Scholarship (Graduate/Scholarship) [10739]

James E. Hoff, S.J. Scholar (Undergraduate/Scholarship) [12223]

James E. Long Memorial Post Doctoral Fellowship (Postdoctorate/Fellowship) [5984]

James E. West Fellowship (Graduate/Fellowship) [62]

James F. Hurley III Bicentennial Merit Scholarship (Undergraduate/Scholarship) [11191]

James L. Biggane Fellowship in Finance (Graduate/Fellowship) [8325]

James L. and Genevieve H. Goodwin Scholarship (Undergraduate/Scholarship) [5334]

James L. Plafkin Memorial Scholarship (Undergraduate/Scholarship) [11626]

James Wisecup Memorial Flight Training Scholarship (Vocational/Occupational, Advanced Professional/Scholarship) [12011]

J. Franklin Jameson Fellowship in American History (Doctorate/Fellowship) [960]

Jan DiMartino Delany Memorial Scholarship (Undergraduate/Scholarship) [4780]

Jan Jancin Award (Undergraduate/Award) [4697]

Jane Beattie Memorial Scholarship (Graduate/Scholarship) [10378]

Jane C. Waldbaum Archaeological Field School Scholarship (Undergraduate, Graduate/Scholarship, Award) [1777]

Jane Coffin Childs Memorial Fund - Medical Research Postdoctoral Fellowship (Postdoctorate, Doctorate/Fellowship) [3303]

Janet Cullen Tanaka Geosciences Undergraduate Scholarship (Undergraduate/Scholarship) [2316]

Japan Foundation, New York Doctoral Candidates (Doctorate/Fellowship) [6233]

Japan Foundation, New York Scholars and Researchers (Long-Term) (Professional development/Fellowship) [6234]

Japan Foundation, New York Scholars and Researchers (Short-Term) (Professional development/Fellowship) [6235]

Japan Society for the Promotion of Science Fellowship (JSPS) (Doctorate/Fellowship) [10247]

Jacob K. Javits Fellowships Program (Master's, Doctorate/Fellowship) [11310]

Jay C. and B. Nadine Leggett Charitable Fund (Undergraduate/Scholarship) [10769]

Jay Hammond Memorial Scholarship (Graduate/Scholarship) [11518]

J.B. and Marilyn McKenzie Graduate Student Fellowship (Graduate/Fellowship) [11627]

JCC Association Graduate Education Scholarships (Graduate/Scholarship) [6257]

JCCF Equal Voice Journalism Scholarship (Professional development/Scholarship) [11591]

JDBNOW Scholarship (Two Year College, Undergraduate, Graduate/Scholarship) [6259]

Advanced Postdoctoral Fellowships (Postdoctorate, Master's/Fellowship) [6349]

Career Development Awards (Professional development, Postdoctorate/Grant, Award) [6350]

JDRF Outreach Scholarship (Undergraduate, Master's, Doctorate/Scholarship) [5705]

JDRF Postdoctoral Fellowships (Postdoctorate/Fellowship) [6351]

JEA Future Journalism Teacher Scholarships (Undergraduate, Master's/Scholarship) [6336]

Jean Bennett Memorial Student Travel Grant (Graduate, Undergraduate/Grant) [8678]

Jean Dearth Dickerscheid Fellowship (Graduate/Fellowship) [9115]

Jeannette K. Watson Fellowship (Undergraduate/Fellowship) [11938]

Jeff Oliphant Memorial Post-Graduate Scholarship (Postgraduate/Scholarship) [12114]

Jefferson Graduate Fellowship (Doctorate, Graduate/Fellowship) [6263]

Jeffrey D. Ralston Memorial Scholarship (Undergraduate/Scholarship) [7562]

John H. Jenkins Research Fellowships in Texas History (Professional development/Fellowship) [10998]

Jennifer Curtis Byler Scholarship (Undergraduate/Scholarship) [8133]

Gaynold Jensen Education Stipends (Postdoctorate, Other/Scholarship) [4084]

Walter J. Jensen Fellowships (Other/Fellowship) [9081]

Jerome Fellowships (Other/Fellowship) [9196]

Jerome M. Sullivan Research Fund (Professional development/Fellowship) [1354]

Jerome Robbins Bogliasco Fellowships in Dance (Professional development/Fellowship) [2645]

Jet Business Scholarship (Graduate/Scholarship) [6267]

Jim Anderson Memorial Scholarship *(Undergraduate/Scholarship)* [8363]

Jim Doogan Memorial Scholarship *(Undergraduate/Scholarship)* [11519]

Jim & Nancy Hinkle Travel Grants *(Graduate/Grant)* [5476]

Jimmy Edwards Scholarship Fund *(Undergraduate/Scholarship)* [3625]

Jimmy Guild Memorial Scholarship *(Undergraduate/Scholarship)* [6802]

JMJ Phillip Group College Scholarships *(Graduate, University, Four Year College, Two Year College/Scholarship)* [6312]

Joe Francis Haircare Scholarship *(Undergraduate/Scholarship)* [4811]

Joe Perdue Scholarship *(Undergraduate/Scholarship, Award)* [3443]

Joel T. Heinen Student Research Fellowship *(Undergraduate, Graduate/Fellowship)* [11628]

Joel T. Heinen Undergraduate Support Scholarship *(Undergraduate/Scholarship)* [11629]

John and Alice Egan Multi-Year Mentioning Scholarship Program *(Undergraduate/Scholarship)* [3955]

John C. Lincoln Memorial Scholarship *(Undergraduate/Scholarship)* [1666]

John E. Mayfield ABLE Scholarship Fund *(Graduate/Scholarship)* [3626]

John Flynn Memorial Scholarship *(Undergraduate/Scholarship)* [3682]

John G. Brokaw Scholarship *(Undergraduate/Scholarship)* [8173]

John J. Bonica Trainee Fellowship *(Professional development/Fellowship)* [5944]

John Jeffries Meteorology Scholarship *(Graduate/Scholarship)* [4502]

John Marshall Everglades Internship Program *(Undergraduate/Internship)* [4457]

John McLendon Minority Postgraduate Scholarship *(Postdoctorate/Scholarship)* [7639]

John & Ruth Childe Scholarship Fund *(Undergraduate/Scholarship)* [10691]

John Streiff Memorial Scholarship *(Undergraduate/Scholarship)* [6803]

John W. Webb Lecture Award *(Other/Award, Recognition, Monetary)* [1466]

Johnny Lineberry Memorial Scholarship *(Undergraduate, Vocational/Occupational/Scholarship)* [12080]

Johns Hopkins Medicine Disaster Fellowships *(Professional development/Fellowship)* [6317]

Johns Hopkins Medicine Emergency Medical Services Fellowship *(Professional development/Fellowship)* [6318]

Johns Hopkins Medicine International Emergency and Public Health Fellowships *(Graduate, Professional development/Fellowship)* [6319]

Johns Hopkins Medicine Medical Education Fellowships *(Professional development/Fellowship)* [6320]

Johns Hopkins Medicine Observation Medicine Fellowships *(Professional development/Fellowship)* [6321]

Johns Hopkins Medicine Research Fellowships *(Professional development/Fellowship)* [6322]

Johns Hopkins Medicine Ultrasound Fellowships *(Professional development/Fellowship)* [6323]

Johns Hopkins University/Applied Physics Laboratory Alexander Kossiakoff Scholarship *(Doctorate, Graduate, Master's/Scholarship)* [5985]

Wilma Winberg Johnson Adelphe Scholarship for Chapter Consultants *(Undergraduate/Scholarship)* [6448]

Johnson and Johnson/AACN Minority Nurse Faculty Scholars *(Graduate/Scholarship)* [543]

MCCA Lloyd M. Johnson, Jr. Scholarships *(Graduate/Scholarship)* [7412]

Joseph C. Johnson Memorial Grant *(Undergraduate/Grant)* [1392]

Gregory D. Johnson Memorial Scholarships *(Doctorate, Graduate, Master's/Scholarship)* [7970]

The Dr. Richard Allen Williams and Genita Evangelista Johnson Scholarship,AMA Foundation Scholarship *(Undergraduate/Scholarship)* [2066]

Joint Japan/World Bank Graduate Scholarship Program for Developing Country National (JJ/WBGSP) *(Graduate/Scholarship)* [12192]

Joint Japan/World Bank Graduate Scholarship Program for Japanese National (JJ/WBGSP) *(Graduate, Master's, Doctorate/Scholarship)* [12193]

George E. Jonas Scholarships *(Graduate, Undergraduate/Scholarship)* [6894]

Jones-Lovich Grants in Southwestern Herpetology *(Master's, Doctorate/Grant)* [5500]

NASSP/Herff Jones Principal's Leadership Award *(Undergraduate/Scholarship)* [7690]

Jordan B. Tatter Scholarship *(Undergraduate, Graduate/Scholarship)* [7334]

The Barbara Jordan Scholarship *(Undergraduate/Scholarship)* [11150]

Joseph A. Holmes Safety Association Scholarship *(High School/Scholarship)* [5544]

Joseph and Amelia Saks Scholarship *(Undergraduate/Scholarship)* [3656]

Joseph Frasca Excellence in Aviation Scholarship *(Undergraduate, Graduate/Scholarship)* [11527]

Joseph J. Fitzsimmons Scholarship Fund *(Doctorate/Scholarship)* [11384]

Joseph S. Steinberg Emerging Jewish Filmmaker Fellowship *(Undergraduate, Graduate/Fellowship)* [3226]

Joseph Sumner Smith Scholarship *(Undergraduate/Scholarship)* [11250]

Josephine de Karman Fellowship *(Doctorate/Fellowship)* [6503]

Joshua Esch Mitchell Aviation Scholarship *(Undergraduate/Scholarship)* [5160]

Journalist of the Year Scholarships *(Undergraduate/Monetary, Scholarship)* [6337]

Joyce C. Hall College Scholarship *(Undergraduate/Scholarship)* [8981]

Leslie W. Joyce and Paul W. Thayer Graduate Fellowship in I-O Psychology *(Graduate/Fellowship)* [10335]

JSA/Jefferson Lab Graduate Fellowship *(Doctorate, Graduate/Fellowship)* [6265]

Judge Delmas C. Hill Scholarship *(Undergraduate/Scholarship)* [11877]

Judge Edward Y. Kakita Memorial Scholarship *(Undergraduate/Scholarship)* [6238]

Judge Sidney M. Aronovitz Memorial Scholarship Fund *(Undergraduate/Scholarship)* [7298]

Juliann and Joe Maxwell Scholarship Fund for Employees of Tractor Supply *(Undergraduate/Scholarship)* [3627]

Juliann King Maxwell Scholarship Fund for Riverview High School *(Undergraduate, Vocational/Occupational/Scholarship)* [3628]

Julio C. Diaz Academic Scholarship Fund *(Undergraduate/Scholarship)* [10770]

The Junior Firefighter of the Year Award *(Undergraduate/Scholarship)* [8154]

Justin G. Schiller Fellowship *(Doctorate, Postdoctorate/Fellowship)* [492]

Justin Scot Alston Memorial Scholarship *(Undergraduate/Scholarship)* [5665]

JW Surety Bonds Scholarships *(Undergraduate, Graduate/Scholarship)* [6353]

Annette Kade Fellowships *(Graduate/Fellowship)* [7277]

Kaia Lynn Markwalter Endowed Scholarship *(Undergraduate/Scholarship)* [6804]

Kaiser Permanente Northern California Delivery Science Fellowship Program *(Postgraduate/Fellowship)* [6357]

Armenag and Armenhooi Kalustian Memorial Grant *(Undergraduate/Scholarship)* [1887]

Kamehameha Schools Class of 1968 "Ka Poli O Kaiona" Scholarships *(Graduate, Undergraduate/Scholarship)* [8930]

Kamehameha Schools Class of 1972 Scholarship *(Graduate, Undergraduate/Scholarship)* [8931]

Aram and Adrine Kamparosyan Memorial Grant *(Undergraduate/Scholarship)* [1888]

WLALA Fran Kandel Public Interest Grants *(Postgraduate/Grant)* [12143]

Bill Kane Undergraduate Scholarship *(Undergraduate/Scholarship, Award, Monetary)* [10349]

Penny Kanner Dissertation Research Fellowship *(Doctorate/Fellowship)* [11541]

The Walter S. Kapala Scholarship Trust *(Undergraduate/Scholarship)* [5335]

Kaplan Lawyers PC Legal Scholarships *(Graduate/Scholarship)* [6376]

Don Kaplan Legacy Scholarships *(Undergraduate/Scholarship)* [2803]

Kaplan Scholarships *(Undergraduate/Scholarship)* [5524]

The Olympia Brown and Max Kapp Award *(Master's/Scholarship)* [11251]

Kappa Kappa Gamma Foundation Project 2000 Scholarship *(Undergraduate/Scholarship)* [6450]

Kappa Omicron Nu National Alumni Fellowships *(Graduate/Fellowship)* [6489]

Kappa Project 2000 Scholarship *(Undergraduate/Scholarship)* [6451]

Karen D. Carsel Memorial Scholarship *(Undergraduate/Scholarship)* [916]

Karen Schuvie Scholarship *(Undergraduate/Scholarship, Loan)* [6368]

Karl Mehlmann Scholarship *(Undergraduate/Scholarship)* [3530]

KASF scholarships *(Graduate, Undergraduate/Scholarship)* [6597]

KASF Designated Scholarships *(Graduate, Undergraduate/Scholarship)* [6598]

KASF General Scholarships *(Undergraduate, Graduate, Professional development/Scholarship)* [6599]

Ken Kashiwahara Scholarships *(Undergraduate/Scholarship)* [9466]

Koren and Alice Odian Kasparian Memorial Grant *(Undergraduate/Scholarship)* [1889]

Kathryn M. Cronin Scholarship *(Undergraduate, Graduate/Scholarship)* [11192]

Kathy D. and Stephen J. Anderson Scholarship Fund *(Undergraduate/Scholarship)* [3629]

Lucile B. Kaufman Women's Scholarship *(Undergraduate/Scholarship)* [10403]

E. Wayne Kay Community College Scholarship *(Undergraduate, Community College/Scholarship)* [10405]

E. Wayne Kay Graduate Scholarships *(Graduate, Doctorate/Scholarship)* [10406]

E. Wayne Kay High School Scholarship *(Undergraduate/Scholarship)* [10407]

Kays Gary Scholarship *(Undergraduate/Scholarship)* [11193]

KCC Foundation Gold Key Scholarship *(Undergraduate/Scholarship)* [6513]

KCC Foundation Scholarship *(Undergraduate/Scholarship)* [6514]

KCC-JEE Graduate Fellowships *(Graduate/Fellowship)* [6580]

KCC Trustee Scholarship *(Undergraduate/Scholarship)* [6515]

KDP International Scholarship Program - President Scholarship *(Undergraduate, Graduate, Doctorate/Scholarship)* [6385]

Ezra Jack Keats/Kerlan Memorial Fellowship *(Professional development/Fellowship)* [11643]

Araxy Kechejian Memorial Grant *(Undergraduate/Scholarship)* [1890]

Keepers Preservation Education Fund *(Undergraduate/Award)* [6990]

KEF General Scholarships *(Undergraduate, Graduate/Scholarship)* [6590]

Kegler Brown Diversity Scholarship *(Undergraduate/Scholarship)* [6511]

Keiko Fukuda Scholarship *(Undergraduate, Postgraduate/Scholarship)* [11385]

Keith Maffioli Scholarship *(Undergraduate/Scholarship)* [3683]

Robert E. Kelsey Annual Scholarship *(Undergraduate/Scholarship)* [8954]

Ken LaFountaine First Nations Scholarship *(Undergraduate/Scholarship)* [10056]

Willmoore H. Kendall Scholarships *(Professional development/Scholarship)* [3444]

Kennedy T. Friend Scholarship Fund *(Graduate, Undergraduate/Scholarship)* [348]

Kenneth and Barbara Starks Plant Resistance to Insects Graduate Student Award *(Graduate/Award)* [4396]

Kenneth G. Weckel Scholarship *(Undergraduate/Scholarship)* [7378]

Kenneth H. Breeden Scholarship *(Undergraduate/Scholarship)* [6658]

Kenneth J. Osborn Scholarship (Undergraduate/ Scholarship) [2007]

Kenneth Rogers Memorial Scholarship (Undergraduate/Scholarship) [6805]

Oscar Kenshur Book Prize (Other/Prize) [1435]

Kentucky Paralegal Association Paralegal Student Scholarships (Undergraduate/Scholarship) [6535]

Kenyon T. Payne Outstanding Student Award (Undergraduate/Award, Monetary) [7344]

Ketchum Excellence in Public Relations Research Award (Graduate/Fellowship, Internship) [5858]

George Keverian Public Service Scholarship (Undergraduate/Scholarship) [1891]

Key to a Bright Future Scholarship (Graduate, College/Scholarship) [6714]

Dr. Arthur A. Kezian DDS Science Scholarship (Undergraduate, Graduate, College, University/Scholarship) [6541]

KGP Cornaro Scholarship (Graduate/Scholarship) [6397]

Graduate Fellowship Program - Mahboob Khan/Advanced Micro Devices Fellowships (Doctorate, Graduate/Fellowship) [10000]

KHIMA Graduate Scholarship (Graduate/Scholarship) [6369]

Michael Kidger Memorial Scholarship in Optical Design (Undergraduate/Scholarship) [10726]

Kids and Community Scholarship Program (College, University/Scholarship) [6552]

Julia Kiene Fellowships in Electrical Energy (Graduate/Fellowship) [12159]

Kilbuck Family Native American Scholarship (Undergraduate/Scholarship) [2484]

Killam Fellowships (Undergraduate/Fellowship) [4771]

Elson T. Killam Memorial Scholarship (Undergraduate, Graduate/Scholarship) [8249]

Kimberly Elementary School PTA Scholarship (Undergraduate/Scholarship) [9552]

Kimmel Scholar Award (Doctorate/Grant) [6554]

Kit C. King Graduate Scholarships (Graduate/Scholarship) [8048]

Martin Luther King Jr. Scholarships (Graduate/ Scholarship) [6558]

Martin Luther King Law Scholarship (Undergraduate/Scholarship) [4165]

Steven G. King Play Environments Scholarship (Undergraduate, Master's/Scholarship) [6648]

Jessica King Scholarships (Other/Scholarship) [3938]

Don King Student Fellowships (Undergraduate/Fellowship) [5659]

Kingsbury Elementary School PTA Scholarship (Undergraduate/Scholarship) [9553]

Southwest Chapter Roy Kinslow Scholarship (Undergraduate/Scholarship) [1566]

Treva C. Kintner Scholarships (Undergraduate/ Scholarship) [9116]

Kislak Fellowship for the Study of the History and Cultures of the Early Americas (Undergraduate, Graduate/Fellowship) [6572]

Tamo Kitaura Scholarships (Other/Scholarship) [11386]

AACT John Kitt Memorial Scholarship (Undergraduate/Scholarship) [538]

Kiwanis Club of Redlands Foundation Academic Excellence Scholarship (Undergraduate/Scholarship) [9554]

Kiwanis Club of Redlands Foundation - Martin and Dorothy Munz Scholarship (Undergraduate/Scholarship) [9555]

Klarman Family Foundation Grants Program in Eating Disorders Research (Professional development/Grant) [5439]

Jane M. Klausman Women in Business Scholarships (Graduate, Undergraduate/Scholarship) [12421]

Gerda and Kurt Klein Scholarships (Undergraduate/Scholarship) [5592]

Klingenstein Fellowships in the Neurosciences (Doctorate, Master's/Fellowship) [6566]

Kluge Fellowship (Doctorate, Graduate/Fellowship) [6573]

J. Merrill Knapp Research Fellowship (Graduate/ Fellowship) [952]

John A. Knauss Marine Policy Fellowship (Graduate/Fellowship) [11304]

David Knight Graduate Scholarship (Graduate/ Scholarship) [10656]

John S. Knight Journalism Fellowships (Other/Fellowship) [6576]

Robert E. Knight Professional Scholarship (Graduate/Scholarship) [10979]

Knight-Wallace Reporting Fellowships (Professional development/Fellowship) [11870]

Knox Hume Scholarship Fund (Undergraduate/ Scholarship) [3630]

Glenn Knudsvig Memorial Scholarships (Graduate, Undergraduate/Scholarship) [754]

Koch Scholars Program (Undergraduate/Scholarship) [11878]

Kodak Fellowships in Film Preservation (Graduate/ Fellowship) [2247]

James P. Kohn Memorial Scholarship (Doctorate/ Scholarship) [1567]

P. Johnson and C. Kolb Memorial Scholarships (Undergraduate, Graduate, Master's, Doctorate/Scholarship) [9873]

Susan G. Komen for the Cure College Scholarship Awards (Two Year College/Award, Scholarship) [6586]

Susan G. Komen for the Cure Post-doctoral Fellowships - Clinical Research Grants (Postdoctorate/ Grant, Fellowship) [6587]

KON/GEICO LeaderShape Undergraduate Scholarship (Undergraduate/Scholarship) [6490]

KON National Alumni Chapter Grant (Professional development/Grant) [6491]

KON New Initiatives Grant (Professional development/Grant) [6492]

Emily Day Koppell Memorial Adelphe Scholarship (Undergraduate, Graduate/Scholarship) [6452]

Korean Language Study Awards (Graduate, Professional development/Scholarship) [6595]

Korean Studies Dissertation Workshop (Graduate/ Fellowship) [10248]

AIST Willy Korf Memorial Fund (Undergraduate, Graduate/Scholarship) [2221]

Kosciuszko Foundation Graduate Study and Research in Poland Scholarships (Graduate, Postgraduate/Scholarship) [6601]

Kosciuszko Foundation Tuition Scholarships (Graduate/Scholarship) [6602]

Kosciuszko Foundation Year Abroad Scholarships (Graduate, Undergraduate/Scholarship) [6603]

Marcia J. Koslov Scholarship (Professional development/Scholarship) [598]

Haig Koumjian Memorial Grant (Undergraduate/ Scholarship) [1892]

William D. Krahling Excellence in Journalism Scholarship (Undergraduate/Scholarship) [403]

Michael Kraus Research Grants (Doctorate/Grant) [961]

Sharon Kreikemeier Memorial Scholarships (Undergraduate/Scholarship) [8189]

Kress/AAR Fellowships (Professional development/ Fellowship) [2058]

Kress Conservation Fellowships (Postgraduate/Fellowship) [6614]

Samuel H. Kress Grants for Research and Publication in Classical Art and Architecture (Professional development, Graduate/Grant, Award) [1778]

Kristin Bjurstrom Krueger Student Scholarship Program (Undergraduate/Scholarship) [7240]

KTA Chapter Adviser Research Grant Award (Professional development/Grant) [6501]

Harry A. Kuljian Memorial Grant (Undergraduate/ Scholarship) [1893]

Kurt H. and Donna M. Schuler Cash Grant (Undergraduate/Scholarship, Grant) [1393]

Henry and Chiyo Kuwahara Creative Arts Award (Graduate/Scholarship) [6248]

Sam and Florice Kuwahara Memorial Scholarship (Undergraduate/Scholarship) [6249]

Anne Emery Kyllo Professional Scholarship (Professional development/Scholarship) [1136]

L-3 Communications Avionics Systems Scholarships (Undergraduate/Scholarship) [186]

L. Gordon, Jr. and June D. Pfefferkorn Scholarship (Undergraduate/Scholarship) [12082]

L'Oréal USA For Women in Science Fellowship (Postdoctorate/Fellowship) [8696]

LA Tutors 123 Innovation in Education Scholarship (All/Scholarship) [6626]

Gretchen Laatsch Scholarships (Graduate/Scholarship) [2139]

Ladah Law Firm, PLLC Injury Scholarships (Undergraduate, Graduate/Scholarship) [6630]

Jeffery P. LaFage Graduate Student Research Award (Master's, Doctorate/Grant) [4397]

Lawrence Gelfand - Armin Rappaport - Walter LaFeber Dissertation Fellowship (Graduate/Fellowship) [10357]

The Lagrant Foundation - Graduate Scholarships (Graduate/Scholarship) [6632]

The Lagrant Foundation - Undergraduate Scholarships (Undergraduate/Scholarship) [6633]

Ray and Kathy LaHood Scholarships for the Study of American Government (Undergraduate/Scholarship) [4102]

Laine - Casey Laine Armed Services Scholarship (Undergraduate/Scholarship) [3479]

Lakselaget Foundation Scholarship Fund (Graduate, Undergraduate/Scholarship) [6635]

Lalor Foundation Merit Awards (Postdoctorate/ Award, Recognition, Prize) [10533]

Lalor Foundation Post-Doctoral Fellowships (Postdoctorate/Fellowship) [6637]

Paul C. K. Lam Memorial Scholarship at The University of Akron (Undergraduate/Scholarship) [8597]

Lamar University College of Engineering Scholarships (Undergraduate/Scholarship) [7852]

Hedy Lamarr Achievement Award for Emerging Leaders in Entertainment Technology (Undergraduate/Award) [4086]

Verne LaMarr Lyons Memorial MSW Scholarship (Graduate, Master's/Fellowship) [7698]

Lambda Project 2000 Scholarship (Undergraduate/ Scholarship) [6453]

Elaine Johnson Lampert Journalism Memorial Adelphe Scholarship (Undergraduate/Award) [6454]

Lance Surety College Scholarships (Undergraduate, Graduate/Scholarship) [6644]

Harold Lancour Scholarship for Foreign Study (Professional development/Scholarship) [2498]

Robert S. Landauer, Sr. Memorial Fellowship (Graduate, Undergraduate/Fellowship) [5430]

Lanford Family Highway Worker Memorial Scholarship Program (High School/Scholarship) [1362]

Frank H. Lang Merit Scholarships (Undergraduate/ Scholarship) [6656]

Lapides Fellowships in Pre-1865 Juvenile Literature and Ephemera (Graduate, Postdoctorate/Fellowship) [493]

Arnold "Les" Larsen, FAIA, Memorial Scholarships (Graduate/Scholarship) [1010]

David B. Larson Fellowships in Health and Spirituality (Postdoctorate/Fellowship) [6574]

LaRue A. Ditmore Music Scholarship (Undergraduate/Scholarship) [12148]

Las Vegas Chinatown Scholarship (Undergraduate/ Scholarship) [9409]

Laser Technology, Engineering and Applications Scholarship (Graduate, Undergraduate/Scholarship) [10727]

The LasikPlus My Vision Essay Scholarship (Undergraduate, Graduate/Scholarship) [6669]

Jay and Deborah Last Fellowships (Doctorate/Fellowship) [494]

Latham Diversity Scholars - 2L Diversity Scholars (Undergraduate/Scholarship) [6673]

Candia Baker Laughlin Certification Scholarship (Undergraduate/Scholarship) [428]

Laura Ann Peck Memorial Endowed Scholarship (Undergraduate/Scholarship) [6806]

Laura M. Fleming Scholarship (Undergraduate, Vocational/Occupational/Scholarship) [4740]

Law Enforcement Memorial Scholarship Endowment Fund (Undergraduate/Scholarship) [4741]

Law Fellows Program (Undergraduate/Fellowship) [7607]

Community Leadership in Justice Fellowship - The Law Foundation of Ontario (Other/Fellowship) [6683]

Law Office of A. Sam Jubran Scholarship Contest *(University, College, Undergraduate/Scholarship)* [6685]

Law Office of David P. Shapiro Annual Leukemia Scholarships *(Vocational/Occupational, Community College, University, Undergraduate, College/Scholarship)* [6691]

The Law Offices of Scott Henry Scholarship Contest *(Undergraduate/Scholarship)* [6710]

The Law Offices of Sean M. Cleary Scholarship *(Undergraduate/Scholarship)* [6712]

Law School Scholarship *(Graduate/Scholarship)* [2618, 9714]

Law and Society Association Article Prize *(Other/Prize, Award)* [6724]

Law and Society Association Dissertation Prize *(Other/Prize)* [6725]

Law and Society Association Undergraduate Student Paper Prize *(Undergraduate/Prize)* [6727]

Law Student Scholarship *(Graduate/Scholarship)* [4539, 6520]

Lawrence Fellowship *(Doctorate/Fellowship)* [11321]

Lawrence Madeiros Scholarship *(Undergraduate/Scholarship)* [7925]

Lawsuit Legal American Nursing Support Scholarships *(Undergraduate, Graduate/Scholarship)* [6738]

LCRF Grant *(Advanced Professional, Professional development/Grant)* [6933]

LCSC Presidential Out-of-State Tuition Scholarships *(Undergraduate/Scholarship)* [6808]

LCSC Welding Club Scholarship *(Undergraduate/Scholarship)* [6809]

Leadership Conference Scholarship *(Other/Scholarship)* [7738]

League Foundation Scholarships *(Undergraduate/Scholarship)* [6745]

League of Latin American Citizens General Electric Scholarships *(Undergraduate/Scholarship)* [6747]

Leakey Foundation Research Grants *(Doctorate, Advanced Professional/Grant)* [6752]

Lebbeus F. Bissell Scholarship Fund *(Undergraduate/Scholarship)* [5336]

LeClairRyan 1L Diversity Scholarship *(Undergraduate/Scholarship)* [6762]

Lee Epstein Fund Scholarship *(Graduate, Undergraduate/Scholarship)* [7107]

Lee Tarbox Memorial Scholarship *(Undergraduate/Scholarship)* [187]

Lee Teng Undergraduate Fellowship in Accelerator Science and Engineering *(Undergraduate/Fellowship)* [11318]

Leesfield/AAJ Scholarship *(Undergraduate/Scholarship)* [583]

Judge William B. Leffler Scholarship *(Graduate/Scholarship)* [11607]

The Legacy Fellowship *(Doctorate/Fellowship)* [495]

Legal Internships *(Professional development/Internship)* [3228]

Charles LeGeyt Fortescue Scholarship *(Graduate/Scholarship, Award, Monetary)* [5817]

Doreen Legg Memorial Scholarships *(Undergraduate/Scholarship)* [9556]

The Herbert Lehman Education Fund Scholarship *(Undergraduate/Scholarship)* [7540]

Leiber and Stoller Music Scholarship *(Undergraduate/Scholarship)* [1410]

Leif and Inger Sjöberg Award *(Advanced Professional, Professional development/Award)* [1376]

Leighton M. Ballew Directing Scholarship *(Undergraduate/Scholarship)* [10635]

Lemelson Center Travel to Collections Awards *(Graduate, Professional development/Award)* [10195]

The Stan Lencki Scholarship *(Undergraduate/Scholarship)* [7172]

John Lennon Scholarships *(Undergraduate/Scholarship)* [2635]

Leo Gilmartin Scholarship *(Undergraduate/Scholarship)* [9211]

Leonard Hawk Founders Scholarship *(Graduate, Undergraduate, Vocational/Occupational/Scholarship)* [1334]

Leopold Education Project Scholarship *(Undergraduate/Scholarship)* [3685]

Leopold Schepp Foundation Scholarship *(Undergraduate, Graduate/Scholarship)* [9932]

Lerner-Scott Prize *(Doctorate/Prize)* [8728]

Leslie and Mary Ella Scales Scholarship *(Undergraduate/Scholarship)* [3657]

Lester G. Benz Memorial Scholarship for College Journalism Study *(Other/Scholarship)* [9463]

Jack A. and Louise S. Levine Memorial Scholarships *(Undergraduate/Scholarship)* [9557]

Harry and Miriam Levinson Scholarship *(Graduate, Master's, Doctorate/Scholarship)* [1284]

Herbert Levy Memorial Scholarship *(Undergraduate/Scholarship)* [10479]

Lewis-Clark Coin Club Endowed Scholarship *(Undergraduate/Scholarship)* [6810]

Lewis and Clark Fund for Exploration and Field Research *(Doctorate/Grant)* [1215]

Military Order of the Purple Heart *(Undergraduate/Scholarship)* [6813]

Lloyd Lewis Fellowships in American History *(Postdoctorate/Fellowship)* [8375]

George T. Lewis, Jr. Academic Scholarship Fund *(Undergraduate/Scholarship)* [4742]

S. Evelyn Lewis Memorial Scholarships in Medical Health Sciences *(Graduate, Undergraduate/Scholarship)* [12414]

Lewis-Reynolds-Smith Founders Fellowship *(Graduate/Fellowship)* [5477]

Lewiston Service League Memorial Scholarship *(Undergraduate/Scholarship)* [6815]

Lexington Alumni Scholarships *(Undergraduate/Scholarship)* [6827]

Lexington Community Foundation Annual Scholarships *(Undergraduate/Scholarship)* [6828]

Lexington Community Foundation/CCC Scholarships *(Undergraduate/Scholarship)* [6829]

Jack G. Lezman Scholarship Contest *(College, University, Undergraduate/Scholarship)* [6836]

Liberty Mutual Scholarships *(Undergraduate/Scholarship)* [1568]

Dolores Zohrab Liebmann Fund - Graduate School Fellowships *(Graduate/Fellowship)* [6845]

Dolores Zohrab Liebmann Fund - Independent Research/Study Grants *(Graduate, Undergraduate/Grant)* [6846]

Dolores Zohrab Liebmann Fund - Publication Grants *(Graduate, Undergraduate/Grant)* [6847]

LIFE Lessons Scholarship Program *(Undergraduate/Scholarship)* [6849]

Life Sciences Research Foundation Postdoctoral Fellowship Program *(Postdoctorate/Fellowship)* [6851]

Lighting the Way for Nursing Scholarship *(Doctorate/Scholarship)* [25]

Lillian and Alex Feir Graduate Student Travel Award in Insect Physiology, Biochemistry, or Molecular Biology *(Master's, Doctorate/Award)* [4398]

Lillie Hope-McGarvey Health Scholarship *(Undergraduate, Vocational/Occupational, Graduate, Master's/Scholarship)* [330]

Ruth Lilly and Dorothy Sargent Rosenberg Poetry Fellowships *(Professional development/Fellowship, Prize)* [9216]

Lilly Scholarships in Religion for Journalists *(Other/Scholarship)* [9633]

Lily H. Gridley Memorial Scholarship *(Undergraduate/Scholarship)* [12149]

Esther Lim Memorial Scholarships *(Undergraduate/Scholarship)* [3308]

Lime Connect Pathways Scholarship for High School Seniors with Disabilities *(Undergraduate/Scholarship)* [6863]

LimNexus Foundation Scholarship *(Undergraduate/Scholarship)* [6239]

AIST Ronald E. Lincoln Memorial Scholarship *(Undergraduate/Scholarship)* [2222]

Linda J. Murphy Scholarship *(Undergraduate/Scholarship)* [12141]

Lindenwood University Scouting Scholarships *(Undergraduate/Scholarship)* [7853]

Lindsay M. Entz Memorial Scholarship Fund *(Undergraduate/Scholarship)* [4595]

Margaret B. Lindsey Award for Distinguished Research in Teacher Education *(Other/Award, Recognition)* [551]

Lineups.com Future of Sports Scholarship Program *(Undergraduate, Graduate/Scholarship)* [6871]

Link Foundation/Smithsonian Graduate Fellowships in Marine Science *(Graduate/Fellowship)* [10201]

Linsley Scholarship Fund *(Undergraduate, Vocational/Occupational/Scholarship)* [3301]

LionsDeal.com Scholarships *(Undergraduate/Scholarship)* [6875]

F. Maynard Lipe Scholarship Award *(Master's, Postgraduate/Scholarship)* [759]

The Lawrence Lipking Fellowship *(Postdoctorate/Fellowship)* [8376]

Emil S. Liston Award *(Other/Scholarship)* [7662]

Litherland/FTEE Undergraduate Scholarships *(Undergraduate/Scholarship)* [6125]

Litner + Deganian College Scholarship Program *(College, University/Scholarship)* [6879]

Davis Levin Livingston Public Interest Law Scholarships *(Postgraduate/Scholarship)* [3975]

Lizette Peterson Homer Injury Prevention Grant *(Other, Undergraduate, Graduate/Grant)* [1739]

LLN Student Scholarships *(Undergraduate/Scholarship)* [6677]

Lloyd Bridges Scholarship *(Graduate/Scholarship)* [3204]

E.C. Lloyd and J.C.U. Johnson Scholarship Fund *(Undergraduate/Scholarship)* [3658]

Loan for Service for Graduates *(Graduate/Loan)* [995]

Local 827 Peter J. Casey Scholarship *(Undergraduate/Scholarship)* [5957]

Local A&WMA Sections and Chapter Scholarships *(Graduate/Scholarship)* [162]

Miriam "Doc" Locke Memorial Adelphe Scholarships *(Graduate/Scholarship)* [6456]

Mary Elizabeth Lockwood Beneventi MBA Scholarship *(Graduate/Scholarship, Award, Monetary)* [8098]

The Loewenstein-Wiener Fellowship *(Professional development, Doctorate, Postdoctorate/Fellowship)* [1061]

Stephen Logan Memorial Scholarship *(Undergraduate/Scholarship)* [4872]

Lois Widly Student Scholarships *(Graduate, Undergraduate/Scholarship)* [6046]

Lone Star GIA Associate and Alumni Scholarships *(Undergraduate/Scholarship)* [4879]

Lawrence A. Long Memorial Law Scholarship *(Graduate/Scholarship)* [404]

The Robert A. Catlin/David W. Long Scholarship *(Graduate/Scholarship)* [1244]

Long-term International Fellowships *(Professional development/Fellowship)* [3778]

Kay Longcope Scholarship Award *(Graduate, Undergraduate/Scholarship)* [7990]

Michael Lorenzen Foundation Scholarship *(Undergraduate, Graduate/Scholarship)* [6890]

Suzanne and Caleb Loring Research Fellowships *(Professional development/Fellowship)* [7145]

Lorraine E. Swain Scholarship *(Undergraduate/Scholarship)* [10114]

Barbara Lotze Scholarships for Future Teachers *(Undergraduate/Scholarship)* [625]

Lou Hochberg Awards - Thesis and Dissertation Awards *(Graduate/Award, Monetary)* [8757]

Louis Armstrong Award Honoring W.C. Handy *(Undergraduate/Scholarship)* [1411]

Louis I. Jaffe Memorial Scholarship-ODU *(Graduate/Scholarship)* [5274]

Louis M. Connor, Jr. Scholarship *(Undergraduate/Scholarship)* [11194]

Louis Pelzer Memorial Award *(Graduate/Award)* [8729]

Louis T. Klauder Scholarship *(Undergraduate, Graduate/Scholarship)* [1303]

Louisiana Agricultural Consultants Association Scholarship *(Graduate, Undergraduate/Scholarship)* [6896]

Louisville Institute Dissertation Fellowships (DF) *(Doctorate/Fellowship)* [6912]

Louisville Institute Project Grant for Researchers (PGR) *(Doctorate/Grant)* [6913]

Louisville Institute Sabbatical Grants for Researchers (SGR) *(Doctorate/Grant)* [6914]

Louisville Institute's First Book Grant Program for Minority Scholars (FBM) *(Doctorate/Grant)* [6915]

Louthian Law School Scholarships *(Advanced Professional/Scholarship)* [6919]

Lowe Family First Summer Student Scholarship *(Undergraduate/Scholarship)* [11630]

Gertie S. Lowe Nursing Scholarship Awards *(Undergraduate/Scholarship)* [3659]

The Lozano Law Firm Scholarship Contest *(College, University, Undergraduate/Scholarship)* [6925]

LPHA Scholarships *(Graduate, Undergraduate/Scholarship)* [6906]

LSU Eye Center Clinical Retina Fellowships *(Undergraduate/Fellowship)* [6910]

Lt. Holly Adams Memorial Scholarship Fund *(Undergraduate/Scholarship)* [3632]

Lucidchart Scholarship *(Undergraduate, Graduate/Scholarship)* [6927]

Lucidpress Scholarship *(Undergraduate, Graduate/Scholarship)* [6928]

Lucile Cheever Graubart/Lambda Scholarship *(Undergraduate/Scholarship)* [10115]

Lucy and Charles W.E. Clarke Scholarship *(Undergraduate/Scholarship, Award)* [2000]

Lucy Hilty Research Grant *(Graduate/Grant)* [1312]

Lugonia Alumni/Harrison Lightfoot Scholarship *(Undergraduate/Scholarship)* [9558]

Lula Faye Clegg Memorial Scholarship Endowment Fund *(Undergraduate/Scholarship)* [4743]

LULAC National Scholarship Fund (LNSF) *(Graduate, Undergraduate/Scholarship)* [6749]

Lee G. Luna Foreign Travel Scholarship *(Professional development/Scholarship)* [8109]

Lung Cancer Discovery Award (LCD) *(Doctorate/Award)* [1100]

Lung Health Dissertation Grants (LH) *(Doctorate/Grant)* [1101]

Lutheran Student Scholastic and Service Scholarships - College and University Students *(Undergraduate/Scholarship)* [2562]

Lyle Mamer Fellowship *(Graduate/Fellowship)* [12160]

Lymphatic Research Foundation Additional Support for NIH-funded F32 Postdoctoral Fellows Awards *(Postdoctorate/Award)* [5440]

Lymphatic Research Foundation Postdoctoral Fellowship Awards Program *(Postdoctorate/Fellowship)* [5441]

M. Hildred Blewett Fellowship *(Postdoctorate/Fellowship, Award, Monetary)* [1225]

MABF Scholarships *(Professional development/Scholarship)* [7286]

John Mabry Forestry Scholarships *(Undergraduate/Scholarship)* [9489]

MAC Emeritus Membership Award *(Professional development/Award)* [7366]

Bill MacAloney Legacy Scholarships *(Undergraduate/Scholarship)* [2805]

MacArthur Fellows Program *(Professional development/Fellowship)* [6954]

Catherine Macaulay Prize *(Graduate/Prize)* [1436]

MACC Scholarships *(Other/Scholarship)* [7288]

Katie MacDonald Memorial Scholarships *(Graduate, Undergraduate/Scholarship)* [11273]

Warren Mack Scholarship *(Undergraduate/Scholarship)* [6333]

Robert Mack Scholarships *(Graduate, Undergraduate/Scholarship)* [6956]

Thermoset Division/James I. Mackenzie and James H. Cunningham Scholarships *(Undergraduate, Graduate/Scholarship)* [10490]

Mackey-Byars Scholarship for Communication Excellence *(Undergraduate/Scholarship)* [11195]

MACPA Scholarships *(Undergraduate, Graduate/Scholarship)* [7114]

Carol E. Macpherson Memorial Scholarship *(Graduate, Undergraduate/Scholarship)* [11645]

Andrew Macrina Scholarships *(Undergraduate/Scholarship)* [845]

Eileen C. Maddex Fellowships *(Graduate/Fellowship)* [6493]

Dorothy L. Maddy Academic Scholarship *(Undergraduate/Scholarship)* [10744]

Dorothy L. Maddy Workshop/Seminar Scholarship *(Other/Scholarship)* [10745]

James Madison Foundation - Junior Fellowships *(Advanced Professional, Graduate/Fellowship)* [6227]

James Madison Foundation - Senior Fellowships *(Advanced Professional/Fellowship)* [6228]

James Madison Graduate Fellowships *(Graduate/Fellowship)* [6229]

Madson Graduate Scholarship *(Graduate/Scholarship)* [10083]

MAES General Scholarships *(Graduate, Undergraduate/Scholarship)* [6965]

MAES Pipeline Scholarship *(Graduate, Undergraduate/Scholarship)* [6967]

MAES Presidential Scholarship *(Graduate, Undergraduate/Scholarship)* [6968]

Magnetic Interfaces & Nanostructures Division - Leo M. Falicov Student Award *(Graduate/Grant)* [2384]

Dr. Edward May Magruder Medical Scholarships *(Undergraduate/Scholarship)* [751]

Maibach Travel Grant *(Professional development/Grant)* [799]

Maiman Student Paper Competition *(Graduate, Undergraduate/Award)* [8679]

Maine Graphic Arts Association Scholarships *(Undergraduate/Scholarship)* [6997]

Maine Nutrition Council Scholarships *(Undergraduate/Scholarship)* [7001]

Maintenance Technical Reward and Career Scholarship *(Undergraduate/Scholarship)* [7739]

The Make It Move Scholarships *(Undergraduate/Scholarship)* [1762]

Make Me Laugh Scholarship *(Undergraduate, High School/Scholarship)* [11231]

Make Your Mark Scholarship *(Graduate, College/Scholarship)* [5294]

MALDEF Dream Act Student Activist Scholarships *(Undergraduate, Graduate/Scholarship)* [7290]

Maley/FTE Scholarships *(Graduate/Scholarship)* [6126]

Maley/FTEE Teacher Professional Development Scholarships *(Professional development/Scholarship)* [6127]

Margaret Mallett Nursing Scholarship *(Undergraduate/Scholarship)* [10058]

Malmberg Scholarships *(Undergraduate/Scholarship)* [1619]

Malyon Smith Scholarship Research Award *(Graduate/Scholarship)* [1737]

Louisan Mamer Fellowship *(Postgraduate/Fellowship)* [12161]

Mamie Adams Memorial Award *(Undergraduate, Four Year College, Two Year College/Scholarship)* [6816]

Manasel Manasselian Memorial Grant *(Undergraduate/Scholarship)* [1894]

Manchester Scholarship Foundation - Adult Learners Scholarship *(Undergraduate/Scholarship)* [5337]

Mangum & Associates PC Scholarship Contest *(Undergraduate/Scholarship)* [7014]

Mann Law Firm Scholarships *(Advanced Professional/Scholarship)* [7018]

Mansfield Soccer Association Scholarship *(Undergraduate/Scholarship)* [7020]

Honorable Carol Los Mansmann Memorial Fund *(Graduate, Undergraduate/Scholarship)* [349]

Mantle Cell Lymphoma Therapeutic Studies Grant *(Advanced Professional/Grant)* [6950]

Many Voices Fellowships *(Other/Fellowship)* [9197]

March of Dimes General Research Grants *(Professional development/Grant)* [7026]

March of Dimes Graduate Nursing Scholarships *(Graduate/Scholarship)* [7027]

The Albert H. Marckwardt Travel Grants *(Graduate, Doctorate/Grant)* [10969]

Harold and Inge Marcus Scholarship *(Undergraduate/Scholarship)* [5833]

Arif Mardin Music Fellowship *(Other/Fellowship)* [11141]

Margaret A. Blanchard Scholarship *(Graduate/Scholarship)* [11196]

Margaret Dowell-Gravatt, M.D. Scholarship *(Undergraduate/Scholarship)* [2486]

Margaret E. Phillips Scholarship *(Undergraduate/Scholarship)* [11716]

Margaret E. Waldron Memorial Fund *(Undergraduate/Scholarship)* [4596]

Margaret J. Andrew Memorial Scholarship *(Undergraduate, Graduate/Scholarship)* [10116]

Margaret Mead Award *(Doctorate/Award)* [10272]

Margarian Scholarship *(Undergraduate, Graduate/Scholarship)* [7032]

Art Margosian Scholarship *(Undergraduate/Scholarship)* [6334]

Maria Gonzalez Borrero Scholarship Fund *(Undergraduate/Scholarship)* [5338]

Marian A. Smith Costume Scholarship Award *(Graduate/Scholarship)* [10636]

Marian Johnson Frutiger Sisterhood Scholarship *(Undergraduate/Scholarship)* [10117]

Marine Technology Society ROV Scholarship (MTS ROV) *(Undergraduate, Graduate/Scholarship)* [7069]

Shirley Stone Marinkovich Memorial Scholarships *(Undergraduate/Scholarship)* [6458]

Marion Barr Stanfield Art Scholarship *(Graduate, Undergraduate/Scholarship)* [11252]

Marion and Donald Routh Student Research Grant *(Graduate/Grant)* [1740]

Mariposa Elementary School PTA Scholarship *(Undergraduate/Scholarship)* [9559]

Marisol Scholarship *(Undergraduate/Scholarship)* [6459]

Marjorie Kovler Research Fellowship *(Professional development/Fellowship)* [6532]

Marjorie Usher Ragan Scholarship *(Undergraduate/Scholarship)* [11197]

Mark A. Reid Memorial Scholarship *(Undergraduate/Scholarship)* [3687]

Howard T. Markey Memorial Scholarship *(Undergraduate/Scholarship)* [4507]

Markley Family Scholarship Fund *(Undergraduate/Scholarship)* [10778]

Markley Scholarship *(Undergraduate, Graduate/Scholarship)* [7623]

Marla Schwartz Education Grant *(Professional development, Graduate/Grant)* [599]

Marliave Scholarship Fund *(Graduate/Scholarship)* [2161]

George Perkins Marsh Prize *(Other/Prize)* [1455]

Marsh Risk Consulting Scholarships *(Undergraduate/Scholarship)* [1569]

Marshall-Baruch Fellowships *(Doctorate/Fellowship)* [7111]

Marshall Cavendish Scholarships *(Graduate/Scholarship, Monetary)* [1079]

Marshall Foundation Scholars Program *(Undergraduate/Scholarship)* [7112]

Marshall Memorial Fellowship *(Other/Fellowship)* [4946]

Marshall Phelps Athletic Memorial Scholarship *(Undergraduate/Scholarship)* [9560]

Ray and Gertrude Marshall Scholarships *(Undergraduate/Scholarship)* [846]

Martha Combs Jenkins Scholarship *(Undergraduate/Scholarship)* [9117]

Martha Delman and Milton Arthur Krug Endowed Law Scholarship *(Undergraduate/Scholarship)* [9016]

Martha Weston Grant *(Advanced Professional/Grant)* [10301]

Martin Frank Diversity Travel Award *(Undergraduate, Postdoctorate/Fellowship, Award, Monetary)* [1237]

Edna L. Martin Scholarship Fund *(Undergraduate/Scholarship)* [3633]

Susan B. Martin Scholarship *(Graduate/Scholarship)* [892]

Eric Martinez Memorial Scholarships *(Graduate, Undergraduate/Scholarship)* [11274]

The Anthony A. Martino Memorial Scholarship *(Undergraduate/Scholarship)* [5010]

A. Lucchetti Martino Scholarship *(Undergraduate/Scholarship)* [7961]

Marty Rosness Student Scholarship *(Other/Scholarship)* [1798]

Marvin H. and Kathleen G. Teget Leadership Scholarship *(Undergraduate/Scholarship)* [10866]

Mary Ann Mikulic Scholarship *(Other/Scholarship)* [2273]

Mary and Elliot Wood Foundation Graduate Scholarship *(Graduate/Scholarship)* [4744]

The Mary and Elliott Wood Foundation Undergraduate Scholarship *(Undergraduate/Scholarship)* [4745]

Mary L. Brown Scholarship DMACC *(Undergraduate/Scholarship)* [6161]

Mary Minglen Scholarship *(Postgraduate/Scholarship)* [1180]

Mary Mouzon Darby Undergraduate Scholarship *(Undergraduate/Scholarship)* [5622]

Mary Stuart Rogers Scholarship *(Undergraduate/Scholarship)* [12035]

Mary Turnbull Schacht Memorial Scholarship *(Undergraduate/Scholarship)* [10118]

The Maschhoffs Pork Production Scholarships *(Undergraduate/Scholarship)* [7971]

MASNA Student Scholarships *(Undergraduate, Graduate/Scholarship)* [7036]

Masonic-Range Science Scholarship *(Undergraduate/Scholarship)* [10520]

Clinical Translational Fellowship at Pfizer *(Advanced Professional/Fellowship)* [7134]

Massachusetts General Hospital/Harvard Medical School Internship *(Doctorate/Internship)* [7135]

MAT Scholarship *(Undergraduate, Vocational/Occupational/Scholarship)* [7406]

Ruth G. and Joseph D. Matarazzo Scholarship *(Graduate, Master's, Doctorate/Scholarship)* [1285]

Material Handling Education Foundation Scholarships *(Doctorate, Graduate, Undergraduate/Scholarship)* [7293]

Mathematics Mentoring Travel Grants *(Doctorate/Grant)* [2319]

Mathilde Krim Fellowships in Biomedical Research *(Doctorate/Fellowship)* [1685]

Noel D. Matkin Awards *(Undergraduate/Award)* [4301]

Matt Harmon Memorial Scholarship Fund *(Undergraduate/Scholarship)* [10697]

Matt Stager Memorial Scholarship *(Undergraduate/Scholarship)* [11929]

Elizabeth M. Mauro Reimbursement Awards *(Advanced Professional/Award)* [72]

Ann Lane Mavromatis Scholarship *(Undergraduate/Scholarship)* [967]

The Maxwell Scholarship in Graduate Medical Journalism *(Graduate/Scholarship)* [11198]

May-Cassioppi Scholarship *(Undergraduate/Scholarship)* [3688]

Howard Mayer Brown Fellowship *(Graduate/Fellowship)* [1146]

The Clara Mayo Grants *(Graduate/Grant)* [10510]

Charles "Chuck" McAdams Memorial Scholarships *(Graduate, Undergraduate/Scholarship)* [10921]

McAllister Fellowship *(Professional development/Fellowship)* [2072]

Doreen McMullan McCarthy Memorial Academic Scholarship for Women with Bleeding Disorders *(Undergraduate/Scholarship)* [7926]

McClatchy Minority Scholarship and Fellowship *(Undergraduate/Scholarship)* [10617]

The First Lieutenant Scott McClean Love Memorial Scholarship - Children of Soldiers *(Undergraduate, Vocational/Occupational/Scholarship)* [1917]

The First Lieutenant Scott McClean Love Memorial Scholarship - Spouses of Soldiers *(Undergraduate, Vocational/Occupational/Scholarship)* [1918]

McCloy Fellowships in Agriculture *(Professional development/Fellowship)* [810]

McCloy Fellowships in Environmental Policy *(Professional development/Fellowship)* [811]

McCloy Fellowships in Journalism *(Professional development/Fellowship)* [812]

McCloy Fellowships in Urban Affairs *(Professional development/Fellowship)* [813]

Anne O'Hare McCormick Memorial Scholarship *(Graduate/Scholarship)* [8393]

Michele L. McDonald Scholarships *(Undergraduate/Scholarship)* [4304]

McDonald's Inspiration Celebration Scholarship *(Undergraduate, Graduate/Scholarship)* [11026]

MCEA Financial Assistance Award *(Undergraduate/Scholarship)* [7062]

Foster G. McGaw Scholarship *(Undergraduate, Graduate/Scholarship)* [2306]

Nancy B. Woolridge McGee Graduate Fellowships *(Graduate/Fellowship)* [12415]

Thomas R. McGetchin Memorial Scholarship Award *(Undergraduate/Scholarship)* [11423]

The William P. McHugh Memorial Fund *(Doctorate, Graduate/Grant)* [1338]

Mary Bowles McInnis Adelphe Scholarship *(Undergraduate/Scholarship)* [6461]

C.A. "Pete" McKnight Scholarships *(High School/Scholarship)* [11199]

The McLean Scholarship for Nursing and Physician Assistant Majors *(Undergraduate/Scholarship)* [2194]

McMurray Stern - Scholarship Opportunity *(Undergraduate, College, University/Scholarship)* [7197]

Ronald E. McNair Scholarships in Space and Optical Physics *(Undergraduate/Scholarship)* [8089]

National Association of Pediatric Nurse Practitioners McNeil Annual Scholarships *(Undergraduate/Scholarship)* [7679]

National Association of Pediatric Nurse Practitioners McNeil Rural and Underserved Scholarships *(Graduate/Scholarship)* [7680]

Joan Reagin McNeill Scholarships - Alpha Theta *(Undergraduate/Scholarship)* [10119]

Joan Reagin McNeill Scholarships - Theta Phi *(Undergraduate/Scholarship)* [10120]

O. Ruth McQuown Scholarship - Graduate Award for Current Students *(Graduate/Scholarship)* [11572]

MDA Development Grants *(Doctorate/Grant)* [7509]

MDA Research Grants *(Advanced Professional/Grant)* [7510]

MDF Postdoctoral Fellowship *(Postdoctorate/Fellowship)* [7536]

MDI Biological Laboratory High school Student Summer Research Fellowship *(High School/Fellowship)* [7484]

MDI Biological Laboratory Undergraduate Summer Research Fellowships *(Undergraduate/Fellowship)* [7485]

Mead Leadership Fellowships *(Professional development/Fellowship)* [8482]

David Meador Foundation - Club Management Student Scholarships *(Undergraduate/Scholarship)* [8242]

Medford Rogue Rotary Scholarship *(Undergraduate/Scholarship)* [7209]

MediaMister $1000 Student Scholarship *(Undergraduate, Graduate/Scholarship)* [7211]

Medical Scrubs Collection Scholarship *(Undergraduate, Graduate/Scholarship)* [7225]

Medical Student Rotation for Underrepresented Populations *(Graduate, Master's/Grant)* [3779]

MedicalFieldCareers.com Healthcare Scholarship *(Professional development/Scholarship)* [7227]

Medieval Academy Dissertation Grants *(Graduate/Grant)* [7230]

Carl J. Megel Scholarship *(Undergraduate/Scholarship)* [884]

Susan R. Meisinger Fellowship for Graduate Study in HR *(Graduate, Master's, Advanced Professional/Fellowship)* [10367]

Dr. Roger E. Meisner Veterinary Medicine Educational Scholarship Fund *(Undergraduate, Graduate/Scholarship)* [8474]

Melanie and Todd Edmondson Memorial Scholarship *(Undergraduate/Scholarship)* [3660]

Frederic G. Melcher Scholarships *(Graduate/Scholarship)* [2240]

K. Cyrus Melikian Memorial Grant *(Undergraduate/Scholarship)* [1895]

Mellon/ACLS Dissertation Completion Fellowships *(Graduate, Doctorate/Fellowship)* [825]

Mellon-CES Dissertation Completion Fellowships in European Studies. *(Graduate/Fellowship)* [3858]

Mellon Fellowships for Dissertation Research in Original Sources *(Doctorate/Fellowship)* [3870]

MHS Andrew W. Mellon Fellowships *(Professional development, Doctorate/Fellowship)* [7146]

Mellon Fellowships in Urban Landscape Studies *(Graduate, Master's, Doctorate/Fellowship)* [4233]

Andrew W. Mellon Foundation Fellowships *(Graduate/Fellowship)* [8749]

Institute Andrew W. Mellon Postdoctoral Research Fellowships *(Graduate/Fellowship)* [8621]

Terry Mellor Continuing Education Grant *(Undergraduate/Grant)* [10735]

MELNA Scholarship *(Undergraduate, Graduate/Scholarship)* [6999]

Melvin Kruger Endowed Scholarship Program *(Graduate, Undergraduate/Scholarship)* [8063, 9739]

Member Student Scholarships *(Undergraduate/Scholarship)* [9050]

Memorial Fund Scholarship *(Undergraduate/Scholarship)* [7785]

Mensa Education and Research Foundation U.S. Scholarship *(Undergraduate/Scholarship)* [7262]

Mentored Research Fellowship *(Postdoctorate/Fellowship)* [7534]

Mentored Research Scholar Grant *(Doctorate, Professional development/Grant)* [717]

Merchants Exchange Scholarship *(Undergraduate, Vocational/Occupational, Graduate, Professional development/Scholarship)* [7266]

Meredith P. Crawford Fellowship in I-O Psychology *(Doctorate/Fellowship)* [5626]

Merial Excellence in Preventive Medicine in Beef Award *(Other/Grant)* [526]

Merial Excellence in Preventive Medicine in Dairy Award *(Other/Grant)* [527]

Christopher Mesi Memorial Music Scholarships *(Undergraduate/Scholarship)* [3179]

Mesothelioma Memorial Scholarships *(Undergraduate, Vocational/Occupational/Scholarship)* [10859]

Nicholas Metropolis Award for Outstanding Doctoral Thesis Work in Computational Physics *(Doctorate, Postdoctorate/Award, Recognition, Monetary)* [1226]

Meyer D. and Dorothy C. Silverman Scholarship Fund *(Undergraduate/Scholarship)* [3639]

Theodore Meyer Scholarship *(Undergraduate, Graduate/Scholarship)* [1137]

MFJC Doctoral Scholarships *(Doctorate/Scholarship)* [7250]

MGH Department of Psychiatry Behavioral Neurology and Neuropsychiatry Fellowship Program *(Advanced Professional, Professional development/Fellowship)* [7136]

Eating Disorders Summer Research Fellowship *(Advanced Professional, Professional development/Fellowship)* [7137]

MGH Department of Psychiatry Forensic Psychiatry Fellowship *(Professional development/Fellowship)* [7138]

MGH Department of Psychiatry Global Psychiatric Clinical Research Training Program *(Advanced Professional/Fellowship)* [7139]

MHS African American Studies Fellowships *(Professional development/Fellowship)* [7147]

MHS/Cushing Academy Fellowships on Environmental History *(Professional development/Fellowship)* [7148]

MHS Long-Term Research Fellowships *(Professional development/Fellowship)* [7149]

MHS/Massachusetts Society of the Cincinnati Fellowships *(Professional development/Fellowship)* [7150]

MICA Scholarships *(Undergraduate/Scholarship)* [7386]

Michael D. Curtin Renaissance Student Memorial Scholarship *(Graduate/Scholarship)* [4257]

Michael Moody Fitness Scholarship *(Undergraduate, Graduate/Scholarship)* [7464]

Michael P. Spadafora Medical Toxicology Travel Award *(Professional development/Grant)* [766]

Michael R. Losey Excellence In HR Research Award *(Graduate, Undergraduate/Award, Recognition)* [10368]

Michigan Accountancy Foundation Final Year Accounting Scholarship *(Graduate/Scholarship)* [7301]

Michigan Education Association Scholarships *(Undergraduate/Scholarship)* [7313]

Michigan League for Nursing Student Scholarships *(Undergraduate/Scholarship)* [7315]

Michigan Realtors Scholarship Trust *(Graduate, Undergraduate/Scholarship)* [7324]

Michigan Society of Fellows Three-Year Fellowships *(Postdoctorate/Fellowship)* [7326]

Michigan Sugar Queen Scholarship *(Undergraduate/Scholarship)* [7342]

John G. and Betty J. Mick Scholarship Fund *(Undergraduate/Scholarship)* [10781]

Micklin Law Group Scholarship *(College, University/Scholarship)* [7352]

Microsoft Research Graduate Women's Scholarships *(Graduate/Scholarship)* [7356]

Microsoft Research PhD Fellowships *(Doctorate/Fellowship)* [7357]

Mid-Continent Instruments and Avionics Scholarship *(Undergraduate/Scholarship)* [188]

Beth Middleton Memorial Scholarships *(Undergraduate/Scholarship)* [4486]

Midlothian Rotary Club "Service Above Self" Scholarships *(Undergraduate/Scholarship)* [7363]

Midwest Modern Language Association Fellowship *(Doctorate, Postdoctorate/Fellowship)* [7380, 8377]

Albert and Eloise Midyette Memorial Scholarship Fund *(Undergraduate/Scholarship)* [4746]

Migrant Health Scholarships *(Other/Scholarship)* [7749]

Mike Hylton Memorial Scholarship *(Undergraduate/Scholarship)* [5480]

Mike Niemeyer Memorial Football Scholarship *(Undergraduate/Scholarship)* [9563]

Mikimoto Scholarship *(Graduate/Scholarship)* [4880]

Miklos Faust International Travel Award *(Doctorate/Grant)* [1481]

Mila Boyd Law Offices Scholarship Contest *(Undergraduate/Scholarship)* [2667]

Milan Getting Scholarship *(Undergraduate/Scholarship)* [10574]

Mildred Colodny Diversity Scholarships for Graduate Program in Historic Preservation *(Graduate/Scholarship, Award, Monetary)* [8145]

William F. Miles Scholarships *(Graduate/Scholarship)* [5276]

Military Service Scholarship *(Graduate, Undergraduate/Scholarship)* [10084]

The Cheryl Allyn Miller Award *(Doctorate, Graduate/Award)* [10567]

Ruth R. and Alyson R. Miller Fellowships *(Professional development/Fellowship)* [7151]

Raymond W. Miller, PE Scholarships *(Undergraduate/Scholarship)* [4631]

Glenn Miller Scholarship *(Undergraduate/Scholarship)* [7395]

Millie Gonzalez Memorial Scholarship *(Undergraduate/Scholarship)* [5481]

Dolphus E. Milligan Graduate Fellowships *(Graduate/Fellowship)* [8029]

Carolina Panthers Players Sam Mills Memorial Scholarships *(Undergraduate/Scholarship)* [4747]

Abby and Howard Milstein Innovation Award in Reproductive Medicine *(Advanced Professional, Professional development, Graduate/Grant)* [6329]

Abby and Howard Milstein Reproductive Medicine Research Award *(Advanced Professional, Professional development/Grant)* [6330]

Milton Postgraduate Fellowship *(Postgraduate/Fellowship)* [3214]

Mineral & Metallurgical Processing Division Scholarships and Richard Klimpel Memorial Scholarships (MPD) *(Undergraduate, Graduate/Scholarship)* [10428]

Minnesota Association County Probation Officers Scholarships *(Undergraduate/Scholarship)* [7402]

Minnesota Division Scholarships *(Undergraduate/Scholarship)* [7371]

Jacque I. Minnotte Health Reporting Fellowship *(Other/Fellowship)* [9474]

Minorities in Government Finance Scholarship *(Graduate, Undergraduate/Scholarship)* [5054]

Minority Scholarship in Classics and Classical Archaeology *(Undergraduate/Fellowship)* [10311]

Molly Ann Mishler Memorial Scholarships *(College/Scholarship)* [11457]

Miss America Social Impact Initiative Scholarship *(Undergraduate/Scholarship)* [7417]

Missigman Scholarship Fund *(Undergraduate/Scholarship)* [4598]

Dikran Missirlian Scholarship Grant *(Undergraduate/Scholarship)* [1896]

George J. Mitchell Postgraduate Scholarships *(Postgraduate/Scholarship)* [7646]

MJSA Education Foundation Scholarship *(Undergraduate/Scholarship)* [7024]

MLA Continuing Education Grants (CE) *(Graduate/Grant)* [7219]

MLA Financial Assistance *(Graduate, Advanced Professional/Grant)* [7426]

MLA/NLM Spectrum Scholarship *(Undergraduate/Scholarship)* [7220]

MLA Research, Development, and Demonstration Project Grant *(Graduate/Grant)* [7221]

MLA Scholarship *(Graduate, Master's/Scholarship)* [7222]

MLA Scholarship for Minority Students *(Graduate/Scholarship)* [7223]

MMC Scholarships *(Other/Scholarship)* [6027]

MMRF Research Fellow Awards *(Postdoctorate, Professional development/Grant)* [7495]

MMUF Dissertation Grants *(Graduate/Grant)* [12047]

MMUF Travel and Research Grants *(Graduate, Undergraduate/Grant)* [12048]

MNLA Academic Scholarship *(Undergraduate/Scholarship)* [7317]

MODNA Nursing Education Scholarship *(Doctorate, Graduate/Scholarship)* [7359]

Molded Dimensions, LLC Scholarship *(College, University/Scholarship)* [7428]

Antoinette M. Molinari Memorial Scholarships *(Doctorate/Scholarship)* [467]

Molly McKay Scholarship *(Undergraduate/Scholarship)* [11200]

Momeni Foundation Scholastic Achievement Scholarships *(Undergraduate/Scholarship)* [7955]

Monaghan/Trudell Fellowships for Aerosol Technique Development *(Professional development/Fellowship)* [1355]

The Montana Advocates Scholarship *(All/Scholarship)* [90]

Montana Broadcasters Association Broadcast Engineering Scholarships *(Undergraduate/Scholarship)* [7453]

Letitia Moore Charitable Trust Scholarship *(Undergraduate/Scholarship)* [12243]

Moore Middle School PTA Scholarship *(Undergraduate/Scholarship)* [9564]

Annabelle Moore Scholarship *(Undergraduate/Scholarship)* [2745]

Willie Hobbs Moore Scholarships *(Undergraduate/Scholarship)* [8090]

Thomas S. Morgan Memorial Scholarship *(Graduate, Master's/Scholarship)* [9075]

Morgan Stanley Pediatrics Fellowships *(Postgraduate, Graduate/Fellowship)* [686]

Morgan Stanley Tribal Scholars Program *(Undergraduate/Scholarship)* [982]

Robert L. Morlan Redlands Area Interfaith Council Scholarships *(Undergraduate/Scholarship)* [9565]

Morphisec's Women in Cybersecurity Scholarships *(Undergraduate, Graduate/Scholarship)* [7470]

Morris L. and Rebecca Ziskind Memorial Scholarship *(Undergraduate/Scholarship)* [5666]

June Morrison Scholarship Fund *(Undergraduate/Scholarship)* [11990]

Harry L. Morrison Scholarships *(Undergraduate/Scholarship)* [8091]

Dorothy Morrison Undergraduate Scholarships *(Undergraduate/Scholarship, Monetary)* [1400]

Mortar Board National Foundation Fellowship *(Postdoctorate/Fellowship, Award)* [7476]

Morton Bahr Scholarship *(Undergraduate/Scholarship)* [3559]

Morton M. Traum Surface Science Student Award *(Graduate, Doctorate/Prize)* [2385]

Mother's Day Scholarship *(All/Scholarship)* [7443]

Gerald O. Mott Award *(Graduate/Award)* [3916]

John R. Mott Scholarships *(Undergraduate, Graduate/Scholarship)* [7482]

Mt. Hood Chapter Scholarship Awards *(Undergraduate/Scholarship)* [8708]

MPI CRV Membership Scholarships *(Other/Scholarship)* [7238]

MPI-WI Founders Grant Program *(Professional development/Grant)* [7241]

MSA Graduate Fellowship *(Graduate/Fellowship)* [7532]

MSA Grant for Research in Crystallography *(Professional development/Grant)* [7397]

MSA Grant for Student Research in Mineralogy and Petrology *(Undergraduate, Graduate/Grant)* [7398]

MSAA Scholarship Program *(Graduate/Scholarship)* [7410]

MSGC Undergraduate-Under-Represented Minority Fellowship Program *(Undergraduate/Fellowship)* [7331]

MSHQ Premed Scholarship *(Undergraduate, Graduate, Postgraduate/Scholarship)* [7205]

The MTS Student Scholarship for Graduate Students *(Graduate/Scholarship)* [7070]

The MTS Student Scholarship for Graduating High School Seniors *(Undergraduate/Scholarship)* [7071]

The MTS Student Scholarship for Two-Year, Technical, Engineering and Community College Students *(Undergraduate/Scholarship)* [7072]

Mu Alpha Theta Summer Grants *(Undergraduate, Graduate/Grant)* [7493]

Mueller Undergraduate Scholarship *(Undergraduate/Scholarship)* [12115]

Multi-Country Research Fellowship *(Doctorate, Postdoctorate/Fellowship)* [3851]

Multicultural Work-in-Progress Grant *(Advanced Professional/Grant)* [10302]

Muncy Rotary Club Scholarship Fund *(Undergraduate/Scholarship)* [4600]

Muncy Scholars Awards Fund *(Undergraduate/Scholarship)* [4601]

Marvin Mundel Memorial Scholarship *(Undergraduate/Scholarship)* [5834]

The Jack K. & Gertrude Murphy Award *(Graduate/Award)* [9871]

NACCED Annual John C. Murphy Scholarships *(Graduate, Undergraduate/Scholarship)* [7643]

Murrietta Circuits Scholarship Opportunity *(Undergraduate, College, University/Scholarship)* [7505]

Edward R. Murrow Press Fellowships *(Professional development/Fellowship)* [3866]

Murse World Scholarship *(Undergraduate, Graduate, Postdoctorate/Scholarship)* [7507]

My Life As A Lawyer Scholarship *(Graduate/Scholarship)* [3837]

Myasthenia Gravis Foundation of America Nursing Research Fellowships *(Undergraduate/Fellowship)* [7529]

Myrna F. Bernath Fellowship *(Doctorate, Graduate/Fellowship)* [10358]

NAAE Upper Division Scholarship *(Undergraduate/Scholarship)* [7609]

NAAMA Scholarships *(Undergraduate/Scholarship)* [7598]

NABA National Scholarship Program *(Graduate, Undergraduate/Scholarship, Award, Monetary)* [7613]

NACA Foundation Graduate Scholarships *(Graduate, Master's, Doctorate/Scholarship)* [7624]

NACA Mid Atlantic Undergraduate Scholarship *(Undergraduate/Scholarship)* [7626]

NACA Multicultural Professional Development Grant *(Undergraduate, Graduate, Professional development/Grant)* [7627]

NACA Scholarship for Student Leaders in the Central & Northern Plains Regions *(Undergraduate/Scholarship)* [7628]

NACA Silver Anniversary Scholarship for Student Leaders *(Undergraduate/Scholarship)* [7630]

NACA South Student Leadership Scholarships *(Undergraduate/Scholarship)* [7631]

NACADA Scholarships *(Graduate, Postdoctorate/Scholarship)* [7568]

NACBS Dissertation Fellowship *(Graduate, Doctorate/Fellowship)* [8420]

NACBS-Huntington Library Fellowship *(Doctorate, Postdoctorate/Fellowship)* [8422]

The Nadia Christensen Prize *(All/Prize)* [1377]

NRMRL Postdoctoral Research Program *(Postdoctorate, Advanced Professional, Professional development/Fellowship)* [11356]

NSA Scholarship Foundation *(Undergraduate/Scholarship)* [8079]

NSBRI First Award Fellowships *(Postdoctorate/Fellowship)* [8121]

NSHSS Academic Paper Awards *(High School/Scholarship)* [8104]

NSHSS National Scholar Awards *(High School, College/Scholarship)* [8105]

NSPS Berntsen International Scholarship in Surveying Technology *(Undergraduate/Scholarship)* [8118]

NSPS and AAGS Scholarships *(Undergraduate/Scholarship)* [8119]

NSS Conservation Grants *(Advanced Professional/Grant)* [8126]

NSSA/NSCA Collegiate High School Senior Scholarships *(Undergraduate/Scholarship)* [8131]

NTHS/HOSA Scholarships *(Undergraduate/Scholarship)* [8140]

NURSE Corps Scholarship Program *(Professional development/Scholarship)* [11335]

NWF Campus Ecology Fellowships *(Graduate, Undergraduate/Fellowship)* [8161]

NWRI Fellowship *(Graduate, Doctorate/Fellowship)* [8158]

NWSA Graduate Scholarship *(Master's, Doctorate/Scholarship)* [8166]

NYCT Paid Graduate Student Philanthropy Fellowships - Arts and Historic Preservation *(Graduate/Fellowship)* [8305]

NYCT Paid Graduate Student Philanthropy Fellowships - Children, Youth, Families, Education, Human Justice and Workforce *(Graduate/Fellowship)* [8306]

NYCT Paid Graduate Student Philanthropy Fellowships - Community Development and the Environment *(Graduate/Fellowship)* [8307]

NYCT Paid Graduate Student Philanthropy Fellowships - Health and People with Special Needs *(Graduate/Fellowship)* [8308]

The NYCTutoring.com Scholarship *(Undergraduate/Scholarship)* [8569]

NYLA-Dewey Fellowship Award *(Graduate/Award, Fellowship)* [8314]

NYLA-Dewey Scholarship *(Master's, Undergraduate/Award, Scholarship)* [8315]

OAB Kids Scholarships *(Undergraduate/Scholarship)* [8575]

WillEtta "Willie" Long Oates, Gamma Nu, Memorial Scholarship *(Undergraduate, Graduate/Scholarship)* [6463]

Dennis J. O'Brien USAEE Best Student Paper Award *(Undergraduate/Award)* [11296]

Oceanic Research Group Scholarships *(Graduate, Undergraduate/Scholarship)* [8573]

Basil O'Connor Starter Scholar Research Awards (BOC) *(Professional development/Grant)* [7028]

Odd Fellows Lodge #8 Endowed Scholarship *(Undergraduate/Scholarship)* [6818]

The Captain Jennifer Shafer Odom Memorial Scholarship - Children of Soldiers *(Undergraduate, Vocational/Occupational/Scholarship)* [1919]

The Captain Jennifer Shafer Odom Memorial Scholarship - Spouses of Soldiers *(Undergraduate, Vocational/Occupational/Scholarship)* [1920]

OGR Award of Excellence Scholarships *(Undergraduate/Scholarship)* [6048]

OAB Kids Scholarship *(Undergraduate/Scholarship)* [8576]

Ohio Space Grant Consortium Graduate Fellowships *(Graduate, Doctorate, Master's/Fellowship)* [8598]

Ohio Space Grant Consortium Special Minority Fellowships *(Doctorate, Graduate, Master's/Fellowship)* [8599]

Seth Okin Good Deeds Scholarships *(Undergraduate, Graduate, Community College/Scholarship)* [9283]

Oklahoma City University Full-Time Merit Scholarships *(Undergraduate/Scholarship)* [8609]

Oklahoma Restaurant Association Scholarships *(Other/Scholarship)* [8612]

Rhonda J.B. O'Leary Memorial Scholarship *(Undergraduate, Graduate/Scholarship)* [4305]

Olin-Searle-Smith-Darling Fellows in Law *(Other/Fellowship)* [4523]

Robert B. Oliver ASNT Scholarship *(Undergraduate/Scholarship)* [1532]

MHS Andrew Oliver Research Fellowships *(Professional development/Fellowship)* [7152]

Olivia James Traveling Fellowship *(Professional development/Fellowship)* [1779]

Roy C. and Dorothy Jean Olson Memorial Scholarship *(Graduate/Scholarship)* [6042]

Charlie O'Meilia Scholarship *(Undergraduate/Scholarship, Monetary, Award)* [5973]

Omicron Nu Research Fellowship *(Postdoctorate, Graduate/Fellowship)* [6497]

Omohundro Institute-NEH Postdoctoral Fellowships *(Graduate/Fellowship)* [8622]

Oncology Nursing Society Foundation - Doctoral Scholarships *(Doctorate/Scholarship)* [8628]

Oncology Nursing Society Foundation - Master's Scholarships *(Graduate, Master's/Scholarship)* [8629]

One Source Process Inc. Scholarship *(Undergraduate, Graduate/Scholarship)* [8634]

ONS Foundation Congress Scholarships *(Professional development/Scholarship)* [8630]

ONWA Annual Scholarship *(Undergraduate/Scholarship)* [8582]

OOIDA Mary Johnston Scholarship Program *(Undergraduate/Scholarship)* [8798]

Open Society Fellowship *(Other/Fellowship)* [8664]

Open Society Presidential Fellowship *(Graduate/Fellowship)* [8665]

Opera Foundation Scholarship *(Other/Scholarship)* [8671]

OPERF Small Grants *(Doctorate/Grant)* [8768]

OppU Achievers Scholarship *(Undergraduate/Scholarship)* [8673]

Optical Design and Engineering Scholarship *(Graduate, Undergraduate/Scholarship)* [10728]

Optimist Club of Redlands Scholarship- Ralph Maloof *(Undergraduate/Scholarship)* [9568]

Order of Omega Doctoral Fellowships *(Doctorate, Graduate/Fellowship)* [8687]

Oregon Association of Nurseries Scholarship Program *(Graduate/Scholarship)* [8711]

Oregon Farm Bureau Memorial Scholarship *(Undergraduate, Graduate, High School/Scholarship)* [8716]

Organization of American States AOS-Placed Scholarships *(Graduate, Undergraduate/Scholarship)* [8736]

Organization of American States Graduate Scholarships *(Doctorate, Graduate/Scholarship)* [8737]

Organization of American States Self-Placed Scholarships *(Doctorate, Graduate/Scholarship)* [8738]

Organization of Chinese Americans Scholarships *(Undergraduate/Scholarship)* [1986]

Oronzio de Nora Industrial Electrochemistry Fellowships *(Postdoctorate/Fellowship)* [4363]

Orthopaedic Foot and Ankle Fellowships *(Graduate, Professional development/Fellowship)* [1194]

Orthopaedic Specialists of the Carolinas Nursing Scholarship *(Undergraduate/Scholarship)* [12086]

Royce Osborn Minority Scholarship *(Undergraduate/Scholarship)* [1552]

OSCA Graduate Student Scholarship Program *(Graduate/Scholarship)* [8594]

OSGC Community College Scholarships *(Undergraduate/Scholarship)* [8600]

OSGC Education Scholarships *(Undergraduate/Scholarship)* [8601]

OSHA Graduate Scholarship *(Doctorate, Master's/Scholarship)* [8614]

Oslo International Summer School Scholarship *(Undergraduate/Scholarship)* [10591]

Osteopathic Medical Student Research Fellowship Program *(Undergraduate/Fellowship)* [10867]

M. Dick Osumi Civil Rights and Public Interest Scholarship *(Graduate, Undergraduate/Scholarship)* [6240]

The Otis and Florence Lapham Memorial Scholarship *(Graduate/Scholarship)* [6205]

Ellis R. Ott Scholarships *(Graduate, Master's/Scholarship)* [1543]

Otto M. Stanfield Law Scholarship *(Graduate/Scholarship)* [11253]

Satenik & Adom Ourian Education Foundation Scholarship *(Undergraduate/Scholarship)* [1897]

Out to Innovate Scholarship *(Graduate, Undergraduate, Community College/Scholarship)* [8019]

Outlaw Student's Medical Professions Scholarships *(Undergraduate/Scholarship)* [10860]

Outlaw Student's Minority Scholarships *(Undergraduate/Scholarship)* [10861]

Outlaw Student's Nursing School Scholarships *(Undergraduate/Scholarship)* [10862]

Outlaw Student's Teacher Scholarships *(Undergraduate/Scholarship)* [10863]

Cecilia Payne-Gaposchkin Doctoral Dissertation Award in Astrophysics *(Doctorate, Postdoctorate/Award, Recognition, Monetary)* [1227]

Overflow Scholarships *(Undergraduate/Scholarship)* [1803]

The Pac-12 Postgraduate Scholarships *(Graduate/Scholarship)* [8802]

Packard Fellowships for Science and Engineering *(Professional development/Fellowship)* [8808]

The Arthur J. Packard Memorial Scholarship *(Undergraduate/Scholarship)* [973]

The Barbara L. Packer Fellowship *(Doctorate, Postdoctorate/Fellowship)* [496]

PALCUS National Scholarship Program *(Undergraduate/Scholarship)* [9250]

Paleontological Society Student Research Award *(Graduate, Undergraduate/Grant)* [29]

Palmer Farley Memorial Scholarship *(Graduate/Scholarship)* [5277]

Pan Pacific Law Enforcement Scholarships *(Undergraduate/Scholarship)* [9868]

The PanHellenic Scholarship *(Undergraduate/Scholarship)* [8816]

Pappaioanou Veterinary Public Health and Applied Epidemiology Fellowships *(Undergraduate/Fellowship)* [3202]

Parapsychological Association Research Endowment *(Undergraduate/Recognition, Grant)* [8822]

Joseph M. Parish Memorial Grants *(Undergraduate/Grant)* [1394]

Parker B. Francis Respiratory Research Grant *(Advanced Professional, Professional development/Grant)* [1357]

Cissy McDaniel Parker Scholarships *(Undergraduate/Scholarship)* [4010]

E.U. and Gene Parker Scholarships *(Undergraduate/Scholarship, Monetary)* [7880]

Parking Industry Institute Scholarship Program *(Undergraduate/Scholarship)* [8036]

Parkinson's Disease Foundation International Research Grants Program (IRGP) *(Postdoctorate/Grant)* [8899]

The Paros-Digiquartz Scholarship *(Graduate, Undergraduate/Scholarship)* [7073]

Parsons Brinckerhoff / Jim Lammie Scholarship *(Undergraduate, Graduate/Scholarship)* [1304]

Part the Cloud: Translational Research Funding *(Postgraduate/Grant)* [416]

Participation-Based Scholarships *(Undergraduate/Scholarship)* [9101]

Partners HealthCare Geriatric Psychiatry Fellowship *(Professional development/Fellowship)* [7140]

Pasteur Foundation Postdoctoral Fellowship *(Postdoctorate/Fellowship)* [8913]

Pat Dermargosian Memorial Scholarship *(Undergraduate/Scholarship)* [9570]

Patricia Buchanan Memorial Scholarship *(Undergraduate/Scholarship)* [11742]

Gail Patrick Charitable Trust Scholarships *(Graduate/Scholarship)* [4041]

Walter S. Patterson Scholarships *(Graduate/Scholarship)* [2704]

Joanne Holbrook Patton Military Spouse Scholarships *(Graduate, Undergraduate/Scholarship)* [8009]

Paul A. Whelan Aviation and Aerospace Scholarship *(Graduate, Undergraduate/Scholarship)* [11528]

Paul B. & Aline Flynn Scholarship Fund *(Undergraduate/Scholarship)* [10698]

Paul and Ellen Ruckes Scholarship *(Graduate, Undergraduate/Scholarship)* [917]

Paul Green Houston Scholarship (Undergraduate/Scholarship) [11201]

Paul Mansur Award (Undergraduate/Scholarship) [6021]

Paul S. Robinson Award (Postgraduate/Award) [10322]

Courtland P. Paul Scholarships (Undergraduate/Scholarship) [6650]

Paula Backscheider Archival Fellowship (Other/Fellowship) [1437]

PCBA Diversity Scholarship (Undergraduate/Scholarship) [8983]

PCF Challenge Awards (Professional development/Award) [9370]

PCF Young Investigator Award (Professional development, Postdoctorate/Award) [9371]

PCH Architects LLP - Steven J. Lehnhof Memorial Architectural Scholarship (Undergraduate/Scholarship) [9571]

PDEF Professional Development Scholarship (Professional development/Scholarship) [10440]

Peale Scholarship Grant (Professional development/Scholarship) [9094]

Pearl I. Young Scholarship (Undergraduate/Scholarship) [8472]

The Scott Pearlman Field Awards (Professional development/Award) [4470]

Oliver P. Pearson Award (Doctorate/Fellowship) [1506]

Pediatric Endocrinology Nursing Society Academic Education Scholarships (Undergraduate/Scholarship) [8941]

Peermusic Latin Scholarship (Undergraduate/Scholarship) [2636]

The Melissa Pellegrin Memorial Scholarship Fund (Undergraduate, Graduate/Scholarship) [8759]

Pembroke Center's Faculty Research Fellowships (Professional development/Fellowship) [2724]

Pembroke Center Graduate Student Fellowships (Graduate, Postdoctorate/Fellowship) [2725]

Pembroke Center Seed Grants (Professional development/Grant) [2726]

Pembroke Center for Teaching and Research on Women Postdoctoral Research Associateships (Postdoctorate/Fellowship) [2727]

PennyGeeks.com Car Insurance Essay Scholarship (Undergraduate/Scholarship) [8971]

PENS Conference Reimbursement Scholarship (Undergraduate/Scholarship) [8942]

P.E.O. Scholar Awards (PSA) (Doctorate/Award, Scholarship) [8977]

Pepperdine University Diversity Scholarships (Doctorate, Graduate/Scholarship) [9019]

Pepperdine University School of Law JD/MBA Endowed Scholarship (Undergraduate/Scholarship) [9023]

PepsiCo Foundation Scholarships (Undergraduate/Scholarship) [974, 9034]

Gilberto and Lennetta Pesquera Medical School Scholarships (Graduate/Scholarship) [5001]

PETA Foundation Law Internship (Graduate/Internship) [8979]

Peter and Malina James and Dr. Louis P. James Legacy Scholarship (Graduate, Master's, Doctorate/Scholarship) [1286]

Peter T. Steinwedell Scholarship (Graduate/Scholarship) [5341]

Larry A. Peters Endowment Fund Scholarship (Undergraduate/Scholarship) [1898]

Paul Evan Peters Fellowship (Master's, Doctorate, Graduate/Fellowship) [3452]

Ruth D. Peterson Fellowship for Racial and Ethnic Diversity (Doctorate/Fellowship) [1420]

Kate B. and Hall J. Peterson Fellowships (Doctorate/Fellowship) [497]

Captain James H. Peterson Memorial Scholarships (Undergraduate/Scholarship) [5290]

Petro Law Firm Scholarship Contest (Graduate, College/Scholarship) [9046]

Petroleum Engineering Scholarships (Undergraduate/Scholarship) [10473]

Pfafftown Jaycees/Lynn Canada Memorial Scholarship (Undergraduate/Scholarship, Award) [12088]

The Ruth Cook Pfautz Memorial Scholarship Fund (Undergraduate/Scholarship) [4782]

Carl H. Pforzheimer, Jr., Research Grants (Graduate, Other/Grant) [6507]

PGSF Scholarship (Undergraduate/Scholarship) [9332]

PHA Research Fellowships (Professional development/Fellowship) [9449]

Pharmaceutics Post Doctoral Fellowships (Doctorate/Fellowship) [9059]

Pharmaceutics Sabbatical Fellowships (Master's, Doctorate/Fellowship) [9061]

Pharmacology/Toxicology Pre Doctoral Fellowships (Doctorate/Fellowship) [9062]

Phi Alpha Theta Doctoral Scholarship (Doctorate/Scholarship) [9076]

Phi Alpha Theta Faculty Advisor Research Grant (Other/Grant) [9077]

Phi Delta Gamma Academic Achievement Awards (Undergraduate/Scholarship) [9095]

Phi Eta Sigma Graduate Scholarships (Graduate, Other/Scholarship) [9089]

Phi Eta Sigma Undergraduate Scholarships (Undergraduate/Scholarship) [9091]

Phi Kappa Phi Fellowship (Graduate, Undergraduate/Fellowship) [9098]

Phi Kappa Sigma Foundation Scholarship (Undergraduate/Scholarship) [9102]

Phi Sigma Epsilon Past National President Scholarships (Graduate, Undergraduate/Scholarship) [9172]

Phi Theta Kappa Scholarship (Undergraduate/Scholarship) [5765]

Phi Upsilon Omicron Candle Fellowships (Graduate, Postgraduate/Fellowship) [9119]

Phi Upsilon Omicron Challenge Scholarships (Undergraduate/Scholarship) [9120]

Phi Upsilon Omicron Diamond Anniversary Fellowships (Graduate/Fellowship) [9121]

Phi Upsilon Omicron Founders Fellowship (Graduate/Fellowship) [9122]

Phi Upsilon Omicron Golden Anniversary Scholarships (Undergraduate/Scholarship) [9123]

Phi Upsilon Omicron Past Presidents Scholarships (Undergraduate/Scholarship) [9124]

Phi Upsilon Omicron Presidents Research Fellowship (Graduate, Master's, Doctorate, Postdoctorate/Fellowship) [9125]

The Philadelphia Public Interest Fellowship Program (Undergraduate/Fellowship) [9133]

Philip Alston Scholarship (Undergraduate/Scholarship) [11203]

Philip F. Greco Memorial Scholarship (Undergraduate/Scholarship) [6960]

Philip H. Melanson Memorial Scholarship (Undergraduate, Graduate/Scholarship) [11593]

The Walter T. Philippy Scholarship (Undergraduate/Scholarship) [7175]

Philips Respironics Fellowships in Mechanical Ventilation (Professional development/Fellowship) [1358]

Philips Respironics Fellowships in Non-Invasive Respiratory Care (Professional development/Fellowship) [1359]

Jean L. Phillips Auburn Scholarship Fund (Undergraduate/Scholarship) [3662]

Phillips Fund for Native American Research (Doctorate, Master's/Grant) [1217]

Ed Phinney Commemorative Scholarships (Graduate, Undergraduate/Scholarship) [755]

PhRMA Foundation Health Outcomes Pre Doctoral Fellowships (Doctorate/Fellowship) [9063]

PhRMA Foundation Health Outcomes Research Starter Grants (Doctorate/Grant) [9064]

PhRMA Foundation Health Outcomes Sabbatical Fellowships (Postdoctorate, Master's/Fellowship) [9065]

PhRMA Foundation Informatics Research Starter Grants (Doctorate/Grant) [9066]

PhRMA Foundation Pharmaceutics Pre Doctoral Fellowships (Postdoctorate/Fellowship) [9067]

PhRMA Foundation Pharmacology/Toxicology Post Doctoral Fellowships (Postdoctorate/Fellowship) [9068]

PhRMA Foundation Pharmacology/Toxicology Research Starter Grants (Doctorate/Grant) [9069]

PhRMA Foundation Pharmacology/Toxicology Sabatical Fellowships (Postdoctorate, Master's/Fellowship) [9070]

PhRMA Foundation Post Doctoral Health Outcomes Fellowships (Postdoctorate/Fellowship) [9071]

PEN/Phyllis Naylor Grant for Children's and Young Adult Novelists (Other/Grant) [8952]

The Physical Therapy Faculty Scholarship Endowment (Graduate/Scholarship) [10846]

Helen Edwards Summer Internship (Undergraduate/Internship) [11319]

Pi Kapp Scholars Award (Undergraduate/Scholarship) [9162]

Pi Project 2000 Tali James Memorial Scholarship (Undergraduate/Scholarship) [6465]

The Thomas R. Pickering Foreign Affairs Fellowship (Graduate, Undergraduate/Fellowship) [11346, 12050]

Mary Pickford Scholarships (Graduate/Scholarship) [2248]

Peter L. Picknelly Honorary Scholarships (Graduate/Scholarship) [711]

David Pilon Scholarships for Training in Professional Psychology (Graduate/Scholarship) [1271]

Pilot Project Grant (Professional development/Award, Grant) [10456]

The John Pine Memorial Award (Doctorate, Graduate, Undergraduate/Scholarship) [9078]

Julia T. Pingree Student Scholarship (Undergraduate/Scholarship) [8252]

The PinProsPlus Scholarship (College, University, Graduate/Scholarship) [9178]

The Pinto Ranch Western Achievement Scholarship (Graduate/Scholarship) [9180]

Stephen D. Pisinski Memorial Scholarship (Undergraduate/Scholarship) [9436]

Robert Pittman Scholarships-Internships (Undergraduate/Scholarship, Internship) [11204]

Carter Pitts Scholarships (Undergraduate/Scholarship) [6168]

PKD Foundation Fellowships (Doctorate, Graduate/Fellowship) [9184]

Wayne F. Placek Grants (Graduate, Doctorate/Grant) [1287]

Betsy Plank/PRSSA Scholarships (Undergraduate/Scholarship) [9437]

PlasticPlace Young Entrepreneurs Scholarship Award (Undergraduate/Scholarship) [9192]

Platt Excavation Fellowships (Other, Undergraduate/Fellowship) [1379]

PLP Scholarships (Undergraduate/Scholarship, Award, Monetary) [8985]

Plumbing-Heating-Cooling Contractors Association Educational Foundation Need-Based Scholarships (Undergraduate/Scholarship) [9206]

PLUS Foundation Financial Aid Scholarship (Undergraduate/Scholarship) [9212]

PNAA Nursing Scholarship Award (Master's, Doctorate/Scholarship) [9135]

Pokross/Curhan Family Fund Prize (Graduate, Undergraduate/Prize) [1064]

Polaire Weissman Fund Fellowship (Graduate/Fellowship) [7279]

Donald and Susie Polden Dean's Scholarships (Graduate/Scholarship) [11611]

Polish American Club of North Jersey Scholarships (Undergraduate/Scholarship) [6605]

Polish National Alliance of Brooklyn, USA Scholarships (Undergraduate/Scholarship) [6606]

A. H. Pollard Travelling PhD Scholarships (Postdoctorate/Scholarship) [5810]

The David J. Pollini Scholarship (Undergraduate/Scholarship) [7176]

Francis Poloshian Memorial Grant (Undergraduate/Scholarship) [1899]

James Poloshian Memorial Grant (Undergraduate/Scholarship) [1900]

Harold F. Polston Scholarships (Graduate, Undergraduate/Scholarship) [1571]

Harriet and Leon Pomerance Fellowships (Graduate/Fellowship) [1780]

PON Graduate Student Grants (Graduate/Grant) [5368]

PON Next Generation Grants (Doctorate, Postdoctorate/Grant) [5369]

PON Summer Fellowships (Graduate/Fellowship) [5370]

The Pope Scholarship Award (Undergraduate/Scholarship) [7177]

Porter Physiology Development Fellowship (Doctorate/Fellowship, Award, Monetary) [1238]

AFT Robert G. Porter Scholars Program (Undergraduate/Scholarship) [881]

Robert Porterfield Scholarship (Graduate/Scholarship) [10639]

Portland Cement Association Scholarship (Graduate/Scholarship) [4503]

Post-Doctoral Summer Travel-Research Grants (Postdoctorate/Grant) [5871]

Post-High School Tuition Scholarship Program (Undergraduate/Scholarship) [3190]

Postdoctoral Fellowships for Basic Scientists Program (Postdoctorate/Fellowship) [8900]

Postdoctoral Fellowships for Clinical Neurologists (Postdoctorate/Fellowship) [8901]

Poteet Strawberry Festival Association Scholarships (Graduate, Undergraduate/Scholarship) [9256]

Barbara Potter Scholarship Fund (Professional development/Scholarship) [1188]

Ralph H. Potts Memorial Fellowship Award (Graduate/Award, Fellowship) [1184]

George V. Powell Diversity Scholarships (Graduate/Scholarship) [6654]

Gerald Powell Scholarships (Undergraduate/Scholarship) [3663]

Powers-Knapp Scholarship Program (Undergraduate/Scholarship) [11744]

Practising Law Institute Scholarships (Advanced Professional, Professional development/Scholarship) [9262]

Lou and Carole Prato Sports Reporting Scholarship (Undergraduate/Scholarship) [9475]

Praxair International Scholarship (Undergraduate/Scholarship) [1669]

PREA Scholarship (Undergraduate, Graduate/Scholarship) [8973]

Catherine Prelinger Award (Postdoctorate/Scholarship) [3830]

Presidential Management Fellows (PMF) (Graduate, Master's/Fellowship) [11330]

Presidents Scholarship (Undergraduate/Scholarship) [9476]

Prevent Cancer Foundation Fellowships (Postdoctorate/Fellowship) [9277]

Preventive Medicine Residency and Fellowship (PMR) (Other/Fellowship) [11331]

Price Benowitz Social Justice Scholarships (Undergraduate, Graduate, Community College/Scholarship) [9285]

Peridian International, Inc./Rae L. Price, FASLA Scholarship (Undergraduate/Scholarship) [1492]

Peridian International, Inc./Rae L. Price, FASLA Scholarships (Undergraduate/Scholarship) [6651]

Judith McManus Price Scholarship (Undergraduate, Graduate/Scholarship) [1245]

Lendon N. Pridgen, GlaxoSmithKline - NOBCChE Fellowships (Graduate/Fellowship) [8031]

Eric Primavera Memorial Scholarships (Undergraduate/Scholarship) [4632]

Print and Graphics Scholarship Foundation Awards (Graduate, Undergraduate/Award) [9330]

Miguel Pro Scholarships (Undergraduate/Scholarship) [12224]

Professional Certification Exam Scholarship (Undergraduate, Professional development/Scholarship) [9797]

Professional Woman's Magazine Scholarship Opportunity (Undergraduate/Scholarship) [9347]

Professional Women of Redlands, PoWeR to Continue Learning Scholarships (Undergraduate/Scholarship) [9572]

Professor Emeritus Dr. Bill Johnson Memorial Scholarship (Undergraduate/Scholarship) [10061]

Progressive Dairy Producer Awards (All/Grant) [7826]

Property and Environment Research Center Graduate Fellowships (Graduate/Fellowship) [9351]

Property and Environment Research Center Lone Mountain Fellowships (Other/Fellowship) [9352]

Property and Environment Research Center Media Fellowships (Other/Fellowship) [9353]

Prospanica Scholarship (Graduate, Undergraduate/Scholarship) [9360]

Proven Data Recovery Technology Scholarships (All/Scholarship) [9373]

Barbara F. Prowant Nursing Research Grants (Graduate/Grant) [1153]

PRSA Diversity Multicultural Scholarships (Undergraduate/Scholarship) [9438]

Neil Pruitt, Sr. Memorial Scholarships (Undergraduate/Scholarship) [7778]

Joseph E. Pryor Graduate Fellowships (Graduate/Fellowship) [379]

Phillis Brinton Pryor Panhellenic Scholarship (Undergraduate/Scholarship) [6466]

PSAI Scholarship Fund (Undergraduate/Scholarship) [9248]

PSF Research Fellowship Grants (Master's, Doctorate/Grant, Fellowship) [9190]

Psychosocial Research Pilot Grants (Professional development/Grant) [8201]

Psychosocial Research - Postdoctoral Psychosocial Fellowships (Postdoctorate/Fellowship) [8202]

Psychosocial Research Studies and Demonstration Projects (Professional development/Grant) [8203]

PTAC Crew Scholarship for HVAC Students (Vocational/Occupational/Scholarship) [9381]

Public Interest Environmental Law Fellowships (Graduate/Fellowship) [4415]

Public Interest Fellowship (Undergraduate/Fellowship) [797]

Pulaski Scholarships for Advanced Studies (Graduate, Master's/Scholarship) [827]

Eugene C. Pulliam Fellowship for Editorial Writing (Other/Fellowship) [10502]

Eugene C. Pulliam Fellowships for Editorial Writing (Other/Fellowship) [10086]

Pulliam/Kilgore Freedom of Information Internships (Undergraduate/Internship) [10503]

The Purpose Challenge (Undergraduate/Scholarship) [9358]

PVA Research Foundation Fellowships (Postdoctorate/Fellowship) [8820]

PWC Core Apprentice Program (Other/Internship) [9200]

PWIPM Professional Empowerment Grant (Graduate/Grant) [8038]

Harry V. Quadracci Memorial Scholarship (Undergraduate, Graduate/Scholarship) [5209]

Quality Bath.com Scholarship (Community College, College, University, Undergraduate, Graduate/Scholarship) [9453]

Quarter Century Wireless Association Scholarship Program (Undergraduate/Scholarship) [9457]

The Michael J. Quill Scholarship (Undergraduate/Scholarship) [11075]

Quincy Brown Memorial Scholarship (Undergraduate/Scholarship) [9573]

AIST Judith A. Quinn Detroit Member Chapter Scholarship (Undergraduate/Scholarship) [2223]

R. Garn Haycock Memorial Scholarship (Undergraduate/Scholarship) [9574]

Rachel Graham Memorial Scholarship (Undergraduate/Scholarship) [9575]

Natalie and Mendel Racolin Memorial Fellowship (Postdoctorate, Doctorate/Fellowship) [12239]

RADM William A. Sullivan, USN (Ret.) Scholarship (Undergraduate/Scholarship) [8174]

The Raffin-Gathercole Scholarship (Undergraduate/Scholarship) [4873]

Railroad and Mine Workers Memorial Scholarship (Graduate/Scholarship) [6250]

Rain Bird Intelligent Use of Water Scholarship (Undergraduate/Scholarship) [6652, 9491]

Rains - J.J. Rains Memorial Scholarship (Undergraduate/Scholarship) [3483]

Raleigh Mann Scholarship (Undergraduate/Scholarship) [11206]

Tom D. Ralls Memorial Scholarship (Professional development/Scholarship) [4807]

Ralph and Josephine Smith Fund (Undergraduate/Scholarship) [4602]

Rama Scholarships for the American Dream (Graduate, Undergraduate/Scholarship) [975]

Commander Newell S. Rand Jr. Scholarship Program (Undergraduate/Scholarship) [8828]

Helen F. "Jerri" Rand Memorial Scholarships (Undergraduate, Vocational/Occupational/Scholarship) [3715]

Jennings Randolph Peace Scholarship Dissertation Program (Doctorate/Scholarship, Fellowship) [11380]

United States Institute of Peace Jennings Randolph Senior Fellowship Program (Advanced Professional/Fellowship) [11381]

Edward C. Raney Fund Award (Professional development/Grant) [1484]

Rangel Graduate Fellowship (Graduate/Fellowship) [9499]

Jeannette Rankin Scholarships (Undergraduate, Vocational/Occupational/Scholarship) [9501]

Ratingle Scholarship Program (College, University, Community College, Undergraduate, Graduate/Scholarship) [9506]

W.B. Ray High School Class of '56 Averill Johnson Scholarship (Undergraduate/Scholarship) [3484]

Ray and Pearl Sams Scholarship (Undergraduate/Scholarship) [12089]

Raymond A. Kent-Navy V-12/ROTC (Undergraduate/Scholarship) [11579]

Raymond and Donald Beeler Memorial Scholarship (Undergraduate/Scholarship) [9576]

RBPA Scholarship (Undergraduate, Graduate, Doctorate/Scholarship) [9493]

Read Carlock Memorial Scholarship Fund (Other/Scholarship) [1800]

Real Estate Elevated Scholarship (Community College, Undergraduate, Graduate/Scholarship) [9510]

Reba Malone Scholarship (Undergraduate, Graduate/Scholarship) [1305]

Carl C. and Abbie Rebman Trust Scholarship (Undergraduate/Scholarship) [5124]

The Recovery Village Health Care Scholarship (Undergraduate/Scholarship) [9514]

Redlands Baseball/Softball for Youth Scholarship (Undergraduate/Scholarship) [9577]

Redlands Council PTA - Dorathy Jolley Memorial Scholarship (Undergraduate/Scholarship) [9579]

Redlands Evening Lions Club - Barbara Westen Memorial Scholarship (Undergraduate/Scholarship) [9580]

Redlands High School Academic Decathlon Scholarship (Undergraduate/Scholarship) [9582]

Redlands High School Boy's Varsity Volleyball Scholarships (Undergraduate/Scholarship) [9584]

Redlands High School Girls' Volleyball Boosters Scholarship Awards (Undergraduate/Scholarship) [9585]

Redlands High School Mock Trial Scholarship (Undergraduate/Scholarship) [9586]

Redlands High School-PTSA Scholarship (Undergraduate/Scholarship) [9587]

Redlands High School Softball Booster Scholarship (Undergraduate/Scholarship) [9588]

Redlands High School Spiritleaders Scholarship (Undergraduate/Scholarship) [9589]

Redlands High School Terrier Band Boosters Club Scholarship (Undergraduate/Scholarship) [9590]

Redlands High School Vocal Music Boosters Scholarship (Undergraduate/Scholarship) [9591]

Redlands Rotary Club Scholarship - Donald C. Anderson (Undergraduate/Scholarship) [9594]

The Reedsy National Creative Writing Scholarship (Undergraduate/Scholarship) [9607]

Rees Scholarship Foundation - HVACR and Water Heating Technician Program (Community College, Undergraduate, Vocational/Occupational/Scholarship) [9610]

Rees Scholarship Foundation - Veterans Program (Vocational/Occupational, Undergraduate/Scholarship) [9611]

The Reese Fellowship (Doctorate/Fellowship) [498]

REFORMA Scholarship (Undergraduate, Graduate/Scholarship) [9615]

REFORMA Scholarship Program (Undergraduate/Scholarship) [9616]

Regina B. Shearn Scholarship (Graduate, Undergraduate/Scholarship) [398]

Regina Brown Undergraduate Student Fellowship (Undergraduate/Fellowship) [7788]

Regina Higdon Scholarship (Undergraduate/Scholarship) [3642]

Rehabmart.com $25,000 Scholarship Fund (Undergraduate/Scholarship) [9627]

Reid Blackburn Scholarship (Undergraduate/Scholarship) [8051]

Reiff & Bily Legal Scholarship (Graduate, Undergraduate/Scholarship) [9631]

George Reinke Scholarships (Other/Scholarship) [1587]

REMSA Scholarships (Undergraduate/Scholarship) [1330]

Renardo A. Matteucci Family Scholarship (Undergraduate/Scholarship) [3597]

Betty Rendel Scholarships (Undergraduate/Scholarship) [7886]

Rene Matos Memorial Scholarship Program (Undergraduate, Vocational/Occupational/Scholarship) [7928]

James Renwick Fellowship in American Craft (Doctorate, Postdoctorate/Fellowship) [10217]

Research Career Development Award (Professional development/Grant) [8631]

Research Fellowships for Yale Graduate & Professional School Students (Graduate, Professional development/Fellowship) [2465]

Research Grant Funding (RE01) (Advanced Professional/Grant) [8632]

Research Internships in Science and Engineering (RISE) (Undergraduate/Internship) [4065]

Research Resident/Fellow Grant (Professional development/Grant) [9483]

Research Scholarship in Photograph Conservation (Graduate/Scholarship) [7280]

Resident Travel Award for Underrepresented Populations (Professional development/Award) [3783]

Resilience Action Fund Scholarship (Graduate/Scholarship) [4504]

Restoring Self Scholarship (Undergraduate/Scholarship) [5559]

Retired League Postmasters Scholarship Program (Undergraduate/Scholarship) [9655]

Returning Adult and Single-Parent Scholarships (Undergraduate/Scholarship) [11745]

Reuters Fellowship (Graduate, Undergraduate/Fellowship) [8788]

Reuters Institute Visiting Fellowships (Professional development/Fellowship) [11660]

Rev. Alfred E. Monson Scholarship (Other/Fellowship) [4862]

RFDF MBA Preparation Fellowships (Graduate/Fellowship) [9708]

R.G. and Ruth Crossno Scholarship (Undergraduate/Scholarship) [4258]

Lori Rhett Memorial Scholarships (Graduate, Undergraduate/Scholarship) [7632]

Rho Chi, AFPE First Year Graduate Fellowships (Graduate/Fellowship) [9683]

Rice-Cullimore Scholarship (Graduate/Scholarship) [2001]

Richard A. Wiebe Public Service Fellowship (Graduate/Fellowship) [8327]

Richard Cecil Todd and Clauda Pennock Todd Tripod Scholarship (Graduate, Undergraduate/Scholarship) [9104]

Richard Goolsby Scholarship - Created by William and Martha Debrule (Graduate, Undergraduate/Scholarship) [4751]

Richard J. Bouchard - AECOM Scholarship (Undergraduate, Graduate/Scholarship) [1306]

Richard J. Burk, Jr., Fellowship (Graduate, Undergraduate/Fellowship) [5431]

Richard J. Roth Journalism Fellowship (Graduate/Fellowship) [8328]

Richard J. Schnell Memorial Scholarship (Postdoctorate/Scholarship) [3692]

Richard L. Greene Dissertation Award in Experimental Condensed Matter or Materials Physics (Doctorate, Postdoctorate/Award, Recognition, Monetary) [1228]

Richard McGrath Memorial Fund Award (Undergraduate/Award) [839]

Richard P. Covert, Ph.D., LFHIMSS Scholarships for Management Systems (Graduate, Postgraduate, Undergraduate/Scholarship) [5450]

Richard R. Tufenkian Scholarships (Undergraduate/Scholarship) [1848]

Richard Stessel Memorial Scholarship (Graduate/Scholarship) [163]

Henry and Sylvia Richardson Research Grant (Postdoctorate/Grant) [4401]

J. Milton Richardson Theological Fellowship (Graduate/Fellowship) [405]

Frank J. Richter Scholarship (Graduate, Undergraduate/Scholarship) [633]

Rick Arkans Eagle Scout Scholarship (Undergraduate/Scholarship) [7856]

Rick Brewer Scholarship (Undergraduate/Scholarship) [11207]

Rick Munoz Memorial Scholarship (Undergraduate/Scholarship) [9597]

John Riddick Student Grant (Graduate/Grant) [7559]

The Honorable Joseph H. Ridge Memorial Scholarship Fund (Undergraduate/Scholarship) [350]

The Jasper Ridge Restoration Fellowship (Graduate, Undergraduate/Fellowship) [4279]

ANN Ingrid Josefin Ridky Academic Scholarships (Undergraduate, Graduate/Scholarship) [56]

The Don Riebhoff Memorial Scholarship (Undergraduate/Scholarship) [1957]

Bryon Riesch Paralysis Foundation Research Grants (Professional development/Grant) [9703]

Rieser Fellowships (Undergraduate/Fellowship) [2743]

Ameen Rihani Scholarship Program (Undergraduate/Scholarship) [1768]

RA Consulting Service/Maria Riley Scholarships (Graduate, Undergraduate/Scholarship) [7893]

Lois McDonald Rinehart Adelphe Scholarship (Undergraduate, Graduate/Scholarship) [6468]

John T. Riordan Professional Education Scholarships (Professional development/Fellowship) [5981]

Rise to Shine Scholarship (Undergraduate/Scholarship) [353]

Ritchie-Jennings Memorial Scholarship Program (Undergraduate, Graduate/Scholarship) [2132]

Paul H. Rittle Sr. Professional Development Grants (Other/Grant) [5863]

Riverside Sheriffs Association Member Scholarship Program (Graduate, Undergraduate/Scholarship) [9710]

R.L. Gillette Scholarship (Undergraduate/Scholarship) [918]

RMACRAO Professional Development Scholarship (Professional development/Scholarship) [9725]

RMHC African American Future Achievers Scholarship (Undergraduate/Scholarship) [9734]

RMHC Asia Scholarship (Undergraduate/Scholarship) [9735]

RMHC HACER Scholarship (Undergraduate/Scholarship) [9736]

RMNP Research Fellowship (Graduate/Fellowship) [9730]

Road to Success Scholarship (Undergraduate/Scholarship) [8551]

Rob and Bessie Welder Wildlife Foundation's graduate research fellowship (Graduate, Master's, Doctorate/Fellowship) [11958]

Robbie Miller Memorial Endowed Scholarship (Undergraduate/Scholarship) [6819]

Robert D. Greenberg Scholarship (Graduate, Other/Scholarship) [10286]

Robert Gardner Memorial Fellowship (Graduate, Undergraduate/Fellowship) [5432]

Robert Hancock Memorial Scholarship Award (Undergraduate/Scholarship) [7346]

Robert J. McNamara Student Paper Award (Graduate/Award, Monetary) [2291]

Robert L. Peaslee Brazing Scholarship (Undergraduate/Scholarship) [1671]

Robert N. Colwell Fellowship (Doctorate/Fellowship) [2009]

Robert O. Wagner Professional Development Scholarship (Professional development/Scholarship) [2328]

Robert R. Palmer Research Travel Fellowship (Other/Fellowship) [1438]

Robert S. McNamara Fellowships Program (RSMFP) (Doctorate/Fellowship, Monetary) [12194]

Robert Toigo Foundation Fellowship (Master's/Fellowship) [11048]

Robert Winchester Dodson Scholarship (Undergraduate/Scholarship) [11208]

Clinical Scholars (Professional development/Scholarship) [6325]

Robert Wood Johnson Foundation Health Policy Fellows (Advanced Professional, Professional development/Fellowship) [6326]

Robert Wood Johnson Health Policy Fellowships (Advanced Professional, Professional development/Fellowship) [6327]

Clifford Roberts Graduate Fellowships (Doctorate/Fellowship) [4963]

Eugene L. Roberts, Jr. Prize (Undergraduate/Prize) [11209]

Elliott C. Roberts Scholarships (Graduate/Scholarship) [5815]

Robinson G. Allen Athletic Memorial Scholarship (Undergraduate/Scholarship) [9599]

Helen M. Robinson Grants (Doctorate/Grant) [6037]

Robinson Helicopter R22/R44 Safety Course Scholarship (Professional development/Scholarship) [12012]

NKA Dr. Violet B. Robinson Memorial Graduate Scholarship (Advanced Professional/Scholarship) [7978]

Sara Roby Fellowship in Twentieth-Century American Realism (Doctorate, Postdoctorate/Fellowship) [10218]

August M. Rocco Scholarship Fund (Undergraduate/Scholarship) [10788]

Rochelle Scholarship (College/Scholarship) [6908]

Rockford Area Habitat for Humanity College Scholarship (Undergraduate/Scholarship) [3693]

Rockwell Collins Scholarships (Undergraduate/Scholarship) [190]

Rodger Doxsey Travel Prize (Graduate, Postdoctorate/Prize) [684]

Paul W. Rodgers Scholarship (Undergraduate/Scholarship) [5925]

Rodney Williams Legacy Scholarship (Graduate/Scholarship) [11580]

R.O.E.A. Dumitru Golea Goldy-Gemu Scholarships (Undergraduate, High School/Scholarship) [1369]

Roger K. Summit Scholarship (Graduate/Scholarship) [9356]

Kimberly Marie Rogers Memorial Scholarship Fund (Undergraduate, Vocational/Occupational/Scholarship) [4603]

Roland E. Murphy, O.Carm., Scholarship (Undergraduate/Scholarship) [3186]

Sandra Journey Rolf Scholarship Fund (Undergraduate, Graduate/Scholarship) [6469]

Rome Prize (Postdoctorate, Graduate, Undergraduate/Prize, Award) [476]

Ronald B. Linsky Fellowship for Outstanding Water Research (Graduate, Master's, Doctorate/Fellowship) [8159]

Ronald McDonald House Charities Scholarship (Undergraduate/Scholarship) [9737]

Dorothy Worden Ronken Scholarships (Graduate/Scholarship) [4042]

Susanna Stover Root Memorial Scholarship (Undergraduate/Scholarship) [6470]

Roothbert Fund Scholarships (Undergraduate, Graduate/Scholarship) [9741]

Dr. Wayne F. Rose Scholarship Fund (Undergraduate/Scholarship) [4604]

Clarence J. Rosecrans Scholarship (Graduate, Master's, Doctorate/Scholarship) [1288]

Esther Katz Rosen Fund Grants (Graduate/Grant) [1289]

Jack Rosen Scholarship (Undergraduate/Scholarship) [6393]

Walter A. Rosenblith New Investigator Award (Postdoctorate/Award) [5426]

Marshall N. Rosenbluth Outstanding Doctoral Thesis Award (Doctorate, Postdoctorate/Award, Recognition, Monetary) [1229]

ASPPH/CDC Allan Rosenfield Global Health Fellowship Program (Postdoctorate, Postgraduate/Fellowship) [2284]

The Bea and Harry Ross Scholarship Endowment (Graduate/Scholarship) [10847]

Ross Trust Future School Counselors Essay Competition (Undergraduate/Award, Prize) [834]

The Rotary Club of Charlotte Public Safety Scholarship Fund (Undergraduate/Scholarship) [4752]

Rotary Club of Corpus Christi Scholarship (Undergraduate/Scholarship) [3485]

Rotary Foundation Global Grant Scholarships Supplement (Graduate/Scholarship, Grant) [9745]

Edward S. Roth Scholarship (Graduate, Undergraduate/Scholarship) [10411]

Marjorie Roy Rothermel Scholarship (Master's/Scholarship) [2002]

Theodore Rousseau Fellowships (Graduate/Fellowship) [7281]

Regie Routman Teacher Recognition Grant (Advanced Professional/Grant, Recognition) [6038]

Rove Pest Control Scholarships (Undergraduate/Scholarship) [9747]

Rovelstad Scholarship (Undergraduate, Graduate/Scholarship) [3871]

Roy Rowan Scholarship (Graduate, Undergraduate/Scholarship) [8789]

Rowe Family Fellowships (Graduate/Fellowship) [8752]

Leo S. Rowe Pan American Fund (Graduate, Undergraduate/Loan) [8739]

Travis Roy Foundation Individual Grants (All/Grant) [9749]

Roy H. Pollack Scholarship (Graduate, Master's/Scholarship) [11254]

Lucille and Edward R. Roybal Foundation Public Health Scholarships (Graduate, Undergraduate/Scholarship) [9753]

RSDSA Research Grants (Other/Grant) [9613]

RSNA/AAPM Graduate Fellowship (Graduate/Fellowship) [622]

RSNA/AUR/APDR/SCARD Radiology Education Research Development Grant (Professional development/Grant) [9484]

RSNA Education Scholar Grant (Professional development/Grant) [9485]

Research Scholar Grant (Professional development/Grant) [9486]

RSNA Research Seed Grant (Professional development/Grant) [9487]

Joe Rudd Scholarships (Graduate/Scholarship) [9732]

Rudolph Dillman Memorial Scholarship (Graduate, Undergraduate/Scholarship) [919]

Damon Runyon Clinical Investigator Awards (Postgraduate/Award) [9761]

Russell Athletics Scholarship (Undergraduate/Scholarship) [2336]

Russell C. McCaughan Heritage Scholarship (Undergraduate/Scholarship, Award) [1199]

Russell & Lazarus Safety Scholarship Contest (Undergraduate, College, University/Scholarship) [9763]

Russell Sage Foundation's Visiting Scholars Program (Postdoctorate, Doctorate/Fellowship) [9774]

Russell & Sigurd Varian Award (Graduate/Recognition) [2386]

NPELRA Foundation - Anthony C. Russo Scholarships (Graduate/Scholarship) [8057]

Lucile Rust Scholarships (Undergraduate/Scholarship) [9126]

Ruth K. Jacobs Memorial Scholarship (Graduate/Scholarship) [3317]

Ruth L. Kirschstein Individual Predoctoral NRSA for MD/PhD and other Dual Degree Fellowships (Doctorate, Master's/Fellowship) [11337]

Ruth Liu Memorial Scholarship (Undergraduate/Scholarship) [3309]

Ruth McMillan Academic Excellence Student Scholarship (Undergraduate, Four Year College, Two Year College/Grant) [2836]

The Ryan Law Group Scholarship (Undergraduate/Scholarship) [9768]

S. Penny Chappell Scholarship (Undergraduate/Scholarship) [9127]

Arthur C. Parker Scholarship (Undergraduate, Graduate/Scholarship) [10270]

SABA NC - Public Interest Post-Bar Fellowships (Professional development/Fellowship) [10599]

SABA NC - Public Interest Summer Fellowships (Undergraduate/Fellowship) [10600]

Safer Athletic Field Environments Scholarships (SAFE) (Graduate, Undergraduate, Two Year College/Scholarship) [10736]

SAH Study Tour Fellowships (Graduate/Fellowship) [10276]

Don Sahli-Kathy Woodall Graduate Scholarships (Graduate/Scholarship) [10960]

Sons and Daughters Don Sahli-Kathy Woodall Scholarships (Graduate, Undergraduate/Scholarship) [10961]

Saint Elizabeth Health Care Scholarship for Community Health Nursing (Undergraduate/Scholarship) [2170]

St. Francis Xavier Scholarship (Undergraduate/Scholarship) [12225]

St. Louis Paralegal Student Scholarships (Undergraduate/Scholarship) [9783]

St. Patrick's Day Scholarship (All/Scholarship) [7444]

Saints Cyril and Methodius Scholarships (Undergraduate/Scholarship) [9766]

SAJA Student Scholarship (Undergraduate, Graduate/Scholarship) [10604]

Sakura Finetek Student Scholarship (Undergraduate/Scholarship) [8113]

The Bill, W2ONV, and Ann Salerno Memorial Scholarship (Undergraduate/Scholarship) [1958]

Sally Beauty Scholarships for High School Graduates (High School/Scholarship) [9336]

Salon Supply Store Cosmetology Scholarships (Undergraduate/Scholarship) [9789]

Samfund grants (Other/Grant) [9793]

Margaret Jerome Sampson Scholarships (Undergraduate/Scholarship) [9128]

Samsung American Legion Scholarship (Undergraduate/Scholarship) [1073]

Samuel H. Kress Foundation Fellowships (Doctorate/Fellowship) [10277]

Samuel P. Hays Research Fellowship (Other/Fellowship) [1459]

Samuel Robinson Award (Undergraduate/Award) [9267]

Leonard H. Sandler Fellowships (Graduate/Fellowship) [5636]

Sandra Jo Hornick Scholarship (Undergraduate/Scholarship) [6394]

SAO Predoctoral Fellowship (Graduate/Fellowship) [5359]

Frank Sarli Memorial Scholarship (Undergraduate/Scholarship) [7820]

Sho Sato Memorial Scholarship (Undergraduate, Graduate/Scholarship) [6251]

Satter Human Rights Fellowship (Graduate, Master's, Juris Doctorate/Fellowship) [5366]

John A. Savoy Scholarship Fund (Undergraduate/Scholarship) [4605]

Bill Sawyer Memorial Scholarship (Undergraduate/Scholarship) [6820]

Herbert M. Saylor Memorial Scholarship (Graduate/Scholarship) [10586]

SBE/Ennes Youth Scholarships (Graduate/Scholarship) [10287]

SC&R Foundation Grant Program (Undergraduate/Grant) [10717]

SCBWI Work-in-Progress Awards (WIP) (Advanced Professional/Award) [10303]

SCC Part-Time Continuing Student Scholarship (Undergraduate/Scholarship) [10063]

SCCLA Fellowships (Graduate/Fellowship) [10647]

SCCLA Scholarships (Graduate/Scholarship) [10648]

SCDAA Post-Doctoral Research Fellowships (Postdoctorate/Fellowship) [10074]

Schallek Award (Graduate/Award) [7231]

Schallek Fellowship (Graduate/Fellowship) [7232]

Abe Schechter Graduate Scholarships (Graduate/Scholarship) [9467]

Schedulers and Dispatchers Monetary Scholarship (Other/Scholarship) [7740]

Harold W. Schloss Memorial Scholarship Fund (Undergraduate/Scholarship, Monetary) [3184]

Julie Schmid Research Scholarship (Advanced Professional/Scholarship) [2255]

Schneider/Bingle PLTW Scholarship (Undergraduate/Scholarship) [10412]

Prof. George Schneider Scholarship (Undergraduate/Scholarship) [10413]

Lillian P. Schoephoerster Scholarships (Undergraduate/Scholarship) [9129]

Dale M. Schoettler Scholarship for Visually Impaired Students (Undergraduate, Graduate/Scholarship) [9874]

Scholarship for Disabled Veterans (High School, Community College, Four Year College, Graduate, Professional development, Vocational/Occupational/Scholarship) [6702]

Scholarship Foundation of Santa Barbara General Scholarship Program (Undergraduate, Graduate/Scholarship) [9951]

Scholarship-Leadership Awards (Undergraduate/Scholarship) [6499]

Scholarship in Medical Education Award (Advanced Professional, Professional development/Scholarship) [10339]

The Scholarship of the Morris Radio Club of New Jersey (Undergraduate/Scholarship) [1960]

School Nutrition Association of Kansas Education Scholarship (Undergraduate/Scholarship) [9965]

Schools first Federal Credit Union Scholarship (Undergraduate/Scholarship) [9602]

Schrank Family Scholarship (Undergraduate/Scholarship) [11631]

Alice Southworth Schulman, Class of 1954, Simmons Scholarships for Unitarian Universalist Women (Undergraduate/Scholarship) [11255]

Schurgin Family Foundation Scholarship (Undergraduate/Scholarship) [5982]

AIST William E. Schwabe Memorial Scholarship (Undergraduate/Scholarship) [2225]

Schwan's Food Service Scholarship (Vocational/Occupational, Professional development/Scholarship, Award) [9961]

Frances M. Schwartz Fellowship (Other/Fellowship) [1171, 10026]

Fritz Schwartz Serials Education Scholarship (Graduate/Scholarship) [7560]

Evalee C. Schwarz Educational Loans (Undergraduate, Graduate/Loan) [9967]

David R. Schweisberg Memorial Scholarship (Graduate, Undergraduate/Scholarship) [8790]

Science and Engineering Apprenticeship Program (SEAP) (High School/Internship) [1444]

Science History Institute Travel Grants (All/Grant) [9972]

Science, Mathematics And Research for Transformation Scholarship for Service Program (SMART) (Undergraduate, Graduate/Scholarship) [1445, 9974]

ScienceSoft Scholarship (Graduate, Undergraduate/Scholarship) [9976]

SCIRTS (Spinal Cord Injury Research on the Translational Spectrum) Pilot Research Grants (Professional development)/Grant) [8204]

SCIRTS (Spinal Cord Injury Research on the Translational Spectrum) Postdoctoral Fellowships (Postdoctorate/Fellowship) [8205]

SCIRTS (Spinal Cord Injury Research on the Translational Spectrum) Senior Research Grants (Professional development/Grant) [8206]

Scleroderma Foundation Established Investigator Grants (Doctorate/Grant) [9979]

Scleroderma Foundation New Investigator Grants (Doctorate/Grant) [9980]

SCSPA Scholarship (Graduate/Scholarship) [10618]

SCSPA Yearbook Scholarship (Undergraduate/Scholarship) [10619]

SDE Fellowship (Graduate, Postgraduate/Fellowship) [5060]

Seabee Memorial Scholarship Association Scholarships (Undergraduate/Scholarship) [10231]

Seaman Family Scholarship (Undergraduate/Scholarship) [3487]

Seasons in Malibu Annual Scholarship (Undergraduate, Graduate/Scholarship) [9994]

SEE Education Foundation Scholarship (Undergraduate, Graduate, Doctorate/Scholarship) [6107]

Aaron Seesan Memorial Scholarship Fund (Undergraduate/Scholarship) [10790]

Dr. Eugene M. Seidner Student Scholarship Program (Undergraduate, Graduate/Scholarship) [46]

Selena Danette Brown Book Scholarship (Graduate, Undergraduate/Scholarship) [7620]

D. Mitchell Self Memorial Scholarship (Undergraduate/Scholarship) [8536]

David W. Self Scholarship (Undergraduate/Scholarship) [11263]

SEMA Memorial Scholarship and Loan Forgiveness Award (Graduate, Undergraduate/Loan, Scholarship) [10720]

SEMA Memorial Scholarships (Graduate, Undergraduate/Scholarship) [10721]

Dr. Henry Seneca Charitable Trust Scholarship (Undergraduate/Scholarship) [1901]

Archak and Meroum Senekjian Memorial Grant (Undergraduate/Scholarship) [1902]

Senior Scholar Scholarship Presented by 65Medicare.org (Two Year College, Four Year College/Scholarship) [18]

Senior Wisdom Scholarship (Undergraduate, Graduate/Scholarship, Award) [9186]

SeniorAdvice Caregiver Scholarships (Undergraduate/Scholarship) [10008]

Sentinels of Freedom Scholarship (Advanced Professional/Scholarship) [10011]

SEO Optimizers Scholarships (All/Scholarship) [10015]

Sequoyah Graduate Scholarship (Master's/Scholarship) [2040]

Serbian Bar Association of America Scholarships (Graduate/Scholarship) [10017]

Charles W. Serby COPD Research Fellowship (Professional development/Fellowship) [1360]

Sertoma Communicative Disorders Scholarship (Undergraduate/Scholarship) [10019]

Sertoma Hard of Hearing and Deaf Scholarship (Undergraduate/Scholarship) [10020]

Frank B. Sessa Scholarship (Professional development/Scholarship) [2499]

Roger Sessions Memorial Bogliasco Fellowships in Music (Professional development/Fellowship) [2647]

Margaret B. Ševenko Prize in Islamic Art and Culture (Doctorate, Graduate/Prize) [5535]

John R. Sevier Memorial Scholarship Award (Undergraduate/Scholarship) [11424]

SFP Junior Investigator's Career Development Awards (Other/Grant) [10330]

SFP Mid-Career/Mentor Award (Other/Grant) [10331]

SFP Student Research Grants (Graduate/Grant) [10332]

SHAFR Dissertation Completion Fellowship (Doctorate/Fellowship) [10359]

Julia Shahan and Shahan Siran Nevshehir Memorial Grant (Undergraduate/Scholarship) [1903]

Shamberg Scholars Program (Undergraduate/Scholarship) [11879]

Albert F. Shanker Scholarship (Undergraduate/Scholarship) [885]

Shannon Fellowships (Professional development/Fellowship) [6133]

Sharon D. Banks Memorial Undergraduate Scholarship (Undergraduate/Scholarship) [12171]

Sharp Criminal Lawyers Autism Scholarship (College, Undergraduate, Vocational/Occupational/Scholarship) [10035]

Luci Shaw Fellowship (Undergraduate/Fellowship) [3215]

The Ann Shaw International TYA Fellowship (Professional development/Fellowship) [11014]

Josephine Kerbey Shaw Memorial Undergraduate Scholarship (Undergraduate/Scholarship) [6472]

Shear-Miles Agricultural Scholarship (Graduate, Doctorate/Scholarship) [11647]

Shear-Miles Agricultural Scholarship/Fellowship (Graduate, Doctorate/Fellowship, Scholarship) [11648]

Sheep Heritage Foundation Memorial Scholarship (Graduate, Doctorate/Scholarship) [1383]

The Jim Sheerin Scholarship (Undergraduate/Scholarship) [7178]

Sheet Metal And Air Conditioning Contractors' National Association College of Fellows Scholarship Program (Undergraduate/Scholarship) [10039]

Sheldon Wechsler and George Mertz Contact Lens Residency Award (Professional development, Advanced Professional/Award) [464]

Shell Incentive Fund Scholarship (Undergraduate/Scholarship) [10041]

Shell Oil Company Technical Scholarship (Undergraduate/Scholarship) [10042]

Shell Process Technology Scholarships (Undergraduate/Scholarship) [10043]

Susan Goldsmith Shelley Scholarship (Undergraduate/Scholarship) [6473]

Robert P. Sheppard Leadership Awards (High School, College/Scholarship) [8106]

Sheriff W. Bruce Umpleby Law Enforcement Memorial Scholarship Fund (Undergraduate/Scholarship) [10791]

Sherman Fairchild Post-Graduate Fellowship in Conservation (Graduate/Fellowship) [7468]

Shields-Gillespie Scholarship (Other/Scholarship) [1189]

Chiyoko and Thomas Shimazaki Scholarship (Graduate/Scholarship) [6252]

Shinn Family Scholarship (Undergraduate/Scholarship) [6821]

Joseph Shinoda Memorial Scholarship (Undergraduate/Scholarship) [10047]

Jason Shipley Memorial Scholarships (Undergraduate/Scholarship) [7974]

Shohet Scholars Grant Program (SSG) (Professional development/Grant) [5962]

Short-term Senior Fellowships in Iranian Studies (Graduate, Master's, Doctorate/Fellowship) [1031]

SHOT-NASA Fellowship (Doctorate/Fellowship) [10365]

Shout It Out Scholarship (Undergraduate, High School/Scholarship) [11232]

SHPE Dissertation Scholarship (Doctorate/Scholarship) [10351]

SHPE Professional Scholarship (Master's, Doctorate/Scholarship) [10352]

Ralph W. Shrader Diversity Scholarship (Graduate/Scholarship) [107]

Shripat Kamble Urban Entomology Graduate Student Award for Innovative Research (Doctorate/Award) [4399]

SHRM Certification Scholarships - Individual (Professional development/Scholarship) [10369]

Mary Isabel Sibley Fellowship (Doctorate/Fellowship) [9082]

SICB Fellowship of Graduate Student Travel (FGST) (Graduate/Fellowship) [10374]

SICB Grants-in-Aid of Research Program (GIAR) (Graduate/Grant) [10375]

Sidley Diversity and Inclusion Scholarships (Undergraduate/Scholarship) [10076]

Sidley Prelaw Scholars Program (Undergraduate/Scholarship) [10077]

Jeff Siegel Memorial Scholarships (Undergraduate/Scholarship) [8317]

E.J. Sierleja Memorial Fellowship (Graduate/Fellowship) [5835]

Sigma Iota Epsilon Undergraduate National Scholar Awards (Undergraduate/Scholarship) [10088]

Sigma Kappa Foundation Alumnae Continuing Education Scholarship (Graduate, Undergraduate/Scholarship) [10121]

Sigma Kappa Foundation Alzheimer's/Gerontology Scholarship (Graduate/Scholarship) [10122]

Sigma Kappa Foundation Founders' Scholarships (Undergraduate/Scholarship) [10123]

Sigma Kappa Foundation Michigan Scholarship (Undergraduate/Scholarship) [10124]

Sigma Phi Alpha Graduate Scholarship (Graduate/Scholarship) [861]

Willard B. Simmons Sr. Memorial Scholarships (Undergraduate/Scholarship) [7779]

Julian Simon Fellowships (Postgraduate/Fellowship) [9354]

Simon Youth Community Scholarship Program (Undergraduate/Scholarship) [10140]

Simonton Windows Scholarship (Undergraduate/Scholarship) [8880]

Carole Simpson Scholarship (Undergraduate/Scholarship) [9477]

Aaron B. Singleton Memorial Scholarship (Undergraduate/Scholarship) [8538]

Sino-American Pharmaceutical Professionals Association Scholarships (Undergraduate/Scholarship) [10150]

Helen J. Sioussat/Fay Wells Scholarships (Graduate/Scholarship) [2705]

Skadden Fellowship (Graduate/Fellowship) [10157]

Skalny Scholarship for Polish Studies (Undergraduate/Scholarship) [828]

Francelene Skinner Memorial Scholarships (Undergraduate/Scholarship) [6832]

Skooblie Scholarships (Undergraduate/Scholarship) [10163]

Skubiak & Rivas - Justice in Action Scholarship (College, University, Vocational/Occupational, Undergraduate/Scholarship) [10165]

Robert W. Sledge Fellowships (Graduate/Fellowship) [380]

Sleeping Angels Co. Scholarships (College, University/Scholarship) [10169]

The Slifka Foundation Interdisciplinary Fellowship (Doctorate, Master's/Fellowship) [7282]

Alfred P. Sloan Foundation Graduate Scholarships - Sloan Indigenous Graduate Partnership (SIGP) (Master's, Doctorate/Scholarship) [7581]

Alfred P. Sloan Foundation Graduate Scholarships - Sloan Minority Ph.D. Program (MPHD) (Doctorate/Scholarship) [7582]

Sloan Northwood University Heavy-Duty Scholarships (Undergraduate/Scholarship) [2353]

Sloan Research Fellowships (Doctorate/Fellowship) [10171]

Thomas J. Slocum Memorial Scholarships to Redstone College (Undergraduate/Scholarship) [191]

The Aaron and Rita Slom Scholarships (Undergraduate/Scholarship) [11069]

SMA Foundation Scholarship Fund (Undergraduate/Scholarship) [10707]

Ann Kelsay Small Scholarship (Undergraduate/Scholarship) [6475]

SmartMeasurement's Dream for a Better Future: Student Scholarship (High School, Vocational/Occupational, College, University, Undergraduate/Scholarship) [10173]

SME Coal & Energy Division Scholarship (Undergraduate/Scholarship) [10429]

SME Education Foundation Family Scholarships (Undergraduate/Scholarship) [10415]

SME Environmental Division Scholarship (Undergraduate, Graduate/Scholarship) [10430]

SMFM/AAOGF Scholarship Awards (Graduate/Scholarship) [10423]

Smile Marketing Dental Scholarship (Doctorate/Scholarship) [10177]

James I. Smith, III Notre Dame Law School Scholarship Fund (Graduate, Undergraduate/Scholarship) [351]

Hy Smith Endowment Fund (Undergraduate/Scholarship) [5280]

Smith Family Awards Program for Excellence in Biomedical Research (Advanced Professional, Professional development/Award) [5443]

Henry DeWitt Smith Graduate Scholarship (Graduate/Scholarship) [10431]

Stanley Smith Horticultural Fellowships (Graduate, Undergraduate/Fellowship) [8753]

Brian and Cathy Smith Memorial Fund (Graduate/Scholarship) [1138]

Colonel Nate Smith Scholarship (Graduate, Undergraduate/Scholarship) [7201]

A.O. Smith Scholarships (Undergraduate/Scholarship) [9208]

Richard S. Smith Scholarships (Undergraduate/Scholarship) [11264]

William E. Smith Scholarships (Graduate/Scholarship) [220]

Smithsonian Fellowships in Museum Practice (Professional development, Graduate/Fellowship) [10188]

Smithsonian Minority Awards Program - Visiting Student (Graduate/Fellowship) [10209]

Smithsonian Native American Awards Program - Community Scholars (Graduate, Doctorate, Postdoctorate, Professional development/Fellowship) [10210]

Smithsonian Native American Awards Program - Visiting Student (Graduate/Fellowship) [10211]

The SMPE NY Scholarship Loan Program (Undergraduate/Scholarship, Loan) [10421]

SNF Professional Growth Scholarship (Graduate, Undergraduate, Vocational/Occupational, Postgraduate/Scholarship, Award) [9962]

SNMMI-TS Advanced Practitioner Program Scholarship (Professional development/Scholarship) [10441]

SNMMI-TS Bachelor's Degree Completion Scholarships (Undergraduate/Scholarship) [10442]

A.C. Snow and Katherine Snow Smith Scholarship (High School/Scholarship) [11210]

Helen D. Snow Memorial Scholarship (Undergraduate, Graduate, Doctorate/Scholarship) [9085]

Snowmobile Association of Massachusetts Awards / Scholarships (Undergraduate/Scholarship) [10235]

SNRS Research Grants (Professional development/ Grant) [10660]

SNRS/STTI Research Grants (Professional development/Grant) [10661]

SOAP/Kybele International Outreach Grant (Advanced Professional, Professional development/ Grant) [10448]

SOBP Travel Fellowship Award-Early Career Investigator-International (Postdoctorate/Fellowship) [10283]

Society of Allied Weight Engineers Scholarships (Undergraduate/Scholarship) [10268]

Society for the Arts in Healthcare Student Scholarships (Doctorate, Graduate, Undergraduate/Scholarship) [10281]

Society for Linguistic Anthropology Annual Student Essay Prize (Graduate, Undergraduate/Monetary) [10380]

Society of Pediatric Nurses Academic Educational Scholarship (Undergraduate, Graduate/Scholarship) [10459]

SPU Research Grant (Undergraduate/Grant) [10470]

Society for the Scientific Study of Sexuality Student Research Grant (Undergraduate/Grant) [10528]

Society of Vacuum Coaters Foundation Scholarship (Undergraduate, Graduate/Scholarship) [10553]

Sodowsky Law Firm Scholarship (College, University, Undergraduate/Scholarship) [10570]

SOHN Allied Health to BSN Degree Scholarship (Undergraduate/Scholarship) [10450]

Louis B. Sohn Fellowships in Human Rights and Environment (Graduate/Fellowship) [3219]

SOHN Graduate Degree Scholarship (Undergraduate/Scholarship) [10451]

SOHN RN to BSN Degree Scholarship (Undergraduate/Scholarship) [10452]

The Solano Law Firm Scholarship Contest (College, University, Undergraduate/Scholarship) [10576]

Solvable.com Debt-Free Scholarship (Two Year College, College, University, Undergraduate/Scholarship) [10584]

SOM Foundation Structural Engineering Travel Fellowships (Doctorate, Graduate, Master's, Undergraduate/Fellowship) [10160]

Sonia Morgan Scholarship (Undergraduate/Scholarship) [8292]

Dr. Kiyoshi Sonoda Memorial Scholarship (Graduate, Master's/Scholarship) [6253]

Sony Pictures Scholarship (Graduate/Scholarship) [2249]

SOPHE/ATSDR Student Fellowships in Environmental Health or Emergency Preparedness (Graduate/ Fellowship) [10513]

SOPHE/CDC Student Fellowship in Unintentional Injury Prevention (Doctorate, Master's/Fellowship) [10514]

SOPHE/CDC Student Fellowships in Child, Adolescent and School Health (Doctorate, Graduate, Master's/Fellowship) [10515]

Soroptimist International of Chambersburg Fund (Undergraduate/Scholarship) [4783]

Paul & Daisy Soros Fellowships (Graduate/Fellowship) [10597]

Soros Justice Advocacy Fellowships - Track I (Professional development/Fellowship) [8666]

Soros Justice Advocacy Fellowships - Track II (Professional development/Fellowship) [8667]

Soros Justice Media Fellowships - Track I (Professional development/Fellowship) [8668]

Soros Justice Media Fellowships - Track II (Professional development/Fellowship) [8669]

SORP Student Conference Scholarship (Graduate, Undergraduate/Scholarship) [10454]

Eastman Kodak Dr. Theophilus Sorrell Fellowships (Graduate/Fellowship) [8032]

South Carolina Association for Financial Professionals Certified Treasury Professional Scholarships (Other/Scholarship) [10606]

South Central Modern Language Association Fellowships (Doctorate, Postdoctorate/Fellowship) [8383]

South Dakota Division Scholarships (Undergraduate/Scholarship) [7375]

South Jersey Golf Association Scholarships (Undergraduate/Scholarship) [10627]

Southeastern Theatre Conference Secondary School Scholarship (Undergraduate/Scholarship) [10640]

Southern Scholarship Foundation Scholarships (Undergraduate, Graduate, Postgraduate/Scholarship) [10666]

Southwest Native-American Foundation Scholarships (Undergraduate, University, Four Year College/Scholarship) [10709]

Sovereign Nations Scholarships (Undergraduate/ Scholarship) [984]

SPA/Lemelson Fellowship Program (Graduate/ Award) [10506]

Amy E. Spain Memorial Scholarships (Graduate/ Scholarship) [11614]

Spangenberg Shibley & Liber Video PSA Scholarship Awards (Undergraduate/Scholarship) [10715]

Sparking the Future in Healthcare Scholarship (Doctorate/Scholarship) [26]

Nathan Sparks Memorial Scholarship (Undergraduate/Scholarship) [3664]

SPE Foundation General Scholarships (Undergraduate, Graduate/Scholarship) [10495]

SPE Student Awards for Innovations in Imaging (Undergraduate, Graduate/Scholarship) [10475]

Special Events Internship- New York (Undergraduate, Graduate/Internship) [4987]

Special Events Internships - Los Angeles (Undergraduate, Graduate/Internship) [4988]

Specialty Equipment Market Association Scholarships (Graduate, Undergraduate, Vocational/Occupational/Scholarship) [10722]

Specialty Nursing Scholarships (Undergraduate/ Scholarship) [4792]

Spice Box Grants (Advanced Professional/Grant) [848]

SPIE Student Author Travel Grants (Graduate, Undergraduate/Grant) [10729]

Phillip A. Spiegel IASP Congress Trainee Scholarship (Graduate, Undergraduate/Scholarship) [5945]

Spirit of Anne Frank Scholarship Award (Undergraduate/Scholarship) [4813]

The Spirit Square Center for Arts and Education Scholarship Fund (Undergraduate/Scholarship) [4754]

Spokeo Connections Scholarships (Undergraduate/ Scholarship) [10733]

SPOOM Research Grants (Graduate/Grant) [10500]

Sports Internships - Los Angeles (Undergraduate, Graduate/Internship) [4989]

Sporty's/Cincinnati Avionics Scholarships (Undergraduate, Vocational/Occupational/Scholarship) [192]

Spouse Tuition Aid Loan Program (STAP) (Undergraduate, Graduate/Loan) [8181]

SPS Future Teacher Scholarships (Undergraduate/ Scholarship) [10480]

SPS Leadership Scholarships (Undergraduate/ Scholarship) [10481]

SPSmedical CS Scholarships (Other/Scholarship) [5928]

SPSSI Grants-In-Aid Program (Graduate, Postdoctorate/Grant) [10511]

Blanche Squires Memorial Senior Brass Scholarship (Undergraduate/Scholarship) [9917]

SRC Master's Scholarships Program (Graduate, Master's/Scholarship) [10001]

SREB-State Doctoral Scholars Program - Dissertation Award (Doctorate/Scholarship, Award) [10663]

SREB-State Doctoral Scholars Program - Doctoral Award (Doctorate, Graduate/Scholarship) [10664]

SRF Post-doctoral Fellowships (Postdoctorate/Fellowship) [9982]

SSF Research Grants (Other/Grant) [10154]

SSF Student Fellowships (Doctorate, Undergraduate/Fellowship) [10155]

Stacey Scholarship Fund (All/Scholarship) [7822]

Stand Watie Scholarship (Undergraduate/Scholarship) [10588]

Standard and Poor's Award for Economic and Business Reporting - S&P Scholarships (Graduate, Undergraduate/Scholarship) [8791]

Stanford Advanced Materials $1,000 College Scholarship (College/Scholarship) [10747]

A.R.O.Y. Stanitz Scholarships (Undergraduate/ Scholarship) [1370]

Stanley Moore FUI Foundation Regional Scholarships (Four Year College, High School, Two Year College/Scholarship) [8464]

Stanley Moore National Scholarships (Undergraduate/Scholarship) [8465]

Stantec Scholarship (Master's, Doctorate/Scholarship, Monetary) [1644]

Thomas J. Stanton, Jr. Scholarships (Graduate/ Scholarship) [10029]

Star-Ledger Scholarships for the Performing Arts (Undergraduate/Scholarship) [8280]

STC-PSC Scholarships (Undergraduate, Graduate/ Scholarship) [10541]

STC Scholarships (Graduate, Undergraduate/Scholarship) [6884]

The Stanley H. Stearman Awards (Undergraduate/ Scholarship) [8080]

The Robert P. Stearns/SCS Engineers Scholarship Award (Graduate/Scholarship) [10582]

Tom Steel Post-Graduate Fellowships (Postgraduate, Professional development/Fellowship) [9322]

Stephen Gates Memorial Scholarship (Undergraduate/Scholarship) [11211]

Stephen K. Hall ACWA Water Law and Policy Scholarship (Graduate/Scholarship) [2078]

Mike Stephenson Legal Scholarships (Graduate/ Scholarship) [7199]

Steve Hymans Extended Stay Scholarship Program (Undergraduate/Scholarship) [976]

Steve Kaplan TV & Film Studies Award (Other/ Award) [1412]

Steve Mason Sports Media Scholarship (Graduate, Undergraduate/Scholarship) [7991]

Christine K. Stevens Development Scholarship (Undergraduate, Graduate/Scholarship) [1139]

Stevens Doctoral Award (Doctorate/Award) [5986]

Benjamin F. Stevens Fellowships (Professional development/Fellowship) [7153]

H.L. Stevenson Fellowship (Graduate, Undergraduate/Fellowship) [8792]

Richie Stevenson Scholarship Fund (Undergraduate/Scholarship) [3645]

Stewardson Keefe LeBrun Travel Grant (Professional development/Grant, Award) [139]

Allegheny Branch of Mid-America Chapter - Nancy Stewart Professional Development Scholarships (Professional development/Scholarship) [1588]

Dell Chenoweth Stifel Scholarship (Graduate/Scholarship) [6476]

The Richard Stockton College of New Jersey Foundation Alumni Association Graduate Awards (Graduate/Scholarship) [10848]

Louis Stokes Health Scholars Program (Undergraduate/Scholarship) [3742]

Louis Stokes Urban Health Policy Fellows Program (Other/Fellowship) [3743]

Ralph W. Stone Graduate Fellowships (Graduate/ Fellowship) [8129]

Stout Law Firm Family Matters Scholarship *(College, University, Vocational/Occupational, Undergraduate/Scholarship)* [10854]

Martin L. Stout Scholarships *(Graduate, Undergraduate/Scholarship)* [2162]

Robert "Bob" Strahan Memorial Scholarship *(Undergraduate, Graduate/Scholarship)* [5210]

George A. Strait Minority Scholarship *(Graduate/Scholarship)* [600]

The Donald A. Strauss Scholarship *(Undergraduate/Scholarship)* [11532]

The Carole J. Streeter, KB9JBR, Scholarship *(Undergraduate/Scholarship)* [1963]

Stanley W. Strew Scholarship *(Undergraduate/Scholarship)* [2785]

Striving for Greatness Accounting & Finance Scholarship *(Undergraduate/Scholarship)* [9214]

Stuart Cameron and Margaret McLeod Memorial Scholarship (SCMS) *(Graduate, Undergraduate/Scholarship)* [5850]

Stuart L. Bernath Dissertation Research Grant *(Graduate/Grant)* [10360]

Student travel awards *(Graduate/Award)* [30]

Student Essay Contest *(High School/Prize)* [1683]

Student Illustrator Scholarship *(Undergraduate, Graduate/Scholarship)* [10304]

Student Investigator Research Grant - General Audiology/Hearing Science *(Graduate, Doctorate/Grant)* [433]

Student Investigator Research Grant - Hearing Aids, Clinical Protocols and Patient Outcomes *(Graduate, Doctorate/Grant)* [434]

Student Investigator Research Grant - Vestibular *(Graduate, Doctorate/Grant)* [435]

Student Loan Relief Scholarship *(All/Scholarship)* [7445]

Student Research Foundation Personal Achievement Scholarship *(Undergraduate/Scholarship)* [4309]

Student Researcher Award, From the Behavioral Gerontology SIG *(Undergraduate, Graduate/Award)* [2064]

Student Summer Research Fellowship *(Undergraduate, Graduate/Fellowship)* [436]

Student Training and Research in Tumor Immunology Grants *(Graduate/Grant)* [3142]

Student Travel Grant *(Undergraduate/Grant)* [7361]

Student Writer Scholarship *(Graduate, Doctorate, Undergraduate/Scholarship)* [10305]

Students of History Scholarship *(Undergraduate/Scholarship)* [10869]

Study Scholarship for Artists or Musicians *(Graduate, Postdoctorate/Scholarship)* [4066]

Study.com CLEP Scholarship *(Other/Scholarship)* [10871]

Study.com Scholarship Florida Students *(Undergraduate, College/Scholarship)* [10872]

Study.com Scholarship Texas Students *(Undergraduate, College/Scholarship)* [10873]

Subic Bay-Cubi Point Scholarships *(Undergraduate/Scholarship)* [8176]

Caroline tum Suden/Frances Hellebrandt Professional Opportunity Awards *(Postdoctorate, Graduate/Award, Monetary)* [1239]

Sue A. Malone Scholarship *(Doctorate, Graduate, Professional development/Scholarship)* [6370]

Sue & Ken Dyer Foundation Travel Scholarship *(Other/Scholarship)* [4784]

John A. and Jean Quinn Sullivan Scholarship Funds *(Undergraduate/Scholarship)* [4220]

Phil Sullivan Scholarships *(Undergraduate/Scholarship)* [9314]

Summer Intern Scholarships In Cardiothoracic Surgery *(Undergraduate/Scholarship, Internship)* [663]

Summer Language Study Grants in Turkey *(Graduate/Grant)* [5872]

Summer Scholarship *(All/Scholarship)* [7446]

Lee Summer Student Fellowship *(Undergraduate, Master's/Fellowship)* [10652]

Summer Undergraduate Fellowship Program *(Undergraduate/Fellowship)* [623]

Hatton W. Sumners Endowed Law Schools Scholarships *(Undergraduate, Graduate/Scholarship)* [10877]

Hatton W. Sumners Endowed Undergraduate School Scholarships *(Undergraduate/Scholarship)* [10878]

Hatton W. Sumners Non-Endowed Undergraduate and Graduate Scholarships *(Undergraduate, Graduate/Scholarship)* [10879]

Superior District Legislative Mentoring Student Grants *(Undergraduate/Grant)* [2837]

Superpower Scholarship *(Undergraduate, High School/Scholarship)* [11233]

Surety and Fidelity Industry Intern and Scholarship Program *(Undergraduate, Graduate/Scholarship)* [10885]

The Susan Kelly Power and Helen Hornbeck Tanner Fellowship *(Doctorate, Postdoctorate/Fellowship)* [8384]

Sussman-Miller Educational Assistance Award Program *(Undergraduate/Scholarship)* [323]

SUT Houston Graduate Scholarships *(Graduate/Scholarship)* [10547]

SUT Houston Undergraduate Scholarships *(Undergraduate/Scholarship)* [10548]

Sutherland/Purdy Scholarship *(Undergraduate/Scholarship)* [9130]

Sutton Scholarship Award *(Undergraduate/Award, Scholarship)* [10891]

SUVCW Scholarships *(Undergraduate/Scholarship)* [10595]

SVS Vascular Surgery Trainee Advocacy Travel Scholarship *(Advanced Professional, Professional development/Scholarship, Grant)* [10556]

Swede Swanson Memorial Scholarships *(Undergraduate/Scholarship)* [8190]

The Hanns Swarzenski and Brigitte Horney Swarzenski Fellowship *(Graduate/Fellowship)* [7283]

Sweep All Scholarship *(College, University/Scholarship)* [10893]

Sweet and Simple Scholarship *(Undergraduate, High School/Scholarship)* [11234]

Swensrud Teacher Fellowships at MHS (Massachusetts Historical Society) *(Professional development/Fellowship)* [7154]

Stan Swinton Fellowship *(Graduate, Undergraduate/Fellowship)* [8793]

Switzer Environmental Fellowship *(Graduate/Fellowship)* [9721]

SWS Barbara Rosenblum Scholarship *(Doctorate/Fellowship, Scholarship)* [10568]

SWS Student Scholarships *(Undergraduate/Scholarship)* [10562]

Sylvia Parkinson Fund *(Undergraduate/Scholarship)* [5344]

Sylvia Taylor Johnson Minority Fellowships in Educational Measurement *(Doctorate/Fellowship)* [4313]

Symantec Research Labs Graduate Fellowships *(Doctorate, Graduate/Fellowship)* [8547]

S. Leonard Syme Training Fellowship *(Master's, Doctorate/Fellowship)* [5877]

Symee Ruth Feinberg Memorial Scholarship Fund *(Undergraduate/Scholarship)* [5345]

Ta Liang Award *(Graduate/Award)* [2010]

Harry Taback 9/11 Memorial Scholarships *(Undergraduate/Scholarship)* [1572]

Tabat Scholarship Award *(Graduate/Scholarship)* [4533]

TACL-LA Taiwanese American Community Scholarship (TACS) *(Undergraduate/Scholarship)* [10911]

Tacy Anna Smith Memorial Scholarship Endowment Fund *(Undergraduate/Scholarship)* [4757]

Tag and Label Manufacturers Institute Scholarships - Four-Year Colleges *(Undergraduate/Scholarship)* [10904]

Tag and Label Manufacturers Institute Scholarships - Two-Year Colleges *(Undergraduate/Scholarship)* [10905]

Tailhook Educational Foundation Scholarship *(Undergraduate, Postdoctorate/Scholarship)* [10907]

Robert M. Takasugi Public Interest Fellowships *(Postgraduate/Fellowship)* [10913]

Kei Takemoto Memorial Scholarships *(Undergraduate/Scholarship)* [193]

The Donald H. Bernstein and John B. Talbert Jr. Scholarship *(Undergraduate/Scholarship)* [4758]

Justice Stephen K. Tamura Scholarship *(Undergraduate/Scholarship)* [6241]

Mitsuyoshi Tanaka Dissertation Award in Experimental Particle Physics *(Doctorate, Postdoctorate/Award, Recognition, Monetary)* [1230]

Alexander M. Tanger Scholarships *(Graduate/Scholarship)* [2706]

Alex Tanous Scholarship Award *(Undergraduate/Scholarship)* [10919]

Frederick A. Tarantino Memorial Scholarship Award *(Undergraduate/Scholarship)* [11425]

Targeted Research Initiative for Health Outcomes *(Doctorate/Grant)* [4427]

Raymond J. Tarleton Graduate Fellowships *(Graduate/Fellowship)* [3267]

TaskEasy Scholarships for Future Entrepreneurs *(Undergraduate/Scholarship)* [10923]

Taylor/Blakeslee University Fellowships *(Graduate/Award)* [3848]

Joshua C. Taylor Fellowships *(Doctorate, Postdoctorate/Fellowship)* [10219]

Ryan "Munchie" Taylor Memorial Scholarships *(Undergraduate/Scholarship)* [6944]

TCA-ACBH Scholarship to Turkey Program *(Undergraduate/Scholarship)* [86, 11142]

TCA Outstanding Graduate Student Award *(Graduate/Award)* [10981]

TCA Scholarship Fund *(Undergraduate/Scholarship)* [11121]

TCA-UMD Scholarship to Turkey Program *(Undergraduate/Scholarship)* [11143]

TCAdvance Scholarship *(Undergraduate/Scholarship)* [11144]

TCATA College Scholarship Fund *(Undergraduate/Scholarship)* [11004]

TCDA Abbott IPCO Professional Scholarships *(Other/Scholarship)* [742]

TCDA Bill Gorham Student Scholarship *(Undergraduate/Scholarship)* [743]

TCDA Cloys Webb Student Scholarship *(Undergraduate/Scholarship)* [744]

TCDA Gandy Ink Professional Scholarship *(Professional development/Scholarship)* [745]

TCDA General Fund Scholarships *(Undergraduate/Scholarship)* [746]

TCDA Past Presidents Student Scholarship *(Undergraduate/Scholarship)* [747]

Teacher Education Scholarship *(Advanced Professional/Scholarship)* [1130]

TeamMates Mentoring Program Scholarship *(Undergraduate/Scholarship)* [5125]

Tech Mastery Scholarships *(Undergraduate, Graduate/Scholarship)* [9635]

Technical Scholarship *(Undergraduate/Scholarship)* [8592]

Technical Women's Organization Education Scholarship *(Advanced Professional, Graduate/Scholarship)* [10933]

Ted Ousley Scholarship Endowment Fund *(Undergraduate/Scholarship)* [4759]

Teddy Wilburn Scholarship Fund *(Undergraduate/Scholarship)* [3646]

Telecommunications Association of Michigan - Category II - IV Scholarship *(Undergraduate/Scholarship)* [10944]

Telluride Association Summer Program Scholarships *(Undergraduate/Scholarship)* [10946]

Mary L. Tenopyr Graduate Student Scholarship *(Graduate/Scholarship)* [10336]

The Terra Foundation Fellowships in American Art *(Undergraduate, Doctorate, Postdoctorate/Fellowship)* [10220]

Terra Summer Residency Fellowships *(Master's, Doctorate/Fellowship)* [10966]

The TESOL/TEFL Travel Grant *(Advanced Professional/Grant, Monetary)* [10970]

Marc Tetalman, MD, Memorial Award *(Professional development, Doctorate/Recognition)* [10444]

Texas Mutual Scholarship Program *(Undergraduate, Vocational/Occupational/Scholarship)* [10990]

Texas Scholarship of Academic Excellence *(Undergraduate, Graduate/Scholarship)* [1708]

Texas State Technical College Scholarships *(Undergraduate/Scholarship)* [194]

Text=Wrecks Scholarship *(Graduate, College/Scholarship)* [4968]

TFOS Fellowship Awards (Graduate, Postdoctorate/Fellowship) [10929]

Jim and Pat Thacker Sports Communication Internship (Undergraduate/Internship) [11212]

ThanksUSA Scholarship (Undergraduate, Vocational/Occupational/Scholarship) [11006]

THEO WILSON SCHOLARSHIP (Graduate, Undergraduate/Scholarship) [8794]

Theodore C. Sorensen Research Fellowship (Other/Fellowship) [6533]

Theodore E.D. Braun Research Travel Fellowship (Other/Fellowship) [1439]

Thermo Fisher Scientific Antibody Scholarship (Undergraduate, Graduate/Scholarship) [11016]

Thermo Scientific Educational Scholarships (Professional development/Scholarship) [8115]

Thermoforming Division Scholarship (Undergraduate, Graduate/Scholarship) [10497]

Thesaurus Linguae Latinae Fellowship (TTL) (Doctorate/Fellowship) [10312]

Werner B. Thiele Memorial Scholarship (Graduate, Undergraduate/Scholarship) [5211]

Elizabeth R. Thomas Alumni Nursing Scholarship (Undergraduate/Scholarship) [10065]

Thomas Arkle Clark Scholar-Leader of the Year (Graduate, Undergraduate/Scholarship) [9092]

Thomas E. Shown, M.D. Memorial Scholarship (Undergraduate/Scholarship) [12094]

Thomas J. Watson Fellowship (Undergraduate/Fellowship) [11939]

Thomas and Ruth River International Scholarship (Undergraduate, Graduate/Scholarship) [12201]

Cheryl M. Thomas Scholarship (Undergraduate, Graduate, Postdoctorate/Scholarship) [27]

The Rev. Chuck and Nancy Thomas Scholarship (Professional development/Scholarship) [11256]

Thomas W. Gallagher Scholarship Fund (Undergraduate/Scholarship) [10797]

Thome Foundation Awards Program in Age-Related Macular Degeneration Research (Professional development/Grant) [5444]

Thome Foundation Awards Program in Alzheimer's Disease Drug Discovery Research (Professional development/Grant) [5445]

Katrina Thompson Scholarship (Community College, College, University, Undergraduate, Vocational/Occupational/Scholarship) [9856]

Thompson Scholarship for Women in Safety (Doctorate/Scholarship) [1573]

Thomas P. Thornton Scholarship (Undergraduate, Graduate/Scholarship) [5731]

Arthur A. Thovmasian, Jr. Memorial Grant (Undergraduate/Scholarship) [1904]

The Thurgood Marshall College Fund (Undergraduate/Scholarship) [10856]

Thurgood Marshall Fellowships Program (Undergraduate/Fellowship) [8301]

Tibor T. Polgar Fellowship (Graduate, Undergraduate/Fellowship) [5613]

Tien Bui Memorial Scholarship (Undergraduate/Scholarship) [12095]

Tiftickjian Law Firm, P.C. Juvenile Justice Law School Scholarships (Graduate/Scholarship) [11030]

The Tikvah Fellowship (Undergraduate/Fellowship) [11034]

Tillman Scholars Program (Undergraduate, Graduate/Scholarship) [11036]

The Jack Tillson Scholarship Fund (Graduate/Scholarship) [6164]

The Tingen & Williams Undergraduate Scholarship (Undergraduate/Scholarship) [11040]

Titan Web Agency Bi-Annual Scholarship Program (Community College, Four Year College, Two Year College/Scholarship) [11042]

Mario J. Tocco Hydrocephalus Foundation Scholarships (Undergraduate/Scholarship) [5667]

Tom Bost Scholarship (Undergraduate/Scholarship) [11213]

Tom Cory Scholarships (Undergraduate, Graduate/Scholarship) [1787]

Tom Taylor Memorial Scholarship to Spartan College of Aeronautics & Technology (Undergraduate/Scholarship) [195]

The Adelle and Erwin Tomash Fellowship in the History of Information Technology (Doctorate, Graduate/Fellowship) [11641]

Tommie J. Hamner Scholarship (Undergraduate/Scholarship) [9131]

Sally Kress Tompkins Fellowship (Graduate/Fellowship) [10278]

TonaLaw Veteran's Scholarship (Undergraduate, Graduate, Professional development, Vocational/Occupational/Scholarship) [11050]

Top Ten List Scholarship (Undergraduate, High School/Scholarship) [11235]

Ferdinand Torres Scholarships (Graduate, Undergraduate/Scholarship) [920]

Tourette Association of America Research Grant Awards (Master's, Doctorate/Grant) [11067]

Dr. Harry Jeffrey Tourigian Memorial Grant (Undergraduate/Scholarship) [1905]

The Town and County Club Scholarship (Undergraduate/Scholarship) [5346]

Toyota/TELACU Scholarships (Undergraduate/Scholarship) [10942]

The Joyce Tracy Fellowship (Doctorate/Fellowship) [499]

TRALA Industry Scholarship Awards (Undergraduate/Scholarship) [11119]

Vera Tran Memorial Scholarships (Undergraduate/Scholarship) [11825]

Trans Issues Internships - New York (Undergraduate, Graduate/Internship) [4990]

Transatlantic Fellows Program (Other/Fellowship) [4947]

The TranscriptionServices.com Scholarship (Undergraduate/Scholarship) [11073]

Translational Research Professorship (Professional development/Internship) [3784]

Transoft Solutions, Inc. Ahead of the Curve Scholarship (AOTC) (Graduate, Undergraduate/Scholarship) [5867]

Traub-Dicker Rainbow Scholarships (TDRS) (Undergraduate/Scholarship) [10851]

Triadex Scholarship (Undergraduate/Scholarship) [11106]

Tribute Fund Community Grant (Professional development/Grant) [10306]

Tim Triner Letter Carriers Scholarship Fund (Undergraduate/Scholarship) [10798]

Triple Crown Award (Other/Recognition, Award) [8075]

TRIUMF Summer Research Award (Undergraduate/Award, Scholarship) [11115]

Charlie Trotters's Culinary Education Foundation Scholarships (Other, Undergraduate/Scholarship) [849]

Jo Anne J. Trow Undergraduate Scholarships (Undergraduate/Scholarship) [393]

Truckload Carriers Association Scholarships (Undergraduate/Scholarship) [11122]

The William H. Truettner Fellowship Endowment Fund (Undergraduate, Doctorate, Postdoctorate/Fellowship) [10221]

TrustedPros Scholarships (Undergraduate/Scholarship) [11131]

Trustees College Scholarships (Undergraduate/Scholarship) [6961]

Trustees Law School Scholarship (Undergraduate/Scholarship) [6962]

TSGC Graduate Fellowships (Graduate/Fellowship) [10994]

TSHP R&E Foundation Scholarship Program (Undergraduate, Graduate/Scholarship) [11135]

Tucker Family Scholarship (Undergraduate/Scholarship) [11214]

Barry Tuckwell Award (All/Scholarship) [6022]

Edward Tuinier Memorial Scholarship (Undergraduate/Scholarship) [907]

Turf and Ornamental Communicators Association Scholarship Program (Undergraduate/Scholarship) [11139]

Hans Turley Prize in Queer Eighteenth-Century Studies (Graduate, Other/Prize) [1440]

Jeff Turner-Forsyth Audubon Society Scholarship (Undergraduate/Scholarship) [12096]

James A. Turner, Jr. Memorial Scholarship (Undergraduate/Scholarship) [1672]

Mark and Vera Turner Memorial Scholarships (Undergraduate/Scholarship) [6833]

Scott Alan Turner Personal Finance Scholarship (High School, Undergraduate/Scholarship) [11152]

Lydia Donaldson Tutt-Jones Memorial Research Grant (Graduate, Other, Master's/Grant) [109]

Twenty Four Seven Hotels Scholarship Opportunity (Undergraduate, College, University/Scholarship) [11156]

Two Year/Community Broadcast Education Association Scholarship Awards (Other/Scholarship) [2707]

William R. Tyler Fellowships (Graduate/Fellowship) [4234]

Florence Tyson Grant to Study Music Psychotherapy (Professional development/Grant) [1140]

UAB Health Policy Fellowship (Graduate, Master's, Doctorate/Scholarship) [11430]

UAF Alumni Association Scholarship (Undergraduate/Scholarship) [11520]

UC-Berkeley/ISEEES/CCS Postdoctoral Fellowships (Postdoctorate/Fellowship) [11535]

UC MEXUS-CICESE Graduate Student Short-Term Research and Training Program (Master's, Doctorate, Postdoctorate/Grant) [11539]

UC MEXUS - CICESE Graduate Student Short-Term Research and Non-degree Training (Graduate/Grant) [11550]

UC MEXUS-CONACYT Collaborative Grants (Professional development/Grant) [11551]

UC MEXUS-CONACYT Postdoctoral Research Fellowships (Postdoctorate/Fellowship) [11553]

UC MEXUS Dissertation Research Grants (Graduate/Grant) [11554]

UC MEXUS Scholars in Residence Program - Graduate (Graduate/Scholarship) [11555]

UC MEXUS Scholars in Residence Program - Recent University Graduates (Postgraduate, Graduate/Scholarship) [11556]

UC MEXUS Scholars in Residence Program - Visiting Faculty (Professional development/Scholarship) [11557]

UC MEXUS Small Grants for UC Postdocs (Postdoctorate/Grant) [11558]

UC MEXUS Small Grants for UC Students (Graduate, Postdoctorate/Grant) [11559]

UCLA-CSW Travel Grants (Graduate, Undergraduate/Grant) [11542]

UCSD Black Alumni Scholarships for Engineering, Mathematics and Science (Undergraduate/Scholarship) [9858]

UCT Scholarship (Other/Scholarship) [8693]

Udall Scholarship (Undergraduate/Scholarship) [11533]

Udall Undergraduate Scholarship (Undergraduate/Scholarship) [11165]

UF Center for Latin American Studies FLAS Summer Fellowships (Master's, Graduate, Undergraduate/Award, Fellowship) [11570]

Ugly Sweater Scholarship (High School, College, University, Graduate, Undergraduate/Scholarship) [9957]

Sandy Ulm Scholarships (Undergraduate, Master's/Scholarship) [4625]

UMBS Istock Family Scholarship (Undergraduate/Scholarship) [11632]

UMBS Returning Student Award (Undergraduate/Scholarship) [11633]

UMDF Clinical Research Fellowship Training Awards (Professional development/Fellowship) [11266]

UNCF Merck Graduate Science Research Dissertation Fellowships (Graduate/Fellowship) [7268, 11270]

UNCF/Merck Postdoctoral Science Research Fellowships (Postdoctorate/Scholarship) [7269, 11271]

Undergraduate/Graduate Scholarships (Undergraduate, Graduate/Scholarship) [5989]

Undergraduate Scholars Program (Graduate/Scholarship) [5606]

Undergraduate Session Assistants Program (Undergraduate/Other) [8329]

Underrepresented in Medicine award (Graduate/Scholarship) [1112]

Richard M. Weaver Fellowships (Graduate/Fellowship) [5886]

Web Design Scholarship (Undergraduate/Scholarship) [2665]

W.E.B. Du Bois Program (Doctorate/Fellowship) [7944]

Webb – Faye and Rendell C Webb JR Scholarship (Undergraduate/Scholarship) [3491]

WEDA Scholarship Program (Professional development/Scholarship) [11979]

John V. Wehausen Graduate Scholarships for Advanced Study in Ship Hydrodynamics and Wave Theory (Graduate/Scholarship) [10435]

The Arthur and Lila Weinberg Fellowship for Independent Researchers (Other, Graduate/Fellowship) [8385]

The Bee Winkler Weinstein Scholarship Fund (Undergraduate, Vocational/Occupational/Scholarship) [10852]

William E. Weisel Scholarship (Undergraduate/Scholarship) [10418]

Susan C. Weiss Clinical Advancement Scholarship (Other/Scholarship) [10446]

Welch Scholars Grants (Undergraduate/Grant) [1200]

Wells Fargo American Indian Scholarship Program (Undergraduate/Scholarship) [996]

Jean Hess Wells Memorial Adelphe Graduate Scholarship (Graduate/Scholarship) [6480]

Jean Hess Wells Memorial Adelphe Scholarship (Undergraduate/Scholarship) [6481]

Wellstone Fellowships for Social Justice (Graduate/Fellowship) [4484]

Peter R. Weitz Prize (Other/Prize) [4949]

Francis X. Weninger Scholarships (Undergraduate/Scholarship) [12226]

Wenner-Gren Foundation Dissertation Fieldwork Grants (Doctorate/Grant) [11966]

Wenner-Gren Foundation Post-PhD Research Grants (Doctorate, Postdoctorate/Grant) [11967]

John R. and Joan F. Werren Scholarships Fund (Undergraduate/Scholarship) [10801]

Wes Burton Memorial Scholarship (Undergraduate/Scholarship) [12097]

Wesley C. Cameron Scholarship (Undergraduate/Scholarship) [8177]

Wesley R. Habley Summer Institute Scholarships (Professional development/Scholarship) [7569]

Western University - Endourology Fellowship (Professional development/Fellowship) [4385]

Mary Elizabeth Westpheling - Long Beach (Calif.) Alumnae Association Memorial Scholarhip (Undergraduate/Scholarship) [6482]

Frederick K. Weyerhaeuser Forest History Fellowship (Graduate/Fellowship) [4682]

Stan Wheeler Mentorship Awards (Other/Award) [6728]

Nellie Yeoh Whetten Award (Graduate/Recognition) [2387]

Whirly-Girls Helicopter Add-On Flight Training Scholarship (Professional development, Vocational/Occupational/Scholarship) [12013]

Whirly-Girls Jean Tinsley Memorial HELI-EXPO Scholarship (Professional development, Vocational/Occupational/Scholarship) [12014]

The Whistleblower Lawyer-Louthian Law Legal Scholarship Award (Graduate/Scholarship) [6920]

Law Office of David D. White Annual Traumatic Brain Injury Scholarships (College, Community College, University, Vocational/Occupational/Scholarship) [6687]

White Collar Defense Diversity Scholarships (Undergraduate, Graduate/Scholarship) [9286]

Bradford White Corporation Scholarships (Undergraduate/Scholarship) [9209]

White House Fellows (Other/Fellowship) [9271]

Paul D. White Scholarship Program (Undergraduate/Scholarship) [2409]

Ann Cook Whitman Scholarships for Perry High School (Undergraduate/Scholarship) [4964]

Jane and Morgan Whitney Fellowships (Graduate/Fellowship) [7284]

Why Get Your Blue On? Video Scholarships (Graduate, Undergraduate/Award, Scholarship) [11997]

Tom Wicker Award (Graduate/Award) [11216]

Larry B. Wickham Memorial Scholarship for Graduate Studies (Graduate/Scholarship) [7487]

Elie Wiesel Prize in Ethics (Undergraduate/Prize, Award) [12022]

WIFLE Regular Scholarship Program (Graduate, Postdoctorate, Undergraduate/Scholarship) [12139]

WIGA College Scholarships (Postgraduate, Graduate, Undergraduate/Scholarship) [11894]

Hair Loss Scholarship (College, University, Undergraduate, Graduate, Two Year College, Vocational/Occupational/Scholarship) [12024]

The Fred C. Wikoff Jr. Scholarship (Undergraduate, Vocational/Occupational/Scholarship) [4763]

Wilder Dimension Scholarships for Advanced Study in Theatre Arts (Graduate/Scholarship) [4178]

James B. Willett Educational Memorial Scholarship Award (Undergraduate/Scholarship) [11426]

William A. and Ann M. Brothers Scholarship (Undergraduate/Scholarship) [1673]

William B. Howell Memorial Scholarship (Undergraduate/Scholarship) [1674]

William "Buddy" Sentner Scholarship Award (Undergraduate, High School/Scholarship) [629]

William E. Parrish Scholarship (Graduate, Master's/Scholarship) [9079]

William G. and Mayme J. Green Fund (Undergraduate/Scholarship) [5349]

William Goldberg Scholarship (Undergraduate/Scholarship) [4883]

William H. Andrews/HAWS Scholarship (Undergraduate/Scholarship) [12098]

William J. Tangye Scholarship (Undergraduate/Scholarship, Monetary, Award) [5974]

William J. Yankee Memorial Scholarship (Undergraduate/Scholarship, Monetary, Recognition) [1263]

William M. Fanning Maintenance Scholarship (Undergraduate/Scholarship) [7742]

William P. Elrod Memorial Scholarship (Undergraduate/Scholarship) [10938]

William P. Van Wagenen Fellowship (Undergraduate/Fellowship) [608]

William Pigott Memorial Scholarship (Undergraduate/Scholarship) [3694]

William "Sully" Sullivan Scholarship (Graduate, Undergraduate/Scholarship) [11864]

William T. Hartzell Memorial Scholarship (Undergraduate/Scholarship) [9605]

Williams Chorale Bacardi Fallon Scholarships (High School/Award, Scholarship) [12037]

Sidney B. Williams, Jr. Scholarships (Undergraduate/Scholarship) [4698]

BM1 James Elliott Williams Memorial Scholarship Fund (Undergraduate/Scholarship) [8936]

Maxine Williams Scholarship (Undergraduate/Scholarship) [605]

Lippincott Williams and Wilkins Scholarships (LWW Scholarship) (Master's, Doctorate/Scholarship) [3440]

Willie T. Loud scholarship (Undergraduate, Graduate/Scholarship) [7894]

Wilma Sackett Dressel Scholarship (Undergraduate/Scholarship) [10126]

Wilshire Law Firm Scholarship (Undergraduate, Graduate/Scholarship) [12041]

Woodrow Wilson Dissertation Fellowship in Women's Studies (Doctorate/Fellowship) [12051]

The Wilson Fellowship (Postdoctorate/Fellowship) [11677]

Pete Wilson Journalism Scholarship (Graduate, Undergraduate/Scholarship) [9478]

Saul T. Wilson, Jr. Internship (Graduate, Undergraduate/Internship) [11301]

Bob Wilson Legacy Scholarships (Undergraduate/Scholarship) [2810]

Winston Build Your Future Scholarship (Graduate, Undergraduate, Vocational/Occupational/Scholarship) [9963]

David A. Winston Health Policy Scholarship (Graduate/Scholarship) [2307]

Winterthur Research Fellowships (Graduate/Fellowship) [12101]

Wisconsin Laboratory Association Graduate Student Scholarships (Graduate/Scholarship) [12123]

WLA Scholarships (Undergraduate, Graduate/Scholarship) [12124]

Wisconsin Laboratory Association Undergraduate University Student Scholarships (Undergraduate/Scholarship) [12125]

Wisconsin Lawton Minority Retention Grants (Undergraduate/Grant) [11753]

The William B. Wisdom Grants in Aid of Research (Undergraduate, Graduate/Grant) [12130]

WLA Conference Attendance Grants (Undergraduate, Professional development/Grant) [11896]

WLALA Scholarships (Postgraduate/Scholarship) [12144]

Woksape Oyate: "Wisdom of the People" Distinguished Scholars Awards (Undergraduate/Grant) [986]

Paul R. Wolf Memorial Scholarships (Graduate/Scholarship) [2012]

Emil Wolf Outstanding Student Paper Competition (Graduate, Undergraduate/Award) [8680]

The Wolf Trap Accounting Internship Program (Graduate, Other, Undergraduate/Internship) [12127]

Wolf Trap's Grants for High School Performing Arts Teachers (Other/Grant) [12128]

Nona Hobbs Wolfe Memorial Scholarship (Undergraduate/Scholarship) [6483]

Eleanor M. Wolfson Memorial Scholarship Fund (Undergraduate/Scholarship) [4607]

Women In Defense HORIZONS Scholarship (Graduate, Undergraduate/Scholarship) [12133]

Women In Need Scholarships (Undergraduate/Scholarship) [4306]

Women In Transition Scholarships (Undergraduate/Scholarship) [4307]

Women Techmakers Udacity Scholarship (Graduate, Undergraduate/Scholarship) [5048]

Women of Today's Manufacturing Scholarship (Undergraduate/Scholarship) [3697]

Women of WSAJ Bar Preparation Scholarship (Undergraduate/Scholarship) [11904]

Women's Army Corps Veterans Association Scholarships (Undergraduate/Scholarship) [12153]

Women's Jewelry Association Member Grants (Professional development/Grant) [12163]

Women's Leadership in Agriculture Scholarship (Undergraduate/Scholarship) [8578]

Women's Leadership Training Grant (Advanced Professional, Professional development/Grant) [10557]

Women's Overseas and Service League Scholarships for Women (Undergraduate/Scholarship) [12168]

Wood Fruitticher Grocery Company, Inc. Scholarships (Graduate, Undergraduate/Scholarship) [222]

Rolla F. Wood Graduate Scholarships (Graduate, Undergraduate/Scholarship) [9105]

Woodrow Wilson International Center for Scholars Fellowships (Doctorate, Postdoctorate/Fellowship) [12043]

Woodrow Wilson-Rockefeller Brothers Fund Fellowships for Aspiring Teachers of Color (Undergraduate/Fellowship) [12052]

Helen M. Woodruff Fellowships (Postdoctorate/Fellowship) [1781]

Woody Guthrie Fellowship (Professional development/Fellowship) [2637]

Worcester District Medical Society Scholarship Fund (Undergraduate/Scholarship) [12188]

Work Ethic Scholarship (Vocational/Occupational, Two Year College/Scholarship) [7384]

John W. Work III Memorial Foundation Scholarship Fund (Undergraduate/Scholarship) [3650]

Working for Farmers' Success Scholarships (Undergraduate/Scholarship) [3240]

World Book Graduate Scholarships in Library and Information Science (Graduate/Scholarship) [3038]

The World Forest Institute International Fellowship (Undergraduate/Fellowship) [12198]

Worldstudio AIGA Scholarships (Graduate, Undergraduate/Scholarship) [12205]

Worthy Gemological Scholarships (Undergraduate/Scholarship) [12211]

Worthy Women's Professional Studies Scholarship *(Vocational/Occupational/Scholarship)* [12212]

Wpromote Digital Marketing Scholarship *(Undergraduate, Graduate/Scholarship)* [12219]

WRI Education Foundation Scholarships - Graduate *(Graduate/Scholarship)* [12103]

WRI Education Foundation Scholarships - High School Seniors *(Undergraduate/Scholarship)* [12104]

WRI Education Foundation Scholarships - Undergraduate *(Undergraduate/Scholarship)* [12105]

Writing the Future *(Undergraduate, College, University/Scholarship)* [4078]

WSAJ Diversity Bar Preparation Scholarship *(Undergraduate/Scholarship)* [11906]

WSGC Scholarships for Incoming Freshmen *(Undergraduate/Scholarship)* [11902]

WSSA Student Paper Competition *(Undergraduate, Graduate/Award, Monetary)* [11987]

WTVD Scholarship *(Undergraduate/Scholarship)* [11217]

WYCUP Scholarship Program *(Other/Scholarship)* [12196]

Wyeth Foundation For American Art Publication Grant *(Other/Grant)* [3504]

Wyeth Foundation Predoctoral Fellowship *(Postdoctorate/Fellowship)* [10222]

Margaret Wyeth Scholarships *(Undergraduate/Scholarship)* [3698]

Xavier Community-Engaged Fellowships *(Undergraduate/Fellowship)* [12227]

Xavier University Presidential Scholarships *(Undergraduate/Scholarship)* [12228]

Xavier University ROTC Scholarships - Air Force ROTC *(Undergraduate/Scholarship)* [12229]

Xavier University ROTC Scholarships - Army ROTC *(Undergraduate/Scholarship)* [12230]

Xavier University Williams Scholarships *(Undergraduate/Scholarship)* [12231]

Reverend H. John and Asako Yamashita Memorial Scholarship *(Graduate/Scholarship)* [6254]

Yamhill County Farm Bureau Scholarships *(Undergraduate/Scholarship)* [8717]

The YASME Foundation Scholarship *(Undergraduate/Scholarship)* [1968]

Minoru Yasui Memorial Scholarship *(Graduate/Scholarship)* [6255]

Willa Yeck Memorial Scholarship Fund *(Undergraduate/Scholarship)* [7108]

The YFU Americas Scholarship *(Undergraduate/Scholarship)* [12276]

Gary Yoshimura Scholarship *(Undergraduate/Scholarship)* [9439]

Young Birder Scholarships *(Undergraduate/Scholarship, Monetary)* [695]

Young Investigators Achievement Award *(Advanced Professional, Professional development, Graduate/Grant)* [6331]

Young People For Fellowships *(Professional development/Fellowship)* [12270]

Donnell B. Young Scholarships *(Undergraduate/Scholarship)* [326]

Yount, Hyde & Barbour Scholarships *(Undergraduate, Graduate/Scholarship)* [11850]

Your Time to Climb Scholarship *(Undergraduate/Scholarship)* [10958]

Youth Empowerment Summit Scholarships *(Undergraduate/Scholarship)* [7722]

Youth Partners Accessing Capital (YPAC) *(Undergraduate/Scholarship)* [390]

YWA Foundation Scholarship *(Graduate, Undergraduate/Scholarship)* [12272]

Zagunis Student Leader Scholarship *(Graduate, Undergraduate/Scholarship)* [7633]

Lisa Zaken Award For Excellence *(Graduate, Undergraduate/Award, Monetary)* [5838]

Aram Zakian Memorial Fund Scholarship *(Undergraduate/Scholarship)* [1906]

Araxie Zakian Memorial Grant *(Undergraduate/Scholarship)* [1907]

James P. and Joy Y. Zana Scholarship *(Undergraduate/Scholarship)* [5127]

Charles Zarigian, Esq. Memorial Award *(Undergraduate/Scholarship)* [1908]

George Zartarian Memorial Grant *(Undergraduate/Scholarship)* [1909]

The Zebra "Show Off Your Stripes" Scholarship *(Undergraduate, Graduate, Vocational/Occupational, Community College/Scholarship)* [12403]

Zelda Walling Vicha Memorial Scholarship *(Undergraduate/Scholarship)* [1540]

The Zenith Fellows Award Program (Zenith) *(Postdoctorate/Fellowship)* [418]

Zenon C. R. Hansen Leadership Scholarship *(Undergraduate/Scholarship)* [7861]

Zeta Chapter Memorial Award *(Undergraduate/Award)* [3699]

Zeta Phi Beta General Undergraduate Scholarship *(Undergraduate/Scholarship)* [12416]

Zeta Phi Beta Sorority General Graduate Fellowships *(Graduate/Fellowship)* [12417]

Zeta Sigma Project 2000 Scholarship *(Undergraduate/Scholarship)* [6484]

Amelia Zollner IPPR/UCL Internship Award *(Undergraduate/Internship)* [5855]

Zombie Apocalypse Scholarship *(Undergraduate, High School/Scholarship)* [11237]

Zuckerman STEM Leadership Program *(Postdoctorate/Scholarship)* [12423]

Zumper Apartments Scholarship *(College, High School/Scholarship)* [12425]

UNITED STATES (BY REGION)

Mid Atlantic Region
NACA Mid Atlantic Higher Education Research Scholarships *(Master's/Scholarship)* [7625]

Midwestern States
Archie Motley Memorial Scholarships for Minority Students *(Graduate/Scholarship)* [7367]

New England States
Dvora Brodie Scholarships *(Graduate, Postgraduate, Undergraduate/Scholarship)* [5447]

Charles H. Hood Foundation Child Health Research Awards Program *(Doctorate/Award)* [5438]

NEEBC Scholarship Award *(Undergraduate, Graduate/Scholarship)* [8244]

NELA Conference Scholarships *(All/Scholarship)* [8246]

Shaw-Worth Memorial Scholarship *(Undergraduate/Scholarship)* [5638]

Northwestern States
The William Bennett, W7PHO, Memorial Scholarship *(Undergraduate/Scholarship)* [1929]

Clair Shirey Scholarships *(Undergraduate/Scholarship)* [11464]

Pacific States
The William Bennett, W7PHO, Memorial Scholarship *(Undergraduate/Scholarship)* [1929]

San Diego County
Doris Hendren Memorial Scholarship *(Undergraduate/Scholarship)* [9811]

Southeastern States
Leighton M. Ballew Directing Scholarship *(Undergraduate/Scholarship)* [10635]

Marian A. Smith Costume Scholarship Award *(Graduate/Scholarship)* [10636]

Polly Holliday Scholarship Award *(Undergraduate/Scholarship, Monetary)* [10637]

Robert Porterfield Graduate Scholarship *(Graduate/Scholarship)* [10638]

Southeastern Theatre Conference Secondary School Scholarship *(Undergraduate/Scholarship)* [10640]

William E. Wilson Scholarship *(Graduate/Scholarship)* [10641]

Southern States
SNRS Dissertation Research Grants *(Doctorate/Grant)* [10659]

Southwestern States
The William Bennett, W7PHO, Memorial Scholarship *(Undergraduate/Scholarship)* [1929]

Stark County
Stark County Bar Association Scholarship Fund *(Undergraduate/Scholarship)* [10793]

U.S. Territories
A.G. Bell School Age Financial Aid Program *(High School/Scholarship, Monetary)* [333]

APIASF Scholarships *(Undergraduate/Scholarship)* [1994]

Barbara A. Cooley Master's Scholarship *(Master's/Scholarship, Award, Monetary)* [10348]

Bill Kane Undergraduate Scholarship *(Undergraduate/Scholarship, Award, Monetary)* [10349]

National MS Society New Jersey Metro Chapter Scholarship Program *(Undergraduate/Scholarship)* [8015]

OAS Scholarships for Professional Development - The ABC of Telecommunications *(Professional development/Scholarship)* [8735]

Western States
Elena Sanchez Memorial WSWS Outstanding Student Scholarship Program *(Graduate, Undergraduate/Scholarship)* [11993]

Western District fellowship *(Graduate/Fellowship)* [5866]

UNITED STATES (BY STATE)

Alabama
ACHE/American Legion Auxiliary Scholarship Program *(Undergraduate/Scholarship)* [205]

ACHE Police Officer's and Firefighter's Survivors Educational Assistance Program (POFSEAP) *(Undergraduate/Scholarship)* [208]

ACHE Senior Adult Scholarship Program *(Undergraduate/Scholarship)* [209]

Alabama Gi Dependents' Educational Benefit Program *(Undergraduate/Scholarship)* [211]

Alabama Horse Council Scholarships *(Undergraduate/Scholarship)* [224]

Alabama National Guard Educational Assistance Program *(Undergraduate/Scholarship)* [212]

Alabama Scholarships for Dependents of Blind Parents *(Undergraduate/Scholarship)* [213]

Alabama Student Assistance Program (ASAP) *(Undergraduate/Scholarship, Grant)* [214]

Alabama Student Grant Program *(Undergraduate/Grant)* [215]

American Legion Florence/Lauderdale Post 11 Scholarship *(Undergraduate, Community College/Scholarship)* [8501]

Diana Ashe-Clayton Memorial Scholarship *(Undergraduate/Scholarship)* [8502]

Birmingham District Alabama Dietetic Association Scholarships *(Graduate, Undergraduate/Scholarship)* [217]

Birmingham Student Scholarships *(Undergraduate/Scholarship)* [2580]

Leon Bradley Scholarship Program *(Undergraduate/Scholarship)* [638]

Johnston Cabaniss Scholarships *(Graduate/Scholarship)* [226]

The Charles Clarke Cordle Memorial Scholarship *(Undergraduate/Scholarship)* [1937]

Don't Wait to Reach Your Potential *(High School/Scholarship)* [9258]

Edward Fennel Mauldin Endowed Scholarship *(Undergraduate, Community College/Scholarship)* [8509]

GIST - Mattie Lou Gist Memorial Scholarship Endowment (Undergraduate, Community College/Scholarship) [8510]

GIST - Orben F. Gist Memorial Scholarship Endowment (Undergraduate, Community College/Scholarship) [8511]

Joshua "Josh" Green Memorial Scholarship Endowment (Undergraduate, Community College/Scholarship) [8512]

Shelby Grissom Memorial Scholarship (Undergraduate, Community College/Scholarship) [8514]

Gulf Coast Hurricane Scholarship (Undergraduate/Scholarship) [10488]

Walston and Jewel Hester Memorial Scholarship Endowment (Undergraduate, Community College/Scholarship) [8516]

Esther McAfee Flippo Hunt Memorial Scholarship (Undergraduate/Scholarship) [8517]

ICS Scholarship (Undergraduate/Scholarship) [8518]

Justice Janie L. Shores Scholarship (Undergraduate/Scholarship) [227]

Legacy Inc. College Undergraduate and Graduate Scholarships (Other/Scholarship) [6766]

Lockheed Martin Scholarship (Undergraduate/Scholarship) [8521]

Bill Lucas Memorial Scholarship Endowment (Undergraduate, Community College/Scholarship) [8522]

McFarffels Scholarships (Undergraduate/Scholarship) [9304]

The Medalist Club Post Graduate Scholarship (Postgraduate/Scholarship) [7203]

NAJA Scholarship (Graduate/Scholarship) [7664]

North Alabama Dietetic Association Scholarships (Undergraduate, Graduate/Scholarship) [218]

Northeast Alabama District Dietetic Association Scholarships (Graduate, Undergraduate/Scholarship) [219]

NW-SCC Faculty and Staff Scholarship (Undergraduate/Scholarship) [8533]

NW-SCC General Foundation Scholarship (Undergraduate/Scholarship) [8534]

Regions Riding Forward Scholarship Essay Contest (Undergraduate, High School/Scholarship) [9618]

Barry "Tyler" Rhea Memorial Scholarship (Undergraduate, Community College/Scholarship) [8535]

Simms Scholarship (Undergraduate, Community College/Scholarship) [8537]

J. Craig and Page T. Smith Scholarship (Undergraduate/Scholarship) [10186]

Southeast Alabama Dietetic Association Scholarships (Graduate, Undergraduate/Scholarship) [221]

Southern Section A&WMA Scholarships (Graduate/Scholarship) [10668]

Karen Thompson Memorial Scholarship (Undergraduate, Community College/Scholarship) [8539]

VFW Post 5140/Paul W. Shockley Sr. Memorial Scholarship (Undergraduate/Scholarship) [8541]

Joseph W. Wade Memorial Scholarship Endowment (Undergraduate, Community College/Scholarship) [8542]

William Verbon Black Scholarship (Undergraduate/Scholarship) [228]

Mary Katherine "Kathy" Williamson Scholarship Fund (Undergraduate/Scholarship) [3665]

Alaska

Accounting Club Scholarship (Undergraduate/Scholarship) [11469]

AIA Alaska College Scholarship Program (Graduate, Undergraduate/Scholarship) [1007]

Alaska Aerospace Development Corporation Scholarships (Undergraduate/Scholarship) [11433]

Alaska Native Medical Center Auxiliary Scholarships (Undergraduate/Scholarship) [11434]

Alaska Press Club Scholarships (Undergraduate/Scholarship) [11435]

Mike Ardaw Scholarships (Undergraduate/Scholarship) [11436]

Paul Arnold Memorial Scholarships (Other/Scholarship) [9288]

Asian and Pacific Islander Queer Sisters Scholarship (APIQS) (Undergraduate/Scholarship) [9289]

Associates in Behavioral Health Scholarships (Graduate/Scholarship) [9290]

Elaine Atwood Scholarship (Undergraduate, Graduate/Scholarship) [11470]

Dr. Jon Baker Memorial Scholarship (Other/Scholarship) [11471]

UAA Michael Baring-Gould Memorial Scholarship (Graduate, Undergraduate/Scholarship) [11472]

Lawrence Bayer Business Administration Scholarships (Undergraduate/Scholarship) [11437]

Charles E. Behlke Engineering Memorial Scholarships (Undergraduate/Scholarship) [11438]

Mark A. Beltz Scholarship (Graduate, Undergraduate/Scholarship) [11473]

Bill and Nell Biggs Scholarship (Undergraduate/Scholarship) [11508]

Bolick Foreign Student Scholarships (Undergraduate/Scholarship) [11439]

Pat Brakke Political Science Scholarship (Undergraduate/Scholarship) [11474]

The Mary Lou Brown Scholarship (Undergraduate/Scholarship) [1931]

Bunnell Scholarships (Undergraduate/Scholarship) [11441]

Loyal D. Burkett Memorial Scholarships (Undergraduate/Scholarship) [11442]

Lyle Carlson Wildlife Management Scholarships (Undergraduate/Scholarship) [11443]

Emi Chance for Aspiring Artists Scholarship (Undergraduate/Scholarship) [11475]

Mable B. Crawford Memorial Scholarships (Undergraduate/Scholarship) [11444]

Brian M. Day Scholarships (Undergraduate, Graduate/Scholarship) [9295]

Deloris Carter Hampton Scholarship (Undergraduate/Scholarship) [9296]

Dennis Coleman Scholarship (Undergraduate/Scholarship) [9297]

Dennis Coleman Scholarships (Undergraduate/Scholarship) [9298]

Donald O. Coffman Scholarship (Graduate, Undergraduate/Scholarship) [9300]

Patricia Hughes Eastaugh Teaching Scholarship (Undergraduate/Scholarship) [11445]

Edward Rollin Clinton Memorial for Music Scholarship (Undergraduate/Scholarship) [11476]

Excellence in Geographic Information Systems Scholarships (Graduate/Scholarship) [11446]

Lydia Fohn-Hansen/Lola Hill Memorial Scholarships (Undergraduate, Graduate/Scholarship) [11447]

Michael D. Ford Memorial Scholarship (Graduate, Undergraduate/Scholarship) [11477]

Johnny & Sarah Frank Scholarships (Undergraduate/Scholarship) [11448]

Jan and Glenn Fredericks Scholarship (Graduate, Undergraduate/Scholarship) [11478]

Glenn Godfrey Sr. Memorial Scholarship (Undergraduate, Graduate/Scholarship) [6589]

Charles F. Gould Endowment Scholarships (Undergraduate/Scholarship) [11449]

Governor William A. Egan Award (Undergraduate/Award) [11480]

Ken Gray Scholarship (Undergraduate/Scholarship) [11481]

Patty Hamilton Early Childhood Development Scholarships (Undergraduate/Scholarship) [11450]

Lenore and George Hedla Accounting Scholarship (Undergraduate/Scholarship) [11482]

John Henderson Endowment Scholarships (Undergraduate/Scholarship) [11451]

Donald Wills Jacobs Scholarships (Undergraduate/Scholarship) [11452]

Chris L. Kleinke Scholarship (Graduate/Scholarship) [11483]

Iver and Cora Knapstad Scholarships (Undergraduate/Scholarship) [11453]

Kris Knudson Memorial Scholarship (Graduate, Undergraduate/Scholarship) [11484]

Arlene Kuhner Memorial Scholarship (Undergraduate/Scholarship) [11485]

Austin E. Lathrop Scholarships (Undergraduate/Scholarship) [11454]

Franklin M. Leach Scholarships (Undergraduate/Scholarship) [11455]

Linda Simmons Memorial Scholarship (Graduate/Scholarship) [240]

Larry Matfay Cultural Heritage Scholarship (Undergraduate, Graduate/Scholarship) [6592]

Dave McCloud Aviation Memorial Scholarships (Undergraduate/Scholarship) [11456]

Melissa J. Wolf Accounting Scholarship (Undergraduate/Scholarship) [11486]

Jack D. Motteler Scholarship (Undergraduate/Scholarship) [9305]

Muriel Hannah Scholarship in Art (Undergraduate, Graduate/Scholarship) [11487]

Andrew Nerland Scholarships (Undergraduate/Scholarship) [11458]

Maureen E. Nolan-Cahill Memorial Scholarship (Undergraduate/Scholarship) [11459]

Nordic Skiing Association of Anchorage Scholarship (Graduate/Scholarship) [242]

Don and Jan O'Dowd/SAA Statewide Scholarships (Undergraduate/Scholarship) [11460]

Diane Olsen Memorial Scholarship (Undergraduate/Scholarship) [11488]

Alvin G. Ott Fish & Wildlife Scholarship (Undergraduate/Scholarship) [11461]

Pat and Cliff Rogers Nursing Scholarship (Undergraduate/Scholarship) [11509]

Pignalberi Public Policy Scholarship (Graduate/Scholarship) [11489]

Pride Foundation Political Leadership Scholarships (Undergraduate/Scholarship) [9306]

Pride Foundation Regional Scholarships (Undergraduate/Scholarship) [9307]

Pride Foundation Scholarships (Undergraduate/Scholarship) [9771]

Pride Foundation Social Work Scholarships (Undergraduate/Scholarship) [9308]

Pt. Lay Memorial Scholarships (Undergraduate/Scholarship) [11462]

April Relyea Scholarship (Graduate, Undergraduate/Scholarship) [11490]

A.D. Al and Maxine Robertson Memorial Scholarship (Undergraduate/Scholarship) [11463]

Dr. Orrin Rongstad Wildlife Scholarship (Undergraduate/Scholarship) [11510]

Rosenberg-Ibarra Scholarships (Graduate/Scholarship) [9312]

RRANN Program Scholarship (Undergraduate/Scholarship) [11491]

Brown Schoenheit Memorial Scholarship (Undergraduate/Scholarship) [11492]

Seldovia Native Association Achievement Scholarships (Undergraduate, Graduate/Scholarship) [9996]

Seldovia Native Association General Scholarships (Undergraduate, Graduate/Scholarship) [9997]

Clair Shirey Scholarships (Undergraduate/Scholarship) [11464]

Kathy Spadoni Memorial Scholarships (Graduate/Scholarship) [9313]

Sheri Stears Education Scholarship (Undergraduate/Scholarship) [11494]

Sturgulewski Family Scholarship (Graduate, Undergraduate/Scholarship) [11495]

UAA Alaska Kidney Foundation Scholarship (Graduate, Undergraduate/Scholarship) [11496]

UAA Alumni Association Scholarship (Undergraduate/Scholarship) [11497]

UAA Ardell French Memorial Scholarship (Undergraduate/Scholarship) [11498]

UAA College of Business and Public Policy Scholarships - American Marketing Association & F.X. Dale Tran Memorial Scholarship (Graduate, Undergraduate/Scholarship) [11499]

UAA Eveline Schuster Memorial Award/Scholarship (Graduate, Undergraduate/Scholarship) [11500]

UAA Friends of the Performing Arts Scholarship (Undergraduate/Scholarship) [11501]

UAA GCI Scholarship (Undergraduate/Scholarship) [11502]

UAA Kimura Scholarship Fund for Illustration (Undergraduate/Scholarship) [11503]

UAA Kimura Scholarship Fund for Photography (Undergraduate/Scholarship) [11504]

UAA Quanterra Scholarship (Master's, Doctorate/Scholarship) [11505]

UAF College of Liberal Arts - Anchorage Daily News Journalism Awards (Undergraduate/Scholarship) [11514]

Ric Ulrich and Chuck Pischke Scholarships (Undergraduate/Scholarship) [9315]

University of Alaska Regents' Scholarship (Undergraduate/Scholarship) [11512]

Wells Fargo Career Scholarship (Undergraduate/Scholarship) [11506]

Arthur N. Wilson, MD, Scholarships (Undergraduate/Scholarship) [1113]

Guy A. Woodings Scholarships (Undergraduate/Scholarship) [11465]

Wozumi Family Scholarships (Undergraduate/Scholarship) [9318]

Ralph Yetka Memorial Scholarships (Undergraduate/Scholarship) [11466]

Joan C. Yoder Memorial Nursing Scholarships (Undergraduate/Scholarship) [11467]

Arizona

Marvin A. Andrews Scholarships/Internships (Graduate, Undergraduate/Internship, Scholarship) [1805]

Arizona Nursery Association Scholarships (Undergraduate, Graduate, College, University/Scholarship) [1812]

ASCPA High School Scholarships (Graduate/Scholarship, Monetary) [1816]

ASCPA Private University Scholarships (Master's, Graduate/Scholarship) [1817]

Walt Bartram Memorial Education Scholarship (Undergraduate/Scholarship) [10384]

BOCA Scholarship (Undergraduate/Scholarship) [8796]

The Central Arizona DX Association Scholarship (Undergraduate/Scholarship) [1932]

Charles A. Esser Memorial Scholarships (Graduate/Scholarship) [1806]

Gail Goodell Folsom Memorial Scholarships (Undergraduate/Scholarship) [7542]

Kappa Delta Phi Scholarship (Postgraduate/Scholarship) [1179]

Los Abogados LSAT Pipeline Fellowship (Graduate/Fellowship) [6892]

Phoenix Pride Scholarship (Undergraduate/Scholarship) [9137]

Rocky Mountain Coal Mining Institute Engineering/Geology Scholarships (Four Year College/Scholarship) [9727]

Rocky Mountain Coal Mining Institute Technical Scholarships (Two Year College/Scholarship) [9728]

Graduate Research Fellows (GRF) (Graduate/Fellowship) [9969]

William C. Ray, CIH, CSP Arizona Scholarship (Doctorate/Scholarship) [1575]

Arkansas

APHA Student Scholarship (Undergraduate, Graduate/Scholarship) [1834]

ARAFCS Doctoral Scholarship (Doctorate, Graduate/Scholarship) [1821]

ARAFCS Masters Scholarship (Graduate, Master's/Scholarship) [1822]

Arkansas Single Parent Scholarship (Undergraduate, Graduate/Scholarship) [1836]

ArLA Scholarship (Graduate/Scholarship) [1829]

Benbrook Scholarship (Graduate/Scholarship) [1838]

Arkansas Nursing Foundation - Dorothea Fund Scholarships (Other/Scholarship) [1831]

Arkansas Nursing Foundation - Mary Gray Scholarships (Other/Scholarship) [1832]

Randy Henry Memorial Scholarship (Undergraduate/Scholarship) [9343]

Lone Star GIA Associate and Alumni Scholarships (Undergraduate/Scholarship) [4879]

Randall Mathis Scholarship for Environmental Studies Fund (Undergraduate/Scholarship) [1824]

The Fred R. McDaniel Memorial Scholarship (Undergraduate/Scholarship) [1948]

Memphis Access and Diversity Scholarships (Graduate/Scholarship) [11609]

NAJA Scholarship (Graduate/Scholarship) [7664]

North Dakota Division Scholarships (Undergraduate, Graduate/Scholarship) [7373]

Ozarks Division of Midwest Dairy Educational Award (Undergraduate/Scholarship) [7374]

Regions Riding Forward Scholarship Essay Contest (Undergraduate, High School/Scholarship) [9618]

Hatton W. Sumners Scholarships (Undergraduate/Scholarship) [8610]

California

The Abas Law Foundation Scholarship (Graduate, Postgraduate/Scholarship) [1992]

Above and Beyond Scholarship (Graduate/Scholarship) [2826]

Alice Newell Joslyn Medical Scholarship (Undergraduate, Doctorate, Master's/Scholarship) [2460]

Marvin Anmuth Scholarship (Undergraduate, Graduate/Scholarship) [6269]

Connie "Chelo" Armendariz Memorial Scholarships (Undergraduate/Scholarship) [9521]

Richard E. Arnason Court Scholarship Program (Undergraduate/Scholarship) [3816]

Association of California Water Agencies Scholarship (Undergraduate/Scholarship) [2076]

Association for Women in Architecture Scholarships (Undergraduate/Scholarship) [2309]

Athena San Diego Pinnacle Scholarship (Undergraduate/Scholarship) [9799]

Ballard Family Foundation Scholarships (Undergraduate/Scholarship) [9800]

Barta-Lehman Musical Scholarship (Undergraduate/Scholarship) [9801]

Walt Bartram Memorial Education Scholarship (Undergraduate/Scholarship) [10384]

Hazel Reed Baumeister Scholarship Program (Undergraduate/Scholarship) [10130]

Bay Area Minority Law Student Scholarship (Graduate, Undergraduate/Scholarship) [2433]

BECA General Scholarship (Undergraduate/Scholarship) [2461]

James R. and Geraldine F. Bertelsen Scholarship (Undergraduate/Scholarship) [9802]

The Brandenburg Education Scholarship (College, University, Undergraduate/Scholarship) [6270]

Breslauer Family Scholarships (Undergraduate/Scholarship) [9803]

Louise A. Broderick San Diego County Scholarship (Undergraduate/Scholarship) [9804]

California Association of Family and Consumer Sciences - San Diego Chapter Scholarship (Undergraduate, Graduate/Scholarship) [9805]

California Council of the Blind Scholarships (Undergraduate, Graduate, Vocational/Occupational/Scholarship) [2794]

Career Development Grant in molecular genetics (Advanced Professional, Professional development/Grant) [11071]

CGA Scholarships (Undergraduate/Scholarship) [2812]

CHEA Undergraduate Scholarship Program for Students with Disabilities (Undergraduate/Scholarship) [2814]

Chicana / Latina Foundation Scholarship Program (Graduate, Undergraduate/Scholarship) [3289]

Clair A. Hill Scholarship (Undergraduate/Scholarship) [2077]

Community Bank - Lee Guggisberg Foundation Memorial Scholarships (Undergraduate/Scholarship) [9535]

CPYC/CNOA Youth Leadership Scholarship (Undergraduate/Scholarship) [2820, 2822]

Crain Scholarship Program (Undergraduate/Scholarship) [10131]

Crawford Scholarship (Undergraduate/Scholarship) [9808]

Curry Awards for Girls and Young Women (Undergraduate/Scholarship) [10132]

David Weiss Scholarship Program (Undergraduate/Scholarship) [12268]

Death Valley '49ers Scholarships (Undergraduate/Scholarship) [3985]

Distracted Driving Scholarship (High School, Two Year College, University/Scholarship) [6188]

Hans and Margaret Doe Charitable Trust Scholarship (Community College, Vocational/Occupational, College, University, Undergraduate, Graduate/Scholarship) [9810]

Dorothy M. Bolyard Memorial Scholarship (Undergraduate/Scholarship) [9812]

James Echols Scholarship Award (Undergraduate/Recognition, Award, Scholarship) [2781]

Edith Macias Vann Southern California (Undergraduate/Scholarship) [12151]

Escondido High School (EHS) Class of '56 Scholarship (Community College, Vocational/Occupational/Scholarship) [9813]

James Mackenzie Fellows Scholarships Honoring Gertrude Baccus (Undergraduate/Scholarship) [9543]

James Mackenzie Fellows Scholarships Honoring William Cunningham (Undergraduate/Scholarship) [9544]

Frank H. Ault Scholarship (Undergraduate/Scholarship) [9814]

The Nathan J. and Virginia H. Friedman College Scholarship (Undergraduate, Four Year College, University/Scholarship) [6271]

G-2 Summer Portuguese Language Program (Undergraduate/Grant) [6942]

G-3 Summer Program in Portugal (Postgraduate/Grant) [6943]

Getty Foundation Library Research Grants (Professional development/Grant) [4954]

The Elaine and Barry Gilbert College Scholarship (Undergraduate/Scholarship) [6272]

Glendale Latino Association Scholarships (Undergraduate/Scholarship) [4999]

Bobette Bibo Gugliotta Memorial Scholarships for Creative Writing (Undergraduate/Scholarship) [10133]

Leslie Jane Hahn Memorial Scholarships (Undergraduate/Scholarship) [9816]

Ralph Hale and Martha L. Ruppert Educational Scholarship (Undergraduate/Grant) [10134]

Hans H. and Margaret B. Doe Scholarship (Graduate, Undergraduate/Scholarship) [9817]

Harry Munoz Memorial Scholarship (Undergraduate/Scholarship) [9550]

Herman H. Derksen Scholarship (Undergraduate/Scholarship) [9820]

The Stephanie G. Hoffman Scholarship (Graduate, Undergraduate/Scholarship) [6274]

Cathy Hopper Memorial Scholarship (Undergraduate/Scholarship) [9821]

Albert W. and Mildred Hubbard Scholarships (Undergraduate/Scholarship) [9822]

Jean Wright-Elson Scholarship (Doctorate, Graduate, Undergraduate/Scholarship) [9823]

The Robert L. Johns Vocational Scholarship (Vocational/Occupational/Scholarship) [4871]

Nancy Johnston Memorial Scholarships (Graduate, Undergraduate/Scholarship) [10956]

Judith Keller Marx Krumholz Scholarship (Graduate/Scholarship) [9824]

Kappa Delta Phi Scholarship (Postgraduate/Scholarship) [1179]

Kawano Family Scholarships (Undergraduate/Scholarship) [9825]

John F. Kennedy Scholarship Award (Undergraduate/Recognition, Award, Scholarship) [2782]

Kiwanis Club of Escondido Scholarship (Undergraduate/Scholarship) [9826]

LAFS - Cal State University San Marcos General Scholarships (Undergraduate/Scholarship) [2462]

Latinos in Technology Scholarship (Undergraduate/Scholarship) [10136]

Leadership for Diversity Paraprofessional Scholarship (Advanced Professional/Scholarship) [2828]

Leadership for Diversity TL Scholarship (Master's/Scholarship) [2829]

Patrick Ledden Honorary Scholarships (Undergraduate/Scholarship) [9827]

Lemon Grove Education Foundation Scholarship (Undergraduate, Graduate/Scholarship) [9829]

David C. Lizárraga Fellowship (Graduate/Fellowship) [10941]

Luis Arreola Memorial Scholarship (Undergraduate/Scholarship) [9831]

Alexander M. and June L. Maisin Foundation Scholarship (Undergraduate/Scholarship) [6275]

Malini E. Sathyadev Memorial Scholarship (Undergraduate/Scholarship) [9832]

Mario Pedrozzi Scholarship *(Undergraduate, Graduate/Scholarship)* [8950]

Marvin Arnold and Irene Jaquetta Heye Scholarship *(Undergraduate/Scholarship)* [9833]

McKinley Elementary School PTA Scholarship *(Undergraduate/Scholarship)* [9561]

Mission Bay Hospital Auxiliary Scholarship *(Undergraduate/Scholarship)* [9834]

MKC/Preuss Scholarship *(Undergraduate, Community College, University/Scholarship)* [9835]

Music Teachers' Association of California Goodlin Scholarship *(High School/Scholarship)* [9836]

Napoleon A. Jones, III Memorial Scholarship *(Undergraduate/Scholarship)* [9837]

Northside Booster Club - Felix R. Sepulveda Memorial Scholarship *(Undergraduate/Scholarship)* [9567]

The Gail Karp Orgell Scholarship *(Four Year College, University, Undergraduate/Scholarship)* [6276]

Pacific Beacon Scholarship *(Community College, University, Undergraduate, Vocational/Occupational/Scholarship)* [9838]

Casilda Pagan Educational/Vocational Scholarships *(Graduate, Undergraduate, Postgraduate/Scholarship)* [5594]

Ben Palacio Scholarships *(Undergraduate/Scholarship)* [11387]

Pearman Family Scholarship *(Undergraduate/Scholarship)* [9839]

Pollard-Bailey Scholarship *(Undergraduate/Scholarship)* [9840]

Qualcomm San Diego Science, Technology, Engineering and Mathematics Scholarship *(Undergraduate/Scholarship)* [9841]

Rancho Bernardo/Smith Scholarship *(Undergraduate/Scholarship)* [9842]

Randy Williams Scholarship *(Undergraduate/Scholarship)* [9843]

Ray And Mary Bell Scholarship *(Undergraduate/Scholarship)* [9844]

The Shirley and Robert Raymer College Scholarship *(Four Year College, University, Undergraduate/Scholarship)* [6277]

Rebecca Lee Crumpler, M.D. Scholarship *(Advanced Professional/Scholarship)* [2070]

Redlands Footlighters, Inc. - Merle and Peggy Williams Scholarship *(Undergraduate/Scholarship)* [9581]

Redlands High School Aquatics Booster Club Scholarship *(Undergraduate/Scholarship)* [9583]

Redlands Rotary Club Foundation Discretionary Scholarship *(Undergraduate/Scholarship)* [9593]

Redlands Rotary Club Scholarship - Ernest L. Cronemeyer *(Undergraduate/Scholarship)* [9595]

Redlands Teachers Association Scholarship *(Undergraduate/Scholarship)* [9596]

Reuben H. Fleet Memorial Scholarship *(Undergraduate/Scholarship)* [9845]

Robert G. Campbell Scholarship *(Undergraduate/Scholarship)* [9598]

Charles and Ruth Ronin Memorial Scholarships *(Undergraduate/Scholarship)* [9600]

The Rotary Club of Rancho Bernardo Sunrise Community Service Scholarships *(Undergraduate/Scholarship)* [9846]

Ruppert Scholarship *(Undergraduate/Scholarship)* [2831]

Ruth E. Jenkins Scholarship *(Undergraduate/Scholarship)* [9847]

SALEF Health Career Scholarships *(Undergraduate, Graduate/Scholarship)* [9791]

The San Diego Foundation Community Scholarship I *(Undergraduate/Scholarship)* [9848]

The San Diego Foundation Community Scholarship II *(Undergraduate/Scholarship)* [9849]

San Pasqual Academy Scholarship *(Undergraduate/Scholarship)* [9850]

Leo and Trinidad Sanchez Scholarships *(Undergraduate/Scholarship)* [10138]

Schatz Energy Fellowships for Graduate Studies *(Graduate/Fellowship, Recognition)* [5640]

The S.F. Humanities, Inc: Leo Hills Scholarship *(Undergraduate, Graduate/Scholarship)* [6278]

Harvey L. Simmons Memorial Scholarships *(Undergraduate/Scholarship)* [9851]

Smiley Elementary School PTA Scholarship - Beverly Roberts Memorial *(Undergraduate/Scholarship)* [9603]

Soroptimist International of Redlands Scholarship *(Undergraduate/Scholarship)* [9604]

Southern California Lambda Medical Student Scholarships *(Undergraduate, Graduate/Scholarship)* [10650]

SPROWT Scholarship for Women *(Undergraduate/Scholarship)* [5201]

Steve Petix Journalism Scholarship *(Undergraduate/Scholarship)* [9853]

Mark and Karla Stuart Family Scholarship *(Undergraduate/Scholarship)* [9854]

Stuart L. Noderer Memorial Scholarship *(Undergraduate/Scholarship)* [9855]

UCSD Black Alumni Scholarship for Arts and Humanities *(Undergraduate/Scholarship)* [9857]

U.S. Bank Scholarships *(Undergraduate/Scholarship)* [9859]

University Club Lamp of Learning Scholarship *(Undergraduate, University/Scholarship)* [9860]

Winifred Van Hagen/Rosalind Cassidy Scholarship Award *(Undergraduate, Graduate/Recognition, Award)* [2783]

Diana Venable Scholarship *(Undergraduate, Community College/Scholarship)* [9861]

Vincent Trotter Health Care Scholarship *(Undergraduate/Scholarship)* [9862]

Marjorie Rose Warren Scholarship *(Undergraduate/Scholarship)* [9863]

Weissbuch Family Scholarship *(Undergraduate/Scholarship)* [9864]

The Leon And Margaret Williams Scholarship *(Undergraduate/Scholarship)* [9866]

Willis W. and Ethel M. Clark Foundation Investment in Community Fellowship *(Graduate/Fellowship)* [3432]

Wilma Motley Memorial California Merit Scholarship *(Undergraduate/Scholarship)* [862]

The Ronald P. Wilmot Scholarship *(Undergraduate, Graduate/Scholarship)* [6280]

Colorado

All Smiles Dental Group Scholarship *(Undergraduate/Scholarship)* [342]

Broadcast Education and Development Program *(Other/Scholarship)* [3526]

Colorado Nurses Association: Virginia Paulson Memorial Scholarship *(Graduate, Undergraduate/Scholarship)* [3532]

Dwight A. Hamilton Scottish Rite Foundation of Colorado Graduate Scholarship in Speech-Language Pathology *(Graduate/Scholarship)* [9984]

El Pomar Fellowship *(Graduate/Fellowship)* [4330]

Highlands Ranch Dental Group Scholarship *(Undergraduate, High School/Scholarship)* [5508]

H.M. Muffly Memorial Scholarship *(Graduate, Undergraduate/Scholarship)* [3535]

Iris Scholarship *(Undergraduate/Scholarship)* [6447]

Kip Dental and Orthodontics Scholarship *(Undergraduate/Scholarship)* [6562]

LAEF Scholarships *(Undergraduate/Scholarship)* [6675]

Rocky Mountain Coal Mining Institute Engineering/Geology Scholarships *(Four Year College/Scholarship)* [9727]

Rocky Mountain Coal Mining Institute Technical Scholarships *(Two Year College/Scholarship)* [9728]

Roy Anderson Memorial Scholarship *(Graduate, Undergraduate/Scholarship)* [3536]

Stephen T. Marchello Scholarship *(Graduate/Scholarship)* [7030]

Patty Walter Memorial Scholarships *(Graduate, Undergraduate/Scholarship)* [3537]

Connecticut

Frederick G. Adams Scholarship Fund *(Undergraduate/Scholarship)* [5312]

Ann Liguori Foundation Sports Media Scholarship *(Graduate, Undergraduate/Scholarship)* [8366]

Associated General Contractors of Connecticut Scholarships (AGC/CT Scholarship) *(Undergraduate/Scholarship)* [3759]

Bar President's Scholarship *(Undergraduate/Scholarship)* [11931]

Thomas M. Blake Memorial Scholarships *(Undergraduate/Scholarship)* [3753]

Gerald J. and Helen Bogen Fund *(Undergraduate/Scholarship)* [5225]

Brian Cummins Memorial Scholarship *(Undergraduate/Scholarship)* [5317]

C. Rodney Demarest Memorial Scholarship *(Undergraduate/Scholarship)* [5318]

Casey Family Services Alumni Scholarship *(Undergraduate, Master's, Vocational/Occupational/Scholarship)* [4693]

The College Club of Hartford Scholarships *(Undergraduate/Scholarship)* [5319]

CALS Memorial Scholarship *(Undergraduate/Scholarship)* [3751]

Connecticut Association of Latinos in Higher Education Scholarships *(Undergraduate/Scholarship)* [3754, 5320]

Julia B. DeCapua Fund *(Undergraduate/Scholarship)* [5226]

Dorothy E. Hofmann Pembroke Scholarship *(Undergraduate/Scholarship)* [5325]

Charles Dubose Scholarships *(Undergraduate/Scholarship)* [5326]

Edward Traurig Scholarship *(Undergraduate/Scholarship)* [11932]

Herman and Bess Glazer Scholarship Fund *(Undergraduate/Scholarship)* [5227]

Hartford Whalers Booster Club Scholarship *(Undergraduate/Scholarship)* [5353]

Eileen Kraus Scholarship *(Two Year College, Four Year College/Scholarship)* [3763]

Les Dames D'Escoffier New York Corporate Scholarship *(Undergraduate/Scholarship)* [6777]

Lighthouse International Scholarships - College-bound Awards *(High School, Undergraduate/Scholarship)* [6856]

Lighthouse International Scholarships - Graduate Awards *(Graduate, Postgraduate/Scholarship)* [6857]

Lighthouse International Scholarships - Undergraduate Awards *(Undergraduate/Scholarship)* [6858]

Mary Main Memorial Scholarship *(Undergraduate/Scholarship)* [5339]

ARTC Glenn Moon Scholarships *(Undergraduate/Scholarship)* [5340]

NASSLEO Scholarships - Region I *(Undergraduate/Scholarship)* [7688]

The New England FEMARA Scholarship *(Undergraduate/Scholarship)* [1951]

Full Pellegrini Scholarship *(Undergraduate, Graduate/Scholarship)* [10896]

Rosa Quezada Memorial Education Scholarships *(Undergraduate/Scholarship)* [3755]

Mary C. Rawlins Scholarships *(Graduate/Scholarship)* [5342]

Rhea Sourifman Caplin Memorial Scholarship *(Undergraduate/Scholarship)* [5343]

John Soto Scholarships *(Undergraduate/Scholarship)* [3756]

Hazaros Tabakoglu Scholarship Fund *(Undergraduate/Scholarship)* [8309]

Marta Vallin Memorial Scholarships *(Undergraduate/Scholarship)* [3757]

Waterbury Bar Association Scholarship *(Undergraduate/Scholarship)* [11933]

WBA Paralegal/Legal Assistant Scholarship *(Undergraduate/Scholarship)* [11934]

Yankee Clipper Contest Club Youth Scholarship *(Undergraduate/Scholarship)* [1967]

Young Christian Leaders Scholarships *(Undergraduate/Scholarship)* [12266]

Zimmermann Scholarship *(Graduate/Scholarship)* [10898]

Delaware

Horatio Alger Delaware Scholarships *(Undergraduate/Scholarship)* [5562]

Chrysler Technical Scholarship Fund *(Undergraduate/Scholarship)* [3996]

Drew Smith Memorial Scholarship (Undergraduate/
Scholarship) [3563]

Dunkin' Donuts Philadelphia Regional Scholarship
Program (Undergraduate/Scholarship) [9941]

Generation III Scholarship (Undergraduate/Scholarship) [4285]

German Society Scholarships (Undergraduate/
Scholarship) [4951]

Gruwell Scholarship (Undergraduate/Scholarship)
[3569]

Lighthouse International Scholarships - College-
bound Awards (High School, Undergraduate/
Scholarship) [6856]

Lighthouse International Scholarships - Graduate
Awards (Graduate, Postgraduate/Scholarship)
[6857]

Lighthouse International Scholarships - Undergraduate Awards (Undergraduate/Scholarship) [6858]

NASSLEO Scholarships - Region I (Undergraduate/
Scholarship) [7688]

Full Pellegrini Scholarship (Undergraduate, Gradu-
ate/Scholarship) [10896]

Richard and Patricia Hazel Minority Scholarship
Award (Undergraduate/Scholarship) [3577]

ROFL Scholarship (Undergraduate, College, Univer-
sity/Scholarship) [9236]

Zimmermann Scholarship (Graduate/Scholarship)
[10898]

District of Columbia

Abramson Scholarship (Undergraduate/Scholar-
ship) [37]

Horatio Alger District of Columbia, Maryland and
Virginia Scholarships (Undergraduate/Scholar-
ship) [5563]

Dr. Johnella Banks Memorial Scholarships (Under-
graduate/Scholarship) [2610]

FCBA Foundation College Scholarship Program
(Undergraduate/Scholarship) [4511]

ILSA Internships (Undergraduate/Internship) [6029]

Dwight P. Jacobus Scholarships (Undergraduate/
Scholarship) [2277]

Lighthouse International Scholarships - College-
bound Awards (High School, Undergraduate/
Scholarship) [6856]

Lighthouse International Scholarships - Graduate
Awards (Graduate, Postgraduate/Scholarship)
[6857]

Lighthouse International Scholarships - Undergraduate Awards (Undergraduate/Scholarship) [6858]

NASSLEO Scholarships - Region I (Undergraduate/
Scholarship) [7688]

National Federation of the Blind Scholarship Program (Undergraduate/Scholarship, Monetary)
[7878]

Margaret Pemberton Scholarships (Undergraduate/
Scholarship) [2611]

Public Service Fellows Internship Program - Center
for Government Leadership (Undergraduate,
Graduate/Internship) [8904]

Public Service Fellows Internship Program - Education and Outreach (Undergraduate, Graduate,
Professional development/Internship) [8905]

Public Service Fellows Internship Program - Government Transformation and Agency Partnerships
(Undergraduate, Graduate, Professional develop-
ment/Internship) [8906]

Public Service Fellows Internship Program - Human
Resources (Professional development, Other/In-
ternship) [8907]

Public Service Internship Program - Communications (Undergraduate, Graduate, Professional de-
velopment/Internship) [8908]

Public Service Internship Program - Development
(Undergraduate, Graduate, Professional develop-
ment/Internship) [8909]

Public Service Internship Program - Government
Affairs (Undergraduate, Graduate, Professional
development/Internship) [8910]

Public Service Internship Program - Research and
Program Evaluation Focus (Undergraduate,
Graduate, Professional development/Internship)
[8911]

Florida

Emily and Roland Abraham Educational Fund (Un-
dergraduate/Scholarship) [3708]

Horatio Alger Florida Scholarships (Undergraduate/
Scholarship) [5564]

American Association of University Women(AAUW)
Sue Gottcent Memorial Scholarship Fund (Undergraduate, Graduate/Scholarship) [10670]

Anne Sturrock Nursing Scholarship Fund (Undergraduate, Graduate/Scholarship) [10672]

The Bailey Family Foundation College Scholarship
Program (Undergraduate/Scholarship) [2403]

The Bailey Family Foundation High School Scholarships Program (Undergraduate/Scholarship)
[2404]

Leon Bradley Scholarship Program (Undergraduate/
Scholarship) [638]

Celler Legal P.A. Employment Skills Scholarship
Program (Undergraduate/Scholarship) [3206]

Central Florida Jazz Society Scholarships (Under-
graduate/Scholarship) [3242]

ChairScholars Florida Scholarship Program (Under-
graduate/Scholarship) [3274]

Chip Johnson Memorial Scholarship Fund (Under-
graduate/Scholarship) [10675]

COUSE-Gram Scholarship Fund (Undergraduate/
Scholarship) [10677]

D&A Florida Scholarships (Undergraduate/Scholar-
ship) [10678]

David G. Robinson Arts Scholarship Fund (Under-
graduate/Scholarship) [10679]

The Davis Educational Fund (Undergraduate, Voca-
tional/Occupational/Scholarship) [3711]

Doc Keen Memorial Scholarship Fund (Undergradu-
ate/Scholarship) [10680]

Doris W. Frey Memorial Scholarship Fund (Gradu-
ate/Scholarship) [10681]

Drs. Ira and Udaya Dash Nursing Scholarship Fund
(Undergraduate, Graduate/Scholarship) [10682]

Dunbar Heritage Scholarship Fund (Undergraduate/
Scholarship) [10683]

Faye Lynn Roberts Education Scholarship Fund
(Undergraduate, Graduate/Scholarship) [10684]

FICPA Educational Foundation 1040K Race Scholarships (Undergraduate/Scholarship, Award)
[4636]

Florida Education Fund McKnight Doctoral Fellowship (Graduate/Fellowship) [4629]

Florida Nurses Foundation Scholarships (Undergraduate, Master's, Doctorate/Scholarship) [4640]

Florida Public Transportation Association Scholarships (FPTA) (Undergraduate, Graduate/Scholar-
ship) [1301]

Clay Ford Florida Board of Accountancy Minority
Scholarships (Undergraduate/Scholarship) [4627]

Francis Harris Gresham Scholarship Fund (Under-
graduate/Scholarship) [10685]

James Franklin and Dorothy J. Warnell Scholarship
Fund (Undergraduate, Vocational/Occupational/
Scholarship) [3713]

Gulf Coast Hurricane Scholarship (Undergraduate/
Scholarship) [10488]

IRARC Memorial, Joseph P. Rubino, WA4MMD,
Scholarship (Undergraduate/Scholarship) [1946]

Isabel Mayer Kirkpatrick Scholarship Fund (Under-
graduate/Scholarship) [10687]

James Bilder Scholarship Fund (Undergraduate/
Scholarship) [10688]

John I. & Madeleine R. Taeni Scholarship Fund (Un-
dergraduate/Scholarship) [10689]

John M. & Mary A. Shanley Memorial Scholarship
(Undergraduate, Graduate/Scholarship) [10690]

V.J. Johnson Memorial Scholarships (Undergradu-
ate/Scholarship) [642]

Jordan Abdo Memorial Scholarship Fund (Under-
graduate/Scholarship) [10692]

Judge Isaac Anderson, Jr. Scholarship Fund (Under-
graduate/Scholarship) [10693]

Judge William J. Nelson Scholarship Fund (Under-
graduate/Scholarship) [10694]

Kappa Delta Phi Scholarship (Postgraduate/Scholar-
ship) [1179]

The Kids' Chance of Florida Scholarship Program
(All/Scholarship) [6550]

Lewis B. Barber Memorial Scholarship Fund (Under-
graduate/Scholarship) [10695]

Lighthouse International Scholarships - College-
bound Awards (High School, Undergraduate/
Scholarship) [6856]

Lighthouse International Scholarships - Graduate
Awards (Graduate, Postgraduate/Scholarship)
[6857]

Lighthouse International Scholarships - Undergraduate Awards (Undergraduate/Scholarship) [6858]

Love Of Bonita Empowerment Scholarship Fund
(Undergraduate/Scholarship) [10696]

NAJA Scholarship (Graduate/Scholarship) [7664]

Regions Riding Forward Scholarship Essay Contest
(Undergraduate, High School/Scholarship) [9618]

Reuben R. Cowles Youth Educational Award (Undergraduate, Graduate/Award) [1059]

Robert A. Kleckner Scholarship Fund (Undergraduate, Graduate/Scholarship) [10699]

Robert B. And Dorothy Pence Scholarship Fund
(Undergraduate/Scholarship) [10700]

Robert C. & Margaret A. Schikora Scholarship Fund
(Undergraduate/Scholarship) [10701]

The Rotary Club of Cape Coral Goldcoast Scholarship (Undergraduate/Scholarship) [3149]

Roy W. Likins Scholarship (Undergraduate, Gradu-
ate/Scholarship) [1646]

Ruth Messmer Scholarship Fund (Undergraduate/
Scholarship) [10702]

ServiceMaster By Glenns Preparation Scholarship
(University, Undergraduate, Vocational/Occupa-
tional/Scholarship) [10022]

Southwest Florida Community Foundation College
Assistance Scholarships (Undergraduate/Scholar-
ship) [10703]

Southwest Florida Deputy Sheriffs Association Fund
(Undergraduate/Scholarship) [10704]

Jacki Tuckfield Memorial Graduate Business Scholarship Fund (Doctorate, Graduate, Master's/Schol-
arship) [7299]

William L. Graddy Law School Scholarship Fund
(Graduate/Scholarship) [10705]

Ted G. Wilson Memorial Scholarships (Undergradu-
ate/Scholarship) [9338]

Georgia

Horatio Alger Georgia Scholarships (Undergraduate/
Scholarship) [5565]

Annual Eichholz Scholarship (Graduate/Scholar-
ship) [4324]

Best Foot Forward Scholarship (Undergraduate,
College, University/Scholarship) [5203]

Leon Bradley Scholarship Program (Undergraduate/
Scholarship) [638]

The Charles Clarke Cordle Memorial Scholarship
(Undergraduate/Scholarship) [1937]

E. Lanier (Lanny) Finch Scholarship (Undergradu-
ate/Scholarship) [4923]

GACFE Scholarship Program (Graduate, Under-
graduate/Scholarship) [2134]

George and Pearl Strickland Scholarship Fund
(Graduate, Undergraduate/Scholarship) [3586]

Georgia Engineering Foundation Scholarships
(Graduate/Scholarship) [4928]

Gene Henson Scholarship (Undergraduate/Scholar-
ship) [2340]

Philip R. Karr, III Scholarship Fund (Graduate/Schol-
arship) [4926]

Larry Dean Davis Scholarship (Undergraduate/
Scholarship) [8938]

Lighthouse International Scholarships - College-
bound Awards (High School, Undergraduate/
Scholarship) [6856]

Lighthouse International Scholarships - Graduate
Awards (Graduate, Postgraduate/Scholarship)
[6857]

Lighthouse International Scholarships - Undergraduate Awards (Undergraduate/Scholarship) [6858]

Durwood McAlister Scholarship (Undergraduate/
Scholarship) [4935]

Mollie Lukken Memorial Scholarship (Graduate,
Other/Scholarship) [6345]

Morris Newspaper Corporation Scholarship (Under-
graduate/Scholarship) [4936]

The Edna A. Noblin Scholarship (Undergraduate/
Scholarship) [6659]

NWAG Georgia Students Scholarship *(Undergraduate/Scholarship)* [8395]

Reglons Riding Forward Scholarship Essay Contest *(Undergraduate, High School/Scholarship)* [9618]

Reuben R. Cowles Youth Educational Award *(Undergraduate, Graduate/Award)* [1059]

William C. Rogers Scholarship *(Undergraduate/Scholarship)* [4937]

Southern Section A&WMA Scholarships *(Graduate/Scholarship)* [10668]

The Charles B. Staat Memorial Scholarship *(Graduate/Scholarship)* [10741]

Steve Dearduff Scholarship Fund *(Graduate, Undergraduate/Scholarship)* [3587]

United Way Of Forsyth County Scholarship *(Other/Scholarship)* [6660]

Virginia M. Smyth Scholarship *(Graduate/Scholarship)* [4930]

Watson-Brown Scholarship *(Undergraduate/Scholarship)* [11936]

Ted G. Wilson Memorial Scholarships *(Undergraduate/Scholarship)* [9338]

Guam

ABC Stores Jumpstart Scholarship Fund *(Undergraduate, University, College, Vocational/Occupational, Graduate/Scholarship)* [5377]

Hawaii

A&B Ohana Scholarship Fund *(Undergraduate, College, Two Year College, Vocational/Occupational/Scholarship)* [5375]

AAUW Honolulu Branch Education Funds *(Undergraduate, Graduate, Master's/Scholarship)* [5376]

ABC Stores Jumpstart Scholarship Fund *(Undergraduate, University, College, Vocational/Occupational, Graduate/Scholarship)* [5377]

Aiea General Hospital Association Scholarship *(Undergraduate, College, Two Year College, University/Scholarship)* [5378]

Daniel K. and Millie Akaka Ohana Scholarship Fund *(Undergraduate/Scholarship)* [5379]

Anthony Alexander, Andrew Delos Reyes & Jeremy Tolentino Memorial Fund *(Undergraduate, University, College, Two Year College/Scholarship)* [5380]

Aloha Prince Hall Hawaii Foundation Fund Scholarship *(Undergraduate, College, University/Scholarship)* [5381]

Bank of Hawaii Foundation Scholarship Fund *(Undergraduate, University, College, Two Year College/Scholarship)* [5382]

Bick Bickson Scholarship Fund *(Undergraduate, Graduate/Award)* [5383]

Booz Allen Hawaii Scholarship Fund *(Undergraduate, Four Year College, University/Scholarship)* [5384]

Candon, Todd, & Seabolt Scholarship Fund *(Undergraduate, Four Year College, University/Scholarship)* [5385]

Castle & Cooke George W.Y. Yim Scholarship Fund *(Undergraduate, Graduate, Two Year College, Four Year College, University/Scholarship)* [5386]

Castle & Cooke Mililani Technology Park Scholarship Fund *(Undergraduate, University, Four Year College/Scholarship)* [5387]

Catrala - Hawaii Scholarship Fund *(Undergraduate, University, Two Year College, Four Year College/Scholarship)* [5388]

Ben and Vicky Cayetano Scholarship Fund *(Undergraduate, College, University, Two Year College/Scholarship)* [5389]

Central Pacific Bank Scholarship Fund *(Undergraduate/Scholarship)* [5390]

CHEA Undergraduate Scholarship Program for Students with Disabilities *(Undergraduate/Scholarship)* [2814]

CHEA Vocational Grants *(Vocational/Occupational, Two Year College/Grant)* [2815]

Camille C. Chidiac Fund Scholarship *(Undergraduate, Four Year College, Two Year College, Vocational/Occupational/Scholarship)* [5391]

Donald W. F. Ching Memorial Scholarship Fund *(Undergraduate, Two Year College, Four Year College/Scholarship)* [5392]

Dolly Ching Scholarship *(Undergraduate, Two Year College, Four Year College/Scholarship)* [5393]

Clem Judd Jr. Memorial Scholarship *(Undergraduate/Scholarship)* [5418]

Bal Dasa Scholarship Fund *(Undergraduate, University, College, Two Year College, Vocational/Occupational/Scholarship)* [5394]

Deja Vu Surf Hawaii Scholarship Fund *(Undergraduate, Two Year College, Four Year College/Scholarship)* [5395]

Frank Der Yuen Aviation Scholarship *(Undergraduate/Scholarship)* [8804]

Diamond Resort Scholarship Fund *(Undergraduate, Two Year College, Four Year College/Scholarship)* [5396]

Allan Eldin & Agnes Sutorik Geiger Scholarship Fund *(Undergraduate, Graduate/Scholarship)* [5397]

Blossom Kalama Evans Memorial Scholarship Fund *(Undergraduate, University, Four Year College, Two Year College/Scholarship)* [5398]

Ambassador Minerva Jean Falcon Hawaii Scholarship *(Undergraduate, Graduate, Two Year College, College, University/Scholarship)* [5399]

Victoria S. and Bradley L. Geist Scholarships *(Undergraduate, University, College, Vocational/Occupational/Scholarship)* [5400, 5437]

Doris and Clarence Glick Classical Music Scholarship Fund *(Undergraduate, Graduate, Two Year College, Four Year College, University/Scholarship)* [5401]

Goldman Sachs/Matsuo Takabuki Commemorative Scholarship *(Graduate/Scholarship)* [8926]

Anna K. Gower and Annabelle K. Gower Scholarship Fund *(Undergraduate, University, College, Two Year College, Vocational/Occupational/Scholarship)* [5402]

Isaac and Mary Harbottle Scholarship *(Graduate, Undergraduate/Scholarship)* [8927]

Hawaii Chapter/David T. Woolsey Scholarship *(Undergraduate, Graduate, Professional development/Scholarship)* [6647]

Celeste Hayo Memorial Scholarship Fund *(Undergraduate, College, University/Scholarship)* [5403]

HCF Community Scholarships Fund *(Undergraduate, Graduate/Scholarship)* [5404]

R.W. "Bob" Holden Memorial Scholarships *(Undergraduate/Scholarship)* [5419]

Hpgs Graduate Scholarships *(Graduate/Scholarship)* [5421]

HPGS Undergraduate Scholarships *(Undergraduate/Scholarship)* [5422]

David L. Irons Memorial Scholarship Fund *(Undergraduate, Two Year College, Four Year College/Scholarship)* [5405]

Arthur Jackman Scholarship *(Community College, Vocational/Occupational/Scholarship)* [5406]

Gladys Kamakakokalani 'Ainoa Brandt Scholarships *(Graduate, Undergraduate/Scholarship)* [8929]

Ka'u Chamber of Commerce Scholarship *(Undergraduate/Scholarship)* [6505]

Dan & Pauline Lutkenhouse & Hawaii Tropical Botanical Garden Scholarship and Educational Fund *(Undergraduate, Graduate/Scholarship)* [5407]

Cora Aguda Manayan Fund Scholarship *(Undergraduate/Scholarship)* [5408]

Craig D. Newman Memorial Scholarship *(Undergraduate/Scholarship)* [5409]

Charles & Mitch Ota Foundation Scholarship *(Undergraduate, Two Year College, Four Year College/Scholarship)* [5410]

PSHF Good Idea Grant *(Other/Grant)* [9441]

Doris Hardinger Roome Scholarship Fund *(Undergraduate, Graduate, Two Year College, Four Year College/Scholarship)* [5411]

Albert and Dorothy Shigekuni Scholarship Fund *(Undergraduate/Scholarship)* [5412]

The Jane Suganuma Memorial Scholarship Fund *(Undergraduate, Graduate, University, College, Two Year College/Scholarship)* [5413]

Alan and Grace Tenn Scholarship Fund *(Undergraduate, Graduate/Scholarship)* [5414]

Alma White - Delta Chapter, Delta Kappa Gamma Scholarship *(Undergraduate, University, College, Two Year College/Scholarship)* [5415]

William S. Richardson Commemorative Scholarship *(Graduate/Scholarship)* [8934]

Clarence and Virginia Young Trust Scholarship *(Undergraduate/Scholarship)* [5416]

Idaho

Horatio Alger Idaho University Scholarships *(Undergraduate/Scholarship)* [5566]

Horatio Alger Lola and Duane Hagadone Idaho Scholarships *(Undergraduate/Scholarship)* [5570]

Alois and Marie Goldmann Scholarship *(Graduate/Scholarship)* [5675]

American Legion Boys/Girls State Scholarship *(High School/Scholarship)* [6782]

Paul Arnold Memorial Scholarships *(Other/Scholarship)* [9288]

Asian and Pacific Islander Queer Sisters Scholarship (APIQS) *(Undergraduate/Scholarship)* [9289]

Associates in Behavioral Health Scholarships *(Graduate/Scholarship)* [9290]

The Mary Lou Brown Scholarship *(Undergraduate/Scholarship)* [1931]

Mike Crapo Math and Science Scholarship Fund *(Undergraduate/Scholarship)* [5676]

Brian M. Day Scholarships *(Undergraduate, Graduate/Scholarship)* [9295]

Deloris Carter Hampton Scholarship *(Undergraduate/Scholarship)* [9296]

Dennis Coleman Scholarship *(Undergraduate/Scholarship)* [9297]

Dennis Coleman Scholarships *(Undergraduate/Scholarship)* [9298]

Donald O. Coffman Scholarship *(Graduate, Undergraduate/Scholarship)* [9300]

Eugene Northrup Scholarship *(Undergraduate/Scholarship)* [6791]

Idaho Governor's Cup Scholarship *(Undergraduate/Scholarship)* [6799]

Idaho Nursery and Landscape Association Scholarships *(Undergraduate/Scholarship)* [5683]

Idaho Nursing and Health Professions Scholarship Fund *(Undergraduate/Scholarship)* [5677]

Idaho Opportunity Scholarship *(Undergraduate/Scholarship)* [10805]

Idaho Society of CPA's Scholarships *(Other/Scholarship)* [5678, 5685]

Inland Northwest Business Alliance Scholarships (INBA) *(Undergraduate/Scholarship)* [9302]

Intermountain Medical Imaging Scholarship *(Undergraduate, Community College/Scholarship)* [5892]

Jim Poore Memorial Scholarship Fund *(Undergraduate/Scholarship)* [5679]

Laura Moore Cunningham Foundation General Scholarship *(Undergraduate/Scholarship)* [6807]

Lewis-Clark State College Foundation Scholars *(Undergraduate/Scholarship)* [6811]

Lewis-Clark State College In-State Non-Traditional Student Scholarship *(Undergraduate/Scholarship)* [6812]

Lewis-Clark State College Provost Scholarship *(Undergraduate/Scholarship)* [6814]

Margaret G. Johnson and Marge J. Stout Scholarship *(Undergraduate/Scholarship)* [6817]

McFarffels Scholarships *(Undergraduate/Scholarship)* [9304]

Jack D. Motteler Scholarship *(Undergraduate/Scholarship)* [9305]

Pride Foundation Political Leadership Scholarships *(Undergraduate/Scholarship)* [9306]

Pride Foundation Regional Scholarships *(Undergraduate/Scholarship)* [9307]

Pride Foundation Scholarships *(Undergraduate/Scholarship)* [9771]

Pride Foundation Social Work Scholarships *(Undergraduate/Scholarship)* [9308]

Rosenberg-Ibarra Scholarships *(Graduate/Scholarship)* [9312]

Roger C. Sathre Memorial Scholarship Fund *(Graduate/Scholarship)* [5680]

Kathy Spadoni Memorial Scholarships *(Graduate/Scholarship)* [9313]

Susan P. Schroeder Memorial Scholarship (Undergraduate/Scholarship) [6822]

Trinity Scholars Program (Undergraduate/Scholarship) [11113]

Tschudy Family Scholarship (Undergraduate/Scholarship) [5687]

Ric Ulrich and Chuck Pischke Scholarships (Undergraduate/Scholarship) [9315]

W. L. Shattuck Scholarship (Undergraduate, Graduate, High School/Scholarship) [5681]

Wozumi Family Scholarships (Undergraduate/Scholarship) [9318]

Illinois

AIA Northeast Illinois Student Scholarships (Undergraduate, Graduate/Scholarship) [1009]

Horatio Alger Illinois Scholarships (Undergraduate/Scholarship) [5567]

Allied Health Care Professional Scholarship (Undergraduate/Scholarship) [5711]

James M. Banovetz Illinois Local Government Fellowships (Graduate, Undergraduate/Fellowship) [5698]

Beta Lambda Project 2000 Scholarship (Undergraduate/Scholarship) [6404]

The Gloria Bousley Graduate Scholarship (Graduate/Scholarship) [5696]

The Chicago FM Club Scholarship (Undergraduate/Scholarship) [1934]

Community Foundation of Northern Illinois Scholarship (Undergraduate/Scholarship) [3675]

DMSF Scholarship (High School/Scholarship) [7503]

Sergeant Paul Fisher Scholarship (Undergraduate/Scholarship) [7830]

GFAI Industry Immersion Scholarship Program (Undergraduate/Scholarship) [5064]

Graduate Student Fellowships (Graduate/Fellowship) [4547]

Harold B. Halter Memorial Scholarship (Undergraduate/Scholarship) [4497]

IAAI Scholarship Foundation Accounting Scholarships (Undergraduate/Scholarship) [5733]

Illinois Division of Midwest Dairy Educational Award (Undergraduate/Scholarship) [7369]

Illinois Lake Management Association Undergraduate/Graduate Scholarships (Graduate, Undergraduate/Scholarship) [5700]

Illinois Landscape Contractors Association Scholarships (Undergraduate/Scholarship) [5703]

Illinois Special Education Teacher Tuition Waiver Scholarship (SETTW) (Undergraduate/Scholarship) [5712]

Illinois Student Assistance Commission Medical Student Scholarship (Undergraduate/Scholarship) [5713]

Illinois Student Assistance Commission Nursing Education Scholarship (Undergraduate, Graduate, College/Scholarship) [5714]

International Management Council Scholarship (IMC) (Undergraduate/Scholarship) [3681]

ISPE Foundation Scholarship (Undergraduate/Scholarship) [5707]

Jewish Federation Academic Scholarship (Graduate, Undergraduate/Scholarship) [6310]

La Voz Latina Scholarship (Undergraduate/Scholarship) [3684]

Louisa Bowen Memorial Scholarship for Graduate Students in Archival Administration (Graduate/Scholarship) [7365]

Margaret T. Craig Community Service Scholarship (Undergraduate/Scholarship) [3686]

Minority Teachers of Illinois Scholarship (MTI) (Undergraduate/Scholarship) [5715]

North Dakota Division Scholarships (Undergraduate, Graduate/Scholarship) [7373]

The Peoria Area Amateur Radio Club Scholarship (Undergraduate/Scholarship) [1953]

Regions Riding Forward Scholarship Essay Contest (Undergraduate, High School/Scholarship) [9618]

Robert Esser Student Achievement Scholarship (Graduate, Undergraduate/Scholarship) [5701]

The Six Meter Club of Chicago Scholarship (Undergraduate/Scholarship) [1961]

William R. Durham Drama and Theater Scholarship (Undergraduate/Scholarship) [3695]

Indiana

Horatio Alger Indiana Scholarships (Undergraduate/Scholarship) [5568]

Anthony Munoz Scholarship Fund (Undergraduate/Scholarship) [7501]

Ralph Burkhardt Scholarship Fund (Undergraduate, High School/Scholarship) [11942]

Betty J. Cecere Memorial Scholarship Endowment Fund (Graduate/Scholarship) [11944]

Central Indiana Jim Kriner Memorial Scholarship (Undergraduate/Scholarship) [1563]

The Church, Langdon, Lopp, Banet Law Scholarships (Undergraduate, Four Year College/Scholarship) [3329]

Corinne and Fred Capuder Memorial Scholarship (Undergraduate/Scholarship) [3349]

Deana Kendrick Foundation Scholarship (Undergraduate/Scholarship) [6522]

Erika A. and George E. Brattain, Sr. Donor Advised Scholarship Fund (Undergraduate, High School/Scholarship) [11947]

Granger Business Association College Scholarship (Graduate/Scholarship) [5199]

Indiana Broadcasters Association College Scholarship Program (Undergraduate/Scholarship) [5750]

Indiana State University Academic Excellence Scholarship (Undergraduate/Scholarship) [5757]

Indiana State University Creative and Performing Arts Awards (Undergraduate/Scholarship) [5769]

Indiana State University President's Scholarships (Undergraduate/Scholarship) [5759]

Indiana State University Rural Health Scholarship (Undergraduate/Scholarship) [5760]

ISU Gongaware Scholarship (Undergraduate/Scholarship) [5762]

Jewish Federation Academic Scholarship (Graduate, Undergraduate/Scholarship) [6310]

Kappa Delta Phi Scholarship (Postgraduate/Scholarship) [1179]

Katherine M. Grosscup Scholarships in Horticulture (Undergraduate, Graduate/Scholarship) [4860]

KDP Huntington Bank Scholarship (Undergraduate/Scholarship) [6384]

Louisa Bowen Memorial Scholarship for Graduate Students in Archival Administration (Graduate/Scholarship) [7365]

Nixon Family Scholarship Fund (Undergraduate, High School/Scholarship) [11950]

Nicholas H. Noyes, Jr. Scholarship (Undergraduate/Scholarship) [6391]

Phi Theta Kappa Scholarship (Undergraduate/Scholarship) [5765]

Frederick Rakestraw Law Scholarship (Graduate/Scholarship) [8489]

Regions Riding Forward Scholarship Essay Contest (Undergraduate, High School/Scholarship) [9618]

Reid Hospital Graduate Student Scholarships (Graduate/Scholarship) [11951]

Esther Schlundt Memorial Scholarship Fund (Graduate, Undergraduate/Scholarship) [5754]

The Six Meter Club of Chicago Scholarship (Undergraduate/Scholarship) [1961]

Eric E. Smoker Memorial Scholarship (Undergraduate, Two Year College, Four Year College/Scholarship) [8490]

Sue Marsh Weller Memorial Scholarship Fund (Graduate/Scholarship) [5755]

Sycamore Hills Dentistry Scholarship (College, University/Scholarship) [10900]

University of Louisville Eagle Scout Scholarships (Undergraduate/Scholarship, Award) [7857]

Warren M. Anderson Scholarship (Undergraduate/Scholarship) [5766]

Iowa

Horatio Alger Ak-Sar-Ben Scholarships (Undergraduate/Scholarship) [5561]

Grace O. Doane Scholarship (Undergraduate/Scholarship) [4150]

Sergeant Paul Fisher Scholarship (Undergraduate/Scholarship) [7830]

The Paul and Helen L. Grauer Scholarships (Undergraduate/Scholarship) [1941]

John M. Helmick Law Scholarship (Undergraduate/Scholarship) [4162]

Herbert Hoover Uncommon Student Award (Undergraduate/Scholarship) [5557]

INF Scholarships (Undergraduate/Scholarship) [6166]

Iowa Division of Midwest Dairy Educational Award (Undergraduate/Scholarship) [7370]

James P. Irish Scholarship (Undergraduate/Scholarship) [4164]

Kappa Delta Phi Scholarship (Postgraduate/Scholarship) [1179]

Louisa Bowen Memorial Scholarship for Graduate Students in Archival Administration (Graduate/Scholarship) [7365]

James B. Morris Scholarship (Undergraduate/Scholarship) [7474]

North Dakota Division Scholarships (Undergraduate, Graduate/Scholarship) [7373]

The PHD Scholarship (Undergraduate/Scholarship) [1954]

The Ray, NØRP, & Katie, WØKTE, Pautz Scholarship (Undergraduate/Scholarship) [1956]

Regions Riding Forward Scholarship Essay Contest (Undergraduate, High School/Scholarship) [9618]

Kansas

The Irving W. Cook WA0CGS Scholarship (Undergraduate/Scholarship) [1936]

The Paul and Helen L. Grauer Scholarships (Undergraduate/Scholarship) [1941]

James B. Pearson Fellowship (Graduate/Scholarship) [6361]

J.L. Weigand, Jr. Legal Education Trust Scholarship (Undergraduate/Scholarship) [11876]

Kansas Association of Broadcasters Scholarships (Undergraduate/Scholarship) [6359]

Kansas Dental Education Opportunities Program (Graduate/Scholarship) [6362]

Kansas Distinguished Scholarship Program (Graduate/Scholarship) [6363]

Kansas Nurse Educator Service Scholarship (Graduate/Scholarship) [6364]

Kansas Optometry Service Scholarship (Graduate, Undergraduate/Scholarship) [6365]

Kansas Osteopathic Medical Service Scholarship (Graduate, Other/Scholarship) [6366]

Louisa Bowen Memorial Scholarship for Graduate Students in Archival Administration (Graduate/Scholarship) [7365]

Mingenback Family Scholarship Fund (Undergraduate, Graduate/Scholarship) [5016]

MoKan Division of Midwest Dairy Educational Award (Undergraduate/Scholarship) [7372]

North Dakota Division Scholarships (Undergraduate, Graduate/Scholarship) [7373]

Martha Mitchell Pearson Memorial Scholarship (Undergraduate, Graduate/Scholarship) [6464]

The PHD Scholarship (Undergraduate/Scholarship) [1954]

The Ray, NØRP, & Katie, WØKTE, Pautz Scholarship (Undergraduate/Scholarship) [1956]

Hatton W. Sumners Scholarships (Undergraduate/Scholarship) [8610]

Lynn McNabb Walton Adelphe Scholarhship (Undergraduate/Scholarship) [6479]

Kentucky

Horatio Alger Kentucky Scholarships (Undergraduate/Scholarship) [5569]

Anthony Munoz Scholarship Fund (Undergraduate/Scholarship) [7501]

The Betty Bell Scholarship Fund (Undergraduate/Scholarship) [5548]

Leon Bradley Scholarship Program (Undergraduate/Scholarship) [638]

The Tommy Bright Scholarship Fund (Undergraduate/Scholarship) [5549]

The Church, Langdon, Lopp, Banet Law Scholarships (Undergraduate, Four Year College/Scholarship) [3329]

Covington-Cincinnati/Northern Kentucky Alumni Chapter - Dane Wagge Scholarships *(University/Scholarship)* [11575]

Dr. Mubin Syed And Mrs. Afshan Syed Scholarship Program *(Undergraduate/Scholarship)* [6176]

Frankfort/Capital Region Alumni Chapter *(University/Scholarship)* [11576]

Graduate Realtor Institute Scholarships *(Graduate/Scholarship)* [6537]

Kappa Delta Phi Scholarship *(Postgraduate/Scholarship)* [1179]

Katherine M. Grosscup Scholarships in Horticulture *(Undergraduate, Graduate/Scholarship)* [4860]

Kentucky Alumni Club Scholarships - Lexington/Central Kentucky Alumni Chapter *(Graduate, High School/Scholarship)* [11577]

Kentucky Alumni Club Scholarships - Somerset/Lake Cumberland Area Alumni Chapter *(University/Scholarship)* [11578]

Kentucky Educational Excellence Scholarship *(Undergraduate/Scholarship)* [2572]

KHEAA Teacher Scholarship *(Undergraduate/Scholarship)* [2573]

Louisa Bowen Memorial Scholarship for Graduate Students in Archival Administration *(Graduate/Scholarship)* [7365]

Regions Riding Forward Scholarship Essay Contest *(Undergraduate, High School/Scholarship)* [9618]

Sam J. Hord Memorial Scholarship *(Undergraduate/Scholarship)* [10629]

South Kentucky RECC High School Senior Scholarship Program *(Undergraduate/Scholarship)* [10630]

University of Louisville Eagle Scout Scholarships *(Undergraduate/Scholarship, Award)* [7857]

Women In Rural Electrification Scholarships (W.I.R.E.) *(Undergraduate/Scholarship)* [10631]

Louisiana

Horatio Alger Louisiana Scholarships *(Undergraduate/Scholarship)* [5571]

AWMA Louisiana Section Scholarship *(Undergraduate, Graduate/Scholarship)* [167]

Camille F. Gravel, Jr. Scholarship *(Professional development/Scholarship)* [6898]

Frank L. Dautriel Memorial Scholarships for Graduates *(Graduate/Scholarship)* [6900]

Frank L. Dautriel Memorial Scholarships for Undergraduates *(Undergraduate/Scholarship)* [6901]

Gulf Coast Hurricane Scholarship *(Undergraduate/Scholarship)* [10488]

LLA Scholarships (LLA) *(Graduate/Scholarship)* [6903]

Lone Star GIA Associate and Alumni Scholarships *(Undergraduate/Scholarship)* [4879]

Mary Moore Mitchell Scholarship *(Graduate/Scholarship)* [6904]

NAJA Scholarship *(Graduate/Scholarship)* [7664]

Regions Riding Forward Scholarship Essay Contest *(Undergraduate, High School/Scholarship)* [9618]

Scholarships for a Higher Education in Law *(Graduate/Scholarship)* [2683]

Society of Louisiana Certified Public Accountants Scholarships *(Undergraduate, Master's, Doctorate/Scholarship)* [10382]

Hatton W. Sumners Scholarships *(Undergraduate/Scholarship)* [8610]

Maine

Benjamin Riggs Scholarship *(Undergraduate/Scholarship)* [4916]

Casey Family Services Alumni Scholarship *(Undergraduate, Master's, Vocational/Occupational/Scholarship)* [4693]

Catharine Wilder Guiles Scholarship *(Graduate/Scholarship)* [6976]

Brent R. Churchill Memorial Scholarship *(Undergraduate/Scholarship)* [6977]

Downeast Feline Fund *(Graduate/Scholarship)* [6978]

Edwina Foye Award for Outstanding Graduate Student *(Undergraduate, Graduate/Scholarship)* [4805]

Gary Merrill Memorial Scholarship Fund *(Undergraduate/Scholarship)* [6979]

Georgetown Working League Scholarship *(Undergraduate/Scholarship)* [4917]

Ronald P. Guerrette FFA Scholarship Fund *(Undergraduate/Scholarship)* [6980]

Guy P. Gannett Scholarship Fund *(Undergraduate/Scholarship)* [6981]

Henry L.P. Schmelzer College Transitions Scholarship Fund *(Undergraduate/Scholarship)* [6982]

Horch Roofing Trade School Scholarship *(Vocational/Occupational/Scholarship)* [5584]

Hugh and Elizabeth Montgomery Scholarship Fund *(Undergraduate/Scholarship)* [6983]

Iberdrola USA Scholarships *(Undergraduate/Scholarship)* [6984]

Ella R. Ifill Fund *(Undergraduate/Scholarship)* [6985]

James and Marilyn Rockefeller Scholarship Fund *(Undergraduate/Scholarship)* [6986]

Jerome Peters Family Fund *(Undergraduate/Scholarship)* [6987]

John S. and Marjoria R. Cunningham Camp Scholarship *(Other/Scholarship)* [6988]

Joseph W. Mayo ALS Scholarship Fund *(Graduate/Scholarship)* [6989]

Josephine Hooker Shain Scholarship *(Undergraduate/Scholarship)* [4918]

Lawrence and Louise Robbins Scholarship Fund *(Undergraduate/Scholarship)* [6991]

The Dr. James L. Lawson Memorial Scholarship *(Undergraduate/Scholarship)* [1947]

Lighthouse International Scholarships - College-bound Awards *(High School, Undergraduate/Scholarship)* [6856]

Lighthouse International Scholarships - Graduate Awards *(Graduate, Postgraduate/Scholarship)* [6857]

Lighthouse International Scholarships - Undergraduate Awards *(Undergraduate/Scholarship)* [6858]

Maine Community Foundation - Rice Scholarships *(Undergraduate/Scholarship)* [6992]

Maine Vietnam Veterans Scholarship *(Advanced Professional/Scholarship)* [6993]

NASSLEO Scholarships - Region I *(Undergraduate/Scholarship)* [7688]

The New England FEMARA Scholarship *(Undergraduate/Scholarship)* [1951]

Patriot Education Scholarship Fund *(Undergraduate/Scholarship)* [6994]

Riggs Cove Foundation Scholarship *(Undergraduate/Scholarship)* [4919]

Robinhood Marine Center Scholarship *(Undergraduate/Scholarship)* [4920]

Ruth Milan-Altrusa Scholarship Fund *(Undergraduate/Scholarship)* [6995]

Susan Vincent Memorial Scholarship *(Undergraduate/Scholarship)* [6973]

Woodex Bearing Company Scholarship *(Undergraduate/Scholarship)* [4921]

Yankee Clipper Contest Club Youth Scholarship *(Undergraduate/Scholarship)* [1967]

Maryland

Horatio Alger District of Columbia, Maryland and Virginia Scholarships *(Undergraduate/Scholarship)* [5563]

BCCC Foundation General Scholarship Fund *(Undergraduate/Scholarship)* [2414]

BCCC Workforce Creation Scholarship *(Undergraduate/Scholarship)* [2415]

Letitia B. Carter Scholarships *(Undergraduate, Advanced Professional/Scholarship)* [9649]

Casey Family Services Alumni Scholarship *(Undergraduate, Master's, Vocational/Occupational/Scholarship)* [4693]

Drew Smith Memorial Scholarship *(Undergraduate/Scholarship)* [3563]

Duane V. Puerde Memorial Scholarship Fund *(Undergraduate/Scholarship)* [3564]

Elizabeth Brittingham Pusey Scholarship *(Graduate/Scholarship)* [3565]

Esther M. Smith Scholarship Fund *(Undergraduate/Scholarship)* [3566]

Federalsburg Rotary Club Scholarship *(Undergraduate/Scholarship)* [3567]

Generation III Scholarship *(Undergraduate/Scholarship)* [4285]

Green Hill Yacht and Country Club Scholarship *(Undergraduate, High School/Scholarship)* [3568]

Hancock Family Snow Hill High School Scholarship *(Graduate/Scholarship)* [3570]

Marcia S. Harris Legacy Fund Scholarships *(Undergraduate, Advanced Professional/Scholarship)* [9650]

Dwight P. Jacobus Scholarships *(Undergraduate/Scholarship)* [2277]

Martin S. Kane Memorial Community Service Award Scholarships *(Undergraduate/Scholarship)* [3572]

Kathleen Kelly Undergraduate Scholarship *(Undergraduate/Scholarship)* [9434]

Lighthouse International Scholarships - College-bound Awards *(High School, Undergraduate/Scholarship)* [6856]

Lighthouse International Scholarships - Graduate Awards *(Graduate, Postgraduate/Scholarship)* [6857]

Lighthouse International Scholarships - Undergraduate Awards *(Undergraduate/Scholarship)* [6858]

M. William and Frances J. Tilghman Scholarship *(Undergraduate/Scholarship)* [3573]

Maryland Building Industry Association, Eastern Shore Chapter Scholarship Fund *(Undergraduate, High School/Scholarship)* [3574]

Maryland Poison Center Clinical Toxicology Fellowship *(Doctorate, Graduate/Fellowship)* [7116]

Minority Scholarship Award *(Undergraduate/Scholarship)* [3575]

NASSLEO Scholarships - Region I *(Undergraduate/Scholarship)* [7688]

NFBPA Land-Use Planning Scholarships *(Master's, Doctorate/Scholarship)* [7892]

Northrop Grumman Engineering Scholars Program *(Undergraduate/Scholarship)* [8498]

NRAEF Scholarship *(Undergraduate/Scholarship)* [9651]

PFLAG Howard County Scholarship *(Undergraduate/Scholarship)* [9054]

Progress Lane Scholarship Fund *(Undergraduate/Scholarship)* [3576]

Richard and Patricia Hazel Minority Scholarship Award *(Undergraduate/Scholarship)* [3577]

Lana K. Rinehart Scholarships *(Undergraduate/Scholarship)* [3578]

Rotary Club of Annapolis Scholarship *(Graduate/Scholarship)* [1719]

TFC Edward A. Plank, Jr. Memorial Scholarship *(Undergraduate/Scholarship)* [3579]

The Gary Wagner, K3OMI, Scholarship *(Undergraduate/Scholarship)* [1965]

WFMC Ride for the Fallen Memorial Scholarship *(Two Year College, Four Year College, Vocational/Occupational/Scholarship)* [11872]

Wicomico High School Class of '55 Schloarship *(Undergraduate/Scholarship)* [3580]

William R. Bowen Scholarship *(Undergraduate/Scholarship)* [3581]

William T. Burbage Family Memorial Scholarship *(Undergraduate/Scholarship)* [3582]

Massachusetts

Adler Pollock & Sheehan Diversity Scholarships *(Undergraduate/Fellowship)* [77]

African American Achievement Scholarship Fund *(Undergraduate/Scholarship)* [3727]

Alexander G. Gray, Jr., Scholarship Award *(Graduate/Scholarship)* [7156]

Arts Foundation of Cape Cod Scholarships *(Undergraduate, Vocational/Occupational/Scholarship)* [1975]

Boston City Federation "Return to School" Scholarships *(Undergraduate, Graduate/Scholarship)* [4897]

Casey Family Services Alumni Scholarship *(Undergraduate, Master's, Vocational/Occupational/Scholarship)* [4693]

Catherine E. Philbin Scholarship *(Undergraduate, Graduate/Scholarship)* [4898]

Sgt. Cherven Scholarship (Undergraduate/Scholarship) [7128]

Communication Disorder/Speech Therapy Scholarship (Graduate/Scholarship) [4899]

Early Childhood Educators Scholarship Program (Undergraduate/Scholarship) [7158]

Gehring Memorial Foundation Scholarships (Graduate, Undergraduate/Scholarship) [5742]

Hai Guin Scholarships (Undergraduate, Graduate/Scholarship) [5260]

Law Offices of Mark E. Salomone Scholarship for Road Safety (Undergraduate/Scholarship) [6706]

The Dr. James L. Lawson Memorial Scholarship (Undergraduate/Scholarship) [1947]

Rebecca Christine Lenci Thespian Memorial Scholarship (Undergraduate/Scholarship) [9830]

Lighthouse International Scholarships - College-bound Awards (High School, Undergraduate/Scholarship) [6856]

Lighthouse International Scholarships - Graduate Awards (Graduate, Postgraduate/Scholarship) [6857]

Lighthouse International Scholarships - Undergraduate Awards (Undergraduate/Scholarship) [6858]

MALSCE Memorial Scholarship (Undergraduate/Scholarship) [7122]

Massachusetts Bar Foundation Legal Intern Fellowship Program (LIFP) (Graduate/Fellowship) [7126]

Massachusetts Federation of Polish Women's Clubs Scholarships (Undergraduate/Scholarship) [6604]

MEFA Graduate Loans (Graduate/Loan) [7130]

Music Scholarship for Undergraduate in Voice (Undergraduate/Scholarship) [4900]

NASSLEO Scholarships - Region I (Undergraduate/Scholarship) [7688]

The New England FEMARA Scholarship (Undergraduate/Scholarship) [1951]

Nickels for Notes Music Scholarship (Undergraduate/Scholarship) [4901]

Pennies for Art Scholarship (Undergraduate/Scholarship) [4902]

Plumbing-Heating-Cooling Contractors Association Educational Foundation Massachusetts Auxiliary Scholarships (Undergraduate/Scholarship) [9205]

Portuguese American Police Association Scholarships (Undergraduate/Scholarship) [9252]

The Scholarship Foundation of Wakefield Scholarships (All/Scholarship) [9955]

Percy W. Wadman, M.D. Scholarship (Postgraduate/Scholarship) [4815]

Women's Italian Club of Boston Scholarships (Undergraduate/Scholarship) [4903]

Yankee Clipper Contest Club Youth Scholarship (Undergraduate/Scholarship) [1967]

Dr. Marie E. Zakrzewski Medical Scholarships (Doctorate/Scholarship) [6607]

Jacob Ziskind Memorial Fund for Upperclassmen (Graduate, Undergraduate/Scholarship) [5746]

Michigan

Achille & Irene Despres, William & Andre Scholarship (Undergraduate/Scholarship) [5131]

Altrusa International of Grand Rapids Scholarship (Undergraduate/Scholarship) [5133]

Amos and Marilyn Winsand - Detroit Section Named Scholarship (Undergraduate/Scholarship) [1656]

Antonia Dellas Memorial Scholarship (Undergraduate/Scholarship) [6192]

Arts Council of Greater Grand Rapids Minority Scholarship (Undergraduate/Scholarship) [5134]

Audrey L. Wright Scholarship (Undergraduate/Scholarship) [5135]

Barbara and Nicole Heacox Foreign Study & Travel Scholarship (Undergraduate/Scholarship) [5068]

Dennis J. Beck Memorial Scholarship (Undergraduate/Scholarship) [6193]

Bernice Barabash Sports Scholarship (Graduate/Scholarship) [6194]

Black Men Building Resources Scholarship (Undergraduate/Scholarship) [5137]

Bob and Dawn Hardy Automotive Scholarship (Undergraduate/Scholarship) [6195]

Harry and Lucille Brown Scholarship (Undergraduate/Scholarship) [5138]

Carolyn Gallmeyer Scholarship (Undergraduate/Scholarship) [5140]

Charles (Charlie) A. Bassett Endowed Scholarship (Undergraduate/Scholarship) [5070]

Charles and Eleanor Rycenga Education Scholarship (Undergraduate/Scholarship) [5071]

Clarke Adams Memorial Fund (Undergraduate/Scholarship) [6662]

Paul Collins Scholarship (Undergraduate/Scholarship) [5143]

Consumers Credit Union Scholarship (Undergraduate, College, Vocational/Occupational, Two Year College, University/Scholarship) [3814]

Gerald M. Crane Music Award Scholarship (Undergraduate/Scholarship) [5144]

Daniel Gerber, Sr. Medallion Scholarship (Undergraduate/Scholarship) [4939]

Daniel L. Reiss Memorial Scholarship (Undergraduate/Scholarship) [5073]

Darooge Family Scholarship (Undergraduate/Scholarship) [5145]

Antenore C. "Butch" Davanzo Scholarships (Graduate, Undergraduate/Scholarship) [7348]

David and Sharon Seaver Family Scholarship Fund in Memory of Timothy D. Seaver (Undergraduate/Scholarship) [5074]

Detroit Economic Club Scholarship (Undergraduate/Scholarship) [3719]

Dr. William A. and Marceleine J. Sautter Hanover-Horton Youth of Promise Scholarship (Graduate/Scholarship) [6196]

Donald J. DeYoung Scholarship (Undergraduate/Scholarship) [5147]

Dorothy and Dick Burgess Scholarship (Undergraduate/Scholarship) [6197]

Economic Club Business Study Abroad Scholarships (Undergraduate/Scholarship) [5149]

Economic Club of Grand Rapids Scholarship (Undergraduate/Scholarship) [5150]

The Eileen J. Smith, R.N. Memorial Scholarship (Undergraduate/Scholarship) [6198]

The Eleanor A. Ernest Scholarship (Graduate/Scholarship) [6199]

Erickson Education Scholarship (Undergraduate/Scholarship) [5075]

Melissa Eleanor Ernest Scholarship (Undergraduate/Scholarship) [6200]

Faith Speckhard Scholarship (Graduate/Scholarship) [6201]

Floto-Peel Family Scholarship Fund (Undergraduate, Vocational/Occupational/Scholarship) [5076]

John L. and Victory E. Frantz Scholarship (Undergraduate/Scholarship) [5077]

Geraldine Geistert Boss Scholarship (Undergraduate/Scholarship) [5151]

Irma Gelhausen Scholarship Fund (Graduate/Scholarship) [6663]

Gerber Foundation Merit Scholarship (Graduate/Scholarship) [4940]

Geri Coccodrilli Culinary Scholarship (Undergraduate/Scholarship) [5079]

Grand Haven Offshore Challenge Scholarship (Undergraduate/Scholarship) [5080]

Guy D. & Mary Edith Halladay Music Scholarship (Graduate, Undergraduate/Scholarship) [5154]

H. Wayne VanAgtmael Cosmetology Scholarship (Undergraduate/Scholarship) [5081]

Martha and Oliver Hansen Memorial Scholarships (Undergraduate/Scholarship) [6202]

Harold and Eleanor Ringelberg Scholarship (Undergraduate/Scholarship) [5082]

Harry J. Morris, Jr. Emergency Services (Undergraduate/Scholarship) [5157]

Hazel Simms Nursing Scholarship (Other/Scholarship) [6664]

John P. Hennessey Scholarship (Graduate, Undergraduate/Scholarship) [7349]

Wayne Hildebrant Police Scholarship Fund (Undergraduate/Scholarship) [6665]

Hoffman Family Scholarship (Undergraduate/Scholarship) [5085]

Robert Holmes Scholarship (Undergraduate/Scholarship) [3720]

Detroit Tigers Willie Horton Scholarship (Undergraduate/Scholarship) [3721]

Jacob R. & Mary M. VanLoo & Lenore K. VanLoo Scholarship (Undergraduate/Scholarship) [5159]

James W. Junior and Jane T. Brown Scholarship (Undergraduate, Vocational/Occupational/Scholarship) [5160]

June Danby and Pat Pearse Education Scholarship (Undergraduate/Scholarship) [6203]

Katherine M. Grosscup Scholarships in Horticulture (Undergraduate, Graduate/Scholarship) [4860]

Kelsey's Law Distracted Driving Awareness Scholarship (High School, Undergraduate/Scholarship) [7305]

Kevin Ernst Memorial Scholarship (Undergraduate/Scholarship) [5087]

Kyle R. Moreland Memorial Scholarship (Undergraduate/Scholarship) [5088]

Ladies Literary Club Scholarship (Undergraduate/Scholarship) [5161]

Paul J. Laninga Memorial Scholarship (Undergraduate/Scholarship) [5089]

Lapeer County Medical Fund (Undergraduate/Scholarship) [6666]

Lavina Laible Scholarship (Undergraduate/Scholarship) [5162]

Jack W. Leatherman Family Scholarship (Undergraduate, Vocational/Occupational/Scholarship) [5090]

Imelda (Graduate, High School/Scholarship) [3722]

Louisa Bowen Memorial Scholarship for Graduate Students in Archival Administration (Graduate/Scholarship) [7365]

John T. & Frances J. Maghielse Scholarship (Undergraduate/Scholarship) [5163]

Margery J. Seeger Scholarship (Undergraduate/Scholarship) [5164]

Marjorie M. Hendricks Environmental Education Scholarship (Undergraduate/Scholarship) [5094]

Marvin R. and Pearl E. Patterson Family Scholarship (Undergraduate/Scholarship) [5095]

Mathilda & Carolyn Gallmeyer Scholarship (Undergraduate/Scholarship) [5165]

Melbourne & Alice E. Frontjes Scholarship (Undergraduate/Scholarship) [5167]

Michael Herman Scholarship (Undergraduate, Vocational/Occupational/Scholarship) [5096]

Michael J. Wolf Scholarship (Undergraduate/Scholarship) [5168]

Michigan Auto Law Student Diversity Scholarships (Undergraduate/Scholarship) [7306]

Michigan Council of Women in Technology High School Scholarship Program (High School/Scholarship) [7310]

Michigan Council of Women in Technology Undergraduate Scholarship Program (Undergraduate, Graduate/Scholarship) [7311]

Michigan Society of Professional Engineers Scholarships (Undergraduate/Scholarship) [7328]

Michigan Stormwater-Floodplain Association Scholarships (Graduate, Undergraduate/Scholarship) [7338]

Mildred E. Troske Music Scholarship (Undergraduate/Scholarship) [5169]

Miller G. Sherwood Family Scholarship (Undergraduate/Scholarship) [5097]

Millicent Mary Schaffner Endowed Memorial Scholarship (Undergraduate/Scholarship) [5098]

MNF Scholarships (Undergraduate, Graduate/Scholarship) [7320]

NAIFA West Michigan Scholarship (Undergraduate/Scholarship) [5170]

NALS of Michigan Scholarship (Undergraduate/Scholarship) [7546]

North Ottawa Hospital Auxiliary Scholarship (Undergraduate/Scholarship) [5099]

Carl Parsell Scholarship Fund (Undergraduate/Scholarship) [7303]

Pat and John MacTavish Scholarship (Undergraduate/Scholarship) [5100]

Patricia & Armen Oumedian Scholarship (Undergraduate/Scholarship) [5172]

Paul Tejada Memorial Scholarship (Undergraduate/Scholarship) [6206]

Peggy (Kommer) Novosad Scholarship (Graduate, Postgraduate/Scholarship) [5173]

P.E.O. Chapter DS Scholarship (Undergraduate, Vocational/Occupational/Scholarship) [5101]

Phillip Guy Richardson Memorial Scholarship (Undergraduate/Scholarship) [6207]

Reach for Your Goal Scholarship (Undergraduate/Scholarship) [5174]

Jacob L. Reinecke Memorial Scholarship (Undergraduate/Scholarship) [5102]

Rick and Beverly Lattin Education Scholarship (Undergraduate/Scholarship) [5103]

Robert L. & Hilda Treasure Mitchell Scholarship (Undergraduate/Scholarship) [5176]

Robert P. Ernest Scholarship (Undergraduate/Scholarship) [6208]

Jean and Tom Rosenthal Scholarship Program (Undergraduate/Scholarship) [3723]

Ross P. Broesamle Education Fund (Undergraduate/Scholarship) [6667]

Dave & Laurie Russell Family Scholarships for Habitat for Humanity of Kent County Families (Undergraduate/Scholarship) [5180]

David and Jinny Schultz Family Scholarship (Undergraduate/Scholarship) [5104]

Jeptha Wade Schureman Scholarship Program (Undergraduate/Scholarship) [3724]

Scott A. Flahive Memorial Scholarship (Undergraduate/Scholarship) [5105]

Seth Koehler Central High School (Undergraduate, Vocational/Occupational/Scholarship) [5106]

Ken and Sandy Sharkey Family Scholarship (Undergraduate/Scholarship) [5107]

Sherman L. & Mabel C. Lepard Scholarship (Undergraduate/Scholarship) [5181]

Dr. William E. & Norma Sprague Scholarship (Undergraduate, Graduate/Scholarship) [5183]

Stephen Lankester Scholarship (Undergraduate/Scholarship) [5184]

The Zachary Taylor Stevens Scholarship (Undergraduate/Scholarship) [1962]

Edward P. Suchecki Family Scholarship (Undergraduate/Scholarship) [5109]

Henry D. and Ruth G. Swartz Family Scholarship (Undergraduate/Scholarship) [5110]

Terry Linda Potter Scholarship (Undergraduate/Scholarship) [5111]

Barbara and Howard Thompson Scholarships (Undergraduate/Scholarship) [6209]

Dorothy J. Thurston Graduate Scholarship (Undergraduate/Scholarship) [5186]

Tom Gifford Scholarship (Undergraduate/Scholarship) [5112]

U-M Alumnae Club (University of Michigan) Scholarships (Undergraduate/Scholarship) [5187]

Virginia Valk Fehsenfeld Scholarship (Undergraduate/Scholarship) [5189]

Sue Walicki Nursing Scholarships (Undergraduate/Scholarship) [6210]

Warner Norcross & Judd Minority Scholarships (Undergraduate/Scholarship) [11874]

West Michigan Nursery and Landscape Association Scholarship (Undergraduate/Scholarship) [5113]

William and Beatrice Kavanaugh Memorial Scholarship (Graduate/Scholarship) [6211]

WMSHP Scholarship (Graduate/Scholarship) [11985]

Women's Club of Grand Haven Scholarship (Undergraduate/Scholarship) [5114]

Violet Wondergem Health Science Scholarships (Undergraduate/Scholarship) [5195]

Zenko Family Scholarship (Undergraduate/Scholarship) [5115]

Minnesota

Horatio Alger Minnesota Scholarships (Undergraduate/Scholarship) [5572]

Amelia and Emanuel Nessell Family Scholarship Fund (Undergraduate/Scholarship) [4197]

Anderson Niskanen Scholarship Fund (Graduate/Scholarship) [4198]

Darrell and Palchie Asselin Scholarship Fund (Undergraduate/Scholarship) [4199]

William E. Barto Scholarship Fund (Undergraduate/Scholarship) [4200]

Bernard B. and Mary L. Brusin Scholarship Fund (Undergraduate/Scholarship) [4201]

Dr. Mark Rathke Family Scholarship Fund (Graduate/Scholarship) [4202]

DSACF Modern Woodmen of America Scholarship Fund (Undergraduate/Scholarship) [4203]

Patricia S. Gustafson '56 Memorial Scholarship Fund (Graduate/Scholarship) [4207]

Gus and Henrietta Hill Scholarship Fund (Graduate/Scholarship) [4209]

Max and Julia Houghton Duluth Central Scholarships (Undergraduate/Scholarship) [4210]

Greg Irons Award Fund (Undergraduate/Award) [4211]

Jackson Club Scholarship Fund (Undergraduate/Scholarship) [4212]

Cory Jam Memorial Award (Undergraduate/Scholarship) [4213]

Lawrence E. and Mabel Jackson Rudberg Scholarship Fund (Undergraduate/Scholarship) [4214]

Lilly Lorenzen Scholarships (Undergraduate/Scholarship) [1618]

Louisa Bowen Memorial Scholarship for Graduate Students in Archival Administration (Graduate/Scholarship) [7365]

McKnight Fellowships (Other/Fellowship) [9198]

McKnight Theater Artist Fellowships (Other/Fellowship) [9199]

Minneapolis Jewish Federation Camp Scholarships (Undergraduate, Other/Scholarship) [7400]

Minnesota Association of Public Accountant Scholarship (Undergraduate/Scholarship) [7404]

Minnesota Health Information Management Association Scholarships (Undergraduate/Scholarship) [7408]

Minnesota Power Community Involvement Scholarship Fund (Undergraduate/Scholarship) [4215]

North Dakota Division Scholarships (Undergraduate, Graduate/Scholarship) [7373]

Phil Shykes Memorial Scholarship Fund (Graduate/Scholarship) [4217]

Robert B. and Sophia Whiteside Scholarship Fund (Graduate/Scholarship) [4218]

Sterbenz-Ryan Scholarship (Undergraduate, Vocational/Occupational/Scholarship) [9778]

Upper Midwest Human Rights Fellowship Program (Graduate/Scholarship, Fellowship) [5632]

Mississippi

Buster Pool Memorial Scholarship Fund (Undergraduate/Scholarship) [3605]

Gulf Coast Hurricane Scholarship (Undergraduate/Scholarship) [10488]

The Fred R. McDaniel Memorial Scholarship (Undergraduate/Scholarship) [1948]

Memphis Access and Diversity Scholarships (Graduate/Scholarship) [11609]

The Mississippi Scholarship (Undergraduate/Scholarship) [1950]

MSCPA Undergraduate Scholarship (Undergraduate/Scholarship) [7421]

NAJA Scholarship (Graduate/Scholarship) [7664]

Regions Riding Forward Scholarship Essay Contest (Undergraduate, High School/Scholarship) [9618]

Ross/Nickey Scholarships (Graduate/Scholarship) [7422]

Southern Section A&WMA Scholarships (Graduate/Scholarship) [10668]

University of Southern Mississippi Eagle Scout Scholarship (Undergraduate/Scholarship) [7858]

Missouri

Horatio Alger Missouri Scholarships (Undergraduate/Scholarship) [5573]

Ava's Grace Scholarship Program (Graduate, Undergraduate/Scholarship) [9949]

The Paul and Helen L. Grauer Scholarships (Undergraduate/Scholarship) [1941]

Health Professional Nursing Student Loans (Undergraduate, Graduate, Community College, Doctorate/Loan) [7424]

John Allen Love Scholarship (Graduate, Undergraduate/Scholarship) [11715]

Kappa Delta Phi Scholarship (Postgraduate/Scholarship) [1179]

Louisa Bowen Memorial Scholarship for Graduate Students in Archival Administration (Graduate/Scholarship) [7365]

Megan Meier Memorial Scholarships (Undergraduate/Scholarship) [7243]

MoKan Division of Midwest Dairy Educational Award (Undergraduate/Scholarship) [7372]

NAJA Scholarship (Graduate/Scholarship) [7664]

North Dakota Division Scholarships (Undergraduate, Graduate/Scholarship) [7373]

Ozarks Division of Midwest Dairy Educational Award (Undergraduate/Scholarship) [7374]

Martha Mitchell Pearson Memorial Scholarship (Undergraduate, Graduate/Scholarship) [6464]

The PHD Scholarship (Undergraduate/Scholarship) [1954]

The Ray, NØRP, & Katie, WØKTE, Pautz Scholarship (Undergraduate/Scholarship) [1956]

Regions Riding Forward Scholarship Essay Contest (Undergraduate, High School/Scholarship) [9618]

Hatton W. Sumners Scholarships (Undergraduate/Scholarship) [8610]

Montana

Horatio Alger Montana Scholarships (Undergraduate/Scholarship) [5574]

Anthony Gerharz Scholarship (Undergraduate, Graduate/Scholarship) [7457]

Paul Arnold Memorial Scholarships (Other/Scholarship) [9288]

Asian and Pacific Islander Queer Sisters Scholarship (APIQS) (Undergraduate/Scholarship) [9289]

Associates in Behavioral Health Scholarships (Graduate/Scholarship) [9290]

The Mary Lou Brown Scholarship (Undergraduate/Scholarship) [1931]

Brian M. Day Scholarships (Undergraduate, Graduate/Scholarship) [9295]

Deloris Carter Hampton Scholarship (Undergraduate/Scholarship) [9296]

Dennis Coleman Scholarship (Undergraduate/Scholarship) [9297]

Dennis Coleman Scholarships (Undergraduate/Scholarship) [9298]

Donald E. Pizzini Memorial Nurse Scholarship (Undergraduate, Professional development/Scholarship) [7455]

Donald O. Coffman Scholarship (Graduate, Undergraduate/Scholarship) [9300]

EAA Members Memorial Scholarship (Undergraduate/Scholarship) [4391]

EAA Workshop Scholarships (Undergraduate/Scholarship) [4392]

Eldon E. and JoAnn C. Kuhns Family Scholarship (Undergraduate, Graduate/Scholarship) [7458]

McFarffels Scholarships (Undergraduate/Scholarship) [9304]

Jack D. Motteler Scholarship (Undergraduate/Scholarship) [9305]

MSCPA Scholarship - Montana Tech (Undergraduate, Graduate/Scholarship) [7459]

MSCPA Scholarship - MSU Bozeman (Undergraduate, Graduate/Scholarship) [7460]

MSCPA Scholarship - University of Montana (Undergraduate, Graduate/Scholarship) [7461]

Pride Foundation Political Leadership Scholarships (Undergraduate/Scholarship) [9306]

Pride Foundation Regional Scholarships (Undergraduate/Scholarship) [9307]

Pride Foundation Scholarships (Undergraduate/Scholarship) [9771]

Pride Foundation Social Work Scholarships (Undergraduate/Scholarship) [9308]

Rocky Mountain Coal Mining Institute Engineering/Geology Scholarships (Four Year College/Scholarship) [9727]

Rocky Mountain Coal Mining Institute Technical Scholarships (Two Year College/Scholarship) [9728]

Rosenberg-Ibarra Scholarships (Graduate/Scholarship) [9312]

Scott Brownlee Memorial Scholarship (Undergraduate, Graduate/Scholarship) [7462]

Kathy Spadoni Memorial Scholarships (Graduate/Scholarship) [9313]

Stanley Moore FUI Foundation Regional Scholarships (Four Year College, High School, Two Year College/Scholarship) [8464]

Stephen T. Marchello Scholarship *(Graduate/Scholarship)* [7030]

Trinity Scholars Program *(Undergraduate/Scholarship)* [11113]

Ric Ulrich and Chuck Pischke Scholarships *(Undergraduate/Scholarship)* [9315]

Upper Midwest Human Rights Fellowship Program *(Graduate/Scholarship, Fellowship)* [5632]

Wozumi Family Scholarships *(Undergraduate/Scholarship)* [9318]

Nebraska

Horatio Alger Ak-Sar-Ben Scholarships *(Undergraduate/Scholarship)* [5561]

BSF General Scholarship Awards *(College, University/Scholarship)* [2439]

The Paul and Helen L. Grauer Scholarships *(Undergraduate/Scholarship)* [1941]

Louisa Bowen Memorial Scholarship for Graduate Students in Archival Administration *(Graduate/Scholarship)* [7365]

Nebraska Farm Bureau Greater Horizon Scholarship *(Undergraduate/Scholarship)* [8187]

Nebraska Paralegal Association Student Scholarships *(Undergraduate/Scholarship)* [8194]

Louise A. Nixon Scholarship *(Graduate/Scholarship)* [8192]

North Dakota Division Scholarships *(Undergraduate, Graduate/Scholarship)* [7373]

The PHD Scholarship *(Undergraduate/Scholarship)* [1954]

Jim and Dee Price Family Scholarship *(Undergraduate, Community College, College, University/Scholarship)* [5123]

The Ray, NØRP, & Katie, WØKTE, Pautz Scholarship *(Undergraduate/Scholarship)* [1956]

Hatton W. Sumners Scholarships *(Undergraduate/Scholarship)* [8610]

Wyman and Cleo Woodyard Family Scholarship *(Undergraduate, University, College/Scholarship)* [5126]

WYCUP Scholarship Program *(Other/Scholarship)* [12196]

Nevada

Aaron Edward Arnoldsen Memorial Scholarship *(Undergraduate/Scholarship)* [1922]

ABC Stores Jumpstart Scholarship Fund *(Undergraduate, University, College, Vocational/Occupational, Graduate/Scholarship)* [5377]

Adelson Scholarship *(Undergraduate/Scholarship)* [9387]

American Nuclear Society Nevada Section Scholarship *(Undergraduate/Scholarship)* [1161, 9390]

Cheyenne High School Desert Shields Scholarship *(Undergraduate/Scholarship)* [9392]

Cimarron-Memorial Spartan Staff Scholarships *(Undergraduate/Scholarship)* [9393]

Clark High School Academy of Finance Scholarship *(Undergraduate/Scholarship)* [9394]

Corporal Joseph Martinez U.S. Army/Durango High School AFJROTC Scholarship *(Undergraduate/Scholarship)* [9396]

Dan Mordecai Educational Scholarship Award *(Graduate, Undergraduate/Scholarship)* [8210]

Edwin F. Wiegand Science & Technology Scholarship *(Undergraduate/Scholarship)* [9397]

Elizabeth Shafer Memorial Scholarship *(Undergraduate/Scholarship)* [9398]

Evelyn Abrams Memorial Scholarship *(Undergraduate/Scholarship)* [9399]

Brendan Flores Alumni Leadership Circle Scholarship - Clark High School *(Undergraduate/Scholarship)* [9400]

Glazing Industry Scholarship *(Advanced Professional/Scholarship)* [9402]

Gordy Fink Memorial Scholarship *(Undergraduate/Scholarship)* [9403]

Gretchen Hauff Memorial Scholarship *(Undergraduate/Scholarship)* [9404]

JMA Architecture Studios Scholarship *(Undergraduate/Scholarship)* [9405]

John Caoile Memorial Scholarship *(Other/Scholarship)* [9406]

Josef Princ Memorial Scholarship *(Undergraduate/Scholarship)* [9407]

Mesquite Club Evening Chapter Inc. Scholarship *(Undergraduate/Scholarship)* [9410]

Michael Koizumi APWA Internship Scholarship *(Undergraduate/Scholarship, Internship)* [1308]

Mickey Donnelly Memorial Scholarship *(Undergraduate/Scholarship)* [9412]

National Security Technologies Engineering and Science Scholarships *(Undergraduate/Scholarship)* [9414]

Palo Verde High School Barbara Edwards Memorial Scholarship *(Undergraduate/Scholarship)* [9416]

Palo Verde High School Faculty Follies Scholarship *(Undergraduate/Scholarship)* [9417]

Panther Cafe Scholarships *(Undergraduate/Scholarship)* [9418]

Pardee Community Building Scholarship *(Undergraduate/Scholarship)* [9419]

Rich Abjian Leadership Scholarship *(Undergraduate/Scholarship)* [9420]

Rose Marie Princ Memorial Scholarship *(Undergraduate/Scholarship)* [9421]

Sheila Tarr-Smith Memorial Scholarship *(Undergraduate/Scholarship)* [9422]

Smith's Personal Best Scholarships *(Undergraduate/Scholarship)* [9423]

Tall Awareness Scholarships *(Graduate/Scholarship)* [9425]

Tarkanian Teacher Education Academy at Clark High School Scholarship *(Undergraduate/Scholarship)* [9426]

Travis Dunning Memorial Scholarship *(Undergraduate/Scholarship)* [9427]

Veronica Gantt Memorial Scholarship *(Undergraduate/Scholarship)* [9429]

New Hampshire

The Bruce Clement Post-Secondary Education Scholarship *(Undergraduate/Scholarship)* [8267]

Casey Family Services Alumni Scholarship *(Undergraduate, Master's, Vocational/Occupational/Scholarship)* [4693]

Community Project Grants *(Other/Grant)* [8261]

Edwina Foye Award for Outstanding Graduate Student *(Undergraduate, Graduate/Scholarship)* [4805]

Caroline and Martin Gross Fellowship *(Professional development/Fellowship)* [8256]

The Dr. James L. Lawson Memorial Scholarship *(Undergraduate/Scholarship)* [1947]

Lighthouse International Scholarships - College-bound Awards *(High School, Undergraduate/Scholarship)* [6856]

Lighthouse International Scholarships - Graduate Awards *(Graduate, Postgraduate/Scholarship)* [6857]

Lighthouse International Scholarships - Undergraduate Awards *(Undergraduate/Scholarship)* [6858]

Louise Tillotson Teaching Fellowship *(Professional development/Fellowship)* [8257]

Louise Tillotson Teaching Professional Development Scholarship *(Professional development/Scholarship)* [8258]

The Rick Mahoney Scholarship *(Undergraduate/Scholarship)* [7173]

Manning & Zimmerman Distracted Driving Scholarship *(College, University, Undergraduate, Vocational/Occupational/Scholarship)* [6697]

The Medallion Fund Scholarship *(Undergraduate/Scholarship)* [8254]

NASSLEO Scholarships - Region I *(Undergraduate/Scholarship)* [7688]

The New England FEMARA Scholarship *(Undergraduate/Scholarship)* [1951]

Piscataqua Region Artist Advancement Grant *(Professional development/Grant)* [8259]

Plan NH's Scholarship and Fellowship Program *(Community College, Four Year College, Undergraduate, Graduate, Vocational/Occupational/Scholarship)* [9188]

Small Grants for Community Projects and Educational Programs *(Other/Grant)* [8262]

Johnny Trombly Memorial Scholarship *(Undergraduate/Scholarship)* [7433]

Yankee Clipper Contest Club Youth Scholarship *(Undergraduate/Scholarship)* [1967]

New Jersey

Ann Liguori Foundation Sports Media Scholarship *(Graduate, Undergraduate/Scholarship)* [8366]

Benjamin Asbell Memorial Awards *(Graduate, Undergraduate/Scholarship)* [2846]

CentraState Associated Auxiliaries Scholarship *(Undergraduate/Scholarship)* [3248]

CentraState Healthcare Foundation Health Professions Scholarships *(Undergraduate/Scholarship)* [3250]

Hon. Joseph W. Cowgill Memorial Award *(Undergraduate, Graduate/Scholarship)* [2848]

George Dale Scholarship Fund *(Undergraduate/Scholarship)* [1973]

DuBois Brothers Award *(Undergraduate, Graduate/Scholarship)* [2850]

Dunkin' Donuts Philadelphia Regional Scholarship Program *(Undergraduate/Scholarship)* [9941]

Gallo Blue Chip Scholarships *(Undergraduate/Scholarship)* [5301]

Generation III Scholarship *(Undergraduate/Scholarship)* [4285]

German Society Scholarships *(Undergraduate/Scholarship)* [4951]

HRET Health Career Scholarships *(Postgraduate, Undergraduate/Scholarship)* [8275]

Jeffrey Carollo Music Scholarship *(Undergraduate/Scholarship)* [8279]

Bernadine Johnson-Marshall and Martha Bell Williams Scholarships *(Undergraduate/Scholarship)* [2068]

Les Dames D'Escoffier New York Corporate Scholarship *(Undergraduate/Scholarship)* [6777]

Lighthouse International Scholarships - College-bound Awards *(High School, Undergraduate/Scholarship)* [6856]

Lighthouse International Scholarships - Graduate Awards *(Graduate, Postgraduate/Scholarship)* [6857]

Lighthouse International Scholarships - Undergraduate Awards *(Undergraduate/Scholarship)* [6858]

NASSLEO Scholarships - Region I *(Undergraduate/Scholarship)* [7688]

NCNJ-AWMA Undergraduate Scholarship *(Undergraduate/Scholarship)* [172]

NJCBIR Individual Research Grants *(Graduate, Professional development, Postdoctorate, Doctorate/Grant)* [10807]

NJCBIR Programmatic Multi-Investigator Project Grants *(Other/Grant)* [10810]

NJLA Scholarships *(Graduate, Postgraduate/Scholarship)* [8277]

NJSBF Labor Law Scholarship *(Undergraduate/Scholarship)* [8291]

NJSCPA College Scholarships *(Graduate, Undergraduate/Scholarship)* [8287]

NJSCPA High School Seniors *(Undergraduate/Scholarship)* [8288]

Osteopathic Medical School Scholarship *(Undergraduate/Scholarship)* [8271]

Full Pellegrini Scholarship *(Undergraduate, Graduate/Scholarship)* [10896]

The Vincent S. Haneman - Joseph B. Perskie Scholarship *(Graduate, Undergraduate/Fellowship)* [2342]

Louis C. Portella Memorial Award *(Undergraduate, Graduate/Scholarship)* [2853]

Riding Into the Future *(Undergraduate, College, University/Scholarship)* [6775]

ROFL Scholarship *(Undergraduate, College, University/Scholarship)* [9236]

Jay A. Strassberg Memorial Scholarship *(Undergraduate/Scholarship)* [2855]

Hazaros Tabakoglu Scholarship Fund *(Undergraduate/Scholarship)* [8309]

Daniel B. Toll Memorial Award *(Undergraduate, Graduate/Scholarship)* [2856]

Bruce A. Wallace Memorial Award *(Undergraduate, Graduate/Scholarship)* [2858]

Yankee Clipper Contest Club Youth Scholarship *(Undergraduate/Scholarship)* [1967]

Young Christian Leaders Scholarships (*Undergraduate/Scholarship*) [12266]

Zimmermann Scholarship (*Graduate/Scholarship*) [10898]

New Mexico

Walt Bartram Memorial Education Scholarship (*Undergraduate/Scholarship*) [10384]

Notah Begay III Scholarship Program (*Undergraduate/Scholarship*) [317]

Excel Staffing Companies Scholarships for Excellence in Continuing Education (*Undergraduate/Scholarship*) [319]

Don Fox Memorial Scholarship (*Undergraduate/Scholarship*) [232]

Martha Julian Memorial Scholarship (*Undergraduate/Scholarship*) [233]

Ted Lewis Memorial Scholarship (*Undergraduate/Scholarship*) [234]

Lone Star GIA Associate and Alumni Scholarships (*Undergraduate/Scholarship*) [4879]

The Fred R. McDaniel Memorial Scholarship (*Undergraduate/Scholarship*) [1948]

New Mexico Manufactured Housing Association Scholarship Fund (*Undergraduate/Scholarship*) [320]

Robby Baker Memorial Scholarship (*Graduate/Scholarship*) [321]

Rocky Mountain Coal Mining Institute Engineering/Geology Scholarships (*Four Year College/Scholarship*) [9727]

Rocky Mountain Coal Mining Institute Technical Scholarships (*Two Year College/Scholarship*) [9728]

Barnes W. Rose, Jr. and Eva Rose Nichol Scholarship Fund (*Graduate/Scholarship*) [322]

Hatton W. Sumners Scholarships (*Undergraduate/Scholarship*) [8610]

Woodcock Family Education Scholarship Program (*Undergraduate/Scholarship*) [324]

New York

Ann Liguori Foundation Sports Media Scholarship (*Graduate, Undergraduate/Scholarship*) [8366]

Robert L. Bernstein Fellowships in International Human Rights (*Graduate/Fellowship*) [5630]

The Henry Broughton, K2AE, Memorial Scholarship (*Undergraduate/Scholarship*) [1930]

CHRGJ Emerging Human Rights Scholarship Conference (*Graduate/Scholarship*) [8358]

Emerald Creek Capital Scholarship (*Undergraduate/Scholarship*) [4374]

Eunice Miles Scholarship (*Graduate/Scholarship*) [4876]

Fellowship on Women & Public Policy (*Graduate/Fellowship*) [11522]

Gallo Blue Chip Scholarships (*Undergraduate/Scholarship*) [5301]

The Dr. James L. Lawson Memorial Scholarship (*Undergraduate/Scholarship*) [1947]

Les Dames D'Escoffier New York Corporate Scholarship (*Undergraduate/Scholarship*) [6777]

Lighthouse International Scholarships - College-bound Awards (*High School, Undergraduate/Scholarship*) [6856]

Lighthouse International Scholarships - Graduate Awards (*Graduate, Postgraduate/Scholarship*) [6857]

Lighthouse International Scholarships - Undergraduate Awards (*Undergraduate/Scholarship*) [6858]

David J. Moynihan Scholarships (*Undergraduate, Graduate/Scholarship*) [8331]

NASSLEO Scholarships - Region I (*Undergraduate/Scholarship*) [7688]

New York State Association of Agricultural Fairs Scholarship (*Undergraduate/Scholarship*) [8319]

The New York Times College Scholarship (*Undergraduate/Scholarship, Internship*) [8354]

NYFWA Scholarships (*Undergraduate, Graduate/Scholarship*) [8312]

Faith E. O'Neal Scholarship (*Graduate/Scholarship*) [9459]

Full Pellegrini Scholarship (*Undergraduate, Graduate/Scholarship*) [10896]

Harry B. Pulver Scholarships (*Undergraduate/Scholarship*) [5002]

Richard T. Liddicoat Scholarship (*Graduate/Scholarship*) [4882]

Herbert Roback Scholarship (*Graduate, Master's/Scholarship*) [7579]

Saint Andrews Scholarships (*Undergraduate/Scholarship*) [9776]

Saratoga County Bar Association Law Student Scholarship (*Undergraduate/Scholarship*) [9880]

Stanley M. Schoenfeld Memorial Scholarship (*Postgraduate/Scholarship*) [8321]

Senator Patricia K. McGee Nursing Faculty Scholarship (*Doctorate, Graduate/Scholarship*) [8323]

The Norman E. Strohmeier, W2VRS, Memorial Scholarship (*Undergraduate/Scholarship*) [1964]

Hazaros Tabakoglu Scholarship Fund (*Undergraduate/Scholarship*) [8309]

Victoria Ovis Memorial Scholarship (*Undergraduate/Scholarship*) [7982]

Albert E. Wischmeyer Scholarship (*Undergraduate/Scholarship*) [10419]

Yankee Clipper Contest Club Youth Scholarship (*Undergraduate/Scholarship*) [1967]

Young Christian Leaders Scholarships (*Undergraduate/Scholarship*) [12266]

Zimmermann Scholarship (*Graduate/Scholarship*) [10898]

Lorraine Zitone Memorial Scholarship Fund (*Undergraduate/Scholarship*) [7109]

North Carolina

African American Network - Carolinas Scholarship Fund (*Undergraduate/Scholarship*) [4715]

The William Tasse Alexander Scholarship (*Undergraduate/Scholarship*) [4716]

Art and Dannie Weber Scholarship (*Undergraduate/Scholarship*) [12061]

Ben Robinette Scholarship Fund (*Undergraduate/Scholarship*) [4720]

Pete and Ellen Bensley Memorial Scholarship Fund (*Undergraduate/Scholarship*) [4721]

Blanche Raper Zimmerman Scholarship (*Other/Scholarship*) [12062]

Leon Bradley Scholarship Program (*Undergraduate/Scholarship*) [638]

Kasie Ford Capling Memorial Scholarship Endowment Fund (*Undergraduate/Scholarship*) [4723]

William F. Carl Scholarships (*Undergraduate/Scholarship*) [8443]

Childrens Scholarship Fund-Charlotte (*Undergraduate/Scholarship*) [4728]

Dan Stewart Scholarship (*Other/Scholarship*) [8433]

David Julian Whichard Scholarship (*Undergraduate/Scholarship*) [11180]

Davidson and Jones Hotel Corporation Scholarship (*Undergraduate/Scholarship*) [8445]

Edward Jackson International Travel Award (*Undergraduate/Award*) [11184]

Edwin H. and Louise N. Williamson Endowed Scholarship (*Undergraduate/Scholarship*) [12072]

Virginia Elizabeth and Alma Vane Taylor Nursing Scholarship (*Undergraduate/Scholarship*) [12073]

Elizabeth T. Williams Memorial Scholarship (*Undergraduate/Scholarship*) [12074]

Elmer and Rosa Lee Collins Scholarship (*Undergraduate/Scholarship*) [12075]

Forsyth County Nursing Scholarship (*Undergraduate/Scholarship*) [12077]

The Garden Club Council of Winston-Salem and Forsyth County Scholarship (*Undergraduate/Scholarship*) [12079]

Governor James E. Holshouser Professional Development Scholarship (*Other/Scholarship*) [8434]

Henry S. and Carolyn Adams Scholarship (*Undergraduate/Scholarship*) [4734]

Hughes Memorial Foundatio n (*Other/Scholarship*) [5619]

Jack Ervin Economic Development Institute Scholarship (*Other/Scholarship*) [8435]

James Davis Scholarship (*Undergraduate/Scholarship*) [11190]

James V. Johnson Scholarship Endowment Fund (*Undergraduate/Scholarship*) [4737]

Jim Graham Scholarship (*Undergraduate/Scholarship*) [8455]

Julian E. Carnes Scholarship Endowment Fund (*Undergraduate/Scholarship*) [4738]

The Mary and Millard Kiker Scholarship (*Undergraduate/Scholarship*) [4739]

Douglas Gray Kimel Scholarship (*Undergraduate/Scholarship*) [12081]

L.D. and Elsie Long Memorial Scholarship (*Graduate/Scholarship*) [12083]

Lighthouse International Scholarships - College-bound Awards (*High School, Undergraduate/Scholarship*) [6856]

Lighthouse International Scholarships - Graduate Awards (*Graduate, Postgraduate/Scholarship*) [6857]

Lighthouse International Scholarships - Undergraduate Awards (*Undergraduate/Scholarship*) [6858]

North Carolina Hospitality Education Foundation Scholarship (*Undergraduate/Scholarship*) [8446]

NC Hospitality Education Foundation Scholarships - Graduate (*Graduate/Scholarship*) [8447]

NC Hospitality Education Foundation Scholarships - High School (*Undergraduate/Scholarship*) [8448]

NC Hospitality Education Foundation Scholarships - Two Year Community or Junior College (*Undergraduate/Scholarship*) [8449]

NCACPA Outstanding Minority Accounting Student Scholarships (*Undergraduate/Scholarship*) [8426]

NCRLA Golden Corral Scholarship (*Undergraduate/Scholarship*) [8450]

Nell and Spencer Waggoner Scholarship (*Undergraduate/Scholarship*) [12084]

North Carolina Association of Health Care Recruiters Scholarship (*Undergraduate/Scholarship*) [8429]

North Carolina CPA Foundation Scholarships (*Undergraduate/Scholarship*) [8427]

North Carolina Heroes Financial Hardship Grant (*Other/Grant*) [8439]

The North Carolina League For Nursing Academic Scholarship (*Graduate, Master's/Scholarship*) [4748]

Oliver Joel and Ellen Pell Denny Healthcare Scholarship (*Undergraduate/Scholarship*) [12085]

Peter DeWitt Pruden and Phyllis Harrill Pruden Scholarship (*Undergraduate/Scholarship*) [11202]

William H. and Lena M. Petree Scholarship (*Graduate/Scholarship*) [12087]

Regions Riding Forward Scholarship Essay Contest (*Undergraduate, High School/Scholarship*) [9618]

Reuben R. Cowles Youth Educational Award (*Undergraduate, Graduate/Award*) [1059]

Rider Family Scholarship (*Undergraduate/Scholarship, Award*) [12090]

The Sally Cole Visual Arts Scholarship Program (*Undergraduate/Scholarship*) [4753]

Serena D. Dalton Scholarship (*Undergraduate/Scholarship*) [12091]

Stella B. Johnson Scholarship (*Undergraduate/Scholarship*) [12092]

Mary Stewart and William T. Covington, Jr. Scholarship Fund (*Undergraduate/Scholarship*) [4755]

Stultz Scholarship (*Undergraduate/Scholarship*) [12093]

T. Frank Booth Memorial Scholarship Endowment Fund (*Undergraduate/Scholarship*) [4756]

Tailor Made Lawns Scholarship Fund (*Undergraduate/Scholarship*) [10909]

Turner Family Scholarships (*Undergraduate, Vocational/Occupational/Scholarship*) [4760]

The Gary Wagner, K3OMI, Scholarship (*Undergraduate/Scholarship*) [1965]

The L. Phil and Alice J. Wicker Scholarship (*Undergraduate/Scholarship*) [1966]

Gary S. Wilmer/RAMI Music Scholarship (*Undergraduate/Scholarship*) [3696]

The Harriet Glen Wilmore Scholarship (*Undergraduate, Vocational/Occupational/Scholarship*) [4765]

Ted G. Wilson Memorial Scholarships (*Undergraduate/Scholarship*) [9338]

The Winston-Salem Foundation Scholarship (*Undergraduate/Scholarship*) [12099]

North Dakota

Horatio Alger North Dakota Scholarships (Undergraduate/Scholarship) [5576]
Louisa Bowen Memorial Scholarship for Graduate Students in Archival Administration (Graduate/Scholarship) [7365]
North Dakota Division Scholarships (Undergraduate, Graduate/Scholarship) [7373]
North Dakota Veterinary Medical Association Scholarships (Undergraduate/Scholarship) [8475]
Rocky Mountain Coal Mining Institute Engineering/Geology Scholarships (Four Year College/Scholarship) [9727]
Rocky Mountain Coal Mining Institute Technical Scholarships (Two Year College/Scholarship) [9728]
Stanley Moore FUI Foundation Regional Scholarships (Four Year College, High School, Two Year College/Scholarship) [8464]
Upper Midwest Human Rights Fellowship Program (Graduate/Scholarship, Fellowship) [5632]

Northern Mariana Islands

Christian Pharmacists Fellowship International (CPFI) (Advanced Professional/Scholarship) [3321]

Ohio

Ach Family Scholarship Fund (Undergraduate/Scholarship) [3335]
AISC/Ohio Structural Steel Association Scholarships (Undergraduate, Master's/Scholarship) [1052]
Akron Bar Association Foundation Scholarships (Undergraduate/Scholarship) [203]
Alex Family Scholarship (Undergraduate/Scholarship) [7077]
Alice J. Foit Scholarship Fund (Undergraduate/Scholarship) [10750]
Ora E. Anderson Scholarship (Undergraduate, High School/Scholarship) [4706]
Anthony Munoz Scholarship Fund (Undergraduate/Scholarship) [7501]
A. B. and Hazel Augenstein Scholarship (Undergraduate/Scholarship) [7078]
Irene Ballinger Memorial Scholarship (Undergraduate/Scholarship) [7079]
Barr Foundation Scholarship (Undergraduate/Scholarship) [3337]
Barrett Family Scholarship Fund (Undergraduate/Scholarship) [3338]
Bergmann Family Scholarship (Undergraduate/Scholarship) [7080]
Helen & Bob Bintz Scholarship (Undergraduate/Scholarship) [7081]
Bob and Linda Kohlhepp Scholarship Fund (Undergraduate/Scholarship) [3339]
Borden Inc. Scholarship Fund (Undergraduate/Scholarship) [3340]
Catherine Amelia Thew Brown Memorial Scholarship (Undergraduate/Scholarship) [7082]
William & Martha Buckingham Scholarship (Undergraduate/Scholarship) [7083]
Stephen J. Byrnes & Mary "Sally" Byrnes Scholarship (Undergraduate, Two Year College, Four Year College/Scholarship) [7084]
Caledonia Alumni Association Scholarship (Graduate/Scholarship) [7085]
Harry D. Callahan Educational Trust (Undergraduate/Scholarship) [10754]
Carey Family Scholarship (Undergraduate/Scholarship) [7086]
Carl H. Lindner Family Fund (Undergraduate/Scholarship) [3341]
Joe & Peggy Casey Memorial Scholarship (Undergraduate/Scholarship) [7087]
George H. and Anna Casper Fund (Undergraduate, Graduate/Scholarship, Loan) [10755]
Castellini Foundation Scholarship (Undergraduate/Scholarship) [3342]
CFT/ACPSOP Scholarship Fund (Undergraduate/Scholarship) [3343]
Charles and Claire Phillips Scholarship Fund (Undergraduate/Scholarship) [3344]

Charlotte R. SchmidLapp Scholarship Fund (Undergraduate/Scholarship) [3345]
Christopher Todd Grant Memorial Fund (Undergraduate/Scholarship) [3346]
Cincinnati Bell Foundation Scholarship (Undergraduate/Scholarship) [3347]
Cincinnati Financial Corporation Fund (Undergraduate/Scholarship) [3348]
Cleveland Executive Fellowships (CEF) (Other/Fellowship) [3434]
Collier Scholarship (Undergraduate, College, University/Scholarship) [7088]
Community's Memorial Scholarship (Undergraduate, College, University/Scholarship) [7089]
Bill & Joan Cones Scholarship (Undergraduate, College, University/Scholarship) [7090]
Clare Cooke Performing Arts Scholarship (Undergraduate, College, University/Scholarship) [7091]
Alex Cooper Memorial Scholarship (Undergraduate, College, University/Scholarship) [7092]
Corinne and Fred Capuder Memorial Scholarship (Undergraduate/Scholarship) [3349]
Cornell/Goodman Scholarship (Undergraduate, College, University, Vocational/Occupational/Scholarship) [7093]
Corwin Nixon Scholarship Fund (Undergraduate/Scholarship) [3350]
David A. Couch Memorial Scholarship (Undergraduate/Scholarship) [8839]
Covington-Cincinnati/Northern Kentucky Alumni Chapter - Dane Wagge Scholarships (University/Scholarship) [11575]
Craig Scholarship (Undergraduate, College, University/Scholarship) [7094]
Crosset Family Foundation Scholarship (Undergraduate/Scholarship) [3351]
Stormy Ray Cushing Scholarship (Undergraduate, College, University/Scholarship) [7095]
Dater Foundation Scholarship (Undergraduate/Scholarship) [3352]
David J. Joseph Company Scholarship Fund (Undergraduate/Scholarship) [3353]
Marge Sorreles Davies Memorial Scholarship (Undergraduate, College, University/Scholarship) [7096]
Dee Wacksman Scholarship Fund (Undergraduate/Scholarship) [3354]
Robert Martz DiGiacomo Memorial Scholarship Fund (Undergraduate/Scholarship) [10756]
Dr. Kathy Dixon Memorial Scholarship (Undergraduate, University, College/Scholarship) [7097]
Don and Madalyn Sickafoose Educational Trust Fund (Undergraduate/Scholarship, Loan) [10757]
The Harold K. Douthit Scholarship (Undergraduate/Scholarship) [8580]
Dwight Hibbard Scholarship Fund (Undergraduate/Scholarship) [3355]
Brenda Dye Music Boosters Scholarship (Undergraduate, University, College/Scholarship) [7098]
Elgin Alumni Association Scholarship (Undergraduate, University, College/Scholarship) [7099]
Ella Wilson Johnson Scholarship Fund (Undergraduate/Scholarship) [3356]
Helen E. Evans Scholarship (Undergraduate, College, University/Scholarship) [7100]
Everett Family Scholarship (Undergraduate, College, University/Scholarship) [7101]
E.W. Scripps Foundation Scholarship (Undergraduate/Scholarship) [3357]
Farmer Family Scholarship Fund (Undergraduate/Scholarship) [3358]
Fifth Third Bank Scholarship Fund (Undergraduate/Scholarship) [3359]
Fletemeyer Family Scholarship Fund (Undergraduate/Scholarship) [3360]
Florette B. Hoffheimer Scholarship Fund (Undergraduate/Scholarship) [3361]
Frank Foster Skillman Fund (Undergraduate/Scholarship) [3362]
Gardner Foundation Scholarship (Undergraduate/Scholarship) [3363]
David A. and Pamela A. Gault Charitable Fund (Undergraduate/Scholarship) [10759]
GE Aviation Scholarship Fund (Undergraduate/Scholarship) [3364]

Laverne L. Gibson Memorial Scholarship (Undergraduate/Scholarship) [8848]
Goldman, Sachs and Company Fund (Undergraduate/Scholarship) [3365]
James H. and Shirley L. Green Scholarship Fund (Undergraduate/Scholarship) [10761]
Velma Shotwell Griffin Memorial Scholarship Fund (Undergraduate/Scholarship) [10762]
H.C. Schott Foundation Scholarship (Undergraduate/Scholarship) [3366]
HCRTA/Glen O. & Wyllabeth Scholarship Fund (Undergraduate/Scholarship) [3367]
Dr. James H. Heckman Memorial Scholarship Fund (Undergraduate/Scholarship) [10763]
Heidelberg Distributing Scholarship Fund (Undergraduate/Scholarship) [3368]
Heinz Pet Products Scholarship Fund (Undergraduate/Scholarship) [3369]
Helen Steiner Rice Scholarship Fund (Undergraduate/Scholarship) [3370]
Raymond T. Hoge Scholarship Fund (Undergraduate/Scholarship) [10765]
Jackson High School Alumni Scholarship Fund (Graduate/Scholarship) [10768]
Johnny Bench Scholarship Fund (Undergraduate/Scholarship) [3371]
Joseph S. Stern Scholarship Fund (Undergraduate/Scholarship) [3372]
Judge Benjamin Schwartz Memorial Fund (Undergraduate/Scholarship) [3373]
Juilfs Foundation Scholarship (Undergraduate/Scholarship) [3374]
The Junior Achievement of East Central Ohio, Inc. Scholarship Fund (Undergraduate, High School/Scholarship) [10771]
David A. Kaiser Memorial Scholarship Fund (Undergraduate/Scholarship) [10772]
Kappa Delta Phi Scholarship (Postgraduate/Scholarship) [1179]
Katherine M. Grosscup Scholarships in Horticulture (Undergraduate, Graduate/Scholarship) [4860]
KDP Huntington Bank Scholarship (Undergraduate/Scholarship) [6384]
Kroger Cincinnati/Dayton Scholarship Fund (Undergraduate/Scholarship) [3375]
Samuel Krugliak Legal Scholarship Fund (Undergraduate/Scholarship) [10773]
L. & T. Woolfolk Memorial Scholarship Fund (Undergraduate/Scholarship) [3376]
Lake Dollars for Scholars Endowment Fund (Undergraduate/Scholarship) [10774]
Lester and Eleanor Webster Foundation Fund (Undergraduate/Scholarship) [10775]
Louis B. Zapoleon Memorial Fund (Undergraduate/Scholarship) [3377]
Louisa Bowen Memorial Scholarship for Graduate Students in Archival Administration (Graduate/Scholarship) [7365]
Lowe Simpson Scholarship Fund (Undergraduate/Scholarship) [3378]
Lyle Everingham Scholarship Fund (Undergraduate/Scholarship) [3379]
Lyle and Rlene Everingham Family Fund (Undergraduate/Scholarship) [3380]
Manzer-Keener-Wefler Scholarship Fund (Undergraduate/Scholarship) [10777]
Martha W. Tanner Memorial Fund (Undergraduate/Scholarship) [3381]
Marvin Rammelsberg Scholarship Fund (Undergraduate/Scholarship) [3382]
Mary Roberts Scholarship Fund (Undergraduate/Scholarship) [3383]
McCall Educational Fund (Undergraduate/Scholarship) [3384]
MCRTA Book Scholarships (Undergraduate/Scholarship) [7295]
Medina County Retired Teachers Association Scholarship (Graduate/Scholarship) [7236]
Sanders J. Mestel Legal Scholarship Fund (Undergraduate/Scholarship) [10779]
Harry Mestel Memorial Accounting Scholarship Fund (Undergraduate/Scholarship) [10780]
Michael Bany Memorial Scholarship Fund (Undergraduate/Scholarship) [3385]
Midland Company Scholarship Fund (Undergraduate/Scholarship) [3386]

Milacron Geier Scholarship Fund (Undergraduate/ Scholarship) [3387]

Milton and Edith Brown Memorial Scholarship Fund (Undergraduate/Scholarship) [3388]

Lt. Colonel Robert G. Moreland Vocational/Technical Fund (Undergraduate/Scholarship) [10783]

Nelson Schwab Jr. Scholarship Fund (Undergraduate/Scholarship) [3389]

Nethercott Family Scholarship Fund (Undergraduate/Scholarship) [3390]

NOHIMSS Student Scholarship Program (Undergraduate, Master's, Doctorate/Scholarship) [8494]

Ohio National Foundation Scholarship (Undergraduate/Scholarship) [3391]

Ohio Newspaper Association Minority Scholarship (Undergraduate/Scholarship) [8581]

O'Jay's Scholarship Fund (Undergraduate/Scholarship) [10786]

Pepper Family Scholarship Fund (Undergraduate/ Scholarship) [3392]

Perry Township School Memorial Scholarship Fund (Undergraduate/Scholarship) [10787]

Pichler Family Scholarship Fund (Undergraduate/ Scholarship) [3393]

PNC Scholarship Fund (Undergraduate/Scholarship) [3394]

The Thomas W. Porter, W8KYZ, Scholarship Honoring Michael Daugherty, W8LSE (Undergraduate/ Scholarship) [1955]

Priscilla Gamble Scholarship Fund (Undergraduate/ Scholarship) [3395]

Procter and Gamble Foundation Scholarship (Undergraduate/Scholarship) [3396]

Raymond and Augusta Klink Scholarship Fund (Undergraduate/Scholarship) [3397]

Reid Hospital Graduate Student Scholarships (Graduate/Scholarship) [11951]

Reynoldsburg-Pickerington Rotary Club High School Scholarship (Undergraduate/Scholarship) [9681]

Richard Heekin Scholarship Fund (Undergraduate/ Scholarship) [3398]

Robert H. Reakirt Scholarship Fund (Undergraduate/Scholarship) [3399]

Thomas Warren Roberts Memorial Scholarship (Undergraduate/Scholarship) [8873]

Roger and Joyce Howe Scholarship Fund (Undergraduate/Scholarship) [3400]

Ruth M. Cogan Foundation Trust (Undergraduate/ Scholarship) [10789]

S. David Shor Scholarship Fund (Undergraduate/ Scholarship) [3401]

St. Joseph's Hospital School of Nursing Alumnae Scholarship (Undergraduate/Scholarship) [8876]

S.C. Johnson, A Family Company Scholarship Fund (Undergraduate/Scholarship) [3402]

Semple Foundation Scholarship (Undergraduate/ Scholarship) [3403]

Ruth Skeeles Memorial Scholarship Fund (Undergraduate/Scholarship) [10792]

Stark County Dairy Promoters Scholarship Fund (Graduate/Scholarship) [10794]

Stephen Schwartz Musical Theatre Scholarship (Undergraduate/Scholarship) [5624]

The Zachary Taylor Stevens Scholarship (Undergraduate/Scholarship) [1962]

Jeffrey Tyler Sweitzer Wrestling Memorial Scholarship Fund (Undergraduate/Scholarship) [10795]

Timothy S. Sweterlitsch Memorial Scholarship Fund (Undergraduate/Scholarship) [10796]

Thomas J. Emery Memorial Fund Scholarship (Undergraduate/Scholarship) [3404]

T.L. Conlan Scholarship Fund (Undergraduate/ Scholarship) [3405]

US Bank NA Scholarship Fund (Undergraduate/ Scholarship) [3406]

Walter and Marilyn Bartlett Scholarship Fund (Undergraduate/Scholarship) [3407]

Western-Southern Foundation Scholarship (Undergraduate/Scholarship) [3408]

Whitaker-Minard Memorial Scholarship (Undergraduate/Scholarship) [8886]

Mary Kean White Memorial Scholarship Fund (Undergraduate, Doctorate/Scholarship) [10802]

Bob Evans And Wayne White Scholarship (Graduate, High School/Scholarship) [4708]

William A. Friedlander Scholarship Fund (Undergraduate/Scholarship) [3409]

William J. Rielly/MCURC Scholarship Fund (Undergraduate/Scholarship) [3410]

Glenn Wilson Broadcast Journalism Scholarship (Undergraduate/Scholarship) [8887]

Wood County Bar Association Memorial Scholarship (Graduate/Scholarship) [8888]

Woodward Trustees Foundation Scholarship (Undergraduate/Scholarship) [3411]

Wynne Family Memorial Fund (Undergraduate/ Scholarship) [3412]

The Youth Scholarship Program (Undergraduate/ Scholarship) [5725]

Zelma Gray Medical School Scholarship (Graduate, Doctorate/Scholarship) [4709]

Oklahoma

The Tom and Judith Comstock Scholarship (Undergraduate/Scholarship) [1935]

Lone Star GIA Associate and Alumni Scholarships (Undergraduate/Scholarship) [4879]

The Fred R. McDaniel Memorial Scholarship (Undergraduate/Scholarship) [1948]

Ozarks Division of Midwest Dairy Educational Award (Undergraduate/Scholarship) [7374]

Hatton W. Sumners Scholarships (Undergraduate/ Scholarship) [8610]

Lynn McNabb Walton Adelphe Scholarhship (Undergraduate/Scholarship) [6479]

Oregon

Paul Arnold Memorial Scholarships (Other/Scholarship) [9288]

Asian and Pacific Islander Queer Sisters Scholarship (APIQS) (Undergraduate/Scholarship) [9289]

Associates in Behavioral Health Scholarships (Graduate/Scholarship) [9290]

The Mary Lou Brown Scholarship (Undergraduate/ Scholarship) [1931]

Clackamas County Farm Bureau Agricultural Scholarships (Undergraduate/Scholarship) [8715]

Brian M. Day Scholarships (Undergraduate, Graduate/Scholarship) [9295]

Deloris Carter Hampton Scholarship (Undergraduate/Scholarship) [9296]

Dennis Coleman Scholarship (Undergraduate/Scholarship) [9297]

Dennis Coleman Scholarships (Undergraduate/ Scholarship) [9298]

Donald O. Coffman Scholarship (Graduate, Undergraduate/Scholarship) [9300]

Oregon Latino Scholarship Fund (Graduate, Undergraduate/Scholarship) [5526]

McFarffels Scholarships (Undergraduate/Scholarship) [9304]

Jack D. Motteler Scholarship (Undergraduate/Scholarship) [9305]

OAIA Scholarships (Undergraduate, Graduate/ Scholarship) [8700]

Oregon College/University Scholarships (Undergraduate/Scholarship) [8721]

Oregon Literary Fellowships (Advanced Professional/Fellowship) [6877]

OSCPA Educational Foundation High School Scholarships (Undergraduate/Scholarship) [8722]

Pride Foundation Political Leadership Scholarships (Undergraduate/Scholarship) [9306]

Pride Foundation Regional Scholarships (Undergraduate/Scholarship) [9307]

Pride Foundation Scholarships (Undergraduate/ Scholarship) [9771]

Pride Foundation Social Work Scholarships (Undergraduate/Scholarship) [9308]

Pride of the Rose Scholarship (Undergraduate/ Scholarship) [9309]

Robert W. and Bernice Ingalls Staton Scholarships (Undergraduate/Scholarship) [11654]

Rosenberg-Ibarra Scholarships (Graduate/Scholarship) [9312]

The Seneca Scholarship (High School, College/ Scholarship) [10006]

Kathy Spadoni Memorial Scholarships (Graduate/ Scholarship) [9313]

Trinity Scholars Program (Undergraduate/Scholarship) [11113]

Ric Ulrich and Chuck Pischke Scholarships (Undergraduate/Scholarship) [9315]

University of Oregon Presidential Scholarship (Undergraduate/Scholarship) [11658]

Wozumi Family Scholarships (Undergraduate/Scholarship) [9318]

Pennsylvania

Ruth Abernathy Presidential Scholarship (Professional development, Graduate/Scholarship) [10346]

Albert and Alice Nacinovich Music Scholarship Fund (Undergraduate/Scholarship) [4582]

Horatio Alger Pennsylvania Scholarships (Undergraduate/Scholarship) [5577]

Allegheny County Medical Society Medical Student Scholarship (Advanced Professional/Scholarship) [4796]

Allen Allured Fellowship (Graduate/Fellowship) [9345]

Alliance Medical Education Scholarship (AMES) (Undergraduate, Graduate/Scholarship) [4797]

Ann Liguori Foundation Sports Media Scholarship (Graduate, Undergraduate/Scholarship) [8366]

Bailey/Hollister Scholarship (Graduate, Professional development/Scholarship) [8956]

Joseph R. Calder, Jr., MD Scholarship Fund (Undergraduate/Scholarship) [4586]

Carrie and George Lyter Scholarship (Undergraduate/Scholarship) [4775]

Irene R. Christman Scholarship (Undergraduate/ Scholarship) [8960]

Dr. Michael Dorizas Memorial Scholarships (Undergraduate/Scholarship) [5464]

Dunkin' Donuts Philadelphia Regional Scholarship Program (Undergraduate/Scholarship) [9941]

Erin L. Jenkins Memorial Scholarship (Undergraduate/Scholarship) [4776]

Gallo Blue Chip Scholarships (Undergraduate/ Scholarship) [5301]

Generation III Scholarship (Undergraduate/Scholarship) [4285]

Green Knight Economic Development Corporation Scholarships (Undergraduate/Scholarship) [5235]

Scott A. Gunder, MD, DCMS Presidential Scholarship (Undergraduate, Graduate/Scholarship) [4798]

Hellenic University Club of Philadelphia Founders Scholarship (Undergraduate/Scholarship) [5465]

Nicholas S. Hetos, DDS, Memorial Graduate Scholarship (Graduate, Doctorate/Scholarship) [5466]

Hope Through Learning Award (Undergraduate/ Award) [5551]

Howard Fox Memorial Law Scholarship Fund (Graduate/Scholarship) [2488]

Individual K-Grants (All/Grant) [6564]

J. Ward Sleichter and Frances F. Sleichter Memorial Fund (Undergraduate/Scholarship) [4779]

John G. Williams Scholarship Foundation (Undergraduate/Scholarship) [12039]

Judge Ross Leadership Scholarship (Professional development/Scholarship) [7764]

Katherine M. Grosscup Scholarships in Horticulture (Undergraduate, Graduate/Scholarship) [4860]

Short-Term Library Resident Research Fellowships (Doctorate/Fellowship) [1216]

Lighthouse International Scholarships - Collegebound Awards (High School, Undergraduate/ Scholarship) [6856]

Lighthouse International Scholarships - Graduate Awards (Graduate, Postgraduate/Scholarship) [6857]

Lighthouse International Scholarships - Undergraduate Awards (Undergraduate/Scholarship) [6858]

Lycoming County Medical Society Scholarship (Undergraduate, Graduate/Scholarship) [4799]

Olivia M. Marquart Scholarships (Graduate, Master's, Doctorate/Scholarship) [11169]

Montgomery County Medical Society – William W. Lander, MD, Medical Student Scholarship (Undergraduate/Scholarship) [4800]

Robert E. and Judy More Scholarship Fund (Undergraduate/Scholarship) [4599]

NASSLEO Scholarships - Region I (Undergraduate/ Scholarship) [7688]

Northampton County Medical Society Alliance Scholarships (Undergraduate/Scholarship) [8480]

NTHA Forest Resources Scholarships for College Students (Undergraduate/Scholarship) [8496]

Oliver Rosenberg Educational Trust (Undergraduate/Scholarship) [4781]

Dr. Nicholas Padis Memorial Graduate Scholarship (Graduate/Scholarship) [5467]

Full Pellegrini Scholarship (Undergraduate, Graduate/Scholarship) [10896]

Pennsylvania Engineering Foundation (PEF) Grants: Undergraduate (Undergraduate/Scholarship) [8964]

Pennsylvania Heartland Unit Scholarship (Undergraduate/Scholarship) [5489]

Pennsylvania Land Surveyors' Foundation Scholarship (Undergraduate/Scholarship) [8962]

Pennsylvania Library Association MLS Scholarships (Graduate/Scholarship) [8958]

ROFL Scholarship (Undergraduate, College, University/Scholarship) [9236]

Schmidt Kramer Annual Scholarship For Academic Excellence (Undergraduate/Scholarship) [9936]

Minnie Patton Stayman Scholarships (Undergraduate/Scholarship) [8968]

Dr. Peter A. Theodos Memorial Graduate Scholarship (Graduate/Scholarship) [5468]

Dimitri J. Ververelli Memorial Scholarship for Architecture and/or Engineering (Undergraduate/Scholarship) [5469]

Myrtle Siegfried, MD, and Michael Vigilante, MD Scholarship (Undergraduate/Scholarship) [4801]

Monica M. Weaver Memorial Fund (Undergraduate/Scholarship) [4606]

William H. Davis, Jr. Scholarship (Undergraduate/Scholarship) [3599]

Yankee Clipper Contest Club Youth Scholarship (Undergraduate/Scholarship) [1967]

Zimmermann Scholarship (Graduate/Scholarship) [10898]

Puerto Rico

Army Health Professions Scholarship Program (HPSP) (Professional development/Scholarship) [11288]

CHCI Congressional Internship Program (Undergraduate/Internship) [3745]

HACU/KIA Motors America, Inc. STEAM Scholarships (Undergraduate, Graduate/Scholarship) [5516, 6543]

HRSA Scholarships for Disadvantaged Students (Undergraduate/Scholarship) [11334]

Imagine America College Scholarships for High School Students (Undergraduate/Scholarship) [5717]

National Federation of the Blind Scholarship Program (Undergraduate/Scholarship, Monetary) [7878]

Rhode Island

Adler Pollock & Sheehan Diversity Scholarships (Undergraduate/Fellowship) [77]

Antonio Cirino Memorial Scholarship (Graduate/Scholarship) [9688]

Bach Organ Scholarship (Undergraduate/Scholarship) [9689]

Bruce and Marjorie Sundlun Scholarship (Undergraduate/Scholarship) [9690]

Casey Family Services Alumni Scholarship (Undergraduate, Master's, Vocational/Occupational/Scholarship) [4693]

Constant Memorial Scholarship (Undergraduate/Scholarship) [9691]

Edward Leon Duhamel Freemasons Scholarship (Undergraduate/Scholarship) [9692]

GFWC Women's Club of South County scholarship program (Undergraduate/Scholarship) [9693]

The Dr. James L. Lawson Memorial Scholarship (Undergraduate/Scholarship) [1947]

Lighthouse International Scholarships - College-bound Awards (High School, Undergraduate/Scholarship) [6856]

Lighthouse International Scholarships - Graduate Awards (Graduate, Postgraduate/Scholarship) [6857]

Lighthouse International Scholarships - Undergraduate Awards (Undergraduate/Scholarship) [6858]

Lily and Catello Sorrentino Memorial Scholarship (Undergraduate/Scholarship) [9694]

Marilynne Graboys Wool Scholarship (Graduate/Scholarship) [9695]

NASSLEO Scholarships - Region I (Undergraduate/Scholarship) [7688]

The New England FEMARA Scholarship (Undergraduate/Scholarship) [1951]

Rhode Island Association of Former Legislators Scholarship (Graduate/Scholarship) [9696]

Rhode Island Commission on Women/Freda H. Goldman Education Award (Undergraduate/Award) [9697]

RISLA Student Loans (Undergraduate, Graduate/Loan) [9701]

Thomas F. Black Jr. Memorial Scholarship (Undergraduate/Scholarship) [9686]

Yankee Clipper Contest Club Youth Scholarship (Undergraduate/Scholarship) [1967]

South Carolina

African American Network - Carolinas Scholarship Fund (Undergraduate/Scholarship) [4715]

Leon Bradley Scholarship Program (Undergraduate/Scholarship) [638]

Judy Crocker Memorial Scholarship Fund (Undergraduate/Scholarship) [4730]

Harry Hampton Fund Scholarship (Undergraduate/Scholarship) [5266]

Howard B. Higgins South Carolina Dental Scholarships (Undergraduate/Scholarship) [4736]

Julian E. Carnes Scholarship Endowment Fund (Undergraduate/Scholarship) [4738]

Lighthouse International Scholarships - College-bound Awards (High School, Undergraduate/Scholarship) [6856]

Lighthouse International Scholarships - Graduate Awards (Graduate, Postgraduate/Scholarship) [6857]

Lighthouse International Scholarships - Undergraduate Awards (Undergraduate/Scholarship) [6858]

Peter DeWitt Pruden and Phyllis Harrill Pruden Scholarship (Undergraduate/Scholarship) [11202]

The Henry Dewitt Plyler Scholarship (Undergraduate/Scholarship) [4750]

Regions Riding Forward Scholarship Essay Contest (Undergraduate, High School/Scholarship) [9618]

Reuben R. Cowles Youth Educational Award (Undergraduate, Graduate/Award) [1059]

SCLEOA Scholarships (Undergraduate, Professional development/Scholarship) [10609]

South Carolina Association for Financial Professionals College Education Scholarships (Undergraduate/Scholarship) [10607]

South Carolina Undergraduate Scholarships (Undergraduate/Scholarship) [10615]

Watson-Brown Scholarship (Undergraduate/Scholarship) [11936]

The L. Phil and Alice J. Wicker Scholarship (Undergraduate/Scholarship) [1966]

The Wilbert L. and Zora F. Holmes Scholarship (Undergraduate/Scholarship) [4764]

Ted G. Wilson Memorial Scholarships (Undergraduate/Scholarship) [9338]

South Dakota

Horatio Alger South Dakota Scholarships (Undergraduate/Scholarship) [5578]

Louisa Bowen Memorial Scholarship for Graduate Students in Archival Administration (Graduate/Scholarship) [7365]

Marianne M. Stenvig Scholarship (Master's, Doctorate/Scholarship) [10623]

North Dakota Division Scholarships (Undergraduate, Graduate/Scholarship) [7373]

Stanley Moore FUI Foundation Regional Scholarships (Four Year College, High School, Two Year College/Scholarship) [8464]

Upper Midwest Human Rights Fellowship Program (Graduate/Scholarship, Fellowship) [5632]

Jerry Wheeler Scholarships (Undergraduate/Scholarship) [10625]

Tennessee

Leon Bradley Scholarship Program (Undergraduate/Scholarship) [638]

Ruby A. Brown Memorial Scholarships (Undergraduate/Scholarship) [4255]

The Cheatham County Scholarship Fund (Undergraduate/Scholarship) [3607]

Drue Smith / Society of Professional Journalists' Scholarship Fund (Undergraduate/Scholarship) [3614]

Evans and Petree Law Firm Scholarship (Graduate/Scholarship) [11598]

Federal Court Bench and Bar Scholarships (Graduate/Scholarship) [11599]

George Oliver Benton Memorial Scholarship Fund (Undergraduate/Scholarship) [3619]

Diane G. Lowe and John Gomez, IV Scholarship Fund (Undergraduate/Scholarship) [3620]

Heloise Werthan Kuhn Scholarship Fund (Undergraduate/Scholarship) [3621]

Jerry Newson Scholarship Fund (Undergraduate/Scholarship) [3624]

Mike and Mary Jean Kruse Scholarship Fund (Graduate, Undergraduate/Scholarship) [3631]

Maude Keisling / Cumberland County Extension Homemakers Scholarship Fund (Undergraduate/Scholarship) [3634]

John E. Mayfield Scholarship Fund for Cheatham County Central High School (Undergraduate/Scholarship) [3635]

John E. Mayfield Scholarship Fund for Harpeth High School (Undergraduate/Scholarship) [3636]

John E. Mayfield Scholarship Fund for Pleasant View Christian High School (Undergraduate/Scholarship) [3637]

John E. Mayfield Scholarship Fund for Sycamore High School (Undergraduate/Scholarship) [3638]

Memphis Access and Diversity Scholarships (Graduate/Scholarship) [11609]

Montesi Scholarship (Undergraduate/Scholarship) [4866]

NAJA Scholarship (Graduate/Scholarship) [7664]

Nashville Unit Scholarships (Undergraduate/Scholarship, Grant) [5488]

Pauline LaFon Gore Scholarship Fund (Undergraduate/Scholarship) [3641]

Peter DeWitt Pruden and Phyllis Harrill Pruden Scholarship (Undergraduate/Scholarship) [11202]

Regions Riding Forward Scholarship Essay Contest (Undergraduate, High School/Scholarship) [9618]

Reuben R. Cowles Youth Educational Award (Undergraduate, Graduate/Award) [1059]

Senator Carl O. Koella, Jr. Memorial Scholarship Fund (Undergraduate/Scholarship) [3644]

Southern Section A&WMA Scholarships (Graduate/Scholarship) [10668]

Springfield Family Scholarship (Graduate/Scholarship) [11615]

Steven L. Coffey Memorial Scholarship (Undergraduate/Scholarship) [4259]

Tennessee Trucking Foundation Scholarship Fund (Undergraduate/Scholarship) [3647]

The Gary Wagner, K3OMI, Scholarship (Undergraduate/Scholarship) [1965]

William and Clara Bryan Scholarship Fund (Undergraduate/Scholarship) [3648]

Woman's Club of Nashville Scholarship Endowment Fund (Undergraduate/Scholarship) [3649]

Texas

Horatio Alger Texas Scholarships (Undergraduate/Scholarship) [5579]

Anderson Cummings AC Scholarship for Higher Education (Undergraduate/Scholarship) [1707]

AWMA Louisiana Section Scholarship (Undergraduate, Graduate/Scholarship) [167]

B. J. Runnels Dean Scholarship Fund (Undergraduate/Scholarship) [3602]

BAFTX Early Starters Award *(Undergraduate/ Award)* [2696]

BAFTX Graduate Award *(Graduate/Award)* [2697]

BAFTX Junior Achievers Award *(Undergraduate/ Award)* [2698]

BAFTX Undergraduate Award *(Undergraduate/ Award)* [2699]

Barriger - Zachary Barriger Memorial Scholarship Fund *(Undergraduate/Scholarship)* [3463]

Beck – O.J. Beck, Jr. Memorial Scholarship *(Undergraduate/Scholarship)* [3464]

Bennett – Reverend E.F. Bennett Scholarship *(Undergraduate/Scholarship)* [3465]

Brem - Marion Luna Brem/Pat McNeil Health and Education Endowment *(Undergraduate/Scholarship)* [3466]

Angela Faye Brown Video Essay Contest *(Graduate/Scholarship)* [2717]

Burney – Cecil E. Burney Scholarship *(Undergraduate/Scholarship)* [3468]

C.C.H.R.M.A. Scholarships *(Undergraduate/Scholarship)* [3469]

Evelyn L. Cockrell Memorial Scholarship *(Undergraduate/Scholarship)* [10983]

The Tom and Judith Comstock Scholarship *(Undergraduate/Scholarship)* [1935]

Bill Cormack Scholarships *(Undergraduate/Scholarship)* [10987]

Crosley Law Firm Distracted Driving Scholarship *(Four Year College/Scholarship)* [3918]

DAPA Student Member Scholarships *(Undergraduate, Postgraduate/Scholarship)* [3964]

Lee K. Feine Scholarship *(Undergraduate, Graduate/Scholarship)* [7790]

The Marie Trahan/Susman Godfrey Scholarship *(Undergraduate/Scholarship)* [11148]

Guerra - Melissa Ann (Missy) Guerra Scholarship *(Undergraduate/Scholarship)* [3476]

Gulf Coast Hurricane Scholarship *(Undergraduate/Scholarship)* [10488]

George and Mary Josephine Hamman Foundation Scholarships *(Undergraduate/Scholarship)* [5264]

Hill Country Master Gardeners Horticulture Scholarship *(Undergraduate, Graduate/Scholarship)* [5510]

Houston Alumnae Association Doris Krikham Brokaw Memorial Adelphe Scholarship *(Undergraduate, Graduate/Scholarship)* [6444]

Houston Alumnae Association, Eunice "Scotty" Scott Siverson Memorial Adelphe Scholarship *(Undergraduate, Graduate/Scholarship)* [6445]

Institute of Transportation Engineers - Texas District Fellowships *(Graduate/Fellowship)* [5865]

Mary Jon and J. P. Bryan Leadership in Education Awards *(Advanced Professional/Award)* [10999]

Kae and Kay Brockermeyer Endowed Scholarship Fund *(Undergraduate/Scholarship)* [9011]

Kent S. Butler Memorial Groundwater Stewardship Scholarship Essay Contest *(Undergraduate/Scholarship, Award)* [2443]

Lay – Sue Kay Lay Memorial Scholarship *(Undergraduate/Scholarship)* [3480]

Danny T. Le Memorial Scholarship *(Undergraduate/Scholarship)* [11822]

Local 564 Scholarship Fund *(Undergraduate, Vocational/Occupational/Scholarship)* [6142]

Lone Star GIA Associate and Alumni Scholarships *(Undergraduate/Scholarship)* [4879]

Martin " Marty" Allen Scholarship *(Undergraduate/Scholarship)* [3481]

The Mary E. Bivins Ministry Scholarship Program *(Graduate, Undergraduate/Scholarship)* [2584]

The Fred R. McDaniel Memorial Scholarship *(Undergraduate/Scholarship)* [1948]

Miller – Brian and Colleen Miller Math and Science Scholarship *(Undergraduate/Scholarship)* [3482]

Tad Nelson Law Firm Scholarships *(Undergraduate/Scholarship)* [6716]

Le Hoang Nguyen College Scholarships (LHN) *(Undergraduate/Scholarship)* [11823]

North Texas Relocation Professionals Scholarship *(Undergraduate/Scholarship)* [8478]

PHCC of Texas Auxiliary and PHCC Educational Foundation funds *(Undergraduate/Scholarship)* [9207]

Regions Riding Forward Scholarship Essay Contest *(Undergraduate, High School/Scholarship)* [9618]

Rocky Mountain Coal Mining Institute Engineering/ Geology Scholarships *(Four Year College/Scholarship)* [9727]

Rocky Mountain Coal Mining Institute Technical Scholarships *(Two Year College/Scholarship)* [9728]

San Angelo Area Foundation Scholarship *(All/Scholarship)* [9795]

Saunders – Kevin Saunders Wheelchair Success Scholarship *(Undergraduate/Scholarship)* [3486]

Shamsie – Judge Terry Shamsie Scholarship *(Undergraduate/Scholarship)* [3488]

SLEAMC Scholarships *(Graduate, Undergraduate/Scholarship)* [10045]

Herman J. Smith Scholarship *(Undergraduate, Graduate/Scholarship)* [7935]

South Texas Unit Scholarship *(Undergraduate/Scholarship)* [5490]

Springer - Jim Springer Memorial Scholarship *(Undergraduate/Scholarship)* [3489]

Cecilia Steinfeldt Fellowships for Research in the Arts and Material Culture *(Professional development/Fellowship)* [11000]

Hatton W. Sumners Scholarships *(Undergraduate/Scholarship)* [8610]

TACS/A. Bragas and Associates Student Scholarships *(Undergraduate/Scholarship)* [10972]

TACS/Texas Tech University K-12 *(Undergraduate/Scholarship)* [10973]

Talbert Family Memorial Scholarship *(Undergraduate/Scholarship)* [3490]

Texas Music Educators Association Past-Presidents Memorial Scholarships *(Undergraduate/Scholarship)* [10988]

Texas Telephone Association Foundation Scholarships *(Undergraduate/Scholarship)* [11002]

TSHP R&E Foundation Scholarship Program *(Undergraduate, Graduate/Scholarship)* [11135]

TxHIMA HIA-HIT Scholarship *(Undergraduate/Scholarship)* [10984]

TxHIMA Outstanding Student Scholarship *(Undergraduate/Scholarship)* [10985]

Dr. Juan D. Villarreal/HDA Foundation Scholarships *(Undergraduate/Scholarship)* [5520]

Willa Beach-Porter CTBA Music Scholarship Fund *(Undergraduate/Scholarship)* [3246]

Williams – Dr. Dana Williams Scholarship *(Undergraduate/Scholarship)* [3492]

United States Virgin Islands

Almeric L. Christian Memorial Scholarship *(Graduate/Scholarship)* [11829]

Utah

Horatio Alger Utah Scholarships *(Undergraduate/Scholarship)* [5580]

Rocky Mountain Coal Mining Institute Engineering/ Geology Scholarships *(Four Year College/Scholarship)* [9727]

Rocky Mountain Coal Mining Institute Technical Scholarships *(Two Year College/Scholarship)* [9728]

Utah ROLF Scholarship *(Community College/Award)* [4367]

Vermont

American Legion Department of Vermont Scholarship *(Undergraduate/Scholarship)* [1075]

Casey Family Services Alumni Scholarship *(Undergraduate, Master's, Vocational/Occupational/Scholarship)* [4693]

The Dr. James L. Lawson Memorial Scholarship *(Undergraduate/Scholarship)* [1947]

Lighthouse International Scholarships - Collegebound Awards *(High School, Undergraduate/Scholarship)* [6856]

Lighthouse International Scholarships - Graduate Awards *(Graduate, Postgraduate/Scholarship)* [6857]

Lighthouse International Scholarships - Undergraduate Awards *(Undergraduate/Scholarship)* [6858]

NASSLEO Scholarships - Region I *(Undergraduate/Scholarship)* [7688]

The New England FEMARA Scholarship *(Undergraduate/Scholarship)* [1951]

Johnny Trombly Memorial Scholarship *(Undergraduate/Scholarship)* [7433]

Vermont Paralegal Organization Paralegal Certification Scholarship *(Undergraduate/Scholarship)* [11802]

Yankee Clipper Contest Club Youth Scholarship *(Undergraduate/Scholarship)* [1967]

Virginia

Horatio Alger District of Columbia, Maryland and Virginia Scholarships *(Undergraduate/Scholarship)* [5563]

Bayly-Tiffany Scholarships *(Undergraduate/Scholarship)* [11712]

Leo Bourassa Scholarship *(Undergraduate, Graduate/Scholarship)* [11837]

Leon Bradley Scholarship Program *(Undergraduate/Scholarship)* [638]

Charles Fred Wonson Scholarship *(Graduate/Scholarship)* [11713]

Drew Smith Memorial Scholarship *(Undergraduate/Scholarship)* [3563]

Ellis W. Rowe Memorial Scholarship *(Graduate/Scholarship)* [5268]

Enid W. and Bernard B. Spigel Architectural Scholarship *(Graduate/Scholarship)* [5269]

Florence L. Smith Medical Scholarship *(Graduate/Scholarship)* [5270]

H. Kruger Kaprielian Scholarship *(Undergraduate/Scholarship)* [11714]

Hampton Roads Association of Social Workers Scholarship *(Graduate/Scholarship)* [5271]

Hampton Roads Tara Welch Gallagher Environmental Scholarship *(Graduate/Scholarship)* [5272]

Hughes Memorial Foundatio n *(Other/Scholarship)* [5619]

Jane S. Glenn Memorial Endowed Scholarship *(Undergraduate/Scholarship)* [9718]

James N. Kincanon Scholarship *(Undergraduate/Scholarship)* [9719]

Lex T. Eckenrode Scholarship for PELS *(Professional development/Scholarship)* [11831]

Lighthouse International Scholarships - Collegebound Awards *(High School, Undergraduate/Scholarship)* [6856]

Lighthouse International Scholarships - Graduate Awards *(Graduate, Postgraduate/Scholarship)* [6857]

Lighthouse International Scholarships - Undergraduate Awards *(Undergraduate/Scholarship)* [6858]

L. Gordon "Link" Linkous Scholarship *(Undergraduate/Scholarship)* [11103]

Louis I. Jaffe Memorial Scholarship-NSU Alumni *(Graduate/Scholarship)* [5273]

Lewis K. Martin II, M.D. and Cheryl Rose Martin Scholarship Fund *(Graduate/Scholarship)* [5275]

Peter DeWitt Pruden and Phyllis Harrill Pruden Scholarship *(Undergraduate/Scholarship)* [11202]

Reuben R. Cowles Youth Educational Award *(Undergraduate, Graduate/Award)* [1059]

Richard D. and Sheppard R. Cooke Memorial Scholarship *(Graduate/Scholarship)* [5278]

Drs. Kirkland Ruffin & Willcox Ruffin Scholarships *(Graduate/Scholarship)* [5279]

V. Thomas Forehand, Jr. Scholarship *(Undergraduate/Scholarship)* [11717]

VASWCD College Scholarship *(College, Four Year College, Two Year College, Undergraduate/Scholarship)* [11104]

Virginia Museum of Fine Arts Visual Arts Fellowships *(Graduate, Other, Undergraduate/Fellowship)* [11839]

The Gary Wagner, K3OMI, Scholarship *(Undergraduate/Scholarship)* [1965]

The L. Phil and Alice J. Wicker Scholarship *(Undergraduate/Scholarship)* [1966]

Alice Hinchcliffe Williams, RDH, MS Merit Scholarship *(Graduate/Scholarship)* [11833]

Ted G. Wilson Memorial Scholarships *(Undergraduate/Scholarship)* [9338]

Washington

Horatio Alger Washington Scholarships (Undergraduate/Scholarship) [5581]

American Indian Endowed Scholarship (Graduate, Undergraduate/Scholarship) [11916]

Paul Arnold Memorial Scholarships (Other/Scholarship) [9288]

Asian and Pacific Islander Queer Sisters Scholarship (APIQS) (Undergraduate/Scholarship) [9289]

Associates in Behavioral Health Scholarships (Graduate/Scholarship) [9290]

Bellevue PFLAG Scholarships (Graduate, High School/Scholarship) [9292]

Beta Sigma Phi Visual Arts Scholarship (Undergraduate/Scholarship) [10049]

Boeing Company Scholarship (Undergraduate/Scholarship) [10050]

The Mary Lou Brown Scholarship (Undergraduate/Scholarship) [1931]

CEJIL Legal Internships (Graduate, Professional development/Internship) [3231]

Cole Family Scholarships (All/Scholarship) [9294]

College Success Foundation Chateau Ste. Michelle Scholarship Fund (Undergraduate/Scholarship) [3514]

College Success Foundation Leadership 1000 Scholarship (Undergraduate/Scholarship) [3515]

College Success Foundation Washington State Governors' Scholarship for Foster Youth (Undergraduate/Scholarship) [3516]

Dave Lamb Scholarship (Graduate/Scholarship) [11912]

Brian M. Day Scholarships (Undergraduate, Graduate/Scholarship) [9295]

Deloris Carter Hampton Scholarship (Undergraduate/Scholarship) [9296]

Dennis Coleman Scholarship (Undergraduate/Scholarship) [9297]

Dennis Coleman Scholarships (Undergraduate/Scholarship) [9298]

Derivative Duo Scholarships (Undergraduate/Scholarship) [9299]

Donald O. Coffman Scholarship (Graduate, Undergraduate/Scholarship) [9300]

Graduate Pulmonary Nursing Fellowship (Professional development/Fellowship, Scholarship) [4572]

Educator Conditional Scholarship And Repayment Programs (Other, Undergraduate/Loan, Scholarship) [11918]

George J.Waterman Memorial Scholarship (Undergraduate/Scholarship) [11898]

Greater Seattle Business Association Scholarships (GSBA Scholarships) (Undergraduate, Graduate/Scholarship) [5223]

High School Academic Scholarship (Undergraduate/Scholarship) [10053]

Inland Northwest Business Alliance Scholarships (INBA) (Undergraduate/Scholarship) [9302]

Joseph Wood Rogers Memorial Scholarship in Mathematics (Undergraduate/Scholarship) [10055]

Ron LaFreniere Business Administration Scholarship (Undergraduate/Scholarship) [10057]

Lemelson Center Fellowships (Doctorate, Postdoctorate, Professional development/Fellowship) [10194]

Margaret Svec Scholarship (Undergraduate/Scholarship) [10059]

Marilyn Yetso Memorial Scholarship (Graduate, Master's, Doctorate/Scholarship) [11168]

Edmund F. Maxwell Scholarships (Undergraduate/Scholarship) [7162]

McFarffels Scholarships (Undergraduate/Scholarship) [9304]

Mill Creek Chamber of Commerce Scholarship (Undergraduate/Scholarship) [7393]

Jack D. Motteler Scholarship (Undergraduate/Scholarship) [9305]

Eric Niemitalo Scholarship in Earth and Environmental Science (Undergraduate/Scholarship) [10060]

Northrop-Park Fellowship (Professional development/Fellowship) [4573]

Olympia Tumwater Foundation Traditional Scholarships (Undergraduate, High School/Scholarship) [8616]

Olympia Tumwater Foundation Transitional (non-traditional) Scholarships (Undergraduate/Scholarship) [8617]

Pride Foundation Political Leadership Scholarships (Undergraduate/Scholarship) [9306]

Pride Foundation Regional Scholarships (Undergraduate/Scholarship) [9307]

Pride Foundation Scholarships (Undergraduate/Scholarship) [9771]

Pride Foundation Social Work Scholarships (Undergraduate/Scholarship) [9308]

Pride of the Rose Scholarship (Undergraduate/Scholarship) [9309]

Don Renschler Scholarships (Graduate/Scholarship) [9310]

Rosenberg-Ibarra Scholarships (Graduate/Scholarship) [9312]

SCC Full-Time Continuing Student Scholarship (Undergraduate/Scholarship) [10062]

Shoreline and Lake Forest Park scholarship (Undergraduate/Scholarship) [10064]

Kathy Spadoni Memorial Scholarships (Graduate/Scholarship) [9313]

Trinity Scholars Program (Undergraduate/Scholarship) [11113]

Ric Ulrich and Chuck Pischke Scholarships (Undergraduate/Scholarship) [9315]

University of Puget Sound LGBT Leadership Scholarship (Undergraduate/Scholarship) [9772]

Washington City/County Management Association Scholarships (Graduate/Scholarship) [11885]

Washington College Grant (SNG) (Undergraduate/Grant) [11919]

Washington CPA Foundation Scholarship (Undergraduate/Scholarship) [11899]

Washington State Nurses Association Foundation Scholarships (WSNF) (Graduate, Undergraduate/Scholarship) [11914]

Whidbey Island Giving Circle Scholarships (Undergraduate/Scholarship) [9317]

WIGA College Scholarships (Postgraduate, Graduate, Undergraduate/Scholarship) [11894]

Wolf Trap's Grants for High School Performing Arts Teachers (Other/Grant) [12128]

Wozumi Family Scholarships (Undergraduate/Scholarship) [9318]

WSAJ American Justice Essay Scholarships (Undergraduate/Scholarship) [11905]

WSAJ Presidents' Scholarships (Undergraduate/Scholarship) [11907]

WSGC Community College Transfer Scholarships (Undergraduate/Scholarship) [11901]

West Virginia

Martin K. Alsup and Frank Schroeder Memorial Music Scholarship (Undergraduate/Scholarship) [8830]

The Ambrose-Ramsey Trust (Undergraduate/Scholarship) [8831]

Joe Barbarow Memorial Scholarship (Undergraduate/Scholarship) [8832]

William (Billbo) Boston/Harold Knopp Scholarship (Undergraduate/Scholarship) [8833]

Bryce/Lietzke/Martin Scholarship (Undergraduate/Scholarship) [8834]

Freda Burge Scholarship (Undergraduate/Scholarship) [8835]

Chester H. Bruce Memorial Scholarship (Undergraduate/Scholarship) [8836]

George H. Clinton Scholarship (Undergraduate/Scholarship) [8837]

Dwight O. Connor/Ellen Conner Lepp/Danhart Scholarship (Undergraduate/Scholarship) [8838]

David A. Couch Memorial Scholarship (Undergraduate/Scholarship) [8839]

Jennifer D. Coulter Memorial Scholarship (Undergraduate/Scholarship) [8840]

Cindy Curry Memorial Scholarship (Undergraduate/Scholarship) [8841]

Kenneth D. and Katherine D. Davis Scholarship (Undergraduate/Scholarship) [8842]

Lawrence E. and Jean L. Davis Scholarship (Undergraduate/Scholarship) [8843]

Doddridge County High School Promise Scholarship in Memory of Hattie Leggett (Undergraduate/Scholarship) [8844]

David Edward Farson Scholarships (Undergraduate/Scholarship) [8845]

Fostering Hope Scholarship (Undergraduate/Scholarship) [8846]

William E. "Bill" Gallagher Scholarship (Undergraduate/Scholarship) [8847]

Laverne L. Gibson Memorial Scholarship (Undergraduate/Scholarship) [8848]

Shane Gilbert Memorial Scholarship (Undergraduate/Scholarship) [8849]

S. William & Martha R. Goff Educational Scholarship (Undergraduate/Scholarship) [8850]

Russ Grant Memorial Scholarship for Tennis (Undergraduate/Scholarship) [8851]

Clayburn J. Sr. & Garnet R. Hanna Scholarship (Undergraduate/Scholarship) [8852]

H.G. Hardbarger Science - Mathematics Award (Undergraduate, Vocational/Occupational/Award) [8853]

Harrisville Lion's Club Scholarship (Undergraduate, Vocational/Occupational/Scholarship) [8854]

Harry C. Hartleben III/Gordon Page Corbitt Scholarship (Undergraduate/Scholarship) [8855]

Gail L. Hartshorn Memorial Fund (Other/Scholarship) [8856]

Gregory Linn Haught Citizenship Award (Undergraduate/Scholarship) [8857]

Dorcas Edmonson Haught Scholarship (Undergraduate/Scholarship) [8858]

Ella Beren Hersch Scholarship (Undergraduate/Scholarship) [8859]

Holly Jackson-Wuller Memorial Scholarship (Undergraduate/Scholarship) [8860]

K.A.S.A. Memorial Scholarship (Undergraduate/Scholarship) [8861]

Katherine M. Grosscup Scholarships in Horticulture (Undergraduate, Graduate/Scholarship) [4860]

Dr. Charles Kelly Memorial Scholarships (Undergraduate/Scholarship) [8862]

Langfitt-Ambrose Scholarship (Undergraduate/Scholarship) [8863]

Lighthouse International Scholarships - College-bound Awards (High School, Undergraduate/Scholarship) [6856]

Lighthouse International Scholarships - Graduate Awards (Graduate, Postgraduate/Scholarship) [6857]

Lighthouse International Scholarships - Undergraduate Awards (Undergraduate/Scholarship) [6858]

Megan Nicole Longwell Scholarship (Undergraduate/Scholarship) [8864]

Dudley Mullins/Cabot Corporation Scholarship (Undergraduate/Scholarship) [8865]

NASSLEO Scholarships - Region I (Undergraduate/Scholarship) [7688]

Pennsboro High School Alumni Scholarship (Undergraduate/Scholarship) [8866]

William R. Pfalzgraf Memorial Scholarship (Undergraduate/Scholarship) [8867]

Herschel H. Pifer Scholarship (Undergraduate/Scholarship) [8868]

The Thomas W. Porter, W8KYZ, Scholarship Honoring Michael Daugherty, W8LSE (Undergraduate/Scholarship) [1955]

William R. Reaser Scholarship (Vocational/Occupational, Undergraduate/Scholarship) [8869]

Mary K. Smith Rector Scholarship (Undergraduate, Vocational/Occupational/Scholarship) [8870]

Ripley Rotary Scholarship/The Judge Oliver Kessel Scholarship (Undergraduate, Vocational/Occupational/Scholarship) [8871]

James H. Roberts Athletic Scholarship (Undergraduate/Scholarship) [8872]

Carl M. Rose Memorial Scholarship (Undergraduate/Scholarship) [8874]

S. Byrl Ross Memorial Scholarship (Undergraduate/Scholarship) [8875]

St. Joseph's Hospital School of Nursing Alumnae Scholarship (Undergraduate/Scholarship) [8876]

Sand Plains & Lewis A. and Gurry F. Batten Education Scholarship (Undergraduate/Scholarship) [8877]

Everett Oscar Shimp Memorial Scholarships (Undergraduate/Scholarship) [8878]

Pat Shimp Memorial Scholarships (Undergraduate/Scholarship) [8879]

Bill Six Memorial Scholarship (Undergraduate/Scholarship) [8881]

The Zachary Taylor Stevens Scholarship (Undergraduate/Scholarship) [1962]

C.R. Thomas Scholarship (Undergraduate/Scholarship) [8882]

Charles A. Townsend Scholarship (Undergraduate/Scholarship) [8883]

The Gary Wagner, K3OMI, Scholarship (Undergraduate/Scholarship) [1965]

Wayne-Meador-Elliott Scholarship (Undergraduate/Scholarship) [8884]

West Virginia Nurses Association District No. 3 Professional Nursing Scholarships (Undergraduate/Scholarship) [8885]

West Virginia PTA Scholarship (Undergraduate/Scholarship) [11973]

Whitaker-Minard Memorial Scholarship (Undergraduate/Scholarship) [8886]

The L. Phil and Alice J. Wicker Scholarship (Undergraduate/Scholarship) [1966]

Glenn Wilson Broadcast Journalism Scholarship (Undergraduate/Scholarship) [8887]

Wood County Bar Association Memorial Scholarship (Graduate/Scholarship) [8888]

Wood County Technical/Caperton Center Scholarship (Undergraduate/Scholarship) [8889]

Wisconsin

The Chicago FM Club Scholarship (Undergraduate/Scholarship) [1934]

CMA Private Lesson Program: Instrumental Scholarships for Elementary and Middle School Students (Undergraduate/Scholarship) [3420]

E. H. Marth Food Protection And Food Sciences Scholarship (Undergraduate/Scholarship) [12109]

Eileen Harrison Education Scholarships (Graduate, Undergraduate/Scholarship) [5083]

Herb Kohl Educational Foundation Teacher Fellowship Program (Professional development/Fellowship) [6584]

John P. and Tashia F. Morgridge Scholarship (Undergraduate, Graduate/Scholarship) [11736]

Kemper K. Knapp Scholarship (Undergraduate/Scholarship) [11737]

George Koeppel Scholarship/All School (Undergraduate/Scholarship) [11738]

Louisa Bowen Memorial Scholarship for Graduate Students in Archival Administration (Graduate/Scholarship) [7365]

Menominee Tribal Scholarships (Undergraduate, Graduate, High School/Scholarship) [7256]

Pi Lambda Theta Scholarship (Undergraduate/Scholarship) [11743]

The Six Meter Club of Chicago Scholarship (Undergraduate/Scholarship) [1961]

Sterbenz-Ryan Scholarship (Undergraduate, Vocational/Occupational/Scholarship) [9778]

Upper Midwest Human Rights Fellowship Program (Graduate/Scholarship, Fellowship) [5632]

WHIMA Established Professional Development Scholarship (Graduate/Scholarship) [12119]

WIEA Scholarships (Doctorate, Graduate, Undergraduate, Vocational/Occupational, Master's, Doctorate/Scholarship) [12121]

Wisconsin Broadcasters Association Foundation Student Scholarships (Graduate/Scholarship) [12117]

Wisconsin Minority Teacher Loan (Undergraduate/Loan) [10812]

Wisconsin Nursing Student Loan (Graduate, Undergraduate, Doctorate/Loan) [10813]

Wisconsin Teacher of the Visually Impaired Loan (Undergraduate, Graduate/Loan) [10814]

Wyoming

Horatio Alger Wyoming Scholarships (Undergraduate/Scholarship) [5582]

Find Your Path Scholarship (Graduate, College/Scholarship) [10837]

Iris Scholarship (Undergraduate/Scholarship) [6447]

Marie Mathew Rask-Gamma Omicron Educational Endowment (Undergraduate/Scholarship) [6467]

Rocky Mountain Coal Mining Institute Engineering/Geology Scholarships (Four Year College/Scholarship) [9727]

Rocky Mountain Coal Mining Institute Technical Scholarships (Two Year College/Scholarship) [9728]

CANADA

AABP Amstutz Scholarship (Undergraduate/Scholarship) [522]

AACR Minority and Minority-Serving Institution Faculty Scholar Awards (Doctorate, Postdoctorate/Award) [530]

AAG Provincial Student Award (Graduate/Award) [246]

AAN Medical Student Summer Research Scholarship (Graduate/Scholarship) [460]

AANS Medical Student Summer Research Fellowships (MSSRF) (Undergraduate/Fellowship) [607]

AASLD Autoimmune Liver Diseases Pilot Research Award (Graduate, Doctorate, Postdoctorate, Professional development/Award, Grant) [645]

AASLD Clinical, Translational and Outcomes Research Awards (Professional development/Grant) [646]

The AASSC Gurli Aagaard Woods Undergraduate Publication Award (Undergraduate/Award) [2032]

The AASSC Marna Feldt Graduate Publication Award (Graduate/Award) [2033]

AASSC Norwegian Travel Grant (Undergraduate, College, University/Grant) [2034]

AATS Resident Critical Care Scholarships (Professional development/Scholarship) [661]

Dr. Anderson Abbott Awards (Undergraduate/Scholarship) [11681]

Abel Wolman Fellowship (Doctorate/Fellowship, Award, Monetary) [1634]

Jack Ackroyd Scholarships (Other/Scholarship) [2083]

ACS Faculty Research Fellowships (Professional development/Fellowship) [773]

AEBC Toronto Chapter Scholarships (Undergraduate/Scholarship) [361]

AEF Educational Scholarship (Undergraduate/Scholarship) [255]

Affiliated Distributors Electrical Industry Scholarship Awards (Undergraduate/Scholarship) [4337]

A.G. Bell School Age Financial Aid Program (High School/Scholarship, Monetary) [333]

AGE-WELL Graduate Student and Postdoctoral Awards in Technology and Aging (Master's, Doctorate, Postdoctorate/Award) [128]

AHNS Pilot Grant (Other, Doctorate/Grant) [955]

AIA and the Global Automotive Aftermarket Symposium Scholarships (Undergraduate/Scholarship) [2357]

AIHS Postgraduate Fellowships (Postgraduate, Advanced Professional/Fellowship) [273]

Airgas - Terry Jarvis Memorial Scholarship (Undergraduate/Scholarship) [1650]

AiryHair Cosmetology Scholarship (Undergraduate, Graduate/Scholarship) [201]

Albert W. Dent Graduate Student Scholarship (Undergraduate/Scholarship) [763]

Alberta Award for the Study of Canadian Human Rights and Multiculturalism (Doctorate, Graduate, Master's/Award) [280]

Alberta Centennial Award (Undergraduate/Scholarship) [281]

Alberta Child Care Association Professional Development Grants (Professional development/Grant) [253]

Alberta Innovates Graduate Student Scholarships (Graduate/Scholarship) [275]

Alberta Innovates - Technology Futures Graduate Student Scholarships in ICT (Doctorate, Graduate, Master's/Scholarship) [276]

Alberta Innovates - Technology Futures Graduate Student Scholarships in Nanotechnology (Doctorate, Graduate/Scholarship) [277]

Alberta Innovates - Technology Futures Graduate Student Scholarships in Omics (Doctorate, Master's, Professional development/Scholarship) [278]

Alberta Teachers Association Doctoral Fellowships in Education (Doctorate/Fellowship) [312]

Alberta Teachers Association Educational Research Award (Other/Scholarship) [313]

Alexander D. Pringle Memorial Scholarship (Advanced Professional/Scholarship) [9328]

Alexander Graham Bell Canada Graduate Scholarships-Doctoral Program (Doctorate, Master's/Scholarship) [3803]

Hon. Lincoln Alexander Scholarship (Undergraduate, Graduate/Scholarship) [2586]

Alex's Lemonade Stand Foundation Innovation Grants (Other/Grant) [337]

AlgaeCal Health Scholarship (Undergraduate, Graduate, Vocational/Occupational/Scholarship) [340]

Stephanie Ali Memorial Scholarships (Undergraduate/Scholarship) [11682]

ALIS Graduate Student Scholarship (Graduate/Scholarship) [283]

ALIS International Education Awards - Ukraine (Undergraduate/Scholarship) [284]

Allen T. Lambert Scholarship (Postgraduate/Scholarship) [12247]

Lorraine Allison Scholarship (Graduate/Scholarship) [1789]

ALSC Bound to Stay Bound Books Scholarship (Graduate/Scholarship) [2237]

America Express Travel Scholarships (Undergraduate/Scholarship) [1581]

American Association for Cancer Research Minority Scholar in Cancer Research Awards (Graduate/Award) [533]

American College of Surgeons International Guest Scholarship (Professional development/Scholarship) [776]

American Judges Association Law Student Essay Competition (Undergraduate/Prize) [1066]

Dr. Andy Anderson Young Professional Awards (Professional development/Award) [9146]

Andrew Thomson Prize in Applied Meteorology (Professional development/Award, Prize) [3040]

Ann C. Beckingham Scholarship (Graduate, Other/Scholarship) [2989]

Annette Urso Rickel Foundation Dissertation Award for Public Policy (Graduate/Scholarship) [1273]

Annie Kirshenblatt Memorial Scholarship (Graduate, Undergraduate/Scholarship) [11062]

Annual Research Doctoral and Postgraduate Fellowship Grant Program (Doctorate, Postdoctorate, Postgraduate, Advanced Professional/Fellowship, Grant) [2923]

ANS Research Grant Award (Professional development/Grant) [1158]

ANSER Graduate Student Awards for Research on Nonprofits and the Social Economy (Graduate/Award) [2252]

APALA Scholarship (Doctorate, Master's/Scholarship) [1990]

APLA Merit Award (Professional development/Scholarship) [2344]

Aplastic Anemia and Myelodysplasia Association of Canada Scholarships (Graduate, Master's/Scholarship) [3054]

ARA Region 10/Dorothy Wellnitz Scholarship – Canada (Undergraduate, Vocational/Occupational/Scholarship) [1332]

Architects Association of PEI Scholarship (Master's, Doctorate, Graduate/Scholarship) [3701]

Arctic Physical Therapy Scholarship (Undergraduate/Scholarship) [1794]

ARIT Fellowships in the Humanities and Social Sciences in Turkey (Postdoctorate, Graduate/Fellowship) [1342, 3850, 11345, 11348]

Erin J.C. Arsenault Fellowships in Space Governance (Graduate/Fellowship) [7188]

ASA Graduate Scholarships *(Graduate/Scholarship)* [1385]

ASAC-CJAS PhD Research Grant Award *(Doctorate/Grant, Award)* [79]

Asia Pacific Foundation of Canada Junior Research Fellowships *(Undergraduate, Master's/Fellowship)* [4711]

Asia Pacific Foundation of Canada Media Fellowships *(Professional development/Fellowship)* [4712]

Asia Pacific Foundation of Canada Post-Graduate Research Fellowships *(Master's, Doctorate/Fellowship)* [4713]

ASTA Alaska Airlines Scholarships *(Undergraduate/Scholarship)* [1582]

ASTA Holland America Line Graduate Research Scholarships *(Graduate/Scholarship)* [1583]

ASTA Rigby, Healy, Simmons Scholarships *(Graduate, Undergraduate/Scholarship)* [1584]

AstraZeneca Award *(Doctorate/Award)* [3055]

Martha and Robert Atherton Ministerial Scholarship *(Master's/Scholarship)* [11245]

Atkinson Fellowships in Public Policy *(Professional development/Fellowship)* [2338]

Atlantic Salmon Federation Olin Fellowships *(Graduate/Fellowship)* [2347]

Auto Body Technician Certificate Scholarship *(Graduate/Scholarship)* [9884]

Avis Budget Group Scholarships *(Graduate/Scholarship)* [1585]

The B. Harper Bull Scholarship Awards *(Graduate, Doctorate, Postgraduate/Award)* [11060]

James L. Baillie Memorial Fund - Student Award for Field Research *(Graduate/Grant)* [4451]

Airgas - Jerry Baker Scholarship *(Undergraduate/Scholarship)* [1658]

Ball Horticultural Company Scholarship *(Undergraduate/Scholarship)* [894]

Ballantyne Resident Research Grant *(Other, Graduate/Grant)* [956]

Bank of Canada Fellowship Award *(Doctorate, Other/Fellowship)* [2423]

Bank of Canada Governor's Awards *(Doctorate, Other/Award)* [2424]

Banting Postdoctoral Fellowships Program *(Postdoctorate/Fellowship)* [3804]

Baxter Corporation Canadian Research Awards in Anesthesia *(Other/Award, Monetary)* [2877]

BCPF Bursaries *(Undergraduate/Scholarship)* [10731]

William B. Bean Student Research Award *(Undergraduate/Grant)* [1196]

Suzanne Beauregard Scholarships *(Undergraduate, Graduate/Scholarship)* [5027]

Beaverbrook Media at McGill Student Paper Prize *(Undergraduate/Prize)* [2955]

Ed Becker Conference Travel Awards *(Undergraduate, Graduate/Award)* [4403]

Dr. Ann C. Beckingham Scholarships *(Doctorate/Scholarship)* [3056]

Jenny Panitch Beckow Memorial Scholarship - Israel *(Graduate/Scholarship)* [6284]

Harvey Bell Memorial Prize *(Graduate/Prize, Scholarship)* [11674]

Beverlee Bell Scholarships in Human Rights and Democracy *(Graduate/Scholarship)* [4136]

Max Bell Senior Fellow Grants *(Advanced Professional/Grant)* [2469]

Viscount Bennett Fellowship *(Graduate/Fellowship)* [2918]

The Bentley Cropping Systems Fellowship *(Graduate/Fellowship)* [3263]

The E. Alexander Bergstrom Memorial Research Award *(Undergraduate, Master's/Award)* [2177]

Bernard Amtmann Fellowship *(Postgraduate, Other/Fellowship)* [2569]

Bernard Michel Scholarship *(Undergraduate/Scholarship)* [2862]

Harold Bettinger Scholarship *(Undergraduate, Graduate/Scholarship)* [896]

Leonard Bettinger Vocational Scholarship *(Undergraduate, Vocational/Occupational/Scholarship)* [897]

Beverley Mascoll Scholarship *(Undergraduate/Scholarship)* [2588]

Dr. Noorali and Sabiya Bharwani Endowment *(Undergraduate/Scholarship)* [8413]

Hussein Jina Bharwani Memorial Endowment *(Undergraduate/Scholarship)* [8414]

BHCRI Cancer Research Training Program (CRTP) Awards *(Graduate, Postdoctorate, Advanced Professional, Professional development/Grant)* [5649]

BHCRI Studentship Awards *(Undergraduate, Graduate, Advanced Professional/Grant)* [5653]

Timothy Bierlmeier Memorial Scholarships *(Undergraduate, Master's/Scholarship)* [12288]

Biological Survey of Canada Scholarship *(Postgraduate/Scholarship)* [4404]

Biomedical Research Grants *(Postdoctorate/Grant)* [6545]

Blaski Alex Memorial Scholarship *(Undergraduate/Scholarship)* [9657]

BMO Capital Markets Lime Connect Equity through Education Scholarships *(Undergraduate, Graduate/Scholarship)* [6860]

BMO Financial Group Lime Connect Canada Scholarship Program for Students with Disabilities *(Undergraduate, Graduate/Scholarship)* [6861]

Edith and Arnold N. Bodtker Grants *(Undergraduate, Graduate/Grant, Internship)* [3968]

Yvonne L. Bombardier Visual Arts Scholarship Program *(Master's, Doctorate/Scholarship)* [2651]

Steve Bonk Scholarship *(Undergraduate, Graduate/Scholarship)* [3136]

John H. Borden Scholarship *(Postgraduate/Scholarship)* [4405]

Borek Maria and Czeslaw Scholarship *(Undergraduate/Scholarship)* [9658]

Jim Bourque Scholarship *(Undergraduate/Scholarship)* [1790]

Margery Boyce Bursary Award *(Graduate/Award, Scholarship)* [2893]

Geoffrey Bradshaw Memorial Scholarship *(Graduate/Scholarship)* [12294]

Brain Canada-ALS Canada Career Transition Awards *(Postdoctorate, Advanced Professional, Professional development/Grant)* [2672]

Brain Canada-ALS Canada Discovery Grants *(Advanced Professional, Professional development/Grant)* [2673]

Brain Canada-ALS Canada Hudson Translational Team Grants *(Advanced Professional, Professional development/Grant)* [2674]

Brain Canada/CQDM *(Advanced Professional/Grant)* [2675]

Brain Canada/NeuroDevNet Developmental Neurosciences Research Training Awards *(Postdoctorate, Advanced Professional, Professional development/Grant)* [2676]

James Bridenbaugh Memorial Scholarship *(Undergraduate/Scholarship)* [898]

Margaret Brine Graduate Scholarships For Women *(Graduate, Master's, Doctorate/Scholarship)* [2978]

Louis J. Brody Q.C. Entrance Scholarships *(Graduate/Scholarship)* [12248]

Norm Bromberger Research Bursary *(Undergraduate, Graduate/Scholarship)* [11672]

Peter F. Bronfman Scholarships of Merit *(Postgraduate/Scholarship)* [12249]

Brooks Scholarship *(Graduate/Scholarship)* [4411]

CFSA Randal Brown & Associates Awards *(Undergraduate/Award)* [2114]

Robert K. Brown Scholarships *(Undergraduate, Master's/Scholarship)* [2589]

Pamfil and Maria Bujea Family Orthodox Christian Seminarian Scholarships *(Undergraduate/Scholarship)* [1367]

Burger King Scholars Program *(Undergraduate/Scholarship)* [2748]

Burndy Canada Inc. Academic Achievement Awards *(Undergraduate/Scholarship)* [4338]

Burroughs Wellcome Fund Collaborative Research Travel Grants (CRTG) *(Doctorate, Postdoctorate/Grant)* [2750]

Burroughs Wellcome Travel Fellowships *(Undergraduate, Graduate/Fellowship)* [10531]

Business, Education and Technology Scholarships *(Graduate, Undergraduate/Scholarship)* [362]

Leon C. Bynoe Memorial Scholarships *(Undergraduate/Scholarship)* [11683]

CAC Gerry Bruno Scholarship *(Graduate, Undergraduate/Scholarship)* [199]

CACCN/Baxter Corporation Guardian Scholarship *(Professional development/Scholarship)* [2889]

CALL/ACBD Education Reserve Fund Grant *(Professional development/Grant)* [2899]

CALL/ACBD Research Grants *(Graduate/Grant)* [2900]

CALT Prize for Academic Excellence *(Other/Prize)* [2904]

Cameco Corporation Scholarships in the Geological Sciences - Continuing Students *(Undergraduate/Scholarship)* [2863]

Cameco Corporation Scholarships in the Geological Sciences - Entering Students *(Undergraduate/Scholarship)* [2864]

Dalton Camp Awards *(Professional development/Award, Monetary)* [4829]

Canadian Association of Cardiac Rehabilitation Graduate Scholarship Awards *(Graduate/Scholarship)* [2887]

Canadian Association for Studies in Co-operation Scholarships - Alexander Fraser Laidlaw Fellowship *(Graduate/Fellowship)* [2951]

Canadian Association for Studies in Co-operation Scholarships - Amy and Tim Dauphinee Scholarship *(Graduate/Scholarship)* [2952]

Canadian Association for Studies in Co-operation Scholarships Lemaire Co-operative Studies Award *(Graduate, Undergraduate/Scholarship)* [2953]

Canadian Blood Services Postdoctoral Fellowship Program *(Postdoctorate/Fellowship)* [2921]

Canadian Cancer Society Travel Awards *(Doctorate, Master's, Postdoctorate/Award)* [2942]

Canadian Derivatives Scholarship *(Postgraduate/Scholarship)* [2663]

Canadian Energy Law Foundation Graduate Scholarship in Law *(Advanced Professional/Scholarship)* [2962]

Canadian Federation of Independent Grocers National Scholarship *(Undergraduate/Scholarship)* [4531]

Canadian Federation of University Women Etobicoke Bursary *(Undergraduate/Scholarship)* [11684]

Canadian Hard of Hearing Association Scholarship Program *(Undergraduate/Scholarship)* [2997]

Canadian Historical Geography Award *(Master's, Graduate, Undergraduate/Prize)* [2086]

Canadian Home Economics Association Fellowship (CHEA) *(Postgraduate/Fellowship)* [2969]

Canadian Hydrographic Association Student Award *(Undergraduate/Award)* [3008]

Canadian Identification Society Essay/Scholarship Awards *(Advanced Professional, Professional development/Award)* [3010]

Canadian Institute for Advanced Legal Studies French Language Scholarships *(Graduate, Advanced Professional/Scholarship)* [5793]

Canadian Iranian Foundation Scholarship *(Undergraduate/Scholarship)* [3035]

Canadian IT Law Association Student Writing Contest *(Undergraduate/Prize)* [3132]

Canadian Japanese-Mennonite Scholarship *(Undergraduate/Scholarship)* [7254]

Canadian Nurses Foundation Northern Award *(Undergraduate/Scholarship)* [3057]

Canadian Nurses Foundation Scholarships *(Undergraduate, Master's, Doctorate/Scholarship)* [3058]

The Canadian Parking Association Scholarship (CPA) *(Undergraduate/Scholarship)* [2125]

Canadian Picture Pioneers Scholarship *(Undergraduate/Scholarship)* [3100]

The Canadian Poultry Research Council Postgraduate Scholarship *(Postgraduate/Scholarship)* [3102]

Canadian Seniors' Golf Association Scholarships *(Undergraduate/Scholarship)* [5028]

Canadian Society for Pharmacology and Therapeutics Clinical Fellowship Award *(Advanced Professional/Fellowship)* [6624]

Canadian Studies Postdoctoral Fellowships *(Postdoctorate/Fellowship)* [3800]

Canadian Technical Asphalt Association Scholarships *(Undergraduate/Scholarship)* [3130]

Canadian Water Resources Association Harker/Cameron Women in Water Scholarship *(Graduate/Scholarship)* [2107]

Canadian Zionist Federation - Dr. Leon Aryeh Kronitz Scholarship *(Undergraduate, Graduate/Scholarship)* [2984]

CAPSLE Bursary. *(Graduate/Fellowship)* [2908]

Cardiac Health Foundation of Canada Scholarship *(Graduate/Scholarship)* [3158]

Career Awards for Medical Scientists (CAMS) *(Postdoctorate/Grant)* [2751]

Career Awards at the Scientific Interface (CASI) *(Undergraduate, Postdoctorate, Graduate/Grant)* [2753]

Carin Alma E. Somers Scholarship *(Undergraduate/Scholarship)* [2345]

Herb Carnegie Scholarship *(Undergraduate/Scholarship)* [2590]

CARO-ELEKTA Research Fellowship Program *(Professional development/Fellowship)* [2102]

Carol Anne Letheren Entrance Award *(Postgraduate/Award)* [12250]

Orin Carver Scholarship *(Undergraduate/Scholarship)* [3703]

CAS/GE Healthcare Canada Inc. Research Awards *(Other/Award)* [2878]

CAS Research Award in Neuroanesthesia *(Other/Award)* [2879]

CAS Trust Scholarship Program *(Undergraduate/Scholarship, Monetary, Award)* [3183]

CAS/Vitaid-LMA Residents' Research Grant Competition *(Other/Award)* [2880]

Fraser Milner Casgrain Scholarships *(Other/Scholarship)* [2418]

Catzman Award for Professionalism and Civility *(Advanced Professional, Professional development/Award)* [96]

CBCF - Ontario Nurse and Allied Health Professional Fellowships *(Advanced Professional, Professional development/Fellowship)* [2929]

CBCF - Ontario Physician Fellowships *(Doctorate, Professional development/Fellowship)* [2930]

CBCF - Ontario Research Fellowships *(Doctorate, Postdoctorate, Professional development/Fellowship)* [2931]

CBCF - Ontario Research Project Grants *(Advanced Professional, Professional development/Grant)* [2932]

CCAE Ontario Regional Chapter Scholarship *(Advanced Professional, Professional development/Scholarship)* [6742]

CCCN Research Grant Program *(Professional development/Grant)* [3791]

CCFF Clinical Fellowships *(Doctorate, Graduate/Fellowship)* [4543]

CCFF Fellowships *(Doctorate, Graduate/Fellowship)* [4544]

CCGSE Mentorship Award *(Graduate/Award)* [10261]

CEMF Engineering Ambassador Awards *(Undergraduate/Award)* [2964]

CEMF Rona Hatt Chemical Engineering Ambassador Award *(Graduate, Undergraduate/Award)* [2965]

CESEF Postgraduate Scholarship Program *(Postdoctorate/Scholarship)* [4660]

CFN Interdisciplinary Fellowships Program *(Graduate, Postdoctorate, Advanced Professional/Fellowship)* [2982]

CFSA Aon Fire Protection Engineering Award *(Undergraduate/Scholarship)* [2115]

CFSA City of Markham, Buildings Standards Department Award *(Undergraduate/Scholarship)* [2116]

CFSA Fire Safety Awards *(Postgraduate/Scholarship)* [2117]

CFSA Founders Award for Leadership & Excellence *(Graduate, Postgraduate/Scholarship)* [2118]

CFSA Leber Rubes Inc. Awards *(Postgraduate/Award, Monetary)* [2119]

CFSA LRI Engineering Award *(Undergraduate/Scholarship)* [2120]

CFSA Nadine International Awards *(Undergraduate/Scholarship)* [2121]

CFSA Siemens Canada Award *(Undergraduate/Scholarship)* [2122]

CFSA Underwriters' Laboratories of Canada Awards *(Undergraduate/Scholarship)* [2123]

CFUW Memorial Fellowship *(Master's/Fellowship)* [2971]

CGNA Memorial Scholarship *(Graduate, Other/Scholarship)* [2990]

CGPF Endowments Conference Scholarships *(Undergraduate/Scholarship)* [2994]

Chapter 1 - Detroit Associate Scholarship *(Graduate, Undergraduate, Vocational/Occupational, Two Year College, Four Year College/Award)* [10386]

Chapter 1 Detroit Undergraduate Scholarship *(Undergraduate, Vocational/Occupational, Two Year College, Four Year College/Scholarship)* [10387]

Chapter 6 - Fairfield County Scholarship *(Undergraduate/Scholarship)* [10394]

Bernard Chernos Essay Contest *(High School/Prize)* [2949]

Shirley Cheshire Memorial Scholarship Awards *(Undergraduate/Scholarship)* [7756]

Chevalier Award Scholarship *(Undergraduate/Scholarship)* [2958]

Childhood Cancer Survivor Scholarship *(Undergraduate, College, University, Vocational/Occupational/Scholarship)* [3291]

Chinese Professionals Association of Canada Professional Achievement Awards (PAA) *(Professional development/Award)* [3311]

CHS - Bursary Program Scholarships *(Undergraduate/Scholarship)* [3001]

CHS - Mature Student Bursary Program Scholarships *(Undergraduate/Scholarship)* [3002]

C.I.B.C Scholarship *(Undergraduate, Graduate/Scholarship)* [2591, 3014]

CICC Postdoctoral Fellowship *(Postdoctorate/Fellowship)* [3255]

CIFAR Azrieli Global Scholars program *(Professional development/Scholarship)* [3020]

CISDL Global Research Fellowship - Associate Fellows *(Graduate/Fellowship)* [3257]

CISDL Global Research Fellowship - Legal Research Fellows *(Graduate/Fellowship)* [3258]

CISDL Global Research Fellowships - Senior Research Fellows *(Other/Fellowship)* [3259]

CitizenshipTests.org Engineering and Science Scholarship *(Undergraduate/Scholarship)* [3991]

City of Toronto Graduate Scholarships for Women in Mathematics *(Master's, Doctorate/Scholarship)* [11685]

City of Toronto Queen Elizabeth II Sesquicentennial Scholarships in Community Health Nursing for Graduates *(Graduate/Scholarship)* [11686]

City of Toronto Queen Elizabeth II Sesquicentennial Scholarships in Community Health Nursing for Undergraduates *(Undergraduate/Scholarship)* [11687]

City of Toronto Scholarships for Aboriginal Health *(Graduate, Undergraduate/Scholarship)* [11688]

City of Toronto Women's Studies Scholarships *(Graduate, Undergraduate/Scholarship)* [11689]

CJF Canadian Journalism Fellowships *(Graduate, Other, Undergraduate/Fellowship)* [6620]

Clarivate Analytics/MLA Doctoral Fellowship *(Doctorate, Graduate/Fellowship)* [7215]

CMOS-SCMO President's Prize *(Professional development/Prize)* [3041]

CN Scholarships for Women *(Undergraduate/Scholarship)* [3052]

CNIB Master's Scholarships *(Master's/Scholarship)* [3047]

CNST Scholarship *(Doctorate, Graduate/Scholarship)* [2146]

Marshall A. Cohen Entrance Awards *(Postgraduate/Award)* [12251]

Anna C. and Oliver C. Colburn Fellowships *(Doctorate/Fellowship)* [1775]

College of Fellows Travel Scholarship *(Undergraduate/Scholarship)* [3024]

Desmond Conacher Scholarship *(Graduate/Scholarship)* [10259]

Connaught Fellowship *(Graduate/Fellowship)* [11704]

Convectair Sustainable Development Scholarship Awards *(Undergraduate/Scholarship)* [4339]

Fred Cooke Student Award *(Undergraduate/Grant)* [10294]

COPA Scholarship Fund *(Undergraduate/Scholarship)* [3084]

COTF Graduate Scholarships *(Doctorate, Master's/Scholarship)* [3077]

COTF/Invacare Master's Scholarship *(Master's/Scholarship)* [3078]

Steve Cowan Memorial Scholarships *(Undergraduate/Scholarship)* [3906]

Helene and George Coward Award in Gerontology *(Graduate/Award)* [11709]

CPS Clinical Pain Management Fellowship Awards *(Postgraduate/Fellowship)* [3087]

CPS Outstanding Pain Mentorship Award *(Other/Award)* [3093]

CPS Trainee Research Awards *(Doctorate/Grant, Award)* [3094]

CRM-ISM Postdoctoral Fellowship *(Postdoctorate/Fellowship)* [5807, 11417]

Crohn's and Colitis Canada Innovations in IBD Research *(Advanced Professional, Professional development/Grant)* [3909]

CSCI Distinguished Scientist Lectures and Awards *(Advanced Professional/Award)* [10264]

CSEG Scholarship Trust Fund *(Graduate, Undergraduate/Scholarship)* [3116]

CSLA Leaders of Distinction Award *(Professional development/Recognition)* [3127]

CSMLS Student Scholarship *(Postgraduate/Scholarship, Monetary, Award)* [3118]

CSSE New Scholar Fellowship (CSSE) *(Professional development/Fellowship)* [10262]

CSSHE Masters Thesis/Project Awards *(Master's/Award)* [3124]

CSSHE Research and Scholarship Award *(Professional development/Award)* [3125]

CTRF Scholarships for Graduate Study in Transportation *(Graduate/Scholarship)* [3134]

Culinary Scholarship (2-year Program) *(Undergraduate/Scholarship)* [3005]

D. Glenn Hilts Scholarship *(Graduate, Undergraduate/Scholarship)* [2288]

DAAD Learn German in Germany Grants *(Doctorate/Grant)* [4058]

DAAD Study Scholarship Awards *(Graduate, Undergraduate/Scholarship)* [4059]

DAAD Undergraduate Scholarship Program *(Undergraduate/Scholarship)* [4060]

Dafoe Scholarship *(Undergraduate, Master's/Scholarship)* [3037]

Roger Daley Postdoctoral Publication Awards *(Postdoctorate/Monetary, Award)* [3043]

D&R Sobey Scholarships *(Undergraduate/Scholarship)* [10237]

Dante Prize *(Undergraduate/Prize, Monetary)* [3970]

David A. Kronick Travelling Fellowship *(Doctorate, Graduate/Fellowship)* [7216]

David H. Clift Scholarship *(Graduate/Scholarship, Monetary)* [1077]

David Pohl Scholarship *(Master's/Scholarship)* [11247]

Dawson District Renewable Resources Council Scholarship *(Undergraduate, College, University, Vocational/Occupational/Scholarship)* [12306]

Laurence Decore Awards for Student Leadership *(Undergraduate/Scholarship)* [288]

Earl Dedman Memorial Scholarship *(Undergraduate/Scholarship)* [900]

Deed of Award *(Undergraduate/Scholarship, Award)* [2944]

Delta Faucet Scholarships *(Undergraduate/Scholarship)* [9204]

The Dendel Scholarship *(Graduate, Undergraduate/Scholarship)* [5284]

Helen L. Dewar Scholarship *(Undergraduate/Scholarship)* [11020]

D.F. Plett Graduate Fellowship *(Graduate/Fellowship)* [9202]

Diabetes Hope Scholarship Program *(Undergraduate/Scholarship)* [4072]

Diana M. Priestly Memorial Scholarship *(Undergraduate/Scholarship)* [2901]

Dillon Consulting Scholarship *(Graduate/Scholarship)* [2108]

Dr. Allan A. Dixon Memorial Scholarships (Post-graduate/Scholarship) [3106]

The William Donald Dixon Research Grant (Graduate, Undergraduate, Advanced Professional/Grant) [3011]

Dobranowski Julian Memorial Scholarship (Undergraduate/Scholarship) [9659]

Dr. Biljan Memorial Awards (Advanced Professional/Award, Grant) [2980]

Dr. Ezra Nesbeth Foundation Scholarship (Undergraduate/Scholarship) [6213]

Dr. Paul and Gayle Sohi Medical Education Scholarship (Advanced Professional/Scholarship) [8230]

Dominion of Canada General Insurance Company Graduate Scholarship in Actuarial Science (Graduate, Master's, Doctorate/Scholarship) [11728]

Donald A. B. Lindberg Research Fellowship (Doctorate, Graduate/Fellowship) [7217]

Marusia and Michael Dorosh Fellowship (Master's, Graduate/Fellowship) [3027]

Dr. Lloyd M. Dosdall Memorial Scholarships (Post-graduate/Scholarship) [4406]

Douglas-Coldwell Foundation Scholarships in Social Affairs (Graduate/Scholarship) [4137]

Dr Piotrowski Adolph Memorial Art Scholarship (Undergraduate/Scholarship) [9660]

Tom and Roberta Drewes Scholarship (Graduate/Scholarship, Monetary) [6839]

DriversEdHub.com Scholarship (Undergraduate/Scholarship) [3992]

Drzymala Janusz & Roma Scholarship (Undergraduate/Scholarship) [9661]

Lise M. Duchesneau Scholarship (Undergraduate/Scholarship) [2097]

Dulemba Aleksander & Stefania Scholarship (Undergraduate/Scholarship) [9662]

Peter Dwyer Scholarships (Undergraduate/Scholarship) [2872]

Bob Dyer/OEL Apprenticeship Scholarships (Undergraduate/Scholarship) [4340]

Joshua Dyke Family Scholarship (Undergraduate/Scholarship) [11021]

e8 Sustainable Energy Development Post-Doctoral Scholarship Programme (Master's/Scholarship) [5008]

Earl and Countess of Wessex - World Championships in Athletics Scholarship (Undergraduate/Scholarship) [289]

Eaton Awards of Academic Achievement (Undergraduate/Scholarship) [4341]

David Eaton Scholarship (Master's/Scholarship) [11249]

The École Nationale des Chartes Exchange Fellowship (Postdoctorate/Fellowship) [8371]

École Polytechnique Commemorative Awards (Master's, Doctorate, Graduate/Fellowship) [2972]

The Edit My Paper Proofreading Scholarships (Undergraduate/Scholarship) [4287]

Edmonton Chapter Student Award (Graduate/Award) [247]

Edmonton Epilepsy Association Scholarship (Undergraduate/Scholarship) [4294]

Edmonton Epilepsy Continuing Education Scholarships (Undergraduate/Scholarship) [4295]

Educational Excellence Award (Graduate/Award) [3120]

Edward Foster Award (Advanced Professional/Award) [3012]

EFC Atlantic Region Scholarships (Undergraduate/Scholarship) [4342]

EFC University and College Scholarships (Undergraduate/Scholarship) [4343]

E.J. Josey Scholarship (Graduate/Scholarship) [2606]

Eli Lilly Graduate Scholarship (Graduate, Postgraduate/Scholarship) [2091]

endMS Doctoral Studentship Awards (Doctorate/Internship) [7497]

endMS Master's Studentship Awards (Master's/Internship) [7498]

endMS Postdoctoral Fellowships (Postdoctorate/Fellowship) [7499]

Entomological Society of Canada Danks Scholarship (Postgraduate/Scholarship) [4407]

Entomological Society of Saskatchewan Student Presentation Award (Undergraduate/Award) [4412]

Entomological Society of Saskatchewan Travel Awards (Professional development/Award) [4413]

Eugene Boyko Memorial Scholarship (Undergraduate/Scholarship) [249]

Extendicare Scholarships in Gerontology (Master's/Scholarship) [3059]

Faculty Research Visit Grants (Doctorate/Grant) [4061]

Fahs-Beck Fund for Research and Experimentation - Doctoral Dissertation Grants (Doctorate/Grant) [8303]

Fahs-Beck Fund for Research and Experimentation - Postdoctoral Grants (Postdoctorate/Grant) [8304]

Fellowship in the PMAC-AGPC (Professional development/Fellowship) [9349]

FFB-C Postdoctoral Fellowships (Postdoctorate/Fellowship) [4788]

Firefly Foundation/ASRP Spark Award (Postdoctorate/Grant) [412, 4570]

Flamenco Student Scholarship (Undergraduate, Professional development/Scholarship) [4614]

Flis Walter & Anna Memorial Scholarship (Undergraduate/Scholarship) [9663]

Judge Daniel F. Foley Memorial Scholarship (Undergraduate/Scholarship) [1913]

Foresters Competitive Scholarship (Undergraduate, Vocational/Occupational, Four Year College, Two Year College/Scholarship) [5737]

Foster G. McGaw Graduate Student Scholarship (Graduate/Scholarship) [764]

Terry Fox Memorial Scholarship (Undergraduate/Scholarship) [8147]

Francis H. Moffitt Scholarship (Graduate, Undergraduate/Scholarship) [2006]

Franklin Empire Scholarship Awards (Undergraduate/Scholarship) [4344]

William Taylor in Radiocommunications Scholarships (Undergraduate/Scholarship) [3795]

GAAC Project Grants (Undergraduate, Professional development/Grant) [4995]

Gabriel Dumont College Graduate Student Bursary (Postgraduate, Master's, Doctorate/Scholarship) [4236]

Gadzala Franciszek Memorial Scholarship (Undergraduate/Scholarship) [9664]

Harry Gairey Scholarship (Undergraduate/Scholarship) [2592]

NWT Law Foundation/Graeme Garson Scholarships (Advanced Professional/Scholarship) [8545]

GCFI Student Travel Awards (Undergraduate/Award) [5252]

G.E. Lighting Canada Community Leadership Awards (Undergraduate/Award) [4345]

Geological Society of America Graduate Student Research Grants (Doctorate, Graduate/Grant) [4910]

Gerrie Electric Memorial Scholarship Awards (Undergraduate/Scholarship) [4346]

Gertrude M. Cox Scholarship (Master's, Doctorate/Scholarship) [1611]

Get A Boost $2,000 Scholarship (All/Scholarship) [2608]

Keith Gilmore Foundation - Diploma Scholarships (Other/Scholarship) [4970]

Keith Gilmore Foundation - Postgraduate Scholarships (Postgraduate/Scholarship) [4971]

Keith Gilmore Foundation - Undergraduate Scholarships (Undergraduate/Scholarship) [4972]

Dr. Helen Preston Glass Fellowships (Master's/Fellowship) [3060]

Glogowski Franciszek Memorial Scholarship (Undergraduate/Scholarship) [9665]

Daniel B. Goldberg Scholarship (Graduate/Scholarship, Recognition) [5052]

Goldia.com Jewelry Scholarships (Undergraduate, Graduate/Scholarship) [5025]

Goldwin Howland Scholarship (Master's, Doctorate/Scholarship) [3080]

Charles D. Gonthier Research Fellowship (Graduate, Advanced Professional/Fellowship) [3018]

Google Lime Scholarship (Undergraduate, Graduate, Doctorate/Scholarship) [6862]

Lucille May Gopie Scholarships (Undergraduate, Graduate/Scholarship) [2593]

Wilhelmina Gordon Foundation Scholarships (Undergraduate/Scholarship) [7757]

Carl W. Gottschalk Research Scholar Grants (Professional development/Grant) [1526]

Graduate Research Awards for Disarmament, Arms Control and Non-Proliferation (Master's, Doctorate/Award) [10142]

Graduate Research Travel Scholarships (Graduate/Scholarship) [4408]

Graduate Student Pest Management Award (Graduate/Grant, Award) [3108]

Charles Hall Grandgent Award (Graduate/Award, Monetary) [3971]

Grant Assistance Program for Autism Professionals - College Programs (Undergraduate/Grant) [8652]

Grant Assistance Program for Autism Professionals - Doctoral Programs (Doctorate/Grant) [8653]

Grant Assistance Program for Autism Professionals - Institutional Standards (Undergraduate, Graduate/Grant) [8654]

Grant Assistance Program for Autism Professionals - Masters Programs (Master's/Grant) [8655]

Grant Assistance Program for Autism Professionals - Professional Certification Programs (Undergraduate, Professional development/Grant) [8656]

Grant Assistance Program for Autism Professionals - Retroactive Assistance (Advanced Professional, Professional development/Grant) [8657]

Grant Assistance Program for Autism Professionals - Undergraduate Programs (Undergraduate/Grant) [8658]

Graybar Canada Award of Excellence Scholarships (Undergraduate/Scholarship) [4347]

Frank L. Greathouse Government Accounting Scholarship (Graduate, Undergraduate/Award, Scholarship) [5053]

Greg Clerk Award (Advanced Professional, Professional development/Award) [6621]

Jennifer C. Groot Memorial Fellowship (Undergraduate, Graduate/Fellowship) [727]

John Simon Guggenheim Memorial Fellowships - United States & Canadian Competition (Graduate, Postgraduate, Undergraduate/Fellowship) [5250]

Gunild Keetman Scholarship (Other, Undergraduate/Scholarship) [8724]

Guntley-Lorimer Science and Arts Scholarships (Undergraduate/Scholarship) [2594]

David J. Hallissey Memorial Internships (Graduate, Undergraduate/Internship) [1586]

Al Hamilton Scholarship (Undergraduate/Scholarship) [2595]

Stan Hamilton Scholarship (Graduate/Scholarship) [9885]

Hammond Power Solutions Inc. Outstanding Electrical Scholar Awards (HPS) (Undergraduate/Award) [4348]

Hans McCorriston Grant (Undergraduate/Grant) [2358]

Harkness Fellowships in Health Care Policy and Practice (Doctorate, Graduate/Fellowship) [3555]

Harry Steele Entrance Award (Postgraduate/Award) [12252]

Centre on Aging Betty Havens Memorial Graduate Fellowship (Graduate, Doctorate, Master's/Fellowship) [11584]

Heather McCallum Scholarship (Professional development/Scholarship, Award) [2104]

Helen and George Kilik Scholarship (Undergraduate/Scholarship) [290]

Mary Jane Hendrie Memorial Scholarships (Graduate, Undergraduate/Scholarship) [11690]

Henry Friesen Awards and Lecture (Doctorate/Award) [10265]

Frances C. Hidell Scholarship (Undergraduate/Scholarship) [2144]

HII Scholarship Fund (Community College, Two Year College, Four Year College, Undergraduate, University/Scholarship) [5655]

Judy Hill Memorial Scholarships (Undergraduate/Scholarship) [3061]

Geordie Hilton Academic Scholarships (Undergraduate/Scholarship) [5030]

Jack MacDonell Scholarship for Research in Aging *(Graduate, Doctorate, Master's/Scholarship)* [11585]

Mackenzie King Open Scholarship *(Graduate, Postgraduate, Undergraduate/Scholarship)* [7182]

Mackenzie King Travelling Scholarship *(Graduate/Scholarship, Monetary)* [7183]

MAF Canada Scholarship Fund *(Undergraduate/Scholarship)* [7419]

Maibach Travel Grant *(Professional development/Grant)* [799]

Manulife Financial Scholarship *(Undergraduate/Scholarship)* [3793]

Marie Tremaine Fellowship *(Postgraduate, Other/Fellowship)* [2570]

Markham-Colegrave International Scholarships *(Undergraduate/Scholarship)* [901]

Marshall Cavendish Scholarships *(Graduate/Scholarship, Monetary)* [1079]

Eleanor Jean Martin Award *(Master's/Scholarship)* [3065]

Martin Fischer Training Award *(Undergraduate/Award)* [2995]

Dick Martin Scholarships *(Postgraduate/Scholarship, Award)* [2946]

Right Honourable Paul Martin Sr. Scholarships *(Graduate/Scholarship)* [5794]

Martin Walmsley Award for Entrepreneurship *(Graduate/Award)* [8636]

Bill Mason Memorial Scholarship Fund *(Undergraduate/Scholarship)* [8810]

Elizabeth Massey Award *(Postgraduate/Award)* [2974]

Maziarz Tadeusz Scholarship *(Undergraduate/Scholarship)* [9671]

John Mazurek Memorial-Morgex Insurance Scholarship *(Other/Scholarship)* [314]

Joseph McCulley Educational Trust Fund *(Graduate, Undergraduate/Grant)* [11695]

William H. McGannon Foundation Scholarships *(Graduate, Undergraduate/Scholarship)* [7180]

Douglas McRorie Memorial Scholarships *(Doctorate, Master's/Scholarship, Award)* [131]

MediaMister $1000 Student Scholarship *(Undergraduate, Graduate/Scholarship)* [7211]

Dr. Ernest and Minnie Mehl Scholarships *(Undergraduate/Scholarship)* [298]

Frederic G. Melcher Scholarships *(Graduate/Scholarship)* [2240]

Mensa Canada Scholarship Programme *(Undergraduate/Scholarship)* [7259]

Donald Menzies Bursary Award *(Postgraduate/Scholarship, Award)* [2894]

Merck Frosst Canada Inc. Postgraduate Pharmacy Fellowship Award *(Postgraduate, Graduate, Doctorate/Fellowship)* [2172]

Merck Frosst Canada Ltd. Postgraduate Pharmacy Fellowships *(Graduate, Postgraduate, Doctorate/Fellowship)* [2173]

Al Mercury Scholarships *(Undergraduate/Scholarship)* [11696]

Metcalf Innovation Fellowship program *(Advanced Professional, Professional development/Fellowship)* [7271]

Michael Oykhman Criminal Law and Evidence Scholarship *(Juris Doctorate, Advanced Professional/Scholarship)* [8800]

The Michener-Deacon Fellowship for Investigative Journalism *(Professional development/Fellowship)* [4655]

The Michener-Deacon Fellowship for Journalism Education *(Professional development/Fellowship)* [4656]

Michno Bronislaw Memorial Scholarship *(Undergraduate/Scholarship)* [9672]

Miles Spencer Nadal Entrance Award *(Master's/Award)* [12258]

Military Nurses Association Scholarships *(Master's/Scholarship)* [3066]

Mineralogical Association of Canada Scholarships *(Doctorate, Graduate/Scholarship)* [2244]

Minerva Scholarships *(Undergraduate/Scholarship)* [2598]

Minorities in Government Finance Scholarship *(Graduate, Undergraduate/Scholarship)* [5054]

MLA Research, Development, and Demonstration Project Grant *(Graduate/Grant)* [7221]

MLA Scholarship *(Graduate, Master's/Scholarship)* [7222]

MLA Scholarship for Minority Students *(Graduate/Scholarship)* [7223]

Murray Montague Memorial Scholarship *(Undergraduate/Scholarship)* [5129]

Morris M. Pulver Scholarship Fund *(Undergraduate, Graduate, Postgraduate/Scholarship)* [2986]

John H. Moss Scholarships *(Undergraduate/Scholarship)* [11697]

Movember Clinical Trials *(Advanced Professional/Grant)* [9362]

Movember Discovery Grants *(Advanced Professional, Professional development/Grant)* [9363]

Movember Rising Star in Prostate Cancer Research Awards *(Advanced Professional, Professional development/Grant)* [9364]

Movember Team Grants *(Advanced Professional, Professional development/Grant)* [9365]

MSA Graduate Fellowship *(Graduate/Fellowship)* [7532]

Marvin Mundel Memorial Scholarship *(Undergraduate/Scholarship)* [5834]

Margaret Munro Award *(Undergraduate/Scholarship)* [3067]

Dr. Helen K. Mussallem Fellowships *(Master's/Fellowship)* [3068]

NAAMA Scholarships *(Undergraduate/Scholarship)* [7598]

NACBS Dissertation Fellowship *(Graduate, Doctorate/Fellowship)* [8420]

NACBS-Huntington Library Fellowship *(Doctorate, Postdoctorate/Fellowship)* [8422]

Nadene M Thomas Graduate Research Bursary *(Graduate/Scholarship)* [315]

National Board Technical Scholarship *(College, Four Year College, University/Scholarship)* [7730]

National Greenhouse Manufacturers Association (NGMA) Scholarships *(Undergraduate/Scholarship)* [902]

Nawrot Marek Memorial Scholarship *(Undergraduate/Scholarship)* [9673]

NBHRF/ASRP Doctoral Training Awards *(Doctorate/Award)* [413, 8212]

NBHRF Doctoral Studentship *(Doctorate/Grant)* [8214]

NBHRF Master's Studentship *(Master's/Grant)* [8217]

NBHRF Postdoctoral Fellowships *(Postdoctorate/Fellowship)* [8218]

NCLEJ Law School Graduate Fellows and Volunteers *(Graduate, Advanced Professional/Fellowship)* [7751]

Neuroscience Certification Bursary Awards *(Other/Award)* [2095]

Alan H. Neville Memorial Scholarships *(Graduate/Scholarship)* [363]

Sharon Nield Memorial Scholarships *(Undergraduate/Scholarship)* [3070]

NLM Associate Fellowship *(Postgraduate/Fellowship)* [11339]

Norfolk Southern Foundation Scholarships *(Undergraduate/Scholarship)* [1329]

Nortel Institute for Telecommunications Graduate Scholarship *(Graduate, Master's/Scholarship)* [11706]

North American Society Fellowship Award (NAS Fellowship) *(Professional development/Fellowship)* [9147]

Northern Scientific Training Program *(Graduate/Scholarship)* [1791]

Mike and Flo Novovesky Scholarship *(Undergraduate/Scholarship)* [903]

Novus Biologicals Scholarship Program *(All/Scholarship)* [8553]

NSA Scholarship Foundation *(Undergraduate/Scholarship)* [8079]

NSERC Postgraduate Scholarships-Doctoral Program *(Doctorate/Scholarship)* [3806]

Nuffield Canada Farming Scholarships *(Undergraduate/Scholarship)* [8555]

AEBC Rick Oakes Scholarships for the Arts *(Undergraduate/Scholarship)* [364]

O'Brien Foundation Fellowships *(Professional development/Fellowship)* [8571]

Lawrence "Bud" Ohlman Memorial Scholarships *(Undergraduate/Scholarship)* [904]

Omatsu FACL Scholarships *(Juris Doctorate, Advanced Professional/Scholarship)* [4529]

OMHF Postdoctoral Fellowships *(Postdoctorate/Fellowship)* [7264]

ONECA Four Directions Scholarship *(Undergraduate/Scholarship)* [8660]

OOBS Student Leadership Scholarships *(Undergraduate/Scholarship)* [8778]

Orford String Quartet Scholarship *(Professional development/Scholarship)* [3786]

Organization of American States Graduate Scholarships *(Doctorate, Graduate/Scholarship)* [8737]

Osram Sylvania Scholastic Achievement Awards *(Undergraduate/Scholarship)* [4352]

Parkinson Canada Basic Research Fellowship *(Advanced Professional/Fellowship)* [8891]

Parkinson Canada Clinical Movement Disorder Fellowship *(Advanced Professional, Professional development/Fellowship)* [8892]

Parkinson Canada Clinical Research Fellowship *(Professional development/Fellowship)* [8893]

Parkinson Canada Graduate Student Award *(Graduate, Advanced Professional/Award)* [8894]

Parkinson Canada New Investigator Award *(Professional development/Grant)* [8895]

Parkinson Canada Pilot Project Grant *(Advanced Professional/Grant)* [8896]

Senator Norman Paterson Fellowships (TBC) *(Doctorate/Scholarship)* [3071]

Q. O. (Quint) Patrick Scholarships *(Undergraduate/Scholarship)* [12006]

Arthur Paulin Automotive Aftermarket Scholarship Awards *(Postgraduate, Undergraduate/Scholarship)* [2359]

PEA Bursaries *(Undergraduate/Scholarship)* [9340]

PEA Scholarships *(Undergraduate/Scholarship)* [9341]

P.E.O. Scholar Awards (PSA) *(Doctorate/Award, Scholarship)* [8977]

Nalini Perera Little Lotus Bud Master's Scholarships *(Master's/Scholarship)* [3048]

Persons Case Scholarship *(Undergraduate, Graduate/Scholarship)* [303]

Peter F. Bronfman Entrance Award *(Postgraduate/Award)* [12259]

Petroleum History Society Graduate Scholarships *(Graduate/Scholarship)* [9048]

PHE Canada National Award for Teaching Excellence in Physical Education *(Professional development/Recognition)* [9148]

PHE Canada Student Awards *(Undergraduate/Award)* [9149]

Philip F. Vineberg Travelling Fellowship in the Humanities *(Undergraduate/Scholarship, Monetary)* [7184]

Shoshana Philipp (Kirshenblatt) R.N. Memorial Scholarships *(Graduate, Undergraduate/Scholarship)* [11063]

Philips Lighting Continuing Education Awards *(Undergraduate/Scholarship)* [4353]

Physiotherapy Foundation of Canada Research Grant *(Other/Grant)* [3096]

Pidperyhora Eleonora Scholarship *(Undergraduate/Scholarship)* [9674]

PIMS Postdoctoral Fellowship *(Doctorate, Postdoctorate/Fellowship)* [8806]

PLCAC Student Award Program *(Postgraduate/Award)* [9182]

Platform Support Grants *(Advanced Professional/Grant)* [2678]

Plumbing-Heating-Cooling Contractors Association Educational Foundation Need-Based Scholarships *(Undergraduate/Scholarship)* [9206]

PHCC of Texas Auxiliary and PHCC Educational Foundation funds *(Undergraduate/Scholarship)* [9207]

POLAR Northern Resident Scholarship *(Doctorate, Master's/Scholarship)* [2147]

Polar Scholarship *(Doctorate, Graduate/Scholarship)* [2148]

Harriet and Leon Pomerance Fellowships *(Graduate/Fellowship)* [1780]

Gail Posluns Fellowships in Hematology *(Postdoctorate/Fellowship)* [6931]

Post-Doctoral Mellon Fellowships *(Postdoctorate/Fellowship)* [9246]

Postdoctoral Fellowships *(Postdoctorate/Fellowship)* [4809]

Fields Postdoctoral Fellowships (FPDF) *(Postdoctorate/Fellowship)* [4552]

Prairie Baseball Academy Scholarship *(Undergraduate/Scholarship)* [304]

The Preston Robb Fellowship *(Professional development, College, Master's/Fellowship)* [7191]

Prince Edward Island Law Student Scholarships *(Undergraduate/Scholarship)* [6732]

Prostate Cancer Canada Clinical Research Fellowships *(Advanced Professional/Fellowship)* [9366]

Prostate Cancer Canada Graduate Studentships *(Graduate, Doctorate/Grant)* [9367]

Prostate Cancer Canada Postdoctoral Research Fellowships *(Postdoctorate, Advanced Professional/Fellowship)* [9368]

Provincial and Regional 4-H Scholarship *(Undergraduate/Scholarship)* [15]

PSAC-AGR National Scholarship *(Postgraduate/Scholarship, Monetary)* [9444]

PSAC - Coughlin National Scholarships *(Postgraduate/Scholarship, Monetary)* [9445]

PSAC National Member Scholarship *(Postgraduate/Scholarship, Monetary)* [9446]

PSAC Regional Scholarships *(Postgraduate/Scholarship, Monetary)* [9447]

Ross C. Purse Doctoral Fellowship *(Graduate/Award, Fellowship)* [3049]

Doug Purvis Prize *(Other/Prize)* [2885]

Queen Elizabeth II Graduate Scholarship *(Doctorate, Graduate, Master's/Scholarship)* [305]

R. Roy McMurtry Fellowship in Legal History *(Doctorate, Graduate/Fellowship)* [8772]

R. Tait Mckenzie Award *(Professional development/Award)* [9150]

RAB Design Lighting Award of Excellence *(Undergraduate/Scholarship)* [4354]

James K. Rathmell Jr. Memorial Scholarship *(Undergraduate, Graduate/Scholarship)* [905]

The Reedsy National Creative Writing Scholarship *(Undergraduate/Scholarship)* [9607]

Registered Apprenticeship Program/CTS Scholarships (RAP) *(Undergraduate/Scholarship)* [306]

J.H. Stewart Reid Memorial Fellowship Trust *(Doctorate/Fellowship)* [9629]

Siobhan Isabella Reid Memorial Scholarships *(Graduate, Undergraduate/Scholarship)* [6754]

George Reinke Scholarships *(Other/Scholarship)* [1587]

Research Internships in Science and Engineering (RISE) *(Undergraduate/Internship)* [4065]

W. Reymont Scholarships *(Undergraduate/Scholarship)* [9675]

Richard J. Schmeelk Fellowship *(Graduate/Fellowship)* [9934]

Robert Krembil Scholarship of Merit *(Master's/Scholarship)* [12260]

Robert L. Peaslee Brazing Scholarship *(Undergraduate/Scholarship)* [1671]

Robert N. Colwell Fellowship *(Doctorate/Fellowship)* [2009]

Robert Sutherland/Harry Jerome Entrance Award *(Undergraduate/Scholarship)* [2599, 9461]

Robin P. Armstrong Memorial Prize for Excellence in Indigenous Studies *(Graduate/Award, Monetary)* [2087]

Gertrude J. Robinson Book Prize *(Professional development/Prize, Award)* [2956]

Isobel Robinson Historical Research Grant *(Professional development/Grant)* [3081]

Jennifer Robinson Memorial Scholarship *(Graduate/Scholarship)* [1792]

Rodziny Krawczyk-Krane Family Scholarship *(Undergraduate/Scholarship)* [9676]

R.O.E.A. Dumitru Golea Goldy-Gemu Scholarships *(Undergraduate, High School/Scholarship)* [1369]

Roy Seymour Rogers and Geraldine Ruth Rogers Scholarship *(Undergraduate/Scholarship)* [11023]

Ross A. Wilson Science Scholarship *(Undergraduate/Scholarship)* [11024]

Rothberg International School Graduate Merit Scholarship *(Graduate, Master's/Scholarship)* [2987]

Robert Roy Award *(Advanced Professional/Award, Recognition)* [2099]

Roy Cooper Memorial Scholarship *(Undergraduate/Scholarship)* [6758]

Roy H. Pollack Scholarship *(Graduate, Master's/Scholarship)* [11254]

Royal Bank Scholarships *(Undergraduate, Master's, Graduate/Scholarship)* [2600]

Royal Canadian Regiment Association Bursaries *(Undergraduate/Scholarship)* [9751]

RPNAS Baccalaureate Level Program Scholarship *(Undergraduate/Scholarship)* [9620]

RPNAS Doctorate Level Program Scholarship *(Doctorate/Scholarship)* [9621]

RPNAS Master's Level Program Scholarship *(Master's/Scholarship)* [9622]

R.S. Williamson & Eliford Mott Memorial Scholarships *(Undergraduate/Scholarship)* [12007]

RTDNF Scholarships *(Undergraduate/Scholarship)* [9480]

Glen Ruby Memorial Scholarships *(Undergraduate/Scholarship)* [3122]

Rutherford Scholars *(Undergraduate/Scholarship)* [308]

Ryerson Scholarships *(Undergraduate/Scholarship)* [6219]

Chester & Maria Sadowski Memorial Scholarships *(Undergraduate/Scholarship)* [9677]

Burton MacDonald and Rosemarie Sampson Fellowship *(Undergraduate, Graduate/Fellowship)* [730]

AIST David H. Samson Canadian Scholarship *(Undergraduate/Scholarship)* [2224]

Sanofi Pasteur Scholarships *(Master's/Scholarship)* [3072]

Saskatchewan Government Insurance Actuarial Science Scholarship *(Graduate/Scholarship)* [9887]

Saskatchewan Government Insurance Anniversary Scholarships *(Undergraduate/Scholarship)* [9888]

Saskatchewan Hockey Association Scholarships *(Undergraduate/Scholarship)* [9893]

Saskatchewan Pulse Growers Undergraduate Scholarships *(Undergraduate/Scholarship)* [9923]

Saskatchewan School Boards Association Graduate Student Award *(Graduate/Award)* [9926]

François J. Saucier Prize in Applied Oceanography *(Professional development/Award, Prize)* [3045]

Schlegel-UW RIA Scholarship *(Doctorate/Scholarship)* [2895]

Schneider/Bingle PLTW Scholarship *(Undergraduate/Scholarship)* [10412]

Schneider Electric Student Merit Awards *(Undergraduate/Scholarship)* [4355]

B.E. Schnurr Memorial Fund Research Grants *(Other/Grant)* [3097]

Scholarship for Indigenous Students *(Undergraduate/Scholarship)* [8148]

Scholarship for Students of Colour *(Undergraduate/Scholarship)* [8149]

Scholarships for the Next Generation of Scientists *(Postdoctorate/Scholarship)* [3144]

Fritz Schwartz Serials Education Scholarship *(Graduate/Scholarship)* [7560]

Scotiabank Scholarship *(Undergraduate/Scholarship)* [2426, 2601]

Wilfred George Scott Fellowship in Gerontology *(Graduate/Fellowship)* [11710]

Senior Wisdom Scholarship *(Undergraduate, Graduate/Scholarship, Award)* [9186]

SFP Scholarships *(Undergraduate/Scholarship)* [9947]

SGI Business Insurance Diploma Scholarships *(Undergraduate/Scholarship)* [9890]

SGI Graduate Research Grant *(Graduate/Grant)* [9891]

Shastri Scholar Travel Subsidy Grants (SSTSG) *(Graduate, Professional development/Grant)* [10037]

Dr. Robert Norman Shaw Scholarship *(Undergraduate/Scholarship)* [310]

David S. Sheridan Canadian Research Awards *(Other/Award)* [2881]

Siemens Canada Academic Awards *(Undergraduate/Scholarship)* [4356, 10079]

Sigma Theta Tau International Scholarships *(Doctorate/Scholarship)* [3073]

Sloan Research Fellowships *(Doctorate/Fellowship)* [10171]

SME Education Foundation Family Scholarships *(Undergraduate/Scholarship)* [10415]

Donald Smiley Prize *(Advanced Professional/Prize, Award, Recognition)* [2111]

Eva Smith Bursary *(Postgraduate/Scholarship)* [6220]

Brian Smith Memorial Scholarships *(Undergraduate/Scholarship)* [2669]

A.O. Smith Scholarships *(Undergraduate/Scholarship)* [9208]

Boleslaw & Irena Sobczak Scholarships *(Undergraduate/Scholarship)* [9678]

The Frank H. Sobey Awards for Excellence in Business Studies *(Undergraduate/Award)* [10238]

Sobeys & Empire Work Experience & Scholarship Program - Future Leaders Awards *(Other/Scholarship)* [10239]

Society of Graphic Designers of Canada Adobe Scholarships *(Undergraduate/Scholarship)* [10255]

Society of Graphic Designers of Canada Applied Arts Scholarships *(Undergraduate/Scholarship)* [10256]

Society of Graphic Designers of Canada Veer Scholarships *(Undergraduate/Scholarship)* [10257]

Sonepar Canada Scholarship Awards *(Undergraduate/Scholarship)* [4357]

Betty Spalton Scholarships *(Undergraduate/Scholarship)* [2454]

SPEATBC Entrance Scholarship *(Graduate, High School/Scholarship)* [10518]

SSHRC Doctoral Fellowship Program *(Doctorate/Fellowship, Scholarship)* [3797]

SSHRC Postdoctoral Fellowships *(Postdoctorate/Fellowship)* [3798]

The Standard Recognition of Excellence Awards *(Undergraduate/Scholarship)* [4358]

Lasek Stanisław and Aniela Scholarship *(Undergraduate/Scholarship)* [9679]

Stasiuk Master's Research Fellowship *(Master's/Fellowship)* [3032]

Taylor Statten Memorial Fellowships *(Graduate/Scholarship)* [11698]

The Stanley H. Stearman Awards *(Undergraduate/Scholarship)* [8080]

Stelpro Scholarship 360: Energizing Potential *(Undergraduate/Scholarship)* [4359]

H.H. Stern Award *(Advanced Professional/Award)* [2100]

The David Stockwood Memorial Prize *(Advanced Professional, Professional development/Prize)* [97]

Glenna Stone Memorial Scholarship *(Undergraduate/Scholarship)* [2999]

Herb Stovel Scholarship - National Trust Conference Bursaries *(Undergraduate, Graduate, Professional development/Scholarship)* [8142]

Herb Stovel Scholarship - Project Research Bursaries *(Undergraduate, Graduate, Professional development/Scholarship)* [8143]

Student Investigator Research Grant - Vestibular *(Graduate, Doctorate/Grant)* [435]

Study Scholarship for Artists or Musicians *(Graduate, Postdoctorate/Scholarship)* [4066]

Summer Undergraduate Fellowship Program *(Undergraduate/Fellowship)* [623]

Summerside-Natick International Friendship Hockey Fund *(Undergraduate/Scholarship)* [3706]

Syncrude/Athabasca University Aboriginal Scholarships *(Undergraduate/Scholarship)* [10902]

TAC Foundation – 3M Canada "Bob Margison Memorial" Scholarship *(Graduate, Undergraduate/Scholarship)* [11077]

TAC Foundation-407 ETR Scholarships *(Undergraduate, Graduate/Scholarship)* [11078]

TAC Foundation-Amec Foster Wheeler Scholarships *(Undergraduate, Graduate/Scholarship)* [11079]

TAC Foundation-ATS Traffic Scholarships *(Undergraduate, Graduate/Scholarship)* [11080]

CANADA (BY PROVINCE)

Alberta

Sir James Lougheed Award of Distinction (Doctorate, Graduate, Master's/Award) [297]

Al Maurer Awards (Undergraduate, Graduate, Advanced Professional/Scholarship) [4292]

Louise McKinney Post-secondary Scholarship (Undergraduate/Scholarship) [299]

Charles S. Noble Scholarships for Study at Harvard (Undergraduate/Scholarship) [300]

Northern Alberta Development Council Bursaries Program (Undergraduate/Scholarship) [301]

Northern Alberta Development Council Bursary (Undergraduate/Scholarship) [302]

Oil & Gas, Trades & Technology (OGTT) Bursary and Scholarship Awards (OGTT) (Undergraduate/Scholarship) [5776]

Risk Management and Insurance Scholarship (Graduate/Scholarship) [9886]

Alexander Rutherford High School Achievement Scholarship (Undergraduate/Scholarship) [307]

Saskatchewan Government Insurance Corporate Scholarships (Undergraduate/Scholarship) [9889]

Servus Credit Union 4-H Scholarship (College, University, Undergraduate/Scholarship) [16]

Dr. Robert and Anna Shaw Scholarship (Undergraduate/Scholarship) [309]

Dr. Robert Norman Shaw Scholarship (Undergraduate/Scholarship) [310]

The Kennett Y. Spencer Memorial Scholarship (Graduate/Scholarship) [11524]

Ukrainian Canadian Professional and Business Club Scholarships in Education (Undergraduate/Scholarship) [3033]

Viscount Bennett Scholarship (Graduate/Scholarship) [6721]

Visual Arts and New Media Individual Project Funding (Professional development/Grant) [265]

Robert E. Walter Memorial Scholarship (Undergraduate/Scholarship) [6958]

British Columbia

Alliance Pipeline Scholarships (Other/Scholarship) [2417]

CBCF - BC/Yukon Region Breast Cancer Research Grants Competition (Advanced Professional/Grant) [2924]

CBCF - BC/Yukon Region Breast Cancer Survivor Dragon Boat Grants (Professional development/Grant) [2925]

CBCF - BC/Yukon Region Community Health Grants (Professional development/Grant) [2926]

CBCF - BC/Yukon Region Small Initiative Funds (Professional development/Grant) [2927]

MSFHR Research Trainee Award (Postdoctorate, Professional development/Grant) [10181]

MSFHR Scholar Awards (Advanced Professional, Professional development/Grant) [10182]

Risk Management and Insurance Scholarship (Graduate/Scholarship) [9886]

Manitoba

CBCF - Prairies/NWT Grants in Clinical Research (Advanced Professional, Professional development/Grant) [2935]

CBCF - Prairies/NWT Grants in Health Services and Policy Research (Advanced Professional, Professional development/Grant) [2936]

CBCF - Prairies/NWT Postdoctoral Fellowships (Postdoctorate, Professional development/Fellowship) [2937]

CBCF - Prairies/NWT Research Grants in Psychosocial, Cultural and Environmental Determinants of Health (Advanced Professional, Professional development/Grant) [2938]

Mark & Dorothy Danzker Scholarship (Postgraduate/Scholarship) [6305]

Mona Gray Creative Arts Scholarship (Graduate, Undergraduate/Scholarship) [6306]

Judaic Studies and/or Studies in Israel (Undergraduate, Postgraduate/Scholarship) [6307]

Esther and Samuel Milmot Scholarship (Graduate, Undergraduate/Scholarship) [11586]

Risk Management and Insurance Scholarship (Graduate/Scholarship) [9886]

Saskatchewan Government Insurance Corporate Scholarships (Undergraduate/Scholarship) [9889]

New Brunswick

Astra Zeneca Medical Scholarship (Advanced Professional/Scholarship) [8222]

Bell Aliant Medical Education Scholarship (Advanced Professional/Scholarship) [8223]

Berton W. Huestis Memorial Scholarship (Advanced Professional/Scholarship) [8224]

BMO Medical Education Scholarship (Advanced Professional/Scholarship) [8225]

CIBC Medical Education Scholarships (Advanced Professional/Scholarship) [8226]

Dr. Frank and Audrey Wanamaker Medical Scholarship (Advanced Professional/Scholarship) [8227]

Dr. Henrik and Wanda Tonning Memorial Scholarship (Advanced Professional/Scholarship) [8228]

Dr. Isaac Keillor Farrer, Advanced Medical Education Scholarship (Advanced Professional/Scholarship) [8229]

Friends of the Christofor Foundation Scholarship (Advanced Professional/Scholarship) [8231]

Horizon Health Network Scholarship (Advanced Professional/Scholarship) [8232]

G. William McQuade Memorial Scholarships (Advanced Professional/Scholarship) [8233]

NB College of Physicians and Surgeons Medical Education Scholarship (Advanced Professional/Scholarship) [8234]

NBHRF Bridge Grants (Professional development/Grant) [8213]

NBHRF Establishment Grants (Professional development/Grant) [8215]

NBHRF Health Research Strategic Initiative Grants (Professional development/Grant) [8216]

New Brunswick Nurses Association Scholarships (Master's/Scholarship) [3069]

O'Brien Foundation Fellowships (Professional development/Fellowship) [8571]

RBC Medical Education Scholarship (Advanced Professional/Scholarship) [8235]

Regional Development Corporation Scholarship (Advanced Professional/Scholarship) [8236]

Robert R. McCain Memorial Scholarship (Advanced Professional/Scholarship) [8237]

Scotiabank Medical Education Scholarship (Advanced Professional/Scholarship) [8238]

TD Bank Medical Education Scholarship (Advanced Professional/Scholarship) [8239]

Newfoundland and Labrador

Jim Hierlihy Memorial Scholarship (Undergraduate/Scholarship) [4429]

Law Foundation of Newfoundland and Labrador Law School Scholarships (Advanced Professional/Scholarship) [6681]

Mature Student Scholarship (Undergraduate/Scholarship) [4430]

Ocean Industry Student Research Awards (Undergraduate, Graduate, Postdoctorate/Award) [9641]

Northwest Territories

CBCF - Prairies/NWT Grants in Clinical Research (Advanced Professional, Professional development/Grant) [2935]

CBCF - Prairies/NWT Grants in Health Services and Policy Research (Advanced Professional, Professional development/Grant) [2936]

CBCF - Prairies/NWT Postdoctoral Fellowships (Postdoctorate, Professional development/Fellowship) [2937]

CBCF - Prairies/NWT Research Grants in Psychosocial, Cultural and Environmental Determinants of Health (Advanced Professional, Professional development/Grant) [2938]

NWT Law Foundation/Graeme Garson Scholarships (Advanced Professional/Scholarship) [8545]

The Kennett Y. Spencer Memorial Scholarship (Graduate/Scholarship) [11524]

Nova Scotia

Scholarship Award of the Bell Aliant Pioneer Volunteers (Graduate/Scholarship) [3050]

Nunavut

CBCF - Prairies/NWT Grants in Clinical Research (Advanced Professional, Professional development/Grant) [2935]

CBCF - Prairies/NWT Grants in Health Services and Policy Research (Advanced Professional, Professional development/Grant) [2936]

CBCF - Prairies/NWT Postdoctoral Fellowships (Postdoctorate, Professional development/Fellowship) [2937]

CBCF - Prairies/NWT Research Grants in Psychosocial, Cultural and Environmental Determinants of Health (Advanced Professional, Professional development/Grant) [2938]

The Kennett Y. Spencer Memorial Scholarship (Graduate/Scholarship) [11524]

Ontario

AEBC Toronto Chapter Scholarships (Undergraduate/Scholarship) [361]

Albert C.W. Chan Foundation Award (Graduate/Fellowship) [12264]

BBPA First Generation Scholarships (College, University, Undergraduate/Scholarship) [2587]

Burlington Medical Student Bursary (Undergraduate/Grant) [8646]

CAA National Capital Region Writing Contest (All/Award, Prize, Monetary) [2916]

Diabetes Hope Scholarship Program (Undergraduate/Scholarship) [4072]

Doreen Brady Memorial Scholarship (Postgraduate/Scholarship) [8639]

Educational Fellowship For Practicing Physicians (Advanced Professional, Professional development/Fellowship) [9155]

Dr. E. Bruce Hendrick Scholarship Program (All/Scholarship) [5669]

Dr. Gilbert Hopson Medical Student Bursary (Undergraduate/Grant) [8647]

Joan Rogers Kamps Bursary (Undergraduate, Postgraduate, Professional development/Scholarship) [8641]

Richard Lim Professional Development Scholarship (Advanced Professional, Professional development/Scholarship, Recognition) [6743]

Dr. Arlene MacIntyre Medical Student Bursary (Undergraduate/Grant, Recognition) [8648]

Margaret Lynch Memorial Fellowship (Postgraduate/Fellowship) [8642]

Mary C. Babcock Fellowship (Postgraduate/Fellowship) [8643]

OMSBF District Four - Physician Care Bursary (Undergraduate/Grant) [8649]

Ontario Women's Institute Scholarships (Undergraduate/Scholarship) [4525]

PSI Graham Farquharson Knowledge Translation Fellowship (Advanced Professional, Professional development/Fellowship) [9156]

PSI Healthcare Research by Community Physicians Grants (Advanced Professional, Professional development/Grant) [9157]

Resident Research Grant (Postgraduate, Professional development/Grant) [9158]

Risk Management and Insurance Scholarship (Graduate/Scholarship) [9886]

Rose Cassin Memorial Scholarship (Postgraduate/Scholarship) [8644]

Wilfred George Scott Fellowship in Gerontology (Graduate/Fellowship) [11710]

Brian Smith Memorial Scholarships (Undergraduate/Scholarship) [2669]

Beatrice Drinnan Spence Scholarship (Undergraduate, Vocational/Occupational/Scholarship) [4268]

Sun Life Financial Medical Student Bursary (Undergraduate/Grant) [8650]

Tristin Memorial Scholarships (Undergraduate, Vocational/Occupational/Scholarship) [6756]

University of Toronto Nortel Institute Undergraduate Scholarships (Undergraduate/Scholarship) [11701]

Prince Edward Island

Joan Auld Scholarship *(Undergraduate/Scholarship)* [3702]

Lowell Phillips Scholarship *(Undergraduate/Scholarship)* [3705]

Scholarship Award of the Bell Aliant Pioneer Volunteers *(Graduate/Scholarship)* [3050]

Quebec

Evelyn Joy Abramowicz Memorial Scholarship *(Undergraduate/Scholarship)* [6282]

BCSF Scholarships *(Undergraduate/Scholarship)* [2604]

Therese and David Bohbot Scholarship *(Undergraduate/Scholarship)* [6285]

Stephen Bronfman Scholarship *(Graduate/Scholarship)* [6286]

Bernice & Gordon Brown Scholarship *(Undergraduate/Scholarship)* [6287]

Hadar J. Chemtob Memorial Scholarship *(Undergraduate/Scholarship)* [6288]

Doctoral Scholarship Outside Québec *(Doctorate/Scholarship)* [5796]

Harry Feldman Memorial Scholarship *(Undergraduate/Scholarship)* [6290]

Jack Gitlitz Memorial Scholarship - Israel *(Graduate, Undergraduate/Scholarship)* [6291]

Harry Hopmeyer Memorial Scholarship *(Undergraduate/Scholarship)* [6292]

IRSST Doctoral Scholarship *(Doctorate/Scholarship)* [5797]

IRSST Doctoral Scholarships Supplement *(Doctorate/Scholarship)* [5798]

IRSST Master's Scholarships *(Master's/Scholarship)* [5799]

IRSST Master's Scholarships Supplement *(Master's/Scholarship)* [5800]

IRSST postdoctoral fellowship *(Postdoctorate/Fellowship)* [5801]

Mitchell Karper Memorial Scholarship *(Undergraduate/Scholarship)* [6293]

Joseph Katz Memorial Scholarship *(Undergraduate/Scholarship)* [6294]

Henriette & Marcel Korner Scholarship *(Undergraduate/Scholarship)* [6295]

Liela Klinger Kurztman Memorial Scholarship *(Undergraduate/Scholarship)* [6296]

Irene Brand Lieberman Memorial Scholarship *(Graduate/Scholarship)* [6298]

Postdoctoral Fellowship in Québec *(Postdoctorate/Fellowship)* [5802]

Musia & Leon Schwartz Scholarship *(Graduate/Scholarship)* [6299]

Stelpro Scholarship 360: Energizing Potential *(Undergraduate/Scholarship)* [4359]

Bernard Michael Tarshis Memorial Scholarship *(Undergraduate/Scholarship)* [6300]

Dr. Steven S. Zalcman Memorial Scholarship *(Graduate, Postgraduate/Scholarship)* [6301]

Saskatchewan

Alliance Pipeline Scholarships *(Other/Scholarship)* [2417]

Norm Bromberger Research Bursary *(Undergraduate, Graduate/Scholarship)* [11672]

CBCF - Prairies/NWT Grants in Clinical Research *(Advanced Professional, Professional development/Grant)* [2935]

CBCF - Prairies/NWT Grants in Health Services and Policy Research *(Advanced Professional, Professional development/Grant)* [2936]

CBCF - Prairies/NWT Postdoctoral Fellowships *(Postdoctorate, Professional development/Fellowship)* [2937]

CBCF - Prairies/NWT Research Grants in Psychosocial, Cultural and Environmental Determinants of Health *(Advanced Professional, Professional development/Grant)* [2938]

Dr. Alfred E. Slinkard Scholarship *(Graduate/Scholarship)* [9921]

Don Jaques Memorial Fellowship *(Graduate/Fellowship)* [9922]

LDAS Scholarship *(Undergraduate/Scholarship)* [6760]

Poundmaker Memorial Scholarships *(Undergraduate/Scholarship)* [11675]

Risk Management and Insurance Scholarship *(Graduate/Scholarship)* [9886]

Saskatchewan Government Insurance Corporate Scholarships *(Undergraduate/Scholarship)* [9889]

Saskatchewan School Boards Association Education Scholarships *(Graduate/Scholarship)* [9925]

Yukon Territory

Alano Club Scholarship *(Undergraduate, College, University, Vocational/Occupational/Scholarship)* [12280]

Marjorie Almstrom Scholarship *(Undergraduate, Master's/Scholarship)* [12281]

Jaedyn Amann Memorial Scholarship *(Undergraduate, Master's/Scholarship)* [12282]

Fay Anthony Scholarship *(Undergraduate, College, University, Vocational/Occupational/Scholarship)* [12283]

Robert Armstrong Memorial Scholarship *(Undergraduate, Master's/Scholarship)* [12284]

Victoria Baldwin Memorial Scholarship *(Undergraduate, Master's/Scholarship)* [12285]

Alec Berry Scholarship *(Undergraduate, College, Vocational/Occupational/Scholarship)* [12286]

Henry Besner Memorial Scholarship *(Undergraduate, Master's/Scholarship)* [12287]

Joan Bilton Scholarship *(Undergraduate, College, University, Vocational/Occupational/Scholarship)* [12289]

Thomas J. Black Scholarship *(Undergraduate, University, College/Scholarship)* [12290]

Boreal Alternate Energy Centre Scholarship *(Undergraduate, University, College, Vocational/Occupational/Scholarship)* [12291]

Herbie Bouwman Memorial Scholarship *(Undergraduate, Master's/Scholarship)* [12292]

Bill Bowie Scholarship *(University, Undergraduate, College, Vocational/Occupational/Scholarship)* [12293]

Archie Bruce Scholarship *(Undergraduate, Vocational/Occupational/Scholarship)* [12295]

Gladys Bruce Scholarship *(Undergraduate/Scholarship)* [12296]

John Bunker Scholarship *(Vocational/Occupational, College/Scholarship)* [12297]

G.I. and Martha Cameron Scholarship *(Undergraduate/Scholarship)* [12298]

Robert & Jean Campbell Scholarship *(Undergraduate, University, College, Vocational/Occupational/Scholarship)* [12299]

Brian Campion Scholarship *(Graduate, Undergraduate/Scholarship)* [12300]

CBCF - BC/Yukon Region Breast Cancer Research Grants Competition *(Advanced Professional/Grant)* [2924]

CBCF - BC/Yukon Region Breast Cancer Survivor Dragon Boat Grants *(Professional development/Grant)* [2925]

CBCF - BC/Yukon Region Community Health Grants *(Professional development/Grant)* [2926]

CBCF - BC/Yukon Region Small Initiative Funds *(Professional development/Grant)* [2927]

Chechahko Consumers Co-Op Ltd. Scholarship *(Master's/Scholarship)* [12301]

Helen & Orval Couch Memorial Scholarship *(Undergraduate/Scholarship)* [12302]

Douglas B. Craig Scholarship *(Undergraduate, College, University, Vocational/Occupational/Scholarship)* [12303]

Marvin Crawford Scholarship *(College, Vocational/Occupational/Scholarship)* [12304]

Jim Davie Memorial Scholarship *(Undergraduate, Master's/Scholarship)* [12305]

Dawson District Renewable Resources Council Scholarship *(Undergraduate, College, University, Vocational/Occupational/Scholarship)* [12306]

Belle & Curly Desrosiers Scholarship *(Undergraduate, College, University, Vocational/Occupational/Scholarship)* [12307]

Anne & Konrad Domes Scholarship *(Undergraduate, University, College, Vocational/Occupational/Scholarship)* [12308]

Marnie & Bill Drury Scholarship *(Undergraduate, University, College, Vocational/Occupational/Scholarship)* [12309]

Dr. Allan Duncan Memorial Scholarship *(Undergraduate, Master's/Scholarship)* [12310]

Debra Dungey Scholarship *(Undergraduate, Graduate, University, College/Scholarship)* [12311]

David Eby Memorial Scholarship *(Undergraduate, Master's, Graduate/Scholarship)* [12312]

Mark & Heinz Eichhorn Scholarship *(College, Vocational/Occupational/Scholarship)* [12313]

Firth Family Scholarship *(Undergraduate, Graduate, Master's/Scholarship)* [12314]

Bea Firth Scholarship *(Undergraduate, Graduate/Scholarship)* [12315]

Adrian Fisher Scholarship *(Undergraduate, College, University/Scholarship)* [12316]

Maureen & Gilles Fontaine Scholarship *(Undergraduate, College, University, Vocational/Occupational/Scholarship)* [12317]

Donald Frizzell Memorial Scholarship *(Undergraduate, Graduate, Master's/Scholarship)* [12318]

Joe Goodeill Scholarship *(Undergraduate, University, College/Scholarship)* [12319]

Tamara Guttman Memorial Scholarship *(Undergraduate, University, College, Vocational/Occupational/Scholarship)* [12320]

Bert & Karen Hadvick Scholarship *(Undergraduate, University, College, Vocational/Occupational/Scholarship)* [12321]

Chuck Halliday Scholarship *(Undergraduate, University, College, Vocational/Occupational/Scholarship)* [12322]

Ted & Nicky Harrison Memorial Fund *(Undergraduate, Master's/Scholarship)* [12323]

Dereen Hildebrand Scholarship *(Undergraduate, College, University, Vocational/Occupational/Scholarship)* [12324]

Nedien Hoganson Memorial Scholarship *(Undergraduate, Master's/Scholarship)* [12325]

The Hougen Family Fund Scholarship *(Undergraduate, College, University, Vocational/Occupational/Scholarship)* [12326]

Donald Hoy Memorial Scholarship *(Undergraduate/Scholarship)* [12327]

John Hoyt Memorial Scholarship *(Undergraduate, Master's/Scholarship)* [12328]

Indian River Scholarship *(Undergraduate, University, College, Vocational/Occupational/Scholarship)* [12329]

Helen Janko Memorial Scholarship *(Undergraduate, Master's/Scholarship)* [12330]

Harry Johannes Scholarship *(Undergraduate, Graduate/Scholarship)* [12331]

Douglas Johnson Memorial Scholarship *(Master's, Graduate, Undergraduate/Scholarship)* [12332]

Marilyn King Scholarship *(Undergraduate, University, College, Vocational/Occupational/Scholarship)* [12333]

Flo Kitz Memorial Scholarship *(Undergraduate, Master's/Scholarship)* [12334]

Klondike Defence Force Grant *(Undergraduate, College, University, Vocational/Occupational/Scholarship)* [12335]

Mariel Lacasse Scholarship *(Undergraduate, University, College, Vocational/Occupational/Scholarship)* [12336]

Queenie Leader Memorial Scholarship *(Undergraduate, Master's/Scholarship)* [12337]

Nesta Leduc Scholarship *(Undergraduate, University, College, Vocational/Occupational/Scholarship)* [12338]

Grant Livingston Memorial Scholarship *(Undergraduate, Master's/Scholarship)* [12339]

Claudia-Ann Lowry Scholarship *(Undergraduate, College, University, Vocational/Occupational/Scholarship)* [12340]

Peter Lucas Scholarship *(Undergraduate, University, College, Vocational/Occupational/Scholarship)* [12341]

Ole & Mary Lunde Scholarship *(Undergraduate, University, College, Vocational/Occupational, Graduate/Scholarship)* [12342]

Dr. Sally Macdonald Scholarship *(Undergraduate, Master's/Scholarship)* [12343]

Norman Matechuk Memorial Scholarship *(Undergraduate, Master's/Scholarship)* [12344]

James McLachlan Scholarship *(Undergraduate, University, College/Scholarship)* [12345]

Les McLaughlin Scholarship *(Undergraduate, University, College, Vocational/Occupational/Scholarship)* [12346]

Bea & George McLeod Scholarship *(Undergraduate, University, College, Vocational/Occupational, Other/Scholarship)* [12347]

Pat & Donald Merrill Scholarship *(Undergraduate, University, College, Vocational/Occupational/Scholarship)* [12348]

Rita & Frank Mooney Scholarship *(Undergraduate, University, College, Vocational/Occupational/Scholarship)* [12349]

Brian Morris Scholarship *(Undergraduate, University, College, Vocational/Occupational/Scholarship)* [12350]

James W. Murdoch Scholarship *(Undergraduate, University, College, Vocational/Occupational/Scholarship)* [12351]

Gordon Newman Recreation Scholarship *(Undergraduate, University, College, Vocational/Occupational/Scholarship)* [12352]

Erik Nielsen Memorial Scholarship *(Undergraduate, Master's/Scholarship)* [12353]

Al Oster Music Legacy Scholarship *(Other, Professional development/Scholarship)* [12354]

Ted Parnell Scholarship *(Undergraduate/Scholarship)* [12278]

Patnode Family Scholarship *(Undergraduate, University, College, Vocational/Occupational/Scholarship)* [12355]

Herman Peterson Scholarship *(Vocational/Occupational, Undergraduate, University, College/Scholarship)* [12356]

J. L. Phelps Scholarship *(Undergraduate, University, College, Vocational/Occupational/Scholarship)* [12357]

Garry Phillips Scholarship *(Undergraduate, University, College, Vocational/Occupational/Scholarship)* [12358]

The Porter Creek Citizens' Assoc. Scholarship *(Undergraduate, University, College, Vocational/Occupational/Scholarship)* [12359]

Diamond & James Quong Memorial Scholarship *(Graduate, Master's, Undergraduate/Scholarship)* [12360]

Ivan & Dianna Raketti Scholarship *(Undergraduate, Graduate, Master's/Scholarship)* [12361]

Gary Reynolds Scholarship *(Undergraduate, University, College, Vocational/Occupational/Scholarship)* [12362]

Evelyn (Babe) Richards Scholarship *(Undergraduate, University, College, Vocational/Occupational/Scholarship)* [12363]

Paula Joan Riehl Memorial Scholarship *(High School/Scholarship)* [12364]

Red Rogers Memorial Scholarship *(Undergraduate, Master's/Scholarship)* [12365]

John Rowan Scholarship *(Undergraduate, University, College, Vocational/Occupational/Scholarship)* [12366]

Schmidt Family Scholarship *(Undergraduate, University, College/Scholarship)* [12367]

Senyk Memorial Scholarship *(Undergraduate, Master's/Scholarship)* [12368]

Joan Shaxon Scholarship *(Undergraduate, University, College, Vocational/Occupational/Scholarship)* [12369]

Ben Sheardown Scholarship *(Undergraduate, University, College/Scholarship)* [12370]

Dr. Brent Slobodin Memorial Scholarship in the Humanities *(Undergraduate, Graduate, University, College/Scholarship)* [12371]

Smyth Family Scholarship *(Undergraduate, University, College, Vocational/Occupational/Scholarship)* [12372]

The Kennett Y. Spencer Memorial Scholarship *(Graduate/Scholarship)* [11524]

Steele Family Memorial Scholarship *(Undergraduate, Master's/Scholarship)* [12373]

John & Doris Stenbraten Scholarship *(Undergraduate, University, College, Vocational/Occupational/Scholarship)* [12374]

Stuart/SIM Northern Education Scholarship *(Undergraduate, University, College, Vocational/Occupational/Scholarship)* [12375]

Rod Tait Memorial Scholarship *(Undergraduate, College, University, Vocational/Occupational/Scholarship)* [12376]

Peg & Aubrey Tanner Scholarship *(Undergraduate, College, University, Vocational/Occupational/Scholarship)* [12377]

Betty & Charles Taylor Scholarship *(Graduate, Undergraduate/Scholarship)* [12378]

Edith & Victor Thomas Scholarship *(Undergraduate, University, College/Scholarship)* [12379]

J.J. Van Bibber Scholarship *(Undergraduate, University, College, Vocational/Occupational/Scholarship)* [12380]

Vancouver Yukoners Legacy Scholarship *(Vocational/Occupational, College, Undergraduate/Scholarship)* [12381]

Joan Veinott Scholarship *(Undergraduate, University, College/Scholarship)* [12382]

Village of Mayo Heritage Fund Scholarship *(Undergraduate, University, College, Vocational/Occupational/Scholarship)* [12383]

Dorreene & Herb Wahl Scholarship *(Undergraduate, University, College/Scholarship)* [12384]

Matthew Watson Scholarship *(Undergraduate, University, College, Graduate/Scholarship)* [12385]

Matthew Webster Scholarship *(Undergraduate, College, Vocational/Occupational/Scholarship)* [12386]

Whitehorse Business & Professional Women's Club Bursary *(Undergraduate, University, College, Vocational/Occupational/Scholarship)* [12387]

Whitehorse Copper Mines Scholarship *(Undergraduate, University, College, Vocational/Occupational/Scholarship)* [12388]

Whitehorse Glacier Bears Swim Club Scholarship *(Undergraduate, University, College, Vocational/Occupational/Scholarship)* [12389]

Whitehorse Shotokan Karate Club Scholarship *(Undergraduate, Master's/Scholarship)* [12390]

Flo Whyard-Holland America Line-Westours Scholarship *(Undergraduate/Scholarship)* [12391]

Dr. Anne Williams Scholarship *(Undergraduate, Graduate/Scholarship)* [12392]

Shirley Williams Scholarship *(Undergraduate, University, College/Scholarship)* [12393]

Robert Wilson Scholarship *(Undergraduate, College, Vocational/Occupational/Scholarship)* [12394]

Jeff Young Memorial Scholarship *(Undergraduate, Master's/Scholarship)* [12395]

Yukon Anniversaries Commission Scholarship *(Undergraduate, University, College, Vocational/Occupational/Scholarship)* [12396]

The Yukon Foundation Medical Laboratory Scholarship *(Graduate, Master's, Undergraduate/Scholarship)* [12397]

Yukon Outdoors Club Scholarship *(Undergraduate, University, College, Vocational/Occupational/Scholarship)* [12398]

Y.W.C.A. of Yukon Scholarship *(Undergraduate, University, College, Vocational/Occupational/Scholarship)* [12399]

INTERNATIONAL

AAMC Foundation Engagement Program for International Curators Grants *(Advanced Professional, Professional development/Grant)* [2057]

AAN International Scholarship Award *(Professional development/Scholarship, Award)* [459]

American Association of University Women International Fellowships *(Graduate, Postgraduate, Master's/Fellowship)* [666]

AWS International Scholarship Program *(Undergraduate, Graduate/Scholarship)* [1657]

Franklin Mosher Baldwin Memorial Fellowships *(Master's, Doctorate/Fellowship)* [6751]

The Bentley Cropping Systems Fellowship *(Graduate/Fellowship)* [3263]

Conference and Workshop Grants *(Professional development/Grant)* [11960]

Deborah Partridge Wolfe International Fellowship (Graduate) *(Graduate, Undergraduate/Fellowship)* [12410]

Fermilab Internships for Physics Majors *(Undergraduate/Internship)* [11315]

HHMI International Student Research Fellowships *(Doctorate/Fellowship)* [5616]

IOIA Organic Community Initiative Scholarships *(Other/Scholarship)* [6054]

Law and Society Association International Prize *(Other/Award, Recognition)* [6726]

National Geographic Expedition Council Grants *(Advanced Professional/Grant)* [7907]

National Geographic Young Explorers Grants *(Advanced Professional/Grant)* [7909]

Rice-Cullimore Scholarship *(Graduate/Scholarship)* [2001]

IOIA Andrew Rutherford Scholarships *(Other/Scholarship)* [6055]

Terra Foundation Research Travel Grants *(Doctorate, Undergraduate/Grant)* [10965]

Tourette Association of America Research Grant Awards *(Master's, Doctorate/Grant)* [11067]

INTERNATIONAL (BY REGION)

Africa

American Society for Microbiology International Fellowships for Africa *(Postdoctorate/Fellowship)* [1510]

Documentary Film Grants *(Professional development/Grant)* [409]

Wadsworth African Fellowships *(Doctorate/Fellowship)* [11964]

Asia and Pacific

East-West Center Graduate Degree Fellowship *(Master's, Doctorate, Graduate/Fellowship)* [4262]

Asia

American Society for Microbiology International Fellowships for Asia *(Postdoctorate/Fellowship)* [1511]

Documentary Film Grants *(Professional development/Grant)* [409]

Asian Pacific America

SCCLA Scholarships *(Graduate/Scholarship)* [10648]

Baltic States

Abram and Fannie Gottlieb Immerman and Abraham Nathan and Bertha Daskal Weinstein Memorial Fellowship *(Postdoctorate, Doctorate/Fellowship)* [12238]

Caribbean

Caribbean Hotel and Tourism Association Scholarship *(Graduate, Undergraduate/Scholarship)* [3167]

GCFI Student Travel Awards *(Undergraduate/Award)* [5252]

IAF Fellowships *(Doctorate/Fellowship)* [5883]

OAS Academic Scholarship for Undergraduate Studies *(Undergraduate/Scholarship)* [8731]

Paleontological Society International Research Program Sepkoski Grants *(Advanced Professional, Graduate/Grant)* [8814]

Leo S. Rowe Pan American Fund *(Graduate, Undergraduate/Loan)* [8739]

TFI Latin America Media Arts Fund *(Professional development/Grant)* [11110]

Central America

OAS Scholarships for Professional Development - Disaster Communications Management *(Professional development/Scholarship)* [8732]

OAS Scholarships for Professional Development - Radio Spectrum Monitoring Techniques and Procedures *(Professional development/Scholarship)* [8733]

OAS Scholarships for Professional Development - Satellite Communications *(Professional development/Scholarship)* [8734]
Paleontological Society International Research Program Sepkoski Grants *(Advanced Professional, Graduate/Grant)* [8814]

Eastern Europe

CJH-Prins Foundation Fellowships for Senior Scholars *(Doctorate/Fellowship)* [3223]
CJH-Prins Foundation Post-Doctoral and Early Career Fellowship for Emigrating Scholars *(Professional development, Postdoctorate/Fellowship)* [3224]
Paleontological Society International Research Program Sepkoski Grants *(Advanced Professional, Graduate/Grant)* [8814]

Europe

HAESF Graduate Scholarships *(Graduate/Scholarship)* [5644]
HAESF Professional Internship Program *(Doctorate/Internship)* [5645]

Latin America and the Caribbean

American Society for Microbiology International Fellowships for Latin America and the Caribbean *(Postdoctorate/Fellowship)* [1512]

Latin America

The E. Alexander Bergstrom Memorial Research Award *(Undergraduate, Master's/Award)* [2177]
Documentary Film Grants *(Professional development/Grant)* [409]
IAF Fellowships *(Doctorate/Fellowship)* [5883]
Pew Latin American Fellows Program in the Biomedical Sciences *(Other/Fellowship)* [9052]
Leo S. Rowe Pan American Fund *(Graduate, Undergraduate/Loan)* [8739]

Middle East

IDRC Research Awards *(Master's, Doctorate/Award)* [3264]

North America

AAPA Student Research Scholarship *(Graduate, Undergraduate/Scholarship)* [631]
A.C. Elias, Jr. Irish-American Research Travel Fellowship *(Other/Fellowship)* [1425]
Afdhal / McHutchison LIFER Award *(Postdoctorate, Professional development/Award)* [649]
American Wine Society Educational Foundation Scholarships (AWSEF) *(Graduate/Scholarship)* [1676]
Aubrey L. Williams Research Travel Fellowship *(Doctorate/Fellowship)* [1429]
Chronic Pain Medicine Research Grant *(Professional development/Grant)* [1556]
Galvanize the Future: A Richard L. Brooks Memorial Scholarship *(Undergraduate, Graduate/Scholarship)* [934]
ILMA foundation Scholarship Program *(Undergraduate/Scholarship)* [5735]
International Scholars Program for Young Vascular Surgeons *(Graduate/Scholarship)* [10555]
Carl Koller Memorial Research Grants *(Professional development/Grant)* [1557]
OAS Scholarships for Professional Development - Disaster Communications Management *(Professional development/Scholarship)* [8732]
OAS Scholarships for Professional Development - Radio Spectrum Monitoring Techniques and Procedures *(Professional development/Scholarship)* [8733]
OAS Scholarships for Professional Development - Satellite Communications *(Professional development/Scholarship)* [8734]
OTA Member Full Research Grant *(Other/Grant)* [8763]

Wexner Graduate Fellowship / Davidson Scholars Program *(Graduate/Fellowship)* [12003]

North and Central America

IDRC Research Awards *(Master's, Doctorate/Award)* [3264]

North of Sahara

IDRC Research Awards *(Master's, Doctorate/Award)* [3264]

Oceania

IDRC Research Awards *(Master's, Doctorate/Award)* [3264]

Pacific Islands

APIASF Scholarships *(Undergraduate/Scholarship)* [1994]

Scandinavia

Annika Teig Fellowship *(Postgraduate/Internship)* [1375]

South America

IDRC Research Awards *(Master's, Doctorate/Award)* [3264]
OAS Scholarships for Professional Development - Disaster Communications Management *(Professional development/Scholarship)* [8732]
OAS Scholarships for Professional Development - Radio Spectrum Monitoring Techniques and Procedures *(Professional development/Scholarship)* [8733]
OAS Scholarships for Professional Development - Satellite Communications *(Professional development/Scholarship)* [8734]
Paleontological Society International Research Program Sepkoski Grants *(Advanced Professional, Graduate/Grant)* [8814]
TFI Latin America Media Arts Fund *(Professional development/Grant)* [11110]

South Asia

IDRC Research Awards *(Master's, Doctorate/Award)* [3264]

South of Sahara

IDRC Research Awards *(Master's, Doctorate/Award)* [3264]

Southeast Asia

William L. Bradley Memorial Scholarship *(Master's/Scholarship)* [8334]

Soviet Union (former)

CJH-Prins Foundation Fellowships for Senior Scholars *(Doctorate/Fellowship)* [3223]
CJH-Prins Foundation Post-Doctoral and Early Career Fellowship for Emigrating Scholars *(Professional development, Postdoctorate/Fellowship)* [3224]
Paleontological Society International Research Program Sepkoski Grants *(Advanced Professional, Graduate/Grant)* [8814]

West Indies

IDRC Research Awards *(Master's, Doctorate/Award)* [3264]

INTERNATIONAL (BY COUNTRY)

Argentina

CEJIL Communications Internships *(Professional development, Graduate/Internship)* [3230]

CEJIL Legal Internships *(Graduate, Professional development/Internship)* [3231]
Organization of American States Graduate Scholarships *(Doctorate, Graduate/Scholarship)* [8737]

Australia

Harkness Fellowships in Health Care Policy and Practice *(Doctorate, Graduate/Fellowship)* [3555]
Morgan Stanley Pediatrics Fellowships *(Postgraduate, Graduate/Fellowship)* [686]
The Reedsy National Creative Writing Scholarship *(Undergraduate/Scholarship)* [9607]

Bangladesh

ICNL Research Fellowships *(Advanced Professional, Professional development/Fellowship)* [5964]

Barbados

Organization of American States Graduate Scholarships *(Doctorate, Graduate/Scholarship)* [8737]

Benin

ICNL Research Fellowships *(Advanced Professional, Professional development/Fellowship)* [5964]

Bolivia

Organization of American States Graduate Scholarships *(Doctorate, Graduate/Scholarship)* [8737]

Brazil

CEJIL Communications Internships *(Professional development, Graduate/Internship)* [3230]
CEJIL Legal Internships *(Graduate, Professional development/Internship)* [3231]
Organization of American States Graduate Scholarships *(Doctorate, Graduate/Scholarship)* [8737]

Burundi

ICNL Research Fellowships *(Advanced Professional, Professional development/Fellowship)* [5964]

Cambodia

ICNL Research Fellowships *(Advanced Professional, Professional development/Fellowship)* [5964]

Chile

Organization of American States Graduate Scholarships *(Doctorate, Graduate/Scholarship)* [8737]

China

Lucy Hsu Ho Scholarship *(Undergraduate/Scholarship)* [2485]

Colombia

ICNL Research Fellowships *(Advanced Professional, Professional development/Fellowship)* [5964]
Organization of American States Graduate Scholarships *(Doctorate, Graduate/Scholarship)* [8737]

Costa Rica

CEJIL Communications Internships *(Professional development, Graduate/Internship)* [3230]
CEJIL Legal Internships *(Graduate, Professional development/Internship)* [3231]
Organization of American States Graduate Scholarships *(Doctorate, Graduate/Scholarship)* [8737]

Cuba

Brandon Fradd Fellowship in Music Composition (*Professional development/Fellowship*) [3416]

CINTAS Foundation Fellowship in Architecture & Design (*Professional development/Fellowship*) [3417]

Mas Family Scholarship (*Graduate, Undergraduate/Scholarship*) [7120]

Denmark

American-Scandinavian Foundation Fellowships/Grants in the United States (*Graduate, Professional development/Fellowship, Grant*) [1372]

Edith and Arnold N. Bodtker Grants (*Undergraduate, Graduate/Grant, Internship*) [3968]

SSOC Scholarship (*Undergraduate/Scholarship*) [9930]

Ecuador

Organization of American States Graduate Scholarships (*Doctorate, Graduate/Scholarship*) [8737]

El Salvador

Organization of American States Graduate Scholarships (*Doctorate, Graduate/Scholarship*) [8737]

Finland

American-Scandinavian Foundation Fellowships/Grants in the United States (*Graduate, Professional development/Fellowship, Grant*) [1372]

SSOC Scholarship (*Undergraduate/Scholarship*) [9930]

France

Jenny d'Héricourt Fellowship (*Doctorate/Fellowship*) [487]

Gambia

ICNL Research Fellowships (*Advanced Professional, Professional development/Fellowship*) [5964]

Germany

APSA Congressional Fellowships (*Other/Fellowship*) [4945]

DAI Fellowship for Study in Berlin (*Postdoctorate/Fellowship*) [1776]

The Christoph Daniel Ebeling Fellowship (*Postdoctorate, Doctorate/Fellowship*) [489, 4055]

Harkness Fellowships in Health Care Policy and Practice (*Doctorate, Graduate/Fellowship*) [3555]

Anna-Maria and Stephen M. Kellen Fellowships (*Professional development/Fellowship*) [809]

McCloy Fellowships in Agriculture (*Professional development/Fellowship*) [810]

McCloy Fellowships in Environmental Policy (*Professional development/Fellowship*) [811]

McCloy Fellowships in Journalism (*Professional development/Fellowship*) [812]

McCloy Fellowships in Urban Affairs (*Professional development/Fellowship*) [813]

Ghana

African Humanities Program (*Postdoctorate/Fellowship*) [819]

ICNL Research Fellowships (*Advanced Professional, Professional development/Fellowship*) [5964]

Next Generation Social Sciences in Africa: Doctoral Dissertation Completion Fellowship (*Doctorate/Fellowship*) [3169, 10249]

Next Generation Social Sciences in Africa: Doctoral Dissertation Proposal Fellowship (*Doctorate/Fellowship*) [3170, 10250]

Next Generation Social Sciences in Africa: Doctoral Dissertation Research Fellowship (*Doctorate/Fellowship*) [3171, 10251]

Greenland

Fritz Schwartz Serials Education Scholarship (*Graduate/Scholarship*) [7560]

Grenada

Organization of American States Graduate Scholarships (*Doctorate, Graduate/Scholarship*) [8737]

Hungary

Dr. Elemer and Eva Kiss Scholarship Fund (*Undergraduate/Scholarship*) [5642]

Iceland

American-Scandinavian Foundation Fellowships/Grants in the United States (*Graduate, Professional development/Fellowship, Grant*) [1372]

SSOC Scholarship (*Undergraduate/Scholarship*) [9930]

India

Chereddi NarayanaRao & Radhamanohari Scholarships (*Graduate/Scholarship*) [10948]

Gadde Sitaramamma & Tirupataiah Scholarship (*Graduate/Scholarship*) [10949]

Guthikonda BasavapunnaRao & Umadevi Scholarship (*Graduate/Scholarship*) [10950]

Guthikonda Ramabrahmam & Balamani Scholarship (*Graduate/Scholarship*) [10951]

Kodali Veeraiah & Sarojini Scholarship (*Graduate/Scholarship*) [10952]

Malayalee Engineers Association Scholarships (*Undergraduate/Scholarship*) [7012]

Shastri Scholar Travel Subsidy Grants (SSTSG) (*Graduate, Professional development/Grant*) [10037]

TANA Foundation Graduate Scholarships (*Graduate/Scholarship*) [10953]

Vallabhaneni Sukundamma & Lakshmaiah Scholarship (*Graduate/Scholarship*) [10954]

Indonesia

William L. Bradley Memorial Scholarship (*Master's/Scholarship*) [8334]

ICNL Research Fellowships (*Advanced Professional, Professional development/Fellowship*) [5964]

Indonesian Directorate General of Higher Education Scholarships (DIKTI) (*Graduate/Scholarship*) [4263]

Iran

Lee Teng Undergraduate Fellowship in Accelerator Science and Engineering (*Undergraduate/Fellowship*) [11318]

Helen Edwards Summer Internship (*Undergraduate/Internship*) [11319]

Ireland

A.C. Elias, Jr. Irish-American Research Travel Fellowship (*Other/Fellowship*) [1425]

Israel

Jenny Panitch Beckow Memorial Scholarship - Canada (*Graduate/Scholarship*) [6283]

Ruth and Victor David Scholarship (*Undergraduate, Graduate/Scholarship*) [6289]

International Scholarship Programs for Community Service (*Undergraduate/Scholarship*) [7249]

Klarman Family Foundation Grants Program in Eating Disorders Research (*Professional development/Grant*) [5439]

Morphisec's Women in Cybersecurity Scholarships (*Undergraduate, Graduate/Scholarship*) [7470]

The Tikvah Fellowship (*Undergraduate/Fellowship*) [11034]

Italy

John R. Mott Scholarships (*Undergraduate, Graduate/Scholarship*) [7482]

Jamaica

Marcus Mosiah Garvey Scholarships (*Undergraduate/Scholarship*) [6216]

Organization of American States Graduate Scholarships (*Doctorate, Graduate/Scholarship*) [8737]

Japan

Abe Fellowship (*Professional development/Fellowship*) [10241]

Abe Fellowships for Journalists (*Professional development/Fellowship*) [10242]

Crown Prince Akihito Scholarship Foundation (*Graduate/Scholarship*) [6231]

Goldia.com Jewelry Scholarships (*Undergraduate, Graduate/Scholarship*) [5025]

Mary Jane Hendrie Memorial Scholarships (*Graduate, Undergraduate/Scholarship*) [11690]

Obuchi Student Scholarship (*Graduate/Scholarship*) [4264]

Wagner-Torizuka Fellowship (*Professional development/Fellowship*) [10445]

Kazakhstan

Russian Student Scholarship (*Undergraduate/Scholarship*) [11511]

Kosovo

ICNL Research Fellowships (*Advanced Professional, Professional development/Fellowship*) [5964]

Kyrgyzstan

Russian Student Scholarship (*Undergraduate/Scholarship*) [11511]

Malawi

ICNL Research Fellowships (*Advanced Professional, Professional development/Fellowship*) [5964]

Mexico

AASLD Autoimmune Liver Diseases Pilot Research Award (*Graduate, Doctorate, Postdoctorate, Professional development/Award, Grant*) [645]

AASLD Clinical, Translational and Outcomes Research Awards (*Professional development/Grant*) [646]

Abel Wolman Fellowship (*Doctorate/Fellowship, Award, Monetary*) [1634]

GCFI Student Travel Awards (*Undergraduate/Award*) [5252]

Geological Society of America Graduate Student Research Grants (*Doctorate, Graduate/Grant*) [4910]

ICNL Research Fellowships (*Advanced Professional, Professional development/Fellowship*) [5964]

John J. McKetta Undergraduate Scholarship (*Undergraduate/Scholarship*) [1023]

Marvin Mundel Memorial Scholarship (*Undergraduate/Scholarship*) [5834]

Organization of American States Graduate Scholarships (*Doctorate, Graduate/Scholarship*) [8737]

Fritz Schwartz Serials Education Scholarship (*Graduate/Scholarship*) [7560]

TFI Latin America Media Arts Fund (*Professional development/Grant*) [11110]

UC MEXUS-CICESE Graduate Student Short-Term Research and Training Program (*Master's, Doctorate, Postdoctorate/Grant*) [11539]

UC MEXUS-CONACYT Collaborative Grants (*Professional development/Grant*) [11551]

UC MEXUS-CONACYT Doctoral Fellowship (*Doctorate/Fellowship*) [11552]

UC MEXUS-CONACYT Postdoctoral Research Fellowships *(Postdoctorate/Fellowship)* [11553]

UC MEXUS Dissertation Research Grants *(Graduate/Grant)* [11554]

UC MEXUS Scholars in Residence Program - Graduate *(Graduate/Scholarship)* [11555]

UC MEXUS Scholars in Residence Program - Recent University Graduates *(Postgraduate, Graduate/Scholarship)* [11556]

UC MEXUS Scholars in Residence Program - Visiting Faculty *(Professional development/Scholarship)* [11557]

UC MEXUS Small Grants for UC Postdocs *(Postdoctorate/Grant)* [11558]

UC MEXUS Small Grants for UC Students *(Graduate, Postdoctorate/Grant)* [11559]

UPS Scholarship for Female Students *(Undergraduate/Scholarship)* [5836]

UPS Scholarship for Minority Students *(Undergraduate/Scholarship)* [5837]

Moldova

ICNL Research Fellowships *(Advanced Professional, Professional development/Fellowship)* [5964]

Nepal

Hugh & Helen Wood Nepalese Scholarship *(Undergraduate/Scholarship)* [2482]

Netherlands

Harkness Fellowships in Health Care Policy and Practice *(Doctorate, Graduate/Fellowship)* [3555]

New Zealand

Harkness Fellowships in Health Care Policy and Practice *(Doctorate, Graduate/Fellowship)* [3555]

Nigeria

African Humanities Program *(Postdoctorate/Fellowship)* [819]

Next Generation Social Sciences in Africa: Doctoral Dissertation Completion Fellowship *(Doctorate/Fellowship)* [3169, 10249]

Next Generation Social Sciences in Africa: Doctoral Dissertation Proposal Fellowship *(Doctorate/Fellowship)* [3170, 10250]

Next Generation Social Sciences in Africa: Doctoral Dissertation Research Fellowship *(Doctorate/Fellowship)* [3171, 10251]

NWAG Nigeria Scholarships *(Undergraduate/Scholarship)* [8396]

North Korea

Asia-Pacific Biomedical Research Foundation Merit Awards *(Postdoctorate/Award, Recognition, Prize)* [10530]

Norway

American-Scandinavian Foundation Fellowships/Grants in the United States *(Graduate, Professional development/Fellowship, Grant)* [1372]

Harkness Fellowships in Health Care Policy and Practice *(Doctorate, Graduate/Fellowship)* [3555]

SSOC Scholarship *(Undergraduate/Scholarship)* [9930]

Pakistan

AIPS Post-Doctoral Fellowship *(Postdoctorate/Fellowship)* [1037]

AIPS Pre-Doctoral Fellowship *(Doctorate, Postdoctorate/Fellowship)* [1038]

Panama

Organization of American States Graduate Scholarships *(Doctorate, Graduate/Scholarship)* [8737]

Peru

David and Deborah Clark Fellowship *(Graduate/Fellowship)* [8744]

Dole Food Fellowship *(Graduate/Fellowship)* [8745]

Emily P. Foster Fellowship *(Graduate/Fellowship)* [8746]

F. Christian and Betty Thompson Fellowship *(Graduate/Fellowship)* [8747]

ICNL Research Fellowships *(Advanced Professional, Professional development/Fellowship)* [5964]

Lillian and Murray Slatkin Fellowship *(Graduate/Fellowship)* [8748]

Organization of American States Graduate Scholarships *(Doctorate, Graduate/Scholarship)* [8737]

Peace Frogs Fellowships *(Graduate/Fellowship)* [8750]

Rexford Daubenmire Fellowship *(Graduate/Fellowship)* [8751]

William L. Brown Fellowship *(Graduate/Fellowship)* [8754]

Philippines

William L. Bradley Memorial Scholarship *(Master's/Scholarship)* [8334]

PNAA Nursing Scholarship Award *(Master's, Doctorate/Scholarship)* [9135]

Portugal

Edilia and François Auguste de Montêquin Fellowships *(Doctorate/Fellowship)* [10274]

Russia

East-West Center Graduate Degree Fellowship *(Master's, Doctorate, Graduate/Fellowship)* [4262]

Russian Student Scholarship *(Undergraduate/Scholarship)* [11511]

Serbia

Dr. Elemer and Eva Kiss Scholarship Fund *(Undergraduate/Scholarship)* [5642]

Slovakia

Dr. Elemer and Eva Kiss Scholarship Fund *(Undergraduate/Scholarship)* [5642]

South Africa

African Humanities Program *(Postdoctorate/Fellowship)* [819]

Next Generation Social Sciences in Africa: Doctoral Dissertation Completion Fellowship *(Doctorate/Fellowship)* [3169, 10249]

Next Generation Social Sciences in Africa: Doctoral Dissertation Proposal Fellowship *(Doctorate/Fellowship)* [3170, 10250]

Next Generation Social Sciences in Africa: Doctoral Dissertation Research Fellowship *(Doctorate/Fellowship)* [3171, 10251]

South Korea

Asia-Pacific Biomedical Research Foundation Merit Awards *(Postdoctorate/Award, Recognition, Prize)* [10530]

Spain

Edilia and François Auguste de Montêquin Fellowships *(Doctorate/Fellowship)* [10274]

Sudan

Lee Teng Undergraduate Fellowship in Accelerator Science and Engineering *(Undergraduate/Fellowship)* [11318]

Helen Edwards Summer Internship *(Undergraduate/Internship)* [11319]

Suriname

OAS Academic Scholarship for Undergraduate Studies *(Undergraduate/Scholarship)* [8731]

Sweden

American-Scandinavian Foundation Fellowships/Grants in the United States *(Graduate, Professional development/Fellowship, Grant)* [1372]

Harkness Fellowships in Health Care Policy and Practice *(Doctorate, Graduate/Fellowship)* [3555]

SSOC Scholarship *(Undergraduate/Scholarship)* [9930]

Switzerland

Harkness Fellowships in Health Care Policy and Practice *(Doctorate, Graduate/Fellowship)* [3555]

Syria

Lee Teng Undergraduate Fellowship in Accelerator Science and Engineering *(Undergraduate/Fellowship)* [11318]

Helen Edwards Summer Internship *(Undergraduate/Internship)* [11319]

Taiwan

Joel R. Friend Scholarship *(Undergraduate/Scholarship)* [2483]

Tanzania

African Humanities Program *(Postdoctorate/Fellowship)* [819]

Godparents for Tanzania Scholarship *(Undergraduate/Scholarship)* [5012]

Next Generation Social Sciences in Africa: Doctoral Dissertation Completion Fellowship *(Doctorate/Fellowship)* [3169, 10249]

Next Generation Social Sciences in Africa: Doctoral Dissertation Proposal Fellowship *(Doctorate/Fellowship)* [3170, 10250]

Next Generation Social Sciences in Africa: Doctoral Dissertation Research Fellowship *(Doctorate/Fellowship)* [3171, 10251]

Thailand

ICNL Research Fellowships *(Advanced Professional, Professional development/Fellowship)* [5964]

Joel R. Friend Scholarship *(Undergraduate/Scholarship)* [2483]

Trinidad and Tobago

Organization of American States Graduate Scholarships *(Doctorate, Graduate/Scholarship)* [8737]

Turkey

Getty Research Exchange Fellowship Program for Cultural Heritage Preservation *(Doctorate/Fellowship)* [1347]

Ilse B. Hanfmann, George Hanfmann and Machteld J. Mellink Burslari Fellowship. *(Doctorate/Fellowship)* [1348]

Turkmenistan

Russian Student Scholarship *(Undergraduate/Scholarship)* [11511]

Uganda

African Humanities Program *(Postdoctorate/Fellowship)* [819]

Next Generation Social Sciences in Africa: Doctoral Dissertation Completion Fellowship *(Doctorate/Fellowship)* [3169, 10249]

Next Generation Social Sciences in Africa: Doctoral Dissertation Proposal Fellowship *(Doctorate/Fellowship)* [3170, 10250]

Next Generation Social Sciences in Africa: Doctoral Dissertation Research Fellowship *(Doctorate/Fellowship)* [3171, 10251]

SSSP Racial/Ethnic Minority Graduate Fellowship *(Graduate/Fellowship, Award, Monetary)* [10537]

Ukraine

Alberta Ukrainian Centennial Commemorative Scholarship *(Graduate/Scholarship)* [11887]

ALIS International Education Awards - Ukraine *(Undergraduate/Scholarship)* [284]

Canada-Ukraine Parliamentary Program Internship Scholarships (CUPP) *(Undergraduate/Scholarship, Internship)* [11888]

Chopivsky Fellowships *(Graduate/Fellowship)* [11889]

ICNL Research Fellowships *(Advanced Professional, Professional development/Fellowship)* [5964]

Dr. Elemer and Eva Kiss Scholarship Fund *(Undergraduate/Scholarship)* [5642]

Kovaluk Scholarship Fund *(Undergraduate/Scholarship)* [11412]

USA/USA-Ukramerazha Scholarships *(Undergraduate/Scholarship)* [11413]

United Kingdom

ALA Century Scholarship *(Master's, Doctorate/Scholarship)* [2293]

BAFTX Early Starters Award *(Undergraduate/Award)* [2696]

BAFTX Graduate Award *(Graduate/Award)* [2697]

BAFTX Junior Achievers Award *(Undergraduate/Award)* [2698]

BAFTX Undergraduate Award *(Undergraduate/Award)* [2699]

Hilda E. Bretzlaff Foundation Scholarships *(Undergraduate/Scholarship, Grant)* [2687]

Goldia.com Jewelry Scholarships *(Undergraduate, Graduate/Scholarship)* [5025]

Harkness Fellowships in Health Care Policy and Practice *(Doctorate, Graduate/Fellowship)* [3555]

Lloyd Bridges Scholarship *(Graduate/Scholarship)* [3204]

Novus Biologicals Scholarship Program *(All/Scholarship)* [8553]

Saint Andrews Scholarships *(Undergraduate/Scholarship)* [9776]

U.S.-U.K. Young Investigator Exchange Fellowship *(Postdoctorate/Fellowship)* [417]

Uruguay

Organization of American States Graduate Scholarships *(Doctorate, Graduate/Scholarship)* [8737]

Uzbekistan

Russian Student Scholarship *(Undergraduate/Scholarship)* [11511]

Vietnam

Seameo-Vietnam Scholarship Program *(Graduate/Scholarship)* [4265]

Zimbabwe

ICNL Research Fellowships *(Advanced Professional, Professional development/Fellowship)* [5964]

Legal Residence Index

Place of Study Index

This index lists awards that carry restrictions on where study may take place. Award citations are arranged alphabetically under the following geographic headings: United States, United States (by Region), United States (by State), Canada, Canada (by Province), International, International (by Region), and International (by Country). Each citation is followed by the study level and award type, which appear in parentheses. Numbers following the parenthetical information indicate book entry numbers for particular awards, not page numbers.

UNITED STATES

1-800-Pain-Free Scholarship *(Two Year College, Undergraduate, Graduate/Scholarship)* [141]

$1000 uPONICS Hydroponics/Aquaponics Scholarship *(Undergraduate/Scholarship)* [11761]

100th Infantry Battalion Veterans Memorial Scholarship Fund *(Undergraduate, University, College, Vocational/Occupational/Scholarship)* [5374]

10x Digital Marketing Scholarship *(Undergraduate, Graduate/Scholarship)* [4]

$1500 College Monk Short Essay Scholarship *(Undergraduate, Graduate/Scholarship)* [3508]

180 Medical College Scholarship Program *(Undergraduate, Graduate, Professional development/Scholarship)* [6]

1Dental Scholarship *(Undergraduate, Graduate/Scholarship)* [8]

1L and 2L Diversity Fellowship Programs *(Undergraduate/Fellowship)* [5042]

$2,000 College Scholarship for the Business Leaders of Tomorrow *(Undergraduate/Scholarship)* [2759]

$2,000 Nitro College Scholarship *(Community College, University, Undergraduate, Graduate/Scholarship)* [8407]

2020 The Nuclear Family Scholarship *(College, University, Undergraduate/Scholarship)* [6689]

$5000 Imagine Scholarship *(College, University/Scholarship)* [9755]

The 86211 Scholarship *(Undergraduate/Scholarship)* [9643]

A-2 Joaquim Pereira Memorial Scholarship *(Undergraduate/Scholarship)* [6935]

A-4 António Mattos Memorial Scholarship *(Undergraduate/Scholarship)* [6936]

AAA Education Research Scholarship *(Graduate, Postdoctorate/Scholarship)* [512]

AAA Postdoctoral Fellowship *(Postdoctorate/Fellowship)* [513]

AAAA Scholarship Program *(Undergraduate, Graduate/Scholarship)* [1911]

AAACN Conference Scholarship for Nursing Students *(Undergraduate/Scholarship)* [424]

AAACN Education Scholarship *(Undergraduate/Scholarship)* [425]

AAACN Research/Evidence Based Practice Project Awards *(Undergraduate/Grant, Scholarship)* [426]

AAAS Mass Media Science & Engineering Fellows Program *(Undergraduate, Graduate, Postdoctorate/Fellowship)* [506]

AABP Amstutz Scholarship *(Undergraduate/Scholarship)* [522]

AABP Bovine Veterinary Student Recognition Award *(Undergraduate/Scholarship, Award)* [523]

AABP Education Grants *(Graduate, Postgraduate, Master's/Grant)* [524]

AABP Student Externship Program *(Undergraduate/Scholarship)* [525]

AACD Dentist Fellowships *(Professional development/Fellowship)* [446]

AACE International Competitive Scholarships *(Undergraduate/Scholarship)* [22]

AACPDM Student Travel Scholarship *(Professional development/Scholarship)* [438]

AACTE Outstanding Book Awards *(Other/Award, Recognition)* [547]

AACTE Outstanding Dissertation Awards *(Doctorate/Award)* [548]

AAEP/ALSIC Scholarships *(Undergraduate/Scholarship)* [558]

AAEP Foundation Past Presidents' Research Fellow *(Graduate, Professional development/Scholarship)* [559]

AAFSW Merit Scholarship for College Students *(College, Undergraduate/Scholarship)* [2025]

AAIA Allogan Slagle Memorial Scholarship *(Undergraduate, Graduate/Scholarship)* [2036]

AAIDD Fellowship *(Advanced Professional, Professional development/Fellowship)* [577]

AALL Technical Services SIS Active Member Grant *(Professional development/Grant)* [588]

AALL Technical Services SIS Experienced Member General Grant *(Professional development/Grant)* [589]

AALL Technical Services SIS Leadership Academy Grant *(Professional development/Grant)* [590]

AALL Technical Services SIS Management Institute Grant *(Professional development/Grant)* [591]

AALL Technical Services SIS New Member General Grant *(Professional development/Grant)* [592]

AAMC Foundation Engagement Program for International Curators Grants *(Advanced Professional, Professional development/Grant)* [2057]

AAMFT Minority Fellowship Program (MFP) *(Doctorate, Graduate/Fellowship)* [602]

AAN Clinical Research Training Fellowship *(Other/Scholarship)* [458]

AAN International Scholarship Award *(Professional development/Scholarship, Award)* [459]

AAN Medical Student Summer Research Scholarship *(Graduate/Scholarship)* [460]

A&B Ohana Scholarship Fund *(Undergraduate, College, Two Year College, Vocational/Occupational/Scholarship)* [5375]

AANS Medical Student Summer Research Fellowships (MSSRF) *(Undergraduate/Fellowship)* [607]

AAOHN Professional Development Scholarships - Academic Study *(Graduate/Scholarship)* [613]

AAOHN Professional Development Scholarships - Continuing Education *(Professional development/Scholarship)* [614]

AAP Educator Scholarship *(Postdoctorate/Scholarship)* [472]

Leroy F. Aarons Scholarship Award *(Graduate, Undergraduate/Scholarship)* [7988]

AAS/AAS Trainee Research Fellowship Awards *(Professional development/Fellowship)* [2028]

AAS-American Society for Eighteenth-Century Studies Fellowships *(Doctorate/Fellowship)* [482]

AAS Korean Studies Scholarship Program *(Graduate/Scholarship)* [2061]

AAS National Endowment for the Humanities Long-Term Fellowships *(Postdoctorate/Fellowship)* [483]

AASLD Advanced/Transplant Hepatology Award *(Professional development/Award)* [644]

AASLD Autoimmune Liver Diseases Pilot Research Award *(Graduate, Doctorate, Postdoctorate, Professional development/Award, Grant)* [645]

AASLD Clinical, Translational and Outcomes Research Awards *(Professional development/Grant)* [646]

AASLD NP/PA Clinical Hepatology Fellowship *(Professional development/Fellowship)* [647]

AASLD Pinnacle Research Award in Liver Disease *(Professional development/Award)* [648]

AAST/ETHICON Research Grants in Local Wound Haemostatics and Hemorrhage Control Scholarships *(Graduate, Postgraduate/Grant)* [651]

AAST/KCI Research Grant *(Doctorate/Grant)* [652]

AATS Perioperative/Team-Based Care Poster Competition *(Professional development/Award)* [660]

AATS Resident Critical Care Scholarships *(Professional development/Scholarship)* [661]

AATS/STS Cardiothoracic Ethics Forum Scholarships *(Professional development/Scholarship)* [662, 10543]

AAUW American Fellowships *(Doctorate, Postdoctorate/Fellowship)* [32]

AAUW Career Development Grants *(Graduate, Advanced Professional, Professional development/Grant)* [33]

AAUW International Fellowships *(Master's, Doctorate, Postdoctorate/Fellowship)* [34]

AAUW Selected Professions Fellowships *(Graduate, Master's, Doctorate/Fellowship)* [35]

ABA Diversity Scholarships *(Graduate/Scholarship)* [707]

ABA Members Scholarships *(Undergraduate, Graduate/Scholarship)* [708]

Abba P. Schwartz Research Fellowship *(Professional development/Fellowship)* [6530]

Anthony Abbene Scholarship Fund *(Undergraduate/Scholarship)* [5663]

AbbVie Immunology Scholarship *(Community College, Undergraduate, Graduate, Vocational/Occupational, Doctorate/Scholarship)* [9938]

ABC-Clio Research Grants *(Graduate/Grant)* [10425]

Abe Fellowship *(Professional development/Fellowship)* [10241]

Abe Fellowships for Journalists *(Professional development/Fellowship)* [10242]

Abe Voron Award *(Graduate/Scholarship)* [2703]

Abel Wolman Fellowship *(Doctorate/Fellowship, Award, Monetary)* [1634]

ABF Law and Social Science Dissertation Fellowship and Mentoring Program *(Graduate/Fellowship)* [690]

ABF Montgomery Summer Research Diversity Fellowships in Law and Social Science *(Undergraduate/Fellowship)* [691]

ABF/NSF Doctoral Fellowships Program in Law & Inequality *(Doctorate/Fellowship, Award)* [692]

ABFSE National Scholarship Program *(Undergraduate/Scholarship)* [697]

Kyutaro and Yasuo Abiko Memorial Scholarship *(Undergraduate/Scholarship)* [6243]

Above and Beyond Scholarship *(Graduate/Scholarship)* [2826]

ABTA Basic Research Fellowships *(Postdoctorate/Fellowship)* [699]

ABTA Discovery Grant *(Professional development/ Grant)* [700]

ABTA Medical Student Summer Fellowship Program *(Undergraduate/Fellowship)* [701]

ABTA Translational Grant Program *(Postdoctorate/ Grant)* [702]

The ABWA Sunrise Chapter Scholarship Fund *(Undergraduate, Vocational/Occupational/Scholarship)* [3709]

Academic Hero Scholarship *(College, University/ Scholarship)* [3886]

Academy of Motion Picture Arts and Sciences Student Academy Awards *(Undergraduate/Award)* [53]

Academy of Neonatal Nursing Conference Scholarships *(Professional development/Scholarship)* [55]

Accenture American Indian Scholarship Fund *(Graduate, Undergraduate/Scholarship)* [993]

Ach Family Scholarship Fund *(Undergraduate/ Scholarship)* [3335]

Achille & Irene Despres, William & Andre Scholarship *(Undergraduate/Scholarship)* [5131]

ACI BASF Construction Chemicals Student Fellowship *(Graduate, Undergraduate/Fellowship)* [782]

ACI Cagley Student Fellowship *(Graduate, Master's, Undergraduate/Fellowship)* [783]

ACI Charles Pankow Student Fellowship *(Graduate, Undergraduate/Fellowship)* [784]

ACI Elmer Baker Student Fellowship *(Undergraduate/Fellowship)* [785]

ACI Foundation Scholarships *(Graduate/Scholarship)* [786]

ACI President's Fellowships *(Doctorate, Master's/ Fellowship)* [787]

ACI Richard N. White Student Fellowship *(Graduate, Undergraduate/Fellowship)* [788]

ACI W.R. Grace Scholarships *(Graduate/Scholarship)* [789]

ACJA/LAE Student Paper Competition *(Undergraduate, Graduate/Scholarship)* [836]

ACJA/LAE Student Scholarship Program *(Undergraduate/Scholarship)* [837]

ACJA/LAE Student Scholarship Program - Graduate Level *(Graduate, Master's, Doctorate/Scholarship)* [838]

ACLS Collaborative Research Fellowships *(Doctorate/Fellowship)* [817]

ACLS Fellowships *(Advanced Professional, Professional development/Fellowship)* [818]

A.C.N.M. Foundation, Inc. Fellowship for Graduate Education *(Doctorate, Postdoctorate/Fellowship)* [768]

ACNM Foundation Midwives of Color-Watson Midwifery Student Scholarship *(Undergraduate/Scholarship)* [769]

ACS/ASA Health Policy and Management Scholarships *(Professional development/Scholarship)* [1616]

ACS Faculty Research Fellowships *(Professional development/Fellowship)* [773]

ACS Resident Research Scholarships *(Advanced Professional/Scholarship)* [774]

ACS Scholarship *(Undergraduate/Scholarship)* [795]

ACSUS Distinguished Dissertation Award *(Doctorate/Award)* [2080]

ACUI Research and Education Grant *(Undergraduate, Graduate, Professional development/Grant)* [2138]

ACVO Best Resident Manuscript Awards *(Undergraduate/Recognition)* [780]

Nancy Ashley Adams/Ashley Adams Koetje Scholarships *(Undergraduate/Scholarship)* [3998]

EFWA Moss Adams Foundation Scholarships *(Undergraduate/Scholarship)* [4303]

Ruth D. Adams Fund *(Undergraduate/Scholarship)* [4581]

RPMDA/Ed Adams Memorial Scholarships *(Other/ Scholarship)* [9653]

Adelman Travel Scholarship *(Undergraduate, College/Scholarship)* [75]

Adelson Scholarship *(Undergraduate/Scholarship)* [9387]

ADMA International Scholarship *(Undergraduate/ Scholarship)* [2372]

Admiral Mike Boorda Loan Program *(Undergraduate/Loan)* [8179]

Adolf Van Pelt Scholarship *(Undergraduate/Scholarship)* [2037]

ADR Postdoctoral Fellowship Awards *(Advanced Professional, Professional development/Fellowship)* [2691]

Harry E. Adrian Memorial Grant *(Undergraduate/ Scholarship)* [1857]

Adrienne Zoe Fedok Art and Music Scholarship *(Undergraduate/Scholarship)* [4773]

Advance Degree and Clinical Research Training Grants in Alpha-1 Antitrypsin Deficiency *(Master's/ Grant)* [1351]

Advance Prevention Lawsuit Legal Scholarships *(Undergraduate, Graduate/Scholarship)* [6737]

Advanced Light Source Collaborative Postdoctoral Fellowship Program *(Postdoctorate/Fellowship)* [6734]

Advanced Mountain Flight Training Scholarship *(Professional development, Vocational/Occupational/Scholarship)* [12009]

The Advocates Law Scholarship *(All/Scholarship)* [94]

AE Flight Training Scholarship *(Other/Scholarship)* [8400]

AE Jet Type Rating Scholarships *(Other/Scholarship)* [8401]

A.E. Robert Friedman Scholarship *(Undergraduate, High School/Scholarship)* [8812]

AE Technical Training Scholarship *(Other/Scholarship)* [8402]

AECT Foundation Mentor Endowment Scholarship *(Doctorate, Graduate/Scholarship)* [2155]

AECT Legacy Graduate Scholarship *(Master's, Graduate, Professional development/Scholarship)* [2156]

AECT McJulien Graduate Student Scholarship Award *(Graduate, Doctorate/Scholarship)* [2157]

AED Student/Early Career Investigator Travel Fellowship Program *(Postgraduate/Fellowship)* [43]

AED Student Research Grants *(Undergraduate, Graduate, Postgraduate/Grant)* [44]

AERA-ETS Fellowship Program in Measurement and Education Research *(Doctorate/Fellowship)* [868]

AERA Fellows Program *(Postdoctorate/Fellowship)* [869]

AERA Minority Dissertation Fellowship in Education Research *(Doctorate/Fellowship)* [870]

AES Graduate Studies Grants *(Graduate/Grant, Award)* [2349]

A.F. Zimmerman Scholarship *(Graduate, Master's/ Scholarship)* [9073]

AFAR Scholarships for Research in the Biology of Aging *(Graduate, Doctorate/Scholarship)* [874]

AFCEA Cyber Security Scholarship *(Undergraduate, Graduate/Scholarship)* [103]

AFCEA STEM Teacher Graduate Scholarships *(Graduate/Scholarship)* [104, 7022]

AFCEA War Veterans Scholarships *(Undergraduate/ Scholarship)* [105]

Afdhal / McHutchison LIFER Award *(Postdoctorate, Professional development/Award)* [649]

Affirm Scholarship Program *(Undergraduate/Scholarship)* [2175]

Affirmative Action Student Scholarship Mini-Grant Travel Awards *(Undergraduate, Master's/Grant)* [41]

AFPE Gateway Research Scholarships *(Doctorate/ Scholarship)* [922]

AFPE Pre-Doctoral Fellowships in Pharmaceutical Sciences *(Doctorate/Fellowship)* [923]

AFPE Pre-Doctoral Fellowships in Pharmaceutical Sciences for Underrepresented Minorities *(Doctorate, Graduate/Fellowship)* [924]

African American Achievement Scholarship Fund *(Undergraduate/Scholarship)* [3727]

AFSA Chapter 155 Division 1 Scholarships - Category 1 *(Undergraduate/Scholarship)* [111]

AFSA Chapter 155 Division 1 Scholarships - Category 2 *(Undergraduate/Scholarship)* [112]

AFSA Chapter 155 Division 1 Scholarships - Category 3 *(Undergraduate/Scholarship)* [113]

AFSA Scholarship Program *(Undergraduate/Scholarship)* [153]

AFSP Distinguished Investigator Grants *(Postgraduate/Grant)* [926]

AFSP Pilot Innovation Grants *(Postgraduate/Grant)* [927]

AFSP Postdoctoral Research Fellowships Innovation Grants *(Postgraduate/Fellowship)* [928]

AFSP Standard Research Innovation Grants *(Postgraduate/Grant)* [929]

AFSP Young Investigator Innovation Grants *(Postgraduate/Grant)* [930]

AfterCollege/AACN Nursing Scholarship *(Undergraduate, Master's, Doctorate/Scholarship)* [118]

AfterCollege Business Student Scholarship *(Undergraduate, Graduate, Doctorate/Scholarship)* [119]

AfterCollege Engineering & Technology Student Scholarship *(Undergraduate, Graduate, Doctorate, Master's/Scholarship)* [120]

AfterCollege Science Student Scholarship *(Undergraduate, Graduate, Doctorate/Scholarship)* [121]

AfterCollege STEM Inclusion Scholarship *(Undergraduate, Graduate/Scholarship)* [122]

AfterCollege Succurro Scholarship *(Undergraduate, Graduate, Doctorate/Scholarship)* [123]

AFWA Masters Scholarships *(Master's/Scholarship)* [58]

AFWA Undergraduate Scholarships *(Undergraduate/ Scholarship)* [59]

A.G. Bell College Scholarship Program *(Undergraduate, Graduate/Scholarship, Award)* [332]

A.G. Bell School Age Financial Aid Program *(High School/Scholarship, Monetary)* [333]

AGA Student Research Fellowship Award *(Undergraduate, Graduate/Fellowship)* [941]

Samuel Agabian Memorial Grant *(Undergraduate/ Scholarship)* [1858]

AGBU Heritage Scholar Grant *(Undergraduate/ Scholarship, Grant)* [1850]

AGC Foundation Outstanding Educator Awards *(Other/Award, Monetary)* [2016]

AGC NYS Scholarship Program *(Undergraduate, Graduate/Scholarship)* [2018]

Agnes E. Vaghi Scholarship *(Undergraduate/Scholarship)* [7960]

The Agnes Sopcak Memorial Scholarship *(Undergraduate/Scholarship)* [12146]

Agriculture Future of America Community Scholarships *(Undergraduate/Scholarship)* [133]

Agriculture Future of America Scholarships *(Undergraduate/Scholarship)* [134]

AGWT Baroid Scholarships *(Undergraduate/Scholarship)* [948]

AGWT Thomas M. Stetson Scholarships *(Undergraduate/Scholarship)* [949]

AH&LEF American Express Scholarship *(Undergraduate/Scholarship)* [969]

AHCJ Reporting Fellowships on Health Care Performance *(Other/Fellowship)* [3552]

Ahepa Buckeye Scholarship Awards *(Undergraduate/Scholarship, Award)* [136]

AHETEMS/ExxonMobil Scholarships *(Undergraduate/Scholarship)* [10067]

AHETEMS General Scholarships *(Undergraduate, Graduate/Scholarship)* [10068]

AHETEMS Professional Scholarships *(Graduate/ Scholarship)* [10069]

AHNS/AAO-HNS Young Investigator combined Award *(Other/Award)* [470, 954]

AHNS Pilot Grant *(Other, Doctorate/Grant)* [955]

AHRQ Mentored Clinical Scientist Research Career Development Award *(Doctorate, Master's/Award)* [11325]

AIA Alaska College Scholarship Program *(Graduate, Undergraduate/Scholarship)* [1007]

AIA and the Global Automotive Aftermarket Symposium Scholarships *(Undergraduate/Scholarship)* [2357]

AIA Graduate Student Travel Awards *(Graduate/ Grant, Award)* [1772]

AIA Northeast Illinois Student Scholarships *(Undergraduate, Graduate/Scholarship)* [1009]

AIAA Foundation Scholarship Program *(Graduate, Undergraduate/Scholarship, Award, Monetary)* [1005]

AICA Orthopedics Scholarship *(Undergraduate, Two Year College, Graduate/Scholarship)* [142]

AIChE Minority Scholarship Awards for College Students *(Undergraduate/Scholarship)* [1020]

AIChE Minority Scholarship Awards for Incoming College Freshmen (*Undergraduate/Scholarship*) [1021]

AICPA John L. Carey Scholarship Awards (*Graduate/Scholarship*) [1016]

Aiea General Hospital Association Scholarship (*Undergraduate, College, Two Year College, University/Scholarship*) [5378]

AIEA Presidential Fellows Program (*Undergraduate/Fellowship*) [2201]

Aiello Harris Legal Scholarships (*Undergraduate, Graduate/Scholarship*) [144]

AIERF Undergraduate Scholarship (*Undergraduate/Scholarship*) [1764]

AIGC Fellowships - Graduate (*Graduate/Fellowship*) [994]

Melkon and Negdar Aijian Memorial Grant (*Undergraduate/Scholarship*) [1859]

Aim High Jerry Clay Scholarship (*Undergraduate/Scholarship*) [5132]

AIPS Post-Doctoral Fellowship (*Postdoctorate/Fellowship*) [1037]

AIPS Pre-Doctoral Fellowship (*Doctorate, Postdoctorate/Fellowship*) [1038]

AIR Dissertation Grants (*Doctorate/Grant*) [2196]

Air Force Association/Grantham Scholarships (*Undergraduate/Scholarship*) [146]

Air Products and Chemicals, Inc. Scholarships (*Undergraduate/Scholarship*) [2191]

Air Traffic Control Association Full-time Employee Student Scholarship (*Other/Scholarship*) [155]

Air Traffic Control Association Non-employee Student Scholarships (*Undergraduate/Scholarship*) [156]

Aircraft Owners and Pilots Association Scholarships (*Undergraduate/Scholarship*) [174]

Airgas - Terry Jarvis Memorial Scholarship (*Undergraduate/Scholarship*) [1650]

AISES Intel Growing The Legacy Scholarship Program (*Graduate, Undergraduate/Scholarship*) [1001]

AISES Oracle Academy Scholarship (*Graduate, Undergraduate/Scholarship*) [1002, 5044]

AISES Summer Internships (*Undergraduate, Graduate/Internship*) [1003]

Justice John F. Aiso Scholarship (*Undergraduate/Scholarship*) [6237]

AIST Globe-Trotters Member Chapter Scholarship (*Undergraduate, Postgraduate/Scholarship*) [2206]

AIST Midwest Member Chapter - Betty McKern Scholarship (*Undergraduate/Scholarship*) [2208]

AIST Midwest Member Chapter - Don Nelson Scholarship (*Undergraduate/Scholarship*) [2209]

AIST Midwest Member Chapter - Engineering Scholarships (*Undergraduate/Scholarship*) [2210]

AIST Midwest Member Chapter - Jack Gill Scholarship (*Undergraduate/Scholarship*) [2211]

AIST Midwest Member Chapter - Mel Nickel Scholarship (*Undergraduate/Scholarship*) [2212]

AIST Midwest Member Chapter – Tom Cipich Non-Engineering Scholarship (*Undergraduate/Scholarship*) [2207]

AIST Midwest Member Chapter - Western States Award (*Undergraduate/Scholarship*) [2213]

AIST Northeastern Ohio Member Chapter - Alfred B. Glossbrenner Scholarship (*Undergraduate/Scholarship*) [2214]

AIST Northern Pacific Member Chapter Scholarships (*Undergraduate/Scholarship*) [2216]

AIST Ohio Valley Member Chapter Scholarships (*Undergraduate/Scholarship*) [2217]

AIST Southeast Member Chapter - Gene Suave Scholarship (*Undergraduate/Scholarship*) [2218]

AIST Southern California Member Chapter Scholarship (*Undergraduate/Scholarship*) [2219]

AJL Scholarship Fund (*Graduate/Scholarship*) [2228]

AKCNL Nightingale Scholarship (*Graduate, Undergraduate/Scholarship*) [2074]

Crown Prince Akihito Scholarship Foundation (*Graduate/Scholarship*) [6231]

Al Conklin and Bill de Decker Business Aviation Management Scholarship (*Undergraduate/Scholarship*) [7732]

Al Shackleford and Dan Martin Professional Scholarship (*Professional development/Scholarship*) [2430]

Alan Compton and Bob Stanley Professional Scholarship (*Professional development/Scholarship*) [2431]

Jonathan Alan Scholarship Fund (*Undergraduate/Scholarship*) [11941]

Alaska Airlines Pilot Scholarship (*All/Scholarship*) [8741]

Albert and Alice Nacinovich Music Scholarship Fund (*Undergraduate/Scholarship*) [4582]

Albert Flegenheimer Memorial Scholarship (*Undergraduate/Scholarship*) [7340]

Bette Lou Albert, New Mexico, Memorial Scholarship Fund (*Undergraduate, Graduate/Scholarship*) [6399]

Albert R. and Alma Shadle Fellowship (*Graduate/Fellowship*) [1499]

Albert W. Dent Graduate Student Scholarship (*Undergraduate/Scholarship*) [763]

Alberta Holstein Association Scholarships (*Undergraduate/Scholarship*) [267]

Alcoa Scholarship (*Undergraduate, Graduate/Scholarship*) [5207]

ALD Graduate Fellowships (*Graduate/Fellowship*) [392]

Owen F. Aldis Scholarship Fund (*Doctorate/Scholarship*) [6109]

Alex Family Scholarship (*Undergraduate/Scholarship*) [7077]

Anthony Alexander, Andrew Delos Reyes & Jeremy Tolentino Memorial Fund (*Undergraduate, University, College, Two Year College/Scholarship*) [5380]

The William Tasse Alexander Scholarship (*Undergraduate/Scholarship*) [4716]

Neil Alexander Scholarships (*Undergraduate/Scholarship*) [7586]

ALF Postdoctoral Research Fellowship Award (*Postdoctorate, Professional development/Fellowship*) [1090]

Floyd S. Alford Jr. Scholarships (*Undergraduate/Scholarship*) [11173]

AlgaeCal Health Scholarship (*Undergraduate, Graduate, Vocational/Occupational/Scholarship*) [340]

Horatio Alger Ak-Sar-Ben Scholarships (*Undergraduate/Scholarship*) [5561]

Horatio Alger Delaware Scholarships (*Undergraduate/Scholarship*) [5562]

Horatio Alger District of Columbia, Maryland and Virginia Scholarships (*Undergraduate/Scholarship*) [5563]

Horatio Alger Florida Scholarships (*Undergraduate/Scholarship*) [5564]

Horatio Alger Georgia Scholarships (*Undergraduate/Scholarship*) [5565]

Horatio Alger Illinois Scholarships (*Undergraduate/Scholarship*) [5567]

Horatio Alger Indiana Scholarships (*Undergraduate/Scholarship*) [5568]

Horatio Alger Kentucky Scholarships (*Undergraduate/Scholarship*) [5569]

Horatio Alger Minnesota Scholarships (*Undergraduate/Scholarship*) [5572]

Horatio Alger Missouri Scholarships (*Undergraduate/Scholarship*) [5573]

Horatio Alger National Scholarships (*Undergraduate/Scholarship*) [5575]

Horatio Alger North Dakota Scholarships (*Undergraduate/Scholarship*) [5576]

Horatio Alger Pennsylvania Scholarships (*Undergraduate/Scholarship*) [5577]

Horatio Alger South Dakota Scholarships (*Undergraduate/Scholarship*) [5578]

Horatio Alger Texas Scholarships (*Undergraduate/Scholarship*) [5579]

Horatio Alger Utah Scholarships (*Undergraduate/Scholarship*) [5580]

Horatio Alger Washington Scholarships (*Undergraduate/Scholarship*) [5581]

Horatio Alger Wyoming Scholarships (*Undergraduate/Scholarship*) [5582]

Alice Hersey Wick Award (*Undergraduate/Scholarship*) [10090]

Alice J. Foit Scholarship Fund (*Undergraduate/Scholarship*) [10750]

All-American Vector Marketing Scholarship Program (*Undergraduate/Scholarship*) [11793]

All Star Purchasing (*Undergraduate/Scholarship*) [344]

The Frances C. Allen Fellowship (*Graduate/Fellowship*) [8368]

Allen Law Firm Personal Injury Scholarship (*College, Undergraduate/Scholarship*) [355]

Dorothea E. Allen Scholarship (*Undergraduate/Scholarship*) [4974]

Alliance of Black Culinarians Scholarships (*Undergraduate/Scholarship*) [9389]

Alliance Defending Freedom - Blackstone Legal Fellowships (*Undergraduate/Fellowship*) [359]

Alliance Francaise of Hartford Harpin/Rohinsky Scholarships (*Undergraduate/Scholarship*) [5313]

Allied Dental Student Scholarship Program (*Undergraduate/Scholarship*) [853]

Allied Van Lines Military Scholarship (*Undergraduate/Scholarship*) [370]

Allison E. Fisher Scholarship (*Undergraduate, Graduate/Scholarship*) [7615]

Dr. and Mrs. David B. Allman Medical Scholarship (*Undergraduate/Scholarship*) [7414]

Allmand Law Scholarship Contest (*Undergraduate/Scholarship*) [372]

Almeric L. Christian Memorial Scholarship (*Graduate/Scholarship*) [11829]

ALOA Scholarship Foundation (*Undergraduate/Scholarship*) [374]

ALPFA Scholarship (*Graduate, Undergraduate, Master's/Scholarship*) [2231]

Alpha Chi Sigma Scholarship Awards (*Graduate, Undergraduate/Scholarship*) [384]

Alpha Delta Gamma Educational Foundation Scholarship (*Undergraduate, Graduate/Scholarship*) [386]

Alpha Mu Tau Undergraduate Scholarships (*Undergraduate/Scholarship, Monetary*) [1398]

Alpha Tau Omega Graduate Scholarship (*Graduate/Scholarship*) [401]

Alpha Tau Omega Undergraduate Scholarships (*Undergraduate/Scholarship*) [402]

The Alsandor Law Firm Scholarship Contest (*Undergraduate/Scholarship*) [407]

Martin K. Alsup and Frank Schroeder Memorial Music Scholarship (*Undergraduate/Scholarship*) [8830]

Robert E. Altenhofen Memorial Scholarships (*Graduate, Undergraduate/Scholarship*) [2004]

Alumni Endowed Scholarship (*Undergraduate/Scholarship*) [2840]

Luis W. Alvarez Postdoctoral Fellowships in Computational Science (*Doctorate/Fellowship*) [6735]

Alwin B. Newton Scholarship (*Undergraduate/Scholarship*) [1468]

Alzheimer's/Gerontology Scholarship (*Graduate/Scholarship*) [10092]

Alzheimer's Disease Research Standard Award (*Doctorate/Award*) [2692]

AMA/Charles H. Grant Scholarship Program (*Undergraduate/Scholarship*) [50]

AMA Foundation Physicians of Tomorrow Scholarships (*Graduate/Scholarship*) [1111]

AMACESP Student Scholarships (*Undergraduate/Scholarship*) [197]

The Amato Sanita Brighter Future Scholarship (*Undergraduate, Graduate, Advanced Professional/Scholarship*) [9876]

The Ambrose-Ramsey Trust (*Undergraduate/Scholarship*) [8831]

Ameel J. Fisher Scholarship (*Undergraduate/Scholarship*) [11174]

Amelia and Emanuel Nessell Family Scholarship Fund (*Undergraduate/Scholarship*) [4197]

America Express Travel Scholarships (*Undergraduate/Scholarship*) [1581]

Americal Legacy Foundation Scholarship (*Undergraduate/Scholarship*) [420]

American Acne and Rosacea Society Mentorship Grant (*Professional development/Grant*) [480]

American Art Therapy Association Anniversary Scholarship (*Graduate/Scholarship*) [501]

American Association of Blacks in Energy Scholarships (Undergraduate/Scholarship) [517]

American Association of Cereal Chemists Graduate Fellowship Program (Graduate/Fellowship) [3266]

American Association of Plastic Surgeons Academic Scholar Program (Professional development/Scholarship) [627]

American Association of State Troopers Scholarship Foundation First Scholarships (Undergraduate/Scholarship) [640]

American Association of State Troopers Scholarship Foundation Second Scholarships (Undergraduate/Scholarship) [641]

American Association of University Women Career Development Grants (Postgraduate/Grant) [665]

American Association of University Women International Fellowships (Graduate, Postgraduate, Master's/Fellowship) [666]

American Association of University Women Selected Professions Fellowships (Other/Fellowship) [668]

American Association of University Women(AAUW) Sue Gottcent Memorial Scholarship Fund (Undergraduate, Graduate/Scholarship) [10670]

American Association for Women in Community Colleges Doctoral Scholarship (Undergraduate/Scholarship) [671]

American Association for Women in Community Colleges LEADERS Institute Scholarship (Other/Scholarship) [672]

American Astronomical Society Small Research Grants (Doctorate/Grant) [681]

American Bus Association Academic Merit Scholarships (Undergraduate, Graduate/Scholarship) [709]

American College of Surgeons Australia/New Zealand Traveling Fellowship (Undergraduate/Fellowship) [775]

American Council of Independent Laboratories Academic Scholarships (Undergraduate/Scholarship, Award) [815]

American Councils for International Education Critical Language Scholarship Program (Undergraduate, Graduate/Scholarship) [830]

American Darts Organization Memorial Youth National Scholarship (Undergraduate/Scholarship) [851]

American Dental Association Dental Assisting Scholarship Program (Undergraduate/Scholarship) [854]

American Dental Association Dental Hygiene Scholarship Program (Undergraduate/Scholarship) [855]

American Dental Association Dental Laboratory Technology Scholarship Program (Undergraduate/Scholarship) [856]

American Dental Association Minority Dental Student Scholarships (Undergraduate/Scholarship) [857]

American Dental Hygienists' Association Institute for Oral Health Research Grants (Master's/Grant) [859]

American Dissertation Fellowships (Doctorate, Postdoctorate/Fellowship) [669]

American Express Professional Development Scholarship (Other/Scholarship) [970]

American Foreign Service Association Scholarship Fund Program (Undergraduate/Scholarship) [912]

American Historical Association Fellowships in Aerospace History (Doctorate/Fellowship) [958]

American Historical Print Collectors Society Fellowship (Doctorate/Fellowship) [484, 965]

American Indian Endowed Scholarship (Graduate, Undergraduate/Scholarship) [11916]

American Institute for Economic Research Student Summer Fellowship (Graduate, Undergraduate/Fellowship) [1028]

American Institute of Physics Congressional Science Fellowship (Doctorate/Fellowship) [1042]

American Institute of Physics State Department Science Fellowship (Doctorate/Fellowship) [1043]

American Judges Association Law Student Essay Competition (Undergraduate/Prize) [1066]

American Legion Eagle Scout of the Year (Undergraduate/Scholarship) [7843]

The American Legion Legacy Scholarship (Undergraduate/Scholarship) [1070]

American Liver Foundation Liver Scholar Award (Doctorate/Award) [1091]

American Lung Association Biomedical Research Grants (RG) (Doctorate/Grant) [1094]

American Marketing Association-Connecticut Chapter, Anna C. Klune Memorial Scholarship (Graduate/Scholarship) [5314]

American Nuclear Society Incoming Freshman Scholarships (Undergraduate/Scholarship) [1160]

American Nuclear Society Undergraduates Scholarships (Undergraduate/Scholarship) [1162]

American Patriot Scholarship (Undergraduate/Scholarship, Monetary) [7388]

American Physical Society Minority Undergraduate Scholarships (Undergraduate/Scholarship) [1220]

American Planning Association ENRE Student Fellowship Program (Graduate/Fellowship) [1242]

American Psychology-Law Society Dissertation Awards (Graduate/Award) [1291]

American Psychology-Law Society Student Grants-In-Aid (Graduate/Grant) [1292]

American Research in the Humanities in China Fellowships (Doctorate/Fellowship) [820]

American-Scandinavian Foundation Fellowships/Grants in the United States (Graduate, Professional development/Fellowship, Grant) [1372]

American Society of Colon and Rectal Surgeons International Fellowships (Other/Fellowship) [1404]

American Society of Colon and Rectal Surgeons International Travel Scholarships (Other/Scholarship) [1405]

American Society of Electroneurodiagnostic Technologists Student Education Grants (Undergraduate/Grant) [1981]

American Society of Heating, Refrigerating, and Air-Conditioning Memorial Scholarships (Undergraduate/Scholarship) [1469]

American Society for Horticultural Science Travel Grants (Graduate, Undergraduate/Grant) [1478]

American Society for Microbiology International Fellowships for Africa (Postdoctorate/Fellowship) [1510]

American Society for Microbiology International Fellowships for Asia (Postdoctorate/Fellowship) [1511]

American Society for Microbiology International Fellowships for Latin America and the Caribbean (Postdoctorate/Fellowship) [1512]

American Society for Microbiology Undergraduate Research Fellowship (Undergraduate/Fellowship, Award, Monetary) [1513]

American Society of Mining and Reclamation Memorial Scholarship Award (Undergraduate, Community College, College, University/Scholarship, Recognition) [1522]

American Society Of Mammalogists Fellowship In Mammalogy (Graduate/Fellowship) [1501]

American Sokol Merit Award (Undergraduate/Scholarship, Recognition) [1593]

American Speech Language Hearing Foundation Clinical Research Grant (Doctorate/Grant) [1595]

American Speech Language Hearing Foundation Endowed Scholarships (Graduate, Master's, Doctorate/Scholarship) [1596]

American Speech Language Hearing Foundation General Scholarships (Graduate, Master's, Doctorate/Scholarship) [1597]

American Speech Language Hearing Foundation International Student Scholarship (Graduate, Master's, Doctorate/Scholarship) [1598]

American Speech Language Hearing Foundation Minority Student Scholarship (Graduate, Master's, Doctorate/Scholarship) [1599]

American Speech Language Hearing Foundation Scholarship for Student with A Disability (Graduate, Master's, Doctorate/Scholarship) [1600]

American Water Ski Educational Foundation Scholarships (Undergraduate/Scholarship) [11778]

American Watercolor Society Scholarship Program for Art Teachers (Undergraduate, Graduate/Scholarship) [1648]

American Welding Society District Scholarships (Undergraduate/Scholarship) [1651]

American Welding Society Graduate Research Fellowships (Graduate/Fellowship) [1652]

American Welding Society National Scholarships (Undergraduate/Scholarship) [1653]

American Welding Society Past Presidents Scholarships (Undergraduate, Graduate, Master's, Doctorate/Scholarship) [1654]

AmericanMuscle's Student Scholarship Program (College, University/Scholarship) [1681]

Americans for Informed Democracy Global Scholar Program (Undergraduate/Scholarship) [1687]

T. Thomas Amirian Memorial Grant (Undergraduate/Scholarship) [1860]

Arsham Amirikian Engineering Scholarship (Undergraduate/Scholarship) [1655]

AMLN Scholarships for Arab American Students (Graduate, Undergraduate/Scholarship) [1127]

AMS Centennial Fellowships (Postdoctorate/Fellowship, Monetary) [1107]

AMS Freshman Undergraduate Scholarship (Undergraduate/Scholarship) [1119]

AMS Graduate Fellowship in the History of Science (Graduate/Fellowship) [1120]

AMS Graduate Fellowships (Graduate/Fellowship) [1121]

AMS/Industry/Government Graduate Fellowships (Graduate/Fellowship) [1122]

AMS Minority Scholarships (Undergraduate/Scholarship) [1123]

AMS Senior Named Scholarships (Undergraduate/Scholarship) [1124]

AMS Teacher Education Scholarships (Undergraduate/Scholarship) [1129]

AMSN Career Mobility Scholarship (Undergraduate, Doctorate/Scholarship) [48]

AMTA Past Presidents' Conference Scholar (Professional development/Scholarship) [1132]

AMTA Student Conference Scholar (Undergraduate, Graduate/Scholarship) [1133]

AMTF Graduate Scholarships (Graduate/Scholarship, Monetary) [1399]

Amtrol Scholarship (High School/Scholarship) [950, 1689]

AMVETS National Scholarships - Entering College Freshmen (Undergraduate/Scholarship) [1696]

AMVETS National Scholarships - For Veterans (Undergraduate/Scholarship) [1697]

AMVETS National Scholarships - JROTC (Undergraduate, College/Medal) [1698]

Anaheim Police Survivors and Scholarship Fund (Undergraduate/Scholarship) [1703]

Anchor Scholarship Foundation Scholarships (Undergraduate, Four Year College, Two Year College/Scholarship) [1705]

Andersen Nontraditional Scholarships for Women's Education and Retraining (ANSWER) (Undergraduate/Scholarship) [4717]

Mary Louise Andersen Scholarship (Undergraduate/Scholarship) [1742]

Anderson Cummings AC Scholarship for Higher Education (Undergraduate/Scholarship) [1707]

William G. Anderson, DO, Minority Scholarships (Undergraduate/Scholarship) [1198]

Michael P. Anderson Scholarships in Space Science (Undergraduate/Scholarship) [8082]

Grace Andow Memorial Scholarship (Undergraduate, Graduate/Scholarship) [6244]

Andrew Gronholdt Arts Scholarship (Undergraduate, Vocational/Occupational, Graduate, Master's/Scholarship) [328]

Andrew W. Mellon Fellowships For Conservation Training Programs (Graduate/Fellowship) [10197]

Richard E. Andrews Memorial Scholarship (Undergraduate/Scholarship, Monetary) [694]

Androscoggin County Chamber of Commerce Adult Scholarships (Professional development/Scholarship) [6825]

Sigma Theta Tau, International Nursing Research Grants (STTI) (Master's, Doctorate/Grant) [1175]

Angus Foundation Graduate Student Degree Scholarship Program (Graduate/Scholarship) [1712]

Angus Foundation Scholarships (Undergraduate, Graduate/Scholarship) [7965]

Angus Foundation Undergraduate Student Scholarships (Undergraduate/Scholarship) [1713]

Angus/Talon Youth Educational Learning Program Endowment Fund (Graduate, Undergraduate/Scholarship) [1714]

Anheuser-Busch NAPABA Law Foundation Presidential Scholarships *(Undergraduate/Scholarship)* [7601]

Marvin Anmuth Scholarship *(Undergraduate, Graduate/Scholarship)* [6269]

Ann Liguori Foundation Sports Media Scholarship *(Graduate, Undergraduate/Scholarship)* [8366]

Ann Marie Bredefeld Scholarship *(Undergraduate/Scholarship)* [8988]

Anne L. "Annie" Alexander and Blaise Robert "B R" Alexander *(Undergraduate/Scholarship)* [4583]

Anne Lowe Scholarship *(Undergraduate/Scholarship, Award)* [3323]

Anne M. Fassett Scholarship Fund *(Undergraduate, Graduate/Scholarship)* [10671]

Anne Sturrock Nursing Scholarship Fund *(Undergraduate, Graduate/Scholarship)* [10672]

Leonore Annenberg Teaching Fellowships *(Graduate/Fellowship)* [12045]

Annette and Ernest Keith Memorial Scholarship *(Undergraduate/Scholarship)* [9520]

Annette Urso Rickel Foundation Dissertation Award for Public Policy *(Graduate/Scholarship)* [1273]

Annie Jump Cannon Award in Astronomy *(Doctorate/Award, Recognition)* [682]

Annie Wagner Memorial Scholarship Fund *(Undergraduate/Scholarship)* [3336]

Annika Teig Fellowship *(Postgraduate/Internship)* [1375]

Annual Educational Scholarships *(Undergraduate/Scholarship)* [7566]

Annual Eichholz Scholarship *(Graduate/Scholarship)* [4324]

Annual Pool Cleaner Scholarship *(Undergraduate, Postgraduate/Scholarship)* [7523]

Annual Research Doctoral and Postgraduate Fellowship Grant Program *(Doctorate, Postdoctorate, Postgraduate, Advanced Professional/Fellowship, Grant)* [2923]

ANS Research Grant Award *(Professional development/Grant)* [1158]

Hettie M. Anthony Fellowship *(Doctorate/Fellowship)* [6495]

Anthony Munoz Scholarship Fund *(Undergraduate/Scholarship)* [7501]

Antonio Cirino Memorial Scholarship *(Graduate/Scholarship)* [9688]

A.O. Putnam Memorial Scholarship *(Undergraduate/Scholarship)* [5826]

AOF/Johnson & Johnson Vision Care - Innovation in Education Grants *(Advanced Professional, Professional development/Grant)* [462]

AOFAS Research Grants Program *(Graduate/Grant)* [1193]

AORN Academic Scholarships *(Undergraduate, Master's, Doctorate/Scholarship, Monetary)* [2257]

AORN Foundation Scholarship Program *(Undergraduate, Doctorate, Master's/Scholarship, Monetary)* [2258]

AOSA Research Grant *(Professional development/Grant)* [1186]

AOSA Research Partnership Grant *(Professional development/Grant)* [1187]

APA Society Convention Research Awards *(Undergraduate, Graduate/Award)* [9375]

APABA Silicon Valley Achievement Scholarship *(Advanced Professional/Scholarship)* [1988]

APALA Scholarship *(Doctorate, Master's/Scholarship)* [1990]

APC High School Scholarship *(Graduate/Scholarship)* [84]

APDA Post-Doctoral Research Fellowship *(Postdoctorate/Fellowship)* [1206]

APDA Research Grants *(Postgraduate, Professional development/Grant)* [1207]

APF High School Psychology Outreach Grants *(Advanced Professional, Professional development/Grant)* [1275]

APF Professional Development Awards for High School Psychology Teachers *(Advanced Professional, Professional development/Grant)* [1276]

APF Visionary Grants *(Graduate/Grant)* [1277]

APhA Foundation Scholarship *(Undergraduate/Scholarship)* [1743]

APHF Academic Scholarship *(Undergraduate/Scholarship)* [1204]

APHL-CDC Infectious Diseases Laboratory Fellowship *(Doctorate/Fellowship)* [2269]

APIASF Scholarships *(Undergraduate/Scholarship)* [1994]

Applied Urban Communication Research Grants *(Professional development/Grant)* [4270]

APS Convention Society Research Awards *(Undergraduate, Graduate/Award)* [9376]

APS Student Research Award (APS) *(Undergraduate, Graduate/Award)* [2266]

APSA Congressional Fellowships *(Other/Fellowship)* [4945]

APSA Congressional Fellowships for Journalists *(Advanced Professional, Professional development/Fellowship)* [1247]

APSA Congressional Fellowships for Political Scientists *(Advanced Professional, Professional development, Postdoctorate/Fellowship)* [1248]

APSA-MCI Communications Congressional Fellowship *(Advanced Professional, Professional development, Postdoctorate/Fellowship)* [1250]

APSA Small Research Grant Program *(Professional development/Grant)* [1252]

APSA U.S. Federal Executives Fellowships *(Advanced Professional, Professional development/Fellowship)* [1253]

APTA Minority Scholarships - Faculty Development Scholarships *(Postdoctorate/Scholarship, Award, Recognition)* [1232]

APTA Minority Scholarships - Physical Therapist Assistant Students *(Undergraduate/Scholarship, Award, Recognition)* [1233]

APTA Minority Scholarships - Physical Therapist Students *(Undergraduate/Scholarship, Award, Recognition)* [1234]

ARA Region Two/Ron Marshall Scholarship *(Undergraduate/Scholarship)* [1333]

Ararat Association Scholarship Grant *(Undergraduate/Scholarship)* [1861]

ARCADIS Scholarship *(Master's, Doctorate/Scholarship, Monetary)* [1635]

ARCE Funded Fellowships *(Doctorate, Postdoctorate/Fellowship)* [1336]

ARCE Research Associates Fellowship *(Doctorate, Postdoctorate, Professional development/Fellowship)* [1337]

Archaeological Institute of America Fellowships for Study in the US *(Postdoctorate/Fellowship)* [1773]

George F. Archambault Scholarship *(Undergraduate/Scholarship)* [1744]

Arctic Physical Therapy Scholarship *(Undergraduate/Scholarship)* [1794]

Ardis Kipp Cohoon Scholarship *(Undergraduate/Scholarship)* [11175]

AREMA Committee 12 - Rail Transit Scholarships *(Undergraduate/Scholarship)* [1316]

AREMA Committee 18 - Light Density and Short Line Railways Scholarships *(Undergraduate/Scholarship)* [1317]

AREMA Committee 24 - Education and Training Scholarships *(Undergraduate/Scholarship)* [1318]

AREMA Committee 27 - Maintenance-of-Way Work Equipment Scholarships *(Undergraduate/Scholarship)* [1319]

AREMA Committee 33 - Electric Energy Utilization Scholarships *(Undergraduate/Scholarship)* [1320]

AREMA Presidential Spouse Scholarship *(Undergraduate/Scholarship)* [1322]

A.R.F.O.R.A. Undergraduate Scholarships for Women *(Undergraduate/Scholarship)* [1366]

Arizona Nursery Association Scholarships *(Undergraduate, Graduate, College, University/Scholarship)* [1812]

Arkansas Single Parent Scholarship *(Undergraduate, Graduate/Scholarship)* [1836]

Connie "Chelo" Armendariz Memorial Scholarships *(Undergraduate/Scholarship)* [9521]

Armenian American Medical Association Scholarship Program *(Undergraduate, Graduate/Scholarship)* [1842]

Armenian American Veterans' Association of Worcester Scholarship *(Undergraduate/Scholarship)* [1862]

Armenian Bar Association Scholarships *(Graduate/Scholarship)* [1846]

Army Health Professions Scholarship Program (HPSP) *(Professional development/Scholarship)* [11288]

Richard E. Arnason Court Scholarship Program *(Undergraduate/Scholarship)* [3816]

Paul Arnold Memorial Scholarships *(Other/Scholarship)* [9288]

Kush Arora Federal Criminal Justice Reform Scholarships *(Undergraduate, Graduate/Scholarship)* [9279]

The ARRL General Fund Scholarship *(Undergraduate/Scholarship)* [1926]

ARS Lazarian Graduate Scholarship *(Graduate, Master's, Doctorate/Scholarship)* [1854]

ARS Undergraduate Scholarship *(Undergraduate/Scholarship)* [1855]

Ardemis, Armenoohy, and Arpi Arsenian Memorial Grant *(Undergraduate/Scholarship)* [1863]

Art and Dannie Weber Scholarship *(Undergraduate/Scholarship)* [12061]

Arthritis Foundation Investigator Awards *(Doctorate/Award)* [1971]

Arthur B.C. Walker II Scholarship *(Undergraduate/Scholarship)* [8083]

Arthur H. Daniels Memorial Scholarship *(Undergraduate/Scholarship)* [9522]

Arthur Lockwood Beneventi Law Scholarship *(Undergraduate/Scholarship, Award, Monetary)* [8093]

Arthur M. & Berdena King Eagle Scout Scholarship *(Undergraduate/Scholarship)* [7844]

Arthur M. Schlesinger Jr. Research Fellowship *(Professional development/Fellowship)* [6531]

Arthur Patch McKinlay Scholarship *(Graduate, Undergraduate/Scholarship)* [753]

Artist-in-Residence Workspace Grant *(Professional development/Grant)* [3210]

Arts Council of Greater Grand Rapids Minority Scholarship *(Undergraduate/Scholarship)* [5134]

ASA Graduate Scholarships *(Graduate/Scholarship)* [1385]

ASA Inc. Journalism Internship Program *(Undergraduate/Internship)* [1864]

ASA/NSF/BLS Fellowships *(Graduate/Fellowship, Recognition, Grant)* [1609, 8065, 11343]

ASA Student Forum Travel Awards *(Undergraduate, Graduate/Award)* [1591]

ASBC Foundation Graduate Scholarships *(Graduate/Scholarship)* [1387]

ASBC Foundation Undergraduate Scholarships *(Undergraduate/Scholarship)* [1388]

ASCLD Scholarship Program *(Graduate, Undergraduate, Master's, Doctorate/Scholarship, Award, Monetary)* [1417]

ASCP Foundation Garza & Becan-McBride Endowed Scholarship *(Undergraduate/Scholarship, Monetary)* [1402]

ASECS Graduate Student Research Paper Award *(Graduate/Prize)* [1426]

ASECS Innovative Course Design Competition *(Undergraduate/Award)* [1427]

ASECS Women's Caucus Editing and Translation Fellowship *(Doctorate/Fellowship)* [1428]

ASEE/NSF Small Business Postdoctoral Research Diversity Fellowship (SBPRDF) *(Postdoctorate/Fellowship)* [1442, 8066]

ASET Scholarships *(Other/Scholarship)* [1982]

ASEV Traditional Scholarship *(Graduate, Undergraduate/Scholarship)* [1447]

ASGP Graduate Research Fellowships *(Graduate/Fellowship)* [244]

ASHARE Undergraduate Engineering Scholarships *(Undergraduate/Scholarship)* [1470]

ASHFoundation New Century Scholars Doctoral Scholarship *(Doctorate/Scholarship)* [1601]

ASHFoundation New Century Scholars Research Grant *(Doctorate/Grant)* [1602]

ASHFoundation New Investigators Research Grant *(Doctorate/Grant)* [1603]

ASHFoundation NSSLHA Scholarship *(Graduate/Scholarship)* [1604]

ASHFoundation Speech Science Research Grant *(Doctorate/Grant)* [1605]

ASHFoundation Student Research Grant in Audiology *(Doctorate/Grant)* [1606]

ASHFoundation Student Research Grant in Early Childhood Language Development *(Doctorate, Master's/Grant)* [1607]

Ashley E. Ketcher Memorial Scholarship *(Undergraduate/Scholarship)* [3667]

ASHP Student Research Awards *(Doctorate/Award)* [1465]

ASHS Industry Division Student Travel Grant *(Graduate, Undergraduate/Grant)* [1479]

ASHS Scholars Award *(Undergraduate/Scholarship)* [1480]

Asian and Pacific Islander Queer Sisters Scholarship (APIQS) *(Undergraduate/Scholarship)* [9289]

ASID Foundation Legacy Scholarships for Graduate Students *(Graduate/Scholarship)* [1486]

ASIS Foundation Chapter Matching Scholarship *(Undergraduate/Scholarship)* [1996]

ASIST Scholarship (ASIST) *(Professional development/Scholarship)* [4463]

ASLA Council of Fellows *(Undergraduate/Scholarship)* [1491]

ASLA Council of Fellows Scholarships *(Undergraduate/Scholarship)* [6646]

ASLMS Educational Grants *(Undergraduate, Graduate, Professional development/Grant)* [1494]

ASLMS Research Grant *(Postdoctorate/Grant, Monetary)* [1495]

ASM/CDC Program in Infectious Disease and Public Health Microbiology *(Postdoctorate/Fellowship)* [1514]

ASM Congressional Science Fellowship *(Postdoctorate/Fellowship)* [1515]

ASM Robert D. Watkins Graduate Research Fellowship *(Postdoctorate/Fellowship, Monetary)* [1517]

ASM Science Teaching Fellowships - Student *(Undergraduate/Fellowship)* [1518]

ASMC National Scholarship Program *(Graduate/Scholarship)* [1520]

ASMS Research Awards *(Other/Award)* [1508]

ASNT Fellowship Award *(Graduate/Fellowship, Award)* [1531]

Myron "Ted" Asplin Foundation Scholarships *(Professional development/Scholarship)* [5739]

ASPPH/CDC Public Health Fellowship Program *(Doctorate, Graduate/Fellowship)* [2279]

ASPPH/EPA Environmental Health Fellowship Program *(Doctorate, Postdoctorate/Fellowship)* [2280]

ASPPH/NHTSA Public Health Fellowship Program *(Doctorate, Master's/Fellowship)* [2281]

ASPPH Public Health Fellowship Program *(Doctorate, Postdoctorate/Fellowship)* [2282]

ASPPH Public Health Preparedness Fellowship Program *(Postdoctorate/Fellowship)* [2283]

ASPT General Graduate Student Research Grant Fund *(Master's, Doctorate/Grant)* [1538]

ASRT Research Grants *(Professional development/Grant)* [1550]

Len Assante Scholarship Program *(Undergraduate/Scholarship)* [7911]

Darrell and Palchie Asselin Scholarship Fund *(Undergraduate/Scholarship)* [4199]

Associated General Contractors of Connecticut Scholarships (AGC/CT Scholarship) *(Undergraduate/Scholarship)* [3759]

Associates in Behavioral Health Scholarships *(Graduate/Scholarship)* [9290]

Association for the Advancement of Baltic Studies Dissertation Grants for Graduate Students *(Doctorate/Grant)* [2030]

Association for Compensatory Educators of Texas Paraprofessionals Scholarships *(Other/Scholarship)* [2141]

Association for Compensatory Educators of Texas Students *(Graduate/Scholarship)* [2142]

Association of Donor Recruitment Professionals Hughes Scholarships *(Other/Scholarship)* [2150]

Association of Donor Recruitment Professionals Presidential Scholarships *(Other/Scholarship)* [2151]

Association of Energy Engineers Foundation Scholarship Program *(Graduate, Undergraduate/Scholarship)* [2159]

Association of Flight Attendants Scholarship Fund *(Undergraduate/Scholarship)* [2179]

Association of Government Accountants Graduate Scholarships for Community Service *(Graduate/Scholarship)* [2187]

Association of Government Accountants Graduate Scholarships for Full-time study *(Graduate/Scholarship)* [2188]

Association of Government Accountants Graduate Scholarships for Part-time study *(Graduate/Scholarship)* [2189]

Association for Psychological Science Student Grants (APS) *(Graduate, Undergraduate/Grant)* [2267]

Association of State Dam Safety Officials memorial Undergraduate Scholarship *(Undergraduate/Scholarship)* [2296]

Association of the United States Navy Scholarships *(Undergraduate/Scholarship)* [2303]

Association for Women in Sports Media Internship Program *(Undergraduate/Scholarship, Internship)* [2321]

ASSP Diversity Committee Scholarship *(Doctorate/Scholarship)* [1559]

ASSP Foundation Academic Scholarship Program *(Undergraduate, Graduate, Doctorate, Vocational/Occupational/Scholarship)* [1560]

ASSP Foundation Professional Education Grant Program *(Professional development/Grant)* [1561]

ASTA Alaska Airlines Scholarships *(Undergraduate/Scholarship)* [1582]

ASTA Holland America Line Graduate Research Scholarships *(Graduate/Scholarship)* [1583]

ASTA Rigby, Healy, Simmons Scholarships *(Graduate, Undergraduate/Scholarship)* [1584]

ASTRO Junior Faculty Career Research Training Award *(Advanced Professional, Professional development/Award)* [1545]

ASTRO Minority Summer Fellowship Award *(Postgraduate, Professional development/Fellowship, Award)* [1546]

ASTRO/ROI Comparative Effectiveness Research Awards *(Professional development/Award)* [1548]

Astronaut Scholarship Foundation Scholarship *(Undergraduate/Scholarship)* [2332]

Marguerite Chapootian Atamian Memorial Grant *(Undergraduate/Scholarship)* [1865]

AT&T Business Internship Awards *(Undergraduate, Graduate/Internship)* [11176]

Martha and Robert Atherton Ministerial Scholarship *(Master's/Scholarship)* [11245]

Atlanta Alumnae Chapter Achievement Scholarship *(Undergraduate/Scholarship)* [3999]

Atlantic Salmon Federation Olin Fellowships *(Graduate/Fellowship)* [2347]

Atlas Shrugged Essay Contest *(Graduate, Undergraduate, High School/Prize)* [2395]

Attorney-CPA Foundation Scholarships *(Postgraduate/Scholarship)* [430]

AUA Foundation Urology Research Bridge Awards *(Postgraduate/Award)* [11771]

Aubespin Scholarships *(Undergraduate/Scholarship)* [801]

Aubrey L. Williams Research Travel Fellowship *(Doctorate/Fellowship)* [1429]

Audrey L. Wright Scholarship *(Undergraduate/Scholarship)* [5135]

Audrey Lumsden-Kouvel Fellowship *(Postdoctorate/Fellowship)* [8369]

A. B. and Hazel Augenstein Scholarship *(Undergraduate/Scholarship)* [7078]

Austin Alumnae Association Beta Xi Scholarship in Memory of Katherine Peeres Woolridge *(Undergraduate/Scholarship)* [6400]

Autism Scholarship *(High School, Two Year College, Four Year College, Graduate, Vocational/Occupational, Professional development/Scholarship)* [2617]

Autism Scholarship *(Two Year College, Four Year College, Vocational/Occupational/Scholarship)* [9712]

Auto Accident Law Firm Survivor Scholarships *(Graduate/Scholarship)* [1758]

Auto-Pets "Out-of-the-Box Thinking" Scholarships *(All/Scholarship)* [2355]

Automotive Technician Scholarship Program *(Undergraduate/Scholarship)* [7160]

Automotive Women's Alliance Foundation Scholarships *(Undergraduate/Scholarship)* [2366]

Auxiliary Undergraduate Scholarships *(Undergraduate/Scholarship)* [1998]

Avis Budget Group Scholarships *(Graduate/Scholarship)* [1585]

AVMA Fellowship Program *(Professional development/Fellowship)* [1628]

AVS Applied Surface Science Division *(Graduate/Award)* [2374]

AVS Biomaterial Interfaces Division - Early Career Researchers Awards (BID-ECR) *(Graduate/Monetary)* [2375]

AVS Electronic Materials and Photonic Division Postdoctoral Award *(Postdoctorate/Award)* [2376]

AVS Manufacturing Science and Technology Group *(Graduate/Award)* [2377]

AVS MEMS and NEMS Technical Group Best Paper Award *(Undergraduate, Graduate/Monetary)* [2378]

AVS Nanometer-Scale Science and Technology Division Graduate Award *(Graduate/Monetary)* [2379]

AVS Spectroscopic Ellipsometry Focus Topic Graduate Student Awards *(Graduate/Award)* [2380]

AVS Thin Film Division James Harper Awards *(Graduate/Monetary)* [2381]

AWG Minority Scholarship *(Undergraduate/Scholarship)* [2313]

AWM Mathematics Travel Grants *(Doctorate/Grant)* [2318]

AWMA Louisiana Section Scholarship *(Undergraduate, Graduate/Scholarship)* [167]

AWWA American Water Scholarship *(Master's, Doctorate/Scholarship, Monetary)* [1636]

AXA Achievement Scholarship *(Undergraduate/Scholarship)* [2393]

Susan Ayers Memorial Scholarships *(Undergraduate/Scholarship)* [9391]

Ayn Rand Institute Anthem Essay Contest *(High School, Undergraduate/Prize)* [2396]

Ayn Rand Institute Fountainhead Essay Contest *(High School, Undergraduate/Prize)* [2397]

John M. Azarian Memorial Armenian Youth Scholarship Fund *(Undergraduate/Scholarship)* [2399]

AZVT Laurie Page-Peck Scholarship *(Graduate/Scholarship)* [2325]

B-2 LAFF 20-30's Financial Aid Scholarship *(Postgraduate/Scholarship)* [6937]

B-3 LAFF 20-30's Financial Aid Scholarship *(Professional development/Scholarship)* [6938]

B-4 Albert S. Vieira Memorial Scholarship *(Professional development/Scholarship)* [6939]

Tom Babcox Memorial Scholarships *(Professional development/Scholarship)* [2351]

Carroll Preston Baber Research Grant *(Professional development/Grant)* [1081]

Bach Organ Scholarship *(Undergraduate/Scholarship)* [9689]

Bachelor of Science in Nursing Academic Scholarships *(Graduate/Scholarship)* [7548]

Bachelor's in Nursing Degree Scholarship *(Undergraduate/Scholarship)* [8626]

BACUS Scholarship *(Graduate, Undergraduate/Scholarship)* [10724]

The Bailey Family Foundation College Scholarship Program *(Undergraduate/Scholarship)* [2403]

The Bailey Family Foundation High School Scholarships Program *(Undergraduate/Scholarship)* [2404]

Bailey/Hollister Scholarship *(Graduate, Professional development/Scholarship)* [8956]

Esther Tuttle Bailey Memorial Scholarship *(Undergraduate/Scholarship)* [6401]

Lincoln C. Bailey Memorial Scholarship Fund *(Undergraduate/Scholarship)* [6079]

Barbara Bailey Scholarship *(Undergraduate/Scholarship)* [9291]

Marian Wood Baird Scholarship *(Undergraduate/Scholarship)* [11401]

Baker Donelson Diversity Scholarship *(Undergraduate/Scholarship)* [2406]

Baker McKenzie Diversity Fellowship *(Postgraduate, Professional development/Fellowship)* [2411]

Francis Warren Baker Memorial Scholarships *(Undergraduate/Scholarship)* [10094]

Baker Scholarship (Doctorate, Professional development/Scholarship) [4888]

Airgas - Jerry Baker Scholarship (Undergraduate/Scholarship) [1658]

ACI Baker Student Fellowships (Undergraduate/Fellowship) [790]

BakerHostetler Diversity Fellowship Program (Undergraduate/Fellowship) [2408]

Bernt Balchen, Jr. and Olav Jorgen Hegge Hardingfele Scholarships (Other/Scholarship) [5292]

Norman S. Baldwin Fishery Science Scholarship (Doctorate, Master's/Scholarship) [5923]

Donald A. Baldwin Sr. Business Aviation Management Scholarship (Professional development/Scholarship) [7733]

Vic and Margaret Ball Student Intern Scholarships (Undergraduate/Internship) [895]

Ballantyne Resident Research Grant (Other, Graduate/Grant) [956]

Ballard Family Foundation Scholarships (Undergraduate/Scholarship) [9800]

Bambi Bailey Scholarship Fund (Undergraduate/Scholarship) [3589]

Bank of Hawaii Foundation Scholarship Fund (Undergraduate, University, College, Two Year College/Scholarship) [5382]

Dr. Johnella Banks Memorial Scholarships (Undergraduate/Scholarship) [2610]

Mark T. Banner Scholarships for Law Students (Postdoctorate/Scholarship) [6873]

Bar President's Scholarship (Undergraduate/Scholarship) [11931]

Barakat Trust and Barakat Foundation Scholarships (Graduate, Postdoctorate/Scholarship) [1767]

Barbara A. Cooley Master's Scholarship (Master's/Scholarship, Award, Monetary) [10348]

Barbara Bonnema Memorial Scholarship (Undergraduate/Scholarship) [9525]

Barbara Jordan Memorial Scholarships (Undergraduate, Graduate/Scholarship) [2300]

Joe Barbarow Memorial Scholarship (Undergraduate/Scholarship) [8832]

UAA Janice K. Barden Aviation Scholarship (Undergraduate/Scholarship) [7734]

Gina L. Barnhart Memorial Scholarship Fund (Undergraduate/Scholarship) [4585]

Baron and Budd Attorneys Mesothelioma Cancer Victims Memorial Scholarships (College, University/Scholarship) [2437]

Barrett Family Scholarship Fund (Undergraduate/Scholarship) [3338]

Barta-Lehman Musical Scholarship (Undergraduate/Scholarship) [9801]

The Jean Bartel Military Scholarship (Undergraduate/Scholarship) [7415]

The Bascom Hill Society Scholarship (Undergraduate/Scholarship) [11734]

Forrest Bassford Student Award (Undergraduate/Award) [6881]

W. H. (Bert) Bates Oxford Cup Scholarship (Undergraduate, Graduate/Scholarship) [2503]

Jim Batten Community Newspaper Internship (Undergraduate/Internship) [11177]

Marian Sims Baughn Scholarship (Undergraduate/Scholarship) [6402]

The Ernest L. Baulch, W2TX, and Marcia E. Baulch, WA2AKJ, Scholarship (Undergraduate/Scholarship) [1927]

Timothy Baylink Good Fellowship Awards (Undergraduate/Fellowship) [9526]

John Bayliss Broadcast Foundation Internship Programs (Undergraduate/Internship) [2451]

John Bayliss Broadcast Foundation Radio Scholarships (Undergraduate/Scholarship) [2452]

BCCC Workforce Creation Scholarship (Undergraduate/Scholarship) [2415]

BDC Visiting Fellowship (Advanced Professional, Professional development/Fellowship) [2715]

William B. Bean Student Research Award (Undergraduate/Grant) [1196]

Catherine H. Beattie Fellowships (Graduate/Fellowship) [3238, 4858]

Beaver Medical Clinic Foundation - H.E.A.R.T. Academy Award (Undergraduate/Scholarship) [9528]

Beaver Medical Clinic Foundation - Premedical Award (Undergraduate/Scholarship) [9529]

Becas Univision Scholarship Program (Undergraduate, Graduate/Scholarship) [5528]

Louise Seaman Bechtel Fellowship (Professional development/Fellowship) [2239]

Stephen D. Bechtel, Jr. Oxford Cup Scholarship (Undergraduate, Graduate/Scholarship) [2504]

Dennis J. Beck Memorial Scholarship (Undergraduate/Scholarship) [6193]

Beck – O.J. Beck, Jr. Memorial Scholarship (Undergraduate/Scholarship) [3464]

Beck-Pfann Memorial Scholarship (Undergraduate/Scholarship) [8991]

Garvin L. Beck Scholarships (Undergraduate/Scholarship) [9530]

BEF General Academic Scholarships (Undergraduate, Graduate/Scholarship) [4438]

BEF Sacks For CF Scholarship (Graduate, Undergraduate/Scholarship) [4439]

BEF Scholarship of the Arts (Graduate, Undergraduate/Scholarship) [4440]

Belfer-Aptman Dissertation Research Awards (Doctorate/Award) [7247]

John Bell and Lawrence Thornton Scholarship Fund (Undergraduate/Scholarship) [5315]

Bellevue PFLAG Scholarships (Graduate, High School/Scholarship) [9292]

Samuel Flagg Bemis Dissertation Research Grants (Graduate/Grant) [10354]

Ben C. Francis Risk Management Education Fund (Undergraduate/Scholarship) [9385]

Benchwarmers Club of Redlands Scholarship- Jess Mercado Memorial (Undergraduate/Scholarship) [9531]

Reckitt Benckiser Student Scholarships (Graduate/Scholarship) [7677]

The Richard W. Bendicksen, N7ZL, Memorial Scholarship (Undergraduate/Scholarship) [1928]

Bill Bendiner and Doug Morgenson Scholarship (Undergraduate/Scholarship) [9293]

H. Y. Benedict Fellowships (Graduate/Fellowship) [376]

George Benes, MD & Michael Mallee, EdD Point Scholarships (Undergraduate, Graduate, Doctorate/Scholarship) [9218]

Benign Essential Blepharospasm Research Foundation Research Grants (Doctorate/Grant) [2473]

Benjamin G. Shatz Scholarship (Undergraduate/Scholarship) [8992]

Benjamin Riggs Scholarship (Undergraduate/Scholarship) [4916]

HDR/Henry "Bud" Benjes Scholarships (Master's/Scholarship, Monetary) [1637]

Bertram W. Bennett Memorial Scholarship (Undergraduate, Graduate/Scholarship) [2505]

The William Bennett, W7PHO, Memorial Scholarship (Undergraduate/Scholarship) [1929]

Benson & Bingham First Annual Scholarship (Graduate/Scholarship) [2475]

Benson Law Firm Scholarship Contest (Undergraduate/Scholarship) [2477]

Benton-Meier Scholarships (Graduate/Scholarship) [1278]

Rosalie Bentzinger Scholarships (Doctorate/Scholarship) [4889]

Bergman Scholarship (Undergraduate/Scholarship) [8460]

Bergmann Family Scholarship (Undergraduate/Scholarship) [7080]

The E. Alexander Bergstrom Memorial Research Award (Undergraduate, Master's/Award) [2177]

The Joseph Berkman, and Michael and Sarah Chipkin Holocaust/Genocide Studies Award (Graduate/Scholarship) [10842]

Louise Berman Fellows Award (Graduate, Master's, Doctorate/Fellowship) [6378]

Bernard B. and Mary L. Brusin Scholarship Fund (Undergraduate/Scholarship) [4201]

Bernard Kilgore Memorial Scholarship (Undergraduate/Scholarship) [8282]

Richard L. Bernardi Memorial Scholarship (Undergraduate/Scholarship) [3668]

Bernice Barabash Sports Scholarship (Graduate/Scholarship) [6194]

Jean Clark Berry Scholarship (Undergraduate, Graduate/Scholarship) [6403]

Booksrun Scholarship Financial Aid (Undergraduate, Graduate/Scholarship) [2653]

Beta Lambda Project 2000 Scholarship (Undergraduate/Scholarship) [6404]

Beta Mu Project 2000 Scholarship (Undergraduate/Scholarship) [6405]

Beta Pi Project 2000 Scholarship in Memory of Kristy LeMond (Undergraduate/Scholarship) [6406]

Beta Pi Sigma Sorority Local Chapter Scholarship (BPSSS) (Undergraduate/Scholarship) [2501]

Beta Province Project 2000 Scholarship (Undergraduate/Scholarship) [6407]

Beta Sigma Scholarship (Undergraduate/Scholarship) [10096]

Beta Tau Scholarship Fund (Undergraduate/Scholarship) [6408]

Beta Theta Memorial Scholarship (Graduate, Undergraduate/Scholarship) [6409]

Beta Xi Project 2000 Scholarship (Undergraduate/Scholarship) [6410]

Beta Zeta Project 2000 Scholarship (Undergraduate/Scholarship) [6411]

Beth Carew Memorial Scholarship Program (Undergraduate/Scholarship) [7920]

Betty Rose Scholarship (Undergraduate/Scholarship) [1407]

William and Dorothy Bevan Scholarship (Graduate, Master's, Doctorate/Scholarship) [1279]

Albert J. Beveridge Grant for Research in the History of the Western Hemisphere (Doctorate/Grant) [959]

Beyond the Cure Ambassador Scholarship Program (Community College, College, Undergraduate, Graduate, Vocational/Occupational/Scholarship) [7767]

Bick Bickson Scholarship Fund (Undergraduate, Graduate/Award) [5383]

Bill McCarthy Boy Scout Scholarship Fund (Undergraduate/Scholarship) [10752]

Jan Bingle Scholarships (Master's, Doctorate/Scholarship) [3438]

Birgit Baldwin Fellowship (Graduate/Fellowship) [7229]

Birmingham District Alabama Dietetic Association Scholarships (Graduate, Undergraduate/Scholarship) [217]

Bisexual Foundation Scholarships (Graduate/Scholarship, Award) [1736]

Dr. Richard E. Bjork Memorial Graduate Study Award (Graduate/Scholarship) [10843]

Law Offices of David A. Black Annual Hearing Impaired Scholarships (All/Scholarship) [6701]

Black Men Building Resources Scholarship (Undergraduate/Scholarship) [5137]

NICSA/William T. Blackwell Scholarship Fund (Undergraduate/Scholarship) [7952]

Mitzi & William Blahd, MD, Pilot Research Grant (Professional development/Grant) [10437]

Beatrice K. Blair Scholarships (Undergraduate/Scholarship) [2620]

Thomas M. Blake Memorial Scholarships (Undergraduate/Scholarship) [3753]

Blake-Nuttall Fund Grants (Other/Grant) [8565]

Blanche E. Woolls Scholarship (Graduate/Scholarship) [2496]

Blanche Raper Zimmerman Scholarship (Other/Scholarship) [12062]

Kyle R. Blanco Memorial Scholarship (Undergraduate, Graduate/Scholarship) [2507]

Joan Blend Scholarship Fund (Undergraduate, Graduate/Scholarship) [10753]

Everitt P. Blizard Memorial Scholarship (Graduate/Scholarship) [1163]

Ellin Bloch and Pierre Ritchie Diversity Dissertation Grant (Graduate/Grant) [1269]

Jeanne Humphrey Block Dissertation Award (Postdoctorate/Award) [5363]

Bluepay Stem Scholarship (Graduate, Undergraduate/Scholarship) [2630]

BMO Capital Markets Lime Connect Equity through Education Scholarships (Undergraduate, Graduate/Scholarship) [6860]

California ChangeLawyers 1L scholarship *(Graduate/Scholarship)* [2790]

California Waterfowl Association College Scholarships *(Undergraduate/Scholarship)* [2842]

Calihan Academic Grants *(Graduate, Professional development/Fellowship, Grant)* [65]

Calihan Travel Grants *(Other, Graduate/Grant)* [66]

John L. Calvert Memorial Scholarship *(Undergraduate, Graduate/Scholarship)* [2514]

W.L. Calvert Memorial Scholarships *(Graduate/Scholarship)* [5596]

Camille F. Gravel, Jr. Scholarship *(Professional development/Scholarship)* [6898]

Camp Network Counselor Appreciation Scholarships *(Undergraduate/Scholarship)* [2866]

Thomas R. Camp Scholarship *(Graduate/Scholarship, Monetary)* [1639]

Lucille Campbell Scholarship Fund *(Undergraduate, High School/Scholarship)* [11943]

CAMS Summer Research Fellowship *(Undergraduate/Fellowship)* [3307]

Candon, Todd, & Seabolt Scholarship Fund *(Undergraduate, Four Year College, University/Scholarship)* [5385]

Canham Graduate Studies Scholarship *(Graduate/Scholarship)* [11927]

The Lester J. Cappon Fellowship in Documentary Editing *(Postdoctorate/Fellowship)* [8370]

CAPT Winifred Quick Collins, USN (Ret.) Scholarship *(Undergraduate/Scholarship)* [8172]

Captain Jodi Callahan Memorial Scholarship *(Graduate, Master's/Scholarship)* [147]

The CarBrain.com Scholarship *(Two Year College, Undergraduate, Graduate, High School/Scholarship)* [3155]

Daniel Cardillo Charitable Fund *(Professional development/Scholarship)* [6975]

Career Awards for Medical Scientists (CAMS) *(Postdoctorate/Grant)* [2751]

Career Awards at the Scientific Interface (CASI) *(Undergraduate, Postdoctorate, Graduate/Grant)* [2753]

Career Development Scholarships *(Postgraduate/Scholarship)* [4666]

Career Enhancement Grant *(Professional development/Grant)* [4432]

Career Mobility Scholarships *(Graduate, Undergraduate, Vocational/Occupational/Scholarship)* [4791]

CareerFitter Online Scholarship *(Undergraduate, Graduate/Scholarship)* [3165]

Vyaire Fellowship for Neonatal and Pediatric Therapists *(Professional development/Fellowship)* [1352]

John Carew Memorial Scholarship *(Graduate/Scholarship)* [899]

Carl A. Scott Book Scholarship *(Undergraduate/Scholarship)* [3873]

Carl E. Brooks Scholarship Fund *(Undergraduate/Scholarship)* [10673]

Carl H. Lindner Family Fund *(Undergraduate/Scholarship)* [3341]

Carl & Lucille Jarrett Scholarship Fund *(Undergraduate/Scholarship)* [4587]

Carli Edwards Memorial Scholarship *(Undergraduate/Scholarship)* [10051]

Gladys Ross Carlson Adelphe Scholarship Fund *(Undergraduate, Graduate/Scholarship)* [6413]

Carnegie Observatories Graduate Research Fellowships *(Graduate, Doctorate/Fellowship)* [3173]

Caroline M. Hewins Scholarship *(Graduate, Undergraduate/Scholarship)* [5351]

Carolyn Gallmeyer Scholarship *(Undergraduate/Scholarship)* [5140]

Carolyn Wones Recruitment Grant *(Undergraduate/Grant)* [3671]

Gene Carte Student Paper Competition Awards *(Undergraduate, Graduate/Prize)* [1419]

Carter G. Woodson Institute Post-doctoral Residential Research & Teaching Fellowship *(Postdoctorate/Fellowship)* [12183]

Carter G. Woodson Institute Pre-doctoral Fellowship *(Doctorate/Fellowship)* [12184]

Letitia B. Carter Scholarships *(Undergraduate, Advanced Professional/Scholarship)* [9649]

CASBS Fellowships *(Doctorate, Other/Fellowship)* [3208]

George H. and Anna Casper Fund *(Undergraduate, Graduate/Scholarship, Loan)* [10755]

Thomas D. and Karen H. Cassady Scholarship *(Undergraduate, Graduate/Scholarship)* [2515]

Castellini Foundation Scholarship *(Undergraduate/Scholarship)* [3342]

Kerri Castellini Women's Leadership Scholarship *(Undergraduate, Graduate, Community College/Scholarship)* [9280]

Castle & Cooke George W.Y. Yim Scholarship Fund *(Undergraduate, Graduate, Two Year College, Four Year College, University/Scholarship)* [5386]

Castle & Cooke Mililani Technology Park Scholarship Fund *(Undergraduate, University, Four Year College/Scholarship)* [5387]

Catholic Relief Services Summer Internship *(Undergraduate, Graduate/Internship)* [3188]

Catrala - Hawaii Scholarship Fund *(Undergraduate, University, Two Year College, Four Year College/Scholarship)* [5388]

Ben and Vicky Cayetano Scholarship Fund *(Undergraduate, College, University, Two Year College/Scholarship)* [5389]

Llewellyn L. Cayvan String Instrument Scholarship *(Undergraduate, Graduate/Scholarship)* [5141]

CBC Spouses Education Scholarship *(Graduate, Undergraduate/Scholarship)* [3738]

CBC Spouses Performing Arts Scholarship *(Undergraduate/Scholarship)* [3739]

CBC Spouses Visual Arts Scholarship *(Undergraduate/Scholarship)* [3740]

CCFA Career Development Awards *(Doctorate/Grant, Award)* [3911]

CCFA Research Fellowship Awards *(Doctorate, Graduate/Fellowship, Award)* [3912]

CCFA Student Research Fellowship Awards *(Graduate, Undergraduate/Grant, Fellowship, Award)* [3913]

CCWH / Berks Graduate Student Fellowship *(Graduate/Fellowship)* [3828]

C.D. Howard Scholarship *(Undergraduate/Scholarship, Monetary, Award)* [5970]

CDC Steven M. Teutsch Prevention Effectiveness (PE) *(Doctorate/Fellowship)* [11328]

Cecelia Connelly Graduate Scholarship in Underwater Archaeology *(Graduate, Undergraduate/Scholarship)* [12135]

Betty J. Cecere Memorial Scholarship Endowment Fund *(Graduate/Scholarship)* [11944]

Cedarcrest Farms Scholarships *(Graduate, Undergraduate/Scholarship)* [1058]

CEJIL Communications Internships *(Professional development, Graduate/Internship)* [3230]

CEJIL Legal Internships *(Graduate, Professional development/Internship)* [3231]

Cengage Travel Award for Teachers of Reading at a Community College *(Professional development/Monetary)* [3512]

Cenie Jomo Williams Tuition Scholarship *(Graduate, Undergraduate/Scholarship)* [7617]

DAR Centennial Scholarship *(Undergraduate/Scholarship, Award, Monetary)* [8094]

The Central Arizona DX Association Scholarship *(Undergraduate/Scholarship)* [1932]

Central Pacific Bank Scholarship Fund *(Undergraduate/Scholarship)* [5390]

CentraState Associated Auxiliaries Scholarship *(Undergraduate/Scholarship)* [3248]

CentraState Healthcare Foundation Health Professions Scholarships *(Undergraduate/Scholarship)* [3250]

Certified in Care Coordination and Transition Management (CCCTM) Certification Grant *(Undergraduate/Scholarship)* [427]

Certified Neuroscience Registered Nurse Recertification Grant Program *(Other/Grant)* [610]

The Cerutti Group Scholarship *(Undergraduate/Scholarship)* [5208]

Arthur and Gladys Cervenka Scholarship *(Undergraduate/Scholarship)* [10385]

CES Conference Travel Grants *(Graduate, Professional development/Grant)* [3856]

CfA Postdoctoral Fellowship *(Postdoctorate/Fellowship)* [5357]

CFCC Foundation Merit Scholarship *(Undergraduate/Scholarship)* [3151]

CFNIL Senior Memorial Scholarship *(Undergraduate/Scholarship)* [3672]

CFR National Intelligence Fellowships *(Professional development/Fellowship)* [3861]

CFT/ACPSOP Scholarship Fund *(Undergraduate/Scholarship)* [3343]

Rick Chace Foundation Scholarships *(Graduate/Scholarship)* [2246]

Chaîne des Rôtisseurs Scholarships *(Undergraduate/Scholarship)* [842]

ChairScholars National Scholarship Program *(Undergraduate/Scholarship)* [3275]

Jeanne S. Chall Research Fellowship *(Doctorate, Graduate/Fellowship, Grant)* [6033]

The Challenge Met Scholarship *(Undergraduate/Scholarship)* [1933]

Mariam K. Chamberlain Fellowship in Women and Public Policy *(Graduate/Fellowship)* [5874]

Bryan A. Champion Memorial Scholarship *(Undergraduate/Scholarship)* [5586]

Harry H. and Floy B. Chapin Scholarships *(Undergraduate/Scholarship)* [3673]

Oscar Chapman Memorial Scholarship *(Undergraduate, Graduate/Scholarship)* [2516]

Nancy J. Chapman Scholarships *(Other/Scholarship)* [2152]

Chappie Hall Scholarship *(Undergraduate/Scholarship)* [2]

Chapter 17 - St. Louis Scholarship *(Undergraduate/Scholarship)* [10388]

Chapter 23 - Quad Cities Scholarship *(Undergraduate/Scholarship)* [10389]

Chapter 6 - Fairfield County Scholarship *(Undergraduate/Scholarship)* [10394]

Chapter 79/198/311 Scholarship *(Graduate, Undergraduate, Vocational/Occupational, Community College/Scholarship)* [10398]

Charles and Carol Spielberger Scholarship *(Graduate, Master's, Doctorate/Scholarship)* [1280]

Charles (Charlie) A. Bassett Endowed Scholarship *(Undergraduate/Scholarship)* [5070]

Charles E. Peterson Fellowships *(Other/Fellowship)* [2334]

Charles H. Bussmann Graduate Scholarship *(Graduate, Undergraduate/Scholarship)* [7068]

Charles Lee Anderson Memorial Scholarship *(Undergraduate/Scholarship)* [3674]

Charles McCorkle Hauser Scholarship *(Undergraduate/Scholarship)* [11179]

Charles S. Houston Grant *(Advanced Professional/Grant)* [12028]

Charlotte Housing Authority Scholarship Fund (CHASF) *(Undergraduate/Scholarship)* [4726]

Charlotte R. SchmidLapp Scholarship Fund *(Undergraduate/Scholarship)* [3345]

Charlotte V. Bergen Scholarship *(Undergraduate/Scholarship)* [1408]

CCWH Nupur Chaudhuri Article Prize *(Professional development/Prize)* [3829]

CHEA Undergraduate Scholarship Program for Students with Disabilities *(Undergraduate/Scholarship)* [2814]

CHEA Vocational Grants *(Vocational/Occupational, Two Year College/Grant)* [2815]

The Cheatham County Scholarship Fund *(Undergraduate/Scholarship)* [3607]

Chereddi NarayanaRao & Radhamanohari Scholarships *(Graduate/Scholarship)* [10948]

Cherokee Nation Graduate Scholarship *(Graduate/Scholarship)* [3283]

Cherokee Nation Pell Scholarships *(Undergraduate/Scholarship)* [3284]

Sgt. Cherven Scholarship *(Undergraduate/Scholarship)* [7128]

Chester H. Bruce Memorial Scholarship *(Undergraduate/Scholarship)* [8836]

Chet And Janett Perry Rotary Club Of Fort Myers Scholarship Fund *(Undergraduate/Scholarship)* [10674]

The Chicago FM Club Scholarship *(Undergraduate/Scholarship)* [1934]

Camille C. Chidiac Fund Scholarship *(Undergraduate, Four Year College, Two Year College, Vocational/Occupational/Scholarship)* [5391]

Kevin Child Scholarship (Undergraduate/Scholarship) [7921]

Child Welfare and Development (CWD) Scholarship (Undergraduate/Scholarship) [4489]

Childbirth Educator Program Scholarships (Other/Scholarship) [6641]

Children of Evangeline Section Scholarships (Graduate, Undergraduate/Scholarship) [10472]

Children of Unitarian Universalist Religious Professionals Grant (Undergraduate/Grant) [11246]

Children's National Health System Pediatric Nursing Student Scholarships (Undergraduate/Scholarship) [124]

Childrens Scholarship Fund-Charlotte (Undergraduate/Scholarship) [4728]

Dolly Ching Scholarship (Undergraduate, Two Year College, Four Year College/Scholarship) [5393]

ChiroHealthUSA Foxworth Family Scholarship (Doctorate/Scholarship) [3313]

Choose Your Future Scholarship Fund (Undergraduate/Scholarship) [3608]

Chrétien International Research Grants (Doctorate/Grant) [683]

Chris M. Kurzweil Scholarship (Undergraduate/Scholarship) [3717]

Christian Larew Memorial Scholarship (Graduate/Scholarship, Monetary) [6838]

Frances N. Christian Memorial Endowment Nursing Scholarship (Graduate, Undergraduate/Scholarship) [10844]

Christian Pharmacists Fellowship International (CPFI) (Advanced Professional/Scholarship) [3321]

Christine Kerr Cawthorne Scholarship (Undergraduate/Scholarship) [10097]

Irene R. Christman Scholarship (Undergraduate/Scholarship) [8960]

Christopher Todd Grant Memorial Fund (Undergraduate/Scholarship) [3346]

Commander Daniel J. Christovich Scholarship (Undergraduate/Scholarship) [3455]

Chrysalis Scholarship (Graduate/Scholarship) [2314]

Chuck Peacock Memorial Scholarship (Undergraduate/Scholarship) [175]

Chuck Pezzano Scholarship (College, Graduate/Scholarship) [5955]

The Church, Langdon, Lopp, Banet Law Scholarships (Undergraduate, Four Year College/Scholarship) [3329]

Brent R. Churchill Memorial Scholarship (Undergraduate/Scholarship) [6977]

The Churchill Scholarships (Postgraduate/Scholarship) [3331]

CIA Undergraduate Scholarships (Undergraduate/Scholarship) [2185, 3244]

CIGNA Healthcare Graduate Scholarships (Graduate/Scholarship) [7888]

CIGNA Undergraduate Scholarships (Undergraduate/Scholarship) [7889]

Cimarron-Memorial Spartan Staff Scholarships (Undergraduate/Scholarship) [9393]

CIMON Inc Scholarship (College, University/Scholarship) [3333]

Cincinnati Bell Foundation Scholarship (Undergraduate/Scholarship) [3347]

Cincinnati Financial Corporation Fund (Undergraduate/Scholarship) [3348]

Cindy Andrews Educational Scholarship (Undergraduate/Scholarship) [9534]

CINTAS Foundation Fellowship in Architecture & Design (Professional development/Fellowship) [3417]

CIRMMT Student Awards (Graduate, Master's, Doctorate/Award) [3253]

CISDL Global Research Fellowship - Associate Fellows (Graduate/Fellowship) [3257]

CISDL Global Research Fellowship - Legal Research Fellows (Graduate/Fellowship) [3258]

CISDL Global Research Fellowships - Senior Research Fellows (Other/Fellowship) [3259]

Citi/TELACU Scholars Mentoring Program (Undergraduate/Scholarship) [10940]

CitizenshipTests.org Engineering and Science Scholarship (Undergraduate/Scholarship) [3991]

City Bar Diversity Fellowship Program (Undergraduate/Fellowship) [8300]

City of Boston Disability Scholarship Contest (Undergraduate/Scholarship) [4535]

City Of Sanibel Employee Dependent Scholarship Fund (Undergraduate/Scholarship) [10676]

Civitan Shropshire Scholarship (Undergraduate, Vocational/Occupational/Scholarship) [3424]

CJH Graduate Research Fellowships (Doctorate/Fellowship) [3221]

CJH-NEH Fellowships for Senior Scholars (Doctorate/Fellowship) [3222]

CJH-Prins Foundation Fellowships for Senior Scholars (Doctorate/Fellowship) [3223]

CJH-Prins Foundation Post-Doctoral and Early Career Fellowship for Emigrating Scholars (Professional development, Postdoctorate/Fellowship) [3224]

CJH Visiting Scholars Program (Doctorate/Fellowship) [3225]

Claes Nobel Academic Scholarships for Members (High School, College/Scholarship) [8103]

Clan Ross Foundation Scholarships (Undergraduate/Scholarship) [3426]

Clarivate Analytics/MLA Doctoral Fellowship (Doctorate, Graduate/Fellowship) [7215]

Vickie Clark-Flaherty Scholarships (Undergraduate/Scholarship) [8444]

Clarke Adams Memorial Fund (Undergraduate/Scholarship) [6662]

Classic Wines of California Scholarships (Undergraduate/Scholarship) [2797]

Claude B. Hart Memorial Scholarship (Undergraduate/Scholarship) [12066]

Claude Robinson Memorial Scholarship (Undergraduate/Scholarship) [7969]

Clay Maitland CGF Scholarship (Undergraduate/Scholarship) [3456]

Clay Postdoctoral Fellowship (Postdoctorate/Fellowship) [5358]

Clem Judd Jr. Memorial Scholarship (Undergraduate/Scholarship) [5418]

Clement T. Hanson Scholarship (Undergraduate/Scholarship) [7430]

Cleve Holloway Memorial Scholarship (Undergraduate/Scholarship) [3652]

Cleveland Alumni Association Scholarship (Undergraduate, Graduate/Scholarship) [2517]

Geraldine Clewell Fellowships - Doctoral Student (Graduate/Fellowship) [9107]

Geraldine Clewell Fellowships - Masteral (Graduate/Fellowship) [9108]

James L. Clifford Prize (Other/Prize, Monetary) [1430]

Clinical Project Funding for Advanced Practice Oncology Nurses (Advanced Professional, Professional development/Grant) [8627]

Clinician Research Awards (Postgraduate, Professional development, Other/Fellowship) [8898]

George H. Clinton Scholarship (Undergraduate/Scholarship) [8837]

Closs/Parnitzke/Clarke Scholarship (Undergraduate/Scholarship) [9109]

L. Robert Clough Memorial Scholarship (Undergraduate, Graduate/Scholarship) [2518]

The Club at Morningside Scholarship (Undergraduate, Graduate/Scholarship) [9806]

CMAA Student Conference Travel Grants (Undergraduate/Grant, Award) [3442]

CMC-KLI Leadership Research Fellowship (Undergraduate/Fellowship) [3428]

CMC-KLI Leadership Thesis Fellowship (Undergraduate/Fellowship) [3429]

CMC-KLI Social Sector Internship Program (Undergraduate/Internship) [3430]

CMC/MMC Scholarships (CMC) (Other/Scholarship) [6026]

CME Beef Industry Scholarship (Undergraduate/Scholarship) [7744]

Coast Guard Foundation Enlisted Education Scholarship (Advanced Professional/Scholarship) [3457]

J.C. and Rheba Cobb Memorial Scholarships (Undergraduate/Scholarship) [7775]

John Coburn and Harold Winters Student Award in Plasma Science and Technology (Graduate/Award) [2382]

Johnnie L. Cochran, Jr./MWH Scholarships (Graduate, Undergraduate/Scholarship) [7890]

Code Play LEARN Scholarship (Two Year College, Undergraduate, Graduate/Scholarship) [3496]

American Academy of Periodontology Dr. D. Walter Cohen Teaching Fellowships (Professional development/Fellowship) [474]

The COIT Clean GIF Scholarship Contest (Undergraduate, Graduate/Scholarship) [3498]

Col Mary Feik Cadet Flight Scholarship (Undergraduate/Scholarship) [3422]

Cole Family Scholarships (All/Scholarship) [9294]

Arthur H. Cole Grants in Aid (Doctorate/Grant) [4281]

Paul Cole Student Technologist Scholarship (Undergraduate/Scholarship) [10438]

The College Bound Scholarship (Undergraduate/Scholarship) [11917]

Colonel Theodore A. Leisen Memorial and Training Endowment Fund (Graduate/Grant) [8196]

Color Masters Scholarship (Undergraduate/Scholarship) [4875]

Columbus Citizens Foundation College Scholarships (Undergraduate/Scholarship) [3543]

Columbus Citizens Foundation High School Scholarships (Undergraduate/Scholarship) [3544]

John Colvin Law Award (Graduate/Scholarship) [3546]

Colwell Law Group Single Parent Scholarship (Community College, University, Undergraduate/Scholarship) [3548]

The Commonwealth Fund Mongan Fellowship in Minority Health Policy (Other/Fellowship) [3554]

Communal Studies Association Research Fellowships (Graduate/Fellowship) [3557]

The Communities in Schools Jack Tate ThinkCollege Scholarship (Undergraduate/Scholarship) [4729]

Community Bank - Lee Guggisberg Foundation Memorial Scholarships (Undergraduate/Scholarship) [9535]

Community Foundation of the Fox River Valley Scholarship (Undergraduate, Graduate, High School/Scholarship) [3584]

Community Foundation of Northern Illinois Scholarship (Undergraduate/Scholarship) [3675]

Community Legal Services of Philadelphia Fellowships (Postgraduate, Graduate/Fellowship) [3729]

Comparative Effectiveness Research Professorship (CERP) (Professional development, Doctorate/Grant) [3772]

Comparative Perspectives on Chinese Culture and Society Grantees (Doctorate/Grant) [823]

The Tom and Judith Comstock Scholarship (Undergraduate/Scholarship) [1935]

Condon Prize for Best Student Essay in Psychological Anthropology (Graduate, Undergraduate/Prize, Recognition) [10505]

Maridell Braham Condon Scholarships (Undergraduate/Scholarship) [10098]

Conference and Workshop Grants (Professional development/Grant) [11960]

Congressional Fellowship (Other/Fellowship) [3741]

Connecticut Association of Latinos in Higher Education Scholarships (Undergraduate/Scholarship) [3754, 5320]

Connecticut Mortgage Bankers Social Affairs Fund (Undergraduate/Scholarship) [5321]

Connecticut Space Grant College Consortium Undergraduate Research Fellowships (Undergraduate/Fellowship) [3761]

Dwight O. Connor/Ellen Conner Lepp/Danhart Scholarship (Undergraduate/Scholarship) [8838]

The Connor Group Kids & Community Partners Scholarship (Two Year College, Undergraduate, Graduate/Scholarship) [3765]

Conservation and Scientific Research Fellowships (Graduate/Fellowship) [7274]

Constant Memorial Scholarship (Undergraduate/Scholarship) [9691]

Consumers Credit Union Scholarship (Undergraduate, College, Vocational/Occupational, Two Year College, University/Scholarship) [3814]

Contemporary Club Scholarship (Undergraduate/Scholarship) [9536]

Convergence Assistantship Grants (Undergraduate/Grant) [5283]

Deloris Carter Hampton Scholarship *(Undergraduate/Scholarship)* [9296]

Delta Chi Alumnae Memorial Scholarship *(Undergraduate/Scholarship)* [10099]

Delta Epsilon Sigma Graduate Fellowship *(Graduate/Fellowship)* [4017]

Delta Epsilon Sigma Undergraduate Scholarships *(Undergraduate/Scholarship)* [4018]

Delta Faucet Scholarships *(Undergraduate/Scholarship)* [9204]

Delta Gamma Foundation Florence Margaret Harvey Memorial Scholarship *(Graduate, Undergraduate/Scholarship)* [914]

Delta Kappa Project 2000 Scholarship *(Undergraduate/Scholarship)* [6417]

Delta Nu Project 2000 Scholarship *(Undergraduate/Scholarship)* [6418]

Delta Project 2000 Scholarship *(Undergraduate/Scholarship)* [6419]

Delta Tau Project 2000 Scholarship *(Undergraduate/Scholarship)* [6420]

Delta Tau Scholarship *(Undergraduate, Graduate/Scholarship)* [2520]

Delta Upsilon Project 2000 Nowell Memorial Scholarship *(Undergraduate/Scholarship)* [6421]

Christopher Demetris Memorial Scholarships *(Undergraduate/Scholarship)* [5463]

Inez Demonet Scholarship *(Graduate/Scholarship)* [11804]

Dena Epstein Award for Archival and Library Research in American Music *(Professional development/Award)* [7513]

The Dendel Scholarship *(Graduate, Undergraduate/Scholarship)* [5284]

Denis Wong & Associates Scholarship *(Graduate, Undergraduate/Scholarship)* [8923]

Dennis Coleman Scholarship *(Undergraduate/Scholarship)* [9297]

Dennis Coleman Scholarships *(Undergraduate/Scholarship)* [9298]

Denton Scholarship *(Graduate/Scholarship)* [10081]

Dick Depaolis Memorial Scholarship *(Undergraduate/Scholarship)* [3718]

Garabed and Almast Der Megrditchian Scholarship Grants *(Undergraduate/Scholarship)* [1874]

Frank Der Yuen Aviation Scholarship *(Undergraduate/Scholarship)* [8804]

Derivative Duo Scholarships *(Undergraduate/Scholarship)* [9299]

Descendants Scholarships *(Undergraduate/Scholarship)* [3954]

Libby Deschenes Prize for Applied Research *(Undergraduate/Prize)* [11989]

Detroit Economic Club Scholarship *(Undergraduate/Scholarship)* [3719]

DeVries Law School Scholarship *(Undergraduate/Scholarship)* [4070]

DFA Production Grant *(Professional development/Grant)* [3966]

Jenny d'Héricourt Fellowship *(Doctorate/Fellowship)* [487]

Beta Nu/Caryl Cordis D'hondt Scholarship *(Undergraduate/Scholarship)* [10100]

Theta/Caryl Cordis D'hondt Scholarship *(Undergraduate/Scholarship)* [10101]

Diamond Resort Scholarship Fund *(Undergraduate, Two Year College, Four Year College/Scholarship)* [5396]

Edwina Eustis Dick Scholarship for Music Therapy Interns *(Graduate/Scholarship)* [1134]

Robert Martz DiGiacomo Memorial Scholarship Fund *(Undergraduate/Scholarship)* [10756]

DirectTextbook.com Scholarship Essay Contest *(College, Undergraduate, University/Scholarship)* [4097]

Disabled Veteran Scholarship *(College, Vocational/Occupational/Scholarship)* [9713]

Disabled Veteran Student Scholarship *(Two Year College, Four Year College/Scholarship)* [12018]

Disabled Veterans Scholarship *(Vocational/Occupational, Community College, Four Year College, Graduate, Professional development/Scholarship)* [6519]

Discover Bar Exam Loans *(Graduate/Loan, Scholarship)* [4109]

Discover Graduate Loans *(Graduate, Master's, Doctorate/Loan, Scholarship)* [4110]

Discover Health Professions Loans *(Graduate/Loan, Scholarship)* [4111]

Discover Law Loans *(Graduate/Loan, Scholarship)* [4112]

Discover MBA Loans *(Graduate/Loan, Scholarship)* [4113]

Discover Residency Loans *(Graduate/Loan, Scholarship)* [4114]

Dissertation Proposal Development Fellowship *(Doctorate/Fellowship)* [10243]

Dissertation Writing Grants *(Graduate/Grant)* [5869]

Diversity Executive Leadership Program Scholarship (DELP) *(Other/Scholarship)* [1977]

Diversity Scholarship *(Graduate/Scholarship, Award)* [1796]

Robert A. and Barbara Divine Graduate Student Travel Fund *(Graduate/Grant)* [10355]

Peggy Dixon Two-Year Scholarships *(Undergraduate/Scholarship)* [10477]

D.J. Lovell Scholarship *(Graduate, Undergraduate/Scholarship)* [10725]

Charles Dobbins FTA Scholarships *(Undergraduate, Vocational/Occupational/Scholarship)* [4846]

Doc Keen Memorial Scholarship Fund *(Undergraduate/Scholarship)* [10680]

Dr. Ali Jarrahi Merit Scholarship *(Undergraduate/Scholarship)* [6172]

Dr. Aura-Lee A. and James Hobbs Pittenger American History Scholarship *(Undergraduate/Scholarship, Award, Monetary)* [8095]

Dr. Edward G. Voss Memorial Scholarship *(Undergraduate/Scholarship)* [11618]

Dr. F. Ross Byrd Scholarship *(Graduate/Scholarship)* [11909]

Dr. Frank and Florence Marino Scholarship *(Undergraduate/Scholarship)* [5322]

Dr. George and Isabelle Elanjian Scholarship *(Undergraduate/Scholarship)* [11638]

Dr. George M. Smerk Scholarship *(Undergraduate, Graduate/Scholarship)* [1300]

Dr. Gunnar B. Stickler Scholarship *(Undergraduate, Vocational/Occupational/Scholarship)* [10839]

Dr. James A. Ferguson Emerging Infectious Diseases Research Initiatives for Student Enhancement Fellowship (RISE) *(Graduate/Fellowship)* [6526]

Dr. Joyce Beckett Scholarship *(Graduate, Undergraduate/Scholarship)* [7618]

Dr. Julianne Malveaux Scholarship *(Undergraduate/Scholarship)* [7668]

Dr. Mark Rathke Family Scholarship Fund *(Graduate/Scholarship)* [4202]

Dr. Mubin Syed And Mrs. Afshan Syed Scholarship Program *(Undergraduate/Scholarship)* [6176]

Dr. Nancy Smith Midgette Scholarship *(Undergraduate/Scholarship)* [10102]

Dr. Nicholas J. Piergrossi Memorial Scholarship *(Undergraduate/Scholarship)* [5323]

Dr. Stephen J. Fortgang / University of Northern Iowa Chapter Scholarship *(Undergraduate/Scholarship)* [6379]

Documentary Film Grants *(Professional development/Grant)* [409]

F. Atlee Dodge Maintenance Scholarship *(Undergraduate/Scholarship)* [237]

Jim Dodson Law Scholarship for Brain Injury Victims & Their Caregivers *(Undergraduate/Scholarship)* [4124]

Dody Boyd Scholarship Fund *(Undergraduate/Scholarship)* [3613]

Hans and Margaret Doe Charitable Trust Scholarship *(Community College, Vocational/Occupational, College, University, Undergraduate, Graduate/Scholarship)* [9810]

DOE Computational Science Graduate Fellowship (DOE CSGF) *(Doctorate, Graduate/Fellowship)* [6611]

Office of Science Graduate Student Research (SCGSR) Program *(Graduate, Master's, Postdoctorate/Fellowship)* [11323]

Emmett J. Doerr Memorial Distinguished Scout Scholarship *(High School/Scholarship)* [7846]

Dofflemyer Scholarship *(Undergraduate/Scholarship)* [7847]

Dollar-A-Day Academic Scholarships *(Graduate, Undergraduate/Scholarship)* [4126]

Scott Dominguez - Craters of the Moon Chapter Scholarship *(Graduate, Undergraduate/Scholarship)* [1564]

Don Aron Scholarship *(Undergraduate/Scholarship)* [7783]

Don and Barbara Curtis Excellence Fund for Extracurricular Activities *(Undergraduate/Scholarship)* [11181]

Don C. Beaver Memorial Scholarship *(Undergraduate/Scholarship)* [2798]

Don Freeman Illustrator Grants *(Advanced Professional/Grant)* [10300]

Don and Madalyn Sickafoose Educational Trust Fund *(Undergraduate/Scholarship, Loan)* [10757]

Don S. Maurer Advertising Scholarship *(Undergraduate/Scholarship)* [11182]

Donald A. B. Lindberg Research Fellowship *(Doctorate, Graduate/Fellowship)* [7217]

Donald F. & Mildred Topp Othmer Scholarship Awards *(Undergraduate/Scholarship)* [1022]

Donald J. DeYoung Scholarship *(Undergraduate/Scholarship)* [5147]

Donald O. Coffman Scholarship *(Graduate, Undergraduate/Scholarship)* [9300]

Donald and Shirley Hastings Scholarship *(Undergraduate/Scholarship)* [1660]

Marion Jones Donaldson Scholarship Fund *(Undergraduate/Scholarship)* [4589]

Donna Gail Scholarship for Chapter Service *(Undergraduate, Graduate, Doctorate/Scholarship)* [6380]

Joseph M. Dorgan Scholarship *(Undergraduate/Scholarship)* [4151]

Doris W. Frey Memorial Scholarship Fund *(Graduate/Scholarship)* [10681]

Pauly D'Orlando Memorial Art Scholarship *(Graduate, Undergraduate/Scholarship)* [11248]

Dotcom-Monitor Women in Computing Scholarship *(Undergraduate/Scholarship)* [4134]

Dottie Martin Teacher Scholarship *(Graduate, Undergraduate/Scholarship)* [8437]

The Father Connie Dougherty Scholarship Fund *(Undergraduate, Vocational/Occupational/Scholarship)* [3712]

Douglas Lake Improvement Association Scholarship *(Undergraduate/Scholarship)* [11619]

The Douglas Psychotherapy Do Good General Education Scholarship *(Undergraduate, Graduate/Scholarship)* [4140]

Douglass Foundation Fellowship in American Art *(Doctorate/Fellowship)* [10214]

The Douglass Foundation Fellowship in American Art *(Graduate/Fellowship)* [7276]

Dow Chemical Company Fellowships *(Graduate/Fellowship)* [8027]

Downeast Feline Fund *(Graduate/Scholarship)* [6978]

Tim Downing Memorial Scholarship Program *(Professional development/Scholarship)* [2906]

Downtown Apartment Companys Scholarship Program *(Undergraduate/Scholarship)* [4144]

Helen Cashatt Drais Memorial Adelphe Scholarship *(Undergraduate/Scholarship)* [6422]

Drake University Law School Law Opportunity Scholarship - Diversity *(Undergraduate/Scholarship)* [4153]

The Drawn to Art Fellowship *(Doctorate/Fellowship)* [488]

DREAM - Diversity Recruitment Recruitment through Education and Mentoring Program *(Undergraduate/Fellowship)* [621]

Margaret Drew Alpha Scholarship *(Graduate/Scholarship)* [9110]

Charles Drew Scholarships *(Other/Scholarship)* [2153]

Drew Smith Memorial Scholarship *(Undergraduate/Scholarship)* [3563]

Camille and Henry Dreyfus Foundation - Senior Scientist Mentor Program *(Professional development/Grant)* [4180]

DriversEdHub.com Scholarship *(Undergraduate/Scholarship)* [3992]

Drone Technology College Scholarshi p *(High School, Undergraduate/Scholarship)* [4183]

Drue Smith / Society of Professional Journalists' Scholarship Fund (*Undergraduate/Scholarship*) [3614]

Drug Development Research Professorship (*Professional development/Internship*) [3773]

Richard Drukker Memorial Scholarships (*Undergraduate/Scholarship*) [8283]

Drummond Law Firm Scholarship (*Graduate, College/Scholarship*) [4189]

Harold D. Drummond Scholarships (*Undergraduate, Graduate/Scholarship*) [6381]

DSACF Modern Woodmen of America Scholarship Fund (*Undergraduate/Scholarship*) [4203]

Emilie Du Chatelet Award (*Doctorate/Award*) [1431]

Henry Belin du Pont Dissertation Fellowships (*Doctorate, Graduate/Fellowship*) [5257]

Henry Belin du Pont Research Grants (*Graduate/Grant*) [5258]

Duane Hanson Scholarship (*Undergraduate/Scholarship*) [1473]

Duane V. Puerde Memorial Scholarship Fund (*Undergraduate/Scholarship*) [3564]

Lee Dubin Memorial Scholarship (*Undergraduate/Scholarship*) [3500]

Charles Dubose Scholarships (*Undergraduate/Scholarship*) [5326]

Julia M. Duckwall Scholarship (*Professional development/Scholarship*) [2199]

Mark Duda Scholarship Fund (*Graduate, Undergraduate/Scholarship*) [7104]

Doris Duke Conservation Fellows Program (*Master's/Fellowship*) [12046]

Duluth Building and Construction Trades Council Scholarship Fund (*Graduate/Scholarship*) [4204]

Duluth Central High School Alumni Scholarship Fund (*Graduate/Scholarship*) [4205]

Dunbar Heritage Scholarship Fund (*Undergraduate/Scholarship*) [10683]

Duncan Aviation Scholarship (*Undergraduate/Scholarship*) [178, 4238]

John Holt Duncan Memorial Scholarship (*Undergraduate, Graduate/Scholarship*) [2521]

Wade and Marcelene Duncan Scholarship (*Undergraduate/Scholarship*) [12070]

Dunkin' Donuts Philadelphia Regional Scholarship Program (*Undergraduate/Scholarship*) [9941]

Durning Sisters Scholarships (*Graduate/Scholarship*) [4001]

Joe Durso, Jr. Memorial Scholarship (*Undergraduate/Scholarship*) [7451]

Dutch and Ginger Arver Scholarship (*Undergraduate/Scholarship*) [179]

Dwight Hibbard Scholarship Fund (*Undergraduate/Scholarship*) [3355]

Dwight Mosley Scholarship Award (*Undergraduate/Scholarship*) [11403]

Dwight Teed Scholarship Fund (*Undergraduate/Scholarship*) [10881]

Marvin and Joanell Dyrstad Scholarship (*Undergraduate/Scholarship*) [1746]

Dystonia Medical Research Foundation Clinical Fellowships (*Postdoctorate/Fellowship*) [4244]

E. H. Marth Food Protection And Food Sciences Scholarship (*Undergraduate/Scholarship*) [12109]

E. Lanier (Lanny) Finch Scholarship (*Undergraduate/Scholarship*) [4923]

EAA Members Memorial Scholarship (*Undergraduate/Scholarship*) [4391]

EAA Workshop Scholarships (*Undergraduate/Scholarship*) [4392]

EAIA Research Grants (*Other/Grant*) [4248]

Earl Warren Civil Rights Training Scholarships (*Graduate/Scholarship*) [7538]

Earl Warren Scholarship (*Graduate/Scholarship*) [7539]

Early-Career Patient-Oriented Diabetes Research Awards (*Professional development/Award*) [6347]

Early Childhood Educators Scholarship Program (*Undergraduate/Scholarship*) [7158]

Robert E. Early Memorial Scholarship (*Undergraduate/Scholarship*) [4155]

East Carolina Scholarship (*Undergraduate, Graduate/Scholarship*) [2522]

Eastern Orthodox Scouting Scholarships (*Undergraduate/Scholarship*) [7848]

The Eating Recovery Center Foundation Early Career Investigator Grants (*Professional development/Grant*) [7863]

David Eaton Scholarship (*Master's/Scholarship*) [11249]

Eben Tisdale Fellowship (*Undergraduate/Fellowship, Monetary*) [4838]

ECA Centennial Scholarships (*Master's, Doctorate/Scholarship*) [4271]

Echoing Green Black Male Achievement Fellowships (*Professional development/Fellowship*) [4275]

Echoing Green Climate Fellowships (*Professional development/Fellowship*) [4276]

Echoing Green Global Fellowships (*Professional development/Fellowship*) [4277]

Ecolab Scholarship (*Undergraduate/Scholarship*) [971]

Edgecliff McAuley Art Scholarships (*Undergraduate/Scholarship*) [12221]

Edgecliff McAuley Music Scholarship (*Undergraduate/Scholarship*) [12222]

Edith Weingarten Scholarship (*Postgraduate/Scholarship*) [1177]

S. Randolph Edmonds Young Scholars Competition (*Graduate, Undergraduate/Scholarship*) [2615]

Edon Farmers Cooperative Scholarships (*Undergraduate/Scholarship*) [4297]

Education Factor Scholarships (*Graduate, Undergraduate/Scholarship*) [7207]

"Education is Power" Scholarships (*Undergraduate/Scholarship*) [7923]

Educational and Cultural Affairs Alumni Small Grants Program (ECA) (*Other/Grant*) [6069]

Educational Loan Program for Gay and Lesbian Students (*Undergraduate/Loan*) [3615]

Edward C. Pomeroy Award for Outstanding Contributions to Teacher Education (*Other/Award, Recognition*) [550]

Edward C. Roy, Jr. Award For Excellence in K-8 Earth Science Teaching (*Professional development/Award*) [944]

Edward Heywood Megson Scholarship (*Undergraduate/Scholarship*) [11183]

Edward Kent Welch Memorial Scholarship (*Undergraduate/Scholarship*) [12071]

Edward Leon Duhamel Freemasons Scholarship (*Undergraduate/Scholarship*) [9692]

Edward Traurig Scholarship (*Undergraduate/Scholarship*) [11932]

The Edwards Annual College Scholarships (*Undergraduate/Scholarship*) [4320]

Esther Edwards Graduate Scholarships (*Doctorate, Professional development/Scholarship*) [4890]

Edwyna Wheadon Postgraduate Training Scholarship (*Postgraduate/Scholarship*) [7799]

E.E. Williams Research Grant (*Master's, Doctorate/Grant*) [5498]

EERI/FEMA NEHRP Graduate Fellowship in Earthquake Hazard Reduction (*Graduate/Fellowship*) [4250, 11362]

EGIA Foundation Scholarship Program (*Vocational/Occupational, Two Year College/Scholarship*) [4322]

EHA Exploratory Travel and Data Grants (*Doctorate/Grant*) [4282]

EHA Graduate Dissertation Fellowships (*Graduate/Fellowship*) [4283]

E.I. DuPont Graduate Fellowship (*Graduate/Fellowship*) [8028]

Eight and Forty Lung and Respiratory Disease Nursing Scholarships (*Other/Scholarship*) [1071]

The Eileen J. Smith, R.N. Memorial Scholarship (*Undergraduate/Scholarship*) [6198]

Hillel Einhorn New Investigator Award (*Doctorate/Award*) [10377]

Jeri Eiserman, RRT Professional Education Research Fellowship (*Professional development/Fellowship*) [1353]

Farouk El-Baz Student Research Grants (*Graduate, Undergraduate, Doctorate, Master's/Grant*) [4909]

El Dorado County Mineral and Gem Society Scholarship (*Graduate/Scholarship*) [4328]

Allan Eldin & Agnes Sutorik Geiger Scholarship Fund (*Undergraduate, Graduate/Scholarship*) [5397]

The Eleanor A. Ernest Scholarship (*Graduate/Scholarship*) [6199]

Electronics Division: Lewis C. Hoffman Scholarship (*Undergraduate/Scholarship*) [733]

Elements Behavioral Health Scholarship (*College, University, Undergraduate/Scholarship*) [4365]

Elena Sanchez Memorial WSWS Outstanding Student Scholarship Program (*Graduate, Undergraduate/Scholarship*) [11993]

Elevating Healthcare Scholarship (*Undergraduate/Scholarship*) [24]

W. Todd Elias Memorial Scholarship (*Undergraduate, Graduate/Scholarship*) [2523]

Elin J. Stene/Xi Scholarship (*Undergraduate/Scholarship*) [10103]

Elisabeth M. and Winchell M. Parsons Scholarship (*Doctorate/Scholarship*) [1999]

Elise Reed Jenkins Memorial Scholarship (*Undergraduate/Scholarship*) [10104]

Elite Entrepreneurs Scholarship Contest (*Undergraduate, Graduate, High School/Scholarship*) [4369]

Elizabeth Benson Scholarship Award (*Undergraduate/Scholarship*) [9625]

Elizabeth Brittingham Pusey Scholarship (*Graduate/Scholarship*) [3565]

Elizabeth Munsterberg Koppitz Child Psychology Graduate Student Fellowship (*Graduate/Fellowship*) [1281]

Elizabeth Nash Foundation Scholarship (*Undergraduate, Graduate/Scholarship*) [7554]

Elizabeth Neuffer Fellowship (*Other/Fellowship*) [6148]

Elizabeth Shafer Memorial Scholarship (*Undergraduate/Scholarship*) [9398]

Elizabeth and Sherman Asche Memorial Scholarship (*Graduate, Undergraduate/Scholarship*) [2038]

Elks National Foundation Most Valuable Student Scholarship Contest (*Undergraduate/Scholarship*) [2816, 4371]

Ella Wilson Johnson Scholarship Fund (*Undergraduate/Scholarship*) [3356]

The Dr. Robert Elliott Memorial Scholarship (*Undergraduate/Scholarship*) [7167, 8264]

The Pauline Elliott Scholarship (*Undergraduate/Scholarship*) [7168, 8265]

Robert A. Ellis Scholarships in Physics (*Undergraduate/Scholarship*) [8085]

Ellis W. Rowe Memorial Scholarship (*Graduate/Scholarship*) [5268]

Elmer and Rosa Lee Collins Scholarship (*Undergraduate/Scholarship*) [12075]

Albinas Elskus Scholarship (*Other/Scholarship*) [10743]

Elton Casey Scholarship (*Undergraduate/Scholarship*) [11185]

Elva Knight Research Grant (*Professional development, Graduate/Grant, Award*) [6034]

EMLF Law Student Scholarships (*Undergraduate/Scholarship*) [4387]

Emma and Meloid Algood Tuition Scholarship (*Graduate, Undergraduate/Scholarship*) [7619]

Employment Boost College Scholarship (*College, University/Scholarship*) [4381]

ENA Foundation Undergraduate State Challenge Scholarship (*Undergraduate/Scholarship*) [4379]

Enders Student Fellowship (*Graduate/Fellowship*) [2081]

Alice Yuriko Endo Memorial Scholarship (*Undergraduate/Scholarship*) [6245]

Endowment Fund for Education Grants (*Undergraduate/Grant*) [2575]

Endowment Fund for Education Scholarships (EFFE) (*Undergraduate/Grant, Scholarship*) [2576]

Most Valuable Student scholarships (*Undergraduate/Scholarship*) [4372]

Enid Hall Griswold Memorial Scholarship (*Undergraduate/Scholarship, Award, Monetary*) [8096]

Enid W. and Bernard B. Spigel Architectural Scholarship (*Graduate/Scholarship*) [5269]

Enkababian Family and Sarian Family Memorial Grant (*Undergraduate/Scholarship*) [1875]

EPA Science to Achieve Results Fellowships (STAR) (*Graduate/Fellowship*) [11350]

Florida Automotive Industry Scholarships (Undergraduate/Scholarship) [2352]

Florida Nurses Foundation Scholarships (Undergraduate, Master's, Doctorate/Scholarship) [4640]

Florida Public Transportation Association Scholarships (FPTA) (Undergraduate, Graduate/Scholarship) [1301]

Floto-Peel Family Scholarship Fund (Undergraduate, Vocational/Occupational/Scholarship) [5076]

Flow Feet Foot the Bill Scholarship (Two Year College, University/Award) [4653]

James Fonseca Scholarship (Undergraduate, Graduate/Scholarship) [395]

Ford Foundation Dissertation Fellowship (Postdoctorate/Fellowship) [4672, 7572]

Ford Foundation Diversity Fellowships (Graduate, Doctorate, Postdoctorate, Postgraduate/Fellowship) [7573]

Ford Foundation Postdoctoral Fellowship (Postdoctorate/Fellowship) [4673, 7574]

Ford Foundation Predoctoral Fellowship (Graduate, Doctorate/Fellowship) [4674, 7575]

A. Ward Ford Memorial Research Grant (Postdoctorate, Professional development/Grant) [1497]

Anne Ford Scholarships (High School/Scholarship) [7753]

Nancy B. Forest and L. Michael Honaker Master's Grant for Research in Psychology (Graduate/Grant) [1270]

Foresters Competitive Scholarship (Undergraduate, Vocational/Occupational, Four Year College, Two Year College/Scholarship) [5737]

ForEverglades Scholarship (Graduate, Master's, Doctorate/Scholarship) [4456]

Forsyth County Nursing Scholarship (Undergraduate/Scholarship) [12077]

Genevieve Forthun Scholarships (Undergraduate/Scholarship) [9111]

Foster G. McGaw Graduate Student Scholarship (Graduate/Scholarship) [764]

Dr. Nancy Foster Scholarship Program (Doctorate/Scholarship) [8017]

Fostering Hope Scholarship (Undergraduate/Scholarship) [8846]

Foundation of American Institute for Conservation Lecture Grants (Other/Grant) [1026]

Foundation for Neonatal Research and Education Scholarship (Doctorate, Graduate, Postgraduate, Undergraduate/Scholarship) [4794]

Foundation for the Preservation of Honey Bees Scholarship (Graduate/Scholarship) [4803]

Foundation Scholarships (Graduate/Scholarship) [8619]

Founding Mothers Student Scholarships - Graduate (Graduate/Scholarship) [2233]

Mary Metzger Fouse Memorial Scholarship Fund (Undergraduate/Scholarship) [6428]

Don Fox Memorial Scholarship (Undergraduate/Scholarship) [232]

Captain Ernest W. Fox Perpetual Scholarship (Advanced Professional/Scholarship) [3459]

Frame My Future Scholarship Contest (Undergraduate, Graduate/Scholarship, Prize) [3327]

Fran Morgenstern Davis Scholarship (Undergraduate/Scholarship) [1409]

Francis H. Moffitt Scholarship (Graduate, Undergraduate/Scholarship) [2006]

Francis Harris Gresham Scholarship Fund (Undergraduate/Scholarship) [10685]

Gloria Francke Scholarship (Undergraduate/Scholarship) [1747]

Frank and Charlene Harris Scholarship Fund (Undergraduate/Scholarship) [3618]

Frank Foster Skillman Fund (Undergraduate/Scholarship) [3362]

Frank G. Araujo Memorial Scholarship (Undergraduate/Scholarship) [9545]

Frank H. Ault Scholarship (Undergraduate/Scholarship) [9814]

Frank L. Weil Memorial Eagle Scout Scholarship (Undergraduate/Scholarship) [7850]

Frank Oppenheimer Scholarship (Postgraduate/Scholarship) [1178]

Mayme and Herb Frank Scholarship Program (Graduate/Scholarship) [1984]

Loren Frankel Memorial Scholarship (Undergraduate, Graduate/Scholarship) [1117]

Mary Weiking Franken Scholarships (Undergraduate/Scholarship) [9112]

The Ginny Frankenthaler Memorial Scholarships (Undergraduate/Scholarship) [10633]

James Franklin and Dorothy J. Warnell Scholarship Fund (Undergraduate, Vocational/Occupational/Scholarship) [3713]

John Hope Franklin Prize (Other/Prize) [6723]

Franklin Research Grants (Doctorate/Grant) [1214]

Violet and Cyril Franks Scholarship (Graduate/Scholarship) [1282]

John L. and Victory E. Frantz Scholarship (Undergraduate/Scholarship) [5077]

Fraser Family Scholarships (Undergraduate/Scholarship) [9401]

Fraser Stryker Diversity Scholarship Program (Undergraduate/Scholarship) [4817]

FRAXA Fellowships (Postdoctorate, Master's/Fellowship, Recognition, Monetary) [4819]

Fred and Avery Test Scholarship (Undergraduate/Scholarship) [11620]

Frederick V. Hunt Postdoctoral Research Fellowship in Acoustics (Postdoctorate/Fellowship) [61]

Freedom Alliance Scholarship Fund (Undergraduate/Scholarship) [4821]

Kevin Freeman Travel Grant (Graduate, Other/Grant) [7514]

The Ludo Frevel Crystallography Scholarship (Graduate/Scholarship) [5966]

Dale E. Fridell Memorial Scholarships (Undergraduate, Vocational/Occupational/Scholarship) [10858]

The Nathan J. and Virginia H. Friedman College Scholarship (Undergraduate, Four Year College, University/Scholarship) [6271]

The Phil Friel Scholarship (Undergraduate/Scholarship) [7170]

Friends of Mary Automotive Scholarship (Undergraduate/Scholarship) [10052]

Friends of Project 10 Models of Excellence Scholarship (Undergraduate/Scholarship) [4831]

Froberg-Suess JD/MBA Scholarship (Undergraduate/Scholarship) [8999]

Patricia and Phillip Frost Fellowships (Doctorate, Postdoctorate/Fellowship) [10215]

Fruits and Vegetable Industries Scholarships (Undergraduate/Scholarship) [7333]

The William and Francis Fry Honorary Fellowship for Contributions to Therapeutic Ultrasound (Professional development/Fellowship) [6118]

Mary Alice Fry Memorial Scholarship (Undergraduate, Graduate/Scholarship) [6429]

FSF Student Travel Grant (Undergraduate, Graduate/Grant) [4678]

Full Circle Scholarship (Graduate, Undergraduate/Scholarship) [980, 2042]

Full Stack Student Scholarship (Graduate/Scholarship) [4833]

Kathryn Fuller Science for Nature Fund (Graduate, Postdoctorate/Fellowship) [12203]

Arthur Flagler Fultz Research Award (Professional development/Grant) [1135]

Donald M. Furbush Professional Development Grants (Other/Grant) [5862]

The Future of Bariatric Surgery Scholarship (Undergraduate, Graduate, Vocational/Occupational/Scholarship) [2435]

Future Digital Marketers Scholarship (College, University/Scholarship) [2657]

Future Educators Scholarship (College, University/Scholarship) [7491]

Future Leader Initial NCTM Annual Meeting Attendance Awards (Advanced Professional/Award, Monetary) [7804]

G-1 Research Project Grants (Undergraduate/Grant) [6941]

G-2 Summer Portuguese Language Program (Undergraduate/Grant) [6942]

G-3 Summer Program in Portugal (Postgraduate/Grant) [6943]

Gabrial A. Hartl Scholarship (Undergraduate/Scholarship) [157]

Gabe Stepetin Business Scholarship (Undergraduate, Vocational/Occupational, Graduate, Master's/Scholarship) [329]

Gadde Sitaramamma & Tirupataiah Scholarship (Graduate/Scholarship) [10949]

Joe E. Gaddy, Jr. and Margaret W. Gaddy Scholarship (Undergraduate/Scholarship) [12078]

Gaebe Eagle Scout Award (Undergraduate/Scholarship) [7851]

Frederick and Helen Gaige Award (Professional development/Grant) [1483]

Gail Garner Memorial R.I.S.E. Scholarship (Undergraduate/Scholarship) [9548]

GALAS Scholarship (Undergraduate, Graduate/Scholarship) [4868]

Farley Moody Galbraith Scholarship (Graduate/Scholarship) [3653]

Whitney Laine Gallahar Memorial Scholarship Fund (Undergraduate/Scholarship) [3654]

The Gallery Collection's Create-A-Greeting-Card Scholarship (Undergraduate/Scholarship) [4848]

Gallo Blue Chip Scholarships (Undergraduate/Scholarship) [5301]

Lionel Galstaun Memorial Grant (Undergraduate/Scholarship) [1877]

Maro Ajemian Galstaun Memorial Grant (Undergraduate/Scholarship) [1878]

Gamma Chi Project 2000 Scholarship (Undergraduate/Scholarship) [6430]

Gamma Iota Scholarship (Undergraduate/Scholarship) [10108]

Gamma Iota Scholarships - Gamma Tau (Undergraduate/Scholarship) [10109]

Gamma Iota Scholarships - Zeta Kappa (Undergraduate/Scholarship) [10110]

Gamma Iota Scholarships - Zeta Nu (Undergraduate/Scholarship) [10111]

Gamma Lambda Scholarship (Undergraduate/Scholarship) [10112]

Gamma Mu Project 2000 Scholarship (Undergraduate/Scholarship) [6431]

The Gamma Mu Scholarships Program (Vocational/Occupational, Professional development, Undergraduate, Graduate, Postgraduate/Scholarship) [4854]

Gamma Pi Project 2000 Scholarship (Undergraduate/Scholarship) [6432]

Gamma Sigma Alpha Graduate Scholarship (Graduate/Scholarship) [4856]

Gamma Theta Project 2000 Scholarship (Undergraduate/Scholarship) [6433]

Gamma Zeta Project 2000 Scholarship (Undergraduate/Scholarship) [6434]

John A. Gans Scholarship (Undergraduate/Scholarship) [1748]

Gantenbein Medical Fund Fellowship (Graduate/Fellowship) [4092]

Michael and Gina Garcia Rail Engineering Scholarships (Undergraduate, Graduate/Scholarship) [1328]

William R. Gard Memorial Scholarships (Graduate/Scholarship) [7666]

Garden Club of America Awards in Tropical Botany (GCA) (Doctorate/Award) [4859]

The Garden Club Council of Winston-Salem and Forsyth County Scholarship (Undergraduate/Scholarship) [12079]

Gardner Foundation Education Scholarship (Professional development/Scholarship) [5786]

Dwight D. Gardner Scholarship (Undergraduate/Scholarship) [5828]

Eugene Garfield Doctoral Dissertation Fellowship (Doctorate/Fellowship) [2497]

Peter M. Gargano Scholarship Fund (Undergraduate/Scholarship) [4206]

Gary and Gussie Williams Scholarship (Undergraduate/Scholarship) [11621]

Gary Merrill Memorial Scholarship Fund (Undergraduate/Scholarship) [6979]

Edwin W. Gaston Scholarships (Undergraduate/Scholarship) [377]

The Gates Millennium Scholars (Undergraduate/Scholarship) [5529]

Marian P. and David M. Gates Scholarship for Non-Residents (Undergraduate/Scholarship) [11622]

James L. Gavin Memorial Scholarship (Undergraduate, Graduate/Scholarship) [2524]

A.R.F.O.R.A. Martha Gavrila Scholarships for Women (Postgraduate/Scholarship) [1368]

GAWP Graduate Scholarships (Graduate/Scholarship) [4925]

Lowell Gaylor Memorial Scholarships (Undergraduate/Scholarship) [181]

The Florence Gaynor Award (Graduate/Scholarship) [7654]

GCSAA Scholars Competition (Undergraduate/Scholarship) [5032]

GCSAA Student Essay Contest (Graduate, Undergraduate/Prize) [5033]

GE Aviation Scholarship Fund (Undergraduate/Scholarship) [3364]

GED Jump Start Scholarships (Professional development/Scholarship) [9959]

Geeta Rastogi Memorial Scholarship (Undergraduate/Scholarship) [11757]

Irma Gelhausen Scholarship Fund (Graduate/Scholarship) [6663]

The Gene & John Athletic Fund (Undergraduate/Scholarship) [10850]

General Falcon Scholarships (Undergraduate/Scholarship) [9243]

General John Paul Ratay Educational Fund Grants (Undergraduate/Grant) [7389]

Generation III Scholarship (Undergraduate/Scholarship) [4285]

Geological Society of America Graduate Student Research Grants (Doctorate, Graduate/Grant) [4910]

George C. Balch Scholarship (Graduate/Scholarship) [11383]

George E. Judd Scholarship Fund (Undergraduate/Scholarship) [10686]

George E. Nichols Undergraduate Scholarship (Undergraduate/Scholarship) [11624]

George H. A. Clowes, Jr. MD, FACS, Memorial Research Career Development Award (Professional development/Fellowship) [777]

George Hi'ilani Mills Scholarship (Graduate/Scholarship) [8925]

George N. Lindsay Fellowship (Graduate/Fellowship) [6740]

George Torkildsen Literary Award (Professional development/Award, Trophy) [12200]

George W. Juno Scholarship (Graduate/Scholarship) [4877]

Georgelis Injury Law Firm, P.C. Scholarship Award (Graduate/Scholarship) [4912]

Georgetown Working League Scholarship (Undergraduate/Scholarship) [4917]

Gerald V. Henderson Memorial Scholarship (Undergraduate, Graduate/Scholarship) [10427]

Geraldine Clewell Scholarship (Undergraduate/Scholarship) [9113]

Gerard Swartz Fudge Memorial Scholarship (Postgraduate/Scholarship) [5664]

Gerber Foundation Merit Scholarship (Graduate/Scholarship) [4940]

Burton L. Gerber Scholarship (Undergraduate/Scholarship) [2525]

Doris Y. and John J. Gerber Scholarship (Undergraduate/Scholarship) [11910]

Walter Gerboth Award (Other/Award, Monetary) [7515]

German Historical Institute Doctoral and Postdoctoral Fellowships (Doctorate, Postgraduate/Fellowship) [4942]

German Historical Institute Fellowships at the Horner Library (Postdoctorate, Master's/Fellowship) [4943]

German Society Scholarships (Undergraduate/Scholarship) [4951]

German Studies Research Grants (Undergraduate/Grant) [4062]

Bunny Kline Gerner & Robin Gerner Doty Memorial Adelphe Scholarship (Undergraduate/Scholarship) [6435]

Gertrude M. Cox Scholarship (Master's, Doctorate/Scholarship) [1611]

Elizabeth Tucker Gessley Scholarship (Undergraduate/Scholarship) [6436]

Get Ahead Scholarship (Undergraduate, Graduate/Scholarship) [4474]

Getty GRI-NEH Postdoctoral Fellowships (Postdoctorate/Fellowship) [4955]

Getty Research Exchange Fellowship Program for Cultural Heritage Preservation (Doctorate/Fellowship) [1347]

GFWC Women's Club of South County scholarship program (Undergraduate/Scholarship) [9693]

GIA Scholarship - Distance Education eLearning (Graduate/Scholarship) [4878]

John J. Gibbons Fellowship in Public Interest & Constitutional Law (Professional development/Fellowship) [4966]

Joy Gibson MATC Cohort Award (Undergraduate/Scholarship) [11188]

Laverne L. Gibson Memorial Scholarship (Undergraduate/Scholarship) [8848]

Robert D. Gibson Scholarship (Undergraduate/Scholarship) [1749]

Shane Gilbert Memorial Scholarship (Undergraduate/Scholarship) [8849]

Gilbreth Memorial Fellowship (Graduate/Fellowship) [5829]

Gilder Lehrman Short-Term research Fellowships (Graduate, Postdoctorate/Fellowship) [6773]

Terry M. Giles Honor Scholar Program (Undergraduate/Scholarship) [9001]

Gilliam Fellowships for Advanced Study (Postdoctorate, Master's, Graduate/Fellowship) [5615]

Benjamin A. Gilman International Scholarship (Undergraduate/Scholarship) [11479]

Susan Kay Munson Gilmore Memorial Scholarship (Undergraduate, Vocational/Occupational, Graduate/Scholarship) [3678]

Lawrence Ginocchio Aviation Scholarships (Undergraduate/Scholarship) [7736]

The Alex Gissler Memorial Scholarship (Undergraduate/Scholarship) [7171]

Gladys C. Anderson Memorial Scholarship (Undergraduate/Scholarship) [915]

John Glaser Scholarships (Undergraduate/Scholarship) [3506]

GLATA Living Memorial Doctorate Scholarship (Doctorate/Scholarship) [5215]

GLATA Living Memorial Graduate Scholarship (Graduate/Fellowship, Scholarship) [5216]

Glazing Industry Scholarship (Advanced Professional/Scholarship) [9402]

Glendale Latino Association Scholarships (Undergraduate/Scholarship) [4999]

Glenn Keever Scholarship (Undergraduate/Scholarship) [11189]

Glenn T. Seaborg Congressional Science and Engineering Fellowship (Professional development/Fellowship) [1165]

Bud Glover Memorial Scholarships (Undergraduate/Scholarship) [182]

Goddard, Indovina & Krakowski Scholarship (Undergraduate, Graduate/Scholarship) [396]

The Dr. Robert H. Goddard Memorial Scholarship (Graduate, Undergraduate/Scholarship) [8123]

The Marie Trahan/Susman Godfrey Scholarship (Undergraduate/Scholarship) [11148]

Glenn Godfrey Sr. Memorial Scholarship (Undergraduate, Graduate/Scholarship) [6589]

S. William & Martha R. Goff Educational Scholarship (Undergraduate/Scholarship) [8850]

Shirley J. Gold Scholarship (Undergraduate, Vocational/Occupational/Scholarship) [883]

Daniel B. Goldberg Scholarship (Graduate/Scholarship, Recognition) [5052]

Golden Door Scholarship (Graduate/Scholarship) [5018]

William R. Goldfarb Memorial Scholarships (Undergraduate/Scholarship) [1940]

Goldia.com Jewelry Scholarships (Undergraduate, Graduate/Scholarship) [5025]

Dr. Guido Goldman Fellowships (Postdoctorate/Fellowship) [807]

Goldman, Sachs and Company Fund (Undergraduate/Scholarship) [3365]

Goldman Sachs/Matsuo Takabuki Commemorative Scholarship (Undergraduate/Scholarship) [8926]

Joshua Gomes Memorial Scholarship Fund (Graduate/Scholarship) [7924]

Diane G. Lowe and John Gomez, IV Scholarship Fund (Undergraduate/Scholarship) [3620]

Goodman Acker Scholarships (Graduate/Scholarship) [5040]

Google Lime Scholarship (Undergraduate, Graduate, Doctorate/Scholarship) [6862]

Google US/Canada PhD Fellowships (Graduate, Doctorate/Fellowship) [5047]

Thomas Boston Gordon Memorial Scholarship (Undergraduate, Graduate/Scholarship) [2526]

Gordon W. and Agnes P. Cobb Scholarship (Undergraduate/Scholarship) [4256]

FAMU Presidential Scholarship - George W. Gore Assistantship Scholarship (Undergraduate/Scholarship) [4621]

Sarah "Sally" Ives Gore Gamma Kappa Sapphire Scholarships (Graduate, Undergraduate/Scholarship) [6437]

Louis Gottschalk Prize (Other/Prize) [1432]

Carl W. Gottschalk Research Scholar Grants (Professional development/Grant) [1526]

Wilford Hayes Gowen Scholarship Fund (Undergraduate/Scholarship) [11600]

Anna K. Gower and Annabelle K. Gower Scholarship Fund (Undergraduate, University, College, Two Year College, Vocational/Occupational/Scholarship) [5402]

Goya Scholarships (Graduate/Scholarship) [10028]

Graduate Fellowships for Study of International Affairs (Graduate, Master's/Fellowship) [4093]

Graduate Student Award (Doctorate, Master's, Graduate/Award) [515]

Grand Canyon Historical Society Scholarships (Graduate/Scholarship) [5066]

Grand Rapids University Prep Founders' Scholarship (Undergraduate/Scholarship) [5153]

Charles Hall Grandgent Award (Graduate/Award, Monetary) [3971]

Granger Business Association College Scholarship (Graduate/Scholarship) [5199]

Grant H. Flint International Scholarship Program - Category I (Undergraduate/Scholarship) [10580]

Russ Grant Memorial Scholarship for Tennis (Undergraduate/Scholarship) [8851]

Grants in Aid for Early Career Professionals (Graduate/Grant) [1294]

The Paul and Helen L. Grauer Scholarships (Undergraduate/Scholarship) [1941]

Graydon A. Tunstall Undergraduate Student Scholarship (Undergraduate/Scholarship) [9074]

Greater Seattle Business Association Scholarships (GSBA Scholarships) (Undergraduate, Graduate/Scholarship) [5223]

Frank L. Greathouse Government Accounting Scholarship (Graduate, Undergraduate/Award, Scholarship) [5053]

Bishop Charles P. Greco Graduate Fellowships (Graduate, Master's/Fellowship) [6578]

Greek Orthodox Archdiocese of America Paleologos Graduate Scholarships (Graduate/Scholarship) [5231]

Green Hill Yacht and Country Club Scholarship (Undergraduate, High School/Scholarship) [3568]

Green Knight Economic Development Corporation Scholarships (Undergraduate/Scholarship) [5235]

Crystal Green Memorial Scholarship (Graduate/Scholarship) [2626]

James H. and Shirley L. Green Scholarship Fund (Undergraduate/Scholarship) [10761]

Howard L. Green Scholarships (Undergraduate/Scholarship) [8273]

The K2TEO Martin J. Green, Sr. Memorial Scholarship (Undergraduate/Scholarship) [1942]

Michael Greenberg Student Writing Competition (Graduate/Monetary, Scholarship) [7986]

Curt Greene Memorial Scholarships (Undergraduate/Scholarship) [5302]

Elizabeth Greenhalgh Memorial Scholarships in Journalism, Graphic Arts, or Photography (Undergraduate/Scholarship) [12136]

Greenlining Institute Policy Fellowship (Undergraduate/Fellowship) [5237]

Anna Munger Greenwood Memorial Adelphe Scholarship (Undergraduate/Scholarship) [6438]

Gretchen Hauff Memorial Scholarship (Undergraduate/Scholarship) [9404]

Caroline and Martin Gross Fellowship (Professional development/Fellowship) [8256]

Kathern F. Gruber Scholarship Program (Undergraduate, Graduate/Scholarship) [2624]

Gruwell Scholarship *(Undergraduate/Scholarship)* [3569]

GSA Scholarships for International Nurses *(Undergraduate, Master's/Scholarship)* [5006]

Ronald P. Guerrette FFA Scholarship Fund *(Undergraduate/Scholarship)* [6980]

Eleanor Guetzloe Undergraduate Scholarship *(Undergraduate/Scholarship)* [3853]

Harry Frank Guggenheim Dissertation Fellowships *(Doctorate/Fellowship)* [5247]

Harry Frank Guggenheim Foundation Research Grants *(Professional development/Grant)* [5248]

John Simon Guggenheim Memorial Fellowships - United States & Canadian Competition *(Graduate, Postgraduate, Undergraduate/Fellowship)* [5250]

Bobette Bibo Gugliotta Memorial Scholarships for Creative Writing *(Undergraduate/Scholarship)* [10133]

Hai Guin Scholarships *(Undergraduate, Graduate/Scholarship)* [5260]

Guin-Stanford Scholarship *(Advanced Professional/Scholarship)* [3655]

George Gurdjian Memorial Grant *(Undergraduate/Scholarship)* [1879]

Antranik and Alice Gurdjian Scholarship Grant *(Undergraduate/Scholarship)* [1880]

The George Gurney Fellowship Endowment Fund *(Doctorate, Postdoctorate/Fellowship)* [10216]

Patricia S. Gustafson '56 Memorial Scholarship Fund *(Graduate/Scholarship)* [4207]

Guthikonda BasavapunnaRao & Umadevi Scholarship *(Graduate/Scholarship)* [10950]

Guthikonda Ramabrahmam & Balamani Scholarship *(Graduate/Scholarship)* [10951]

Guy D. & Mary Edith Halladay Music Scholarship *(Graduate, Undergraduate/Scholarship)* [5154]

Guy P. Gannett Scholarship Fund *(Undergraduate/Scholarship)* [6981]

Guzkowski Family Scholarships *(Undergraduate/Scholarship)* [9549]

Gwen Yarnell Theatre Scholarship *(Undergraduate/Scholarship)* [4566]

Gwin J. and Ruth Kolb Research Travel Fellowship *(Doctorate, Other/Fellowship)* [1433]

GWS Scholarship Program *(Undergraduate, Graduate/Scholarship)* [165]

H. Wayne VanAgtmael Cosmetology Scholarship *(Undergraduate/Scholarship)* [5081]

Garabed, Zabel and Vahe Hachikian Scholarship Grant *(Undergraduate/Scholarship)* [1881]

Hackett Family Scholarship *(Undergraduate/Scholarship)* [5155]

Louise Wallace Hackney Fellowships for the Study of Chinese Art *(Doctorate/Fellowship)* [1191]

HACU/KIA Motors America, Inc. STEAM Scholarships *(Undergraduate, Graduate/Scholarship)* [5516, 6543]

Perry F. Hadlock Memorial Scholarships *(Undergraduate/Scholarship)* [1943]

Suzanne Lovell Hadsell Memorial Scholarship *(Undergraduate, Graduate/Scholarship)* [6440]

Leslie Jane Hahn Memorial Scholarships *(Undergraduate/Scholarship)* [9816]

Jack Hajinian Memorial Grant *(Undergraduate/Scholarship)* [1882]

Lee Hakel Graduate Student Scholarship *(Graduate/Scholarship)* [10334]

Half Chrome Drones Scholarship *(Other/Scholarship)* [5262]

Hall of Achievement Scholarship *(Undergraduate/Scholarship)* [2799]

Anna E. Hall Memorial Scholarships *(Undergraduate, Graduate, Doctorate/Scholarship)* [9084]

David J. Hallissey Memorial Internships *(Graduate, Undergraduate/Internship)* [1586]

The Caitlin Hammaren Memorial Scholarship *(Undergraduate/Scholarship)* [6441]

Harry Hampton Fund Scholarship *(Undergraduate/Scholarship)* [5266]

Hampton Roads Association of Social Workers Scholarship *(Graduate/Scholarship)* [5271]

HANA Scholars *(Undergraduate, Graduate, Doctorate/Scholarship)* [4891]

Hancock Family Snow Hill High School Scholarship *(Graduate/Scholarship)* [3570]

Byron Hanke Fellowships *(Doctorate, Graduate, Undergraduate/Fellowship)* [4767]

Clayburn J. Sr. & Garnet R. Hanna Scholarship *(Undergraduate/Scholarship)* [8852]

Hans H. and Margaret B. Doe Scholarship *(Graduate, Undergraduate/Scholarship)* [9817]

Charles Henry Hardin Memorial Scholarship *(Undergraduate, Graduate/Scholarship)* [2527]

Dolores Ruth Heady Hardy Memorial Scholarship *(Undergraduate/Scholarship)* [6442]

Harkness Fellowships in Health Care Policy and Practice *(Doctorate, Graduate/Fellowship)* [3555]

Margaret Shumavonian Harnischfeger Scholarship *(Undergraduate/Scholarship)* [1883]

Harold E. Ennes Scholarship *(Graduate/Scholarship)* [10285]

Harold Gulliksen Psychometric Research Fellowship *(Doctorate, Graduate/Fellowship)* [4312]

Harriet Irsay Scholarship *(Graduate, Undergraduate/Scholarship)* [1045]

Marcia S. Harris Legacy Fund Scholarships *(Undergraduate, Advanced Professional/Scholarship)* [9650]

Eileen Harrison Education Scholarships *(Graduate, Undergraduate/Scholarship)* [5083]

Lullelia W. Harrison Scholarships in Counseling *(Graduate, Undergraduate/Scholarship)* [12411]

Harrisville Lion's Club Scholarship *(Undergraduate, Vocational/Occupational/Scholarship)* [8854]

Harry A. Donn Scholarship *(Undergraduate/Scholarship)* [5329]

Harry Munoz Memorial Scholarship *(Undergraduate/Scholarship)* [9550]

Dave Hart Graduate Scholarship *(Graduate/Scholarship)* [10654]

Ida L. Hartenberg Charitable Scholarships *(Undergraduate/Scholarship)* [5330]

Hartford Grammar School Scholarship Fund *(Undergraduate/Scholarship)* [5331]

Hartford Whalers Booster Club Scholarship *(Undergraduate/Scholarship)* [5353]

Harry C. Hartleben III/Gordon Page Corbitt Scholarship *(Undergraduate/Scholarship)* [8855]

Gail L. Hartshorn Memorial Fund *(Other/Scholarship)* [8856]

Harvey Fellows Program *(Graduate/Fellowship)* [7519]

Harvey M. Pollicove Memorial Scholarship *(Undergraduate, Graduate/Scholarship)* [8676]

Harvey Washington Banks Scholarship in Astronomy *(Undergraduate/Scholarship)* [8086]

Donald F. Hastings Scholarship *(Undergraduate/Scholarship)* [1661]

Gregory Linn Haught Citizenship Award *(Undergraduate/Scholarship)* [8857]

Hawaii Chapter/David T. Woolsey Scholarship *(Undergraduate, Graduate, Professional development/Scholarship)* [6647]

Don C. Hawkins Memorial Scholarships *(Undergraduate/Scholarship)* [184]

Thomas T. Hayashi Memorial Scholarship *(Graduate, Undergraduate/Scholarship)* [6246]

Celeste Hayo Memorial Scholarship Fund *(Undergraduate, College, University/Scholarship)* [5403]

Hazel D. Isbell Foundation Fellowships *(Graduate/Fellowship)* [4003]

Hazen and Sawyer Scholarship *(Master's/Scholarship, Monetary)* [1641]

HBO Point Scholarship *(Graduate, Undergraduate, Doctorate/Scholarship)* [9222]

H.C. Schott Foundation Scholarship *(Undergraduate/Scholarship)* [3366]

HCF Community Scholarships Fund *(Undergraduate, Graduate/Scholarship)* [5404]

HCRTA/Glen O. & Wyllabeth Scholarship Fund *(Undergraduate/Scholarship)* [3367]

HDSA Research Grants *(Graduate/Grant)* [5657]

Health and Aging Policy Fellows Program *(Advanced Professional, Professional development/Fellowship)* [1255]

Health is a Right Not a Privilege Scholarship *(Advanced Professional, Master's, Graduate/Scholarship)* [8561]

Health Services Research Dissertation Awards *(Doctorate/Award)* [11326]

Healthcare Information Management Systems Scholarships *(Graduate, Postgraduate, Undergraduate/Scholarship)* [5448]

Healthy Communities Scholarship *(Undergraduate, Graduate, Community College/Scholarship)* [9282]

Dr. James H. Heckman Memorial Scholarship Fund *(Undergraduate/Scholarship)* [10763]

HECUA Scholarship for Community Engagement *(Undergraduate/Scholarship)* [5505]

HECUA Scholarship for Social Justice *(Undergraduate, Graduate/Scholarship)* [5506]

Vladimir and Pearl Heifetz Memorial Fellowship *(Undergraduate, Graduate, Postgraduate/Fellowship)* [12236]

Hekemian Family Scholarship Grants *(Undergraduate/Scholarship)* [1884]

Helen Hay Whitney Foundation Postdoctoral Research Fellowship *(Postdoctorate, Master's/Fellowship)* [12020]

Helen R. (Finley) Loescher and Stephen B. Loescher Scholarship *(High School/Scholarship)* [3679]

Helen Steiner Rice Scholarship Fund *(Undergraduate/Scholarship)* [3370]

Helena B. Cobb Higher Education (four Year) Scholarship *(Undergraduate, Vocational/Occupational/Scholarship)* [12165]

The Helena B. Cobb Scholarships *(Undergraduate, Vocational/Occupational/Scholarship)* [12166]

Helene M. Overly Memorial Graduate Scholarship *(Graduate/Scholarship)* [12170]

Commercial Helicopter Pilot Rating Scholarships *(Other/Scholarship)* [5456]

Helicopter Foundation International Maintenance Technician Certificate Scholarships *(Other/Scholarship)* [5457]

Hellenic Times Scholarships *(Undergraduate, Graduate/Scholarship)* [5461]

Joseph T. Helling Scholarship Fund *(Undergraduate/Scholarship)* [5748]

Ronald, Randall and Roger Helman Scholarship *(Undergraduate, Graduate/Scholarship)* [2528]

Helmer, Conley & Kasselman Annual College Scholarship *(Undergraduate/Scholarship)* [5471]

Heloise Werthan Kuhn Scholarship Fund *(Undergraduate/Scholarship)* [3621]

"Help to Save" Scholarship *(College, University/Scholarship)* [3880]

Clinton J. Helton Manufacturing Scholarship *(Undergraduate/Scholarship)* [10402]

Hemlow Prize in Burney Studies *(Graduate/Prize)* [1434]

Hench Post-Dissertation Fellowship *(Postdoctorate/Fellowship)* [491]

Henigson Human Rights Fellowship *(Graduate, Master's, Juris Doctorate/Fellowship)* [5365]

SNMMI Robert E. Henkin, MD, Government Relations Fellowship *(Professional development/Fellowship)* [10439]

Henley-Putnam University Scholarships *(Other/Scholarship)* [5931]

Henry Adams Scholarship *(Undergraduate/Scholarship)* [1474]

Randy Henry Memorial Scholarship *(Undergraduate/Scholarship)* [9343]

Allan F. Henry/Paul A. Greebler Scholarship *(Graduate/Scholarship)* [1166]

Henry S. and Carolyn Adams Scholarship *(Undergraduate/Scholarship)* [4734]

Henry Salvatori Fellowships *(Graduate/Fellowship)* [5885]

Henry Salvatori Scholarship *(Undergraduate/Scholarship)* [8689]

Herb Adrian Memorial Scholarship Endowment *(Undergraduate/Scholarship)* [4735]

Herb And Ann Fincher Scholarship Fund *(Undergraduate/Scholarship)* [3571]

Herbert Law Office Scholarship Contest *(Undergraduate/Scholarship)* [5492]

Herbert Scoville Jr. Peace Fellowship *(Graduate/Fellowship)* [9988]

Hermann Law Group, PLLC Safety Scholarship Contest *(Undergraduate/Scholarship)* [5496]

Hernandez – Manuel Hernandez, Jr. Memorial Scholarship *(Undergraduate/Scholarship)* [3477]

George L. and June L. Herpel Memorial Scholarship *(Graduate/Scholarship)* [2529]

The Herpetologists' League Graduate Research Award *(Graduate/Award)* [5499]

Purdue University Ray W. Herrick Laboratories Research Fellowship *(Graduate/Fellowship)* [9451]

Jessica M. Herron, Epsilon Nu, Memorial Scholarship *(Undergraduate, Graduate/Scholarship)* [6443]

Ella Beren Hersch Scholarship *(Undergraduate/ Scholarship)* [8859]

Herschede Engineering Scholarship *(Graduate/ Scholarship)* [10082]

Isabel M. Herson Scholarships in Education *(Graduate, Undergraduate/Scholarship)* [12412]

Hertz Foundation Graduate Fellowship Award *(Graduate/Fellowship)* [5502]

Aleksander and Alicja Hertz Memorial Fellowship *(Doctorate, Postdoctorate/Fellowship)* [12237]

Wayne E. Hesch Memorial Scholarship *(Undergraduate, Graduate/Scholarship)* [1691]

Beth B. Hess Memorial Scholarship *(Doctorate, Graduate/Fellowship, Award)* [10566]

HFA Educational Scholarship *(Undergraduate/Scholarship)* [5479]

HFMH Bilingual Scholarships for Mental Health Workforce Diversity *(Graduate/Scholarship)* [5539]

HGS Foundation Undergraduate Scholarships *(Undergraduate/Scholarship)* [5597]

H.H. Harris Foundation Scholarship *(Professional development, Undergraduate/Scholarship, Monetary)* [932]

HHMI International Student Research Fellowships *(Doctorate/Fellowship)* [5616]

HHMI Medical Research Fellowship *(Undergraduate/Fellowship)* [5617]

HIAA Graduate Student Travel Grants *(Graduate/ Grant)* [5534]

Dorothy Hicks Graduate Scholarship *(Graduate/ Scholarship)* [10655]

Frances C. Hidell Scholarship *(Undergraduate/ Scholarship)* [2144]

Jim Hierlihy Memorial Scholarship *(Undergraduate/ Scholarship)* [4429]

Howard B. Higgins South Carolina Dental Scholarships *(Undergraduate/Scholarship)* [4736]

HII Scholarship Fund *(Community College, Two Year College, Four Year College, Undergraduate, University/Scholarship)* [5655]

Robert S. Hilbert Memorial Student Travel Grants *(Graduate, Undergraduate/Grant)* [8677]

Wayne Hildebrant Police Scholarship Fund *(Undergraduate/Scholarship)* [6665]

Douglas W. Hill, Jr. Scholarship *(Undergraduate, Graduate/Scholarship)* [2530]

John A. Hill Memorial Scholarship *(Undergraduate, Graduate/Scholarship)* [2531]

Gus and Henrietta Hill Scholarship Fund *(Graduate/ Scholarship)* [4209]

HIPLA Fellowship *(Undergraduate/Fellowship)* [5599]

HIPLA Scholarships for University of Houston Law Center Students *(Graduate, Undergraduate/Scholarship)* [5600]

Oregon Latino Scholarship Fund *(Graduate, Undergraduate/Scholarship)* [5526]

Hispanic Scholarship Fund General College Scholarship Program (HSF) *(Undergraduate/Scholarship)* [5530]

Hispanic Serving Institution Scholarships (HSIS) *(Undergraduate/Scholarship)* [11280]

Historically Black College or University Scholarships (HBCUS) *(Undergraduate/Scholarship)* [11281]

History of Art: Institutional Fellowships *(Graduate/ Fellowship)* [6613]

HIV Prevention Research Advocacy Fellowships *(Professional development/Fellowship)* [2368]

The Albert H. Hix, W8AH, Memorial Scholarship *(Undergraduate/Scholarship)* [1944]

HLS/MLA Professional Development Grants *(Other/ Grant)* [7218]

Lou Hochberg Awards - University/College Essay Awards *(Undergraduate/Award, Monetary)* [8756]

Jeri Hodges Leadership Scholarship *(Professional development/Scholarship)* [10978]

The George W. and Ethel B. Hoefler Fund *(Undergraduate/Scholarship)* [3714]

Dorothy M. and Earl S. Hoffman Award *(Graduate/ Award)* [2383]

Hoffman Family Scholarship *(Undergraduate/Scholarship)* [5085]

Henry Hoffman Memorial Scholarship *(Undergraduate/Scholarship)* [7641]

Miriam Hoffman Scholarship *(Undergraduate, Graduate/Scholarship)* [4892]

The Stephanie G. Hoffman Scholarship *(Graduate, Undergraduate/Scholarship)* [6274]

The Michael J. Hogan Foreign Language Fellowship *(Graduate/Fellowship)* [10356]

The Thelma S. Hoge Memorial Scholarship *(Graduate/Scholarship)* [3596]

Raymond T. Hoge Scholarship Fund *(Undergraduate/Scholarship)* [10765]

R.W. "Bob" Holden Memorial Scholarships *(Undergraduate/Scholarship)* [5419]

Dr. Marshall E. Hollis Scholarship *(Undergraduate, Graduate/Scholarship)* [2532]

Holly A. Cornell Scholarship *(Master's/Scholarship, Monetary)* [1642, 3272]

Robert Holmes Scholarship *(Undergraduate/Scholarship)* [3720]

George Holopigian Memorial Grants *(Undergraduate/Scholarship)* [1885]

The Arthur and Janet Holzheimer Fellowship in the History of Cartography *(Postdoctorate, Doctorate/ Fellowship)* [8373]

Holzheimer Memorial Student Scholarship *(Graduate, Master's/Scholarship)* [1243]

Hon. Peggy Bernheim Memorial Scholarship *(Undergraduate/Scholarship)* [2711]

Honeywell Avionics Scholarships *(Undergraduate/ Scholarship)* [185]

Hope Through Learning Award *(Undergraduate/ Award)* [5551]

Seth Horen, K1LOM Memorial Scholarships *(Undergraduate/Scholarship)* [1945]

Edward Horne Scholarship *(Advanced Professional/ Scholarship)* [8742]

Saul Horowitz Jr. Memorial Graduate Award *(Graduate/Scholarship, Award)* [126]

Judge and Mrs. Robert D. Horowitz Legal Scholarship Fund *(Graduate, Undergraduate/Scholarship)* [10766]

Horticulture Scholarship from Frances Sylvia Zverina *(Undergraduate/Scholarship)* [5486]

Horticulture Scholarship of the Western Reserve Herb Society *(Undergraduate/Scholarship)* [5487]

Detroit Tigers Willie Horton Scholarship *(Undergraduate/Scholarship)* [3721]

HostingAdvice.com Future Web Developers Annual Scholarship *(Undergraduate/Scholarship)* [5590]

Max and Julia Houghton Duluth Central Scholarships *(Undergraduate/Scholarship)* [4210]

Houston Alumnae Chapter Graduate Fellowship *(Graduate/Fellowship)* [4004]

The HoustonMovers.com Scholarship *(Undergraduate/Scholarship)* [5602]

The Hirair and Anna Hovnanian Foundation Presidential Scholarship *(Undergraduate/Scholarship)* [5512]

Howard A. Clark Horticulture Scholarship Fund *(Undergraduate/Scholarship)* [3622]

Howard A. Crum Memorial Scholarship *(Undergraduate/Scholarship)* [11625]

Howard E. and Wilma J. Adkins Memorial Scholarship *(Undergraduate/Scholarship)* [1662]

William C. Howell Scholarship *(Graduate, Master's, Doctorate/Scholarship)* [1283]

Christopher Hoy/ERT Scholarship *(Graduate/Scholarship, Monetary)* [1078]

Carol Hoy Scholarship Fund *(Undergraduate/Scholarship)* [4778]

HRET Health Career Scholarships *(Postgraduate, Undergraduate/Scholarship)* [8275]

HRH Prince Alwaleed Bin Talal ISNA Fellowships *(Graduate/Fellowship)* [6180]

HRSA Scholarships for Disadvantaged Students *(Undergraduate/Scholarship)* [11334]

HSF/Marathon Oil College Scholarship Program *(Undergraduate/Scholarship)* [5531]

HSF/Wells Fargo Scholarship Program *(Undergraduate, Graduate, High School/Scholarship)* [5532]

HSMAI Foundation Scholarship *(Graduate/Scholarship)* [5608]

Albert W. and Mildred Hubbard Scholarships *(Undergraduate/Scholarship)* [9822]

Huber Engineered Woods Product Evaluation Scholarships *(Graduate/Scholarship)* [4500]

Amber Huber Memorial Scholarship *(Undergraduate/Scholarship)* [3680]

Hubert K. and JoAnn Seymour Scholarship *(Undergraduate/Scholarship)* [8461]

Huenefeld/Denton Scholarships *(Undergraduate/ Scholarship)* [4038]

Hugh and Elizabeth Montgomery Scholarship Fund *(Undergraduate/Scholarship)* [6983]

Hughes Memorial Foundatio n *(Other/Scholarship)* [5619]

Paul A. Hughes Memorial Scholarships *(Undergraduate/Scholarship)* [2800]

Huguenot Society of South Carolina Graduate Scholarship *(Graduate/Scholarship)* [5621]

Humane Studies Fellowship *(Graduate/Fellowship)* [5824]

Humanism in Medicine Scholarships *(Undergraduate/Scholarship)* [10865]

Anna C. Hume Scholarship *(Undergraduate/Scholarship)* [4976]

Kevin Hummer Point Scholarship *(Graduate, Undergraduate, Doctorate/Scholarship)* [9223]

Betty Jo Creighton Hunkele Adelphe Scholarship *(Undergraduate/Scholarship)* [6446]

Dr. Richard M. Hunt Fellowships *(Doctorate, Postdoctorate/Fellowship)* [808]

The Donald A. King Summer Research Fellowship *(Undergraduate/Fellowship)* [5658]

Zora Neale Hurston Scholarships *(Graduate/Scholarship)* [12413]

The Husenig Foundation Scholarship Grant *(Undergraduate/Scholarship)* [1886]

The Hyatt Hotels Fund For Minority Lodging Management Students *(Undergraduate/Scholarship)* [972]

Janet Hyde Graduate Student Research Grant *(Doctorate, Graduate/Grant)* [1732]

Hydro Research Foundation Fellowships *(Advanced Professional/Fellowship)* [5661]

Hylan Family Scholarship *(Two Year College, Four Year College/Scholarship)* [5671]

Hypertherm International HyTech Leadership Scholarships *(Graduate/Scholarship)* [1663]

I Have a Dream Scholarship *(Graduate, High School/Scholarship)* [11230]

IAAP Wings Chapter Scholarships *(Undergraduate/ Scholarship)* [5901]

IABA Scholarship *(Graduate/Scholarship)* [6170]

IAEM Scholarship Program *(Undergraduate, Graduate/Scholarship)* [5919]

IAESTE United States Internships *(Undergraduate/ Internship)* [3937]

IAHCSMM-Purdue University Scholarship *(Professional development/Scholarship)* [5927]

IALL Regular Bursaries *(Other/Scholarship)* [5933]

IARS Mentored Research Award (IMRA) *(Professional development/Award, Grant)* [5899]

IASC Doctoral Fellowships - Dissertation *(Doctorate/ Fellowship)* [11720]

IASC Doctoral Fellowships - Pre-Dissertation *(Doctorate/Fellowship)* [11721]

IASC Postdoctoral Fellowships *(Postdoctorate/Fellowship)* [11722]

IASC Visiting Fellowships *(Professional development/Fellowship)* [11723]

IASP Collaborative Research Grants *(Professional development/Grant)* [5939]

IASP Visiting Professor Grant *(Professional development/Grant)* [5943]

IAWP International Scholarship *(Other/Scholarship)* [5949]

Iberdrola USA Scholarships *(Undergraduate/Scholarship)* [6984]

ICC General Scholarship Fund *(Undergraduate/ Scholarship, Monetary, Award)* [5971]

Ice Skating Institute of America Education Foundation Scholarships *(Undergraduate/Scholarship)* [5673]

ICJS Short-Term Fellowships *(Doctorate, Postdoctorate, Advanced Professional/Fellowship)* [10184]

ICMA Local Government Management Fellowship *(Master's/Fellowship)* [5968]

ICNL Research Fellowships *(Advanced Professional, Professional development/Fellowship)* [5964]

ICRS Graduate Fellowships *(Doctorate, Graduate/Fellowship)* [5976]

The Idaho Advocates Scholarship *(University, Graduate/Scholarship)* [92]

David Iden Memorial Safety Scholarships *(Undergraduate/Scholarship)* [1565]

IEHA Education/Scholarship Foundation Award *(Undergraduate/Scholarship)* [5998]

IFDA Student Member Scholarship *(Undergraduate/Scholarship)* [6014]

Ella R. Ifill Fund *(Undergraduate/Scholarship)* [6985]

IILJ Scholarships *(Doctorate/Scholarship)* [5845]

IILJ Visiting Fellowships and Research *(Postdoctorate/Fellowship)* [5846]

IISE Presidents Scholarship *(Undergraduate/Scholarship)* [5831]

Illinois Association of Chamber of Commerce Executives Scholarships *(Professional development/Scholarship)* [5693]

Illinois Division of Midwest Dairy Educational Award *(Undergraduate/Scholarship)* [7369]

Illuminator Educational Foundation Scholarships *(Undergraduate, Graduate/Scholarship)* [2801]

IMA Memorial Education Fund Scholarships (MEF) *(Graduate, Undergraduate/Scholarship)* [5848]

Imagine America College Scholarships for High School Students *(Undergraduate/Scholarship)* [5717]

Imagine America Scholarships for Adults *(Undergraduate/Scholarship)* [5719]

Elmer S. Imes Scholarships in Physics *(Undergraduate/Scholarship)* [8087]

John L. Imhoff Scholarship *(Graduate, Undergraduate/Scholarship)* [5832]

Imprex Scholarship *(College, University/Scholarship)* [5727]

Ina Knutsen Scholarship *(Undergraduate/Scholarship)* [10054]

Independent Professional Seed Association Student Recognition Awards *(Undergraduate/Scholarship)* [5740]

Indian Health Service Professionals Program *(Undergraduate/Scholarship)* [988]

Indiana FFA Association State Fair Scholarship *(Undergraduate/Scholarship)* [5752]

Individual K-Grants *(All/Grant)* [6564]

INF Scholarships *(Undergraduate/Scholarship)* [6166]

Influenster Code Like a Girl Scholarships *(Undergraduate, Graduate/Scholarship)* [5782]

Informatics Post Doctoral Fellowships *(Doctorate/Fellowship)* [9056]

Informatics Pre Doctoral Fellowships *(Doctorate/Fellowship)* [9057]

Terrance N. Ingraham Pediatric Optometry Residency Award *(Graduate/Award)* [463]

Jennifer Ingrum Scholarship Fund *(Undergraduate/Scholarship)* [3623]

Injury Scholarship *(Undergraduate/Scholarship)* [7164]

INKAS Rising Star Scholarship *(University/Scholarship)* [5789]

Inland Northwest Business Alliance Scholarships (INBA) *(Undergraduate/Scholarship)* [9302]

Innovative Grants-Pilot and Research Tool Grants *(Postdoctorate/Grant)* [6348]

Institute for Health Metrics and Evaluation Post Bachelor Fellowship (PBF) *(Graduate/Fellowship)* [5821]

Institute for Health Metrics and Evaluation Post Graduate Fellowships (PGF) *(Doctorate, Postdoctorate/Fellowship)* [5822]

Institute for the International Education of Students Faculty Fellowships *(Postdoctorate/Fellowship)* [5843, 8374]

Institute of Management Accountants FAR Doctoral Student Grants Program *(Doctorate/Grant)* [5849]

Integra Foundation NNF Research Grant Awards *(Professional development/Grant)* [611]

Inter American Press Association Scholarships *(Undergraduate/Scholarship)* [10253]

International Affairs Fellowships in Nuclear Security (IAF-NS) *(Professional development/Fellowship)* [3865]

International Association of Foundation Drilling Scholarships for Civil Engineering Students *(Graduate/Scholarship)* [81]

International Association of Foundation Drilling Scholarships for Part-time Civil Engineering Graduate School Students *(Graduate/Scholarship)* [82]

International Association of Wildland Fire Graduate-Level Scholarships *(Graduate/Scholarship)* [5947]

International Code Council Scholarship *(Graduate/Scholarship)* [4501]

International Dissertation Research Fellowship (IDRF) *(Graduate, Doctorate/Fellowship)* [10246]

International Executive Housekeepers Association Spartan Scholarship Award *(Undergraduate/Scholarship)* [5999]

International Foodservice Editorial Council Scholarship *(Graduate/Scholarship)* [6007]

International Furnishings and Design Association Part-time Student Scholarship *(Undergraduate/Scholarship)* [6015]

International Management Council Scholarship (IMC) *(Undergraduate/Scholarship)* [3681]

International Operators Scholarship *(Professional development/Scholarship)* [7737]

International Order of the King's Daughters and Sons North American Indian Scholarship Program *(Undergraduate/Scholarship)* [989]

International Radio and Television Society Foundation Summer Fellowships Program *(Undergraduate, Graduate/Fellowship)* [6067]

International Sanitary Supply Association Foundation Scholarships *(Undergraduate/Scholarship)* [6081]

International Scholars Program for Young Vascular Surgeons *(Graduate/Scholarship)* [10555]

International Society for Humor Studies Graduate Student Awards (GSA) *(Graduate/Award, Scholarship)* [6111]

International Society for Humor Studies Scholarly Contribution Awards (SCA) *(Other/Award)* [6112]

International Women's Fishing Association Scholarship Trust *(Graduate/Scholarship)* [6146]

The Interracial Scholarship Fund of Greater Hartford *(Undergraduate/Scholarship)* [5333]

Investigators in the Pathogenesis of Infectious Disease *(Doctorate, Postdoctorate/Grant)* [2754]

IOIA Organic Community Initiative Scholarships *(Other/Scholarship)* [6054]

IOKDS Health Careers Scholarship *(College, University, Undergraduate, Graduate, Doctorate/Scholarship)* [6050]

IOKDS Student Ministry Scholarships *(Master's/Scholarship)* [6052]

Iowa Division of Midwest Dairy Educational Award *(Undergraduate/Scholarship)* [7370]

IPPR North Events Internship *(Undergraduate/Internship)* [5854]

Iranian-American Scholarship Fund *(Undergraduate, Graduate/Scholarship)* [7954]

IRARC Memorial, Joseph P. Rubino, WA4MMD, Scholarship *(Undergraduate/Scholarship)* [1946]

Irene Winifred Eno Grant *(Professional development/Grant)* [1487]

Irene Woodall Graduate Scholarship *(Graduate/Scholarship)* [860]

Iris Scholarship *(Undergraduate/Scholarship)* [6447]

Irma E. Voigt Memorial Scholarship *(Undergraduate/Scholarship)* [10113]

Greg Irons Award Fund *(Undergraduate/Award)* [4211]

David L. Irons Memorial Scholarship Fund *(Undergraduate, Two Year College, Four Year College/Scholarship)* [5405]

Irwin S. Lerner Student Scholarship *(Undergraduate/Scholarship)* [8108]

ISA Educational Foundation Scholarship *(Undergraduate, Graduate/Scholarship)* [6086]

ISA Section and District Scholarships - Southwestern Wyoming *(Graduate, Undergraduate/Scholarship)* [6091]

ISA Section and District Scholarships - Texas, Louisiana and Mississippi *(Graduate, Undergraduate/Scholarship)* [6092]

ISA Section and District Scholarships - Wilmington *(Graduate, Undergraduate/Scholarship)* [6093]

Isabel Mayer Kirkpatrick Scholarship Fund *(Undergraduate/Scholarship)* [10687]

ISCALC International Scholarship Fund *(Undergraduate/Scholarship)* [4594]

ISDS Graduate Student Scholarships *(Doctorate, Graduate/Scholarship)* [6105]

ISF Excellence in Community Service Scholarship *(Undergraduate/Scholarship)* [6173]

ISF Undergraduate Scholarship *(Undergraduate/Scholarship)* [6174]

ISID Small Grants *(Postdoctorate, Professional development/Grant)* [6114]

Islamic Scholarship Fund Scholarship (ISF) *(Graduate, Undergraduate/Scholarship)* [6178]

ISOPE Offshore Mechanics Scholarships for Outstanding Students *(Graduate/Scholarship)* [6116]

ISTTE Scholarship *(Graduate, Undergraduate/Scholarship)* [6122]

ISTU Student Prizes *(Undergraduate/Prize)* [6119]

ITAA Graduate Student Best Paper Award *(Graduate/Award, Monetary)* [6129]

Italian Language Scholarship *(Undergraduate/Scholarship)* [8690]

ITMS Shannon Fellowships *(Graduate, Undergraduate/Fellowship)* [6132]

ITNS Research Grants *(Other/Grant)* [6137]

ITW Welding Companies Scholarships *(Undergraduate/Scholarship)* [1664]

Ivanhoe Foundation Fellowship *(Master's/Fellowship)* [6184]

Bob and Mary Ives Scholarship *(Graduate, Undergraduate/Scholarship)* [6102]

Iwalani Carpenter Sowa Scholarship *(Graduate/Scholarship)* [8928]

J. Jay Hostetler Scholarship *(Undergraduate/Scholarship)* [6383]

J. Newell Stannard Fellowship *(Graduate, Undergraduate/Fellowship)* [5429]

J. Ward Sleichter and Frances F. Sleichter Memorial Fund *(Undergraduate/Scholarship)* [4779]

Jack H. Brown Future Leaders Scholarships *(Undergraduate/Scholarship)* [2802]

The Jack and Jill of America Foundation's National Scholarship Program *(Undergraduate/Scholarship)* [6190]

Jack Kent Cooke Foundation College Scholarship Program *(Undergraduate/Scholarship)* [3820]

Jack Kent Cooke Foundation Undergraduate Transfer Scholarship *(Undergraduate/Scholarship)* [3821]

Jack Kent Cooke Foundation Young Scholars Program *(Undergraduate/Scholarship)* [3822]

Jack M. Nagasaka Memorial Scholarship *(Undergraduate/Scholarship)* [9551]

Jack R. Gilstrap Scholarship *(Undergraduate, Graduate/Scholarship)* [1302]

Jackie Robinson Scholarship Award *(Undergraduate/Scholarship)* [9723]

Jackman Scholarships *(Undergraduate/Scholarship)* [9114]

Graduate Student Honoraria - Anna M. Jackson Awards *(Master's, Doctorate/Award)* [1504]

Jackson Club Scholarship Fund *(Undergraduate/Scholarship)* [4212]

Jackson High School Alumni Scholarship Fund *(Graduate/Scholarship)* [10768]

Dwight P. Jacobus Scholarships *(Undergraduate/Scholarship)* [2277]

Jacque Placette Chapman Master's Fellowships *(Graduate, Master's/Fellowship)* [8686]

Jacqueline Shields Memorial Scholarship *(Graduate/Scholarship)* [161]

Cory Jam Memorial Award *(Undergraduate/Scholarship)* [4213]

James Bilder Scholarship Fund *(Undergraduate/Scholarship)* [10688]

The James Davidson Innovative Student Scholarship *(Graduate/Scholarship)* [10739]

James Davis Scholarship *(Undergraduate/Scholarship)* [11190]

James E. Hoff, S.J. Scholar *(Undergraduate/Scholarship)* [12223]

James E. Long Memorial Post Doctoral Fellowship *(Postdoctorate/Fellowship)* [5984]

James E. West Fellowship *(Graduate/Fellowship)* [62]

James F. Hurley III Bicentennial Merit Scholarship *(Undergraduate/Scholarship)* [11191]

James L. Biggane Fellowship in Finance *(Graduate/Fellowship)* [8325]

James L. and Genevieve H. Goodwin Scholarship *(Undergraduate/Scholarship)* [5334]

James L. Plafkin Memorial Scholarship *(Undergraduate/Scholarship)* [11626]

James and Marilyn Rockefeller Scholarship Fund *(Undergraduate/Scholarship)* [6986]

James W. Junior and Jane T. Brown Scholarship *(Undergraduate, Vocational/Occupational/Scholarship)* [5086]

James Wisecup Memorial Flight Training Scholarship *(Vocational/Occupational, Advanced Professional/Scholarship)* [12011]

J. Franklin Jameson Fellowship in American History *(Doctorate/Fellowship)* [960]

Jan Jancin Award *(Undergraduate/Award)* [4697]

Jane Beattie Memorial Scholarship *(Graduate/Scholarship)* [10378]

Jane C. Waldbaum Archaeological Field School Scholarship *(Undergraduate, Graduate/Scholarship, Award)* [1777]

Jane Coffin Childs Memorial Fund - Medical Research Postdoctoral Fellowship *(Postdoctorate, Doctorate/Fellowship)* [3303]

Janssen Infectious Disease Point Scholarships *(Undergraduate, Graduate, Doctorate/Scholarship)* [9224]

Jason Chaney Memorial Scholarship *(High School/Scholarship)* [11948]

Jacob K. Javits Fellowships Program *(Master's, Doctorate/Fellowship)* [11310]

Jay C. and B. Nadine Leggett Charitable Fund *(Undergraduate/Scholarship)* [10769]

J.B. and Marilyn McKenzie Graduate Student Fellowship *(Graduate/Fellowship)* [11627]

JCC Association Graduate Education Scholarships *(Graduate/Scholarship)* [6257]

JCCF Equal Voice Journalism Scholarship *(Professional development/Scholarship)* [11591]

JDBNOW Scholarship *(Two Year College, Undergraduate, Graduate/Scholarship)* [6259]

Advanced Postdoctoral Fellowships *(Postdoctorate, Master's/Fellowship)* [6349]

Career Development Awards *(Professional development, Postdoctorate/Grant, Award)* [6350]

JDRF Outreach Scholarship *(Undergraduate, Master's, Doctorate/Scholarship)* [5705]

JDRF Postdoctoral Fellowships *(Postdoctorate/Fellowship)* [6351]

JEA Future Journalism Teacher Scholarships *(Undergraduate, Master's/Scholarship)* [6336]

Jean Bennett Memorial Student Travel Grant *(Graduate, Undergraduate/Grant)* [8678]

Jean Dearth Dickerscheid Fellowship *(Graduate/Fellowship)* [9115]

Jean Wright-Elson Scholarship *(Doctorate, Graduate, Undergraduate/Scholarship)* [9823]

Jeff Oliphant Memorial Post-Graduate Scholarship *(Postgraduate/Scholarship)* [12114]

Jeffrey Carollo Music Scholarship *(Undergraduate/Scholarship)* [8279]

Jeffrey D. Ralston Memorial Scholarship *(Undergraduate/Scholarship)* [7562]

Walter J. Jensen Fellowships *(Other/Fellowship)* [9081]

Jerome M. Sullivan Research Fund *(Professional development/Fellowship)* [1354]

Jerry Newson Scholarship Fund *(Undergraduate/Scholarship)* [3624]

Jet Business Scholarship *(Graduate/Scholarship)* [6267]

Jewell Gardiner Scholarship *(Undergraduate/Scholarship)* [2827]

Jim Anderson Memorial Scholarship *(Undergraduate/Scholarship)* [8363]

Jim Graham Scholarship *(Undergraduate/Scholarship)* [8455]

Jim & Nancy Hinkle Travel Grants *(Graduate/Grant)* [5476]

Jimmy Edwards Scholarship Fund *(Undergraduate/Scholarship)* [3625]

JMA Architecture Studios Scholarship *(Undergraduate/Scholarship)* [9405]

JMJ Phillip Group College Scholarships *(Graduate, University, Four Year College, Two Year College/Scholarship)* [6312]

Joe Francis Haircare Scholarship *(Undergraduate/Scholarship)* [4811]

Joe Perdue Scholarship *(Undergraduate/Scholarship, Award)* [3443]

Joel T. Heinen Student Research Fellowship *(Undergraduate, Graduate/Fellowship)* [11628]

Joel T. Heinen Undergraduate Support Scholarship *(Undergraduate/Scholarship)* [11629]

John and Alice Egan Multi-Year Mentioning Scholarship Program *(Undergraduate/Scholarship)* [3955]

John C. Lincoln Memorial Scholarship *(Undergraduate/Scholarship)* [1666]

John E. Mayfield ABLE Scholarship Fund *(Graduate/Scholarship)* [3626]

John Flynn Memorial Scholarship *(Undergraduate/Scholarship)* [3682]

John G. Brokaw Scholarship *(Undergraduate/Scholarship)* [8173]

John G. Williams Scholarship Foundation *(Undergraduate/Scholarship)* [12039]

John I. & Madeleine R. Taeni Scholarship Fund *(Undergraduate/Scholarship)* [10689]

John J. McKetta Undergraduate Scholarship *(Undergraduate/Scholarship)* [1023]

John Jeffries Meteorology Scholarship *(Graduate/Scholarship)* [4502]

John M. & Mary A. Shanley Memorial Scholarship *(Undergraduate, Graduate/Scholarship)* [10690]

John Marshall Everglades Internship Program *(Undergraduate/Internship)* [4457]

John McLendon Minority Postgraduate Scholarship *(Postdoctorate/Scholarship)* [7639]

John & Ruth Childe Scholarship Fund *(Undergraduate/Scholarship)* [10691]

John S. and Marjoria R. Cunningham Camp Scholarship *(Other/Scholarship)* [10692]

John W. Webb Lecture Award *(Other/Award, Recognition, Monetary)* [1466]

Johnny Bench Scholarship Fund *(Undergraduate/Scholarship)* [3371]

Johnny Lineberry Memorial Scholarship *(Undergraduate, Vocational/Occupational/Scholarship)* [12080]

Johns Hopkins University/Applied Physics Laboratory Alexander Kossiakoff Scholarship *(Doctorate, Graduate, Master's/Scholarship)* [5985]

Wilma Winberg Johnson Adelphe Scholarship for Chapter Consultants *(Undergraduate/Scholarship)* [6448]

Alvin H. Johnson AMS 50 Dissertation Fellowships *(Doctorate/Fellowship)* [1143]

Johnson and Johnson/AACN Minority Nurse Faculty Scholars *(Graduate/Scholarship)* [543]

Joseph C. Johnson Memorial Grant *(Undergraduate/Grant)* [1392]

Gregory D. Johnson Memorial Scholarships *(Doctorate, Graduate, Master's/Scholarship)* [7970]

V.J. Johnson Memorial Scholarships *(Undergraduate/Scholarship)* [642]

The Dr. Richard Allen Williams and Genita Evangelista Johnson Scholarship, AMA Foundation Scholarship *(Undergraduate/Scholarship)* [2066]

Joint Japan/World Bank Graduate Scholarship Program for Developing Country National (JJ/WBGSP) *(Graduate/Scholarship)* [12192]

Joint Japan/World Bank Graduate Scholarship Program for Japanese National (JJ/WBGSP) *(Graduate, Master's, Doctorate/Scholarship)* [12193]

George E. Jonas Scholarships *(Graduate, Undergraduate/Scholarship)* [6894]

NASSP/Herff Jones Principal's Leadership Award *(Undergraduate/Scholarship)* [7690]

Jordan Abdo Memorial Scholarship Fund *(Undergraduate/Scholarship)* [10692]

Jordan B. Tatter Scholarship *(Undergraduate, Graduate/Scholarship)* [7334]

The Barbara Jordan Scholarship *(Undergraduate/Scholarship)* [11150]

Josef Princ Memorial Scholarship *(Undergraduate/Scholarship)* [9407]

Joseph A. Holmes Safety Association Scholarship *(High School/Scholarship)* [5544]

Joseph and Amelia Saks Scholarship *(Undergraduate/Scholarship)* [3656]

Joseph H. Fichter Research Grant *(Postdoctorate/Grant)* [2290]

Joseph J. Fitzsimmons Scholarship Fund *(Doctorate/Scholarship)* [11384]

Joseph S. Stern Scholarship Fund *(Undergraduate/Scholarship)* [3372]

Joseph W. Mayo ALS Scholarship Fund *(Graduate/Scholarship)* [6989]

Josephine Hooker Shain Scholarship *(Undergraduate/Scholarship)* [4918]

Joshua Esch Mitchell Aviation Scholarship *(Undergraduate/Scholarship)* [5160]

Journalist of the Year Scholarships *(Undergraduate/Monetary, Scholarship)* [6337]

Journey Toward Ordained Ministry Scholarships *(Undergraduate, Graduate/Scholarship)* [4893]

Joyce C. Hall College Scholarship *(Undergraduate/Scholarship)* [8981]

Leslie W. Joyce and Paul W. Thayer Graduate Fellowship in I-O Psychology *(Graduate/Fellowship)* [10335]

JPGtoPDF College Scholarship *(Undergraduate, Graduate/Scholarship)* [6339]

Judge Edward Y. Kakita Memorial Scholarship *(Undergraduate/Scholarship)* [6238]

Judge Isaac Anderson, Jr. Scholarship Fund *(Undergraduate/Scholarship)* [10693]

Judge Ross Leadership Scholarship *(Professional development/Scholarship)* [7764]

Judge Sidney M. Aronovitz Memorial Scholarship Fund *(Undergraduate/Scholarship)* [7298]

Julian E. Carnes Scholarship Endowment Fund *(Undergraduate/Scholarship)* [4738]

Martha Julian Memorial Scholarship *(Undergraduate/Scholarship)* [233]

Juliann and Joe Maxwell Scholarship Fund for Employees of Tractor Supply *(Undergraduate/Scholarship)* [3627]

Juliann King Maxwell Scholarship Fund for Riverview High School *(Undergraduate, Vocational/Occupational/Scholarship)* [3628]

June Danby and Pat Pearse Education Scholarship *(Undergraduate/Scholarship)* [6203]

The Junior Achievement of East Central Ohio, Inc. Scholarship Fund *(Undergraduate, High School/Scholarship)* [10771]

Justin G. Schiller Fellowship *(Doctorate, Postdoctorate/Fellowship)* [492]

Justin Scot Alston Memorial Scholarship *(Undergraduate/Scholarship)* [5665]

Annette Kade Fellowships *(Graduate/Fellowship)* [7277]

Kae and Kay Brockermeyer Endowed Scholarship Fund *(Undergraduate/Scholarship)* [9011]

David A. Kaiser Memorial Scholarship Fund *(Undergraduate/Scholarship)* [10772]

Sam Kalman Scholarship *(Undergraduate/Scholarship)* [1750]

Armenag and Armenhooi Kalustian Memorial Grant *(Undergraduate/Scholarship)* [1887]

Gladys Kamakakokalani 'Ainoa Brandt Scholarships *(Graduate, Undergraduate/Scholarship)* [8929]

Kamehameha Schools Class of 1968 "Ka Poli O Kaiona" Scholarships *(Graduate, Undergraduate/Scholarship)* [8930]

Kamehameha Schools Class of 1972 Scholarship *(Graduate, Undergraduate/Scholarship)* [8931]

Aram and Adrine Kamparosyan Memorial Grant *(Undergraduate/Scholarship)* [1888]

Martin S. Kane Memorial Community Service Award Scholarships *(Undergraduate/Scholarship)* [3572]

Bill Kane Undergraduate Scholarship *(Undergraduate/Scholarship, Award, Monetary)* [10349]

Kansas Osteopathic Medical Service Scholarship *(Graduate, Other/Scholarship)* [6366]

The Walter S. Kapala Scholarship Trust *(Undergraduate/Scholarship)* [5335]

Don Kaplan Legacy Scholarships *(Undergraduate/Scholarship)* [2803]

Kaplan Scholarships *(Undergraduate/Scholarship)* [5524]

The Olympia Brown and Max Kapp Award *(Master's/Scholarship)* [11251]

Kappa Delta Phi Scholarship *(Postgraduate/Scholarship)* [1179]

Kappa Kappa Gamma Foundation - Mary Maxwell Gates Scholarship *(Undergraduate, Graduate/Scholarship)* [6449]

Kappa Kappa Gamma Foundation Project 2000 Scholarship *(Undergraduate/Scholarship)* [6450]

Kappa Omicron Nu National Alumni Fellowships *(Graduate/Fellowship)* [6489]

Kappa Project 2000 Scholarship *(Undergraduate/Scholarship)* [6451]

The ISASI Rudolf Kapustin Memorial Scholarship *(Undergraduate/Scholarship)* [6083]

Karen D. Carsel Memorial Scholarship *(Undergraduate/Scholarship)* [916]

Karl Mehlmann Scholarship *(Undergraduate/Scholarship)* [3530]

K.A.S.A. Memorial Scholarship *(Undergraduate/Scholarship)* [8861]

KASF scholarships *(Graduate, Undergraduate/Scholarship)* [6597]

KASF Designated Scholarships *(Graduate, Undergraduate/Scholarship)* [6598]

KASF General Scholarships *(Undergraduate, Graduate, Professional development/Scholarship)* [6599]

Koren and Alice Odian Kasparian Memorial Grant *(Undergraduate/Scholarship)* [1889]

Katherine M. Grosscup Scholarships in Horticulture *(Undergraduate, Graduate/Scholarship)* [4860]

Kathryn M. Cronin Scholarship *(Undergraduate, Graduate/Scholarship)* [11192]

Kathy D. and Stephen J. Anderson Scholarship Fund *(Undergraduate/Scholarship)* [3629]

Lucile B. Kaufman Women's Scholarship *(Undergraduate/Scholarship)* [10403]

Kawano Family Scholarships *(Undergraduate/Scholarship)* [9825]

E. Wayne Kay Co-op Scholarship *(Undergraduate/Scholarship)* [10404]

E. Wayne Kay Community College Scholarship *(Undergraduate, Community College/Scholarship)* [10405]

E. Wayne Kay High School Scholarship *(Undergraduate/Scholarship)* [10407]

Kays Gary Scholarship *(Undergraduate/Scholarship)* [11193]

KCC Foundation Gold Key Scholarship *(Undergraduate/Scholarship)* [6513]

KCC Foundation Scholarship *(Undergraduate/Scholarship)* [6514]

KCC Trustee Scholarship *(Undergraduate/Scholarship)* [6515]

KDP Huntington Bank Scholarship *(Undergraduate/Scholarship)* [6384]

KDP International Scholarship Program - President Scholarship *(Undergraduate, Graduate, Doctorate/Scholarship)* [6385]

KDP MBNA Scholarships *(Undergraduate, Graduate/Scholarship)* [6386]

Ezra Jack Keats/Kerlan Memorial Fellowship *(Professional development/Fellowship)* [11643]

Araxy Kechejian Memorial Grant *(Undergraduate/Scholarship)* [1890]

Keepers Preservation Education Fund *(Undergraduate/Award)* [6990]

Keepers Preservation Education Fund Fellowship *(Graduate/Fellowship)* [10275]

KEF General Scholarships *(Undergraduate, Graduate/Scholarship)* [6590]

Keiko Fukuda Scholarship *(Undergraduate, Postgraduate/Scholarship)* [11385]

Keith Maffioli Scholarship *(Undergraduate/Scholarship)* [3683]

Anna-Maria and Stephen M. Kellen Fellowships *(Professional development/Fellowship)* [809]

Ken LaFountaine First Nations Scholarship *(Undergraduate/Scholarship)* [10056]

Willmoore H. Kendall Scholarships *(Professional development/Scholarship)* [3444]

Kennedy T. Friend Scholarship Fund *(Graduate, Undergraduate/Scholarship)* [348]

Kenneth J. Osborn Scholarship *(Undergraduate/Scholarship)* [2007]

Oscar Kenshur Book Prize *(Other/Prize)* [1435]

Kenyon T. Payne Outstanding Student Award *(Undergraduate/Award, Monetary)* [7344]

Kerrigan Scholarship Foundation *(Undergraduate/Scholarship)* [9012]

George Keverian Public Service Scholarship *(Undergraduate/Scholarship)* [1891]

Kevin Ernst Memorial Scholarship *(Undergraduate/Scholarship)* [5087]

Dr. Arthur A. Kezian DDS Science Scholarship *(Undergraduate, Graduate, College, University/Scholarship)* [6541]

Graduate Fellowship Program - Mahboob Khan/Advanced Micro Devices Fellowships *(Doctorate, Graduate/Fellowship)* [10000]

Michael Kidger Memorial Scholarship in Optical Design *(Undergraduate/Scholarship)* [10726]

Kids and Community Scholarship Program *(College, University/Scholarship)* [6552]

The Mary and Millard Kiker Scholarship *(Undergraduate/Scholarship)* [4739]

Killam Fellowships *(Undergraduate/Fellowship)* [4771]

Douglas Gray Kimel Scholarship *(Undergraduate/Scholarship)* [12081]

James N. Kincanon Scholarship *(Undergraduate/Scholarship)* [9017]

Kit C. King Graduate Scholarships *(Graduate/Scholarship)* [8048]

Larry King/Jeffrey Fashion Cares Point Scholarship *(Undergraduate, Graduate, Doctorate/Scholarship)* [9225]

Martin Luther King Law Scholarship *(Undergraduate/Scholarship)* [4165]

Steven G. King Play Environments Scholarship *(Undergraduate, Master's/Scholarship)* [6648]

Jessica King Scholarships *(Other/Scholarship)* [3938]

Don King Student Fellowships *(Undergraduate/Fellowship)* [5659]

Kingsbury Elementary School PTA Scholarship *(Undergraduate/Scholarship)* [9553]

Treva C. Kintner Scholarships *(Undergraduate/Scholarship)* [9116]

James P. Kirkgasser Memorial Scholarship *(Undergraduate, Graduate/Scholarship)* [2533]

Dr. Elemer and Eva Kiss Scholarship Fund *(Undergraduate/Scholarship)* [5642]

Tamo Kitaura Scholarships *(Other/Scholarship)* [11386]

Kiwanis Club of Escondido Scholarship *(Undergraduate/Scholarship)* [9826]

Kiwanis Club of Redlands Foundation Academic Excellence Scholarship *(Undergraduate/Scholarship)* [9554]

Kiwanis Club of Redlands Foundation - Martin and Dorothy Munz Scholarship *(Undergraduate/Scholarship)* [9555]

Klarman Family Foundation Grants Program in Eating Disorders Research *(Professional development/Grant)* [5439]

Jane M. Klausman Women in Business Scholarships *(Graduate, Undergraduate/Scholarship)* [12421]

The Margie Klein "Paper Plate" Scholarships *(All/Scholarship)* [2053]

Gerda and Kurt Klein Scholarships *(Undergraduate/Scholarship)* [5592]

Dr. Eva Kleinpeter Scholarship *(Undergraduate/Scholarship)* [6387]

John A. Knauss Marine Policy Fellowship *(Graduate/Fellowship)* [11304]

David Knight Graduate Scholarship *(Graduate/Scholarship)* [10656]

John G. F. Knight Memorial Scholarship *(Undergraduate, Graduate/Scholarship)* [2534]

Robert E. Knight Professional Scholarship *(Graduate/Scholarship)* [10979]

Knox Hume Scholarship Fund *(Undergraduate/Scholarship)* [3630]

Glenn Knudsvig Memorial Scholarships *(Graduate, Undergraduate/Scholarship)* [754]

Kodak Fellowships in Film Preservation *(Graduate/Fellowship)* [2247]

Kodali Veeraiah & Sarojini Scholarship *(Graduate/Scholarship)* [10952]

James P. Kohn Memorial Scholarship *(Doctorate/Scholarship)* [1567]

Susan G. Komen for the Cure College Scholarship Awards *(Two Year College/Award, Scholarship)* [6586]

Susan G. Komen for the Cure Post-doctoral Fellowships - Clinical Research Grants *(Postdoctorate/Grant, Fellowship)* [6587]

KON/GEICO LeaderShape Undergraduate Scholarship *(Undergraduate/Scholarship)* [6490]

KON National Alumni Chapter Grant *(Professional development/Grant)* [6491]

KON New Initiatives Grant *(Professional development/Grant)* [6492]

Emily Day Koppell Memorial Adelphe Scholarship *(Undergraduate, Graduate/Scholarship)* [6452]

Korean Studies Dissertation Workshop *(Graduate/Fellowship)* [10248]

AIST Willy Korf Memorial Fund *(Undergraduate, Graduate/Scholarship)* [2221]

Kosciuszko Foundation Tuition Scholarships *(Graduate/Scholarship)* [6602]

Marcia J. Koslov Scholarship *(Professional development/Scholarship)* [598]

Haig Koumjian Memorial Grant *(Undergraduate/Scholarship)* [1892]

William D. Krahling Excellence in Journalism Scholarship *(Undergraduate/Scholarship)* [403]

Michael Kraus Research Grants *(Doctorate/Grant)* [961]

Eileen Kraus Scholarship *(Two Year College, Four Year College/Scholarship)* [3763]

Sharon Kreikemeier Memorial Scholarships *(Undergraduate/Scholarship)* [8189]

Kress Conservation Fellowships *(Postgraduate/Fellowship)* [6614]

Krist-Reavley Minority Scholarship *(Undergraduate/Scholarship)* [9013]

Carl A. Kroch Oxford Cup Memorial Scholarship *(Undergraduate, Graduate/Scholarship)* [2535]

Kristin Bjurstrom Krueger Student Scholarship Program *(Undergraduate/Scholarship)* [7240]

Samuel Krugliak Legal Scholarship Fund *(Undergraduate/Scholarship)* [10773]

Harry A. Kuljian Memorial Grant *(Undergraduate/Scholarship)* [1893]

Kurt H. and Donna M. Schuler Cash Grant *(Undergraduate/Scholarship, Grant)* [1393]

Kurz Industrial Solutions Wind Energy Scholarship Fund *(Graduate/Scholarship)* [6618]

Henry and Chiyo Kuwahara Creative Arts Award *(Graduate/Scholarship)* [6248]

Sam and Florice Kuwahara Memorial Scholarship *(Undergraduate/Scholarship)* [6249]

Kyle R. Moreland Memorial Scholarship *(Undergraduate/Scholarship)* [5088]

Anne Emery Kyllo Professional Scholarship *(Professional development/Scholarship)* [1136]

L. Gordon, Jr. and June D. Pfefferkorn Scholarship *(Undergraduate/Scholarship)* [12082]

L. & T. Woolfolk Memorial Scholarship Fund *(Undergraduate/Scholarship)* [3376]

L'Oréal USA For Women in Science Fellowship *(Postdoctorate/Fellowship)* [8696]

LA Tutors 123 Innovation in Education Scholarship *(All/Scholarship)* [6626]

La Voz Latina Scholarship *(Undergraduate/Scholarship)* [3684]

Gretchen Laatsch Scholarships *(Graduate/Scholarship)* [2139]

Ladah Law Firm, PLLC Injury Scholarships *(Undergraduate, Graduate/Scholarship)* [6630]

LAEF Scholarships *(Undergraduate/Scholarship)* [6675]

Jeffery P. LaFage Graduate Student Research Award *(Master's, Doctorate/Grant)* [4397]

Lawrence Gelfand - Armin Rappaport - Walter LaFeber Dissertation Fellowship *(Graduate/Fellowship)* [10357]

The Lagrant Foundation - Graduate Scholarships *(Graduate/Scholarship)* [6632]

The Lagrant Foundation - Undergraduate Scholarships *(Undergraduate/Scholarship)* [6633]

Ray and Kathy LaHood Scholarships for the Study of American Government *(Undergraduate/Scholarship)* [4102]

Lake Dollars for Scholars Endowment Fund *(Undergraduate/Scholarship)* [10774]

Lakselaget Foundation Scholarship Fund *(Graduate, Undergraduate/Scholarship)* [6635]

Lalor Foundation Merit Awards *(Postdoctorate/Award, Recognition, Prize)* [10533]

Lalor Foundation Post-Doctoral Fellowships *(Postdoctorate/Fellowship)* [6637]

Paul C. K. Lam Memorial Scholarship at The University of Akron *(Undergraduate/Scholarship)* [8597]

Lamar University College of Engineering Scholarships *(Undergraduate/Scholarship)* [7852]

Hedy Lamarr Achievement Award for Emerging Leaders in Entertainment Technology *(Undergraduate/Award)* [4086]

Lambda Project 2000 Scholarship *(Undergraduate/Scholarship)* [6453]

Elaine Johnson Lampert Journalism Memorial Adelphe Scholarship *(Undergraduate/Award)* [6454]

Lance Surety College Scholarships *(Undergraduate, Graduate/Scholarship)* [6644]

Robert S. Landauer, Sr. Memorial Fellowship *(Graduate, Undergraduate/Fellowship)* [5430]

Otho E. Lane Memorial Scholarship *(Undergraduate, Graduate/Scholarship)* [2536]

Lanford Family Highway Worker Memorial Scholarship Program *(High School/Scholarship)* [1362]

Langfitt-Ambrose Scholarship *(Undergraduate/Scholarship)* [8863]

Paul J. Laninga Memorial Scholarship *(Undergraduate/Scholarship)* [5089]

Lapeer County Medical Fund *(Undergraduate/Scholarship)* [6666]

Lapides Fellowships in Pre-1865 Juvenile Literature and Ephemera *(Graduate, Postdoctorate/Fellowship)* [493]

Katherine Roberts LaPorte Memorial Adelphe Scholarship *(Undergraduate/Scholarship)* [6455]

Larry Dean Davis Scholarship *(Undergraduate/Scholarship)* [8938]

Larson Aquatic Research Support Scholarships (LARS) *(Graduate/Scholarship, Monetary, Recognition)* [1643]

LaRue A. Ditmore Music Scholarship *(Undergraduate/Scholarship)* [12148]

Laser Technology, Engineering and Applications Scholarship *(Graduate, Undergraduate/Scholarship)* [10727]

Jay and Deborah Last Fellowships *(Doctorate/Fellowship)* [494]

Latham Diversity Scholars - 2L Diversity Scholars *(Undergraduate/Scholarship)* [6673]

Candia Baker Laughlin Certification Scholarship *(Undergraduate/Scholarship)* [428]

Laura M. Fleming Scholarship *(Undergraduate, Vocational/Occupational/Scholarship)* [4740]

Law Fellows Program *(Undergraduate/Fellowship)* [7607]

Community Leadership in Justice Fellowship - The Law Foundation of Ontario *(Other/Fellowship)* [6683]

Law Office of A. Sam Jubran Scholarship Contest *(University, College, Undergraduate/Scholarship)* [6685]

Law Office of David P. Shapiro Annual Leukemia Scholarships *(Vocational/Occupational, Community College, University, Undergraduate, College/Scholarship)* [6691]

Law Offices of Mark E. Salomone Scholarship for Road Safety *(Undergraduate/Scholarship)* [6706]

The Law Offices of Scott Henry Scholarship Contest *(Undergraduate/Scholarship)* [6710]

Law School Scholarship *(Graduate/Scholarship)* [2618, 9714]

Law and Society Association Article Prize *(Other/Prize, Award)* [6724]

Law and Society Association Dissertation Prize *(Other/Prize)* [6725]

Law and Society Association International Prize *(Other/Award, Recognition)* [6726]

Law and Society Association Undergraduate Student Paper Prize *(Undergraduate/Prize)* [6727]

Law Student Scholarship *(Graduate/Scholarship)* [4539, 6520]

Lawrence E. and Mabel Jackson Rudberg Scholarship Fund *(Undergraduate/Scholarship)* [4214]

Lawrence Fellowship *(Doctorate/Fellowship)* [11321]

Lawrence and Louise Robbins Scholarship Fund *(Undergraduate/Scholarship)* [6991]

Lawrence Madeiros Scholarship *(Undergraduate/Scholarship)* [7925]

The Dr. James L. Lawson Memorial Scholarship *(Undergraduate/Scholarship)* [1947]

Lawsuit Legal American Nursing Support Scholarships *(Undergraduate, Graduate/Scholarship)* [6738]

L.D. and Elsie Long Memorial Scholarship *(Graduate/Scholarship)* [12083]

Leadership Conference Scholarship *(Other/Scholarship)* [7738]

Leadership for Diversity Paraprofessional Scholarship *(Advanced Professional/Scholarship)* [2828]

Leadership for Diversity TL Scholarship *(Master's/Scholarship)* [2829]

Leadership Scholarships *(Undergraduate/Scholarship)* [10478]

League Foundation Scholarships *(Undergraduate/Scholarship)* [6745]

League of Latin American Citizens General Electric Scholarships *(Undergraduate/Scholarship)* [6747]

Leakey Foundation Research Grants *(Doctorate, Advanced Professional/Grant)* [6752]

Jack W. Leatherman Family Scholarship *(Undergraduate, Vocational/Occupational/Scholarship)* [5090]

Lebbeus F. Bissell Scholarship Fund *(Undergraduate/Scholarship)* [5336]

LeClairRyan 1L Diversity Scholarship *(Undergraduate/Scholarship)* [6762]

Lee Epstein Fund Scholarship *(Graduate, Undergraduate/Scholarship)* [7107]

Lee Tarbox Memorial Scholarship *(Undergraduate/Scholarship)* [187]

Lee Teng Undergraduate Fellowship in Accelerator Science and Engineering *(Undergraduate/Fellowship)* [11318]

The Legacy Fellowship *(Doctorate/Fellowship)* [495]

Charles LeGeyt Fortescue Scholarship *(Graduate/Scholarship, Award, Monetary)* [5817]

Doreen Legg Memorial Scholarships *(Undergraduate/Scholarship)* [9556]

The Herbert Lehman Education Fund Scholarship *(Undergraduate/Scholarship)* [7540]

Leiber and Stoller Music Scholarship *(Undergraduate/Scholarship)* [1410]

Leica Scholarship *(Graduate/Scholarship)* [2008]

Leighton M. Ballew Directing Scholarship *(Undergraduate/Scholarship)* [10635]

Imelda *(Graduate, High School/Scholarship)* [3722]

Lemelson Center Fellowships *(Doctorate, Postdoctorate, Professional development/Fellowship)* [10194]

Lemelson Center Travel to Collections Awards *(Graduate, Professional development/Award)* [10195]

The Stan Lencki Scholarship *(Undergraduate/Scholarship)* [7172]

John Lennon Scholarships *(Undergraduate/Scholarship)* [2635]

Leo Gilmartin Scholarship *(Undergraduate/Scholarship)* [9211]

Leopold Education Project Scholarship *(Undergraduate/Scholarship)* [3685]

Lerner-Scott Prize *(Doctorate/Prize)* [8728]

Les Dames D'Escoffier New York Corporate Scholarship *(Undergraduate/Scholarship)* [6777]

Leslie Baranowski Scholarship for Professional Excellence *(Professional development/Scholarship)* [5787]

Leslie and Mary Ella Scales Scholarship *(Undergraduate/Scholarship)* [3657]

Lester G. Benz Memorial Scholarship for College Journalism Study *(Other/Scholarship)* [9463]

Saul Levine Memorial Scholarship *(Graduate/Scholarship)* [1167]

Jack A. and Louise S. Levine Memorial Scholarships *(Undergraduate/Scholarship)* [9557]

Harry and Miriam Levinson Scholarship *(Graduate, Master's, Doctorate/Scholarship)* [1284]

Herbert Levy Memorial Scholarship *(Undergraduate/Scholarship)* [10479]

William J. Levy Point Scholarship *(Undergraduate, Graduate, Doctorate/Scholarship)* [9226]

Lewis B. Barber Memorial Scholarship Fund *(Undergraduate/Scholarship)* [10695]

Lewis and Clark Fund for Exploration and Field Research *(Doctorate/Grant)* [1215]

Lloyd Lewis Fellowships in American History *(Postdoctorate/Fellowship)* [8375]

George T. Lewis, Jr. Academic Scholarship Fund *(Undergraduate/Scholarship)* [4742]

Ted Lewis Memorial Scholarship *(Undergraduate/Scholarship)* [234]

S. Evelyn Lewis Memorial Scholarships in Medical Health Sciences *(Graduate, Undergraduate/Scholarship)* [12414]

Lewis-Reynolds-Smith Founders Fellowship *(Graduate/Fellowship)* [5477]

Lexington Alumni Scholarships *(Undergraduate/Scholarship)* [6827]

Lexington Community Foundation Annual Scholarships *(Undergraduate/Scholarship)* [6828]

Lexington Community Foundation/CCC Scholarships *(Undergraduate/Scholarship)* [6829]

Jack G. Lezman Scholarship Contest *(College, University, Undergraduate/Scholarship)* [6836]

Liberty Mutual Scholarships *(Undergraduate/Scholarship)* [1568]

Short-Term Library Resident Research Fellowships *(Doctorate/Fellowship)* [1216]

Dolores Zohrab Liebmann Fund - Graduate School Fellowships *(Graduate/Fellowship)* [6845]

Dolores Zohrab Liebmann Fund - Independent Research/Study Grants *(Graduate, Undergraduate/Grant)* [6846]

Dolores Zohrab Liebmann Fund - Publication Grants *(Graduate, Undergraduate/Grant)* [6847]

LIFE Lessons Scholarship Program *(Undergraduate/Scholarship)* [6849]

Lighthouse International Scholarships - College-bound Awards *(High School, Undergraduate/Scholarship)* [6856]

Lighthouse International Scholarships - Graduate Awards *(Graduate, Postgraduate/Scholarship)* [6857]

Lighting the Way for Nursing Scholarship *(Doctorate/Scholarship)* [25]

Lillie Hope-McGarvey Health Scholarship *(Undergraduate, Vocational/Occupational, Graduate, Master's/Scholarship)* [330]

Lily H. Gridley Memorial Scholarship *(Undergraduate/Scholarship)* [12149]

Esther Lim Memorial Scholarships *(Undergraduate/Scholarship)* [3308]

Lim, Ruger & Kim Scholarships *(Undergraduate/Scholarship)* [7602]

Lime Connect Pathways Scholarship for High School Seniors with Disabilities *(Undergraduate/Scholarship)* [6863]

LimNexus Foundation Scholarship *(Undergraduate/Scholarship)* [6239]

AIST Ronald E. Lincoln Memorial Scholarship *(Undergraduate/Scholarship)* [2222]

Linda J. Murphy Scholarship *(Undergraduate/Scholarship)* [12141]

Lindenwood University Scouting Scholarships *(Undergraduate/Scholarship)* [7853]

Margaret B. Lindsey Award for Distinguished Research in Teacher Education *(Other/Award, Recognition)* [551]

Lineups.com Future of Sports Scholarship Program *(Undergraduate, Graduate, Scholarship)* [6871]

Link Foundation/Smithsonian Graduate Fellowships in Marine Science *(Graduate/Fellowship)* [10201]

Linsley Scholarship Fund *(Undergraduate, Vocational/Occupational/Scholarship)* [3301]

David Linton Memorial Scholarship *(Undergraduate, Graduate/Scholarship)* [2537]

LionsDeal.com Scholarships *(Undergraduate/Scholarship)* [6875]

F. Maynard Lipe Scholarship Award *(Master's, Postgraduate/Scholarship)* [759]

The Lawrence Lipking Fellowship *(Postdoctorate/Fellowship)* [8376]

Litherland/FTEE Undergraduate Scholarships *(Undergraduate/Scholarship)* [6125]

Littleton-Griswold Research Grant *(Doctorate/Grant)* [962]

Davis Levin Livingston Public Interest Law Scholarships *(Postgraduate/Scholarship)* [3975]

David C. Lizárraga Fellowship *(Graduate/Fellowship)* [10941]

Lizette Peterson Homer Injury Prevention Grant *(Other, Undergraduate, Graduate/Grant)* [1739]

LLA Scholarships (LLA) *(Graduate/Scholarship)* [6903]

LLN Student Scholarships *(Undergraduate/Scholarship)* [6677]

Lloyd Bridges Scholarship *(Graduate/Scholarship)* [3204]

E.C. Lloyd and J.C.U. Johnson Scholarship Fund *(Undergraduate/Scholarship)* [3658]

Loan for Service for Graduates *(Graduate/Loan)* [995]

Local 827 Peter J. Casey Scholarship *(Undergraduate/Scholarship)* [5957]

Local A&WMA Sections and Chapter Scholarships *(Graduate/Scholarship)* [162]

Miriam "Doc" Locke Memorial Adelphe Scholarships *(Graduate/Scholarship)* [6456]

Mary Elizabeth Lockwood Beneventi MBA Scholarship *(Graduate/Scholarship, Award, Monetary)* [8098]

The Loewenstein-Wiener Fellowship *(Professional development, Doctorate, Postdoctorate/Fellowship)* [1061]

Logojoy Student Entrepreneur Scholarship *(Undergraduate, Graduate/Scholarship)* [6888]

Lois Widly Student Scholarships *(Graduate, Undergraduate/Scholarship)* [6046]

Lone Star GIA Associate and Alumni Scholarships *(Undergraduate/Scholarship)* [4879]

Lawrence A. Long Memorial Law Scholarship *(Graduate/Scholarship)* [404]

The Robert A. Catlin/David W. Long Scholarship *(Graduate/Scholarship)* [1244]

Long-term International Fellowships *(Professional development/Fellowship)* [3778]

Kay Longcope Scholarship Award *(Graduate, Undergraduate/Scholarship)* [7990]

Bart Longo Memorial Scholarship Program *(Undergraduate, Graduate/Scholarship)* [7762]

Megan Nicole Longwell Scholarship *(Undergraduate/Scholarship)* [8864]

Louise Loomis Memorial Adelphe Scholarships *(Undergraduate/Scholarship)* [6457]

Michael Lorenzen Foundation Scholarship *(Undergraduate, Graduate/Scholarship)* [6890]

Lorraine E. Swain Scholarship *(Undergraduate/Scholarship)* [10114]

Barbara Lotze Scholarships for Future Teachers *(Undergraduate/Scholarship)* [625]

Lou & Dorie Amen Legacy Scholarship *(Undergraduate/Scholarship)* [2804]

Lou Hochberg Awards - Thesis and Dissertation Awards *(Graduate/Award, Monetary)* [8757]

Louis Armstrong Award Honoring W.C. Handy *(Undergraduate/Scholarship)* [1411]

Louis B. Zapoleon Memorial Fund *(Undergraduate/Scholarship)* [3377]

Louis I. Jaffe Memorial Scholarship-NSU Alumni *(Graduate/Scholarship)* [5273]

Louis M. Connor, Jr. Scholarship *(Undergraduate/Scholarship)* [11194]

Louis Pelzer Memorial Award *(Graduate/Award)* [8729]

Louis T. Klauder Scholarship *(Undergraduate, Graduate/Scholarship)* [1303]

Louisa Anne Oriente Scholarship *(Graduate, Doctorate/Scholarship)* [6388]

Louisa Bowen Memorial Scholarship for Graduate Students in Archival Administration *(Graduate/Scholarship)* [7365]

Louise Bales Gallagher Scholarship *(Undergraduate/Scholarship)* [4005]

Louise Wachter Wickham Scholarship *(Undergraduate/Scholarship)* [5092]

Louisiana Agricultural Consultants Association Scholarship *(Graduate, Undergraduate/Scholarship)* [6896]

Louisville Institute Dissertation Fellowships (DF) *(Doctorate/Fellowship)* [6912]

Louisville Institute Project Grant for Researchers (PGR) *(Doctorate/Grant)* [6913]

Louisville Institute Sabbatical Grants for Researchers (SGR) *(Doctorate/Grant)* [6914]

Louisville Institute's First Book Grant Program for Minority Scholars (FBM) *(Doctorate/Grant)* [6915]

Louthian Law School Scholarships *(Advanced Professional/Scholarship)* [6919]

Love Of Bonita Empowerment Scholarship Fund *(Undergraduate/Scholarship)* [10696]

Lowe Family First Summer Student Scholarship *(Undergraduate/Scholarship)* [11083]

Lowe Simpson Scholarship Fund *(Undergraduate/Scholarship)* [3378]

The Lozano Law Firm Scholarship Contest *(College, University, Undergraduate/Scholarship)* [6925]

Horace G. Lozier Memorial Scholarship *(Undergraduate, Graduate/Scholarship)* [2538]

LPHA Scholarships *(Graduate, Undergraduate/Scholarship)* [6906]

Lt Col Romeo - Josephine Bass Ferretti Scholarship *(Undergraduate/Scholarship)* [148]

Lt. Holly Adams Memorial Scholarship Fund *(Undergraduate/Scholarship)* [3632]

Luce/ACLS Dissertation Fellowships in American Art *(Graduate, Doctorate/Fellowship)* [824]

Lucidchart Scholarship *(Undergraduate, Graduate/Scholarship)* [6927]

Lucidpress Scholarship *(Undergraduate, Graduate/Scholarship)* [6928]

Lucile Cheever Graubart/Lambda Scholarship *(Undergraduate/Scholarship)* [10115]

Lucy and Charles W.E. Clarke Scholarship *(Undergraduate/Scholarship, Award)* [2000]

Lucy Hilty Research Grant *(Graduate/Grant)* [1312]

Luis Arreola Memorial Scholarship *(Undergraduate/Scholarship)* [9831]

LULAC National Scholarship Fund (LNSF) *(Graduate, Undergraduate/Scholarship)* [6749]

Lee G. Luna Foreign Travel Scholarship *(Professional development/Scholarship)* [8109]

Juan and Esperanza Luna Scholarship *(Undergraduate/Scholarship)* [1751]

Lutheran Student Scholastic and Service Scholarships - College and University Students *(Undergraduate/Scholarship)* [2562]

Dan & Pauline Lutkenhouse & Hawaii Tropical Botanical Garden Scholarship and Educational Fund *(Undergraduate, Graduate/Scholarship)* [5407]

Lycoming County Medical Society Scholarship *(Undergraduate, Graduate/Scholarship)* [4799]

Lyle Mamer Fellowship *(Graduate/Fellowship)* [12160]

Lyle and Rlene Everingham Family Fund *(Undergraduate/Scholarship)* [3380]

Lymphatic Research Foundation Additional Support for NIH-funded F32 Postdoctoral Fellows Awards *(Postdoctorate/Award)* [5440]

Lymphatic Research Foundation Postdoctoral Fellowship Awards Program *(Postdoctorate/Fellowship)* [5441]

The C. Lyons Fellowship Program *(Advanced Professional/Fellowship)* [7984]

M. Hildred Blewett Fellowship *(Postdoctorate/Fellowship, Award, Monetary)* [1225]

M. William and Frances J. Tilghman Scholarship *(Undergraduate/Scholarship)* [3573]

MAC Emeritus Membership Award *(Professional development/Award)* [7366]

Bill MacAloney Legacy Scholarships *(Undergraduate/Scholarship)* [2805]

Catherine Macaulay Prize *(Graduate/Prize)* [1436]

Katie MacDonald Memorial Scholarships *(Graduate, Undergraduate/Scholarship)* [11273]

Warren Mack Scholarship *(Undergraduate/Scholarship)* [6333]

Robert Mack Scholarships *(Graduate, Undergraduate/Scholarship)* [6956]

Thermoset Division/James I. Mackenzie and James H. Cunningham Scholarships *(Undergraduate, Graduate/Scholarship)* [10490]

Mackenzie King Travelling Scholarship *(Graduate/Scholarship, Monetary)* [7183]

Mackey-Byars Scholarship for Communication Excellence *(Undergraduate/Scholarship)* [11195]

Andrew Macrina Scholarships *(Undergraduate/Scholarship)* [845]

Dorothy L. Maddy Workshop/Seminar Scholarship *(Other/Scholarship)* [10745]

James Madison Foundation - Junior Fellowships *(Advanced Professional, Graduate/Fellowship)* [6227]

James Madison Foundation - Senior Fellowships *(Advanced Professional/Fellowship)* [6228]

James Madison Graduate Fellowships *(Graduate/Fellowship)* [6229]

Madson Graduate Scholarship *(Graduate/Scholarship)* [10083]

MAES Founders Scholarship *(Graduate, Undergraduate/Scholarship)* [6964]

MAES General Scholarships *(Graduate, Undergraduate/Scholarship)* [6965]

MAES Padrino/Madrina Scholarships *(Graduate, Undergraduate/Scholarship)* [6966]

MAES Pipeline Scholarship *(Graduate, Undergraduate/Scholarship)* [6967]

MAES Presidential Scholarship *(Graduate, Undergraduate/Scholarship)* [6968]

MAES Scholarships *(Graduate/Scholarship)* [6969]

Magnetic Interfaces & Nanostructures Division - Leo M. Falicov Student Award *(Graduate/Grant)* [2384]

Lillian Grace Mahan Scholarship Fund *(Graduate/Scholarship)* [10776]

The Rick Mahoney Scholarship *(Undergraduate/Scholarship)* [7173]

Maiman Student Paper Competition *(Graduate, Undergraduate/Award)* [8679]

Maine Community College Scholarships (MCCS) *(Undergraduate, Vocational/Occupational/Scholarship)* [7008]

Maine Community Foundation - Rice Scholarships *(Undergraduate/Scholarship)* [6992]

Maine Vietnam Veterans Scholarship *(Advanced Professional/Scholarship)* [6993]

Maintenance Technical Reward and Career Scholarship *(Undergraduate/Scholarship)* [7739]

Alexander M. and June L. Maisin Foundation Scholarship *(Undergraduate/Scholarship)* [6275]

MALDEF Law School Scholarship Program *(Undergraduate, Graduate/Scholarship)* [7291]

Maley/FTE Scholarships *(Graduate/Scholarship)* [6126]

Maley/FTEE Teacher Professional Development Scholarships *(Professional development/Scholarship)* [6127]

Malini E. Sathyadev Memorial Scholarship *(Undergraduate/Scholarship)* [9832]

Malyon Smith Scholarship Research Award *(Graduate/Scholarship)* [1737]

Manasel Manasselian Memorial Grant *(Undergraduate/Scholarship)* [1894]

Cora Aguda Manayan Fund Scholarship *(Undergraduate/Scholarship)* [5408]

Manchester Scholarship Foundation - Adult Learners Scholarship *(Undergraduate/Scholarship)* [5337]

Lazaro J. Mandel Young Investigator Award *(Advanced Professional/Monetary, Award)* [1236]

Mangum & Associates PC Scholarship Contest *(Undergraduate/Scholarship)* [7014]

Manhattan Street Capital National Scholarship *(Undergraduate/Scholarship)* [7016]

Manning & Zimmerman Distracted Driving Scholarship *(College, University, Undergraduate, Vocational/Occupational/Scholarship)* [6697]

Honorable Carol Los Mansmann Memorial Fund *(Graduate, Undergraduate/Scholarship)* [349]

Manzer-Keener-Wefler Scholarship Fund *(Undergraduate/Scholarship)* [10777]

March of Dimes General Research Grants *(Professional development/Grant)* [7026]

March of Dimes Graduate Nursing Scholarships *(Graduate/Scholarship)* [7027]

The Albert H. Marckwardt Travel Grants *(Graduate, Doctorate/Grant)* [10969]

Harold and Inge Marcus Scholarship *(Undergraduate/Scholarship)* [5833]

Arif Mardin Music Fellowship *(Other/Fellowship)* [11141]

Margaret A. Blanchard Scholarship *(Graduate/Scholarship)* [11196]

Margaret E. Waldron Memorial Fund *(Undergraduate/Scholarship)* [4596]

Margaret J. Andrew Memorial Scholarship *(Undergraduate, Graduate/Scholarship)* [10116]

Margaret T. Craig Community Service Scholarship *(Undergraduate/Scholarship)* [3686]

Margarian Scholarship *(Undergraduate, Graduate/Scholarship)* [7032]

Margery J. Seeger Scholarship *(Undergraduate/Scholarship)* [5164]

Art Margosian Scholarship *(Undergraduate/Scholarship)* [6334]

Maria Gonzalez Borrero Scholarship Fund *(Undergraduate/Scholarship)* [5338]

Marian Johnson Frutiger Sisterhood Scholarship *(Undergraduate/Scholarship)* [10117]

Maricopa County Community College District Scholarships (MCCCD) *(Undergraduate/Scholarship)* [7034]

Marilyn Yetso Memorial Scholarship *(Graduate, Master's, Doctorate/Scholarship)* [11168]

Marilynne Graboys Wool Scholarship *(Graduate/Scholarship)* [9695]

Marine Technology Society ROV Scholarship (MTS ROV) *(Undergraduate, Graduate/Scholarship)* [7069]

Shirley Stone Marinkovich Memorial Scholarships *(Undergraduate/Scholarship)* [6458]

Marion Barr Stanfield Art Scholarship *(Graduate, Undergraduate/Scholarship)* [11252]

Marion and Donald Routh Student Research Grant *(Graduate/Grant)* [1740]

Mariposa Elementary School PTA Scholarship *(Undergraduate/Scholarship)* [9559]

Marisol Scholarship *(Undergraduate/Scholarship)* [6459]

Marjorie Kovler Research Fellowship *(Professional development/Fellowship)* [6532]

Marjorie Usher Ragan Scholarship *(Undergraduate/Scholarship)* [11197]

Mark A. Reid Memorial Scholarship *(Undergraduate/Scholarship)* [3687]

Marliave Scholarship Fund *(Graduate/Scholarship)* [2161]

Olivia M. Marquart Scholarships *(Graduate, Master's, Doctorate/Scholarship)* [11169]

Marsh Risk Consulting Scholarships *(Undergraduate/Scholarship)* [1569]

Marsh Writing/Research Scholarship Awards *(Undergraduate, Graduate, Doctorate/Scholarship)* [6389]

Marshall-Baruch Fellowships *(Doctorate/Fellowship)* [7111]

Marshall Cavendish Scholarships *(Graduate/Scholarship, Monetary)* [1079]

Marshall Memorial Fellowship *(Other/Fellowship)* [4946]

Samuel Taylor Marshall Scholarship *(Graduate, Undergraduate/Scholarship)* [2539]

Ray and Gertrude Marshall Scholarships *(Undergraduate/Scholarship)* [846]

Martha Combs Jenkins Scholarship *(Undergraduate/Scholarship)* [9117]

Martha Delman and Milton Arthur Krug Endowed Law Scholarship *(Undergraduate/Scholarship)* [9016]

Martha Weston Grant *(Advanced Professional/Grant)* [10301]

Edna L. Martin Scholarship Fund *(Undergraduate/Scholarship)* [3633]

Martin Sisters Scholarship *(Undergraduate/Scholarship)* [4007]

John S. Martinez and Family Scholarship Fund *(Undergraduate/Scholarship)* [3591]

Eric Martinez Memorial Scholarships *(Graduate, Undergraduate/Scholarship)* [11274]

The Anthony A. Martino Memorial Scholarship *(Undergraduate/Scholarship)* [5010]

A. Lucchetti Martino Scholarship *(Undergraduate/Scholarship)* [7961]

Marvin H. and Kathleen G. Teget Leadership Scholarship *(Undergraduate/Scholarship)* [10866]

Mary and Elliot Wood Foundation Graduate Scholarship *(Graduate/Scholarship)* [4744]

Mary L. Brown Scholarship DMACC *(Undergraduate/Scholarship)* [6161]

Mary Minglen Scholarship *(Postgraduate/Scholarship)* [1180]

Mary Moore Mitchell Scholarship *(Graduate/Scholarship)* [6904]

Mary Mouzon Darby Undergraduate Scholarship *(Undergraduate/Scholarship)* [5622]

Mary Roberts Scholarship Fund *(Undergraduate/Scholarship)* [3383]

Mary Turnbull Schacht Memorial Scholarship *(Undergraduate/Scholarship)* [10118]

Maryland Building Industry Association, Eastern Shore Chapter Scholarship Fund *(Undergraduate, High School/Scholarship)* [3574]

Maryland Speech Language Hearing Association Graduate Scholarships *(Graduate/Scholarship)* [7118]

Mas Family Scholarship *(Graduate, Undergraduate/Scholarship)* [7120]

The Maschhoffs Pork Production Scholarships *(Undergraduate/Scholarship)* [7971]

MASNA Student Scholarships *(Undergraduate, Graduate/Scholarship)* [7036]

Margaret Edwards Mason Adelphe Scholarship *(Undergraduate/Scholarship)* [6460]

Masonic-Range Science Scholarship *(Undergraduate/Scholarship)* [10520]

Massachusetts Federation of Polish Women's Clubs Scholarships *(Undergraduate/Scholarship)* [6604]

The Robert Masur Fellowship in Civil Liberties *(Undergraduate/Fellowship)* [11160]

MAT Scholarship *(Undergraduate, Vocational/Occupational/Scholarship)* [7406]

Ruth G. and Joseph D. Matarazzo Scholarship *(Graduate, Master's, Doctorate/Scholarship)* [1285]

Material Handling Education Foundation Scholarships *(Doctorate, Graduate, Undergraduate/Scholarship)* [7293]

Larry Matfay Cultural Heritage Scholarship *(Undergraduate, Graduate/Scholarship)* [6592]

Mathematics Mentoring Travel Grants *(Doctorate/Grant)* [2319]

Katharine & Bryant Mather Scholarship *(Graduate/Scholarship)* [791]

Mathilde Krim Fellowships in Biomedical Research *(Doctorate/Fellowship)* [1685]

Matt Harmon Memorial Scholarship Fund *(Undergraduate/Scholarship)* [10697]

Matt Stager Memorial Scholarship *(Undergraduate/Scholarship)* [11929]

Mature Student Scholarship *(Undergraduate/Scholarship)* [4430]

Maude Keisling / Cumberland County Extension Homemakers Scholarship Fund *(Undergraduate/Scholarship)* [3634]

Elizabeth M. Mauro Reimbursement Awards *(Advanced Professional/Award)* [72]

Ann Lane Mavromatis Scholarship *(Undergraduate/Scholarship)* [967]

The Maxwell Scholarship in Graduate Medical Journalism *(Graduate/Scholarship)* [11198]

May-Cassioppi Scholarship *(Undergraduate/Scholarship)* [3688]

Howard Mayer Brown Fellowship *(Graduate/Fellowship)* [1146]

John E. Mayfield Scholarship Fund for Cheatham County Central High School *(Undergraduate/Scholarship)* [3635]

John E. Mayfield Scholarship Fund for Harpeth High School *(Undergraduate/Scholarship)* [3636]

John E. Mayfield Scholarship Fund for Pleasant View Christian High School *(Undergraduate/Scholarship)* [3637]

John E. Mayfield Scholarship Fund for Sycamore High School *(Undergraduate/Scholarship)* [3638]

The Clara Mayo Grants *(Graduate/Grant)* [10510]

Giuliano Mazzetti Scholarship *(Undergraduate/Scholarship)* [10408]

Walter Samuel McAfee Scholarships in Space Physics *(Undergraduate/Scholarship)* [8088]

MCBA Scholarship (MCBA) *(Undergraduate/Scholarship)* [7308]

McCall Educational Fund *(Undergraduate/Scholarship)* [3384]

Doreen McMullan McCarthy Memorial Academic Scholarship for Women with Bleeding Disorders *(Undergraduate/Scholarship)* [7926]

McClatchy Minority Scholarship and Fellowship *(Undergraduate/Scholarship)* [10617]

The First Lieutenant Scott McClean Love Memorial Scholarship - Children of Soldiers *(Undergraduate, Vocational/Occupational/Scholarship)* [1917]

The First Lieutenant Scott McClean Love Memorial Scholarship - Spouses of Soldiers *(Undergraduate, Vocational/Occupational/Scholarship)* [1918]

McCleary Law Fellows Program *(Graduate, Undergraduate/Fellowship)* [5628]

McCloy Fellowships in Agriculture *(Professional development/Fellowship)* [810]

McCloy Fellowships in Environmental Policy *(Professional development/Fellowship)* [811]

McCloy Fellowships in Journalism *(Professional development/Fellowship)* [812]

McCloy Fellowships in Urban Affairs *(Professional development/Fellowship)* [813]

Niqui McCown Honor and Memorial Scholarship Fund *(Undergraduate/Scholarship)* [11949]

The Fred R. McDaniel Memorial Scholarship *(Undergraduate/Scholarship)* [1948]

Michele L. McDonald Scholarships *(Undergraduate/Scholarship)* [4304]

McFarffels Scholarships *(Undergraduate/Scholarship)* [9304]

Foster G. McGaw Scholarship *(Undergraduate, Graduate/Scholarship)* [2306]

Nancy B. Woolridge McGee Graduate Fellowships *(Graduate/Fellowship)* [12415]

Thomas R. McGetchin Memorial Scholarship Award *(Undergraduate/Scholarship)* [11423]

Linda and Vincent McGrath Scholarship *(Undergraduate/Scholarship)* [6390]

Mary Bowles McInnis Adelphe Scholarship *(Undergraduate/Scholarship)* [6461]

The McKelvey Scholarship *(Undergraduate/Scholarship)* [7193]

McKinley Elementary School PTA Scholarship *(Undergraduate/Scholarship)* [9561]

McKinney Sisters Scholarship *(Undergraduate/Scholarship)* [4008]

C.A. "Pete" McKnight Scholarships *(High School/Scholarship)* [11199]

McKnight Theater Artist Fellowships *(Other/Fellowship)* [9199]

The McLean Scholarship for Nursing and Physician Assistant Majors *(Undergraduate/Scholarship)* [2194]

Ronald E. McNair Scholarships in Space and Optical Physics *(Undergraduate/Scholarship)* [8089]

National Association of Pediatric Nurse Practitioners McNeil Annual Scholarships *(Undergraduate/Scholarship)* [7679]

National Association of Pediatric Nurse Practitioners McNeil Rural and Underserved Scholarships *(Graduate/Scholarship)* [7680]

Joan Reagin McNeill Scholarships - Alpha Theta *(Undergraduate/Scholarship)* [10119]

Joan Reagin McNeill Scholarships - Theta Phi *(Undergraduate/Scholarship)* [10120]

O. Ruth McQuown Scholarship - Graduate Award for Current Students *(Graduate/Scholarship)* [11572]

MDA Development Grants *(Doctorate/Grant)* [7509]

MDA Research Grants *(Advanced Professional/Grant)* [7510]

MDF Postdoctoral Fellowship *(Postdoctorate/Fellowship)* [7536]

MDI Biological Laboratory High school Student Summer Research Fellowship *(High School/Fellowship)* [7484]

MDI Biological Laboratory Undergraduate Summer Research Fellowships *(Undergraduate/Fellowship)* [7485]

David Meador Foundation - Club Management Student Scholarships *(Undergraduate/Scholarship)* [8242]

The Medallion Fund Scholarship *(Undergraduate/Scholarship)* [8254]

Medical Scrubs Collection Scholarship *(Undergraduate, Graduate/Scholarship)* [7225]

Medical Student Rotation for Underrepresented Populations *(Graduate, Master's/Grant)* [3779]

MedicalFieldCareers.com Healthcare Scholarship *(Professional development/Scholarship)* [7227]

Medieval Academy Dissertation Grants *(Graduate/Grant)* [7230]

The MEDIGO Scholarship Program *(Undergraduate, Graduate/Scholarship)* [7234]

Medina County Retired Teachers Association Scholarship *(Undergraduate/Scholarship)* [7236]

Carl J. Megel Scholarship *(Undergraduate/Scholarship)* [884]

Kumar Mehta Scholarship *(Graduate/Scholarship)* [792]

Dr. Roger E. Meisner Veterinary Medicine Educational Scholarship Fund *(Undergraduate, Graduate/Scholarship)* [8474]

Melanie and Todd Edmondson Memorial Scholarship *(Undergraduate/Scholarship)* [3660]

K. Cyrus Melikian Memorial Grant *(Undergraduate/Scholarship)* [1895]

Mellon/ACLS Dissertation Completion Fellowships *(Graduate, Doctorate/Fellowship)* [825]

Mellon-CES Dissertation Completion Fellowships in European Studies. *(Graduate/Fellowship)* [3858]

Mellon Fellowships for Dissertation Research in Original Sources *(Doctorate/Fellowship)* [3870]

Andrew W. Mellon Foundation Fellowships *(Graduate/Fellowship)* [8749]

Terry Mellor Continuing Education Grant *(Undergraduate/Grant)* [10735]

Melvin Kruger Endowed Scholarship Program *(Graduate, Undergraduate/Scholarship)* [8063, 9739]

Member Student Scholarships *(Undergraduate/Scholarship)* [9050]

Memorial Fund Scholarship *(Undergraduate/Scholarship)* [7785]

Menominee Tribal Scholarships *(Undergraduate, Graduate, High School/Scholarship)* [7256]

Mentored Research Fellowship *(Postdoctorate/Fellowship)* [7534]

Mentored Research Scholar Grant *(Doctorate, Professional development/Grant)* [717]

Merchants Exchange Scholarship *(Undergraduate, Vocational/Occupational, Graduate, Professional development/Scholarship)* [7266]

Meredith P. Crawford Fellowship in I-O Psychology *(Doctorate/Fellowship)* [5626]

Merial Excellence in Preventive Medicine in Beef Award *(Other/Grant)* [526]

Merial Excellence in Preventive Medicine in Dairy Award *(Other/Grant)* [527]

John K. Merrell Scholarship *(Undergraduate, Graduate/Scholarship)* [2541]

Steven Craig Merrill Memorial Scholarship *(Undergraduate, Graduate/Scholarship)* [2542]

Mesothelioma Memorial Scholarships *(Undergraduate, Vocational/Occupational/Scholarship)* [10859]

Sanders J. Mestel Legal Scholarship Fund *(Undergraduate/Scholarship)* [10779]

Meyer D. and Dorothy C. Silverman Scholarship Fund *(Undergraduate/Scholarship)* [3639]

Theodore Meyer Scholarship *(Undergraduate, Graduate/Scholarship)* [1137]

MFJC Doctoral Scholarships *(Doctorate/Scholarship)* [7250]

MICA Scholarships *(Undergraduate/Scholarship)* [7386]

Michael D. Curtin Renaissance Student Memorial Scholarship *(Graduate/Scholarship)* [4257]

Michael Herman Scholarship *(Undergraduate, Vocational/Occupational/Scholarship)* [5096]

Michael J. Hoggard Memorial Scholarship *(Undergraduate/Scholarship)* [9411]

Michael Moody Fitness Scholarship *(Undergraduate, Graduate/Scholarship)* [7464]

Michael P. Spadafora Medical Toxicology Travel Award *(Professional development/Grant)* [766]

Michael R. Losey Excellence In HR Research Award *(Graduate, Undergraduate/Award, Recognition)* [10368]

Michigan Council of Women in Technology High School Scholarship Program *(High School/Scholarship)* [7310]

Michigan Council of Women in Technology Undergraduate Scholarship Program *(Undergraduate, Graduate/Scholarship)* [7311]

Michigan Realtors Scholarship Trust *(Graduate, Undergraduate/Scholarship)* [7324]

Michigan Society of Fellows Three-Year Fellowships *(Postdoctorate/Fellowship)* [7326]

Michigan Sugar Company Hotel Restaurant/Resort Management Scholarship *(Undergraduate/Scholarship)* [7341]

Michigan Sugar Queen Scholarship *(Undergraduate/Scholarship)* [7342]

Micklin Law Group Scholarship *(College, University/Scholarship)* [7352]

Microsoft Research Graduate Women's Scholarships *(Graduate/Scholarship)* [7356]

Microsoft Research PhD Fellowships *(Doctorate/Fellowship)* [7357]

Mid-Continent Instruments and Avionics Scholarship *(Undergraduate/Scholarship)* [188]

Beth Middleton Memorial Scholarships *(Undergraduate/Scholarship)* [4486]

Midland Company Scholarship Fund *(Undergraduate/Scholarship)* [3386]

Midwest Modern Language Association Fellowship *(Doctorate, Postdoctorate/Fellowship)* [7380, 8377]

Mike and Gail Donley Spouse Scholarship *(Undergraduate, Graduate, Postgraduate/Scholarship)* [149]

Mike Hylton Memorial Scholarship *(Undergraduate/Scholarship)* [5480]

Mike Niemeyer Memorial Football Scholarship *(Undergraduate/Scholarship)* [9563]

Mike Reynolds Scholarship *(Undergraduate/Scholarship)* [9473]

Mikimoto Scholarship *(Graduate/Scholarship)* [4880]

Miklos Faust International Travel Award *(Doctorate/Grant)* [1481]

Mila Boyd Law Offices Scholarship Contest *(Undergraduate/Scholarship)* [2667]

Milacron Geier Scholarship Fund *(Undergraduate/Scholarship)* [3387]

Milan Getting Scholarship *(Undergraduate/Scholarship)* [10574]

Mildred Colodny Diversity Scholarships for Graduate Program in Historic Preservation *(Graduate/Scholarship, Award, Monetary)* [8145]

Mildred E. Troske Music Scholarship *(Undergraduate/Scholarship)* [5169]

William F. Miles Scholarships *(Graduate/Scholarship)* [5276]

Military Service Scholarship *(Graduate, Undergraduate/Scholarship)* [10084]

The MILK Scholarship *(University/Scholarship)* [7391]

The Cheryl Allyn Miller Award *(Doctorate, Graduate/Award)* [10567]

Millicent Mary Schaffner Endowed Memorial Scholarship *(Undergraduate/Scholarship)* [5098]

Millie Gonzalez Memorial Scholarship *(Undergraduate/Scholarship)* [5481]

Abby and Howard Milstein Innovation Award in Reproductive Medicine *(Advanced Professional, Professional development, Graduate/Grant)* [6329]

Milton and Edith Brown Memorial Scholarship Fund *(Undergraduate/Scholarship)* [3388]

Milton Postgraduate Fellowship *(Postgraduate/Fellowship)* [3214]

Mineral & Metallurgical Processing Division Scholarships and Richard Klimpel Memorial Scholarships (MPD) *(Undergraduate, Graduate/Scholarship)* [10428]

Minneapolis Jewish Federation Camp Scholarships *(Undergraduate, Other/Scholarship)* [7400]

Minnesota Power Community Involvement Scholarship Fund *(Undergraduate/Scholarship)* [4215]

Jacque I. Minnotte Health Reporting Fellowship *(Other/Fellowship)* [9474]

Minorities in Government Finance Scholarship *(Graduate, Undergraduate/Scholarship)* [5054]

Minority Scholarship Award *(Undergraduate/Scholarship)* [3575]

Minority Scholarship in Classics and Classical Archaeology *(Undergraduate/Fellowship)* [10311]

Minton-Spidell-Jackowski Point Scholarship *(Undergraduate, Graduate, Doctorate/Scholarship)* [9227]

Miss America Social Impact Initiative Scholarship *(Undergraduate/Scholarship)* [7417]

Mission Bay Hospital Auxiliary Scholarship *(Undergraduate/Scholarship)* [9834]

Dikran Missirlian Scholarship Grant *(Undergraduate/Scholarship)* [1896]

MJSA Education Foundation Scholarship *(Undergraduate/Scholarship)* [7024]

MKC/Preuss Scholarship *(Undergraduate, Community College, University/Scholarship)* [9835]

MLA Financial Assistance *(Graduate, Advanced Professional/Grant)* [7426]

MLA/NLM Spectrum Scholarship *(Undergraduate/Scholarship)* [7220]

MLA Research, Development, and Demonstration Project Grant *(Graduate/Grant)* [7221]

MLA Scholarship *(Graduate, Master's/Scholarship)* [7222]

MLA Scholarship for Minority Students *(Graduate/Scholarship)* [7223]

MMC Scholarships *(Other/Scholarship)* [6027]

MMRF Research Fellow Awards *(Postdoctorate, Professional development/Grant)* [7495]

MMUF Dissertation Grants *(Graduate/Grant)* [12047]

MMUF Travel and Research Grants *(Graduate, Undergraduate/Grant)* [12048]

MNLA Academic Scholarship *(Undergraduate/Scholarship)* [7317]

MODNA Nursing Education Scholarship *(Doctorate, Graduate/Scholarship)* [7359]

MoKan Division of Midwest Dairy Educational Award *(Undergraduate/Scholarship)* [7372]

Molded Dimensions, LLC Scholarship *(College, University/Scholarship)* [7428]

Antoinette M. Molinari Memorial Scholarships *(Doctorate/Scholarship)* [467]

Mollie Lukken Memorial Scholarship *(Graduate, Other/Scholarship)* [6345]

Molly McKay Scholarship *(Undergraduate/Scholarship)* [11200]

Shelby L. Molter Music Education Scholarship *(Undergraduate, Graduate/Scholarship)* [2543]

Momeni Foundation Scholastic Achievement Scholarships *(Undergraduate/Scholarship)* [7955]

Monaghan/Trudell Fellowships for Aerosol Technique Development *(Professional development/Fellowship)* [1355]

The Montana Advocates Scholarship *(All/Scholarship)* [90]

Montana Broadcasters Association Broadcast Engineering Scholarships *(Undergraduate/Scholarship)* [7453]

Monte Mitchell Scholarship *(Undergraduate/Scholarship)* [189]

Montgomery County Medical Society – William W. Lander, MD, Medical Student Scholarship *(Undergraduate/Scholarship)* [4800]

ARTC Glenn Moon Scholarships *(Undergraduate/Scholarship)* [5340]

M. Steve Moore Memorial Scholarship *(Undergraduate, Graduate/Award)* [2544]

Annabelle Moore Scholarship *(Undergraduate/Scholarship)* [2745]

Willie Hobbs Moore Scholarships *(Undergraduate/Scholarship)* [8090]

The Dr. Blanca Moore-Velez Woman of Substance Scholarship *(Undergraduate/Scholarship)* [7669]

Thomas S. Morgan Memorial Scholarship *(Graduate, Master's/Scholarship)* [9075]

Morgan Stanley Pediatrics Fellowships *(Postgraduate, Graduate/Fellowship)* [686]

Robert L. Morlan Redlands Area Interfaith Council Scholarships *(Undergraduate/Scholarship)* [9565]

Morphisec's Women in Cybersecurity Scholarships *(Undergraduate, Graduate/Scholarship)* [7470]

Morris L. and Rebecca Ziskind Memorial Scholarship *(Undergraduate/Scholarship)* [5666]

Edith Cantor Morrison Memorial Scholarship *(Undergraduate, Graduate/Scholarship)* [2545]

June Morrison Scholarship Fund *(Undergraduate/Scholarship)* [11990]

Harry L. Morrison Scholarships *(Undergraduate/Scholarship)* [8091]

Dorothy Morrison Undergraduate Scholarships *(Undergraduate/Scholarship, Monetary)* [1400]

Mortar Board National Foundation Fellowship *(Postdoctorate/Fellowship, Award)* [7476]

Morton Bahr Scholarship *(Undergraduate/Scholarship)* [3559]

Morton M. Traum Surface Science Student Award *(Graduate, Doctorate/Prize)* [2385]

Archie Motley Memorial Scholarships for Minority Students *(Graduate/Scholarship)* [7367]

Gerald O. Mott Award *(Graduate/Award)* [3916]

John R. Mott Scholarships *(Undergraduate, Graduate/Scholarship)* [7482]

Jack D. Motteler Scholarship *(Undergraduate/Scholarship)* [9305]

Mt. Hood Chapter Scholarship Awards *(Undergraduate/Scholarship)* [8708]

David J. Moynihan Scholarships *(Undergraduate, Graduate/Scholarship)* [8331]

MPI CRV Membership Scholarships *(Other/Scholarship)* [7238]

MPI-WI Founders Grant Program *(Professional development/Grant)* [7241]

MPOWER Financing's Global Citizen Scholarship *(College, University, Undergraduate/Scholarship)* [7489]

MSA Graduate Fellowship *(Graduate/Fellowship)* [7532]

MSA Grant for Research in Crystallography *(Professional development/Grant)* [7397]

MSA Grant for Student Research in Mineralogy and Petrology *(Undergraduate, Graduate/Grant)* [7398]

MSAA Scholarship Program *(Graduate/Scholarship)* [7410]

MSEA/SEIU Part-time Student Members Scholarships *(Undergraduate/Scholarship)* [7010]

The MTS Student Scholarship for Graduate Students *(Graduate/Scholarship)* [7070]

The MTS Student Scholarship for Graduating High School Seniors *(Undergraduate/Scholarship)* [7071]

The MTS Student Scholarship for Two-Year, Technical, Engineering and Community College Students *(Undergraduate/Scholarship)* [7072]

Mu Alpha Theta Summer Grants *(Undergraduate, Graduate/Grant)* [7493]

Mueller Undergraduate Scholarship *(Undergraduate/Scholarship)* [12115]

Dudley Mullins/Cabot Corporation Scholarship *(Undergraduate/Scholarship)* [8865]

Multicultural Work-in-Progress Grant *(Advanced Professional/Grant)* [10302]

Muncy Rotary Club Scholarship Fund *(Undergraduate/Scholarship)* [4600]

Muncy Scholars Awards Fund *(Undergraduate/Scholarship)* [4601]

Marvin Mundel Memorial Scholarship *(Undergraduate/Scholarship)* [5834]

NACCED Annual John C. Murphy Scholarships *(Graduate, Undergraduate/Scholarship)* [7643]

Murse World Scholarship *(Undergraduate, Graduate, Postdoctorate/Scholarship)* [7507]

Murtha Cullina LLP Scholarship Fund *(Undergraduate/Scholarship)* [3592]

My Life As A Lawyer Scholarship *(Graduate/Scholarship)* [3837]

Myasthenia Gravis Foundation of America Nursing Research Fellowships *(Undergraduate/Fellowship)* [7529]

Myra Levick Scholarship Fund *(Graduate/Scholarship)* [502]

Myrna F. Bernath Fellowship *(Doctorate, Graduate/Fellowship)* [10358]

NAAE Upper Division Scholarship *(Undergraduate/Scholarship)* [7609]

NAAMA Scholarships *(Undergraduate/Scholarship)* [7598]

NABA National Scholarship Program *(Graduate, Undergraduate/Scholarship, Award, Monetary)* [7613]

NACA Multicultural Professional Development Grant *(Undergraduate, Graduate, Professional development/Grant)* [7627]

NACA Silver Anniversary Scholarship for Student Leaders *(Undergraduate/Scholarship)* [7630]

NACADA Scholarships *(Graduate, Postdoctorate/Scholarship)* [7568]

NACBS Dissertation Fellowship *(Graduate, Doctorate/Fellowship)* [8420]

NACBS-Huntington Library Fellowship *(Doctorate, Postdoctorate/Fellowship)* [8422]

Nadine Barrie Smith Student Award *(Undergraduate/Award)* [6120]

NAED/Spencer Dissertation Fellowship Program *(Graduate, Doctorate/Fellowship)* [7577]

NAFA Corporate Aviation Business Scholarship *(Undergraduate, Graduate/Scholarship)* [7592]

NAFA Scholarship Program *(Undergraduate/Scholarship)* [7590]

NAGAP Graduate Student Enrollment Management Research Grants *(Graduate/Grant)* [7651]

NAJA Scholarship *(Graduate/Scholarship)* [7664]

NALS of Detroit Scholarships *(Undergraduate/Scholarship)* [7544]

NANBPWC National Scholarship *(Undergraduate/Scholarship)* [7670]

Robyn Nance Memorial Scholarships *(Undergraduate/Scholarship)* [9566]

Nancy Curry Scholarship *(Vocational/Occupational, Undergraduate, Graduate, Postgraduate/Scholarship, Award)* [9960]

Nancy Lorraine Jensen Memorial Scholarship Fund *(Undergraduate/Scholarship)* [10590]

NAPC Forum Student Scholarships *(Undergraduate, Graduate/Scholarship)* [7594]

Napoleon A. Jones, III Memorial Scholarship *(Undergraduate/Scholarship)* [9837]

NAPT Continuing Education Award *(Undergraduate/Award)* [7684]

NASA RISGC Graduate Fellowships *(Master's, Postdoctorate, Graduate/Fellowship)* [9699]

NASA WVSGC Undergraduate Research Fellowship *(Undergraduate/Fellowship)* [11975]

NASE Future Entrepreneur *(Undergraduate/Scholarship)* [7692]

Nashville Unit Scholarships *(Undergraduate/Scholarship, Grant)* [5488]

NASLR Mined Land Reclamation Educational Grant *(Undergraduate/Grant)* [7700]

Nate Mack/Cindi Turner Scholarship *(Undergraduate/Scholarship)* [9413]

National American Arab Nurses Association Scholarships for Nursing Study *(Undergraduate, Master's/Scholarship)* [7596]

National Association of Abandoned Mine Land Programs Scholarship *(Undergraduate/Scholarship)* [7605]

National Association of Biology Teachers BioClub Student Award *(Undergraduate/Scholarship)* [7611]

National Association for the Self-Employed Scholarships *(Undergraduate, High School/Scholarship)* [7693]

National Association of Women in Construction Construction Trades Scholarship *(Undergraduate/Scholarship)* [7708]

National Association of Women in Construction Founders Undergraduate Scholarship *(Undergraduate/Scholarship)* [7709]

National Ataxia Foundation Postdoctoral Fellowship Award *(Postdoctorate/Fellowship, Award)* [7711]

National Ataxia Foundation Research Grants *(Other/Grant)* [7712]

The National Center for Health Statistics Postdoctoral Research Program (NCHS) *(Postdoctorate/Fellowship)* [11329]

National Co-op Scholarship Program *(Undergraduate/Scholarship)* [12190]

National Council on Public History Graduate Student Travel Awards *(Doctorate, Graduate, Master's/Grant)* [7792]

National Council on Public History Student Project Awards *(Undergraduate/Grant)* [7793]

National Court Reporters Association Student Intern Scholarship *(Undergraduate/Scholarship)* [7818]

National Debt Relief Scholarship *(University, Four Year College, Undergraduate/Scholarship)* [7828]

National Dental Hygienists' Association Scholarships *(Undergraduate/Scholarship)* [7839]

National Federation of the Blind Scholarship Program *(Undergraduate/Scholarship, Monetary)* [7878]

National GEM Consortium - MS Engineering Fellowships *(Master's/Fellowship)* [7902]

National GEM Consortium - PhD Engineering Fellowships *(Master's, Graduate/Fellowship)* [7903]

National GEM Consortium - PhD Science Fellowships *(Doctorate, Graduate/Fellowship)* [7904]

National Geographic Conservation Trust Grants *(Doctorate, Advanced Professional/Grant)* [7906]

National Geographic Expedition Council Grants *(Advanced Professional/Grant)* [7907]

National Geographic Society/Waitt Grants *(Advanced Professional/Grant, Award)* [7908]

National Geographic Young Explorers Grants *(Advanced Professional/Grant)* [7909]

National Guard Association of Rhode Island Scholarship *(Undergraduate/Scholarship)* [7913]

National High School Oratorical Contest Scholarship *(Undergraduate/Scholarship)* [1072]

National Huguenot Society College and Postgraduate Student Scholarships *(Undergraduate, Postgraduate/Scholarship)* [7937]

National Humanities Center Fellowships *(Doctorate, Postdoctorate/Fellowship)* [7939]

National Institute of Health Undergraduate Scholarship Program (NIH UGSP) *(Undergraduate/Scholarship)* [11341]

National Iranian American Council Fellowships *(Graduate, Undergraduate/Fellowship)* [7956]

National Junior Swine Association Outstanding Member Scholarships *(Graduate/Scholarship)* [7972]

National Medical Fellowships Need-Based Scholarships *(Undergraduate/Scholarship)* [8001]

National Merit Scholarship Program *(Undergraduate/Scholarship)* [8003]

National Military Intelligence Foundation Scholarship *(Undergraduate, Graduate/Scholarship)* [8011]

National Organization of Italian-American Women Scholarships *(Undergraduate, Graduate/Scholarship)* [8025]

National Pathfinder Scholarship *(Graduate, Master's, Undergraduate/Scholarship)* [7885]

National Science Foundation Graduate Research Fellowship Program (GRFP) *(Graduate/Fellowship)* [8068]

National Sculpture Society Participation Scholarships *(Undergraduate/Scholarship)* [8073]

National Security Technologies Engineering and Science Scholarships *(Undergraduate/Scholarship)* [9414]

National Technical Honor Society Scholarships (NTHS) *(Undergraduate/Scholarship)* [4487]

Native American Education Grants *(Graduate, Undergraduate/Grant)* [990]

Native Hawaiian Chamber of Commerce Scholarship *(Graduate, Undergraduate/Scholarship)* [8932]

Native Hawaiian Visual Arts Scholarship *(Graduate, Undergraduate/Scholarship)* [8933]

Naval Helicopter Association Scholarship *(Graduate, Undergraduate/Scholarship)* [8170]

Naval Research Enterprise Internship Program (NREIP) *(Graduate, Undergraduate/Internship)* [1443]

The Nazareth Scholarships - Sr. Kevin Whelan Scholarship *(Undergraduate/Scholarship)* [8183]

NBCUniversal Point Scholarship *(Undergraduate, Graduate, Doctorate/Scholarship)* [9228]

NBCUniversal Tony Coelho Media Scholarship *(Undergraduate, Graduate/Scholarship)* [618]

NBRC Frederic Helmholz, Jr., MD Educational Research Fund *(Master's, Doctorate/Grant)* [1356]

NBT Trade School, Community/Technical College, or University Scholarships *(Undergraduate/Scholarship)* [8563]

NCCF Survivor Scholarship *(Undergraduate/Scholarship)* [7773]

NCEA Postdoctoral Research Program *(Postdoctorate/Fellowship)* [11360]

NCECA Graduate Student Fellowships *(Graduate/Fellowship)* [7787]

NCPA Foundation Presidential Scholarships *(Undergraduate/Scholarship)* [7776]

NCPA Summer Internship Program *(Undergraduate/Internship)* [7777]

NCRF New Professional Reporter Grant *(Other/Grant)* [7819]

NCSGC Undergraduate Research Scholarships *(Undergraduate/Scholarship)* [8457]

NCSGC Undergraduate Scholarships *(Undergraduate/Scholarship)* [8458]

NCTE Research Foundation Grants *(Other/Grant)* [7800]

NCTM Emerging Teacher-Leaders in Elementary School Mathematics Grants for Grades PreK-5 *(Other/Grant)* [7806]

NCTM Prospective 7-12 Secondary Teacher Course Work Scholarships *(Professional development/Scholarship)* [7807]

NCTM School In-Service Training Grants for Grades 6-8 *(Undergraduate/Grant)* [7808]

NCTM School In-Service Training Grants for Grades 9-12 *(Undergraduate/Grant)* [7809]

NCTM School In-Service Training Grants for Grades PreK-5 *(Undergraduate/Grant)* [7810]

NDFU Scholarship *(Undergraduate/Scholarship)* [8462]

NDIA Picatinny Chapter Scholarships *(Undergraduate/Scholarship)* [7832]

NDSEG Fellowship *(Graduate/Fellowship)* [7834]

NDSGC American Indian Scholarships *(Undergraduate/Scholarship)* [8467]

NDSGC Graduate Fellowships *(Graduate, Master's, Doctorate/Scholarship, Fellowship)* [8468]

NDSGC Summer Faculty Fellowship *(Professional development/Scholarship, Fellowship)* [8469]

NDSGC Undergraduate Fellowships *(Undergraduate/Scholarship, Fellowship)* [8470]

NDSGC Undergraduate Scholarship *(Undergraduate/Scholarship)* [8471]

NDTA Academic Scholarship Program A *(Undergraduate/Scholarship)* [7836]

NDTA Academic Scholarship Program B *(Undergraduate/Scholarship)* [7837]

Nebraska Farm Bureau Greater Horizon Scholarship *(Undergraduate/Scholarship)* [8187]

Need-based and Merit Scholarships *(Undergraduate/Scholarship)* [4273]

Need-Based Scholarships *(Doctorate/Scholarship)* [4508]

Need-Based Scholarships *(Undergraduate/Scholarship)* [9100]

Douglas J. Neeley Memorial Scholarship *(Undergraduate, Graduate/Scholarship)* [2546]

J.W. "Bill" Neese Scholarship *(Undergraduate/Scholarship, Monetary, Award)* [5972]

NEHA/AAS Scholarship *(Graduate, Undergraduate/Scholarship)* [478, 7873]

Paul and Ruth Neidhold Business Scholarship *(Undergraduate/Scholarship)* [3689]

Aryeh Neier Fellowships *(Graduate/Fellowship)* [5635]

Nell Bryant Robinson Scholarship *(Undergraduate/Scholarship)* [9118]

Edward J. Nell Memorial Scholarships in Journalism *(Undergraduate/Scholarship)* [9464]

Dave Nelsen Scholarships *(Undergraduate/Scholarship)* [7672]

Tad Nelson Law Firm Scholarships *(Undergraduate/Scholarship)* [6716]

Carol Nelson Scholarship *(Undergraduate/Scholarship)* [6462]

Bill Nelson Scholarship Endowment (BNSE) *(Undergraduate, Graduate/Scholarship)* [8780]

NEMLA Summer Fellowships *(Graduate/Fellowship)* [8484]

NeMLA-University at Buffalo Special Collections Fellowship *(Undergraduate, Graduate/Fellowship)* [8485]

NEMRA Educational Scholarship Foundation *(Undergraduate, Vocational/Occupational/Scholarship)* [7866]

Nephrology Nurse Researcher Awards *(Doctorate/Award)* [1152]

NERRS Graduate Research Fellowship *(Graduate/Fellowship)* [7875]

Netfloor USA Access Flooring College Scholarships *(Undergraduate/Scholarship)* [8208]

Nethercott Family Scholarship Fund *(Undergraduate/Scholarship)* [3390]

Nettie and Jesse Gorov Scholarship *(Undergraduate/Scholarship)* [3690]

Reverend John S. Nettles Scholarships *(Undergraduate/Scholarship)* [3661]

The New England FEMARA Scholarship *(Undergraduate/Scholarship)* [1951]

New Hampshire Snowmobile Association Book Scholarships *(Undergraduate/Scholarship)* [8269]

New Investigator Grant *(Postdoctorate/Grant)* [9978]

New Investigator Research Grant *(Doctorate/Grant)* [432]

New York State Senate - Legislative Fellowship *(Graduate, Postgraduate/Fellowship)* [8326]

The New York Times College Scholarship *(Undergraduate/Scholarship, Internship)* [8354]

Ted and Ruth Neward Scholarships *(Undergraduate, Graduate/Scholarship)* [10492]

Newberry Consortium on American Indian Studies Faculty Fellowships *(Professional development/Fellowship)* [8378]

The Newberry Consortium in American Indian Studies Graduate Student Fellowships *(Graduate/Fellowship)* [8379]

Newberry Library ACM/GLCA Faculty Fellowships *(Other/Fellowship)* [2014, 8380]

Newberry Library National Endowment for the Humanities Fellowships *(Postdoctorate/Fellowship)* [8381]

The Newberry Library Short-Term Residential Fellowships for Individual Research *(Postdoctorate, Doctorate/Fellowship)* [8382]

The Shanon Newberry Physical Therapy Scholarship Endowment *(Doctorate/Scholarship)* [10845]

Newcomer Supply Student Scholarship *(Undergraduate/Scholarship)* [8110]

Newfangled Networks $1,000 Scholarship *(Undergraduate, Graduate/Scholarship)* [8389]

Caroline H. Newhouse Scholarship Fund *(Professional development/Scholarship, Grant)* [3163]

Newman Civic Fellowship *(Undergraduate/Fellowship)* [2868]

Craig D. Newman Memorial Scholarship *(Undergraduate/Scholarship)* [5409]

Edsel Newman Scholarships *(Undergraduate/Scholarship)* [6830]

Newman University Scouting Scholarships *(Undergraduate/Scholarship)* [7855]

NFBPA Future Colleagues Scholarships *(Undergraduate/Scholarship)* [7891]

NFDA Professional Women's Conference Scholarship *(Undergraduate/Scholarship)* [4844]

NFPA PCCE Scholarship *(Other, Professional development/Scholarship)* [7882]

NFPA/Thomson Reuters Scholarships *(Undergraduate, Two Year College/Scholarship)* [7883]

NFPA Youth Scholarships *(Undergraduate/Scholarship)* [7896]

N.G. Kaul Memorial Scholarship *(Doctorate, Graduate/Scholarship)* [8364]

NGA Conservation Fellowships *(Graduate/Fellowship)* [7898]

NGAT Educational Foundation Scholarship *(Graduate, Undergraduate/Scholarship)* [7915]

NGC College Scholarships *(Graduate, Undergraduate/Scholarship)* [7900]

NHAEOP Member Scholarships *(Undergraduate/Scholarship)* [8251]

NHEERL Postdoctoral Research Program *(Postdoctorate, Advanced Professional, Professional development/Fellowship)* [11354]

NHFA Scholarships *(Graduate/Scholarship)* [7930]

NHS Scholarships *(Undergraduate/Scholarship)* [7932]

NIABA/NIAF Scholarships *(Graduate/Scholarship)* [7958]

NIBA Presidential Scholarships *(Undergraduate/Scholarship)* [7941]

Helen W. Nies Memorial Scholarship *(Postgraduate/Scholarship)* [4509]

NIJ Visiting Fellows Program *(Other/Fellowship)* [7943]

Nikko Cosmetic Surgery Center Annual Breast Cancer Survivor Scholarships *(All/Scholarship)* [8398]

Nila Banton Smith Research Dissemination Support Grant *(Professional development/Grant)* [6036]

NING Scholarship *(Undergraduate, Graduate/Scholarship)* [8405]

Nissan North America, Inc. Scholarships *(Undergraduate/Scholarship)* [983]

NIU-CSEAS Foreign Language and Area Studies (FLAS) Graduate Fellowship *(Undergraduate, Graduate/Fellowship)* [8487]

Nixon Family Scholarship Fund *(Undergraduate, High School/Scholarship)* [11950]

Louise A. Nixon Scholarship *(Graduate/Scholarship)* [8192]

Stan and Mary Stark Alumni Scholarship *(Other/Scholarship)* [7967]

NJLA Scholarships *(Graduate, Postgraduate/Scholarship)* [8277]

NJPA Foundation Scholarship for Research on Diversity Issues *(Graduate/Scholarship)* [8285]

NJSA Visionary Leader Scholarships *(Graduate/Scholarship)* [7973]

NJSCPA High School Seniors *(Undergraduate/Scholarship)* [8288]

NLBRA Age-Out Scholarship *(Undergraduate/Scholarship)* [7993]

NLBRA National Royalty Scholarship *(Other/Scholarship)* [7994]

NLBRA Rainwater Scholarships *(Undergraduate/Scholarship)* [7995]

NLBRA World All Around Scholarships *(Undergraduate/Scholarship)* [7996]

NLBRA World Event Scholarships *(Undergraduate/Scholarship)* [7997]

NLBRA/Wrangler Academic Scholarships *(Undergraduate/Scholarship)* [7998]

NLBRA Youth Board Officer Scholarships *(Undergraduate/Scholarship)* [7999]

NLF Scholarships *(Undergraduate/Scholarship)* [7603]

NLM Associate Fellowship *(Postgraduate/Fellowship)* [11339]

NMCRS Gold Star Scholarship Program *(Undergraduate/Scholarship)* [8180]

NMHM Global Volcanism Program for Visiting Scientist/Postdoctoral Fellowships *(Postdoctorate, Advanced Professional/Fellowship)* [10202]

NMNH American Indian Program Fellowships *(Graduate/Fellowship)* [10203]

NMPF National Dairy Leadership Scholarship Program *(Graduate, Master's, Doctorate/Scholarship)* [8013]

NMSC College and University Sponsorship of Merit Scholarship Awards *(Undergraduate/Scholarship)* [8004]

NMSC Corporate-Sponsored merit Scholarship Awards *(Undergraduate/Scholarship)* [8005]

NMSC National Achievement Scholarship Program *(Undergraduate/Scholarship)* [8006]

NMSC Special Scholarships *(Undergraduate/Scholarship)* [8007]

NOBCChE Procter and Gamble Fellowships *(Graduate/Fellowship)* [8030]

Leonard Noble Educational Scholarships *(Professional development/Scholarship)* [8111]

Charles S. Noble Scholarships for Study at Harvard *(Undergraduate/Scholarship)* [300]

Alfred H. Nolle Scholarships *(Undergraduate/Scholarship)* [378]

Helen Woodruff Nolop Scholarships in Audiology and Allied Fields *(Graduate/Scholarship)* [4040]

Non Commissioned Officers Association Scholarships *(Undergraduate/Scholarship)* [8409]

Nor' Easters Scholarships - Two-year Program *(Undergraduate/Scholarship)* [5542]

Norall Scholarship Trust *(Undergraduate, Postdoctorate/Scholarship)* [6831]

Marian Norby Scholarships *(Other/Scholarship)* [6883]

Norm Manly YMTA Maritime Education Scholarship *(Undergraduate/Scholarship)* [4691, 12274]

Norman E. and Mary-Belle Huston Scholarship *(Graduate, Undergraduate/Scholarship)* [6103]

Norman Siegel Research Scholar Grants in Pediatrics *(Doctorate/Grant)* [1527]

Norman W. Kramer Outstanding Scholar Award *(Undergraduate/Scholarship)* [7345]

North Alabama Dietetic Association Scholarships *(Undergraduate, Graduate/Scholarship)* [218]

North American Van Lines Military Scholarship Competition *(Undergraduate/Scholarship)* [8424]

North Carolina Heroes Financial Hardship Grant *(Other/Grant)* [8439]

The North Carolina League For Nursing Academic Scholarship *(Graduate, Master's/Scholarship)* [4748]

North Carolina Nursery and Landscape Association Horticulture Scholarships *(Undergraduate/Scholarship)* [8441]

North Dakota Farmers Union Co-op House Scholarship *(Undergraduate/Scholarship)* [8463]

North Ottawa Hospital Auxiliary Scholarship *(Undergraduate/Scholarship)* [5099]

North Texas GIA Alumni Association Scholarship *(Undergraduate/Scholarship)* [4881]

Northampton County Medical Society Alliance Scholarships *(Undergraduate/Scholarship)* [8480]

NorthCoast Medical Scholarship *(Postgraduate/Scholarship)* [1181]

Northeast Alabama District Dietetic Association Scholarships *(Graduate, Undergraduate/Scholarship)* [219]

Northern California DX Foundation Scholarships *(Undergraduate/Scholarship)* [1952]

Northrop Grumman Engineering Scholars Program *(Undergraduate/Scholarship)* [8498]

Northside Booster Club - Felix R. Sepulveda Memorial Scholarship *(Undergraduate/Scholarship)* [9567]

Northwest Community Center Scholarship *(Undergraduate/Scholarship)* [3691]

Northwest-Shoals Community College Athletic Scholarships *(Undergraduate/Scholarship)* [8526]

Northwest-Shoals Community College High School Academic Scholarships *(Undergraduate/Scholarship)* [8530]

NOVA Foundation Scholarships *(Doctorate, Master's/Scholarship)* [8559]

Novak Awards *(Doctorate/Monetary, Award)* [67]

Novus Biologicals Scholarship Program *(All/Scholarship)* [8553]

NPC Scholarship *(Graduate/Scholarship)* [8040]

NPM Academic Scholarship *(Graduate, Undergraduate/Scholarship)* [7674]

NPM Program Scholarship *(Graduate, Undergraduate/Scholarship)* [7675]

NPPF Still & Multimedia Scholarship *(Undergraduate/Scholarship)* [8049]

NPPF TV News Scholarship *(Undergraduate/Scholarship)* [8050]

NRAEF Scholarship *(Undergraduate/Scholarship)* [9651]

NSA Scholarship Foundation *(Undergraduate/Scholarship)* [8079]

NSHSS Academic Paper Awards *(High School/Scholarship)* [8104]

NSPS Berntsen International Scholarship in Surveying Technology *(Undergraduate/Scholarship)* [8118]

NSS Conservation Grants *(Advanced Professional/Grant)* [8126]

NSS Education Grants *(Undergraduate/Grant)* [8127]

NSSA/NSCA Collegiate High School Senior Scholarships *(Undergraduate/Scholarship)* [8131]

Nuclear Criticality Safety Pioneers Scholarship *(Graduate/Scholarship)* [1168]

NURSE Corps Scholarship Program *(Professional development/Scholarship)* [11335]

NWRI Fellowship *(Graduate, Doctorate/Fellowship)* [8158]

NYCT Paid Graduate Student Philanthropy Fellowships - Arts and Historic Preservation *(Graduate/Fellowship)* [8305]

NYCT Paid Graduate Student Philanthropy Fellowships - Children, Youth, Families, Education, Human Justice and Workforce *(Graduate/Fellowship)* [8306]

NYCT Paid Graduate Student Philanthropy Fellowships - Health and People with Special Needs *(Graduate/Fellowship)* [8308]

The NYCTutoring.com Scholarship *(Undergraduate/Scholarship)* [8569]

NYFWA Scholarships *(Undergraduate, Graduate/Scholarship)* [8312]

OAB Kids Scholarships *(Undergraduate/Scholarship)* [8575]

OAIA Scholarships *(Undergraduate, Graduate/Scholarship)* [8700]

OAS Academic Scholarship for Undergraduate Studies *(Undergraduate/Scholarship)* [8731]

OAS Scholarships for Professional Development - Disaster Communications Management *(Professional development/Scholarship)* [8732]

OAS Scholarships for Professional Development - Radio Spectrum Monitoring Techniques and Procedures *(Professional development/Scholarship)* [8733]

OAS Scholarships for Professional Development - Satellite Communications *(Professional development/Scholarship)* [8734]

WillEtta "Willie" Long Oates, Gamma Nu, Memorial Scholarship *(Undergraduate, Graduate/Scholarship)* [6463]

Dennis J. O'Brien USAEE Best Student Paper Award *(Undergraduate/Award)* [11296]

Oceanic Research Group Scholarships *(Graduate, Undergraduate/Scholarship)* [8573]

Edward A. O'Connor Founder's Scholarship *(Undergraduate/Scholarship)* [99]

Basil O'Connor Starter Scholar Research Awards (BOC) *(Professional development/Grant)* [7028]

The Captain Jennifer Shafer Odom Memorial Scholarship - Children of Soldiers *(Undergraduate, Vocational/Occupational/Scholarship)* [1919]

The Captain Jennifer Shafer Odom Memorial Scholarship - Spouses of Soldiers *(Undergraduate, Vocational/Occupational/Scholarship)* [1920]

OGR Award of Excellence Scholarships *(Undergraduate/Scholarship)* [6048]

OAB Kids Scholarship *(Undergraduate/Scholarship)* [8576]

Ohio National Foundation Scholarship *(Undergraduate/Scholarship)* [3391]

Ohio Space Grant Consortium Graduate Fellowships *(Graduate, Doctorate, Master's/Fellowship)* [8598]

Ohio Space Grant Consortium Special Minority Fellowships *(Doctorate, Graduate, Master's/Fellowship)* [8599]

O'Jay's Scholarship Fund *(Undergraduate/Scholarship)* [10786]

Seth Okin Good Deeds Scholarships *(Undergraduate, Graduate, Community College/Scholarship)* [9283]

Oklahoma Restaurant Association Scholarships *(Other/Scholarship)* [8612]

Robert B. Oliver ASNT Scholarship *(Undergraduate/Scholarship)* [1532]

Roy C. and Dorothy Jean Olson Memorial Scholarship *(Graduate/Scholarship)* [6042]

Charlie O'Meilia Scholarship *(Undergraduate/Scholarship, Monetary, Award)* [5973]

Omicron Nu Research Fellowship *(Postdoctorate, Graduate/Fellowship)* [6497]

Oncology Nursing Society Foundation - Doctoral Scholarships *(Doctorate/Scholarship)* [8628]

Oncology Nursing Society Foundation - Master's Scholarships *(Graduate, Master's/Scholarship)* [8629]

One Source Process Inc. Scholarship *(Undergraduate, Graduate/Scholarship)* [8634]

ONS Foundation Congress Scholarships *(Professional development/Scholarship)* [8630]

OOIDA Mary Johnston Scholarship Program *(Undergraduate/Scholarship)* [8798]

Open Society Fellowship *(Other/Fellowship)* [8664]

Opera Foundation Scholarship *(Other/Scholarship)* [8671]

OPERF Small Grants *(Doctorate/Grant)* [8768]

OppU Achievers Scholarship *(Undergraduate/Scholarship)* [8673]

Optical Design and Engineering Scholarship *(Graduate, Undergraduate/Scholarship)* [10728]

Optimist Club of Redlands Scholarship- Ralph Maloof *(Undergraduate/Scholarship)* [9568]

Optimist Club of Redlands Scholarship- Virgina Elliott *(Undergraduate/Scholarship)* [9569]

Order of Omega Doctoral Fellowships *(Doctorate, Graduate/Fellowship)* [8687]

Oregon Association of Nurseries Scholarship Program *(Graduate/Scholarship)* [8711]

Oregon Farm Bureau Memorial Scholarship *(Undergraduate, Graduate, High School/Scholarship)* [8716]

Oregon Literary Fellowships *(Advanced Professional/Fellowship)* [6877]

Organization of American States AOS-Placed Scholarships *(Graduate, Undergraduate/Scholarship)* [8736]

Organization of American States Graduate Scholarships *(Doctorate, Graduate/Scholarship)* [8737]

Organization of American States Self-Placed Scholarships *(Doctorate, Graduate/Scholarship)* [8738]

Organization of Chinese Americans Scholarships *(Undergraduate/Scholarship)* [1986]

Oronzio de Nora Industrial Electrochemistry Fellowships *(Postdoctorate/Fellowship)* [4363]

Orthopaedic Foot and Ankle Fellowships *(Graduate, Professional development/Fellowship)* [1194]

Orthopaedic Specialists of the Carolinas Nursing Scholarship *(Undergraduate/Scholarship)* [12086]

OSGC Community College Scholarships *(Undergraduate/Scholarship)* [8600]

OSGC Education Scholarships *(Undergraduate/Scholarship)* [8601]

Osteopathic Medical School Scholarship *(Undergraduate/Scholarship)* [8271]

Osteopathic Medical Student Research Fellowship Program *(Undergraduate/Fellowship)* [10867]

M. Dick Osumi Civil Rights and Public Interest Scholarship *(Graduate, Undergraduate/Scholarship)* [6240]

Charles & Mitch Ota Foundation Scholarship *(Undergraduate, Two Year College, Four Year College/Scholarship)* [5410]

OTA Member Full Research Grant *(Other/Grant)* [8763]

The Otis and Florence Lapham Memorial Scholarship *(Graduate/Scholarship)* [6205]

Ellis R. Ott Scholarships *(Graduate, Master's/Scholarship)* [1543]

Otto M. Stanfield Law Scholarship *(Graduate/Scholarship)* [11253]

Satenik & Adom Ourian Education Foundation Scholarship *(Undergraduate/Scholarship)* [1897]

Out to Innovate Scholarship *(Graduate, Undergraduate, Community College/Scholarship)* [8019]

Outlaw Student's Medical Professions Scholarships *(Undergraduate/Scholarship)* [10860]

Outlaw Student's Minority Scholarships *(Undergraduate/Scholarship)* [10861]

Outlaw Student's Nursing School Scholarships *(Undergraduate/Scholarship)* [10862]

Outlaw Student's Teacher Scholarships *(Undergraduate/Scholarship)* [10863]

Overflow Scholarships *(Undergraduate/Scholarship)* [1803]

Elvina Jane Owen Scholarship *(Graduate, Undergraduate/Scholarship)* [4894]

Ozarks Division of Midwest Dairy Educational Award *(Undergraduate/Scholarship)* [7374]

The Pac-12 Postgraduate Scholarships *(Graduate/Scholarship)* [8802]

Pacific Beacon Scholarship *(Community College, University, Undergraduate, Vocational/Occupational/Scholarship)* [9838]

Packard Fellowships for Science and Engineering *(Professional development/Fellowship)* [8808]

The Arthur J. Packard Memorial Scholarship *(Undergraduate/Scholarship)* [973]

The Barbara L. Packer Fellowship *(Doctorate, Postdoctorate/Fellowship)* [496]

Casilda Pagan Educational/Vocational Scholarships *(Graduate, Undergraduate, Postgraduate/Scholarship)* [5594]

Platt Excavation Fellowships (Other, Undergraduate/ Fellowship) [1379]

Platt Family Scholarship Prize Essay Contest (Undergraduate/Scholarship, Monetary) [6867]

Plumbing-Heating-Cooling Contractors Association Educational Foundation Massachusetts Auxiliary Scholarships (Undergraduate/Scholarship) [9205]

Plumbing-Heating-Cooling Contractors Association Educational Foundation Need-Based Scholarships (Undergraduate/Scholarship) [9206]

PHCC of Texas Auxiliary and PHCC Educational Foundation funds (Undergraduate/Scholarship) [9207]

PLUS Foundation Financial Aid Scholarship (Undergraduate/Scholarship) [9212]

The Henry Dewitt Plyler Scholarship (Undergraduate/Scholarship) [4750]

PNAA Nursing Scholarship Award (Master's, Doctorate/Scholarship) [9135]

Point Community College Scholarship Program (Undergraduate, Community College/Scholarship) [9229]

Polaire Weissman Fund Fellowship (Graduate/Fellowship) [7279]

Polish American Club of North Jersey Scholarships (Undergraduate/Scholarship) [6605]

Polish National Alliance of Brooklyn, USA Scholarships (Undergraduate/Scholarship) [6606]

A. H. Pollard Travelling PhD Scholarships (Postdoctorate/Scholarship) [5810]

The David J. Pollini Scholarship (Undergraduate/Scholarship) [7176]

Francis Poloshian Memorial Grant (Undergraduate/Scholarship) [1899]

James Poloshian Memorial Grant (Undergraduate/Scholarship) [1900]

Harold F. Polston Scholarships (Graduate, Undergraduate/Scholarship) [1571]

Harriet and Leon Pomerance Fellowships (Graduate/Fellowship) [1780]

PON Graduate Student Grants (Graduate/Grant) [5368]

PON Next Generation Grants (Doctorate, Postdoctorate/Grant) [5369]

PON Summer Fellowships (Graduate/Fellowship) [5370]

The Pope Scholarship Award (Undergraduate/Scholarship) [7177]

Karin Riley Porter Good Works Scholarships (Undergraduate, Graduate/Scholarship) [9284]

AFT Robert G. Porter Scholars Program (Undergraduate/Scholarship) [881]

The Thomas W. Porter, W8KYZ, Scholarship Honoring Michael Daugherty, W8LSE (Undergraduate/Scholarship) [1955]

Robert Porterfield Scholarship (Graduate/Scholarship) [10639]

Portland Cement Association Scholarship (Graduate/Scholarship) [4503]

Portuguese American Police Association Scholarships (Undergraduate/Scholarship) [9252]

Post-High School Tuition Scholarship Program (Undergraduate/Scholarship) [3190]

Postdoctoral Fellowships for Basic Scientists Program (Postdoctorate/Fellowship) [8900]

Postdoctoral Fellowships for Clinical Neurologists (Postdoctorate/Fellowship) [8901]

Poteet Strawberry Festival Association Scholarships (Graduate, Undergraduate/Scholarship) [9256]

George V. Powell Diversity Scholarships (Graduate/Scholarship) [6654]

Lou and Carole Prato Sports Reporting Scholarship (Undergraduate/Scholarship) [9475]

Praxair International Scholarship (Undergraduate/Scholarship) [1669]

PREA Scholarship (Undergraduate, Graduate/Scholarship) [8973]

Presidential Management Fellows (PMF) (Graduate, Master's/Fellowship) [11330]

Presidents Scholarship (Undergraduate/Scholarship) [9476]

Pretty Photoshop Actions Bi-Annual Scholarship (Undergraduate, Graduate, Graduate/Scholarship) [9273]

Prevent Cancer Foundation Fellowships (Postdoctorate/Fellowship) [9277]

Preventive Medicine Residency and Fellowship (PMR) (Other/Fellowship) [11331]

Price Benowitz Social Justice Scholarships (Undergraduate, Graduate, Community College/Scholarship) [9285]

Judith McManus Price Scholarship (Undergraduate, Graduate/Scholarship) [1245]

Pride Foundation Political Leadership Scholarships (Undergraduate/Scholarship) [9306]

Pride Foundation Regional Scholarships (Undergraduate/Scholarship) [9307]

Pride Foundation Scholarships (Undergraduate/Scholarship) [9771]

Pride Foundation Social Work Scholarships (Undergraduate/Scholarship) [9308]

Pride of the Rose Scholarship (Undergraduate/Scholarship) [9309]

Lendon N. Pridgen, GlaxoSmithKline - NOBCChE Fellowships (Graduate/Fellowship) [8031]

Prince Henry Society Scholarships (Undergraduate/Scholarship) [9326]

Print and Graphics Scholarship Foundation Awards (Graduate, Undergraduate/Award) [9330]

Priscilla Gamble Scholarship Fund (Undergraduate/Scholarship) [3395]

Miguel Pro Scholarships (Undergraduate/Scholarship) [12224]

Procter and Gamble Foundation Scholarship (Undergraduate/Scholarship) [3396]

Professional Certification Exam Scholarship (Undergraduate, Professional development/Scholarship) [9797]

Professional Woman's Magazine Scholarship Opportunity (Undergraduate/Scholarship) [9347]

Professor Emeritus Dr. Bill Johnson Memorial Scholarship (Undergraduate/Scholarship) [10061]

Progress Lane Scholarship Fund (Undergraduate/Scholarship) [3576]

Progressive Dairy Producer Awards (All/Grant) [7826]

Property and Environment Research Center Graduate Fellowships (Graduate/Fellowship) [9351]

Property and Environment Research Center Lone Mountain Fellowships (Other/Fellowship) [9352]

Property and Environment Research Center Media Fellowships (Other/Fellowship) [9353]

Prospanica Scholarship (Graduate, Undergraduate/Scholarship) [9360]

Barbara F. Prowant Nursing Research Grants (Graduate/Grant) [1153]

PRSA Diversity Multicultural Scholarships (Undergraduate/Scholarship) [9438]

Neil Pruitt, Sr. Memorial Scholarships (Undergraduate/Scholarship) [7778]

Joseph E. Pryor Graduate Fellowships (Graduate/Fellowship) [379]

Cheryl White Pryor Memorial Scholarship (Undergraduate/Scholarship) [4012]

Phillis Brinton Pryor Panhellenic Scholarship (Undergraduate/Scholarship) [6466]

Psychosocial Research - Postdoctoral Psychosocial Fellowships (Postdoctorate/Fellowship) [8202]

PTAC Crew Scholarship for HVAC Students (Vocational/Occupational/Scholarship) [9381]

Public Interest Environmental Law Fellowships (Graduate/Fellowship) [4415]

Public Interest Fellowship (Undergraduate/Fellowship) [797]

Eugene C. Pulliam Fellowships for Editorial Writing (Other/Fellowship) [10086]

Pulliam/Kilgore Freedom of Information Internships (Undergraduate/Internship) [10503]

Paul Pumpian Scholarship (Undergraduate/Scholarship) [1752]

PVA Research Foundation Fellowships (Postdoctorate/Fellowship) [8820]

PWC Core Apprentice Program (Other/Internship) [9200]

Harry V. Quadracci Memorial Scholarship (Undergraduate, Graduate/Scholarship) [5209]

Quality Bath.com Scholarship (Community College, College, University, Undergraduate, Graduate/Scholarship) [9453]

Quality Company Formations Scholarship (College, University, Undergraduate/Scholarship) [9455]

Quarter Century Wireless Association Scholarship Program (Undergraduate/Scholarship) [9457]

Rosa Quezada Memorial Education Scholarships (Undergraduate/Scholarship) [3755]

Quincy Brown Memorial Scholarship (Undergraduate/Scholarship) [9573]

Quincy Sharpe Mills Memorial Scholarship (Undergraduate/Scholarship) [11205]

AIST Judith A. Quinn Detroit Member Chapter Scholarship (Undergraduate/Scholarship) [2223]

R. Garn Haycock Memorial Scholarship (Undergraduate/Scholarship) [9574]

Rachel Graham Memorial Scholarship (Undergraduate/Scholarship) [9575]

RADM William A. Sullivan, USN (Ret.) Scholarship (Undergraduate/Scholarship) [8174]

Railroad and Mine Workers Memorial Scholarship (Graduate/Scholarship) [6250]

Rain Bird Intelligent Use of Water Scholarship (Undergraduate/Scholarship) [6652, 9491]

Rains - J.J. Rains Memorial Scholarship (Undergraduate/Scholarship) [3483]

Frederick Rakestraw Law Scholarship (Graduate/Scholarship) [8489]

Raleigh Mann Scholarship (Undergraduate/Scholarship) [11206]

Ralph and Josephine Smith Fund (Undergraduate/Scholarship) [4602]

Rama Scholarships for the American Dream (Graduate, Undergraduate/Scholarship) [975]

Commander Newell S. Rand Jr. Scholarship Program (Undergraduate/Scholarship) [8828]

Helen F. "Jerri" Rand Memorial Scholarships (Undergraduate, Vocational/Occupational/Scholarship) [3715]

Jennings Randolph Peace Scholarship Dissertation Program (Doctorate/Scholarship, Fellowship) [11380]

United States Institute of Peace Jennings Randolph Senior Fellowship Program (Advanced Professional/Fellowship) [11381]

Randy Williams Scholarship (Undergraduate/Scholarship) [9843]

Edward C. Raney Fund Award (Professional development/Grant) [1484]

Rangel Graduate Fellowship (Graduate/Fellowship) [9499]

Jeannette Rankin Scholarships (Undergraduate, Vocational/Occupational/Scholarship) [9501]

Marie Mathew Rask-Gamma Omicron Educational Endowment (Undergraduate/Scholarship) [6467]

Lenny Ravich "Shalom" Scholarships (Advanced Professional/Scholarship) [2054]

Rawley Silver Award for Excellence (Graduate/Scholarship) [503]

Rawley Silver Research Award (Postgraduate, Postdoctorate/Award, Recognition) [504]

Mary C. Rawlins Scholarships (Graduate/Scholarship) [5342]

Ray And Mary Bell Scholarship (Undergraduate/Scholarship) [9844]

W.B. Ray High School Class of '56 Averill Johnson Scholarship (Undergraduate/Scholarship) [3484]

The Ray, NØRP, & Katie, WØKTE, Pautz Scholarship (Undergraduate/Scholarship) [1956]

Ray and Pearl Sams Scholarship (Undergraduate/Scholarship) [12089]

Raymond A. Kent-Navy V-12/ROTC (Undergraduate/Scholarship) [11579]

Raymond and Augusta Klink Scholarship Fund (Undergraduate/Scholarship) [3397]

RBPA Scholarship (Undergraduate, Graduate, Doctorate/Scholarship) [9493]

William R. Reaser Scholarship (Vocational/Occupational, Undergraduate/Scholarship) [8869]

Reba Malone Scholarship (Undergraduate, Graduate/Scholarship) [1305]

Redlands Baseball/Softball for Youth Scholarship (Undergraduate/Scholarship) [9577]

Redlands Community Scholarship Foundation Awards (Undergraduate/Scholarship) [9578]

Redlands Council PTA - Dorathy Jolley Memorial Scholarship (Undergraduate/Scholarship) [9579]

Redlands Evening Lions Club - Barbara Westen Memorial Scholarship (Undergraduate/Scholarship) [9580]

Robinson G. Allen Athletic Memorial Scholarship *(Undergraduate/Scholarship)* [9599]

Helen M. Robinson Grants *(Doctorate/Grant)* [6037]

Robinson Helicopter R22/R44 Safety Course Scholarship *(Professional development/Scholarship)* [12012]

Sara Roby Fellowship in Twentieth-Century American Realism *(Doctorate, Postdoctorate/Fellowship)* [10218]

Rockford Area Habitat for Humanity College Scholarship *(Undergraduate/Scholarship)* [3693]

Rockwell Collins Scholarships *(Undergraduate/Scholarship)* [190]

Rocky Mountain Coal Mining Institute Engineering/Geology Scholarships *(Four Year College/Scholarship)* [9727]

Rocky Mountain Coal Mining Institute Technical Scholarships *(Two Year College/Scholarship)* [9728]

Paul W. Rodgers Scholarship *(Undergraduate/Scholarship)* [5925]

Rodney Williams Legacy Scholarship *(Graduate/Scholarship)* [11580]

R.O.E.A. Dumitru Golea Goldy-Gemu Scholarships *(Undergraduate, High School/Scholarship)* [1369]

Roger and Jacquelyn Vander Laan Family Scholarship *(Undergraduate/Scholarship)* [5177]

Roger and Joyce Howe Scholarship Fund *(Undergraduate/Scholarship)* [3400]

Roger K. Summit Scholarship *(Graduate/Scholarship)* [9356]

Kimberly Marie Rogers Memorial Scholarship Fund *(Undergraduate, Vocational/Occupational/Scholarship)* [4603]

Sandra Journey Rolf Scholarship Fund *(Undergraduate, Graduate/Scholarship)* [6469]

Rome Prize *(Postdoctorate, Graduate, Undergraduate/Prize, Award)* [476]

Ronald B. Linsky Fellowship for Outstanding Water Research *(Graduate, Master's, Doctorate/Fellowship)* [8159]

Ronald McDonald House Charities Scholarship *(Undergraduate/Scholarship)* [9737]

Ronald T. Smith Family Scholarship *(Undergraduate, Graduate/Scholarship)* [5178]

Charles and Ruth Ronin Memorial Scholarships *(Undergraduate/Scholarship)* [9600]

Dorothy Worden Ronken Scholarships *(Graduate/Scholarship)* [4042]

Rose Marie Princ Memorial Scholarship *(Undergraduate/Scholarship)* [9421]

Carl M. Rose Memorial Scholarship *(Undergraduate/Scholarship)* [8874]

Dr. Wayne F. Rose Scholarship Fund *(Undergraduate/Scholarship)* [4604]

Clarence J. Rosecrans Scholarship *(Graduate, Master's, Doctorate/Scholarship)* [1288]

Esther Katz Rosen Fund Grants *(Graduate/Grant)* [1289]

Jack Rosen Scholarship *(Undergraduate/Scholarship)* [6393]

Walter A. Rosenblith New Investigator Award *(Postdoctorate/Award)* [5426]

ASPPH/CDC Allan Rosenfield Global Health Fellowship Program *(Postdoctorate, Postgraduate/Fellowship)* [2284]

Jean and Tom Rosenthal Scholarship Program *(Undergraduate/Scholarship)* [3723]

S. Byrl Ross Memorial Scholarship *(Undergraduate/Scholarship)* [8875]

Ross P. Broesamle Education Fund *(Undergraduate/Scholarship)* [6667]

Colonel Jerry W. Ross Scholarship *(Undergraduate/Scholarship)* [1753]

The Bea and Harry Ross Scholarship Endowment *(Graduate/Scholarship)* [10847]

Ross Trust Future School Counselors Essay Competition *(Undergraduate/Award, Prize)* [834]

Rotary Club of Annapolis Scholarship *(Graduate/Scholarship)* [1719]

The Rotary Club of Charlotte Public Safety Scholarship Fund *(Undergraduate/Scholarship)* [4752]

The Rotary Club of Rancho Bernardo Sunrise Community Service Scholarships *(Undergraduate/Scholarship)* [9846]

Marjorie Roy Rothermel Scholarship *(Master's/Scholarship)* [2002]

Theodore Rousseau Fellowships *(Graduate/Fellowship)* [7281]

Regie Routman Teacher Recognition Grant *(Advanced Professional/Grant, Recognition)* [6038]

Rovelstad Scholarship *(Undergraduate, Graduate/Scholarship)* [3871]

Leo S. Rowe Pan American Fund *(Graduate, Undergraduate/Loan)* [8739]

Roy H. Pollack Scholarship *(Graduate, Master's/Scholarship)* [11254]

Roy W. Likins Scholarship *(Undergraduate, Graduate/Scholarship)* [1646]

RSNA/AUR/APDR/SCARD Radiology Education Research Development Grant *(Professional development/Grant)* [9484]

RSNA Education Scholar Grant *(Professional development/Grant)* [9485]

Research Scholar Grant *(Professional development/Grant)* [9486]

RSNA Research Seed Grant *(Professional development/Grant)* [9487]

Joe Rudd Scholarships *(Graduate/Scholarship)* [9732]

Rudolph Dillman Memorial Scholarship *(Graduate, Undergraduate/Scholarship)* [919]

Damon Runyon Clinical Investigator Awards *(Postgraduate/Award)* [9761]

Ruppert Scholarship *(Undergraduate/Scholarship)* [2831]

Russell Athletics Scholarship *(Undergraduate/Scholarship)* [2336]

Russell C. McCaughan Heritage Scholarship *(Undergraduate/Scholarship, Award)* [1199]

Dave & Laurie Russell Family Scholarships for Habitat for Humanity of Kent County Families *(Undergraduate/Scholarship)* [5180]

Russell & Lazarus Safety Scholarship Contest *(Undergraduate, College, University/Scholarship)* [9763]

Russell & Sigurd Varian Award *(Graduate/Recognition)* [2386]

NPELRA Foundation - Anthony C. Russo Scholarships *(Graduate/Scholarship)* [8057]

Lucile Rust Scholarships *(Undergraduate/Scholarship)* [9126]

Ruth E. Jenkins Scholarship *(Undergraduate/Scholarship)* [9847]

Ruth L. Kirschstein Individual Predoctoral NRSA for MD/PhD and other Dual Degree Fellowships *(Doctorate, Master's/Fellowship)* [11337]

Ruth Liu Memorial Scholarship *(Undergraduate/Scholarship)* [3309]

Ruth Messmer Scholarship Fund *(Undergraduate/Scholarship)* [10702]

Ruth and Sherman Zudekoff Scholarship Fund *(Undergraduate/Scholarship)* [3593]

IOIA Andrew Rutherford Scholarships *(Other/Scholarship)* [6055]

The Ryan Law Group Scholarship *(Undergraduate/Scholarship)* [9768]

Michael Clarkson Ryan Memorial Scholarship *(Undergraduate, Graduate/Scholarship)* [2551]

S. David Shor Scholarship Fund *(Undergraduate/Scholarship)* [3401]

S. Penny Chappell Scholarship *(Undergraduate/Scholarship)* [9127]

SABA NC - Public Interest Post-Bar Fellowships *(Professional development/Fellowship)* [10599]

SABA NC - Public Interest Summer Fellowships *(Undergraduate/Fellowship)* [10600]

Safer Athletic Field Environments Scholarships (SAFE) *(Graduate, Undergraduate, Two Year College/Scholarship)* [10736]

St. Francis Xavier Scholarship *(Undergraduate/Scholarship)* [12225]

St. James Armenian Apostolic Church Scholarships *(Undergraduate, Vocational/Occupational/Scholarship)* [9780]

St. Joseph's Hospital School of Nursing Alumnae Scholarship *(Undergraduate/Scholarship)* [8876]

St. Louis Paralegal Student Scholarships *(Undergraduate/Scholarship)* [9783]

St. Petersburg Personal Injury Attorneys McQuaid & Douglas $2,000 Scholarship Contest *(College, Undergraduate, Vocational/Occupational, Professional development/Scholarship)* [9787]

Saints Cyril and Methodius Scholarships *(Undergraduate/Scholarship)* [9766]

Sakura Finetek Student Scholarship *(Undergraduate/Scholarship)* [8113]

The Bill, W2ONV, and Ann Salerno Memorial Scholarship *(Undergraduate/Scholarship)* [1958]

The Eugene "Gene" Sallee, W4YFR, Memorial Scholarship *(Undergraduate, Graduate/Scholarship)* [1959]

Sally Beauty Scholarships for High School Graduates *(High School/Scholarship)* [9336]

The Sally Cole Visual Arts Scholarship Program *(Undergraduate/Scholarship)* [4753]

Margaret Jerome Sampson Scholarships *(Undergraduate/Scholarship)* [9128]

Samsung American Legion Scholarship *(Undergraduate/Scholarship)* [1073]

Samuel Robinson Award *(Undergraduate/Award)* [9267]

The San Diego Foundation Community Scholarship I *(Undergraduate/Scholarship)* [9848]

San Pasqual Academy Scholarship *(Undergraduate/Scholarship)* [9850]

Sand Plains & Lewis A. and Gurry F. Batten Education Scholarship *(Undergraduate/Scholarship)* [8877]

Leonard H. Sandler Fellowships *(Graduate/Fellowship)* [5636]

Sandra Jo Hornick Scholarship *(Undergraduate/Scholarship)* [6394]

SAO Predoctoral Fellowship *(Graduate/Fellowship)* [5359]

Sarah Shinn Marshall Scholarship *(Undergraduate, Graduate/Scholarship)* [4013]

Frank Sarli Memorial Scholarship *(Undergraduate/Scholarship)* [7820]

Sho Sato Memorial Scholarship *(Undergraduate, Graduate/Scholarship)* [6251]

Curtis M. Saulsbury Scholarship Fund *(Undergraduate/Scholarship)* [3594]

Saunders – Kevin Saunders Wheelchair Success Scholarship *(Undergraduate/Scholarship)* [3486]

Save a Life Scholarship *(College, University, Vocational/Occupational, Undergraduate, Graduate/Scholarship)* [448]

Save Mart Legacy Scholarships *(Undergraduate/Scholarship)* [2808]

Herbert M. Saylor Memorial Scholarship *(Graduate/Scholarship)* [10586]

SBE/Ennes Youth Scholarships *(Graduate/Scholarship)* [10287]

S.C. Johnson, A Family Company Scholarship Fund *(Undergraduate/Scholarship)* [3402]

SC&R Foundation Grant Program *(Undergraduate/Grant)* [10717]

SCBWI Work-in-Progress Awards (WIP) *(Advanced Professional/Award)* [10303]

SCC Full-Time Continuing Student Scholarship *(Undergraduate/Scholarship)* [10062]

SCC Part-Time Continuing Student Scholarship *(Undergraduate/Scholarship)* [10063]

SCDAA Post-Doctoral Research Fellowships *(Postdoctorate/Fellowship)* [10074]

Schallek Award *(Graduate/Award)* [7231]

Schallek Fellowship *(Graduate/Fellowship)* [7232]

Abe Schechter Graduate Scholarships *(Graduate/Scholarship)* [9467]

Schedulers and Dispatchers Monetary Scholarship *(Other/Scholarship)* [7740]

Julie Schmid Research Scholarship *(Advanced Professional/Scholarship)* [2255]

Schmidt Kramer Annual Scholarship For Academic Excellence *(Undergraduate/Scholarship)* [9936]

Bernadotte E. Schmitt Grant *(Doctorate/Grant)* [963]

Schneider/Bingle PLTW Scholarship *(Undergraduate/Scholarship)* [10412]

Lillian P. Schoephoerster Scholarships *(Undergraduate/Scholarship)* [9129]

Scholarship Foundation of Santa Barbara General Scholarship Program *(Undergraduate, Graduate/Scholarship)* [9951]

The Scholarship Foundation of Wakefield Scholarships (All/Scholarship) [9955]

Scholarship from Law Office of Yuriy Moshes, P.C. (Undergraduate/Award, Scholarship) [6699]

The Scholarship of the Morris Radio Club of New Jersey (Undergraduate/Scholarship) [1960]

Scholarships for a Higher Education in Law (Graduate/Scholarship) [2683]

School Nutrition Association of Kansas Education Scholarship (Undergraduate/Scholarship) [9965]

Schrank Family Scholarship (Undergraduate/Scholarship) [11631]

David and Jinny Schultz Family Scholarship (Undergraduate/Scholarship) [5104]

James F. Schumar Scholarship (Graduate/Scholarship) [1169]

AIST William E. Schwabe Memorial Scholarship (Undergraduate/Scholarship) [2225]

Schwan's Food Service Scholarship (Vocational/Occupational, Professional development/Scholarship, Award) [9961]

Frances M. Schwartz Fellowship (Other/Fellowship) [1171, 10026]

Evalee C. Schwarz Educational Loans (Undergraduate, Graduate/Loan) [9967]

Science and Engineering Apprenticeship Program (SEAP) (High School/Internship) [1444]

Science, Mathematics And Research for Transformation Scholarship for Service Program (SMART) (Undergraduate, Graduate/Scholarship) [1445, 9974]

ScienceSoft Scholarship (Graduate, Undergraduate/Scholarship) [9976]

SCIRTS (Spinal Cord Injury Research on the Translational Spectrum) Postdoctoral Fellowships (Postdoctorate/Fellowship) [8205]

SCLEOA Scholarships (Undergraduate, Professional development/Scholarship) [10609]

Scleroderma Foundation Established Investigator Grants (Doctorate/Grant) [9979]

Scleroderma Foundation New Investigator Grants (Doctorate/Grant) [9980]

Scott A. Flahive Memorial Scholarship (Undergraduate/Scholarship) [5105]

SDE Fellowship (Graduate, Postgraduate/Fellowship) [5060]

Seabee Memorial Scholarship Association Scholarships (Undergraduate/Scholarship) [10231]

Fred A. Seaton Memorial Scholarship (Undergraduate, Graduate/Scholarship) [2552]

SEE Education Foundation Scholarship (Undergraduate, Graduate, Doctorate/Scholarship) [6107]

Dr. Eugene M. Seidner Student Scholarship Program (Undergraduate, Graduate/Scholarship) [46]

Seldovia Native Association Achievement Scholarships (Undergraduate, Graduate/Scholarship) [9996]

Seldovia Native Association General Scholarships (Undergraduate, Graduate/Scholarship) [9997]

Selena Danette Brown Book Scholarship (Graduate, Undergraduate/Scholarship) [7620]

David W. Self Scholarship (Undergraduate/Scholarship) [11263]

SEMA Memorial Scholarship and Loan Forgiveness Award (Graduate, Undergraduate/Loan, Scholarship) [10720]

SEMA Memorial Scholarships (Graduate, Undergraduate/Scholarship) [10721]

Semple Foundation Scholarship (Undergraduate/Scholarship) [3403]

Senator Carl O. Koella, Jr. Memorial Scholarship Fund (Undergraduate/Scholarship) [3644]

Dr. Henry Seneca Charitable Trust Scholarship (Undergraduate/Scholarship) [1901]

The Seneca Scholarship (High School, College/Scholarship) [10006]

Archak and Meroum Senekjian Memorial Grant (Undergraduate/Scholarship) [1902]

Senior Master Sergeant William Sowers Memorial Scholarship (Undergraduate/Grant) [114]

Senior Scholar Scholarship Presented by 65Medicare.org (Two Year College, Four Year College/Scholarship) [18]

Senior Wisdom Scholarship (Undergraduate, Graduate/Scholarship, Award) [9186]

SeniorAdvice Caregiver Scholarships (Undergraduate/Scholarship) [10008]

SEO Optimizers Scholarships (All/Scholarship) [10015]

Sequoyah Graduate Scholarship (Master's/Scholarship) [2040]

Charles W. Serby COPD Research Fellowship (Professional development/Fellowship) [1360]

Serena D. Dalton Scholarship (Undergraduate/Scholarship) [12091]

Sertoma Communicative Disorders Scholarship (Undergraduate/Scholarship) [10019]

Sertoma Hard of Hearing and Deaf Scholarship (Undergraduate/Scholarship) [10020]

Service League Volunteer Scholarships (Undergraduate/Scholarship) [11891]

Frank B. Sessa Scholarship (Professional development/Scholarship) [2499]

Seth Koehler Central High School (Undergraduate, Vocational/Occupational/Scholarship) [5106]

Margaret B. Ševenko Prize in Islamic Art and Culture (Doctorate, Graduate/Prize) [5535]

John R. Sevier Memorial Scholarship Award (Undergraduate/Scholarship) [11424]

SFP Junior Investigator's Career Development Awards (Other/Grant) [10330]

SFP Mid-Career/Mentor Award (Other/Grant) [10331]

SFP Student Research Grants (Graduate/Grant) [10332]

SGM Law Group $1,000 Bi-Annual Scholarship (Undergraduate, Graduate/Scholarship) [10033]

SHAFR Dissertation Completion Fellowship (Doctorate/Fellowship) [10359]

Julia Shahan and Shahan Siran Nevshehir Memorial Grant (Undergraduate/Scholarship) [1903]

Albert F. Shanker Scholarship (Undergraduate/Scholarship) [885]

Ken and Sandy Sharkey Family Scholarship (Undergraduate/Scholarship) [5107]

Sharon D. Banks Memorial Undergraduate Scholarship (Undergraduate/Scholarship) [12171]

Luci Shaw Fellowship (Undergraduate/Fellowship) [3215]

Josephine Kerbey Shaw Memorial Undergraduate Scholarship (Undergraduate/Scholarship) [6472]

Shear-Miles Agricultural Scholarship (Graduate, Doctorate/Scholarship) [11647]

Shear-Miles Agricultural Scholarship/Fellowship (Graduate, Doctorate/Fellowship, Scholarship) [11648]

Sheep Heritage Foundation Memorial Scholarship (Graduate, Doctorate/Scholarship) [1383]

The Jim Sheerin Scholarship (Undergraduate/Scholarship) [7178]

Sheet Metal And Air Conditioning Contractors' National Association College of Fellows Scholarship Program (Undergraduate/Scholarship) [10039]

William C. Scheetz Memorial Scholarship (Undergraduate, Graduate/Scholarship) [2553]

Sheldon Wechsler and George Mertz Contact Lens Residency Award (Professional development, Advanced Professional/Award) [464]

Susan Goldsmith Shelley Scholarship (Undergraduate/Scholarship) [6473]

Robert P. Sheppard Leadership Awards (High School, College/Scholarship) [8106]

Sheriff W. Bruce Umpleby Law Enforcement Memorial Scholarship Fund (Undergraduate/Scholarship) [10791]

Sherman L. & Mabel C. Lepard Scholarship (Undergraduate/Scholarship) [5181]

Shields-Gillespie Scholarship (Other/Scholarship) [1189]

Chiyoko and Thomas Shimazaki Scholarship (Graduate/Scholarship) [6252]

Everett Oscar Shimp Memorial Scholarships (Undergraduate/Scholarship) [8878]

Pat Shimp Memorial Scholarships (Undergraduate/Scholarship) [8879]

Joseph Shinoda Memorial Scholarship (Undergraduate/Scholarship) [10047]

Jason Shipley Memorial Scholarships (Undergraduate/Scholarship) [7974]

Shirley J. Brooke Endowed Scholarship (Undergraduate/Scholarship) [9026]

Lynn Brower Shonk Memorial Scholarship (Undergraduate/Scholarship) [6474]

Col. Richard R. (Misty) and Sally Shoop Scholarship (Undergraduate, Graduate/Scholarship) [2554]

Shoreline and Lake Forest Park scholarship (Undergraduate/Scholarship) [10064]

SHOT-NASA Fellowship (Doctorate/Fellowship) [10365]

SHPE Dissertation Scholarship (Doctorate/Scholarship) [10351]

SHPE Professional Scholarship (Master's, Doctorate/Scholarship) [10352]

Ralph W. Shrader Diversity Scholarship (Graduate/Scholarship) [107]

Shred Nations Scholarship (Undergraduate, Graduate/Scholarship) [10071]

Shripat Kamble Urban Entomology Graduate Student Award for Innovative Research (Doctorate/Award) [4399]

SHRM Certification Scholarships - Individual (Professional development/Scholarship) [10369]

Mary Isabel Sibley Fellowship (Doctorate/Fellowship) [9082]

SICB Grants-in-Aid of Research Program (GIAR) (Graduate/Grant) [10375]

Sidley Diversity and Inclusion Scholarships (Undergraduate/Scholarship) [10076]

Sidley Prelaw Scholars Program (Undergraduate/Scholarship) [10077]

Sigma Diagnostics Student Scholarships (Undergraduate/Scholarship) [8114]

Sigma Kappa Foundation Alumnae Continuing Education Scholarship (Graduate, Undergraduate/Scholarship) [10121]

Sigma Kappa Foundation Alzheimer's/Gerontology Scholarship (Graduate/Scholarship) [10122]

Sigma Kappa Foundation Founders' Scholarships (Undergraduate/Scholarship) [10123]

Sigma Phi Alpha Graduate Scholarship (Graduate/Scholarship) [861]

Harvey L. Simmons Memorial Scholarships (Undergraduate/Scholarship) [9851]

Willard B. Simmons Sr. Memorial Scholarships (Undergraduate/Scholarship) [7779]

Julian Simon Fellowships (Postgraduate/Fellowship) [9354]

Simon Youth Community Scholarship Program (Undergraduate/Scholarship) [10140]

Simonton Windows Scholarship (Undergraduate/Scholarship) [8880]

Col. John R. Simpson Memorial Scholarship (Undergraduate, Graduate/Scholarship) [2555]

Carole Simpson Scholarship (Undergraduate/Scholarship) [9477]

Single Mother Scholarship (Undergraduate, Graduate, College, University/Scholarship) [9743]

Helen J. Sioussat/Fay Wells Scholarships (Graduate/Scholarship) [2705]

Bill Six Memorial Scholarship (Undergraduate/Scholarship) [8881]

The Six Meter Club of Chicago Scholarship (Undergraduate/Scholarship) [1961]

Skadden Fellowship (Graduate/Fellowship) [10157]

Skalny Scholarship for Polish Studies (Undergraduate/Scholarship) [828]

Ruth Skeeles Memorial Scholarship Fund (Undergraduate/Scholarship) [10792]

Francelene Skinner Memorial Scholarships (Undergraduate/Scholarship) [6832]

Rand Skolnick Point Scholarship (Undergraduate, Graduate, Doctorate/Scholarship) [9231]

Skooblie Scholarships (Undergraduate/Scholarship) [10163]

Skubiak & Rivas - Justice in Action Scholarship (College, University, Vocational/Occupational, Undergraduate/Scholarship) [10165]

The Skylight Effect Scholarship Contest (Undergraduate, Graduate/Scholarship) [10167]

SLEAMC Scholarships (Graduate, Undergraduate/Scholarship) [10045]

Robert W. Sledge Fellowships (Graduate/Fellowship) [380]

Sleeping Angels Co. Scholarships (College, University/Scholarship) [10169]

The Slifka Foundation Interdisciplinary Fellowship (Doctorate, Master's/Fellowship) [7282]

Alfred P. Sloan Foundation Graduate Scholarships - Sloan Indigenous Graduate Partnership (SIGP) *(Master's, Doctorate/Scholarship)* [7581]

Alfred P. Sloan Foundation Graduate Scholarships - Sloan Minority Ph.D. Program (MPHD) *(Doctorate/ Scholarship)* [7582]

Sloan Northwood University Heavy-Duty Scholarships *(Undergraduate/Scholarship)* [2353]

Sloan Research Fellowships *(Doctorate/Fellowship)* [10171]

SMA Foundation Scholarship Fund *(Undergraduate/ Scholarship)* [10707]

Ann Kelsay Small Scholarship *(Undergraduate/ Scholarship)* [6475]

SmartMeasurement's Dream for a Better Future: Student Scholarship *(High School, Vocational/ Occupational, College, University, Undergraduate/ Scholarship)* [10173]

SME Coal & Energy Division Scholarship *(Undergraduate/Scholarship)* [10429]

SME Directors Scholarships *(Undergraduate/Scholarship)* [10414]

SME Education Foundation Family Scholarships *(Undergraduate/Scholarship)* [10415]

SME Environmental Division Scholarship *(Undergraduate, Graduate/Scholarship)* [10430]

SME Future Leaders of Manufacturing Scholarship *(Graduate, Undergraduate/Scholarship)* [10416]

SMFM/AAOGF Scholarship Awards *(Graduate/ Scholarship)* [10423]

Smile Marketing Dental Scholarship *(Doctorate/ Scholarship)* [10177]

Smiley Elementary School PTA Scholarship - Beverly Roberts Memorial *(Undergraduate/Scholarship)* [9603]

James I. Smith, III Notre Dame Law School Scholarship Fund *(Graduate, Undergraduate/Scholarship)* [351]

Henry DeWitt Smith Graduate Scholarship *(Graduate/Scholarship)* [10431]

Gladys Ann Smith Greater Los Angeles Women's Council Scholarship *(Undergraduate/Scholarship)* [8175]

Brian and Cathy Smith Memorial Fund *(Graduate/ Scholarship)* [1138]

James George Smith Memorial Scholarship *(Undergraduate, Graduate/Scholarship)* [2556]

Colonel Nate Smith Scholarship *(Graduate, Undergraduate/Scholarship)* [7201]

A.O. Smith Scholarships *(Undergraduate/Scholarship)* [9208]

Richard S. Smith Scholarships *(Undergraduate/ Scholarship)* [11264]

William E. Smith Scholarships *(Graduate/Scholarship)* [220]

Smith's Personal Best Scholarships *(Undergraduate/Scholarship)* [9423]

Smithsonian Fellowships in Museum Practice *(Professional development, Graduate/Fellowship)* [10188]

Smithsonian Minority Awards Program - Visiting Student *(Graduate/Fellowship)* [10209]

Smithsonian Native American Awards Program - Visiting Student *(Graduate/Fellowship)* [10211]

Smithsonian Postgraduate/Postdoctoral Fellowships in Conservation of Museum Collections *(Postgraduate, Postdoctorate/Fellowship)* [10212]

Eric E. Smoker Memorial Scholarship *(Undergraduate, Two Year College, Four Year College/Scholarship)* [8490]

The SMPE NY Scholarship Loan Program *(Undergraduate/Scholarship, Loan)* [10421]

Gladys Snauble Scholarship *(Undergraduate/Scholarship)* [5182]

SNF Professional Growth Scholarship *(Graduate, Undergraduate, Vocational/Occupational, Postgraduate/Scholarship, Award)* [9962]

SNMMI-TS Advanced Practitioner Program Scholarship *(Professional development/Scholarship)* [10441]

SNMMI-TS Bachelor's Degree Completion Scholarships *(Undergraduate/Scholarship)* [10442]

A.C. Snow and Katherine Snow Smith Scholarship *(High School/Scholarship)* [11210]

Helen D. Snow Memorial Scholarship *(Undergraduate, Graduate, Doctorate/Scholarship)* [9085]

SNRS Dissertation Research Grants *(Doctorate/ Grant)* [10659]

SNRS Research Grants *(Professional development/ Grant)* [10660]

SNRS/STTI Research Grants *(Professional development/Grant)* [10661]

SOAP/Kybele International Outreach Grant *(Advanced Professional, Professional development/ Grant)* [10448]

SOBP Travel Fellowship Award-Early Career Investigator-International *(Postdoctorate/Fellowship)* [10283]

Society for the Arts in Healthcare Student Scholarships *(Doctorate, Graduate, Undergraduate/Scholarship)* [10281]

Society of Exploration Geophysicists Scholarships *(Graduate, Undergraduate/Scholarship, Monetary, Award)* [10328]

Society for Linguistic Anthropology Annual Student Essay Prize *(Graduate, Undergraduate/Monetary)* [10380]

Society of Pediatric Nurses Academic Educational Scholarship *(Undergraduate, Graduate/Scholarship)* [10459]

SPU Research Grant *(Undergraduate/Grant)* [10470]

Society for the Scientific Study of Sexuality Student Research Grant *(Undergraduate/Grant)* [10528]

Society of Vacuum Coaters Foundation Scholarship *(Undergraduate, Graduate/Scholarship)* [10553]

Sodowsky Law Firm Scholarship *(College, University, Undergraduate/Scholarship)* [10570]

Softer H2O Scholarship Program *(Undergraduate, Graduate/Scholarship)* [10572]

The Solano Law Firm Scholarship Contest *(College, University, Undergraduate/Scholarship)* [10576]

SOM Foundation Structural Engineering Travel Fellowships *(Doctorate, Graduate, Master's, Undergraduate/Fellowship)* [10160]

Sonja S. Maguire Outstanding Scholastic Achievement Awards *(Graduate, Undergraduate/Scholarship)* [10897]

Dr. Kiyoshi Sonoda Memorial Scholarship *(Graduate, Master's/Scholarship)* [6253]

Sony Pictures Scholarship *(Graduate/Scholarship)* [2249]

SOPHE/ATSDR Student Fellowships in Environmental Health or Emergency Preparedness *(Graduate/ Fellowship)* [10513]

SOPHE/CDC Student Fellowship in Unintentional Injury Prevention *(Doctorate, Master's/Fellowship)* [10514]

SOPHE/CDC Student Fellowships in Child, Adolescent and School Health *(Doctorate, Graduate, Master's/Fellowship)* [10515]

Soroptimist International of Redlands Scholarship *(Undergraduate/Scholarship)* [9604]

Paul & Daisy Soros Fellowships *(Graduate/Fellowship)* [10597]

Soros Justice Advocacy Fellowships - Track I *(Professional development/Fellowship)* [8666]

Soros Justice Advocacy Fellowships - Track II *(Professional development/Fellowship)* [8667]

Soros Justice Media Fellowships - Track I *(Professional development/Fellowship)* [8668]

Soros Justice Media Fellowships - Track II *(Professional development/Fellowship)* [8669]

SORP Student Conference Scholarship *(Graduate, Undergraduate/Scholarship)* [10454]

Eastman Kodak Dr. Theophilus Sorrell Fellowships *(Graduate/Fellowship)* [8032]

John Soto Scholarships *(Undergraduate/Scholarship)* [3756]

South Central Modern Language Association Fellowships *(Doctorate, Postdoctorate/Fellowship)* [8383]

South Jersey Golf Association Scholarships *(Undergraduate/Scholarship)* [10627]

South Kentucky RECC High School Senior Scholarship Program *(Undergraduate/Scholarship)* [10630]

Southeast Alabama Dietetic Association Scholarships *(Graduate, Undergraduate/Scholarship)* [221]

Southwest Florida Community Foundation College Assistance Scholarships *(Undergraduate/Scholarship)* [10703]

Southwest Florida Deputy Sheriffs Association Fund *(Undergraduate/Scholarship)* [10704]

SPA/Lemelson Fellowship Program *(Graduate/ Award)* [10506]

Kathy Spadoni Memorial Scholarships *(Graduate/ Scholarship)* [9313]

Spangenberg Shibley & Liber Video PSA Scholarship Awards *(Undergraduate/Scholarship)* [10715]

Sparking the Future in Healthcare Scholarship *(Doctorate/Scholarship)* [26]

Nathan Sparks Memorial Scholarship *(Undergraduate/Scholarship)* [3664]

SPE Foundation General Scholarships *(Undergraduate, Graduate/Scholarship)* [10495]

SPE Student Awards for Innovations in Imaging *(Undergraduate, Graduate/Scholarship)* [10475]

Specialty Equipment Market Association Scholarships *(Graduate, Undergraduate, Vocational/Occupational/Scholarship)* [10722]

Specialty Nursing Scholarships *(Undergraduate/ Scholarship)* [4792]

Spice Box Grants *(Advanced Professional/Grant)* [848]

SPIE Student Author Travel Grants *(Graduate, Undergraduate/Grant)* [10729]

Phillip A. Spiegel IASP Congress Trainee Scholarship *(Graduate, Undergraduate/Scholarship)* [5945]

The Lawrence Alan Spiegel Remembrance Scholarship *(Undergraduate/Scholarship)* [5546]

Spirit of Anne Frank Scholarship Award *(Undergraduate/Scholarship)* [4813]

The Spirit Square Center for Arts and Education Scholarship Fund *(Undergraduate/Scholarship)* [4754]

Spokeo Connections Scholarships *(Undergraduate/ Scholarship)* [10733]

Sporty's/Cincinnati Avionics Scholarships *(Undergraduate, Vocational/Occupational/Scholarship)* [192]

Spouse Tuition Aid Loan Program (STAP) *(Undergraduate, Graduate/Loan)* [8181]

Springer - Jim Springer Memorial Scholarship *(Undergraduate/Scholarship)* [3489]

SPS Future Teacher Scholarships *(Undergraduate/ Scholarship)* [10480]

SPS Leadership Scholarships *(Undergraduate/ Scholarship)* [10481]

SPSmedical CS Scholarships *(Other/Scholarship)* [5928]

SRC Master's Scholarships Program *(Graduate, Master's/Scholarship)* [10001]

SREB-State Doctoral Scholars Program - Dissertation Award *(Doctorate/Scholarship, Award)* [10663]

SREB-State Doctoral Scholars Program - Doctoral Award *(Doctorate, Graduate/Scholarship)* [10664]

SSF Research Grants *(Other/Grant)* [10154]

SSF Student Fellowships *(Doctorate, Undergraduate/Fellowship)* [10155]

Stand Watie Scholarship *(Undergraduate/Scholarship)* [10588]

Stanford Advanced Materials $1,000 College Scholarship *(College/Scholarship)* [10747]

A.R.O.Y. Stanitz Scholarships *(Undergraduate/ Scholarship)* [1370]

Stanley Moore FUI Foundation Regional Scholarships *(Four Year College, High School, Two Year College/Scholarship)* [8464]

Stanley Moore National Scholarships *(Undergraduate/Scholarship)* [8465]

Stantec Scholarship *(Master's, Doctorate/Scholarship, Monetary)* [1644]

Thomas J. Stanton, Jr. Scholarships *(Graduate/ Scholarship)* [10029]

Star-Ledger Scholarships for the Performing Arts *(Undergraduate/Scholarship)* [8280]

Stark County Bar Association Scholarship Fund *(Undergraduate/Scholarship)* [10793]

Stark County Dairy Promoters Scholarship Fund *(Graduate/Scholarship)* [10794]

STC Scholarships *(Graduate, Undergraduate/Scholarship)* [6884]

The Stanley H. Stearman Awards (Undergraduate/ Scholarship) [8080]

The Robert P. Stearns/SCS Engineers Scholarship Award (Graduate/Scholarship) [10582]

Tom Steel Post-Graduate Fellowships (Postgraduate, Professional development/Fellowship) [9322]

Stella B. Johnson Scholarship (Undergraduate/ Scholarship) [12092]

Stephen Gates Memorial Scholarship (Undergraduate/Scholarship) [11211]

Stephen K. Hall ACWA Water Law and Policy Scholarship (Graduate/Scholarship) [2078]

Stephen Schwartz Musical Theatre Scholarship (Undergraduate/Scholarship) [5624]

Stephen T. Marchello Scholarship (Graduate/Scholarship) [7030]

H. H. Stephenson, Jr. Oxford Cup Scholarship (Undergraduate, Graduate/Scholarship) [2557]

Hugh E. Stephenson, Jr. Oxford Cup Scholarship (Undergraduate, Graduate/Scholarship) [2558]

Mike Stephenson Legal Scholarships (Graduate/ Scholarship) [7199]

Elizabeth Coulter Stephenson Scholarships (Undergraduate/Scholarship) [4044]

Raymond H. Stetson Scholarship in Phonetics and Speech Science (Graduate/Scholarship) [63]

Steve Dearduff Scholarship Fund (Graduate, Undergraduate/Scholarship) [3587]

Steve Hymans Extended Stay Scholarship Program (Undergraduate/Scholarship) [976]

Steve Kaplan TV & Film Studies Award (Other/ Award) [1412]

Steve Mason Sports Media Scholarship (Graduate, Undergraduate/Scholarship) [7991]

Steve Petix Journalism Scholarship (Undergraduate/ Scholarship) [9853]

Christine K. Stevens Development Scholarship (Undergraduate, Graduate/Scholarship) [1139]

Stevens Doctoral Award (Doctorate/Award) [5986]

The Zachary Taylor Stevens Scholarship (Undergraduate/Scholarship) [1962]

Richie Stevenson Scholarship Fund (Undergraduate/Scholarship) [3645]

Stewardson Keefe LeBrun Travel Grant (Professional development/Grant, Award) [139]

Mary Stewart and William T. Covington, Jr. Scholarship Fund (Undergraduate/Scholarship) [4755]

Dell Chenoweth Stifel Scholarship (Graduate/Scholarship) [6476]

The Richard Stockton College of New Jersey Foundation Alumni Association Graduate Awards (Graduate/Scholarship) [10848]

Louis Stokes Health Scholars Program (Undergraduate/Scholarship) [3742]

Louis Stokes Urban Health Policy Fellows Program (Other/Fellowship) [3743]

Ralph W. Stone Graduate Fellowships (Graduate/ Fellowship) [8129]

Stout Law Firm Family Matters Scholarship (College, University, Vocational/Occupational, Undergraduate/Scholarship) [10854]

Martin L. Stout Scholarships (Graduate, Undergraduate/Scholarship) [2162]

Robert "Bob" Strahan Memorial Scholarship (Undergraduate, Graduate/Scholarship) [5210]

George A. Strait Minority Scholarship (Graduate/ Scholarship) [600]

The Carole J. Streeter, KB9JBR, Scholarship (Undergraduate/Scholarship) [1963]

Stanley W. Strew Scholarship (Undergraduate/ Scholarship) [2785]

The Norman E. Strohmeier, W2VRS, Memorial Scholarship (Undergraduate/Scholarship) [1964]

Stuart Cameron and Margaret McLeod Memorial Scholarship (SCMS) (Graduate, Undergraduate/ Scholarship) [5850]

Mark and Karla Stuart Family Scholarship (Undergraduate/Scholarship) [9854]

Stuart L. Bernath Dissertation Research Grant (Graduate/Grant) [10360]

Stuart L. Noderer Memorial Scholarship (Undergraduate/Scholarship) [9855]

Student Entrepreneur Scholarship (Undergraduate, Graduate/Scholarship) [5355]

Student Fellowship (Graduate, Undergraduate/Fellowship) [7530]

Student Illustrator Scholarship (Undergraduate, Graduate/Scholarship) [10304]

Student Investigator Research Grant - General Audiology/Hearing Science (Graduate, Doctorate/ Grant) [433]

Student Investigator Research Grant - Hearing Aids, Clinical Protocols and Patient Outcomes (Graduate, Doctorate/Grant) [434]

Student Investigator Research Grant - Vestibular (Graduate, Doctorate/Grant) [435]

Student Research Foundation Personal Achievement Scholarship (Undergraduate/Scholarship) [4309]

Student Summer Research Fellowship (Undergraduate, Graduate/Fellowship) [436]

Student Travel Grant (Undergraduate/Grant) [7361]

Student Writer Scholarship (Graduate, Doctorate, Undergraduate/Scholarship) [10305]

Students of History Scholarship (Undergraduate/ Scholarship) [10869]

Stultz Scholarship (Undergraduate/Scholarship) [12093]

Subic Bay-Cubi Point Scholarships (Undergraduate/ Scholarship) [8176]

Substance Abuse and Mental Health Awareness in Veterans Scholarship (Undergraduate, Graduate/ Scholarship) [4187]

Edward P. Suchecki Family Scholarship (Undergraduate/Scholarship) [5109]

Sugar Spun Scholarship (Undergraduate, Graduate/ Scholarship) [10875]

Summer Intern Scholarships In Cardiothoracic Surgery (Undergraduate/Scholarship, Internship) [663]

Summer Undergraduate Fellowship Program (Undergraduate/Fellowship) [623]

Hatton W. Sumners Endowed Undergraduate School Scholarships (Undergraduate/Scholarship) [10878]

Hatton W. Sumners Non-Endowed Undergraduate and Graduate Scholarships (Undergraduate, Graduate/Scholarship) [10879]

Surety and Fidelity Industry Intern and Scholarship Program (Undergraduate, Graduate/Scholarship) [10885]

The Susan Kelly Power and Helen Hornbeck Tanner Fellowship (Doctorate, Postdoctorate/Fellowship) [8384]

SUT Houston Graduate Scholarships (Graduate/ Scholarship) [10547]

SUT Houston Undergraduate Scholarships (Undergraduate/Scholarship) [10548]

Sutherland/Purdy Scholarship (Undergraduate/ Scholarship) [9130]

SUVCW Scholarships (Undergraduate/Scholarship) [10595]

SVS Vascular Surgery Trainee Advocacy Travel Scholarship (Advanced Professional, Professional development/Scholarship, Grant) [10556]

Swede Swanson Memorial Scholarships (Undergraduate/Scholarship) [8190]

Henry D. and Ruth G. Swartz Family Scholarship (Undergraduate/Scholarship) [5110]

The Hanns Swarzenski and Brigitte Horney Swarzenski Fellowship (Graduate/Fellowship) [7283]

Sweep All Scholarship (College, University/Scholarship) [10893]

Jeffrey Tyler Sweitzer Wrestling Memorial Scholarship Fund (Undergraduate/Scholarship) [10795]

Timothy S. Sweterlitsch Memorial Scholarship Fund (Undergraduate/Scholarship) [10796]

SWS Barbara Rosenblum Scholarship (Doctorate/ Fellowship, Scholarship) [10568]

Sycamore Hills Dentistry Scholarship (College, University/Scholarship) [10900]

Sylvia Taylor Johnson Minority Fellowships in Educational Measurement (Doctorate/Fellowship) [4313]

Symantec Research Labs Graduate Fellowships (Doctorate, Graduate/Fellowship) [8547]

Symee Ruth Feinberg Memorial Scholarship Fund (Undergraduate/Scholarship) [5345]

T. Frank Booth Memorial Scholarship Endowment Fund (Undergraduate/Scholarship) [4756]

Ta Liang Award (Graduate/Award) [2010]

Harry Taback 9/11 Memorial Scholarships (Undergraduate/Scholarship) [1572]

TAC Foundation-Stantec Consulting Dr. Ralph Haas Scholarships (Graduate, Undergraduate/Scholarship) [11099]

TACL-LA Taiwanese American Community Scholarship (TACS) (Undergraduate/Scholarship) [10911]

Kei Takemoto Memorial Scholarships (Undergraduate/Scholarship) [193]

The Donald H. Bernstein and John B. Talbert Jr. Scholarship (Undergraduate/Scholarship) [4758]

Tall Awareness Scholarships (Graduate/Scholarship) [9425]

Justice Stephen K. Tamura Scholarship (Undergraduate/Scholarship) [6241]

TANA Foundation Graduate Scholarships (Graduate/ Scholarship) [10953]

Alexander M. Tanger Scholarships (Graduate/Scholarship) [2706]

Alex Tanous Scholarship Award (Undergraduate/ Scholarship) [10919]

Frederick A. Tarantino Memorial Scholarship Award (Undergraduate/Scholarship) [11425]

Targeted Research Initiative for Health Outcomes (Doctorate/Grant) [4427]

Tarkanian Teacher Education Academy at Clark High School Scholarship (Undergraduate/Scholarship) [9426]

Raymond J. Tarleton Graduate Fellowships (Graduate/Fellowship) [3267]

Joshua C. Taylor Fellowships (Doctorate, Postdoctorate/Fellowship) [10219]

Ryan "Munchie" Taylor Memorial Scholarships (Undergraduate/Scholarship) [6944]

TCA-ACBH Scholarship to Turkey Program (Undergraduate/Scholarship) [86, 11142]

TCA-UMD Scholarship to Turkey Program (Undergraduate/Scholarship) [11143]

TCAdvance Scholarship (Undergraduate/Scholarship) [11144]

Teacher Education Scholarship (Advanced Professional/Scholarship) [1130]

Tech Mastery Scholarships (Undergraduate, Graduate/Scholarship) [9635]

Technical, vocational or associate's degree programs (Undergraduate/Scholarship) [10621]

Technical Scholarship (Undergraduate/Scholarship) [8592]

Mary L. Tenopyr Graduate Student Scholarship (Graduate/Scholarship) [10336]

The Terra Foundation Fellowships in American Art (Undergraduate, Doctorate, Postdoctorate/Fellowship) [10220]

Terry Linda Potter Scholarship (Undergraduate/ Scholarship) [5111]

The TESOL/TEFL Travel Grant (Advanced Professional/Grant, Monetary) [10970]

Marc Tetalman, MD, Memorial Award (Professional development, Doctorate/Recognition) [10444]

Texas Scholarship of Academic Excellence (Undergraduate, Graduate/Scholarship) [1708]

Texas State Technical College Scholarships (Undergraduate/Scholarship) [194]

TFC Edward A. Plank, Jr. Memorial Scholarship (Undergraduate/Scholarship) [3579]

Jim and Pat Thacker Sports Communication Internship (Undergraduate/Internship) [11212]

Theodore C. Sorensen Research Fellowship (Other/ Fellowship) [6533]

Theodore E.D. Braun Research Travel Fellowship (Other/Fellowship) [1439]

Thermo Fisher Scientific Antibody Scholarship (Undergraduate, Graduate/Scholarship) [11016]

Thermo Scientific Educational Scholarships (Professional development/Scholarship) [8115]

Thermoforming Division Scholarship (Undergraduate, Graduate/Scholarship) [10497]

Thesaurus Linguae Latinae Fellowship (TTL) (Doctorate/Fellowship) [10312]

Werner B. Thiele Memorial Scholarship (Graduate, Undergraduate/Scholarship) [5211]

Elizabeth R. Thomas Alumni Nursing Scholarship (Undergraduate/Scholarship) [10065]

Thomas Arkle Clark Scholar-Leader of the Year (Graduate, Undergraduate/Scholarship) [9092]

Thomas E. Shown, M.D. Memorial Scholarship *(Undergraduate/Scholarship)* [12094]

Thomas F. Black Jr. Memorial Scholarship *(Undergraduate/Scholarship)* [9686]

Thomas J. Emery Memorial Fund Scholarship *(Undergraduate/Scholarship)* [3404]

Thomas and Ruth River International Scholarship *(Undergraduate, Graduate/Scholarship)* [12201]

Charles C. Thomas Scholarship *(Undergraduate/Scholarship)* [1754]

Cheryl M. Thomas Scholarship *(Undergraduate, Graduate, Postdoctorate/Scholarship)* [27]

C.R. Thomas Scholarship *(Undergraduate/Scholarship)* [8882]

The Rev. Chuck and Nancy Thomas Scholarship *(Professional development/Scholarship)* [11256]

Thome Foundation Awards Program in Age-Related Macular Degeneration Research *(Professional development/Grant)* [5444]

Thome Foundation Awards Program in Alzheimer's Disease Drug Discovery Research *(Professional development/Grant)* [5445]

Katrina Thompson Scholarship *(Community College, College, University, Undergraduate, Vocational/Occupational/Scholarship)* [9856]

Thompson Scholarship for Women in Safety *(Doctorate/Scholarship)* [1573]

Barbara and Howard Thompson Scholarships *(Undergraduate/Scholarship)* [6209]

Thomas P. Thornton Scholarship *(Undergraduate, Graduate/Scholarship)* [5731]

Arthur A. Thovmasian, Jr. Memorial Grant *(Undergraduate/Scholarship)* [1904]

The Thurgood Marshall College Fund *(Undergraduate/Scholarship)* [10856]

Thurgood Marshall Fellowships Program *(Undergraduate/Fellowship)* [8301]

Tiftickjian Law Firm, P.C. Juvenile Justice Law School Scholarships *(Graduate/Scholarship)* [11030]

The Tikvah Fellowship *(Undergraduate/Fellowship)* [11034]

Tillman Scholars Program *(Undergraduate, Graduate/Scholarship)* [11036]

Titan Web Agency Bi-Annual Scholarship Program *(Community College, Four Year College, Two Year College/Scholarship)* [11042]

T.L. Conlan Scholarship Fund *(Undergraduate/Scholarship)* [3405]

Tobi's Scholarship *(Undergraduate/Scholarship)* [11044]

Mario J. Tocco Hydrocephalus Foundation Scholarships *(Undergraduate/Scholarship)* [5667]

Michael W. Toennis Scholarship *(Undergraduate, Graduate/Scholarship)* [2559]

Tom Best Scholarship *(Undergraduate/Scholarship)* [11213]

Tom Cory Scholarships *(Undergraduate, Graduate/Scholarship)* [1787]

Tommie J. Hamner Scholarship *(Undergraduate/Scholarship)* [9131]

TonaLaw Veteran's Scholarship *(Undergraduate, Graduate, Professional development, Vocational/Occupational/Scholarship)* [11050]

Took Trust Point Scholarship *(Undergraduate, Graduate/Scholarship)* [9232]

Ferdinand Torres Scholarships *(Graduate, Undergraduate/Scholarship)* [920]

Dr. Harry Jeffrey Tourigian Memorial Grant *(Undergraduate/Scholarship)* [1905]

The Town and County Club Scholarship *(Undergraduate/Scholarship)* [5346]

Toyota Point Scholarship *(Undergraduate, Graduate, Doctorate/Scholarship)* [9233]

Toyota/TELACU Scholarships *(Undergraduate/Scholarship)* [10942]

The Joyce Tracy Fellowship *(Doctorate/Fellowship)* [499]

Vera Tran Memorial Scholarships *(Undergraduate/Scholarship)* [11825]

Transatlantic Fellows Program *(Other/Fellowship)* [4947]

The TranscriptionServices.com Scholarship *(Undergraduate/Scholarship)* [11073]

Translational Research Professorship *(Professional development/Internship)* [3784]

Transoft Solutions, Inc. Ahead of the Curve Scholarship (AOTC) *(Graduate, Undergraduate/Scholarship)* [5867]

Traub-Dicker Rainbow Scholarships (TDRS) *(Undergraduate/Scholarship)* [10851]

Travis Dunning Memorial Scholarship *(Undergraduate/Scholarship)* [9427]

Tri Delta Alpha Eta Scholarships *(Undergraduate/Scholarship)* [4014]

Tri Delta Alpha Rho Leadership Scholarships *(Undergraduate/Scholarship)* [4015]

Triadex Scholarship *(Undergraduate/Scholarship)* [11106]

Tribute Fund Community Grant *(Professional development/Grant)* [10306]

Tim Triner Letter Carriers Scholarship Fund *(Undergraduate/Scholarship)* [10798]

Trinity Education Foundation Seminary Scholarship *(Graduate/Scholarship)* [11112]

Johnny Trombly Memorial Scholarship *(Undergraduate/Scholarship)* [7433]

Charlie Trotters's Culinary Education Foundation Scholarships *(Other, Undergraduate/Scholarship)* [849]

Jo Anne J. Trow Undergraduate Scholarships *(Undergraduate/Scholarship)* [393]

The William H. Truettner Fellowship Endowment Fund *(Undergraduate, Doctorate, Postdoctorate/Fellowship)* [10221]

TrustedPros Scholarships *(Undergraduate/Scholarship)* [11131]

Trustees College Scholarships *(Undergraduate/Scholarship)* [6961]

Tucker Family Scholarship *(Undergraduate/Scholarship)* [11214]

Hans Turley Prize in Queer Eighteenth-Century Studies *(Graduate, Other/Prize)* [1440]

Jeff Turner-Forsyth Audubon Society Scholarship *(Undergraduate/Scholarship)* [12096]

James A. Turner, Jr. Memorial Scholarship *(Undergraduate/Scholarship)* [1672]

Scott Alan Turner Personal Finance Scholarship *(High School, Undergraduate/Scholarship)* [11152]

Lydia Donaldson Tutt-Jones Memorial Research Grant *(Graduate, Other, Master's/Grant)* [109]

Florence Tyson Grant to Study Music Psychotherapy *(Professional development/Grant)* [1140]

UC MEXUS - CICESE Graduate Student Short-Term Research and Non-degree Training *(Graduate/Grant)* [11550]

UC MEXUS-CONACYT Collaborative Grants *(Professional development/Grant)* [11551]

UC MEXUS-CONACYT Doctoral Fellowship *(Doctorate/Fellowship)* [11552]

UC MEXUS-CONACYT Postdoctoral Research Fellowships *(Postdoctorate/Fellowship)* [11553]

UC MEXUS Dissertation Research Grants *(Graduate/Grant)* [11554]

UC MEXUS Scholars in Residence Program - Graduate *(Graduate/Scholarship)* [11555]

UC MEXUS Scholars in Residence Program - Recent University Graduates *(Postgraduate, Graduate/Scholarship)* [11556]

UC MEXUS Scholars in Residence Program - Visiting Faculty *(Professional development/Scholarship)* [11557]

UC MEXUS Small Grants for UC Postdocs *(Postdoctorate/Grant)* [11558]

UC MEXUS Small Grants for UC Students *(Graduate, Postdoctorate/Grant)* [11559]

UCT Scholarship *(Other/Scholarship)* [8693]

Udall Undergraduate Scholarship *(Undergraduate/Scholarship)* [11165]

Ugly Sweater Scholarship *(High School, College, University, Graduate, Undergraduate/Scholarship)* [9957]

Sandy Ulm Scholarships *(Undergraduate, Master's/Scholarship)* [4625]

Ric Ulrich and Chuck Pischke Scholarships *(Undergraduate/Scholarship)* [9315]

Ultrsound Schools Info Student Scholarship *(Two Year College, Undergraduate/Scholarship)* [11171]

UMBS Istock Family Scholarship *(Undergraduate/Scholarship)* [11632]

UMBS Returning Student Award *(Undergraduate/Scholarship)* [11633]

UMDF Clinical Research Fellowship Training Awards *(Professional development/Fellowship)* [11266]

Undergraduate Scholars Program *(Graduate/Scholarship)* [5606]

Undergraduate Scholarship *(Undergraduate/Scholarship)* [3285]

Underrepresented in Medicine award *(Graduate/Scholarship)* [1112]

UNICO Merrimack Valley Scholarships *(Graduate/Scholarship)* [11219]

Unigo $10K Scholarship *(Undergraduate, High School/Scholarship)* [11236]

Union Plus Scholarship Program *(Undergraduate, Graduate/Scholarship)* [11243]

Union Plus Scholarship Program *(Undergraduate/Scholarship)* [6139]

United Engineering Foundation Grants *(All/Grant)* [11259]

United Health Foundation National Association of Hispanic Nurses Scholarships *(High School/Scholarship)* [7659]

United Methodist General Scholarships *(Undergraduate, Graduate/Scholarship)* [4895]

U.S. Air Force ROTC High School Scholarship - Type 1 *(High School/Scholarship)* [11282]

U.S. Air Force ROTC High School Scholarship - Type 2 *(High School/Scholarship)* [11283]

U.S. Air Force ROTC In-College Scholarships - Type 2 *(High School/Scholarship)* [11284]

U.S. Aircraft Insurance Group Professional Development Program (USAIG PDP) Scholarships *(Undergraduate/Scholarship)* [7741]

U.S. Bates Scholarship *(Undergraduate/Scholarship)* [6140]

U.S. BIA Indian Higher Education Grants *(Undergraduate/Grant)* [991]

United States Capitol Historical Society Fellowships *(Graduate/Fellowship)* [11299]

U.S.-U.K. Young Investigator Exchange Fellowship *(Postdoctorate/Fellowship)* [417]

UnitedAg Scholarship Program *(Undergraduate/Scholarship)* [11415]

Universal Studios Preservation Scholarships *(Graduate/Scholarship)* [2250]

University of the Aftermarket Foundation Scholarship *(Community College/Scholarship)* [11428]

University Club Lamp of Learning Scholarship *(Undergraduate, University/Scholarship)* [9860]

University of Louisville Eagle Scout Scholarships *(Undergraduate/Scholarship, Award)* [7857]

University of Southern Mississippi Eagle Scout Scholarship *(Undergraduate/Scholarship)* [7858]

University of Wisconsin-Madison Chancellor's Scholarship Program *(Undergraduate/Scholarship)* [11746]

UPE Scholarship Awards *(Graduate, Undergraduate/Scholarship)* [11765]

Upper Midwest Human Rights Fellowship Program *(Graduate/Scholarship, Fellowship)* [5632]

UPS Diversity Scholarship *(Undergraduate/Scholarship)* [1574]

UPS Scholarship for Female Students *(Undergraduate/Scholarship)* [5836]

UPS Scholarship for Minority Students *(Undergraduate/Scholarship)* [5837]

Urban and Regional Policy Fellowship *(Other/Fellowship)* [4948]

Urgent.ly Driving Transportation Innovation Scholarship *(Undergraduate, Graduate, Vocational/Occupational/Scholarship)* [11769]

Urology Care Foundation/Astellas Rising Star in Urology Research Awards *(Postdoctorate, Other/Award)* [11772]

US Bank NA Scholarship Fund *(Undergraduate/Scholarship)* [3406]

USA Cargo Trailer Scholarship *(Undergraduate, Graduate/Scholarship)* [11776]

USA/USA-Ukramerazha Scholarships *(Undergraduate/Scholarship)* [11413]

USAEE/IAEE North American Conference Registration Fee Scholarships *(Undergraduate/Scholarship)* [11297]

USAWOASF Regular Scholarship *(Graduate/Scholarship)* [11291]

USC Latino Alumni Association Scholarships (Graduate, Undergraduate/Scholarship) [11783]

USDA-NIFA-AFRI Merit Awards (Postdoctorate/Award, Recognition, Prize) [10534]

USET Scholarship Fund (Undergraduate/Scholarship) [11278]

USGA/Chevron STEM Scholarship Program (Undergraduate/Scholarship) [11373]

USHJA Foundation Hamel Scholarship for Further Education (Undergraduate/Scholarship) [11375]

USPAACC Ampcus Hallmark Scholarship (Undergraduate/Scholarship) [11395]

USPAACC College Hallmark Scholarships (Undergraduate/Scholarship) [11396]

USPAACC Denny's Hungry for Education Scholarship (Undergraduate/Scholarship) [11397]

USS Coral Sea - Scholarship Program (Undergraduate/Scholarship) [11785]

USTA Serves College Education Scholarship (Undergraduate/Scholarship) [11405]

USTA Serves College Textbook Scholarship (Undergraduate/Scholarship) [11406]

The Utah Advocates Scholarship (College, University/Scholarship) [88]

Utility Workers Union of America Scholarship Program (Undergraduate/Scholarship) [11789]

UW-Madison GLBT Alumni Council Scholarships (Undergraduate, Graduate/Scholarship) [11749]

V.A. Leonard Scholarship (Graduate, Undergraduate/Scholarship) [399]

VABANC Scholarships (Graduate, Undergraduate/Scholarship) [11820]

Vallabhaneni Sukundamma & Lakshmaiah Scholarship (Graduate/Scholarship) [10954]

Marta Vallin Memorial Scholarships (Undergraduate/Scholarship) [3757]

ValuePenguin Scholarships (Undergraduate/Scholarship) [11791]

Valuing Diversity PhD Scholarship (Doctorate/Scholarship) [1105]

Patricia Van Kirk Scholarship (Undergraduate/Scholarship) [9316]

Gary Vanden Berg Internship Grant (Undergraduate/Grant) [10737]

Roy Vander Putten (Advanced Professional/Scholarship) [3460]

René M. Vandervelde Research Grants (Professional development/Grant) [2049]

Vector Marketing Canadian Scholarship Award (Undergraduate/Scholarship) [11794]

Vectorworks Design Scholarship (Undergraduate, Graduate/Scholarship) [11796]

Ventana Medical Systems In Situ Hybridization Awards (Other/Award) [8116]

Graduate Fellowship Program - Peter Verhofstadt Fellowships (Graduate/Fellowship) [10002]

Vern Parish Award (Graduate, Postgraduate, Doctorate/Scholarship) [1088]

Chester M. Vernon Memorial Eagle Scout Scholarships (Undergraduate/Scholarship) [7859]

Veronica Gantt Memorial Scholarship (Undergraduate/Scholarship) [9429]

Vesalius Trust Student Research Scholarship Program (Graduate, Undergraduate/Scholarship) [11805]

Veterans of Foreign Wars Scout of the Year (Undergraduate/Scholarship) [7860]

Vicki Cruse Memorial Emergency Maneuver Training Scholarship (Undergraduate/Scholarship) [8403]

Victor and Ruth N. Goodman Memorial Scholarship (Graduate/Scholarship) [5281]

Victoria M. Gardner Scholarship (Undergraduate/Scholarship) [11215]

Myrtle Siegfried, MD, and Michael Vigilante, MD Scholarship (Undergraduate/Scholarship) [4801]

Vincent T. Wasilewski Award (Graduate/Scholarship) [2708]

Vincent Trotter Health Care Scholarship (Undergraduate/Scholarship) [9862]

Violin Society of America Scholarships (Undergraduate/Scholarship) [11827]

VIP Women in Technology Scholarship (Two Year College, Undergraduate, Graduate/Scholarship) [11856]

Virgil K. Lobring Scholarship Program (Undergraduate/Scholarship) [3725]

Virginia C. Jack and Ralph L. Jack Scholarship Fund (Undergraduate/Scholarship) [10800]

Virginia M. Smyth Scholarship (Graduate/Scholarship) [4930]

Virginia Mathews Memorial Scholarship (Graduate/Scholarship) [998]

Virginia Museum of Fine Arts Visual Arts Fellowships (Graduate, Other, Undergraduate/Fellowship) [11839]

Virginia Tech Student Travel Award (Undergraduate, Graduate/Award) [2167]

Vision Tech Camps Scholarship (Community College, Four Year College/Scholarship) [11854]

Vision Zero Auto Accident Prevention Scholarships (Postgraduate/Scholarship) [6693]

Vivian M. Kommer Scholarship (Undergraduate/Scholarship) [5190]

John D. Voelker Foundation Native American Scholarships (Undergraduate/Scholarship) [11858]

Gupton A. Vogt Oxford Cup Memorial Scholarship (Undergraduate, Graduate/Scholarship) [2560]

Von Ogden Vogt Scholarship (Master's/Scholarship) [11257]

Miki Vohryzek-Bolden Student Paper Competition (Undergraduate/Prize) [11991]

VPPPA June Brothers Scholarship (Graduate, Undergraduate/Scholarship) [11862]

VPPPA Stephen Brown Scholarship (Graduate, Undergraduate/Scholarship) [11863]

W. Kaye Lamb Award for the Best Student works (Undergraduate/Scholarship) [2701]

W. Philip Braender and Nancy Coleman Braender Scholarship Fund (Undergraduate/Scholarship) [5347]

W. Stull Holt Dissertation Fellowship (Graduate/Fellowship) [10361]

W. Wesley Eckenfelder Graduate Research Award (Master's, Doctorate/Award) [2168]

Jane and Gregg Waddill Memorial Adelphe Scholarship (Undergraduate/Scholarship) [6477]

Wadsworth International Fellowships (Graduate/Fellowship) [11965]

The Gary Wagner, K3OMI, Scholarship (Undergraduate/Scholarship) [1965]

Wagner-Torizuka Fellowship (Professional development/Fellowship) [10445]

Wakeford Gelini Driver Safety Scholarship (Undergraduate, Graduate, Vocational/Occupational, College/Scholarship) [11866]

Laramie Walden Memorial Fund (Undergraduate/Scholarship) [4762]

Helen Zick Walker Adelphe Scholarship (Undergraduate/Scholarship) [6478]

Myrtle & Earl Walker Scholarships (Undergraduate/Scholarship) [10417]

Walta Wilkinson Carmichael Scholarship (Graduate/Scholarship) [10125]

Walter "Doc" Hurley Scholarship Fund of Greater Hartford (Undergraduate/Scholarship) [5348]

Walter and Lucille Harper Transfer Scholarship (Graduate/Scholarship) [6516]

Walter and Marilyn Bartlett Scholarship Fund (Undergraduate/Scholarship) [3407]

Walter Samek III Memorial Scholarship (Graduate/Scholarship) [3598]

Shih-Chun Wang Young Investigator Award (Advanced Professional/Monetary, Award) [1240]

Louis Dreyfus Warner-Chappell City College Scholarship (Undergraduate/Scholarship) [1413]

Warner Norcross & Judd Minority Scholarships (Undergraduate/Scholarship) [11874]

Washington College Grant (SNG) (Undergraduate/Grant) [11919]

Waterbury Bar Association Scholarship (Undergraduate/Scholarship) [11933]

Watson-Brown Scholarship (Undergraduate/Scholarship) [11936]

Wayne G. Failor Scholarship Fund (Undergraduate/Scholarship) [8969]

Wayne-Meador-Elliott Scholarship (Undergraduate/Scholarship) [8884]

WBA Paralegal/Legal Assistant Scholarship (Undergraduate/Scholarship) [11934]

WDHOF Undergraduate Scholarships in Marine Conservation (Undergraduate/Scholarship) [12137]

Richard M. Weaver Fellowships (Graduate/Fellowship) [5886]

Monica M. Weaver Memorial Fund (Undergraduate/Scholarship) [4606]

Web Design Scholarship (College, University, Undergraduate, Vocational/Occupational, Graduate/Scholarship, Award) [6917]

Web Design Scholarship (Undergraduate/Scholarship) [2665]

W.E.B. Du Bois Program (Doctorate/Fellowship) [7944]

Websauce Web Design Scholarship (Undergraduate/Scholarship) [11954]

WEDA Scholarship Program (Professional development/Scholarship) [11979]

John V. Wehausen Graduate Scholarships for Advanced Study in Ship Hydrodynamics and Wave Theory (Graduate/Scholarship) [10435]

The Arthur and Lila Weinberg Fellowship for Independent Researchers (Other, Graduate/Fellowship) [8385]

Bertold E. Weinberg Scholarship (Graduate/Scholarship) [793]

The Bee Winkler Weinstein Scholarship Fund (Undergraduate, Vocational/Occupational/Scholarship) [10852]

William E. Weisel Scholarship (Undergraduate/Scholarship) [10418]

Susan C. Weiss Clinical Advancement Scholarship (Other/Scholarship) [10446]

Welch Scholars Grants (Undergraduate/Grant) [1200]

Wells Fargo American Indian Scholarship Program (Undergraduate/Scholarship) [996]

Wells Fargo Point Scholarship (Undergraduate, Graduate/Scholarship) [9234]

Wells Fargo Scholarship Program for People with Disabilities (Undergraduate/Scholarship) [9944]

Jean Hess Wells Memorial Adelphe Graduate Scholarship (Graduate/Scholarship) [6480]

Jean Hess Wells Memorial Adelphe Scholarship (Undergraduate/Scholarship) [6481]

Peter R. Weitz Prize (Other/Prize) [4949]

Judy Kay Wendland-Young Scholarship (Undergraduate/Scholarship) [6279]

Francis X. Weninger Scholarships (Undergraduate/Scholarship) [12226]

Wes Burton Memorial Scholarship (Undergraduate/Scholarship) [12097]

Wesley C. Cameron Scholarship (Undergraduate/Scholarship) [8177]

Wesley R. Habley Summer Institute Scholarships (Professional development/Scholarship) [7569]

West Michigan Nursery and Landscape Association Scholarship (Undergraduate/Scholarship) [5113]

West Virginia Nurses Association District No. 3 Professional Nursing Scholarships (Undergraduate/Scholarship) [8885]

West Virginia PTA Scholarship (Undergraduate/Scholarship) [11973]

Western-Southern Foundation Scholarship (Undergraduate/Scholarship) [3408]

Mary Elizabeth Westpheling - Long Beach (Calif.) Alumnae Association Memorial Scholarhip (Undergraduate/Scholarship) [6482]

Dr. William "Tim" Whalen Memorial Scholarships (Undergraduate/Scholarship) [8476]

Stan Wheeler Mentorship Awards (Other/Award) [6728]

Nellie Yeoh Whetten Award (Graduate/Recognition) [2387]

Whidbey Island Giving Circle Scholarships (Undergraduate/Scholarship) [9317]

WHIMA Established Professional Development Scholarship (Graduate/Scholarship) [12119]

Whirly-Girls Helicopter Add-On Flight Training Scholarship (Professional development, Vocational/Occupational/Scholarship) [12013]

Whirly-Girls Jean Tinsley Memorial HELI-EXPO Scholarship (Professional development, Vocational/Occupational/Scholarship) [12014]

Whitaker-Minard Memorial Scholarship (Undergraduate/Scholarship) [8886]

Law Office of David D. White Annual Traumatic Brain Injury Scholarships *(College, Community College, University, Vocational/Occupational/ Scholarship)* [6687]

White Collar Defense Diversity Scholarships *(Undergraduate, Graduate/Scholarship)* [9286]

Bradford White Corporation Scholarships *(Undergraduate/Scholarship)* [9209]

Alma White - Delta Chapter, Delta Kappa Gamma Scholarship *(Undergraduate, University, College, Two Year College/Scholarship)* [5415]

The Brian J. White Endowed Law Scholarship *(Undergraduate/Scholarship)* [9031]

Mary Kean White Memorial Scholarship Fund *(Undergraduate, Doctorate/Scholarship)* [10802]

Paul D. White Scholarship Program *(Undergraduate/Scholarship)* [2409]

Ann Cook Whitman Scholarships for Perry High School *(Undergraduate/Scholarship)* [4964]

Jane and Morgan Whitney Fellowships *(Graduate/ Fellowship)* [7284]

Tom Wicker Award *(Graduate/Award)* [11216]

Larry B. Wickham Memorial Scholarship for Graduate Studies *(Graduate/Scholarship)* [7487]

Wicomico High School Class of '55 Schloarship *(Undergraduate/Scholarship)* [3580]

Elmo Wierenga Alumni Scholarship *(Undergraduate/ Scholarship)* [5194]

Elie Wiesel Prize in Ethics *(Undergraduate/Prize, Award)* [12022]

Fred Wiesner Educational Excellence Scholarships *(Undergraduate, Graduate/Scholarship)* [2301]

WIGA College Scholarships *(Postgraduate, Graduate, Undergraduate/Scholarship)* [11894]

Hair Loss Scholarship *(College, University, Undergraduate, Graduate, Two Year College, Vocational/Occupational/Scholarship)* [12024]

The Fred C. Wikoff Jr. Scholarship *(Undergraduate, Vocational/Occupational/Scholarship)* [4763]

Wild Felid Legacy Scholarship *(Graduate/Scholarship)* [12026]

Wilder Dimension Scholarships for Advanced Study in Theatre Arts *(Graduate/Scholarship)* [4178]

Willa Beach-Porter CTBA Music Scholarship Fund *(Undergraduate/Scholarship)* [3246]

Willard & Spackman Scholarship Program *(Postgraduate/Scholarship)* [1182]

James B. Willett Educational Memorial Scholarship Award *(Undergraduate/Scholarship)* [11426]

William A. Fischer Scholarship *(Graduate/Scholarship)* [2011]

William B. Howell Memorial Scholarship *(Undergraduate/Scholarship)* [1674]

William and Beatrice Kavanaugh Memorial Scholarship *(Graduate/Scholarship)* [6211]

William C. Ray, CIH, CSP Arizona Scholarship *(Doctorate/Scholarship)* [1575]

William and Clara Bryan Scholarship Fund *(Undergraduate/Scholarship)* [3648]

William E. Parrish Scholarship *(Graduate, Master's/ Scholarship)* [9079]

William G. and Mayme J. Green Fund *(Undergraduate/Scholarship)* [5349]

William Goldberg Scholarship *(Undergraduate/ Scholarship)* [4883]

William H. Andrews/HAWS Scholarship *(Undergraduate/Scholarship)* [12098]

William J. Tangye Scholarship *(Undergraduate/ Scholarship, Monetary, Award)* [5974]

William J. Yankee Memorial Scholarship *(Undergraduate/Scholarship, Monetary, Recognition)* [1263]

William L. Graddy Law School Scholarship Fund *(Graduate/Scholarship)* [10705]

William M. Fanning Maintenance Scholarship *(Undergraduate/Scholarship)* [7742]

William Pigott Memorial Scholarship *(Undergraduate/Scholarship)* [3694]

William R. Bowen Scholarship *(Undergraduate/ Scholarship)* [3581]

William R. Durham Drama and Theater Scholarship *(Undergraduate/Scholarship)* [3695]

William "Sully" Sullivan Scholarship *(Graduate, Undergraduate/Scholarship)* [11864]

William T. Burbage Family Memorial Scholarship *(Undergraduate/Scholarship)* [3582]

Sidney B. Williams, Jr. Scholarships *(Undergraduate/Scholarship)* [4698]

BM1 James Elliott Williams Memorial Scholarship Fund *(Undergraduate/Scholarship)* [8936]

Alice Hinchcliffe Williams, RDH, MS Merit Scholarship *(Graduate/Scholarship)* [11833]

The Leon And Margaret Williams Scholarship *(Undergraduate/Scholarship)* [9866]

Maxine Williams Scholarship *(Undergraduate/Scholarship)* [605]

Williams – Dr. Dana Williams Scholarship *(Undergraduate/Scholarship)* [3492]

Lippincott Williams and Wilkins Scholarships (LWW Scholarship) *(Master's, Doctorate/Scholarship)* [3440]

Mary Katherine "Kathy" Williamson Scholarship Fund *(Undergraduate/Scholarship)* [3665]

Willie T. Loud scholarship *(Undergraduate, Graduate/Scholarship)* [7894]

Beverly Willis Architecture Foundation Travel Fellowship *(Doctorate/Fellowship)* [10279]

Wilma Sackett Dressel Scholarship *(Undergraduate/ Scholarship)* [10126]

Gary S. Wilmer/RAMI Music Scholarship *(Undergraduate/Scholarship)* [3696]

The Harriet Glen Wilmore Scholarship *(Undergraduate, Vocational/Occupational/Scholarship)* [4765]

Glenn Wilson Broadcast Journalism Scholarship *(Undergraduate/Scholarship)* [8887]

Woodrow Wilson Dissertation Fellowship in Women's Studies *(Doctorate/Fellowship)* [12051]

Pete Wilson Journalism Scholarship *(Graduate, Undergraduate/Scholarship)* [9478]

Saul T. Wilson, Jr. Internship *(Graduate, Undergraduate/Internship)* [11301]

Bob Wilson Legacy Scholarships *(Undergraduate/ Scholarship)* [2810]

Arthur N. Wilson, MD, Scholarships *(Undergraduate/ Scholarship)* [1113]

Michael Wilson Scholarships *(Undergraduate/Scholarship)* [151]

Winston Build Your Future Scholarship *(Graduate, Undergraduate, Vocational/Occupational/Scholarship)* [9963]

David A. Winston Health Policy Scholarship *(Graduate/Scholarship)* [2307]

The Winston-Salem Foundation Scholarship *(Undergraduate/Scholarship)* [12099]

Winterthur Research Fellowships *(Graduate/Fellowship)* [12101]

Wirefly.com Scholarhip: Wireless Technology and Society *(Undergraduate, Graduate/Scholarship)* [12107]

Wisconsin Laboratory Association Graduate Student Scholarships *(Graduate/Scholarship)* [12123]

WLA Scholarships *(Undergraduate, Graduate/Scholarship)* [12124]

Wisconsin Laboratory Association Undergraduate University Student Scholarships *(Undergraduate/ Scholarship)* [12125]

Wisconsin Teacher of the Visually Impaired Loan *(Undergraduate, Graduate/Loan)* [10814]

WLA Conference Attendance Grants *(Undergraduate, Professional development/Grant)* [11896]

WMSHP Scholarship *(Graduate/Scholarship)* [11985]

Paul R. Wolf Memorial Scholarships *(Graduate/ Scholarship)* [2012]

Emil Wolf Outstanding Student Paper Competition *(Graduate, Undergraduate/Award)* [8680]

The Wolf Trap Accounting Internship Program *(Graduate, Other, Undergraduate/Internship)* [12127]

Wolf Trap's Grants for High School Performing Arts Teachers *(Other/Grant)* [12128]

Nona Hobbs Wolfe Memorial Scholarship *(Undergraduate/Scholarship)* [6483]

Eleanor M. Wolfson Memorial Scholarship Fund *(Undergraduate/Scholarship)* [4607]

Wendy Y. Wolfson Memorial Scholarship Fund *(Undergraduate/Scholarship)* [4608]

Woman's Club of Nashville Scholarship Endowment Fund *(Undergraduate/Scholarship)* [3649]

Women In Defense HORIZONS Scholarship *(Graduate, Undergraduate/Scholarship)* [12133]

Women In Need Scholarships *(Undergraduate/ Scholarship)* [4306]

Women In Transition Scholarships *(Undergraduate/ Scholarship)* [4307]

Women Techmakers Udacity Scholarship *(Graduate, Undergraduate/Scholarship)* [5048]

Women of Today's Manufacturing Scholarship *(Undergraduate/Scholarship)* [3697]

Women of WSAJ Bar Preparation Scholarship *(Undergraduate/Scholarship)* [11904]

Women's Army Corps Veterans Association Scholarships *(Undergraduate/Scholarship)* [12153]

Women's Club of Grand Haven Scholarship *(Undergraduate/Scholarship)* [5114]

Women's Jewelry Association Member Grants *(Professional development/Grant)* [12163]

Women's Leadership in Agriculture Scholarship *(Undergraduate/Scholarship)* [8578]

Women's Leadership Training Grant *(Advanced Professional, Professional development/Grant)* [10557]

Women's Overseas and Service League Scholarships for Women *(Undergraduate/Scholarship)* [12168]

Wood County Bar Association Memorial Scholarship *(Graduate/Scholarship)* [8888]

Wood County Technical/Caperton Center Scholarship *(Undergraduate/Scholarship)* [8889]

Wood Fruitticher Grocery Company, Inc. Scholarships *(Graduate, Undergraduate/Scholarship)* [222]

Rolla F. Wood Graduate Scholarships *(Graduate, Undergraduate/Scholarship)* [9105]

Woodex Bearing Company Scholarship *(Undergraduate/Scholarship)* [4921]

Woodrow Wilson International Center for Scholars Fellowships *(Doctorate, Postdoctorate/Fellowship)* [12043]

Woodrow Wilson-Rockefeller Brothers Fund Fellowships for Aspiring Teachers of Color *(Undergraduate/Fellowship)* [12052]

Betsy B. Woodward Scholarships *(Undergraduate/ Scholarship)* [2182]

Patty Wooten Scholarships *(Professional development/Scholarship, Award, Recognition)* [2055]

Worcester District Medical Society Scholarship Fund *(Undergraduate/Scholarship)* [12188]

Work Ethic Scholarship *(Vocational/Occupational, Two Year College/Scholarship)* [7384]

John W. Work III Memorial Foundation Scholarship Fund *(Undergraduate/Scholarship)* [3650]

Working for Farmers' Success Scholarships *(Undergraduate/Scholarship)* [3240]

Worldstudio AIGA Scholarships *(Graduate, Undergraduate/Scholarship)* [12205]

Worthy Gemological Scholarships *(Undergraduate/ Scholarship)* [12211]

Wozumi Family Scholarships *(Undergraduate/Scholarship)* [9318]

WRI Education Foundation Scholarships - Graduate *(Graduate/Scholarship)* [12103]

WRI Education Foundation Scholarships - High School Seniors *(Undergraduate/Scholarship)* [12104]

WRI Education Foundation Scholarships - Undergraduate *(Undergraduate/Scholarship)* [12105]

WSAJ American Justice Essay Scholarships *(Undergraduate/Scholarship)* [11905]

WSAJ Diversity Bar Preparation Scholarship *(Undergraduate/Scholarship)* [11906]

WSAJ Presidents' Scholarships *(Undergraduate/ Scholarship)* [11907]

WSGC Scholarships for Incoming Freshmen *(Undergraduate/Scholarship)* [11902]

WSSA Student Paper Competition *(Undergraduate, Graduate/Award, Monetary)* [11987]

WTVD Scholarship *(Undergraduate/Scholarship)* [11217]

WYCUP Scholarship Program *(Other/Scholarship)* [12196]

Wyeth Foundation Predoctoral Fellowship *(Postdoctorate/Fellowship)* [10222]

Margaret Wyeth Scholarships *(Undergraduate/ Scholarship)* [3698]

Xavier Community-Engaged Fellowships *(Undergraduate/Fellowship)* [12227]

Xavier University Presidential Scholarships (Undergraduate/Scholarship) [12228]
Xavier University ROTC Scholarships - Air Force ROTC (Undergraduate/Scholarship) [12229]
Xavier University ROTC Scholarships - Army ROTC (Undergraduate/Scholarship) [12230]
Xavier University Williams Scholarships (Undergraduate/Scholarship) [12231]
Reverend H. John and Asako Yamashita Memorial Scholarship (Graduate/Scholarship) [6254]
Yankee Clipper Contest Club Youth Scholarship (Undergraduate/Scholarship) [1967]
The YASME Foundation Scholarship (Undergraduate/Scholarship) [1968]
Minoru Yasui Memorial Scholarship (Graduate/Scholarship) [6255]
Willa Yeck Memorial Scholarship Fund (Undergraduate/Scholarship) [7108]
Gary Yoshimura Scholarship (Undergraduate/Scholarship) [9439]
Young Birder Scholarships (Undergraduate/Scholarship, Monetary) [695]
Young Investigators Achievement Award (Advanced Professional, Professional development, Graduate/Grant) [6331]
Lisa Zaken Award For Excellence (Graduate, Undergraduate/Award, Monetary) [5838]
Aram Zakian Memorial Fund Scholarship (Undergraduate/Scholarship) [1906]
Araxie Zakian Memorial Grant (Undergraduate/Scholarship) [1907]
Dr. Marie E. Zakrzewski Medical Scholarships (Doctorate/Scholarship) [6607]
Pedro Zamora Young Leaders Scholarship (Undergraduate, Graduate/Scholarship) [7588]
Charles Zarigian, Esq. Memorial Award (Undergraduate/Scholarship) [1908]
George Zartarian Memorial Grant (Undergraduate/Scholarship) [1909]
The Zebra "Show Off Your Stripes" Scholarship (Undergraduate, Graduate, Vocational/Occupational, Community College/Scholarship) [12403]
Zelda Walling Vicha Memorial Scholarship (Undergraduate/Scholarship) [1540]
Zelus Recovery College Scholarship (Undergraduate, Graduate/Scholarship) [12407]
Zenko Family Scholarship (Undergraduate/Scholarship) [5115]
Zenon C. R. Hansen Leadership Scholarship (Undergraduate/Scholarship) [7861]
Zeta Chapter Memorial Award (Undergraduate/Award) [3699]
Zeta Phi Beta General Undergraduate Scholarship (Undergraduate/Scholarship) [12416]
Zeta Phi Beta Sorority General Graduate Fellowships (Graduate/Fellowship) [12417]
Zeta Sigma Project 2000 Scholarship (Undergraduate/Scholarship) [6484]
Zimmermann Scholarship (Graduate/Scholarship) [10898]
Lorraine Zitone Memorial Scholarship Fund (Undergraduate/Scholarship) [7109]
Amelia Zollner IPPR/UCL Internship Award (Undergraduate/Internship) [5855]
Zumper Apartments Scholarship (College, High School/Scholarship) [12425]

UNITED STATES (BY REGION)

Central Region
Markley Scholarship (Undergraduate, Graduate/Scholarship) [7623]

Eastern States
Diversity Scholars Awards (Undergraduate/Award, Recognition) [3810]

Mid Atlantic Region
Tese Caldarelli Memorial Scholarship (Graduate, Undergraduate/Scholarship) [7622]
NACA Mid Atlantic Higher Education Research Scholarships (Master's/Scholarship) [7625]

Zagunis Student Leader Scholarship (Graduate, Undergraduate/Scholarship) [7633]

Mid-Western States
Diversity Scholars Awards (Undergraduate/Award, Recognition) [3810]

New England States
Dvora Brodie Scholarships (Graduate, Postgraduate, Undergraduate/Scholarship) [5447]
Elson T. Killam Memorial Scholarship (Undergraduate, Graduate/Scholarship) [8249]
NEEBC Scholarship Award (Undergraduate, Graduate/Scholarship) [8244]
NELA Conference Scholarships (All/Scholarship) [8246]
Shaw-Worth Memorial Scholarship (Undergraduate/Scholarship) [5638]
Switzer Environmental Fellowship (Graduate/Fellowship) [9721]

Southeastern States
Leighton M. Ballew Directing Scholarship (Undergraduate/Scholarship) [10635]
Marian A. Smith Costume Scholarship Award (Graduate/Scholarship) [10636]
Polly Holliday Scholarship Award (Undergraduate/Scholarship, Monetary) [10637]
Robert Porterfield Graduate Scholarship (Graduate/Scholarship) [10638]
Southeastern Theatre Conference Secondary School Scholarship (Undergraduate/Scholarship) [10640]
William E. Wilson Scholarship (Graduate/Scholarship) [10641]

Southern States
CANS/SNRS Dissertation Research Grant (Doctorate/Grant) [10658]
Diversity Scholars Awards (Undergraduate/Award, Recognition) [3810]

Southwestern States
Jones-Lovich Grants in Southwestern Herpetology (Master's, Doctorate/Grant) [5500]

U.S. Territories
Barbara A. Cooley Master's Scholarship (Master's/Scholarship, Award, Monetary) [10348]
Birmingham-Southern College Eagle Scout Scholarships (Undergraduate/Scholarship) [7845]
Bill Kane Undergraduate Scholarship (Undergraduate/Scholarship, Award, Monetary) [10349]
Klingenstein Fellowships in the Neurosciences (Doctorate, Master's/Fellowship) [6566]
National MS Society New Jersey Metro Chapter Scholarship Program (Undergraduate/Scholarship) [8015]
OAS Scholarships for Professional Development - The ABC of Telecommunications (Professional development/Scholarship) [8735]
Alice Southworth Schulman, Class of 1954, Simmons Scholarships for Unitarian Universalist Women (Undergraduate/Scholarship) [11255]

Western States
Diversity Scholars Awards (Undergraduate/Award, Recognition) [3810]
IMS AWWA Graduate Science and Engineering Scholarships (Graduate/Scholarship) [5895]
Western District fellowship (Graduate/Fellowship) [5866]

UNITED STATES (BY STATE)

Alabama
ACHE/American Legion Auxiliary Scholarship Program (Undergraduate/Scholarship) [205]

ACHE Junior and Community College Athletic Scholarship Program (Undergraduate/Scholarship) [206]
ACHE Junior and Community College Performing Arts Scholarship Program (Undergraduate/Scholarship) [207]
ACHE Police Officer's and Firefighter's Survivors Educational Assistance Program (POFSEAP) (Undergraduate/Scholarship) [208]
ACHE Senior Adult Scholarship Program (Undergraduate/Scholarship) [209]
ACHE Two-Year College Academic Scholarship Program (Undergraduate/Scholarship) [210]
AISC/Southern Association of Steel Fabricators Scholarships (Undergraduate, Master's/Scholarship) [1054]
Alabama Gi Dependents' Educational Benefit Program (Undergraduate/Scholarship) [211]
Alabama National Guard Educational Assistance Program (Undergraduate/Scholarship) [212]
Alabama Power Scholarships (Undergraduate/Scholarship) [8500]
Alabama Scholarships for Dependents of Blind Parents (Undergraduate/Scholarship) [213]
Alabama Student Assistance Program (ASAP) (Undergraduate/Scholarship, Grant) [214]
Alabama Student Grant Program (Undergraduate/Grant) [215]
American Legion Florence/Lauderdale Post 11 Scholarship (Undergraduate, Community College/Scholarship) [8501]
Diana Ashe-Clayton Memorial Scholarship (Undergraduate/Scholarship) [8502]
Barry "Tyler" Rhea Memorial Scholarship (Undergraduate/Scholarship) [8503]
Birmingham-Southern College Eagle Scout Scholarships (Undergraduate/Scholarship) [7845]
Billy Bowling Memorial Scholarship (Undergraduate/Scholarship) [8504]
Leon Bradley Scholarship Program (Undergraduate/Scholarship) [638]
Calhoun Valedictorian, Salutatorian/Top 5 Scholarships (Other/Scholarship) [2777]
Cecil Earl Clapp, Sr. Memorial Scholarship (Undergraduate/Scholarship) [8505]
Marvin E. Daly Memorial Scholarship (Undergraduate/Scholarship) [8506]
Ashley Darby Memorial Scholarship (Community College, Undergraduate/Scholarship) [8507]
EJI Justice Fellowship (Graduate, Postgraduate, Professional development/Fellowship) [4434]
Edward Fennel Mauldin Endowed Scholarship (Undergraduate, Community College/Scholarship) [8509]
GIST - Mattie Lou Gist Memoral Scholarship Endowment (Undergraduate, Community College/Scholarship) [8510]
GIST - Orben F. Gist Memorial Scholarship Endowment (Undergraduate, Community College/Scholarship) [8511]
Joshua "Josh" Green Memorial Scholarship Endowment (Undergraduate, Community College/Scholarship) [8512]
Homajean Grisham Memorial Scholarship (Undergraduate/Scholarship) [8513]
Shelby Grissom Memorial Scholarship (Undergraduate, Community College/Scholarship) [8514]
Gulf Coast Hurricane Scholarship (Undergraduate/Scholarship) [10488]
Harriet Erich Graduate Fellowship (Graduate/Fellowship) [4002]
Howell Heflin Memorial Scholarship (Undergraduate/Scholarship) [8515]
Walston and Jewel Hester Memorial Scholarship Endowment (Undergraduate, Community College/Scholarship) [8516]
Esther McAfee Flippo Hunt Memorial Scholarship (Undergraduate/Scholarship) [8517]
ICS Scholarship (Undergraduate/Scholarship) [8518]
Broughton Isom Memorial Scholarship (Undergraduate/Scholarship) [8519]
Justice Janie L. Shores Scholarship (Undergraduate/Scholarship) [227]
Franklin A. Lenfesty Memorial Scholarship (Undergraduate/Scholarship) [8520]

Lockheed Martin Scholarship *(Undergraduate/Scholarship)* [8521]

Gertie S. Lowe Nursing Scholarship Awards *(Undergraduate/Scholarship)* [3659]

Bill Lucas Memorial Scholarship Endowment *(Undergraduate, Community College/Scholarship)* [8522]

The Medalist Club Post Graduate Scholarship *(Postgraduate/Scholarship)* [7203]

Muscle Shoals Kiwanis Club/Wal-mart *(Undergraduate/Scholarship)* [8523]

Norfolk Southern Foundation Scholarships *(Undergraduate/Scholarship)* [1329]

Northwest-Shoals Community College Fine Arts Scholarships - Art *(Undergraduate/Scholarship)* [8527]

Northwest-Shoals Community College Fine Arts Scholarships - Drama *(Undergraduate/Scholarship)* [8528]

Northwest-Shoals Community College Fine Arts Scholarships - Music *(Undergraduate/Scholarship)* [8529]

Northwest-Shoals Community College Independent Computer Scholarships *(Undergraduate/Scholarship)* [8531]

Northwest-Shoals Community College Student Activities Scholarships *(Undergraduate/Scholarship)* [8532]

NW-SCC Faculty and Staff Scholarship *(Undergraduate/Scholarship)* [8533]

NW-SCC General Foundation Scholarship *(Undergraduate/Scholarship)* [8534]

Regions Riding Forward Scholarship Essay Contest *(Undergraduate, High School/Scholarship)* [9618]

Barry "Tyler" Rhea Memorial Scholarship *(Undergraduate, Community College/Scholarship)* [8535]

Simms Scholarship *(Undergraduate, Community College/Scholarship)* [8537]

J. Craig and Page T. Smith Scholarship *(Undergraduate/Scholarship)* [10186]

Southern Section A&WMA Scholarships *(Graduate/Scholarship)* [10668]

Karen Thompson Memorial Scholarship *(Undergraduate, Community College/Scholarship)* [8539]

UAB Health Policy Fellowship *(Graduate, Master's, Doctorate/Scholarship)* [11430]

VFW Post 5140/Paul W. Shockley Sr. Memorial Scholarship *(Undergraduate/Scholarship)* [8541]

Joseph W. Wade Memorial Scholarship Endowment *(Undergraduate, Community College/Scholarship)* [8542]

Wayne County Bank Scholarship *(Undergraduate/Scholarship)* [8543]

William Verbon Black Scholarship *(Undergraduate/Scholarship)* [228]

Alaska

Accounting Club Scholarship *(Undergraduate/Scholarship)* [11469]

Alaska Aerospace Development Corporation Scholarships *(Undergraduate/Scholarship)* [11433]

Alaska Native Medical Center Auxiliary Scholarships *(Undergraduate/Scholarship)* [11434]

Alaska Press Club Scholarships *(Undergraduate/Scholarship)* [11435]

Mike Ardaw Scholarships *(Undergraduate/Scholarship)* [11436]

Elaine Atwood Scholarship *(Undergraduate, Graduate/Scholarship)* [11470]

Audrey Loftus Memorial Scholarship *(University/Scholarship)* [11516]

Dr. Jon Baker Memorial Scholarship *(Other/Scholarship)* [11471]

UAA Michael Baring-Gould Memorial Scholarship *(Graduate, Undergraduate/Scholarship)* [11472]

Lawrence Bayer Business Administration Scholarships *(Undergraduate/Scholarship)* [11437]

Charles E. Behlke Engineering Memorial Scholarships *(Undergraduate/Scholarship)* [11438]

Mark A. Beltz Scholarship *(Graduate, Undergraduate/Scholarship)* [11473]

Bill and Nell Biggs Scholarship *(Undergraduate/Scholarship)* [11508]

Bolick Foreign Student Scholarships *(Undergraduate/Scholarship)* [11439]

Dr. Betty J. Boyd-Beu and Edwin G. Beu, Jr. Scholarships *(Undergraduate/Scholarship)* [11440]

Pat Brakke Political Science Scholarship *(Undergraduate/Scholarship)* [11474]

Bunnell Scholarships *(Undergraduate/Scholarship)* [11441]

Loyal D. Burkett Memorial Scholarships *(Undergraduate/Scholarship)* [11442]

Lyle Carlson Wildlife Management Scholarships *(Undergraduate/Scholarship)* [11443]

Emi Chance for Aspiring Artists Scholarship *(Undergraduate/Scholarship)* [11475]

Mable B. Crawford Memorial Scholarships *(Undergraduate/Scholarship)* [11444]

CTC Culinary Arts Scholarship Endowment *(Undergraduate, Vocational/Occupational/Scholarship)* [11162]

APTRA-Clete Roberts/Kathryn Dettman Memorial Journalism Scholarship *(Undergraduate/Scholarship)* [2022]

Patricia Hughes Eastaugh Teaching Scholarship *(Undergraduate/Scholarship)* [11445]

Edward Rollin Clinton Memorial for Music Scholarship *(Undergraduate/Scholarship)* [11476]

Excellence in Geographic Information Systems Scholarships *(Graduate/Scholarship)* [11446]

Fairbanks Chapter Legacy Scholarship *(Undergraduate/Scholarship)* [11517]

Lydia Fohn-Hansen/Lola Hill Memorial Scholarships *(Undergraduate, Graduate/Scholarship)* [11447]

Michael D. Ford Memorial Scholarship *(Graduate, Undergraduate/Scholarship)* [11477]

Johnny & Sarah Frank Scholarships *(Undergraduate/Scholarship)* [11448]

Jan and Glenn Fredericks Scholarship *(Graduate, Undergraduate/Scholarship)* [11478]

Charles F. Gould Endowment Scholarships *(Undergraduate/Scholarship)* [11449]

Governor William A. Egan Award *(Undergraduate/Award)* [11480]

Ken Gray Scholarship *(Undergraduate/Scholarship)* [11481]

Patty Hamilton Early Childhood Development Scholarships *(Undergraduate/Scholarship)* [11450]

Lenore and George Hedla Accounting Scholarship *(Undergraduate/Scholarship)* [11482]

John Henderson Endowment Scholarships *(Undergraduate/Scholarship)* [11451]

Donald Wills Jacobs Scholarships *(Undergraduate/Scholarship)* [11452]

Jay Hammond Memorial Scholarship *(Graduate/Scholarship)* [11518]

Jim Doogan Memorial Scholarship *(Undergraduate/Scholarship)* [11519]

Kilbuck Family Native American Scholarship *(Undergraduate/Scholarship)* [2484]

Chris L. Kleinke Scholarship *(Graduate/Scholarship)* [11483]

Iver and Cora Knapstad Scholarships *(Undergraduate/Scholarship)* [11453]

Kris Knudson Memorial Scholarship *(Graduate, Undergraduate/Scholarship)* [11484]

Arlene Kuhner Memorial Scholarship *(Undergraduate/Scholarship)* [11485]

Austin E. Lathrop Scholarships *(Undergraduate/Scholarship)* [11454]

Franklin M. Leach Scholarships *(Undergraduate/Scholarship)* [11455]

William C. Leary Memorial Emergency Services Scholarship *(Undergraduate, Vocational/Occupational/Scholarship)* [11163]

Dave McCloud Aviation Memorial Scholarships *(Undergraduate/Scholarship)* [11456]

Melissa J. Wolf Accounting Scholarship *(Undergraduate/Scholarship)* [11486]

Molly Ann Mishler Memorial Scholarships *(College/Scholarship)* [11457]

Muriel Hannah Scholarship in Art *(Undergraduate, Graduate/Scholarship)* [11487]

Andrew Nerland Scholarships *(Undergraduate/Scholarship)* [11458]

Maureen E. Nolan-Cahill Memorial Scholarship *(Undergraduate/Scholarship)* [11459]

Don and Jan O'Dowd/SAA Statewide Scholarships *(Undergraduate/Scholarship)* [11460]

Diane Olsen Memorial Scholarship *(Undergraduate/Scholarship)* [11488]

Alvin G. Ott Fish & Wildlife Scholarship *(Undergraduate/Scholarship)* [11461]

Pat and Cliff Rogers Nursing Scholarship *(Undergraduate/Scholarship)* [11509]

Pignalberi Public Policy Scholarship *(Graduate/Scholarship)* [11489]

Pt. Lay Memorial Scholarships *(Undergraduate/Scholarship)* [11462]

April Relyea Scholarship *(Graduate, Undergraduate/Scholarship)* [11490]

A.D. Al and Maxine Robertson Memorial Scholarship *(Undergraduate/Scholarship)* [11463]

Dr. Orrin Rongstad Wildlife Scholarship *(Undergraduate/Scholarship)* [11510]

RRANN Program Scholarship *(Undergraduate/Scholarship)* [11491]

Russian Student Scholarship *(Undergraduate/Scholarship)* [11511]

Brown Schoenheit Memorial Scholarship *(Undergraduate/Scholarship)* [11492]

Clair Shirey Scholarships *(Undergraduate/Scholarship)* [11464]

Sheri Stears Education Scholarship *(Undergraduate/Scholarship)* [11494]

Sturgulewski Family Scholarship *(Graduate, Undergraduate/Scholarship)* [11495]

UAA Alaska Kidney Foundation Scholarship *(Graduate, Undergraduate/Scholarship)* [11496]

UAA Alumni Association Scholarship *(Undergraduate/Scholarship)* [11497]

UAA Ardell French Memorial Scholarship *(Undergraduate/Scholarship)* [11498]

UAA College of Business and Public Policy Scholarships - American Marketing Association & F.X. Dale Tran Memorial Scholarship *(Graduate, Undergraduate/Scholarship)* [11499]

UAA Eveline Schuster Memorial Award/Scholarship *(Graduate, Undergraduate/Scholarship)* [11500]

UAA Friends of the Performing Arts Scholarship *(Undergraduate/Scholarship)* [11501]

UAA GCI Scholarship *(Undergraduate/Scholarship)* [11502]

UAA Kimura Scholarship Fund for Illustration *(Undergraduate/Scholarship)* [11503]

UAA Kimura Scholarship Fund for Photography *(Undergraduate/Scholarship)* [11504]

UAA Quanterra Scholarship *(Master's, Doctorate/Scholarship)* [11505]

UAF Alumni Association Scholarship *(Undergraduate/Scholarship)* [11520]

UAF College of Liberal Arts - Anchorage Daily News Journalism Awards *(Undergraduate/Scholarship)* [11514]

University of Alaska Regents' Scholarship *(Undergraduate/Scholarship)* [11512]

Wells Fargo Career Scholarship *(Undergraduate/Scholarship)* [11506]

Guy A. Woodings Scholarships *(Undergraduate/Scholarship)* [11465]

Ralph Yetka Memorial Scholarships *(Undergraduate/Scholarship)* [11466]

Joan C. Yoder Memorial Nursing Scholarships *(Undergraduate/Scholarship)* [11467]

Arizona

Marvin A. Andrews Scholarships/Internships *(Graduate, Undergraduate/Internship, Scholarship)* [1805]

Arizona Hydrological Society Academic Scholarships *(Graduate, Undergraduate/Scholarship)* [1808]

ASCPA High School Scholarships *(Graduate/Scholarship, Monetary)* [1816]

ASCPA Private University Scholarships *(Master's, Graduate/Scholarship)* [1817]

Chapter 67 - Phoenix Scholarship *(Undergraduate/Scholarship)* [10397]

APTRA-Clete Roberts/Kathryn Dettman Memorial Journalism Scholarship *(Undergraduate/Scholarship)* [2022]

Charles A. Esser Memorial Scholarships *(Graduate/Scholarship)* [1806]

Gail Goodell Folsom Memorial Scholarships *(Undergraduate/Scholarship)* [7542]

The San Diego Foundation Community Scholarship II *(Undergraduate/Scholarship)* [9849]

Leo and Trinidad Sanchez Scholarships *(Undergraduate/Scholarship)* [10138]

Southern California Lambda Medical Student Scholarships *(Undergraduate, Graduate/Scholarship)* [10650]

SouthWest Sun Solar $500 Scholarship *(Undergraduate/Scholarship)* [10711]

Special Events Internships - Los Angeles *(Undergraduate, Graduate/Internship)* [4988]

SPROWT Scholarship for Women *(Undergraduate/Scholarship)* [5201]

Lee Summer Student Fellowship *(Undergraduate, Master's/Fellowship)* [10652]

Superior District Legislative Mentoring Student Grants *(Undergraduate/Grant)* [2837]

Superior District Legislative Mentoring Student Grants RT to DC *(Undergraduate/Grant)* [2838]

Switzer Environmental Fellowship *(Graduate/Fellowship)* [9721]

Robert M. Takasugi Public Interest Fellowships *(Postgraduate/Fellowship)* [10913]

Thomas and Glenna Trimble Endowed Scholarship *(Graduate/Scholarship)* [9028]

The Honorable Raymond Thompson Endowed Scholarship *(Undergraduate/Scholarship)* [9029]

UC MEXUS-CICESE Graduate Student Short-Term Research and Training Program *(Master's, Doctorate, Postdoctorate/Grant)* [11539]

UCLA-CSW Travel Grants *(Graduate, Undergraduate/Grant)* [11542]

UCSD Black Alumni Scholarship for Arts and Humanities *(Undergraduate/Scholarship)* [9857]

UCSD Black Alumni Scholarships for Engineering, Mathematics and Science *(Undergraduate/Scholarship)* [9858]

U.S. Bank Scholarships *(Undergraduate/Scholarship)* [9859]

USC Latino Alumni Association Scholarships *(Graduate, Undergraduate/Scholarship)* [11783]

Winifred Van Hagen/Rosalind Cassidy Scholarship Award *(Undergraduate, Graduate/Recognition, Award)* [2783]

Warren and Rosalie Gummow Endowed Scholarship *(Undergraduate/Scholarship)* [9030]

Marjorie Rose Warren Scholarship *(Undergraduate/Scholarship)* [9863]

Webb Family Grant *(Postdoctorate/Scholarship)* [3200]

Weissbuch Family Scholarship *(Undergraduate/Scholarship)* [9864]

Robert L. Wiegel Scholarship for Coastal Studies *(Graduate/Scholarship)* [9865]

Wilma Motley Memorial California Merit Scholarship *(Undergraduate/Scholarship)* [862]

WLALA Scholarships *(Postgraduate/Scholarship)* [12144]

Woodrow Judkins Endowed Scholarship *(Undergraduate/Scholarship)* [9032]

Colorado

AISC/Rocky Mountain Steel Construction Association Scholarships *(Undergraduate, Master's/Scholarship)* [1053]

CASFM-Ben Urbonas Scholarship *(Graduate/Scholarship)* [3524]

Colorado Nurses Association: Virginia Paulson Memorial Scholarship *(Graduate, Undergraduate/Scholarship)* [3532]

CSCPA College Scholarships *(Graduate, Undergraduate/Scholarship)* [3539]

CSCPA Sophomore Scholarships *(Undergraduate/Scholarship)* [3541]

Denver Scholarship Foundation General Scholarship Fund *(Graduate/Scholarship)* [4053]

APTRA-Clete Roberts/Kathryn Dettman Memorial Journalism Scholarship *(Undergraduate/Scholarship)* [2022]

Dorothy Mountain Memorial Scholarship *(Graduate/Scholarship)* [6922]

Dwight A. Hamilton Scottish Rite Foundation of Colorado Graduate Scholarship in Speech-Language Pathology *(Graduate/Scholarship)* [9984]

El Pomar Fellowship *(Graduate/Fellowship)* [4330]

Lola Fehr: Nightingale Scholarships *(Graduate, Undergraduate/Scholarship)* [3534]

William Harrison Gill Education Fund *(Undergraduate/Scholarship)* [2480]

Griffin Foundation Scholarships *(Undergraduate/Scholarship)* [5243]

Harry Walts Memorial Graduate Scholarship *(Graduate/Scholarship)* [6923]

Rich Herbert Memorial Scholarship *(Undergraduate, Master's, Doctorate/Scholarship)* [1630]

H.M. Muffly Memorial Scholarship *(Graduate, Undergraduate/Scholarship)* [3535]

Roy Anderson Memorial Scholarship *(Graduate, Undergraduate/Scholarship)* [3536]

Thomas J. Slocum Memorial Scholarships to Redstone College *(Undergraduate/Scholarship)* [191]

Patty Walter Memorial Scholarships *(Graduate, Undergraduate/Scholarship)* [3537]

Connecticut

Frederick G. Adams Scholarship Fund *(Undergraduate/Scholarship)* [5312]

AMLN Scholarships for Arab American Students *(Graduate, Undergraduate/Scholarship)* [1127]

Brian Cummins Memorial Scholarship *(Undergraduate/Scholarship)* [5317]

C. Rodney Demarest Memorial Scholarship *(Undergraduate/Scholarship)* [5318]

Chopivsky Fellowships *(Graduate/Fellowship)* [11889]

The College Club of Hartford Scholarships *(Undergraduate/Scholarship)* [5319]

Dorothy E. Hofmann Pembroke Scholarship *(Undergraduate/Scholarship)* [5325]

Priscilla Green Scholarships *(Undergraduate/Scholarship)* [3894]

Kennedy T. Friend Scholarship Fund *(Graduate, Undergraduate/Scholarship)* [348]

Martin Luther King Jr. Scholarships *(Graduate/Scholarship)* [6558]

Mary Main Memorial Scholarship *(Undergraduate/Scholarship)* [5339]

Mead Leadership Fellowships *(Professional development/Fellowship)* [8482]

Smith Family Awards Program for Excellence in Biomedical Research *(Advanced Professional, Professional development/Award)* [5443]

Sylvia Parkinson Fund *(Undergraduate/Scholarship)* [5344]

Delaware

Mead Leadership Fellowships *(Professional development/Fellowship)* [8482]

Norfolk Southern Foundation Scholarships *(Undergraduate/Scholarship)* [1329]

Richard and Patricia Hazel Minority Scholarship Award *(Undergraduate/Scholarship)* [3577]

District of Columbia

Abramson Scholarship *(Undergraduate/Scholarship)* [37]

Andrew Foster Scholarship *(Undergraduate/Scholarship)* [7720]

CAPAL Public Service Scholarships *(Graduate, Undergraduate/Scholarship)* [3734]

Charles A. Lindbergh Fellowships *(Graduate/Fellowship)* [10191]

CHCI Congressional Internship Program *(Undergraduate/Internship)* [3745]

CHCI Graduate Fellowship Program *(Graduate, Professional development/Fellowship)* [3746]

CHCI Public Policy Fellowships *(Professional development/Fellowship)* [3747]

Congressional and Business Leadership Awards *(Undergraduate/Scholarship)* [4837]

Dumbarton Oaks Fellowship *(Doctorate, Graduate/Fellowship)* [4222]

Dumbarton Oaks Junior Fellowship *(Graduate/Fellowship)* [4223]

Dumbarton Oaks Research Library and Collection Post-Doctoral Teaching Fellowships *(Postdoctorate/Fellowship)* [4232]

The Dwight D. Eisenhower/Ann Cook Whitman Washington, D.C. Scholarship Program *(Undergraduate/Scholarship)* [4961]

Guggenheim Fellowships *(Doctorate/Fellowship)* [10192]

ILSA Internships *(Undergraduate/Internship)* [6029]

Kislak Fellowship for the Study of the History and Cultures of the Early Americas *(Undergraduate, Graduate/Fellowship)* [6572]

Kluge Fellowship *(Doctorate, Graduate/Fellowship)* [6573]

David B. Larson Fellowships in Health and Spirituality *(Postdoctorate/Fellowship)* [6574]

Howard T. Markey Memorial Scholarship *(Undergraduate/Scholarship)* [4507]

Mead Leadership Fellowships *(Professional development/Fellowship)* [8482]

Perkins Coie 1L Political Law Diversity Fellowships *(Undergraduate/Fellowship)* [9040]

PETA Foundation Law Internship *(Graduate/Internship)* [8979]

Presidency Research Fund *(Graduate, Postdoctorate, Undergraduate, Professional development/Grant)* [1259]

Public Service Fellows Internship Program - Center for Government Leadership *(Undergraduate, Graduate/Internship)* [8904]

Public Service Fellows Internship Program - Education and Outreach *(Undergraduate, Graduate, Professional development/Internship)* [8905]

Public Service Fellows Internship Program - Government Transformation and Agency Partnerships *(Undergraduate, Graduate, Professional development/Internship)* [8906]

Public Service Internship Program - Communications *(Undergraduate, Graduate, Professional development/Internship)* [8908]

Public Service Internship Program - Government Affairs *(Undergraduate, Graduate, Professional development/Internship)* [8910]

Public Service Internship Program - Research and Program Evaluation Focus *(Undergraduate, Graduate, Professional development/Internship)* [8911]

Roland E. Murphy, O.Carm., Scholarship *(Undergraduate/Scholarship)* [3186]

Florida

Emily and Roland Abraham Educational Fund *(Undergraduate/Scholarship)* [3708]

AISC/Southern Association of Steel Fabricators Scholarships *(Undergraduate, Master's/Scholarship)* [1054]

Bill Bernbach Diversity Scholarships *(Undergraduate/Scholarship)* [510]

Beta Gamma Memorial Scholarship *(Undergraduate/Scholarship)* [4000]

Leon Bradley Scholarship Program *(Undergraduate/Scholarship)* [638]

Celler Legal P.A. Employment Skills Scholarship Program *(Undergraduate/Scholarship)* [3206]

Central Florida Jazz Society Scholarships *(Undergraduate/Scholarship)* [3242]

ChairScholars Florida Scholarship Program *(Undergraduate/Scholarship)* [3274]

Chip Johnson Memorial Scholarship Fund *(Undergraduate/Scholarship)* [10675]

Cuban American Bar Association Scholarships *(Professional development/Scholarship)* [3935]

D&A Florida Scholarships *(Undergraduate/Scholarship)* [10678]

The James H. Davis Memorial Scholarship *(Undergraduate, Graduate, Postgraduate/Scholarship)* [4638]

Drs. Ira and Udaya Dash Nursing Scholarship Fund *(Undergraduate, Graduate/Scholarship)* [10682]

FICPA Educational Foundation 1040K Race Scholarships *(Undergraduate/Scholarship, Award)* [4636]

FLAS Academic Year Fellowships *(Graduate, Undergraduate/Fellowship)* [11569]

Florida Education Fund McKnight Doctoral Fellowship *(Graduate/Fellowship)* [4629]

Florida Outdoor Writers Association Scholarships (FOWA) *(Undergraduate/Scholarship)* [4644]

Clay Ford Florida Board of Accountancy Minority Scholarships *(Undergraduate/Scholarship)* [4627]

Donald L. Frendberg Program *(Undergraduate, Vocational/Occupational/Scholarship)* [9609]

Gulf Coast Hurricane Scholarship *(Undergraduate/Scholarship)* [10488]

Judge William J. Nelson Scholarship Fund *(Undergraduate/Scholarship)* [10694]

Raymond W. Miller, PE Scholarships *(Undergraduate/Scholarship)* [4631]

Norfolk Southern Foundation Scholarships *(Undergraduate/Scholarship)* [1329]

North Florida Chapter Safety Education Scholarships *(Undergraduate/Scholarship)* [1570]

The Melissa Pellegrin Memorial Scholarship Fund *(Undergraduate, Graduate/Scholarship)* [8759]

Eric Primavera Memorial Scholarships *(Undergraduate/Scholarship)* [4632]

Regions Riding Forward Scholarship Essay Contest *(Undergraduate, High School/Scholarship)* [9618]

Edward S. Roth Scholarship *(Graduate, Undergraduate/Scholarship)* [10411]

ServiceMaster By Glenns Preparation Scholarship *(University, Undergraduate, Vocational/Occupational/Scholarship)* [10022]

Southern Scholarship Foundation Scholarships *(Undergraduate, Graduate, Postgraduate/Scholarship)* [10666]

William V. Storch Student Award *(Undergraduate, Graduate/Award)* [1632]

Study.com Scholarship Florida Students *(Undergraduate, College/Scholarship)* [10872]

Jacki Tuckfield Memorial Graduate Business Scholarship Fund *(Doctorate, Graduate, Master's/Scholarship)* [7299]

UF Center for Latin American Studies FLAS Summer Fellowships *(Master's, Graduate, Undergraduate/Award, Fellowship)* [11570]

Ted G. Wilson Memorial Scholarships *(Undergraduate/Scholarship)* [9338]

Georgia

AISC/Southern Association of Steel Fabricators Scholarships *(Undergraduate, Master's/Scholarship)* [1054]

Annual Eichholz Scholarship *(Graduate/Scholarship)* [4324]

Brenda S. Bank Educational Workshop Scholarship *(Undergraduate/Scholarship)* [10341]

Bill Bernbach Diversity Scholarships *(Undergraduate/Scholarship)* [510]

Leon Bradley Scholarship Program *(Undergraduate/Scholarship)* [638]

Anthony R. Dees Educational Workshop Scholarship *(Graduate/Scholarship)* [10342]

GACFE Scholarship Program *(Graduate, Undergraduate/Scholarship)* [2134]

George and Pearl Strickland Scholarship Fund *(Graduate, Undergraduate/Scholarship)* [3586]

Georgia Engineering Foundation Scholarships *(Graduate/Scholarship)* [4928]

Larry Gulley Scholarship *(Undergraduate/Scholarship)* [10343]

Connie and Robert T. Gunter Scholarship *(Undergraduate/Scholarship)* [10401]

Richard A. Hammill Scholarship Fund *(Undergraduate/Scholarship)* [1103]

Carroll Hart Scholarship *(Graduate/Scholarship)* [10344]

Gene Henson Scholarship *(Undergraduate/Scholarship)* [2340]

Philip R. Karr, III Scholarship Fund *(Graduate/Scholarship)* [4926]

Kenneth H. Breeden Scholarship *(Undergraduate/Scholarship)* [6658]

Durwood McAlister Scholarship *(Undergraduate/Scholarship)* [4935]

Morris Newspaper Corporation Scholarship *(Undergraduate/Scholarship)* [4936]

NERL Postdoctoral Research Program *(Postdoctorate, Advanced Professional, Professional development/Fellowship)* [11352]

The Edna A. Noblin Scholarship *(Undergraduate/Scholarship)* [6659]

Norfolk Southern Foundation Scholarships *(Undergraduate/Scholarship)* [1329]

Public Health Informatics Fellowship Program (PHIFP) *(Professional development, Master's, Graduate/Fellowship)* [11332]

Regions Riding Forward Scholarship Essay Contest *(Undergraduate, High School/Scholarship)* [9618]

William C. Rogers Scholarship *(Undergraduate/Scholarship)* [4937]

Southern Section A&WMA Scholarships *(Graduate/Scholarship)* [10668]

SREB-State Doctoral Scholars Program - Dissertation Award *(Doctorate/Scholarship, Award)* [10663]

SREB-State Doctoral Scholars Program - Doctoral Award *(Doctorate, Graduate/Scholarship)* [10664]

United Way Of Forsyth County Scholarship *(Other/Scholarship)* [6660]

Ted G. Wilson Memorial Scholarships *(Undergraduate/Scholarship)* [9338]

Guam

Thomas R. Camp Scholarships *(Graduate/Scholarship, Monetary)* [1639]

Larson Aquatic Research Support Scholarships (LARS) *(Graduate/Scholarship, Monetary, Recognition)* [1643]

Hawaii

AAUW Honolulu Branch Education Funds *(Undergraduate, Graduate, Master's/Scholarship)* [5376]

Asian Development Bank - Japan Scholarship Program *(Graduate, Master's/Scholarship)* [4261]

APTRA-Clete Roberts/Kathryn Dettman Memorial Journalism Scholarship *(Undergraduate/Scholarship)* [2022]

East-West Center Graduate Degree Fellowship *(Master's, Doctorate, Graduate/Fellowship)* [4262]

Blossom Kalama Evans Memorial Scholarship Fund *(Undergraduate, University, Four Year College, Two Year College/Scholarship)* [5398]

Ambassador Minerva Jean Falcon Hawaii Scholarship *(Undergraduate, Graduate, Two Year College, College, University/Scholarship)* [5399]

Isaac and Mary Harbottle Scholarship *(Graduate, Undergraduate/Scholarship)* [8927]

Hpgs Graduate Scholarships *(Graduate/Scholarship)* [5421]

HPGS Undergraduate Scholarships *(Undergraduate/Scholarship)* [5422]

Indonesian Directorate General of Higher Education Scholarships (DIKTI) *(Graduate/Scholarship)* [4263]

Arthur Jackman Scholarship *(Community College, Vocational/Occupational/Scholarship)* [5406]

Gladys Kamakakokalani 'Ainoa Brandt Scholarships *(Graduate, Undergraduate/Scholarship)* [8929]

Obuchi Student Scholarship *(Graduate/Scholarship)* [4264]

PATCH Early Childhood Education Scholarships *(Graduate/Scholarship)* [8915]

Seameo-Vietnam Scholarship Program *(Graduate/Scholarship)* [4265]

Albert and Dorothy Shigekuni Scholarship Fund *(Undergraduate/Scholarship)* [5412]

The Jane Suganuma Memorial Scholarship Fund *(Undergraduate, Graduate, University, College, Two Year College/Scholarship)* [5413]

Alan and Grace Tenn Scholarship Fund *(Undergraduate, Graduate/Scholarship)* [5414]

William S. Richardson Commemorative Scholarship *(Graduate/Scholarship)* [8934]

Clarence and Virginia Young Trust Scholarship *(Undergraduate/Scholarship)* [5416]

Idaho

Horatio Alger Idaho University Scholarships *(Undergraduate/Scholarship)* [5566]

Horatio Alger Lola and Duane Hagadone Idaho Scholarships *(Undergraduate/Scholarship)* [5570]

Alois and Marie Goldmann Scholarship *(Graduate/Scholarship)* [5675]

American Legion Boys/Girls State Scholarship *(High School/Scholarship)* [6782]

Banner Bank Business Scholarship *(Undergraduate/Scholarship)* [6783]

Coeur d'Alene Alumni Scholarship *(Undergraduate/Scholarship)* [6784]

Rob Copeland Memorial Scholarship *(Undergraduate/Scholarship)* [6785]

Rick Crane Group Real Estate Scholarship Fund *(Undergraduate/Scholarship)* [6786]

Mike Crapo Math and Science Scholarship Fund *(Undergraduate/Scholarship)* [5676]

Dave Lamb Scholarship *(Graduate/Scholarship)* [11912]

Dean A. Froehlich Endowed Scholarship *(Undergraduate/Scholarship)* [6787]

APTRA-Clete Roberts/Kathryn Dettman Memorial Journalism Scholarship *(Undergraduate/Scholarship)* [2022]

Eleanor Perry Memorial Endowed Scholarship *(Undergraduate/Scholarship)* [6789]

Elizabeth McKissick Memorial Scholarship *(Undergraduate/Scholarship)* [6790]

Eugene Northrup Scholarship *(Undergraduate/Scholarship)* [6791]

The Fisher-Clark Memorial Endowed Scholarship *(Undergraduate/Scholarship)* [6792]

Foundation Transfer Scholarship *(Undergraduate/Scholarship)* [6793]

William Harrison Gill Education Fund *(Undergraduate/Scholarship)* [2480]

Glen and Babs Carlson Endowed Scholarship *(Undergraduate/Scholarship)* [6794]

Gretchen Dimico Memorial Scholarship *(Undergraduate/Scholarship)* [6795]

Henderson Memorial Endowed Scholarship *(Undergraduate/Scholarship)* [6796]

Hinman-Jensen Endowed Scholarship *(Undergraduate/Scholarship)* [6797]

Frank and Gladys Hopkins Endowed Scholarships *(Undergraduate/Scholarship)* [6798]

ICAFS Idaho Graduate Student Scholarship *(Graduate/Scholarship)* [889]

ICAFS Idaho High School Student Scholarship *(Undergraduate/Scholarship)* [890]

ICAFS Idaho Undergraduate Student Scholarship *(Undergraduate/Scholarship)* [891]

Idaho Governor's Cup Scholarship *(Undergraduate/Scholarship)* [6799]

Idaho Nursery and Landscape Association Scholarships *(Undergraduate/Scholarship)* [5683]

Idaho Nursing and Health Professions Scholarship Fund *(Undergraduate/Scholarship)* [5677]

Idaho Opportunity Scholarship *(Undergraduate/Scholarship)* [10805]

Idaho Society of CPA's Scholarships *(Other/Scholarship)* [5678, 5685]

Irene Carlson Gnaedinger Memorial Scholarship *(Undergraduate/Scholarship)* [6800]

Jack M. & Mary Lou Gruber Scholarship *(Undergraduate/Scholarship)* [6801]

Jim Poore Memorial Scholarship Fund *(Undergraduate/Scholarship)* [5679]

Jimmy Guild Memorial Scholarship *(Undergraduate/Scholarship)* [6802]

John Streiff Memorial Scholarship *(Undergraduate/Scholarship)* [6803]

Kaia Lynn Markwalter Endowed Scholarship *(Undergraduate/Scholarship)* [6804]

Kenneth Rogers Memorial Scholarship *(Undergraduate/Scholarship)* [6805]

Laura Ann Peck Memorial Endowed Scholarship *(Undergraduate/Scholarship)* [6806]

Laura Moore Cunningham Foundation General Scholarship *(Undergraduate/Scholarship)* [6807]

LCSC Presidential Out-of-State Tuition Scholarships *(Undergraduate/Scholarship)* [6808]

LCSC Welding Club Scholarship *(Undergraduate/Scholarship)* [6809]

Lewis-Clark Coin Club Endowed Scholarship *(Undergraduate/Scholarship)* [6810]

Lewis-Clark State College Foundation Scholars *(Undergraduate/Scholarship)* [6811]

Lewis-Clark State College In-State Non-Traditional Student Scholarship *(Undergraduate/Scholarship)* [6812]

Military Order of the Purple Heart *(Undergraduate/Scholarship)* [6813]

Lewis-Clark State College Provost Scholarship *(Undergraduate/Scholarship)* [6814]

Lewiston Service League Memorial Scholarship *(Undergraduate/Scholarship)* [6815]

Margaret G. Johnson and Marge J. Stout Scholarship *(Undergraduate/Scholarship)* [6817]

Susan B. Martin Scholarship *(Graduate/Scholarship)* [892]

Odd Fellows Lodge #8 Endowed Scholarship *(Undergraduate/Scholarship)* [6818]

Robbie Miller Memorial Endowed Scholarship *(Undergraduate/Scholarship)* [6819]

Rosenberg-Ibarra Scholarships *(Graduate/Scholarship)* [9312]

Roger C. Sathre Memorial Scholarship Fund *(Graduate/Scholarship)* [5680]

Bill Sawyer Memorial Scholarship *(Undergraduate/Scholarship)* [6820]

Shinn Family Scholarship *(Undergraduate/Scholarship)* [6821]

Susan P. Schroeder Memorial Scholarship *(Undergraduate/Scholarship)* [6822]

Tschudy Family Scholarship *(Undergraduate/Scholarship)* [5687]

Washington City/County Management Association Scholarships *(Graduate/Scholarship)* [11885]

W. L. Shattuck Scholarship *(Undergraduate, Graduate, High School/Scholarship)* [5681]

Illinois

Allied Health Care Professional Scholarship *(Undergraduate/Scholarship)* [5711]

American Council of Engineering Companies of Illinois Scholarships *(Undergraduate, Postdoctorate/Scholarship)* [805]

Andrea Will Memorial Scholarship *(Undergraduate/Scholarship)* [10093]

Ava's Grace Scholarship Program *(Graduate, Undergraduate/Scholarship)* [9949]

James M. Banovetz Illinois Local Government Fellowships *(Graduate, Undergraduate/Fellowship)* [5698]

The Dora J. Beattie IBEA Scholarship *(Undergraduate/Scholarship)* [5695]

The Gloria Bousley Graduate Scholarship *(Graduate/Scholarship)* [5696]

Chapter 31 - Peoria Scholarship *(Undergraduate/Scholarship)* [10390]

CMSF Scholarship *(Graduate/Scholarship)* [3319]

Larry L. Etherton Scholarships *(Graduate, Undergraduate/Scholarship)* [1326]

Michael W. and Jean D. Franke Family Foundation Scholarships *(Graduate, Undergraduate/Scholarship)* [1327]

Graduate Student Fellowships *(Graduate/Fellowship)* [4547]

IAAI Scholarship Foundation Accounting Scholarships *(Undergraduate/Scholarship)* [5733]

Illinois Landscape Contractors Association Scholarships *(Undergraduate/Scholarship)* [5703]

Illinois Special Education Teacher Tuition Waiver Scholarship (SETTW) *(Undergraduate/Scholarship)* [5712]

Illinois Student Assistance Commission Medical Student Scholarship *(Undergraduate/Scholarship)* [5713]

Illinois Student Assistance Commission Nursing Education Scholarship *(Undergraduate, Graduate, College/Scholarship)* [5714]

ISPE Foundation Scholarship *(Undergraduate/Scholarship)* [5707]

Jewish Federation Academic Scholarship *(Graduate, Undergraduate/Scholarship)* [6310]

Arnold "Les" Larsen, FAIA, Memorial Scholarships *(Graduate/Scholarship)* [1010]

Minority Teachers of Illinois Scholarship (MTI) *(Undergraduate/Scholarship)* [5715]

Muddy Waters Scholarships *(Undergraduate, Graduate/Scholarship)* [2632]

Norfolk Southern Foundation Scholarships *(Undergraduate/Scholarship)* [1329]

Regions Riding Forward Scholarship Essay Contest *(Undergraduate, High School/Scholarship)* [9618]

Robert Esser Student Achievement Scholarship *(Graduate, Undergraduate/Scholarship)* [5701]

Edward S. Roth Scholarship *(Graduate, Undergraduate/Scholarship)* [10411]

Donald M. Wells Scholarships *(Undergraduate/Scholarship)* [5193]

Indiana

The Artist in Landscape Design Scholarship *(Undergraduate/Scholarship)* [8585]

Warren K. Brown Scholarship *(Undergraduate/Scholarship)* [1562]

Central Indiana Jim Kriner Memorial Scholarship *(Undergraduate/Scholarship)* [1563]

Chapter 56 - Ft. Wayne Scholarship *(Graduate, Undergraduate, Vocational/Occupational, Community College/Scholarship)* [10393]

Illinois Landscape Contractors Association Scholarships *(Undergraduate/Scholarship)* [5703]

Indiana Broadcasters Association College Scholarship Program *(Undergraduate/Scholarship)* [5750]

Indiana State University Academic Excellence Scholarship *(Undergraduate/Scholarship)* [5757]

Indiana State University Academic Promise Scholarships *(Undergraduate/Scholarship)* [5768]

Indiana State University Creative and Performing Arts Awards *(Undergraduate/Scholarship)* [5769]

Indiana State University Incentive Scholarship *(Undergraduate/Scholarship)* [5758]

Indiana State University President's Scholarships *(Undergraduate/Scholarship)* [5759]

Indiana State University Rural Health Scholarship *(Undergraduate/Scholarship)* [5760]

Indiana State University Transfer Student Scholarships *(Undergraduate/Scholarship)* [5761]

ISU Child of Alumni Book Voucher Awards *(Undergraduate/Scholarship)* [5770]

ISU Gongaware Scholarship *(Undergraduate/Scholarship)* [5762]

ISU Networks Scholarship *(Undergraduate/Scholarship)* [5763]

Clarence & Josephine Myers Undergraduate Scholarships *(Graduate, Undergraduate, Vocational/Occupational, Community College/Scholarship)* [10409]

Norfolk Southern Foundation Scholarships *(Undergraduate/Scholarship)* [1329]

Noyce Scholarships for Secondary Math and Science Education *(Undergraduate/Scholarship)* [5764]

Nicholas H. Noyes, Jr. Scholarship *(Undergraduate/Scholarship)* [6391]

Phi Theta Kappa Scholarship *(Undergraduate/Scholarship)* [5765]

Regions Riding Forward Scholarship Essay Contest *(Undergraduate, High School/Scholarship)* [9618]

Robert Esser Student Achievement Scholarship *(Graduate, Undergraduate/Scholarship)* [5701]

August M. Rocco Scholarship Fund *(Undergraduate/Scholarship)* [10788]

Roland E. Murphy, O.Carm., Scholarship *(Undergraduate/Scholarship)* [3186]

Esther Schlundt Memorial Scholarship Fund *(Graduate, Undergraduate/Scholarship)* [5754]

Sue Marsh Weller Memorial Scholarship Fund *(Graduate/Scholarship)* [5755]

Warren M. Anderson Scholarship *(Undergraduate/Scholarship)* [5766]

Iowa

William Stone Ayres Scholarship *(Graduate/Scholarship)* [4146]

Beverly Estate Scholarship *(Undergraduate/Scholarship)* [4147]

George and Mary Brammer Scholarship *(Undergraduate/Scholarship)* [4148]

CMSF Scholarship *(Graduate/Scholarship)* [3319]

Raymond DiPaglia Endowment Scholarship *(Undergraduate/Scholarship)* [4149]

Drake University Law School Law Opportunity Scholarship - Disadvantage *(Undergraduate/Scholarship)* [4152]

Drake University Law School Public Service Scholarships *(Undergraduate/Scholarship)* [4154]

Herman E. Elgar Memorial Scholarship *(Undergraduate/Scholarship)* [4156]

D.J. Fairgrave Education Trust *(Undergraduate/Scholarship)* [4157]

Leland Stanford Forrest Scholarship *(Undergraduate/Scholarship)* [4158]

Lex and Scott Hawkins Endowed Scholarship *(Undergraduate/Scholarship)* [4159]

Edward and Cora Hayes Scholarship *(Undergraduate/Scholarship)* [4160]

Annamae Heaps Law Scholarship *(Undergraduate/Scholarship)* [4161]

John M. Helmick Law Scholarship *(Undergraduate/Scholarship)* [4162]

Herbert Hoover Uncommon Student Award *(Undergraduate/Scholarship)* [5557]

Illinois Landscape Contractors Association Scholarships *(Undergraduate/Scholarship)* [5703]

Iowa Association of Electric Cooperatives - Electric Cooperative Pioneer Trust Fund Scholarship *(Undergraduate/Scholarship)* [4163]

Iowa Association for Energy Efficiency Scholarship *(Undergraduate/Scholarship)* [6154]

Iowa Journalism Institute Scholarships *(Graduate, Undergraduate/Scholarship)* [6167]

Iowa Library Association Foundation Scholarships *(Graduate/Scholarship)* [6163]

James P. Irish Scholarship *(Undergraduate/Scholarship)* [4164]

Forest A. King Scholarship *(Undergraduate/Scholarship)* [4166]

Verne Lawyer Scholarship *(Undergraduate/Scholarship)* [4167]

Frederick D. Lewis Jr. Scholarships *(Undergraduate/Scholarship)* [4168]

Gordon and Delores Madson Scholarship *(Undergraduate/Scholarship)* [4169]

Jake S. More Scholarship *(Undergraduate/Scholarship)* [4170]

James B. Morris Scholarship *(Undergraduate/Scholarship)* [7474]

Norfolk Southern Foundation Scholarships *(Undergraduate/Scholarship)* [1329]

North Central Region 9 Scholarship *(Undergraduate/Scholarship)* [10410]

Dwight D. Opperman Scholarships *(Undergraduate/Scholarship)* [4171]

Regions Riding Forward Scholarship Essay Contest *(Undergraduate, High School/Scholarship)* [9618]

Janet Reynoldson Memorial Scholarship *(Other/Scholarship)* [4172]

Walter and Rita Selvy Scholarship *(Undergraduate/Scholarship)* [4173]

Charles "Buck" and Dora Taylor Scholarship *(Undergraduate/Scholarship)* [4174]

The Jack Tillson Scholarship Fund *(Graduate/Scholarship)* [6164]

Haemer Wheatcraft Scholarship *(Undergraduate/Scholarship)* [4175]

Zarley, McKee, Thomte, Voorhees, Sease Law Scholarship *(Undergraduate/Scholarship)* [4176]

Kansas

Mary A. Bancroft Memorial Scholarship *(Graduate/Scholarship)* [6372]

Chapter 52 - Wichita Scholarship *(Graduate, Undergraduate, Vocational/Occupational, Community College/Scholarship)* [10392]

J.L. Weigand, Jr. Legal Education Trust Scholarship *(Undergraduate/Scholarship)* [11876]

Judge Delmas C. Hill Scholarship *(Undergraduate/Scholarship)* [11877]

Kansas Dental Education Opportunities Program *(Graduate/Scholarship)* [6362]

Kansas Distinguished Scholarship Program *(Graduate/Scholarship)* [6363]

Kansas Nurse Educator Service Scholarship *(Graduate/Scholarship)* [6364]

Karen Schuvie Scholarship *(Undergraduate/Scholarship, Loan)* [6368]

KHIMA Graduate Scholarship *(Graduate/Scholarship)* [6369]

Koch Scholars Program *(Undergraduate/Scholarship)* [11878]

Mingenback Family Scholarship Fund *(Undergraduate, Graduate/Scholarship)* [5016]

Martha Mitchell Pearson Memorial Scholarship (Undergraduate, Graduate/Scholarship) [6464]

Sue A. Malone Scholarship (Doctorate, Graduate, Professional development/Scholarship) [6370]

USAWOASF/Grantham University On-Line Scholarship (Graduate/Scholarship) [11290]

Lynn McNabb Walton Adelphe Scholarhship (Undergraduate/Scholarship) [6479]

Washburn University School of Law Business and Transactional Law Center Scholarships (Undergraduate/Scholarship) [11880]

Washburn University School of Law Child and Family Advocacy Fellowships (Undergraduate/Fellowship) [11881]

Kentucky

AISC/Southern Association of Steel Fabricators Scholarships (Undergraduate, Master's/Scholarship) [1054]

The Artist in Landscape Design Scholarship (Undergraduate/Scholarship) [8585]

Ballard Breaux Visiting Fellowships (Postdoctorate/Fellowship) [4558]

Beth K. Fields Scholarship (University/Scholarship) [11574]

Leon Bradley Scholarship Program (Undergraduate/Scholarship) [638]

Warren K. Brown Scholarship (Undergraduate/Scholarship) [1562]

Covington-Cincinnati/Northern Kentucky Alumni Chapter - Dane Wagge Scholarships (University/Scholarship) [11575]

The Educational Foundation of KyCPA Scholarships (Undergraduate/Scholarship) [6539]

Filson Fellowships (Postdoctorate, Doctorate/Fellowship) [4559]

Filson Historical Society Master's Thesis Fellowship (Master's/Fellowship) [4560]

Frankfort/Capital Region Alumni Chapter (University/Scholarship) [11576]

Kentucky Alumni Club Scholarships - Lexington/Central Kentucky Alumni Chapter (Graduate, High School/Scholarship) [11577]

Kentucky Alumni Club Scholarships - Somerset/Lake Cumberland Area Alumni Chapter (University/Scholarship) [11578]

Kentucky Educational Excellence Scholarship (Undergraduate/Scholarship) [2572]

Kentucky Paralegal Association Paralegal Student Scholarships (Undergraduate/Scholarship) [6535]

KHEAA Teacher Scholarship (Undergraduate/Scholarship) [2573]

Norfolk Southern Foundation Scholarships (Undergraduate/Scholarship) [1329]

Regions Riding Forward Scholarship Essay Contest (Undergraduate, High School/Scholarship) [9618]

Sam J. Hord Memorial Scholarship (Undergraduate/Scholarship) [10629]

SREB-State Doctoral Scholars Program - Dissertation Award (Doctorate/Scholarship, Award) [10663]

SREB-State Doctoral Scholars Program - Doctoral Award (Doctorate, Graduate/Scholarship) [10664]

Women In Rural Electrification Scholarships (W.I.R.E.) (Undergraduate/Scholarship) [10631]

Louisiana

AISC/Southern Association of Steel Fabricators Scholarships (Undergraduate, Master's/Scholarship) [1054]

Horatio Alger Louisiana Scholarships (Undergraduate/Scholarship) [5571]

American Radio Relay League Louisiana Memorial Scholarships (Undergraduate/Scholarship) [1924]

Gulf Coast Hurricane Scholarship (Undergraduate/Scholarship) [10488]

Norfolk Southern Foundation Scholarships (Undergraduate/Scholarship) [1329]

Petroleum Engineering Scholarships (Undergraduate/Scholarship) [10473]

Regions Riding Forward Scholarship Essay Contest (Undergraduate, High School/Scholarship) [9618]

Rochelle Scholarship (College/Scholarship) [6908]

Society of Louisiana Certified Public Accountants Scholarships (Undergraduate, Master's, Doctorate/Scholarship) [10382]

SREB-State Doctoral Scholars Program - Dissertation Award (Doctorate/Scholarship, Award) [10663]

SREB-State Doctoral Scholars Program - Doctoral Award (Doctorate, Graduate/Scholarship) [10664]

Maine

Catharine Wilder Guiles Scholarship (Graduate/Scholarship) [6976]

Henry L.P. Schmelzer College Transitions Scholarship Fund (Undergraduate/Scholarship) [6982]

Horch Roofing Trade School Scholarship (Vocational/Occupational/Scholarship) [5584]

Maine Nutrition Council Scholarships (Undergraduate/Scholarship) [7001]

Mead Leadership Fellowships (Professional development/Fellowship) [8482]

Patriot Education Scholarship Fund (Undergraduate/Scholarship) [6994]

Ruth Milan-Altrusa Scholarship Fund (Undergraduate/Scholarship) [6995]

Susan Vincent Memorial Scholarship (Undergraduate/Scholarship) [6973]

Maryland

Baltimore Community Fellowships (Advanced Professional/Fellowship) [8663]

Dr. Johnella Banks Memorial Scholarships (Undergraduate/Scholarship) [2610]

BCCC Foundation General Scholarship Fund (Undergraduate/Scholarship) [2414]

Johns Hopkins Medicine Disaster Fellowships (Professional development/Fellowship) [6317]

Johns Hopkins Medicine International Emergency and Public Health Fellowships (Graduate, Professional development/Fellowship) [6319]

Kathleen Kelly Undergraduate Scholarship (Undergraduate/Scholarship) [9434]

MACPA Scholarships (Undergraduate, Graduate/Scholarship) [7114]

McDaniel College Eagle Scout Scholarship (Undergraduate/Scholarship) [7854]

Mead Leadership Fellowships (Professional development/Fellowship) [8482]

Dolphus E. Milligan Graduate Fellowships (Graduate/Fellowship) [8029]

NFBPA Land-Use Planning Scholarships (Master's, Doctorate/Scholarship) [7892]

Norfolk Southern Foundation Scholarships (Undergraduate/Scholarship) [1329]

Margaret Pemberton Scholarships (Undergraduate/Scholarship) [2611]

PFLAG Howard County Scholarship (Undergraduate/Scholarship) [9054]

Richard and Patricia Hazel Minority Scholarship Award (Undergraduate/Scholarship) [3577]

Lana K. Rinehart Scholarships (Undergraduate/Scholarship) [3578]

SREB-State Doctoral Scholars Program - Dissertation Award (Doctorate/Scholarship, Award) [10663]

SREB-State Doctoral Scholars Program - Doctoral Award (Doctorate, Graduate/Scholarship) [10664]

Charles A. Townsend Scholarship (Undergraduate/Scholarship) [8883]

Massachusetts

Boston City Federation "Return to School" Scholarships (Undergraduate, Graduate/Scholarship) [4897]

Catherine E. Philbin Scholarship (Undergraduate, Graduate/Scholarship) [4898]

Charles A. King Trust Postdoctoral Research Fellowship (Postdoctorate/Fellowship) [5434]

Communication Disorder/Speech Therapy Scholarship (Graduate/Scholarship) [4899]

HBI Gilda Slifka Internship Program (Graduate, Undergraduate/Internship) [2680]

HBI Scholar-in-Residence Program (Undergraduate, Graduate, Postgraduate/Scholarship) [2681]

Jerome Peters Family Fund (Undergraduate/Scholarship) [6987]

Joseph Sumner Smith Scholarship (Undergraduate/Scholarship) [11250]

Clinical Translational Fellowship at Pfizer (Advanced Professional/Fellowship) [7134]

Massachusetts General Hospital/Harvard Medical School Internship (Doctorate/Internship) [7135]

Mead Leadership Fellowships (Professional development/Fellowship) [8482]

MEFA Graduate Loans (Graduate/Loan) [7130]

MGH Department of Psychiatry Behavioral Neurology and Neuropsychiatry Fellowship Program (Advanced Professional, Professional development/Fellowship) [7136]

Eating Disorders Summer Research Fellowship (Advanced Professional, Professional development/Fellowship) [7137]

MGH Department of Psychiatry Forensic Psychiatry Fellowship (Professional development/Fellowship) [7138]

MGH Department of Psychiatry Global Psychiatric Clinical Research Training Program (Advanced Professional/Fellowship) [7139]

Mountain Memorial Fund (Undergraduate/Award) [7054]

Music Scholarship for Undergraduate in Voice (Undergraduate/Scholarship) [4900]

Nickels for Notes Music Scholarship (Undergraduate/Scholarship) [4901]

Partners HealthCare Geriatric Psychiatry Fellowship (Professional development/Fellowship) [7140]

Pennies for Art Scholarship (Undergraduate/Scholarship) [4902]

Philip H. Melanson Memorial Scholarship (Undergraduate, Graduate/Scholarship) [11593]

Harry B. Pulver Scholarships (Undergraduate/Scholarship) [5002]

Edward S. Roth Scholarship (Graduate, Undergraduate/Scholarship) [10411]

Tom Gifford Scholarship (Undergraduate/Scholarship) [5112]

Women's Italian Club of Boston Scholarships (Undergraduate/Scholarship) [4903]

Michigan

AISC/Great Lakes Fabricators and Erectors Association Scholarships (Graduate/Scholarship) [1051]

Altrusa International of Grand Rapids Scholarship (Undergraduate/Scholarship) [5133]

Amos and Marilyn Winsand - Detroit Section Named Scholarship (Undergraduate/Scholarship) [1656]

Antonia Dellas Memorial Scholarship (Undergraduate/Scholarship) [6192]

AREMA Michigan Tech Alumni Scholarships (Graduate, Undergraduate/Scholarship) [1321]

Dr. Noyes L. Avery, Jr. & Ann E. Avery Scholarship (Undergraduate, Graduate/Scholarship) [5136]

Clifford L. Bedford Scholarship Award (Undergraduate/Scholarship) [5220]

Bertha M. Fase Memorial Scholarship (Undergraduate/Scholarship) [5069]

Bob and Dawn Hardy Automotive Scholarship (Undergraduate/Scholarship) [6195]

Calvin Alumni Association-Washington, D.C. Scholarships (Undergraduate/Scholarship) [2844]

Center for the Education of Women Scholarships (Graduate, Undergraduate/Scholarship) [11635]

Center for the Education of Women Student Research Grants (Graduate, Undergraduate/Grant) [11636]

Chapter 1 Detroit Undergraduate Scholarship (Undergraduate, Vocational/Occupational, Two Year College, Four Year College/Scholarship) [10387]

Charles and Eleanor Rycenga Education Scholarship (Undergraduate/Scholarship) [5071]

Christine Soper Scholarship (Undergraduate/Scholarship) [5142]

CMSF Scholarship (Graduate/Scholarship) [3319]

Paul Collins Scholarship (Undergraduate/Scholarship) [5143]

Gerald M. Crane Music Award Scholarship (Undergraduate/Scholarship) [5144]

Daniel L. Reiss Memorial Scholarship (Undergraduate/Scholarship) [5073]

Darooge Family Scholarship *(Undergraduate/Scholarship)* [5145]

Antenore C. "Butch" Davanzo Scholarships *(Graduate, Undergraduate/Scholarship)* [7348]

Dr. William A. and Marceleine J. Sautter Hanover-Horton Youth of Promise Scholarship *(Graduate/Scholarship)* [6196]

Dorothy B. & Charles E. Thomas Scholarship *(Undergraduate/Scholarship)* [5148]

Dorothy and Dick Burgess Scholarship *(Undergraduate/Scholarship)* [6197]

Chapter 116 - Roscoe Douglas Scholarship *(Undergraduate/Scholarship)* [10400]

Erickson Education Scholarship *(Undergraduate/Scholarship)* [5075]

Gauthier Family Scholarship Fund *(Undergraduate/Scholarship)* [5078]

Geraldine Geistert Boss Scholarship *(Undergraduate/Scholarship)* [5151]

The Elaine and Barry Gilbert College Scholarship *(Undergraduate/Scholarship)* [6272]

Grand Haven Offshore Challenge Scholarship *(Undergraduate/Scholarship)* [5080]

Grand Rapids Scholarship Association *(Undergraduate/Scholarship)* [5152]

Grand Rapids Trans Foundation Academic Scholarship *(Undergraduate, Two Year College, Vocational/Occupational/Scholarship)* [5197]

Great Lakes Section Diversity Scholarship *(Graduate, Undergraduate/Scholarship)* [5221]

Guy D. & Mary Edith Halladay Graduate Scholarship *(Undergraduate/Scholarship)* [5156]

Martha and Oliver Hansen Memorial Scholarships *(Undergraduate/Scholarship)* [6202]

Harold and Eleanor Ringelberg Scholarship *(Undergraduate/Scholarship)* [5082]

Harry J. Morris, Jr. Emergency Services *(Undergraduate/Scholarship)* [5157]

Hazel Simms Nursing Scholarship *(Other/Scholarship)* [6664]

John P. Hennessey Scholarship *(Graduate, Undergraduate/Scholarship)* [7349]

Hierholzer-Fojtik Scholarship *(Undergraduate/Scholarship)* [5084]

Illinois Landscape Contractors Association Scholarships *(Undergraduate/Scholarship)* [5703]

Jack Family Scholarship *(Undergraduate/Scholarship)* [5158]

Jacob R. & Mary M. VanLoo & Lenore K. VanLoo Scholarship *(Undergraduate/Scholarship)* [5159]

Kelsey's Law Distracted Driving Awareness Scholarship *(High School, Undergraduate/Scholarship)* [7305]

Ladies Literary Club Scholarship *(Undergraduate/Scholarship)* [5161]

Lavina Laible Scholarship *(Undergraduate/Scholarship)* [5162]

Leo Zupin Memorial Scholarship *(Undergraduate, Vocational/Occupational/Scholarship)* [5091]

John T. & Frances J. Maghielse Scholarship *(Undergraduate/Scholarship)* [5163]

Marion A. and Ruth K. Sherwood Business Scholarship *(Undergraduate/Scholarship)* [5093]

Marjorie M. Hendricks Environmental Education Scholarship *(Undergraduate/Scholarship)* [5094]

Marvin R. and Pearl E. Patterson Family Scholarship *(Undergraduate/Scholarship)* [5095]

Mathilda & Carolyn Gallmeyer Scholarship *(Undergraduate/Scholarship)* [5165]

Melbourne & Alice E. Frontjes Scholarship *(Undergraduate/Scholarship)* [5167]

Michael J. Wolf Scholarship *(Undergraduate/Scholarship)* [5168]

Michigan Accountancy Foundation Final Year Accounting Scholarship *(Graduate/Scholarship)* [7301]

Michigan Auto Law Student Diversity Scholarships *(Undergraduate/Scholarship)* [7306]

Michigan Education Association Scholarships *(Undergraduate/Scholarship)* [7313]

Michigan Society of Professional Engineers Scholarships *(Undergraduate/Scholarship)* [7328]

Michigan Stormwater-Floodplain Association Scholarships *(Graduate, Undergraduate/Scholarship)* [7338]

Miller G. Sherwood Family Scholarship *(Undergraduate/Scholarship)* [5097]

MNF Scholarships *(Undergraduate, Graduate/Scholarship)* [7320]

NAIFA West Michigan Scholarship *(Undergraduate/Scholarship)* [5170]

NALS of Michigan Scholarship *(Undergraduate/Scholarship)* [7546]

Norfolk Southern Foundation Scholarships *(Undergraduate/Scholarship)* [1329]

North Central Region 9 Scholarship *(Undergraduate/Scholarship)* [10410]

Orrie & Dorothy Cassada Scholarship *(Undergraduate/Scholarship)* [5171]

Patricia & Armen Oumedian Scholarship *(Undergraduate/Scholarship)* [5172]

Peggy (Kommer) Novosad Scholarship *(Graduate, Postgraduate/Scholarship)* [5173]

P.E.O. Chapter DS Scholarship *(Undergraduate, Vocational/Occupational/Scholarship)* [5101]

Philip F. Greco Memorial Scholarship *(Undergraduate/Scholarship)* [6960]

Reach for Your Goal Scholarship *(Undergraduate/Scholarship)* [5174]

Josephine Ringold Scholarship *(Undergraduate/Scholarship)* [5175]

Prof. George Schneider Scholarship *(Undergraduate/Scholarship)* [10413]

Jeptha Wade Schureman Scholarship Program *(Undergraduate/Scholarship)* [3724]

Marion A. and Ruth K. Sherwood Engineering Scholarship *(Undergraduate/Scholarship)* [5108]

Sigma Kappa Foundation Michigan Scholarship *(Undergraduate/Scholarship)* [10124]

Stephen Lankester Scholarship *(Undergraduate/Scholarship)* [5184]

Thomas D. Coffield Scholarship *(Undergraduate/Scholarship)* [5185]

Dorothy J. Thurston Graduate Scholarship *(Undergraduate/Scholarship)* [5186]

Trustees Law School Scholarship *(Undergraduate/Scholarship)* [6962]

Edward Tuinier Memorial Scholarship *(Undergraduate/Scholarship)* [907]

U-M Alumnae Club (University of Michigan) Scholarships *(Undergraduate/Scholarship)* [5187]

Virginia Valk Fehsenfeld Scholarship *(Undergraduate/Scholarship)* [5189]

Jack H. Wagner Scholarship *(Graduate, Undergraduate/Scholarship)* [7350]

Sue Walicki Nursing Scholarships *(Undergraduate/Scholarship)* [6210]

Walter C. Winchester Scholarship *(Undergraduate/Scholarship)* [5192]

Donald M. Wells Scholarships *(Undergraduate/Scholarship)* [5193]

Violet Wondergem Health Science Scholarships *(Undergraduate/Scholarship)* [5195]

Minnesota

Anderson Niskanen Scholarship Fund *(Graduate/Scholarship)* [4198]

William E. Barto Scholarship Fund *(Undergraduate/Scholarship)* [4200]

General Mills Foundation Scholarships *(Undergraduate/Scholarship)* [981]

Illinois Lake Management Association Undergraduate/Graduate Scholarships *(Graduate, Undergraduate/Scholarship)* [5700]

Jerome Fellowships *(Other/Fellowship)* [9196]

Many Voices Fellowships *(Other/Fellowship)* [9197]

McKnight Fellowships *(Other/Fellowship)* [9198]

Minnesota Association of Public Accountant Scholarship *(Undergraduate/Scholarship)* [7404]

Minnesota Division Scholarships *(Undergraduate/Scholarship)* [7371]

Minnesota Health Information Management Association Scholarships *(Undergraduate/Scholarship)* [7408]

North Central Region 9 Scholarship *(Undergraduate/Scholarship)* [10410]

Robert Esser Student Achievement Scholarship *(Graduate, Undergraduate/Scholarship)* [5701]

Edward S. Roth Scholarship *(Graduate, Undergraduate/Scholarship)* [10411]

The Adelle and Erwin Tomash Fellowship in the History of Information Technology *(Doctorate, Graduate/Fellowship)* [11641]

Mississippi

AISC/Southern Association of Steel Fabricators Scholarships *(Undergraduate, Master's/Scholarship)* [1054]

Gulf Coast Hurricane Scholarship *(Undergraduate/Scholarship)* [10488]

The Mississippi Scholarship *(Undergraduate/Scholarship)* [1950]

MSCPA Undergraduate Scholarship *(Undergraduate/Scholarship)* [7421]

Norfolk Southern Foundation Scholarships *(Undergraduate/Scholarship)* [1329]

Regions Riding Forward Scholarship Essay Contest *(Undergraduate, High School/Scholarship)* [9618]

Ross/Nickey Scholarships *(Graduate/Scholarship)* [7422]

Southern Section A&WMA Scholarships *(Graduate/Scholarship)* [10668]

Missouri

Walter Moran Farmer Scholarships *(Juris Doctorate/Scholarship)* [11922]

Health Professional Nursing Student Loans *(Undergraduate, Graduate, Community College, Doctorate/Loan)* [7424]

Illinois Landscape Contractors Association Scholarships *(Undergraduate/Scholarship)* [5703]

Kansas Optometry Service Scholarship *(Graduate, Undergraduate/Scholarship)* [6365]

Norfolk Southern Foundation Scholarships *(Undergraduate/Scholarship)* [1329]

Martha Mitchell Pearson Memorial Scholarship *(Undergraduate, Graduate/Scholarship)* [6464]

Regions Riding Forward Scholarship Essay Contest *(Undergraduate, High School/Scholarship)* [9618]

Montana

Horatio Alger Montana Scholarships *(Undergraduate/Scholarship)* [5574]

Anthony Gerharz Scholarship *(Undergraduate, Graduate/Scholarship)* [7457]

APTRA-Clete Roberts/Kathryn Dettman Memorial Journalism Scholarship *(Undergraduate/Scholarship)* [2022]

Donald E. Pizzini Memorial Nurse Scholarship *(Undergraduate, Professional development/Scholarship)* [7455]

Eldon E. and JoAnn C. Kuhns Family Scholarship *(Undergraduate, Graduate/Scholarship)* [7458]

William Harrison Gill Education Fund *(Undergraduate/Scholarship)* [2480]

Great Falls Broadcasters Association Scholarships *(Undergraduate/Scholarship)* [7452]

MSCPA Scholarship - Montana Tech *(Undergraduate, Graduate/Scholarship)* [7459]

MSCPA Scholarship - MSU Bozeman *(Undergraduate, Graduate/Scholarship)* [7460]

MSCPA Scholarship - University of Montana *(Undergraduate, Graduate/Scholarship)* [7461]

Scott Brownlee Memorial Scholarship *(Undergraduate, Graduate/Scholarship)* [7462]

Nebraska

Henry and Maria Ahrens Charitable Trust Scholarship *(Undergraduate, Graduate/Scholarship)* [5117]

Alpha Kappa Trust Scholarship-Beta Omega *(Undergraduate/Scholarship)* [10091]

Edgar Barge Memorial Scholarship *(Undergraduate/Scholarship)* [5118]

BSF General Scholarship Awards *(College, University/Scholarship)* [2439]

Karen A. Connick Memorial Scholarship *(Undergraduate/Scholarship)* [5119]

Dave Sauer Memorial College Scholarship *(Undergraduate/Scholarship)* [170]

Doniphan Community Foundation Scholarships *(Undergraduate, Community College, Vocational/Occupational/Scholarship)* [5120]

Howard and Gladys Eakes Memorial Scholarship *(Undergraduate/Scholarship)* [5121]

Hall County Medical Society Scholarship *(Undergraduate, Graduate/Scholarship)* [5122]

Lehman Family Scholarship *(Undergraduate/Scholarship)* [9828]

Nebraska Paralegal Association Student Scholarships *(Undergraduate/Scholarship)* [8194]

NESCPA Fifth-year (150 hour) scholarships *(Graduate/Scholarship)* [8198]

NESCPA General Scholarship *(Graduate, Undergraduate/Scholarship)* [8199]

North Central Region 9 Scholarship *(Undergraduate/Scholarship)* [10410]

Jim and Dee Price Family Scholarship *(Undergraduate, Community College, College, University/Scholarship)* [5123]

Carl C. and Abbie Rebman Trust Scholarship *(Undergraduate/Scholarship)* [5124]

Susan Thompson Buffett Foundation Scholarship *(Undergraduate, Two Year College/Scholarship)* [2739]

TeamMates Mentoring Program Scholarship *(Undergraduate/Scholarship)* [5125]

Mark and Vera Turner Memorial Scholarships *(Undergraduate/Scholarship)* [6833]

Robert & Barbara Wade Scholarships *(Undergraduate/Scholarship)* [6834]

Wyman and Cleo Woodyard Family Scholarship *(Undergraduate, University, College/Scholarship)* [5126]

James P. and Joy Y. Zana Scholarship *(Undergraduate/Scholarship)* [5127]

Nevada

Aaron Edward Arnoldsen Memorial Scholarship *(Undergraduate/Scholarship)* [1922]

Agustin Cano Memorial Scholarship *(Undergraduate/Scholarship)* [9388]

American Nuclear Society Nevada Section Scholarship *(Undergraduate/Scholarship)* [1161, 9390]

Cheyenne High School Desert Shields Scholarship *(Undergraduate/Scholarship)* [9392]

Clark High School Academy of Finance Scholarship *(Undergraduate/Scholarship)* [9394]

Coronado High School Counselors' Scholarship *(Undergraduate/Scholarship)* [9395]

Dan Mordecai Educational Scholarship Award *(Graduate, Undergraduate/Scholarship)* [8210]

APTRA-Clete Roberts/Kathryn Dettman Memorial Journalism Scholarship *(Undergraduate/Scholarship)* [2022]

Edwin F. Wiegand Science & Technology Scholarship *(Undergraduate/Scholarship)* [9397]

Brendan Flores Alumni Leadership Circle Scholarship - Clark High School *(Undergraduate/Scholarship)* [9400]

William Harrison Gill Education Fund *(Undergraduate/Scholarship)* [2480]

Gordy Fink Memorial Scholarship *(Undergraduate/Scholarship)* [9403]

John Caoile Memorial Scholarship *(Other/Scholarship)* [9406]

Judith Warner Memorial Scholarship *(Undergraduate/Scholarship)* [9408]

Las Vegas Chinatown Scholarship *(Undergraduate/Scholarship)* [9409]

Mesquite Club Evening Chapter Inc. Scholarship *(Undergraduate/Scholarship)* [9410]

Michael Koizumi APWA Internship Scholarship *(Undergraduate/Scholarship, Internship)* [1308]

Mickey Donnelly Memorial Scholarship *(Undergraduate/Scholarship)* [9412]

NERL Postdoctoral Research Program *(Postdoctorate, Advanced Professional, Professional development/Fellowship)* [11352]

North Las Vegas Firefighters William J. Harnedy Memorial Scholarship *(Undergraduate/Scholarship)* [9415]

Palo Verde High School Barbara Edwards Memorial Scholarship *(Undergraduate/Scholarship)* [9416]

Palo Verde High School Faculty Follies Scholarship *(Undergraduate/Scholarship)* [9417]

Pardee Community Building Scholarship *(Undergraduate/Scholarship)* [9419]

Sheila Tarr-Smith Memorial Scholarship *(Undergraduate/Scholarship)* [9422]

Tsutako Curo Scholarship *(Undergraduate/Scholarship)* [9428]

New Hampshire

College of Engineering and Physical Sciences Industry Scholarship *(Undergraduate/Scholarship)* [11650]

Louise Tillotson Teaching Fellowship *(Professional development/Fellowship)* [8257]

Louise Tillotson Teaching Professional Development Scholarship *(Professional development/Scholarship)* [8258]

Mead Leadership Fellowships *(Professional development/Fellowship)* [8482]

The NHPGA Apprentice Scholarship *(Undergraduate/Scholarship)* [7174]

The Walter T. Philippy Scholarship *(Undergraduate/Scholarship)* [7175]

Piscataqua Region Artist Advancement Grant *(Professional development/Grant)* [8259]

Harry B. Pulver Scholarships *(Undergraduate/Scholarship)* [5002]

The UNH Alumni Association Legacy Scholarship *(Undergraduate/Scholarship)* [11651]

UNH Parents Association Endowed Scholarship *(Undergraduate/Scholarship)* [11652]

New Jersey

Abram D. and Maxine H. Londa Scholarship *(Undergraduate/Scholarship)* [8290]

Benjamin Asbell Memorial Awards *(Graduate, Undergraduate/Scholarship)* [2846]

Eivind H. Barth, Jr. Memorial Award *(Undergraduate, Graduate/Scholarship)* [2847]

CentraState Band Aid Open Committee Scholarship *(Undergraduate/Scholarship)* [3249]

Hon. Joseph W. Cowgill Memorial Award *(Undergraduate, Graduate/Scholarship)* [2848]

George Dale Scholarship Fund *(Undergraduate/Scholarship)* [1973]

DCH Freehold Toyota Scholarship *(Undergraduate/Scholarship)* [3251]

Hon. Ralph W.E. Donges Memorial Award *(Undergraduate, Graduate/Scholarship)* [2849]

DuBois Brothers Award *(Undergraduate, Graduate/Scholarship)* [2850]

Bernadine Johnson-Marshall and Martha Bell Williams Scholarships *(Undergraduate/Scholarship)* [2068]

George F. Kugler, Jr. Award *(Undergraduate, Graduate/Scholarship)* [2851]

Mead Leadership Fellowships *(Professional development/Fellowship)* [8482]

NCNJ-AWMA Undergraduate Scholarship *(Undergraduate/Scholarship)* [172]

NJCBIR Individual Research Grants *(Graduate, Professional development, Postdoctorate, Doctorate/Grant)* [10807]

NJCBIR Pilot Research Grants *(Other/Grant)* [10808]

NJCBIR Postdoctoral and Graduate Student Fellowships *(Graduate, Postdoctorate, Professional development, Doctorate/Fellowship)* [10809]

NJCBIR Programmatic Multi-Investigator Project Grants *(Other/Grant)* [10810]

NJSBF Labor Law Scholarship *(Undergraduate/Scholarship)* [8291]

NJSCPA College Scholarships *(Graduate, Undergraduate/Scholarship)* [8287]

Norfolk Southern Foundation Scholarships *(Undergraduate/Scholarship)* [1329]

Louis C. Portella Memorial Award *(Undergraduate, Graduate/Scholarship)* [2853]

Hon. Rudolph J. Rossetti Memorial Award *(Undergraduate, Graduate/Scholarship)* [2854]

Sonia Morgan Scholarship *(Undergraduate/Scholarship)* [8292]

Jay A. Strassberg Memorial Scholarship *(Undergraduate/Scholarship)* [2855]

Daniel B. Toll Memorial Award *(Undergraduate, Graduate/Scholarship)* [2856]

William Tomar Memorial Award *(Undergraduate, Graduate/Scholarship)* [2857]

Bruce A. Wallace Memorial Award *(Undergraduate, Graduate/Scholarship)* [2858]

Wallace Vail Scholarship *(Undergraduate/Scholarship)* [8293]

New Mexico

Chapter 93 - Albuquerque Scholarship *(Undergraduate/Scholarship)* [10399]

APTRA-Clete Roberts/Kathryn Dettman Memorial Journalism Scholarship *(Undergraduate/Scholarship)* [2022]

General Mills Foundation Scholarships *(Undergraduate/Scholarship)* [981]

William Harrison Gill Education Fund *(Undergraduate/Scholarship)* [2480]

New Mexico Association for Bilingual Education Scholarships (NMABE) *(Undergraduate/Scholarship)* [8295]

Charles A. Townsend Scholarship *(Undergraduate/Scholarship)* [8883]

New York

Eleanor Allwork Scholarship *(Undergraduate/Scholarship)* [138]

AWMA Niagara Frontier Section College Scholarship *(Graduate, Undergraduate/Scholarship)* [169]

Leo Baeck Institute - DAAD Fellowships *(Doctorate/Fellowship)* [4057]

Mark B. Bain Graduate Fellowship *(Doctorate, Master's, Graduate/Fellowship)* [5612]

Berkowitz Fellowship *(Professional development/Fellowship)* [11032]

Robert L. Bernstein Fellowships in International Human Rights *(Graduate/Fellowship)* [5630]

Ellen Blodgett Memorial Scholarship *(Master's/Scholarship)* [8333]

William L. Bradley Memorial Scholarship *(Master's/Scholarship)* [8334]

Paul W. Bradley Scholarship *(Master's/Scholarship)* [8335]

CFR Stanton Nuclear Security Fellowship *(Doctorate, Postdoctorate, Advanced Professional/Fellowship)* [3862]

CFR Volunteer Internships *(Undergraduate, Graduate/Internship)* [3863]

CHRGJ Emerging Human Rights Scholarship Conference *(Graduate/Scholarship)* [8358]

Esther Cummings Memorial Scholarship *(Master's/Scholarship)* [8336]

Davis Wright Tremaine 1L Diversity Scholarship *(Undergraduate/Scholarship)* [3979]

Design and Multimedia Internships - New York *(Undergraduate, Graduate/Internship)* [4980]

Margaret Eddy Scholarship *(Graduate, Master's/Scholarship)* [8337]

Faith Initiatives Internships - New York *(Undergraduate, Graduate/Internship)* [4981]

Fellowship on Women & Public Policy *(Graduate/Fellowship)* [11522]

Ethel Mae Gaston Memorial Scholarship *(Master's/Scholarship)* [8338]

Emily V. Gibbes Scholarship *(Master's/Scholarship)* [8339]

GLAAD Communications/PR Internships - New York *(Undergraduate, Graduate/Internship)* [4983]

GLAAD Spanish-Language and Latino Media Internships - Los Angeles *(Undergraduate, Graduate/Internship)* [4984]

GLAAD Youth Issues Internships - New York *(Undergraduate, Graduate/Internship)* [4985]

The William Randolph Hearst Endowed Scholarship *(Master's/Scholarship)* [8340]

Vladimir and Pearl Heifetz Memorial Fellowship *(Undergraduate, Graduate, Postgraduate/Fellowship)* [12236]

The Melvyn F. Hester Scholarship *(Master's/Scholarship)* [8341]

The Barbara J. and M. William Howard Jr. Scholarship *(Master's/Scholarship)* [8342]

The Sang Ok Hur Scholarships *(Master's/Scholarship)* [8343]

Jeannette K. Watson Fellowship *(Undergraduate/Fellowship)* [11938]

Joseph H. Gellert Scholarship *(Graduate/Scholarship)* [4240]

Ketchum Excellence in Public Relations Research Award *(Graduate/Fellowship, Internship)* [5858]

The Hwain Chang Lee scholarship *(Master's/Scholarship)* [8344]

The William K. Lee Scholarship *(Master's/Scholarship)* [8345]

The Margaret Smith Maase Scholarships *(Master's/Scholarship)* [8346]

The Ann M. Mallouk Scholarships *(Master's/Scholarship)* [8347]

The Rev. Richard S. McCarroll and Mrs. E. Allison McCarroll Scholarship *(Master's/Scholarship)* [8348]

Anne O'Hare McCormick Memorial Scholarship *(Graduate/Scholarship)* [8393]

Mead Leadership Fellowships *(Professional development/Fellowship)* [8482]

The Ella and Harold Midtbo Scholarship *(Master's/Scholarship)* [8349]

The William Howard Morton Scholarship *(Master's/Scholarship)* [8350]

Edward R. Murrow Press Fellowships *(Professional development/Fellowship)* [3866]

New York Financial Writers' Associations Scholarships *(Graduate, Undergraduate/Scholarship)* [8311]

New York State Association of Agricultural Fairs Scholarship *(Undergraduate/Scholarship)* [8319]

News and Rapid Response Internship *(Undergraduate, Graduate/Internship)* [4986]

Norfolk Southern Foundation Scholarships *(Undergraduate/Scholarship)* [1329]

NYCT Paid Graduate Student Philanthropy Fellowships - Community Development and the Environment *(Graduate/Fellowship)* [8307]

Faith E. O'Neal Scholarship *(Graduate/Scholarship)* [9459]

Open Society Presidential Fellowship *(Graduate/Fellowship)* [8665]

Abraham A. Oyedeji Scholarship *(Master's/Scholarship)* [8351]

Richard T. Liddicoat Scholarship *(Graduate/Scholarship)* [4882]

Roland E. Murphy, O.Carm., Scholarship *(Undergraduate/Scholarship)* [3186]

Saint Andrews Scholarships *(Undergraduate/Scholarship)* [9776]

Stanley M. Schoenfeld Memorial Scholarship *(Postgraduate/Scholarship)* [8321]

Senator Patricia K. McGee Nursing Faculty Scholarship *(Doctorate, Graduate/Scholarship)* [8323]

Special Events Internship- New York *(Undergraduate, Graduate/Internship)* [4987]

Sports Internships - Los Angeles *(Undergraduate, Graduate/Internship)* [4989]

Tibor T. Polgar Fellowship *(Graduate, Undergraduate/Fellowship)* [5613]

Trans Issues Internships - New York *(Undergraduate, Graduate/Internship)* [4990]

Undergraduate Session Assistants Program *(Undergraduate/Other)* [8329]

Victoria Ovis Memorial Scholarship *(Undergraduate/Scholarship)* [7982]

Albert E. Wischmeyer Scholarship *(Undergraduate/Scholarship)* [10419]

Woody Guthrie Fellowship *(Professional development/Fellowship)* [2637]

The George D. Younger Scholarship *(Graduate/Scholarship)* [8352]

North Carolina

African American Network - Carolinas Scholarship Fund *(Undergraduate/Scholarship)* [4715]

Alice Conger Patterson Scholarship *(Undergraduate/Scholarship)* [12060]

Annabel Lambeth Jones Brevard College Merit Scholarship Fund *(Undergraduate/Scholarship)* [4718]

Ben Robinette Scholarship Fund *(Undergraduate/Scholarship)* [4720]

Pete and Ellen Bensley Memorial Scholarship Fund *(Undergraduate/Scholarship)* [4721]

Leon Bradley Scholarship Program *(Undergraduate/Scholarship)* [638]

Cadmus Communications Corporation Graphics Scholarship Endowment Fund *(Undergraduate/Scholarship)* [4722]

Campus Pride Summer Fellows *(Undergraduate, Graduate, Postgraduate/Fellowship)* [2870]

Kasie Ford Capling Memorial Scholarship Endowment Fund *(Undergraduate/Scholarship)* [4723]

Career Awards for Science and Mathematics Teachers *(Other/Award)* [2752]

William F. Carl Scholarships *(Undergraduate/Scholarship)* [8443]

Carol Bond Scholarship *(Undergraduate/Scholarship)* [8453]

The Carolina Panthers Players Sam Mills Memorial Scholarship *(Undergraduate/Scholarship)* [4724]

Charlotte-Mecklenburg Schools Scholarship Incentive Fund *(Undergraduate/Scholarship)* [3277, 4727]

Charlotte Pride Scholarship *(Community College, Two Year College, Undergraduate, Four Year College/Scholarship)* [3279]

Chester Arzell and Helen Miller Montgomery Scholarship *(Undergraduate/Scholarship)* [12065]

Lloyd E. and Rachel S. Collins Scholarship *(Undergraduate, Graduate, High School/Scholarship)* [12067]

Dan Stewart Scholarship *(Other/Scholarship)* [8433]

Davidson and Jones Hotel Corporation Scholarship *(Undergraduate/Scholarship)* [8445]

Edward Jackson International Travel Award *(Undergraduate/Award)* [11184]

Edwin H. and Louise N. Williamson Endowed Scholarship *(Undergraduate/Scholarship)* [12072]

Virginia Elizabeth and Alma Vane Taylor Nursing Scholarship *(Undergraduate/Scholarship)* [12073]

Elizabeth T. Williams Memorial Scholarship *(Undergraduate/Scholarship)* [12074]

F.A. and Charlotte Blount Scholarship *(Undergraduate/Scholarship)* [12076]

Governor James E. Holshouser Professional Development Scholarship *(Other/Scholarship)* [8434]

Jack Ervin Economic Development Institute Scholarship *(Other/Scholarship)* [8435]

James V. Johnson Scholarship Endowment Fund *(Undergraduate/Scholarship)* [8437]

Law Enforcement Memorial Scholarship Endowment Fund *(Undergraduate/Scholarship)* [4741]

Lula Faye Clegg Memorial Scholarship Endowment Fund *(Undergraduate/Scholarship)* [4743]

The Mary and Elliott Wood Foundation Undergraduate Scholarship *(Undergraduate/Scholarship)* [4745]

Carolina Panthers Players Sam Mills Memorial Scholarships *(Undergraduate/Scholarship)* [4747]

North Carolina Hospitality Education Foundation Scholarship *(Undergraduate/Scholarship)* [8446]

NC Hospitality Education Foundation Scholarships - Graduate *(Graduate/Scholarship)* [8447]

NC Hospitality Education Foundation Scholarships - High School *(Undergraduate/Scholarship)* [8448]

NC Hospitality Education Foundation Scholarships - Two Year Community or Junior College *(Undergraduate/Scholarship)* [8449]

NCACPA Outstanding Minority Accounting Student Scholarships *(Undergraduate/Scholarship)* [8426]

NCRLA Golden Corral Scholarship *(Undergraduate/Scholarship)* [8450]

Nell and Spencer Waggoner Scholarship *(Undergraduate/Scholarship)* [12084]

NERL Postdoctoral Research Program *(Postdoctorate, Advanced Professional, Professional development/Fellowship)* [11352]

Norfolk Southern Foundation Scholarships *(Undergraduate/Scholarship)* [1329]

North Carolina CPA Foundation Scholarships *(Undergraduate/Scholarship)* [8427]

North Mecklenburg Teachers' Memorial Scholarship Fund *(Undergraduate/Scholarship)* [4749]

NRMRL Postdoctoral Research Program *(Postdoctorate, Advanced Professional, Professional development/Fellowship)* [11356]

Oliver Joel and Ellen Pell Denny Healthcare Scholarship *(Undergraduate/Scholarship)* [12085]

Peter DeWitt Pruden and Phyllis Harrill Pruden Scholarship *(Undergraduate/Scholarship)* [11202]

Regions Riding Forward Scholarship Essay Contest *(Undergraduate, High School/Scholarship)* [9618]

Tacy Anna Smith Memorial Scholarship Endowment Fund *(Undergraduate/Scholarship)* [4757]

Ted Ousley Scholarship Endowment Fund *(Undergraduate/Scholarship)* [4759]

Tien Bui Memorial Scholarship *(Undergraduate/Scholarship)* [12095]

Turner Family Scholarships *(Undergraduate, Vocational/Occupational/Scholarship)* [4760]

UNC-CGI C.V. Starr Scholarship *(Undergraduate, Graduate/Scholarship)* [3217]

The Sybil Jennings Vorheis Memorial Undergraduate Scholarships *(Undergraduate/Scholarship)* [4761]

The L. Phil and Alice J. Wicker Scholarship *(Undergraduate/Scholarship)* [1966]

William B. Martin East Carolina University Scholarship *(Undergraduate/Scholarship)* [6395]

Ted G. Wilson Memorial Scholarships *(Undergraduate/Scholarship)* [9338]

North Dakota

North Central Region 9 Scholarship *(Undergraduate/Scholarship)* [10410]

North Dakota Division Scholarships *(Undergraduate, Graduate/Scholarship)* [7373]

North Dakota Veterinary Medical Association Scholarships *(Undergraduate/Scholarship)* [8475]

Matilda B. Thompson Scholarship *(Undergraduate/Scholarship)* [5555]

Ohio

Wayne D. Ackerman Family Scholarship Fund *(Undergraduate/Scholarship)* [10749]

AISC/Ohio Structural Steel Association Scholarships *(Undergraduate, Master's/Scholarship)* [1052]

Akron Bar Association Foundation Scholarships *(Undergraduate/Scholarship)* [203]

Ora E. Anderson Scholarship *(Undergraduate, High School/Scholarship)* [4706]

The Artist in Landscape Design Scholarship *(Undergraduate/Scholarship)* [8585]

Barr Foundation Scholarship *(Undergraduate/Scholarship)* [3337]

Helen & Bob Bintz Scholarship *(Undergraduate/Scholarship)* [7081]

William (Billbo) Boston/Harold Knopp Scholarship *(Undergraduate/Scholarship)* [8833]

William & Martha Buckingham Scholarship *(Undergraduate/Scholarship)* [7083]

Harry D. Callahan Educational Trust *(Undergraduate/Scholarship)* [10754]

CCTS services, resources, and pilot awards *(Postdoctorate, Professional development/Grant)* [8603]

Charles and Claire Phillips Scholarship Fund *(Undergraduate/Scholarship)* [3344]

Corinne and Fred Capuder Memorial Scholarship *(Undergraduate/Scholarship)* [3349]

Crosset Family Foundation Scholarship *(Undergraduate/Scholarship)* [3351]

Dater Foundation Scholarship *(Undergraduate/Scholarship)* [3352]

Lawrence E. and Jean L. Davis Scholarship *(Undergraduate/Scholarship)* [8843]

Dee Wacksman Scholarship Fund *(Undergraduate/Scholarship)* [3354]

Dr. Kathy Dixon Memorial Scholarship *(Undergraduate, University, College/Scholarship)* [7097]

The Harold K. Douthit Scholarship *(Undergraduate/Scholarship)* [8580]

Epsilon Tau Pi's Soaring Eagle Scholarship *(Undergraduate/Scholarship)* [7849]

FFA Scholarship *(Undergraduate/Scholarship)* [8586]

Fifth Third Bank Scholarship Fund *(Undergraduate/Scholarship)* [3359]

Fletemeyer Family Scholarship Fund *(Undergraduate/Scholarship)* [3360]

Florette B. Hoffheimer Scholarship Fund (Undergraduate/Scholarship) [3361]

Gardner Foundation Scholarship (Undergraduate/Scholarship) [3363]

David A. and Pamela A. Gault Charitable Fund (Undergraduate/Scholarship) [10759]

Margaret S. Gilbert Scholarship Fund (Graduate/Scholarship) [10760]

Velma Shotwell Griffin Memorial Scholarship Fund (Undergraduate/Scholarship) [10762]

Mary Ewing Guthrey/Mary Keller Moyer Memorial Scholarship (Undergraduate, Graduate/Scholarship) [6439]

Dorcas Edmonson Haught Scholarship (Undergraduate/Scholarship) [8858]

Heidelberg Distributing Scholarship Fund (Undergraduate/Scholarship) [3368]

Dale O. Heimberger CRNA Memorial Scholarship Fund (Graduate/Scholarship) [10764]

Heinz Pet Products Scholarship Fund (Undergraduate/Scholarship) [3369]

Illinois Lake Management Association Undergraduate/Graduate Scholarships (Graduate, Undergraduate/Scholarship) [5700]

Susan K. Ipacs Nursing Legacy Scholarship (Undergraduate, High School/Scholarship) [4707]

Ira G. Turpin Scholar Program Fund (Undergraduate/Scholarship) [10767]

Jack R. Barckhoff Welding Management Scholarship (Undergraduate/Scholarship) [1665]

Judge Benjamin Schwartz Memorial Fund (Undergraduate/Scholarship) [3373]

Juilfs Foundation Scholarship (Undergraduate/Scholarship) [3374]

Julio C. Diaz Academic Scholarship Fund (Undergraduate/Scholarship) [10770]

Phil Kozel Memorial Scholarship (Undergraduate/Scholarship) [8588]

Kroger Cincinnati/Dayton Scholarship Fund (Undergraduate/Scholarship) [3375]

Lester and Eleanor Webster Foundation Fund (Undergraduate/Scholarship) [10775]

Lyle Everingham Scholarship Fund (Undergraduate/Scholarship) [3379]

Markley Family Scholarship Fund (Undergraduate/Scholarship) [10778]

Martha W. Tanner Memorial Fund (Undergraduate/Scholarship) [3381]

Marvin Rammelsberg Scholarship Fund (Undergraduate/Scholarship) [3382]

Harry Mestel Memorial Accounting Scholarship Fund (Undergraduate/Scholarship) [10780]

Michael Bany Memorial Scholarship Fund (Undergraduate/Scholarship) [3385]

John G. and Betty J. Mick Scholarship Fund (Undergraduate/Scholarship) [10781]

Lt. Colonel Robert G. Moreland Vocational/Technical Fund (Undergraduate/Scholarship) [10783]

Nelson Schwab Jr. Scholarship Fund (Undergraduate/Scholarship) [3389]

NERL Postdoctoral Research Program (Postdoctorate, Advanced Professional, Professional development/Fellowship) [11352]

NOHIMSS Student Scholarship Program (Undergraduate, Master's, Doctorate/Scholarship) [8494]

Norfolk Southern Foundation Scholarships (Undergraduate/Scholarship) [1329]

Notre Dame Club of Canton, Ohio Scholarship Fund (Undergraduate/Scholarship) [10785]

NRMRL Postdoctoral Research Program (Postdoctorate, Advanced Professional, Professional development/Fellowship) [11356]

Ohio Newspaper Association Minority Scholarship (Undergraduate/Scholarship) [8581]

ONLA President's Scholarship (Undergraduate/Scholarship) [8589]

ONLA Scholarships (Undergraduate, Two Year College, College/Scholarship) [8590]

ONWA Annual Scholarship (Undergraduate/Scholarship) [8582]

OSCA Graduate Student Scholarship Program (Graduate/Scholarship) [8594]

Pichler Family Scholarship Fund (Undergraduate/Scholarship) [3393]

PNC Scholarship Fund (Undergraduate/Scholarship) [3394]

Robert Esser Student Achievement Scholarship (Graduate, Undergraduate/Scholarship) [5701]

Robert H. Reakirt Scholarship Fund (Undergraduate/Scholarship) [3399]

Edward S. Roth Scholarship (Graduate, Undergraduate/Scholarship) [10411]

Ruth M. Cogan Foundation Trust (Undergraduate/Scholarship) [10789]

Prof. George Schneider Scholarship (Undergraduate/Scholarship) [10413]

Aaron Seesan Memorial Scholarship Fund (Undergraduate/Scholarship) [10790]

Dr. William E. & Norma Sprague Scholarship (Undergraduate, Graduate/Scholarship) [5183]

Thomas W. Gallagher Scholarship Fund (Undergraduate/Scholarship) [10797]

University Journalism Scholarships (Undergraduate/Scholarship) [8583]

Keith C. Vanderhyde Scholarship (Undergraduate/Scholarship) [5188]

Bob Evans And Wayne White Scholarship (Graduate, High School/Scholarship) [4708]

William A. Friedlander Scholarship Fund (Undergraduate/Scholarship) [3409]

William J. Rielly/MCURC Scholarship Fund (Undergraduate/Scholarship) [3410]

Woodward Trustees Foundation Scholarship (Undergraduate/Scholarship) [3411]

Wynne Family Memorial Fund (Undergraduate/Scholarship) [3412]

Zelma Gray Medical School Scholarship (Graduate, Doctorate/Scholarship) [4709]

Oklahoma

Leon Harris/Les Nichols Memorial Scholarships to Spartan College of Aeronautics & Technology (Undergraduate/Scholarship) [183]

Kansas Optometry Service Scholarship (Graduate, Undergraduate/Scholarship) [6365]

Southwest Chapter Roy Kinslow Scholarship (Undergraduate/Scholarship) [1566]

L-3 Communications Avionics Systems Scholarships (Undergraduate/Scholarship) [186]

Oklahoma City University Full-Time Merit Scholarships (Undergraduate/Scholarship) [8609]

Hatton W. Sumners Scholarships (Undergraduate/Scholarship) [8610]

Tom Taylor Memorial Scholarship to Spartan College of Aeronautics & Technology (Undergraduate/Scholarship) [195]

Lynn McNabb Walton Adelphe Scholarhship (Undergraduate/Scholarship) [6479]

Oregon

Clackamas County Farm Bureau Agricultural Scholarships (Undergraduate/Scholarship) [8715]

Davis Wright Tremaine 1L Diversity Scholarship (Undergraduate/Scholarship) [3979]

APTRA-Clete Roberts/Kathryn Dettman Memorial Journalism Scholarship (Undergraduate/Scholarship) [2022]

William Harrison Gill Education Fund (Undergraduate/Scholarship) [2480]

Janet Cullen Tanaka Geosciences Undergraduate Scholarship (Undergraduate/Scholarship) [2316]

Kilbuck Family Native American Scholarship (Undergraduate/Scholarship) [2484]

Christopher Mesi Memorial Music Scholarships (Undergraduate/Scholarship) [3179]

Oregon College/University Scholarships (Undergraduate/Scholarship) [8721]

OSCPA Educational Foundation High School Scholarships (Undergraduate/Scholarship) [8722]

Robert W. and Bernice Ingalls Staton Scholarships (Undergraduate/Scholarship) [11654]

University of Oregon Dean's Scholarships (Undergraduate/Scholarship) [11655]

University of Oregon Diversity Excellence Scholarship (Undergraduate/Scholarship) [11656]

University of Oregon General University Scholarship (Undergraduate, Graduate/Scholarship) [11657]

University of Oregon Presidential Scholarship (Undergraduate/Scholarship) [11658]

Washington City/County Management Association Scholarships (Graduate/Scholarship) [11885]

Yamhill County Farm Bureau Scholarships (Undergraduate/Scholarship) [8717]

Pennsylvania

Allegheny County Medical Society Medical Student Scholarship (Advanced Professional/Scholarship) [4796]

Allen Allured Fellowship (Graduate/Fellowship) [9345]

Alliance Medical Education Scholarship (AMES) (Undergraduate, Graduate/Scholarship) [4797]

Anil and Neema Thakrar Family Fund #1 (Undergraduate/Scholarship) [4774]

B-Brave McMahon/Stratton Scholarship Fund (Undergraduate/Scholarship) [4584]

Michael Baker Corp. Scholarship for Diversity in Engineering (Undergraduate/Scholarship) [2192]

Carrie and George Lyter Scholarship (Undergraduate/Scholarship) [4775]

CHOPR Fellowship Program (Postdoctorate/Fellowship) [11664]

The Warren E. "Whitey" Cole A.S.H.E. Scholarship Fund (Undergraduate/Scholarship) [4588]

Commonwealth "Good Citizen" Scholarships (Undergraduate/Scholarship) [2193]

Daniel B. Dixon Scholarship Fund (Undergraduate/Scholarship) [346]

F.C. Grote Fund (Graduate, Undergraduate/Scholarship) [347]

Nolan W. Feeser Scholarship Fund (Undergraduate/Scholarship) [4590]

Benjamin Franklin Trust Fund (Undergraduate, Vocational/Occupational/Scholarship) [4591]

Daniel G. and Helen I. Fultz Scholarship Fund (Undergraduate/Scholarship) [4592]

Norma Gotwalt Scholarship Fund (Undergraduate/Scholarship) [4777]

Scott A. Gunder, MD, DCMS Presidential Scholarship (Undergraduate, Graduate/Scholarship) [4798]

Morton and Beatrice Harrison Scholarship Fund (Undergraduate/Scholarship) [4593]

Conrad N. Hilton Scholarships (Undergraduate/Scholarship) [4962]

Jan DiMartino Delany Memorial Scholarship (Undergraduate/Scholarship) [4780]

Lindsay M. Entz Memorial Scholarship Fund (Undergraduate/Scholarship) [4595]

Mead Leadership Fellowships (Professional development/Fellowship) [8482]

Joseph and Catherine Missigman Memorial Nursing Scholarships (Undergraduate/Scholarship) [4597]

Missigman Scholarship Fund (Undergraduate/Scholarship) [4598]

Robert E. and Judy More Scholarship Fund (Undergraduate/Scholarship) [4599]

Norfolk Southern Foundation Scholarships (Undergraduate/Scholarship) [1329]

Oliver Rosenberg Educational Trust (Undergraduate/Scholarship) [4781]

Pennsylvania Engineering Foundation (PEF) Grants: Undergraduate (Undergraduate/Scholarship) [8964]

The Ruth Cook Pfautz Memorial Scholarship Fund (Undergraduate/Scholarship) [4782]

Russell Ackoff Doctoral Student Fellowship (Doctorate/Fellowship) [11662]

John A. Savoy Scholarship Fund (Undergraduate/Scholarship) [4605]

Soroptimist International of Chambersburg Fund (Undergraduate/Scholarship) [4783]

Minnie Patton Stayman Scholarships (Undergraduate/Scholarship) [8968]

Sue & Ken Dyer Foundation Travel Scholarship (Other/Scholarship) [4784]

John R. and Joan F. Werren Scholarships Fund (Undergraduate/Scholarship) [10801]

William H. Davis, Jr. Scholarship (Undergraduate/Scholarship) [3599]

Puerto Rico

Horatio Alger National Scholarships (Undergraduate/Scholarship) [5575]

Army Health Professions Scholarship Program (HPSP) (Professional development/Scholarship) [11288]

Buick Achievers Scholarship Program (Undergraduate/Scholarship) [4905]

Thomas R. Camp Scholarships (Graduate/Scholarship, Monetary) [1639]

Get Ahead Scholarship (Undergraduate, Graduate/Scholarship) [4474]

HACU/KIA Motors America, Inc. STEAM Scholarships (Undergraduate, Graduate/Scholarship) [5516, 6543]

Larson Aquatic Research Support Scholarships (LARS) (Graduate/Scholarship, Monetary, Recognition) [1643]

LIFE Lessons Scholarship Program (Undergraduate/Scholarship) [6849]

Peermusic Latin Scholarship (Undergraduate/Scholarship) [2636]

SHPE Dissertation Scholarship (Doctorate/Scholarship) [10351]

SHPE Professional Scholarship (Master's, Doctorate/Scholarship) [10352]

Rhode Island

Bach Organ Scholarship (Undergraduate/Scholarship) [9689]

Bruce and Marjorie Sundlun Scholarship (Undergraduate/Scholarship) [9690]

Lily and Catello Sorrentino Memorial Scholarship (Undergraduate/Scholarship) [9694]

Mead Leadership Fellowships (Professional development/Fellowship) [8482]

RISLA Student Loans (Undergraduate, Graduate/Loan) [9701]

Smith Family Awards Program for Excellence in Biomedical Research (Advanced Professional, Professional development/Award) [5443]

South Carolina

African American Network - Carolinas Scholarship Fund (Undergraduate/Scholarship) [4715]

Leon Bradley Scholarship Program (Undergraduate/Scholarship) [638]

The Carolina Panthers Players Sam Mills Memorial Scholarship (Undergraduate/Scholarship) [4724]

Charlotte Pride Scholarship (Community College, Two Year College, Undergraduate, Four Year College/Scholarship) [3279]

Judy Crocker Memorial Scholarship Fund (Undergraduate/Scholarship) [4730]

Albert and Eloise Midyette Memorial Scholarship Fund (Undergraduate/Scholarship) [4746]

Carolina Panthers Players Sam Mills Memorial Scholarships (Undergraduate/Scholarship) [4747]

Norfolk Southern Foundation Scholarships (Undergraduate/Scholarship) [1329]

Peter DeWitt Pruden and Phyllis Harrill Pruden Scholarship (Undergraduate/Scholarship) [11202]

Regions Riding Forward Scholarship Essay Contest (Undergraduate, High School/Scholarship) [9618]

SCSPA Scholarship (Graduate/Scholarship) [10618]

SCSPA Yearbook Scholarship (Undergraduate/Scholarship) [10619]

South Carolina Undergraduate Scholarships (Undergraduate/Scholarship) [10615]

SREB-State Doctoral Scholars Program - Dissertation Award (Doctorate/Scholarship, Award) [10663]

SREB-State Doctoral Scholars Program - Doctoral Award (Doctorate, Graduate/Scholarship) [10664]

The L. Phil and Alice J. Wicker Scholarship (Undergraduate/Scholarship) [1966]

The Wilbert L. and Zora F. Holmes Scholarship (Undergraduate/Scholarship) [4764]

Ted G. Wilson Memorial Scholarships (Undergraduate/Scholarship) [9338]

South Dakota

Marianne M. Stenvig Scholarship (Master's, Doctorate/Scholarship) [10623]

North Central Region 9 Scholarship (Undergraduate/Scholarship) [10410]

South Dakota Division Scholarships (Undergraduate/Scholarship) [7375]

Jerry Wheeler Scholarships (Undergraduate/Scholarship) [10625]

Tennessee

AISC/Southern Association of Steel Fabricators Scholarships (Undergraduate, Master's/Scholarship) [1054]

Tillie B. Alperin Scholarship (Graduate/Scholarship) [11595]

Archie Hartwell Nash Memorial Scholarship Fund (Graduate, Undergraduate/Scholarship) [3601]

B&W Y-12 Scholarship Fund (Undergraduate/Scholarship) [4254]

Barbara Hagan Richards Scholarship Fund (Undergraduate/Scholarship) [3603]

Belmont University Commercial Music Showcase Scholarship Fund (Undergraduate/Scholarship) [2471, 3604]

Leon Bradley Scholarship Program (Undergraduate/Scholarship) [638]

Leigh Carter Scholarship Fund (Undergraduate/Scholarship) [3606]

Claude T Coffman Scholarship (Graduate/Scholarship) [11596]

Dr. Mac Scholarship Fund (Undergraduate/Scholarship) [3612]

C. Cleveland Drennon, Jr. Memorial Scholarship (Graduate/Scholarship) [11597]

Eloise Pitts O'More Scholarship Fund (Undergraduate/Scholarship) [3616]

Emmett H. Turner Scholarship Fund (Undergraduate/Scholarship) [3617]

Evans and Petree Law Firm Scholarship (Graduate/Scholarship) [11598]

Federal Court Bench and Bar Scholarships (Graduate/Scholarship) [11599]

George Oliver Benton Memorial Scholarship Fund (Undergraduate/Scholarship) [3619]

Herbert Herff Presidential Law Scholarships (Graduate/Scholarship) [11601]

Robert and Elaine Hoffman Memorial Scholarships (Graduate/Scholarship) [11602]

Kathryn Hookanson Law Fellowship (Graduate/Fellowship) [11603]

John C. "Jack" Hough Memorial Law Scholarship (Graduate/Scholarship) [11604]

Cecil C. Humphreys Law Fellowships (Graduate/Fellowship, Internship) [11605]

Kansas Optometry Service Scholarship (Graduate, Undergraduate/Scholarship) [6365]

Mike and Mary Jean Kruse Scholarship Fund (Graduate, Undergraduate/Scholarship) [3631]

The Law Alumni Honor Student Scholarship (Graduate/Scholarship) [11606]

Judge William B. Leffler Scholarship (Graduate/Scholarship) [11607]

H. H. McKnight Memorial Scholarship (Graduate/Scholarship) [11608]

Memphis Access and Diversity Scholarships (Graduate/Scholarship) [11609]

Sam A. Myar, Jr. Law Scholarship (Graduate/Scholarship) [11610]

JoAhn Brown Nash Memorial Scholarship Fund (Undergraduate/Scholarship) [3640]

NCBWL Scholarships (Graduate/Scholarship) [7557]

Donald E. Nichols Scholarships (Undergraduate/Scholarship) [1475]

Norfolk Southern Foundation Scholarships (Undergraduate/Scholarship) [1329]

Pauline LaFon Gore Scholarship Fund (Undergraduate/Scholarship) [3641]

Peter DeWitt Pruden and Phyllis Harrill Pruden Scholarship (Undergraduate/Scholarship) [11202]

Donald and Susie Polden Dean's Scholarships (Graduate/Scholarship) [11611]

Ratner and Sugarmon Scholarship (Graduate/Scholarship) [11612]

Regina Higdon Scholarship (Undergraduate/Scholarship) [3642]

Regions Riding Forward Scholarship Essay Contest (Undergraduate, High School/Scholarship) [9618]

Joseph Henry Shepherd Scholarship (Graduate/Scholarship) [11613]

Southern Section A&WMA Scholarships (Graduate/Scholarship) [10668]

Amy E. Spain Memorial Scholarships (Graduate/Scholarship) [11614]

Springfield Family Scholarship (Graduate/Scholarship) [11615]

Steven L. Coffey Memorial Scholarship (Undergraduate/Scholarship) [4259]

Teddy Wilburn Scholarship Fund (Undergraduate/Scholarship) [3646]

Tennessee Learner's Scholarship (College, High School/Scholarship) [3888]

Tennessee Trucking Foundation Scholarship Fund (Undergraduate/Scholarship) [3647]

The Wilson Fellowship (Postdoctorate/Fellowship) [11677]

Wyatt, Tarrant & Combs, LLP, Dr. Benjamin L. Hooks Scholarship (Graduate/Scholarship) [11616]

Texas

AAMA Houston Chapter Health Training Scholarships (Other/Scholarship) [1770]

Alejandro "Alex" Abecia Reaching High Scholarships (Undergraduate/Scholarship) [3462]

BAFTX Early Starters Award (Undergraduate/Award) [2696]

BAFTX Graduate Award (Graduate/Award) [2697]

BAFTX Junior Achievers Award (Undergraduate/Award) [2698]

BAFTX Undergraduate Award (Undergraduate/Award) [2699]

TCDA Carroll Barnes Student Scholarships (Undergraduate/Scholarship) [740]

Barriger - Zachary Barriger Memorial Scholarship Fund (Undergraduate/Scholarship) [3463]

Bennett – Reverend E.F. Bennett Scholarship (Undergraduate/Scholarship) [3465]

Bill Bernbach Diversity Scholarships (Undergraduate/Scholarship) [510]

Brem - Marion Luna Brem/Pat McNeil Health and Education Endowment (Undergraduate/Scholarship) [3466]

D.C. and Virginia Brown Scholarship (Undergraduate/Scholarship) [3467]

Angela Faye Brown Video Essay Contest (Graduate/Scholarship) [2717]

TCDA Jim and Glenda Casey Professional Scholarships (Other/Scholarship) [741]

C.C.H.R.M.A. Scholarships (Undergraduate/Scholarship) [3469]

Dean – Derek Lee Dean Soccer Scholarships (Undergraduate/Scholarship) [3471]

Downes - Jay and Rheba Downes Memorial Scholarship (Undergraduate/Scholarship) [3473]

Eidson - John R. Eidson Jr.,'38 Scholarship (Undergraduate/Scholarship) [3474]

Flynn - Barney Flynn Memorial Scholarship (Undergraduate/Scholarship) [3475]

George Foreman Tribute to Lyndon B. Johnson (Undergraduate/Scholarship) [9472]

Gorrondona & Associates, Inc. / WTS High School Scholarships (Two Year College, Four Year College/Scholarship) [12174]

Guerra - Melissa Ann (Missy) Guerra Scholarship (Undergraduate/Scholarship) [3476]

Gulf Coast Hurricane Scholarship (Undergraduate/Scholarship) [10488]

George and Mary Josephine Hamman Foundation Scholarships (Undergraduate/Scholarship) [5264]

Hill Country Master Gardeners Horticulture Scholarship (Undergraduate, Graduate/Scholarship) [5510]

Houston Alumnae Association Doris Krikham Brokaw Memorial Adelphe Scholarship (Undergraduate, Graduate/Scholarship) [6444]

Houston Alumnae Association, Eunice "Scotty" Scott Siverson Memorial Adelphe Scholarship (Undergraduate, Graduate/Scholarship) [6445]

A. Joseph Huerta "Puedo" Scholarships (Undergraduate/Scholarship) [3478]

Institute of Transportation Engineers - Texas District Fellowships (Graduate/Fellowship) [5865]

Jamail/Long Challenge Grant Scholarships *(Undergraduate, Graduate/Scholarship)* [5522]

Financial Need Minority Scholarships *(Undergraduate/Scholarship)* [11149]

Laine - Casey Laine Armed Services Scholarship *(Undergraduate/Scholarship)* [3479]

Lay – Sue Kay Lay Memorial Scholarship *(Undergraduate/Scholarship)* [3480]

Danny T. Le Memorial Scholarship *(Undergraduate/Scholarship)* [11822]

Martin " Marty" Allen Scholarship *(Undergraduate/Scholarship)* [3481]

Miller – Brian and Colleen Miller Math and Science Scholarship *(Undergraduate/Scholarship)* [3482]

Le Hoang Nguyen College Scholarships (LHN) *(Undergraduate/Scholarship)* [11823]

The Thuy Nguyen Scholarships *(High School/Scholarship)* [11824]

Regions Riding Forward Scholarship Essay Contest *(Undergraduate, High School/Scholarship)* [9618]

Rotary Club of Corpus Christi Scholarship *(Undergraduate/Scholarship)* [3485]

Edward S. Roth Scholarship *(Graduate, Undergraduate/Scholarship)* [10411]

Seaman Family Scholarship *(Undergraduate/Scholarship)* [3487]

Shamsie – Judge Terry Shamsie Scholarship *(Undergraduate/Scholarship)* [3488]

Herman J. Smith Scholarship *(Undergraduate, Graduate/Scholarship)* [7935]

South Texas Unit Scholarship *(Undergraduate/Scholarship)* [5490]

Study.com Scholarship Texas Students *(Undergraduate, College/Scholarship)* [10873]

TACS/Texas Tech University K-12 *(Undergraduate/Scholarship)* [10973]

Talbert Family Memorial Scholarship *(Undergraduate/Scholarship)* [3490]

TCDA Abbott IPCO Professional Scholarships *(Other/Scholarship)* [742]

TCDA Bill Gorham Student Scholarship *(Undergraduate/Scholarship)* [743]

TCDA Cloys Webb Student Scholarship *(Undergraduate/Scholarship)* [744]

TCDA Gandy Ink Professional Scholarship *(Professional development/Scholarship)* [745]

TCDA General Fund Scholarships *(Undergraduate/Scholarship)* [746]

TCDA Past Presidents Student Scholarship *(Undergraduate/Scholarship)* [747]

Webb – Faye and Rendell C Webb JR Scholarship *(Undergraduate/Scholarship)* [3491]

YWA Foundation Scholarship *(Graduate, Undergraduate/Scholarship)* [12272]

Utah

APTRA-Clete Roberts/Kathryn Dettman Memorial Journalism Scholarship *(Undergraduate/Scholarship)* [2022]

William Harrison Gill Education Fund *(Undergraduate/Scholarship)* [2480]

Red Olive Women in STEM Scholarship *(Undergraduate, Graduate/Scholarship)* [9516]

Edward S. Roth Scholarship *(Graduate, Undergraduate/Scholarship)* [10411]

Vermont

Mead Leadership Fellowships *(Professional development/Fellowship)* [8482]

Vermont Paralegal Organization Paralegal Certification Scholarship *(Undergraduate/Scholarship)* [11802]

Virginia

Appalachian School of Law Merit Scholarship Program *(Undergraduate/Scholarship)* [1756]

H. Burton Bates Jr. Scholarships *(Graduate, Undergraduate/Scholarship)* [11843]

Bayly-Tiffany Scholarships *(Undergraduate/Scholarship)* [11712]

Bill Bernbach Diversity Scholarships *(Undergraduate/Scholarship)* [510]

Thomas M. Berry Jr. Scholarships *(Graduate, Undergraduate/Scholarship)* [11844]

Leo Bourassa Scholarship *(Undergraduate, Graduate/Scholarship)* [11837]

Leon Bradley Scholarship Program *(Undergraduate/Scholarship)* [638]

Charles Fred Wonson Scholarship *(Graduate/Scholarship)* [11713]

Betty Sams Christian Fellowships *(Doctorate/Fellowship)* [11835]

Doddridge County High School Promise Scholarship in Memory of Hattie Leggett *(Undergraduate/Scholarship)* [8844]

Florence L. Smith Medical Scholarship *(Graduate/Scholarship)* [5270]

H. Kruger Kaprielian Scholarship *(Undergraduate/Scholarship)* [11714]

Hampton Roads Tara Welch Gallagher Environmental Scholarship *(Graduate/Scholarship)* [5272]

Dixon Hughes Goodman Scholarships *(Undergraduate, Graduate/Scholarship)* [11845]

Jane S. Glenn Memorial Endowed Scholarship *(Undergraduate/Scholarship)* [9718]

Jefferson Graduate Fellowship *(Doctorate, Graduate/Fellowship)* [6263]

John Allen Love Scholarship *(Graduate, Undergraduate/Scholarship)* [11715]

Louis I. Jaffe Memorial Scholarship-ODU *(Graduate/Scholarship)* [5274]

Marshall Foundation Scholars Program *(Undergraduate/Scholarship)* [7112]

Lewis K. Martin II, M.D. and Cheryl Rose Martin Scholarship Fund *(Graduate/Scholarship)* [5275]

Mead Leadership Fellowships *(Professional development/Fellowship)* [8482]

Norfolk Southern Foundation Scholarships *(Undergraduate/Scholarship)* [1329]

Palmer Farley Memorial Scholarship *(Graduate/Scholarship)* [5277]

Peter DeWitt Pruden and Phyllis Harrill Pruden Scholarship *(Undergraduate/Scholarship)* [11202]

Richard D. and Sheppard R. Cooke Memorial Scholarship *(Graduate/Scholarship)* [5278]

Drs. Kirkland Ruffin & Willcox Ruffin Scholarships *(Graduate/Scholarship)* [5279]

Hy Smith Endowment Fund *(Undergraduate/Scholarship)* [5280]

SREB-State Doctoral Scholars Program - Dissertation Award *(Doctorate/Scholarship, Award)* [10663]

SREB-State Doctoral Scholars Program - Doctoral Award *(Doctorate, Graduate/Scholarship)* [10664]

The Tingen & Williams Undergraduate Scholarship *(Undergraduate/Scholarship)* [11040]

V. Thomas Forehand, Jr. Scholarship *(Undergraduate/Scholarship)* [11717]

VA AWWA Graduate Student Scholarships *(Graduate/Scholarship)* [11841]

Virginia Tech Doctoral Scholarship *(Doctorate/Scholarship)* [11846]

VSCPA Educational Foundation Minority Accounting Scholarship *(Graduate, Undergraduate/Scholarship)* [11847]

VSCPA Educational Foundation Undergraduate Accounting Scholarships *(Undergraduate/Scholarship)* [11848]

VSCPA Graduate and PhD Accounting Scholarship *(Doctorate, Graduate/Scholarship)* [11849]

The L. Phil and Alice J. Wicker Scholarship *(Undergraduate/Scholarship)* [1966]

Ted G. Wilson Memorial Scholarships *(Undergraduate/Scholarship)* [9338]

Yount, Hyde & Barbour Scholarships *(Undergraduate, Graduate/Scholarship)* [11850]

Washington

Beta Sigma Phi Visual Arts Scholarship *(Undergraduate/Scholarship)* [10049]

Boeing Company Scholarship *(Undergraduate/Scholarship)* [10050]

CFR Volunteer Internships *(Undergraduate, Graduate/Internship)* [3863]

College Success Foundation Chateau Ste. Michelle Scholarship Fund *(Undergraduate/Scholarship)* [3514]

College Success Foundation Leadership 1000 Scholarship *(Undergraduate/Scholarship)* [3515]

College Success Foundation Washington State Governors' Scholarship for Foster Youth *(Undergraduate/Scholarship)* [3516]

Dave Lamb Scholarship *(Graduate/Scholarship)* [11912]

Davis Wright Tremaine 1L Diversity Scholarship *(Undergraduate/Scholarship)* [3979]

APTRA-Clete Roberts/Kathryn Dettman Memorial Journalism Scholarship *(Undergraduate/Scholarship)* [2022]

Graduate Pulmonary Nursing Fellowship *(Professional development/Fellowship, Scholarship)* [4572]

Educator Conditional Scholarship And Repayment Programs *(Other, Undergraduate/Loan, Scholarship)* [11918]

William Harrison Gill Education Fund *(Undergraduate/Scholarship)* [2480]

High School Academic Scholarship *(Undergraduate/Scholarship)* [10053]

Janet Cullen Tanaka Geosciences Undergraduate Scholarship *(Undergraduate/Scholarship)* [2316]

Joseph Wood Rogers Memorial Scholarship in Mathematics *(Undergraduate/Scholarship)* [10055]

Ron LaFreniere Business Administration Scholarship *(Undergraduate/Scholarship)* [10057]

Margaret Mallett Nursing Scholarship *(Undergraduate/Scholarship)* [10058]

Margaret Svec Scholarship *(Undergraduate/Scholarship)* [10059]

Christopher Mesi Memorial Music Scholarships *(Undergraduate/Scholarship)* [3179]

Mill Creek Chamber of Commerce Scholarship *(Undergraduate/Scholarship)* [7393]

Eric Niemitalo Scholarship in Earth and Environmental Science *(Undergraduate/Scholarship)* [10060]

Rhonda J.B. O'Leary Memorial Scholarship *(Undergraduate, Graduate/Scholarship)* [4305]

Olympia Tumwater Foundation Traditional Scholarships *(Undergraduate, High School/Scholarship)* [8616]

Olympia Tumwater Foundation Transitional (nontraditional) Scholarships *(Undergraduate/Scholarship)* [8617]

STC-PSC Scholarships *(Undergraduate, Graduate/Scholarship)* [10541]

University of Puget Sound LGBT Leadership Scholarship *(Undergraduate/Scholarship)* [9772]

Washington City/County Management Association Scholarships *(Graduate/Scholarship)* [11885]

Washington CPA Foundation Scholarship *(Undergraduate/Scholarship)* [11899]

Washington State Nurses Association Foundation Scholarships (WSNF) *(Graduate, Undergraduate/Scholarship)* [11914]

Why Get Your Blue On? Video Scholarships *(Graduate, Undergraduate/Award, Scholarship)* [11997]

WIGA College Scholarships *(Postgraduate, Graduate, Undergraduate/Scholarship)* [11894]

WSGC Community College Transfer Scholarships *(Undergraduate/Scholarship)* [11901]

West Virginia

William (Billbo) Boston/Harold Knopp Scholarship *(Undergraduate/Scholarship)* [8833]

Freda Burge Scholarship *(Undergraduate/Scholarship)* [8835]

Cindy Curry Memorial Scholarship *(Undergraduate/Scholarship)* [8841]

Lawrence E. and Jean L. Davis Scholarship *(Undergraduate/Scholarship)* [8843]

David Edward Farson Scholarships *(Undergraduate/Scholarship)* [8845]

William E. "Bill" Gallagher Scholarship *(Undergraduate/Scholarship)* [8847]

H.G. Hardbarger Science - Mathematics Award *(Undergraduate, Vocational/Occupational/Award)* [8853]

Holly Jackson-Wuller Memorial Scholarship *(Undergraduate/Scholarship)* [8860]

Dr. Charles Kelly Memorial Scholarships *(Undergraduate/Scholarship)* [8862]

Mead Leadership Fellowships *(Professional development/Fellowship)* [8482]

Norfolk Southern Foundation Scholarships *(Undergraduate/Scholarship)* [1329]

Mary K. Smith Rector Scholarship *(Undergraduate, Vocational/Occupational/Scholarship)* [8870]

James H. Roberts Athletic Scholarship *(Undergraduate/Scholarship)* [8872]

SREB-State Doctoral Scholars Program - Dissertation Award *(Doctorate/Scholarship, Award)* [10663]

SREB-State Doctoral Scholars Program - Doctoral Award *(Doctorate, Graduate/Scholarship)* [10664]

The L. Phil and Alice J. Wicker Scholarship *(Undergraduate/Scholarship)* [1966]

Wisconsin

Ahlswede, Norman & Marie Endowed Engineering Scholarship *(Undergraduate/Scholarship)* [11732]

Barry M. Goldwater Scholarship *(Undergraduate/Scholarship)* [11733]

William E. Barto Scholarship Fund *(Undergraduate/Scholarship)* [4200]

Mary Ann Brichta Scholarships *(Undergraduate/Scholarship)* [11735]

Chapter 4 - Lawrence A. Wacker Memorial Scholarship *(Undergraduate/Scholarship)* [10391]

CMA Private Lesson Program: Instrumental Scholarships for Elementary and Middle School Students *(Undergraduate/Scholarship)* [3420]

Founding Fathers Leadership Scholarships *(Undergraduate/Scholarship)* [12113]

Carleton A. Friday Scholarship *(Undergraduate/Scholarship)* [7377]

Illinois Landscape Contractors Association Scholarships *(Undergraduate/Scholarship)* [5703]

John P. and Tashia F. Morgridge Scholarship *(Undergraduate, Graduate/Scholarship)* [11736]

Kemper K. Knapp Scholarship *(Undergraduate/Scholarship)* [11737]

Kenneth G. Weckel Scholarship *(Undergraduate/Scholarship)* [7378]

George Koeppel Scholarship/All School *(Undergraduate/Scholarship)* [11738]

Kraft Foods Food Science Minority Scholarship *(Undergraduate/Scholarship)* [11739]

Abby Marlatt Scholarship *(Undergraduate/Scholarship)* [11740]

McBurney Disability Resource Center General Scholarships *(Undergraduate/Scholarship)* [11741]

North Central Region 9 Scholarship *(Undergraduate/Scholarship)* [10410]

Patricia Buchanan Memorial Scholarship *(Undergraduate/Scholarship)* [11742]

Pi Lambda Theta Scholarship *(Undergraduate/Scholarship)* [11743]

Powers-Knapp Scholarship Program *(Undergraduate/Scholarship)* [11744]

Returning Adult and Single-Parent Scholarships *(Undergraduate/Scholarship)* [11745]

Robert Esser Student Achievement Scholarship *(Graduate, Undergraduate/Scholarship)* [5701]

John A. and Jean Quinn Sullivan Scholarship Funds *(Undergraduate/Scholarship)* [4220]

University of Wisconsin-Madison National Merit Scholarship *(Undergraduate/Scholarship)* [11747]

UW-Madison Engineering Diversity Scholarship *(Undergraduate/Scholarship)* [11748]

UW-Madison Reserve Officers Training Corps Scholarships (ROTC) *(Undergraduate/Scholarship)* [11750]

UW-Madison School of Education Minority Scholarship *(Undergraduate/Scholarship)* [11751]

WASBO Safety, Security and Wellness Grant *(Other/Grant)* [12111]

William F. Vilas Merit Scholarship *(Undergraduate/Scholarship)* [11752]

Wisconsin Broadcasters Association Foundation Student Scholarships *(Graduate/Scholarship)* [12117]

Wisconsin Lawton Minority Retention Grants *(Undergraduate/Grant)* [11753]

Wisconsin Minority Teacher Loan *(Undergraduate/Loan)* [10812]

Wisconsin Nursing Student Loan *(Graduate, Undergraduate, Doctorate/Loan)* [10813]

Wyoming

AISC/Rocky Mountain Steel Construction Association Scholarships *(Undergraduate, Master's/Scholarship)* [1053]

APTRA-Clete Roberts/Kathryn Dettman Memorial Journalism Scholarship *(Undergraduate/Scholarship)* [2022]

Dorothy Mountain Memorial Scholarship *(Graduate/Scholarship)* [6922]

William Harrison Gill Education Fund *(Undergraduate/Scholarship)* [2480]

Griffin Foundation Scholarships *(Undergraduate/Scholarship)* [5243]

Harry Walts Memorial Graduate Scholarship *(Graduate/Scholarship)* [6923]

CANADA

AABP Amstutz Scholarship *(Undergraduate/Scholarship)* [522]

AABP Student Externship Program *(Undergraduate/Scholarship)* [525]

AAG Provincial Student Award *(Graduate/Award)* [246]

AAN Medical Student Summer Research Scholarship *(Graduate/Scholarship)* [460]

AANS Medical Student Summer Research Fellowships (MSSRF) *(Undergraduate/Fellowship)* [607]

AAS Korean Studies Scholarship Program *(Graduate/Scholarship)* [2061]

The AASSC Gurli Aagaard Woods Undergraduate Publication Award *(Undergraduate/Award)* [2032]

The AASSC Marna Feldt Graduate Publication Award *(Graduate/Award)* [2033]

AASSC Norwegian Travel Grant *(Undergraduate, College, University/Grant)* [2034]

Abel Wolman Fellowship *(Doctorate/Fellowship, Award, Monetary)* [1634]

Evelyn Joy Abramowicz Memorial Scholarship *(Undergraduate/Scholarship)* [6282]

ABTA Basic Research Fellowships *(Postdoctorate/Fellowship)* [699]

ABTA Medical Student Summer Fellowship Program *(Undergraduate/Fellowship)* [701]

Jack Ackroyd Scholarships *(Other/Scholarship)* [2083]

ACS Faculty Research Fellowships *(Professional development/Fellowship)* [773]

AEBC Toronto Chapter Scholarships *(Undergraduate/Scholarship)* [361]

AECT Foundation Mentor Endowment Scholarship *(Doctorate, Graduate/Scholarship)* [2155]

AEF Educational Scholarship *(Undergraduate/Scholarship)* [255]

AFA Film and Video Arts Project Grants *(Professional development/Grant)* [257]

Music Individual Project Funding *(Professional development/Grant)* [258]

AFA Theatre & Performance Art Project Grants *(Professional development/Grant)* [259]

Affiliated Distributors Electrical Industry Scholarship Awards *(Undergraduate/Scholarship)* [4337]

A.G. Bell School Age Financial Aid Program *(High School/Scholarship, Monetary)* [333]

AGE-WELL Graduate Student and Postdoctoral Awards in Technology and Aging *(Master's, Doctorate, Postdoctorate/Award)* [128]

AIA and the Global Automotive Aftermarket Symposium Scholarships *(Undergraduate/Scholarship)* [2357]

Airgas - Terry Jarvis Memorial Scholarship *(Undergraduate/Scholarship)* [1650]

Alberta Centennial Award *(Undergraduate/Scholarship)* [281]

Alberta Child Care Association Professional Development Grants *(Professional development/Grant)* [253]

Alberta Innovates Graduate Student Scholarships *(Graduate/Scholarship)* [275]

Alexander D. Pringle Memorial Scholarship *(Advanced Professional/Scholarship)* [9328]

Alexander Graham Bell Canada Graduate Scholarships-Doctoral Program *(Doctorate, Master's/Scholarship)* [3803]

Hon. Lincoln Alexander Scholarship *(Undergraduate, Graduate/Scholarship)* [2586]

AlgaeCal Health Scholarship *(Undergraduate, Graduate, Vocational/Occupational/Scholarship)* [340]

Stephanie Ali Memorial Scholarships *(Undergraduate/Scholarship)* [11682]

ALIS Fellowships for Full-time Studies in French *(Undergraduate/Fellowship)* [282]

ALIS Graduate Student Scholarship *(Graduate/Scholarship)* [283]

ALIS International Education Awards - Ukraine *(Undergraduate/Scholarship)* [284]

Allen T. Lambert Scholarship *(Postgraduate/Scholarship)* [12247]

Alliance Pipeline Scholarships *(Other/Scholarship)* [2417]

Lorraine Allison Scholarship *(Graduate/Scholarship)* [1789]

America Express Travel Scholarships *(Undergraduate/Scholarship)* [1581]

American Judges Association Law Student Essay Competition *(Undergraduate/Prize)* [1066]

American Liver Foundation Liver Scholar Award *(Doctorate/Award)* [1091]

Dr. Andy Anderson Young Professional Awards *(Professional development/Award)* [9146]

Ann C. Beckingham Scholarship *(Graduate, Other/Scholarship)* [2989]

Annette Urso Rickel Foundation Dissertation Award for Public Policy *(Graduate/Scholarship)* [1273]

Annie Kirshenblatt Memorial Scholarship *(Graduate, Undergraduate/Scholarship)* [11062]

Annual Research Doctoral and Postgraduate Fellowship Grant Program *(Doctorate, Postdoctorate, Postgraduate, Advanced Professional/Fellowship, Grant)* [2923]

ANS Research Grant Award *(Professional development/Grant)* [1158]

ANSER Graduate Student Awards for Research on Nonprofits and the Social Economy *(Graduate/Award)* [2252]

A.O. Putnam Memorial Scholarship *(Undergraduate/Scholarship)* [5826]

APLA Merit Award *(Professional development/Scholarship)* [2344]

Aplastic Anemia and Myelodysplasia Association of Canada Scholarships *(Graduate, Master's/Scholarship)* [3054]

Architects Association of PEI Scholarship *(Master's, Doctorate, Graduate/Scholarship)* [3701]

Arctic Physical Therapy Scholarship *(Undergraduate/Scholarship)* [1794]

Art Acquisition by Application *(Professional development/Grant)* [260]

Arts Graduate Scholarship *(Graduate/Scholarship)* [285]

ASA Graduate Scholarships *(Graduate/Scholarship)* [1385]

ASAC-CJAS PhD Research Grant Award *(Doctorate/Grant, Award)* [79]

Asia Pacific Foundation of Canada Junior Research Fellowships *(Undergraduate, Master's/Fellowship)* [4711]

Asia Pacific Foundation of Canada Media Fellowships *(Professional development/Fellowship)* [4712]

Asia Pacific Foundation of Canada Post-Graduate Research Fellowships *(Master's, Doctorate/Fellowship)* [4713]

ASTA Holland America Line Graduate Research Scholarships *(Graduate/Scholarship)* [1583]

Astra Zeneca Medical Scholarship *(Advanced Professional/Scholarship)* [8222]

AstraZeneca Award *(Doctorate/Award)* [3055]

Atkinson Fellowships in Public Policy *(Professional development/Fellowship)* [2338]

Atlantic Salmon Federation Olin Fellowships *(Graduate/Fellowship)* [2347]

Joan Auld Scholarship *(Undergraduate/Scholarship)* [3702]

Avis Budget Group Scholarships *(Graduate/Scholarship)* [1585]

James L. Baillie Memorial Fund - Student Award for Field Research *(Graduate/Grant)* [4451]

Airgas - Jerry Baker Scholarship (Undergraduate/ Scholarship) [1658]

Lynn Ann Baldwin Scholarships (Master's/Scholarship) [2093]

Ball Horticultural Company Scholarship (Undergraduate/Scholarship) [894]

Banting Postdoctoral Fellowships Program (Postdoctorate/Fellowship) [3804]

Baxter Corporation Canadian Research Awards in Anesthesia (Other/Award, Monetary) [2877]

BCPF Bursaries (Undergraduate/Scholarship) [10731]

William B. Bean Student Research Award (Undergraduate/Grant) [1196]

Suzanne Beauregard Scholarships (Undergraduate, Graduate/Scholarship) [5027]

Beaverbrook Media at McGill Student Paper Prize (Undergraduate/Prize) [2955]

Ed Becker Conference Travel Awards (Undergraduate, Graduate/Award) [4403]

Dr. Ann C. Beckingham Scholarships (Doctorate/ Scholarship) [3056]

Jenny Panitch Beckow Memorial Scholarship - Canada (Graduate/Scholarship) [6283]

Bell Aliant Medical Education Scholarship (Advanced Professional/Scholarship) [8223]

Harvey Bell Memorial Prize (Graduate/Prize, Scholarship) [11674]

Viscount Bennett Fellowship (Graduate/Fellowship) [2918]

The Bentley Cropping Systems Fellowship (Graduate/Fellowship) [3263]

The E. Alexander Bergstrom Memorial Research Award (Undergraduate, Master's/Award) [2177]

Bernard Amtmann Fellowship (Postgraduate, Other/ Fellowship) [2569]

Berton W. Huestis Memorial Scholarship (Advanced Professional/Scholarship) [8224]

Harold Bettinger Scholarship (Undergraduate, Graduate/Scholarship) [896]

Leonard Bettinger Vocational Scholarship (Undergraduate, Vocational/Occupational/Scholarship) [897]

Beverley Mascoll Scholarship (Undergraduate/ Scholarship) [2588]

Dr. Noorali and Sabiya Bharwani Endowment (Undergraduate/Scholarship) [8413]

Hussein Jina Bharwani Memorial Endowment (Undergraduate/Scholarship) [8414]

BHCRI Cancer Research Training Program (CRTP) Awards (Graduate, Postdoctorate, Advanced Professional, Professional development/Grant) [5649]

BHCRI Studentship Awards (Undergraduate, Graduate, Advanced Professional/Grant) [5653]

Timothy Bierlmeier Memorial Scholarships (Undergraduate, Master's/Scholarship) [12288]

Biological Survey of Canada Scholarship (Postgraduate/Scholarship) [4404]

Biomedical Research Grants (Postdoctorate/Grant) [6545]

Blaski Alex Memorial Scholarship (Undergraduate/ Scholarship) [9657]

BMO Capital Markets Lime Connect Equity through Education Scholarships (Undergraduate, Graduate/Scholarship) [6860]

BMO Financial Group Lime Connect Canada Scholarship Program for Students with Disabilities (Undergraduate, Graduate/Scholarship) [6861]

BMO Medical Education Scholarship (Advanced Professional/Scholarship) [8225]

Edith and Arnold N. Bodtker Grants (Undergraduate, Graduate/Grant, Internship) [3968]

Steve Bonk Scholarship (Undergraduate, Graduate/ Scholarship) [3136]

John H. Borden Scholarship (Postgraduate/Scholarship) [4405]

Borek Maria and Czeslaw Scholarship (Undergraduate/Scholarship) [9658]

Margery Boyce Bursary Award (Graduate/Award, Scholarship) [2893]

Geoffrey Bradshaw Memorial Scholarship (Graduate/Scholarship) [12294]

Brain Canada-ALS Canada Career Transition Awards (Postdoctorate, Advanced Professional, Professional development/Grant) [2672]

Brain Canada-ALS Canada Hudson Translational Team Grants (Advanced Professional, Professional development/Grant) [2674]

James Bridenbaugh Memorial Scholarship (Undergraduate/Scholarship) [898]

Margaret Brine Graduate Scholarships For Women (Graduate, Master's, Doctorate/Scholarship) [2978]

Louis J. Brody Q.C. Entrance Scholarships (Graduate/Scholarship) [12248]

Norm Bromberger Research Bursary (Undergraduate, Graduate/Scholarship) [11672]

Peter F. Bronfman Scholarships of Merit (Postgraduate/Scholarship) [12249]

Brooks Scholarship (Graduate/Scholarship) [4411]

CFSA Randal Brown & Associates Awards (Undergraduate/Award) [2114]

Robert K. Brown Scholarships (Undergraduate, Master's/Scholarship) [2978]

Pamfil and Maria Bujea Family Orthodox Christian Seminarian Scholarships (Undergraduate/Scholarship) [1367]

Burger King Scholars Program (Undergraduate/ Scholarship) [2748]

Burlington Medical Student Bursary (Undergraduate/ Grant) [8646]

Burndy Canada Inc. Academic Achievement Awards (Undergraduate/Scholarship) [4338]

Burroughs Wellcome Fund Collaborative Research Travel Grants (CRTG) (Doctorate, Postdoctorate/ Grant) [2750]

Business, Education and Technology Scholarships (Graduate, Undergraduate/Scholarship) [362]

Joan Butler Award in Perinatal Intensive Care Nursing (Advanced Professional/Award) [7755]

Leon C. Bynoe Memorial Scholarships (Undergraduate/Scholarship) [11683]

CAC Gerry Bruno Scholarship (Graduate, Undergraduate/Scholarship) [199]

CALL/ACBD Education Reserve Fund Grant (Professional development/Grant) [2899]

CALL/ACBD Research Grants (Graduate/Grant) [2900]

CALT Prize for Academic Excellence (Other/Prize) [2904]

Cameco Corporation Scholarships in the Geological Sciences - Continuing Students (Undergraduate/ Scholarship) [2863]

Cameco Corporation Scholarships in the Geological Sciences - Entering Students (Undergraduate/ Scholarship) [2864]

Dalton Camp Awards (Professional development/ Award, Monetary) [4829]

Thomas R. Camp Scholarships (Graduate/Scholarship, Monetary) [1639]

Theodore R. Campbell Scholarship (Undergraduate/ Scholarship) [286]

Canada-Ukraine Parliamentary Program Internship Scholarships (CUPP) (Undergraduate/Scholarship, Internship) [11888]

Canadian Association of Cardiac Rehabilitation Graduate Scholarship Awards (Graduate/Scholarship) [2887]

Canadian Association for Studies in Co-operation Scholarships - Alexander Fraser Laidlaw Fellowship (Graduate/Fellowship) [2951]

Canadian Association for Studies in Co-operation Scholarships - Amy and Tim Dauphinee Scholarship (Graduate/Scholarship) [2952]

Canadian Association for Studies in Co-operation Scholarships Lemaire Co-operative Studies Award (Graduate, Undergraduate/Scholarship) [2953]

Canadian Blood Services Graduate Fellowship Program (Graduate/Fellowship) [2920]

Canadian Blood Services Postdoctoral Fellowship Program (Postdoctorate/Fellowship) [2921]

Canadian Cancer Society Travel Awards (Doctorate, Master's, Postdoctorate/Award) [2942]

Canadian Derivatives Scholarship (Postgraduate/ Scholarship) [2663]

Canadian Energy Law Foundation Graduate Scholarship in Law (Advanced Professional/Scholarship) [2962]

Canadian Federation of Independent Grocers National Scholarship (Undergraduate/Scholarship) [4531]

Canadian Federation of University Women Etobicoke Bursary (Undergraduate/Scholarship) [11684]

Canadian Hard of Hearing Association Scholarship Program (Undergraduate/Scholarship) [2997]

Canadian Historical Geography Award (Master's, Graduate, Undergraduate/Prize) [2086]

Canadian Home Economics Association Fellowship (CHEA) (Postgraduate/Fellowship) [2969]

Canadian Hydrographic Association Student Award (Undergraduate/Award) [3008]

Canadian Identification Society Essay/Scholarship Awards (Advanced Professional, Professional development/Award) [3010]

Canadian Iranian Foundation Scholarship (Undergraduate/Scholarship) [3035]

Canadian IT Law Association Student Writing Contest (Undergraduate/Prize) [3132]

Canadian Japanese-Mennonite Scholarship (Undergraduate/Scholarship) [7254]

Canadian Nurses Foundation Northern Award (Undergraduate/Scholarship) [3057]

Canadian Nurses Foundation Scholarships (Undergraduate, Master's, Doctorate/Scholarship) [3058]

Canadian Pain Society Post-Doctoral Fellowship Awards (Postdoctorate/Fellowship) [3086]

The Canadian Parking Association Scholarship (CPA) (Undergraduate/Scholarship) [2125]

Canadian Picture Pioneers Scholarship (Undergraduate/Scholarship) [3100]

The Canadian Poultry Research Council Postgraduate Scholarship (Postgraduate/Scholarship) [3102]

Canadian Seniors' Golf Association Scholarships (Undergraduate/Scholarship) [5028]

Canadian Studies Postdoctoral Fellowships (Postdoctorate/Fellowship) [3800]

Canadian Technical Asphalt Association Scholarships (Undergraduate/Scholarship) [3130]

Canadian Water Resources Association Harker/ Cameron Women in Water Scholarship (Graduate/ Scholarship) [2107]

CAP Student Leadership Award (Undergraduate/ Scholarship) [2910]

CAPSLE Bursary. (Graduate/Fellowship) [2908]

Cardiac Health Foundation of Canada Scholarship (Graduate/Scholarship) [3158]

Career Awards at the Scientific Interface (CASI) (Undergraduate, Postdoctorate, Graduate/Grant) [2753]

John Carew Memorial Scholarship (Graduate/Scholarship) [899]

Carin Alma E. Somers Scholarship (Undergraduate/ Scholarship) [2345]

Herb Carnegie Scholarship (Undergraduate/Scholarship) [2590]

Carol Anne Letheren Entrance Award (Postgraduate/Award) [12250]

CAS/Vitaid-LMA Residents' Research Grant Competition (Other/Award) [2880]

Fraser Milner Casgrain Scholarships (Other/Scholarship) [2418]

Catzman Award for Professionalism and Civility (Advanced Professional, Professional development/ Award) [96]

CBCF - Ontario Research Project Grants (Advanced Professional, Professional development/Grant) [2932]

CCAE Ontario Regional Chapter Scholarship (Advanced Professional, Professional development/ Scholarship) [6742]

CCCN Research Grant Program (Professional development/Grant) [3791]

CCFF Clinical Fellowships (Doctorate, Graduate/ Fellowship) [4543]

CCFF Fellowships (Doctorate, Graduate/Fellowship) [4544]

CCFF Scholarships (Doctorate, Graduate/Scholarship) [4545]

CCGSE Mentorship Award (Graduate/Award) [10261]

CCLA Summer Legal Volunteer Opportunities for Law Students and Law Graduates (Graduate, Undergraduate/Internship) [2948]

CEMF Engineering Ambassador Awards (Undergraduate/Award) [2964]

Johnson & Johnson Scholarships (Undergraduate/
Scholarship) [3062]

J.R. (Joe) Power National Scholarship (Postgradu-
ate/Scholarship, Monetary) [9443]

Juchniewicz Kazimiera Memorial Scholarship (Un-
dergraduate/Scholarship) [9666]

Kacperski Stefan & Weronika Memorial Scholarship
(Undergraduate/Scholarship) [9667]

Karl C. Ivarson Scholarship for Students in Soil Science and Related Studies (Master's, Doctorate/
Scholarship, Award) [130]

Katharine Whiteside Taylor Grant (Professional de-
velopment/Scholarship) [8826]

Lucile B. Kaufman Women's Scholarship (Under-
graduate/Scholarship) [10403]

The Dr. Terry Kavanagh Fellowship (Graduate/Fel-
lowship) [3159]

E. Wayne Kay Co-op Scholarship (Undergraduate/
Scholarship) [10404]

E. Wayne Kay Community College Scholarship (Undergraduate, Community College/Scholarship)
[10405]

Kenneth Laundy Entrance Scholarship (Graduate/
Scholarship) [12255]

Dr. Dorothy J. Kergin Fellowships (Doctorate, Master's/Fellowship) [3063]

Kerrwil's J.W. Kerr Continuing Education Scholarship Awards (Undergraduate/Scholarship) [4351]

Keith Kevan Scholarship (Postgraduate/Scholarship)
[4409]

Dr. Arthur A. Kezian DDS Science Scholarship (Undergraduate, Graduate, College, University/Schol-
arship) [6541]

KFOC Allied Health Doctoral Fellowships (Doctor-
ate/Fellowship) [6546]

KFOC Allied Health Scholarships (Graduate/Schol-
arship) [6547]

KFOC Biomedical Scholarships (Doctorate/Scholar-
ship) [6548]

Khaki University and Y.M.C.A. Memorial Scholarships (Undergraduate/Scholarship) [11694]

Killam Fellowships (Undergraduate/Fellowship)
[4771]

Klimt Stefan & Janina Scholarship (Undergraduate/
Scholarship) [9668]

Hans Klinkenberg Memorial Scholarship (Under-
graduate/Scholarship) [3022]

George Kokociski Memorial Scholarships (Under-
graduate/Scholarship) [9669]

Anna and John Kolesar Memorial Scholarship (Un-
dergraduate/Scholarship) [293]

The Bernie Kom Memorial Award (Postgraduate/
Award) [12256]

Korean Studies Dissertation Workshop (Graduate/
Fellowship) [10248]

CHS James Kreppner Memorial Scholarship and
Bursary Program (Undergraduate/Scholarship)
[3003]

Doreen Kronick Scholarships (Graduate/Scholar-
ship) [2130]

Kuropas Jan Memorial Scholarship (Undergraduate/
Scholarship) [9670]

Liela Klinger Kurztman Memorial Scholarship (Un-
dergraduate/Scholarship) [6296]

LA Tutors 123 Innovation in Education Scholarship
(All/Scholarship) [6626]

Lafarge Community Leaders Scholarships (Other/
Scholarship) [2420]

James D. Lang Memorial Scholarship (Graduate/
Scholarship) [2902]

Language Teacher Bursary Program (Other/Award)
[294]

Languages In Teacher Education Scholarship (Un-
dergraduate/Scholarship) [295]

Larson Aquatic Research Support Scholarships
(LARS) (Graduate/Scholarship, Monetary, Recognition) [1643]

Claudette Mackay Lassonde Ambassador Award
(Doctorate, Undergraduate/Award) [2966]

Karen E. Latt Memorial Scholarship (Graduate/
Scholarship) [6297]

Graduate Fellowships (Graduate/Fellowship) [6679]

Law Foundation of Newfoundland and Labrador
Law School Scholarships (Advanced Professional/
Scholarship) [6681]

Lawrence Bloomberg Entrance Award (Postgradu-
ate/Award) [12257]

Robert G. Lawrence Prize (Doctorate, Graduate/
Prize, Award) [2105]

Bourse Georgette LeMoyne (Graduate/Fellowship)
[2973]

Leslie C. Green Veterans Scholarship (Juris Doctorate, Advanced Professional/Scholarship) [3878]

Lila Fahlman Scholarship (Undergraduate, Gradu-
ate/Scholarship) [2960]

Richard Lim Professional Development Scholarship
(Advanced Professional, Professional develop-
ment/Scholarship, Recognition) [6743]

Lime Connect Pathways Scholarship for High
School Seniors with Disabilities (Undergraduate/
Scholarship) [6863]

Tecla Lin & Nelia Laroza Memorial Scholarships
(Undergraduate/Scholarship) [3064]

Lineups.com Future of Sports Scholarship Program
(Undergraduate, Graduate/Scholarship) [6871]

LionsDeal.com Scholarships (Undergraduate/Schol-
arship) [6875]

Literary Individual Project Funding (Professional de-
velopment/Grant) [264]

Lloyd Houlden Fellowship (Advanced Professional,
Professional development/Fellowship) [2897]

Lois Hole Humanities and Social Sciences Scholarship (Undergraduate/Scholarship) [296]

Long-term International Fellowships (Professional
development/Fellowship) [3778]

Lorne and Ruby Bonnell Scholarship (Master's,
Graduate/Scholarship) [3704]

Sir James Lougheed Award of Distinction (Doctorate, Graduate, Master's/Award) [297]

M. Hildred Blewett Fellowship (Postdoctorate/Fel-
lowship, Award, Monetary) [1225]

Dr. Arlene MacIntyre Medical Student Bursary (Un-
dergraduate/Grant, Recognition) [8648]

Mackenzie King Open Scholarship (Graduate, Postgraduate, Undergraduate/Scholarship) [7182]

Manhattan Street Capital National Scholarship (Un-
dergraduate/Scholarship) [7016]

Manulife Financial Scholarship (Undergraduate/
Scholarship) [3793]

Marie Tremaine Fellowship (Postgraduate, Other/
Fellowship) [2570]

Shirley Stone Marinkovich Memorial Scholarships
(Undergraduate/Scholarship) [6458]

Markham-Colegrave International Scholarships (Un-
dergraduate/Scholarship) [901]

Marshall Cavendish Scholarships (Graduate/Schol-
arship, Monetary) [1079]

Eleanor Jean Martin Award (Master's/Scholarship)
[3065]

Martin Fischer Training Award (Undergraduate/
Award) [2995]

Dick Martin Scholarships (Postgraduate/Scholarship,
Award) [2946]

Martin Walmsley Award for Entrepreneurship
(Graduate/Award) [8636]

Elizabeth Massey Award (Postgraduate/Award)
[2974]

Mature Student Scholarship (Undergraduate/Schol-
arship) [4430]

Al Maurer Awards (Undergraduate, Graduate, Advanced Professional/Scholarship) [4292]

Maziarz Tadeusz Scholarship (Undergraduate/Schol-
arship) [9671]

John Mazurek Memorial-Morgex Insurance Scholarship (Other/Scholarship) [314]

Giuliano Mazzetti Scholarship (Undergraduate/
Scholarship) [10408]

Joseph McCulley Educational Trust Fund (Graduate,
Undergraduate/Grant) [11695]

G. William McQuade Memorial Scholarships (Advanced Professional/Scholarship) [8233]

Douglas McRorie Memorial Scholarships (Doctorate,
Master's/Scholarship, Award) [131]

Dr. Margaret McWilliams Pre-Doctoral Fellowship
(Doctorate/Fellowship) [2975]

Dr. Ernest and Minnie Mehl Scholarships (Under-
graduate/Scholarship) [298]

Mensa Canada Scholarship Programme (Under-
graduate/Scholarship) [7259]

Donald Menzies Bursary Award (Postgraduate/
Scholarship, Award) [2894]

Merck Frosst Canada Ltd. Postgraduate Pharmacy
Fellowships (Graduate, Postgraduate, Doctorate/
Fellowship) [2173]

Al Mercury Scholarships (Undergraduate/Scholar-
ship) [11696]

The Michener-Deacon Fellowship for Investigative
Journalism (Professional development/Fellowship)
[4655]

The Michener-Deacon Fellowship for Journalism
Education (Professional development/Fellowship)
[4656]

Michno Bronislaw Memorial Scholarship (Under-
graduate/Scholarship) [9672]

Microsoft Research Graduate Women's Scholarships (Graduate/Scholarship) [7356]

Microsoft Research PhD Fellowships (Doctorate/
Fellowship) [7357]

Miles Spencer Nadal Entrance Award (Master's/
Award) [12258]

Military Nurses Association Scholarships (Master's/
Scholarship) [3066]

Mineralogical Association of Canada Scholarships
(Doctorate, Graduate/Scholarship) [2244]

Minerva Scholarships (Undergraduate/Scholarship)
[2598]

MLA Continuing Education Grants (CE) (Graduate/
Grant) [7219]

MLA Scholarship (Graduate, Master's/Scholarship)
[7222]

John H. Moss Scholarships (Undergraduate/Schol-
arship) [11697]

Movember Clinical Trials (Advanced Professional/
Grant) [9362]

Movember Discovery Grants (Advanced Professional, Professional development/Grant) [9363]

Movember Rising Star in Prostate Cancer Research
Awards (Advanced Professional, Professional de-
velopment/Grant) [9364]

Movember Team Grants (Advanced Professional,
Professional development/Grant) [9365]

MSA Graduate Fellowship (Graduate/Fellowship)
[7532]

Marvin Mundel Memorial Scholarship (Undergradu-
ate/Scholarship) [5834]

Margaret Munro Award (Undergraduate/Scholarship)
[3067]

Dr. Helen K. Mussallem Fellowships (Master's/Fel-
lowship) [3068]

NAAMA Scholarships (Undergraduate/Scholarship)
[7598]

NACBS Dissertation Fellowship (Graduate, Doctor-
ate/Fellowship) [8420]

NACBS-Huntington Library Fellowship (Doctorate,
Postdoctorate/Fellowship) [8422]

Nadene M Thomas Graduate Research Bursary
(Graduate/Scholarship) [315]

National Board Technical Scholarship (College, Four
Year College, University/Scholarship) [7730]

National Greenhouse Manufacturers Association
(NGMA) Scholarships (Undergraduate/Scholar-
ship) [902]

Nawrot Marek Memorial Scholarship (Undergradu-
ate/Scholarship) [9673]

NB College of Physicians and Surgeons Medical
Education Scholarship (Advanced Professional/
Scholarship) [8234]

NCLEJ Law School Graduate Fellows and Volunteers (Graduate, Advanced Professional/Fellow-
ship) [7751]

Neuroscience Certification Bursary Awards (Other/
Award) [2095]

Alan H. Neville Memorial Scholarships (Graduate/
Scholarship) [363]

New Brunswick Nurses Association Scholarships
(Master's/Scholarship) [3069]

Sharon Nield Memorial Scholarships (Undergradu-
ate/Scholarship) [3070]

Louise McKinney Post-secondary Scholarship (Un-
dergraduate/Scholarship) [299]

North American Society Fellowship Award (NAS Fellowship) (Professional development/Fellowship)
[9147]

Northern Alberta Development Council Bursaries
Program (Undergraduate/Scholarship) [301]

Northern Alberta Development Council Bursary (Un-
dergraduate/Scholarship) [302]

Place of Study Index

Dr. Robert and Anna Shaw Scholarship (Undergraduate/Scholarship) [309]

Dr. Robert Norman Shaw Scholarship (Undergraduate/Scholarship) [310]

David S. Sheridan Canadian Research Awards (Other/Award) [2881]

Joseph Shinoda Memorial Scholarship (Undergraduate/Scholarship) [10047]

Siemens Canada Academic Awards (Undergraduate/Scholarship) [4356, 10079]

Sigma Theta Tau International Scholarships (Doctorate/Scholarship) [3073]

Sloan Research Fellowships (Doctorate/Fellowship) [10171]

SME Directors Scholarships (Undergraduate/Scholarship) [10414]

SME Education Foundation Family Scholarships (Undergraduate/Scholarship) [10415]

SME Future Leaders of Manufacturing Scholarship (Graduate, Undergraduate/Scholarship) [10416]

Brian Smith Memorial Scholarships (Undergraduate/Scholarship) [2669]

Boleslaw & Irena Sobczak Scholarships (Undergraduate/Scholarship) [9678]

The Frank H. Sobey Awards for Excellence in Business Studies (Undergraduate/Award) [10238]

Sobeys & Empire Work Experience & Scholarship Program - Future Leaders Awards (Other/Scholarship) [10239]

Society of Graphic Designers of Canada Adobe Scholarships (Undergraduate/Scholarship) [10255]

Society of Graphic Designers of Canada Applied Arts Scholarships (Undergraduate/Scholarship) [10256]

Society of Graphic Designers of Canada Veer Scholarships (Undergraduate/Scholarship) [10257]

Sonepar Canada Scholarship Awards (Undergraduate/Scholarship) [4357]

Sons of Scotland Past Grand Chiefs Scholarship (Undergraduate/Scholarship) [10593]

Betty Spalton Scholarships (Undergraduate/Scholarship) [2454]

Beatrice Drinnan Spence Scholarship (Undergraduate, Vocational/Occupational/Scholarship) [4268]

SSHRC Doctoral Fellowship Program (Doctorate/Fellowship, Scholarship) [3797]

SSHRC Postdoctoral Fellowships (Postdoctorate/Fellowship) [3798]

The Standard Recognition of Excellence Awards (Undergraduate/Scholarship) [4358]

Lasek Stanisław and Aniela Scholarship (Undergraduate/Scholarship) [9679]

Taylor Statten Memorial Fellowships (Graduate/Scholarship) [11698]

The Stanley H. Stearman Awards (Undergraduate/Scholarship) [8080]

Stelpro Scholarship 360: Energizing Potential (Undergraduate/Scholarship) [4359]

The David Stockwood Memorial Prize (Advanced Professional, Professional development/Prize) [97]

Glenna Stone Memorial Scholarship (Undergraduate/Scholarship) [2999]

Student Investigator Research Grant - Vestibular (Graduate, Doctorate/Grant) [435]

Summerside-Natick International Friendship Hockey Fund (Undergraduate/Scholarship) [3706]

Sun Life Financial Medical Student Bursary (Undergraduate/Grant) [8650]

TAC Foundation-ATS Traffic Scholarships (Undergraduate, Graduate/Scholarship) [11080]

TAC Foundation-Canadian Council of Independent Laboratories Graduate Student Scholarships (CCIL) (Graduate/Scholarship) [11081]

TAC Foundation-Dr. Ralph Haas Graduate Student Scholarships (Graduate/Scholarship) [11085]

TAC Foundation-exp Scholarships (Undergraduate, Graduate/Scholarship) [11087]

TAC Foundation-SNC Lavalin Scholarships (Undergraduate, Graduate/Scholarship) [11098]

TAC Foundation-Stantec Consulting Dr. Ralph Haas Scholarships (Graduate, Undergraduate/Scholarship) [11099]

TAC Foundation-Tetra Tech EBA Inc. Scholarships (Undergraduate, Graduate/Scholarship) [11100]

Tanna H. Schulich MBA Entrance Scholarship (Graduate/Scholarship) [12261]

Taverner Awards (Undergraduate/Grant) [10296]

RABC William Taylor Scholarships (Undergraduate/Scholarship) [4360]

TD Bank Medical Education Scholarship (Advanced Professional/Scholarship) [8239]

TD Meloche Monnex Centennial Doctoral Scholarship (Doctorate/Scholarship) [3074]

TEVA Canada Survivor Scholarship (Undergraduate, University/Scholarship) [3292]

Thelma Cardwell Scholarship (Master's, Doctorate/Scholarship) [3082]

THFC Medical Research Grants (Professional development/Grant) [5454]

The Rev. Chuck and Nancy Thomas Scholarship (Professional development/Scholarship) [11256]

Ken Thomson Scholarship (Graduate/Scholarship) [2109]

Tom Hanson Photojournalism Award (All/Internship) [6622]

John L. Tomasovic, Sr. Scholarship (Undergraduate/Scholarship) [906]

Tommy Douglas Scholarship (Undergraduate/Scholarship) [8150]

Torchia Scholarship in Public Relations (Undergraduate/Scholarship) [3104]

Evald Torokvei Foundation Scholarships (Graduate/Scholarship) [11699]

Transoft Solutions, Inc. Ahead of the Curve Scholarship (AOTC) (Graduate, Undergraduate/Scholarship) [5867]

Tristin Memorial Scholarships (Undergraduate, Vocational/Occupational/Scholarship) [6756]

TrustedPros Scholarships (Undergraduate/Scholarship) [11131]

Sam Tughan Scholarships (Undergraduate/Scholarship) [6182]

UMDF Clinical Research Fellowship Training Awards (Professional development/Fellowship) [11266]

University of the Aftermarket Foundation Scholarship (Community College/Scholarship) [11428]

University of Toronto Nortel Institute Undergraduate Scholarships (Undergraduate/Scholarship) [11701]

University of Toronto Student Union (UTSU) Undergraduate Grant (Undergraduate/Grant) [11702]

UPS Scholarship for Female Students (Undergraduate/Scholarship) [5836]

UPS Scholarship for Minority Students (Undergraduate/Scholarship) [5837]

Claudette Upton Scholarships (Undergraduate/Scholarship) [4289]

USA/USA-Ukramerazha Scholarships (Undergraduate/Scholarship) [11413]

Val Mason Scholarship (Graduate, Professional development/Scholarship, Award) [3114]

Vale Manitoba Operations Post-secondary Scholarship (Undergraduate/Scholarship, Internship) [11421]

Vale Master's Engineering Ambassador Award (Master's/Award) [2967]

Jacob and Rita Van Namen Marketing Scholarship (Undergraduate/Scholarship) [908]

John Vanderlee Award (Undergraduate/Scholarship) [3075]

Vanier Canada Graduate Scholarships Program (Graduate/Scholarship) [3808]

Vectorworks Design Scholarship (Undergraduate, Graduate/Scholarship) [11796]

Mair Verthuy Scholarship (Undergraduate/Scholarship) [3732]

Visual Arts and New Media Individual Project Funding (Professional development/Grant) [265]

Vocational (Bettinger, Holden & Perry) scholarship (Undergraduate, Vocational/Occupational/Scholarship) [909]

Wagner-Torizuka Fellowship (Professional development/Fellowship) [10445]

Myrtle & Earl Walker Scholarships (Undergraduate/Scholarship) [10417]

Robert E. Walter Memorial Scholarship (Undergraduate/Scholarship) [6958]

Colin Wasacase Scholarship (Undergraduate/Scholarship) [8661]

William E. Weisel Scholarship (Undergraduate/Scholarship) [10418]

The WESCO Student Achievement Award (Undergraduate/Scholarship) [4361, 11969]

Portia White Scholarship (Undergraduate/Scholarship) [2602]

Ann Collins Whitmore Memorial Scholarship (ACWMS) (Graduate/Scholarship) [3098]

Ernest Wilby Memorial Scholarship (Undergraduate/Scholarship) [5805]

Wilkinson and Company LLP Scholarships (Undergraduate/Scholarship) [12033]

William A. and Ann M. Brothers Scholarship (Undergraduate/Scholarship) [1673]

Dr. Alice E. Wilson Awards (Master's, Doctorate/Fellowship) [2976]

Women in Coaching National Coaching Institute Scholarships (Undergraduate/Scholarship) [3448]

Violet Wondergem Health Science Scholarship (Undergraduate, Graduate/Scholarship) [910]

WRI Education Foundation Scholarships - Graduate (Graduate/Scholarship) [12103]

WRI Education Foundation Scholarships - High School Seniors (Undergraduate/Scholarship) [12104]

WRI Education Foundation Scholarships - Undergraduate (Undergraduate/Scholarship) [12105]

York Graduate Scholarship (YGS) (Master's, Doctorate/Scholarship) [12262]

York Regional Police Scholarships (Undergraduate/Scholarship) [6222]

Youth or the Environment Scholarships (Other/Scholarship) [2421]

Dr. Steven S. Zalcman Memorial Scholarship (Graduate, Postgraduate/Scholarship) [6301]

CANADA (BY PROVINCE)

Alberta

AAG Provincial Student Award (Graduate/Award) [246]

AIHS Graduate Studentships (Master's, Doctorate/Fellowship) [272]

AIHS Postgraduate Fellowships (Postgraduate, Advanced Professional/Fellowship) [273]

Alberta Award for the Study of Canadian Human Rights and Multiculturalism (Doctorate, Graduate, Master's/Award) [280]

Alberta Blue Cross Scholarships for Aboriginal Students (Undergraduate/Scholarship) [251]

Alberta Centennial Award (Undergraduate/Scholarship) [281]

Alberta Child Care Association Professional Development Grants (Professional development/Grant) [253]

Alberta Innovates Graduate Student Scholarships (Graduate/Scholarship) [275]

Alberta Innovates - Technology Futures Graduate Student Scholarships in ICT (Doctorate, Graduate, Master's/Scholarship) [276]

Alberta Innovates - Technology Futures Graduate Student Scholarships in Nanotechnology (Doctorate, Graduate/Scholarship) [277]

Alberta Innovates - Technology Futures Graduate Student Scholarships in Omics (Doctorate, Master's, Professional development/Scholarship) [278]

Alberta Teachers Association Doctoral Fellowships in Education (Doctorate/Fellowship) [312]

Alberta Teachers Association Educational Research Award (Other/Scholarship) [313]

Alberta Ukrainian Centennial Commemorative Scholarship (Graduate/Scholarship) [11887]

ALIS Graduate Student Scholarship (Graduate/Scholarship) [283]

ALIS International Education Awards - Ukraine (Undergraduate/Scholarship) [284]

Robert C. Carson Memorial Bursary (Undergraduate/Scholarship) [287]

CBCF - Prairies/NWT Grants in Clinical Research (Advanced Professional, Professional development/Grant) [2935]

CBCF - Prairies/NWT Grants in Health Services and Policy Research (Advanced Professional, Professional development/Grant) [2936]

CBCF - Prairies/NWT Postdoctoral Fellowships *(Postdoctorate, Professional development/Fellowship)* [2937]

CBCF - Prairies/NWT Research Grants in Psychosocial, Cultural and Environmental Determinants of Health *(Advanced Professional, Professional development/Grant)* [2938]

Helen Darcovich Memorial Doctoral Fellowship *(Doctorate/Fellowship)* [3026]

Marusia and Michael Dorosh Fellowship *(Master's, Graduate/Fellowship)* [3027]

Earl and Countess of Wessex - World Championships in Athletics Scholarship *(Undergraduate/Scholarship)* [289]

Grande Prairie 4-H District Scholarship *(Undergraduate/Scholarship)* [14]

Helen and George Kilik Scholarship *(Undergraduate/Scholarship)* [290]

Jason Lang Scholarship *(Undergraduate/Scholarship)* [292]

Steven Kobrynsky Memorial Scholarship *(Undergraduate/Scholarship)* [3029]

Siobhan Isabella Reid Memorial Scholarships *(Graduate, Undergraduate/Scholarship)* [6754]

Servus Credit Union 4-H Scholarship *(College, University, Undergraduate/Scholarship)* [16]

Dr. Robert Norman Shaw Scholarship *(Undergraduate/Scholarship)* [310]

The Kennett Y. Spencer Memorial Scholarship *(Graduate/Scholarship)* [11524]

Stasiuk Master's Research Fellowship *(Master's/Fellowship)* [3032]

Viscount Bennett Scholarship *(Graduate/Scholarship)* [6721]

British Columbia

CBCF - BC/Yukon Region Breast Cancer Research Grants Competition *(Advanced Professional/Grant)* [2924]

CBCF - BC/Yukon Region Breast Cancer Survivor Dragon Boat Grants *(Professional development/Grant)* [2925]

CBCF - BC/Yukon Region Community Health Grants *(Professional development/Grant)* [2926]

CBCF - BC/Yukon Region Small Initiative Funds *(Professional development/Grant)* [2927]

Law Society Scholarship *(Graduate/Scholarship)* [6730]

MSFHR Research Trainee Award *(Postdoctorate, Professional development/Grant)* [10181]

MSFHR Scholar Awards *(Advanced Professional, Professional development/Grant)* [10182]

SPEATBC Entrance Scholarship *(Graduate, High School/Scholarship)* [10518]

Women's Health Research Foundation of Canada Scholarship Program *(Graduate/Scholarship)* [12157]

Manitoba

CBCF - Prairies/NWT Grants in Clinical Research *(Advanced Professional, Professional development/Grant)* [2935]

CBCF - Prairies/NWT Grants in Health Services and Policy Research *(Advanced Professional, Professional development/Grant)* [2936]

CBCF - Prairies/NWT Postdoctoral Fellowships *(Postdoctorate, Professional development/Fellowship)* [2937]

CBCF - Prairies/NWT Research Grants in Psychosocial, Cultural and Environmental Determinants of Health *(Advanced Professional, Professional development/Grant)* [2938]

Centre on Aging Betty Havens Memorial Graduate Fellowship *(Graduate, Doctorate, Master's/Fellowship)* [11584]

Health, Leisure and Human Performance Research Institute Graduate Student Travel Award *(Graduate/Grant, Award)* [11589]

Jack MacDonell Scholarship for Research in Aging *(Graduate, Doctorate, Master's/Scholarship)* [11585]

Esther and Samuel Milmot Scholarship *(Graduate, Undergraduate/Scholarship)* [11586]

University of Manitoba Centre on Aging Research Fellowship *(Advanced Professional/Fellowship)* [11587]

New Brunswick

Dr. Frank and Audrey Wanamaker Medical Scholarship *(Advanced Professional/Scholarship)* [8227]

Dr. Paul and Gayle Sohi Medical Education Scholarship *(Advanced Professional/Scholarship)* [8230]

EFC Atlantic Region Scholarships *(Undergraduate/Scholarship)* [4342]

NBHRF/ASRP Doctoral Training Awards *(Doctorate/Award)* [413, 8212]

NBHRF Bridge Grants *(Professional development/Grant)* [8213]

NBHRF Doctoral Studentship *(Doctorate/Grant)* [8214]

NBHRF Establishment Grants *(Professional development/Grant)* [8215]

NBHRF Health Research Strategic Initiative Grants *(Professional development/Grant)* [8216]

NBHRF Master's Studentship *(Master's/Grant)* [8217]

NBHRF Postdoctoral Fellowships *(Postdoctorate/Fellowship)* [8218]

Newfoundland and Labrador

Ocean Industry Student Research Awards *(Undergraduate, Graduate, Postdoctorate/Award)* [9641]

Northwest Territories

CBCF - Prairies/NWT Grants in Clinical Research *(Advanced Professional, Professional development/Grant)* [2935]

CBCF - Prairies/NWT Grants in Health Services and Policy Research *(Advanced Professional, Professional development/Grant)* [2936]

CBCF - Prairies/NWT Postdoctoral Fellowships *(Postdoctorate, Professional development/Fellowship)* [2937]

CBCF - Prairies/NWT Research Grants in Psychosocial, Cultural and Environmental Determinants of Health *(Advanced Professional, Professional development/Grant)* [2938]

NWT Law Foundation/Graeme Garson Scholarships *(Advanced Professional/Scholarship)* [8545]

Nova Scotia

EFC Atlantic Region Scholarships *(Undergraduate/Scholarship)* [4342]

Nunavut

CBCF - Prairies/NWT Grants in Clinical Research *(Advanced Professional, Professional development/Grant)* [2935]

CBCF - Prairies/NWT Grants in Health Services and Policy Research *(Advanced Professional, Professional development/Grant)* [2936]

CBCF - Prairies/NWT Postdoctoral Fellowships *(Postdoctorate, Professional development/Fellowship)* [2937]

CBCF - Prairies/NWT Research Grants in Psychosocial, Cultural and Environmental Determinants of Health *(Advanced Professional, Professional development/Grant)* [2938]

Ontario

Dr. Anderson Abbott Awards *(Undergraduate/Scholarship)* [11681]

AEBC Toronto Chapter Scholarships *(Undergraduate/Scholarship)* [361]

CBCF - Ontario Nurse and Allied Health Professional Fellowships *(Advanced Professional, Professional development/Fellowship)* [2929]

CBCF - Ontario Physician Fellowships *(Doctorate, Professional development/Fellowship)* [2930]

CBCF - Ontario Research Fellowships *(Doctorate, Postdoctorate, Professional development/Fellowship)* [2931]

CJF Canadian Journalism Fellowships *(Graduate, Other, Undergraduate/Fellowship)* [6620]

Connaught Fellowship *(Graduate/Fellowship)* [11704]

Helene and George Coward Award in Gerontology *(Graduate/Award)* [11709]

Dr. Ezra Nesbeth Foundation Scholarship *(Undergraduate/Scholarship)* [6213]

Doreen Brady Memorial Scholarship *(Postgraduate/Scholarship)* [8639]

Educational Fellowship For Practicing Physicians *(Advanced Professional, Professional development/Fellowship)* [9155]

Franklin Empire Scholarship Awards *(Undergraduate/Scholarship)* [4344]

Marcus Mosiah Garvey Scholarships *(Undergraduate/Scholarship)* [6216]

Gerrie Electric Memorial Scholarship Awards *(Undergraduate/Scholarship)* [4346]

Grant Assistance Program for Autism Professionals - Institutional Standards *(Undergraduate, Graduate/Grant)* [8654]

Hammond Power Solutions Inc. Outstanding Electrical Scholar Awards (HPS) *(Undergraduate/Award)* [4348]

Norm Hollend Fellowships in Oncology *(Postdoctorate/Fellowship)* [6930]

Joan Rogers Kamps Bursary *(Undergraduate, Postgraduate, Professional development/Scholarship)* [8641]

John Alexander McLean Scholarship *(Undergraduate/Scholarship)* [11022]

Margaret Lynch Memorial Fellowship *(Postgraduate/Fellowship)* [8642]

Mary C. Babcock Fellowship *(Postgraduate/Fellowship)* [8643]

Norfolk Southern Foundation Scholarships *(Undergraduate/Scholarship)* [1329]

Nortel Institute for Telecommunications Graduate Scholarship *(Graduate, Master's/Scholarship)* [11706]

Ontario Women's Institute Scholarships *(Undergraduate/Scholarship)* [4525]

Gail Posluns Fellowships in Hematology *(Postdoctorate/Fellowship)* [6931]

Post-Doctoral Mellon Fellowships *(Postdoctorate/Fellowship)* [9246]

PSI Graham Farquharson Knowledge Translation Fellowship *(Advanced Professional, Professional development/Fellowship)* [9156]

PSI Healthcare Research by Community Physicians Grants *(Advanced Professional, Professional development/Grant)* [9157]

Resident Research Grant *(Postgraduate, Professional development/Grant)* [9158]

Rose Cassin Memorial Scholarship *(Postgraduate/Scholarship)* [8644]

Ryerson Scholarships *(Undergraduate/Scholarship)* [6219]

Wilfred George Scott Fellowship in Gerontology *(Graduate/Fellowship)* [11710]

Eva Smith Bursary *(Postgraduate/Scholarship)* [6220]

Brian Smith Memorial Scholarships *(Undergraduate/Scholarship)* [2669]

Toronto Rehabilitation Institute Graduate Student Scholarships - Ontario Student Opportunities Trust Fund (OSOTF) *(Graduate/Scholarship)* [11065]

University of Toronto Accenture Scholarships *(Undergraduate/Scholarship)* [11700]

Prince Edward Island

Orin Carver Scholarship *(Undergraduate/Scholarship)* [3703]

EFC Atlantic Region Scholarships *(Undergraduate/Scholarship)* [4342]

Quebec

Erin J.C. Arsenault Fellowships in Space Governance *(Graduate/Fellowship)* [7188]

Therese and David Bohbot Scholarship *(Undergraduate/Scholarship)* [6285]

Yvonne L. Bombardier Visual Arts Scholarship Program *(Master's, Doctorate/Scholarship)* [2651]

Harry Feldman Memorial Scholarship *(Undergraduate/Scholarship)* [6290]

Franklin Empire Scholarship Awards (Undergraduate/Scholarship) [4344]

Hammond Power Solutions Inc. Outstanding Electrical Scholar Awards (HPS) (Undergraduate/Award) [4348]

Harry Hopmeyer Memorial Scholarship (Undergraduate/Scholarship) [6292]

Joseph Katz Memorial Scholarship (Undergraduate/Scholarship) [6294]

Henriette & Marcel Korner Scholarship (Undergraduate/Scholarship) [6295]

Liela Klinger Kurztman Memorial Scholarship (Undergraduate/Scholarship) [6296]

Irene Brand Lieberman Memorial Scholarship (Graduate/Scholarship) [6298]

Philip F. Vineberg Travelling Fellowship in the Humanities (Undergraduate/Scholarship, Monetary) [7184]

Saskatchewan

Auto Body Technician Certificate Scholarship (Graduate/Scholarship) [9884]

Bernard Michel Scholarship (Undergraduate/Scholarship) [2862]

Norm Bromberger Research Bursary (Undergraduate, Graduate/Scholarship) [11672]

CBCF - Prairies/NWT Grants in Clinical Research (Advanced Professional, Professional development/Grant) [2935]

CBCF - Prairies/NWT Grants in Health Services and Policy Research (Advanced Professional, Professional development/Grant) [2936]

CBCF - Prairies/NWT Postdoctoral Fellowships (Postdoctorate, Professional development/Fellowship) [2937]

CBCF - Prairies/NWT Research Grants in Psychosocial, Cultural and Environmental Determinants of Health (Advanced Professional, Professional development/Grant) [2938]

Dr. Alfred E. Slinkard Scholarship (Graduate/Scholarship) [9921]

Don Jaques Memorial Fellowship (Graduate/Fellowship) [9922]

Stan Hamilton Scholarship (Graduate/Scholarship) [9885]

LDAS Scholarship (Undergraduate/Scholarship) [6760]

Poundmaker Memorial Scholarships (Undergraduate/Scholarship) [11675]

Saskatchewan Government Insurance Actuarial Science Scholarship (Graduate/Scholarship) [9887]

Saskatchewan Hockey Association Scholarships (Undergraduate/Scholarship) [9893]

Saskatchewan Pulse Growers Undergraduate Scholarships (Undergraduate/Scholarship) [9923]

Saskatchewan School Boards Association Education Scholarships (Graduate/Scholarship) [9925]

Saskatchewan School Boards Association Graduate Student Award (Graduate/Award) [9926]

SGI Business Insurance Diploma Scholarships (Undergraduate/Scholarship) [9890]

SGI Graduate Research Grant (Graduate/Grant) [9891]

Yukon Territory

CBCF - BC/Yukon Region Breast Cancer Research Grants Competition (Advanced Professional/Grant) [2924]

CBCF - BC/Yukon Region Breast Cancer Survivor Dragon Boat Grants (Professional development/Grant) [2925]

CBCF - BC/Yukon Region Community Health Grants (Professional development/Grant) [2926]

CBCF - BC/Yukon Region Small Initiative Funds (Professional development/Grant) [2927]

Yukon Law Foundation Scholarship (Undergraduate/Scholarship) [12401]

INTERNATIONAL

AAMC Foundation Engagement Program for International Curators Grants (Advanced Professional, Professional development/Grant) [2057]

AWS International Scholarship Program (Undergraduate, Graduate/Scholarship) [1657]

Franklin Mosher Baldwin Memorial Fellowships (Master's, Doctorate/Fellowship) [6751]

Barbara and Nicole Heacox Foreign Study & Travel Scholarship (Undergraduate/Scholarship) [5068]

The Bentley Cropping Systems Fellowship (Graduate/Fellowship) [3263]

Boren Fellowships (Graduate/Fellowship) [5840]

Boren Scholarships (Undergraduate, College/Scholarship) [5841]

Deborah Partridge Wolfe International Fellowship (Graduate) (Graduate, Undergraduate/Fellowship) [12410]

Economic Club Business Study Abroad Scholarships (Undergraduate/Scholarship) [5149]

Conrad N. Hilton Scholarships (Undergraduate/Scholarship) [4962]

James B. Pearson Fellowship (Graduate/Scholarship) [6361]

Harold Lancour Scholarship for Foreign Study (Professional development/Scholarship) [2498]

Multi-Country Research Fellowship (Doctorate, Postdoctorate/Fellowship) [3851]

Satter Human Rights Fellowship (Graduate, Master's, Juris Doctorate/Fellowship) [5366]

SDE Fellowship (Graduate, Postgraduate/Fellowship) [5060]

Thomas J. Watson Fellowship (Undergraduate/Fellowship) [11939]

The Tikvah Fellowship (Undergraduate/Fellowship) [11034]

UNIMA-USA Scholarship (Professional development/Scholarship) [11239]

Weston Brain Institute International Fellowships in Neuroscience (Graduate/Fellowship) [12000]

INTERNATIONAL (BY REGION)

Africa

AIMS Long-term Research Grants (Doctorate, Graduate/Grant) [1033]

AIMS Short-term Research Grants (Doctorate, Graduate/Grant) [1034]

Baker McKenzie Graduate Legal Studies Scholarships (Graduate, Professional development/Scholarship) [2412]

L'Oréal-UNESCO For Women in Science International Rising Talents (Doctorate, Postdoctorate/Fellowship) [8695, 11268]

Learning from Peace in Sub-Saharan Africa (Professional development/Grant) [11377]

Arab States

L'Oréal-UNESCO For Women in Science International Rising Talents (Doctorate, Postdoctorate/Fellowship) [8695, 11268]

Asia and Pacific

Baker McKenzie Graduate Legal Studies Scholarships (Graduate, Professional development/Scholarship) [2412]

Asia

EAPSI Fellowships (Doctorate, Graduate/Fellowship, Award) [8067]

International Society Travel Grant (Professional development/Grant) [450]

Baltic States

Abraham and Rachela Melezin Memorial Fellowship (Doctorate, Postdoctorate/Fellowship) [12235]

Maria Salit-Gitelson Tell Memorial Fellowship (Postdoctorate, Doctorate/Fellowship) [12240]

Caribbean

AABP Student Externship Program (Undergraduate/Scholarship) [525]

Caribbean Hotel and Tourism Association Scholarship (Graduate, Undergraduate/Scholarship) [3167]

IAF Fellowships (Doctorate/Fellowship) [5883]

Paleontological Society International Research Program Sepkoski Grants (Advanced Professional, Graduate/Grant) [8814]

TFI Latin America Media Arts Fund (Professional development/Grant) [11110]

Central America

Paleontological Society International Research Program Sepkoski Grants (Advanced Professional, Graduate/Grant) [8814]

East Asia

IDRC Research Awards (Master's, Doctorate/Award) [3264]

Eastern Europe

Paleontological Society International Research Program Sepkoski Grants (Advanced Professional, Graduate/Grant) [8814]

Eurasia

Individual Advanced Research Opportunities Program For Master's Students (Graduate, Master's/Fellowship) [6070]

IREX Individual Advanced Research Opportunities Program For Postdoctoral Scholars (Postdoctorate/Fellowship) [6071]

IREX Individual Advanced Research Opportunities Program For Pre-doctoral Students (Doctorate/Fellowship) [6072]

IREX Individual Advanced Research Opportunities Program For Professionals (Other/Fellowship) [6073]

Europe

Alliance-CES Pre-Dissertation Research Fellowship (Graduate/Fellowship) [3855]

Baker McKenzie Graduate Legal Studies Scholarships (Graduate, Professional development/Scholarship) [2412]

Canadian Institute for Advanced Legal Studies French Language Scholarships (Graduate, Advanced Professional/Scholarship) [5793]

DLF Graduate Scholarship Program (Graduate/Scholarship) [3960]

Google European Doctoral Fellowships (Doctorate/Fellowship) [5046]

HAESF Professional Internship Program (Doctorate/Internship) [5645]

Individual Advanced Research Opportunities Program For Master's Students (Graduate, Master's/Fellowship) [6070]

International Society Travel Grant (Professional development/Grant) [450]

IREX Individual Advanced Research Opportunities Program For Postdoctoral Scholars (Postdoctorate/Fellowship) [6071]

IREX Individual Advanced Research Opportunities Program For Pre-doctoral Students (Doctorate/Fellowship) [6072]

IREX Individual Advanced Research Opportunities Program For Professionals (Other/Fellowship) [6073]

Terra Summer Residency Fellowships (Master's, Doctorate/Fellowship) [10966]

Latin America

Baker McKenzie Graduate Legal Studies Scholarships (Graduate, Professional development/Scholarship) [2412]

The E. Alexander Bergstrom Memorial Research Award (Undergraduate, Master's/Award) [2177]

IAF Fellowships (Doctorate/Fellowship) [5883]

International Society Travel Grant (Professional development/Grant) [450]

Latin American Student Field Research Award (Graduate/Fellowship) [1505]

Oliver P. Pearson Award *(Doctorate/Fellowship)* [1506]

Middle East

Baker McKenzie Graduate Legal Studies Scholarships *(Graduate, Professional development/Scholarship)* [2412]

North America

AAPA Student Research Scholarship *(Graduate, Undergraduate/Scholarship)* [631]

A.C. Elias, Jr. Irish-American Research Travel Fellowship *(Other/Fellowship)* [1425]

American Wine Society Educational Foundation Scholarships (AWSEF) *(Graduate/Scholarship)* [1676]

Baker McKenzie Graduate Legal Studies Scholarships *(Graduate, Professional development/Scholarship)* [2412]

Gloria Barron Wilderness Society Scholarship *(Graduate, Undergraduate/Scholarship)* [12031]

Chronic Pain Medicine Research Grant *(Professional development/Grant)* [1556]

DLF Graduate Scholarship Program *(Graduate/Scholarship)* [3960]

Foundation for the Preservation of Honey Bees Scholarship *(Graduate/Scholarship)* [4803]

Galvanize the Future: A Richard L. Brooks Memorial Scholarship *(Undergraduate, Graduate/Scholarship)* [934]

David Hudak Memorial Essay Contest for Freethinking Students of Color *(Undergraduate/Scholarship)* [4825]

ILMA foundation Scholarship Program *(Undergraduate/Scholarship)* [5735]

Ilse B. Hanfmann, George Hanfmann and Machteld J. Mellink Burslari Fellowship. *(Doctorate/Fellowship)* [1348]

Carl Koller Memorial Research Grants *(Professional development/Grant)* [1557]

Our World Underwater Scholarship Society North American Rolex Scholarships *(Undergraduate, Graduate/Scholarship)* [8776]

Wexner Graduate Fellowship / Davidson Scholars Program *(Graduate/Fellowship)* [12003]

Scandinavia

American-Scandinavian Foundation Fellowships to Study in Scandinavia *(Graduate/Fellowship)* [1373]

American-Scandinavian Foundation Grants to Study in Scandinavia *(Graduate/Grant)* [1374]

South America

DLF Graduate Scholarship Program *(Graduate/Scholarship)* [3960]

Paleontological Society International Research Program Sepkoski Grants *(Advanced Professional, Graduate/Grant)* [8814]

TFI Latin America Media Arts Fund *(Professional development/Grant)* [11110]

Southeast Asia

NIU-CSEAS Foreign Language and Area Studies (FLAS) Graduate Fellowship *(Undergraduate, Graduate/Fellowship)* [8487]

Soviet Union (former)

Paleontological Society International Research Program Sepkoski Grants *(Advanced Professional, Graduate/Grant)* [8814]

INTERNATIONAL (BY COUNTRY)

Afghanistan

Promoting the Rule of Law and Access to Justice *(Other/Grant)* [11379]

Sue & Ken Dyer Foundation Travel Scholarship *(Other/Scholarship)* [4784]

Argentina

CEJIL Communications Internships *(Professional development, Graduate/Internship)* [3230]

CEJIL Legal Internships *(Graduate, Professional development/Internship)* [3231]

Organization of American States Graduate Scholarships *(Doctorate, Graduate/Scholarship)* [8737]

The YFU Americas Scholarship *(Undergraduate/Scholarship)* [12276]

Armenia

The Hirair and Anna Hovnanian Foundation Presidential Scholarship *(Undergraduate/Scholarship)* [5512]

Australia

Australian-American Health Policy Fellowships *(Doctorate, Graduate/Fellowship)* [3553]

DLF Graduate Scholarship Program *(Graduate/Scholarship)* [3960]

"Help to Save" Scholarship *(College, University/Scholarship)* [3880]

Morgan Stanley Pediatrics Fellowships *(Postgraduate, Graduate/Fellowship)* [686]

Austria

Barbara Potter Scholarship Fund *(Professional development/Scholarship)* [1188]

Bangladesh

AIBS Junior Fellowships *(Doctorate/Fellowship)* [1012]

AIBS Senior Fellowships *(Doctorate/Fellowship)* [1013]

ICNL Research Fellowships *(Advanced Professional, Professional development/Fellowship)* [5964]

Barbados

Organization of American States Graduate Scholarships *(Doctorate, Graduate/Scholarship)* [8737]

Benin

ICNL Research Fellowships *(Advanced Professional, Professional development/Fellowship)* [5964]

Bolivia

Organization of American States Graduate Scholarships *(Doctorate, Graduate/Scholarship)* [8737]

Brazil

CEJIL Communications Internships *(Professional development, Graduate/Internship)* [3230]

CEJIL Legal Internships *(Graduate, Professional development/Internship)* [3231]

Organization of American States Graduate Scholarships *(Doctorate, Graduate/Scholarship)* [8737]

The YFU Americas Scholarship *(Undergraduate/Scholarship)* [12276]

Burundi

ICNL Research Fellowships *(Advanced Professional, Professional development/Fellowship)* [5964]

Cambodia

ICNL Research Fellowships *(Advanced Professional, Professional development/Fellowship)* [5964]

Chile

Organization of American States Graduate Scholarships *(Doctorate, Graduate/Scholarship)* [8737]

China

China and East Asia Google PhD Fellowships *(Doctorate/Fellowship)* [5045]

Colombia

ICNL Research Fellowships *(Advanced Professional, Professional development/Fellowship)* [5964]

Organization of American States Graduate Scholarships *(Doctorate, Graduate/Scholarship)* [8737]

Costa Rica

CEJIL Communications Internships *(Professional development, Graduate/Internship)* [3230]

CEJIL Legal Internships *(Graduate, Professional development/Internship)* [3231]

Organization of American States Graduate Scholarships *(Doctorate, Graduate/Scholarship)* [8737]

Rowe Family Fellowships *(Graduate/Fellowship)* [8752]

Cuba

Brandon Fradd Fellowship in Music Composition *(Professional development/Fellowship)* [3416]

CINTAS Foundation Fellowship in Architecture & Design *(Professional development/Fellowship)* [3417]

Mas Family Scholarship *(Graduate, Undergraduate/Scholarship)* [7120]

Cyprus

Olivia James Traveling Fellowship *(Professional development/Fellowship)* [1779]

Denmark

Edith and Arnold N. Bodtker Grants *(Undergraduate, Graduate/Grant, Internship)* [3968]

J. B. C. Watkins Award *(Professional development/Fellowship)* [2873]

Dominican Republic

Organization of American States Graduate Scholarships *(Doctorate, Graduate/Scholarship)* [8737]

Ecuador

Organization of American States Graduate Scholarships *(Doctorate, Graduate/Scholarship)* [8737]

The YFU Americas Scholarship *(Undergraduate/Scholarship)* [12276]

Egypt

ARCE Funded Fellowships *(Doctorate, Postdoctorate/Fellowship)* [1336]

ARCE Research Associates Fellowship *(Doctorate, Postdoctorate, Professional development/Fellowship)* [1337]

El Salvador

Organization of American States Graduate Scholarships *(Doctorate, Graduate/Scholarship)* [8737]

France

The École Nationale des Chartes Exchange Fellowship *(Postdoctorate/Fellowship)* [8371]

Kennedy T. Friend Scholarship Fund *(Graduate, Undergraduate/Scholarship)* [348]

Symantec Research Labs Graduate Fellowships *(Doctorate, Graduate/Fellowship)* [8547]

Gambia

ICNL Research Fellowships *(Advanced Professional, Professional development/Fellowship)* [5964]

Germany

Leo Baeck Institute - DAAD Fellowships *(Doctorate/Fellowship)* [4057]

DAAD Learn German in Germany Grants *(Doctorate/Grant)* [4058]

DAAD Study Scholarship Awards *(Graduate, Undergraduate/Scholarship)* [4059]

DAAD Undergraduate Scholarship Program *(Undergraduate/Scholarship)* [4060]

DAI Fellowship for Study in Berlin *(Postdoctorate/Fellowship)* [1776]

The Christoph Daniel Ebeling Fellowship *(Postdoctorate, Doctorate/Fellowship)* [489, 4055]

European College of Liberal Arts Scholarships (ECLA) *(Undergraduate/Scholarship)* [11411]

Faculty Research Visit Grants *(Doctorate/Grant)* [4061]

Herzog August Bibliothek Wolfenbüttel Fellowships *(Postdoctorate/Fellowship)* [8372]

Hochschulsommerkurse *(Undergraduate/Award)* [4063]

Intensive Language Course Grant *(Graduate, Undergraduate/Grant)* [4064]

McCloy Fellowships in Agriculture *(Professional development/Fellowship)* [810]

McCloy Fellowships in Environmental Policy *(Professional development/Fellowship)* [811]

McCloy Fellowships in Journalism *(Professional development/Fellowship)* [812]

McCloy Fellowships in Urban Affairs *(Professional development/Fellowship)* [813]

Research Internships in Science and Engineering (RISE) *(Undergraduate/Internship)* [4065]

Study Scholarship for Artists or Musicians *(Graduate, Postdoctorate/Scholarship)* [4066]

Ghana

African Humanities Program *(Postdoctorate/Fellowship)* [819]

ICNL Research Fellowships *(Advanced Professional, Professional development/Fellowship)* [5964]

Next Generation Social Sciences in Africa: Doctoral Dissertation Completion Fellowship *(Doctorate/Fellowship)* [3169, 10249]

Next Generation Social Sciences in Africa: Doctoral Dissertation Proposal Fellowship *(Doctorate/Fellowship)* [3170, 10250]

Next Generation Social Sciences in Africa: Doctoral Dissertation Research Fellowship *(Doctorate/Fellowship)* [3171, 10251]

Greece

Olivia James Traveling Fellowship *(Professional development/Fellowship)* [1779]

Grenada

Organization of American States Graduate Scholarships *(Doctorate, Graduate/Scholarship)* [8737]

Guyana

Organization of American States Graduate Scholarships *(Doctorate, Graduate/Scholarship)* [8737]

Iceland

J. B. C. Watkins Award *(Professional development/Fellowship)* [2873]

India

Malayalee Engineers Association Scholarships *(Undergraduate/Scholarship)* [7012]

Indonesia

ICNL Research Fellowships *(Advanced Professional, Professional development/Fellowship)* [5964]

Iran

AIIrS Persian Language Study in Tehran Fellowship *(Graduate, Master's, Doctorate/Fellowship)* [1030]

Short-term Senior Fellowships in Iranian Studies *(Graduate, Master's, Doctorate/Fellowship)* [1031]

Ireland

A.C. Elias, Jr. Irish-American Research Travel Fellowship *(Other/Fellowship)* [1425]

George J. Mitchell Scholarship *(Postgraduate/Scholarship)* [11774]

George J. Mitchell Postgraduate Scholarships *(Postgraduate/Scholarship)* [7646]

Symantec Research Labs Graduate Fellowships *(Doctorate, Graduate/Fellowship)* [8547]

Israel

Jenny Panitch Beckow Memorial Scholarship - Israel *(Graduate/Scholarship)* [6284]

Bernice & Gordon Brown Scholarship *(Undergraduate/Scholarship)* [6287]

Canadian Zionist Federation - Dr. Leon Aryeh Kronitz Scholarship *(Undergraduate, Graduate/Scholarship)* [2984]

Ruth and Victor David Scholarship *(Undergraduate, Graduate/Scholarship)* [6289]

Harry Feldman Memorial Scholarship *(Undergraduate/Scholarship)* [6290]

Jack Gitlitz Memorial Scholarship - Israel *(Graduate, Undergraduate/Scholarship)* [6291]

Jane R. Glaser Scholarship *(Undergraduate/Scholarship)* [1626]

Hushy Lipton Memorial Scholarship Fund *(Undergraduate, Graduate, Postgraduate/Scholarship)* [2985]

Judaic Studies and/or Studies in Israel *(Undergraduate, Postgraduate/Scholarship)* [6307]

Morris M. Pulver Scholarship Fund *(Undergraduate, Graduate, Postgraduate/Scholarship)* [2986]

Rothberg International School Graduate Merit Scholarship *(Graduate, Master's/Scholarship)* [2987]

Joel A. Weinstein Memorial Scholarship *(Postgraduate, Undergraduate/Scholarship)* [6308]

Zuckerman STEM Leadership Program *(Postdoctorate/Scholarship)* [12423]

Italy

Leo Biaggi de Blasys Bogliasco Fellowships *(Undergraduate/Scholarship)* [2642]

Jerome Robbins Bogliasco Fellowships in Dance *(Professional development/Fellowship)* [2645]

Kress/AAR Fellowships *(Professional development/Fellowship)* [2058]

Olivia James Traveling Fellowship *(Professional development/Fellowship)* [1779]

Roger Sessions Memorial Bogliasco Fellowships in Music *(Professional development/Fellowship)* [2647]

Helen M. Woodruff Fellowships *(Postdoctorate/Fellowship)* [1781]

Jamaica

Organization of American States Graduate Scholarships *(Doctorate, Graduate/Scholarship)* [8737]

Japan

Abe Fellowship *(Professional development/Fellowship)* [10241]

Crown Prince Akihito Scholarship Foundation *(Graduate/Scholarship)* [6231]

International Affairs Fellowships in Japan (IAF) *(Professional development/Fellowship)* [3864]

Japan Foundation, New York Doctoral Candidates *(Doctorate/Fellowship)* [6233]

Japan Foundation, New York Scholars and Researchers (Long-Term) *(Professional development/Fellowship)* [6234]

Japan Foundation, New York Scholars and Researchers (Short-Term) *(Professional development/Fellowship)* [6235]

Japan Society for the Promotion of Science Fellowship (JSPS) *(Doctorate/Fellowship)* [10247]

Jordan

ACOR-CAORC Post-Doctoral Fellowships *(Postdoctorate/Fellowship)* [723]

ACOR-CAORC Pre-Doctoral Fellowships *(Graduate, Doctorate/Fellowship)* [724]

Pierre and Patricia Bikai Fellowship *(Graduate/Fellowship)* [725]

Bert and Sally de Vries Fellowship *(Undergraduate, Graduate/Fellowship)* [726]

Jennifer C. Groot Memorial Fellowship *(Undergraduate, Graduate/Fellowship)* [727]

Harrell Family Fellowship *(Graduate/Fellowship)* [728]

Kenneth W. Russell Memorial Fellowships *(Graduate/Fellowship)* [729]

Burton MacDonald and Rosemarie Sampson Fellowship *(Undergraduate, Graduate/Fellowship)* [730]

James A. Sauer Memorial Fellowships *(Graduate/Fellowship)* [731]

Kosovo

ICNL Research Fellowships *(Advanced Professional, Professional development/Fellowship)* [5964]

Malawi

ICNL Research Fellowships *(Advanced Professional, Professional development/Fellowship)* [5964]

Mexico

Abel Wolman Fellowship *(Doctorate/Fellowship, Award, Monetary)* [1634]

American Liver Foundation Liver Scholar Award *(Doctorate/Award)* [1091]

A.O. Putnam Memorial Scholarship *(Undergraduate/Scholarship)* [5826]

Thomas R. Camp Scholarships *(Graduate/Scholarship, Monetary)* [1639]

Dwight D. Gardner Scholarship *(Undergraduate/Scholarship)* [5828]

Geological Society of America Graduate Student Research Grants *(Doctorate, Graduate/Grant)* [4910]

Gilbreth Memorial Fellowship *(Graduate/Fellowship)* [5829]

ICNL Research Fellowships *(Advanced Professional, Professional development/Fellowship)* [5964]

John J. McKetta Undergraduate Scholarship *(Undergraduate/Scholarship)* [1023]

Jones-Lovich Grants in Southwestern Herpetology *(Master's, Doctorate/Grant)* [5500]

Larson Aquatic Research Support Scholarships (LARS) *(Graduate/Scholarship, Monetary, Recognition)* [1643]

Marvin Mundel Memorial Scholarship *(Undergraduate/Scholarship)* [5834]

Organization of American States Graduate Scholarships *(Doctorate, Graduate/Scholarship)* [8737]

UC MEXUS-CONACYT Postdoctoral Research Fellowships *(Postdoctorate/Fellowship)* [11553]

UPS Scholarship for Female Students *(Undergraduate/Scholarship)* [5836]

UPS Scholarship for Minority Students *(Undergraduate/Scholarship)* [5837]

Moldova

ICNL Research Fellowships *(Advanced Professional, Professional development/Fellowship)* [5964]

Mongolia

ACMS Field Research Fellowship Program *(Post-doctorate/Fellowship)* [719]

ACMS Library Fellowship *(Graduate, Professional development, Postgraduate/Fellowship)* [721]

Nigeria

African Humanities Program *(Postdoctorate/Fellowship)* [819]

Next Generation Social Sciences in Africa: Doctoral Dissertation Completion Fellowship *(Doctorate/Fellowship)* [3169, 10249]

Next Generation Social Sciences in Africa: Doctoral Dissertation Proposal Fellowship *(Doctorate/Fellowship)* [3170, 10250]

Next Generation Social Sciences in Africa: Doctoral Dissertation Research Fellowship *(Doctorate/Fellowship)* [3171, 10251]

NWAG Nigeria Scholarships *(Undergraduate/Scholarship)* [8396]

Norway

Oslo International Summer School Scholarship *(Undergraduate/Scholarship)* [10591]

J. B. C. Watkins Award *(Professional development/Fellowship)* [2873]

Pakistan

Dr. Feroz Ahmed Memorial Educational Post-Graduate Scholarships *(Doctorate, Postgraduate/Scholarship)* [10144]

AIPS Long Term Fellowships *(Doctorate, Postdoctorate/Fellowship)* [1036]

AIPS Post-Doctoral Fellowship *(Postdoctorate/Fellowship)* [1037]

AIPS Pre-Doctoral Fellowship *(Doctorate, Postdoctorate/Fellowship)* [1038]

AIPS Short Term Fellowships *(Doctorate, Postdoctorate/Fellowship)* [1039]

Panama

A. Stanley Rand Fellowship Program *(Undergraduate, Doctorate, Postdoctorate/Fellowship)* [10224]

Organization of American States Graduate Scholarships *(Doctorate, Graduate/Scholarship)* [8737]

Peru

ICNL Research Fellowships *(Advanced Professional, Professional development/Fellowship)* [5964]

Organization of American States Graduate Scholarships *(Doctorate, Graduate/Scholarship)* [8737]

William L. Brown Fellowship *(Graduate/Fellowship)* [8754]

Poland

Kosciuszko Foundation Graduate Study and Research in Poland Scholarships *(Graduate, Postgraduate/Scholarship)* [6601]

Kosciuszko Foundation Year Abroad Scholarships *(Graduate, Undergraduate/Scholarship)* [6603]

Portugal

Archaeology of Portugal Fellowship *(Professional development, Graduate/Fellowship)* [1774]

South Africa

African Humanities Program *(Postdoctorate/Fellowship)* [819]

Next Generation Social Sciences in Africa: Doctoral Dissertation Completion Fellowship *(Doctorate/Fellowship)* [3169, 10249]

Next Generation Social Sciences in Africa: Doctoral Dissertation Proposal Fellowship *(Doctorate/Fellowship)* [3170, 10250]

Next Generation Social Sciences in Africa: Doctoral Dissertation Research Fellowship *(Doctorate/Fellowship)* [3171, 10251]

Sri Lanka

AISLS Fellowships Program *(Doctorate/Fellowship)* [1048]

Sweden

Lilly Lorenzen Scholarships *(Undergraduate/Scholarship)* [1618]

Malmberg Scholarships *(Undergraduate/Scholarship)* [1619]

J. B. C. Watkins Award *(Professional development/Fellowship)* [2873]

Switzerland

Medicus Student Exchange Scholarship *(Graduate, Undergraduate/Scholarship)* [10895]

Tanzania

African Humanities Program *(Postdoctorate/Fellowship)* [819]

Godparents for Tanzania Scholarship *(Undergraduate/Scholarship)* [5012]

Next Generation Social Sciences in Africa: Doctoral Dissertation Completion Fellowship *(Doctorate/Fellowship)* [3169, 10249]

Next Generation Social Sciences in Africa: Doctoral Dissertation Proposal Fellowship *(Doctorate/Fellowship)* [3170, 10250]

Next Generation Social Sciences in Africa: Doctoral Dissertation Research Fellowship *(Doctorate/Fellowship)* [3171, 10251]

Thailand

ICNL Research Fellowships *(Advanced Professional, Professional development/Fellowship)* [5964]

Trinidad and Tobago

Organization of American States Graduate Scholarships *(Doctorate, Graduate/Scholarship)* [8737]

Turkey

ARIT Fellowships in the Humanities and Social Sciences in Turkey *(Postdoctorate, Graduate/Fellowship)* [1342, 3850, 11345, 11348]

ARIT/NEH Fellowships *(Postgraduate/Fellowship)* [1343]

ARIT Summer Fellowships for Intensive Advanced Turkish Language Study *(Graduate, Undergraduate/Fellowship)* [655, 1344, 4914, 11307, 11309]

Institute of Turkish Studies Sabbatical Research Grants *(Other/Grant)* [5870]

National Endowment for the Humanities Advanced Fellowships for Research in Turkey *(Postdoctorate/Fellowship)* [1349, 7871]

Olivia James Traveling Fellowship *(Professional development/Fellowship)* [1779]

Post-Doctoral Summer Travel-Research Grants *(Postdoctorate/Grant)* [5871]

Summer Language Study Grants in Turkey *(Graduate/Grant)* [5872]

Uganda

African Humanities Program *(Postdoctorate/Fellowship)* [819]

Next Generation Social Sciences in Africa: Doctoral Dissertation Completion Fellowship *(Doctorate/Fellowship)* [3169, 10249]

Next Generation Social Sciences in Africa: Doctoral Dissertation Proposal Fellowship *(Doctorate/Fellowship)* [3170, 10250]

Next Generation Social Sciences in Africa: Doctoral Dissertation Research Fellowship *(Doctorate/Fellowship)* [3171, 10251]

Ukraine

Alberta Ukrainian Centennial Commemorative Scholarship *(Graduate/Scholarship)* [11887]

ALIS International Education Awards - Ukraine *(Undergraduate/Scholarship)* [284]

Mychajlo Dmytrenko Fine Arts Foundation Scholarships *(Undergraduate/Scholarship)* [11410]

Ivan Franko School of Ukrainian Studies Ukraine Travel Award *(Undergraduate/Grant)* [3028]

ICNL Research Fellowships *(Advanced Professional, Professional development/Fellowship)* [5964]

United Kingdom

Baker McKenzie Graduate Legal Studies Scholarships *(Graduate, Professional development/Scholarship)* [2412]

Hilda E. Bretzlaff Foundation Scholarships *(Undergraduate/Scholarship, Grant)* [2687]

The Churchill Scholarships *(Postgraduate/Scholarship)* [3331]

Edward C. Roy, Jr. Award For Excellence in K-8 Earth Science Teaching *(Professional development/Award)* [944]

"Help to Save" Scholarship *(College, University/Scholarship)* [3880]

London Goodenough Association of Canada Scholarships *(Graduate/Scholarship)* [6886]

Mackenzie King Travelling Scholarship *(Graduate/Scholarship, Monetary)* [7183]

Right Honourable Paul Martin Sr. Scholarships *(Graduate/Scholarship)* [5794]

George J. Mitchell Postgraduate Scholarships *(Postgraduate/Scholarship)* [7646]

MSGC Undergraduate-Under-Represented Minority Fellowship Program *(Undergraduate/Fellowship)* [7331]

Saint Andrews Scholarships *(Undergraduate/Scholarship)* [9776]

U.S.-U.K. Young Investigator Exchange Fellowship *(Postdoctorate/Fellowship)* [417]

USA/USA-Ukramerazha Scholarships *(Undergraduate/Scholarship)* [11413]

Uruguay

Organization of American States Graduate Scholarships *(Doctorate, Graduate/Scholarship)* [8737]

The YFU Americas Scholarship *(Undergraduate/Scholarship)* [12276]

Zimbabwe

ICNL Research Fellowships *(Advanced Professional, Professional development/Fellowship)* [5964]

This index arranges awards according to qualifying factors related to membership or affiliation. Awards are listed under all appropriate headings. Each citation is followed by the study level and award type, which appear in parentheses. Numbers following the parenthetical information indicate the book entry number for particular awards, not page numbers.

African American

AAMFT Minority Fellowship Program (MFP) *(Doctorate, Graduate/Fellowship)* [602]

Actuarial Diversity Scholarship *(Undergraduate/Scholarship)* [69]

AFPE Pre-Doctoral Fellowships in Pharmaceutical Sciences for Underrepresented Minorities *(Doctorate, Graduate/Fellowship)* [924]

African American Network - Carolinas Scholarship Fund *(Undergraduate/Scholarship)* [4715]

AIChE Minority Scholarship Awards for College Students *(Undergraduate/Scholarship)* [1020]

Air Products and Chemicals, Inc. Scholarships *(Undergraduate/Scholarship)* [2191]

American Association for Cancer Research Minority Scholar in Cancer Research Awards *(Graduate/Award)* [533]

American Physical Society Minority Undergraduate Scholarships *(Undergraduate/Scholarship)* [1220]

AMS Minority Scholarships *(Undergraduate/Scholarship)* [1123]

Andrew Foster Scholarship *(Undergraduate/Scholarship)* [7720]

APS Scholarships for Minority Undergraduate Physics Majors *(Undergraduate/Scholarship)* [1221]

APSA Minority Fellowship Program *(Doctorate/Fellowship)* [1251]

APTA Minority Scholarships - Faculty Development Scholarships *(Postdoctorate/Scholarship, Award, Recognition)* [1232]

APTA Minority Scholarships - Physical Therapist Assistant Students *(Undergraduate/Scholarship, Award, Recognition)* [1233]

APTA Minority Scholarships - Physical Therapist Students *(Undergraduate/Scholarship, Award, Recognition)* [1234]

ASA Minority Fellowship Program (ASA MFP) *(Doctorate/Fellowship)* [1590]

ASGP Graduate Research Fellowships *(Graduate/Fellowship)* [244]

AWG Minority Scholarship *(Undergraduate/Scholarship)* [2313]

Dr. Johnella Banks Memorial Scholarships *(Undergraduate/Scholarship)* [2610]

Bill Bernbach Diversity Scholarships *(Undergraduate/Scholarship)* [510]

Black Men Building Resources Scholarship *(Undergraduate/Scholarship)* [5137]

Leon Bradley Scholarship Program *(Undergraduate/Scholarship)* [638]

Ron Brown Scholarship *(Undergraduate/Scholarship)* [2722]

Angela Faye Brown Video Essay Contest *(Graduate/Scholarship)* [2717]

CANFIT Nutrition, Physical Education and Culinary Arts Scholarships *(Graduate, Undergraduate/Scholarship)* [3561]

CBC Spouses Education Scholarship *(Graduate, Undergraduate/Scholarship)* [3738]

CBC Spouses Performing Arts Scholarship *(Undergraduate/Scholarship)* [3739]

CBC Spouses Visual Arts Scholarship *(Undergraduate/Scholarship)* [3740]

Cenie Jomo Williams Tuition Scholarship *(Graduate, Undergraduate/Scholarship)* [7617]

CIGNA Healthcare Graduate Scholarships *(Graduate/Scholarship)* [7888]

CIGNA Undergraduate Scholarships *(Undergraduate/Scholarship)* [7889]

Johnnie L. Cochran, Jr./MWH Scholarships *(Graduate, Undergraduate/Scholarship)* [7890]

Congressional Fellowship *(Other/Fellowship)* [3741]

Development Fund for Black Students in Science and Technology Scholarship *(Undergraduate/Scholarship)* [4068]

Dr. Joyce Beckett Scholarship *(Graduate, Undergraduate/Scholarship)* [7618]

Dr. Julianne Malveaux Scholarship *(Undergraduate/Scholarship)* [7668]

Joseph M. Dorgan Scholarship *(Undergraduate/Scholarship)* [4151]

Dunbar Heritage Scholarship Fund *(Undergraduate/Scholarship)* [10683]

The Dwight D. Eisenhower/Ann Cook Whitman Washington, D.C. Scholarship Program *(Undergraduate/Scholarship)* [4961]

E.J. Josey Scholarship *(Graduate/Scholarship)* [2606]

Emma and Meloid Algood Tuition Scholarship *(Graduate, Undergraduate/Scholarship)* [7619]

Evans and Petree Law Firm Scholarship *(Graduate/Scholarship)* [11598]

F.A. and Charlotte Blount Scholarship *(Undergraduate/Scholarship)* [12076]

FICPA Educational Foundation 1040K Race Scholarships *(Undergraduate/Scholarship, Award)* [4636]

Florida Education Fund McKnight Doctoral Fellowship *(Graduate/Fellowship)* [4629]

Fraser Stryker Diversity Scholarship Program *(Undergraduate/Scholarship)* [4817]

Sam Gallant Memorial Scholarships *(Graduate, Undergraduate/Scholarship)* [1818]

The Gates Millennium Scholars *(Undergraduate/Scholarship)* [5529]

Glenn B. Anderson Scholarship *(Graduate, Undergraduate/Scholarship)* [7721]

The Marie Trahan/Susman Godfrey Scholarship *(Undergraduate/Scholarship)* [11148]

Ruth Simms Hamilton Research Fellowship *(Graduate/Fellowship)* [10927]

HSF/Marathon Oil College Scholarship Program *(Undergraduate/Scholarship)* [5531]

Huggins-Quarles Award *(Doctorate, Graduate/Award)* [8726]

Hugh & Helen Wood Nepalese Scholarship *(Undergraduate/Scholarship)* [2482]

The Hyatt Hotels Fund For Minority Lodging Management Students *(Undergraduate/Scholarship)* [972]

International Association of Black Actuaries Scholarships *(Undergraduate/Scholarship)* [5907]

The Jack and Jill of America Foundation's National Scholarship Program *(Undergraduate/Scholarship)* [6190]

James E. West Fellowship *(Graduate/Fellowship)* [62]

The Dr. Richard Allen Williams and Genita Evangelista Johnson Scholarship,AMA Foundation Scholarship *(Undergraduate/Scholarship)* [2066]

Martin Luther King Jr. Scholarships *(Graduate/Scholarship)* [6558]

Martin Luther King Law Scholarship *(Undergraduate/Scholarship)* [4165]

L. & T. Woolfolk Memorial Scholarship Fund *(Undergraduate/Scholarship)* [3376]

The Lagrant Foundation - Graduate Scholarships *(Graduate/Scholarship)* [6632]

The Lagrant Foundation - Undergraduate Scholarships *(Undergraduate/Scholarship)* [6633]

The Herbert Lehman Education Fund Scholarship *(Undergraduate/Scholarship)* [7540]

The Robert A. Catlin/David W. Long Scholarship *(Graduate/Scholarship)* [1244]

Howard Mayer Brown Fellowship *(Graduate/Fellowship)* [1146]

McCall Educational Fund *(Undergraduate/Scholarship)* [3384]

Minorities in Government Finance Scholarship *(Graduate, Undergraduate/Scholarship)* [5054]

MLA/NLM Spectrum Scholarship *(Undergraduate/Scholarship)* [7220]

MLA Scholarship for Minority Students *(Graduate/Scholarship)* [7223]

The Dr. Blanca Moore-Velez Woman of Substance Scholarship *(Undergraduate/Scholarship)* [7669]

James B. Morris Scholarship *(Undergraduate/Scholarship)* [7474]

Archie Motley Memorial Scholarships for Minority Students *(Graduate/Scholarship)* [7367]

NABA National Scholarship Program *(Graduate, Undergraduate/Scholarship, Award, Monetary)* [7613]

NACA Multicultural Professional Development Grant *(Undergraduate, Graduate, Professional development/Grant)* [7627]

NANBPWC National Scholarship *(Graduate/Scholarship)* [7670]

National Dental Hygienists' Association Scholarships *(Undergraduate/Scholarship)* [7839]

National Medical Fellowships Need-Based Scholarships *(Undergraduate/Scholarship)* [8001]

NFBPA Future Colleagues Scholarships *(Undergraduate/Scholarship)* [7891]

NFBPA Land-Use Planning Scholarships *(Master's, Doctorate/Scholarship)* [7892]

Pearman Family Scholarship *(Undergraduate/Scholarship)* [9839]

PlasticPlace Young Entrepreneurs Scholarship Award *(Undergraduate/Scholarship)* [9192]

Judith McManus Price Scholarship *(Undergraduate, Graduate/Scholarship)* [1245]

PRSA Diversity Multicultural Scholarships *(Undergraduate/Scholarship)* [9438]

RA Consulting Service/Maria Riley Scholarships *(Graduate, Undergraduate/Scholarship)* [7893]

RMHC African American Future Achievers Scholarship *(Undergraduate/Scholarship)* [9734]

Robert Toigo Foundation Fellowship *(Master's/Fellowship)* [11048]

Ruth E. Jenkins Scholarship *(Undergraduate/Scholarship)* [9847]

Selena Danette Brown Book Scholarship (Graduate, Undergraduate/Scholarship) [7620]

Alfred P. Sloan Foundation Graduate Scholarships - Sloan Minority Ph.D. Program (MPHD) (Doctorate/Scholarship) [7582]

Louis Stokes Health Scholars Program (Undergraduate/Scholarship) [3742]

Jacki Tuckfield Memorial Graduate Business Scholarship Fund (Doctorate, Graduate, Master's/Scholarship) [7299]

UCSD Black Alumni Scholarship for Arts and Humanities (Undergraduate/Scholarship) [9857]

UCSD Black Alumni Scholarships for Engineering, Mathematics and Science (Undergraduate/Scholarship) [9858]

UNCF Merck Graduate Science Research Dissertation Fellowships (Graduate/Fellowship) [7268, 11270]

UNCF/Merck Postdoctoral Science Research Fellowships (Postdoctorate/Scholarship) [7269, 11271]

Underrepresented in Medicine award (Graduate/Scholarship) [1112]

University of Wisconsin-Madison Chancellor's Scholarship Program (Undergraduate/Scholarship) [11746]

Valuing Diversity PhD Scholarship (Doctorate/Scholarship) [1105]

White Collar Defense Diversity Scholarships (Undergraduate, Graduate/Scholarship) [9286]

The Leon And Margaret Williams Scholarship (Undergraduate/Scholarship) [9866]

Willie T. Loud scholarship (Undergraduate, Graduate/Scholarship) [7894]

Woodrow Wilson-Rockefeller Brothers Fund Fellowships for Aspiring Teachers of Color (Undergraduate/Fellowship) [12052]

Youth Empowerment Summit Scholarships (Undergraduate/Scholarship) [7722]

Asian American

AAMFT Minority Fellowship Program (MFP) (Doctorate, Graduate/Fellowship) [602]

Air Products and Chemicals, Inc. Scholarships (Undergraduate/Scholarship) [2191]

Anheuser-Busch NAPABA Law Foundation Presidential Scholarships (Undergraduate/Scholarship) [7601]

APABA Silicon Valley Achievement Scholarship (Advanced Professional/Scholarship) [1988]

APALA Scholarship (Doctorate, Master's/Scholarship) [1990]

APIASF Scholarships (Undergraduate/Scholarship) [1994]

APSA Minority Fellowship Program (Doctorate/Fellowship) [1251]

APTA Minority Scholarships - Faculty Development Scholarships (Postdoctorate/Scholarship, Award, Recognition) [1232]

APTA Minority Scholarships - Physical Therapist Assistant Students (Undergraduate/Scholarship, Award, Recognition) [1233]

APTA Minority Scholarships - Physical Therapist Students (Undergraduate/Scholarship, Award, Recognition) [1234]

ASA Minority Fellowship Program (ASA MFP) (Doctorate/Fellowship) [1590]

Leon Bradley Scholarship Program (Undergraduate/Scholarship) [638]

CANFIT Nutrition, Physical Education and Culinary Arts Scholarships (Graduate, Undergraduate/Scholarship) [3561]

FBANC Foundation NAPABA Convention Scholarship (Advanced Professional/Scholarship) [4554]

Fraser Stryker Diversity Scholarship Program (Undergraduate/Scholarship) [4817]

The Gates Millennium Scholars (Undergraduate/Scholarship) [5529]

HANA Scholars (Undergraduate, Graduate, Doctorate/Scholarship) [4891]

HSF/Marathon Oil College Scholarship Program (Undergraduate/Scholarship) [5531]

Huggins-Quarles Award (Doctorate, Graduate/Award) [8726]

The Hyatt Hotels Fund For Minority Lodging Management Students (Undergraduate/Scholarship) [972]

The Lagrant Foundation - Graduate Scholarships (Graduate/Scholarship) [6632]

The Lagrant Foundation - Undergraduate Scholarships (Undergraduate/Scholarship) [6633]

Las Vegas Chinatown Scholarship (Undergraduate/Scholarship) [9409]

Howard Mayer Brown Fellowship (Graduate/Fellowship) [1146]

Minorities in Government Finance Scholarship (Graduate, Undergraduate/Scholarship) [5054]

MLA/NLM Spectrum Scholarship (Undergraduate/Scholarship) [7220]

MLA Scholarship for Minority Students (Graduate/Scholarship) [7223]

James B. Morris Scholarship (Undergraduate/Scholarship) [7474]

Archie Motley Memorial Scholarships for Minority Students (Graduate/Scholarship) [7367]

NACA Multicultural Professional Development Grant (Undergraduate, Graduate, Professional development/Grant) [7627]

PlasticPlace Young Entrepreneurs Scholarship Award (Undergraduate/Scholarship) [9192]

PRSA Diversity Multicultural Scholarships (Undergraduate/Scholarship) [9438]

Rosa Quezada Memorial Education Scholarships (Undergraduate/Scholarship) [3755]

RMHC Asia Scholarship (Undergraduate/Scholarship) [9735]

Robert Toigo Foundation Fellowship (Master's/Fellowship) [11048]

SCCLA Fellowships (Graduate/Fellowship) [10647]

SCCLA Scholarships (Graduate/Scholarship) [10648]

TACL-LA Taiwanese American Community Scholarship (TACS) (Undergraduate/Scholarship) [10911]

Woodrow Wilson-Rockefeller Brothers Fund Fellowships for Aspiring Teachers of Color (Undergraduate/Fellowship) [12052]

Association membership

1L SUMMER INTERNSHIP PROGRAM Prudential Financial, Inc. (Postgraduate/Internship) [7600]

3M Fellowship Award (Postdoctorate/Fellowship) [12214]

4-H Youth in Action Awards (Graduate, Undergraduate, Vocational/Occupational, High School, College, University/Scholarship) [7564]

A-2 Joaquim Pereira Memorial Scholarship (Undergraduate/Scholarship) [6935]

A-4 António Mattos Memorial Scholarship (Undergraduate/Scholarship) [6936]

AAA Postdoctoral Fellowship (Postdoctorate/Fellowship) [513]

AAAA Scholarship Program (Undergraduate, Graduate/Scholarship) [1911]

AAACN Education Scholarship (Undergraduate/Scholarship) [425]

AAACN Research/Evidence Based Practice Project Awards (Undergraduate/Grant, Scholarship) [426]

AABP Amstutz Scholarship (Undergraduate/Scholarship) [522]

AABP Bovine Veterinary Student Recognition Award (Undergraduate/Scholarship, Award) [523]

AABP Education Grants (Graduate, Postgraduate, Master's/Grant) [524]

AACD Dentist Fellowships (Professional development/Fellowship) [446]

AACN Continuing Professional Development Scholarships (Advanced Professional/Scholarship) [553]

AACOM Scholar in Residence Program (Professional development/Scholarship) [545]

AACPDM Student Travel Scholarship (Professional development/Scholarship) [438]

AACPDM Transformative Practice Grant Award (Professional development/Grant) [439]

AACR Basic Cancer Research Fellowships (Postdoctorate/Fellowship, Award, Recognition) [529]

AACR Scholar-in-Training Awards: Other Conferences and Meetings (Graduate, Postdoctorate/Grant, Award) [531]

AACR-Undergraduate Scholar Awards (Undergraduate/Award) [532]

AACT Junior Investigator Research Grants (Professional development/Grant) [441]

AACT Research Award (Professional development/Grant) [442]

AACT Toxicology Trainee Research Grants (Professional development/Grant) [443]

AADA Student Spouse Scholarship (Professional development/Scholarship) [357]

AAEP Foundation Past Presidents' Research Fellow (Graduate, Professional development/Scholarship) [559]

AAFP Minority Scholarships Program for Residents and Returning Students (Professional development/Scholarship) [454]

AAFP Resident Community Outreach Award (Professional development/Scholarship) [455]

AAFP Tomorrow's Leader Award (Professional development/Scholarship) [456]

AAFSW Merit Scholarship for College Students (College, Undergraduate/Scholarship) [2025]

AAG Dissertation Research Grants (Doctorate/Grant) [563]

AAG Provincial Student Award (Graduate/Award) [246]

AAI Careers in Immunology Fellowship Program (Graduate, Doctorate, Postdoctorate/Fellowship) [572]

AAI Public Policy Fellows Program (PPFP) (Doctorate, Postdoctorate/Fellowship) [573]

AAIDD Fellowship (Advanced Professional, Professional development/Fellowship) [577]

AAJ Trial Advocacy Scholarship (Undergraduate/Scholarship) [581]

AALL Leadership Academy Grant (Professional development/Grant) [585]

AALL Minority Leadership Development Award (Graduate/Award) [586]

AALL Research Fund (Professional development/Grant) [587]

AALL Technical Services SIS Active Member Grant (Professional development/Grant) [588]

AALL Technical Services SIS Experienced Member General Grant (Professional development/Grant) [589]

AALL Technical Services SIS Leadership Academy Grant (Professional development/Grant) [590]

AALL Technical Services SIS Management Institute Grant (Professional development/Grant) [591]

AALL Technical Services SIS New Member General Grant (Professional development/Grant) [592]

AALL/Wolters Kluwer Law & Business Grants (Professional development/Grant) [593]

AAMA Houston Chapter Health Training Scholarships (Other/Scholarship) [1770]

AAMC Foundation Engagement Program for International Curators Grants (Advanced Professional, Professional development/Grant) [2057]

AAN Clinical Research Training Fellowship (Other/Scholarship) [458]

AAN Medical Student Summer Research Scholarship (Graduate/Scholarship) [460]

AANP Education Advancement Scholarships (Graduate/Scholarship, Grant) [12209]

AAOHN Professional Development Scholarships - Academic Study (Graduate/Scholarship) [613]

AAPA Student Research Scholarship (Graduate, Undergraduate/Scholarship) [631]

AAS/AAS Trainee Research Fellowship Awards (Professional development/Fellowship) [2028]

AAS-American Society for Eighteenth-Century Studies Fellowships (Doctorate/Fellowship) [482]

AAS CIAC Small Grants (Graduate/Grant) [2060]

AAS National Endowment for the Humanities Long-Term Fellowships (Postdoctorate/Fellowship) [483]

AASLD Advanced/Transplant Hepatology Award (Professional development/Award) [644]

AASLD Autoimmune Liver Diseases Pilot Research Award (Graduate, Doctorate, Postdoctorate, Professional development/Award, Grant) [645]

AASLD Clinical, Translational and Outcomes Research Awards (Professional development/Grant) [646]

AASLD NP/PA Clinical Hepatology Fellowship *(Professional development/Fellowship)* [647]

AASSC Norwegian Travel Grant *(Undergraduate, College, University/Grant)* [2034]

AATS/STS Cardiothoracic Ethics Forum Scholarships *(Professional development/Scholarship)* [662, 10543]

AAUW Career Development Grants *(Graduate, Advanced Professional, Professional development/Grant)* [33]

AAWD Colgate Research Award *(Undergraduate/Scholarship, Award, Monetary)* [674]

AAZK/AZA Advances in Animal Keeping Course Grants *(Professional development/Grant)* [676]

AAZK Conservation, Preservation and Restoration Grants *(Professional development/Grant)* [677]

AAZK Professional Development Grants *(Professional development/Grant)* [678]

AAZK Research Grants *(Professional development/Grant)* [679]

ABA President's Continuing Education Grant *(Advanced Professional, Professional development/Grant)* [705]

ABC-Clio Research Grants *(Graduate/Grant)* [10425]

Abe Voron Award *(Graduate/Scholarship)* [2703]

Alejandro "Alex" Abecia Reaching High Scholarships *(Undergraduate/Scholarship)* [3462]

Abercrombie and Fitch Global Diversity and Leadership Scholar Awards *(Undergraduate/Scholarship)* [8102]

Ruth Abernathy Presidential Scholarship *(Professional development, Graduate/Scholarship)* [10346]

Ruth Abernathy Presidential Undergraduate Scholarship *(Undergraduate/Scholarship, Fellowship, Award, Monetary)* [10347]

Kyutaro and Yasuo Abiko Memorial Scholarship *(Undergraduate/Scholarship)* [6243]

Above and Beyond Scholarship *(Graduate/Scholarship)* [2826]

ABS Student Research Grant *(Graduate/Grant)* [1716]

A.C. Elias, Jr. Irish-American Research Travel Fellowship *(Other/Fellowship)* [1425]

Academy of Neonatal Nursing Conference Scholarships *(Professional development/Scholarship)* [55]

ACJA/LAE Student Paper Competition *(Undergraduate, Graduate/Scholarship)* [836]

ACJA/LAE Student Scholarship Program - Graduate Level *(Graduate, Master's, Doctorate/Scholarship)* [838]

Jack Ackroyd Scholarships *(Other/Scholarship)* [2083]

ACMS Field Research Fellowship Program *(Postdoctorate/Fellowship)* [719]

ACMS Intensive Mongolian Language Fellowship *(Undergraduate/Fellowship)* [720]

A.C.N.M. Foundation, Inc. Fellowship for Graduate Education *(Doctorate, Postdoctorate/Fellowship)* [768]

ACPA Foundation Annual Fund *(Professional development/Grant)* [771]

ACS/ASA Health Policy and Management Scholarships *(Professional development/Scholarship)* [1616]

ACS Resident Research Scholarships *(Advanced Professional/Scholarship)* [774]

ACS Scholarship *(Undergraduate/Scholarship)* [795]

ACSUS Distinguished Dissertation Award *(Doctorate/Award)* [2080]

RPMDA/Ed Adams Memorial Scholarships *(Other/Scholarship)* [9653]

Advanced Mountain Flight Training Scholarship *(Professional development, Vocational/Occupational/Scholarship)* [12009]

AE Flight Training Scholarship *(Other/Scholarship)* [8400]

AE Jet Type Rating Scholarships *(Other/Scholarship)* [8401]

A.E. Robert Friedman Scholarship *(Undergraduate, High School/Scholarship)* [8812]

AE Technical Training Scholarship *(Other/Scholarship)* [8402]

AECT Foundation Mentor Endowment Scholarship *(Doctorate, Graduate/Scholarship)* [2155]

AECT McJulien Graduate Student Scholarship Award *(Graduate, Doctorate/Scholarship)* [2157]

AED Student/Early Career Investigator Travel Fellowship Program *(Postgraduate/Fellowship)* [43]

AED Student Research Grants *(Undergraduate, Graduate, Postgraduate/Grant)* [44]

AEF Educational Scholarship *(Undergraduate/Scholarship)* [255]

Afdhal / McHutchison LIFER Award *(Postdoctorate, Professional development/Award)* [649]

AFSA Chapter 155 Division 1 Scholarships - Category 1 *(Undergraduate/Scholarship)* [111]

AFSA Chapter 155 Division 1 Scholarships - Category 2 *(Undergraduate/Scholarship)* [112]

AFSA Chapter 155 Division 1 Scholarships - Category 3 *(Undergraduate/Scholarship)* [113]

AFSA Scholarship Program *(Undergraduate/Scholarship)* [153]

AfterCollege/AACN Nursing Scholarship *(Undergraduate, Master's, Doctorate/Scholarship)* [118]

A.G. Bell College Scholarship Program *(Undergraduate, Graduate/Scholarship, Award)* [332]

AGA-R. Robert & Sally Funderburg Research Award in Gastric Cancer *(Postdoctorate/Grant)* [937]

AGA Research Foundation Fellowship to Faculty Transition Award *(Professional development/Fellowship)* [938]

AGA Research Scholar Award (AGA RSA) *(Advanced Professional/Grant)* [939]

AGC Foundation Outstanding Educator Awards *(Other/Award, Monetary)* [2016]

AGC NYS Scholarship Program *(Undergraduate, Graduate/Scholarship)* [2018]

Agnes E. Vaghi Scholarship *(Undergraduate/Scholarship)* [7960]

AH&LEF American Express Scholarship *(Undergraduate/Scholarship)* [969]

Ahepa Buckeye Scholarship Awards *(Undergraduate/Scholarship, Award)* [136]

AHNS/AAO-HNS Young Investigator combined Award *(Other/Award)* [470, 954]

AHRQ Mentored Clinical Scientist Research Career Development Award *(Doctorate, Master's/Award)* [11325]

AIA Graduate Student Travel Awards *(Graduate/Grant, Award)* [1772]

AIBS Junior Fellowships *(Doctorate/Fellowship)* [1012]

AIBS Senior Fellowships *(Doctorate/Fellowship)* [1013]

AIChE Minority Scholarship Awards for College Students *(Undergraduate/Scholarship)* [1020]

AICPA Accountemps Student Scholarship Award *(Graduate/Scholarship)* [1015]

AICPA John L. Carey Scholarship Awards *(Graduate/Scholarship)* [1016]

AICPA Minority Scholarship *(Undergraduate, Graduate/Scholarship)* [1017]

AICPA Two-Year Transfer Scholarship *(Four Year College, Undergraduate/Scholarship)* [1018]

AIMS Long-term Research Grants *(Doctorate, Graduate/Grant)* [1033]

AIMS Short-term Research Grants *(Doctorate, Graduate/Grant)* [1034]

AIP State Department Fellowship *(Postdoctorate/Fellowship, Recognition)* [1041]

AIPS Post-Doctoral Fellowship *(Postdoctorate/Fellowship)* [1037]

AIPS Pre-Doctoral Fellowship *(Doctorate, Postdoctorate/Fellowship)* [1038]

Air Force Association/Grantham Scholarships *(Undergraduate/Scholarship)* [146]

Aises A. T. Anderson Memorial Scholarship *(Graduate, Undergraduate/Scholarship)* [1000]

AISES Intel Growing The Legacy Scholarship Program *(Graduate, Undergraduate/Scholarship)* [1001]

AISES Oracle Academy Scholarship *(Graduate, Undergraduate/Scholarship)* [1002, 5044]

AISES Summer Internships *(Undergraduate, Graduate/Internship)* [1003]

AISLS Grants for Language Instruction *(Graduate/Grant)* [1049]

AIST Foundation Engineering Scholarship *(Undergraduate/Scholarship)* [2205]

AIST Globe-Trotters Member Chapter Scholarship *(Undergraduate, Postgraduate/Scholarship)* [2206]

AIST Midwest Member Chapter - Betty McKern Scholarship *(Undergraduate/Scholarship)* [2208]

AIST Midwest Member Chapter - Don Nelson Scholarship *(Undergraduate/Scholarship)* [2209]

AIST Midwest Member Chapter - Engineering Scholarships *(Undergraduate/Scholarship)* [2210]

AIST Midwest Member Chapter - Jack Gill Scholarship *(Undergraduate/Scholarship)* [2211]

AIST Midwest Member Chapter - Mel Nickel Scholarship *(Undergraduate/Scholarship)* [2212]

AIST Midwest Member Chapter – Tom Cipich Non-Engineering Scholarship *(Undergraduate/Scholarship)* [2207]

AIST Midwest Member Chapter - Western States Award *(Undergraduate/Scholarship)* [2213]

AIST Northeastern Ohio Member Chapter - Alfred B. Glossbrenner Scholarship *(Undergraduate/Scholarship)* [2214]

AIST Northeastern Ohio Member Chapter - John Klusch Scholarships *(Undergraduate/Scholarship)* [2215]

AIST Northern Pacific Member Chapter Scholarships *(Undergraduate/Scholarship)* [2216]

AIST Ohio Valley Member Chapter Scholarships *(Undergraduate/Scholarship)* [2217]

AIST Southeast Member Chapter - Gene Suave Scholarship *(Undergraduate/Scholarship)* [2218]

AIST Southern California Member Chapter Scholarship *(Undergraduate/Scholarship)* [2219]

AJL Conference Stipends *(Graduate/Award)* [2227]

AKF Clinical Scientist in Nephrology Fellowship (CSN) *(Postgraduate/Fellowship)* [1068]

Al Conklin and Bill de Decker Business Aviation Management Scholarship *(Undergraduate/Scholarship)* [7732]

Al Shackleford and Dan Martin Professional Scholarship *(Professional development/Scholarship)* [2430]

Alabama Horse Council Scholarships *(Undergraduate/Scholarship)* [224]

Alan Compton and Bob Stanley Professional Scholarship *(Professional development/Scholarship)* [2431]

Alan Holoch Memorial Grant *(Professional development/Grant)* [594]

Alaska Airlines Pilot Scholarship *(All/Scholarship)* [8741]

Albert W. Dent Graduate Student Scholarship *(Undergraduate/Scholarship)* [763]

Alberta Holstein Association Scholarships *(Undergraduate/Scholarship)* [267]

Alberta Teachers Association Doctoral Fellowships in Education *(Doctorate/Fellowship)* [312]

Alberta Teachers Association Educational Research Award *(Other/Scholarship)* [313]

Neil Alexander Scholarships *(Undergraduate/Scholarship)* [7586]

All Star Purchasing *(Undergraduate/Scholarship)* [344]

The Frances C. Allen Fellowship *(Graduate/Fellowship)* [8368]

J Frances Allen Scholarship Award *(Doctorate/Scholarship)* [887]

Dorothea E. Allen Scholarship *(Undergraduate/Scholarship)* [4974]

Alliance-CES Pre-Dissertation Research Fellowship *(Graduate/Fellowship)* [3855]

Alliance Medical Education Scholarship (AMES) *(Undergraduate, Graduate/Scholarship)* [4797]

Allison E. Fisher Scholarship *(Undergraduate, Graduate/Scholarship)* [7615]

Almeric L. Christian Memorial Scholarship *(Graduate/Scholarship)* [11829]

ALOA Scholarship Foundation *(Undergraduate/Scholarship)* [374]

ALPFA Scholarship *(Graduate, Undergraduate, Master's/Scholarship)* [2231]

Alpha Mu Tau Undergraduate Scholarships *(Undergraduate/Scholarship, Monetary)* [1398]

Alpha Tau Omega Graduate Scholarship *(Graduate/Scholarship)* [401]

Alpha Tau Omega Undergraduate Scholarships (Undergraduate/Scholarship) [402]

ALSC Bound to Stay Bound Books Scholarship (Graduate/Scholarship) [2237]

ALSC Summer Reading Program Grant (Other/Grant) [2238]

Americal Legacy Foundation Scholarship (Undergraduate/Scholarship) [420]

American Art Therapy Association Anniversary Scholarship (Graduate/Scholarship) [501]

American Association of Cereal Chemists Graduate Fellowship Program (Graduate/Fellowship) [3266]

American Association for Hand Surgery Annual Research Awards (Professional development/Grant) [566]

American Association of University Women Career Development Grants (Postgraduate/Grant) [665]

American Association for Women in Community Colleges LEADERS Institute Scholarship (Other/Scholarship) [672]

American Dental Hygienists' Association Institute for Oral Health Research Grants (Master's/Grant) [859]

American Dissertation Fellowships (Doctorate, Postdoctorate/Fellowship) [669]

American Institute of Physics Congressional Science Fellowship (Doctorate/Fellowship) [1042]

American Institute of Physics State Department Science Fellowship (Doctorate/Fellowship) [1043]

American Legion Eagle Scout of the Year (Undergraduate/Scholarship) [7843]

American Legion Florence/Lauderdale Post 11 Scholarship (Undergraduate, Community College/Scholarship) [8501]

American Nephrology Nurses' Association Evidence-Based Research Grants (Other/Grant) [1151]

American Pediatric Surgical Nurses Association Educational Grant (Other/Grant) [1210]

American Psychology-Law Society Dissertation Awards (Graduate/Award) [1291]

American Psychology-Law Society Student Grants-In-Aid (Graduate/Grant) [1292]

American Quarter Horse Foundation Scholarships (Undergraduate, Graduate/Scholarship) [1310]

American-Scandinavian Foundation Grants to Study in Scandinavia (Graduate/Grant) [1374]

American Society of Electroneurodiagnostic Technologists Student Education Grants (Undergraduate/Grant) [1981]

American Society of Mammalogists Grants-in-Aid of Research (Graduate, Undergraduate/Grant) [1500]

American Society for Microbiology Undergraduate Research Fellowship (Undergraduate/Fellowship, Award, Monetary) [1513]

American Society Of Mammalogists Fellowship In Mammalogy (Graduate/Fellowship) [1501]

American Sokol Merit Award (Undergraduate/Scholarship, Recognition) [1593]

American Speech Language Hearing Foundation Endowed Scholarships (Graduate, Master's, Doctorate/Scholarship) [1596]

American Water Ski Educational Foundation Scholarships (Undergraduate/Scholarship) [11778]

AMS Teacher Education Scholarships (Undergraduate/Scholarship) [1129]

AMSA Graduate Student Research Poster Competition (Graduate, Doctorate, Master's/Award) [1109]

AMSN Career Mobility Scholarship (Undergraduate, Doctorate/Scholarship) [48]

AMSSM-ACSM Clinical Research Grants (Professional development/Grant) [1115]

AMTA Past Presidents' Conference Scholar (Professional development/Scholarship) [1132]

AMTA Student Conference Scholar (Undergraduate, Graduate/Scholarship) [1133]

AMTF Graduate Scholarships (Graduate/Scholarship, Monetary) [1399]

ANCA Scholarships (Undergraduate/Scholarship) [1915]

Mary Louise Andersen Scholarship (Undergraduate/Scholarship) [1742]

The Anderson Group Summer Institute Scholarships (Other/Scholarship) [1710]

Dr. Andy Anderson Young Professional Awards (Professional development/Award) [9146]

Grace Andow Memorial Scholarship (Undergraduate, Graduate/Scholarship) [6244]

Andrew Thomson Prize in Applied Meteorology (Professional development/Award, Prize) [3040]

Richard E. Andrews Memorial Scholarship (Undergraduate/Scholarship, Monetary) [694]

ANF/ANN-FNRE Nursing Research Grants (Professional development/Grant) [1173]

ANF/ENRS Nursing Research Society (Professional development/Grant) [1174]

Angus Foundation Graduate Student Degree Scholarship Program (Graduate/Scholarship) [1712]

Angus Foundation Scholarships (Undergraduate, Graduate/Scholarship) [7965]

Angus Foundation Undergraduate Student Scholarships (Undergraduate/Scholarship) [1713]

Anna B. Ames Clinical Excellence Student Grant (Undergraduate/Grant) [2835]

Anne Friedberg Innovative Scholarship Award (Other/Scholarship) [10309]

Anthony Gerharz Scholarship (Undergraduate, Graduate/Scholarship) [7457]

A.O. Putnam Memorial Scholarship (Undergraduate/Scholarship) [5826]

AOFAS Research Grants Program (Graduate/Grant) [1193]

AOSA Research Grant (Professional development/Grant) [1186]

AOSA Research Partnership Grant (Professional development/Grant) [1187]

APA Society Convention Research Awards (Undergraduate, Graduate/Award) [9375]

APALA Scholarship (Doctorate, Master's/Scholarship) [1990]

APhA Foundation Scholarship (Undergraduate/Scholarship) [1743]

APHF Academic Scholarship (Undergraduate/Scholarship) [1204]

Applied Social Issues Internship Program (Undergraduate, Graduate, Doctorate/Internship) [10508]

Applied Urban Communication Research Grants (Professional development/Grant) [4270]

APS Convention Society Research Awards (Undergraduate, Graduate/Award) [9376]

APS Student Research Award (APS) (Undergraduate, Graduate/Award) [2266]

APSA Small Research Grant Program (Professional development/Grant) [1252]

APsaA Fellowship (Doctorate, Postdoctorate/Fellowship) [1265]

APT US&C Scholarships (Advanced Professional/Scholarship) [2271]

ARA Scholarship Awards (Undergraduate/Scholarship) [2364]

ARAFCS Doctoral Scholarship (Doctorate, Graduate/Scholarship) [1821]

ARAFCS Masters Scholarship (Graduate, Master's/Scholarship) [1822]

Archaeological Institute of America Fellowships for Study in the US (Postdoctorate/Fellowship) [1773]

Archaeology of Portugal Fellowship (Professional development, Graduate/Fellowship) [1774]

George F. Archambault Scholarship (Undergraduate/Scholarship) [1744]

AREMA Committee 24 - Education and Training Scholarships (Undergraduate/Scholarship) [1318]

AREMA Michigan Tech Alumni Scholarships (Graduate, Undergraduate/Scholarship) [1321]

A.R.F.O.R.A. Undergraduate Scholarships for Women (Undergraduate/Scholarship) [1366]

Jane B. Aron Doctoral Fellowship (Doctorate/Fellowship) [7695]

Arthur Patch McKinlay Scholarship (Graduate, Undergraduate/Scholarship) [753]

The Artist in Landscape Design Scholarship (Undergraduate/Scholarship) [8585]

ASA Student Forum Travel Awards (Undergraduate, Graduate/Award) [1591]

ASBC Foundation Graduate Scholarships (Graduate/Scholarship) [1387]

ASBC Foundation Undergraduate Scholarships (Undergraduate/Scholarship) [1388]

ASC Ph.D. Research Scholarship Award (Doctorate, Postdoctorate/Scholarship) [1415]

ASCE Freeman Fellowship (Graduate/Fellowship, Award) [1783]

ASCO/CCF Young Investigator Awards (Professional development, Advanced Professional/Grant) [3767]

ASCP Foundation Garza & Becan-McBride Endowed Scholarship (Undergraduate/Scholarship, Monetary) [1402]

ASECS Graduate Student Research Paper Award (Graduate/Prize) [1426]

ASECS Innovative Course Design Competition (Undergraduate/Award) [1427]

ASECS Women's Caucus Editing and Translation Fellowship (Doctorate/Fellowship) [1428]

ASET Scholarships (Other/Scholarship) [1982]

ASEV Traditional Scholarship (Graduate, Undergraduate/Scholarship) [1447]

ASHFoundation New Century Scholars Doctoral Scholarship (Doctorate/Scholarship) [1601]

ASHFoundation NSSLHA Scholarship (Graduate/Scholarship) [1604]

Asian Development Bank - Japan Scholarship Program (Graduate, Master's/Scholarship) [4261]

ASIS Foundation Chapter Matching Scholarship (Undergraduate/Scholarship) [1996]

ASLA Council of Fellows (Undergraduate/Scholarship) [1491]

ASLMS Research Grant (Postdoctorate/Grant, Monetary) [1495]

ASM Congressional Science Fellowship (Postdoctorate/Fellowship) [1515]

ASM Robert D. Watkins Graduate Research Fellowship (Postdoctorate/Fellowship, Monetary) [1517]

ASMS Research Awards (Other/Award) [1508]

ASNE Scholarship (Graduate, Undergraduate/Scholarship) [1524]

ASNT Fellowship Award (Graduate/Fellowship, Award) [1531]

ASRT Research Grants (Professional development/Grant) [1550]

Association for the Advancement of Baltic Studies Dissertation Grants for Graduate Students (Doctorate/Grant) [2030]

Association of Donor Recruitment Professionals Hughes Scholarships (Other/Scholarship) [2150]

Association of Donor Recruitment Professionals Presidential Scholarships (Other/Scholarship) [2151]

Association of Flight Attendants Scholarship Fund (Undergraduate/Scholarship) [2179]

Association of Government Accountants Graduate Scholarships for Community Service (Graduate/Scholarship) [2187]

Association of Government Accountants Graduate Scholarships for Full-time study (Graduate/Scholarship) [2188]

Association of Government Accountants Graduate Scholarships for Part-time study (Graduate/Scholarship) [2189]

Association for Psychological Science Student Grants (APS) (Graduate, Undergraduate/Grant) [2267]

Association of the United States Navy Scholarships (Undergraduate/Scholarship) [2303]

ASSP Foundation Professional Education Grant Program (Professional development/Grant) [1561]

ASTR Research Fellowships (Doctorate/Fellowship) [1577]

ASTRO Junior Faculty Career Research Training Award (Advanced Professional, Professional development/Award) [1545]

ASTRO Residents/Fellows in Radiation Oncology Research Seed Grant (Advanced Professional, Professional development/Grant) [1547]

ASTRO/ROI Comparative Effectiveness Research Awards (Professional development/Award) [1548]

ATS Abstract Scholarships (Undergraduate, Graduate, Doctorate/Scholarship) [1621]

AUA Foundation Urology Research Bridge Awards (Postgraduate/Award) [11771]

Aubrey L. Williams Research Travel Fellowship (Doctorate/Fellowship) [1429]

AVMA Fellowship Program (Professional development/Fellowship) [1628]

Award for Outstanding Doctoral Dissertation in Laser Science *(Doctorate, Postdoctorate/Award)* [1222]

AWMA Niagara Frontier Section College Scholarship *(Graduate, Undergraduate/Scholarship)* [169]

AWS International Scholarship Program *(Undergraduate, Graduate/Scholarship)* [1657]

B-2 LAFF 20-30's Financial Aid Scholarship *(Postgraduate/Scholarship)* [6937]

B-3 LAFF 20-30's Financial Aid Scholarship *(Professional development/Scholarship)* [6938]

B-4 Albert S. Vieira Memorial Scholarship *(Professional development/Scholarship)* [6939]

Carroll Preston Baber Research Grant *(Professional development/Grant)* [1081]

Bachelor of Science in Nursing Academic Scholarships *(Graduate/Scholarship)* [7548]

BACUS Scholarship *(Graduate, Undergraduate/Scholarship)* [10724]

Bailey/Hollister Scholarship *(Graduate, Professional development/Scholarship)* [8956]

Lincoln C. Bailey Memorial Scholarship Fund *(Undergraduate/Scholarship)* [6079]

Baker McKenzie Graduate Legal Studies Scholarships *(Graduate, Professional development/Scholarship)* [2412]

Baker & Taylor/YALSA Collection Development Grant *(Professional development/Grant)* [1083]

Balestreri/Cutino Scholarship *(Undergraduate/Scholarship)* [841]

Brenda S. Bank Educational Workshop Scholarship *(Undergraduate/Scholarship)* [10341]

Bar President's Scholarship *(Undergraduate/Scholarship)* [11931]

TCDA Carroll Barnes Student Scholarships *(Undergraduate/Scholarship)* [740]

Marguerite Ross Barnett Fund *(Graduate, Postdoctorate, Undergraduate/Grant)* [1254]

Walt Bartram Memorial Education Scholarship *(Undergraduate/Scholarship)* [10384]

Suzanne Beauregard Scholarships *(Undergraduate, Graduate/Scholarship)* [5027]

Beaverbrook Media at McGill Student Paper Prize *(Undergraduate/Prize)* [2955]

Bechtel Engineering and Science Scholarship *(Undergraduate/Scholarship)* [7075]

Louise Seaman Bechtel Fellowship *(Professional development/Fellowship)* [2239]

Ed Becker Conference Travel Awards *(Undergraduate, Graduate/Award)* [4403]

Clifford L. Bedford Scholarship Award *(Undergraduate/Scholarship)* [5220]

Hannah Beiter Graduate Student Research Grants *(Master's, Graduate/Grant, Recognition)* [3296]

The Betty Bell Scholarship Fund *(Undergraduate/Scholarship)* [5548]

Samuel Flagg Bemis Dissertation Research Grants *(Graduate/Grant)* [10354]

Reckitt Benckiser Student Scholarships *(Graduate/Scholarship)* [7677]

Viscount Bennett Fellowship *(Graduate/Fellowship)* [2918]

Rosalie Bentzinger Scholarships *(Doctorate/Scholarship)* [4889]

Fred Berg Awards *(Undergraduate/Award)* [4299]

Bergman Scholarship *(Undergraduate/Scholarship)* [8460]

The E. Alexander Bergstrom Memorial Research Award *(Undergraduate, Master's/Award)* [2177]

Bernard Amtmann Fellowship *(Postgraduate, Other/Fellowship)* [2569]

Bernard Kilgore Memorial Scholarship *(Undergraduate/Scholarship)* [8282]

Leslie Bernstein Grant *(Professional development/Grant)* [452]

Beta Sigma Phi Visual Arts Scholarship *(Undergraduate/Scholarship)* [10049]

Betty Rose Scholarship *(Undergraduate/Scholarship)* [1407]

Albert J. Beveridge Grant for Research in the History of the Western Hemisphere *(Doctorate/Grant)* [959]

BHCRI Bridge Funds *(Advanced Professional, Professional development/Grant)* [5648]

BHCRI Matching Funds *(Advanced Professional, Professional development/Grant)* [5650]

BHCRI Miscellaneous Funds *(Advanced Professional, Professional development/Grant)* [5651]

BHCRI Seed Funds *(Advanced Professional, Professional development/Grant)* [5652]

Leo Biaggi de Blasys Bogliasco Fellowships *(Undergraduate/Scholarship)* [2642]

Birgit Baldwin Fellowship *(Graduate/Fellowship)* [7229]

Birmingham District Alabama Dietetic Association Scholarships *(Graduate, Undergraduate/Scholarship)* [217]

BK Lighting / Ron Naus Scholarship *(Graduate, Undergraduate/Scholarship)* [5935]

SETAC/EA Jeff Black Fellowship Award *(Postgraduate/Fellowship)* [10324]

Eileen Blackey Doctoral Fellowship *(Doctorate/Fellowship)* [7696]

NICSA/William T. Blackwell Scholarship Fund *(Undergraduate/Scholarship)* [7952]

Mitzi & William Blahd, MD, Pilot Research Grant *(Professional development/Grant)* [10437]

Beatrice K. Blair Scholarships *(Undergraduate/Scholarship)* [2620]

Ellin Bloch and Pierre Ritchie Diversity Dissertation Grant *(Graduate/Grant)* [1269]

Stella Blum Research Grant *(Graduate, Undergraduate/Grant)* [3843]

BMES Graduate and Undergraduate Student Awards *(Graduate, Undergraduate/Award)* [2578]

Board of Certification for Emergency Nursing (BCEN) Undergraduate Scholarship *(Undergraduate/Scholarship)* [4376]

Sandra Bobbitt Continuing Education Scholarship *(Undergraduate/Scholarship)* [2254]

Edith and Arnold N. Bodtker Grants *(Undergraduate, Graduate/Grant, Internship)* [3968]

Boeing Business Scholarships *(Undergraduate/Scholarship)* [5020]

Boeing Company Scholarship *(Undergraduate/Scholarship)* [10050]

BOMA/NY Scholarship *(Undergraduate/Scholarship)* [2741]

The Ellis Bonner Award *(Graduate/Scholarship)* [7653]

Stephen Botein Fellowships *(Doctorate/Fellowship)* [485]

The Gloria Bousley Graduate Scholarship *(Graduate/Scholarship)* [5696]

Dr. Howard L. Bowen Scholarship *(Undergraduate/Scholarship)* [7005]

Margery Boyce Bursary Award *(Graduate/Award, Scholarship)* [2893]

W. Scott Boyd Group Grant *(Advanced Professional/Grant)* [5951]

Boyle Family Scholarship *(Undergraduate/Scholarship)* [1745]

Wade O. Brinker Resident Research Award *(Postgraduate, Professional development/Grant)* [11813]

Dvora Brodie Scholarships *(Graduate, Postgraduate, Undergraduate/Scholarship)* [5447]

William G. Broughton Fellowship for Outstanding Achievement *(Undergraduate, Graduate, Vocational/Occupational, Other/Fellowship)* [4975]

Murray L. Brown Scholarships *(Undergraduate/Scholarship)* [7006]

Richard A. Brown Student Scholarship *(Undergraduate/Scholarship)* [10977]

Gösta Bruce Scholarship Fund *(Other/Scholarship)* [6059]

The Robert W. Brunsman Memorial Scholarship *(Professional development/Scholarship)* [6041]

Pamfil and Maria Bujea Family Orthodox Christian Seminarian Scholarships *(Undergraduate/Scholarship)* [1367]

Walter Byers Postgraduate Scholarships *(Graduate, Postgraduate/Scholarship)* [7769]

CAA National Capital Region Writing Contest *(All/Award, Prize, Monetary)* [2916]

CACCN/Baxter Corporation Guardian Scholarship *(Professional development/Scholarship)* [2889]

CACCN Educational Awards *(Professional development/Grant)* [2890]

CACCN Research Grant *(Professional development/Grant)* [2891]

CAEYC Presidents Education Award *(Graduate/Award, Scholarship)* [2779]

CAG Health and Health Care Study Group Awards *(Graduate/Award)* [2085]

CALL/ACBD Education Reserve Fund Grant *(Professional development/Grant)* [2899]

CALL/ACBD Research Grants *(Graduate/Grant)* [2900]

Calvin Alumni Association-Washington, D.C. Scholarships *(Undergraduate/Scholarship)* [2844]

Canadian Association of Cardiac Rehabilitation Graduate Scholarship Awards *(Graduate/Scholarship)* [2887]

Canadian Identification Society Essay/Scholarship Awards *(Advanced Professional, Professional development/Award)* [3010]

The Canadian Parking Association Scholarship (CPA) *(Undergraduate/Scholarship)* [2125]

Canadian Water Resources Association Harker/Cameron Women in Water Scholarship *(Graduate/Scholarship)* [2107]

Canham Graduate Studies Scholarship *(Graduate/Scholarship)* [11927]

Therese A. "Teri" Cannon Educational Scholarship *(Other/Scholarship)* [6061]

CANS/SNRS Dissertation Research Grant *(Doctorate/Grant)* [10658]

CAPSLE Bursary. *(Graduate/Fellowship)* [2908]

CAPT Winifred Quick Collins, USN (Ret.) Scholarship *(Undergraduate/Scholarship)* [8172]

Career Development Scholarships *(Postgraduate/Scholarship)* [4666]

Carli Edwards Memorial Scholarship *(Undergraduate/Scholarship)* [10051]

CARO-ELEKTA Research Fellowship Program *(Professional development/Fellowship)* [2102]

Carolinas-Virginias Hardware Scholarship *(Undergraduate/Scholarship)* [4725]

CAS/GE Healthcare Canada Inc. Research Awards *(Other/Award)* [2878]

CAS Research Award in Neuroanesthesia *(Other/Award)* [2879]

CAS Trust Scholarship Program *(Undergraduate/Scholarship, Monetary, Award)* [3183]

TCDA Jim and Glenda Casey Professional Scholarships *(Other/Scholarship)* [741]

CCCN Research Grant Program *(Professional development/Grant)* [3791]

CCF Career Development Award *(Professional development/Grant)* [3769]

CCF Merit Award *(Professional development, Doctorate/Award)* [3771]

CCWH / Berks Graduate Student Fellowship *(Graduate/Fellowship)* [3828]

Cecilia Rowan Memorial Fellowship *(Postgraduate/Fellowship)* [8638]

CEE Cultural Diversity Grant *(Professional development/Grant)* [7798]

CEIBS scholarship *(Graduate/Scholarship)* [7724]

Cengage Travel Award for Teachers of Reading at a Community College *(Professional development/Monetary)* [3512]

Cenie Jomo Williams Tuition Scholarship *(Graduate, Undergraduate/Scholarship)* [7617]

Certified in Care Coordination and Transition Management (CCCTM) Certification Grant *(Undergraduate/Scholarship)* [427]

CFT/ACPSOP Scholarship Fund *(Undergraduate/Scholarship)* [3343]

CGSA Student Scholarship Awards *(Undergraduate/Award, Scholarship)* [2992]

Chaîne des Rôtisseurs Scholarships *(Undergraduate/Scholarship)* [842]

Jeanne S. Chall Research Fellowship *(Doctorate, Graduate/Fellowship, Grant)* [6033]

Logan S. Chambers Individual Scholarship *(Other/Scholarship)* [5952]

Channabasappa Memorial Scholarships *(Graduate, Doctorate/Scholarship)* [5993]

Nancy J. Chapman Scholarships *(Other/Scholarship)* [2152]

Chappie Hall Scholarship *(Undergraduate/Scholarship)* [2]

EHA Graduate Dissertation Fellowships *(Graduate/ Fellowship)* [4283]

Farouk El-Baz Student Research Grants *(Graduate, Undergraduate, Doctorate, Master's/Grant)* [4909]

Eldon E. and JoAnn C. Kuhns Family Scholarship *(Undergraduate, Graduate/Scholarship)* [7458]

Elena Sanchez Memorial WSWS Outstanding Student Scholarship Program *(Graduate, Undergraduate/Scholarship)* [11993]

Eli Lilly And Company/BDPA Scholarship *(Undergraduate, Graduate, Master's/Scholarship)* [2456]

Eli Lilly Graduate Scholarship *(Graduate, Postgraduate/Scholarship)* [2091]

AACR Gertrude B. Elion Cancer Research Award *(Professional development, Graduate/Award, Recognition)* [534]

Elizabeth Benson Scholarship Award *(Undergraduate/Scholarship)* [9625]

Ellen Swallow Richards Travel Grant *(Graduate, Other/Grant)* [1452]

Elva Knight Research Grant *(Professional development, Graduate/Grant, Award)* [6034]

Gladys Anderson Emerson Scholarship *(Undergraduate/Award, Scholarship)* [6152]

Emily P. Foster Fellowship *(Graduate/Fellowship)* [8746]

ENA Foundation Undergraduate State Challenge Scholarship *(Undergraduate/Scholarship)* [4379]

Alice Yuriko Endo Memorial Scholarship *(Undergraduate/Scholarship)* [6245]

Jane Engelberg Memorial Fellowship (JEMF) *(Professional development/Fellowship)* [8100]

Entomological Society of Saskatchewan Travel Awards *(Professional development/Award)* [4413]

Epsilon Mu Scholarship *(Graduate, Undergraduate/ Scholarship)* [6424]

Alan R. Epstein "Reach for the Stars" Scholarships *(College/Scholarship)* [7297]

Equal Justice Works Fellowships *(Graduate, Undergraduate/Fellowship)* [4436]

ERDAS Internship *(Graduate/Internship)* [2005]

NSPF Ray B. Essick Scholarship Awards *(Other/ Scholarship)* [8135]

Estes Memorial *(Graduate/Grant)* [10559]

European Studies First Article Prize *(Professional development/Prize)* [3857]

Lee S. Evans/National Housing Endowment Scholarships *(Undergraduate, Graduate/Scholarship)* [7934]

Richard Evans Schultes Research Award *(Graduate/ Award)* [10320]

William C. Ezell Fellowship *(Graduate, Master's/ Fellowship)* [466]

F. Christian and Betty Thompson Fellowship *(Graduate/Fellowship)* [8747]

FACT "Second Chance" Scholarship Program *(Undergraduate/Scholarship)* [4527]

FAER Mentored Research Training Grants *(Professional development/Grant)* [4702]

FAER Research in Education Grants *(Advanced Professional/Grant)* [4703]

FAER Research Fellowship Grants *(Postdoctorate, Postgraduate, Graduate/Grant)* [4704]

FAIC Individual Professional Development Scholarships *(Professional development/Scholarship)* [4700]

AIST Benjamin F. Fairless Scholarship *(Undergraduate/Scholarship)* [2220]

Families of Freedom Scholarship Fund - Scholarship America *(Undergraduate, Vocational/Occupational/Scholarship)* [4482]

John S.W. Fargher, Jr. Scholarship *(Graduate/ Scholarship)* [5827]

FASSE-International Assembly International Understanding Grants *(Professional development/ Grant)* [7795]

Father J. Harold Conway Memorial Scholarship *(Postgraduate/Scholarship)* [8640]

FCSLA Graduate Scholarships *(Graduate/Scholarship)* [4575]

FCSLA High School Scholarships *(High School, College, Graduate/Scholarship)* [4576]

FCSLA Seminary or Diaconate or Religious Life Scholarships *(Graduate/Scholarship)* [4577]

FCSLA Undergraduate College Scholarships *(Undergraduate, Two Year College, Four Year College/Scholarship)* [4578]

FCSLA Vocational/Technical/Trade Scholarships *(Vocational/Occupational/Scholarship)* [4579]

Feeding Tomorrow Scholarships *(Graduate, Undergraduate/Scholarship)* [5819]

Fellowship in the PMAC-AGPC *(Professional development/Fellowship)* [9349]

Fellowships for Creative and Performing Artists and Writers *(Professional development/Fellowship)* [490]

Fieldwork Fellowship *(Undergraduate, Graduate/ Award, Fellowship)* [4449]

Adele Filene Student Presenter Grant *(Graduate, Undergraduate/Grant)* [3846]

Ruth Fine Memorial Student Loans *(Undergraduate/ Grant, Loan)* [4120]

First Step Award - Wiley Professional Development Grant *(Professional development/Grant, Award)* [2235]

The Judge Ralph Fisch Police Explorer Scholarship Program *(Undergraduate/Scholarship)* [4646]

Flamenco Student Scholarship *(Undergraduate, Professional development/Scholarship)* [4614]

The FLEOA Foundation Scholastic Program *(Undergraduate/Scholarship)* [4519]

Flight Safety International Bell 206/Bell 407 Scholarship *(Professional development, Vocational/Occupational/Scholarship)* [12010]

FMA-FEEA Scholarship Program *(Graduate/Scholarship)* [4516, 4521]

Gail Goodell Folsom Memorial Scholarships *(Undergraduate/Scholarship)* [7542]

Frank Fong Scholarships *(Undergraduate/Scholarship)* [10267]

A. Ward Ford Memorial Research Grant *(Postdoctorate, Professional development/Grant)* [1497]

Nancy B. Forest and L. Michael Honaker Master's Grant for Research in Psychology *(Graduate/ Grant)* [1270]

Foster G. McGaw Graduate Student Scholarship *(Graduate/Scholarship)* [764]

Foundation Scholarships *(Graduate/Scholarship)* [8619]

Founding Fathers Leadership Scholarships *(Undergraduate/Scholarship)* [12113]

Founding Mothers Student Scholarships - Graduate *(Graduate/Scholarship)* [2233]

Terry Fox Memorial Scholarship *(Undergraduate/ Scholarship)* [8147]

Frances Henne/YALSA Grant *(Undergraduate, Professional development/Grant)* [1084]

Gloria Francke Scholarship *(Undergraduate/Scholarship)* [1747]

Frank Oppenheimer Scholarship *(Postgraduate/ Scholarship)* [1178]

Frank S. Land Scholarship *(Undergraduate/Scholarship)* [4049]

Frederick V. Hunt Postdoctoral Research Fellowship in Acoustics *(Postdoctorate/Fellowship)* [61]

Kevin Freeman Travel Grant *(Graduate, Other/ Grant)* [7514]

Friends of Mary Automotive Scholarship *(Undergraduate/Scholarship)* [10052]

Friends of the Oro Valley Public Library Support Staff Scholarship Award *(Undergraduate/Scholarship, Monetary, Award)* [1810]

FSF Field Grant *(Professional development/Grant)* [4677]

FSF Student Travel Grant *(Undergraduate, Graduate/Grant)* [4678]

Arthur Flagler Fultz Research Award *(Professional development/Grant)* [1135]

Future Leader Initial NCTM Annual Meeting Attendance Awards *(Advanced Professional/Award, Monetary)* [7804]

Future STEM Teacher Scholarship *(Undergraduate/ Scholarship)* [10937]

GAAC Project Grants *(Undergraduate, Professional development/Grant)* [4995]

GACFE Scholarship Program *(Graduate, Undergraduate/Scholarship)* [2134]

Frederick and Helen Gaige Award *(Professional development/Grant)* [1483]

Gamewardens Scholarship Program *(High School/ Scholarship)* [4852]

Gamma Sigma Alpha Graduate Scholarship *(Graduate/Scholarship)* [4856]

John A. Gans Scholarship *(Undergraduate/Scholarship)* [1748]

William R. Gard Memorial Scholarships *(Graduate/ Scholarship)* [7666]

Gardner Foundation Education Scholarship *(Professional development/Scholarship)* [5786]

Dwight D. Gardner Scholarship *(Undergraduate/ Scholarship)* [5828]

A.R.F.O.R.A. Martha Gavrila Scholarships for Women *(Postgraduate/Scholarship)* [1368]

GAWP Graduate Scholarships *(Graduate/Scholarship)* [4925]

The Florence Gaynor Award *(Graduate/Scholarship)* [7654]

GCFI Student Travel Awards *(Undergraduate/ Award)* [5252]

GCSAA Scholars Competition *(Undergraduate/ Scholarship)* [5032]

GCSAA Student Essay Contest *(Graduate, Undergraduate/Prize)* [5033]

GED Jump Start Scholarships *(Professional development/Scholarship)* [9959]

GEICO Life Scholarship *(Undergraduate/Scholarship)* [5021]

Generation III Scholarship *(Undergraduate/Scholarship)* [4285]

Geological Society of America Graduate Student Research Grants *(Doctorate, Graduate/Grant)* [4910]

George H. A. Clowes, Jr. MD, FACS, Memorial Research Career Development Award *(Professional development/Fellowship)* [777]

Gerald V. Henderson Memorial Scholarship *(Undergraduate, Graduate/Scholarship)* [10427]

Doris Y. and John J. Gerber Scholarship *(Undergraduate/Scholarship)* [11910]

Walter Gerboth Award *(Other/Award, Monetary)* [7515]

Gianninoto Industrial Design Graduate Scholarship *(Graduate, Undergraduate/Scholarship)* [5778]

Robert D. Gibson Scholarship *(Undergraduate/ Scholarship)* [1749]

Gilbreth Memorial Fellowship *(Graduate/Fellowship)* [5829]

Lawrence Ginocchio Aviation Scholarships *(Undergraduate/Scholarship)* [7736]

GLA Beard Scholarship *(Master's/Scholarship)* [4932]

GLA Hubbard Scholarships *(Master's/Scholarship)* [4933]

J. Robert Gladden Orthopaedic Society PGY5 ABOS Board Preparation Scholarship *(Professional development/Scholarship)* [4992]

J. Robert Gladden Orthopaedic Society Traveling Fellowship Support *(Professional development/ Fellowship)* [4993]

John Glaser Scholarships *(Undergraduate/Scholarship)* [3506]

GLATA Living Memorial Graduate Scholarship *(Graduate/Fellowship, Scholarship)* [5216]

Gleaner Life Insurance Society Scholarship *(Graduate/Scholarship)* [4997]

Glenn B. Anderson Scholarship *(Graduate, Undergraduate/Scholarship)* [7721]

Glenn T. Seaborg Congressional Science and Engineering Fellowship *(Professional development/ Fellowship)* [1165]

Shirley J. Gold Scholarship *(Undergraduate, Vocational/Occupational/Scholarship)* [883]

Golden Key Advisor Professional Development Grant *(Professional development/Grant)* [5022]

Golden Key Graduate Scholar Award *(Graduate/ Scholarship)* [5023]

Sarah "Sally" Ives Gore Gamma Kappa Sapphire Scholarships *(Graduate, Undergraduate/Scholarship)* [6437]

Louis Gottschalk Prize *(Other/Prize)* [1432]

Carl W. Gottschalk Research Scholar Grants *(Professional development/Grant)* [1526]

Governor James E. Holshouser Professional Development Scholarship *(Other/Scholarship)* [8434]

Graduate Realtor Institute Scholarships *(Graduate/ Scholarship)* [6537]

Graduate Student Award *(Doctorate, Master's, Graduate/Award)* [515]

Graduate Student Honoraria - A. Brazier Howell Award *(Master's, Doctorate/Award)* [1502]

Graduate Student Honoraria - Elmer C. Birney Award *(Master's, Doctorate/Award)* [1503]

Graduate Student Pest Management Award *(Graduate/Grant, Award)* [3108]

Graduate Student Travel Grants *(Graduate, Other/ Grant)* [10318]

Grande Prairie 4-H District Scholarship *(Undergraduate/Scholarship)* [14]

Grant H. Flint International Scholarship Program - Category I *(Undergraduate/Scholarship)* [10580]

Grant H. Flint International Scholarship Program - Category II *(Undergraduate/Scholarship)* [10581]

Grants in Aid for Early Career Professionals *(Graduate/Grant)* [1294]

IADR John Gray Fellowship *(Other/Fellowship)* [5914]

Great Lakes Section Diversity Scholarship *(Graduate, Undergraduate/Scholarship)* [5221]

Bishop Charles P. Greco Graduate Fellowships *(Graduate, Master's/Fellowship)* [6578]

Reginald K. Groome Memorial Scholarships *(Undergraduate/Scholarship)* [9986]

Ronald P. Guerrette FFA Scholarship Fund *(Undergraduate/Scholarship)* [6980]

Eleanor Guetzloe Undergraduate Scholarship *(Undergraduate/Scholarship)* [3853]

Larry Gulley Scholarship *(Undergraduate/Scholarship)* [10343]

Scott A. Gunder, MD, DCMS Presidential Scholarship *(Undergraduate, Graduate/Scholarship)* [4798]

Gunild Keetman Scholarship *(Other, Undergraduate/ Scholarship)* [8724]

Gwin J. and Ruth Kolb Research Travel Fellowship *(Doctorate, Other/Fellowship)* [1433]

Lee Hakel Graduate Student Scholarship *(Graduate/ Scholarship)* [10334]

HANA Scholars *(Undergraduate, Graduate, Doctorate/Scholarship)* [4891]

The Harold E. Eisenberg Foundation Scholarship *(Other/Scholarship)* [5979]

Harold E. Ennes Scholarship *(Graduate/Scholarship)* [10285]

Dave Hart Graduate Scholarship *(Graduate/Scholarship)* [10654]

Carroll Hart Scholarship *(Graduate/Scholarship)* [10344]

Thomas T. Hayashi Memorial Scholarship *(Graduate, Undergraduate/Scholarship)* [6246]

Health Policy Scholarship for General Surgeons *(Professional development/Scholarship)* [778]

Healthcare Information Management Systems Scholarships *(Graduate, Postgraduate, Undergraduate/Scholarship)* [5448]

HECUA Scholarship for Social Justice *(Undergraduate, Graduate/Scholarship)* [5506]

Helena B. Cobb Higher Education (four Year) Scholarship *(Undergraduate, Vocational/Occupational/ Scholarship)* [12165]

The Helena B. Cobb Scholarships *(Undergraduate, Vocational/Occupational/Scholarship)* [12166]

Joseph T. Helling Scholarship Fund *(Undergraduate/ Scholarship)* [5748]

Paul E. Henkin School Psychology Travel Grant *(Doctorate/Grant)* [1730]

Henley-Putnam University Scholarships *(Other/ Scholarship)* [5931]

John P. Hennessey Scholarship *(Graduate, Undergraduate/Scholarship)* [7349]

Henry Salvatori Fellowships *(Graduate/Fellowship)* [5885]

The Herpetologists' League Graduate Research Award *(Graduate/Award)* [5499]

Wayne E. Hesch Memorial Scholarship *(Undergraduate, Graduate/Scholarship)* [1691]

Dorothy Hicks Graduate Scholarship *(Graduate/ Scholarship)* [10655]

Jim Hierlihy Memorial Scholarship *(Undergraduate/ Scholarship)* [4429]

HLS/MLA Professional Development Grants *(Other/ Grant)* [7218]

Jeri Hodges Leadership Scholarship *(Professional development/Scholarship)* [10978]

C.H.(Chuck) Hodgson Scholarships *(Undergraduate/ Scholarship)* [12005]

Henry Hoffman Memorial Scholarship *(Undergraduate/Scholarship)* [7641]

Miriam Hoffman Scholarship *(Undergraduate, Graduate/Scholarship)* [4892]

The Michael J. Hogan Foreign Language Fellowship *(Graduate/Fellowship)* [10356]

Hohn-Johnson Research Award *(Professional development/Grant)* [11814]

R.W. "Bob" Holden Memorial Scholarships *(Undergraduate/Scholarship)* [5419]

Robert Holmes Scholarship *(Undergraduate/Scholarship)* [3720]

Edward Horne Scholarship *(Advanced Professional/ Scholarship)* [8742]

HQF New Quality Professional Grant *(Professional development/Award, Grant)* [7657]

Huang Hsing Chun-tu Hsueh Fellowship Fund *(Graduate, Postdoctorate, Undergraduate, Professional development/Grant)* [1256]

Hubert K. and JoAnn Seymour Scholarship *(Undergraduate/Scholarship)* [8461]

Arthur H. Huene Memorial Award *(Doctorate/Grant)* [8947]

Tertia M.C. Hughes Memorial Graduate Student Prize *(Graduate/Award, Prize)* [3044]

Humanism in Medicine Scholarships *(Undergraduate/Scholarship)* [10865]

Anna C. Hume Scholarship *(Undergraduate/Scholarship)* [4976]

IAAI Scholarship Foundation Accounting Scholarships *(Undergraduate/Scholarship)* [5733]

IAESTE United States Internships *(Undergraduate/ Internship)* [3937]

IAGLR Scholarship *(Doctorate/Scholarship)* [5924]

IARS Mentored Research Award (IMRA) *(Professional development/Award, Grant)* [5899]

IASP Developed-Developing Countries Collaborative Research Grants *(Advanced Professional/Grant)* [5940]

IASP Developing Countries Project: Initiative for Improving Pain Education *(Advanced Professional/ Grant)* [5941]

IASP Research Symposium *(Advanced Professional/Grant)* [5942]

IASP Visiting Professor Grant *(Professional development/Grant)* [5943]

IAWP International Scholarship *(Other/Scholarship)* [5949]

Ice Skating Institute of America Education Foundation Scholarships *(Undergraduate/Scholarship)* [5673]

ICRS Graduate Fellowships *(Doctorate, Graduate/ Fellowship)* [5976]

IDA Fellowship/Scholarship Programs *(Other/Fellowship)* [5994]

IDEC Special Project Grant *(Professional development/Grant)* [5888]

IDTA Freestyle Scholarships *(Other/Scholarship)* [5991]

IEEE - Photonics Society Graduate Student Fellowship *(Graduate/Fellowship)* [5691]

IEHA Education/Scholarship Foundation Award *(Undergraduate/Scholarship)* [5998]

IFDA Student Member Scholarship *(Undergraduate/ Scholarship)* [6014]

Ella R. Ifill Fund *(Undergraduate/Scholarship)* [6985]

IISE Council of Fellows Undergraduate Scholarship *(Undergraduate/Scholarship)* [5830]

IISE Presidents Scholarship *(Undergraduate/Scholarship)* [5831]

ILA Teacher as Researcher Grant *(Professional development/Grant)* [6035]

Illinois Association of Chamber of Commerce Executives Scholarships *(Professional development/ Scholarship)* [5693]

Illinois Lake Management Association Undergraduate/Graduate Scholarships *(Graduate, Undergraduate/Scholarship)* [5700]

IMA Memorial Education Fund Scholarships (MEF) *(Graduate, Undergraduate/Scholarship)* [5848]

Ina Knutsen Scholarship *(Undergraduate/Scholarship)* [10054]

Independent Professional Seed Association Student Recognition Awards *(Undergraduate/Scholarship)* [5740]

Indian River Scholarship *(Undergraduate, University, College, Vocational/Occupational/Scholarship)* [12329]

Indiana FFA Association State Fair Scholarship *(Undergraduate/Scholarship)* [5752]

Indonesian Directorate General of Higher Education Scholarships (DIKTI) *(Graduate/Scholarship)* [4263]

Terrance N. Ingraham Pediatric Optometry Residency Award *(Graduate/Award)* [463]

INIA Scholarship Program *(Undergraduate/Scholarship)* [6044]

International Association for Food Protection - Student Travel Scholarship Program *(Undergraduate, Graduate/Scholarship)* [5921]

International Association of Wildland Fire Graduate-Level Scholarships *(Graduate/Scholarship)* [5947]

International Council for Canadian Studies Graduate Student Scholarships *(Graduate/Scholarship)* [3801]

International Development and Education Award in Palliative Care *(Professional development/Award)* [3774]

International Development and Education Awards *(Professional development, Doctorate/Grant)* [3775]

International Door Association Scholarship Foundation Program *(Undergraduate/Scholarship)* [5996]

International Executive Housekeepers Association Spartan Scholarship Award *(Undergraduate/Scholarship)* [5999]

International Innovation Grants *(Professional development/Grant)* [3776]

IOIA Organic Community Initiative Scholarships *(Other/Scholarship)* [6054]

Graduate Study Fellowship *(Professional development/Fellowship)* [6065]

Irene Woodall Graduate Scholarship *(Graduate/ Scholarship)* [860]

Irwin S. Lerner Student Scholarship *(Undergraduate/Scholarship)* [8108]

ISDS Graduate Student Scholarships *(Doctorate, Graduate/Scholarship)* [6105]

Patricia and Gail Ishimoto Memorial Scholarship *(Undergraduate/Scholarship)* [6247]

ISMER Student Financial Assistance *(Master's, Doctorate/Monetary, Grant)* [11670]

ITAA Graduate Student Best Paper Award *(Graduate/Award, Monetary)* [6129]

ITMS Shannon Fellowships *(Graduate, Undergraduate/Fellowship)* [6132]

ITNS Research Grants *(Other/Grant)* [6137]

Jack Ervin Economic Development Institute Scholarship *(Other/Scholarship)* [8435]

Jack Shand Research Grants. *(Advanced Professional/Grant)* [10526]

Graduate Student Honoraria - Anna M. Jackson Awards *(Master's, Doctorate/Award)* [1504]

Freddy L. Jacobs Individual Scholarship *(Undergraduate/Scholarship)* [5953]

James L. Baillie Student Research Award *(Undergraduate/Grant)* [10295]

James Wisecup Memorial Flight Training Scholarship *(Vocational/Occupational, Advanced Professional/Scholarship)* [12011]

JEA Action Research Initiative *(Postgraduate/Grant)* [6303]

Jeff Oliphant Memorial Post-Graduate Scholarship *(Postgraduate/Scholarship)* [12114]

Jeffrey Cook Memorial Faculty Retreat Scholarship *(Professional development/Scholarship)* [10290]

Jeffrey D. Ralston Memorial Scholarship *(Undergraduate/Scholarship)* [7562]

Gaynold Jensen Education Stipends *(Postdoctorate, Other/Scholarship)* [4084]

Stanley "Doc" Jensen Scholarships *(Undergraduate/ Scholarship)* [844]

Jerman-Cahoon Student Scholarship *(Undergraduate/Scholarship)* [1551]

Jessie Young Certification Bursary (Other/Award) [2094]

Jewell Gardiner Scholarship (Undergraduate/Scholarship) [2827]

Jim & Nancy Hinkle Travel Grants (Graduate/Grant) [5476]

Joan Rogers Kamps Bursary (Undergraduate, Postgraduate, Professional development/Scholarship) [8641]

John Charles Wilson and Robert Doran Sr. Scholarship (Undergraduate/Scholarship) [5903]

John D. Wirth Travel Grant (Graduate, Other/Grant) [1454]

John J. Bonica Trainee Fellowship (Professional development/Fellowship) [5944]

John J. McKetta Undergraduate Scholarship (Undergraduate/Scholarship) [1023]

Joseph C. Johnson Memorial Grant (Undergraduate/Grant) [1392]

Jones-Lovich Grants in Southwestern Herpetology (Master's, Doctorate/Grant) [5500]

Joseph C. Menezes Scholarship Fund (Undergraduate/Scholarship) [5905]

Joseph H. Fichter Research Grant (Postdoctorate/Grant) [2290]

Joseph J. Fitzsimmons Scholarship Fund (Doctorate/Scholarship) [11384]

Joseph Wood Rogers Memorial Scholarship in Mathematics (Undergraduate/Scholarship) [10055]

Journalist of the Year Scholarships (Undergraduate/Monetary, Scholarship) [6337]

Journey Toward Ordained Ministry Scholarships (Undergraduate, Graduate/Scholarship) [4893]

Joyce C. Hall College Scholarship (Undergraduate/Scholarship) [8981]

J.R. (Joe) Power National Scholarship (Postgraduate/Scholarship, Monetary) [9443]

Justin G. Schiller Fellowship (Doctorate, Postdoctorate/Fellowship) [492]

Mike Kabo Global Scholarships (Professional development/Scholarship) [5004]

Sam Kalman Scholarship (Undergraduate/Scholarship) [1750]

Kaplan Scholarships (Undergraduate/Scholarship) [5524]

Kappa Delta Phi Scholarship (Postgraduate/Scholarship) [1179]

The ISASI Rudolf Kapustin Memorial Scholarship (Undergraduate/Scholarship) [6083]

Karl C. Ivarson Scholarship for Students in Soil Science and Related Studies (Master's, Doctorate/Scholarship, Award) [130]

Philip R. Karr, III Scholarship Fund (Graduate/Scholarship) [4926]

Martha W. Keister Memorial Travel Grant (Professional development/Grant) [3522]

Rita Mae Kelly Fund (Graduate, Doctorate, Undergraduate, Professional development/Grant) [1257]

Kathleen Kelly Undergraduate Scholarship (Undergraduate/Scholarship) [9434]

Robert E. Kelsey Annual Scholarship (Undergraduate/Scholarship) [8954]

Willmoore H. Kendall Scholarships (Professional development/Scholarship) [3444]

John F. Kennedy Scholarship Award (Undergraduate/Recognition, Award, Scholarship) [2782]

Kenneth and Barbara Starks Plant Resistance to Insects Graduate Student Award (Graduate/Award) [4396]

KGP Cornaro Scholarship (Graduate/Scholarship) [6397]

KHIMA Graduate Scholarship (Graduate/Scholarship) [6369]

Julia Kiene Fellowships in Electrical Energy (Graduate/Fellowship) [12159]

Elson T. Killam Memorial Scholarship (Undergraduate, Graduate/Scholarship) [8249]

The Margie Klein "Paper Plate" Scholarships (All/Scholarship) [2053]

David Knight Graduate Scholarship (Graduate/Scholarship) [10656]

Robert E. Knight Professional Scholarship (Graduate/Scholarship) [10979]

Glenn Knudsvig Memorial Scholarships (Graduate, Undergraduate/Scholarship) [754]

Carl Koller Memorial Research Grants (Professional development/Grant) [1557]

AIST Willy Korf Memorial Fund (Undergraduate, Graduate/Scholarship) [2221]

Marcia J. Koslov Scholarship (Professional development/Scholarship) [598]

William D. Krahling Excellence in Journalism Scholarship (Undergraduate/Scholarship) [403]

Michael Kraus Research Grants (Doctorate/Grant) [961]

Kress/AAR Fellowships (Professional development/Fellowship) [2058]

Samuel H. Kress Grants for Research and Publication in Classical Art and Architecture (Professional development, Graduate/Grant, Award) [1778]

Kurt H. and Donna M. Schuler Cash Grant (Undergraduate/Scholarship, Grant) [1393]

Henry and Chiyo Kuwahara Creative Arts Award (Graduate/Scholarship) [6248]

Sam and Florice Kuwahara Memorial Scholarship (Undergraduate/Scholarship) [6249]

Anne Emery Kyllo Professional Scholarship (Professional development/Scholarship) [1136]

Lawrence Gelfand - Armin Rappaport - Walter LaFeber Dissertation Fellowship (Graduate/Fellowship) [10357]

Ron LaFreniere Business Administration Scholarship (Undergraduate/Scholarship) [10057]

Verne LaMarr Lyons Memorial MSW Scholarship (Graduate, Master's/Fellowship) [7698]

James D. Lang Memorial Scholarship (Graduate/Scholarship) [2902]

Lapides Fellowships in Pre-1865 Juvenile Literature and Ephemera (Graduate, Postdoctorate/Fellowship) [493]

Laser Technology, Engineering and Applications Scholarship (Graduate, Undergraduate/Scholarship) [10727]

Daniel Lasky Scholarship Fund (Undergraduate/Scholarship, Award) [8023]

Jay and Deborah Last Fellowships (Doctorate/Fellowship) [494]

Candia Baker Laughlin Certification Scholarship (Undergraduate/Scholarship) [428]

Leadership for Diversity Paraprofessional Scholarship (Advanced Professional/Scholarship) [2828]

Leadership for Diversity TL Scholarship (Master's/Scholarship) [2829]

Leadership Scholarships (Undergraduate/Scholarship) [10478]

Thomas R. Lee Career Development Award (Professional development/Grant, Award) [865]

Lee Student Support Fund (Undergraduate, Graduate/Award, Monetary, Recognition) [10536]

Leesfield/AAJ Scholarship (Undergraduate/Scholarship) [583]

Leica Scholarship (Graduate/Scholarship) [2008]

Imelda (Graduate, High School/Scholarship) [3722]

Leo Gilmartin Scholarship (Undergraduate/Scholarship) [9211]

Leonard Hawk Founders Scholarship (Graduate, Undergraduate, Vocational/Occupational/Scholarship) [1334]

Leslie Baranowski Scholarship for Professional Excellence (Professional development/Scholarship) [5787]

Janet Levy Fund (Doctorate/Grant) [1145]

Herbert Levy Memorial Scholarship (Undergraduate/Scholarship) [10479]

Lillian and Alex Feir Graduate Student Travel Award in Insect Physiology, Biochemistry, or Molecular Biology (Master's, Doctorate/Award) [4398]

Lillian and Murray Slatkin Fellowship (Graduate/Fellowship) [8748]

AIST Ronald E. Lincoln Memorial Scholarship (Undergraduate/Scholarship) [2222]

Litherland/FTEE Undergraduate Scholarships (Undergraduate/Scholarship) [6125]

Littleton-Griswold Research Grant (Doctorate/Grant) [962]

Local 564 Scholarship Fund (Undergraduate, Vocational/Occupational/Scholarship) [6142]

Loeblich and Tappan Student Research Award (Graduate, Undergraduate/Grant) [3942]

Lawrence A. Long Memorial Law Scholarship (Graduate/Scholarship) [404]

Long-term International Fellowships (Professional development/Fellowship) [3778]

Bart Longo Memorial Scholarship Program (Undergraduate, Graduate/Scholarship) [7762]

Louis Agassiz Fuertes Grant (Professional development/Grant) [12055]

LPHA Scholarships (Graduate, Undergraduate/Scholarship) [6906]

Lucas Grant (Professional development/Grant) [4679]

Lee G. Luna Foreign Travel Scholarship (Professional development/Scholarship) [8109]

Juan and Esperanza Luna Scholarship (Undergraduate/Scholarship) [1751]

Charles Luttman Scholarship (Undergraduate/Scholarship) [2875]

Lyle Mamer Fellowship (Graduate/Fellowship) [12160]

The C. Lyons Fellowship Program (Advanced Professional/Fellowship) [7984]

Carol E. Macpherson Memorial Scholarship (Graduate, Undergraduate/Scholarship) [11645]

Andrew Macrina Scholarships (Undergraduate/Scholarship) [845]

Maibach Travel Grant (Professional development/Grant) [799]

Maine Community College Scholarships (MCCS) (Undergraduate, Vocational/Occupational/Scholarship) [7008]

Maley/FTE Scholarships (Graduate/Scholarship) [6126]

Maley/FTEE Teacher Professional Development Scholarships (Professional development/Scholarship) [6127]

Margaret Mallett Nursing Scholarship (Undergraduate/Scholarship) [10058]

Lazaro J. Mandel Young Investigator Award (Advanced Professional/Monetary, Award) [1236]

Manulife Financial Scholarship (Undergraduate/Scholarship) [3793]

March of Dimes Graduate Nursing Scholarships (Graduate/Scholarship) [7027]

The Albert H. Marckwardt Travel Grants (Graduate, Doctorate/Grant) [10969]

Harold and Inge Marcus Scholarship (Undergraduate/Scholarship) [5833]

Margaret E. Phillips Scholarship (Undergraduate/Scholarship) [11716]

Margaret Lynch Memorial Fellowship (Postgraduate/Fellowship) [8642]

Margaret Svec Scholarship (Undergraduate/Scholarship) [10059]

Marianne M. Stenvig Scholarship (Master's, Doctorate/Scholarship) [10623]

Marie Tremaine Fellowship (Postgraduate, Other/Fellowship) [2570]

Marine Technology Society ROV Scholarship (MTS ROV) (Undergraduate, Graduate/Scholarship) [7069]

Marion and Donald Routh Student Research Grant (Graduate/Grant) [1740]

Marliave Scholarship Fund (Graduate/Scholarship) [2161]

Ray and Gertrude Marshall Scholarships (Undergraduate/Scholarship) [846]

Martha Weston Grant (Advanced Professional/Grant) [10301]

A. Lucchetti Martino Scholarship (Undergraduate/Scholarship) [7961]

Marvin H. and Kathleen G. Teget Leadership Scholarship (Undergraduate/Scholarship) [10866]

Mary C. Babcock Fellowship (Postgraduate/Fellowship) [8643]

Mary Minglen Scholarship (Postgraduate/Scholarship) [1180]

The Maschhoffs Pork Production Scholarships (Undergraduate/Scholarship) [7971]

Master's Degree with a Major in Nursing Academic Scholarships (Graduate/Scholarship) [7549]

Mathematics Graduate Course Work Scholarships for Grades 6-8 Teachers (Graduate/Scholarship) [7805]

Noel D. Matkin Awards (Undergraduate/Award) [4301]

Mature Student Scholarship (Undergraduate/Scholarship) [4430]

Ann Lane Mavromatis Scholarship (Undergraduate/Scholarship) [967]

The Clara Mayo Grants (Graduate/Grant) [10510]

John Mazurek Memorial-Morgex Insurance Scholarship (Other/Scholarship) [314]

A. James McAdams Short-Term Study Stipend (Professional development/Grant) [10461]

MCBA Scholarship (MCBA) (Undergraduate/Scholarship) [7308]

McDonald's Inspiration Celebration Scholarship (Undergraduate, Graduate/Scholarship) [11026]

Richard J. McDonough Scholarship (Undergraduate/Scholarship) [7009]

National Association of Pediatric Nurse Practitioners McNeil Rural and Underserved Scholarships (Graduate/Scholarship) [7680]

MCRTA Book Scholarships (Undergraduate/Scholarship) [7295]

MDA Development Grants (Doctorate/Grant) [7509]

MDA Research Grants (Advanced Professional/Grant) [7510]

David Meador Foundation - Club Management Student Scholarships (Undergraduate/Scholarship) [8242]

Mearl K. Gable II Memorial Grant (Other/Grant) [5285]

The Medalist Club Post Graduate Scholarship (Postgraduate/Scholarship) [7203]

Medical Student Rotation for Underrepresented Populations (Graduate, Master's/Grant) [3779]

Medieval Academy Dissertation Grants (Graduate/Grant) [7230]

Susan R. Meisinger Fellowship for Graduate Study in HR (Graduate, Master's, Advanced Professional/Fellowship) [10367]

Frederic G. Melcher Scholarships (Graduate/Scholarship) [2240]

Mellon-CES Dissertation Completion Fellowships in European Studies. (Graduate/Fellowship) [3858]

Terry Mellor Continuing Education Grant (Undergraduate/Grant) [10735]

MELNA Scholarship (Undergraduate, Graduate/Scholarship) [6999]

E.V. and Nancy Melosi Travel Grants (Graduate, Other/Grant) [1456]

Melvin Kruger Endowed Scholarship Program (Graduate, Undergraduate/Scholarship) [8063, 9739]

Member Student Scholarships (Undergraduate/Scholarship) [9050]

Mentor-Based Minority Postdoctoral Fellowship (Postdoctorate/Fellowship, Monetary) [866]

Donald Menzies Bursary Award (Postgraduate/Scholarship, Award) [2894]

Merck Frosst Canada Inc. Postgraduate Pharmacy Fellowship Award (Postgraduate, Graduate, Doctorate/Fellowship) [2172]

Merck Frosst Canada Ltd. Postgraduate Pharmacy Fellowships (Graduate, Postgraduate, Doctorate/Fellowship) [2173]

Merial Excellence in Preventive Medicine in Beef Award (Other/Grant) [526]

The Edmond A. Metzger Scholarship (Undergraduate/Scholarship) [1949]

Theodore Meyer Scholarship (Undergraduate, Graduate/Scholarship) [1137]

MICA Scholarships (Undergraduate/Scholarship) [7386]

Michael P. Spadafora Medical Toxicology Travel Award (Professional development/Grant) [766]

Michael R. Losey Excellence In HR Research Award (Graduate, Undergraduate/Award, Recognition) [10368]

Michigan Education Association Scholarships (Undergraduate/Scholarship) [7313]

Beth Middleton Memorial Scholarships (Undergraduate/Scholarship) [4486]

Midlothian Rotary Club "Service Above Self" Scholarships (Undergraduate/Scholarship) [7363]

Midwest Modern Language Association Fellowship (Doctorate, Postdoctorate/Fellowship) [7380, 8377]

Milan Getting Scholarship (Undergraduate/Scholarship) [10574]

The Cheryl Allyn Miller Award (Doctorate, Graduate/Award) [10567]

Warren E. Miller Fund in Electoral Politics (Advanced Professional, Graduate, Postdoctorate, Undergraduate/Grant) [1258]

Mineral & Metallurgical Processing Division Scholarships and Richard Klimpel Memorial Scholarships (MPD) (Undergraduate, Graduate/Scholarship) [10428]

Minnesota Health Information Management Association Scholarships (Undergraduate/Scholarship) [7408]

MLA Continuing Education Grants (CE) (Graduate/Grant) [7219]

MLA Financial Assistance (Graduate, Advanced Professional/Grant) [7426]

MLA Research, Development, and Demonstration Project Grant (Graduate/Grant) [7221]

MMC Scholarships (Other/Scholarship) [6027]

MODNA Nursing Education Scholarship (Doctorate, Graduate/Scholarship) [7359]

Antoinette M. Molinari Memorial Scholarships (Doctorate/Scholarship) [467]

Morgan and Jeanie Sherwood Travel Grant (Graduate, Other/Grant) [1457]

Dorothy Morrison Undergraduate Scholarships (Undergraduate/Scholarship, Monetary) [1400]

Mortar Board National Foundation Fellowship (Postdoctorate/Fellowship, Award) [7476]

Morton Bahr Scholarship (Undergraduate/Scholarship) [3559]

Gerald O. Mott Award (Graduate/Award) [3916]

MPI CRV Membership Scholarships (Other/Scholarship) [7238]

MPI-WI Founders Grant Program (Professional development/Grant) [7241]

MSA Graduate Fellowship (Graduate/Fellowship) [7532]

MSA Grant for Student Research in Mineralogy and Petrology (Undergraduate, Graduate/Grant) [7398]

MSAA Scholarship Program (Graduate/Scholarship) [7410]

MSCPA Scholarship - Montana Tech (Undergraduate, Graduate/Scholarship) [7459]

MSCPA Scholarship - MSU Bozeman (Undergraduate, Graduate/Scholarship) [7460]

MSCPA Scholarship - University of Montana (Undergraduate, Graduate/Scholarship) [7461]

MSEA/SEIU Part-time Student Members Scholarships (Undergraduate/Scholarship) [7010]

The MTS Student Scholarship for Graduate Students (Graduate/Scholarship) [7070]

The MTS Student Scholarship for Graduating High School Seniors (Undergraduate/Scholarship) [7071]

The MTS Student Scholarship for Two-Year, Technical, Engineering and Community College Students (Undergraduate/Scholarship) [7072]

Mueller Undergraduate Scholarship (Undergraduate/Scholarship) [12115]

Multicultural Work-in-Progress Grant (Advanced Professional/Grant) [10302]

Marvin Mundel Memorial Scholarship (Undergraduate/Scholarship) [5834]

Clarence & Josephine Myers Undergraduate Scholarships (Graduate, Undergraduate, Vocational/Occupational, Community College/Scholarship) [10409]

Myra Levick Scholarship Fund (Graduate/Scholarship) [502]

NAAE Upper Division Scholarship (Undergraduate/Scholarship) [7609]

NABA National Scholarship Program (Graduate, Undergraduate/Scholarship, Award, Monetary) [7613]

NACADA Scholarships (Graduate, Postdoctorate/Scholarship) [7568]

James B. Nachman Endowed ASCO Junior Faculty Award in Pediatric Oncology (Doctorate, Professional development/Grant, Monetary) [3780]

Nadene M Thomas Graduate Research Bursary (Graduate/Scholarship) [315]

NAFA Scholarship Program (Undergraduate/Scholarship) [7590]

IADR Toshio Nakao Fellowship (Other/Fellowship) [5915]

Nancy Curry Scholarship (Vocational/Occupational, Undergraduate, Graduate, Postgraduate/Scholarship, Award) [9960]

Nancy Lorraine Jensen Memorial Scholarship Fund (Undergraduate/Scholarship) [10590]

NAPT Continuing Education Award (Undergraduate/Award) [7684]

NARFE-FEEA Scholarship Awards Program (Undergraduate/Scholarship) [4517, 7584]

NASE Future Entrepreneur (Undergraduate/Scholarship) [7692]

National AAHAM Scholarship (Undergraduate/Scholarship) [570]

National Association for the Self-Employed Scholarships (Undergraduate, High School/Scholarship) [7693]

National Ataxia Foundation Research Grants (Other/Grant) [7712]

National Beta Club Scholarships (Undergraduate/Scholarship, Monetary) [7714]

National Black Nurses Association Scholarships (Undergraduate/Scholarship) [7726]

National Board Technical Scholarship (College, Four Year College, University/Scholarship) [7730]

National Collegiate Athletic Association Postgraduate Scholarships (Postgraduate/Scholarship) [7771]

National Council on Public History Graduate Student Travel Awards (Doctorate, Graduate, Master's/Grant) [7792]

National Council on Public History Student Project Awards (Undergraduate/Grant) [7793]

National Dairy Herd Information Association Scholarship Program (Undergraduate/Scholarship) [7824]

National Dental Hygienists' Association Scholarships (Undergraduate/Scholarship) [7839]

National Guard Association of Rhode Island Scholarship (Undergraduate/Scholarship) [7913]

National Huguenot Society College and Postgraduate Student Scholarships (Undergraduate, Postgraduate/Scholarship) [7937]

National Judges Association Scholarships (Other/Scholarship) [7963]

National Junior Swine Association Outstanding Member Scholarships (Graduate/Scholarship) [7972]

National Merit Harris Corporation Scholarship Program (Undergraduate/Scholarship) [5306]

National Military Intelligence Foundation Scholarship (Undergraduate, Graduate/Scholarship) [8011]

National Recreation and Park Association Diversity Scholarships (Undergraduate/Scholarship) [8059]

National Swimming Pool Foundation Scholarship Award (Other/Scholarship) [8136]

National Technical Honor Society Scholarships (NTHS) (Undergraduate/Scholarship) [4487]

National Women's Studies Association Lesbian Caucus Award (Master's, Doctorate/Award, Grant) [8165]

NBT Trade School, Community/Technical College, or University Scholarships (Undergraduate/Scholarship) [8563]

NCECA Graduate Student Fellowships (Graduate/Fellowship) [7787]

NCPA Foundation Presidential Scholarships (Undergraduate/Scholarship) [7776]

NCRF New Professional Reporter Grant (Other/Grant) [7819]

NCTE Research Foundation Grants (Other/Grant) [7800]

NCTM Emerging Teacher-Leaders in Elementary School Mathematics Grants for Grades PreK-5 (Other/Grant) [7806]

NCTM Prospective 7-12 Secondary Teacher Course Work Scholarships (Professional development/Scholarship) [7807]

NCTM School In-Service Training Grants for Grades 6-8 (Undergraduate/Grant) [7808]

NCTM School In-Service Training Grants for Grades 9-12 (Undergraduate/Grant) [7809]

NCTM School In-Service Training Grants for Grades PreK-5 (Undergraduate/Grant) [7810]

NDFU Scholarship *(Undergraduate/Scholarship)* [8462]

NDIA Picatinny Chapter Scholarships *(Undergraduate/Scholarship)* [7832]

NDTA Academic Scholarship Program A *(Undergraduate/Scholarship)* [7836]

NDTA Academic Scholarship Program B *(Undergraduate/Scholarship)* [7837]

NEA Foundation Learning and Leadership Grants *(Professional development/Grant)* [8185]

Nebraska Farm Bureau Greater Horizon Scholarship *(Undergraduate/Scholarship)* [8187]

Nebraska Paralegal Association Student Scholarships *(Undergraduate/Scholarship)* [8194]

NEHA/AAS Scholarship *(Graduate, Undergraduate/Scholarship)* [478, 7873]

NELA Conference Scholarships *(All/Scholarship)* [8246]

Bill Nelson Scholarship Endowment (BNSE) *(Undergraduate, Graduate/Scholarship)* [8780]

NEMLA Summer Fellowships *(Graduate/Fellowship)* [8484]

NEMRA Educational Scholarship Foundation *(Undergraduate, Vocational/Occupational/Scholarship)* [7866]

Nephrology Nurse Researcher Awards *(Doctorate/Award)* [1152]

New Hampshire Snowmobile Association Book Scholarships *(Undergraduate/Scholarship)* [8269]

Newberry Consortium on American Indian Studies Faculty Fellowships *(Professional development/Fellowship)* [8378]

Newcomer Supply Student Scholarship *(Undergraduate/Scholarship)* [8110]

NFPA PCCE Scholarship *(Other, Professional development/Scholarship)* [7882]

NFPA Youth Scholarships *(Undergraduate/Scholarship)* [7896]

NGAT Educational Foundation Scholarship *(Graduate, Undergraduate/Scholarship)* [7915]

NHAEOP Member Scholarships *(Undergraduate/Scholarship)* [8251]

NHS Scholarships *(Undergraduate/Scholarship)* [7932]

NIABA/NIAF Scholarships *(Graduate/Scholarship)* [7958]

NIBA Presidential Scholarships *(Undergraduate/Scholarship)* [7941]

Eric Niemitalo Scholarship in Earth and Environmental Science *(Undergraduate/Scholarship)* [10060]

Nila Banton Smith Research Dissemination Support Grant *(Professional development/Grant)* [6036]

Louise A. Nixon Scholarship *(Graduate/Scholarship)* [8192]

NJSA Visionary Leader Scholarships *(Graduate/Scholarship)* [7973]

NLBRA Age-Out Scholarship *(Undergraduate/Scholarship)* [7993]

NLBRA National Royalty Scholarship *(Other/Scholarship)* [7994]

NLBRA Rainwater Scholarships *(Undergraduate/Scholarship)* [7995]

NLBRA World All Around Scholarships *(Undergraduate/Scholarship)* [7996]

NLBRA World Event Scholarships *(Undergraduate/Scholarship)* [7997]

NLBRA/Wrangler Academic Scholarships *(Undergraduate/Scholarship)* [7998]

NLBRA Youth Board Officer Scholarships *(Undergraduate/Scholarship)* [7999]

NLLN Continuing Education Scholarship *(Professional development/Scholarship)* [8492]

NMPF National Dairy Leadership Scholarship Program *(Graduate, Master's, Doctorate/Scholarship)* [8013]

NMSC Corporate-Sponsored merit Scholarship Awards *(Undergraduate/Scholarship)* [8005]

Leonard Noble Educational Scholarships *(Professional development/Scholarship)* [8111]

Non Commissioned Officers Association Scholarships *(Undergraduate/Scholarship)* [8409]

Nor' Easters Scholarships - Two-year Program *(Undergraduate/Scholarship)* [5542]

Nordic Skiing Association of Anchorage Scholarship *(Graduate/Scholarship)* [242]

Norman Siegel Research Scholar Grants in Pediatrics *(Doctorate/Grant)* [1527]

North Alabama Dietetic Association Scholarships *(Undergraduate, Graduate/Scholarship)* [218]

North American Society Fellowship Award (NAS Fellowship) *(Professional development/Fellowship)* [9147]

North Central Region 9 Scholarship *(Undergraduate/Scholarship)* [10410]

North Florida Chapter Safety Education Scholarships *(Undergraduate/Scholarship)* [1570]

NorthCoast Medical Scholarship *(Postgraduate/Scholarship)* [1181]

Northeast Alabama District Dietetic Association Scholarships *(Graduate, Undergraduate/Scholarship)* [219]

Northern California Chapter of HIMSS Scholarships *(Graduate, Postgraduate, Undergraduate/Scholarship)* [5449]

NPM Academic Scholarship *(Graduate, Undergraduate/Scholarship)* [7674]

NPM Program Scholarship *(Graduate, Undergraduate/Scholarship)* [7675]

NSHSS Academic Paper Awards *(High School/Scholarship)* [8104]

NSHSS National Scholar Awards *(High School, College/Scholarship)* [8105]

NSPS and AAGS Scholarships *(Undergraduate/Scholarship)* [8119]

NSS Conservation Grants *(Advanced Professional/Grant)* [8126]

NSSA/NSCA Collegiate High School Senior Scholarships *(Undergraduate/Scholarship)* [8131]

NTHS/HOSA Scholarships *(Undergraduate/Scholarship)* [8140]

NWSA Graduate Scholarship *(Master's, Doctorate/Scholarship)* [8166]

NYLA-Dewey Fellowship Award *(Graduate/Award, Fellowship)* [8314]

NYLA-Dewey Scholarship *(Master's, Undergraduate/Award, Scholarship)* [8315]

OAS Scholarships for Professional Development - The ABC of Telecommunications *(Professional development/Scholarship)* [8735]

Dennis J. O'Brien USAEE Best Student Paper Award *(Undergraduate/Award)* [11296]

Olivia James Traveling Fellowship *(Professional development/Fellowship)* [1779]

Roy C. and Dorothy Jean Olson Memorial Scholarship *(Graduate/Scholarship)* [6042]

OMSF Clinical Surgery Fellowship *(Professional development/Fellowship)* [8682]

OOIDA Mary Johnston Scholarship Program *(Undergraduate/Scholarship)* [8798]

Optical Design and Engineering Scholarship *(Graduate, Undergraduate/Scholarship)* [10728]

Organization of American States Graduate Scholarships *(Doctorate, Graduate/Scholarship)* [8737]

Royce Osborn Minority Scholarship *(Undergraduate/Scholarship)* [1552]

OSCA Graduate Student Scholarship Program *(Graduate/Scholarship)* [8594]

Oslo International Summer School Scholarship *(Undergraduate/Scholarship)* [10591]

Osteopathic Medical Student Research Fellowship Program *(Undergraduate/Fellowship)* [10867]

OTA Member Full Research Grant *(Other/Grant)* [8763]

Elvina Jane Owen Scholarship *(Graduate, Undergraduate/Scholarship)* [4894]

The Barbara L. Packer Fellowship *(Doctorate, Postdoctorate/Fellowship)* [496]

Casilda Pagan Educational/Vocational Scholarships *(Graduate, Undergraduate, Postgraduate/Scholarship)* [5594]

Pain and Symptom Management Special Merit Award *(Postdoctorate, Professional development/Award)* [3781]

PALCUS National Scholarship Program *(Undergraduate/Scholarship)* [9250]

Paleontological Society Student Research Award *(Graduate, Undergraduate/Grant)* [29]

PAM General Conference Scholarships *(Other/Scholarship)* [9264]

Pan Pacific Law Enforcement Scholarships *(Undergraduate/Scholarship)* [9868]

Joseph M. Parish Memorial Grants *(Undergraduate/Grant)* [1394]

Parking Industry Institute Scholarship Program *(Undergraduate/Scholarship)* [8036]

The Paros-Digiquartz Scholarship *(Graduate, Undergraduate/Scholarship)* [7073]

Carl Parsell Scholarship Fund *(Undergraduate/Scholarship)* [7303]

Q. O. (Quint) Patrick Scholarships *(Undergraduate/Scholarship)* [12006]

Patterson Memorial *(Graduate, Undergraduate/Grant, Monetary)* [10560]

Walter S. Patterson Scholarships *(Graduate/Scholarship)* [2704]

Paul S. Robinson Award *(Postgraduate/Award)* [10322]

Paula Backscheider Archival Fellowship *(Other/Fellowship)* [1437]

PDEF Professional Development Scholarship *(Professional development/Scholarship)* [10440]

PEA Bursaries *(Undergraduate/Scholarship)* [9340]

PEA Scholarships *(Undergraduate/Scholarship)* [9341]

Oliver P. Pearson Award *(Doctorate/Fellowship)* [1506]

Pediatric Endocrinology Nursing Society Academic Education Scholarships *(Undergraduate/Scholarship)* [8941]

Penguin Random House Young Readers Group Award *(Professional development/Grant, Award)* [2241]

Pennsylvania Library Association MLS Scholarships *(Graduate/Scholarship)* [8958]

PENS Conference Reimbursement Scholarship *(Undergraduate/Scholarship)* [8942]

PENS Research Grants *(Professional development/Grant)* [8943]

Kate B. and Hall J. Peterson Fellowships *(Doctorate/Fellowship)* [497]

Silvio and Eugenia Petrini Grants *(Other/Grant)* [5286]

PGSF Scholarship *(Undergraduate/Scholarship)* [9332]

Ed Phinney Commemorative Scholarships *(Graduate, Undergraduate/Scholarship)* [755]

PHSC Publication Grant *(Professional development/Grant)* [9139]

PHSC Research Grant *(Professional development/Grant)* [9140]

PEN/Phyllis Naylor Grant for Children's and Young Adult Novelists *(Other/Grant)* [8952]

Peter L. Picknelly Honorary Scholarships *(Graduate/Scholarship)* [711]

David Pilon Scholarships for Training in Professional Psychology *(Graduate/Scholarship)* [1271]

Stephen D. Pisinski Memorial Scholarship *(Undergraduate/Scholarship)* [9436]

Pitsenbarger Award *(Undergraduate, Graduate/Grant, Award)* [150]

Betsy Plank/PRSSA Scholarships *(Undergraduate/Scholarship)* [9437]

Platt Excavation Fellowships *(Other, Undergraduate/Fellowship)* [1379]

PLUS Foundation Financial Aid Scholarship *(Undergraduate/Scholarship)* [9212]

PNAA Nursing Scholarship Award *(Master's, Doctorate/Scholarship)* [9135]

Polish National Alliance of Brooklyn, USA Scholarships *(Undergraduate/Scholarship)* [6606]

Harriet and Leon Pomerance Fellowships *(Graduate/Fellowship)* [1780]

Porter Physiology Development Fellowship *(Doctorate/Fellowship, Award, Monetary)* [1238]

AFT Robert G. Porter Scholars Program *(Undergraduate/Scholarship)* [881]

Post-High School Tuition Scholarship Program *(Undergraduate/Scholarship)* [3190]

Barbara Potter Scholarship Fund *(Professional development/Scholarship)* [1188]

Catherine Prelinger Award *(Postdoctorate/Scholarship)* [3830]

Presidency Research Fund *(Graduate, Postdoctorate, Undergraduate, Professional development/Grant)* [1259]

Prince Edward Island Law Student Scholarships *(Undergraduate/Scholarship)* [6732]

Print and Graphics Scholarship Foundation Awards *(Graduate, Undergraduate/Award)* [9330]

Procter & Gamble Professional Oral Health/HDA Foundation Scholarships *(Undergraduate/Scholarship)* [5519]

Professional Certification Exam Scholarship *(Undergraduate, Professional development/Scholarship)* [9797]

Professor Emeritus Dr. Bill Johnson Memorial Scholarship *(Undergraduate/Scholarship)* [10061]

Provincial and Regional 4-H Scholarship *(Undergraduate/Scholarship)* [15]

Barbara F. Prowant Nursing Research Grants *(Graduate/Grant)* [1153]

Neil Pruitt, Sr. Memorial Scholarships *(Undergraduate/Scholarship)* [7778]

Joseph E. Pryor Graduate Fellowships *(Graduate/Fellowship)* [379]

PSAC-AGR National Scholarship *(Postgraduate/Scholarship, Monetary)* [9444]

PSAC - Coughlin National Scholarships *(Postgraduate/Scholarship, Monetary)* [9445]

PSAC National Member Scholarship *(Postgraduate/Scholarship, Monetary)* [9446]

PSAC Regional Scholarships *(Postgraduate/Scholarship, Monetary)* [9447]

PSAI Scholarship Fund *(Undergraduate/Scholarship)* [9248]

PSF Research Fellowship Grants *(Master's, Doctorate/Grant, Fellowship)* [9190]

Psychosocial Research Pilot Grants *(Professional development/Grant)* [8201]

Paul Pumpian Scholarship *(Undergraduate/Scholarship)* [1752]

AIST Judith A. Quinn Detroit Member Chapter Scholarship *(Undergraduate/Scholarship)* [2223]

RADM William A. Sullivan, USN (Ret.) Scholarship *(Undergraduate/Scholarship)* [8174]

Railroad and Mine Workers Memorial Scholarship *(Graduate/Scholarship)* [6250]

Tom D. Ralls Memorial Scholarship *(Professional development/Scholarship)* [4807]

Jennings Randolph Peace Scholarship Dissertation Program *(Doctorate/Scholarship, Fellowship)* [11380]

Edward C. Raney Fund Award *(Professional development/Grant)* [1484]

Lenny Ravich "Shalom" Scholarships *(Advanced Professional/Scholarship)* [2054]

Rawley Silver Award for Excellence *(Graduate/Scholarship)* [503]

The Ray, NØRP, & Katie, WØKTE, Pautz Scholarship *(Undergraduate/Scholarship)* [1956]

Read Carlock Memorial Scholarship Fund *(Other/Scholarship)* [1800]

Regina Brown Undergraduate Student Fellowship *(Undergraduate/Fellowship)* [7788]

Research Resident/Fellow Grant *(Professional development/Grant)* [9483]

Resident Travel Award for Underrepresented Populations *(Professional development/Award)* [3783]

Rexford Daubenmire Fellowship *(Graduate/Fellowship)* [8751]

Reynoldsburg-Pickerington Rotary Club High School Scholarship *(Undergraduate/Scholarship)* [9681]

The Haynes Rice Award *(Graduate/Scholarship)* [7655]

Richard Cecil Todd and Clauda Pennock Todd Tripod Scholarship *(Graduate, Undergraduate/Scholarship)* [9104]

Richard McGrath Memorial Fund Award *(Undergraduate/Award)* [839]

Richard P. Covert, Ph.D., LFHIMSS Scholarships for Management Systems *(Graduate, Postgraduate, Undergraduate/Scholarship)* [5450]

Henry and Sylvia Richardson Research Grant *(Postdoctorate/Grant)* [4401]

J. Milton Richardson Theological Fellowship *(Graduate/Fellowship)* [405]

ANN Ingrid Josefin Ridky Academic Scholarships *(Undergraduate, Graduate/Scholarship)* [56]

The Don Riebhoff Memorial Scholarship *(Undergraduate/Scholarship)* [1957]

Ritchie-Jennings Memorial Scholarship Program *(Undergraduate, Graduate/Scholarship)* [2132]

Riverside Sheriffs Association Member Scholarship Program *(Graduate, Undergraduate/Scholarship)* [9710]

RMACRAO Professional Development Scholarship *(Professional development/Scholarship)* [9725]

Robert A. Clark Memorial Educational Scholarship *(Professional development/Scholarship)* [8112]

Robert D. Greenberg Scholarship *(Graduate, Other/Scholarship)* [10286]

Robert J. McNamara Student Paper Award *(Graduate/Award, Monetary)* [2291]

Robert O. Wagner Professional Development Scholarship *(Professional development/Scholarship)* [2328]

Robert R. Palmer Research Travel Fellowship *(Other/Fellowship)* [1438]

Robert Wood Johnson Foundation Health Policy Fellows *(Advanced Professional, Professional development/Fellowship)* [6326]

Gertrude J. Robinson Book Prize *(Professional development/Prize, Award)* [2956]

Helen M. Robinson Grants *(Doctorate/Grant)* [6037]

Robinson Helicopter R22/R44 Safety Course Scholarship *(Professional development/Scholarship)* [12012]

NKA Dr. Violet B. Robinson Memorial Graduate Scholarship *(Advanced Professional/Scholarship)* [7978]

Rochelle Scholarship *(College/Scholarship)* [6908]

Rocky Mountain Coal Mining Institute Engineering/Geology Scholarships *(Four Year College/Scholarship)* [9727]

Rocky Mountain Coal Mining Institute Technical Scholarships *(Two Year College/Scholarship)* [9728]

Rodger Doxsey Travel Prize *(Graduate, Postdoctorate/Prize)* [684]

Rose Cassin Memorial Scholarship *(Postgraduate/Scholarship)* [8644]

Jean and Tom Rosenthal Scholarship Program *(Undergraduate/Scholarship)* [3723]

IADR Norton Ross Fellowship *(Postgraduate/Fellowship)* [5916]

Colonel Jerry W. Ross Scholarship *(Undergraduate/Scholarship)* [1753]

Regie Routman Teacher Recognition Grant *(Advanced Professional/Grant, Recognition)* [6038]

Robert Roy Award *(Advanced Professional/Award, Recognition)* [2099]

Royal Canadian Regiment Association Bursaries *(Undergraduate/Scholarship)* [9751]

RPNAS Baccalaureate Level Program Scholarship *(Undergraduate/Scholarship)* [9620]

RPNAS Doctorate Level Program Scholarship *(Doctorate/Scholarship)* [9621]

RPNAS Master's Level Program Scholarship *(Master's/Scholarship)* [9622]

R.S. Williamson & Eliford Mott Memorial Scholarships *(Undergraduate/Scholarship)* [12007]

RSNA/AUR/APDR/SCARD Radiology Education Research Development Grant *(Professional development/Grant)* [9484]

RSNA Education Scholar Grant *(Professional development/Grant)* [9485]

Research Scholar Grant *(Professional development/Grant)* [9486]

RSNA Research Seed Grant *(Professional development/Grant)* [9487]

NPELRA Foundation - Anthony C. Russo Scholarships *(Graduate/Scholarship)* [8057]

Moti L. & Kamla Rustgi International Travel Awards *(Professional development/Grant)* [942]

Ruth McMillan Academic Excellence Student Scholarship *(Undergraduate, Four Year College, Two Year College/Grant)* [2836]

IOIA Andrew Rutherford Scholarships *(Other/Scholarship)* [6055]

Safer Athletic Field Environments Scholarships (SAFE) *(Graduate, Undergraduate, Two Year College/Scholarship)* [10736]

SAH Study Tour Fellowships *(Graduate/Fellowship)* [10276]

Sons and Daughters Don Sahli-Kathy Woodall Scholarships *(Graduate, Undergraduate/Scholarship)* [10961]

Saint Elizabeth Health Care Scholarship for Community Health Nursing *(Undergraduate/Scholarship)* [2170]

St. Giles Young Investigator Award *(Doctorate/Grant)* [8948]

St. Louis Paralegal Student Scholarships *(Undergraduate/Scholarship)* [9783]

Sakura Finetek Student Scholarship *(Undergraduate/Scholarship)* [8113]

Sam J. Hord Memorial Scholarship *(Undergraduate/Scholarship)* [10629]

AIST David H. Samson Canadian Scholarship *(Undergraduate/Scholarship)* [2224]

Samuel Robinson Award *(Undergraduate/Award)* [9267]

ABS Amy R. Samuels Cetacean Behavior and Conservation Award *(Graduate/Grant)* [1717]

Frank Sarli Memorial Scholarship *(Undergraduate/Scholarship)* [7820]

Saskatchewan Hockey Association Scholarships *(Undergraduate/Scholarship)* [9893]

Saskatchewan Trucking Association Scholarships *(Undergraduate/Scholarship)* [9928]

Sho Sato Memorial Scholarship *(Undergraduate, Graduate/Scholarship)* [6251]

François J. Saucier Prize in Applied Oceanography *(Professional development/Award, Prize)* [3045]

SBE/Ennes Youth Scholarships *(Graduate/Scholarship)* [10287]

SBSE Ases Student Travel Scholarship *(Graduate/Scholarship)* [10291]

SBSE Student Retreat Scholarship *(Master's, Doctorate/Scholarship)* [10292]

SCA/IARS Starter Grant *(Graduate/Grant)* [10298]

SC&R Foundation Scholarship *(Undergraduate/Scholarship)* [10718]

SCBWI Work-in-Progress Awards (WIP) *(Advanced Professional/Award)* [10303]

SCC Full-Time Continuing Student Scholarship *(Undergraduate/Scholarship)* [10062]

SCC Part-Time Continuing Student Scholarship *(Undergraduate/Scholarship)* [10063]

Schallek Award *(Graduate/Award)* [7231]

Schallek Fellowship *(Graduate/Fellowship)* [7232]

Schlegel-UW RIA Scholarship *(Doctorate/Scholarship)* [2895]

Harold W. Schloss Memorial Scholarship Fund *(Undergraduate/Scholarship, Monetary)* [3184]

Bernadotte E. Schmitt Grant *(Doctorate/Grant)* [963]

Stanley M. Schoenfeld Memorial Scholarship *(Postgraduate/Scholarship)* [8321]

Scholarship for Indigenous Students *(Undergraduate/Scholarship)* [8148]

Scholarship in Medical Education Award *(Advanced Professional, Professional development/Scholarship)* [10339]

School Nutrition Association of Kansas Education Scholarship *(Undergraduate/Scholarship)* [9965]

Alice Southworth Schulman, Class of 1954, Simmons Scholarships for Unitarian Universalist Women *(Undergraduate/Scholarship)* [11255]

AIST William E. Schwabe Memorial Scholarship *(Undergraduate/Scholarship)* [2225]

Schwan's Food Service Scholarship *(Vocational/Occupational, Professional development/Scholarship, Award)* [9961]

Scott Brownlee Memorial Scholarship *(Undergraduate, Graduate/Scholarship)* [7462]

IADR David B. Scott Fellowship *(Professional development/Fellowship, Award)* [5917]

SCSPA Scholarship *(Graduate/Scholarship)* [10618]

SCSPA Yearbook Scholarship *(Undergraduate/Scholarship)* [10619]

SDE Fellowship *(Graduate, Postgraduate/Fellowship)* [5060]

Seaman Family Scholarship *(Undergraduate/Scholarship)* [3487]

Seameo-Vietnam Scholarship Program *(Graduate/Scholarship)* [4265]

Seldovia Native Association Achievement Scholarships *(Undergraduate, Graduate/Scholarship)* [9996]

Seldovia Native Association General Scholarships *(Undergraduate, Graduate/Scholarship)* [9997]

Selena Danette Brown Book Scholarship *(Graduate, Undergraduate/Scholarship)* [7620]

Senior Master Sergeant William Sowers Memorial Scholarship *(Undergraduate/Grant)* [114]

Senior Scholarships *(Undergraduate, Vocational/ Occupational/Scholarship)* [8077]

Servus Credit Union 4-H Scholarship *(College, University, Undergraduate/Scholarship)* [16]

Margaret B. Ševenko Prize in Islamic Art and Culture *(Doctorate, Graduate/Prize)* [5535]

SHAFR Dissertation Completion Fellowship *(Doctorate/Fellowship)* [10359]

Shannon Fellowships *(Professional development/ Fellowship)* [6133]

The Ann Shaw International TYA Fellowship *(Professional development/Fellowship)* [11014]

Sheet Metal And Air Conditioning Contractors' National Association College of Fellows Scholarship Program *(Undergraduate/Scholarship)* [10039]

Shields-Gillespie Scholarship *(Other/Scholarship)* [1189]

Chiyoko and Thomas Shimazaki Scholarship *(Graduate/Scholarship)* [6252]

Norma J. Shoemaker Award for Critical Care Nursing Excellence *(Professional development/Award)* [10316]

Shoreline and Lake Forest Park scholarship *(Undergraduate/Scholarship)* [10064]

SHPE Dissertation Scholarship *(Doctorate/Scholarship)* [10351]

SHPE Professional Scholarship *(Master's, Doctorate/Scholarship)* [10352]

Shred Nations Scholarship *(Undergraduate, Graduate/Scholarship)* [10071]

Shripat Kamble Urban Entomology Graduate Student Award for Innovative Research *(Doctorate/ Award)* [4399]

SHRM Certification Scholarships - Individual *(Professional development/Scholarship)* [10369]

SICB Fellowship of Graduate Student Travel (FGST) *(Graduate/Fellowship)* [10374]

SICB Grants-in-Aid of Research Program (GIAR) *(Graduate/Grant)* [10375]

Jeff Siegel Memorial Scholarships *(Undergraduate/ Scholarship)* [8317]

Siemens Clinical Advancement Scholarship *(Master's, Doctorate, Professional development/Scholarship)* [1553]

E.J. Sierleja Memorial Fellowship *(Graduate/Fellowship)* [5835]

Sigma Iota Epsilon Undergraduate National Scholar Awards *(Undergraduate/Scholarship)* [10088]

Sigma Phi Alpha Graduate Scholarship *(Graduate/ Scholarship)* [861]

Willard B. Simmons Sr. Memorial Scholarships *(Undergraduate/Scholarship)* [7779]

Helen J. Sioussat/Fay Wells Scholarships *(Graduate/Scholarship)* [2705]

SMA Foundation Scholarship Fund *(Undergraduate/ Scholarship)* [10707]

SME Coal & Energy Division Scholarship *(Undergraduate/Scholarship)* [10429]

SME Education Foundation Family Scholarships *(Undergraduate/Scholarship)* [10415]

SME Environmental Division Scholarship *(Undergraduate, Graduate/Scholarship)* [10430]

SME Future Leaders of Manufacturing Scholarship *(Graduate, Undergraduate/Scholarship)* [10416]

SMFM/AAOGF Scholarship Awards *(Graduate/ Scholarship)* [10423]

Donald Smiley Prize *(Advanced Professional/Prize, Award, Recognition)* [2111]

Henry DeWitt Smith Graduate Scholarship *(Graduate/Scholarship)* [10431]

Gladys Ann Smith Greater Los Angeles Women's Council Scholarship *(Undergraduate/Scholarship)* [8175]

Brian and Cathy Smith Memorial Fund *(Graduate/ Scholarship)* [1138]

The SMPE NY Scholarship Loan Program *(Undergraduate/Scholarship, Loan)* [10421]

SNF Professional Growth Scholarship *(Graduate, Undergraduate, Vocational/Occupational, Postgraduate/Scholarship, Award)* [9962]

SNMMI-TS Advanced Practitioner Program Scholarship *(Professional development/Scholarship)* [10441]

SNMMI-TS Bachelor's Degree Completion Scholarships *(Undergraduate/Scholarship)* [10442]

Snowmobile Association of Massachusetts Awards / Scholarships *(Undergraduate/Scholarship)* [10235]

SNRS Dissertation Research Grants *(Doctorate/ Grant)* [10659]

SNRS Research Grants *(Professional development/ Grant)* [10660]

SNRS/STTI Research Grants *(Professional development/Grant)* [10661]

SOAP/Kybele International Outreach Grant *(Advanced Professional, Professional development/ Grant)* [10448]

SOBP Travel Fellowship Award-Early Career Investigator-International *(Postdoctorate/Fellowship)* [10283]

Society of Allied Weight Engineers Scholarships *(Undergraduate/Scholarship)* [10268]

Society for the Arts in Healthcare Student Scholarships *(Doctorate, Graduate, Undergraduate/Scholarship)* [10281]

Society of Graphic Designers of Canada Adobe Scholarships *(Undergraduate/Scholarship)* [10255]

Society of Graphic Designers of Canada Applied Arts Scholarships *(Undergraduate/Scholarship)* [10256]

Society of Graphic Designers of Canada Veer Scholarships *(Undergraduate/Scholarship)* [10257]

Society of Louisiana Certified Public Accountants Scholarships *(Undergraduate, Master's, Doctorate/Scholarship)* [10382]

Society for Pediatric Radiology Seed Grants *(Graduate, Other/Grant)* [10467]

Society for the Scientific Study of Sexuality Student Research Grant *(Undergraduate/Grant)* [10528]

SOHN Allied Health to BSN Degree Scholarship *(Undergraduate/Scholarship)* [10450]

SOHN Graduate Degree Scholarship *(Undergraduate/Scholarship)* [10451]

SOHN RN to BSN Degree Scholarship *(Undergraduate/Scholarship)* [10452]

Carrie Fox Solin Blow Molding Division Memorial Scholarships *(Undergraduate/Scholarship)* [10494]

Dr. Kiyoshi Sonoda Memorial Scholarship *(Graduate, Master's/Scholarship)* [6253]

Sons of Scotland Past Grand Chiefs Scholarship *(Undergraduate/Scholarship)* [10593]

SOPHE/CDC Student Fellowship in Unintentional Injury Prevention *(Doctorate, Master's/Fellowship)* [10514]

SORP Student Conference Scholarship *(Graduate, Undergraduate/Scholarship)* [10454]

South Carolina Public Health Association Scholarships *(Professional development/Scholarship, Monetary)* [10612]

South Central Modern Language Association Fellowships *(Doctorate, Postdoctorate/Fellowship)* [8383]

South Jersey Golf Association Scholarships *(Undergraduate/Scholarship)* [10627]

Southeast Alabama Dietetic Association Scholarships *(Graduate, Undergraduate/Scholarship)* [221]

SPA/Lemelson Fellowship Program *(Graduate/ Award)* [10506]

SPE Student Awards for Innovations in Imaging *(Undergraduate, Graduate/Scholarship)* [10475]

Spice Box Grants *(Advanced Professional/Grant)* [848]

SPIE Student Author Travel Grants *(Graduate, Undergraduate/Grant)* [10729]

SPOOM Research Grants *(Graduate/Grant)* [10500]

SPP Young Investigator Research Grant *(Postdoctorate, Master's/Grant)* [10462]

SPS Future Teacher Scholarships *(Undergraduate/ Scholarship)* [10480]

SPS Leadership Scholarships *(Undergraduate/ Scholarship)* [10481]

SPSSI Grants-In-Aid Program *(Graduate, Postdoctorate/Grant)* [10511]

SSCP Dissertation Grant Award *(Graduate/Grant)* [10524]

The SSPI Mid-Atlantic Chapter Scholarship *(Graduate, Undergraduate/Scholarship)* [10522]

SSSP Racial/Ethnic Minority Graduate Fellowship *(Graduate/Fellowship, Award, Monetary)* [10537]

Stand Watie Scholarship *(Undergraduate/Scholarship)* [10588]

Alexander Standish Memorial Scholarship *(Professional development/Scholarship)* [3749]

A.R.O.Y. Stanitz Scholarships *(Undergraduate/ Scholarship)* [1370]

Stanley Moore FUI Foundation Regional Scholarships *(Four Year College, High School, Two Year College/Scholarship)* [8464]

Stanley Moore National Scholarships *(Undergraduate/Scholarship)* [8465]

The Stanley H. Stearman Awards *(Undergraduate/ Scholarship)* [8080]

H.H. Stern Award *(Advanced Professional/Award)* [2100]

Charles Sternberg Scholarship *(Graduate/Scholarship)* [2048]

Raymond H. Stetson Scholarship in Phonetics and Speech Science *(Graduate/Scholarship)* [63]

Steve Mason Sports Media Scholarship *(Graduate, Undergraduate/Scholarship)* [7991]

Steven A. Stahl Research Grant *(Graduate/Grant, Award)* [6039]

Christine K. Stevens Development Scholarship *(Undergraduate, Graduate/Scholarship)* [1139]

Allegheny Branch of Mid-America Chapter - Nancy Stewart Professional Development Scholarships *(Professional development/Scholarship)* [1588]

Ralph W. Stone Graduate Fellowship in Cave and Karst Studies *(Graduate/Fellowship)* [8128]

Ralph W. Stone Graduate Fellowships *(Graduate/ Fellowship)* [8129]

Martin L. Stout Scholarships *(Graduate, Undergraduate/Scholarship)* [2162]

George A. Strait Minority Scholarship *(Graduate/ Scholarship)* [600]

Stuart Cameron and Margaret McLeod Memorial Scholarship (SCMS) *(Graduate, Undergraduate/ Scholarship)* [5850]

Stuart L. Bernath Dissertation Research Grant *(Graduate/Grant)* [10360]

Student Travel Grant *(Undergraduate/Grant)* [7361]

Study Scholarship for Artists or Musicians *(Graduate, Postdoctorate/Scholarship)* [4066]

Subic Bay-Cubi Point Scholarships *(Undergraduate/ Scholarship)* [8176]

Caroline tum Suden/Frances Hellebrandt Professional Opportunity Awards *(Postdoctorate, Graduate/Award, Monetary)* [1239]

Sue A. Malone Scholarship *(Doctorate, Graduate, Professional development/Scholarship)* [6370]

SUT Houston Graduate Scholarships *(Graduate/ Scholarship)* [10547]

SUT Houston Undergraduate Scholarships *(Undergraduate/Scholarship)* [10548]

SVS Vascular Surgery Trainee Advocacy Travel Scholarship *(Advanced Professional, Professional development/Scholarship, Grant)* [10556]

SWE Scholarships *(Undergraduate, Graduate, Scholarship)* [10564]

SWS Barbara Rosenblum Scholarship *(Doctorate/ Fellowship, Scholarship)* [10568]

Ta Liang Award *(Graduate/Award)* [2010]

TACS/A. Bragas and Associates Student Scholarships *(Undergraduate/Scholarship)* [10972]

Tailhook Educational Foundation Scholarship *(Undergraduate, Postdoctorate/Scholarship)* [10907]

Alexander M. Tanger Scholarships *(Graduate/Scholarship)* [2706]

Taverner Awards *(Undergraduate/Grant)* [10296]

Ryan "Munchie" Taylor Memorial Scholarships *(Undergraduate/Scholarship)* [6944]

TCA Outstanding Graduate Student Award *(Graduate/Award)* [10981]

TCA Scholarship Fund *(Undergraduate/Scholarship)* [11121]

TCATA College Scholarship Fund *(Undergraduate/ Scholarship)* [11004]

TCDA Abbott IPCO Professional Scholarships *(Other/Scholarship)* [742]

TCDA Bill Gorham Student Scholarship *(Undergraduate/Scholarship)* [743]

TCDA Cloys Webb Student Scholarship *(Undergraduate/Scholarship)* [744]

TCDA Gandy Ink Professional Scholarship *(Professional development/Scholarship)* [745]

TCDA General Fund Scholarships *(Undergraduate/Scholarship)* [746]

TCDA Past Presidents Student Scholarship *(Undergraduate/Scholarship)* [747]

Technical, vocational or associate's degree programs *(Undergraduate/Scholarship)* [10621]

Technical Scholarship *(Undergraduate/Scholarship)* [8592]

Technical Women's Organization Education Scholarship *(Advanced Professional, Graduate/Scholarship)* [10933]

Telecommunications Association of Michigan - Category II - IV Scholarship *(Undergraduate/Scholarship)* [10944]

Mary L. Tenopyr Graduate Student Scholarship *(Graduate/Scholarship)* [10336]

The TESOL/TEFL Travel Grant *(Advanced Professional/Grant, Monetary)* [10970]

TFOS Fellowship Awards *(Graduate, Postdoctorate/Fellowship)* [10929]

Thelma Cardwell Scholarship *(Master's, Doctorate/Scholarship)* [3082]

Theodore E.D. Braun Research Travel Fellowship *(Other/Fellowship)* [1439]

Thermo Scientific Educational Scholarships *(Professional development/Scholarship)* [8115]

Charles C. Thomas Scholarship *(Undergraduate/Scholarship)* [1754]

Tommy Douglas Scholarship *(Undergraduate/Scholarship)* [8150]

TRALA Industry Scholarship Awards *(Undergraduate/Scholarship)* [11119]

Translational Research Professorship *(Professional development/Internship)* [3784]

TriBeta Research Grant Awards *(Undergraduate/Grant)* [2494]

Tribute Fund Community Grant *(Professional development/Grant)* [10306]

Truckload Carriers Association Scholarships *(Undergraduate/Scholarship)* [11122]

Turco Munoz Domestic Violence Survivor Scholarship *(Undergraduate, Graduate/Scholarship)* [11137]

The Turnkey Lender's Scholarship Program *(Undergraduate/Scholarship)* [11154]

TxHIMA HIA-HIT Scholarship *(Undergraduate/Scholarship)* [10984]

TxHIMA Outstanding Student Scholarship *(Undergraduate/Scholarship)* [10985]

Florence Tyson Grant to Study Music Psychotherapy *(Professional development/Grant)* [1140]

UAF Alumni Association Scholarship *(Undergraduate/Scholarship)* [11520]

UC MEXUS-CONACYT Collaborative Grants *(Professional development/Grant)* [11551]

Sandy Ulm Scholarships *(Undergraduate, Master's/Scholarship)* [4625]

Unifor Scholarship *(Professional development, Undergraduate/Scholarship)* [11223]

Union Plus Scholarship Program *(Undergraduate, Graduate/Scholarship)* [11243]

Union Plus Scholarship Program *(Undergraduate/Scholarship)* [6139]

United Methodist General Scholarships *(Undergraduate, Graduate/Scholarship)* [4895]

U.S. Air Force ROTC In-College Scholarships - Type 2 *(High School/Scholarship)* [11284]

U.S. Aircraft Insurance Group Professional Development Program (USAIG PDP) Scholarships *(Undergraduate/Scholarship)* [7741]

U.S. Bates Scholarship *(Undergraduate/Scholarship)* [6140]

United States Society on Dams Scholarships *(Graduate, Undergraduate/Scholarship)* [11399]

UnitedAg Scholarship Program *(Undergraduate/Scholarship)* [11415]

UPE Scholarship Awards *(Graduate, Undergraduate/Scholarship)* [11765]

UPS Scholarship for Female Students *(Undergraduate/Scholarship)* [5836]

Claudette Upton Scholarships *(Undergraduate/Scholarship)* [4289]

USAEE/IAEE North American Conference Registration Fee Scholarships *(Undergraduate/Scholarship)* [11297]

Utah Chiefs of Police Scholarship Program *(College, Undergraduate, University/Scholarship)* [11787]

VA AWWA Graduate Student Scholarships *(Graduate/Scholarship)* [11841]

Val Mason Scholarship *(Graduate, Professional development/Scholarship, Award)* [3114]

Winifred Van Hagen/Rosalind Cassidy Scholarship Award *(Undergraduate, Graduate/Recognition, Award)* [2783]

Gary Vanden Berg Internship Grant *(Undergraduate/Grant)* [10737]

Varian Radiation Therapy Advancement Scholarship *(Master's, Doctorate, Professional development/Scholarship)* [1554]

Vern Parish Award *(Graduate, Postgraduate, Doctorate/Scholarship)* [1088]

Veterans of Foreign Wars Scout of the Year *(Undergraduate/Scholarship)* [7860]

Vicki Cruse Memorial Emergency Maneuver Training Scholarship *(Undergraduate/Scholarship)* [8403]

Dr. Juan D. Villarreal/HDA Foundation Scholarships *(Undergraduate/Scholarship)* [5520]

Vincent T. Wasilewski Award *(Graduate/Scholarship)* [2708]

Virgil K. Lobring Scholarship Program *(Undergraduate/Scholarship)* [3725]

Paul A. Volcker Fund *(Undergraduate, Graduate, Doctorate, Professional development/Grant)* [1260]

VPPPA June Brothers Scholarship *(Graduate, Undergraduate/Scholarship)* [11862]

W. Stull Holt Dissertation Fellowship *(Graduate/Fellowship)* [10361]

Alan D. Waggoner Sonographer Student Scholarship Award *(Undergraduate/Scholarship)* [1423]

Jack H. Wagner Scholarship *(Graduate, Undergraduate/Scholarship)* [7350]

Shih-Chun Wang Young Investigator Award *(Advanced Professional/Monetary, Award)* [1240]

WASBO Scholarship Program *(Undergraduate/Scholarship)* [11883]

Waterbury Bar Association Scholarship *(Undergraduate/Scholarship)* [11933]

Richard M. Weaver Fellowships *(Graduate/Fellowship)* [5886]

WEDA Scholarship Program *(Professional development/Scholarship)* [11979]

John V. Wehausen Graduate Scholarships for Advanced Study in Ship Hydrodynamics and Wave Theory *(Graduate/Scholarship)* [10435]

Susan C. Weiss Clinical Advancement Scholarship *(Other/Scholarship)* [10446]

James R. Welch Scholarship *(Graduate/Scholarship)* [2050]

Ida B. Wells Graduate Student Fellowship *(Graduate/Fellowship)* [3831]

Wesley C. Cameron Scholarship *(Undergraduate/Scholarship)* [8177]

Wesley R. Habley Summer Institute Scholarships *(Professional development/Scholarship)* [7569]

Stan Wheeler Mentorship Awards *(Other/Award)* [6728]

WHIMA Established Professional Development Scholarship *(Graduate/Scholarship)* [12119]

Whirly-Girls Helicopter Add-On Flight Training Scholarship *(Professional development, Vocational/Occupational/Scholarship)* [12013]

Whirly-Girls Jean Tinsley Memorial HELI-EXPO Scholarship *(Professional development, Vocational/Occupational/Scholarship)* [12014]

Larry B. Wickham Memorial Scholarship for Graduate Studies *(Graduate/Scholarship)* [7487]

Wild Felid Legacy Scholarship *(Graduate/Scholarship)* [12026]

Willard & Spackman Scholarship Program *(Postgraduate/Scholarship)* [1182]

William A. Fischer Scholarship *(Graduate/Scholarship)* [2011]

William "Buddy" Sentner Scholarship Award *(Undergraduate, High School/Scholarship)* [629]

William J. Yankee Memorial Scholarship *(Undergraduate/Scholarship, Monetary, Recognition)* [1263]

William L. Brown Fellowship *(Graduate/Fellowship)* [8754]

William M. Fanning Maintenance Scholarship *(Undergraduate/Scholarship)* [7742]

William "Sully" Sullivan Scholarship *(Graduate, Undergraduate/Scholarship)* [11864]

BM1 James Elliott Williams Memorial Scholarship Fund *(Undergraduate/Scholarship)* [11833]

Alice Hinchcliffe Williams, RDH, MS Merit Scholarship *(Graduate/Scholarship)* [11833]

Wilma Motley Memorial California Merit Scholarship *(Undergraduate/Scholarship)* [862]

The Wilson Fellowship *(Postdoctorate/Fellowship)* [11677]

Winston Build Your Future Scholarship *(Graduate, Undergraduate, Vocational/Occupational/Scholarship)* [9963]

David A. Winston Health Policy Scholarship *(Graduate/Scholarship)* [2307]

WLA Conference Attendance Grants *(Undergraduate, Professional development/Grant)* [11896]

Women in Cancer Research Scholar Awards *(Graduate, Postdoctorate/Award, Monetary)* [536]

Women & Politics Fund *(Graduate, Postdoctorate, Undergraduate, Professional development/Grant)* [1261]

Women's Jewelry Association Member Grants *(Professional development/Grant)* [12163]

Women's Leadership Training Grant *(Advanced Professional, Professional development/Grant)* [10557]

Wood Fruitticher Grocery Company, Inc. Scholarships *(Graduate, Undergraduate/Scholarship)* [222]

Helen M. Woodruff Fellowships *(Postdoctorate/Fellowship)* [1781]

Patty Wooten Scholarships *(Professional development/Scholarship, Award, Recognition)* [2055]

Reverend H. John and Asako Yamashita Memorial Scholarship *(Graduate/Scholarship)* [6254]

Minoru Yasui Memorial Scholarship *(Graduate/Scholarship)* [6255]

Jane Yolen Mid-List Author Grant *(Professional development/Grant)* [10307]

Gary Yoshimura Scholarship *(Undergraduate/Scholarship)* [9439]

Young Birder Scholarships *(Undergraduate/Scholarship, Monetary)* [695]

Alma H. Young Emerging Scholar Award *(Doctorate/Award)* [11767]

Young Investigators Achievement Award *(Advanced Professional, Professional development, Graduate/Grant)* [6331]

Lisa Zaken Award For Excellence *(Graduate, Undergraduate/Award, Monetary)* [5838]

Disabled

Anthony Abbene Scholarship Fund *(Undergraduate/Scholarship)* [5663]

Evelyn Joy Abramowicz Memorial Scholarship *(Undergraduate/Scholarship)* [6282]

AEBC Toronto Chapter Scholarships *(Undergraduate/Scholarship)* [361]

A.G. Bell School Age Financial Aid Program *(High School/Scholarship, Monetary)* [333]

ALA Century Scholarship *(Master's, Doctorate/Scholarship)* [2293]

Alabama Scholarships for Dependents of Blind Parents *(Undergraduate/Scholarship)* [213]

American Speech Language Hearing Foundation Endowed Scholarships *(Graduate, Master's, Doctorate/Scholarship)* [1596]

American Speech Language Hearing Foundation Scholarship for Student with A Disability *(Graduate, Master's, Doctorate/Scholarship)* [1600]

Andrew Foster Scholarship *(Undergraduate/Scholarship)* [7720]

Anne M. Fassett Scholarship Fund *(Undergraduate, Graduate/Scholarship)* [10671]

Ethel Louise Armstrong Foundation Scholarships *(Graduate, Master's/Scholarship, Monetary)* [1267]

ASGP Graduate Research Fellowships *(Graduate/Fellowship)* [244]

Autism/ASD Scholarship *(Community College, Four Year College, Graduate, Vocational/Occupational, Professional development/Scholarship)* [6518]

Autism Scholarship *(Community College, Four Year College, Vocational/Occupational/Scholarship)* [4537]

Autism Scholarship *(High School, Two Year College, Four Year College, Graduate, Vocational/Occupational, Professional development/Scholarship)* [2617]

Autism Scholarship *(Two Year College, Four Year College, Vocational/Occupational/Scholarship)* [9712]

BCPF Bursaries *(Undergraduate/Scholarship)* [10731]

BEF General Academic Scholarships *(Undergraduate, Graduate/Scholarship)* [4438]

BEF Sacks For CF Scholarship *(Graduate, Undergraduate/Scholarship)* [4439]

BEF Scholarship of the Arts *(Graduate, Undergraduate/Scholarship)* [4440]

Law Offices of David A. Black Annual Hearing Impaired Scholarships *(All/Scholarship)* [6701]

BMO Capital Markets Lime Connect Equity through Education Scholarships *(Undergraduate, Graduate/Scholarship)* [6860]

BMO Financial Group Lime Connect Canada Scholarship Program for Students with Disabilities *(Undergraduate, Graduate/Scholarship)* [6861]

Business, Education and Technology Scholarships *(Graduate, Undergraduate/Scholarship)* [362]

C. Rodney Demarest Memorial Scholarship *(Undergraduate/Scholarship)* [5318]

California Council of the Blind Scholarships *(Undergraduate, Graduate, Vocational/Occupational/Scholarship)* [2794]

Canadian Hard of Hearing Association Scholarship Program *(Undergraduate/Scholarship)* [2997]

ChairScholars National Scholarship Program *(Undergraduate/Scholarship)* [3275]

CHEA Undergraduate Scholarship Program for Students with Disabilities *(Undergraduate/Scholarship)* [2814]

Kevin Child Scholarship *(Undergraduate/Scholarship)* [7921]

CNIB Master's Scholarships *(Master's/Scholarship)* [3047]

College-Bound Award *(High School/Award, Scholarship)* [6853]

Community Project Grants *(Other/Grant)* [8261]

Arthur E. Copeland Scholarship *(Four Year College, Two Year College/Scholarship)* [11293]

Helen Copeland Scholarship *(Professional development, Undergraduate, Vocational/Occupational/Scholarship)* [11294]

Pfizer Soozie Courter Hemophilia Scholarship Program *(Undergraduate/Scholarship)* [7922]

Delta Gamma Foundation Florence Margaret Harvey Memorial Scholarship *(Graduate, Undergraduate/Scholarship)* [914]

Belle & Curly Desrosiers Scholarship *(Undergraduate, College, University, Vocational/Occupational/Scholarship)* [12307]

Diana Brown Endowed Scholarship *(Undergraduate/Scholarship)* [6788]

Disabled Veteran Scholarship *(College, Vocational/Occupational/Scholarship)* [9713]

Disabled Veteran Student Scholarship *(Two Year College, Four Year College/Scholarship)* [12018]

Disabled Veterans Scholarship *(Community College, College, Vocational/Occupational/Scholarship)* [4538]

Disabled Veterans Scholarship *(Vocational/Occupational, Community College, Four Year College, Graduate, Professional development/Scholarship)* [6519]

Diversity Executive Leadership Program Scholarship (DELP) *(Other/Scholarship)* [1977]

Dr. Gunnar B. Stickler Scholarship *(Undergraduate, Vocational/Occupational/Scholarship)* [10839]

Edmonton Epilepsy Association Scholarship *(Undergraduate/Scholarship)* [4294]

"Education is Power" Scholarships *(Undergraduate/Scholarship)* [7923]

Esther M. Smith Scholarship Fund *(Undergraduate/Scholarship)* [3566]

Exercise For Life Athletic Scholarship *(Undergraduate/Scholarship)* [4441]

Families of Freedom Scholarship Fund - Scholarship America *(Undergraduate, Vocational/Occupational/Scholarship)* [4482]

Maureen & Gilles Fontaine Scholarship *(Undergraduate, College, University, Vocational/Occupational/Scholarship)* [12317]

Terry Fox Memorial Scholarship *(Undergraduate/Scholarship)* [8147]

Gerard Swartz Fudge Memorial Scholarship *(Postgraduate/Scholarship)* [5664]

Gladys C. Anderson Memorial Scholarship *(Undergraduate/Scholarship)* [915]

Google Lime Scholarship *(Undergraduate, Graduate, Doctorate/Scholarship)* [6862]

Graduate Award *(Graduate/Award, Scholarship)* [6854]

Dr. E. Bruce Hendrick Scholarship Program *(All/Scholarship)* [5669]

HFA Educational Scholarship *(Undergraduate/Scholarship)* [5479]

Jim Hierlihy Memorial Scholarship *(Undergraduate/Scholarship)* [4429]

Irving J. Hoffman Memorial Scholarships *(Undergraduate/Scholarship)* [11691]

Individual K-Grants *(All/Grant)* [6564]

Innovative Grants-Pilot and Research Tool Grants *(Postdoctorate/Grant)* [6348]

JDRF Postdoctoral Fellowships *(Postdoctorate/Fellowship)* [6351]

Kenneth Jernigan Scholarships *(Undergraduate/Scholarship, Monetary)* [7877]

John & Ruth Childe Scholarship Fund *(Undergraduate/Scholarship)* [10691]

Justin Scot Alston Memorial Scholarship *(Undergraduate/Scholarship)* [5665]

Kaia Lynn Markwalter Endowed Scholarship *(Undergraduate/Scholarship)* [6804]

Karen D. Carsel Memorial Scholarship *(Undergraduate/Scholarship)* [916]

Lawrence Madeiros Scholarship *(Undergraduate/Scholarship)* [7925]

LDAS Scholarship *(Undergraduate/Scholarship)* [6760]

Lighthouse International Scholarships - College-bound Awards *(High School, Undergraduate/Scholarship)* [6856]

Lighthouse International Scholarships - Graduate Awards *(Graduate, Postgraduate/Scholarship)* [6857]

Lighthouse International Scholarships - Undergraduate Awards *(Undergraduate/Scholarship)* [6858]

Lime Connect Pathways Scholarship for High School Seniors with Disabilities *(Undergraduate/Scholarship)* [6863]

Michael Lorenzen Foundation Scholarship *(Undergraduate, Graduate/Scholarship)* [6890]

Lutheran Student Scholastic and Service Scholarships - College and University Students *(Undergraduate/Scholarship)* [2562]

Katie MacDonald Memorial Scholarships *(Graduate, Undergraduate/Scholarship)* [11273]

Martin Frank Diversity Travel Award *(Undergraduate, Postdoctorate/Fellowship, Award, Monetary)* [1237]

Eric Martinez Memorial Scholarships *(Graduate, Undergraduate/Scholarship)* [11274]

Mary Main Memorial Scholarship *(Undergraduate/Scholarship)* [5339]

Mature Student Scholarship *(Undergraduate/Scholarship)* [4430]

McBurney Disability Resource Center General Scholarships *(Undergraduate/Scholarship)* [11741]

Doreen McMullan McCarthy Memorial Academic Scholarship for Women with Bleeding Disorders *(Undergraduate/Scholarship)* [7926]

Mike Hylton Memorial Scholarship *(Undergraduate/Scholarship)* [5480]

Millie Gonzalez Memorial Scholarship *(Undergraduate/Scholarship)* [5481]

Morris L. and Rebecca Ziskind Memorial Scholarship *(Undergraduate/Scholarship)* [5666]

National Federation of the Blind Scholarship Program *(Undergraduate/Scholarship, Monetary)* [7878]

NBCUniversal Tony Coelho Media Scholarship *(Undergraduate, Graduate/Scholarship)* [618]

Alan H. Neville Memorial Scholarships *(Graduate/Scholarship)* [363]

George H. Nofer Scholarship for Law and Public Policy *(Graduate/Scholarship, Monetary)* [334]

AEBC Rick Oakes Scholarships for the Arts *(Undergraduate/Scholarship)* [364]

Charles and Melva T. Owen Memorial Scholarships *(Undergraduate/Scholarship, Monetary)* [7879]

E.U. and Gene Parker Scholarships *(Undergraduate/Scholarship, Monetary)* [7880]

Paul and Ellen Ruckes Scholarship *(Graduate, Undergraduate/Scholarship)* [917]

Nalini Perera Little Lotus Bud Master's Scholarships *(Master's/Scholarship)* [3048]

Lowell Phillips Scholarship *(Undergraduate/Scholarship)* [3705]

Redlands Evening Lions Club - Barbara Westen Memorial Scholarship *(Undergraduate/Scholarship)* [9580]

Rehabmart.com $25,000 Scholarship Fund *(Undergraduate/Scholarship)* [9627]

Betty Rendel Scholarships *(Undergraduate/Scholarship)* [7886]

R.L. Gillette Scholarship *(Undergraduate/Scholarship)* [918]

Robby Baker Memorial Scholarship *(Graduate/Scholarship)* [321]

Roy Cooper Memorial Scholarship *(Undergraduate/Scholarship)* [6758]

Travis Roy Foundation Individual Grants *(All/Grant)* [9749]

Rudolph Dillman Memorial Scholarship *(Graduate, Undergraduate/Scholarship)* [919]

Saunders – Kevin Saunders Wheelchair Success Scholarship *(Undergraduate/Scholarship)* [3486]

Bill Sawyer Memorial Scholarship *(Undergraduate/Scholarship)* [6820]

Dale M. Schoettler Scholarship for Visually Impaired Students *(Undergraduate, Graduate/Scholarship)* [9874]

Scholarship for Disabled Veterans *(High School, Community College, Four Year College, Graduate, Professional development, Vocational/Occupational/Scholarship)* [6702]

Sentinels of Freedom Scholarship *(Advanced Professional/Scholarship)* [10011]

Sertoma Communicative Disorders Scholarship *(Undergraduate/Scholarship)* [10019]

Sertoma Hard of Hearing and Deaf Scholarship *(Undergraduate/Scholarship)* [10020]

Sharp Criminal Lawyers Autism Scholarship *(College, Undergraduate, Vocational/Occupational/Scholarship)* [10035]

Small Grants for Community Projects and Educational Programs *(Other/Grant)* [8262]

Beatrice Drinnan Spence Scholarship *(Undergraduate, Vocational/Occupational/Scholarship)* [4268]

Glenna Stone Memorial Scholarship *(Undergraduate/Scholarship)* [2999]

Mario J. Tocco Hydrocephalus Foundation Scholarships *(Undergraduate/Scholarship)* [5667]

Toronto Rehab Scholarships in Rehabilitation-Related Research *(Graduate/Scholarship)* [11064]

Ferdinand Torres Scholarships *(Graduate, Undergraduate/Scholarship)* [920]

Wells Fargo Scholarship Program for People with Disabilities *(Undergraduate/Scholarship)* [9944]

Youth Empowerment Summit Scholarships *(Undergraduate/Scholarship)* [7722]

Employer affiliation

A&B Ohana Scholarship Fund (Undergraduate, College, Two Year College, Vocational/Occupational/Scholarship) [5375]

ABA Members Scholarships (Undergraduate, Graduate/Scholarship) [708]

ABC Stores Jumpstart Scholarship Fund (Undergraduate, University, College, Vocational/Occupational, Graduate/Scholarship) [5377]

Adelson Scholarship (Undergraduate/Scholarship) [9387]

AOF/Johnson & Johnson Vision Care - Innovation in Education Grants (Advanced Professional, Professional development/Grant) [462]

APDA Research Grants (Postgraduate, Professional development/Grant) [1207]

APSA U.S. Federal Executives Fellowships (Advanced Professional, Professional development/Fellowship) [1253]

ASA/NSF/BLS Fellowships (Graduate/Fellowship, Recognition, Grant) [1609, 8065, 11343]

Bank of Canada Fellowship Award (Doctorate, Other/Fellowship) [2423]

Bank of Canada Governor's Awards (Doctorate, Other/Award) [2424]

Bank of Hawaii Foundation Scholarship Fund (Undergraduate, University, College, Two Year College/Scholarship) [5382]

Ben C. Francis Risk Management Education Fund (Undergraduate/Scholarship) [9385]

Bill Egan Memorial Award (Undergraduate/Scholarship) [8702]

The Dr. George T. Bottomley Scholarship (Undergraduate/Scholarship) [4835, 7166]

Diana V. Braddom FRFDS Scholarship (Professional development/Scholarship) [6843]

Peter Buck Fellowships Program - Graduate (Graduate/Fellowship) [10199]

Peter Buck Fellowships Program - Postdoctoral (Postdoctorate/Fellowship) [10200]

Burger King Employee Scholars Program (Undergraduate/Scholarship) [2747]

Burndy Canada Inc. Academic Achievement Awards (Undergraduate/Scholarship) [4338]

Bus & Tour Operator Scholarships (Undergraduate, Graduate/Scholarship) [710]

Carolinas-Virginias Hardware Scholarship (Undergraduate/Scholarship) [4725]

CCAE Ontario Regional Chapter Scholarship (Advanced Professional, Professional development/Scholarship) [6742]

Central Pacific Bank Scholarship Fund (Undergraduate/Scholarship) [5390]

Charles H. Stone-Piedmont Scholarship (Undergraduate/Scholarship, Monetary) [657]

COPA Scholarship Fund (Undergraduate/Scholarship) [3084]

Copper and Brass Servicenter Association Scholarship Program (Undergraduate/Scholarship) [3833]

Crowder Scholarship (Undergraduate/Scholarship) [4731]

Colonel Richard M. Dawson Highway Patrol Scholarship Fund (Undergraduate/Scholarship) [3610]

DBI Scholarship Fund (Undergraduate/Scholarship) [3611]

Don Aron Scholarship (Undergraduate/Scholarship) [7783]

Downeast Energy Scholarships (Undergraduate/Scholarship) [4142]

Tim Downing Memorial Scholarship Program (Professional development/Scholarship) [2906]

Bob Dyer/OEL Apprenticeship Scholarships (Undergraduate/Scholarship) [4340]

Howard and Gladys Eakes Memorial Scholarship (Undergraduate/Scholarship) [5121]

Eaton Awards of Academic Achievement (Undergraduate/Scholarship) [4341]

The Dr. Robert Elliott Memorial Scholarship (Undergraduate/Scholarship) [7167, 8264]

The Pauline Elliott Scholarship (Undergraduate/Scholarship) [7168, 8265]

The Robert C. Erb Sr. Scholarship (Undergraduate/Scholarship) [7169]

Fahs-Beck Fund for Research and Experimentation - Postdoctoral Grants (Postdoctorate/Grant) [8304]

Jack B. Fisher Scholarship Fund (Graduate/Scholarship) [10758]

Captain Ernest W. Fox Perpetual Scholarship (Advanced Professional/Scholarship) [3459]

The Phil Friel Scholarship (Undergraduate/Scholarship) [7170]

Peter M. Gargano Scholarship Fund (Undergraduate/Scholarship) [4206]

The Alex Gissler Memorial Scholarship (Undergraduate/Scholarship) [7171]

Grant Assistance Program for Autism Professionals - College Programs (Undergraduate/Grant) [8652]

Grant Assistance Program for Autism Professionals - Doctoral Programs (Doctorate/Grant) [8653]

Grant Assistance Program for Autism Professionals - Institutional Standards (Undergraduate, Graduate/Grant) [8654]

Grant Assistance Program for Autism Professionals - Masters Programs (Master's/Grant) [8655]

Grant Assistance Program for Autism Professionals - Professional Certification Programs (Undergraduate, Professional development/Grant) [8656]

Grant Assistance Program for Autism Professionals - Retroactive Assistance (Advanced Professional, Professional development/Grant) [8657]

Grant Assistance Program for Autism Professionals - Undergraduate Programs (Undergraduate/Grant) [8658]

HII Scholarship Fund (Community College, Two Year College, Four Year College, Undergraduate, University/Scholarship) [5655]

Henry Hoffman Memorial Scholarship (Undergraduate/Scholarship) [7641]

Institute of Turkish Studies Sabbatical Research Grants (Other/Grant) [5870]

International Affairs Fellowships in Nuclear Security (IAF-NS) (Professional development/Fellowship) [3865]

Kerrwil's J.W. Kerr Continuing Education Scholarship Awards (Undergraduate/Scholarship) [4351]

Joseph H. Klupenger Scholarship Awards (Undergraduate/Scholarship, Award) [8707]

Laura M. Fleming Scholarship (Undergraduate, Vocational/Occupational/Scholarship) [4740]

The Stan Lencki Scholarship (Undergraduate/Scholarship) [7172]

Leo Gilmartin Scholarship (Undergraduate/Scholarship) [9211]

Lilly Scholarships in Religion for Journalists (Other/Scholarship) [9633]

Richard Lim Professional Development Scholarship (Advanced Professional, Professional development/Scholarship, Recognition) [6743]

Link Foundation/Smithsonian Graduate Fellowships in Marine Science (Graduate/Fellowship) [10201]

The Rick Mahoney Scholarship (Undergraduate/Scholarship) [7173]

Matt Stager Memorial Scholarship (Undergraduate/Scholarship) [11929]

Al Maurer Awards (Undergraduate, Graduate, Advanced Professional/Scholarship) [4292]

Melvin Kruger Endowed Scholarship Program (Graduate, Undergraduate/Scholarship) [8063, 9739]

Bill Nelson Scholarship Endowment (BNSE) (Undergraduate, Graduate/Scholarship) [8780]

The NHPGA Apprentice Scholarship (Undergraduate/Scholarship) [7174]

Louise A. Nixon Scholarship (Graduate/Scholarship) [8192]

NMHM Global Volcanism Program for Visiting Scientist/Postdoctoral Fellowships (Postdoctorate, Advanced Professional/Fellowship) [10202]

OAB Kids Scholarships (Undergraduate/Scholarship) [8575]

OPERF Student Awards (Professional development/Grant) [8766]

Packard Fellowships for Science and Engineering (Professional development/Fellowship) [8808]

Pembroke Center's Faculty Research Fellowships (Professional development/Fellowship) [2724]

The Walter T. Philippy Scholarship (Undergraduate/Scholarship) [7175]

Philips Lighting Continuing Education Awards (Undergraduate/Scholarship) [4353]

PLCAC Student Award Program (Postgraduate/Award) [9182]

PLUS Foundation Financial Aid Scholarship (Undergraduate/Scholarship) [9212]

The David J. Pollini Scholarship (Undergraduate/Scholarship) [7176]

The Pope Scholarship Award (Undergraduate/Scholarship) [7177]

Retail Chapter Scholarship Awards (Undergraduate/Scholarship) [8712]

Ronald T. Smith Family Scholarship (Undergraduate, Graduate/Scholarship) [5178]

The Rotary Club of Charlotte Public Safety Scholarship Fund (Undergraduate/Scholarship) [4752]

Saskatchewan Government Insurance Corporate Scholarships (Undergraduate/Scholarship) [9889]

Saskatchewan Trucking Association Scholarships (Undergraduate/Scholarship) [9928]

SEMA Memorial Scholarship and Loan Forgiveness Award (Graduate, Undergraduate/Loan, Scholarship) [10720]

The Jim Sheerin Scholarship (Undergraduate/Scholarship) [7178]

Smith Family Awards Program for Excellence in Biomedical Research (Advanced Professional, Professional development/Award) [5443]

Sobeys & Empire Work Experience & Scholarship Program - Future Leaders Awards (Other/Scholarship) [10239]

The Square Up Scholarship Program (Two Year College, Undergraduate, Vocational/Occupational, Four Year College/Scholarship) [6616]

The Donald H. Bernstein and John B. Talbert Jr. Scholarship (Undergraduate/Scholarship) [4758]

Texas Mutual Scholarship Program (Undergraduate, Vocational/Occupational/Scholarship) [10990]

TRALA Industry Scholarship Awards (Undergraduate/Scholarship) [11119]

Turner Family Scholarships (Undergraduate, Vocational/Occupational/Scholarship) [4760]

Laramie Walden Memorial Fund (Undergraduate/Scholarship) [4762]

Walmart Associate Scholarship (Undergraduate/Scholarship) [11868]

WEDA Scholarship Program (Professional development/Scholarship) [11979]

The Fred C. Wikoff Jr. Scholarship (Undergraduate, Vocational/Occupational/Scholarship) [4763]

Willamette Chapter Scholarship Awards (Undergraduate/Scholarship) [8713]

Ethnic group membership

AAMA Houston Chapter Health Training Scholarships (Other/Scholarship) [1770]

Accenture American Indian Scholarship Fund (Graduate, Undergraduate/Scholarship) [993]

Achille & Irene Despres, William & Andre Scholarship (Undergraduate/Scholarship) [5131]

Adler Pollock & Sheehan Diversity Scholarships (Undergraduate/Fellowship) [77]

Harry E. Adrian Memorial Grant (Undergraduate/Scholarship) [1857]

Samuel Agabian Memorial Grant (Undergraduate/Scholarship) [1858]

AGBU Heritage Scholar Grant (Undergraduate/Scholarship, Grant) [1850]

Agnes E. Vaghi Scholarship (Undergraduate/Scholarship) [7960]

AIGC Fellowships - Graduate (Graduate/Fellowship) [994]

Melkon and Negdar Aijian Memorial Grant (Undergraduate/Scholarship) [1859]

Al Muammar Scholarships for Journalism (Undergraduate/Scholarship) [1766]

Alberta Blue Cross Scholarships for Aboriginal Students (Undergraduate/Scholarship) [251]

Alberta Ukrainian Centennial Commemorative Scholarship (Graduate/Scholarship) [11887]

Amelia and Emanuel Nessell Family Scholarship Fund (Undergraduate/Scholarship) [4197]

American Physical Society Minority Undergraduate Scholarships (Undergraduate/Scholarship) [1220]

T. Thomas Amirian Memorial Grant (Undergraduate/Scholarship) [1860]

AMLN Scholarships for Arab American Students (*Graduate, Undergraduate/Scholarship*) [1127]

AMS Freshman Undergraduate Scholarship (*Undergraduate/Scholarship*) [1119]

AMS Graduate Fellowships (*Graduate/Fellowship*) [1121]

APTA Minority Scholarships - Faculty Development Scholarships (*Postdoctorate/Scholarship, Award, Recognition*) [1232]

APTA Minority Scholarships - Physical Therapist Assistant Students (*Undergraduate/Scholarship, Award, Recognition*) [1233]

APTA Minority Scholarships - Physical Therapist Students (*Undergraduate/Scholarship, Award, Recognition*) [1234]

Ararat Association Scholarship Grant (*Undergraduate/Scholarship*) [1861]

Armenian American Medical Association Scholarship Program (*Undergraduate, Graduate/Scholarship*) [1842]

Armenian American Veterans' Association of Worcester Scholarship (*Undergraduate/Scholarship*) [1862]

Armenian Professional Society Graduate Student Scholarship (*Graduate/Scholarship*) [1852]

ARS Lazarian Graduate Scholarship (*Graduate, Master's, Doctorate/Scholarship*) [1854]

ARS Undergraduate Scholarship (*Undergraduate/Scholarship*) [1855]

Ardemis, Armenoohy, and Arpi Arsenian Memorial Grant (*Undergraduate/Scholarship*) [1863]

ASA Inc. Journalism Internship Program (*Undergraduate/Internship*) [1864]

Marguerite Chapootian Atamian Memorial Grant (*Undergraduate/Scholarship*) [1865]

John M. Azarian Memorial Armenian Youth Scholarship Fund (*Undergraduate/Scholarship*) [2399]

Baker McKenzie Diversity Fellowship (*Postgraduate, Professional development/Fellowship*) [2411]

BakerHostetler Diversity Fellowship Program (*Undergraduate/Fellowship*) [2408]

Dennis J. Beck Memorial Scholarship (*Undergraduate/Scholarship*) [6193]

Sarkis Bogosian Memorial Grant (*Undergraduate/Scholarship*) [1866]

Bohemian Lawyers Association of Chicago Scholarships (*Graduate/Scholarship*) [2649]

Ara S. Boyan Scholarship Grant (*Undergraduate/Scholarship*) [1867]

Brandon Fradd Fellowship in Music Composition (*Professional development/Fellowship*) [3416]

Cathy L. Brock Memorial Scholarships (*Graduate/Scholarship*) [5814]

Hermine Buchakian Scholarship Grant (*Undergraduate/Scholarship*) [1868]

Buckfire & Buckfire, P.C. Law School Diversity Scholarships (*Graduate/Scholarship*) [2736]

Buckfire & Buckfire, P.C. Medical Diversity Scholarships (*Advanced Professional/Scholarship*) [2737]

Charlotte Calfian Scholarship Grant (*Undergraduate/Scholarship*) [1869]

California Bar Foundation 3L Diversity Scholarship (*Undergraduate/Scholarship*) [2789, 3812, 10602]

Canada-Ukraine Parliamentary Program Internship Scholarships (CUPP) (*Undergraduate/Scholarship, Internship*) [11888]

CANFIT Nutrition, Physical Education and Culinary Arts Scholarships (*Graduate, Undergraduate/Scholarship*) [3561]

Carlos M. Castaneda Journalism Scholarship (*Graduate/Scholarship*) [4840]

Chereddi NarayanaRao & Radhamanohari Scholarships (*Graduate/Scholarship*) [10948]

CINTAS Foundation Fellowship in Architecture & Design (*Professional development/Fellowship*) [3417]

CINTAS-Knight Fellowship in theVisual Arts (*Professional development/Fellowship*) [3418]

CPA-F Scholarship (*Graduate/Scholarship*) [2824]

Arthur H. Dadian Scholarship Grants (*Undergraduate/Scholarship*) [1870]

Thomas Richard Dadourian Memorial Grant (*Undergraduate/Scholarship*) [1871]

Alexander A. Dadourian Scholarship (*Undergraduate/Scholarship*) [1872]

Dadour Dadourian Scholarship Fund (*Undergraduate/Scholarship*) [1873]

Dan and Rachel Mahi Educational Scholarship (*Graduate, Undergraduate/Scholarship*) [8921]

Daniel Kahikina and Millie Akaka Scholarship (*Graduate, Undergraduate/Scholarship*) [8922]

Denis Wong & Associates Scholarship (*Graduate, Undergraduate/Scholarship*) [8923]

Garabed and Almast Der Megrditchian Scholarship Grants (*Undergraduate/Scholarship*) [1874]

Dr. Ali Jarrahi Merit Scholarship (*Undergraduate/Scholarship*) [6172]

Dr. George and Isabelle Elanjian Scholarship (*Undergraduate/Scholarship*) [11638]

The Dream is Inclusive Scholarship (*Two Year College, Undergraduate, Graduate, Professional development, Vocational/Occupational/Scholarship*) [8624]

James Echols Scholarship Award (*Undergraduate/Recognition, Award, Scholarship*) [2781]

Enkababian Family and Sarian Family Memorial Grant (*Undergraduate/Scholarship*) [1875]

Bruce T. and Jackie Mahi Erickson Scholarship (*Graduate, Undergraduate/Scholarship*) [8924]

Parsegh and Thora Essefian Memorial Grant (*Undergraduate/Scholarship*) [1876]

Clay Ford Florida Board of Accountancy Minority Scholarships (*Undergraduate/Scholarship*) [4627]

Forté Fellowships (*Master's/Fellowship*) [4689]

Gadde Sitaramamma & Tirupataiah Scholarship (*Graduate/Scholarship*) [10949]

GALAS Scholarship (*Undergraduate, Graduate/Scholarship*) [4868]

Lionel Galstaun Memorial Grant (*Undergraduate/Scholarship*) [1877]

Maro Ajemian Galstaun Memorial Grant (*Undergraduate/Scholarship*) [1878]

GAPA Foundation Scholarship (*Undergraduate, Graduate, High School, Vocational/Occupational/Scholarship*) [9334]

Geeta Rastogi Memorial Scholarship (*Undergraduate/Scholarship*) [11757]

George Hi'ilani Mills Scholarship (*Graduate/Scholarship*) [8925]

German Historical Institute Doctoral and Postdoctoral Fellowships (*Doctorate, Postgraduate/Fellowship*) [4942]

Glenn Godfrey Sr. Memorial Scholarship (*Undergraduate, Graduate/Scholarship*) [6589]

Goldman Sachs/Matsuo Takabuki Commemorative Scholarship (*Graduate/Scholarship*) [8926]

Anna K. Gower and Annabelle K. Gower Scholarship Fund (*Undergraduate, University, College, Two Year College, Vocational/Occupational/Scholarship*) [5402]

Ella T. Grasso Literary Scholarship (*Undergraduate/Scholarship*) [11221]

Hai Guin Scholarships (*Undergraduate, Graduate/Scholarship*) [5260]

George Gurdjian Memorial Grant (*Undergraduate/Scholarship*) [1879]

Antranik and Alice Gurdjian Scholarship Grant (*Undergraduate/Scholarship*) [1880]

Guthikonda BasavapunnaRao & Umadevi Scholarship (*Graduate/Scholarship*) [10950]

Guthikonda Ramabrahmam & Balamani Scholarship (*Graduate/Scholarship*) [10951]

H. Kruger Kaprielian Scholarship (*Undergraduate/Scholarship*) [11714]

Garabed, Zabel and Vahe Hachikian Scholarship Grant (*Undergraduate/Scholarship*) [1881]

Jack Hajinian Memorial Grant (*Undergraduate/Scholarship*) [1882]

Stan Hamilton Scholarship (*Graduate/Scholarship*) [9885]

Isaac and Mary Harbottle Scholarship (*Graduate, Undergraduate/Scholarship*) [8927]

Margaret Shumavonian Harnischfeger Scholarship (*Undergraduate/Scholarship*) [1883]

Hekemian Family Scholarship Grants (*Undergraduate/Scholarship*) [1884]

Hellenic University Club of Philadelphia Founders Scholarship (*Undergraduate/Scholarship*) [5465]

George Holopigian Memorial Grants (*Undergraduate/Scholarship*) [1885]

The Hirair and Anna Hovnanian Foundation Presidential Scholarship (*Undergraduate/Scholarship*) [5512]

Hirair and Anna Hovnanian Foundation Scholarship (*Undergraduate/Scholarship*) [5513]

The Husenig Foundation Scholarship Grant (*Undergraduate/Scholarship*) [1886]

IABA Scholarship (*Graduate/Scholarship*) [6170]

Iranian-American Scholarship Fund (*Undergraduate, Graduate/Scholarship*) [7954]

ISF Excellence in Community Service Scholarship (*Undergraduate/Scholarship*) [6173]

ISF Undergraduate Scholarship (*Undergraduate/Scholarship*) [6174]

Journey Toward Ordained Ministry Scholarships (*Undergraduate, Graduate/Scholarship*) [4893]

Armenag and Armenhooi Kalustian Memorial Grant (*Undergraduate/Scholarship*) [1887]

Gladys Kamakakokalani 'Ainoa Brandt Scholarships (*Graduate, Undergraduate/Scholarship*) [8929]

Kamehameha Schools Class of 1968 "Ka Poli O Kaiona" Scholarships (*Graduate, Undergraduate/Scholarship*) [8930]

Kamehameha Schools Class of 1972 Scholarship (*Graduate, Undergraduate/Scholarship*) [8931]

Aram and Adrine Kamparosyan Memorial Grant (*Undergraduate/Scholarship*) [1888]

KASF scholarships (*Graduate, Undergraduate/Scholarship*) [6597]

KASF Designated Scholarships (*Graduate, Undergraduate/Scholarship*) [6598]

Koren and Alice Odian Kasparian Memorial Grant (*Undergraduate/Scholarship*) [1889]

Araxy Kechejian Memorial Grant (*Undergraduate/Scholarship*) [1890]

KEF General Scholarships (*Undergraduate, Graduate/Scholarship*) [6590]

George Keverian Public Service Scholarship (*Undergraduate/Scholarship*) [1891]

Dr. Elemer and Eva Kiss Scholarship Fund (*Undergraduate/Scholarship*) [5642]

Kodali Veeraiah & Sarojini Scholarship (*Graduate/Scholarship*) [10952]

Kosciuszko Foundation Tuition Scholarships (*Graduate/Scholarship*) [6602]

Haig Koumjian Memorial Grant (*Undergraduate/Scholarship*) [1892]

Harry A. Kuljian Memorial Grant (*Undergraduate/Scholarship*) [1893]

Kuropas Jan Memorial Scholarship (*Undergraduate/Scholarship*) [9670]

Latinos in Technology Scholarship (*Undergraduate/Scholarship*) [10136]

Danny T. Le Memorial Scholarship (*Undergraduate/Scholarship*) [11822]

LeClairRyan 1L Diversity Scholarship (*Undergraduate/Scholarship*) [6762]

Loan for Service for Graduates (*Graduate/Loan*) [995]

Louisville Institute's First Book Grant Program for Minority Scholars (FBM) (*Doctorate/Grant*) [6915]

Lucy Hsu Ho Scholarship (*Undergraduate/Scholarship*) [2485]

Manasel Manasselian Memorial Grant (*Undergraduate/Scholarship*) [1894]

Cora Aguda Manayan Fund Scholarship (*Undergraduate/Scholarship*) [5408]

Mangasar M. Mangasarian Scholarship Fund (*Graduate/Scholarship*) [11544]

Margaret Dowell-Gravatt, M.D. Scholarship (*Undergraduate/Scholarship*) [2486]

Martin Frank Diversity Travel Award (*Undergraduate, Postdoctorate/Fellowship, Award, Monetary*) [1237]

A. Lucchetti Martino Scholarship (*Undergraduate/Scholarship*) [7961]

Mas Family Scholarship (*Graduate, Undergraduate/Scholarship*) [7120]

Larry Matfay Cultural Heritage Scholarship (*Undergraduate, Graduate/Scholarship*) [6592]

Howard Mayer Brown Fellowship (*Graduate/Fellowship*) [1146]

K. Cyrus Melikian Memorial Grant (*Undergraduate/Scholarship*) [1895]

Menominee Tribal Scholarships *(Undergraduate, Graduate, High School/Scholarship)* [7256]

Michigan Auto Law Student Diversity Scholarships *(Undergraduate/Scholarship)* [7306]

Dikran Missirlian Scholarship Grant *(Undergraduate/Scholarship)* [1896]

Momeni Foundation Scholastic Achievement Scholarships *(Undergraduate/Scholarship)* [7955]

NAAMA Scholarships *(Undergraduate/Scholarship)* [7598]

NABA National Scholarship Program *(Graduate, Undergraduate/Scholarship, Award, Monetary)* [7613]

NACA Multicultural Professional Development Grant *(Undergraduate, Graduate, Professional development/Grant)* [7627]

National GEM Consortium - PhD Engineering Fellowships *(Master's, Graduate/Fellowship)* [7903]

National GEM Consortium - PhD Science Fellowships *(Doctorate, Graduate/Fellowship)* [7904]

National Iranian American Council Fellowships *(Graduate, Undergraduate/Fellowship)* [7956]

National Medical Fellowships Need-Based Scholarships *(Undergraduate/Scholarship)* [8001]

National Organization of Italian-American Women Scholarships *(Undergraduate, Graduate/Scholarship)* [8025]

National Recreation and Park Association Diversity Scholarships *(Undergraduate/Scholarship)* [8059]

Native Hawaiian Chamber of Commerce Scholarship *(Graduate, Undergraduate/Scholarship)* [8932]

Native Hawaiian Visual Arts Scholarship *(Graduate, Undergraduate/Scholarship)* [8933]

NCACPA Outstanding Minority Accounting Student Scholarships *(Undergraduate/Scholarship)* [8426]

Le Hoang Nguyen College Scholarships (LHN) *(Undergraduate/Scholarship)* [11823]

The Thuy Nguyen Scholarships *(High School/Scholarship)* [11824]

NWAC Helen Bassett Commemorative Student Award *(Undergraduate, Graduate/Scholarship)* [8168]

Omatsu FACL Scholarships *(Juris Doctorate, Advanced Professional/Scholarship)* [4529]

ONECA Four Directions Scholarship *(Undergraduate/Scholarship)* [8660]

M. Dick Osumi Civil Rights and Public Interest Scholarship *(Graduate, Undergraduate/Scholarship)* [6240]

Satenik & Adom Ourian Education Foundation Scholarship *(Undergraduate/Scholarship)* [1897]

Outlaw Student's Minority Scholarships *(Undergraduate/Scholarship)* [10861]

The PanHellenic Scholarship *(Undergraduate/Scholarship)* [8816]

Pepperdine University School of Law Armenian Student Scholarship *(Undergraduate/Scholarship)* [9020]

Larry A. Peters Endowment Fund Scholarship *(Undergraduate/Scholarship)* [1898]

Ruth D. Peterson Fellowship for Racial and Ethnic Diversity *(Doctorate/Fellowship)* [1420]

Polish National Alliance of Brooklyn, USA Scholarships *(Undergraduate/Scholarship)* [6606]

Francis Poloshian Memorial Grant *(Undergraduate/Scholarship)* [1899]

James Poloshian Memorial Grant *(Undergraduate/Scholarship)* [1900]

Porter Physiology Development Fellowship *(Doctorate/Fellowship, Award, Monetary)* [1238]

Poundmaker Memorial Scholarships *(Undergraduate/Scholarship)* [11675]

Powers-Knapp Scholarship Program *(Undergraduate/Scholarship)* [11744]

Prince Henry Society Scholarships *(Undergraduate/Scholarship)* [9326]

Pulaski Scholarships for Advanced Studies *(Graduate, Master's/Scholarship)* [827]

Ralph Modjeski Scholarship *(Graduate, Undergraduate/Scholarship)* [9240]

Richard R. Tufenkian Scholarships *(Undergraduate/Scholarship)* [1848]

Ameen Rihani Scholarship Program *(Undergraduate/Scholarship)* [1768]

Elliott C. Roberts Scholarships *(Graduate/Scholarship)* [5815]

R.O.E.A. Dumitru Golea Goldy-Gemu Scholarships *(Undergraduate, High School/Scholarship)* [1369]

St. James Armenian Apostolic Church Scholarships *(Undergraduate, Vocational/Occupational/Scholarship)* [9780]

SAJA Student Scholarship *(Undergraduate, Graduate/Scholarship)* [10604]

SALEF Health Career Scholarships *(Undergraduate, Graduate/Scholarship)* [9791]

Dr. Henry Seneca Charitable Trust Scholarship *(Undergraduate/Scholarship)* [1901]

Archak and Meroum Senekjian Memorial Grant *(Undergraduate/Scholarship)* [1902]

Serbian Bar Association of America Scholarships *(Graduate/Scholarship)* [10017]

Julia Shahan and Shahan Siran Nevshehir Memorial Grant *(Undergraduate/Scholarship)* [1903]

SREB-State Doctoral Scholars Program - Dissertation Award *(Doctorate/Scholarship, Award)* [10663]

SREB-State Doctoral Scholars Program - Doctoral Award *(Doctorate, Graduate/Scholarship)* [10664]

SSSP Racial/Ethnic Minority Graduate Fellowship *(Graduate/Fellowship, Award, Monetary)* [10537]

Hazaros Tabakoglu Scholarship Fund *(Undergraduate/Scholarship)* [8309]

TANA Foundation Graduate Scholarships *(Graduate/Scholarship)* [10953]

Arthur A. Thovmasian, Jr. Memorial Grant *(Undergraduate/Scholarship)* [1904]

Dr. Harry Jeffrey Tourigian Memorial Grant *(Undergraduate/Scholarship)* [1905]

Vera Tran Memorial Scholarships *(Undergraduate/Scholarship)* [11825]

Udall Undergraduate Scholarship *(Undergraduate/Scholarship)* [11165]

UNICO Merrimack Valley Scholarships *(Graduate/Scholarship)* [11219]

Union of Marash Armenian Student Funds *(Undergraduate, Graduate/Scholarship)* [11241]

University of Wisconsin-Madison Chancellor's Scholarship Program *(Undergraduate/Scholarship)* [11746]

USPAACC Ampcus Hallmark Scholarship *(Undergraduate/Scholarship)* [11395]

USPAACC College Hallmark Scholarships *(Undergraduate/Scholarship)* [11396]

USPAACC Denny's Hungry for Education Scholarship *(Undergraduate/Scholarship)* [11397]

Vallabhaneni Sukundamma & Lakshmaiah Scholarship *(Graduate/Scholarship)* [10954]

Dimitri J. Ververelli Memorial Scholarship for Architecture and/or Engineering *(Undergraduate/Scholarship)* [5469]

VSCPA Educational Foundation Minority Accounting Scholarship *(Graduate, Undergraduate/Scholarship)* [11847]

Colin Wasacase Scholarship *(Undergraduate/Scholarship)* [8661]

Wells Fargo American Indian Scholarship Program *(Undergraduate/Scholarship)* [996]

Wellstone Fellowships for Social Justice *(Graduate/Fellowship)* [4484]

William S. Richardson Commemorative Scholarship *(Graduate/Scholarship)* [8934]

Wisconsin Lawton Minority Retention Grants *(Undergraduate/Grant)* [11753]

York Regional Police Scholarships *(Undergraduate/Scholarship)* [6222]

Aram Zakian Memorial Fund Scholarship *(Undergraduate/Scholarship)* [1906]

Araxie Zakian Memorial Grant *(Undergraduate/Scholarship)* [1907]

Dr. Marie E. Zakrzewski Medical Scholarships *(Doctorate/Scholarship)* [6607]

Charles Zarigian, Esq. Memorial Award *(Undergraduate/Scholarship)* [1908]

George Zartarian Memorial Grant *(Undergraduate/Scholarship)* [1909]

Zelle Diversity in Law Scholarship *(Undergraduate/Scholarship)* [12405]

Fraternal organization membership

A.F. Zimmerman Scholarship *(Graduate, Master's/Scholarship)* [9073]

ALD Graduate Fellowships *(Graduate/Fellowship)* [392]

Alice Hersey Wick Award *(Undergraduate/Scholarship)* [10090]

Alpha Chi Omega Love and Loyalty Grants *(Professional development/Grant)* [382]

Alpha Chi Sigma Scholarship Awards *(Graduate, Undergraduate/Scholarship)* [384]

Alpha Delta Gamma Educational Foundation Scholarship *(Undergraduate, Graduate/Scholarship)* [386]

Alpha Kappa Alpha - Educational Advancement Foundation Undergraduate Financial Need-Based Scholarships *(Undergraduate/Scholarship)* [388]

Alpha Kappa Alpha - Educational Advancement Foundation Undergraduate Merit Scholarships *(Undergraduate/Scholarship)* [389]

Alpha Kappa Trust Scholarship-Beta Omega *(Undergraduate/Scholarship)* [10091]

Alzheimer's/Gerontology Scholarship *(Graduate/Scholarship)* [10092]

Andrea Will Memorial Scholarship *(Undergraduate/Scholarship)* [10093]

Hettie M. Anthony Fellowship *(Doctorate/Fellowship)* [6495]

Francis Warren Baker Memorial Scholarships *(Undergraduate/Scholarship)* [10094]

Barber-Owen-Thomas Scholarship *(Undergraduate/Scholarship)* [10095]

W. H. (Bert) Bates Oxford Cup Scholarship *(Undergraduate, Graduate/Scholarship)* [2503]

Stephen D. Bechtel, Jr. Oxford Cup Scholarship *(Undergraduate, Graduate/Scholarship)* [2504]

Bertram W. Bennett Memorial Scholarship *(Undergraduate, Graduate/Scholarship)* [2505]

Beta Foundation Merit Scholarships *(Graduate, Undergraduate/Scholarship)* [2506]

Beta Lambda Project 2000 Scholarship *(Undergraduate/Scholarship)* [6404]

Beta Mu Project 2000 Scholarship *(Undergraduate/Scholarship)* [6405]

Beta Pi Project 2000 Scholarship in Memory of Kristy LeMond *(Undergraduate/Scholarship)* [6406]

Beta Province Project 2000 Scholarship *(Undergraduate/Scholarship)* [6407]

Beta Sigma Scholarship *(Undergraduate/Scholarship)* [10096]

Beta Tau Scholarship Fund *(Undergraduate/Scholarship)* [6408]

Beta Theta Memorial Scholarship *(Graduate, Undergraduate/Scholarship)* [6409]

Beta Xi Project 2000 Scholarship *(Undergraduate/Scholarship)* [6410]

Beta Zeta Project 2000 Scholarship *(Undergraduate/Scholarship)* [6411]

Kyle R. Blanco Memorial Scholarship *(Undergraduate, Graduate/Scholarship)* [2507]

Mildred Cater Bradham Social Work Fellowships *(Graduate, Professional development/Fellowship)* [12409]

William J. Brennan Graduate Assistant Fellowships *(Graduate/Fellowship)* [8685]

Seth R. and Corinne H. Brooks Memorial Scholarships *(Undergraduate/Scholarship)* [2508]

Fred and Mary Jane Brower Scholarship *(Undergraduate, Graduate/Scholarship)* [2509]

Marjorie M. Brown Dissertation Fellowship *(Doctorate/Fellowship)* [6488]

Marjorie M. Brown Fellowship Program *(Postdoctorate/Fellowship)* [6496]

Edward M. Brown Oxford Cup Scholarship *(Undergraduate, Graduate/Scholarship)* [2510]

Frederick S. Bucholz Scholarship *(Undergraduate, Graduate/Scholarship)* [2511]

Adam S. Burford Memorial Scholarship *(Undergraduate, Graduate/Scholarship)* [2512]

Thad Byrne Memorial Scholarship *(Undergraduate, Graduate/Scholarship)* [2513]

John L. Calvert Memorial Scholarship *(Undergraduate, Graduate/Scholarship)* [2514]

Thomas D. and Karen H. Cassady Scholarship *(Undergraduate, Graduate/Scholarship)* [2515]

Oscar Chapman Memorial Scholarship *(Undergraduate, Graduate/Scholarship)* [2516]

Christine Kerr Cawthorne Scholarship *(Undergraduate/Scholarship)* [10097]

Clan Ross Foundation Scholarships *(Undergraduate/Scholarship)* [3426]

Cleveland Alumni Association Scholarship *(Undergraduate, Graduate/Scholarship)* [2517]

Geraldine Clewell Fellowships - Doctoral Student *(Graduate/Fellowship)* [9107]

Geraldine Clewell Fellowships - Masteral *(Graduate/Fellowship)* [9108]

Closs/Parnitzke/Clarke Scholarship *(Undergraduate/Scholarship)* [9109]

L. Robert Clough Memorial Scholarship *(Undergraduate, Graduate/Scholarship)* [2518]

Maridell Braham Condon Scholarships *(Undergraduate/Scholarship)* [10098]

CSA Fraternal Life Scholarships *(Undergraduate/Scholarship)* [3933]

Dallas Alumnae Association Gamma Phi Chapter Scholarship *(Undergraduate/Scholarship)* [6415]

Lucile Caswell Davids Memorial Adelphe Scholarship *(Undergraduate, Graduate/Scholarship)* [6416]

Arlene Davis Scholarships *(Undergraduate/Scholarship)* [4030]

William W. Dawson Memorial Scholarship *(Undergraduate, Graduate/Scholarship)* [2519]

Delta Chi Alumnae Memorial Scholarship *(Undergraduate/Scholarship)* [10099]

Delta Kappa Project 2000 Scholarship *(Undergraduate/Scholarship)* [6417]

Delta Nu Project 2000 Scholarship *(Undergraduate/Scholarship)* [6418]

Delta Project 2000 Scholarship *(Undergraduate/Scholarship)* [6419]

Delta Tau Project 2000 Scholarship *(Undergraduate/Scholarship)* [6420]

Delta Tau Scholarship *(Undergraduate, Graduate/Scholarship)* [2520]

Delta Upsilon Project 2000 Nowell Memorial Scholarship *(Undergraduate/Scholarship)* [6421]

Denton Scholarship *(Graduate/Scholarship)* [10081]

Beta Nu/Caryl Cordis D'hondt Scholarship *(Undergraduate/Scholarship)* [10100]

Theta/Caryl Cordis D'hondt Scholarship *(Undergraduate/Scholarship)* [10101]

Dr. Nancy Smith Midgette Scholarship *(Undergraduate/Scholarship)* [10102]

Scott Dominguez - Craters of the Moon Chapter Scholarship *(Graduate, Undergraduate/Scholarship)* [1564]

John Holt Duncan Memorial Scholarship *(Undergraduate, Graduate/Scholarship)* [2521]

East Carolina Scholarship *(Undergraduate, Graduate/Scholarship)* [2522]

W. Todd Elias Memorial Scholarship *(Undergraduate, Graduate/Scholarship)* [2523]

Elin J. Stene/Xi Scholarship *(Undergraduate/Scholarship)* [10103]

Elise Reed Jenkins Memorial Scholarship *(Undergraduate/Scholarship)* [10104]

Gladys Anderson Emerson Scholarship *(Undergraduate/Award, Scholarship)* [6152]

Epsilon Delta Project 2000 Scholarship *(Undergraduate/Scholarship)* [6423]

Epsilon Epsilon Scholarship *(Undergraduate/Scholarship)* [10105]

Epsilon Tau Scholarship *(Undergraduate/Scholarship)* [10106]

Evelyn S. Nish Scholarship *(Undergraduate/Scholarship)* [10107]

Falcon Achievement Scholarships *(Undergraduate/Scholarship)* [9242]

James Fonseca Scholarship *(Undergraduate, Graduate/Scholarship)* [395]

Genevieve Forthun Scholarships *(Undergraduate/Scholarship)* [9111]

Foundation Scholarships *(Graduate/Scholarship)* [8619]

Mary Metzger Fouse Memorial Scholarship Fund *(Undergraduate/Scholarship)* [6428]

Mary Weiking Franken Scholarships *(Undergraduate/Scholarship)* [9112]

Gamma Chi Project 2000 Scholarship *(Undergraduate/Scholarship)* [6430]

Gamma Iota Scholarship *(Undergraduate/Scholarship)* [10108]

Gamma Iota Scholarships - Gamma Tau *(Undergraduate/Scholarship)* [10109]

Gamma Iota Scholarships - Zeta Kappa *(Undergraduate/Scholarship)* [10110]

Gamma Iota Scholarships - Zeta Nu *(Undergraduate/Scholarship)* [10111]

Gamma Lambda Scholarship *(Undergraduate/Scholarship)* [10112]

Gamma Mu Project 2000 Scholarship *(Undergraduate/Scholarship)* [6431]

Gamma Pi Project 2000 Scholarship *(Undergraduate/Scholarship)* [6432]

Gamma Theta Project 2000 Scholarship *(Undergraduate/Scholarship)* [6433]

Gamma Zeta Project 2000 Scholarship *(Undergraduate/Scholarship)* [6434]

James L. Gavin Memorial Scholarship *(Undergraduate, Graduate/Scholarship)* [2524]

General Falcon Scholarships *(Undergraduate/Scholarship)* [9243]

Geraldine Clewell Scholarship *(Undergraduate/Scholarship)* [9113]

Burton L. Gerber Scholarship *(Undergraduate/Scholarship)* [2525]

Elizabeth Tucker Gessley Scholarship *(Undergraduate/Scholarship)* [6436]

Goddard, Indovina & Krakowski Scholarship *(Undergraduate, Graduate/Scholarship)* [396]

Thomas Boston Gordon Memorial Scholarship *(Undergraduate, Graduate/Scholarship)* [2526]

Richard C. Gorecki Scholarships *(Graduate/Scholarship)* [9244]

Graydon A. Tunstall Undergraduate Student Scholarship *(Undergraduate/Scholarship)* [9074]

Mary Ewing Guthrey/Mary Keller Moyer Memorial Scholarship *(Undergraduate, Graduate/Scholarship)* [6439]

Suzanne Lovell Hadsell Memorial Scholarship *(Undergraduate, Graduate/Scholarship)* [6440]

Anna E. Hall Memorial Scholarships *(Undergraduate, Graduate, Doctorate/Scholarship)* [9084]

The Caitlin Hammaren Memorial Scholarship *(Undergraduate/Scholarship)* [6441]

Charles Henry Hardin Memorial Scholarship *(Undergraduate, Graduate/Scholarship)* [2527]

Dolores Ruth Heady Hardy Memorial Scholarship *(Undergraduate/Scholarship)* [6442]

Ronald, Randall and Roger Helman Scholarship *(Undergraduate, Graduate/Scholarship)* [2528]

George L. and June L. Herpel Memorial Scholarship *(Graduate/Scholarship)* [2529]

Jessica M. Herron, Epsilon Nu, Memorial Scholarship *(Undergraduate, Graduate/Scholarship)* [6443]

Herschede Engineering Scholarship *(Graduate/Scholarship)* [10082]

Douglas W. Hill, Jr. Scholarship *(Undergraduate, Graduate/Scholarship)* [2530]

John A. Hill Memorial Scholarship *(Undergraduate, Graduate/Scholarship)* [2531]

Dr. Marshall E. Hollis Scholarship *(Undergraduate, Graduate/Scholarship)* [2532]

Houston Alumnae Association Doris Krikham Brokaw Memorial Adelphe Scholarship *(Undergraduate, Graduate/Scholarship)* [6444]

Houston Alumnae Association, Eunice "Scotty" Scott Siverson Memorial Adelphe Scholarship *(Undergraduate, Graduate/Scholarship)* [6445]

Huenefeld/Denton Scholarships *(Undergraduate/Scholarship)* [4038]

Betty Jo Creighton Hunkele Adelphe Scholarship *(Undergraduate/Scholarship)* [6446]

Iris Scholarship *(Undergraduate/Scholarship)* [6447]

Irma E. Voigt Memorial Scholarship *(Undergraduate/Scholarship)* [10113]

Jackman Scholarships *(Undergraduate/Scholarship)* [9114]

Jacque Placette Chapman Master's Fellowships *(Graduate, Master's/Fellowship)* [8686]

Jean Dearth Dickerscheid Fellowship *(Graduate/Fellowship)* [9115]

Wilma Winberg Johnson Adelphe Scholarship for Chapter Consultants *(Undergraduate/Scholarship)* [6448]

Kappa Kappa Gamma Foundation Project 2000 Scholarship *(Undergraduate/Scholarship)* [6450]

Kappa Project 2000 Scholarship *(Undergraduate/Scholarship)* [6451]

KGP Cornaro Scholarship *(Graduate/Scholarship)* [6397]

Treva C. Kintner Scholarships *(Undergraduate/Scholarship)* [9116]

James P. Kirkgasser Memorial Scholarship *(Undergraduate, Graduate/Scholarship)* [2533]

John G. F. Knight Memorial Scholarship *(Undergraduate, Graduate/Scholarship)* [2534]

KON/GEICO LeaderShape Undergraduate Scholarship *(Undergraduate/Scholarship)* [6490]

KON National Alumni Chapter Grant *(Professional development/Grant)* [6491]

KON New Initiatives Grant *(Professional development/Grant)* [6492]

Emily Day Koppell Memorial Adelphe Scholarship *(Undergraduate, Graduate/Scholarship)* [6452]

Carl A. Kroch Oxford Cup Memorial Scholarship *(Undergraduate, Graduate/Scholarship)* [2535]

Elaine Johnson Lampert Journalism Memorial Adelphe Scholarship *(Undergraduate/Award)* [6454]

Otho E. Lane Memorial Scholarship *(Undergraduate, Graduate/Scholarship)* [2536]

David Linton Memorial Scholarship *(Undergraduate, Graduate/Scholarship)* [2537]

Lorraine E. Swain Scholarship *(Undergraduate/Scholarship)* [10114]

Horace G. Lozier Memorial Scholarship *(Undergraduate, Graduate/Scholarship)* [2538]

Lucile Cheever Graubart/Lambda Scholarship *(Undergraduate/Scholarship)* [10115]

Eileen C. Maddex Fellowships *(Graduate/Fellowship)* [6493]

Madson Graduate Scholarship *(Graduate/Scholarship)* [10083]

Margaret J. Andrew Memorial Scholarship *(Undergraduate, Graduate/Scholarship)* [10116]

Marian Johnson Frutiger Sisterhood Scholarship *(Undergraduate/Scholarship)* [10117]

Marisol Scholarship *(Undergraduate/Scholarship)* [6459]

Samuel Taylor Marshall Scholarship *(Graduate, Undergraduate/Scholarship)* [2539]

Martha Combs Jenkins Scholarship *(Undergraduate/Scholarship)* [9117]

Mary Turnbull Schacht Memorial Scholarship *(Undergraduate/Scholarship)* [10118]

Nancy B. Woolridge McGee Graduate Fellowships *(Graduate/Fellowship)* [12415]

Mary Bowles McInnis Adelphe Scholarship *(Undergraduate/Scholarship)* [6461]

Joan Reagin McNeill Scholarships - Alpha Theta *(Undergraduate/Scholarship)* [10119]

Joan Reagin McNeill Scholarships - Theta Phi *(Undergraduate/Scholarship)* [10120]

John K. Merrell Scholarship *(Undergraduate, Graduate/Scholarship)* [2541]

Steven Craig Merrill Memorial Scholarship *(Undergraduate, Graduate/Scholarship)* [2542]

Military Service Scholarship *(Graduate, Undergraduate/Scholarship)* [10084]

Shelby L. Molter Music Education Scholarship *(Undergraduate, Graduate/Scholarship)* [2543]

M. Steve Moore Memorial Scholarship *(Undergraduate, Graduate/Award)* [2544]

Thomas S. Morgan Memorial Scholarship *(Graduate, Master's/Scholarship)* [9075]

Edith Cantor Morrison Memorial Scholarship *(Undergraduate, Graduate/Scholarship)* [2545]

Mu Alpha Theta Summer Grants *(Undergraduate, Graduate/Grant)* [7493]

Need-Based Scholarships *(Undergraduate/Scholarship)* [9100]

Douglas J. Neeley Memorial Scholarship *(Undergraduate, Graduate/Scholarship)* [2546]

Nell Bryant Robinson Scholarship *(Undergraduate/Scholarship)* [9118]

Carol Nelson Scholarship *(Undergraduate/Scholarship)* [6462]

WillEtta "Willie" Long Oates, Gamma Nu, Memorial Scholarship *(Undergraduate, Graduate/Scholarship)* [6463]

Omicron Nu Research Fellowship *(Postdoctorate, Graduate/Fellowship)* [6497]

Order of Omega Doctoral Fellowships *(Doctorate, Graduate/Fellowship)* [8687]

E. William Palmer Memorial Scholarship *(Undergraduate, Graduate/Scholarship)* [2547]

Participation-Based Scholarships *(Undergraduate/Scholarship)* [9101]

Gail Patrick Charitable Trust Scholarships *(Graduate/Scholarship)* [4041]

Peale Scholarship Grant *(Professional development/Scholarship)* [9094]

Phi Alpha Theta Doctoral Scholarship *(Doctorate/Scholarship)* [9076]

Phi Alpha Theta Faculty Advisor Research Grant *(Other/Grant)* [9077]

Phi Delta Gamma Academic Achievement Awards *(Undergraduate/Scholarship)* [9095]

Phi Eta Sigma Graduate Scholarships *(Graduate, Other/Scholarship)* [9089]

Phi Eta Sigma Undergraduate Scholarship Awards *(Undergraduate/Scholarship)* [9090]

Phi Eta Sigma Undergraduate Scholarships *(Undergraduate/Scholarship)* [9091]

Phi Kappa Phi DissertationFellowships *(Doctorate/Fellowship)* [9097]

Phi Kappa Phi Fellowship *(Graduate, Undergraduate/Fellowship)* [9098]

Phi Kappa Sigma Foundation Scholarship *(Undergraduate/Scholarship)* [9102]

Phi Sigma Epsilon Past National President Scholarships *(Graduate, Undergraduate/Scholarship)* [9172]

Phi Theta Kappa Scholarship *(Undergraduate/Scholarship)* [5765]

Phi Upsilon Omicron Candle Fellowships *(Graduate, Postgraduate/Fellowship)* [9119]

Phi Upsilon Omicron Challenge Scholarships *(Undergraduate/Scholarship)* [9120]

Phi Upsilon Omicron Diamond Anniversary Fellowships *(Graduate/Fellowship)* [9121]

Phi Upsilon Omicron Founders Fellowship *(Graduate/Fellowship)* [9122]

Phi Upsilon Omicron Golden Anniversary Scholarships *(Undergraduate/Scholarship)* [9123]

Phi Upsilon Omicron Past Presidents Scholarships *(Undergraduate/Scholarship)* [9124]

Phi Upsilon Omicron Presidents Research Fellowship *(Graduate, Master's, Doctorate, Postdoctorate/Fellowship)* [9125]

Pi Gamma Mu Scholarships *(Graduate/Scholarship)* [9160]

Pi Project 2000 Tali James Memorial Scholarship *(Undergraduate/Scholarship)* [6465]

The John Pine Memorial Award *(Doctorate, Graduate, Undergraduate/Scholarship)* [9078]

Caroline Previdi of Sandy Hook Elementary Memorial Scholarship *(Undergraduate, Graduate/Scholarship)* [2548]

Joseph E. Pryor Graduate Fellowships *(Graduate/Fellowship)* [379]

Phillis Brinton Pryor Panhellenic Scholarship *(Undergraduate/Scholarship)* [6466]

Marie Mathew Rask-Gamma Omicron Educational Endowment *(Undergraduate/Scholarship)* [6467]

Regina B. Shearn Scholarship *(Graduate, Undergraduate/Scholarship)* [398]

Rho Chi, AFPE First Year Graduate Fellowships *(Graduate/Fellowship)* [9683]

Rho Chi Society Clinical Research Scholarships *(Postdoctorate/Scholarship)* [9684]

John J. and Elizabeth Rhodes Scholarship *(Undergraduate, Graduate/Scholarship)* [2549]

Ben C. Rich Memorial Scholarship *(Undergraduate, Graduate/Scholarship)* [2550]

Richard Cecil Todd and Clauda Pennock Todd Tripod Scholarship *(Graduate, Undergraduate/Scholarship)* [9104]

Dorothy Worden Ronken Scholarships *(Graduate/Scholarship)* [4042]

Lucile Rust Scholarships *(Undergraduate/Scholarship)* [9126]

Michael Clarkson Ryan Memorial Scholarship *(Undergraduate, Graduate/Scholarship)* [2551]

S. Penny Chappell Scholarship *(Undergraduate/Scholarship)* [9127]

Saints Cyril and Methodius Scholarships *(Undergraduate/Scholarship)* [9766]

Margaret Jerome Sampson Scholarships *(Undergraduate/Scholarship)* [9128]

Lillian P. Schoephoerster Scholarships *(Undergraduate/Scholarship)* [9129]

A.J. and Lynda Hare Scribante Scholarship Fund *(Undergraduate/Scholarship)* [6471]

Fred A. Seaton Memorial Scholarship *(Undergraduate, Graduate/Scholarship)* [2552]

Josephine Kerbey Shaw Memorial Undergraduate Scholarship *(Undergraduate/Scholarship)* [6472]

William C. Scheetz Memorial Scholarship *(Undergraduate, Graduate/Scholarship)* [2553]

Susan Goldsmith Shelley Scholarship *(Undergraduate/Scholarship)* [6473]

Lynn Brower Shonk Memorial Scholarship *(Undergraduate/Scholarship)* [6474]

Col. Richard R. (Misty) and Sally Shoop Scholarship *(Undergraduate, Graduate/Scholarship)* [2554]

Sigma Kappa Foundation Alumnae Continuing Education Scholarship *(Graduate, Undergraduate/Scholarship)* [10121]

Sigma Kappa Foundation Alzheimer's/Gerontology Scholarship *(Graduate/Scholarship)* [10122]

Sigma Kappa Foundation Founders' Scholarships *(Undergraduate/Scholarship)* [10123]

Sigma Kappa Foundation Michigan Scholarship *(Undergraduate/Scholarship)* [10124]

Sigma Phi Alpha Graduate Scholarship *(Graduate/Scholarship)* [861]

Col. John R. Simpson Memorial Scholarship *(Undergraduate, Graduate/Scholarship)* [2555]

Ann Kelsay Small Scholarship *(Undergraduate/Scholarship)* [6475]

James George Smith Memorial Scholarship *(Undergraduate, Graduate/Scholarship)* [2556]

Helen D. Snow Memorial Scholarship *(Undergraduate, Graduate, Doctorate/Scholarship)* [9085]

SNRS/STTI Research Grants *(Professional development/Grant)* [10661]

H. H. Stephenson, Jr. Oxford Cup Scholarship *(Undergraduate, Graduate/Scholarship)* [2557]

Hugh E. Stephenson, Jr. Oxford Cup Scholarship *(Undergraduate, Graduate/Scholarship)* [2558]

Sutherland/Purdy Scholarship *(Undergraduate/Scholarship)* [9130]

SUVCW Scholarships *(Undergraduate/Scholarship)* [10595]

Thomas Arkle Clark Scholar-Leader of the Year *(Graduate, Undergraduate/Scholarship)* [9092]

Charles C. Thomas Scholarship *(Undergraduate/Scholarship)* [1754]

Matilda B. Thompson Scholarship *(Undergraduate/Scholarship)* [5555]

Michael W. Toennis Scholarship *(Undergraduate, Graduate/Scholarship)* [2559]

Tommie J. Hamner Scholarship *(Undergraduate/Scholarship)* [9131]

Jo Anne J. Trow Undergraduate Scholarships *(Undergraduate/Scholarship)* [393]

V.A. Leonard Scholarship *(Graduate, Undergraduate/Scholarship)* [399]

Gupton A. Vogt Oxford Cup Memorial Scholarship *(Undergraduate, Graduate/Scholarship)* [2560]

Walta Wilkinson Carmichael Scholarship *(Graduate/Scholarship)* [10125]

Lynn McNabb Walton Adelphe Scholarhship *(Undergraduate/Scholarship)* [6479]

Mary Elizabeth Westpheling - Long Beach (Calif.) Alumnae Association Memorial Scholarhip *(Undergraduate/Scholarship)* [6482]

William E. Parrish Scholarship *(Graduate, Master's/Scholarship)* [9079]

Wilma Sackett Dressel Scholarship *(Undergraduate/Scholarship)* [10126]

Rolla F. Wood Graduate Scholarships *(Graduate, Undergraduate/Scholarship)* [9105]

Donnell B. Young Scholarships *(Undergraduate/Scholarship)* [326]

Youth Partners Accessing Capital (YPAC) *(Undergraduate/Scholarship)* [390]

Zeta Sigma Project 2000 Scholarship *(Undergraduate/Scholarship)* [6484]

Hispanic American

AAMFT Minority Fellowship Program (MFP) *(Doctorate, Graduate/Fellowship)* [602]

Actuarial Diversity Scholarship *(Undergraduate/Scholarship)* [69]

AFPE Pre-Doctoral Fellowships in Pharmaceutical Sciences for Underrepresented Minorities *(Doctorate, Graduate/Fellowship)* [924]

AHETEMS General Scholarships *(Undergraduate, Graduate/Scholarship)* [10068]

AHETEMS Professional Scholarships *(Graduate/Scholarship)* [10069]

AIChE Minority Scholarship Awards for College Students *(Undergraduate/Scholarship)* [1020]

Air Products and Chemicals, Inc. Scholarships *(Undergraduate/Scholarship)* [2191]

ALPFA Scholarship *(Graduate, Undergraduate, Master's/Scholarship)* [2231]

American Association for Cancer Research Minority Scholar in Cancer Research Awards *(Graduate/Award)* [533]

American Physical Society Minority Undergraduate Scholarships *(Undergraduate/Scholarship)* [1220]

AMS Minority Scholarships *(Undergraduate/Scholarship)* [1123]

APS Scholarships for Minority Undergraduate Physics Majors *(Undergraduate/Scholarship)* [1221]

APSA Fund for Latino Scholarship *(Undergraduate, Graduate/Scholarship)* [1249]

APSA Minority Fellowship Program *(Doctorate/Fellowship)* [1251]

APTA Minority Scholarships - Faculty Development Scholarships *(Postdoctorate/Scholarship, Award, Recognition)* [1232]

APTA Minority Scholarships - Physical Therapist Assistant Students *(Undergraduate/Scholarship, Award, Recognition)* [1233]

APTA Minority Scholarships - Physical Therapist Students *(Undergraduate/Scholarship, Award, Recognition)* [1234]

ASA Minority Fellowship Program (ASA MFP) *(Doctorate/Fellowship)* [1590]

ASGP Graduate Research Fellowships *(Graduate/Fellowship)* [244]

AWG Minority Scholarship *(Undergraduate/Scholarship)* [2313]

Becas Univision Scholarship Program *(Undergraduate, Graduate/Scholarship)* [5528]

Bill Bernbach Diversity Scholarships *(Undergraduate/Scholarship)* [510]

Thomas M. Blake Memorial Scholarships *(Undergraduate/Scholarship)* [3753]

Leon Bradley Scholarship Program *(Undergraduate/Scholarship)* [638]

Angela Faye Brown Video Essay Contest *(Graduate/Scholarship)* [2717]

BSF General Scholarship Awards *(College, University/Scholarship)* [2439]

Carlos M. Castaneda Journalism Scholarship *(Graduate/Scholarship)* [4840]

CHCI Congressional Internship Program *(Undergraduate/Internship)* [3745]

CHCI Graduate Fellowship Program *(Graduate, Professional development/Fellowship)* [3746]

CHCI Public Policy Fellowships *(Professional development/Fellowship)* [3747]

Columbus Citizens Foundation College Scholarships *(Undergraduate/Scholarship)* [3543]

Columbus Citizens Foundation High School Scholarships *(Undergraduate/Scholarship)* [3544]

Connecticut Association of Latinos in Higher Education Scholarships *(Undergraduate/Scholarship)* [3754, 5320]

Lydia Cruz and Sandra Maria Ramos Scholarships *(Graduate/Scholarship)* [4026]

F.A. and Charlotte Blount Scholarship *(Undergraduate/Scholarship)* [12076]

Fleming/Blaszcak Scholarships *(Undergraduate, Graduate/Scholarship)* [10486]

Florida Education Fund McKnight Doctoral Fellowship *(Graduate/Fellowship)* [4629]

Frank G. Araujo Memorial Scholarship *(Undergraduate/Scholarship)* [9545]

Fraser Stryker Diversity Scholarship Program *(Undergraduate/Scholarship)* [4817]

The Gates Millennium Scholars *(Undergraduate/Scholarship)* [5529]

HANA Scholars *(Undergraduate, Graduate, Doctorate/Scholarship)* [4891]

Henry Salvatori Scholarship *(Undergraduate/Scholarship)* [8689]

HFMH Bilingual Scholarships for Mental Health Workforce Diversity *(Graduate/Scholarship)* [5539]

Oregon Latino Scholarship Fund *(Graduate, Undergraduate/Scholarship)* [5526]

Hispanic Scholarship Fund General College Scholarship Program (HSF) *(Undergraduate/Scholarship)* [5530]

HSF/Marathon Oil College Scholarship Program *(Undergraduate/Scholarship)* [5531]

HSF/Wells Fargo Scholarship Program *(Undergraduate, Graduate, High School/Scholarship)* [5532]

The Hyatt Hotels Fund For Minority Lodging Management Students *(Undergraduate/Scholarship)* [972]

Inter American Press Association Scholarships *(Undergraduate/Scholarship)* [10253]

Italian Language Scholarship *(Undergraduate/Scholarship)* [8690]

James E. West Fellowship *(Graduate/Fellowship)* [62]

Kaplan Scholarships *(Undergraduate/Scholarship)* [5524]

La Voz Latina Scholarship *(Undergraduate/Scholarship)* [3684]

LAEF Scholarships *(Undergraduate/Scholarship)* [6675]

The Lagrant Foundation - Graduate Scholarships *(Graduate/Scholarship)* [6632]

The Lagrant Foundation - Undergraduate Scholarships *(Undergraduate/Scholarship)* [6633]

LLN Student Scholarships *(Undergraduate/Scholarship)* [6677]

LULAC National Scholarship Fund (LNSF) *(Graduate, Undergraduate/Scholarship)* [6749]

MABF Scholarships *(Professional development/Scholarship)* [7286]

Maria Gonzalez Borrero Scholarship Fund *(Undergraduate/Scholarship)* [5338]

Howard Mayer Brown Fellowship *(Graduate/Fellowship)* [1146]

Minorities in Government Finance Scholarship *(Graduate, Undergraduate/Scholarship)* [5054]

MLA/NLM Spectrum Scholarship *(Undergraduate/Scholarship)* [7220]

MLA Scholarship for Minority Students *(Graduate/Scholarship)* [7223]

James B. Morris Scholarship *(Undergraduate/Scholarship)* [7474]

Archie Motley Memorial Scholarships for Minority Students *(Graduate/Scholarship)* [7367]

NACA Multicultural Professional Development Grant *(Undergraduate, Graduate, Professional development/Grant)* [7627]

National Medical Fellowships Need-Based Scholarships *(Undergraduate/Scholarship)* [8001]

NHFA Scholarships *(Graduate/Scholarship)* [7930]

Casilda Pagan Educational/Vocational Scholarships *(Graduate, Undergraduate, Postgraduate/Scholarship)* [5594]

PlasticPlace Young Entrepreneurs Scholarship Award *(Undergraduate/Scholarship)* [9192]

Portuguese American Police Association Scholarships *(Undergraduate/Scholarship)* [9252]

Judith McManus Price Scholarship *(Undergraduate, Graduate/Scholarship)* [1245]

Prospanica Scholarship *(Graduate, Undergraduate/Scholarship)* [9360]

PRSA Diversity Multicultural Scholarships *(Undergraduate/Scholarship)* [9438]

Rosa Quezada Memorial Education Scholarships *(Undergraduate/Scholarship)* [3755]

RMHC HACER Scholarship *(Undergraduate/Scholarship)* [9736]

Robert Toigo Foundation Fellowship *(Master's/Fellowship)* [11048]

Leo S. Rowe Pan American Fund *(Graduate, Undergraduate/Loan)* [8739]

Lucille and Edward R. Roybal Foundation Public Health Scholarships *(Graduate, Undergraduate/Scholarship)* [9753]

SALEF Health Career Scholarships *(Undergraduate, Graduate/Scholarship)* [9791]

Leo and Trinidad Sanchez Scholarships *(Undergraduate/Scholarship)* [10138]

Alfred P. Sloan Foundation Graduate Scholarships - Sloan Minority Ph.D. Program (MPHD) *(Doctorate/Scholarship)* [7582]

John Soto Scholarships *(Undergraduate/Scholarship)* [3756]

Underrepresented in Medicine award *(Graduate/Scholarship)* [1112]

United Health Foundation National Association of Hispanic Nurses Scholarships *(High School/Scholarship)* [7659]

University of Wisconsin-Madison Chancellor's Scholarship Program *(Undergraduate/Scholarship)* [11746]

Marta Vallin Memorial Scholarships *(Undergraduate/Scholarship)* [3757]

Valuing Diversity PhD Scholarship *(Doctorate/Scholarship)* [1105]

White Collar Defense Diversity Scholarships *(Undergraduate, Graduate/Scholarship)* [9286]

Woodrow Wilson-Rockefeller Brothers Fund Fellowships for Aspiring Teachers of Color *(Undergraduate/Fellowship)* [12052]

Military

$1,000 Scholarship for Veterans *(Undergraduate/Scholarship)* [9042]

100th Infantry Battalion Veterans Memorial Scholarship Fund *(Undergraduate, University, College, Vocational/Occupational/Scholarship)* [5374]

AAAA Scholarship Program *(Undergraduate, Graduate/Scholarship)* [1911]

ACHE/American Legion Auxiliary Scholarship Program *(Undergraduate/Scholarship)* [205]

Admiral Mike Boorda Loan Program *(Undergraduate/Loan)* [8179]

AFCEA War Veterans Scholarships *(Undergraduate/Scholarship)* [105]

The Agnes Sopcak Memorial Scholarship *(Undergraduate/Scholarship)* [12146]

Alabama National Guard Educational Assistance Program *(Undergraduate/Scholarship)* [212]

Allied Van Lines Military Scholarship *(Undergraduate/Scholarship)* [370]

The American Legion Legacy Scholarship *(Undergraduate/Scholarship)* [1070]

American Patriot Scholarship *(Undergraduate/Scholarship, Monetary)* [7388]

Anchor Scholarship Foundation Scholarships *(Undergraduate, Four Year College, Two Year College/Scholarship)* [1705]

Seth Bonder Scholarship for Applied Operations Research in Military Applications *(Doctorate/Scholarship, Monetary, Recognition, Award)* [5852]

Lieutenant General Douglas D. Buchholz Memorial Scholarship *(Undergraduate/Scholarship)* [106]

Buick Achievers Scholarship Program *(Undergraduate/Scholarship)* [4905]

Commander Ronald J. Cantin Scholarships *(Undergraduate/Scholarship)* [3454]

Captain Jodi Callahan Memorial Scholarship *(Graduate, Master's/Scholarship)* [147]

CFR Military Fellowships *(Professional development/Fellowship)* [3860]

Children of Fallen Patriots Scholarships *(Community College, Undergraduate, Graduate, Vocational/Occupational/Scholarship)* [3294]

Commander Daniel J. Christovich Scholarship *(Undergraduate/Scholarship)* [3455]

Clay Maitland CGF Scholarship *(Undergraduate/Scholarship)* [3456]

Coast Guard Foundation Enlisted Education Scholarship *(Advanced Professional/Scholarship)* [3457]

Corporal Joseph Martinez U.S. Army/Durango High School AFJROTC Scholarship *(Undergraduate/Scholarship)* [9396]

Drummond Law Firm Scholarship *(Graduate, College/Scholarship)* [4189]

Ethyl and Armin Wiebke Memorial Scholarship *(Undergraduate/Scholarship)* [12147]

The Fallen Heroes Scholarship *(Undergraduate/Scholarship)* [3458]

FEEA-NTEU Scholarships *(Graduate, Postgraduate, Undergraduate/Scholarship)* [4515]

Freedom Alliance Scholarship Fund *(Undergraduate/Scholarship)* [4821]

General John Paul Ratay Educational Fund Grants *(Undergraduate/Grant)* [7389]

Hardy, Wolf & Downing Scholarships *(Undergraduate, Graduate/Scholarship)* [5296]

ICI Military Scholarship *(Undergraduate, Vocational/Occupational/Scholarship)* [5960]

Imagine America Military Awards Program *(Undergraduate/Scholarship)* [5718]

Laine - Casey Laine Armed Services Scholarship *(Undergraduate/Scholarship)* [3479]

LaRue A. Ditmore Music Scholarship *(Undergraduate/Scholarship)* [12148]

Lily H. Gridley Memorial Scholarship *(Undergraduate/Scholarship)* [12149]

Lt Col Romeo - Josephine Bass Ferretti Scholarship *(Undergraduate/Scholarship)* [148]

Maine Vietnam Veterans Scholarship *(Advanced Professional/Scholarship)* [6993]

Marine Corps League National Scholarship *(Undergraduate/Scholarship)* [7064]

The First Lieutenant Scott McClean Love Memorial Scholarship - Children of Soldiers *(Undergraduate, Vocational/Occupational/Scholarship)* [1917]

The First Lieutenant Scott McClean Love Memorial Scholarship - Spouses of Soldiers *(Undergraduate, Vocational/Occupational/Scholarship)* [1918]

MCEA Financial Assistance Award *(Undergraduate/Scholarship)* [7062]

Naval Helicopter Association Scholarship *(Graduate, Undergraduate/Scholarship)* [8170]

North American Van Lines Military Scholarship Competition *(Undergraduate/Scholarship)* [8424]

North Carolina Heroes Financial Hardship Grant *(Other/Grant)* [8439]

The Captain Jennifer Shafer Odom Memorial Scholarship - Children of Soldiers *(Undergraduate, Vocational/Occupational/Scholarship)* [1919]

The Captain Jennifer Shafer Odom Memorial Scholarship - Spouses of Soldiers *(Undergraduate, Vocational/Occupational/Scholarship)* [1920]

Pacific Beacon Scholarship *(Community College, University, Undergraduate, Vocational/Occupational/Scholarship)* [9838]

Joanne Holbrook Patton Military Spouse Scholarships *(Graduate, Undergraduate/Scholarship)* [8009]

Pitsenbarger Award *(Undergraduate, Graduate/Grant, Award)* [150]

Restoring Self Scholarship *(Undergraduate/Scholarship)* [5559]

Robert Wood Johnson Health Policy Fellowships *(Advanced Professional, Professional development/Fellowship)* [6327]

Colonel Jerry W. Ross Scholarship *(Undergraduate/Scholarship)* [1753]

Seabee Memorial Scholarship Association Scholarships *(Undergraduate/Scholarship)* [10231]

Sentinels of Freedom Scholarship *(Advanced Professional/Scholarship)* [10011]

Colonel Nate Smith Scholarship *(Graduate, Undergraduate/Scholarship)* [7201]

Smyth Family Scholarship *(Undergraduate, University, College, Vocational/Occupational/Scholarship)* [12372]

Substance Abuse and Mental Health Awareness in Veterans Scholarship *(Undergraduate, Graduate/Scholarship)* [4187]

ThanksUSA Scholarship *(Undergraduate, Vocational/Occupational/Scholarship)* [11006]

Tillman Scholars Program *(Undergraduate, Graduate/Scholarship)* [11036]

USS Coral Sea - Scholarship Program *(Undergraduate/Scholarship)* [11785]

Roy Vander Putten *(Advanced Professional/Scholarship)* [3460]

VFW Post 5140/Paul W. Shockley Sr. Memorial Scholarship *(Undergraduate/Scholarship)* [8541]

Michael Wilson Scholarships *(Undergraduate/Scholarship)* [151]

Women's Overseas and Service League Scholarships for Women *(Undergraduate/Scholarship)* [12168]

Xavier University ROTC Scholarships - Air Force ROTC *(Undergraduate/Scholarship)* [12229]

Xavier University ROTC Scholarships - Army ROTC *(Undergraduate/Scholarship)* [12230]

Minority

1L and 2L Diversity Fellowship Programs *(Undergraduate/Fellowship)* [5042]

AACR Minority and Minority-Serving Institution Faculty Scholar Awards *(Doctorate, Postdoctorate/Award)* [530]

AALL Minority Leadership Development Award *(Graduate/Award)* [586]

ACNM Foundation Midwives of Color-Watson Midwifery Student Scholarship *(Undergraduate/Scholarship)* [769]

Actuarial Diversity Scholarship *(Undergraduate/Scholarship)* [69]

EFWA Moss Adams Foundation Scholarships *(Undergraduate/Scholarship)* [4303]

Adler Pollock & Sheehan Diversity Scholarships *(Undergraduate/Fellowship)* [77]

AERA Minority Dissertation Fellowship in Education Research *(Doctorate/Fellowship)* [870]

AFPE Pre-Doctoral Fellowships in Pharmaceutical Sciences for Underrepresented Minorities *(Doctorate, Graduate/Fellowship)* [924]

AfterCollege STEM Inclusion Scholarship *(Undergraduate, Graduate/Scholarship)* [122]

AICPA Minority Scholarship *(Undergraduate, Graduate/Scholarship)* [1017]

Albert W. Dent Graduate Student Scholarship *(Undergraduate/Scholarship)* [763]

Hon. Lincoln Alexander Scholarship *(Undergraduate, Graduate/Scholarship)* [2586]

American Association of Blacks in Energy Scholarships *(Undergraduate/Scholarship)* [517]

American Association for Cancer Research Minority Scholar in Cancer Research Awards *(Graduate/Award)* [533]

American Dental Association Minority Dental Student Scholarships *(Undergraduate/Scholarship)* [857]

American Speech Language Hearing Foundation Endowed Scholarships *(Graduate, Master's, Doctorate/Scholarship)* [1596]

American Speech Language Hearing Foundation Minority Student Scholarship *(Graduate, Master's, Doctorate/Scholarship)* [1599]

AMS Freshman Undergraduate Scholarship *(Undergraduate/Scholarship)* [1119]

AMS Graduate Fellowships *(Graduate/Fellowship)* [1121]

William G. Anderson, DO, Minority Scholarships *(Undergraduate/Scholarship)* [1198]

APSA Minority Fellowship Program *(Doctorate/Fellowship)* [1251]

APTA Minority Scholarships - Faculty Development Scholarships *(Postdoctorate/Scholarship, Award, Recognition)* [1232]

APTA Minority Scholarships - Physical Therapist Assistant Students *(Undergraduate/Scholarship, Award, Recognition)* [1233]

APTA Minority Scholarships - Physical Therapist Students *(Undergraduate/Scholarship, Award, Recognition)* [1234]

Arts Council of Greater Grand Rapids Minority Scholarship *(Undergraduate/Scholarship)* [5134]

ASA Minority Fellowship Program (ASA MFP) *(Doctorate/Fellowship)* [1590]

ASEH Minority Travel Grants *(Graduate, Other/Grant)* [1449]

ASGP Graduate Research Fellowships *(Graduate/Fellowship)* [244]

ASTRO Minority Summer Fellowship Award *(Postgraduate, Professional development/Fellowship, Award)* [1546]

Baker McKenzie Diversity Fellowship *(Postgraduate, Professional development/Fellowship)* [2411]

Bay Area Minority Law Student Scholarship *(Graduate, Undergraduate/Scholarship)* [2433]

BBPA First Generation Scholarships *(College, University, Undergraduate/Scholarship)* [2587]

BCSF Scholarships *(Undergraduate/Scholarship)* [2604]

Dennis J. Beck Memorial Scholarship *(Undergraduate/Scholarship)* [6193]

Beverley Mascoll Scholarship *(Undergraduate/Scholarship)* [2588]

Ellen Blodgett Memorial Scholarship *(Master's/Scholarship)* [8333]

Leon Bradley Scholarship Program *(Undergraduate/Scholarship)* [638]

Mary Ann Brichta Scholarships *(Undergraduate/Scholarship)* [11735]

Cathy L. Brock Memorial Scholarships *(Graduate/Scholarship)* [5814]

George M. Brooker, CPM Diversity Collegiate Scholarship *(Graduate, Undergraduate/Scholarship)* [5861]

The Phyllis Lister-Brown Memorial Scholarship *(Undergraduate/Scholarship)* [11146]

Robert K. Brown Scholarships *(Undergraduate, Master's/Scholarship)* [2589]

Buckfire & Buckfire, P.C. Law School Diversity Scholarships *(Graduate/Scholarship)* [2736]

Buckfire & Buckfire, P.C. Medical Diversity Scholarships *(Advanced Professional/Scholarship)* [2737]

Buick Achievers Scholarship Program *(Undergraduate/Scholarship)* [4905]

Burroughs Wellcome Travel Fellowships *(Undergraduate, Graduate/Fellowship)* [10531]

California Bar Foundation 3L Diversity Scholarship *(Undergraduate/Scholarship)* [2789, 3812, 10602]

Herb Carnegie Scholarship *(Undergraduate/Scholarship)* [2590]

C.I.B.C Scholarship *(Undergraduate, Graduate/Scholarship)* [2591, 3014]

Council on Social Work Education Minority Fellowship Program for Doctoral Students *(Postdoctorate/Fellowship)* [3874]

CPA-F Scholarship *(Graduate/Scholarship)* [2824]

CUPRAP Communications Internship Award for Students of Color *(Undergraduate/Award)* [3518]

Dave Caldwell Scholarship *(Graduate/Scholarship, Monetary)* [1640]

Deloris Carter Hampton Scholarship *(Undergraduate/Scholarship)* [9296]

Diversity Executive Leadership Program Scholarship (DELP) *(Other/Scholarship)* [1977]

Diversity in Psychology and Law Research Award *(Undergraduate, Graduate/Grant, Award)* [1293]

Diversity Scholarship *(Graduate/Scholarship, Award)* [1796]

Dr. James A. Ferguson Emerging Infectious Diseases Research Initiatives for Student Enhancement Fellowship (RISE) *(Graduate/Fellowship)* [6526]

Donald W. Banner Diversity Fellowship for Law Students *(Graduate/Fellowship)* [2428]

Dow Chemical Company Fellowships *(Graduate/Fellowship)* [8027]

DREAM - Diversity Recruitment Recruitment through Education and Mentoring Program *(Undergraduate/Fellowship)* [621]

James Echols Scholarship Award *(Undergraduate/Recognition, Award, Scholarship)* [2781]

E.I. DuPont Graduate Fellowship *(Graduate/Fellowship)* [8028]

Eli Lilly And Company/BDPA Scholarship *(Undergraduate, Graduate, Master's/Scholarship)* [2456]

ESA Foundation Scholarship *(Undergraduate/Scholarship)* [4394]

Ethnic Minority and Women's Enhancement Postgraduate Scholarships *(Graduate, Postgraduate/Scholarship)* [7770]

Farella Braun + Martel LLP 1L Diversity Scholarship Program *(Undergraduate/Scholarship)* [4495]

FASEB MARC Travel Awards *(Undergraduate, Graduate, Postdoctorate/Award)* [10532]

Fermilab Summer Internships in Science & Technology (SIST) *(Undergraduate/Internship)* [11317]

The Fred Finch Scholarship *(Undergraduate/Scholarship)* [11147]

Fine Arts Association Minority Scholarship *(Undergraduate/Scholarship)* [4564]

Finnegan Diversity Scholarship *(Juris Doctorate/Scholarship)* [4568]

Clay Ford Florida Board of Accountancy Minority Scholarships *(Undergraduate/Scholarship)* [4627]

Dr. Nancy Foster Scholarship Program *(Doctorate/Scholarship)* [8017]

Franchise Law Diversity Scholarship Awards *(Undergraduate/Scholarship)* [6012]

Kevin Freeman Travel Grant *(Graduate, Other/Grant)* [7514]

Harry Gairey Scholarship *(Undergraduate/Scholarship)* [2592]

J. Robert Gladden Orthopaedic Society PGY5 ABOS Board Preparation Scholarship *(Professional development/Scholarship)* [4992]

The Marie Trahan/Susman Godfrey Scholarship *(Undergraduate/Scholarship)* [11148]

Golden Door Scholarship *(Graduate/Scholarship)* [5018]

Arthur H. Goodman Memorial Scholarship *(Undergraduate, University/Scholarship)* [9815]

Lucille May Gopie Scholarships *(Undergraduate, Graduate/Scholarship)* [2593]

GradSchools.com Minority Graduate Nursing Scholarship *(Graduate/Scholarship)* [4316]

Priscilla Green Scholarships *(Undergraduate/Scholarship)* [3894]

Guntley-Lorimer Science and Arts Scholarships *(Undergraduate/Scholarship)* [2594]

Al Hamilton Scholarship *(Undergraduate/Scholarship)* [2595]

HFMH Bilingual Scholarships for Mental Health Workforce Diversity *(Graduate/Scholarship)* [5539]

Holly A. Cornell Scholarship *(Master's/Scholarship, Monetary)* [1642, 3272]

HRSA Scholarships for Disadvantaged Students *(Undergraduate/Scholarship)* [11334]

David Hudak Memorial Essay Contest for Freethinking Students of Color *(Undergraduate/Scholarship)* [4825]

Indigenous Arts Individual Project Funding *(Professional development/Grant)* [263]

Innovative Grants-Pilot and Research Tool Grants *(Postdoctorate/Grant)* [6348]

IOBSE Scholarships *(Undergraduate/Scholarship)* [6057]

Ira G. Turpin Scholar Program Fund *(Undergraduate/Scholarship)* [10767]

Jackie Robinson Scholarship Award *(Undergraduate/Scholarship)* [9723]

James E. West Fellowship *(Graduate/Fellowship)* [62]

JDRF Postdoctoral Fellowships *(Postdoctorate/Fellowship)* [6351]

Hon. Michaelle Jean Scholarship *(Undergraduate/Scholarship)* [2596]

Harry Jerome Legacy Scholarship *(Undergraduate, Graduate/Scholarship)* [2597]

Financial Need Minority Scholarships *(Undergraduate/Scholarship)* [11149]

John McLendon Minority Postgraduate Scholarship *(Postdoctorate/Scholarship)* [7639]

John P. and Tashia F. Morgridge Scholarship *(Undergraduate, Graduate/Scholarship)* [11736]

Johnson and Johnson/AACN Minority Nurse Faculty Scholars *(Graduate/Scholarship)* [543]

MCCA Lloyd M. Johnson, Jr. Scholarships *(Graduate/Scholarship)* [7412]

The Dr. Richard Allen Williams and Genita Evangelista Johnson Scholarship,AMA Foundation Scholarship *(Undergraduate/Scholarship)* [2066]

The Barbara Jordan Scholarship *(Undergraduate/Scholarship)* [11150]

Judge Isaac Anderson, Jr. Scholarship Fund *(Undergraduate/Scholarship)* [10693]

Judge Sidney M. Aronovitz Memorial Scholarship Fund *(Undergraduate/Scholarship)* [7298]

Native American

The Hyatt Hotels Fund For Minority Lodging Management Students (Undergraduate/Scholarship) [972]

Indian Health Service Professionals Program (Undergraduate/Scholarship) [988]

Indspire Health Careers Bursary and Scholarships (Graduate, Undergraduate/Scholarship) [5774]

International Order of the King's Daughters and Sons North American Indian Scholarship Program (Undergraduate/Scholarship) [989]

IOKDS Native American Scholarships (Undergraduate, University, College, Vocational/Occupational/Scholarship) [6051]

James E. West Fellowship (Graduate/Fellowship) [62]

Kilbuck Family Native American Scholarship (Undergraduate/Scholarship) [2484]

The Lagrant Foundation - Graduate Scholarships (Graduate/Scholarship) [6632]

The Lagrant Foundation - Undergraduate Scholarships (Undergraduate/Scholarship) [6633]

Loan for Service for Graduates (Graduate/Loan) [995]

Howard Mayer Brown Fellowship (Graduate/Fellowship) [1146]

Minorities in Government Finance Scholarship (Graduate, Undergraduate/Scholarship) [5054]

MLA/NLM Spectrum Scholarship (Undergraduate/Scholarship) [7220]

MLA Scholarship for Minority Students (Graduate/Scholarship) [7223]

James B. Morris Scholarship (Undergraduate/Scholarship) [7474]

Archie Motley Memorial Scholarships for Minority Students (Graduate/Scholarship) [7367]

NACA Multicultural Professional Development Grant (Undergraduate, Graduate, Professional development/Grant) [7627]

National Medical Fellowships Need-Based Scholarships (Undergraduate/Scholarship) [8001]

Native American Education Grants (Graduate, Undergraduate/Grant) [990]

NCAIED American Indian Business Scholarship Program (Graduate, Master's, Undergraduate/Scholarship) [7747]

NDSGC American Indian Scholarships (Undergraduate/Scholarship) [8467]

NMNH American Indian Program Fellowships (Graduate/Fellowship) [10203]

Oil & Gas, Trades & Technology (OGTT) Bursary and Scholarship Awards (OGTT) (Undergraduate/Scholarship) [5776]

PlasticPlace Young Entrepreneurs Scholarship Award (Undergraduate/Scholarship) [9192]

Judith McManus Price Scholarship (Undergraduate, Graduate/Scholarship) [1245]

PRSA Diversity Multicultural Scholarships (Undergraduate/Scholarship) [9438]

Robert Toigo Foundation Fellowship (Master's/Fellowship) [11048]

Arthur C. Parker Scholarship (Undergraduate, Graduate/Scholarship) [10270]

Seldovia Native Association Achievement Scholarships (Undergraduate, Graduate/Scholarship) [9996]

Seldovia Native Association General Scholarships (Undergraduate, Graduate/Scholarship) [9997]

Sidley Prelaw Scholars Program (Undergraduate/Scholarship) [10077]

Alfred P. Sloan Foundation Graduate Scholarships - Sloan Indigenous Graduate Partnership (SIGP) (Master's, Doctorate/Scholarship) [7581]

Alfred P. Sloan Foundation Graduate Scholarships - Sloan Minority Ph.D. Program (MPHD) (Doctorate/Scholarship) [7582]

Smithsonian Native American Awards Program - Community Scholars (Graduate, Doctorate, Postdoctorate, Professional development/Fellowship) [10210]

Smithsonian Native American Awards Program - Visiting Student (Graduate/Fellowship) [10211]

Southwest Native-American Foundation Scholarships (Undergraduate, University, Four Year College/Scholarship) [10709]

Udall Scholarship (Undergraduate/Scholarship) [11533]

Udall Undergraduate Scholarship (Undergraduate/Scholarship) [11165]

Underrepresented in Medicine award (Graduate/Scholarship) [1112]

U.S. BIA Indian Higher Education Grants (Undergraduate/Grant) [991]

USET Scholarship Fund (Undergraduate/Scholarship) [11278]

Valuing Diversity PhD Scholarship (Doctorate/Scholarship) [1105]

John D. Voelker Foundation Native American Scholarships (Undergraduate/Scholarship) [11858]

Wells Fargo American Indian Scholarship Program (Undergraduate/Scholarship) [996]

WIEA Scholarships (Doctorate, Graduate, Undergraduate, Vocational/Occupational, Master's, Doctorate/Scholarship) [12121]

WIGA College Scholarships (Postgraduate, Graduate, Undergraduate/Scholarship) [11894]

WMSHP Scholarship (Graduate/Scholarship) [11985]

Woodrow Wilson-Rockefeller Brothers Fund Fellowships for Aspiring Teachers of Color (Undergraduate/Fellowship) [12052]

Other

AfterCollege Succurro Scholarship (Undergraduate, Graduate, Doctorate/Scholarship) [123]

American Association of State Troopers Scholarship Foundation First Scholarships (Undergraduate/Scholarship) [640]

American Association of State Troopers Scholarship Foundation Second Scholarships (Undergraduate/Scholarship) [641]

American Federation of Police and Concerned Citizen Educational Scholarship (Undergraduate/Scholarship) [879]

Annual Bloom Legal Scholarship for Students Affected by Cerebral Palsy (Community College, Undergraduate/Scholarship) [2628]

APS Scholarships for Minority Undergraduate Physics Majors (Undergraduate/Scholarship) [1221]

Army Health Professions Scholarship Program (HPSP) (Professional development/Scholarship) [11288]

BakerHostetler Diversity Fellowship Program (Undergraduate/Fellowship) [2408]

George Benes, MD & Michael Mallee, EdD Point Scholarships (Undergraduate, Graduate, Doctorate/Scholarship) [9218]

Birmingham-Southern College Eagle Scout Scholarships (Undergraduate/Scholarship) [7845]

Bristol-Myers Squibb Scholarship for Cancer Survivors (Community College, Four Year College, Vocational/Occupational, Undergraduate/Scholarship) [9940]

Calamus Foundation Point Scholarship (Undergraduate, Graduate, Doctorate/Scholarship) [9219]

Camp Network Counselor Appreciation Scholarships (Undergraduate/Scholarship) [2866]

CBCF - BC/Yukon Region Breast Cancer Survivor Dragon Boat Grants (Professional development/Grant) [2925]

C.D. Howard Scholarship (Undergraduate/Scholarship, Monetary, Award) [5970]

Chartway Federal Credit Union Director's Memorial Scholarship (Undergraduate, Graduate/Scholarship) [3281]

City Of Sanibel Employee Dependent Scholarship Fund (Undergraduate/Scholarship) [10676]

Convectair Sustainable Development Scholarship Awards (Undergraduate/Scholarship) [4339]

George Dale Scholarship Fund (Undergraduate/Scholarship) [1973]

The Davis-Putter Scholarship Fund (Undergraduate, Graduate/Scholarship) [9770]

Walter M. Decker Point Scholarship (Graduate, Undergraduate/Scholarship) [9220]

The Lilly Diabetes Tomorrow's Leaders Scholarship (Undergraduate/Scholarship) [4074]

Edward Leon Duhamel Freemasons Scholarship (Undergraduate/Scholarship) [9692]

Steven Esposito Memorial Scholarship (Undergraduate, Graduate, Doctorate/Scholarship) [9221]

Federal Court Bench and Bar Scholarships (Graduate/Scholarship) [11599]

Foundation Public Service Scholarship Award (Undergraduate/Scholarship) [4786]

Grand Rapids Trans Foundation Academic Scholarship (Undergraduate, Two Year College, Vocational/Occupational/Scholarship) [5197]

Greater Seattle Business Association Scholarships (GSBA Scholarships) (Undergraduate, Graduate/Scholarship) [5223]

HBO Point Scholarship (Graduate, Undergraduate, Doctorate/Scholarship) [9222]

Hellenic Times Scholarships (Undergraduate, Graduate/Scholarship) [5461]

Kevin Hummer Point Scholarship (Graduate, Undergraduate, Doctorate/Scholarship) [9223]

ICC General Scholarship Fund (Undergraduate/Scholarship, Monetary, Award) [5971]

ICMA Local Government Management Fellowship (Master's/Fellowship) [5968]

ISTTE Scholarship (Graduate, Undergraduate/Scholarship) [6122]

Janssen Infectious Disease Point Scholarships (Undergraduate, Graduate, Doctorate/Scholarship) [9224]

V.J. Johnson Memorial Scholarships (Undergraduate/Scholarship) [642]

Joint Japan/World Bank Graduate Scholarship Program for Developing Country National (JJ/WBGSP) (Graduate/Scholarship) [12192]

KASF General Scholarships (Undergraduate, Graduate, Professional development/Scholarship) [6599]

Larry King/Jeffrey Fashion Cares Point Scholarship (Undergraduate, Graduate, Doctorate/Scholarship) [9225]

Lanford Family Highway Worker Memorial Scholarship Program (High School/Scholarship) [1362]

William J. Levy Point Scholarship (Undergraduate, Graduate, Doctorate/Scholarship) [9226]

Local 827 Peter J. Casey Scholarship (Undergraduate/Scholarship) [5957]

Carl J. Megel Scholarship (Undergraduate/Scholarship) [884]

Fred & Lena Meijer Scholarships (Undergraduate/Scholarship) [5166]

Minton-Spidell-Jackowski Point Scholarship (Undergraduate, Graduate, Doctorate/Scholarship) [9227]

NBCUniversal Point Scholarship (Undergraduate, Graduate, Doctorate/Scholarship) [9228]

J.W. "Bill" Neese Scholarship (Undergraduate/Scholarship, Monetary, Award) [5972]

Charlie O'Meilia Scholarship (Undergraduate/Scholarship, Monetary, Award) [5973]

Ozarks Division of Midwest Dairy Educational Award (Undergraduate/Scholarship) [7374]

Point Community College Scholarship Program (Undergraduate, Community College/Scholarship) [9229]

Psychology Association of Saskatchewan Student Scholarships - Academic Achievement (Master's, Doctorate/Scholarship) [9378]

Psychology Association of Saskatchewan Student Scholarships - Research Based (Master's, Doctorate/Scholarship) [9379]

The Michael J. Quill Scholarship (Undergraduate/Scholarship) [11075]

RBPA Scholarship (Undergraduate, Graduate, Doctorate/Scholarship) [9493]

Redlands High School Boy's Varsity Volleyball Scholarships (Undergraduate/Scholarship) [9584]

Redlands High School Mock Trial Scholarship (Undergraduate/Scholarship) [9586]

Rim-Freeman Point Scholarship (Undergraduate/Scholarship) [9230]

John T. Riordan Professional Education Scholarships (Professional development/Fellowship) [5981]

Robert B. And Dorothy Pence Scholarship Fund (Undergraduate/Scholarship) [10700]

Robert S. McNamara Fellowships Program (RSMFP) *(Doctorate/Fellowship, Monetary)* [12194]

Robert Wood Johnson Health Policy Fellowships *(Advanced Professional, Professional development/Fellowship)* [6327]

Ronald T. Smith Family Scholarship *(Undergraduate, Graduate/Scholarship)* [5178]

Harold W. Rosenthal Fellowship in International Relations *(Professional development/Fellowship)* [2264]

Royal Canadian Regiment Association Bursaries *(Undergraduate/Scholarship)* [9751]

RRANN Program Scholarship *(Undergraduate/Scholarship)* [11491]

Saskatchewan Government Insurance Anniversary Scholarships *(Undergraduate/Scholarship)* [9888]

Albert F. Shanker Scholarship *(Undergraduate/Scholarship)* [885]

Simonton Windows Scholarship *(Undergraduate/Scholarship)* [8880]

Rand Skolnick Point Scholarship *(Undergraduate, Graduate, Doctorate/Scholarship)* [9231]

SMA Alumni Foundation Legacy Scholarship Program *(Other/Scholarship)* [10816]

Southwest Florida Deputy Sheriffs Association Fund *(Undergraduate/Scholarship)* [10704]

SPE Vinyl Plastics Division Educational Grants *(Undergraduate/Grant)* [10496]

Thomas P. Thornton Scholarship *(Undergraduate, Graduate/Scholarship)* [5731]

Took Trust Point Scholarship *(Undergraduate, Graduate/Scholarship)* [9232]

Toyota Point Scholarship *(Undergraduate, Graduate, Doctorate/Scholarship)* [9233]

UW-Madison GLBT Alumni Council Scholarships *(Undergraduate, Graduate/Scholarship)* [11749]

WAEPA Scholarship Program *(Undergraduate, Vocational/Occupational/Scholarship)* [12207]

Wells Fargo Point Scholarship *(Undergraduate, Graduate/Scholarship)* [9234]

Whitehorse Glacier Bears Swim Club Scholarship *(Undergraduate, University, College, Vocational/Occupational/Scholarship)* [12389]

William J. Tangye Scholarship *(Undergraduate/Scholarship, Monetary, Award)* [5974]

The Ronald P. Wilmot Scholarship *(Undergraduate, Graduate/Scholarship)* [6280]

Zelle Diversity in Law Scholarship *(Undergraduate/Scholarship)* [12405]

Religious affiliation

Stephanie Ali Memorial Scholarships *(Undergraduate/Scholarship)* [11682]

American Legion Eagle Scout of the Year *(Undergraduate/Scholarship)* [7843]

Marvin Anmuth Scholarship *(Undergraduate, Graduate/Scholarship)* [6269]

Anne Sturrock Nursing Scholarship Fund *(Undergraduate, Graduate/Scholarship)* [10672]

A.R.F.O.R.A. Undergraduate Scholarships for Women *(Undergraduate/Scholarship)* [1366]

Martha and Robert Atherton Ministerial Scholarship *(Master's/Scholarship)* [11245]

Baker Scholarship *(Doctorate, Professional development/Scholarship)* [4888]

Bernard B. and Mary L. Brusin Scholarship Fund *(Undergraduate/Scholarship)* [4201]

James R. and Geraldine F. Bertelsen Scholarship *(Undergraduate/Scholarship)* [9802]

The Brandenburg Education Scholarship *(College, University, Undergraduate/Scholarship)* [6270]

Pamfil and Maria Bujea Family Orthodox Christian Seminarian Scholarships *(Undergraduate/Scholarship)* [1367]

Children of Unitarian Universalist Religious Professionals Grant *(Undergraduate/Grant)* [11246]

CMSF Scholarship *(Graduate/Scholarship)* [3319]

CSF Graduate Fellowship *(Graduate/Fellowship)* [3325]

David Pohl Scholarship *(Master's/Scholarship)* [11247]

Christopher Demetris Memorial Scholarships *(Undergraduate/Scholarship)* [5463]

Dr. Mubin Syed And Mrs. Afshan Syed Scholarship Program *(Undergraduate/Scholarship)* [6176]

Emmett J. Doerr Memorial Distinguished Scout Scholarship *(High School/Scholarship)* [7846]

Dollar-A-Day Academic Scholarships *(Graduate, Undergraduate/Scholarship)* [4126]

Doris W. Frey Memorial Scholarship Fund *(Graduate/Scholarship)* [10681]

Pauly D'Orlando Memorial Art Scholarship *(Graduate, Undergraduate/Scholarship)* [11248]

Eastern Orthodox Scouting Scholarships *(Undergraduate/Scholarship)* [7848]

David Eaton Scholarship *(Master's/Scholarship)* [11249]

FEF Scholarship *(Undergraduate/Scholarship)* [4478]

Frank L. Weil Memorial Eagle Scout Scholarship *(Undergraduate/Scholarship)* [7850]

The Nathan J. and Virginia H. Friedman College Scholarship *(Undergraduate, Four Year College, University/Scholarship)* [6271]

A.R.F.O.R.A. Martha Gavrila Scholarships for Women *(Postgraduate/Scholarship)* [1368]

The Elaine and Barry Gilbert College Scholarship *(Undergraduate/Scholarship)* [6272]

Helen B. and Lewis E. Goldstein Scholarship *(Undergraduate, Graduate/Scholarship)* [6273]

Greek Orthodox Archdiocese of America Paleologos Graduate Scholarships *(Graduate/Scholarship)* [5231]

Harvey Fellows Program *(Graduate/Fellowship)* [7519]

Helena B. Cobb Higher Education (four Year) Scholarship *(Undergraduate, Vocational/Occupational/Scholarship)* [12165]

The Helena B. Cobb Scholarships *(Undergraduate, Vocational/Occupational/Scholarship)* [12166]

The Stephanie G. Hoffman Scholarship *(Graduate, Undergraduate/Scholarship)* [6274]

HRH Prince Alwaleed Bin Talal ISNA Fellowships *(Graduate/Fellowship)* [6180]

Islamic Scholarship Fund Scholarship (ISF) *(Graduate, Undergraduate/Scholarship)* [6178]

Iwalani Carpenter Sowa Scholarship *(Graduate/Scholarship)* [8928]

Jewish Federation Academic Scholarship *(Graduate, Undergraduate/Scholarship)* [6310]

Joseph Sumner Smith Scholarship *(Undergraduate/Scholarship)* [11250]

The Olympia Brown and Max Kapp Award *(Master's/Scholarship)* [11251]

Lewis B. Barber Memorial Scholarship Fund *(Undergraduate/Scholarship)* [10695]

Lila Fahlman Scholarship *(Undergraduate, Graduate/Scholarship)* [2960]

Linsley Scholarship Fund *(Undergraduate, Vocational/Occupational/Scholarship)* [3301]

Lutheran Student Scholastic and Service Scholarships - College and University Students *(Undergraduate/Scholarship)* [2562]

MACC Scholarships *(Other/Scholarship)* [7288]

Alexander M. and June L. Maisin Foundation Scholarship *(Undergraduate/Scholarship)* [6275]

Margaret E. Phillips Scholarship *(Undergraduate/Scholarship)* [11716]

Marion Barr Stanfield Art Scholarship *(Graduate, Undergraduate/Scholarship)* [11252]

The Mary E. Bivins Ministry Scholarship Program *(Graduate, Undergraduate/Scholarship)* [2584]

NPM Academic Scholarship *(Graduate, Undergraduate/Scholarship)* [7674]

The Gail Karp Orgell Scholarship *(Four Year College, University, Undergraduate/Scholarship)* [6276]

Otto M. Stanfield Law Scholarship *(Graduate/Scholarship)* [11253]

PLP Scholarships *(Undergraduate/Scholarship, Award, Monetary)* [8985]

The Shirley and Robert Raymer College Scholarship *(Four Year College, University, Undergraduate/Scholarship)* [6277]

Rick Arkans Eagle Scout Scholarship *(Undergraduate/Scholarship)* [7856]

R.O.E.A. Dumitru Golea Goldy-Gemu Scholarships *(Undergraduate, High School/Scholarship)* [1369]

Roland E. Murphy, O.Carm., Scholarship *(Undergraduate/Scholarship)* [3186]

Roy H. Pollack Scholarship *(Graduate, Master's/Scholarship)* [11254]

David W. Self Scholarship *(Undergraduate/Scholarship)* [11263]

The S.F. Humanities, Inc: Leo Hills Scholarship *(Undergraduate, Graduate/Scholarship)* [6278]

Richard S. Smith Scholarships *(Undergraduate/Scholarship)* [11264]

The Rev. Chuck and Nancy Thomas Scholarship *(Professional development/Scholarship)* [11256]

Chester M. Vernon Memorial Eagle Scout Scholarships *(Undergraduate/Scholarship)* [7859]

Von Ogden Vogt Scholarship *(Master's/Scholarship)* [11257]

Wexner Graduate Fellowship / Davidson Scholars Program *(Graduate/Fellowship)* [12003]

The Brian J. White Endowed Law Scholarship *(Undergraduate/Scholarship)* [9031]

Young Christian Leaders Scholarships *(Undergraduate/Scholarship)* [12266]

Union affiliation

Duluth Building and Construction Trades Council Scholarship Fund *(Graduate/Scholarship)* [4204]

North Dakota Farmers Union Co-op House Scholarship *(Undergraduate/Scholarship)* [8463]

Raymond A. Kent-Navy V-12/ROTC *(Undergraduate/Scholarship)* [11579]

David C. Sommerville Memorial Scholarship *(Undergraduate, Graduate/Scholarship)* [9852]

Utility Workers Union of America Scholarship Program *(Undergraduate/Scholarship)* [11789]

Veteran

$1,000 Scholarship for Veterans *(Undergraduate/Scholarship)* [9042]

AFCEA War Veterans Scholarships *(Undergraduate/Scholarship)* [105]

The American Legion Legacy Scholarship *(Undergraduate/Scholarship)* [1070]

AMVETS National Scholarships - Entering College Freshmen *(Undergraduate/Scholarship)* [1696]

AMVETS National Scholarships - For Veterans *(Undergraduate/Scholarship)* [1697]

Buick Achievers Scholarship Program *(Undergraduate/Scholarship)* [4905]

Disabled Veteran Scholarship *(College, Vocational/Occupational/Scholarship)* [9713]

Disabled Veteran Student Scholarship *(Two Year College, Four Year College/Scholarship)* [12018]

Disabled Veterans Scholarship *(Community College, College, Vocational/Occupational/Scholarship)* [4538]

Disabled Veterans Scholarship *(Vocational/Occupational, Community College, Four Year College, Graduate, Professional development/Scholarship)* [6519]

Drummond Law Firm Scholarship *(Graduate, College/Scholarship)* [4189]

The eLearners Scholarship for Military Personnel, Veterans, and Spouses *(College, Vocational/Occupational/Scholarship)* [4333]

Forsyth County Nursing Scholarship *(Undergraduate/Scholarship)* [12077]

Kathern F. Gruber Scholarship Program *(Undergraduate, Graduate/Scholarship)* [2624]

Imagine America Military Awards Program *(Undergraduate/Scholarship)* [5718]

Leslie C. Green Veterans Scholarship *(Juris Doctorate, Advanced Professional/Scholarship)* [3878]

Maine Vietnam Veterans Scholarship *(Advanced Professional/Scholarship)* [6993]

H. H. McKnight Memorial Scholarship *(Graduate/Scholarship)* [11608]

Murrietta Circuits Scholarship Opportunity *(Undergraduate, College, University/Scholarship)* [7505]

North American Van Lines Military Scholarship Competition *(Undergraduate/Scholarship)* [8424]

North Carolina Heroes Financial Hardship Grant *(Other/Grant)* [8439]

Rees Scholarship Foundation - Veterans Program *(Vocational/Occupational, Undergraduate/Scholarship)* [9611]

Robert Wood Johnson Health Policy Fellowships *(Advanced Professional, Professional development/Fellowship)* [6327]

Samsung American Legion Scholarship *(Undergraduate/Scholarship)* [1073]

Scholarship for Disabled Veterans *(High School, Community College, Four Year College, Graduate,*

Professional development, Vocational/Occupational/Scholarship) [6702]

Substance Abuse and Mental Health Awareness in Veterans Scholarship *(Undergraduate, Graduate/Scholarship)* [4187]

TonaLaw Veteran's Scholarship *(Undergraduate, Graduate, Professional development, Vocational/Occupational/Scholarship)* [11050]

Wells Fargo Veterans Scholarship Program *(Undergraduate, Graduate, Two Year College, Four Year College/Scholarship)* [9945]

Women's Army Corps Veterans Association Scholarships *(Undergraduate/Scholarship)* [12153]

Sponsor and Scholarship Index

This index lists, in a single alphabetic sequence, all of the administering and sponsoring organizations and awards covered in the "Sponsors and Their Scholarships" section. Also included are co-sponsoring organizations and organization acronyms. The numbers that follow citations indicate the book entry numbers for particular organizations and awards, not page numbers. Book entry numbers for administering organizations appear in boldface type.

Alaska Native Medical Center Auxiliary Scholarships [11434]
Alaska Press Club Scholarships [11435]
Alaska Space Grant Program (ASGP) **[243]**
Albert and Alice Nacinovich Music Scholarship Fund [4582]
Albert C.W. Chan Foundation Award [12264]
Albert Einstein Distinguished Educator Fellowships (AEF) [11108]
Albert Flegenheimer Memorial Scholarship [7340]
Albert J. and Mae Lee Memorial Scholarship [8987]
Bette Lou Albert, New Mexico, Memorial Scholarship Fund [6399]
Albert R. and Alma Shadle Fellowship [1499]
Albert W. Dent Graduate Student Scholarship [763]
Alberta Association on Gerontology **[245]**
Alberta Award for the Study of Canadian Human Rights and Multiculturalism [280]
Alberta Barley **[248]**
Alberta Blue Cross **[250]**
Alberta Blue Cross Scholarships for Aboriginal Students [251]
Alberta Centennial Award [281]
Alberta Child Care Association (ACCA) **[252]**
Alberta Child Care Association Professional Development Grants [253]
Alberta Equestrian Federation (AEF) **[254]**
Alberta Foundation for the Arts (AFA) **[256]**
Alberta Holstein Association **[266]**
Alberta Holstein Association Scholarships [267]
Alberta Indian Investment Corp. (AIIC) **[268]**
Alberta Innovates Graduate Student Scholarships [275]
Alberta Innovates - Health Solutions **[271]**
Alberta Innovates Technology Futures (AITF) **[274]**
Alberta Innovates - Technology Futures Graduate Student Scholarships in ICT [276]
Alberta Innovates - Technology Futures Graduate Student Scholarships in Nanotechnology [277]
Alberta Innovates - Technology Futures Graduate Student Scholarships in Omics [278]
Alberta Learning Information Service - Alberta Scholarship Program **[279]**
Alberta Teachers' Association (ATA) **[311]**
Alberta Teachers Association Doctoral Fellowships in Education [312]
Alberta Teachers Association Educational Research Award [313]
Alberta Ukrainian Centennial Commemorative Scholarship [11887]
Albuquerque Community Foundation (ACF) **[316]**
Alcoa Scholarship [5207]
ALD Graduate Fellowships [392]
Alden Kindred of America (AKA) **[325]**
Owen F. Aldis Scholarship Fund [6109]
Aleut Foundation **[327]**
Alex Family Scholarship [7077]
Anthony Alexander, Andrew Delos Reyes & Jeremy Tolentino Memorial Fund [5380]
Alexander D. Pringle Memorial Scholarship [9328]
Alexander G. Gray, Jr., Scholarship Award [7156]
Alexander Graham Bell Association for the Deaf and Hard of Hearing (AG Bell) **[331]**
Alexander Graham Bell Canada Graduate Scholarships-Doctoral Program [3803]
Hon. Lincoln Alexander Scholarship [2586]
The William Tasse Alexander Scholarship [4716]
Neil Alexander Scholarships [7586]
Alex's Lemonade Stand Foundation (ALSF) **[335]**
Alex's Lemonade Stand Foundation Epidemiology Grants [336]
Alex's Lemonade Stand Foundation Innovation Grants [337]
Alex's Lemonade Stand Foundation Young Investigator Grants [338]
ALF Postdoctoral Research Fellowship Award [1090]
Floyd S. Alford Jr. Scholarships [11173]
AlgaeCal **[339]**
AlgaeCal Health Scholarship [340]
Horatio Alger Ak-Sar-Ben Scholarships [5561]
Horatio Alger Delaware Scholarships [5562]
Horatio Alger District of Columbia, Maryland and Virginia Scholarships [5563]
Horatio Alger Florida Scholarships [5564]
Horatio Alger Georgia Scholarships [5565]

Horatio Alger Idaho University Scholarships [5566]
Horatio Alger Illinois Scholarships [5567]
Horatio Alger Indiana Scholarships [5568]
Horatio Alger Kentucky Scholarships [5569]
Horatio Alger Lola and Duane Hagadone Idaho Scholarships [5570]
Horatio Alger Louisiana Scholarships [5571]
Horatio Alger Minnesota Scholarships [5572]
Horatio Alger Missouri Scholarships [5573]
Horatio Alger Montana Scholarships [5574]
Horatio Alger National Scholarships [5575]
Horatio Alger North Dakota Scholarships [5576]
Horatio Alger Pennsylvania Scholarships [5577]
Horatio Alger South Dakota Scholarships [5578]
Horatio Alger Texas Scholarships [5579]
Horatio Alger Utah Scholarships [5580]
Horatio Alger Washington Scholarships [5581]
Horatio Alger Wyoming Scholarships [5582]
Stephanie Ali Memorial Scholarships [11682]
Alice Conger Patterson Scholarship [12060]
Alice Hersey Wick Award [10090]
Alice J. Foit Scholarship Fund [10750]
Alice Newell Joslyn Medical Scholarship [2460]
ALIS Fellowships for Full-time Studies in French [282]
ALIS Graduate Student Scholarship [283]
ALIS International Education Awards - Ukraine [284]
All About Education Scholarship [11225]
All-American Vector Marketing Scholarship Program [11793]
ALL-SIS Conference of Newer Law Librarians Grants [595]
All Smiles Dental Group **[341]**
All Smiles Dental Group Scholarship [342]
All Star Association **[343]**
All Star Purchasing [344]
Allegheny County Bar Foundation (ACBF) **[345]**
Allegheny County Medical Society Medical Student Scholarship [4796]
Allen Allured Fellowship [9345]
The Frances C. Allen Fellowship [8368]
Allen, Flatt, Balladis & Leslie Inc. **[352]**
Allen Law Firm **[354]**
Allen Law Firm Personal Injury Scholarship [355]
William A. Allen Memorial Metal Shop/Auto Body Scholarships [9519]
J Frances Allen Scholarship Award [887]
Dorothea E. Allen Scholarship [4974]
Allen T. Lambert Scholarship [12247]
Alliance of the American Dental Association (AADA) **[356]**
Alliance of Black Culinarians Scholarships [9389]
Alliance-CES Pre-Dissertation Research Fellowship [3855]
Alliance Defending Freedom (ADF) **[358]**
Alliance Defending Freedom - Blackstone Legal Fellowships [359]
Alliance for Equality of Blind Canadians (AEBC) **[360]**
Alliance Francaise of Hartford Harpin/Rohinsky Scholarships [5313]
Alliance Medical Education Scholarship (AMES) [4797]
Alliance Pipeline Scholarships [2417]
Alliance of Resident Theatres, New York (ART-NY) **[365]**
Alliance of Technology and Women (ATW) **[367]**
Allied Dental Student Scholarship Program [853]
Allied Health Care Professional Scholarship [5711]
Allied Van Lines Inc. **[369]**
Allied Van Lines Military Scholarship [370]
Allison E. Fisher Scholarship [7615]
Lorraine Allison Scholarship [1789]
Dr. and Mrs. David B. Allman Medical Scholarship [7414]
Allmand Law **[371]**
Allmand Law Scholarship Contest [372]
Eleanor Allwork Scholarship [138]
Almeric L. Christian Memorial Scholarship [11829]
Marjorie Almstrom Scholarship [12281]
ALOA Scholarship Foundation [374]
ALOA Security Professionals Association, Inc. (ALOA) **[373]**
Aloha Prince Hall Hawaii Foundation Fund Scholarship [5381]
Alois and Marie Goldmann Scholarship [5675]

Tillie B. Alperin Scholarship [11595]
ALPFA Scholarship [2231]
Alpha Chi **[375]**
Alpha Chi Omega **[381]**
Alpha Chi Omega Love and Loyalty Grants [382]
Alpha Chi Sigma Fraternity Inc. **[383]**
Alpha Chi Sigma Scholarship Awards [384]
Alpha Delta Gamma Educational Foundation Scholarship [386]
Alpha Delta Gamma National Fraternity **[385]**
Alpha Kappa Alpha Educational Advancement Foundation (AKAEAF) **[387]**
Alpha Kappa Alpha - Educational Advancement Foundation Undergraduate Financial Need-Based Scholarships [388]
Alpha Kappa Alpha - Educational Advancement Foundation Undergraduate Merit Scholarships [389]
Alpha Kappa Gamma Trust Scholarship-Beta Omega [10091]
Alpha Lambda Delta **[391]**
Alpha Mu Gamma Honor Society **[394]**
Alpha Mu Tau Undergraduate Scholarships [1398]
Alpha Phi Sigma (APS) **[397]**
Alpha Tau Omega Graduate Scholarship [401]
Alpha Tau Omega Undergraduate Scholarships [402]
Alpha Tau Omegapha Tau Omega Fraternity (ATO) **[400]**
Alphonso Deal Scholarship Award [7728]
The Alsandor Law Firm **[406]**
The Alsandor Law Firm Scholarship Contest [407]
ALSC Bound to Stay Bound Books Scholarship [2237]
ALSC Summer Reading Program Grant [2238]
Martin K. Alsup and Frank Schroeder Memorial Music Scholarship [8830]
Robert E. Altenhofen Memorial Scholarships [2004]
Alter-Cine Foundation **[408]**
Altrusa International of Grand Rapids Scholarship [5133]
Alumni Endowed Scholarship [2840]
Luis W. Alvarez Postdoctoral Fellowships in Computational Science [6735]
Alwin B. Newton Scholarship [1468]
Alzheimer Society of Canada (ASC) **[410]**
Alzheimer's/Gerontology Scholarship [10092]
Alzheimer's Association **[414]**
Alzheimer's Disease Research Standard Award [2692]
AMA/Charles H. Grant Scholarship Program [50]
AMA Foundation Physicians of Tomorrow Scholarships [1111]
AMACESP Student Scholarships [197]
Jaedyn Amann Memorial Scholarship [12282]
The Amato Sanita Brighter Future Scholarship [9876]
The Ambrose-Ramsey Trust [8831]
Ameel J. Fisher Scholarship [11174]
Amelia and Emanuel Nessell Family Scholarship Fund [4197]
America Express Travel Scholarships [1581]
Americal Division Veterans Association (ADVA) **[419]**
Americal Legacy Foundation Scholarship [420]
American Academy of Advertising (AAA) **[421]**
American Academy of Ambulatory Care Nursing (AAACN) **[423]**
American Academy of Attorney-CPAs (AAA-CPA) **[429]**
American Academy of Audiology (AAA) **[431]**
American Academy for Cerebral Palsy and Developmental Medicine (AACPDM) **[437]**
American Academy of Clinical Toxicology (AACT) **[440]**
American Academy of Cosmetic Dentistry (AACD) **[445]**
American Academy of CPR & First Aid, Inc. **[447]**
American Academy of Dermatology (AAD) **[449]**
American Academy of Facial Plastic and Reconstructive Surgery (AAFPRS) **[451]**
American Academy of Family Physicians (AAFP) **[453]**
American Academy of Neurology (AAN) **[457]**
American Academy of Optometry (AAO) **[461]**

American Academy of Optometry Foundation (AOF) **[465]**

American Academy of Otolaryngology - Head and Neck Surgery (AAO-HNS) **[469]**

American Academy of Periodontology (AAP) **[471]**

American Academy in Rome (AAR) **[475]**

American Academy of Sanitarians (AAS) **[477]**

American Acne and Rosacea Society (AARS) **[479]**

American Acne and Rosacea Society Mentorship Grant [480]

American Antiquarian Society (AAS) **[481]**

American Art Therapy Association (AATA) **[500]**

American Art Therapy Association Anniversary Scholarship [501]

American Association for the Advancement of Science (AAAS) **[505]**

American Association of Advertising Agencies (AAAA) **[508]**

American Association of Anatomists (AAA) **[511]**

American Association for Applied Linguistics (AAAL) **[514]**

American Association of Blacks in Energy (AABE) **[516]**

American Association of Blacks in Energy Scholarships [517]

American Association of Blood Banks (AABB) **[518]**

American Association of Bovine Practitioners (AABP) **[521]**

American Association for Cancer Research (AACR) **[528]**

American Association for Cancer Research Minority Scholar in Cancer Research Awards [533]

American Association of Candy Technologists (AACT) **[537]**

American Association of Cereal Chemists Graduate Fellowship Program [3266]

American Association for Clinical Chemistry (AACC) **[539]**

American Association of Colleges of Nursing (AACN) **[542]**

American Association of Colleges of Osteopathic Medicine (AACOM) **[544]**

American Association of Colleges for Teacher Education (AACTE) **[546]**

American Association of Critical-Care Nurses (AACN) **[552]**

American Association of Endodontists (AAE) **[554]**

American Association of Equine Practitioners (AAEP) **[557]**

American Association of Family and Consumer Sciences (AAFCS) **[560]**

American Association of Family and Consumer Sciences Undergraduate Scholarships [561]

American Association of Geographers (AAG) **[562]**

American Association for Hand Surgery (AAHS) **[565]**

American Association for Hand Surgery Annual Research Awards [566]

American Association on Health and Disability (AAHD) **[567]**

American Association of Healthcare Administrative Management (AAHAM) **[569]**

American Association of Immunologists (AAI) **[571]**

American Association for the Improvement of Boxing (AAIB) **[574]**

American Association on Intellectual and Developmental Disabilities (AAIDD) **[576]**

American Association of Japanese University Women (AAJUW) **[578]**

American Association for Justice (AAJ) **[580]**

American Association of Law Libraries (AALL) **[584]**

American Association for Marriage and Family Therapy (AAMFT) **[601]**

American Association of Medical Assistants (AAMA) **[604]**

American Association of Neurological Surgeons (AANS) **[606]**

American Association of Neuroscience Nurses (AANN) **[609]**

American Association of Occupational Health Nurses, Inc. (AAOHN) **[612]**

American Association for Paralegal Education (AAFPE) **[615]**

American Association of People with Disabilities (AAPD) **[617]**

American Association of Physicists in Medicine (AAPM) **[619]**

American Association of Physics Teachers (AAPT) **[624]**

American Association of Plastic Surgeons (AAPS) **[626]**

American Association of Plastic Surgeons Academic Scholar Program [627]

American Association of Police Polygraphists (AAPP) **[628]**

American Association of Professional Apiculturists (AAPA) **[630]**

American Association of Railroad Superintendents (AARS) **[632]**

American Association of School Administrators (AASA) **[634]**

American Association of School Personnel Administrators (AASPA) **[637]**

American Association of State Troopers (AAST) **[639]**

American Association of State Troopers Scholarship Foundation First Scholarships [640]

American Association of State Troopers Scholarship Foundation Second Scholarships [641]

American Association for the Study of Liver Diseases (AASLD) **[643]**

American Association for the Surgery of Trauma (AAST) **[650]**

American Association of Teachers of Turkic Languages (AATT) **[654]**

American Association of Textile Chemists and Colorists (AATCC) **[656]**

American Association for Thoracic Surgery (AATS) **[658]**

American Association of University Women (AAUW) **[664]**

American Association of University Women Career Development Grants [665]

American Association of University Women International Fellowships [666]

American Association of University Women Master's and First Professional Awards [667]

American Association of University Women Selected Professions Fellowships [668]

American Association of University Women(AAUW) Sue Gottcent Memorial Scholarship Fund [10670]

American Association for Women in Community Colleges (AAWCC) **[670]**

American Association for Women in Community Colleges Doctoral Scholarship [671]

American Association for Women in Community Colleges LEADERS Institute Scholarship [672]

American Association of Women Dentists (AAWD) **[673]**

American Association of Zoo Keepers (AAZK) **[675]**

American Astronomical Society (AAS) **[680]**

American Astronomical Society Small Research Grants [681]

American Australian Association (AAA) **[685]**

American Bar Association Commission on Homelessness and Poverty (ABACHP) **[687]**

American Bar Foundation (ABF) **[689]**

American Birding Association (ABA) **[693]**

American Board of Funeral Service Education (ABFSE) **[696]**

American Brain Tumor Association (ABTA) **[698]**

American Burn Association (ABA) **[703]**

American Bus Association (ABA) **[706]**

American Bus Association Academic Merit Scholarships [709]

American Cancer Society (ACS) **[712]**

American Cancer Society - Postdoctoral Fellowships [715]

American Cancer Society - Research Scholar Grants [716]

American Center for Mongolian Studies (ACMS) **[718]**

American Center for Oriental Research **[722]**

American Ceramic Society (ACERS) **[732]**

American Chemical Society (ACS) **[734]**

American Chemical Society - Rubber Division **[737]**

American Choral Directors Association - Texas Chapter **[739]**

American Civil Liberties Union of Northern California, Mid-Peninsula Chapter **[748]**

American Clan Gregor Society (ACGS) **[750]**

American Classical League (ACL) **[752]**

American College of Bankruptcy (ACB) **[756]**

American College of Chiropractic Orthopedists (ACCO) **[758]**

American College of Gastroenterology (ACG) **[760]**

American College of Healthcare Executives (ACHE) **[762]**

American College of Medical Toxicology (ACMT) **[765]**

American College of Nurse-Midwives Foundation (ACNM) **[767]**

American College Personnel Association (ACPA) **[770]**

American College of Surgeons Australia/New Zealand Traveling Fellowship [775]

American College of Surgeons International Guest Scholarship [776]

American College of Surgeons Professional Association (ACSPA) **[772]**

American College of Veterinary Ophthalmologists (ACVO) **[779]**

American Concrete Institute (ACI) **[781]**

American Conifer Society (ACS) **[794]**

American Constitution Society for Law and Policy (ACS) **[796]**

American Contact Dermatitis Society (ACDS) **[798]**

American Copy Editors Society Education Fund (ACES) **[800]**

American Council of the Blind Scholarships [803]

American Council of Blind Students (ACBS) **[802]**

American Council of Engineering Companies of Illinois (ACECIL) **[804]**

American Council of Engineering Companies of Illinois Scholarships [805]

American Council on Germany (ACG) **[806]**

American Council of Independent Laboratories (ACIL) **[814]**

American Council of Independent Laboratories Academic Scholarships [815]

American Council of Learned Societies (ACLS) **[816]**

American Council for Polish Culture (ACPC) **[826]**

American Councils for International Education **[829]**

American Councils for International Education Critical Language Scholarship Program [830]

American Counsel Association (ACA) **[831]**

American Counsel Association Scholarships [832]

American Counseling Association (ACA) **[833]**

American Criminal Justice Association - Lambda Alpha Epsilon (ACJA-LAE) **[835]**

American Culinary Federation (ACF) **[840]**

American Darts Organization (ADO) **[850]**

American Darts Organization Memorial Youth National Scholarship [851]

American Dental Association (ADA) **[852]**

American Dental Association Dental Assisting Scholarship Program [854]

American Dental Association Dental Hygiene Scholarship Program [855]

American Dental Association Dental Laboratory Technology Scholarship Program [856]

American Dental Association Minority Dental Student Scholarships [857]

American Dental Hygienists' Association Institute for Oral Health (ADHA IOH) **[858]**

American Dental Hygienists' Association Institute for Oral Health Research Grants [859]

American Diabetes Association (ADA) **[863]**

American Diabetes Association and Boehringer Ingelheim Research Award: Chronic Kidney Disease and Renal Insufficiency in the Setting of Diabetes [7976]

American Dissertation Fellowships [669]

American Educational Research Association (AERA) **[867]**

American Enterprise Institute **[871]**

American Enterprise Institute National Research Initiative Fellowships (NRI) [872]

American Express Professional Development Scholarship [970]

American Federation for Aging Research (AFAR) **[873]**

American Federation of Police and Concerned Citizen Educational Scholarship [879]

American Federation of Police and Concerned Citizens (AFP&CC) **[878]**

American Federation of Teachers (AFT) **[880]**

American Federation of Teachers - Oregon (AFT) **[882]**

American Fisheries Society (AFS) **[886]**

American Fisheries Society Idaho Chapter **[888]**

American Floral Endowment (AFE) **[893]**

American Foreign Service Association (AFSA) **[911]**

American Foreign Service Association Scholarship Fund Program [912]

American Foundation for the Blind (AFB) **[913]**

American Foundation for Pharmaceutical Education (AFPE) **[921]**

American Foundation for Suicide Prevention (AFSP) **[925]**

American Foundry Society (AFS) **[931]**

American Galvanizers Association (AGA) **[933]**

American Gastroenterological Association (AGA) **[935]**

American Gastroenterological Association Research Foundation (AGAF) **[940]**

American Geosciences Institute (AGI) **[943]**

American Geriatrics Society (AGS) **[945]**

American Ground Water Trust (AGWT) **[947]**

American Guild of Organists, Canton Chapter Charitable Fund [10751]

American Handel Society (AHS) **[951]**

American Head and Neck Society (AHNS) **[953]**

American Historical Association (AHA) **[957]**

American Historical Association Fellowships in Aerospace History [958]

American Historical Print Collectors Society (AHPCS) **[964]**

American Historical Print Collectors Society Fellowship [484], [965]

American Horticultural Therapy Association (AHTA) **[966]**

American Hotel & Lodging Educational Foundation (AHLEF) **[968]**

American Indian College Fund **[977]**

American Indian Education Fund (AIEF) **[987]**

American Indian Endowed Scholarship [11916]

American Indian Graduate Center (AIGC) **[992]**

American Indian Library Association (AILA) **[997]**

American Indian Science and Engineering Society (AISES) **[999]**

American Institute of Aeronautics and Astronautics (AIAA) **[1004]**

American Institute of Architects Alaska **[1006]**

American Institute of Architects - Northeast Illinois (AIA NEI) **[1008]**

American Institute of Bangladesh Studies (AIBS) **[1011]**

American Institute of Certified Public Accountants (AICPA) **[1014]**

American Institute of Chemical Engineers (AICHE) **[1019]**

American Institute for Conservation of Historic & Artistic Works **[1024]**

American Institute for Economic Research (AIER) **[1027]**

American Institute for Economic Research Student Summer Fellowship [1028]

American Institute of Iranian Studies (AIIRS) **[1029]**

American Institute for Maghrib Studies (AIMS) **[1032]**

American Institute of Pakistan Studies (AIPS) **[1035]**

American Institute of Physics (AIP) **[1040]**

American Institute of Physics Congressional Science Fellowship [1042]

American Institute of Physics State Department Science Fellowship [1043]

American Institute of Polish Culture (AIPC) **[1044]**

American Institute for Sri Lankan Studies (AISLS) **[1046]**

American Institute of Steel Construction (AISC) **[1050]**

American Institute of Wine and Food (AIWF) **[1055]**

American Jersey Cattle Association (AJCA) **[1057]**

American Jewish Archives (AJA) **[1060]**

American Jewish Historical Society (AJHS) **[1062]**

American Judges Association (AJA) **[1065]**

American Judges Association Law Student Essay Competition [1066]

American Kidney Fund (AKF) **[1067]**

The American Legion (AL) **[1069]**

American Legion Boys/Girls State Scholarship [6782]

American Legion Department of Vermont **[1074]**

American Legion Department of Vermont Scholarship [1075]

American Legion Eagle Scout of the Year [7843]

American Legion Florence/Lauderdale Post 11 Scholarship [8501]

The American Legion Legacy Scholarship [1070]

American Library Association (ALA) **[1076]**

American Library Association Office for Research and Statistics (ORS) **[1080]**

American Library Association Young Adult Library Services Association (YALSA) **[1082]**

American Life Fund (ALF) **[1085]**

The American Life Fund Scholarship [1086]

American Livebearer Association (ALA) **[1087]**

American Liver Foundation (ALF) **[1089]**

American Liver Foundation Liver Scholar Award [1091]

American Lung Association Biomedical Research Grants (RG) [1094]

American Lung Association Clinical Patient Care Research Grants (CG) [1095]

American Lung Association Dalsemer Research Grants (DA) [1096]

American Lung Association DeSousa Awards [1097]

American Lung Association in the District of Columbia (ALA) **[1092]**

American Lung Association Senior Research Training Fellowships (RT) [1098]

American Lung Association Social-Behavioral Research Grants (SB) [1099]

American Marketing Association-Connecticut Chapter, Anna C. Klune Memorial Scholarship [5314]

American Marketing Association Foundation (AMAF) **[1102]**

American Mathematical Society (AMS) **[1106]**

American Meat Science Association (AMSA) **[1108]**

American Medical Association (AMA) **[1110]**

American Medical Society for Sports Medicine (AMSSM) **[1114]**

American Men's Studies Association (AMSA) **[1116]**

American Meteorological Society (AMS) **[1118]**

American MidEast Leadership Network (AMLN) **[1126]**

American Montessori Society (AMS) **[1128]**

American Music Therapy Association (AMTA) **[1131]**

American Musicological Society (AMS) **[1141]**

American National Red Cross **[1148]**

American Nephrology Nurses' Association (ANNA) **[1150]**

American Nephrology Nurses' Association Evidence-Based Research Grants [1151]

American Neuropsychiatric Association (ANPA) **[1154]**

American Neurotology Society (ANS) **[1156]**

American Nuclear Society (ANS) **[1159]**

American Nuclear Society Incoming Freshman Scholarships [1160]

American Nuclear Society Nevada Section Scholarship [1161], [9390]

American Nuclear Society Undergraduates Scholarships [1162]

American Numismatic Society (ANS) **[1170]**

American Nurses Foundation (ANF) **[1172]**

American Occupational Therapy Foundation (AOTF) **[1176]**

American Oil Chemists' Society (AOCS) **[1183]**

American Orff-Schulwerk Association (AOSA) **[1185]**

American Oriental Society (AOS) **[1190]**

American Orthopaedic Foot and Ankle Society (AOFAS) **[1192]**

American Osler Society (AOS) **[1195]**

American Osteopathic Foundation (AOF) **[1197]**

American Otological Society (AOS) **[1201]**

American Paint Horse Foundation (APHA) **[1203]**

American Parkinson Disease Association (APDA) **[1205]**

American Patriot Scholarship [7388]

American Pediatric Surgical Nurses Association (APSNA) **[1209]**

American Pediatric Surgical Nurses Association Educational Grant [1210]

American Philosophical Society (APS) **[1211]**

American Physical Society (APS) **[1218]**

American Physical Society Minority Undergraduate Scholarships [1220]

American Physical Therapy Association (APTA) **[1231]**

American Physiological Society (APS) **[1235]**

American Planning Association (APA) **[1241]**

American Planning Association ENRE Student Fellowship Program [1242]

American Political Science Association (APSP) **[1246]**

American Polygraph Association (APA) **[1262]**

American Psychoanalytic Association (APSAA) **[1264]**

American Psychological Association (APA) **[1266]**

American Psychological Association of Graduate Students (APAGS) **[1268]**

American Psychological Foundation (APF) **[1272]**

American Psychology-Law Society (AP-LS) **[1290]**

American Psychology-Law Society Dissertation Awards [1291]

American Psychology-Law Society Student Grants-In-Aid [1292]

American Public Power Association (APPA) **[1296]**

American Public Transportation Foundation (APFT) **[1298]**

American Public Works Association - Nevada Chapter (APWA) **[1307]**

American Quarter Horse Foundation Scholarships [1310]

American Quarter Horse Youth Association (AQHYA) **[1309]**

American Quilt Study Group (AQSG) **[1311]**

American Radio Relay League Louisiana Memorial Scholarships [1924]

American Radium Society (ARS) **[1313]**

American Railway Engineering and Maintenance-of-Way Association (AREMA) **[1315]**

American Rental Association Foundation (ARA) **[1331]**

American Research Center in Egypt (ARCE) **[1335]**

American Research in the Humanities in China Fellowships [820]

American Research Institute in Turkey (ARIT) **[1341]**

American Respiratory Care Foundation (ARCF) **[1350]**

American Road & Transportation Builders Association (ARTBA) **[1361]**

American Roentgen Ray Society (ARRS) **[1363]**

American Romanian Orthodox Youth (AROY) **[1365]**

The American-Scandinavian Foundation (ASF) **[1371]**

American-Scandinavian Foundation Fellowships/Grants in the United States [1372]

American-Scandinavian Foundation Fellowships to Study in Scandinavia [1373]

American-Scandinavian Foundation Grants to Study in Scandinavia [1374]

American Schools of Oriental Research (ASOR) **[1378]**

American Senior Benefits Association (ASBA) **[1380]**

American Sheep Industry Association (ASI) **[1382]**

American Shotcrete Association (ASA) **[1384]**

American Society of Brewing Chemists (ASBC) **[1386]**

American Society of Business Publication Editors (ASBPE) **[1389]**

American Society of Certified Engineering Technicians (ASCET) **[1391]**

American Society of Cinematographers (ASC) **[1395]**

American Society for Clinical Laboratory Science (ASCLS) **[1397]**

American Society for Clinical Pathology (ASCP) **[1401]**

American Society of Colon and Rectal Surgeons (ASCRS) **[1403]**

American Society of Colon and Rectal Surgeons International Fellowships [1404]

American Society of Colon and Rectal Surgeons International Travel Scholarships [1405]

American Society of Composers, Authors and Publishers Foundation (ASCAP) **[1406]**

American Society for Composites (ASC) **[1414]**

American Society of Crime Laboratory Directors (ASCLD) **[1416]**

American Society of Criminology (ASC) **[1418]**

American Society of Echocardiography (ASE) **[1421]**

American Society for Eighteenth-Century Studies (ASECS) **[1424]**

American Society of Electroneurodiagnostic Technologists Student Education Grants [1981]

American Society for Engineering Education (ASEE) **[1441]**

American Society for Enology and Viticulture (ASEV) **[1446]**

American Society for Environmental History (ASEH) **[1448]**

American Society For Legal History, Inc. (ASLH) **[1460]**

American Society of Genealogists (ASG) **[1462]**

American Society of Health-System Pharmacists (ASHP) **[1464]**

American Society of Heating, Refrigerating and Air-Conditioning Engineers (ASHRAE) **[1467]**

American Society of Heating, Refrigerating, and Air-Conditioning Memorial Scholarships [1469]

American Society for Horticultural Science (ASHS) **[1477]**

American Society for Horticultural Science Travel Grants [1478]

American Society of Ichthyologists and Herpetologists (ASIH) **[1482]**

American Society of Interior Designers (ASID) **[1485]**

American Society of International Law (ASIL) **[1488]**

American Society of Landscape Architects (ASLA) **[1490]**

American Society for Laser Medicine and Surgery (ASLMS) **[1493]**

American Society of Mammalogists (ASM) **[1498]**

American Society of Mammalogists Grants-in-Aid of Research [1500]

American Society for Mass Spectrometry (ASMS) **[1507]**

American Society for Microbiology (ASM) **[1509]**

American Society for Microbiology International Fellowships for Africa [1510]

American Society for Microbiology International Fellowships for Asia [1511]

American Society for Microbiology International Fellowships for Latin America and the Caribbean [1512]

American Society for Microbiology Undergraduate Research Fellowship [1513]

American Society of Military Comptrollers (ASMC) **[1519]**

American Society of Mining and Reclamation (ASMR) **[1521]**

American Society of Mining and Reclamation Memorial Scholarship Award [1522]

American Society of Naval Engineers (ASNE) **[1523]**

American Society of Nephrology (ASN) **[1525]**

American Society of Neuroradiology (ASNR) **[1528]**

American Society for Nondestructive Testing (ASNT) **[1530]**

American Society Of Mammalogists Fellowship In Mammalogy [1501]

American Society of Pension Professionals and Actuaries (ASPPA) **[1533]**

American Society for Pharmacology and Experimental Therapeutics (ASPET) **[1535]**

American Society of Plant Taxonomists (ASPT) **[1537]**

American Society of Podiatric Medical Assistants (ASPMA) **[1539]**

American Society for Quality (ASQ) **[1541]**

American Society for Radiation Oncology (ASTRO) **[1544]**

American Society of Radiologic Technologists Education and Research Foundation (ASRT) **[1549]**

American Society of Regional Anesthesia and Pain Medicine (ASRA) **[1555]**

American Society of Safety Professionals **[1558]**

American Society for Theatre Research (ASTR) **[1576]**

American Society of Travel Agents (ASTA) **[1580]**

American Sociological Association (ASA) **[1589]**

American Sokol Merit Award [1593]

American Sokol Organization (ASO) **[1592]**

American Speech Language Hearing Foundation (ASHF) **[1594]**

American Speech Language Hearing Foundation Clinical Research Grant [1595]

American Speech Language Hearing Foundation Endowed Scholarships [1596]

American Speech Language Hearing Foundation General Scholarships [1597]

American Speech Language Hearing Foundation International Student Scholarship [1598]

American Speech Language Hearing Foundation Minority Student Scholarship [1599]

American Speech Language Hearing Foundation Scholarship for Student with A Disability [1600]

American Statistical Association (ASA) **[1608]**

American String Teachers Association - New Jersey Chapter (ASTA-NJ) **[1613]**

American Surgical Association (ASA) **[1615]**

American Swedish Institute (ASI) **[1617]**

American Thoracic Society (ATS) **[1620]**

American Tinnitus Association (ATA) **[1623]**

American University School of Public Affairs (AU-SPA) **[1625]**

American Veterinary Medical Association (AVMA) **[1627]**

American Water Resources Association - Colorado Section (AWRA-CO) **[1629]**

American Water Resources Association - Florida Section **[1631]**

American Water Ski Educational Foundation Scholarships [11778]

American Water Works Association (AWWA) **[1633]**

American Water Works Association - Florida Section (FSAWWA) **[1645]**

American Watercolor Society (AWS) **[1647]**

American Watercolor Society Scholarship Program for Art Teachers [1648]

American Welding Society (AWS) **[1649]**

American Welding Society District Scholarships [1651]

American Welding Society Graduate Research Fellowships [1652]

American Welding Society National Scholarships [1653]

American Welding Society Past Presidents Scholarships [1654]

American Wine Society Educational Foundation (AWSEF) **[1675]**

American Wine Society Educational Foundation Scholarships (AWSEF) [1676]

American Woman's Society of Certified Public Accountants (AWSCPA) **[1677]**

AmericanMuscle **[1680]**

AmericanMuscle's Student Scholarship Program [1681]

Americans for Informed Democracy Global Scholar Program [1687]

Americans United for Separation of Church and State (AUSCS) **[1682]**

amfAR, The Foundation for AIDS Research **[1684]**

T. Thomas Amirian Memorial Grant [1860]

Arsham Amirikian Engineering Scholarship [1655]

AMLN Scholarships for Arab American Students [1127]

Amos and Marilyn Winsand - Detroit Section Named Scholarship [1656]

AMP Global Youth **[1686]**

AMS Centennial Fellowships [1107]

AMS Freshman Undergraduate Scholarship [1119]

AMS Graduate Fellowship in the History of Science [1120]

AMS Graduate Fellowships [1121]

AMS/Industry/Government Graduate Fellowships [1122]

AMS Minority Scholarships [1123]

AMS Senior Named Scholarships [1124]

AMS Teacher Education Scholarships [1129]

AMSA Graduate Student Research Poster Competition [1109]

AMSN Career Mobility Scholarship [48]

AMSSM-ACSM Clinical Research Grants [1115]

AMTA Past Presidents' Conference Scholar [1132]

AMTA Student Conference Scholar [1133]

AMTF Graduate Scholarships [1399]

Amtrol Inc. **[1688]**

Amtrol Scholarship [950], [1689]

Amusement & Music Operators Association (AMOA) **[1690]**

AMV **[1692]**

AMVETS **[1695]**

AMVETS National Scholarships - Entering College Freshmen [1696]

AMVETS National Scholarships - For Veterans [1697]

AMVETS National Scholarships - JROTC [1698]

Amyloidosis Foundation **[1699]**

ANA Multicultural Excellence Scholarship Fund (MAIP) [509]

Anaheim Police Association **[1702]**

Anaheim Police Survivors and Scholarship Fund [1703]

ANCA Scholarships [1915]

Anchor Plastics Scholarships [9166]

Anchor Scholarship Foundation **[1704]**

Anchor Scholarship Foundation Scholarships [1705]

Andersen Nontraditional Scholarships for Women's Education and Retraining (ANSWER) [4717]

Mary Louise Andersen Scholarship [1742]

Anderson Cummings AC Scholarship for Higher Education [1707]

Anderson & Cummings, LLP **[1706]**

William G. Anderson, DO, Minority Scholarships [1198]

The Anderson Group Summer Institute **[1709]**

The Anderson Group Summer Institute Scholarships [1710]

Henry H. Anderson, Jr. Sail Training Scholarship [10917]

Mary Anderson Memorial Intermediate Woodwind Scholarship [9895]

Anderson Niskanen Scholarship Fund [4198]

Ora E. Anderson Scholarship [4706]

Earl I. Anderson Scholarships [1925]

Michael P. Anderson Scholarships in Space Science [8082]

Dr. Andy Anderson Young Professional Awards [9146]

Grace Andow Memorial Scholarship [6244]

Andrea Will Memorial Scholarship [10093]

Andrew Foster Scholarship [7720]

Andrew Gronholdt Arts Scholarship [328]

Andrew Thomson Prize in Applied Meteorology [3040]

Andrew W. Mellon Fellowships For Conservation Training Programs [10197]

Richard E. Andrews Memorial Scholarship [694]

Marvin A. Andrews Scholarships/Internships [1805]

Androscoggin County Chamber of Commerce Adult Scholarships [6825]

ANF/ANN-FNRE Nursing Research Grants [1173]

ANF/ENRS Nursing Research Society [1174]

Sigma Theta Tau, International Nursing Research Grants (STTI) [1175]

Joanne Angle Investigator Award [9275]

Angus Foundation **[1711]**

Angus Foundation Graduate Student Degree Scholarship Program [1712]

Angus Foundation Scholarships [7965]

Angus Foundation Undergraduate Student Scholarships [1713]

Angus/Talon Youth Educational Learning Program Endowment Fund [1714]

Anheuser-Busch NAPABA Law Foundation Presidential Scholarships [7601]

Anil and Neema Thakrar Family Fund #1 [4774]

Animal Behavior Society (ABS) **[1715]**

Animal Compassion Undergraduate Scholarships [9044]

Marvin Anmuth Scholarship [6269]

Ann C. Beckingham Scholarship [2989]

Ann Liguori Foundation Sports Media Scholarship [8366]

Ann Marie Bredefeld Scholarship [8988]

The ARRL General Fund Scholarship [1926]
ARRS/ASNR Scholarship in Neuroradiology [1364], [1529]
ARS Lazarian Graduate Scholarship [1854]
ARS Undergraduate Scholarship [1855]
ARS Young Oncologist Travel Grants [1314]
Erin J.C. Arsenault Fellowships in Space Governance [7188]
Ardemis, Armenoohy, and Arpi Arsenian Memorial Grant [1863]
Art Acquisition by Application [260]
Art and Dannie Weber Scholarship [12061]
Arthritis Champions Scholarship [1970]
Arthritis Foundation (AF) **[1969]**
Arthritis Foundation Investigator Awards [1971]
Arthur and Barbara Pape Endowment [11666]
Arthur B.C. Walker II Scholarship [8083]
Arthur H. Daniels Memorial Scholarship [9522]
Arthur and Juna Fisher Memorial Track Scholarship [9523]
Arthur Lockwood Beneventi Law Scholarship [8093]
Arthur M. & Berdena King Eagle Scout Scholarship [7844]
Arthur M. Schlesinger Jr. Research Fellowship [6531]
Arthur Patch McKinlay Scholarship [753]
Artificial Intelligence & Ethics [12]
Artist-in-Residence Workspace Grant [3210]
The Artist in Landscape Design Scholarship [8585]
Arts Council of Greater Grand Rapids Minority Scholarship [5134]
Arts Council of Princeton (ACP) **[1972]**
Arts Foundation of Cape Cod **[1974]**
Arts Foundation of Cape Cod Scholarships [1975]
Arts Graduate Scholarship [285]
ASA Graduate Scholarships [1385]
ASA Inc. Journalism Internship Program [1864]
ASA Minority Fellowship Program (ASA MFP) [1590]
ASA/NSF/BLS Fellowships [1609], [8065], [11343]
ASA Student Forum Travel Awards [1591]
ASAC-CJAS PhD Research Grant Award [79]
ASAE: The Center for Association Leadership **[1976]**
ASBA College Scholarship Grant Program [1381]
ASBC Foundation Graduate Scholarships [1387]
ASBC Foundation Undergraduate Scholarships [1388]
Benjamin Asbell Memorial Awards [2846]
ASBPE Young Leaders Scholarship [1390]
ASC Ph.D. Research Scholarship Award [1415]
ASC Research Grant [411]
ASCE Freeman Fellowship [1783]
Ascend, Inc. **[1978]**
ASCLD Scholarship Program [1417]
ASCO/CCF Young Investigator Awards [3767]
ASCP Foundation Garza & Becan-McBride Endowed Scholarship [1402]
ASCPA High School Scholarships [1816]
ASCPA Private University Scholarships [1817]
ASDSO Undergraduate Scholarship [2295]
ASE Career Development Award [1422]
ASECS Graduate Student Research Paper Award [1426]
ASECS Innovative Course Design Competition [1427]
ASECS Women's Caucus Editing and Translation Fellowship [1428]
ASEE-NRL Postdoctoral Fellowship Program [11389]
ASEE/NSF Small Business Postdoctoral Research Diversity Fellowship (SBPRDF) [1442], [8066]
ASEH Minority Travel Grants [1449]
ASET Scholarships [1982]
ASET - The Neurodiagnostic Society **[1980]**
ASEV Traditional Scholarship [1447]
The ASG Scholar Award [1463]
ASGP Graduate Research Fellowships [244]
ASHARE Undergraduate Engineering Scholarships [1470]
Ashburn Institute (AI) **[1983]**
Diana Ashe-Clayton Memorial Scholarship [8502]
ASHFoundation New Century Scholars Doctoral Scholarship [1601]
ASHFoundation New Century Scholars Research Grant [1602]

ASHFoundation New Investigators Research Grant [1603]
ASHFoundation NSSLHA Scholarship [1604]
ASHFoundation Speech Science Research Grant [1605]
ASHFoundation Student Research Grant in Audiology [1606]
ASHFoundation Student Research Grant in Early Childhood Language Development [1607]
Ashley E. Ketcher Memorial Scholarship [3667]
Larry Ashley Memorial Scholarship Award [2127]
ASHP Student Research Awards [1465]
ASHS Industry Division Student Travel Grant [1479]
ASHS Scholars Award [1480]
Asia-Pacific Biomedical Research Foundation Merit Awards [10530]
Asia Pacific Foundation of Canada Junior Research Fellowships [4711]
Asia Pacific Foundation of Canada Media Fellowships [4712]
Asia Pacific Foundation of Canada Post-Graduate Research Fellowships [4713]
Asian Development Bank - Japan Scholarship Program [4261]
Asian Pacific American Advocates (OCA) **[1985]**
Asian Pacific American Bar Association of Silicon Valley (APABASV) **[1987]**
Asian Pacific American Librarians Association (APALA) **[1989]**
Asian/Pacific Bar Association of Sacramento (ABAS) **[1991]**
Asian and Pacific Islander American Scholarship Fund **[1993]**
Asian and Pacific Islander Queer Sisters Scholarship (APIQS) [9289]
ASID Foundation Legacy Scholarships for Graduate Students [1486]
ASIS Foundation Chapter Matching Scholarship [1996]
ASIS International (ASIS) **[1995]**
ASIST Scholarship (ASIST) [4463]
ASLA Council of Fellows [1491]
ASLA Council of Fellows Scholarships [6646]
ASLMS Educational Grants [1494]
ASLMS Research Grant [1495]
ASM/CDC Program in Infectious Disease and Public Health Microbiology [1514]
ASM Congressional Science Fellowship [1515]
ASM Research Capstone Fellowship [1516]
ASM Robert D. Watkins Graduate Research Fellowship [1517]
ASM Science Teaching Fellowships - Student [1518]
ASMC National Scholarship Program [1520]
ASME International **[1997]**
ASMS Research Awards [1508]
ASNE Scholarship [1524]
ASNT Fellowship Award [1531]
Myron "Ted" Asplin Foundation Scholarships [5739]
ASPPH/CDC Public Health Fellowship Program [2279]
ASPPH/EPA Environmental Health Fellowship Program [2280]
ASPPH/NHTSA Public Health Fellowship Program [2281]
ASPPH Public Health Fellowship Program [2282]
ASPPH Public Health Preparedness Fellowship Program [2283]
ASPRS, The Imaging and Geospatial Information Society **[2003]**
ASPT General Graduate Student Research Grant Fund [1538]
ASRT Research Grants [1550]
Len Assante Scholarship Program [7911]
Darrell and Palchie Asselin Scholarship Fund [4199]
Associated Colleges of the Midwest (ACM) **[2013]**
Associated General Contractors of America (AGC) **[2015]**
Associated General Contractors of Connecticut Scholarships (AGC/CT Scholarship) [3759]
Associated General Contractors of New York State **[2017]**
Associated Medical Services (AMS) **[2019]**
Associated Press Television and Radio Association (APTRA) **[2021]**
Associates of the American Foreign Service Worldwide (AAFSW) **[2023]**

Associates in Behavioral Health Scholarships [9290]
Association for Academic Surgery (AAS) **[2027]**
Association for the Advancement of Baltic Studies (AABS) **[2029]**
Association for the Advancement of Baltic Studies Dissertation Grants for Graduate Students [2030]
Association for the Advancement of Scandinavian Studies in Canada **[2031]**
Association on American Indian Affairs (AAIA) **[2035]**
Association of American Indian Physicians (AAIP) **[2041]**
Association of American Medical Colleges (AAMC) **[2043]**
Association of Applied Paleontological Sciences (AAPS) **[2045]**
Association for Applied and Therapeutic Humor (AATH) **[2051]**
Association of Art Museum Curators (AAMC) **[2056]**
Association for Asian Studies (AAS) **[2059]**
Association for Behavior Analysis International (ABAI) **[2062]**
Association of Black Cardiologists (ABC) **[2065]**
Association of Black Women Lawyers of New Jersey **[2067]**
Association of Black Women Physicians (ABWP) **[2069]**
Association of Business Information & Media Companies (ABM) **[2071]**
Association of California Nurse Leaders Kern County Chapter **[2073]**
Association of California Water Agencies (ACWA) **[2075]**
Association of California Water Agencies Scholarship [2076]
Association for Canadian Studies in the United States (ACSUS) **[2079]**
Association Canadienne des Chefs de Police (ACCP) **[2082]**
L'Association Canadienne Des Géographes (CAG) **[2084]**
Association Canadienne d'Études Cinématographiques (ACEC) **[2088]**
Association Canadienne du Diabete **[2090]**
Association Canadienne des Infirmieres et Infirmiers en Sciences Neurologiques (ACIISN) **[2092]**
Association Canadienne des Parajuristes **[2096]**
Association Canadienne des Professeurs de Langues Secondes (ACPLS) **[2098]**
Association Canadienne de Radio-Oncologie (ACRO) **[2101]**
Assocation Canadienne de la Recherche Théâtrale (ACRT) **[2103]**
Association Canadienne des Ressources Hydriques (ACRH) **[2106]**
Association Canadienne de Science Politique (ACSP) **[2110]**
Association Canadienne de Securite Incendie **[2113]**
Association Canadienne du Stationnement (ACS) **[2124]**
Association Canadienne des Thérapeutes du Sport (CATA) **[2126]**
Association Canadienne des Troubles d'apprentissage (ACTA) **[2128]**
Association of Certified Fraud Examiners (ACFE) **[2131]**
Association of Certified Fraud Examiners - Georgia Area Chapter (ACFE) **[2133]**
Association of College and Research Libraries - Delaware Valley Chapter **[2135]**
Association of College Unions International (ACUI) **[2137]**
Association for Compensatory Educators of Texas (ACET) **[2140]**
Association for Compensatory Educators of Texas Paraprofessionals Scholarships [2141]
Association for Compensatory Educators of Texas Students [2142]
Association of Desk and Derrick Clubs (ADDC) **[2143]**
Association universitaire canadienne d'études nordique (ACUNS) **[2145]**
Association of Donor Recruitment Professionals (ADRP) **[2149]**

Association of Donor Recruitment Professionals Hughes Scholarships [2150]

Association of Donor Recruitment Professionals Presidential Scholarships [2151]

Association for Educational Communications and Technology (AECT) **[2154]**

Association of Energy Engineers (AEE) **[2158]**

Association of Energy Engineers Foundation Scholarship Program [2159]

Association of Environmental & Engineering Geologists **[2160]**

Association of Environmental Engineering and Science Professors Foundation (AEESP) **[2163]**

Association des Etudiantes Infirmiereres du Canada **[2169]**

Association des Facultes de Pharmacie du Canada (AFPC) **[2171]**

Association for Federal Information Resources Management (AFFIRM) **[2174]**

Association of Field Ornithologists (AFO) **[2176]**

Association of Flight Attendants - CWA (AFA-CWA) **[2178]**

Association of Flight Attendants Scholarship Fund [2179]

Association of Food and Drug Officials (AFDO) **[2180]**

Association of Former Intelligence Officers (AFIO) **[2183]**

Association of Government Accountants (AGA) **[2186]**

Association of Government Accountants Graduate Scholarships for Community Service [2187]

Association of Government Accountants Graduate Scholarships for Full-time study [2188]

Association of Government Accountants Graduate Scholarships for Part-time study [2189]

Association of Independent Colleges and Universities of Pennsylvania (AICUP) **[2190]**

Association for Institutional Research (AIR) **[2195]**

Association of International Education Administrators (AIEA) **[2200]**

Association of International Petroleum Negotiators (AIPN) **[2202]**

Association for Iron and Steel Technology (AIST) **[2204]**

Association of Jewish Libraries **[2226]**

Association of Latino Professionals For America (ALPFA) **[2230]**

Association of Leadership Educators, Inc. (ALE) **[2232]**

Association for Library Collections & Technical Services (ALCTS) **[2234]**

Association for Library Service to Children (ALSC) **[2236]**

Association Minéralogique du Canada **[2242]**

Association of Moving Image Archivists (AMIA) **[2245]**

Association for Nonprofit and Social Economy Research **[2251]**

Association of Occupational Health Professionals in Healthcare (AOHP) **[2253]**

Association of PeriOperative Registered Nurses (AORN) **[2256]**

Association of Postgraduate PA Programs (APPAP) **[2259]**

Association for Preservation Technology International (APT) **[2261]**

Association for Preservation Technology International Student Scholarships [2262]

Association of Professional Schools of International Affairs (APSIA) **[2263]**

Association for Psychological Science (APS) **[2265]**

Association for Psychological Science Student Grants (APS) [2267]

Association of Public Health Laboratories (APHL) **[2268]**

Association of Public Treasurers of the United States and Canada (APT US & C) **[2270]**

Association of Rehabilitation Nurses (ARN) **[2272]**

Association for Research on Nonprofit Organizations and Voluntary Action (ARNOVA) **[2274]**

Association of School Business Officials of Maryland and the District of Columbia (ASBO-MD&DC) **[2276]**

Association of Schools and Programs of Public Health (ASPPH) **[2278]**

Association of Science-Technology Centers (ASTC) **[2285]**

Association of Seventh-Day Adventist Librarians (ASDAL) **[2287]**

Association for the Sociology of Religion (ASR) **[2289]**

Association of Specialized and Cooperative Library Agencies (ASCLA) **[2292]**

Association of State Dam Safety Officials (ASDSO) **[2294]**

Association of State Dam Safety Officials memorial Undergraduate Scholarship [2296]

Association of Surgical Technologists (AST) **[2297]**

Association of Texas Professional Educators Foundation (ATPE) **[2299]**

Association of the United States Navy (AUSN) **[2302]**

Association of the United States Navy Scholarships [2303]

Association of University Programs in Health Administration (AUPHA) **[2304]**

Association for Women in Architecture and Design (AWA+D) **[2308]**

Association for Women in Architecture Scholarships [2309]

Association for Women in Computing - Houston Chapter **[2310]**

Association for Women Geoscientists (AWG) **[2312]**

Association for Women in Mathematics (AWM) **[2317]**

Association for Women in Sports Media (AWSM) **[2320]**

Association for Women in Sports Media Internship Program [2321]

Association of Zoo Veterinary Technicians (AZVT) **[2324]**

Association of Zoos and Aquariums (AZA) **[2326]**

ASSP Diversity Committee Scholarship [1559]

ASSP Foundation Academic Scholarship Program [1560]

ASSP Foundation Professional Education Grant Program [1561]

ASTA Alaska Airlines Scholarships [1582]

ASTA Holland America Line Graduate Research Scholarships [1583]

ASTA Rigby, Healy, Simmons Scholarships [1584]

ASTM International **[2329]**

ASTR Research Fellowships [1577]

Astra Zeneca Medical Scholarship [8222]

AstraZeneca Award [3055]

ASTRO Junior Faculty Career Research Training Award [1545]

ASTRO Minority Summer Fellowship Award [1546]

ASTRO Residents/Fellows in Radiation Oncology Research Seed Grant [1547]

ASTRO/ROI Comparative Effectiveness Research Awards [1548]

Astronaut Scholarship Foundation (ASF) **[2331]**

Astronaut Scholarship Foundation Scholarship [2332]

ATA Research Grants [1624]

Marguerite Chapootian Atamian Memorial Grant [1865]

AT&T Business Internship Awards [11176]

Athalie Clarke Endowed Scholarship [8989]

Athena San Diego Pinnacle Scholarship [9799]

Athenaeum of Philadelphia (PAT) **[2333]**

Martha and Robert Atherton Ministerial Scholarship [11245]

Athletic Equipment Managers Association (AEMA) **[2335]**

Atkinson Charitable Foundation **[2337]**

Atkinson Fellowships in Public Policy [2338]

ISA Aerospace Industries Division - William H. Atkinson Scholarships [6085]

Atlanta Alumnae Chapter Achievement Scholarship [3999]

Atlanta Association of Legal Administrators (AALA) **[2339]**

Atlantic County Bar Association **[2341]**

Atlantic Provinces Library Association (APLA) **[2343]**

Atlantic Salmon Federation (ASF) **[2346]**

Atlantic Salmon Federation Olin Fellowships [2347]

Atlas Shrugged Essay Contest [2395]

ATS Abstract Scholarships [1621]

Attorney-CPA Foundation Scholarships [430]

Elaine Atwood Scholarship [11470]

AUA Foundation Urology Research Bridge Awards [11771]

Aubespin Scholarships [801]

Aubrey L. Williams Research Travel Fellowship [1429]

Audio Engineering Society, Inc. (AES) **[2348]**

Audrey L. Wright Scholarship [5135]

Audrey Loftus Memorial Scholarship [11516]

Audrey Lumsden-Kouvel Fellowship [8369]

A. B. and Hazel Augenstein Scholarship [7078]

Joan Auld Scholarship [3702]

H. Thomas Austern Memorial Writing Competition [4664]

Austin Alumnae Association Beta Xi Scholarship in Memory of Katherine Peeres Woolridge [6400]

Australian-American Health Policy Fellowships [3553]

Autism/ASD Scholarship [6518]

Autism Scholarship [2617], [4051], [4537], [9712]

Auto Accident Law Firm Survivor Scholarships [1758]

Auto Body Technician Certificate Scholarship [9884]

Auto Care Association **[2350]**

Auto-Pets **[2354]**

Auto-Pets "Out-of-the-Box Thinking" Scholarships [2355]

Automotive Industries Association of Canada (AIAC) **[2356]**

Automotive Parts and Service Association of Illinois **[2361]**

Automotive Recyclers Association (ARA) **[2363]**

Automotive Technician Scholarship Program [7160]

Automotive Women's Alliance Foundation (AWAF) **[2365]**

Automotive Women's Alliance Foundation Scholarships [2366]

Auxiliary Undergraduate Scholarships [1998]

AVAC: Global Advocacy for HIV Prevention **[2367]**

AvaCare Medical **[2369]**

AvaCare Medical Scholarship [2370]

Ava's Grace Scholarship Program [9949]

Avery Award [11668]

Dr. Noyes L. Avery, Jr. & Ann E. Avery Scholarship [5136]

Aviation Distributors and Manufacturers Association (ADMA) **[2371]**

Avis Budget Group Scholarships [1585]

AVMA Fellowship Program [1628]

AVS Applied Surface Science Division [2374]

AVS Biomaterial Interfaces Division - Early Career Researchers Awards (BID-ECR) [2375]

AVS Electronic Materials and Photonic Division Postdoctoral Award [2376]

AVS Manufacturing Science and Technology Group [2377]

AVS MEMS and NEMS Technical Group Best Paper Award [2378]

AVS Nanometer-Scale Science and Technology Division Graduate Award [2379]

AVS Science and Technology Society (AVS) **[2373]**

AVS Spectroscopic Ellipsometry Focus Topic Graduate Student Awards [2380]

AVS Thin Film Division James Harper Awards [2381]

Award for Outstanding Doctoral Dissertation in Laser Science [1222]

Award for Outstanding Doctoral Thesis Research in Biological Physics [1223]

AWeber Communications **[2388]**

The Aweber Developing Futures Scholarship [2389]

AWG Minority Scholarship [2313]

AWM Mathematics Travel Grants [2318]

AWMA Louisiana Section Scholarship [167]

AWMA Niagara Frontier Section College Scholarship [169]

AWS International Scholarship Program [1657]

AWSCPA National Scholarships [1678]

AWSM Broadcasting Scholarship [2322]

AWSM Public Relations Scholarship/Internships [2323]

AWWA American Water Scholarship [1636]

AX Control Inc. **[2390]**

AX Control, Inc. Academic Scholarship [2391]

AXA Achievement Scholarship [2393]
AXA Equitable Life Insurance Co. **[2392]**
Susan Ayers Memorial Scholarships [9391]
Ayn Rand Institute (ARI) **[2394]**
Ayn Rand Institute Anthem Essay Contest [2396]
Ayn Rand Institute Fountainhead Essay Contest [2397]
William Stone Ayres Scholarship [4146]
The Azarian Group LLC **[2398]**
John M. Azarian Memorial Armenian Youth Scholarship Fund [2399]
Azrieli Neurodevelopmental Research Program [2671]
AZVT Laurie Page-Peck Scholarship [2325]
B-2 LAFF 20-30's Financial Aid Scholarship [6937]
B-3 LAFF 20-30's Financial Aid Scholarship [6938]
B-4 Albert S. Vieira Memorial Scholarship [6939]
B-Brave McMahon/Stratton Scholarship Fund [4584]
The B. Harper Bull Scholarship Awards [11060]
B. J. Runnels Dean Scholarship Fund [3602]
Tom Babcox Memorial Scholarships [2351]
Carroll Preston Baber Research Grant [1081]
Bach Organ Scholarship [9689]
Bachelor of Science in Nursing Academic Scholarships [7548]
Bachelor's in Nursing Degree Scholarship [8626]
Back to School Scholarship [7437]
BACUS Scholarship [10724]
BadCredit.org **[2400]**
BadCredit.orgs Wealth Wise Scholarship [2401]
Leo Baeck Institute - DAAD Fellowships [4057]
BAFTX Early Starters Award [2696]
BAFTX Graduate Award [2697]
BAFTX Junior Achievers Award [2698]
BAFTX Undergraduate Award [2699]
Baha'i Faith Scholarship for Racial Harmony [9524]
Marian Breland Bailey Award [2063]
The Bailey Family Foundation (BFF) **[2402]**
The Bailey Family Foundation College Scholarship Program [2403]
The Bailey Family Foundation High School Scholarships Program [2404]
Bailey/Hollister Scholarship [8956]
Esther Tuttle Bailey Memorial Scholarship [6401]
Lincoln C. Bailey Memorial Scholarship Fund [6079]
Barbara Bailey Scholarship [9291]
James L. Baillie Memorial Fund - Student Award for Field Research [4451]
Mark B. Bain Graduate Fellowship [5612]
Marian Wood Baird Scholarship [11401]
Michael Baker Corp. Scholarship for Diversity in Engineering [2192]
Baker, Donelson, Bearman, Caldwell and Berkowitz, P.C. **[2405]**
Baker Donelson Diversity Scholarship [2406]
Baker and Hostetler LLP **[2407]**
Baker McKenzie **[2410]**
Baker McKenzie Diversity Fellowship [2411]
Baker McKenzie Graduate Legal Studies Scholarships [2412]
Dr. Jon Baker Memorial Scholarship [11471]
Francis Warren Baker Memorial Scholarships [10094]
Baker Scholarship [4888]
Airgas - Jerry Baker Scholarship [1658]
ACI Baker Student Fellowships [790]
Baker and Taylor Entertainment Audio Music/Video Product Award [9431]
Baker & Taylor/YALSA Collection Development Grant [1083]
BakerHostetler Diversity Fellowship Program [2408]
Bernt Balchen, Jr. and Olav Jorgen Hegge Hardingfele Scholarships [5292]
Norman S. Baldwin Fishery Science Scholarship [5923]
Franklin Mosher Baldwin Memorial Fellowships [6751]
Victoria Baldwin Memorial Scholarship [12285]
Lynn Ann Baldwin Scholarships [2093]
Donald A. Baldwin Sr. Business Aviation Management Scholarship [7733]
Balestreri/Cutino Scholarship [841]
Balfour Scholarship [9087]
Ball Horticultural Company Scholarship [894]
Vic and Margaret Ball Student Intern Scholarships [895]

Ballantyne Resident Research Grant [956]
Ballard Breaux Visiting Fellowships [4558]
Ballard Family Foundation Scholarships [9800]
Irene Ballinger Memorial Scholarship [7079]
Baltimore City Community College (BCCC) **[2413]**
Baltimore Community Fellowships [8663]
Bambi Bailey Scholarship Fund [3589]
Mary A. Bancroft Memorial Scholarship [6372]
B&W Y-12 Scholarship Fund [4254]
Banff Centre for Arts and Creativity **[2416]**
Bank of America Junior Achievement Scholarship in honor of Donna Champion Fund [4719]
Bank of Canada **[2422]**
Bank of Canada Fellowship Award [2423]
Bank of Canada Governor's Awards [2424]
Brenda S. Bank Educational Workshop Scholarship [10341]
Bank of Hawaii Foundation Scholarship Fund [5382]
Bank of Nova Scotia - Barbados **[2425]**
Dr. Johnella Banks Memorial Scholarships [2610]
Banner Bank Business Scholarship [6783]
Mark T. Banner Scholarships for Law Students [6873]
Banner & Witcoff Ltd. **[2427]**
James M. Banovetz Illinois Local Government Fellowships [5698]
Banting Postdoctoral Fellowships Program [3804]
Baptist Communicators Association (BCA) **[2429]**
Bar Association of San Francisco (BASF) **[2432]**
Bar President's Scholarship [11931]
Barakat Trust and Barakat Foundation Scholarships [1767]
Barbara A. Cooley Master's Scholarship [10348]
Barbara A. Shacochis Scholarship [8990]
Barbara Bonnema Memorial Scholarship [9525]
Barbara Hagan Richards Scholarship Fund [3603]
Barbara Jordan Memorial Scholarships [2300]
Barbara and Nicole Heacox Foreign Study & Travel Scholarship [5068]
Joe Barbarow Memorial Scholarship [8832]
Barber-Owen-Thomas Scholarship [10095]
UAA Janice K. Barden Aviation Scholarship [7734]
Edgar Barge Memorial Scholarship [5118]
Bariatric Surgery Source, LLC **[2434]**
UAA Michael Baring-Gould Memorial Scholarship [11472]
TCDA Carroll Barnes Student Scholarships [740]
Marguerite Ross Barnett Fund [1254]
Gina L. Barnhart Memorial Scholarship Fund [4585]
Baron and Budd Attorneys Mesothelioma Cancer Victims Memorial Scholarships [2437]
Baron and Budd P.C. **[2436]**
Barr Foundation Scholarship [3337]
Barrett Family Scholarship Fund [3338]
Barrientos Scholarship Foundation (BSF) **[2438]**
Barriger - Zachary Barriger Memorial Scholarship Fund [3463]
Gloria Barron Wilderness Society Scholarship [12031]
Barry "Tyler" Rhea Memorial Scholarship [8503]
Barry M. Goldwater Scholarship [11733]
Barta-Lehman Musical Scholarship [9801]
The Jean Bartel Military Scholarship [7415]
Eivind H. Barth, Jr. Memorial Award [2847]
Barth Syndrome Foundation (BSF) **[2440]**
M. Elizabeth C. Bartlet Fund [1142]
William E. Barto Scholarship Fund [4200]
Barton Springs/Edwards Aquifer Conservation District (BSEACD) **[2442]**
Walt Bartram Memorial Education Scholarship [10384]
The Bascom Hill Society Scholarship [11734]
Jan S. Bashinski Criminalistics Graduate Thesis Assistance Grant [4676]
Forrest Bassford Student Award [6881]
Bat and Ball Game **[2444]**
Bat and Ball Game Womens Sports Scholarship [2445]
Bat Conservation International (BCI) **[2446]**
Bat Conservation International Granting Programs [2447]
H. Burton Bates Jr. Scholarships [11843]
W. H. (Bert) Bates Oxford Cup Scholarship [2503]
Jim Batten Community Newspaper Internship [11177]
Raymond B. Bauer Research Award [7322]

Marian Sims Baughn Scholarship [6402]
The Ernest L. Baulch, W2TX, and Marcia E. Baulch, WA2AKJ, Scholarship [1927]
Hazel Reed Baumeister Scholarship Program [10130]
Baurkot & Baurkot: The Immigration Law Group **[2448]**
Baxter Corporation Canadian Research Awards in Anesthesia [2877]
Bay Area Minority Law Student Scholarship [2433]
Lawrence Bayer Business Administration Scholarships [11437]
Timothy Baylink Good Fellowship Awards [9526]
John Bayliss Broadcast Foundation Internship Programs [2451]
John Bayliss Broadcast Foundation **[2450]**
John Bayliss Broadcast Foundation Radio Scholarships [2452]
Bayly-Tiffany Scholarships [11712]
BBPA First Generation Scholarship [2587]
B.C. Road Builders and Heavy Construction Association (BCRB & HCA) **[2453]**
BCCC Foundation General Scholarship Fund [2414]
BCCC Workforce Creation Scholarship [2415]
BCPF Bursaries [10731]
BCSF Scholarships [2604]
BDC Visiting Fellowship [2715]
BDPA Education and Technology Foundation (BETF) **[2455]**
William B. Bean Student Research Award [1196]
James Beard Foundation Scholarship Program [9939]
Beatitudes Fellowships [2458]
The Beatitudes Society **[2457]**
Catherine H. Beattie Fellowships [3238], [4858]
The Dora J. Beattie IBEA Scholarship [5695]
Suzanne Beauregard Scholarships [5027]
Beaver Medical Clinic Foundation - Dr. Glenn Adams Memorial Award [9527]
Beaver Medical Clinic Foundation - H.E.A.R.T. Academy Award [9528]
Beaver Medical Clinic Foundation - Premedical Award [9529]
Beaverbrook Media at McGill Student Paper Prize [2955]
BECA Foundation **[2459]**
BECA General Scholarship [2461]
Becas Univision Scholarship Program [5528]
Bechtel Engineering and Science Scholarship [7075]
Louise Seaman Bechtel Fellowship [2239]
Stephen D. Bechtel, Jr. Oxford Cup Scholarship [2504]
Dennis J. Beck Memorial Scholarship [6193]
Beck – O.J. Beck, Jr. Memorial Scholarship [3464]
Beck-Pfann Memorial Scholarship [8991]
Garvin L. Beck Scholarships [9530]
Ed Becker Conference Travel Awards [4403]
Dr. Ann C. Beckingham Scholarships [3056]
Jenny Panitch Beckow Memorial Scholarship - Canada [6283]
Jenny Panitch Beckow Memorial Scholarship - Israel [6284]
Clifford L. Bedford Scholarship Award [5220]
The Paul B. Beeson Emerging Leaders Career Development Award in Aging(K76) [875], [5310]
BEF General Academic Scholarships [4438]
BEF Sacks For CF Scholarship [4439]
BEF Scholarship of the Arts [4440]
Notah Begay III Scholarship Program [317]
Charles E. Behlke Engineering Memorial Scholarships [11438]
Beinecke Rare Book & Manuscript Library **[2463]**
Beinecke Rare Book and Manuscript Library Visiting Postdoctoral Scholar Fellowships [2464]
N.S. Beinstock Fellowships [9469]
Hannah Beiter Graduate Student Research Grants [3296]
Bel Canto Vocal Scholarship Foundation **[2466]**, [2467]
Belfer-Aptman Dissertation Research Awards [7247]
Bell Aliant Medical Education Scholarship [8223]
Max Bell Foundation **[2468]**
Alfred D. Bell, Jr. Travel Grants [4681]
John Bell and Lawrence Thornton Scholarship Fund [5315]

Sponsor and Scholarship Index

Harvey Bell Memorial Prize [11674]

The Betty Bell Scholarship Fund [5548]

Beverlee Bell Scholarships in Human Rights and Democracy [4136]

Max Bell Senior Fellow Grants [2469]

Bradley Stuart Beller Special Merit Award [3768]

Bellevue PFLAG Scholarships [9292]

Belmont University **[2470]**

Belmont University Commercial Music Showcase Scholarship Fund [2471], [3604]

Mark A. Beltz Scholarship [11473]

Samuel Flagg Bemis Dissertation Research Grants [10354]

Ben C. Francis Risk Management Education Fund [9385]

Ben Robinette Scholarship Fund [4720]

Benbrook Scholarship [1838]

Benchwarmers Club of Redlands Scholarship- Jess Mercado Memorial [9531]

Reckitt Benckiser Student Scholarships [7677]

The Richard W. Bendicksen, N7ZL, Memorial Scholarship [1928]

Bill Bendiner and Doug Morgenson Scholarship [9293]

H. Y. Benedict Fellowships [376]

George Benes, MD & Michael Mallee, EdD Point Scholarships [9218]

Benign Essential Blepharospasm Research Foundation (BEBRF) **[2472]**

Benign Essential Blepharospasm Research Foundation Research Grants [2473]

Benjamin G. Shatz Scholarship [8992]

Benjamin Kaminer Endowed Scholarship in Physiology [7038]

Benjamin Riggs Scholarship [4916]

HDR/Henry "Bud" Benjes Scholarships [1637]

Viscount Bennett Fellowship [2918]

Bertram W. Bennett Memorial Scholarship [2505]

Bennett – Reverend E.F. Bennett Scholarship [3465]

The William Bennett, W7PHO, Memorial Scholarship [1929]

Pete and Ellen Bensley Memorial Scholarship Fund [4721]

Benson & Bingham **[2474]**

Benson & Bingham First Annual Scholarship [2475]

Benson Law Firm **[2476]**

Benson Law Firm Scholarship Contest [2477]

The Bentley Cropping Systems Fellowship [3263]

Benton Community Foundation (BCF) **[2478]**

Benton-Meier Scholarships [1278]

Linn-Benton County Scholarships [8719]

Rosalie Bentzinger Scholarships [4889]

Fred Berg Awards [4299]

Bergman Scholarship [8460]

Bergmann Family Scholarship [7080]

The E. Alexander Bergstrom Memorial Research Award [2177]

The Joseph Berkman, and Michael and Sarah Chipkin Holocaust/Genocide Studies Award [10842]

Berkowitz Fellowship [11032]

Berks County Community Foundation **[2487]**

Louise Berman Fellows Award [6378]

Bernard Amtmann Fellowship [2569]

Bernard B. and Mary L. Brusin Scholarship Fund [4201]

Bernard Kilgore Memorial Scholarship [8282]

Bernard Michel Scholarship [2862]

Richard L. Bernardi Memorial Scholarship [3668]

Bill Bernbach Diversity Scholarships [510]

Bernice Barabash Sports Scholarship [6194]

Robert L. Bernstein Fellowships in International Human Rights [5630]

Leslie Bernstein Grant [452]

Thomas M. Berry Jr. Scholarships [11844]

Alec Berry Scholarship [12286]

Jean Clark Berry Scholarship [6403]

The Bert Saperstein Communication Scholarship Fund [2490]

The Bert Saperstein Communications Scholarship Fund **[2489]**

James R. and Geraldine F. Bertelsen Scholarship [9802]

Bertha M. Fase Memorial Scholarship [5069]

Berton W. Huestis Memorial Scholarship [8224]

Henry Besner Memorial Scholarship [12287]

Best Foot Forward Scholarship [5203]

The Best Hoverboard **[2491]**

The Best Hoverboard Scholarship Era [2492]

Booksrun Scholarship Financial Aid [2653]

Beta Beta Beta **[2493]**

Beta Foundation Merit Scholarships [2506]

Beta Gamma Memorial Scholarship [4000]

Beta Lambda Project 2000 Scholarship [6404]

Beta Mu Project 2000 Scholarship [6405]

Beta Phi Mu **[2495]**

Beta Pi Project 2000 Scholarship in Memory of Kristy LeMond [6406]

Beta Pi Sigma Sorority, Inc. (BPSSI) **[2500]**

Beta Pi Sigma Sorority Local Chapter Scholarship (BPSSS) [2501]

Beta Province Project 2000 Scholarship [6407]

Beta Sigma Phi Visual Arts Scholarship [10049]

Beta Sigma Scholarship [10096]

Beta Tau Scholarship Fund [6408]

Beta Theta Memorial Scholarship [6409]

Beta Theta Pi **[2502]**

Beta Xi Project 2000 Scholarship [6410]

Beta Zeta Project 2000 Scholarship [6411]

Beth Carew Memorial Scholarship Program [7920]

Beth K. Fields Scholarship [11574]

Bethesda Lutheran Communities **[2561]**

Bethune-Cookman University (B-CU) **[2563]**

Bethune-Cookman University Excelsior Level 1 Scholarship [2564]

Bethune-Cookman University Presidential Scholarship [2565]

Betsy B. and Garold A. Leach Scholarship [4028]

Harold Bettinger Scholarship [896]

Leonard Bettinger Vocational Scholarship [897]

Betty Rose Scholarship [1407]

William and Dorothy Bevan Scholarship [1279]

Albert J. Beveridge Grant for Research in the History of the Western Hemisphere [959]

Beverley Mascoll Scholarship [2588]

Beverly Estate Scholarship [4147]

Beyond the Cure Ambassador Scholarship Program [7767]

Dr. Noorali and Sabiya Bharwani Endowment [8413]

Hussein Jina Bharwani Memorial Endowment [8414]

BHCRI Bridge Funds [5648]

BHCRI Cancer Research Training Program (CRTP) Awards [5649]

BHCRI Matching Funds [5650]

BHCRI Miscellaneous Funds [5651]

BHCRI Seed Funds [5652]

BHCRI Studentship Awards [5653]

Leo Biaggi de Blasys Bogliasco Fellowships [2642]

Bibliographical Society of America (BSA) **[2566]**

Bibliographical Society of Canada (BSC) **[2568]**

Bick Bickson Scholarship Fund [5383]

Timothy Bierlmeier Memorial Scholarships [12288]

Big Sandy Community and Technical College (BSCTC) **[2571]**

Pierre and Patricia Bikai Fellowship [725]

Bill Dickey Scholarship Association Scholarship [4082]

Bill Egan Memorial Award [8702]

Bill McCarthy Boy Scout Scholarship Fund [10752]

Bill and Nell Biggs Scholarship [11508]

Joan Bilton Scholarship [12289]

Jan Bingle Scholarships [3438]

Helen & Bob Bintz Scholarship [7081]

BioCommunications Association (BCA) **[2574]**

Biological Survey of Canada Scholarship [4404]

Biomedical Engineering Society (BMES) **[2577]**

Biomedical Research Grants [6545]

Birgit Baldwin Fellowship [7229]

Birmingham District Alabama Dietetic Association Scholarships [217]

Birmingham Public School **[2579]**

Birmingham-Southern College Eagle Scout Scholarships [7845]

Birmingham Student Scholarships [2580]

Bisexual Foundation Scholarships [1736]

Bisnar Chase, Personal Injury Attorneys LLP **[2581]**

Mary E. Bivins Foundation **[2583]**

Dr. Richard E. Bjork Memorial Graduate Study Award [10843]

BK Lighting / Ron Naus Scholarship [5935]

Law Offices of David A. Black Annual Hearing Impaired Scholarships [6701]

Black Business and Professional Association (BBPA) **[2585]**

Black Canadian Scholarship Fund **[2603]**

Black Caucus of the American Library Association (BCALA) **[2605]**

SETAC/EA Jeff Black Fellowship Award [10324]

Black Men Building Resources Scholarship [5137]

Black Note Inc. **[2607]**

Black Nurses Association of Greater Washington D.C. Area (BNA-GWDCA) **[2609]**

Black Rock Arts Foundation (BRAF) **[2612]**

Thomas J. Black Scholarship [12290]

Black Theatre Network (BTN) **[2614]**

Black Wynn PLLC **[2616]**

Eileen Blackey Doctoral Fellowship [7696]

NICSA/William T. Blackwell Scholarship Fund [7952]

Mitzi & William Blahd, MD, Pilot Research Grant [10437]

Blair Chiropractic Society **[2619]**

Beatrice K. Blair Scholarships [2620]

Thomas M. Blake Memorial Scholarships [3753]

Blake-Nuttall Fund Grants [8565]

Blakemore Foundation **[2621]**

Blakemore Freeman Fellowships [2622]

Blanche E. Woolls Scholarship [2496]

Blanche Raper Zimmerman Scholarship [12062]

Kyle R. Blanco Memorial Scholarship [2507]

Blaski Alex Memorial Scholarship [9657]

Joan Blend Scholarship Fund [10753]

Blinded Veterans Association (BVA) **[2623]**

Everitt P. Blizard Memorial Scholarship [1163]

Ellin Bloch and Pierre Ritchie Diversity Dissertation Grant [1269]

Jeanne Humphrey Block Dissertation Award [5363]

Ellen Blodgett Memorial Scholarship [8333]

Blood Assurance Foundation **[2625]**

Bloom Legal LLC **[2627]**

BluePay Processing L.L.C. **[2629]**

Bluepay Stem Scholarship [2630]

Blues Heaven Foundation (BHF) **[2631]**

Stella Blum Research Grant [3843]

BMES Graduate and Undergraduate Student Awards [2578]

BMI Foundation **[2633]**

BMO Capital Markets Lime Connect Equity through Education Scholarships [6860]

BMO Financial Group Lime Connect Canada Scholarship Program for Students with Disabilities [6861]

BMO Medical Education Scholarship [8225]

Board of Certification for Emergency Nursing (BCEN) Undergraduate Scholarship [4376]

Bob Baxter Scholarship [8046]

Bob and Dawn Hardy Automotive Scholarship [6195]

Bob East Scholarship [8047]

Bob and Linda Kohlhepp Scholarship Fund [3339]

Bob Quincy Scholarship [11178]

Sandra Bobbitt Continuing Education Scholarship [2254]

BOCA Scholarship [8796]

Bodie McDowell Scholarship [8782]

Edith and Arnold N. Bodtker Grants [3968]

Body of Young Adult Advisors Scholarship (BOYAA) [11167]

Boeing Business Scholarships [5020]

Boeing Company Scholarship [10050]

B.O.G. Pest Control **[2638]**

The B.O.G. Pest Control Scholarship Funds [2639]

Gerald J. and Helen Bogen Fund [5225]

Bogliasco Fellowships [2643]

Bogliasco Foundation - Liguria Study Center for the Arts and Humanities **[2640]**

Sarkis Bogosian Memorial Grant [1866]

Therese and David Bohbot Scholarship [6285]

Bohemian Lawyers' Association of Chicago (BLAC) **[2648]**

Bohemian Lawyers Association of Chicago Scholarships [2649]

Bolick Foreign Student Scholarships [11439]

Brian Bolton Graduate/Mature Student Essay Awards [4823]

BOMA/NY Scholarship [2741]

Fondation J. Armand Bombardier **[2650]**

Yvonne L. Bombardier Visual Arts Scholarship Program [2651]

Canadian Hard of Hearing Association Scholarship Program [2997]
Canadian Hemophilia Society (CHS) **[3000]**
Canadian Historical Geography Award [2086]
Canadian Home Economics Association Fellowship (CHEA) [2969]
Canadian Hospitality Foundation (CHF) **[3004]**
Canadian Hydrographic Association **[3007]**
Canadian Hydrographic Association Student Award [3008]
Canadian Identification Society (CIS) **[3009]**
Canadian Identification Society Essay/Scholarship Awards [3010]
Canadian Imperial Bank Of Commerce (CIBC) **[3013]**
Canadian Indigenous Nurses Association (CINA) **[3015]**
Canadian Institute for the Administration of Justice (CIAJ) **[3017]**
Canadian Institute for Advanced Legal Studies French Language Scholarships [5793]
Canadian Institute for Advanced Research (CIFAR) **[3019]**
Canadian Institute of Geomatics (CIG) **[3021]**
Canadian Institute of Planners (CIP) **[3023]**
Canadian Institute of Ukrainian Studies (CIUS) **[3025]**
Canadian Iranian Foundation (CIF) **[3034]**
Canadian Iranian Foundation Scholarship [3035]
Canadian IT Law Association Student Writing Contest [3132]
Canadian Japanese-Mennonite Scholarship [7254]
Canadian Library Association (CLA) **[3036]**
Canadian Meteorological and Oceanographic Society (CMOS) **[3039]**
Canadian National Institute for the Blind (CNIB) **[3046]**
Canadian National Railway Co. **[3051]**
Canadian Nurses Foundation (CNF) **[3053]**
Canadian Nurses Foundation Northern Award [3057]
Canadian Nurses Foundation Scholarships [3058]
Canadian Occupational Therapy Foundation (COTF) **[3076]**
Canadian Office Products Association (COPA) **[3083]**
Canadian Pain Society (CPS) **[3085]**
Canadian Pain Society Post-Doctoral Fellowship Awards [3086]
The Canadian Parking Association Scholarship (CPA) [2125]
Canadian Physiotherapy Association - Physiotherapy Foundation of Canada **[3095]**
Canadian Picture Pioneers (CPP) **[3099]**
Canadian Picture Pioneers Scholarship [3100]
Canadian Poultry Research Council (CPRC) **[3101]**
The Canadian Poultry Research Council Postgraduate Scholarship [3102]
Canadian Public Relations Society (CPRS) **[3103]**
Canadian Seniors' Golf Association Scholarships [5028]
Canadian Simmental Association (CSA) **[3105]**
Canadian Society of Agronomy (CSA) **[3107]**
Canadian Society of Biblical Studies (CSBS) **[3109]**
Canadian Society for Civil Engineering (CSCE) **[3111]**
Canadian Society of Club Managers (CSCM) **[3113]**
Canadian Society of Exploration Geophysicists (CSEG) **[3115]**
Canadian Society for Medical Laboratory Science (CSMLS) **[3117]**
Canadian Society of Otolaryngology - Head and Neck Surgery (CSOHNS) **[3119]**
Canadian Society of Petroleum Geologists (CSPG) **[3121]**
Canadian Society for Pharmacology and Therapeutics Clinical Fellowship Award [6624]
Canadian Society for the Study of Higher Education (CSSHE) **[3123]**
Canadian Student Leadership Association (CSLA) **[3126]**
Canadian Studies Postdoctoral Fellowships [3800]
Canadian Technical Asphalt Association (CTAA) **[3129]**
Canadian Technical Asphalt Association Scholarships [3130]

Canadian Technology Law Association **[3131]**
Canadian Transportation Research Forum (CTRF) **[3133]**
Canadian Water Resources Association Harker/Cameron Women in Water Scholarship [2107]
Canadian Water and Wastewater Association (CWWA) **[3135]**
Canadian Zionist Federation - Dr. Leon Aryeh Kronitz Scholarship [2984]
Cancer for College (CFC) **[3137]**
Cancer for College Scholarship [3138]
Cancer Research Institute (CRI) **[3139]**
Cancer Research Society (CRS) **[3143]**
Cancer Survivors' Fund **[3145]**
Cancer Survivors' Fund Scholarship [3146]
Candon, Todd, & Seabolt Scholarship Fund [5385]
CANFIT Nutrition, Physical Education and Culinary Arts Scholarships [3561]
Canham Graduate Studies Scholarship [11927]
Therese A. "Teri" Cannon Educational Scholarship [6061]
CANS/SNRS Dissertation Research Grant [10658]
Commander Ronald J. Cantin Scholarships [3454]
CAP Student Leadership Award [2910]
CAPAL Public Service Scholarships [3734]
Cape Coral Community Foundation (CCCF) **[3147]**
Cape Fear Community College Foundation (CFCC) **[3150]**
Capital City AIDS Fund (CCAF) **[3152]**
Kasie Ford Capling Memorial Scholarship Endowment Fund [4723]
The Lester J. Cappon Fellowship in Documentary Editing [8370]
CAPSLE Bursary. [2908]
CAPT Winifred Quick Collins, USN (Ret.) Scholarship [8172]
Captain Jodi Callahan Memorial Scholarship [147]
CarBrain LLC **[3154]**
The CarBrain.com Scholarship [3155]
Cardiac Health Foundation of Canada **[3157]**
Cardiac Health Foundation of Canada Scholarship [3158]
Daniel Cardillo Charitable Fund [6975]
CardRates.com **[3160]**
CardRates.com Financial Futures Scholarship [3161]
Career Awards for Medical Scientists (CAMS) [2751]
Career Awards for Science and Mathematics Teachers [2752]
Career Awards at the Scientific Interface (CASI) [2753]
Career Development Grant in molecular genetics [11071]
Career Development Scholarships [4666]
Career Enhancement Grant [4432]
Career Mobility Scholarships [4791]
Career Transition For Dancers (CTFD) **[3162]**
CareerFitter Online Scholarship [3165]
CareerFitter.com **[3164]**
Vyaire Fellowship for Neonatal and Pediatric Therapists [1352]
John Carew Memorial Scholarship [899]
Carey Family Scholarship [7086]
Caribbean Actuarial Scholarship [70]
Caribbean Hotel and Tourism Association (CHTA) **[3166]**
Caribbean Hotel and Tourism Association Scholarship [3167]
Carrie and George Lyter Scholarship [4775]
Carin Alma E. Somers Scholarship [2345]
Carl A. Scott Book Scholarship [3873]
Carl E. Brooks Scholarship Fund [10673]
Carl H. Lindner Family Fund [3341]
Carl & Lucille Jarrett Scholarship Fund [4587]
William F. Carl Scholarships [8443]
Carli Edwards Memorial Scholarship [10051]
Carlos M. Castaneda Journalism Scholarship [4840]
Gladys Ross Carlson Adelphe Scholarship Fund [6413]
Lyle Carlson Wildlife Management Scholarships [11443]
Carnegie Corporation of New York **[3168]**
Carnegie Institution for Science **[3172]**
Carnegie Observatories Graduate Research Fellowships [3173]
Herb Carnegie Scholarship [2590]

CARO-ELEKTA Research Fellowship Program [2102]
Carol Anne Letheren Entrance Award [12250]
Carol Bond Fund Community College Students Scholarship [8452]
Carol Bond Scholarship [8453]
The Carolina Panthers Players Sam Mills Memorial Scholarship [4724]
Carolinas-Virginias Hardware Scholarship [4725]
Caroline M. Hewins Scholarship [5351]
Carolyn Gallmeyer Scholarship [5140]
Carolyn Wones Recruitment Grant [3671]
Pete Carpenter Fellowship [2634]
Carpenters' Company of the City and County of Philadelphia **[3174]**
Carpenters' Company Scholarship Program [3175]
Willis H. Carrier Scholarships [1471]
Robert C. Carson Memorial Bursary [287]
Rachel Carson Prize [1450]
Gene Carte Student Paper Competition Awards [1419]
Carter G. Woodson Institute Post-doctoral Residential Research & Teaching Fellowship [12183]
Carter G. Woodson Institute Pre-doctoral Fellowship [12184]
Leigh Carter Scholarship Fund [3606]
Letitia B. Carter Scholarships [9649]
Karin Carton Scholarship [4850]
CartVela **[3176]**
Orin Carver Scholarship [3703]
CAS/GE Healthcare Canada Inc. Research Awards [2878]
CAS Research Award in Neuroanesthesia [2879]
CAS Trust Scholarship Program [3183]
CAS/Vitaid-LMA Residents' Research Grant Competition [2880]
CASBS Fellowships [3208]
Cascade Blues Association (CBA) **[3178]**
Cascara Vacation Rentals **[3180]**
Cascara Vacation Rentals Hospitality Matters Scholarships [3181]
Casey Family Services Alumni Scholarship [4693]
Joe & Peggy Casey Memorial Scholarship [7087]
TCDA Jim and Glenda Casey Professional Scholarships [741]
CASFM-Ben Urbonas Scholarship [3524]
Fraser Milner Casgrain Scholarships [2418]
George H. and Anna Casper Fund [10755]
Thomas D. and Karen H. Cassady Scholarship [2515]
Castellini Foundation Scholarship [3342]
Kerri Castellini Women's Leadership Scholarship [9280]
Castle & Cooke George W.Y. Yim Scholarship Fund [5386]
Castle & Cooke Mililani Technology Park Scholarship Fund [5387]
Casualty Actuarial Society (CAS) **[3182]**
Caswell Grave Scholarship [7041]
Catharine Wilder Guiles Scholarship [6976]
Catherine E. Philbin Scholarship [4898]
Catholic Biblical Association of America (CBA) **[3185]**
Catholic Relief Services (CRS) **[3187]**
Catholic Relief Services Summer Internship [3188]
Catholic United Financial **[3189]**
Catrala - Hawaii Scholarship Fund [5388]
Catzman Award for Professionalism and Civility [96]
Cave Conservancy Foundation **[3191]**
Graduate and Undergraduate Fellowship Awards [3195]
Cave Conservancy of the Virginias (CCV) **[3194]**
Ben and Vicky Cayetano Scholarship Fund [5389]
Llewellyn L. Cayvan String Instrument Scholarship [5141]
CBC Spouses Education Scholarship [3738]
CBC Spouses Performing Arts Scholarship [3739]
CBC Spouses Visual Arts Scholarship [3740]
CBCF - BC/Yukon Region Breast Cancer Research Grants Competition [2924]
CBCF - BC/Yukon Region Breast Cancer Survivor Dragon Boat Grants [2925]
CBCF - BC/Yukon Region Community Health Grants [2926]
CBCF - BC/Yukon Region Small Initiative Funds [2927]

CBCF - Ontario Nurse and Allied Health Professional Fellowships [2929]
CBCF - Ontario Physician Fellowships [2930]
CBCF - Ontario Research Fellowships [2931]
CBCF - Ontario Research Project Grants [2932]
CBCF - Prairies/NWT Grants in Basic Biomedical Research [2934]
CBCF - Prairies/NWT Grants in Clinical Research [2935]
CBCF - Prairies/NWT Grants in Health Services and Policy Research [2936]
CBCF - Prairies/NWT Postdoctoral Fellowships [2937]
CBCF - Prairies/NWT Research Grants in Psychosocial, Cultural and Environmental Determinants of Health [2938]
CCAE Ontario Regional Chapter Scholarship [6742]
CCCN Research Grant Program [3791]
CCF Academic Fellowships in Karst Studies - Graduate [3192]
CCF Academic Fellowships in Karst Studies - Undergraduate [3193]
CCF Career Development Award [3769]
CCF Improving Cancer Care Grants [3770]
CCF Merit Award [3771]
CCFA Career Development Awards [3911]
CCFA Research Fellowship Awards [3912]
CCFA Student Research Fellowship Awards [3913]
CCFF Clinical Fellowships [4543]
CCFF Fellowships [4544]
CCFF Scholarships [4545]
CCGSE Mentorship Award [10261]
C.C.H.R.M.A. Scholarships [3469]
CCLA Summer Legal Volunteer Opportunities for Law Students and Law Graduates [2948]
CCNMA: Latino Journalists of California [3196]
CCTS services, resources, and pilot awards [8603]
CCU Endowed Scholarships [3528]
CCWH / Berks Graduate Student Fellowship [3828]
C.D. Howard Scholarship [5970]
CDA Foundation [3199]
CDC Foundation [3201]
CDC Steven M. Teutsch Prevention Effectiveness (PE) [11328]
Cecelia Connelly Graduate Scholarship in Underwater Archaeology [12135]
Betty J. Cecere Memorial Scholarship Endowment Fund [11944]
Cecilia Rowan Memorial Fellowship [8638]
CEDAM International [3203]
Cedarcrest Farms Scholarships [1058]
CEE Cultural Diversity Grant [7798]
CEIBS scholarship [7724]
CEJIL Communications Internships [3230]
CEJIL Legal Internships [3231]
Celler Legal, P.A. [3205]
Celler Legal P.A. Employment Skills Scholarship Program [3206]
CEMF Engineering Ambassador Awards [2964]
CEMF Rona Hatt Chemical Engineering Ambassador Award [2965]
Cengage Travel Award for Teachers of Reading at a Community College [3512]
Cenie Jomo Williams Tuition Scholarship [7617]
DAR Centennial Scholarship [8094]
Center for Advanced Study in the Behavioral Sciences (CASBS) [3207]
Center for Book Arts (CBA) [3209]
Center for Craft, Creativity and Design (CCCD) [3211]
Center for the Education of Women Scholarships [11635]
Center for the Education of Women Student Research Grants [11636]
Center for Engineering in Medicine Predoctoral Fellows Program [7132]
Center For Religious Humanism [3213]
Center for Global Initiatives [3216]
Center for International Environmental Law (CIEL) [3218]
Center for Jewish History (CJH) [3220]
The Center for Justice & Accountability [3227]
Center for Justice and International Law [3229]
Center for LGBTQ Studies (CLAGS) [3232]
Center for Plant Conservation (CPC) [3237]
Centerville-Abington Dollars for Scholars [11945]

The Central Arizona DX Association Scholarship [1932]
Central Farm Service [3239]
Central Florida Jazz Society (CFJS) [3241]
Central Florida Jazz Society Scholarships [3242]
Central Indiana Jim Kriner Memorial Scholarship [1563]
Central Intelligence Agency (CIA) [3243]
Central Pacific Bank Scholarship Fund [5390]
Central Texas Bluegrass Association (CTBA) [3245]
CentraState Associated Auxiliaries Scholarship [3248]
CentraState Band Aid Open Committee Scholarship [3249]
CentraState Healthcare Foundation [3247]
CentraState Healthcare Foundation Health Professions Scholarships [3250]
Centre for Interdisciplinary Research in Music Media and Technology (CIRMMT) [3252]
Centre International de Criminologie Comparée (CICC) [3254]
Centre for International Sustainable Development Law (CISDL) [3256]
Centre pour l'Innovation dans la Gouvernance Internationale (CIGI) [3260]
Centre de Recherches pour le Développement International (CRDI) [3262]
Cereals & Grains Association [3265]
Certified in Care Coordination and Transition Management (CCCTM) Certification Grant [427]
Certified Neuroscience Registered Nurse Recertification Grant Program [610]
The Cerutti Group Scholarship [5208]
Arthur and Gladys Cervenka Scholarship [10385]
CES Conference Travel Grants [3856]
CESEF Postgraduate Scholarship Program [4660]
CfA Postdoctoral Fellowship [5357]
CFCC Foundation Merit Scholarship [3151]
CFF Grants [3948]
CFF/NIH-Unfunded Award [3949]
CFF Pilot and Feasibility Awards [3950]
CFN Interdisciplinary Fellowships Program [2982]
CFNIL Senior Memorial Scholarship [3672]
CFR Military Fellowships [3860]
CFR National Intelligence Fellowships [3861]
CFR Stanton Nuclear Security Fellowship [3862]
CFR Volunteer Internships [3863]
CFSA Aon Fire Protection Engineering Award [2115]
CFSA City of Markham, Buildings Standards Department Award [2116]
CFSA Fire Safety Awards [2117]
CFSA Founders Award for Leadership & Excellence [2118]
CFSA Leber Rubes Inc. Awards [2119]
CFSA LRI Engineering Award [2120]
CFSA Nadine International Awards [2121]
CFSA Siemens Canada Award [2122]
CFSA Underwriters' Laboratories of Canada Awards [2123]
CFT/ACPSOP Scholarship Fund [3343]
CFUW Aboriginal Women's Award [2970]
CFUW Memorial Fellowship [2971]
CGA Scholarships [2812]
CGNA Memorial Scholarship [2990]
CGPF Endowments Conference Scholarships [2994]
CGSA Student Scholarship Awards [2992]
CGTrader [3268]
CH2M/AEESP Outstanding Doctoral Dissertation Award [2164], [3271]
CH2M HILL Companies, Ltd. [3270]
Rick Chace Foundation Scholarships [2246]
Chaîne des Rôtisseurs Scholarships [842]
ChairScholars Florida Scholarship Program [3274]
ChairScholars Foundation [3273]
ChairScholars National Program [3275]
Jeanne S. Chall Research Fellowship [6033]
The Challenge Met Scholarship [1933]
Mariam K. Chamberlain Fellowship in Women and Public Policy [5874]
Logan S. Chambers Individual Scholarship [5952]
Bryan A. Champion Memorial Scholarship [5586]
Emi Chance for Aspiring Artists Scholarship [11475]
Channabasappa Memorial Scholarships [5993]
Harry H. and Floy B. Chapin Scholarships [3673]
Oscar Chapman Memorial Scholarship [2516]

Nancy J. Chapman Scholarships [2152]
Chappie Hall Scholarship [2]
Chapter 1 - Detroit Associate Scholarship [10386]
Chapter 1 Detroit Undergraduate Scholarship [10387]
Chapter 17 - St. Louis Scholarship [10388]
Chapter 23 - Quad Cities Scholarship [10389]
Chapter 31 - Peoria Scholarship [10390]
Chapter 4 - Lawrence A. Wacker Memorial Scholarship [10391]
Chapter 52 - Wichita Scholarship [10392]
Chapter 56 - Ft. Wayne Scholarship [10393]
Chapter 6 - Fairfield County Scholarship [10394]
Chapter 63 - Morrow Scholarship [10395]
Chapter 63 - Smith Memorial Scholarship [10396]
Chapter 67 - Phoenix Scholarship [10397]
Chapter 79/198/311 Scholarship [10398]
Chapter 93 - Albuquerque Scholarship [10399]
Charles A. King Trust Postdoctoral Research Fellowship [5434]
Charles A. Lindbergh Fellowships [10191]
Charles and Carol Spielberger Scholarship [1280]
Charles (Charlie) A. Bassett Endowed Scholarship [5070]
Charles and Claire Phillips Scholarship Fund [3344]
Charles E. Peterson Fellowships [2334]
Charles and Eleanor Rycenga Education Scholarship [5071]
Charles Fred Wonson Scholarship [11713]
Charles Grossman Graduate Scholarship [5978]
Charles H. Bussmann Graduate Scholarship [7068]
Charles H. Stone-Piedmont Scholarship [657]
Charles Lee Anderson Memorial Scholarship [3674]
Charles McCorkle Hauser Scholarship [11179]
Charles S. Houston Grant [12028]
Charles Shafae Scholarship [8818]
Charlie Fleming Scholarship Fund (CFEF) [8138]
Charlotte Housing Authority Scholarship Fund (CHASF) [4726]
Charlotte-Mecklenburg Schools Curriculum Research Center [3276]
Charlotte-Mecklenburg Schools Scholarship Incentive Fund [3277], [4727]
Charlotte Pride [3278]
Charlotte Pride Scholarship [3279]
Charlotte R. SchmidLapp Scholarship Fund [3345]
Charlotte V. Bergen Scholarship [1408]
Chartway Federal Credit Union [3280]
Chartway Federal Credit Union Director's Memorial Scholarship [3281]
CCWH Nupur Chaudhuri Article Prize [3829]
CHCI Congressional Internship Program [3745]
CHCI Graduate Fellowship Program [3746]
CHCI Public Policy Fellowships [3747]
CHEA Undergraduate Scholarship Program for Students with Disabilities [2814]
CHEA Vocational Grants [2815]
The Cheatham County Scholarship Fund [3607]
Chechahko Consumers Co-Op Ltd. Scholarship [12301]
Hadar J. Chemtob Memorial Scholarship [6288]
Chereddi NarayanaRao & Radhamanohari Scholarships [10948]
Bernard Chernos Essay Contest [2949]
Cherokee Nation [3282]
Cherokee Nation Graduate Scholarship [3283]
Cherokee Nation Pell Scholarships [3284]
Sgt. Cherven Scholarship [7128]
Shirley Cheshire Memorial Scholarship Awards [7756]
Chester Arzell and Helen Miller Montgomery Scholarship [12065]
Chester H. Bruce Memorial Scholarship [8836]
Chet And Janett Perry Rotary Club Of Fort Myers Scholarship Fund [10674]
Chevalier Award Scholarship [2958]
Cheyenne High School Desert Shields Scholarship [9392]
CHF Travel Grants [9971]
Melba Dawn Chiarenza Scholarship Fund [11946]
The Chicago FM Club Scholarship [1934]
Chicago Railroad Mechanical Association (CRMA) [3286]
Chicana/Latina Foundation (CLF) [3288]
Chicana / Latina Foundation Scholarship Program [3289]

Camille C. Chidiac Fund Scholarship [5391]
Kevin Child Scholarship [7921]
Child Welfare and Development (CWD) Scholarship [4489]
Childbirth Educator Program Scholarships [6641]
Childhood Cancer Canada [3290]
Childhood Cancer Survivor Scholarship [3291]
Children of Evangeline Section Scholarships [10472]
Children of Fallen Patriots Foundation (CFPF) [3293]
Children of Fallen Patriots Scholarships [3294]
Children of Unitarian Universalist Religious Professionals Grant [11246]
Children's Literature Association (CHLA) [3295]
Children's National Health System Pediatric Nursing Student Scholarships [124]
Childrens Scholarship Fund-Charlotte [4728]
The Children's Tumor Foundation (CTF) [3298]
A Child's Hope Int'l, Inc. [3300]
Jane Coffin Childs Memorial Fund for Medical Research [3302]
Charline Chilson Scholarships [4029]
China and East Asia Google PhD Fellowships [5045]
ChinaSona Foundation [3304]
Chinese American Medical Society (CAMS) [3306]
Chinese Professionals Association of Canada (CPAC) [3310]
Chinese Professionals Association of Canada Professional Achievement Awards (PAA) [3311]
Donald W. F. Ching Memorial Scholarship Fund [5392]
Dolly Ching Scholarship [5393]
Chip Johnson Memorial Scholarship Fund [10675]
ChiroHealth USA [3312]
ChiroHealthUSA Foxworth Family Scholarship [3313]
ChLA Faculty Research Grants [3297]
CHOIR MD Post-Residency Fellowship in Health Services Research [11811]
Choose Your Future Scholarship Fund [3608]
Chopin Foundation Scholarship [3315]
Chopin Foundation of the United States [3314]
Chopivsky Fellowships [11889]
CHOPR Fellowship Program [11664]
Choristers Guild (CG) [3316]
CHPI Travel Fellowships [7186]
Chrétien International Research Grants [683]
CHRGJ Emerging Human Rights Scholarship Conference [8358]
CHRGJ International Human Rights Fellowships [8359]
CHRGJ Students Human Rights Scholars Program [8360]
Chris M. Kurzweil Scholarship [3717]
Betty Sams Christian Fellowships [11835]
Christian Larew Memorial Scholarship [6838]
Frances N. Christian Memorial Endowment Nursing Scholarship [10844]
Christian Missionary Scholarship Foundation (CMSF) [3318]
Christian Pharmacists Fellowship International (CPFI) [3320], [3321]
Christian Record Services for the Blind (CRSB) [3322]
Christian Scholarship Foundation, Inc. (CSF) [3324]
Christine Kerr Cawthorne Scholarship [10097]
The Christine Mirzayan Science & Technology Policy Graduate Fellowship Program [7571]
Christine Soper Scholarship [5142]
Irene R. Christman Scholarship [8960]
Christmas Tree Chapter Scholarship Awards [8703]
Christopher Todd Grant Memorial Fund [3346]
Commander Daniel J. Christovich Scholarship [3455]
Chronic Lymphocytic Leukemia Grant [6947]
Chronic Pain Medicine Research Grant [1556]
Chrysalis Scholarship [2314]
Chrysler Technical Scholarship Fund [3996]
CHS - Bursary Program Scholarships [3001]
CHS - Mature Student Bursary Program Scholarships [3002]
Chuck Peacock Memorial Scholarship [175]
Chuck Pezzano Scholarship [5955]

Church Hill Classics Ltd. [3326]
Church, Langdon, Lopp, Banet Law [3328]
The Church, Langdon, Lopp, Banet Law Scholarships [3329]
Winston Churchill Foundation of the United States [3330]
Brent R. Churchill Memorial Scholarship [6977]
The Churchill Scholarships [3331]
CIA Undergraduate Scholarships [2185], [3244]
CIBC Medical Education Scholarships [8226]
C.I.B.C Scholarship [2591], [3014]
CICC Postdoctoral Fellowship [3255]
CIFAR Azrieli Global Scholars program [3020]
CIGNA Healthcare Graduate Scholarships [7888]
CIGNA Undergraduate Scholarships [7889]
Cimarron-Memorial Spartan Staff Scholarships [9393]
CIMON Inc Scholarship [3333]
CIMON Inc. [3332]
Cincinnati Bell Foundation Scholarship [3347]
Cincinnati Financial Corporation Fund [3348]
Cincinnati Scholarship Foundation (CSF) [3334]
Cindy Andrews Educational Scholarship [9534]
CineStory Feature Fellowship [3414]
Cinestory Foundation [3413]
Cintas Foundation [3415]
CINTAS Foundation Fellowship in Architecture & Design [3417]
CINTAS-Knight Fellowship intheVisual Arts [3418]
CIRMMT Student Awards [3253]
CISDL Global Research Fellowship - Associate Fellows [3257]
CISDL Global Research Fellowship - Legal Research Fellows [3258]
CISDL Global Research Fellowships - Senior Research Fellows [3259]
Citi Foundation Scholarship Program [978]
Citi/TELACU Scholars Mentoring Program [10940]
CitizenshipTests.org Engineering and Science Scholarship [3991]
City Bar Diversity Fellowship Program [8300]
City of Boston Disability Scholarship Contest [4535]
City Of Sanibel Employee Dependent Scholarship Fund [10676]
City of Toronto Graduate Scholarships for Women in Mathematics [11685]
City of Toronto Queen Elizabeth II Sesquicentennial Scholarships in Community Health Nursing for Graduates [11686]
City of Toronto Queen Elizabeth II Sesquicentennial Scholarships in Community Health Nursing for Undergraduates [11687]
City of Toronto Scholarships for Aboriginal Health [11688]
City of Toronto Women's Studies Scholarships [11689]
Civic Music Association of Milwaukee [3419]
Civil Air Patrol (CAP) [3421]
Civitan International (CI) [3423]
Civitan Shropshire Scholarship [3424]
CJF Canadian Journalism Fellowships [6620]
CJH Graduate Research Fellowships [3221]
CJH-NEH Fellowships for Senior Scholars [3222]
CJH-Prins Foundation Fellowships for Senior Scholars [3223]
CJH-Prins Foundation Post-Doctoral and Early Career Fellowship for Emigrating Scholars [3224]
CJH Visiting Scholars Program [3225]
CLA/CP Scholarship [9782]
Clackamas Chapter Ed Wood Memorial Award [8704]
Clackamas Chapter Scholarship Awards [8705]
Clackamas County Farm Bureau Agricultural Scholarships [8715]
Claes Nobel Academic Scholarships for Members [8103]
CLAGS Fellowship Award [3233]
Clair A. Hill Scholarship [2077]
Clan Ross America [3425]
Clan Ross Foundation Scholarships [3426]
Cecil Earl Clapp, Sr. Memorial Scholarship [8505]
Claremont McKenna College - Henry Kravis Leadership Institute [3427]
Clarence Olander School In-Service Training Grants for Grades Prek-5 [7802]
Clarivate Analytics/MLA Doctoral Fellowship [7215]

Michele Clark Fellowships [9471]
Vickie Clark-Flaherty Scholarships [8444]
Willis W. and Ethel M. Clark Foundation [3431]
Clark High School Academy of Finance Scholarship [9394]
Neil Clark Memorial Scholarship [8156]
Clarke Adams Memorial Fund [6662]
IADR John Clarkson Fellowship [5913]
Classic Wines of California Scholarships [2797]
Claude B. Hart Memorial Scholarship [12066]
Claude Robinson Memorial Scholarship [7969]
Clay Maitland CGF Scholarship [3456]
Clay Postdoctoral Fellowship [5358]
CLCA Landscape Educational Advancement Foundation Scholarship [2818]
Clem Judd Jr. Memorial Scholarship [5418]
Clement T. Hanson Scholarship [7430]
Cleve Holloway Memorial Scholarship [3652]
Cleveland Alumni Association Scholarship [2517]
Cleveland Executive Fellowships (CEF) [3434]
Cleveland Leadership Center (CLC) [3433]
Geraldine Clewell Fellowships - Doctoral Student [9107]
Geraldine Clewell Fellowships - Masteral [9108]
Cliff and Nancy Telford Scholarship Fund [51]
James L. Clifford Prize [1430]
Bryan Cline Memorial Soccer Scholarship Program [318]
Clinic & Laboratory Integration Program (CLIP) [3140]
Clinic for the Rehabilitation of Wildlife (CROW) [3435]
Clinical Nurse Specialist Foundation [3437]
Clinical Project Funding for Advanced Practice Oncology Nurses [8627]
Clinician Research Awards [8898]
George H. Clinton Scholarship [8837]
Paul W. Clopper Scholarship Grant for Junior Dental Students [5709]
Closs/Parnitzke/Clarke Scholarship [9109]
L. Robert Clough Memorial Scholarship [2518]
Club Managers Association of America (CMAA) [3441]
The Club at Morningside Scholarship [9806]
Clubs of America [3445]
Clubs of America Scholarship Program [3446]
CMA Private Lesson Program: Instrumental Scholarships for Elementary and Middle School Students [3420]
CMAA Student Conference Travel Grants [3442]
CMC-KLI Leadership Research Fellowship [3428]
CMC-KLI Leadership Thesis Fellowship [3429]
CMC-KLI Social Sector Internship Program [3430]
CMC/MMC Scholarships (CMC) [6026]
CME Beef Industry Scholarship [7744]
CMH Dissertation Fellowships [11286]
CMOS-SCMO President's Prize [3041]
CMOS Undergraduate Scholarships [3042]
CMSF Scholarship [3319]
CN Scholarships for Women [3052]
CNIB Master's Scholarships [3047]
CNS-UCSB Graduate Fellowships for Science and Engineering [11563]
CNST Scholarship [2146]
Coaching Association of Canada (CAC) [3447]
Coalition of Higher Education Assistance Organizations (COHEAO) [3449]
Coalition for Networked Information (CNI) [3451]
Coast Guard Foundation (CGF) [3453]
Coast Guard Foundation Enlisted Education Scholarship [3457]
Coastal Bend Community Foundation (CBCF) [3461]
J.C. and Rheba Cobb Memorial Scholarships [7775]
John Coburn and Harold Winters Student Award in Plasma Science and Technology [2382]
Coca-Cola First Generation Scholarships [979]
Coca-Cola Scholars Foundation (CCSF) [3493]
Coca-Cola Scholars Program Scholarships [3494]
Johnnie L. Cochran, Jr./MWH Scholarships [7890]
Evelyn L. Cockrell Memorial Scholarship [10983]
Frank M. Coda Scholarships [1472]
Code Play Learn [3495]
Code Play LEARN Scholarship [3496]
Coeur d'Alene Alumni Scholarship [6784]
COF Dependent Scholarship Program [9142]

Dallas Area Paralegal Association (DAPA) **[3963]**
Dallas/Fort Worth Chapter WTS Undergraduate Scholarship [12173]
Marvin E. Daly Memorial Scholarship [8506]
The DamagedCars.com Summer Scholarship [3156]
Damon Runyon Cancer Research Foundation Fellowships [9757]
Damon Runyon Physician-Scientist Training Awards [9758]
Damon Runyon-Rachleff Innovation Awards [9759]
Damon Runyon-Sohn Pediatric Cancer Fellowship Award [9760]
Dan M. Reichard, Jr. Scholarship [1299]
Dan Mordecai Educational Scholarship Award [8210]
Dan and Rachel Mahi Educational Scholarship [8921]
Dan Rigel Memorial Educational Grant [2046]
Dan Stewart Scholarship [8433]
Dance Films Association (DFA) **[3965]**
Dance Individual Project Funding [262]
D&A Florida Scholarships [10678]
D&R Sobey Scholarships [10237]
Daniel Gerber, Sr. Medallion Scholarship [4939]
Daniel H. Pokorny Memorial Scholarship Award [9624]
Daniel Kahikina and Millie Akaka Scholarship [8922]
Daniel L. Reiss Memorial Scholarship [5073]
Danish America Heritage Society (DAHS) **[3967]**
Margaret A. Dankworth Management Scholarship [2327]
Dante Prize [3970]
Dante Society of America (DSA) **[3969]**
Malcolm U. Dantzler Scholarships [10611]
Mark & Dorothy Danzker Scholarship [6305]
DAPA Student Member Scholarships [3964]
Ashley Darby Memorial Scholarship [8507]
Helen Darcovich Memorial Doctoral Fellowship [3026]
The Hugh and Hazel Darling Dean's Scholarship [8994]
Darling Foundation Endowed School of Law Scholarship [8995]
Darooge Family Scholarship [5145]
Darrel Hess Community College Geography Scholarship [564]
Daryl Cooper Intermediate Piano Beethoven Scholarship [9898]
Bal Dasa Scholarship Fund [5394]
Dater Foundation Scholarship [3352]
Amy and Tim Dauphinee Scholarship [2912]
Frank L. Dautriel Memorial Scholarships for Graduates [6900]
Frank L. Dautriel Memorial Scholarships for Undergraduates [6901]
George A. Davala Scholarship [7007]
Antenore C. "Butch" Davanzo Scholarships [7348]
Dave Benferado Scholarship [159]
Dave Caldwell Scholarship [1640]
Dave Lamb Scholarship [11912]
Dave Sauer Memorial College Scholarship [170]
David A. Kronick Travelling Fellowship [7216]
David Arver Memorial Scholarship [176]
David Beltran Memorial Scholarship [9540]
David C. Maloney Scholarship [8021]
David and Camille Boatwright Endowed Scholarship [8996]
David and Deborah Clark Fellowship [8744]
David G. Imig Award for Distinguished Achievement in Teacher Education [549]
David G. Robinson Arts Scholarship Fund [10679]
David H. Clift Scholarship [1077]
David H. Smith Conservation Research Fellowship [10314]
David J. Joseph Company Scholarship Fund [3353]
David Julian Whichard Scholarship [11180]
David Library of the American Revolution (DLAR) **[3972]**
David Library Fellowships [3973]
David Meador Foundation - Hospitality-Food Service Scholarships [8241]
David Pohl Scholarship [11247]
Ruth and Victor David Scholarship [6289]
David and Sharon Seaver Family Scholarship Fund in Memory of Timothy D. Seaver [5074]

David W. Schacht Native American Student Scholarship [2479]
David Weiss Scholarship Program [12268]
Lucile Caswell Davids Memorial Adelphe Scholarship [6416]
Davidson and Jones Hotel Corporation Scholarship [8445]
Jim Davie Memorial Scholarship [12305]
Marge Sorreles Davies Memorial Scholarship [7096]
The Davis Educational Fund [3711]
Davis Family Scholarship [9809]
Davis Foundation Postdoctoral Fellowships [5435]
Davis Levin Livingston **[3974]**
Davis Memorial Foundation **[3976]**
Davis Memorial Foundation Scholarship [3977]
Dwight F. Davis Memorial Scholarship [11402]
The James H. Davis Memorial Scholarship [4638]
Johnny Davis Memorial Scholarship [177]
The Davis-Putter Scholarship Fund [9770]
Kenneth D. and Katherine D. Davis Scholarship [8842]
Lawrence E. and Jean L. Davis Scholarship [8843]
Arlene Davis Scholarships [4030]
Raymond Davis Scholarships [10371]
Davis Wright Tremaine 1L Diversity Scholarship [3979]
Davis Wright Tremaine L.L.P. (DWT) **[3978]**
Dawson District Renewable Resources Council Scholarship [12306]
Colonel Richard M. Dawson Highway Patrol Scholarship Fund [3610]
William W. Dawson Memorial Scholarship [2519]
Brian M. Day Scholarships [9295]
The Dayton Amateur Radio Association Scholarship [1938]
DBA Scholarships [4130]
DBI Scholarship Fund [3611]
D.C. Cornelius Memorial Scholarship [12068]
DCH Freehold Toyota Scholarship [3251]
Edilia and François Auguste de Montêquin Fellowships [10274]
Bert and Sally de Vries Fellowship [726]
Kenneth J. De Witt NASA/OSGC Scholarship at The University of Toledo [8596]
DealRoom **[3980]**
Dealsshutter **[3982]**
Dealsshutter.com Scholarship [3983]
Dean A. Froehlich Endowed Scholarship [6787]
The Dean Prim Scholarship [12069]
Dean – Derek Lee Dean Soccer Scholarships [3471]
Deana Kendrick Foundation Scholarship [6522]
Death Valley '49ers Inc. **[3984]**
Death Valley '49ers Scholarships [3985]
Debbie Khalil Memorial Scholarship [9167]
Don Debolt Franchising Scholarship Program [6011]
Deborah Jean Rydberg Memorial Scholarship [3676]
Deborah Munroe Noonan Memorial Research Fund [5436]
Deborah Partridge Wolfe International Fellowship (Graduate) [12410]
Debt.com **[3986]**
Debt.com Scholarship [3987]
Julia B. DeCapua Fund [5226]
Walter M. Decker Point Scholarship [9220]
Decommissioning, and Environmental Science Division Graduate Scholarship [1164]
The Decorative Arts Trust **[3988]**
Laurence Decore Awards for Student Leadership [288]
Earl Dedman Memorial Scholarship [900]
Dee Wacksman Scholarship Fund [3354]
Deed of Award [2944]
DEED Student Research Grant/Internships [1297]
Deedal Studio Inc. **[3990]**
Anthony R. Dees Educational Workshop Scholarship [10342]
Defensive Driving scholarship [3994]
DefensiveDriving.com **[3993]**
Deja Vu Surf Hawaii Scholarship Fund [5395]
Frank del Olmo Memorial Scholarships [3197]
Arnold Arboretum Deland Award for Student Research [5361]
Edward Delaney Scholarship [2198]
Jane Delano Student Nurse Scholarships [1149]

Delaware Community Foundation (DCF) **[3995]**
Deloris Carter Hampton Scholarship [9296]
Delta Chi Alumnae Memorial Scholarship [10099]
Delta Delta Delta **[3997]**
Delta Epsilon Sigma **[4016]**
Delta Epsilon Sigma Graduate Fellowship [4017]
Delta Epsilon Sigma Undergraduate Scholarships [4018]
Delta Faucet Scholarships [9204]
Delta Gamma **[4019]**
Delta Gamma Foundation Florence Margaret Harvey Memorial Scholarship [914]
Delta Gamma Undergraduate Merit-Based Scholarships [4020]
Delta Iota Alumni Scholarship [10146]
The Delta Kappa Gamma Society International (DKP) **[4021]**
Delta Kappa Gamma Society International World Fellowship [4022]
Delta Kappa Project 2000 Scholarship [6417]
Delta Nu Project 2000 Scholarship [6418]
Delta Phi Epsilon Educational Foundation Scholarships [4024]
Delta Phi Epsilon Sorority (DPHIE) **[4023]**
Delta Project 2000 Scholarship [6419]
Delta Tau Lambda Sorority, Inc. **[4025]**
Delta Tau Project 2000 Scholarship [6420]
Delta Tau Scholarship [2520]
Delta Upsilon Project 2000 Nowell Memorial Scholarship [6421]
Delta Zeta (DZ) **[4027]**
Gail Patrick Undergraduate Scholarships [4031]
Law Offices of Michael A. DeMayo Scholarships [6708]
DEMCO New Leaders Travel Grants [9432]
Christopher Demetris Memorial Scholarships [5463]
Democrats for Life of America (DFLA) **[4046]**
Democrats for Life of America Scholarship Essay [4047]
DeMolay International **[4048]**
Inez Demonet Scholarship [11804]
Dena Epstein Award for Archival and Library Research in American Music [7513]
The Dendel Scholarship [5284]
Denis Wong & Associates Scholarship [8923]
Dennis Coleman Scholarship [9297]
Dennis Coleman Scholarships [9298]
Dentistry by John Barras DDS **[4050]**
Denton Scholarship [10081]
Bobby Michael Denton Memorial Scholarship [8508]
Denver Scholarship Foundation (DSF) **[4052]**
Denver Scholarship Foundation General Scholarship Fund [4053]
Dick Depaolis Memorial Scholarship [3718]
DEPS Graduate Scholarship [4099]
Garabed and Almast Der Megrditchian Scholarship Grants [1874]
Frank Der Yuen Aviation Scholarship [8804]
Derivative Duo Scholarships [9299]
Descendants Scholarships [3954]
Libby Deschenes Prize for Applied Research [11989]
Design and Multimedia Internships - New York [4980]
Belle & Curly Desrosiers Scholarship [12307]
Detroit Economic Club Scholarship [3719]
APTRA-Clete Roberts/Kathryn Dettman Memorial Journalism Scholarship [2022]
Deutsche Gesellschaft fur Amerikastudien (DGFA) **[4054]**
Deutscher Akademischer Austausch Dienst (DAAD) **[4056]**
Development Fund for Black Students in Science and Technology (DFBSST) **[4067]**
Development Fund for Black Students in Science and Technology Scholarship [4068]
DeVries & Associates **[4069]**
DeVries Law School Scholarship [4070]
Helen L. Dewar Scholarship [11020]
Dewey Lee Curtis Symposium Scholarships [3989]
Dezao Legal Awards [6704]
D.F. Plett Graduate Fellowship [9202]
DFA Cares Foundation Scholarship Program [3958]
DFA Production Grant [3966]
Jenny d'Héricourt Fellowship [487]
Beta Nu/Caryl Cordis D'hondt Scholarship [10100]

Theta/Caryl Cordis D'hondt Scholarship [10101]
Diabetes Hope Foundation (DHF) **[4071]**
Diabetes Hope Scholarship Program [4072]
Diabetes Scholars Foundation (DSF) **[4073]**
The Lilly Diabetes Tomorrow's Leaders Scholarship [4074]
Diagnosis Delayed **[4075]**
Diagnosis Delayed Scholarship [4076]
Diamond Resort Scholarship Fund [5396]
Diana Brown Endowed Scholarship [6788]
Diana M. Priestly Memorial Scholarship [2901]
DiBella Law Offices PC **[4077]**
Edwina Eustis Dick Scholarship for Music Therapy Interns [1134]
Dickey Rural Networks (DRN) **[4079]**
Dickey Rural Networks Scholarship [4080]
Bill Dickey Scholarship Association (BDSA) **[4081]**
Dietetics in Health Care Communities (DHCC) **[4083]**
Diffuse Large B-Cell Lymphoma Grant [6948]
Robert Martz DiGiacomo Memorial Scholarship Fund [10756]
Digital Entertainment Group **[4085]**
Digital Health Canada **[4087]**
Digital Marketing Scholarship Program [3177]
Digital Responsibility **[4089]**
Dillon Consulting Scholarship [2108]
Carol DiMaiti Scholarship [7124]
Raymond DiPaglia Endowment Scholarship [4149]
Diplomatic and Consular Officers, Retired, Inc. (DACOR) **[4091]**
The Direct Energy Live Brighter Scholarship [4095]
Direct Energy L.P. **[4094]**
Direct Textbooks **[4096]**
Directed Energy Professional Society (DEPS) **[4098]**
DirectTextbook.com Scholarship Essay Contest [4097]
Dirksen Congressional Center **[4100]**
The Disability Care Center **[4103]**
Disability Care Center Disabled Student Scholarships [4104]
Disability Care Center Special Education Scholarships [4105]
Disabled American Veterans (DAV) **[4106]**
Disabled Veteran Scholarship [9713]
Disabled Veteran Student Scholarship [12018]
Disabled Veterans Scholarship [4538], [6519]
Discover Bar Exam Loans [4109]
Discover Financial Services (DFS) **[4108]**
Discover Graduate Loans [4110]
Discover Health Professions Loans [4111]
Discover Law Loans [4112]
Discover MBA Loans [4113]
Discover Residency Loans [4114]
Dissertation Award in Hadronic Physics [1224]
Dissertation Completion Fellowship (DCF) [603]
Dissertation Proposal Development Fellowship [10243]
Dissertation Writing Grants [5869]
The Distinguished Flying Cross Society (DFCS) **[4115]**
Distinguished Flying Cross Society Scholarship [4116]
Distinguished Young Women **[4117]**
Distinguished Young Women - Cash Scholarships [4118]
Distracted Driving Scholarship [6188]
District of Columbia Library Association (DCLA) **[4119]**
Diversity Executive Leadership Program Scholarship (DELP) [1977]
Diversity Fellowship Program (DFP) [7466]
Diversity in Psychology and Law Research Award [1293]
Diversity Scholars Awards [3810]
Diversity Scholarship [1796]
Robert A. and Barbara Divine Graduate Student Travel Fund [10355]
Dr. Kathy Dixon Memorial Scholarship [7097]
Dr. Allan A. Dixon Memorial Scholarships [3106]
The William Donald Dixon Research Grant [3011]
Daniel B. Dixon Scholarship Fund [346]
Peggy Dixon Two-Year Scholarships [10477]
D.J. Lovell Scholarship [10725]
DLF Graduate Scholarship Program [3960]

DMSF Scholarship [7503]
Mychajlo Dmytrenko Fine Arts Foundation Scholarships [11410]
Do-Over Scholarship [11226]
DO Supply Academic Scholarship [4122]
DO Supply Inc. **[4121]**
Grace O. Doane Scholarship [4150]
Charles Dobbins FTA Scholarships [4846]
Dobranowski Julian Memorial Scholarship [9659]
Doc Keen Memorial Scholarship Fund [10680]
Dr. Alfred E. Slinkard Scholarship [9921]
Dr. Ali Jarrahi Merit Scholarship [6172]
Dr. Aura-Lee A. and James Hobbs Pittenger American History Scholarship [8095]
Dr. Biljan Memorial Awards [2980]
Dr. Edward G. Voss Memorial Scholarship [11618]
Dr. Ezra Nesbeth Foundation Scholarship [6213]
Dr. F. Ross Byrd Scholarship [11909]
Dr. Frank and Audrey Wanamaker Medical Scholarship [8227]
Dr. Frank and Florence Marino Scholarship [5322]
Dr. George and Isabelle Elanjian Scholarship [11638]
Dr. George M. Smerk Scholarship [1300]
Dr. Gunnar B. Stickler Scholarship [10839]
Dr. Henrik and Wanda Tonning Memorial Scholarship [8228]
Dr. Horace Furumoto Innovations Professional Development - Young Investigator Award [1496]
Dr. Isaac Keillor Farrer, Advanced Medical Education Scholarship [8229]
Dr. J Glenn Radcliffe Scholarship Fund [10822]
Dr. James A. Ferguson Emerging Infectious Diseases Research Initiatives for Student Enhancement Fellowship (RISE) [6526]
Dr. Joyce Beckett Scholarship [7618]
Dr. Julianne Malveaux Scholarship [7668]
Dr, Lancelot Brown Dental Scholarships [6214]
Dr. Mac Scholarship Fund [3612]
Dr. Mark Rathke Family Scholarship Fund [4202]
Dr. Mary Anne Chambers Scholarship [6215]
Dr. Mubin Syed And Mrs. Afshan Syed Scholarship Program [4176]
Dr. Nancy Smith Midgette Scholarship [10102]
Dr. Nicholas J. Piergrossi Memorial Scholarship [5323]
Dr. Paul and Gayle Sohi Medical Education Scholarship [8230]
Dr. Sidney Rafal Memorial Scholarship [5324]
Dr. Stephen J. Fortgang / University of Northern Iowa Chapter Scholarship [6379]
Dr. William A. and Marceleine J. Sautter Hanover-Horton Youth of Promise Scholarship [6196]
Doctoral Dissertation Grants [6075]
Doctoral Scholarship Outside Québec [5796]
Documentary Film Grants [409]
Doddridge County High School Promise Scholarship in Memory of Hattie Leggett [8844]
F. Atlee Dodge Maintenance Scholarship [237]
Jim Dodson Law **[4123]**
Jim Dodson Law Scholarship for Brain Injury Victims & Their Caregivers [4124]
Dody Boyd Scholarship Fund [3613]
Hans and Margaret Doe Charitable Trust Scholarship [9810]
DOE Computational Science Graduate Fellowship (DOE CSGF) [6611]
Office of Science Graduate Student Research (SCGSR) Program [11323]
Emmett J. Doerr Memorial Distinguished Scout Scholarship [7846]
Dofflemyer Scholarship [7847]
Dole Food Fellowship [8745]
Dollar-A-Day Academic Scholarships [4126]
Dollar-A-Day Scholarship Fund, Inc [4125]
Dolphin Scholarship Foundation (DSF) **[4127]**
DOLPHIN SCHOLARSHIPS [4128]
Anne & Konrad Domes Scholarship [12308]
Scott Dominguez - Craters of the Moon Chapter Scholarship [1564]
Dominican Bar Association (DBA) **[4129]**
Dominion of Canada General Insurance Company Graduate Scholarship in Actuarial Science [11728]
Don Aron Scholarship [7783]
Don and Barbara Curtis Excellence Fund for Extracurricular Activities [11181]

Don C. Beaver Memorial Scholarship [2798]
Don and Eileen Fulton Nursing Scholarship Fund [10823]
Don Freeman Illustrator Grants [10300]
Don Jaques Memorial Fellowship [9922]
Don and Madalyn Sickafoose Educational Trust Fund [10757]
Don and Norine Lowry Awards for Women of Excellence [4291]
Don S. Maurer Advertising Scholarship [11182]
Donald A. B. Lindberg Research Fellowship [7217]
Donald E. Pizzini Memorial Nurse Scholarship [7455]
Donald F. & Mildred Topp Othmer Scholarship Awards [1022]
Donald and Florence Hunting Scholarship [5146]
Donald J. DeYoung Scholarship [5147]
Donald O. Coffman Scholarship [9300]
Donald and Shirley Hastings Scholarship [1660]
Donald W. Banner Diversity Fellowship for Law Students [2428]
Donald Worster Travel Grant [1451]
Marion Jones Donaldson Scholarship Fund [4589]
Hon. Ralph W.E. Donges Memorial Award [2849]
Doniphan Community Foundation Scholarships [5120]
Donna Gail Scholarship for Chapter Service [6380]
Don't Wait to Reach Your Potential [9258]
DontPayFull **[4131]**
DontPayFull $500 Annual Student Scholarship [4132]
Doraine "Pursuit of Educational Excellence" Scholarship [3472]
Doreen Brady Memorial Scholarship [8639]
Joseph M. Dorgan Scholarship [4151]
Doris Hendren Memorial Scholarship [9811]
Doris W. Frey Memorial Scholarship Fund [10681]
Dr. Michael Dorizas Memorial Scholarships [5464]
Pauly D'Orlando Memorial Art Scholarship [11248]
Marusia and Michael Dorosh Fellowship [3027]
Dorothy B. & Charles E. Thomas Scholarship [5148]
Dorothy and Dick Burgess Scholarship [6197]
Dorothy E. Hofmann Pembroke Scholarship [5325]
Dorothy M. Bolyard Memorial Scholarship [9812]
Dorothy Mitchell Memorial Scholarship [9541]
Dorothy Mountain Memorial Scholarship [6922]
Dr. Lloyd M. Dosdall Memorial Scholarships [4406]
Dotcom-Monitor, Inc. **[4133]**
Dotcom-Monitor Women in Computing Scholarship [4134]
Dottie Martin Teacher Scholarship [8437]
Donald B. Doty Educational Award [11995]
The Father Connie Dougherty Scholarship Fund [3712]
Douglas-Coldwell Foundation (DCF) **[4135]**
Douglas-Coldwell Foundation Scholarships in Social Affairs [4137]
Douglas Lake Improvement Association Scholarship [11619]
The Douglas Psychotherapy Do Good General Education Scholarship [4140]
Douglas Psychotherapy Service **[4139]**
Chapter 116 - Roscoe Douglas Scholarship [10400]
Douglass Foundation Fellowship in American Art [10214]
The Douglass Foundation Fellowship in American Art [7276]
The Harold K. Douthit Scholarship [8580]
Dow Chemical Company Fellowships [8027]
Downeast Energy and Building Supply **[4141]**
Downeast Energy Scholarships [4142]
Downeast Feline Fund [6978]
Downes - Jay and Rheba Downes Memorial Scholarship [3473]
Tim Downing Memorial Scholarship Program [2906]
Downtown Apartment Company (DAC) **[4143]**
Downtown Apartment Companys Scholarship Program [4144]
W.B.H. Dowse Fellowships [7142]
Dr Piotrowski Adolph Memorial Art Scholarship [9660]
Helen Cashatt Drais Memorial Adelphe Scholarship [6422]
Drake University Law School **[4145]**
Drake University Law School Law Opportunity Scholarship - Disadvantage [4152]

Drake University Law School Law Opportunity Scholarship - Diversity [4153]

Drake University Law School Public Service Scholarships [4154]

The Drama Therapy Fund **[4177]**

The Drawn to Art Fellowship [488]

DRC Pilot and Feasibility Study Award [12233]

DREAM - Diversity Recruitment Recruitment through Education and Mentoring Program [621]

The Dream is Inclusive Scholarship [8624]

C. Cleveland Drennon, Jr. Memorial Scholarship [11597]

Margaret Drew Alpha Scholarship [9110]

Charles Drew Scholarships [2153]

Drew Smith Memorial Scholarship [3563]

Tom and Roberta Drewes Scholarship [6839]

Camille and Henry Dreyfus Foundation, Inc. **[4179]**

Camille and Henry Dreyfus Foundation - Senior Scientist Mentor Program [4180]

Camille Dreyfus Teacher-Scholar Awards [4181]

DriversEdHub.com Scholarship [3992]

Drone Pilot Ground School **[4182]**

Drone Technology College Scholarshi p [4183]

Drones Globe **[4184]**

Drs. Ira and Udaya Dash Nursing Scholarship Fund [10682]

Drue Smith / Society of Professional Journalists' Scholarship Fund [3614]

Drug Development Research Professorship [3773]

DrugRehab.org **[4186]**

Richard Drukker Memorial Scholarships [8283]

Drummond Law Firm **[4188]**

Drummond Law Firm Scholarship [4189]

Harold D. Drummond Scholarships [6381]

Marnie & Bill Drury Scholarship [12309]

Drzymala Janusz & Roma Scholarship [9661]

DSACF Modern Woodmen of America Scholarship Fund [4203]

Emilie Du Chatelet Award [1431]

Henry Belin du Pont Dissertation Fellowships [5257]

Henry Belin du Pont Research Grants [5258]

Duane Hanson Scholarship [1473]

Duane V. Puerde Memorial Scholarship Fund [3564]

The Duberman-Zal Fellowship [3234]

Lee Dubin Memorial Scholarship [3500]

Dublin San Ramon Services District **[4190]**

DuBois Brothers Award [2850]

Charles Dubose Scholarships [5326]

Lise M. Duchesneau Scholarship [2097]

John W. Duckett Jr., AFUD Pediatric Research Scholarships [10469]

Steve Duckett Local Conservation Scholarship [9281]

Julia M. Duckwall Scholarship [2199]

Mark Duda Scholarship Fund [7104]

A. O. Duer Scholarship Award [7661]

A DUI Defense Scholarship [8761]

Doris Duke Charitable Foundation (DDCF) **[4192]**

Doris Duke Conservation Fellows Program [12046]

Duke University and University of North Carolina Rotary Peace Center **[4194]**

Dulemba Aleksander & Stefania Scholarship [9662]

Duluth Building and Construction Trades Council Scholarship Fund [4204]

Duluth Central High School Alumni Scholarship Fund [4205]

Duluth Superior Area Community Foundation (DSACF) **[4196]**

Dumbarton Oaks Fellowship [4222]

Dumbarton Oaks Junior Fellowship [4223]

Dumbarton Oaks Research Library and Collection **[4221]**

Dumbarton Oaks Research Library and Collection Bliss Symposium Award [4224]

Dumbarton Oaks Research Library and Collection Graduate Research Workshops [4225]

Dumbarton Oaks Research Library and Collection One-Month Research Stipends [4226]

Dumbarton Oaks Research Library and Collection Post-Baccalaureate Media Fellowships [4227]

Dumbarton Oaks Research Library and Collection Project Grants [4228]

Dumbarton Oaks Research Library and Collection Short-Term Predoctoral Residencies Grants [4229]

Dumbarton Oaks Research Library and Collection Summer Fellowship [4230]

Dumbarton Oaks Research Library and Collection Summer Internships for Harvard Students [4231]

Dumbarton Oaks Research Library and Collection Post-Doctoral Teaching Fellowships [4232]

Gabriel Dumont Institute of Native Studies and Applied Research (GDI) **[4235]**

Dunbar Heritage Scholarship Fund [10683]

Duncan Aviation Inc. **[4237]**

Duncan Aviation Scholarship [178], [4238]

Dr. Allan Duncan Memorial Scholarship [12310]

John Holt Duncan Memorial Scholarship [2521]

Ernest Duncan - Pre-K-8 Preservice Teacher Action Research Grants [7803]

Wade and Marcelene Duncan Scholarship [12070]

Debra Dungey Scholarship [12311]

Ed Dunkelblau Scholarship [2052]

Dunkin' Donuts Philadelphia Regional Scholarship Program [9941]

Durning Sisters Scholarships [4001]

Joe Durso, Jr. Memorial Scholarship [7451]

Dutch and Ginger Arver Scholarship [179]

Dutchess County Bar Association (DCBA) **[4239]**

DW Simpson Actuarial Science Scholarship [4242]

DW Simpson Global Actuarial Recruitment **[4241]**

Dwight A. Hamilton Scottish Rite Foundation of Colorado Graduate Scholarship in Speech-Language Pathology [9984]

Dwight Hibbard Scholarship Fund [3355]

Dwight Mosley Scholarship Award [11403]

Dwight Teed Scholarship Fund [10881]

Peter Dwyer Scholarships [2872]

Brenda Dye Music Boosters Scholarship [7098]

Bob Dyer/OEL Apprenticeship Scholarships [4340]

Joshua Dyke Family Scholarship [11021]

Marvin and Joanell Dyrstad Scholarship [1746]

Dystonia Medical Research Foundation (DMRF) **[4243]**

Dystonia Medical Research Foundation Clinical Fellowships [4244]

E. H. Marth Food Protection And Food Sciences Scholarship [12109]

E. Lanier (Lanny) Finch Scholarship [4923]

E-Waste Scholarship [4090]

e8 Sustainable Energy Development Post-Doctoral Scholarship Programme [5008]

EAA Members Memorial Scholarship [4391]

EAA Workshop Scholarships [4392]

Eagle Touch Technologies Co. Ltd. **[4245]**

EAIA Research Grants [4248]

Howard and Gladys Eakes Memorial Scholarship [5121]

EAPSI Fellowships [8067]

Amelia Earhart Fellowship [12419]

Earl and Countess of Wessex - World Championships in Athletics Scholarship [289]

Earl Warren Civil Rights Training Scholarships [7538]

Earl Warren Scholarship [7539]

Early American Industries Association (EAIA) **[4247]**

Early-Career Patient-Oriented Diabetes Research Awards [6347]

Early Childhood Educators Scholarship Program [7158]

Robert E. Early Memorial Scholarship [4155]

Earthquake Engineering Research Institute (EERI) **[4249]**

Eason & Tamborini, A Law Corporation **[4251]**

East Carolina Scholarship [2522]

East Tennessee Foundation (ETF) **[4253]**

East-West Center (EWC) **[4260]**

East-West Center Graduate Degree Fellowship [4262]

Patricia Hughes Eastaugh Teaching Scholarship [11445]

Easter Scholarship [7438]

Easter Seals Ontario **[4266]**

Eastern Communication Association (ECA) **[4269]**

Eastern Orthodox Scouting Scholarships [7848]

Eastman Community Music School (ECMS) **[4272]**

The Eating Recovery Center Foundation Early Career Investigator Grants [7863]

Eaton Awards of Academic Achievement [4341]

David Eaton Scholarship [11249]

The Christoph Daniel Ebeling Fellowship [489], [4055]

Eben Tisdale Fellowship [4838]

David Eby Memorial Scholarship [12312]

ECA Centennial Scholarships [4271]

Echoing Green **[4274]**

Echoing Green Black Male Achievement Fellowships [4275]

Echoing Green Climate Fellowships [4276]

Echoing Green Global Fellowships [4277]

James Echols Scholarship Award [2781]

Ecolab Scholarship [971]

The École Nationale des Chartes Exchange Fellowship [8371]

École Polytechnique Commemorative Awards [2972]

Ecological Society of America (ESA) **[4278]**

Economic Club Business Study Abroad Scholarships [5149]

Economic Club of Grand Rapids Scholarship [5150]

Economic History Association (EHA) **[4280]**

Ed Haas Memorial Scholarship Fund [10824]

EDC International Business Scholarships [2940]

Margaret Eddy Scholarship [8337]

Edgecliff McAuley Art Scholarships [12221]

Edgecliff McAuley Music Scholarship [12222]

EDiS Company **[4284]**

The Edit My Paper Proofreading Scholarships [4287]

Edith Head Undergraduate Scholarships [4032]

Edith Macias Vann Southern California [12151]

Edith Weingarten Scholarship [1177]

EditMyPaper.ca **[4286]**

Editors Association of Canada (EAC) **[4288]**

S. Randolph Edmonds Young Scholars Competition [2615]

Edmonton Chapter Student Award [247]

Edmonton Community Foundation **[4290]**

Edmonton Epilepsy Association (EEA) **[4293]**

Edmonton Epilepsy Association Scholarship [4294]

Edmonton Epilepsy Continuing Education Scholarships [4295]

Edon Farmers Cooperative Association Inc. **[4296]**

Edon Farmers Cooperative Scholarships [4297]

Education Factor Scholarships [7207]

Education Matters Scholarship [11227]

"Education is Power" Scholarships [7923]

Educational Audiology Association (EAA) **[4298]**

Educational Audiology Association Doctoral Scholarship [4300]

Educational and Cultural Affairs Alumni Small Grants Program (ECA) [6069]

Educational Excellence Award [3120]

Educational Fellowship For Practicing Physicians [9155]

The Educational Foundation of KyCPA Scholarships [6539]

The Educational Foundation for Women in Accounting (EFWA) **[4302]**

Educational Loan Program for Gay and Lesbian Students [3615]

Educational Research Center of America (ERCA) **[4308]**

Educational Testing Service (ETS) **[4310]**

EducationDynamics L.L.C. **[4314]**

Edvisors Network Inc. **[4317]**

Edward C. Pomeroy Award for Outstanding Contributions to Teacher Education [550]

Edward C. Roy, Jr. Award For Excellence in K-8 Earth Science Teaching [944]

Edward D. Di Loreto-Odell S. McConnell Scholarship [8997]

Edward Foster Award [3012]

Edward Heywood Megson Scholarship [11183]

Edward Jackson International Travel Award [11184]

Edward Kent Welch Memorial Scholarship [12071]

Edward Leon Duhamel Freemasons Scholarship [9692]

Edward Rollin Clinton Memorial for Music Scholarship [11476]

Edward Traurig Scholarship [11932]

The Edwards Annual College Scholarships [4320]

Esther Edwards Graduate Scholarships [4890]

The Edwards Law Firm **[4319]**

Edwin F. Wiegand Science & Technology Scholarship [9397]

Edwin H. and Louise N. Williamson Endowed Scholarship [12072]

Edwina Foye Award for Outstanding Graduate Student [4805]
Edwyna Wheadon Postgraduate Training Scholarship [7799]
E.E. Williams Research Grant [5498]
EERI/FEMA NEHRP Graduate Fellowship in Earthquake Hazard Reduction [4250], [11362]
EFC Atlantic Region Scholarships [4342]
EFC University and College Scholarships [4343]
EGIA Foundation **[4321]**
EGIA Foundation Scholarship Program [4322]
EHA Exploratory Travel and Data Grants [4282]
EHA Graduate Dissertation Fellowships [4283]
E.I. DuPont Graduate Fellowship [8028]
The Eichholz Law Firm **[4323]**
Mark & Heinz Eichhorn Scholarship [12313]
Eidson - John R. Eidson Jr.,'38 Scholarship [3474]
Mike Eidson Scholarship [582]
Eight and Forty Lung and Respiratory Disease Nursing Scholarships [1071]
Eileen J. Garrett Scholarship [8824]
The Eileen J. Smith, R.N. Memorial Scholarship [6198]
Hillel Einhorn New Investigator Award [10377]
Eisbrouch Marsh L.L.C. **[4325]**
Eisbrouch & Marsh Scholarship Awards [4326]
The Dwight D. Eisenhower/Ann Cook Whitman Washington, D.C. Scholarship Program [4961]
Jeri Eiserman, RRT Professional Education Research Fellowship [1353]
E.J. Josey Scholarship [2606]
EJI Justice Fellowship [4434]
Farouk El-Baz Student Research Grants [4909]
El Dorado County Mineral and Gem Society **[4327]**
El Dorado County Mineral and Gem Society Scholarship [4328]
El Pomar Fellowship [4330]
El Pomar Foundation **[4329]**
Elaine Gelman Scholarship [7678]
Allan Eldin & Agnes Sutorik Geiger Scholarship Fund [5397]
Eldon E. and JoAnn C. Kuhns Family Scholarship [7458]
The Eleanor A. Ernest Scholarship [6199]
Eleanor Perry Memorial Endowed Scholarship [6789]
eLearners Online College Scholarship [4332]
The eLearners Scholarship for Military Personnel, Veterans, and Spouses [4333]
eLearners.com **[4331]**
eLearning.net **[4334]**
Electro-Federation Canada (EFC) **[4336]**
Electrochemical Society (ECS) **[4362]**
Electronics Division: Lewis C. Hoffman Scholarship [733]
Elements Behavioral Health **[4364]**
Elements Behavioral Health Scholarship [4365]
Elena Sanchez Memorial WSWS Outstanding Student Scholarship Program [11993]
Elevate Pest Control **[4366]**
Elevating Healthcare Scholarship [24]
Herman E. Elgar Memorial Scholarship [4156]
Elgin Alumni Association Scholarship [7099]
Eli Lilly And Company/BDPA Scholarship [2456]
Eli Lilly Graduate Scholarship [2091]
W. Todd Elias Memorial Scholarship [2523]
Elin J. Stene/Xi Scholarship [10103]
AACR Gertrude B. Elion Cancer Research Award [534]
Elisabeth M. and Winchell M. Parsons Scholarship [1999]
Elise Reed Jenkins Memorial Scholarship [10104]
Elite Entrepreneurs **[4368]**
Elite Entrepreneurs Scholarship Contest [4369]
Virginia Elizabeth and Alma Vane Taylor Nursing Scholarship [12073]
Elizabeth Benson Scholarship Award [9625]
Elizabeth Brittingham Pusey Scholarship [3565]
Elizabeth M. Gruber Scholarship [4033]
Elizabeth McKissick Memorial Scholarship [6790]
Elizabeth Munsterberg Koppitz Child Psychology Graduate Student Fellowship [1281]
Elizabeth Nash Foundation Scholarship [7554]
Elizabeth Neuffer Fellowship [6148]
Elizabeth Shafer Memorial Scholarship [9398]

Elizabeth and Sherman Asche Memorial Scholarship [2038]
Elizabeth T. Williams Memorial Scholarship [12074]
Elks National Foundation (ENF) **[4370]**
Elks National Foundation Most Valuable Student Scholarship Contest [2816], **[4371]**
Ella Wilson Johnson Scholarship Fund [3356]
Ellen Eberhardt Memorial Scholarship Fund [10825]
Ellen Swallow Richards Travel Grant [1452]
The Dr. Robert Elliott Memorial Scholarship [7167], [8264]
The Pauline Elliott Scholarship [7168], [8265]
Robert A. Ellis Scholarships in Physics [8085]
Ellis W. Rowe Memorial Scholarship [5268]
Elmer Cooke Young-Ethel Taylor Young Scholarship Fund [5327]
Elmer and Rosa Lee Collins Scholarship [12075]
Eloise Pitts O'More Scholarship Fund [3616]
Elsa Ludeke Scholarship [4034]
Albinas Elskus Scholarship [10743]
Elton Casey Scholarship [11185]
Elva Knight Research Grant [6034]
Emerald Creek Capital **[4373]**
Emerald Creek Capital Scholarship [4374]
Emerald Empire Chapter Scholarship Awards [8706]
Emergency Nurses Association (ENA) **[4375]**
Emerging Entrepreneur Scholarship Grant [6771]
Emerging Scholars Award [2275]
Gladys Anderson Emerson Scholarship [6152]
Emily P. Foster Fellowship [8746]
EMLF Law Student Scholarships [4387]
Emma and Meloid Algood Tuition Scholarship [7619]
Emmett H. Turner Scholarship Fund [3617]
Emoji Scholarship [7439]
Employment Boost **[4380]**
Employment Boost College Scholarship [4381]
ENA Foundation Annual Conference Scholarships [4377]
ENA Foundation Seed Grants [4378]
ENA Foundation Undergraduate State Challenge Scholarship [4379]
Enders Student Fellowship [2081]
endMS Doctoral Studentship Awards [7497]
endMS Master's Studentship Awards [7498]
endMS Postdoctoral Fellowships [7499]
Alice Yuriko Endo Memorial Scholarship [6245]
Endocrine Society **[4382]**
Endocrine Society Summer Research Fellowships [4383]
Endodontic Educator Fellowship Award [556]
Endourological Society **[4384]**
Endowment Fund for Education Grants [2575]
Endowment Fund for Education Scholarships (EFFE) [2576]
Energy and Mineral Law Foundation (EMLF) **[4386]**
Most Valuable Student scholarships [4372]
Engaged Anthropology Grant [11961]
Jane Engelberg Memorial Fellowship (JEMF) [8100]
Enhanced Insurance Scholarships Program [11763]
Enid Hall Griswold Memorial Scholarship [8096]
Enid W. and Bernard B. Spigel Architectural Scholarship [5269]
Enkababian Family and Sarian Family Memorial Grant [1875]
Enlisted Association of National Guard of the United States (EANGUS) **[4388]**
Ennis Arts Association (EAA) **[4390]**
Enterprise Schlorship [9168]
Entertainment Media Internships - Los Angeles [5029]
Entertainment Software Association (ESA) **[4393]**
The Entomological Foundation **[4395]**
Entomological Society of America (ESA) **[4400]**
Entomological Society of Canada (ESC) **[4402]**
Entomological Society of Canada Danks Scholarship [4407]
Entomological Society of Saskatchewan **[4410]**
Entomological Society of Saskatchewan Student Presentation Award [4412]
Entomological Society of Saskatchewan Travel Awards [4413]
Environmental Law Institute (ELI) **[4414]**
Environmental Research and Education Foundation (EREF) **[4416]**
EPA Science to Achieve Results Fellowships (STAR) [11350]

Epilepsy Foundation **[4418]**
Epilepsy Foundation Behavioral Sciences Post-Doctoral Fellowships [4419]
Epilepsy Foundation Behavioral Sciences Student Fellowships [4420]
Epilepsy Foundation Health Sciences Student Fellowships [4421]
Epilepsy Foundation Post-doctoral Research and Training Fellowships [4422]
Epilepsy Foundation Pre-doctoral Research Training Fellowships [4423]
Epilepsy Foundation Research Grants [4424]
Epilepsy Foundation Research and Training Fellowships for Clinicians [4425]
Epilepsy Newfoundland and Labrador (ENL) **[4428]**
EPP/MSI Undergraduate Scholarship Program (USP) [11303]
Epsilon Delta Project 2000 Scholarship [6423]
Epsilon Epsilon Scholarship [10105]
Epsilon Mu Scholarship [6424]
Epsilon Sigma Alpha (ESA) **[4431]**
Epsilon Tau Pi's Soaring Eagle Scholarship [7849]
Epsilon Tau Scholarship [10106]
Alan R. Epstein "Reach for the Stars" Scholarships [7297]
Equal Justice Initiative (EJI) **[4433]**
Equal Justice Works **[4435]**
Equal Justice Works Fellowships [4436]
E.R. and Lillian B. Dimmette Scholarship [4732]
The Robert C. Erb Sr. Scholarship [7169]
ERDAS Internship [2005]
EREF Doctoral Scholarship [4417]
Eric L. Jacobson Memorial Scholarship [9542]
Erickson Education Scholarship [5075]
Bruce T. and Jackie Mahi Erickson Scholarship [8924]
Erika A. and George E. Brattain, Sr. Donor Advised Scholarship Fund [11947]
Kenan T. Erim Fellowships for Archaeological Research at Aphrodisias [1346]
Erin L. Jenkins Memorial Scholarship [4776]
Ernest and Charlene Stachowiak Memorial Scholarship [3677]
Ernest Hemingway Research Grants [5475], [6528]
Melissa Eleanor Ernest Scholarship [6200]
Ernst and Young Scholarships [1979]
Ervin Fellowship [6768]
Lew Erwin Extrusion Division Scholarship [10485]
Erwin Potts Scholarship [11186]
ESA Foundation Scholarship [4394]
Escondido High School (EHS) Class of '56 Scholarship [9813]
Boomer Esiason Foundation (BEF) **[4437]**
Steven Esposito Memorial Scholarship [9221]
Essay Service **[4444]**
Essay Service Writer's Encouragement Scholarship [4445]
Essay Writing Contest [4447]
EssayPro **[4446]**
Parsegh and Thora Essefian Memorial Grant [1876]
Charles A. Esser Memorial Scholarships [1806]
NSPF Ray B. Essick Scholarship Awards [8135]
Estes Memorial [10559]
Esther M. Smith Scholarship Fund [3566]
Larry L. Etherton Scholarships [1326]
Ethnic Minority and Women's Enhancement Postgraduate Scholarships [7770]
Ethyl and Armin Wiebke Memorial Scholarship [12147]
Etruscan Foundation (EF) **[4448]**
ETS/CGS Award for Innovation in Promoting Success in Graduate Education [3868]
ETS Postdoctoral Fellowships [4311]
Alex J. Ettl Grants [8072]
Études d'Oiseaux Canada **[4450]**
Eugene Boyko Memorial Scholarship [249]
Eugene Northrup Scholarship [6791]
Eugene S. Kropf Scholarship [11526]
Eunice Miles Scholarship [4876]
Eurasia Program Fellowships - Dissertation Development Awards [10244]
Eurasia Program Fellowships - Pre-Dissertation Awards [10245]
European College of Liberal Arts Scholarships (ECLA) [11411]
European Studies First Article Prize [3857]

Eva Nieminski Honorary Graduate Science and Engineering Scholarship [5894]
Chick Evans Caddie Scholarships [11981]
Blossom Kalama Evans Memorial Scholarship Fund [5398]
Lee S. Evans/National Housing Endowment Scholarships [7934]
Evans and Petree Law Firm Scholarship [11598]
Helen E. Evans Scholarship [7100]
Richard Evans Schultes Research Award [10320]
Evans Warncke Robinson LLC **[4452]**
Evans Warncke Robinson, LLC Scholarship Contest [4453]
Eve Kraft Education & College Scholarship [11404]
Evelyn Abrams Memorial Scholarship [9399]
Evelyn S. Nish Scholarship [10107]
Everett Family Scholarship [7101]
Everett Fellowship [6769]
J. Everett and Louise Light Scholarships [6382]
Everglades Foundation **[4454]**
Evoke Strategy LLC **[4458]**
Evoke Strategy Writing Scholarship [4459]
E.W. Scripps Foundation Scholarship [3357]
Exabeam Cyber Security Scholarship [4461]
Exabeam Inc. **[4460]**
Excel Staffing Companies Scholarships for Excellence in Continuing Education [319]
Excellence in Geographic Information Systems Scholarships [11446]
Executive Women International (EWI) **[4462]**
Executive Women International Scholarship Program (EWISP) [4464]
ExeptionalNurse.com **[4465]**
ExeptionalNurse.com Scholarships [4466]
Exercise For Life Athletic Scholarship [4441]
The Exoneration Education Initiative [11028]
The Expert Institute **[4467]**
The Expert Institute Legal Blog Post Writing Contest [4468]
The Explorers Club **[4469]**
Express Medical Supply **[4471]**
Express Medical Supply Scholarship Program [4472]
Extendicare Scholarships in Gerontology [3059]
William C. Ezell Fellowship [466]
EZstorit.com **[4473]**
F. Christian and Betty Thompson Fellowship [8747]
F.A. and Charlotte Blount Scholarship [12076]
Facebook Fellowship Program [4476]
Facebook, Inc. **[4475]**
Facebook Journalism Project Scholarship [7989]
FACS Graduate Fellowships [7706]
FACT "Second Chance" Scholarship Program [4527]
Faculty Research Visit Grants [4061]
Fadel Educational Foundation, Inc. (FEF) **[4477]**
Faegre Baker Daniels Diversity & Inclusion Fellowships [4480]
Faegre Baker Daniels L.L.P. **[4479]**
FAER Mentored Research Training Grants [4702]
FAER Research in Education Grants [4703]
FAER Research Fellowship Grants [4704]
Claire M. Fagin Fellow Award [7917]
Fahs-Beck Fund for Research and Experimentation - Doctoral Dissertation Grants [8303]
Fahs-Beck Fund for Research and Experimentation - Postdoctoral Grants [8304]
FAIC Individual Professional Development Scholarships [4700]
FAIC Latin American and Caribbean Scholars Program [1025]
Fairbanks Chapter Legacy Scholarship [11517]
D.J. Fairgrave Education Trust [4157]
AIST Benjamin F. Fairless Scholarship [2220]
Faith Initiatives Internships - New York [4981]
Faith Speckhard Scholarship [6201]
Falcon Achievement Scholarships [9242]
Ambassador Minerva Jean Falcon Hawaii Scholarship [5399]
Fall Fellowships in Korean Studies [6594]
The Fallen Heroes Scholarship [3458]
James Mackenzie Fallows Scholarships Honoring Gertrude Baccus [9543]
James Mackenzie Fallows Scholarships Honoring William Cunningham [9544]
Families of Freedom Scholarship Fund **[4481]**

Families of Freedom Scholarship Fund - Scholarship America [4482]
Families USA **[4483]**
Family, Career and Community Leaders of America (FCCLA) **[4485]**
Family Life Today **[4488]**
FAMU Presidential Scholarship - Florida Community College Scholarships [4620]
Fanconi Anemia Research Fund (FARF) **[4490]**
Fanconi Anemia Research Grants [4491]
The Fantasy Sports Daily **[4492]**
The Fantasy Sports Daily Scholarship Program - General Scholarship for Advanced Education [4493]
Farella Braun + Martel L.L.P. **[4494]**
Farella Braun + Martel LLP 1L Diversity Scholarship Program [4495]
John S.W. Fargher, Jr. Scholarship [5827]
Fargo Supplier Diversity Scholarship [9301]
Judge McIntyre Faries Scholarship [8998]
Farm Equipment Manufacturers Association (FEMA) **[4496]**
Farmer Family Scholarship Fund [3358]
Walter Moran Farmer Scholarships [11922]
Farmington UNICO Scholarship Fund [5328]
W.D. Farr Scholarship [7745]
David Edward Farson Scholarships [8845]
FASEB MARC Travel Awards [10532]
FASSE-International Assembly International Understanding Grants [7795]
Father J. Harold Conway Memorial Scholarship [8640]
Father's Day Scholarship [7440]
James R. Favor Risk Management Scholarship Fund [6425]
Faye Lynn Roberts Education Scholarship Fund [10684]
FBANC Foundation NAPABA Convention Scholarship [4554]
F.C. Grote Fund [347]
FCBA Foundation College Scholarship Program [4511]
FCBA Foundation Law School Scholarship Programs [4512]
FCBA Foundation Law School Summer Internship Stipend Program [4513]
FCIL Schaffer Grants for Foreign Law Librarians [596]
FCSLA Graduate Scholarships [4575]
FCSLA High School Scholarships [4576]
FCSLA Seminary or Diaconate or Religious Life Scholarships [4577]
FCSLA Undergraduate College Scholarships [4578]
FCSLA Vocational/Technical/Trade Scholarships [4579]
Federal Alliance For Safe Homes (FLASH) **[4498]**
Federal Circuit Bar Association (FCBA) **[4505]**
Federal Communications Bar Association (FCBA) **[4510]**
Federal Court Bench and Bar Scholarships [11599]
Federal Employee Education and Assistance Fund (FEEA) **[4514]**
Federal Law Enforcement Officers Association (FLEOA) **[4518]**
Federal Managers Association (FMA) **[4520]**
Federal Student Loans for Graduate Students [4318]
The Federalist Society **[4522]**
Federalsburg Rotary Club Scholarship [3567]
Federated Insurance Scholarship [9169]
Federated Women's Institutes of Ontario **[4524]**
Federation of American Consumers and Travelers (FACT) **[4526]**
Federation of Asian Canadian Lawyers **[4528]**
Fédération Canadienne des Épiciers Indépendants (FCEI) **[4530]**
Federation of Diocesan Liturgical Commissions (FDLC) **[4532]**
FEEA-NTEU Scholarships [4515]
Feeding Hope Fund for Clinical Research Grants [7864]
Feeding Tomorrow Scholarships [5819]
Nolan W. Feeser Scholarship Fund [4590]
FEF Scholarship [4478]
Lola Fehr: Nightingale Scholarships [3534]
Jonathan M. Feigenbaum, Esquire **[4534]**

Ruth B. Fein Prize [1063]
Lee K. Feine Scholarship [7790]
Fejos Postdoctoral Fellowships in Ethnographic Film [11962]
The Feldman Law Firm, PLLC **[4536]**
Harry Feldman Memorial Scholarship [6290]
Milton Feldstein Memorial Scholarships [160]
Fellowship in the PMAC-AGPC [9349]
Wildlife and Conservation Medicine Internship [3436]
Fellowship on Women & Public Policy [11522]
Fellowships for Creative and Performing Artists and Writers [490]
The Judy Felt Memorial Volunteerism Scholarship [2026]
Reese Felts Scholarships [11187]
Diane Ross Fennekohl Endowment Fund for Education [6426]
Edward Fennel Mauldin Endowed Scholarship [8509]
Fermilab Internships for Physics Majors [11315]
Fermilab Science Undergraduate Laboratory Internship [11316]
Fermilab Summer Internships in Science & Technology (SIST) [11317]
FFA Scholarship [8586]
FFB-C Postdoctoral Fellowships [4788]
FHE Health **[4540]**
Fibrose Kystique Canada (CF) **[4542]**
FICPA Educational Foundation 1040K Race Scholarships [4636]
Field Aviation Co. Inc. Scholarship [180]
Field Museum of Natural History **[4546]**
Fielding Law Group **[4548]**
Fielding Law Group Scholarship Contest [4549]
Carole Fielding Student Grant [11567]
Fields Institute **[4550]**
Fields Research Fellowship [4551]
Fieldwork Fellowship [4449]
Fifth Month Scholarship [11228]
Fifth Third Bank Scholarship Fund [3359]
Adele Filene Student Presenter Grant [3846]
Filipino Bar Association of Northern California (FBANC) **[4553]**
Christine Filipovich Scholarships [3439]
Film Independent **[4555]**
Filson Fellowships [4559]
Filson Historical Society **[4557]**
Filson Historical Society Master's Thesis Fellowship [4560]
Financial CAD Corp. **[4561]**
Alan R. and Barbara D. Finberg Fellowships [5634]
FINCAD Women in Finance Scholarships [4562]
The Fred Finch Scholarship [11147]
Find Your Path Scholarship [10837]
William Robert Findley Graduate Chemistry Scholarship [8097]
Fine Arts Association (FAA) **[4563]**
Fine Arts Association Minority Scholarship [4564]
Fine Arts Association United Way Scholarship [4565]
Ruth Fine Memorial Student Loans [4120]
Finnegan Diversity Scholarship [4568]
Finnegan, Henderson, Farabow, Garrett and Dunner, LLP **[4567]**
Firefly Foundation **[4569]**
Firefly Foundation/ASRP Spark Award [412], [4570]
Firland Foundation **[4571]**
Graduate Pulmonary Nursing Fellowship [4572]
First Catholic Slovak Ladies Association (FCSLA) **[4574]**
First Community Foundation Partnership of Pennsylvania (FCFP) **[4580]**
FIRST Operator Certification Awards [4618]
First Step Award - Wiley Professional Development Grant [2235]
Firth Family Scholarship [12314]
Bea Firth Scholarship [12315]
The Judge Ralph Fisch Police Explorer Scholarship Program [4646]
Eugenia Vellner Fischer Award for the Performing Arts [7416]
Fish Finder Guides **[4609]**
Fish Finder Guides Scholarship [4610]
Fish & Richardson **[4611]**

Frederick V. Hunt Postdoctoral Research Fellowship in Acoustics [61]
Jan and Glenn Fredericks Scholarship [11478]
Emanuel R. Freedman Scholarship [8785]
Freedom Alliance **[4820]**
Freedom Alliance Scholarship Fund [4821]
Freedom From Religion Foundation **[4822]**
Kevin Freeman Travel Grant [7514]
Malcolm and Mildred Freiberg Fellowships [7143]
Donald L. Frendberg Program [9609]
Richard A. Freund International Scholarships [1542]
The Ludo Frevel Crystallography Scholarship [5966]
Carleton A. Friday Scholarship [7377]
Dale E. Fridell Memorial Scholarships [10858]
Fried, Frank, Harris, Shriver and Jacobson L.L.P. **[4826]**
MHS Marc Friedlaender Fellowships [7144]
The Nathan J. and Virginia H. Friedman College Scholarship [6271]
The Phil Friel Scholarship [7170]
Friends of Canadian Broadcasting (FCB) **[4828]**
Friends of the Christofor Foundation Scholarship [8231]
Friends of Coal Scholarships [11971]
Friends and Family of Christopher J. Kohlmeier Scholarship [9547]
Friends of Mary Automotive Scholarship [10052]
Friends of the Oro Valley Public Library Support Staff Scholarship Award [1810]
Friends of Project 10 Inc. **[4830]**
Friends of Project 10 Models of Excellence Scholarship [4831]
Donald Frizzell Memorial Scholarship [12318]
Froberg-Suess JD/MBA Scholarship [8999]
Patricia and Phillip Frost Fellowships [10215]
Fruits and Vegetable Industries Scholarships [7333]
The William and Francis Fry Honorary Fellowship for Contributions to Therapeutic Ultrasound [6118]
Elizabeth Fry Memorial Bursary [6671]
Mary Alice Fry Memorial Scholarship [6429]
FSF Field Grant [4677]
FSF Student Travel Grant [4678]
Full Circle Scholarship [980], [2042]
Full Stack Student Scholarship [4833]
Full Stack Talent **[4832]**
The Fuller Foundation, Inc. **[4834]**
Kathryn Fuller Science for Nature Fund [12203]
Arthur Flagler Fultz Research Award [1135]
Daniel G. and Helen I. Fultz Scholarship Fund [4592]
Fund for American Studies (TFAS) **[4836]**
Arkansas Nursing Foundation - Dorothea Fund Scholarships [1831]
Fund for Small Theatres [366]
Fundación Educativa Carlos M. Castañeda (FECMC) **[4839]**
Funeral Service Foundation, Inc. (FSF) **[4841]**
Fur Takers of America (FTA) **[4845]**
Donald M. Furbush Professional Development Grants [5862]
The Future of Bariatric Surgery Scholarship [2435]
Future Digital Marketers Scholarship [2657]
Future Educators Scholarship [7491]
#thefutureisfemale scholarship [11127]
Future Leader Initial NCTM Annual Meeting Attendance Awards [7804]
William Taylor in Radiocommunications Scholarships [3795]
Future of School Scholarship Program [9942]
Future STEM Teacher Scholarship [10937]
Educator Conditional Scholarship And Repayment Programs [11918]
Loleta D. Fyan Public Library Research Grant [6840]
G-1 Research Project Grants [6941]
G-2 Summer Portuguese Language Program [6942]
G-3 Summer Program in Portugal [6943]
GAAC Project Grants [4995]
Gabrial A. Hartl Scholarship [157]
Gabe Stepetin Business Scholarship [329]
Gabriel Dumont College Graduate Student Bursary [4236]
GACFE Scholarship Program [2134]
Gadde Sitaramamma & Tirupataiah Scholarship [10949]

Joe E. Gaddy, Jr. and Margaret W. Gaddy Scholarship [12078]
Gadzala Franciszek Memorial Scholarship [9664]
Gaebe Eagle Scout Award [7851]
Frederick and Helen Gaige Award [1483]
Gail Garner Memorial R.I.S.E. Scholarship [9548]
Harry Gairey Scholarship [2592]
GALAS Scholarship [4868]
Farley Moody Galbraith Scholarship [3653]
William E. "Bill" Gallagher Scholarship [8847]
Whitney Laine Gallahar Memorial Scholarship Fund [3654]
Sam Gallant Memorial Scholarships [1818]
Gallery Collection **[4847]**
The Gallery Collection's Create-A-Greeting-Card Scholarship [4848]
Gallery Karin Carton **[4849]**
Gallo Blue Chip Scholarships [5301]
Lionel Galstaun Memorial Grant [1877]
Maro Ajemian Galstaun Memorial Grant [1878]
Galvanize the Future: A Richard L. Brooks Memorial Scholarship [934]
Gamewardens Association, Vietnam to Present **[4851]**
Gamewardens Scholarship Program [4852]
Gamma Chi Project 2000 Scholarship [6430]
Gamma Iota Scholarship [10108]
Gamma Iota Scholarships - Gamma Tau [10109]
Gamma Iota Scholarships - Zeta Kappa [10110]
Gamma Iota Scholarships - Zeta Nu [10111]
Gamma Lambda Scholarship [10112]
The Gamma Mu Foundation **[4853]**
Gamma Mu Project 2000 Scholarship [6431]
The Gamma Mu Scholarships Program [4854]
Gamma Pi Project 2000 Scholarship [6432]
Gamma Sigma Alpha (GSA) **[4855]**
Gamma Sigma Alpha Graduate Scholarship [4856]
Gamma Theta Project 2000 Scholarship [6433]
Gamma Zeta Project 2000 Scholarship [6434]
John A. Gans Scholarship [1748]
Gantenbein Medical Fund Fellowship [4092]
GAPA Foundation Scholarship [9334]
Joel Garcia Memorial Scholarship [3198]
Michael and Gina Garcia Rail Engineering Scholarships [1328]
William R. Gard Memorial Scholarships [7666]
Garden Club of America (GCA) **[4857]**
Garden Club of America Awards in Tropical Botany (GCA) [4859]
The Garden Club Council of Winston-Salem and Forsyth County Scholarship [12079]
Garden State Association of Christian Schools **[4861]**
The Gardeners of America **[4863]**
Gardeners of America/Men's Garden Clubs of America Scholarship [4864]
IGS John Gardner Fellowship [11537]
Gardner Foundation Education Scholarship [5786]
Gardner Foundation Scholarship [3363]
Dwight D. Gardner Scholarship [5828]
Eugene Garfield Doctoral Dissertation Fellowship [2497]
Peter M. Gargano Scholarship Fund [4206]
NWT Law Foundation/Graeme Garson Scholarships [8545]
Marcus Mosiah Garvey Scholarships [6216]
Gary and Gussie Williams Scholarship [11621]
Gary Merrill Memorial Scholarship Fund [6979]
Ethel Mae Gaston Memorial Scholarship [8338]
Edwin W. Gaston Scholarships [377]
The Gates Millennium Scholars [5529]
Marian P. and David M. Gates Scholarship for Non-Residents [11622]
Frank Caleb & Margaret Thompson Gates Student Scholarships [11623]
Gatti, Keltner, Bienvenu & Montesi PLC **[4865]**
David A. and Pamela A. Gault Charitable Fund [10759]
Gauthier Family Scholarship Fund [5078]
Mary V. Gaver Scholarship [6841]
James L. Gavin Memorial Scholarship [2524]
A.R.F.O.R.A. Martha Gavrila Scholarships for Women [1368]
GAWP Graduate Scholarships [4925]
Gay and Lesbian Armenian Society (GALAS) **[4867]**

Gay and Lesbian Business Association of Santa Barbara (GLBA) **[4869]**
Lowell Gaylor Memorial Scholarships [181]
The Florence Gaynor Award [7654]
GCFI Student Travel Awards [5252]
GCSAA Scholars Competition [5032]
GCSAA Student Essay Contest [5033]
GE Aviation Scholarship Fund [3364]
G.E. Lighting Canada Community Leadership Awards [4345]
GED Jump Start Scholarships [9959]
Geeta Rastogi Memorial Scholarship [11757]
Gehring Memorial Foundation Scholarships [5742]
GEICO Life Scholarship [5021]
Victoria S. and Bradley L. Geist Scholarships [5400], [5437]
Geraldine Geistert Boss Scholarship [5151]
Irma Gelhausen Scholarship Fund [6663]
Gemological Institute of America (GIA) **[4874]**
The Gene & John Athletic Fund [10850]
General Aviation Manufacturers Association (GAMA) **[4884]**
General Board of Higher Education and Ministry (GBHEM) **[4887]**
General Falcon Scholarships [9243]
General Federation of Women's Clubs of Massachusetts (GFWC) **[4896]**
General John Paul Ratay Educational Fund Grants [7389]
General Mills Foundation Scholarships [981]
General Motors Foundation **[4904]**
Generation III Scholarship [4285]
Genesee Finger Lakes Chapter of the Air and Waste Management Association (GFLAWMA) **[4906]**
Geological Society of America (GSA) **[4908]**
Geological Society of America Graduate Student Research Grants [4910]
George A. Hall / Harold F. Mayfield Grant [12054]
George C. Balch Scholarship [11383]
George E. Judd Scholarship Fund [10686]
George E. Nichols Undergraduate Scholarship [11624]
George Foreman Tribute to Lyndon B. Johnson [9472]
George H. A. Clowes, Jr. MD, FACS, Memorial Research Career Development Award [777]
George Hi'ilani Mills Scholarship [8925]
George J. Mitchell Scholarship [11774]
George J.Waterman Memorial Scholarship [11898]
George N. Lindsay Fellowship [6740]
George Oliver Benton Memorial Scholarship Fund [3619]
George and Pearl Strickland Scholarship Fund [3586]
George Torkildsen Literary Award [12200]
George W. Juno Scholarship [4877]
Georgelis Injury Law Firm, P.C. **[4911]**
Georgelis Injury Law Firm, P.C. Scholarship Award [4912]
Georgetown University **[4913]**
Georgetown Working League (GWL) **[4915]**
Georgetown Working League Scholarship [4917]
Georgia Association of Broadcasters (GAB) **[4922]**
Georgia Association of Water Professionals (GAWP) **[4924]**
Georgia Engineering Foundation (GEF) **[4927]**
Georgia Engineering Foundation Scholarships [4928]
Georgia Gerontology Society **[4929]**
Georgia Library Association **[4931]**
Georgia Press Educational Foundation (GPEF) **[4934]**
Gerald Garner Memorial Scholarship [9000]
Gerald V. Henderson Memorial Scholarship [10427]
Geraldine Clewell Scholarship [9113]
Gerard Swartz Fudge Memorial Scholarship [5664]
Gerber Foundation **[4938]**
Gerber Foundation Merit Scholarship [4940]
Burton L. Gerber Scholarship [2525]
Doris Y. and John J. Gerber Scholarship [11910]
Walter Gerboth Award [7515]
Geri Coccodrilli Culinary Scholarship [5079]
German Historical Institute (GHI) **[4941]**
German Historical Institute Doctoral and Postdoctoral Fellowships [4942]

German Historical Institute Fellowships at the Horner Library [4943]
German Marshall Fund of the United States (GMF) **[4944]**
German Society of Pennsylvania (GSP) **[4950]**
German Society Scholarships [4951]
German Studies Research Grants [4062]
Bunny Kline Gerner & Robin Gerner Doty Memorial Adelphe Scholarship [6435]
Gerrie Electric Memorial Scholarship Awards [4346]
Eloise Gerry Fellowships [5058]
Berek and Regina Gertner OSOTF Bursary in Holocaust Studies [12245]
Gertrude M. Cox Scholarship [1611]
Elizabeth Tucker Gessley Scholarship [6436]
Get A Boost $2,000 Scholarship [2608]
Get Ahead Scholarship [4474]
Getty Conservation Guest Scholars [4953]
Getty Foundation **[4952]**
Getty Foundation Library Research Grants [4954]
Getty GRI-NEH Postdoctoral Fellowships [4955]
Getty Postdoctoral Fellowship in Conservation Science [4956]
Getty Postdoctoral Fellowships [4957]
Getty Predoctoral Fellowships [4958]
Getty Research Exchange Fellowship Program for Cultural Heritage Preservation [1347]
Getty Scholar Grants [4959]
Gettysburg College - Eisenhower Institute **[4960]**
GFAI Industry Immersion Scholarship Program [5064]
GFLC AWMA Scholarship Program [4907]
GFWC Women's Club of South County scholarship program [9693]
GIA Scholarship - Distance Education eLearning [4878]
Gianninoto Industrial Design Graduate Scholarship [5778]
The Robert Giard Fellowship [3235]
Emily V. Gibbes Scholarship [8339]
John J. Gibbons Fellowship in Public Interest & Constitutional Law [4966]
Gibbons P.C. **[4965]**
Joy Gibson MATC Cohort Award [11188]
Laverne L. Gibson Memorial Scholarship [8848]
Robert D. Gibson Scholarship [1749]
GibsonSingleton VA Injury Attorneys **[4967]**
The Elaine and Barry Gilbert College Scholarship [6272]
Shane Gilbert Memorial Scholarship [8849]
Margaret S. Gilbert Scholarship Fund [10760]
Gilbreth Memorial Fellowship [5829]
Gilder Lehrman Short-Term research Fellowships [6773]
Terry M. Giles Honor Scholar Program [9001]
Composites Division/Harold Giles Scholarship [10487]
William Harrison Gill Education Fund [2480]
Gilliam Fellowships for Advanced Study [5615]
Benjamin A. Gilman International Scholarship [11479]
Keith Gilmore Foundation - Diploma Scholarships [4970]
Keith Gilmore Foundation (KGF) **[4969]**
Keith Gilmore Foundation - Postgraduate Scholarships [4971]
Keith Gilmore Foundation - Undergraduate Scholarships [4972]
Susan Kay Munson Gilmore Memorial Scholarship [3678]
Lawrence Ginocchio Aviation Scholarships [7736]
Girls Incorporated of the Greater Capital Region **[4973]**
Girls in Stem (GIS) Scholarship [9716]
The Alex Gissler Memorial Scholarship [7171]
GIST - Mattie Lou Gist Memoral Scholarship Endowment [8510]
GIST - Orben F. Gist Memorial Scholarship Endowment [8511]
Jack Gitlitz Memorial Scholarship - Israel [6291]
GJEC Dissertation Completion Fellowship [7336]
GJEL Accident Attorneys **[4977]**
GLA Beard Scholarship [4932]
GLA Hubbard Scholarships [4933]
GLAAD **[4979]**

GLAAD Communications/PR Internships - New York [4983]
GLAAD Spanish-Language and Latino Media Internships - Los Angeles [4984]
GLAAD Youth Issues Internships - New York [4985]
J. Robert Gladden Orthopaedic Society (JRGOS) **[4991]**
J. Robert Gladden Orthopaedic Society PGY5 ABOS Board Preparation Scholarship [4992]
J. Robert Gladden Orthopaedic Society Traveling Fellowship Support [4993]
Gladys C. Anderson Memorial Scholarship [915]
Jane R. Glaser Scholarship [1626]
John Glaser Scholarships [3506]
Glass Art Association of Canada (GAAC) **[4994]**
Dr. Helen Preston Glass Fellowships [3060]
GLATA Living Memorial Doctorate Scholarship [5215]
GLATA Living Memorial Graduate Scholarship [5216]
Herman and Bess Glazer Scholarship Fund [5227]
Glazing Industry Scholarship [9402]
Gleaner Life Insurance Society (GLIS) **[4996]**
Gleaner Life Insurance Society Scholarship [4997]
Glen and Babs Carlson Endowed Scholarship [6794]
Glendale Latino Association (GLA) **[4998]**
Glendale Latino Association Scholarships [4999]
Glenn/AFAR Breakthroughs in Gerontology Awards [876]
Glenn B. Anderson Scholarship [7721]
Glenn Foundation for Medical Research and AFAR Grants for Junior Faculty [877]
Glenn Keever Scholarship [11189]
Glenn T. Seaborg Congressional Science and Engineering Fellowship [1165]
Glens Falls Foundation **[5000]**
Doris and Clarence Glick Classical Music Scholarship Fund [5401]
Global Art Grant [2613]
Global Business Travel Association (GBTA) **[5003]**
Global Entrepreneur's Award [6314]
Global Sustainability Alliance (GSA) **[5005]**
Global Sustainable Electricity Partnership (GSEP) **[5007]**
Glogowski Franciszek Memorial Scholarship [9665]
Bud Glover Memorial Scholarships [182]
Goddard, Indovina & Krakowski Scholarship [396]
The Dr. Robert H. Goddard Memorial Scholarship [8123]
Goddard Systems Inc. **[5009]**
The Marie Trahan/Susman Godfrey Scholarship [11148]
Glenn Godfrey Sr. Memorial Scholarship [6589]
Godparents for Tanzania **[5011]**
Godparents for Tanzania Scholarship [5012]
Goethe Society of North America (GSNA) **[5013]**
S. William & Martha R. Goff Educational Scholarship [8850]
Shirley J. Gold Scholarship [883]
Daniel B. Goldberg Scholarship [5052]
Golden Belt Community Foundation (GBCF) **[5015]**
Golden Door Scholars **[5017]**
Golden Door Scholarship [5018]
Golden Key Advisor Professional Development Grant [5022]
Golden Key Graduate Scholar Award [5023]
Golden Key International Honour Society (GKIHS) **[5019]**
Keren Goldenberg Public Defender Scholarship [6695]
William R. Goldfarb Memorial Scholarships [1940]
Goldia.com **[5024]**
Goldia.com Jewelry Scholarships [5025]
Dr. Guido Goldman Fellowships [807]
Goldman, Sachs and Company Fund [3365]
Goldman Sachs/Matsuo Takabuki Commemorative Scholarship [8926]
Helen B. and Lewis E. Goldstein Scholarship [6273]
Goldwin Howland Scholarship [3080]
Golf Canada **[5026]**
Golf Course Superintendents Association of America (GCSAA) **[5031]**
Golf Guides Zone **[5035]**
Joshua Gomes Memorial Scholarship Fund [7924]

Diane G. Lowe and John Gomez, IV Scholarship Fund [3620]
Charles D. Gonthier Research Fellowship [3018]
Gonzaga University School of Law **[5037]**
Joe Goodeill Scholarship [12319]
Goodfellow Memorial Canadian Vocal Music Scholarship [9900]
Goodfellow Memorial Grade A Female Voice Scholarship [9901]
Goodfellow Memorial Oratorio Scholarship [9902]
Goodfellow Memorial Senior Grade A Male Voice Scholarship [9903]
Goodfellow Memorial Senior Operatic Scholarship [9904]
Goodman Acker P.C. **[5039]**
Goodman Acker Scholarships [5040]
Arthur H. Goodman Memorial Scholarship [9815]
Goodwin Procter L.L.P. **[5041]**
Google European Doctoral Fellowships [5046]
Google Lime Scholarship [6862]
Google LLC **[5043]**
Google US/Canada PhD Fellowships [5047]
Lucille May Gopie Scholarships [2593]
The Gordon Allport Intergroup Relations Prize [10509]
The Gordon Foundation **[5049]**
Wilhelmina Gordon Foundation Scholarships [7757]
Thomas Boston Gordon Memorial Scholarship [2526]
Barnett D. Gordon Scholarships [5743]
Gordon W. and Agnes P. Cobb Scholarship [4256]
Gordy Fink Memorial Scholarship [9403]
FAMU Presidential Scholarship - George W. Gore Assistantship Scholarship [4621]
Sarah "Sally" Ives Gore Gamma Kappa Sapphire Scholarships [6437]
Richard C. Gorecki Scholarships [9244]
Gorrondona & Associates, Inc. / WTS High School Scholarships [12174]
Louis Gottschalk Prize [1432]
Carl W. Gottschalk Research Scholar Grants [1526]
Norma Gotwalt Scholarship Fund [4777]
Charles F. Gould Endowment Scholarships [11449]
Government Documents Special Interest Section - Veronica Maclay Travel Grant [597]
Government Finance Officers Association of United States and Canada (GFOA) **[5051]**
Governor James E. Holshouser Professional Development Scholarship [8434]
Governor William A. Egan Award [11480]
Wilford Hayes Gowen Scholarship Fund [11600]
Anna K. Gower and Annabelle K. Gower Scholarship Fund [5402]
Goya Scholarships [10028]
GradSchools.com Minority Graduate Nursing Scholarship [4316]
Graduate Award [6854]
Graduate Fellowships for Science, Technology, Engineering, and Mathematics Diversity (GFSD) **[5055]**
Graduate Fellowships for Study of International Affairs [4093]
Graduate Realtor Institute Scholarships [6537]
Graduate Research Awards for Disarmament, Arms Control and Non-Proliferation [10142]
Graduate Research Travel Scholarships [4408]
Graduate Student Award [515]
Graduate Student Fellowships [4547]
Graduate Student Fellowships for Alternatives to the Use of Animals in Science [6009]
Graduate Student Honoraria - A. Brazier Howell Award [1502]
Graduate Student Honoraria - Elmer C. Birney Award [1503]
Graduate Student Pest Management Award [3108]
Graduate Student Scholar Award [9164]
Graduate Student Travel Grants [10318]
Graduate Women in Science (GWIS) **[5057]**
Graduating Texas High School Seniors Scholarship [10992]
A. Allen Graffham Research Grant [2047]
Grain and Feed Association of Illinois (GFAI) **[5063]**
J.L. Granatstein Post-Doctoral Fellowship [11530]
Grand Canyon Historical Society (GCHS) **[5065]**

Grand Canyon Historical Society Scholarships [5066]

Grand Haven Area Community Foundation (GHACF) **[5067]**

Grand Haven Offshore Challenge Scholarship [5080]

Grand Island Community Foundation **[5116]**

Grand Lodge of Saskatchewan **[5128]**

Grand Rapids Community Foundation (GRCF) **[5130]**

Grand Rapids Scholarship Association [5152]

Grand Rapids Trans Foundation **[5196]**

Grand Rapids Trans Foundation Academic Scholarship [5197]

Grand Rapids University Prep Founders' Scholarship [5153]

Grande Prairie 4-H District Scholarship [14]

Charles Hall Grandgent Award [3971]

Granger Business Association (GBA) **[5198]**

Granger Business Association College Scholarship [5199]

Granite Bay Cosmetic Surgery **[5200]**

Grant Assistance Program for Autism Professionals - College Programs [8652]

Grant Assistance Program for Autism Professionals - Doctoral Programs [8653]

Grant Assistance Program for Autism Professionals - Institutional Standards [8654]

Grant Assistance Program for Autism Professionals - Masters Programs [8655]

Grant Assistance Program for Autism Professionals - Professional Certification Programs [8656]

Grant Assistance Program for Autism Professionals - Retroactive Assistance [8657]

Grant Assistance Program for Autism Professionals - Undergraduate Programs [8658]

Grant H. Flint International Scholarship Program - Category I [10580]

Grant H. Flint International Scholarship Program - Category II [10581]

Grant Law Office **[5202]**

Russ Grant Memorial Scholarship for Tennis [8851]

Grants in Aid for Early Career Professionals [1294]

Grants to Artists [4769]

Grants-in-Aid of Research (GIAR) [10128]

Graphic Design Scholarships [8411]

Grass Fellowships at the Marine Biological Laboratory [5205]

Grass Foundation **[5204]**

Ella T. Grasso Literary Scholarship [11221]

The Paul and Helen L. Grauer Scholarships [1941]

Gravure Education Foundation (GEF) **[5206]**

Mona Gray Creative Arts Scholarship [6306]

Ken Gray Scholarship [11481]

IADR John Gray Fellowship [5914]

Arkansas Nursing Foundation - Mary Gray Scholarships [1832]

Graybar Canada Award of Excellence Scholarships [4347]

Graydon A. Tunstall Undergraduate Student Scholarship [9074]

Grays Harbor Community Foundation (GHCF) **[5212]**

Grays Harbor Community Foundation Scholarships [5213]

Great Falls Broadcasters Association Scholarships [7452]

Great Lakes Athletic Trainers Association (GLATA) **[5214]**

Great Lakes Commission (GLC) **[5217]**

Great Lakes Commission Sea Grant Fellowship [5218]

Great Lakes Section Diversity Scholarship [5221]

Great Lakes Section Institute of Food Technologists **[5219]**

GREAT MINDS Collegiate Scholarship Program [368]

Greater DFW WTS Undergraduate Leadership Scholarship [12175]

Greater Seattle Business Association (GSBA) **[5222]**

Greater Seattle Business Association Scholarships (GSBA Scholarships) [5223]

Greater Valley Chamber of Commerce **[5224]**

Greater Washington Society of Certified Public Accountants (GWSCPA) **[5228]**

Frank L. Greathouse Government Accounting Scholarship [5053]

Bishop Charles P. Greco Graduate Fellowships [6578]

Greek Orthodox Archdiocese of America **[5230]**

Greek Orthodox Archdiocese of America Paleologos Graduate Scholarships [5231]

Andy Green, Attorney at Law., P.C. **[5232]**

Green Hill Yacht and Country Club Scholarship [3568]

Green Knight Economic Development Corporation (GKEDC) **[5234]**

Green Knight Economic Development Corporation Scholarships [5235]

Crystal Green Memorial Scholarship [2626]

Joshua "Josh" Green Memorial Scholarship Endowment [8512]

James H. and Shirley L. Green Scholarship Fund [10761]

Howard L. Green Scholarships [8273]

Priscilla Green Scholarships [3894]

The K2TEO Martin J. Green, Sr. Memorial Scholarship [1942]

Michael Greenberg Student Writing Competition [7986]

Curt Greene Memorial Scholarships [5302]

Elizabeth Greenhalgh Memorial Scholarships in Journalism, Graphic Arts, or Photography [12136]

The Greenlining Institute **[5236]**

Greenlining Institute Policy Fellowship [5237]

GreenMatch **[5238]**

Greenwich Scholarship Association (GSA) **[5240]**

Greenwich Scholarship Association Scholarships (GSA) [5241]

Anna Munger Greenwood Memorial Adelphe Scholarship [6438]

Greg Clerk Award [6621]

Greg Matthews Memorial Scholarship [9002]

Gretchen Dimico Memorial Scholarship [6795]

Gretchen Hauff Memorial Scholarship [9404]

Griffin Foundation **[5242]**

Griffin Foundation Scholarships [5243]

Velma Shotwell Griffin Memorial Scholarship Fund [10762]

Homajean Grisham Memorial Scholarship [8513]

Shelby Grissom Memorial Scholarship [8514]

Reginald K. Groome Memorial Scholarships [9986]

Jennifer C. Groot Memorial Fellowship [727]

Caroline and Martin Gross Fellowship [8256]

Kathern F. Gruber Scholarship Program [2624]

Gruwell Scholarship [3569]

GSA Scholarships for International Nurses [5006]

Guajardo & Marks Law School Scholarship [5245]

Guajardo & Marks LLP **[5244]**

Guerra - Melissa Ann (Missy) Guerra Scholarship [3476]

Ronald P. Guerrette FFA Scholarship Fund [6980]

Eleanor Guetzloe Undergraduate Scholarship [3853]

Harry Frank Guggenheim Dissertation Fellowships [5247]

Guggenheim Fellowships [10192]

Harry Frank Guggenheim Foundation (HFG) **[5246]**

Harry Frank Guggenheim Foundation Research Grants [5248]

John Simon Guggenheim Memorial Fellowships - United States & Canadian Competition [5250]

John Simon Guggenheim Memorial Foundation **[5249]**

Bobette Bibo Gugliotta Memorial Scholarships for Creative Writing [10133]

GuildScholar Awards [6855]

Hai Guin Scholarships [5260]

Guin-Stanford Scholarship [3655]

Gulf and Caribbean Fisheries Institute (GCFI) **[5251]**

Gulf Coast Hurricane Scholarship [10488]

Larry Gulley Scholarship [10343]

Scott A. Gunder, MD, DCMS Presidential Scholarship [4798]

Gunild Keetman Scholarship [8724]

Gunnar Nicholson Endowed Scholarship [9003]

Connie and Robert T. Gunter Scholarship [10401]

Guntley-Lorimer Science and Arts Scholarships [2594]

George Gurdjian Memorial Grant [1879]

Antranik and Alice Gurdjian Scholarship Grant [1880]

The George Gurney Fellowship Endowment Fund [10216]

Patricia S. Gustafson '56 Memorial Scholarship Fund [4207]

Guthikonda BasavapunnaRao & Umadevi Scholarship [10950]

Guthikonda Ramabrahmam & Balamani Scholarship [10951]

Mary Ewing Guthrey/Mary Keller Moyer Memorial Scholarship [6439]

Tamara Guttman Memorial Scholarship [12320]

Guy D. & Mary Edith Halladay Music Scholarship [5154]

Guy P. Gannett Scholarship Fund [6981]

Guy P. Greenwald Jr. Endowed Scholarship Fund [9004]

Guzkowski Family Scholarships [9549]

Gwen Yarnell Theatre Scholarship [4566]

Gwin J. and Ruth Kolb Research Travel Fellowship [1433]

GWS Scholarship Program [165]

GWSCPA Scholarship Fund [5229]

Gwynedd Mercy University **[5254]**

Gwynedd Mercy University Presidential Scholarship [5255]

H. Kruger Kaprielian Scholarship [11714]

H. Wayne VanAgtmael Cosmetology Scholarship [5081]

Garabed, Zabel and Vahe Hachikian Scholarship Grant [1881]

Hackett Family Scholarship [5155]

Louise Wallace Hackney Fellowships for the Study of Chinese Art [1191]

HACU/Denny's Hungry for Education Scholarships [5515]

HACU/KIA Motors America, Inc. STEAM Scholarships [5516], [6543]

Perry F. Hadlock Memorial Scholarships [1943]

Suzanne Lovell Hadsell Memorial Scholarship [6440]

Bert & Karen Hadvick Scholarship [12321]

HAESF Graduate Scholarships [5644]

HAESF Professional Internship Program [5645]

Hagley Museum and Library **[5256]**

Leslie Jane Hahn Memorial Scholarships [9816]

Hai Guin Scholarship Association of Boston **[5259]**

Jack Hajinian Memorial Grant [1882]

Michael Hakeem Memorial Essay Contest for Ongoing College Students [4824]

Lee Hakel Graduate Student Scholarship [10334]

Ralph Hale and Martha L. Ruppert Educational Scholarship [10134]

Half Chrome **[5261]**

Half Chrome Drones Scholarship [5262]

Hall of Achievement Scholarship [2799]

Hall County Medical Society Scholarship [5122]

Anna E. Hall Memorial Scholarships [9084]

Guy D. & Mary Edith Halladay Graduate Scholarship [5156]

Chuck Halliday Scholarship [12322]

David J. Hallissey Memorial Internships [1586]

Halloween Costume Scholarship [7441]

Ida Halpern Fellowship and Award [10326]

Harold B. Halter Memorial Scholarship [4497]

Patty Hamilton Early Childhood Development Scholarships [11450]

Alice Hamilton Prize [1453]

Ruth Simms Hamilton Research Fellowship [10927]

Al Hamilton Scholarship [2595]

Stan Hamilton Scholarship [9885]

George and Mary Josephine Hamman Foundation **[5263]**

George and Mary Josephine Hamman Foundation Scholarships [5264]

The Caitlin Hammaren Memorial Scholarship [6441]

Richard A. Hammill Scholarship Fund [1103]

Hammond Power Solutions Inc. Outstanding Electrical Scholar Awards (HPS) [4348]

Harry Hampton Fund Scholarship [5266]

Harry Hampton Memorial Wildlife, Inc. **[5265]**

Hampton Roads Association of Social Workers Scholarship [5271]

Hampton Roads Community Foundation **[5267]**

Hampton Roads Tara Welch Gallagher Environmental Scholarship [5272]
HANA Scholars [4891]
Hancock Family Snow Hill High School Scholarship [3570]
Handweavers Guild of America, Inc. (HGA) [5282]
Byron Hanke Fellowships [4767]
Clayburn J. Sr. & Garnet R. Hanna Scholarship [8852]
Hannah Post-doctoral Fellowship [2020]
Hans H. and Margaret B. Doe Scholarship [9817]
Hans McCorriston Grant [2358]
Martha and Oliver Hansen Memorial Scholarships [6202]
The Haraldson Foundation [5287]
Haraldson Foundation Scholarships [5288]
Harbor Breeze Corp. [5289]
Isaac and Mary Harbottle Scholarship [8927]
Hardanger Fiddle Association of America (HFAA) [5291]
H.G. Hardbarger Science - Mathematics Award [8853]
Charles Henry Hardin Memorial Scholarship [2527]
Hardwick & Pendergast PS [5293]
Dolores Ruth Heady Hardy Memorial Scholarship [6442]
The Alison Hardy Tea and Bursary [7816]
Hardy Wolf & Downing Injury Lawyers [5295]
Hardy, Wolf & Downing Scholarships [5296]
Harkness Fellowships in Health Care Policy and Practice [3555]
Bryce Harlow Foundation [5297]
Harness Horse Youth Foundation (HHYF) [5299]
Harness Tracks of America (HTA) [5303]
Harness Tracks of America Scholarship Fund [5304]
Margaret Shumavonian Harnischfeger Scholarship [1883]
The Harold E. Eisenberg Foundation Scholarship [5979]
Harold E. Ennes Scholarship [10285]
Harold and Eleanor Ringelberg Scholarship [5082]
Harold Gulliksen Psychometric Research Fellowship [4312]
Harper's Magazine Scholarships [8786]
Harrell Family Fellowship [728]
Harriet Erich Graduate Fellowship [4002]
Harriet Irsay Scholarship [1045]
Harris Corporation [5305]
Marcia S. Harris Legacy Fund Scholarships [9650]
Leon Harris/Les Nichols Memorial Scholarships to Spartan College of Aeronautics & Technology [183]
William H. Harris Memorial Scholarships [9170]
Harris Personal Injury Lawyers Inc. [5307]
Eileen Harrison Education Scholarships [5083]
Ted & Nicky Harrison Memorial Fund [12323]
Morton and Beatrice Harrison Scholarship Fund [4593]
Lullelia W. Harrison Scholarships in Counseling [12411]
Harrisville Lion's Club Scholarship [8854]
Harry A. Donn Scholarship [5329]
Harry J. Morris, Jr. Emergency Services [5157]
Harry Munoz Memorial Scholarship [9550]
Harry S. Truman Scholarships [11129]
Harry Steele Entrance Award [12252]
Harry Walts Memorial Graduate Scholarship [6923]
Dave Hart Graduate Scholarship [10654]
Carroll Hart Scholarship [10344]
Ida L. Hartenberg Charitable Scholarships [5330]
John A. Hartford Foundation (JAHF) [5309]
Hartford Foundation for Public Giving (HFPG) [5311]
Hartford Grammar School Scholarship Fund [5331]
Hartford Public Library (HPL) [5350]
Hartford Whalers Booster Club (HWBC) [5352]
Hartford Whalers Booster Club Scholarship [5353]
Harry C. Hartleben III/Gordon Page Corbitt Scholarship [8855]
Gail L. Hartshorn Memorial Fund [8856]
Harvard Business Services Inc. [5354]
Harvard-Smithsonian Center for Astrophysics (CFA) [5356]
Harvard University - Arnold Arboretum [5360]

Harvard University Faculty of Arts & Sciences - Institute for Quantitative Social Science - Henry A. Murray Research Archive [5362]
Harvard University Law School (HLS) [5364]
Harvard University Law School - Program on Negotiation (PON) [5367]
Harvey Fellows Program [7519]
Harvey M. Pollicove Memorial Scholarship [8676]
Harvoy Washington Banks Scholarship in Astronomy [8086]
Hasbrook & Hasbrook [5371]
Donald F. Hastings Scholarship [1661]
Gregory Linn Haught Citizenship Award [8857]
Dorcas Edmonson Haught Scholarship [8858]
Centre on Aging Betty Havens Memorial Graduate Fellowship [11584]
Hawaii Chapter/David T. Woolsey Scholarship [6647]
Hawaii Community Foundation [5373]
Hawaii Lodging & Tourism Association (HLTA) [5417]
Hawaii Pacific Gerontological Society (HPGS) [5420]
Viginia & Susan Hawk Scholarship [9818]
Lex and Scott Hawkins Endowed Scholarship [4159]
Don C. Hawkins Memorial Scholarships [184]
Thomas T. Hayashi Memorial Scholarship [6246]
Edward and Cora Hayes Scholarship [4160]
Celeste Hayo Memorial Scholarship Fund [5403]
Hazel D. Isbell Foundation Fellowships [4003]
Hazel Simms Nursing Scholarship [6664]
Hazen and Sawyer Scholarship [1641]
HBI Gilda Slifka Internship Program [2680]
HBI Scholar-in-Residence Program [2681]
HBO Point Scholarship [9222]
H.C. Schott Foundation Scholarship [3366]
HCF Community Scholarships Fund [5404]
HCRTA/Glen O. & Wyllabeth Scholarship Fund [3367]
HDSA Research Grants [5657]
M.G. "Doc" Headley Scholarships [10826]
Healing Springs Ranch [5423]
Health and Aging Policy Fellows Program [1255]
Health Effects Institute (HEI) [5425]
Health, Leisure and Human Performance Research Institute Graduate Student Travel Award [11589]
Health Physics Society (HPS) [5427]
Health Policy Scholarship for General Surgeons [778]
Health Professional Nursing Student Loans [7424]
Health Resources in Action [5433]
Health is a Right Not a Privilege Scholarship [8561]
Health Services Research Dissertation Awards [11326]
Healthcare Information Management Systems Scholarships [5448]
Healthcare Information and Management Systems Society (HIMSS) [5446]
Healthline Media [5451]
The Healthline & NORD Stronger Scholarship [5452]
Healthy Communities Scholarship [9282]
Annamae Heaps Law Scholarship [4161]
Hearing Foundation of Canada [5453]
The William Randolph Hearst Endowed Scholarship [8340]
Heather McCallum Scholarship [2104]
Dr. James H. Heckman Memorial Scholarship Fund [10763]
HECUA Scholarship for Community Engagement [5505]
HECUA Scholarship for Social Justice [5506]
Lenore and George Hedla Accounting Scholarship [11482]
Howell Heflin Memorial Scholarship [8515]
Heghinian Scholarships [4035]
Heidelberg Distributing Scholarship Fund [3368]
Heidi Patriquin Award for International Education [10465]
Vladimir and Pearl Heifetz Memorial Fellowship [12236]
Dale O. Heimberger CRNA Memorial Scholarship Fund [10764]
Heinz Pet Products Scholarship Fund [3369]
Hekemian Family Scholarship Grants [1884]

Helen G. and Allan D. Cruickshank Education Award [4642]
Helen and George Kilik Scholarship [290]
Helen Hay Whitney Foundation Postdoctoral Research Fellowship [12020]
Helen J. & Harold Gilman Smith Scholarship [2481]
Helen Krich Chinoy Dissertation Fellowship [1578]
Helen R. (Finley) Loescher and Stephen B. Loescher Scholarship [3679]
Helen R Greenamyer Memorial Fund [10827]
Helen Steiner Rice Scholarship Fund [3370]
Helena B. Cobb Higher Education (four Year) Scholarship [12165]
The Helena B. Cobb Scholarships [12166]
Helene M. Overly Memorial Graduate Scholarship [12170]
Helicopter Foundation International (HFI) [5455]
Commercial Helicopter Pilot Rating Scholarships [5456]
Helicopter Foundation International Maintenance Technician Certificate Scholarships [5457]
Hellenic Times Scholarship Fund (HTSF) [5460]
Hellenic Times Scholarships [5461]
Hellenic University Club of Philadelphia (HUC) [5462]
Hellenic University Club of Philadelphia Founders Scholarship [5465]
Joan Heller-Diane Bernard Fellowships [3236]
Joseph T. Helling Scholarship Fund [5748]
Helm Family Scholarship [9819]
Ronald, Randall and Roger Helman Scholarship [2528]
Helmer, Conley & Kasselman Annual College Scholarship [5471]
Helmer, Conley & Kasselman PA [5470]
John M. Helmick Law Scholarship [4162]
Heloise Werthan Kuhn Scholarship Fund [3621]
"Help to Save" Scholarship [3880]
Helsell Fetterman [5472]
Arthur C. Helton Fellowship Program [1489]
Arthur Helton Global Rights Fellowships [8361]
Clinton J. Helton Manufacturing Scholarship [10402]
Hemingway Foundation and Society [5474]
Hemlow Prize in Burney Studies [1434]
Jeanne H. Hemmingway Scholarship Fund [4208]
Hench Post-Dissertation Fellowship [491]
John Henderson Endowment Scholarships [11451]
Henderson Memorial Endowed Scholarship [6796]
Dr. E. Bruce Hendrick Scholarship Program [5669]
Mary Jane Hendrie Memorial Scholarships [11690]
Henigson Human Rights Fellowship [5365]
SNMMI Robert E. Henkin, MD, Government Relations Fellowship [10439]
Paul E. Henkin School Psychology Travel Grant [1730]
Henley-Putnam University Scholarships [5931]
John P. Hennessey Scholarship [7349]
Henry Adams Scholarship [1474]
Henry Friesen Awards and Lecture [10265]
Thomas J. Henry Law [5482]
Thomas J. Henry Leadership Scholarship Program [5483]
Henry L.P. Schmelzer College Transitions Scholarship Fund [6982]
Randy Henry Memorial Scholarship [9343]
Allan F. Henry/Paul A. Greebler Scholarship [1166]
Henry S. and Carolyn Adams Scholarship [4734]
Henry Salvatori Fellowships [5885]
Henry Salvatori Scholarship [8689]
Gene Henson Scholarship [2340]
Herb Adrian Memorial Scholarship Endowment [4735]
Herb And Ann Fincher Scholarship Fund [3571]
Herb Kohl Educational Foundation Student Excellence Scholarship [6582]
Herb Kohl Educational Foundation Student Initiative Scholarship [6583]
Herb Kohl Educational Foundation Teacher Fellowship Program [6584]
Herb Society of America (HSA) [5484]
Herb Society of America Research Grant [5485]
Herbert Hoover Uncommon Student Award [5557]
Herbert Law Office [5491]
Herbert Law Office Scholarship Contest [5492]
Rich Herbert Memorial Scholarship [1630]

Herbert Scoville Jr. Peace Fellowship [9988]

Robert N. Herbert Undergraduate Scholarships [10433]

Herbert W. Rand Fellowship and Scholarship [7045]

Hereditary Disease Foundation (HDF) **[5493]**

Hereditary Disease Foundation Basic Research Grants Program [5494]

Herbert Herff Presidential Law Scholarships [11601]

Herman H. Derksen Scholarship [9820]

Herman P. Kopplemann Fund [5332]

Hermann Law Group PLLC **[5495]**

Hermann Law Group, PLLC Safety Scholarship Contest [5496]

Hernandez – Manuel Hernandez, Jr. Memoral Scholarship [3477]

Catarino and Evangelina Hernández Research Fellowships in Latino History [10996]

George L. and June L. Herpel Memorial Scholarship [2529]

Herpetologists League (HL) **[5497]**

The Herpetologists' League Graduate Research Award [5499]

Purdue University Ray W. Herrick Laboratories Research Fellowship [9451]

Jessica M. Herron, Epsilon Nu, Memorial Scholarship [6443]

Ella Beren Hersch Scholarship [8859]

Herschede Engineering Scholarship [10082]

Isabel M. Herson Scholarships in Education [12412]

The Hertz Foundation **[5501]**

Hertz Foundation Graduate Fellowship Award [5502]

Hertz Doctoral Thesis Prize [5503]

The Hertz Graduate Fellowship Award [7645]

Aleksander and Alicja Hertz Memorial Fellowship [12237]

Herzog August Bibliothek Wolfenbüttel Fellowships [8372]

Wayne E. Hesch Memorial Scholarship [1691]

Beth B. Hess Memorial Scholarship [10566]

Walston and Jewel Hester Memorial Scholarship Endowment [8516]

The Melvyn F. Hester Scholarship [8341]

Nicholas S. Hetos, DDS, Memorial Graduate Scholarship [5466]

HFA Educational Scholarship [5479]

HFMH Bilingual Scholarships for Mental Health Workforce Diversity [5539]

HGS Foundation Undergraduate Scholarships [5597]

H.H. Harris Foundation Scholarship [932]

HHMI International Student Research Fellowships [5616]

HHMI Medical Research Fellowship [5617]

HIAA Graduate Student Travel Grants [5534]

Dorothy Hicks Graduate Scholarship [10655]

Frances C. Hidell Scholarship [2144]

Hierholzer-Fojtik Scholarship [5084]

Jim Hierlihy Memorial Scholarship [4429]

Howard B. Higgins South Carolina Dental Scholarships [4736]

High School Academic Scholarship [10053]

Higher Education Consortium for Urban Affairs (HECUA) **[5504]**

Highlands Ranch Dental Group **[5507]**

Highlands Ranch Dental Group Scholarship [5508]

HII Scholarship Fund [5655]

Robert S. Hilbert Memorial Student Travel Grants [8677]

Dereen Hildebrand Scholarship [12324]

Wayne Hildebrant Police Scholarship Fund [6665]

Hill Country Master Gardeners **[5509]**

Hill Country Master Gardeners Horticulture Scholarship [5510]

Douglas W. Hill, Jr. Scholarship [2530]

John A. Hill Memorial Scholarship [2531]

Judy Hill Memorial Scholarships [3061]

Gus and Henrietta Hill Scholarship Fund [4209]

Geordie Hilton Academic Scholarships [5030]

Conrad N. Hilton Scholarships [4962]

Brooke Hindle Postdoctoral Fellowships [10363]

Hinman-Jensen Endowed Scholarship [6797]

HIPLA Fellowship [5599]

HIPLA Scholarships for University of Houston Law Center Students [5600]

The Hirair and Anna Hovnanian Foundation **[5511]**

Hispanic Association of Colleges and Universities (HACU) **[5514]**

Hispanic Dental Association (HDA) **[5517]**

Hispanic Faculty Staff Association (HFSA) **[5521]**

Hispanic Lawyers Association of Illinois (HLAI) **[5523]**

Hispanic Metropolitan Chamber (HMC) **[5525]**

Oregon Latino Scholarship Fund [5526]

Hispanic Scholarship Fund (HSF) **[5527]**

Hispanic Scholarship Fund General College Scholarship Program (HSF) [5530]

Hispanic Serving Institution Scholarships (HSIS) [11280]

Historians of Islamic Art Association (HIAA) **[5533]**

Historically Black College or University Scholarships (HBCUS) [11281]

History of Art: Institutional Fellowships [6613]

HIV Prevention Research Advocacy Fellowships [2368]

The Albert H. Hix, W8AH, Memorial Scholarship [1944]

HLS/MLA Professional Development Grants [7218]

H.M. Muffly Memorial Scholarship [3535]

Ho-Chunk Nation **[5536]**

Lou Hochberg Awards - University/College Essay Awards [8756]

Hochschulsommerkurse [4063]

Jeri Hodges Leadership Scholarship [10978]

C.H.(Chuck) Hodgson Scholarships [12005]

The George W. and Ethel B. Hoefler Fund [3714]

Dorothy M. and Earl S. Hoffman Award [2383]

Hoffman Family Scholarship [5085]

Henry Hoffman Memorial Scholarship [7641]

Irving J. Hoffman Memorial Scholarships [11691]

Robert and Elaine Hoffman Memorial Scholarships [11602]

Miriam Hoffman Scholarship [4892]

The Stephanie G. Hoffman Scholarship [6274]

The Michael J. Hogan Foreign Language Fellowship [10356]

Nedien Hoganson Memorial Scholarship [12325]

The Thelma S. Hoge Memorial Scholarship [3596]

Raymond T. Hoge Scholarship Fund [10765]

Hogg Foundation for Mental Health **[5538]**

Hohn-Johnson Research Award [11814]

R.W. "Bob" Holden Memorial Scholarships [5419]

Holiday Celebration Scholarship [7442]

Norm Hollend Fellowships in Oncology [6930]

Hollis NorEasters Snowmobile Club **[5540]**

Dr. Marshall E. Hollis Scholarship [2532]

Holly A. Cornell Scholarship [1642], [3272]

The Sharon Holmes ASTA/NJ Scholarship [1614]

Joseph A. Holmes Safety Association (JAHSA) **[5543]**

Robert Holmes Scholarship [3720]

Holocaust and Human Rights Center of Maine (HHRC) **[5545]**

George Holopigian Memorial Grants [1885]

The Arthur and Janet Holzheimer Fellowship in the History of Cartography [8373]

Holzheimer Memorial Student Scholarship [1243]

Home Builders Association of Kentucky (HBAK) **[5547]**

Home Improvement Scholarship [7521]

Homeless Children's Education Fund **[5550]**

Homus **[5552]**

Homus E-Commerce Research Scholarship [5553]

Hon. Peggy Bernheim Memorial Scholarship [2711]

Honest. Wild. Beautiful. Scholarship Program [1721]

Honeywell Avionics Scholarships [185]

Honor Society of Phi Kappa Phi - North Dakota State University Chapter 10 **[5554]**

Charles H. Hood Foundation Child Health Research Awards Program [5438]

Kathryn Hookanson Law Fellowship [11603]

Hoover Presidential Foundation **[5556]**

Hope for Healing Scholarship [4541]

Hope Through Learning Award [5551]

Hope for the Warriors **[5558]**

Johns Hopkins Department of Emergency Medicine Administration Fellowships [6316]

Frank and Gladys Hopkins Endowed Scholarships [6798]

Harry Hopmeyer Memorial Scholarship [6292]

Cathy Hopper Memorial Scholarship [9821]

Dr. Gilbert Hopson Medical Student Bursary [8647]

Horace W. Stunkard Scholarship [7046]

Horatio Alger Association of Distinguished Americans (HAADA) **[5560]**

Horch Roofing **[5583]**

Horch Roofing Trade School Scholarship [5584]

Seth Horen, K1LOM Memorial Scholarships [1945]

Horizon Health Network Scholarship [8232]

Edward Horne Scholarship [8742]

Saul Horowitz Jr. Memorial Graduate Award [126]

Judge and Mrs. Robert D. Horowitz Legal Scholarship Fund [10766]

E.B. Horsman & Son Scholarships [4349]

Horticultural Research Institute (HRI) **[5585]**

Horticulture Scholarship from Frances Sylvia Zverina [5486]

Horticulture Scholarship of the Western Reserve Herb Society [5487]

Detroit Tigers Willie Horton Scholarship [3721]

Hosinec Family Scholarships [11692]

Hospitality Career Scholarship [11038]

HostGator Technology Scholarship [5588]

HostGator.com L.L.C. **[5587]**

HostingAdvice.com **[5589]**

HostingAdvice.com Future Web Developers Annual Scholarship [5590]

The Hougen Family Fund Scholarship [12326]

John C. "Jack" Hough Memorial Law Scholarship [11604]

Max and Julia Houghton Duluth Central Scholarships [4210]

Houghton Mifflin Harcourt Co. **[5591]**

House of Puerto Rico San Diego (HPRSD) **[5593]**

Houston Alumnae Association Doris Krikham Brokaw Memorial Adelphe Scholarship [6444]

Houston Alumnae Association, Eunice "Scotty" Scott Siverson Memorial Adelphe Scholarship [6445]

Houston Alumnae Chapter Graduate Fellowship [4004]

Houston Geological Society (HGS) **[5595]**

Houston Intellectual Property Law Association (HIPLA) **[5598]**

Houston/Nancy Holliman Scholarship [4036]

Sarah Jane Houston Scholarships [4037]

HoustonMovers.com **[5601]**

The HoustonMovers.com Scholarship [5602]

Houtan Scholarship [5604]

Houtan Scholarship Foundation **[5603]**

The Hirair and Anna Hovnanian Foundation Presidential Scholarship [5512]

Hirair and Anna Hovnanian Foundation Scholarship [5513]

Howard A. Clark Horticulture Scholarship Fund [3622]

Howard A. Crum Memorial Scholarship [11625]

Howard A. White Endowed Scholarship [9005]

Howard E. and Wilma J. Adkins Memorial Scholarship [1662]

Howard Fox Memorial Law Scholarship Fund [2488]

Howard Hughes Medical Institute (HHMI) - Janelia Farm Research Campus **[5605]**

The Barbara J. and M. William Howard Jr. Scholarship [8342]

Soldotna Chamber of Commerce/Vera Howarth Memorial Scholarship [10578]

William C. Howell Scholarship [1283]

Christopher Hoy/ERT Scholarship [1078]

Donald Hoy Memorial Scholarship [12327]

Carol Hoy Scholarship Fund [4778]

John Hoyt Memorial Scholarship [12328]

Hpgs Graduate Scholarships [5421]

HPGS Undergraduate Scholarships [5422]

HQF New Quality Professional Grant [7657]

HRET Health Career Scholarships [8275]

HRH Prince Alwaleed Bin Talal ISNA Fellowships [6180]

HRSA Scholarships for Disadvantaged Students [11334]

HSF/Marathon Oil College Scholarship Program [5531]

HSF/Wells Fargo Scholarship Program [5532]

HSMAI Foundation Scholarship [5608]

HSMAI Global **[5607]**

Huang Hsing Chun-tu Hsueh Fellowship Fund [1256]

Albert W. and Mildred Hubbard Scholarships [9822]

Hubbell Canada L.P. **[5609]**

Indian Health Service Professionals Program [988]
Indian River Scholarship [12329]
Indiana Bar Foundation (IBF) **[5747]**
Indiana Broadcasters Association (IBA) **[5749]**
Indiana Broadcasters Association College Scholarship Program [5750]
Indiana FFA Association **[5751]**
Indiana FFA Association State Fair Scholarship [5752]
Indiana Library Federation (ILF) **[5753]**
Indiana State University (ISU) **[5756]**
Indiana State University Academic Excellence Scholarship [5757]
Indiana State University Academic Promise Scholarships [5768]
Indiana State University Alumni Association (ISUAA) **[5767]**
Indiana State University Creative and Performing Arts Awards [5769]
Indiana State University Incentive Scholarship [5758]
Indiana State University President's Scholarships [5759]
Indiana State University Rural Health Scholarship [5760]
Indiana State University Transfer Student Scholarships [5761]
Indigenous Arts Individual Project Funding [263]
Indigenous Bar Association (IBA) **[5771]**
Indigenous Bar Association Law Student Scholarship [5772]
Individual Advanced Research Opportunities Program For Master's Students [6070]
Individual K-Grants [6564]
Indonesian Directorate General of Higher Education Scholarships (DIKTI) [4263]
Indspire **[5773]**
Indspire Health Careers Bursary and Scholarships [5774]
Indspire Post-Secondary Education Scholarships (PSE) [5775]
Industrial Designers Society of America (IDSA) **[5777]**
Industrial R&D Fellowships [3805]
Industrial Supply Association (ISA) **[5779]**
INF Scholarships [6166]
Influenster **[5781]**
Influenster Code Like a Girl Scholarships [5782]
Informatics Post Doctoral Fellowships [9056]
Informatics Pre Doctoral Fellowships [9057]
Informatics Sabbatical Fellowships [9058]
Information Age Publishing HMJ Scholarship award [5784]
Information Age Publishing Inc. (IAP) **[5783]**
Infusion Nurses Society (INS) **[5785]**
Terrance N. Ingraham Pediatric Optometry Residency Award [463]
Jennifer Ingrum Scholarship Fund [3623]
INIA Scholarship Program [6044]
Injection Molding Division Scholarship [10489]
Injury to Opportunity Scholarship [4252]
Injury Scholarship [5308], [7164]
INKAS Armored Vehicle Manufacturing **[5788]**
INKAS Rising Star Scholarship [5789]
Inland Northwest Business Alliance Scholarships (INBA) [9302]
Innovative Grants-Pilot and Research Tool Grants [6348]
Insite Solutions **[5790]**
Institut Canadien d' études Juridiques Supérieures **[5792]**
Institut de Recherche Robert-Sauve en Sante et en Securite du Travail (IRSST) **[5795]**
Institut Royal d'Architecture du Canada (IRAC) **[5803]**
Institut des Sciences Mathematiques (ISM) **[5806]**
Institute of Actuaries of Australia (IAAUST) **[5809]**
Institute for Anarchist Studies (IAS) **[5811]**
Institute for Anarchist Studies Grants for Radical Writers and Translators [5812]
Institute for Diversity and Health Equity **[5813]**
Institute of Electrical and Electronics Engineers (IEEE) **[5816]**
Institute of Food Technologists (IFT) **[5818]**
Institute for Health Metrics and Evaluation (IHME) **[5820]**

Institute for Health Metrics and Evaluation Post Bachelor Fellowship (PBF) [5821]
Institute for Health Metrics and Evaluation Post Graduate Fellowships (PGF) [5822]
Institute of Industrial and Systems Engineers (IISE) **[5825]**
Institute of International Education, Inc. (IIE) **[5839]**
Institute for the International Education of Students (IES) **[5842]**
Institute for the International Education of Students Faculty Fellowships [5843], [8374]
Institute for International Law and Justice (IILJ) **[5844]**
Institute of Management Accountants (IMA) **[5847]**
Institute of Management Accountants FAR Doctoral Student Grants Program [5849]
Institute for Operations Research and the Management Sciences (INFORMS) **[5851]**
Institute for Public Policy Research (IPPR) **[5853]**
Institute for Public Relations (IPR) **[5856]**
Institute of Real Estate Management (IREM) **[5860]**
Institute of Transportation Engineers (ITE) **[5864]**
Institute of Transportation Engineers - Texas District Fellowships [5865]
Western District fellowship [5866]
Institute of Turkish Studies (ITS) **[5868]**
Institute of Turkish Studies Sabbatical Research Grants [5870]
Institute for Women's Policy Research (IWPR) **[5873]**
Institute for Work and Health (IWH) **[5875]**
Instituts de Recherche en Sainté du Canada **[5878]**
Instructional Design & Learning Technologies Scholarships [4335]
Insurify **[5880]**
Insurify Safe Driving Scholarship [5881]
Integra Foundation NNF Research Grant Awards [611]
Intensive Language Course Grant [4064]
Inter-American Foundation (IAF) **[5882]**
Inter American Press Association Scholarships [10253]
Intercollegiate Studies Institute (ISI) **[5884]**
Interior Design Educators Council (IDEC) **[5887]**
Intermediaries & Reinsurance Underwriters Association, Inc. (IRU Inc.) **[5889]**
Intermediaries and Reinsurance Underwriters Association Summer Intern Scholarships Program [5890]
Intermountain Medical Imaging **[5891]**
Intermountain Medical Imaging Scholarship [5892]
Intermountain Section American Water Works Association **[5893]**
International Academy of Aviation and Space Medicine (IAASM) **[5896]**
International Affairs Fellowships in Japan (IAF) [3864]
International Affairs Fellowships in Nuclear Security (IAF-NS) [3865]
International Anesthesia Research Society (IARS) **[5898]**
International Association of Administrative Professionals Wings Chapter **[5900]**
International Association of Arson Investigators (IAAI) **[5902]**
International Association of Arson Investigators Maine Chapter **[5904]**
International Association of Black Actuaries (IABA) **[5906]**
International Association of Black Actuaries Scholarships [5907]
International Association of Chiefs of Police (IACP) **[5908]**
International Association for Cross-Cultural Psychology (IACCP) **[5910]**
International Association for Dental Research (IADR) **[5912]**
International Association of Emergency Managers (IAEM) **[5918]**
International Association for Food Protection (IAFP) **[5920]**
International Association for Food Protection - Student Travel Scholarship Program [5921]
International Association of Foundation Drilling Scholarships for Civil Engineering Students [81]

International Association of Foundation Drilling Scholarships for Part-time Civil Engineering Graduate School Students [82]
International Association for Great Lakes Research (IAGLR) **[5922]**
International Association of Healthcare Central Service Materiel Management (IAHCSMM) **[5926]**
International Association of Law Enforcement Intelligence Analysts (IALEIA) **[5929]**
International Association of Law Libraries (IALL) **[5932]**
International Association of Lighting Designers (IALD) **[5934]**
International Association for Research on Service-Learning and Community Engagement (IARSLCE) **[5936]**
International Association for the Study of Pain (IASP) **[5938]**
International Association of Wildland Fire (IAWF) **[5946]**
International Association of Wildland Fire Graduate-Level Scholarships [5947]
International Association of Women Police (IAWP) **[5948]**
International Association of Workforce Professionals (IAWP) **[5950]**
International Bowling Media Association (IBMA) **[5954]**
International Brotherhood of Electrical Workers - Local Union 827 **[5956]**
International Career Institute (ICI) **[5958]**
International Catacomb Society (ICS) **[5961]**
International Center for Not-for-Profit Law (ICNL) **[5963]**
International Centre for Diffraction Data (ICDD) **[5965]**
International City/County Management Association (ICMA) **[5967]**
International Clinical Research Fellowship [4193]
International Code Council (ICC) **[5969]**
International Code Council Scholarship [4501]
International Coral Reef Society (ICRS) **[5975]**
International Council for Canadian Studies Graduate Student Scholarships [3801]
International Council of Shopping Centers Foundation (ICSC) **[5977]**
International Council on Systems Engineering (INCOSE) **[5983]**
International Dairy-Deli-Bakery Association (IDDBA) **[5987]**
International Dairy-Deli-Bakery Association's Scholarship for Growing the Future [5988]
International Dance Teachers Association (IDTA) **[5990]**
International Desalination Association (IDA) **[5992]**
International Development and Education Award in Palliative Care [3774]
International Development and Education Awards [3775]
International Dissertation Research Fellowship (IDRF) [10246]
International Door Association (IDA) **[5995]**
International Door Association Scholarship Foundation Program [5996]
International Executive Housekeepers Association (IEHA) **[5997]**
International Executive Housekeepers Association Spartan Scholarship Award [5999]
International Facility Management Association Foundation (IFMA) **[6000]**
International Federation of Operational Research Societies (IFORS) **[6002]**
International Food Service Executives Association (IFSEA) **[6004]**
International Foodservice Editorial Council (IFEC) **[6006]**
International Foodservice Editorial Council Scholarship [6007]
International Foundation for Ethical Research (IFER) **[6008]**
International Franchise Association (IFA) **[6010]**
International Furnishings and Design Association (IFDA) **[6013]**
International Furnishings and Design Association Part-time Student Scholarship [6015]
International GI Training Grant [761]

International Grenfell Association (IGA) **[6016]**
International Grenfell Association Bursary [6017]
International Grenfell Association High School Bursaries [6018]
International Grenfell Association Post-Secondary Bursaries [6019]
International Horn Society (IHS) **[6020]**
International Information Systems Security Certification Consortium (ISC2) **[6023]**
International Innovation Grants [3776]
International Institute for Municipal Clerks (IIMC) **[6025]**
International Law Research Program's Graduate Scholarship Competition (CIGI ILRP) [3261]
International Law Students Association (ILSA) **[6028]**
International Life Sciences Institute North America (ILSI) **[6030]**
International Literacy Association (ILA) **[6032]**
International Management Council Scholarship (IMC) [3681]
International Military Community Executives Association (IMCEA) **[6040]**
International Narcotics Interdiction Association (INIA) **[6043]**
International Nurses Society on Addictions (INTNSA) **[6045]**
International Operators Scholarship [7737]
International Order of the Golden Rule (IOGR) **[6047]**
International Order of the King's Daughters and Sons (IOKDS) **[6049]**
International Order of the King's Daughters and Sons North American Indian Scholarship Program [989]
International Organic Inspectors Association (IOIA) **[6053]**
International Organization of Black Security Executives (IOBSE) **[6056]**
International Peace Scholarship Fund (IPS) [8975]
International Phonetic Association (IPA) **[6058]**
International Practice Management Association (IPMA) **[6060]**
International Precious Metals Institute (IPMI) **[6062]**
International Public Management Association for Human Resources (IPMA-HR) **[6064]**
International Radio and Television Society Foundation (IRTS) **[6066]**
International Radio and Television Society Foundation Summer Fellowships Program [6067]
International Research and Exchanges Board (IREX) **[6068]**
The International Research Foundation for English Language Education **[6074]**
International Rett Syndrome Foundation (IRSF) **[6076]**
International Safety Equipment Association (ISEA) **[6078]**
International Sanitary Supply Association (ISSA) **[6080]**
International Sanitary Supply Association Foundation Scholarships [6081]
International Scholars Program for Young Vascular Surgeons [10555]
International Scholarship Programs for Community Service [7249]
International Society of Air Safety Investigators (ISASI) **[6082]**
International Society of Automation (ISA) **[6084]**
International Society for Disease Surveillance **[6104]**
International Society of Explosives Engineers (ISEE) **[6106]**
International Society for Human Ethology (ISHE) **[6108]**
International Society for Humor Studies (ISHS) **[6110]**
International Society for Humor Studies Graduate Student Awards (GSA) [6111]
International Society for Humor Studies Scholarly Contribution Awards (SCA) [6112]
International Society for Infectious Diseases (ISID) **[6113]**
International Society of Offshore and Polar Engineers (ISOPE) **[6115]**

International Society for Therapeutic Ultrasound (ISTU) **[6117]**
International Society Travel Grant [450]
International Society of Travel and Tourism Educators (ISTTE) **[6121]**
International Technology and Engineering Educators Association (ITEEA) **[6123]**
International Textile and Apparel Association (ITAA) **[6128]**
International Thomas Merton Society (ITMS) **[6130]**
International Trademark Association (INTA) **[6134]**
International Trainee Scholarships (ITS) [1622]
International Transplant Nurses Society (ITNS) **[6136]**
International Union of Bricklayers and Allied Craftworkers (BAC) **[6138]**
International Union of Operating Engineers - Local 564 **[6141]**
International Water, Sanitation and Hygiene Foundation (IWSH) **[6143]**
International Women's Fishing Association (IWFA) **[6145]**
International Women's Fishing Association Scholarship Trust [6146]
International Women's Media Foundation (IWMF) **[6147]**
Internet Society **[6149]**
Internet Society Fellowships to the IETF [6150]
The Interracial Scholarship Fund of Greater Hartford [5333]
Investigators in the Pathogenesis of Infectious Disease [2754]
Investors Group Scholarship [2419]
IOBSE Scholarships [6057]
IODE 100th Anniversary Grant [7758]
IODE Labrador Bursary [7759]
IOIA Organic Community Initiative Scholarships [6054]
IOKDS Health Careers Scholarship [6050]
IOKDS Native American Scholarships [6051]
IOKDS Student Ministry Scholarships [6052]
Iota Sigma Pi **[6151]**
Iowa Association of Electric Cooperatives - Electric Cooperative Pioneer Trust Fund Scholarship [4163]
Iowa Association for Energy Efficiency **[6153]**
Iowa Association for Energy Efficiency Scholarship [6154]
Iowa Association for Justice (IAJ) **[6155]**
Iowa Choral Directors Association, Inc. (ICDA) **[6157]**
Iowa Court Reporters Association (ICRA) **[6160]**
Iowa Division of Midwest Dairy Educational Award [7370]
Iowa Journalism Institute Scholarships [6167]
Iowa Library Association (ILA) **[6162]**
Iowa Library Association Foundation Scholarships [6163]
Iowa Newspaper Association (INA) **[6165]**
Susan K. Ipacs Nursing Legacy Scholarship [4707]
Graduate Study Fellowship [6065]
IPPR North Events Internship [5854]
IPR Pathfinder Award [5857]
Ira G. Turpin Scholar Program Fund [10767]
Iranian American Bar Association (IABA) **[6169]**
Iranian-American Scholarship Fund [7954]
Iranian Scholarship Foundation (ISF) **[6171]**
IRARC Memorial, Joseph P. Rubino, WA4MMD, Scholarship [1946]
Irene Carlson Gnaedinger Memorial Scholarship [6800]
Irene Corbally Kuhn Scholarship [8787]
Irene Winifred Eno Grant [1487]
Irene Woodall Graduate Scholarship [860]
IREX Individual Advanced Research Opportunities Program For Postdoctoral Scholars [6071]
IREX Individual Advanced Research Opportunities Program For Pre-doctoral Students [6072]
IREX Individual Advanced Research Opportunities Program For Professionals [6073]
Iris Scholarship [6447]
James P. Irish Scholarship [4164]
Irma E. Voigt Memorial Scholarship [10113]
Greg Irons Award Fund [4211]
David L. Irons Memorial Scholarship Fund [5405]
IRSF Mentored Training Fellowships [6077]

IRSST Doctoral Scholarship [5797]
IRSST Doctoral Scholarships Supplement [5798]
IRSST Master's Scholarships [5799]
IRSST Master's Scholarships Supplement [5800]
IRSST postdoctoral fellowship [5801]
Irwin Allen Nadal Entrance Award [12254]
Irwin S. Lerner Student Scholarship [8108]
ISA Educational Foundation Scholarship [6086]
ISA Executive Board Scholarship [6087]
ISA Section and District Scholarships - Houston [6088]
ISA Section and District Scholarships - Lehigh Valley [6089]
ISA Section and District Scholarships - Richmond Hopewell [6090]
ISA Section and District Scholarships - Southwestern Wyoming [6091]
ISA Section and District Scholarships - Texas, Louisiana and Mississippi [6092]
ISA Section and District Scholarships - Wilmington [6093]
ISA Technical Division Scholarships - Analysis Division [6094]
ISA Technical Division Scholarships - Chemical and Petroleum Industries Division [6095]
ISA Technical Division Scholarships - Food and Pharmaceutical Industries Division [6096]
ISA Technical Division Scholarships - Power Industry Division [6097]
ISA Technical Division Scholarships - Process Measurement and Control Division [6098]
ISA Technical Division Scholarships - Pulp and Paper Industry Division [6099]
ISA Technical Division Scholarships - Test Measurement Division [6100]
ISA Technical Division Scholarships - Water and Wastewater Industries Division [6101]
John D. Isaacs Marine Undergraduate Research Assistant Program [11561]
Isabel Mayer Kirkpatrick Scholarship Fund [10687]
ISBA Scholarship Program [5689]
(ISC)2 Foundation Information Security Undergraduate Scholarships [6024]
ISCALC International Scholarship Fund [4594]
ISDS Graduate Student Scholarships [6105]
ISF Excellence in Community Service Scholarship [6173]
ISF Undergraduate Scholarship [6174]
Patricia and Gail Ishimoto Memorial Scholarship [6247]
ISID Small Grants [6114]
Islamic Research Foundation International, Inc. (IRFI) **[6175]**
Islamic Scholarship Fund (ISF) **[6177]**
Islamic Scholarship Fund Scholarship (ISF) [6178]
Islamic Society of North America (ISNA) **[6179]**
ISM Scholarships for Graduate Studies [5808]
ISMER Student Financial Assistance [11670]
Broughton Isom Memorial Scholarship [8519]
ISOPE Offshore Mechanics Scholarships for Outstanding Students [6116]
ISPE Foundation Scholarship [5707]
ISSA Canada **[6181]**
ISTTE Scholarship [6122]
ISTU Student Prizes [6119]
ISU Child of Alumni Book Voucher Awards [5770]
ISU Gongaware Scholarship [5762]
ISU Networks Scholarship [5763]
ITAA Graduate Student Best Paper Award [6129]
Italian Language Scholarship [8690]
ITEEA Greer/FTE Grants [6124]
ITMS Shannon Fellowships [6132]
ITNS Research Grants [6137]
ITW Welding Companies Scholarships [1664]
Ivanhoe Foundation **[6183]**
Ivanhoe Foundation Fellowship [6184]
Bob and Mary Ives Scholarship [6102]
IvyPanda **[6185]**
Iwalani Carpenter Sowa Scholarship [8928]
IWH Mustard Fellowship in Work and Health [5876]
IWSH Essay Scholarship Contest [6144]
J. Jay Hostetler Scholarship [6383]
J. McDonald and Judy Williams School of Law Scholarship [9006]
J. Newell Stannard Fellowship [5429]

J. Ward Sleichter and Frances F. Sleichter Memorial Fund [4779]

J & Y Law Firm **[6187]**

Jack Ervin Economic Development Institute Scholarship [8435]

Jack Family Scholarship [5158]

Jack H. Brown Future Leaders Scholarships [2802]

The Jack and Jill of America Foundation's National Scholarship Program [6190]

Jack and Jill Foundation **[6189]**

Jack Kent Cooke Foundation College Scholarship Program [3820]

Jack Kent Cooke Foundation Undergraduate Transfer Scholarship [3821]

Jack Kent Cooke Foundation Young Scholars Program [3822]

Jack M. & Mary Lou Gruber Scholarship [6801]

Jack M. Nagasaka Memorial Scholarship [9551]

Jack R. Barckhoff Welding Management Scholarship [1665]

Jack R. Gilstrap Scholarship [1302]

Jack Shand Research Grants. [10526]

Jackie Robinson Scholarship Award [9723]

Arthur Jackman Scholarship [5406]

Jackman Scholarships [9114]

Graduate Student Honoraria - Anna M. Jackson Awards [1504]

Jackson Club Scholarship Fund [4212]

Jackson Community Foundation (JCF) **[6191]**

Jackson High School Alumni Scholarship Fund [10768]

Jackson Memorial Intermediate Piano Recital Scholarship [9905]

Holly Jackson-Wuller Memorial Scholarship [8860]

Jacob R. & Mary M. VanLoo & Lenore K. VanLoo Scholarship [5159]

Freddy L. Jacobs Individual Scholarship [5953]

Donald Wills Jacobs Scholarships [11452]

Dwight P. Jacobus Scholarships [2277]

Jacque Placette Chapman Master's Fellowships [8686]

Jacqueline Shields Memorial Scholarship [161]

Cory Jam Memorial Award [4213]

Jamaican Canadian Association **[6212]**

Jamaican Canadian Association Alberta (JCAA) **[6224]**

Jamaican Canadian Association Alberta Scholarship Program [6225]

Jamail/Long Challenge Grant Scholarships [5522]

James B. Pearson Fellowship [6361]

James Bilder Scholarship Fund [10688]

The James Davidson Innovative Student Scholarship [10739]

James Davis Scholarship [11190]

James E. Hoff, S.J. Scholar [12223]

James E. Long Memorial Post Doctoral Fellowship [5984]

James E. West Fellowship [62]

James F. Hurley III Bicentennial Merit Scholarship [11191]

James H. Patrenos Memorial Scholarship [10147]

James L. Baillie Student Research Award [10295]

James L. Biggane Fellowship in Finance [8325]

James L. and Genevieve H. Goodwin Scholarship [5334]

James L. Plafkin Memorial Scholarship [11626]

James Madison Memorial Fellowship Foundation **[6226]**

James and Marilyn Rockefeller Scholarship Fund [6986]

James V. Johnson Scholarship Endowment Fund [4737]

James W. Junior and Jane T. Brown Scholarship [5086]

James Wisecup Memorial Flight Training Scholarship [12011]

J. Franklin Jameson Fellowship in American History [960]

Jamie Phillips Endowed Scholarship Fund [9007]

Donald Jamieson Fellowship [3112]

Jan DiMartino Delany Memorial Scholarship [4780]

Jan Jancin Award [4697]

Jane Beattie Memorial Scholarship [10378]

Jane C. Waldbaum Archaeological Field School Scholarship [1777]

Jane Coffin Childs Memorial Fund - Medical Research Postdoctoral Fellowship [3303]

Jane Glassco Northern Fellowship [5050]

Jane S. Glenn Memorial Endowed Scholarship [9718]

Janet Cullen Tanaka Geosciences Undergraduate Scholarship [2316]

Janet and Horace Allen Science Scholarship [291]

Helen Janko Memorial Scholarship [12330]

Janssen Infectious Disease Point Scholarships [9224]

Japan-America Society of Hawaii (JASH) **[6230]**

Japan Foundation, New York **[6232]**

Japan Foundation, New York Doctoral Candidates [6233]

Japan Foundation, New York Scholars and Researchers (Long-Term) [6234]

Japan Foundation, New York Scholars and Researchers (Short-Term) [6235]

Japan Society for the Promotion of Science Fellowship (JSPS) [10247]

Japanese American Bar Association (JABA) **[6236]**

Japanese American Citizens League (JACL) **[6242]**

Jason Chaney Memorial Scholarship [11948]

Jason Lang Scholarship [292]

Jacob K. Javits Fellowships Program [11310]

Jay C. and B. Nadine Leggett Charitable Fund [10769]

Jay Hammond Memorial Scholarship [11518]

J.B. and Marilyn McKenzie Graduate Student Fellowship [11627]

JCC Association **[6256]**

JCC Association Graduate Education Scholarships [6257]

JCCF Equal Voice Journalism Scholarship [11591]

JDBNOW **[6258]**

JDBNOW Scholarship [6259]

Advanced Postdoctoral Fellowships [6349]

Career Development Awards [6350]

JDRF Outreach Scholarship [5705]

JDRF Postdoctoral Fellowships [6351]

JEA Action Research Initiative [6303]

JEA Future Journalism Teacher Scholarships [6336]

Jean Bennett Memorial Student Travel Grant [8678]

Jean Dearth Dickerscheid Fellowship [9115]

Jean Goodwill Scholarship [3016]

Hon. Michaelle Jean Scholarship [2596]

Jean Wright-Elson Scholarship [9823]

Jeannette K. Watson Fellowship [11938]

Jeff Oliphant Memorial Post-Graduate Scholarship [12114]

The Jeffcoat Firm **[6260]**

The Jeffcoat Firm Annual Scholarship Essay & Video Competition [6261]

Jefferson Graduate Fellowship [6263]

Jefferson Scholars Foundation **[6262]**

Jefferson Science Associates, LLC (JSA) **[6264]**

Jeffrey Carollo Music Scholarship [8279]

Jeffrey Cook Memorial Faculty Retreat Scholarship [10290]

Jeffrey D. Ralston Memorial Scholarship [7562]

John H. Jenkins Research Fellowships in Texas History [10998]

Jennifer Curtis Byler Scholarship [8133]

Gaynold Jensen Education Stipends [4084]

Walter J. Jensen Fellowships [9081]

Stanley "Doc" Jensen Scholarships [844]

Jerman-Cahoon Student Scholarship [1551]

Kenneth Jernigan Scholarships [7877]

Jerome Fellowships [9196]

Harry Jerome Legacy Scholarship [2597]

Jerome M. Sullivan Research Fund [1354]

Jerome Peters Family Fund [6987]

Jerome Robbins Bogliasco Fellowships in Dance [2645]

Jerry Newson Scholarship Fund [3624]

Jessie Young Certification Bursary [2094]

Jet Business Scholarship [6267]

Jet Insurance Services **[6266]**

Jewell Gardiner Scholarship [2827]

Jewish Community Federation and Endowment Fund **[6268]**

The Jewish Community Foundation of Montreal **[6281]**

Jewish Educators Assembly (JEA) **[6302]**

Jewish Federation Academic Scholarship [6310]

Jewish Foundation of Manitoba **[6304]**

Jewish Vocational Service (JVS) **[6309]**

Jim Anderson Memorial Scholarship [8363]

Jim Doogan Memorial Scholarship [11519]

Jim Graham Scholarship [8455]

Jim & Nancy Hinkle Travel Grants [5476]

Jim Poore Memorial Scholarship Fund [5679]

Jimmy Edwards Scholarship Fund [3625]

Jimmy Guild Memorial Scholarship [6802]

J.L. Weigand, Jr. Legal Education Trust Scholarship [11876]

Financial Need Minority Scholarships [11149]

JMA Architecture Studios Scholarship [9405]

JMJ Phillip Group **[6311]**

JMJ Phillip Group College Scholarships [6312]

Joan Rogers Kamps Bursary [8641]

Joanna Townsend Applied Arts Scholarship [2129]

Jobable **[6313]**

Joe Francis Haircare Scholarship [4811]

Joe Perdue Scholarship [3443]

Joel R. Friend Scholarship [2483]

Joel T. Heinen Student Research Fellowship [11628]

Joel T. Heinen Undergraduate Support Scholarship [11629]

Johanna Mitchell Memorial Intermediate Viola/ Cello/ Double Bass Scholarship [9906]

Harry Johannes Scholarship [12331]

John A. Rothschild Bachelor Degree in Hospitality Scholarship [3006]

John Alexander McLean Scholarship [11022]

John and Alice Egan Multi-Year Mentioning Scholarship Program [3955]

John Allen Love Scholarship [11715]

John C. Lincoln Memorial Scholarship [1666]

John Caoile Memorial Scholarship [12331]

John Charles Wilson and Robert Doran Sr. Scholarship [5903]

John D. Wirth Travel Grant [1454]

John E. Mayfield ABLE Scholarship Fund [3626]

John and Elisabeth Buck Endowed Scholarship [7047]

John Flynn Memorial Scholarship [3682]

John G. Brokaw Scholarship [8173]

John G. Williams Scholarship Foundation [12039]

John Higham Research Fellowship [5723], [8727]

John I. & Madeleine R. Taeni Scholarship Fund [10689]

John J. Bonica Trainee Fellowship [5944]

John J. McKetta Undergraduate Scholarship [1023]

John Jeffries Meteorology Scholarship [4502]

John M. & Mary A. Shanley Memorial Scholarship [10690]

John Marshall Everglades Internship Program [4457]

John McLendon Minority Postgraduate Scholarship [7639]

John P. and Tashia F. Morgridge Scholarship [11736]

John Purfield Endowed Scholarship [9008]

John & Ruth Childe Scholarship Fund [10691]

John S. and Marjoria R. Cunningham Camp Scholarship [6988]

John Streiff Memorial Scholarship [6803]

John W. Kelley Memorial Scholarship Fund [10828]

John W. Webb Lecture Award [1466]

Johnny Bench Scholarship Fund [3371]

Johnny Lineberry Memorial Scholarship [12080]

Johns Hopkins Medicine - Department of Emergency Medicine **[6315]**

Johns Hopkins Medicine Disaster Fellowships [6317]

Johns Hopkins Medicine Emergency Medical Services Fellowship [6318]

Johns Hopkins Medicine International Emergency and Public Health Fellowships [6319]

Johns Hopkins Medicine Medical Education Fellowships [6320]

Johns Hopkins Medicine Observation Medicine Fellowships [6321]

Johns Hopkins Medicine Research Fellowships [6322]

Johns Hopkins Medicine Ultrasound Fellowships [6323]

Johns Hopkins University/Applied Physics Laboratory Alexander Kossiakoff Scholarship [5985]

The Robert L. Johns Vocational Scholarship [4871]

Kathleen Kelly Undergraduate Scholarship [9434]
Robert E. Kelsey Annual Scholarship [8954]
Kelsey's Law Distracted Driving Awareness Scholarship [7305]
Kemper K. Knapp Scholarship [11737]
Ken LaFountaine First Nations Scholarship [10056]
Willmoore H. Kendall Scholarships [3444]
The Deana Kendrick Foundation (TDKF) **[6521]**
Kenhub GmbH **[6523]**
Kenhub Scholarship Program [6524]
Kennedy Krieger Institute (KKI) **[6525]**
John F. Kennedy Library Foundation (JFKLF) **[6527]**
John F. Kennedy Presidential Library and Museum **[6529]**
John F. Kennedy Scholarship Award [2782]
Southwest Ohio Environmental Horticulture Association (SOEHA) Lloyd W. Kennedy Scholarship [8587]
Kennedy T. Friend Scholarship Fund [348]
Kenneth and Barbara Starks Plant Resistance to Insects Graduate Student Award [4396]
Kenneth G. Weckel Scholarship [7378]
Kenneth H. Breeden Scholarship [6658]
Kenneth J. Osborn Scholarship [2007]
Kenneth Laundy Entrance Scholarship [12255]
Kenneth Rogers Memorial Scholarship [6805]
Oscar Kenshur Book Prize [1435]
Kent S. Butler Memorial Groundwater Stewardship Scholarship Essay Contest [2443]
Kentucky Alumni Club Scholarships - Lexington/Central Kentucky Alumni Chapter [11577]
Kentucky Alumni Club Scholarships - Somerset/Lake Cumberland Area Alumni Chapter [11578]
Kentucky Educational Excellence Scholarship [2572]
Kentucky Paralegal Association (KPA) **[6534]**
Kentucky Paralegal Association Paralegal Student Scholarships [6535]
Kentucky REALTORS (KAR) **[6536]**
Kentucky Society of Certified Public Accountants (KYCPA) **[6538]**
Kenyon T. Payne Outstanding Student Award [7344]
Dr. Dorothy J. Kergin Fellowships [3063]
Kerrwil's J.W. Kerr Continuing Education Scholarship Awards [4351]
Kerrigan Scholarship Foundation [9012]
Edgar Kerstan Memorial Scholarship [7258]
Ketchum Excellence in Public Relations Research Award [5858]
Keith Kevan Scholarship [4409]
George Keverian Public Service Scholarship [1891]
Kevin Ernst Memorial Scholarship [5087]
Key to a Bright Future Scholarship [6714]
Dr. Arthur Kezian DDS **[6540]**
Dr. Arthur A. Kezian DDS Science Scholarship [6541]
KFOC Allied Health Doctoral Fellowships [6546]
KFOC Allied Health Scholarships [6547]
KFOC Biomedical Scholarships [6548]
KGP Cornaro Scholarship [6397]
Khaki University and Y.M.C.A. Memorial Scholarships [11694]
Graduate Fellowship Program - Mahboob Khan/Advanced Micro Devices Fellowships [10000]
KHEAA Teacher Scholarship [2573]
KHIMA Graduate Scholarship [6369]
Kia Motors America Inc. **[6542]**
Michael Kidger Memorial Scholarship in Optical Design [10726]
Kidney Foundation of Canada (KFOC) **[6544]**
Kids' Chance of Florida, Inc. **[6549]**
The Kids' Chance of Florida Scholarship Program [6550]
Kids and Community **[6551]**
Kids and Community Scholarship Program [6552]
Julia Kiene Fellowships in Electrical Energy [12159]
The Mary and Millard Kiker Scholarship [4739]
Kilbuck Family Native American Scholarship [2484]
Killam Fellowships [4771]
Elson T. Killam Memorial Scholarship [8249]
Kimberly Elementary School PTA Scholarship [9552]
Douglas Gray Kimel Scholarship [12081]
Sidney Kimmel Foundation for Cancer Research **[6553]**
Kimmel Scholar Award [6554]
James N. Kincanon Scholarship [9719]

Kit C. King Graduate Scholarships [8048]
King Ice **[6555]**
King Ice Scholarship [6556]
Larry King/Jeffrey Fashion Cares Point Scholarship [9225]
Martin Luther King Jr. Scholarship Association **[6557]**
Martin Luther King Jr. Scholarships [6558]
Martin Luther King Law Scholarship [4165]
King of Maids, LLC **[6559]**
King of Maids Scholarship [6560]
Steven G. King Play Environments Scholarship [6648]
Forest A. King Scholarship [4166]
Marilyn King Scholarship [12333]
Jessica King Scholarships [3938]
Don King Student Fellowships [5659]
Kingsbury Elementary School PTA Scholarship [9553]
Southwest Chapter Roy Kinslow Scholarship [1566]
Treva C. Kintner Scholarships [9116]
Kip Dental and Orthodontics **[6561]**
Kip Dental and Orthodontics Scholarship [6562]
Kipling and District Music Festival Intermediate Chopin Scholarship [9907]
Kiplinger Fellowship [8605]
James P. Kirkgasser Memorial Scholarship [2533]
Kislak Fellowship for the Study of the History and Cultures of the Early Americas [6572]
Dr. Elemer and Eva Kiss Scholarship Fund [5642]
Tamo Kitaura Scholarships [11386]
Kevin Kitchnefsky Foundation **[6563]**
AACT John Kitt Memorial Scholarship [538]
Flo Kitz Memorial Scholarship [12334]
Kiwanis Club of Escondido Scholarship [9826]
Kiwanis Club of Redlands Foundation Academic Excellence Scholarship [9554]
Kiwanis Club of Redlands Foundation - Martin and Dorothy Munz Scholarship [9555]
Kiwanis of Wascana Senior Cello/Viola/Double Bass Scholarship [9908]
Klarman Family Foundation Grants Program in Eating Disorders Research [5439]
Jane M. Klausman Women in Business Scholarships [12421]
The Margie Klein "Paper Plate" Scholarships [2053]
Gerda and Kurt Klein Scholarships [5592]
The Kleinhans Fellowship [9495]
Chris L. Kleinke Scholarship [11483]
Dr. Eva Kleinpeter Scholarship [6387]
Klimt Stefan & Janina Scholarship [9668]
Klingenstein Fellowships in the Neurosciences [6566]
Esther A. and Joseph Klingenstein Fund **[6565]**
Klingenstein Third Generation Foundation (KTGF) **[6567]**
Klingon Language Institute (KLI) **[6569]**
Hans Klinkenberg Memorial Scholarship [3022]
Klondike Defence Force Grant [12335]
Arthur Klorfein Scholarship and Fellowship Fund [7049]
John W. Kluge Center at the Library of Congress **[6571]**
Kluge Fellowship [6573]
Joseph H. Klupenger Scholarship Awards [8707]
J. Merrill Knapp Research Fellowship [952]
Iver and Cora Knapstad Scholarships [11453]
John A. Knauss Marine Policy Fellowship [11304]
David Knight Graduate Scholarship [10656]
John S. Knight Journalism Fellowships [6576]
John S. Knight Journalism Fellowships at Stanford (JSK) **[6575]**
John G. F. Knight Memorial Scholarship [2534]
Robert E. Knight Professional Scholarship [10979]
Knight-Wallace Reporting Fellowships [11870]
Knights of Columbus (KofC) **[6577]**
Knox Hume Scholarship Fund [3630]
Kris Knudson Memorial Scholarship [11484]
Glenn Knudsvig Memorial Scholarship [754]
Kobe College Corporation-Japan Education Exchange (KCC-JEE) **[6579]**
Steven Kobrynsky Memorial Scholarship [3029]
Koch Scholars Program [11878]
Kodak Fellowships in Film Preservation [2247]
Kodali Veeraiah & Sarojini Scholarship [10952]
George Koeppel Scholarship/All School [11738]

Herb Kohl Educational Foundation **[6581]**
James P. Kohn Memorial Scholarship [1567]
DSRSD James B. Kohnen Scholarships [4191]
George Kokociski Memorial Scholarships [9669]
P. Johnson and C. Kolb Memorial Scholarships [9873]
Anna and John Kolesar Memorial Scholarship [293]
Carl Koller Memorial Research Grants [1557]
The Bernie Kom Memorial Award [12256]
Susan G. Komen for the Cure College Scholarship Awards [6586]
Susan G. Komen for the Cure Post-doctoral Fellowships - Clinical Research Grants [6587]
Susan G. Komen **[6585]**
KON/GEICO LeaderShape Undergraduate Scholarship [6490]
KON National Alumni Chapter Grant [6491]
KON New Initiatives Grant [6492]
Koniag Education Foundation (KEF) **[6588]**
Emily Day Koppell Memorial Adelphe Scholarship [6452]
Kor Memorial Scholarship [6570]
The Korea Society (TKS) **[6593]**
Korean American Scholarship Foundation (KASF) **[6596]**
Korean Language Study Awards [6595]
Korean Studies Dissertation Workshop [10248]
AIST Willy Korf Memorial Fund [2221]
Henriette & Marcel Korner Scholarship [6295]
Kosciuszko Foundation (KF) **[6600]**
Kosciuszko Foundation Graduate Study and Research in Poland Scholarships [6601]
Kosciuszko Foundation Tuition Scholarships [6602]
Kosciuszko Foundation Year Abroad Scholarships [6603]
Marcia J. Koslov Scholarship [598]
Haig Kournjian Memorial Grant [1892]
Kovaluk Scholarship Fund [11412]
Phil Kozel Memorial Scholarship [8588]
KPMG Foundation **[6608]**
KPMG Foundation Minority Accounting Doctoral Scholarships [6609]
Kraft Foods Food Science Minority Scholarship [11739]
William D. Krahling Excellence in Journalism Scholarship [403]
Melvin Kranzberg Dissertation Fellowships [10364]
Michael Kraus Research Grants [961]
Eileen Kraus Scholarship [3763]
Sharon Kreikemeier Memorial Scholarships [8189]
Krell Institute **[6610]**
CHS James Kreppner Memorial Scholarship and Bursary Program [3003]
Kress/AAR Fellowships [2058]
Kress Conservation Fellowships [6614]
Samuel H. Kress Foundation **[6612]**
Samuel H. Kress Grants for Research and Publication in Classical Art and Architecture [1778]
Krist-Reavley Minority Scholarship [9013]
Carl A. Kroch Oxford Cup Memorial Scholarship [2535]
Kroger Cincinnati/Dayton Scholarship Fund [3375]
Doreen Kronick Scholarships [2130]
Kristin Bjurstrom Krueger Student Scholarship Program [7240]
Samuel Krugliak Legal Scholarship Fund [10773]
Mike and Mary Jean Kruse Scholarship Fund [3631]
Leo J. Krysa Family Undergraduate Scholarships [3030]
The Krystal Co. **[6615]**
KTA Chapter Adviser Research Grant Award [6501]
George F. Kugler, Jr. Award [2851]
Don Kuhn Memorial Scholarship Fund [7106]
Arlene Kuhner Memorial Scholarship [11485]
Harry A. Kuljian Memorial Grant [1893]
Kuropas Jan Memorial Scholarship [9670]
Kurt H. and Donna M. Schuler Cash Grant [1393]
Kurz Industrial Solutions **[6617]**
Kurz Industrial Solutions Wind Energy Scholarship Fund [6618]
Liela Klinger Kurztman Memorial Scholarship [6296]
Henry and Chiyo Kuwahara Creative Arts Award [6248]
Sam and Florice Kuwahara Memorial Scholarship [6249]
Kyle R. Moreland Memorial Scholarship [5088]

Lee Epstein Fund Scholarship [7107]
The Hwain Chang Lee scholarship [8344]
Lee Kimche McGrath Worldwide Fellowship [2286]
The William K. Lee Scholarship [8345]
Lee Student Support Fund [10536]
Lee Tarbox Memorial Scholarship [187]
Lee Teng Undergraduate Fellowship in Accelerator
    Science and Engineering [11318]
Lee Womack Scholarship [7431]
Leesa **[6763]**
Leesa Social Impact Scholarship [6764]
Leesfield/AAJ Scholarship [583]
Judge William B. Leffler Scholarship [11607]
The Legacy Fellowship [495]
Legacy, Inc. **[6765]**
Legacy Inc. College Undergraduate and Graduate
    Scholarships [6766]
Legal Aid of North Carolina Inc. (LANC) **[6767]**
Legal Internships [3228]
Legalzoom **[6770]**
Charles LeGeyt Fortescue Scholarship [5817]
Doreen Legg Memorial Scholarships [9556]
The Herbert Lehman Education Fund Scholar-
    ship [7540]
Lehman Family Scholarship [9828]
Gilder Lehrman Institute of American History **[6772]**
Leiber and Stoller Music Scholarship [1410]
Leica Scholarship [2008]
Leif and Inger Sjöberg Award [1376]
Leighton M. Ballew Directing Scholarship [10635]
Lemaire Co-operative Studies Award [2914]
Imelda [3722]
Lemelson Center Fellowships [10194]
Lemelson Center Travel to Collections
    Awards [10195]
Lemon Grove Education Foundation Scholar-
    ship [9829]
Bourse Georgette LeMoyne [2973]
Rebecca Christine Lenci Thespian Memorial Schol-
    arship [9830]
The Stan Lencki Scholarship [7172]
Franklin A. Lenfesty Memorial Scholarship [8520]
John Lennon Scholarships [2635]
Leo Gilmartin Scholarship [9211]
Leo Zupin Memorial Scholarship [5091]
Leonard Hawk Founders Scholarship [1334]
Leopold Education Project Scholarship [3685]
Leopold Schepp Foundation Scholarship [9932]
Lependorf & Silverstein PC **[6774]**
Lerner-Scott Prize [8728]
Les Dames d'Escoffier New York (LDNY) **[6776]**
Les Dames D'Escoffier New York Corporate Schol-
    arship [6777]
Leslie Baranowski Scholarship for Professional Ex-
    cellence [5787]
Leslie C. Green Veterans Scholarship [3878]
Leslie and Mary Ella Scales Scholarship [3657]
Lester and Eleanor Webster Foundation
    Fund [10775]
Lester G. Benz Memorial Scholarship for College
    Journalism Study [9463]
Brigid Leventhal Special Merit Award [3777]
LeverEdge **[6778]**
LeverEdge Scholarship [6779]
Saul Levine Memorial Scholarship [1167]
Jack A. and Louise S. Levine Memorial Scholar-
    ships [9557]
Harry and Miriam Levinson Scholarship [1284]
Janet Levy Fund [1145]
Herbert Levy Memorial Scholarship [10479]
William J. Levy Point Scholarship [9226]
Lewis B. Barber Memorial Scholarship Fund [10695]
Lewis-Clark Coin Club Endowed Scholarship [6810]
Lewis and Clark Fund for Exploration and Field Re-
    search [1215]
Lewis-Clark State College **[6780]**
Lewis-Clark State College Foundation Schol-
    ars [6811]
Lewis-Clark State College In-State Non-Traditional
    Student Scholarship [6812]
Military Order of the Purple Heart [6813]
Lewis-Clark State College Provost Scholar-
    ship [6814]
Lloyd Lewis Fellowships in American History [8375]
George T. Lewis, Jr. Academic Scholarship
    Fund [4742]

Frederick D. Lewis Jr. Scholarships [4168]
Ted Lewis Memorial Scholarship [234]
S. Evelyn Lewis Memorial Scholarships in Medical
    Health Sciences [12414]
Lewis-Reynolds-Smith Founders Fellowship [5477]
Lewiston Auburn Metropolitan Chamber of Com-
    merce **[6824]**
Lewiston Service League Memorial Scholar-
    ship [6815]
Lex T. Eckenrode Scholarship for PELS [11831]
Lexington Alumni Scholarships [6827]
Lexington Community Foundation (LCF) **[6826]**
Lexington Community Foundation Annual Scholar-
    ships [6828]
Lexington Community Foundation/CCC Scholar-
    ships [6829]
Jack G. Lezman **[6835]**
Jack G. Lezman Scholarship Contest [6836]
Liberty Mutual Scholarships [1568]
Library and Information Technology Association
    (LITA) **[6837]**
Library Leadership and Management Association
    (LLAMA) **[6842]**
Short-Term Library Resident Research Fellow-
    ships [1216]
Irene Brand Lieberman Memorial Scholarship [6298]
Dolores Zohrab Liebmann Fund **[6844]**
Dolores Zohrab Liebmann Fund - Graduate School
    Fellowships [6845]
Dolores Zohrab Liebmann Fund - Independent Re-
    search/Study Grants [6846]
Dolores Zohrab Liebmann Fund - Publication
    Grants [6847]
Life Happens **[6848]**
LIFE Lessons Scholarship Program [6849]
Life Sciences Research Foundation (LSRF) **[6850]**
Life Sciences Research Foundation Postdoctoral
    Fellowship Program [6851]
Lighthouse Guild International **[6852]**
Lighthouse International Scholarships - College-
    bound Awards [6856]
Lighthouse International Scholarships - Graduate
    Awards [6857]
Lighthouse International Scholarships - Undergradu-
    ate Awards [6858]
Lighting the Way for Nursing Scholarship [25]
Lila Fahlman Scholarship [2960]
Lillian and Alex Feir Graduate Student Travel Award
    in Insect Physiology, Biochemistry, or Molecular
    Biology [4398]
Lillian and Murray Slatkin Fellowship [8748]
Lillie Hope-McGarvey Health Scholarship [330]
Ruth Lilly and Dorothy Sargent Rosenberg Poetry
    Fellowships [9216]
Lilly Scholarships in Religion for Journalists [9633]
Lily and Catello Sorrentino Memorial Scholar-
    ship [9694]
Lily H. Gridley Memorial Scholarship [12149]
Esther Lim Memorial Scholarships [3308]
Richard Lim Professional Development Scholar-
    ship [6743]
Lim, Ruger & Kim Scholarships [7602]
Lime Connect, Inc. **[6859]**
Lime Connect Pathways Scholarship for High
    School Seniors with Disabilities [6863]
LimNexus Foundation Scholarship [6239]
Tecla Lin & Nelia Laroza Memorial Scholar-
    ships [3064]
Abraham Lincoln Brigade Archives (ALBA) **[6864]**
Lincoln Forum **[6866]**
AIST Ronald E. Lincoln Memorial Scholar-
    ship [2222]
Linda J. Murphy Scholarship [12141]
Linda Simmons Memorial Scholarship [240]
Charles A. and Anne Morrow Lindbergh Foundation
    [6868]
Lindbergh Grants [6869]
Lindenwood University Scouting Scholarships [7853]
Lindsay M. Entz Memorial Scholarship Fund [4595]
Margaret B. Lindsey Award for Distinguished Re-
    search in Teacher Education [551]
Lineups.com Future of Sports Scholarship Pro-
    gram [6871]
Lineups.com, Inc. **[6870]**
Obrzut Ling Scholarships [9303]

Link Foundation/Smithsonian Graduate Fellowships
    in Marine Science [10201]
L. Gordon "Link" Linkous Scholarship [11103]
Richard Linn American Inn of Court **[6872]**
Lawrence S. Linn Research Grant [10338]
Linsley Scholarship Fund [3301]
David Linton Memorial Scholarship [2537]
Lionsdeal.com **[6874]**
LionsDeal.com Scholarships [6875]
F. Maynard Lipe Scholarship Award [759]
The Lawrence Lipking Fellowship [8376]
Emil S. Liston Award [7662]
Literary Arts **[6876]**
Literary Individual Project Funding [264]
Litherland/FTEE Undergraduate Scholarships [6125]
Litner + Deganian **[6878]**
Litner + Deganian College Scholarship Pro-
    gram [6879]
Littleton-Griswold Research Grant [962]
Livestock Publications Council (LPC) **[6880]**
Grant Livingston Memorial Scholarship [12339]
Davis Levin Livingston Public Interest Law Scholar-
    ships [3975]
David C. Lizárraga Fellowship [10941]
Lizette Peterson Homer Injury Prevention
    Grant [1739]
LLA Scholarships (LLA) [6903]
LLN Student Scholarships [6677]
Lloyd Bridges Scholarship [3204]
Lloyd Houlden Fellowship [2897]
E.C. Lloyd and J.C.U. Johnson Scholarship
    Fund [3658]
Loan for Service for Graduates [995]
Local 564 Scholarship Fund [6142]
Local 827 Peter J. Casey Scholarship [5957]
Local A&WMA Sections and Chapter Scholar-
    ships [162]
Lochmueller Group Inc. **[6882]**
Miriam "Doc" Locke Memorial Adelphe Scholar-
    ships [6456]
Lockheed Martin Scholarship [8521]
Mary Elizabeth Lockwood Beneventi MBA Scholar-
    ship [8098]
Loeblich and Tappan Student Research
    Award [3942]
The Loewenstein-Wiener Fellowship [1061]
Stephen Logan Memorial Scholarship [4872]
Logojoy Student Entrepreneur Scholarship [6888]
Lois Hole Humanities and Social Sciences Scholar-
    ship [296]
Lois Widly Student Scholarships [6046]
Lola Ellis Robertson Scholarship [7050]
London Goodenough Association of Canada
    (LGAC) **[6885]**
London Goodenough Association of Canada Schol-
    arships [6886]
Lone Star GIA Associate and Alumni Scholar-
    ships [4879]
Lawrence A. Long Memorial Law Scholarship [404]
The Robert A. Catlin/David W. Long Scholar-
    ship [1244]
Long-term International Fellowships [3778]
Kay Longcope Scholarship Award [7990]
Bart Longo Memorial Scholarship Program [7762]
Megan Nicole Longwell Scholarship [8864]
Looka Inc. **[6887]**
Louise Loomis Memorial Adelphe Scholar-
    ships [6457]
Michael Lorenzen Foundation **[6889]**
Michael Lorenzen Foundation Scholarship [6890]
Lilly Lorenzen Scholarships [1618]
Suzanne and Caleb Loring Research Fellow-
    ships [7145]
Lorne and Ruby Bonnell Scholarship [3704]
Lorraine E. Swain Scholarship [10114]
Los Abogados Hispanic Bar Association **[6891]**
Los Abogados LSAT Pipeline Fellowship [6892]
Barbara Lotze Scholarships for Future Teach-
    ers [625]
Lou & Dorie Amen Legacy Scholarship [2804]
Lou Hochberg Awards - Thesis and Dissertation
    Awards [8757]
Sir James Lougheed Award of Distinction [297]
Louis Agassiz Fuertes Grant [12055]
Louis Armstrong Award Honoring W.C. Handy [1411]
Louis August Jonas Foundation (LAJF) **[6893]**

Walter Samuel McAfee Scholarships in Space Physics [8088]

Durwood McAlister Scholarship [4935]

McAllister Fellowship [2072]

MCBA Scholarship (MCBA) [7308]

McBurney Disability Resource Center General Scholarships [11741]

McCall Educational Fund [3384]

The Rev. Richard S. McCarroll and Mrs. E. Allison McCarroll Scholarship [8348]

Doreen McMullan McCarthy Memorial Academic Scholarship for Women with Bleeding Disorders [7926]

McClatchy Minority Scholarship and Fellowship [10617]

The First Lieutenant Scott McClean Love Memorial Scholarship - Children of Soldiers [1917]

The First Lieutenant Scott McClean Love Memorial Scholarship - Spouses of Soldiers [1918]

McCleary Law Fellows Program [5628]

Dave McCloud Aviation Memorial Scholarships [11456]

McCloy Fellowships in Agriculture [810]

McCloy Fellowships in Environmental Policy [811]

McCloy Fellowships in Journalism [812]

McCloy Fellowships in Urban Affairs [813]

Anne O'Hare McCormick Memorial Scholarship [8393]

Niqui McCown Honor and Memorial Scholarship Fund [11949]

Joseph McCulley Educational Trust Fund [11695]

McDaniel College Eagle Scout Scholarship [7854]

The Fred R. McDaniel Memorial Scholarship [1948]

Michele L. McDonald Scholarships [4304]

McDonald's Inspiration Celebration Scholarship [11026]

McDonough Scholarship Foundation [7165]

Richard J. McDonough Scholarship [7009]

MCEA Financial Assistance Award [7062]

McFarffels Scholarships [9304]

William H. McGannon Foundation Scholarships [7180]

The William H. McGannon Foundation [7179]

Foster G. McGaw Scholarship [2306]

Nancy B. Woolridge McGee Graduate Fellowships [12415]

Thomas R. McGetchin Memorial Scholarship Award [11423]

McGill University [7181]

McGill University - Centre for Host-Parasite Interactions [7185]

McGill University - Institute and Centre of Air and Space Law (IASL) [7187]

McGill University - Montreal Neurological Institute and Hospital [7189]

Linda and Vincent McGrath Scholarship [6390]

The William P. McHugh Memorial Fund [1338]

Mary Bowles McInnis Adelphe Scholarship [6461]

McKelvey Foundation [7192]

The McKelvey Scholarship [7193]

McKinley Elementary School PTA Scholarship [9561]

John L. and Eleanore I. Mckinley Scholarships [4039]

McKinney Sisters Scholarship [4008]

McKnight Fellowships [9198]

H. H. McKnight Memorial Scholarship [11608]

C.A. "Pete" McKnight Scholarships [11199]

McKnight Theater Artist Fellowships [9199]

James McLachlan Scholarship [12345]

Les McLaughlin Scholarship [12346]

The McLean Scholarship for Nursing and Physician Assistant Majors [2194]

Bea & George McLeod Scholarship [12347]

McMaster University - Ontario Public Interest Research Group-McMaster (OPIRG) [7194]

McMurray Stern [7196]

McMurray Stern - Scholarship Opportunity [7197]

Ronald E. McNair Scholarships in Space and Optical Physics [8089]

McNeely Stephenson Attorneys at Law [7198]

National Association of Pediatric Nurse Practitioners McNeil Annual Scholarships [7679]

National Association of Pediatric Nurse Practitioners McNeil Rural and Underserved Scholarships [7680]

Joan Reagin McNeill Scholarships - Alpha Theta [10119]

Joan Reagin McNeill Scholarships - Theta Phi [10120]

G. William McQuade Memorial Scholarships [8233]

O. Ruth McQuown Scholarship - Graduate Award for Current Students [11572]

MCRD Museum Foundation [7200]

Douglas McRorie Memorial Scholarships [131]

MCRTA Book Scholarships [7295]

Dr. Margaret McWilliams Pre-Doctoral Fellowship [2975]

MDA Development Grants [7509]

MDA Research Grants [7510]

MDF Postdoctoral Fellowship [7536]

MDI Biological Laboratory High school Student Summer Research Fellowship [7484]

MDI Biological Laboratory Undergraduate Summer Research Fellowships [7485]

Mead Leadership Fellowships [8482]

David Meador Foundation - Club Management Student Scholarships [8242]

Ben Meadows Natural Resource Scholarships - Academic Achievement Scholarships [4684]

Ben Meadows Natural Resource Scholarships - Leadership Scholarships [4685]

Mearl K. Gable II Memorial Grant [5285]

The Medalist Club [7202]

The Medalist Club Post Graduate Scholarship [7203]

The Medallion Fund Scholarship [8254]

Meded Media LLC [7204]

Medex Biocare Pharmacy L.L.C. [7206]

Medford Rogue Rotary Club [7208]

Medford Rogue Rotary Scholarship [7209]

Media Mister Inc. [7210]

MediaMister $1000 Student Scholarship [7211]

Medical Group Management Association (MGMA) [7212]

Medical Library Association (MLA) [7214]

Medical Scrubs Collection LLC [7224]

Medical Scrubs Collection Scholarship [7225]

Medical Student Rotation for Underrepresented Populations [3779]

MedicalFieldCareers.com [7226]

MedicalFieldCareers.com Healthcare Scholarship [7227]

Medicus Student Exchange Scholarship [10895]

Medieval Academy of America (MAA) [7228]

Medieval Academy Dissertation Grants [7230]

MEDIGO [7233]

The MEDIGO Scholarship Program [7234]

Medina County Retired Teachers Association [7235]

Medina County Retired Teachers Association Scholarship [7236]

Meeting Professionals International Connecticut River Valley Chapter (MPI CRV) [7237]

Meeting Professionals International - Wisconsin Chapter (MPIWI) [7239]

MEFA Graduate Loans [7130]

Carl J. Megel Scholarship [884]

Dr. Ernest and Minnie Mehl Scholarships [298]

Kumar Mehta Scholarship [792]

Megan Meier Foundation [7242]

Megan Meier Memorial Scholarships [7243]

Fred & Lena Meijer Scholarships [5166]

Susan R. Meisinger Fellowship for Graduate Study in HR [10367]

Dr. Roger E. Meisner Veterinary Medicine Educational Scholarship Fund [8474]

Melanie and Todd Edmondson Memorial Scholarship [3660]

Melanoma Foundation of New England [7244]

Melbourne & Alice E. Frontjes Scholarship [5167]

Frederic G. Melcher Scholarships [2240]

K. Cyrus Melikian Memorial Grant [1895]

The Melissa Institute for Violence Prevention and Treatment [7246]

Melissa J. Wolf Accounting Scholarship [11486]

Mellon/ACLS Dissertation Completion Fellowships [825]

Mellon-CES Dissertation Completion Fellowships in European Studies. [3858]

Mellon Fellowships for Dissertation Research in Original Sources [3870]

MHS Andrew W. Mellon Fellowships [7146]

Mellon Fellowships in Urban Landscape Studies [4233]

Andrew W. Mellon Foundation Fellowships [8749]

Institute Andrew W. Mellon Postdoctoral Research Fellowships [8621]

Terry Mellor Continuing Education Grant [10735]

MELNA Scholarship [6999]

E.V. and Nancy Melosi Travel Grants [1456]

Melvin Kruger Endowed Scholarship Program [8063], [9739]

Member Student Scholarships [9050]

Memorial Foundation for Jewish Culture (MFJC) [7248]

Memorial Fund Scholarship [7785]

Memphis Access and Diversity Scholarships [11609]

Men of Principle Scholarship [2540]

Mrs. Clare K. Mendel Memorial Senior Violin Recital Scholarship [9911]

Mennonite Central Committee (MCCC) [7253]

The Menominee Indian Tribe of Wisconsin (MITW) [7255]

Menominee Tribal Scholarships [7256]

Mensa Canada [7257]

Mensa Canada Scholarship Programme [7259]

Mensa Education and Research Foundation [7261]

Mensa Education and Research Foundation U.S. Scholarship [7262]

Mental Health Research Canada [7263]

Mentor-Based Minority Postdoctoral Fellowship [866]

Mentored Research Fellowship [7534]

Mentored Research Scholar Grant [717]

Donald Menzies Bursary Award [2894]

Merchants Exchange Scholarship [7266]

Merchants Exchange Scholarship Fund [7265]

Merck Company Foundation [7267]

Merck Frosst Canada Inc. Postgraduate Pharmacy Fellowship Award [2172]

Merck Frosst Canada Ltd. Postgraduate Pharmacy Fellowships [2173]

Al Mercury Scholarships [11696]

Meredith P. Crawford Fellowship in I-O Psychology [5626]

Merial Excellence in Preventive Medicine in Beef Award [526]

Merial Excellence in Preventive Medicine in Dairy Award [527]

John K. Merrell Scholarship [2541]

John Merrick Law Scholarship [9017]

Steven Craig Merrill Memorial Scholarship [2542]

Pat & Donald Merrill Scholarship [12348]

Christopher Mesi Memorial Music Scholarships [3179]

Mesothelioma Memorial Scholarships [10859]

Mesquite Club Evening Chapter Inc. Scholarship [9410]

Sanders J. Mestel Legal Scholarship Fund [10779]

Harry Mestel Memorial Accounting Scholarship Fund [10780]

George Cedric Metcalf Charitable Foundation [7270]

Metcalf Innovation Fellowship program [7271]

Nicholas Metropolis Award for Outstanding Doctoral Thesis Work in Computational Physics [1226]

Metropolitan Museum of Art [7272]

The Edmond A. Metzger Scholarship [1949]

Mexican American Bar Foundation [7285]

Mexican American Catholic College (MACC) [7287]

Mexican American Legal Defense and Educational Fund (MALDEF) [7289]

Meyer D. and Dorothy C. Silverman Scholarship Fund [3639]

Theodore Meyer Scholarship [1137]

MFJC Doctoral Scholarships [7250]

MFJC Fellowship Grants [7251]

MGH Department of Psychiatry Behavioral Neurology and Neuropsychiatry Fellowship Program [7136]

Eating Disorders Summer Research Fellowship [7137]

MGH Department of Psychiatry Forensic Psychiatry Fellowship [7138]

MGH Department of Psychiatry Global Psychiatric Clinical Research Training Program [7139]

MHI [7292]

MHS African American Studies Fellowships [7147]
MHS/Cushing Academy Fellowships on Environmental History [7148]
MHS Long-Term Research Fellowships [7149]
MHS/Massachusetts Society of the Cincinnati Fellowships [7150]
Miami County Retired Teachers Association **[7294]**
The Miami Foundation **[7296]**
MICA Scholarships [7386]
Michael A. Russo Memorial Scholarship [9562]
Michael Bany Memorial Scholarship Fund [3385]
Michael D. Curtin Renaissance Student Memorial Scholarship [4257]
Michael Herman Scholarship [5096]
Michael J. Hoggard Memorial Scholarship [9411]
Michael J. Wolf Scholarship [5168]
Michael Koizumi APWA Internship Scholarship [1308]
Michael Moody Fitness Scholarship [7464]
Michael Oykhman Criminal Law and Evidence Scholarship [8800]
Michael P. Spadafora Medical Toxicology Travel Award [766]
Michael R. Losey Excellence In HR Research Award [10368]
The Michener-Deacon Fellowship for Investigative Journalism [4655]
The Michener-Deacon Fellowship for Journalism Education [4656]
Michigan Accountancy Foundation Final Year Accounting Scholarship [7301]
Michigan Association of Certified Public Accountants **[7300]**
Michigan Association of Fire Fighters (MAFF) **[7302]**
Michigan Auto Law **[7304]**
Michigan Auto Law Student Diversity Scholarships [7306]
Michigan Competing Band Association (MCBA) **[7307]**
Michigan Council of Women in Technology (MCWT) **[7309]**
Michigan Council of Women in Technology High School Scholarship Program [7310]
Michigan Council of Women in Technology Undergraduate Scholarship Program [7311]
Michigan Education Association (MEA) **[7312]**
Michigan Education Association Scholarships [7313]
Michigan League for Nursing (MLN) **[7314]**
Michigan League for Nursing Student Scholarships [7315]
Michigan Nursery and Landscape Association (MNLA) **[7316]**
Michigan Nurses Foundation (MNF) **[7318]**
Michigan Parkinson Foundation (MPF) **[7321]**
Michigan Realtors **[7323]**
Michigan Realtors Scholarship Trust [7324]
Michigan Society of Fellows **[7325]**
Michigan Society of Fellows Three-Year Fellowships [7326]
Michigan Society of Professional Engineers (MSPE) **[7327]**
Michigan Society of Professional Engineers Scholarships [7328]
Michigan Space Grant Consortium (MSGC) **[7329]**
Michigan Space Grant Consortium Research Seed Grant Program [7330]
Michigan State Horticultural Society (MSHS) **[7332]**
Michigan State University - Gender, Development and Globalization Program (GDG) **[7335]**
Michigan Stormwater-Floodplain Association (MSFA) **[7337]**
Michigan Stormwater-Floodplain Association Scholarships [7338]
Michigan Sugar Co. **[7339]**
Michigan Sugar Company Hotel Restaurant/Resort Management Scholarship [7341]
Michigan Sugar Queen Scholarship [7342]
Michigan Turfgrass Foundation (MTF) **[7343]**
Michigan Water Environment Association **[7347]**
Michno Bronislaw Memorial Scholarship [9672]
John G. and Betty J. Mick Scholarship Fund [10781]
Mickey Donnelly Memorial Scholarship [9412]
The Micklin Law Group LLC **[7351]**
Micklin Law Group Scholarship [7352]
Microscopy Society of America (MSA) **[7353]**

Microsoft Research **[7355]**
Microsoft Research Graduate Women's Scholarships [7356]
Microsoft Research PhD Fellowships [7357]
Mid-Continent Instruments and Avionics Scholarship [188]
Mid-Ohio District Nurses Association (MODNA) **[7358]**
Middle East Studies Association of North America (MESA) **[7360]**
Beth Middleton Memorial Scholarships [4486]
Midland Company Scholarship Fund [3386]
Midlothian Rotary Club **[7362]**
Midlothian Rotary Club "Service Above Self" Scholarships [7363]
The Ella and Harold Midtbo Scholarship [8349]
Midwest Archives Conference (MAC) **[7364]**
Midwest Dairy Association (MDA) **[7368]**
Midwest Food Processors Association, Inc. **[7376]**
Midwest Modern Language Association (M/MLA) **[7379]**
Midwest Modern Language Association Fellowship [7380], [8377]
Albert and Eloise Midyette Memorial Scholarship Fund [4746]
MIE Solutions **[7381]**
MIE Solutions Scholarship Opportunity [7382]
Migrant Health Scholarships [7749]
Mihaly Russin Scholarship Awards [9765]
Mike and Gail Donley Spouse Scholarship [149]
Mike Hylton Memorial Scholarship [5480]
Mike Niemeyer Memorial Football Scholarship [9563]
Mike Reynolds Scholarship [9473]
mikeroweWORKS Foundation **[7383]**
Mikimoto Scholarship [4880]
Miklos Faust International Travel Award [1481]
Mila Boyd Law Offices Scholarship Contest [2667]
Milacron Geier Scholarship Fund [3387]
Milan Getting Scholarship [10574]
Mildred Colodny Diversity Scholarships for Graduate Program in Historic Preservation [8145]
Mildred E. Troske Music Scholarship [5169]
William F. Miles Scholarships [5276]
Miles Spencer Nadal Entrance Award [12258]
Military Intelligence Corps Association (MICA) **[7385]**
Military Nurses Association Scholarships [3066]
Military Officers Association of America (MOAA) **[7387]**
Military Service Scholarship [10084]
The MILK Scholarship [7391]
MILK Tailor Made Books Ltd. **[7390]**
Mill Creek Chamber of Commerce (MCBA) **[7392]**
Mill Creek Chamber of Commerce Scholarship [7393]
The Cheryl Allyn Miller Award [10567]
Glenn Miller Birthplace Society (GMBS) **[7394]**
Miller – Brian and Colleen Miller Math and Science Scholarship [3482]
Miller Electric International WorldSkills Competition Scholarship [1667]
Ruth R. and Alyson R. Miller Fellowships [7151]
Warren E. Miller Fund in Electoral Politics [1258]
Miller G. Sherwood Family Scholarship [5097]
Raymond W. Miller, PE Scholarships [4631]
Glenn Miller Scholarship [7395]
Millicent Mary Schaffner Endowed Memorial Scholarship [5098]
Millie Gonzalez Memorial Scholarship [5481]
Dolphus E. Milligan Graduate Fellowships [8029]
Carolina Panthers Players Sam Mills Memorial Scholarships [4747]
J. Clawson Mills Scholarships [7278]
Esther and Samuel Milmot Scholarship [11586]
Abby and Howard Milstein Innovation Award in Reproductive Medicine [6329]
Abby and Howard Milstein Reproductive Medicine Research Award [6330]
Milton and Edith Brown Memorial Scholarship Fund [3388]
Milton L. Shifman Endowed Scholarship [7053]
Milton Postgraduate Fellowship [3214]
Mineral & Metallurgical Processing Division Scholarships and Richard Klimpel Memorial Scholarships (MPD) [10428]

Mineralogical Association of Canada Scholarships [2244]
Mineralogical Society of America (MSA) **[7396]**
Minerva Scholarships [2598]
Mingenback Family Scholarship Fund [5016]
Minneapolis Jewish Federation **[7399]**
Minneapolis Jewish Federation Camp Scholarships [7400]
Minnesota Association of County Probation Officers (MACPO) **[7401]**
Minnesota Association County Probation Officers Scholarships [7402]
Minnesota Association of Public Accountant Scholarship [7404]
Minnesota Association of Public Accountants **[7403]**
Minnesota Association of Townships (MAT) **[7405]**
Minnesota Division Scholarships [7371]
Minnesota Health Information Management Association (MHIMA) **[7407]**
Minnesota Health Information Management Association Scholarships [7408]
Minnesota Power Community Involvement Scholarship Fund [4215]
Minnesota State Archery Association (MSAA) **[7409]**
Minnie Hopkins Scholarship Fund [10782]
Jacque I. Minnotte Health Reporting Fellowship [9474]
Minorities in Government Finance Scholarship [5054]
Minority Corporate Counsel Association (MCCA) **[7411]**
Minority Scholarship Award [3575]
Minority Scholarship in Classics and Classical Archaeology [10311]
Minority Teachers of Illinois Scholarship (MTI) [5715]
Minton-Spidell-Jackowski Point Scholarship [9227]
Molly Ann Mishler Memorial Scholarships [11457]
Miss America Organization **[7413]**
Miss America Social Impact Initiative Scholarship [7417]
Joseph and Catherine Missigman Memorial Nursing Scholarships [4597]
Missigman Scholarship Fund [4598]
Mission Aviation Fellowship of Canada (MAF) **[7418]**
Mission Bay Hospital Auxiliary Scholarship [9834]
Dikran Missirlian Scholarship Grant [1896]
The Mississippi Scholarship [1950]
Mississippi Society of Certified Public Accountants (MSCPA) **[7420]**
Missouri Department of Health and Senior Services **[7423]**
George J. Mitchell Postgraduate Scholarships [7646]
MJSA Education Foundation Scholarship [7024]
MKC/Preuss Scholarship [9835]
MLA Continuing Education Grants (CE) [7219]
MLA Financial Assistance [7426]
MLA/NLM Spectrum Scholarship [7220]
MLA Research, Development, and Demonstration Project Grant [7221]
MLA Scholarship [7222]
MLA Scholarship for Minority Students [7223]
MMC Scholarships [6027]
MMRF Research Fellow Awards [7495]
MMUF Dissertation Grants [12047]
MMUF Travel and Research Grants [12048]
MNF Scholarships [7320]
MNLA Academic Scholarship [7317]
Modern Language Association of America (MLA) **[7425]**
MODNA Nursing Education Scholarship [7359]
MoKan Division of Midwest Dairy Educational Award [7372]
Molded Dimensions Inc. **[7427]**
Molded Dimensions, LLC Scholarship [7428]
Antoinette M. Molinari Memorial Scholarships [467]
Moline Foundation **[7429]**
Mollie Lukken Memorial Scholarship [6345]
Molly McKay Scholarship [11200]
Shelby L. Molter Music Education Scholarship [2543]
Momeni Foundation Scholastic Achievement Scholarships [7955]

Monadnock Folklore Society (MFS) **[7432]**
Monaghan/Trudell Fellowships for Aerosol Technique Development [1355]
Nell I. Mondy Fellowships [5059]
Money Metals Exchange (MME) **[7434]**
Money Metals Exchange & Sound Money Defense League Scholarship [7435]
MoneySolver **[7436]**
Monsanto Commitment To Agriculture Scholarships [7449]
Monsanto Co. **[7448]**
Murray Montague Memorial Scholarship [5129]
The Montana Advocates Scholarship [90]
Montana Broadcasters Association (MBA) **[7450]**
Montana Broadcasters Association Broadcast Engineering Scholarships [7453]
Montana Health Care Association (MHCA) **[7454]**
Montana Society of Certified Public Accountants Helena Chapter **[7456]**
Monte Mitchell Scholarship [189]
Salvatore J. Monte Thermoplastic Materials & Foams Division Scholarship [10491]
Montesi Scholarship [4866]
Montgomery County Medical Society – William W. Lander, MD, Medical Student Scholarship [4800]
Michael Moody Fitness **[7463]**
ARTC Glenn Moon Scholarships [5340]
Rita & Frank Mooney Scholarship [12349]
Letitia Moore Charitable Trust Scholarship [12243]
M. Steve Moore Memorial Scholarship [2544]
Moore Middle School PTA Scholarship [9564]
Annabelle Moore Scholarship [2745]
Willie Hobbs Moore Scholarships [8090]
The Dr. Blanca Moore-Velez Woman of Substance Scholarship [7669]
Robert E. and Judy More Scholarship Fund [4599]
Jake S. More Scholarship [4170]
Lt. Colonel Robert G. Moreland Vocational/Technical Fund [10783]
Morgan and Jeanie Sherwood Travel Grant [1457]
Morgan, Lewis & Bockius LLP **[7465]**
Morgan Library & Museum **[7467]**
Thomas S. Morgan Memorial Scholarship [9075]
Morgan Stanley Pediatrics Fellowships [686]
Morgan Stanley Tribal Scholars Program [982]
Robert L. Morlan Redlands Area Interfaith Council Scholarships [9565]
Morphisec **[7469]**
Morphisec's Women in Cybersecurity Scholarships [7470]
Morris L. and Rebecca Ziskind Memorial Scholarship [5666]
The Morris Law Firm **[7471]**
Morris M. Pulver Scholarship Fund [2986]
Morris Newspaper Corporation Scholarship [4936]
Brian Morris Scholarship [12350]
James B. Morris Scholarship Fund **[7473]**
James B. Morris Scholarship [7474]
Edith Cantor Morrison Memorial Scholarship [2545]
June Morrison Scholarship Fund [11990]
Harry L. Morrison Scholarships [8091]
Dorothy Morrison Undergraduate Scholarships [1400]
Mortar Board National College Senior Honor Society **[7475]**
Mortar Board National Foundation Fellowship [7476]
The Mortgage Reports **[7477]**
Morton Bahr Scholarship [3559]
Morton Cure Paralysis Fund **[7479]**
Morton Cure Paralysis Fund Research Grants [7480]
Morton M. Traum Surface Science Student Award [2385]
The William Howard Morton Scholarship [8350]
John H. Moss Scholarship [11697]
Mother's Day Scholarship [7443]
Archie Motley Memorial Scholarships for Minority Students [7367]
Gerald O. Mott Award [3916]
John R. Mott Scholarship Foundation **[7481]**
John R. Mott Scholarships [7482]
Jack D. Motteler Scholarship [9305]
Mount Desert Island Biological Laboratory (MDIBL) **[7483]**
Mt. Hood Chapter Scholarship Awards [8708]
Mountain Memorial Fund [7054]

Mountain Plains Adult Education Association (MPAEA) **[7486]**
Movember Clinical Trials [9362]
Movember Discovery Grants [9363]
Movember Rising Star in Prostate Cancer Research Awards [9364]
Movember Team Grants [9365]
David J. Moynihan Scholarships [8331]
MPAC-DC Graduate Policy Fellowships [7517]
MPI CRV Membership Scholarships [7238]
MPI-WI Founders Grant Program [7241]
MPOWER Financing **[7488]**
MPOWER Financing's Global Citizen Scholarship [7489]
Mrs Prindables **[7490]**
MSA Graduate Fellowship [7532]
MSA Grant for Research in Crystallography [7397]
MSA Grant for Student Research in Mineralogy and Petrology [7398]
MSA Presidential Student Awards (PSA) [7354]
MSAA Scholarship Program [7410]
MSCPA Scholarship - Montana Tech [7459]
MSCPA Scholarship - MSU Bozeman [7460]
MSCPA Scholarship - University of Montana [7461]
MSCPA Undergraduate Scholarship [7421]
MSEA/SEIU Part-time Student Members Scholarships [7010]
MSFHR Research Trainee Award [10181]
MSFHR Scholar Awards [10182]
MSGC Internships [7003]
MSGC Undergraduate-Under-Represented Minority Fellowship Program [7331]
MSHQ Premed Scholarship [7205]
The MTS Student Scholarship for Graduate Students [7070]
The MTS Student Scholarship for Graduating High School Seniors [7071]
The MTS Student Scholarship for Two-Year, Technical, Engineering and Community College Students [7072]
Mu Alpha Theta **[7492]**
Mu Alpha Theta Summer Grants [7493]
Muddy Waters Scholarships [2632]
Mueller Undergraduate Scholarship [12115]
Dudley Mullins/Cabot Corporation Scholarship [8865]
Multi-Country Research Fellowship [3851]
Multicultural Work-in-Progress Grant [10302]
Multiple Myeloma Research Foundation (MMRF) **[7494]**
Multiple Sclerosis Society of Canada **[7496]**
Muncy Rotary Club Scholarship Fund [4600]
Muncy Scholars Awards Fund [4601]
Marvin Mundel Memorial Scholarship [5834]
Anthony Munoz Foundation (AMF) **[7500]**
Margaret Munro Award [3067]
James W. Murdoch Scholarship [12351]
Muriel Hannah Scholarship in Art [11487]
The Jack K. & Gertrude Murphy Award [9871]
Daniel Murphy Scholarship Fund (DMSF) **[7502]**
NACCED Annual John C. Murphy Scholarships [7643]
Murrietta Circuits **[7504]**
Murrietta Circuits Scholarship Opportunity [7505]
Edward R. Murrow Press Fellowships [3866]
Murse World **[7506]**
Murse World Scholarship [7507]
Murtha Cullina LLP Scholarship Fund [3592]
Muscle Shoals Kiwanis Club/Wal-mart [8523]
Muscular Dystrophy Association (MDA) **[7508]**
Music Library Association (MLA) **[7511]**
Music Scholarship for Undergraduate in Voice [4900]
Music Teachers' Association of California Goodlin Scholarship [9836]
Music for Young Children Saskatchewan Teachers' Association Senior Chopin Scholarship [9912]
Music for Young Children Saskatchewan Teachers' Association Senior Piano Chopin Scholarship [9913]
Muslim Public Affairs Council (MPAC) **[7516]**
Dr. Helen K. Mussallem Fellowships [3068]
Mustard Seed Foundation **[7518]**
My Home Improvement Solutions [7520]
My Life As A Lawyer Scholarship [3837]
My Pool Vacuum **[7522]**

My Weather Analyser **[7524]**
MyApartmentMap **[7526]**
MyApartmentMap Housing Fall Scholarship [7527]
Sam A. Myar, Jr. Law Scholarship [11610]
Myasthenia Gravis Foundation of America (MGFA) **[7528]**
Myasthenia Gravis Foundation of America Nursing Research Fellowships [7529]
Mycological Society of America (MSA) **[7531]**
Mary Fran Myers Scholarship [11565]
Clarence & Josephine Myers Undergraduate Scholarships [10409]
The Myositis Association (TMA) **[7533]**
Myotonic Dystrophy Foundation (MDF) **[7535]**
Myra Levick Scholarship Fund [502]
Myrna F. Bernath Fellowship [10358]
NAACP Legal Defense and Educational Fund (LDF) **[7537]**
NAAE Upper Division Scholarship [7609]
NAAMA Scholarships [7598]
NAB Dollars for Scholars $1,000 College Scholarship [8418]
NABA National Scholarship Program [7613]
NACA Foundation Graduate Scholarships [7624]
NACA Mid Atlantic Higher Education Research Scholarships [7625]
NACA Mid Atlantic Undergraduate Scholarship [7626]
NACA Multicultural Professional Development Grant [7627]
NACA Scholarship for Student Leaders in the Central & Northern Plains Regions [7628]
NACA Scholarship for Student Leaders in the Mid America & Central Regions [7629]
NACA Silver Anniversary Scholarship for Student Leaders [7630]
NACA South Student Leadership Scholarships [7631]
NACADA Scholarships [7568]
NACBS Dissertation Fellowship [8420]
NACBS-Dissertation Year Fellowship [8421]
NACBS-Huntington Library Fellowship [8422]
NACDS Foundation Merit-Based Scholarship Awards [7635]
James B. Nachman Endowed ASCO Junior Faculty Award in Pediatric Oncology [3780]
Nadene M Thomas Graduate Research Bursary [315]
The Nadia Christensen Prize [1377]
Nadine Barrie Smith Student Award [6120]
NAED/Spencer Dissertation Fellowship Program [7577]
NAFA Corporate Aviation Business Scholarship [7592]
NAFA International Dissertation Research Fellowships [7647]
NAFA Scholarship Program [7590]
NAGAP Graduate Student Enrollment Management Research Grants [7651]
NAIFA West Michigan Scholarship [5170]
NAJA Scholarship [7664]
IADR Toshio Nakao Fellowship [5915]
NALS of Arizona **[7541]**
NALS of Detroit **[7543]**
NALS of Detroit Scholarships [7544]
NALS of Michigan **[7545]**
NALS of Michigan Scholarship [7546]
NANBPWC National Scholarship [7670]
Robyn Nance Memorial Scholarships [9566]
Nancy Curry Scholarship [9960]
Nancy Lorraine Jensen Memorial Scholarship Fund [10590]
NANOG Scholarship Program [9943]
NanoSTAR Seed Fund Program [11726]
NAON Foundation **[7547]**
NAPC Forum Student Scholarships [7594]
Napoleon A. Jones, III Memorial Scholarship [9837]
NAPRHSW Scholarships [7682]
NAPT Continuing Education Award [7684]
NARAL Pro-Choice America **[7550]**
NARAL Pro-Choice America Development Internships [7551]
NARAL Summer Intership Program [7552]
NARFE-FEEA Scholarship Awards Program [4517], **[7554]**
NASA RISGC Graduate Fellowships [9699]

NASA WVSGC Undergraduate Research Fellowship [11975]
NASCOE Traditional Scholarships [7649]
NASE Future Entrepreneur [7692]
Kermit B. Nash Academic Scholarships [10073]
Elizabeth Nash Foundation (ENF) [7553]
JoAnn Brown Nash Memorial Scholarship Fund [3640]
Nashville Catholic Business Women's League (NCBWL) [7555]
Nashville Unit Scholarships [5488]
NASIG [7558]
NASLR Mined Land Reclamation Educational Grant [7700]
NASP-ERT Minority Scholarship Program [7686]
NASSCO [7561]
NASSLEO Scholarships - Region I [7688]
Nate Mack/Cindi Turner Scholarship [9413]
National 4-H Council (N4-HC) [7563]
National 4th Infantry Ivy Division Association [7565]
National AAHAM Scholarship [570]
National Academic Advising Association (NACADA) [7567]
The National Academies of Sciences, Engineering, and Medicine [7570]
National Academy of Education (NAEd) [7576]
National Academy of Public Administration (NAPA) [7578]
National Action Council for Minorities in Engineering (NACME) [7580]
National Active and Retired Federal Employees Association (NARFE) [7583]
National Administrative Law Judiciary Foundation (NALJF) [7585]
National AIDS Memorial Grove [7587]
National Air Filtration Association (NAFA) [7589]
National Aircraft Finance Association (NAFA) [7591]
National Alliance of Preservation Commissions (NAPC) [7593]
National American Arab Nurses Association (NAANA) [7595]
National American Arab Nurses Association Scholarships for Nursing Study [7596]
National Arab American Medical Association (NAAMA) [7597]
National Asian Pacific American Bar Association (NAPABA) [7599]
National Association of Abandoned Mine Land Programs (NAAMLP) [7604]
National Association of Abandoned Mine Land Programs Scholarship [7605]
National Association for the Advancement of Colored People (NAACP) [7606]
National Association of Agricultural Educators (NAAE) [7608]
National Association of Biology Teachers (NABT) [7610]
National Association of Biology Teachers BioClub Student Award [7611]
National Association of Black Accountants, Inc. (NABA) [7612]
National Association of Black Journalists (NABJ) [7614]
National Association of Black Social Workers (NABSW) [7616]
National Association for Campus Activities (NACA) [7621]
National Association of Chain Drug Stores Foundation [7634]
National Association of Clinical Nurse Specialists (NACNS) [7636]
National Association of Collegiate Directors of Athletics (NACDA) [7638]
National Association of Container Distributors (NACD) [7640]
National Association for County Community and Economic Development (NACCED) [7642]
National Association of Fellowships Advisors (NAFA) [7644]
National Association of FSA County Office Employees (NASCOE) [7648]
National Association of Graduate Admissions Professionals (NAGAP) [7650]
National Association of Health Services Executives (NAHSE) [7652]

National Association for Healthcare Quality (NAHQ) [7656]
National Association of Hispanic Nurses (NAHN) [7658]
National Association of Intercollegiate Athletics (NAIA) [7660]
National Association of Junior Auxiliaries, Inc. (NAJA) [7663]
National Association of Music Merchants (NAMM) [7665]
National Association of Negro Business and Professional Women's Clubs, Inc. (NANBPWC) [7667]
National Association of Oil and Energy Service Professionals (OESP) [7671]
National Association of Pastoral Musicians (NPM) [7673]
National Association of Pediatric Nurse Practitioners (NAPNAP) [7676]
National Association of Puerto Rican Hispanic Social Workers (NAPRHSW) [7681]
National Association for Pupil Transportation (NAPT) [7683]
National Association of School Psychologists (NASP) [7685]
National Association of School Safety and Law Enforcement Officials (NASSLEO) [7687]
National Association of Secondary School Principals (NASSP) [7689]
National Association for the Self-Employed (NASE) [7691]
National Association for the Self-Employed Scholarships [7693]
National Association of Social Workers (NASW) [7694]
National Association of State Land Reclamationists (NASLR) [7699]
National Association of Student Anthropologists (NASA) [7701]
National Association for Surface Finishing (NASF) [7703]
National Association of Teacher Educators for Family and Consumer Sciences (NATEFACS) [7705]
National Association of Women in Construction (NAWIC) [7707]
National Association of Women in Construction Construction Trades Scholarship [7708]
National Association of Women in Construction Founders Undergraduate Scholarship [7709]
National Ataxia Foundation (NAF) [7710]
National Ataxia Foundation Postdoctoral Fellowship Award [7711]
National Ataxia Foundation Research Grants [7712]
National Beta Club [7713]
National Beta Club Scholarships [7714]
National Biosafety and Biocontainment Training Program (NBBTP) [7715]
National Biosafety and Biocontainment Training Program Fellowships [7716]
National Black Coalition of Federal Aviation Employees (NBCFAE) [7717]
National Black Deaf Advocates (NBDA) [7719]
National Black MBA Association (NBMBAA) [7723]
National Black Nurses Association (NBNA) [7725]
National Black Nurses Association Scholarships [7726]
National Black Police Association (NBPA) [7727]
National Board of Boiler and Pressure Vessel Inspectors (NBBI) [7729]
National Board Technical Scholarship [7730]
National Business Aviation Association (NBAA) [7731]
National Cattlemen's Foundation (NCF) [7743]
National Center for American Indian Enterprise Development (NCAIED) [7746]
National Center for Farmworker Health (NCFH) [7748]
The National Center for Health Statistics Postdoctoral Research Program (NCHS) [11329]
National Center for Law and Economic Justice (NCLEJ) [7750]
National Center for Learning Disabilities (NCLD) [7752]
National Chapter of Canada IODE [7754]
National Chief Petty Officers' Association (NCPOA) [7761]

National Child Support Enforcement Association (NCSEA) [7763]
National Children's Cancer Society (NCCS) [7766]
National Co-op Scholarship Program [12190]
National Collegiate Athletic Association (NCAA) [7768]
National Collegiate Athletic Association Postgraduate Scholarships [7771]
National Collegiate Cancer Foundation (NCCF) [7772]
National Community Pharmacists Association (NCPA) [7774]
National Conference of Bar Examiners (NCBE) [7780]
National Conservation District Employees Association (NCDEA) [7782]
National Costumers Association (NCA) [7784]
National Council on Education for the Ceramic Arts (NCECA) [7786]
National Council of Jewish Women, Greater Houston Section [7789]
National Council on Public History (NCPH) [7791]
National Council on Public History Graduate Student Travel Awards [7792]
National Council on Public History Student Project Awards [7793]
National Council for the Social Studies (NCSS) [7794]
National Council of Teachers of English (NCTE) [7797]
National Council of Teachers of Mathematics (NCTM) [7801]
National Council on U.S.-Arab Relations (NCUSAR) [7811]
National Council of University Research Administrators New England Region I (NCURA Region 1) [7813]
National Council of Women of Canada (NCWC) [7815]
National Court Reporters Association (NCRA) [7817]
National Court Reporters Association Student Intern Scholarship [7818]
National Cowboy & Western Heritage Museum [7821]
National Dairy Herd Improvement Association (NDHIA) [7823]
National Dairy Herd Information Association Scholarship Program [7824]
National Dairy Shrine [7825]
National Debt Relief [7827]
National Debt Relief Scholarship [7828]
National Defense Industrial Association - Iowa-Illinois Chapter [7829]
National Defense Industrial Association - Picatinny Chapter [7831]
National Defense Science and Engineering Graduate Fellowship (NDSEG) [7833]
National Defense Transportation Association (NDTA) [7835]
National Dental Hygienists' Association (NDHA) [7838]
National Dental Hygienists' Association Scholarships [7839]
National Driving and Traffic School [7840]
National Eagle Scout Association (NESA) [7842]
National Eating Disorders Association (NEDA) [7862]
National Electrical Manufacturers Representatives Association (NEMRA) [7865]
National Endowment for the Arts (NEA) [7867]
National Endowment for the Humanities (NEH) [7870]
National Endowment for the Humanities Advanced Fellowships for Research in Turkey [1349], [7871]
National Endowment for the Humanities Fellowship [1339]
National Environmental Health Association (NEHA) [7872]
National Estuarine Research Reserve System (NERRS) [7874]
National Federation of the Blind (NFB) [7876]
National Federation of the Blind Scholarship Program [7878]
National Federation of Paralegal Associations (NFPA) [7881]

National Federation of Republican Women (NFRW) **[7884]**

National Forum for Black Public Administrators (NFBPA) **[7887]**

National Foster Parent Association (NFPA) **[7895]**

National Gallery of Art (NGA) **[7897]**

National Garden Clubs (NGC) **[7899]**

National GEM Consortium **[7901]**

National GEM Consortium - MS Engineering Fellowships [7902]

National GEM Consortium - PhD Engineering Fellowships [7903]

National GEM Consortium - PhD Science Fellowships [7904]

National Geographic Conservation Trust Grants [7906]

National Geographic Expedition Council Grants [7907]

National Geographic Society (NGS) **[7905]**

National Geographic Society/Waitt Grants [7908]

National Geographic Young Explorers Grants [7909]

National Glaucoma Research Program Grant [2694]

National Greenhouse Manufacturers Association (NGMA) Scholarships [902]

National Ground Water Association (NGWA) **[7910]**

National Guard Association of Rhode Island (NGARI) **[7912]**

National Guard Association of Rhode Island Scholarship [7913]

National Guard Association of Texas (NGAT) **[7914]**

National Hartford Centers of Gerontological Nursing Excellence **[7916]**

National Hemophilia Foundation (NHF) **[7919]**

National High School Oratorical Contest Scholarship [1072]

National Hispanic Coalition of Federal Aviation Employees (NHCFAE) **[7927]**

National Hispanic Foundation for the Arts (NHFA) **[7929]**

National Honor Society (NHS) **[7931]**

National Housing Endowment **[7933]**

National Huguenot Society (NHS) **[7936]**

National Huguenot Society College and Postgraduate Student Scholarships [7937]

National Humanities Center (NHC) **[7938]**

National Humanities Center Fellowships [7939]

National Industrial Belting Association (NIBA) **[7940]**

National Institute of Health Undergraduate Scholarship Program (NIH UGSP) [11341]

National Institute of Justice (NIJ) **[7942]**

National Institute of Mental Health (NIMH) **[7945]**

National Institute of Nursing Research (NINR) **[7947]**

National Investment Company Service Association (NICSA) **[7951]**

National Iranian American Council (NIAC) **[7953]**

National Iranian American Council Fellowships [7956]

National Italian American Bar Association (NIABA) **[7957]**

National Italian American Foundation (NIAF) **[7959]**

National Judges Association (NJA) **[7962]**

National Judges Association Scholarships [7963]

National Junior Angus Association (NJAA) **[7964]**

National Junior Horticultural Association (NJHA) **[7966]**

National Junior Swine Association (NJSA) **[7968]**

National Junior Swine Association Outstanding Member Scholarships [7972]

National Kidney Foundation (NKF) **[7975]**

National Kindergarten Alliance (NKA) **[7977]**

National Laser Institute **[7979]**

National Law Enforcement and Firefighters Children's Foundation (NLEAFCF) **[7981]**

National Legal Aid and Defender Association (NLADA) **[7983]**

National Lesbian, Gay, Bisexual and Transgender Bar Association (NLGLA) **[7985]**

National Lesbian and Gay Journalists Association (NLGJA) **[7987]**

National Little Britches Rodeo Association (NLBRA) **[7992]**

National Medical Fellowships (NMF) **[8000]**

National Medical Fellowships Need-Based Scholarships [8001]

National Merit Harris Corporation Scholarship Program [5306]

National Merit Scholarship Corporation (NMSC) **[8002]**

National Merit Scholarship Program [8003]

National Military Family Association (NMFA) **[8008]**

National Military Intelligence Foundation (NMIF) **[8010]**

National Military Intelligence Foundation Scholarship [8011]

National Milk Producers Federation (NMPF) **[8012]**

National MS Society New Jersey Metro Chapter Scholarship Program [8015]

National Multiple Sclerosis Society - New Jersey Metro Chapter **[8014]**

National Oceanic and Atmospheric Administration - NOAA Center for Atmospheric Sciences (NCAS) **[8016]**

National Organization of Gay and Lesbian Scientists and Technical Professionals (NOGLSTP) **[8018]**

National Organization for Human Services (NOHS) **[8020]**

National Organization of Industrial Trade Unions (NOITU) **[8022]**

National Organization of Italian-American Women (NOIAW) **[8024]**

National Organization of Italian-American Women Scholarships [8025]

National Organization for the Professional Advancement of Black Chemists and Chemical Engineers (NOBCCHE) **[8026]**

National Orientation Directors Association (NODA) **[8033]**

National Parking Association (NPA) **[8035]**

National Pathfinder Scholarship [7885]

National Pest Management Association (NPMA) **[8037]**

National Potato Council (NPC) **[8039]**

National Poultry and Food Distributors Association (NPFDA) **[8041]**

National Poultry and Food Distributors Association Scholarships [8042]

National Preservation Institute (NPI) **[8043]**

National Preservation Institute Scholarships [8044]

National Press Photographers Association (NPPA) **[8045]**

National Private Truck Council (NPTC) **[8052]**

National PTA **[8054]**

National PTA Reflections - Outstanding Interpretation Awards [8055]

National Public Employer Labor Relations Association (NPELRA) **[8056]**

National Recreation and Park Association (NRPA) **[8058]**

National Recreation and Park Association Diversity Scholarships [8059]

National Restaurant Association Educational Foundation (NRAEF) **[8060]**

National Roofing Contractors Association (NRCA) **[8062]**

National Scholarships [1679]

National Science Foundation (NSF) **[8064]**

National Science Foundation Graduate Research Fellowship Program (GRFP) [8068]

National Science Teachers Association (NSTA) **[8069]**

National Sculpture Society (NSS) **[8071]**

National Sculpture Society Participation Scholarships [8073]

National Security Technologies Engineering and Science Scholarships [9414]

National Sheriffs' Association (NSA) **[8074]**

National Slovak Society of the United States of America (NSS) **[8076]**

National Society of Accountants (NSA) **[8078]**

National Society of Black Physicists (NSBP) **[8081]**

National Society, Daughters of the American Revolution (DAR) **[8092]**

National Society of Genetic Counselors (NSGC) **[8099]**

National Society of High School Scholars (NSHSS) **[8101]**

National Society for HistoTechnology (NSH) **[8107]**

National Society of Professional Surveyors (NSPS) **[8117]**

National Space Biomedical Research Institute **[8120]**

National Space Club and Foundation **[8122]**

National Speleological Society (NSS) **[8124]**

National Sporting Clays Association (NSCA) **[8130]**

National Stone, Sand and Gravel Association (NSSGA) **[8132]**

National Swimming Pool Foundation (NSPF) **[8134]**

National Swimming Pool Foundation Scholarship Award [8136]

National Taxidermists Association (NTA) **[8137]**

National Technical Honor Society (NTHS) **[8139]**

National Technical Honor Society Scholarships [2763]

National Technical Honor Society Scholarships (NTHS) [4487]

National Trust for Canada **[8141]**

National Trust for Historic Preservation **[8144]**

National Union of Public and General Employees (NUPGE) **[8146]**

National Urban Fellows (NUF) **[8151]**

National Volunteer Fire Council (NVFC) **[8153]**

National Walking Horse Association (NWHA) **[8155]**

National Water Research Institute (NWRI) **[8157]**

National Wildlife Federation (NWF) **[8160]**

National Wildlife Rehabilitators Association (NWRA) **[8162]**

National Women's Studies Association (NWSA) **[8164]**

National Women's Studies Association Lesbian Caucus Award [8165]

Native American Education Grants [990]

Native Hawaiian Chamber of Commerce Scholarship [8932]

Native Hawaiian Visual Arts Scholarship [8933]

Native Women's Association of Canada (NWAC) **[8167]**

Naval Helicopter Association Scholarship [8170]

Naval Helicopter Association Scholarship Fund (NHASF) **[8169]**

Naval Research Enterprise Internship Program (NREIP) [1443]

The Naval Weather Service Association Scholarship [1125]

Navy, Army or Air Force ROTC Program [3956]

Navy League of the United States (NLUS) **[8171]**

Navy-Marine Corps Relief Society (NMCRS) **[8178]**

Nawrot Marek Memorial Scholarship [9673]

Nazareth Association **[8182]**

The Nazareth Scholarships - Sr. Kevin Whelan Scholarship [8183]

NB College of Physicians and Surgeons Medical Education Scholarship [8234]

NBCUniversal Point Scholarship [9228]

NBCUniversal Tony Coelho Media Scholarship [618]

NBHRF/ASRP Doctoral Training Awards [413], [8212]

NBHRF Bridge Grants [8213]

NBHRF Doctoral Studentship [8214]

NBHRF Establishment Grants [8215]

NBHRF Health Research Strategic Initiative Grants [8216]

NBHRF Master's Studentship [8217]

NBHRF Postdoctoral Fellowships [8218]

NBIA Scholarship [8220]

NBRC Frederic Helmholz, Jr., MD Educational Research Fund [1356]

NBT Trade School, Community/Technical College, or University Scholarships [8563]

North Carolina Hospitality Education Foundation Scholarship [8446]

NC Hospitality Education Foundation Scholarships - Graduate [8447]

NC Hospitality Education Foundation Scholarships - High School [8448]

NC Hospitality Education Foundation Scholarships - Two Year Community or Junior College [8449]

NCACPA Outstanding Minority Accounting Student Scholarships [8426]

NCAIED American Indian Business Scholarship Program [7747]

NCBWL Scholarships [7557]

NCCF Survivor Scholarship [7773]

NCCT Postdoctoral Research Program [11358]

NCEA Postdoctoral Research Program [11360]

NCECA Graduate Student Fellowships [7787]

Eric Niemitalo Scholarship in Earth and Environmental Science [10060]
Helen W. Nies Memorial Scholarship [4509]
Nigerian Women Association of Georgia (NWAG) **[8394]**
NIJ Visiting Fellows Program [7943]
Nikko Cosmetic Surgery Center **[8397]**
Nikko Cosmetic Surgery Center Annual Breast Cancer Survivor Scholarships [8398]
Nila Banton Smith Research Dissemination Support Grant [6036]
NIMH Postbaccalaureate Intramural Research Awards [7946]
Ninety Nines, Inc. International Organization of Women Pilots **[8399]**
Ning Interactive Inc. **[8404]**
NING Scholarship [8405]
NINR Mentored Patient-Oriented Research Career Development Award [7948]
NINR Midcareer Investigator Award in Patient-Oriented Research [7949]
NINR Pathway to Independence Award [7950]
Nissan North America, Inc. Scholarships [983]
Nitro College **[8406]**
NIU-CSEAS Foreign Language and Area Studies (FLAS) Graduate Fellowship [8487]
Nixon Family Scholarship Fund [11950]
Louise A. Nixon Scholarship [8192]
Louise McKinney Post-secondary Scholarship [299]
NJCBIR Individual Research Grants [10807]
NJCBIR Pilot Research Grants [10808]
NJCBIR Postdoctoral and Graduate Student Fellowships [10809]
NJCBIR Programmatic Multi-Investigator Project Grants [10810]
Stan and Mary Stark Alumni Scholarship [7967]
NJLA Scholarships [8277]
NJPA Foundation Scholarship for Research on Diversity Issues [8285]
NJSA Visionary Leader Scholarships [7973]
NJSBF Labor Law Scholarship [8291]
NJSCPA College Scholarships [8287]
NJSCPA High School Seniors [8288]
NLBRA Age-Out Scholarship [7993]
NLBRA National Royalty Scholarship [7994]
NLBRA Rainwater Scholarships [7995]
NLBRA World All Around Scholarships [7996]
NLBRA World Event Scholarships [7997]
NLBRA/Wrangler Academic Scholarships [7998]
NLBRA Youth Board Officer Scholarships [7999]
NLF Scholarships [7603]
NLLN Continuing Education Scholarship [8492]
NLM Associate Fellowship [11339]
NMCRS Gold Star Scholarship Program [8180]
NMHM Global Volcanism Program for Visiting Scientist/Postdoctoral Fellowships [10202]
NMNH American Indian Program Fellowships [10203]
NMPF National Dairy Leadership Scholarship Program [8013]
NMSC College and University Sponsorship of Merit Scholarship Awards [8004]
NMSC Corporate-Sponsored merit Scholarship Awards [8005]
NMSC National Achievement Scholarship Program [8006]
NMSC Special Scholarships [8007]
NOAA Graduate Sciences Scholarships [11305]
NOBCChE Procter and Gamble Fellowships [8030]
Leonard Noble Educational Scholarships [8111]
Charles S. Noble Scholarships for Study at Harvard [300]
The Edna A. Noblin Scholarship [6659]
George H. Nofer Scholarship for Law and Public Policy [334]
NOHIMSS Student Scholarship Program [8494]
Maureen E. Nolan-Cahill Memorial Scholarship [11459]
Alfred H. Nolle Scholarships [378]
Helen Woodruff Nolop Scholarships in Audiology and Allied Fields [4040]
Non Commissioned Officers Association Scholarships [8409]
Non Commissioned Officers Association of the United States of America (NCOA) **[8408]**
Nonstop Signs and Graphics **[8410]**

Noorali Bharwani Professional Corp. **[8412]**
Noplag **[8415]**
Noplag Scholarship Essay Contest [8416]
Nor' Easters Scholarship [5541]
Nor' Easters Scholarships - Two-year Program [5542]
Norall Scholarship Trust [6831]
Arthur L. Norberg Travel Fund [11640]
Marian Norby Scholarships [6883]
The Deborah J. Norden Fund [1785]
Nordic Skiing Association of Anchorage Scholarship [242]
Norfolk Southern Foundation Scholarships [1329]
Norm Manly YMTA Maritime Education Scholarship [4691], [12274]
Norman E. and Mary-Belle Huston Scholarship [6103]
Norman J. Tschantz, Walter C. Deuble and Dominic J. Bagnoli, Jr. Caddie Scholarship Fund [10784]
Norman K. Russell Scholarship [8034]
Norman Siegel Research Scholar Grants in Pediatrics [1527]
Norman W. Kramer Outstanding Scholar Award [7345]
Nortel Institute for Telecommunications Graduate Scholarship [11706]
Nortel Scholarship [11707]
North Alabama Dietetic Association Scholarships [218]
North American Bancard Holdings, LLC (NABH) **[8417]**
North American Conference on British Studies (NACBS) **[8419]**
North American Society Fellowship Award (NAS Fellowship) [9147]
North American Van Lines Inc. **[8423]**
North American Van Lines Military Scholarship Competition [8424]
North Carolina Association of Certified Public Accountants (NCACPA) **[8425]**
North Carolina Association of Health Care Recruiters Scholarship [8429]
North Carolina Association of Health Care Recruitment (NCAHCR) **[8428]**
North Carolina Council of Epsilon Sigma Alpha **[8430]**
North Carolina Council of Epsilon Sigma Alpha Scholarships [8431]
North Carolina CPA Foundation Scholarships [8427]
North Carolina Economic Development Association (NCEDA) **[8432]**
North Carolina Federation of Republican Women (NCFRW) **[8436]**
North Carolina Heroes Financial Hardship Grant [8439]
North Carolina Heroes Fund **[8438]**
The North Carolina League For Nursing Academic Scholarship [4748]
North Carolina Nursery and Landscape Association (NCNLA) **[8440]**
North Carolina Nursery and Landscape Association Horticulture Scholarships [8441]
North Carolina Restaurant and Lodging Association (NCRLA) **[8442]**
North Carolina Section of the American Water Works Association (NC AWWA-WEA) **[8451]**
North Carolina Simmental Association **[8454]**
North Carolina Space Grant Consortium (NCSGC) **[8456]**
North Central Region 9 Scholarship [10410]
North Dakota Division Scholarships [7373]
North Dakota Farmers Union (NDFU) **[8459]**
North Dakota Farmers Union Co-op House Scholarship [8463]
North Dakota Space Grant Consortium (NDSGC) **[8466]**
North Dakota Veterinary Medical Association (NDVMA) **[8473]**
North Dakota Veterinary Medical Association Scholarships [8475]
North Florida Chapter Safety Education Scholarships [1570]
North Las Vegas Firefighters William J. Harnedy Memorial Scholarship [9415]
North Mecklenburg Teachers' Memorial Scholarship Fund [4749]

North Ottawa Hospital Auxiliary Scholarship [5099]
Michelle North Scholarships for Safety [5458]
North Texas GIA Alumni Association Scholarship [4881]
North Texas Relocation Professionals (NTRP) **[8477]**
North Texas Relocation Professionals Scholarship [8478]
Northampton County Medical Society Alliance (NCMSA) **[8479]**
Northampton County Medical Society Alliance Scholarships [8480]
NorthCoast Medical Scholarship [1181]
Northeast Alabama District Dietetic Association Scholarships [219]
Northeast Conference on the Teaching of Foreign Languages (NECTFL) **[8481]**
Northeast Modern Language Association (NEMLA) **[8483]**
Northern Alberta Development Council Bursaries Program [301]
Northern Alberta Development Council Bursary [302]
Northern California Chapter of HIMSS Scholarships [5449]
Northern California DX Foundation Scholarships [1952]
Northern Illinois University - Center for Southeast Asian Studies **[8486]**
Northern Indiana Community Foundation, Inc. (NICF) **[8488]**
Northern Lights Library Network **[8491]**
Northern Ohio Chapter of Healthcare Information Management Systems Society (NOHIMSS) **[8493]**
Northern Scientific Training Program [1791]
Northern Tier Hardwood Association (NTHA) **[8495]**
Northern Virginia Alumnae Chapter Scholarship [4009]
Northrop Grumman Corporation **[8497]**
Northrop Grumman Engineering Scholars Program [8498]
Northrop-Park Fellowship [4573]
Northside Booster Club - Felix R. Sepulveda Memorial Scholarship [9567]
Northwest Community Center Scholarship [3691]
Northwest-Shoals Community College Academic Scholarship [8524]
Northwest-Shoals Community College Applied Technology Scholarship [8525]
Northwest-Shoals Community College Athletic Scholarships [8526]
Northwest-Shoals Community College Fine Arts Scholarships - Art [8527]
Northwest-Shoals Community College Fine Arts Scholarships - Drama [8528]
Northwest-Shoals Community College Fine Arts Scholarships - Music [8529]
Northwest-Shoals Community College Foundation (NW-SCC) **[8499]**
Northwest-Shoals Community College High School Academic Scholarships [8530]
Northwest-Shoals Community College Independent Computer Scholarships [8531]
Northwest-Shoals Community College Student Activities Scholarships [8532]
Northwest Territories Law Foundation **[8544]**
Northwestern Mutual Scholarship [9171]
Mary R. Norton Memorial Scholarship Award for Women [2330]
NortonLifeLock Inc. **[8546]**
NotMP3 **[8548]**
NotMP3 Scholarship Program [8549]
Notre Dame Club of Canton, Ohio Scholarship Fund [10785]
NOVA Foundation Scholarships [8559]
Novak Awards [67]
Novik & Stanley, A Professional Law Corporation **[8550]**
Mike and Flo Novovesky Scholarship [903]
Novus Biologicals L.L.C. **[8552]**
Novus Biologicals Scholarship Program [8553]
Noyce Scholarships for Secondary Math and Science Education [5764]
Nicholas H. Noyes, Jr. Scholarship [6391]
NPC Scholarship [8040]

NPM Academic Scholarship [7674]
NPM Program Scholarship [7675]
NPPF Still & Multimedia Scholarship [8049]
NPPF TV News Scholarship [8050]
NPSC Fellowship [5056]
NRAEF Scholarship [9651]
NRMRL Postdoctoral Research Program [11356]
NSA Scholarship Foundation [8079]
NSBRI First Award Fellowships [8121]
NSERC Postgraduate Scholarships-Doctoral Program [3806]
NSERC's E.W.R Steacie Memorial Fellowships [3807]
NSHSS Academic Paper Awards [8104]
NSHSS National Scholar Awards [8105]
NSPS Berntsen International Scholarship in Surveying Technology [8118]
NSPS and AAGS Scholarships [8119]
NSS Conservation Grants [8126]
NSS Education Grants [8127]
NSSA/NSCA Collegiate High School Senior Scholarships [8131]
NTHA Forest Resources Scholarships for College Students [8496]
NTHS/HOSA Scholarships [8140]
Nuclear Criticality Safety Pioneers Scholarship [1168]
Nuffield Canada [8554]
Nuffield Canada Farming Scholarships [8555]
Number 1 Auto Transport [8556]
Number 1 Auto Transport Annual Scholarship [8557]
NURSE Corps Scholarship Program [11335]
Nurseries Foundation Scholarship Awards [8709]
Nurseries Memorial Award [8710]
Nurses Organization of Veterans Affairs (NOVA) [8558]
NursingProcess.org [8560]
Nuts, Bolts & Thingamajigs (NBT) [8562]
Nuttall Ornithological Club [8564]
NVIDIA Corporation [8566]
NVIDIA Graduate Fellowships [8567]
NW-SCC Faculty and Staff Scholarship [8533]
NW-SCC General Foundation Scholarship [8534]
NWAC Helen Bassett Commemorative Student Award [8168]
NWAG Georgia Students Scholarship [8395]
NWAG Nigeria Scholarships [8396]
NWF Campus Ecology Fellowships [8161]
NWRA Research Grants [8163]
NWRI Fellowship [8158]
NWSA Graduate Scholarship [8166]
NYCT Paid Graduate Student Philanthropy Fellowships - Arts and Historic Preservation [8305]
NYCT Paid Graduate Student Philanthropy Fellowships - Children, Youth, Families, Education, Human Justice and Workforce [8306]
NYCT Paid Graduate Student Philanthropy Fellowships - Community Development and the Environment [8307]
NYCT Paid Graduate Student Philanthropy Fellowships - Health and People with Special Needs [8308]
NYCTutoring.com [8568]
The NYCTutoring.com Scholarship [8569]
NYFWA Scholarships [8312]
NYLA-Dewey Fellowship Award [8314]
NYLA-Dewey Scholarship [8315]
OAB Kids Scholarships [8575]
OAIA Scholarships [8700]
AEBC Rick Oakes Scholarships for the Arts [364]
OAS Academic Scholarship for Undergraduate Studies [8731]
OAS Scholarships for Professional Development - Disaster Communications Management [8732]
OAS Scholarships for Professional Development - Radio Spectrum Monitoring Techniques and Procedures [8733]
OAS Scholarships for Professional Development - Satellite Communications [8734]
OAS Scholarships for Professional Development - The ABC of Telecommunications [8735]
WillEtta "Willie" Long Oates, Gamma Nu, Memorial Scholarship [6463]
The O'Brien Foundation [8570]
O'Brien Foundation Fellowships [8571]

Dennis J. O'Brien USAEE Best Student Paper Award [11296]
Obuchi Student Scholarship [4264]
Ocean Industry Student Research Awards [9641]
Oceanic Research Group (ORG) [8572]
Oceanic Research Group Scholarships [8573]
Edward A. O'Connor Founder's Scholarship [99]
Basil O'Connor Starter Scholar Research Awards (BOC) [7028]
Odd Fellows Lodge #8 Endowed Scholarship [6818]
The Captain Jennifer Shafer Odom Memorial Scholarship - Children of Soldiers [1919]
The Captain Jennifer Shafer Odom Memorial Scholarship - Spouses of Soldiers [1920]
Don and Jan O'Dowd/SAA Statewide Scholarships [11460]
OGR Award of Excellence Scholarships [6048]
Ohio Association of Broadcasters [8574]
OAB Kids Scholarship [8576]
Ohio Farm Bureau Federation (OFBF) [8577]
Ohio National Foundation Scholarship [3391]
Ohio News Media Association (ONMA) [8579]
Ohio Newspaper Association Minority Scholarship [8581]
Ohio Nursery and Landscape Association (ONLA) [8584]
Ohio Rural Electric Cooperatives Inc. [8591]
Ohio School Counselor Association (OSCA) [8593]
Ohio Space Grant Consortium (OSGC) [8595]
Ohio Space Grant Consortium Graduate Fellowships [8598]
Ohio Space Grant Consortium Special Minority Fellowships [8599]
Ohio State University (OSU) - Center for Clinical and Translational Science (CCTS) [8602]
Ohio State University - Kiplinger Program in Public Affairs Journalism [8604]
Ohioana Library Association [8606]
Lawrence "Bud" Ohlman Memorial Scholarships [904]
Oil & Gas, Trades & Technology (OGTT) Bursary and Scholarship Awards (OGTT) [5776]
O'Jay's Scholarship Fund [10786]
Seth Okin Good Deeds Scholarships [9283]
Oklahoma City University Full-Time Merit Scholarships [8609]
Oklahoma City University School of Law [8608]
Oklahoma Restaurant Association (ORA) [8611]
Oklahoma Restaurant Association Scholarships [8612]
Oklahoma Speech-Language-Hearing Association (OSHA) [8613]
Rhonda J.B. O'Leary Memorial Scholarship [4305]
Olin-Searle-Smith-Darling Fellows in Law [4523]
Robert B. Oliver ASNT Scholarship [1532]
Oliver Joel and Ellen Pell Denny Healthcare Scholarship [12085]
MHS Andrew Oliver Research Fellowships [7152]
Oliver Rosenberg Educational Trust [4781]
Olivia James Traveling Fellowship [1779]
Diane Olsen Memorial Scholarship [11488]
Roy C. and Dorothy Jean Olson Memorial Scholarship [6042]
Olympia Tumwater Foundation (OTF) [8615]
Olympia Tumwater Foundation Traditional Scholarships [8616]
Olympia Tumwater Foundation Transitional (non-traditional) Scholarships [8617]
Omatsu FACL Scholarships [4529]
Charlie O'Meilia Scholarship [5973]
OMHF Postdoctoral Fellowships [7264]
Omicron Delta Kappa Society (ODK) [8618]
Omicron Nu Research Fellowship [6497]
Omohundro Institute of Early American History and Culture (OIEAHC) [8620]
Omohundro Institute-NEH Postdoctoral Fellowships [8622]
OMSBF District Four - Physician Care Bursary [8649]
OMSF Clinical Surgery Fellowship [8682]
On Q Financial [8623]
Oncology Nursing Society Foundation [8625]
Oncology Nursing Society Foundation - Doctoral Scholarships [8628]
Oncology Nursing Society Foundation - Master's Scholarships [8629]

One Source Process Inc. [8633]
One Source Process Inc. Scholarship [8634]
Faith E. O'Neal Scholarship [9459]
ONECA Four Directions Scholarship [8660]
ONLA President's Scholarship [8589]
ONLA Scholarships [8590]
ONS Foundation Congress Scholarships [8630]
Ontario Centres of Excellence (OCE) [8635]
Ontario English Catholic Teachers Association [8637]
Ontario Medical Association (OMA) [8645]
Ontario Ministry of Children and Youth Services [8651]
Ontario Native Education Counselling Association (ONECA) [8659]
Ontario Women's Institute Scholarships [4525]
ONWA Annual Scholarship [8582]
OOBS Student Leadership Scholarships [8778]
OOIDA Mary Johnston Scholarship Program [8798]
Open Society Fellowship [8664]
Open Society Foundations [8662]
Open Society Presidential Fellowship [8665]
Opera Foundation (OF) [8670]
Opera Foundation Scholarship [8671]
OPERF/ABC Resident Travel Award [8765]
OPERF Student Awards [8766]
OPERF Fellowships [8767]
OPERF Small Grants [8768]
OPIRG McMaster Public Interest Research Grant (PIG) [7195]
Dwight D. Opperman Scholarships [4171]
Opportunity Financial, LLC [8672]
OppU Achievers Scholarship [8673]
Optical Design and Engineering Scholarship [10728]
Optical Society of America Foundation (OSAF) [8674]
Optimist Club of Redlands Scholarship- Ralph Maloof [9568]
Optimist Club of Redlands Scholarship- Virgina Elliott [9569]
Oral and Maxillofacial Surgery Foundation (OMS) [8681]
Order of Omega [8684]
Order of Omega Doctoral Fellowships [8687]
Order Sons and Daughters of Italy in America (OS-DIA) [8688]
Order Sons of Italy Foundation General Scholarships [8691]
Order of United Commercial Travelers of America (UCT) [8692]
L'Oreal USA, Inc. [8694]
Oregon Association of Broadcasters (OAB) [8697]
Oregon Association of Broadcasters Scholarships [8698]
Oregon Association of Independent Accountants (OAIA) [8699]
Oregon Association of Nurseries (OAN) [8701]
Oregon Association of Nurseries Scholarship Program [8711]
Oregon College/University Scholarships [8721]
Oregon Farm Bureau (OFB) [8714]
Oregon Farm Bureau Memorial Scholarship [8716]
Oregon Literary Fellowships [6877]
Oregon Medical Association (OMA) [8718]
Oregon Society of Certified Public Accountants (OSCPA) [8720]
Carl Orff Canada - Music for Children (COCMC) [8723]
Orford String Quartet Scholarship [3786]
Organization of American Historians (OAH) [8725]
Organization of American States (OAS) [8730]
Organization of American States AOS-Placed Scholarships [8736]
Organization of American States Graduate Scholarships [8737]
Organization of American States Self-Placed Scholarships [8738]
Organization of Black Aerospace Professionals (OBAP) [8740]
Organization of Chinese Americans Scholarships [1986]
Organization for Tropical Studies (OTS) [8743]
The Gail Karp Orgell Scholarship [6276]
Orgone Biophysical Research Laboratory (OBRL) [8755]
Original Tax Credit Scholarship [1802]

Orlando Central Florida Chapter of the Society for Technical Communication **[8758]**
Oronzio de Nora Industrial Electrochemistry Fellowships [4363]
The Orr Law Firm, LLC **[8760]**
Orrie & Dorothy Cassada Scholarship [5171]
Orthopaedic Foot and Ankle Fellowships [1194]
Orthopaedic Specialists of the Carolinas Nursing Scholarship [12086]
Orthopaedic Trauma Association (OTA) **[8762]**
Orthotic and Prosthetic Education and Research Foundation (OPERF) **[8764]**
OSA Management LLP **[8769]**
Royce Osborn Minority Scholarship [1552]
OSCA Graduate Student Scholarship Program [8594]
OSCPA Educational Foundation High School Scholarships [8722]
OSGC Community College Scholarships [8600]
OSGC Education Scholarships [8601]
Osgoode Society for Canadian Legal History **[8771]**
OSHA Graduate Scholarship [8614]
Oslo International Summer School Scholarship [10591]
Osram Sylvania Scholastic Achievement Awards [4352]
Osteopathic Medical School Scholarship [8271]
Osteopathic Medical Student Research Fellowship Program [10867]
Al Oster Music Legacy Scholarship [12354]
M. Dick Osumi Civil Rights and Public Interest Scholarship [6240]
Charles & Mitch Ota Foundation Scholarship [5410]
The OTA Guide **[8773]**
OTA Member Full Research Grant [8763]
The Otis and Florence Lapham Memorial Scholarship [6205]
Alvin G. Ott Fish & Wildlife Scholarship [11461]
Ellis R. Ott Scholarships [1543]
Otto M. Stanfield Law Scholarship [11253]
Our World-Underwater Scholarship Society (OWUSS) **[8775]**
Our World Underwater Scholarship Society North American Rolex Scholarships [8776]
Satenik & Adom Ourian Education Foundation Scholarship [1897]
Out on Bay Street **[8777]**
Out to Innovate Scholarship [8019]
Outdoor Power Equipment Aftermarket Association (OPEAA) **[8779]**
Outdoor Writers Association of America (OWAA) **[8781]**
Outlaw Student's Medical Professions Scholarships [10860]
Outlaw Student's Minority Scholarships [10861]
Outlaw Student's Nursing School Scholarships [10862]
Outlaw Student's Teacher Scholarships [10863]
Cecilia Payne-Gaposchkin Doctoral Dissertation Award in Astrophysics [1227]
Overflow Scholarships [1803]
Overseas Press Club Foundation **[8783]**
Bill Owen, Cowboy Artist, Memorial Scholarship Fund, Inc. (ACSO) **[8795]**
Charles and Melva T. Owen Memorial Scholarships [7879]
Elvina Jane Owen Scholarship [4894]
Owner-Operator Independent Drivers Association (OOIDA) **[8797]**
Abraham A. Oyedeji Scholarship [8351]
Michael Oykhman Criminal Defense Law **[8799]**
Ozarks Division of Midwest Dairy Educational Award [7374]
The Pac-12 Postgraduate Scholarships [8802]
Pacific 12 Conference (PAC12) **[8801]**
Pacific Aviation Museum - Pearl Harbor **[8803]**
Pacific Beacon Scholarship [9838]
Pacific Institute for the Mathematical Sciences (PIMS) **[8805]**
Packard Fellowships for Science and Engineering [8808]
David and Lucile Packard Foundation **[8807]**
The Arthur J. Packard Memorial Scholarship [973]
The Barbara L. Packer Fellowship [496]
Paddle Canada (PC) **[8809]**

Dr. Nicholas Padis Memorial Graduate Scholarship [5467]
Casilda Pagan Educational/Vocational Scholarships [5594]
Pain and Symptom Management Special Merit Award [3781]
Painting and Decorating Contractors of America (PDCA) **[8811]**
Ben Palacio Scholarships [11387]
PALCUS National Scholarship Program [9250]
Paleontological Society **[8813]**
Paleontological Society International Research Program Sepkoski Grants [8814]
Paleontological Society Student Research Award [29]
Palmer Farley Memorial Scholarship [5277]
E. William Palmer Memorial Scholarship [2547]
Palo Verde High School Barbara Edwards Memorial Scholarship [9416]
Palo Verde High School Faculty Follies Scholarship [9417]
PAM General Conference Scholarships [9264]
PAM Scholarship for Montreat [9265]
Pan Pacific Law Enforcement Scholarships [9868]
Pancreatic Cancer Action Network-AACR Career Development Awards [535]
The PanHellenic Scholarship [8816]
PanHellenic Scholarship Foundation **[8815]**
Panther Cafe Scholarships [9418]
The Katharine Pantzer Fellowship in the British Book Trades [2567]
Papercheck, LLC **[8817]**
Pappaioanou Veterinary Public Health and Applied Epidemiology Fellowships [3202]
Paralyzed Veterans of America (PVA) **[8819]**
Parapsychological Association (PA) **[8821]**
Parapsychological Association Research Endowment [8822]
Parapsychology Foundation (PF) **[8823]**
Pardee Community Building Scholarship [9419]
Parent Cooperative Preschools International (PCPI) **[8825]**
Joseph M. Parish Memorial Grants [1394]
Park Law Enforcement Association (PLEA) **[8827]**
Parker B. Francis Respiratory Research Grant [1357]
Cissy McDaniel Parker Scholarships [4010]
E.U. and Gene Parker Scholarships [7880]
Parkersburg Area Community Foundation (PACF) **[8829]**
Parking Industry Institute Scholarship Program [8036]
Parkinson Canada **[8890]**
Parkinson Canada Basic Research Fellowship [8891]
Parkinson Canada Clinical Movement Disorder Fellowship [8892]
Parkinson Canada Clinical Research Fellowship [8893]
Parkinson Canada Graduate Student Award [8894]
Parkinson Canada New Investigator Award [8895]
Parkinson Canada Pilot Project Grant [8896]
Parkinson's Disease Foundation International Research Grants Program (IRGP) [8899]
Parkinson's Foundation (PF) **[8897]**
Ted Parnell Scholarship [12278]
The Paros-Digiquartz Scholarship [7073]
Carl Parsell Scholarship Fund [7303]
Parsons Brinckerhoff / Jim Lammie Scholarship [1304]
Part the Cloud: Translational Research Funding [416]
Participation-Based Scholarships [9101]
Partners HealthCare Geriatric Psychiatry Fellowship [7140]
Partnership for Pediatric Epilepsy Research [4426]
Partnership for Public Service (PPS) **[8903]**
Pasteur Foundation **[8912]**
Pasteur Foundation Postdoctoral Fellowship [8913]
Pat and Cliff Rogers Nursing Scholarship [11509]
Pat Dermargosian Memorial Scholarship [9570]
Pat and John MacTavish Scholarship [5100]
Patch **[8914]**
PATCH Early Childhood Education Scholarships [8915]
Senator Norman Paterson Fellowships (TBC) [3071]

Pathways College **[8916]**
Pathways College Scholarship [8917]
Patient Advocate Scholarship Program [3782]
Patnode Family Scholarship [12355]
Patricia & Armen Oumedian Scholarship [5172]
Patricia Buchanan Memorial Scholarship [11742]
Gail Patrick Charitable Trust Scholarships [4041]
Q. O. (Quint) Patrick Scholarships [12006]
Patriot Education Scholarship Fund [6994]
Patterson, Belknap, Webb and Tyler L.L.P. **[8918]**
Patterson Belknap Webb & Tyler LLP Diversity Fellowships [8919]
Patterson Memorial [10560]
Walter S. Patterson Scholarships [2704]
Joanne Holbrook Patton Military Spouse Scholarships [8009]
Pauahi Foundation **[8920]**
Paul A. Whelan Aviation and Aerospace Scholarship [11528]
Paul B. & Aline Flynn Scholarship Fund [10698]
Paul and Ellen Ruckes Scholarship [917]
Paul Green Houston Scholarship [11201]
Paul & Inger Friend 4-H Scholarship Fund [10831]
Paul Mansur Award [6021]
Paul S. Robinson Award [10322]
Courtland P. Paul Scholarships [6650]
Paul Tejada Memorial Scholarship [6206]
Paula Backscheider Archival Fellowship [1437]
Arthur Paulin Automotive Aftermarket Scholarship Awards [2359]
Pauline Hand Memorial Scholarship [10832]
Pauline LaFon Gore Scholarship Fund [3641]
PBR Forces Veterans Association (PBR-FVA) **[8935]**
PCBA Diversity Scholarship [8983]
PCF Challenge Awards [9370]
PCF Young Investigator Award [9371]
PCH Architects LLP - Steven J. Lehnhof Memorial Architectural Scholarship [9571]
PDEF Professional Development Scholarship [10440]
PDFelement Scholarship [12181]
PEA Bursaries [9340]
PEA Scholarships [9341]
Peace Dissertation Prize Grant [11378]
Peace Frogs Fellowships [8750]
Peale Scholarship Grant [9094]
Pearl I. Young Scholarship [8472]
The Scott Pearlman Field Awards [4470]
Pearman Family Scholarship [9839]
Oliver P. Pearson Award [1506]
Martha Mitchell Pearson Memorial Scholarship [6464]
Pediatric Brain Tumor Foundation - Georgia **[8937]**
Pediatric Endocrinology Nursing Society (PENS) **[8939]**
Pediatric Endocrinology Nursing Society Academic Education Scholarships [8941]
Pediatric Infectious Diseases Society (PIDS) **[8944]**
Pediatric Orthopedic Society of North America (POSNA) **[8946]**
Pedrozzi Scholarship Foundation **[8949]**
Peermusic Latin Scholarship [2636]
Peg Hart Harrison Memorial Scholarship [4011]
Peggy (Kommer) Novosad Scholarship [5173]
Greater DFW WTS Monique Pegues Graduate Leadership Scholarship [12176]
The Melissa Pellegrin Memorial Scholarship Fund [8759]
Full Pellegrini Scholarship [10896]
Margaret Pemberton Scholarships [2611]
Pembroke Center's Faculty Research Fellowships [2724]
Pembroke Center Graduate Student Fellowships [2725]
Pembroke Center Seed Grants [2726]
Pembroke Center for Teaching and Research on Women Postdoctoral Research Associateships [2727]
PEN American **[8951]**
Penguin Random House Young Readers Group Award [2241]
Pennies for Art Scholarship [4902]
Pennsboro High School Alumni Scholarship [8866]
Pennsylvania Association on Probation, Parole and Corrections (PAPPC) **[8953]**

Pennsylvania Dental Hygienists Association (PDHA) **[8955]**

Pennsylvania Engineering Foundation (PEF) Grants: Undergraduate [8964]

Pennsylvania Heartland Unit Scholarship [5489]

Pennsylvania Land Surveyors' Foundation Scholarship [8962]

Pennsylvania Library Association (PALA) **[8957]**

Pennsylvania Library Association MLS Scholarships [8958]

Pennsylvania Music Educators Association (PMEA) **[8959]**

Pennsylvania Society of Land Surveyors (PSLS) **[8961]**

Pennsylvania Society of Professional Engineers (PSPE) **[8963]**

Pennsylvania Space Grant Consortium (PSGC) **[8965]**

Pennsylvania State System of Higher Education Foundation (PASSHE) **[8967]**

PennyGeeks.com **[8970]**

PennyGeeks.com Car Insurance Essay Scholarship [8971]

PENS Conference Reimbursement Scholarship [8942]

PENS Research Grants [8943]

Pension Real Estate Association (PREA) **[8972]**

P.E.O. Chapter DS Scholarship [5101]

The P.E.O. Educational Loan Fund (ELF) [8976]

PEO International (PEO) **[8974]**

P.E.O. Scholar Awards (PSA) [8977]

People for the Ethical Treatment of Animals (PETA) **[8978]**

People to People International (PTPI) **[8980]**

The Peoria Area Amateur Radio Club Scholarship [1953]

Peoria County Bar Association (PCBA) **[8982]**

Pepper Family Scholarship Fund [3392]

Pepperdine University (PU) **[8984]**

Pepperdine University Caruso School of Law **[8986]**

Pepperdine University Diversity Scholarships [9019]

Pepperdine University School of Law Armenian Student Scholarship [9020]

Pepperdine University School of Law Dean's Merit Scholarship [9021]

Pepperdine University School of Law Faculty Scholars Award [9022]

Pepperdine University School of Law JD/MBA Endowed Scholarship [9023]

Pepperdine University School of Law Special Law School Scholarship [9024]

PepsiCo Foundation, Inc. **[9033]**

PepsiCo Foundation Scholarships [974], [9034]

Nalini Perera Little Lotus Bud Master's Scholarships [3048]

Perfect Plants Nursery **[9035]**

Perfect Plants Scholarship [9036]

Perkins Coie 1L Diversity Fellowship [9038]

Perkins Coie 1L Patent Litigation and Patent Fellowships [9039]

Perkins Coie 1L Political Law Diversity Fellowships [9040]

Perkins Coie L.L.P. **[9037]**

Perry Township School Memorial Scholarship Fund [10787]

The Vincent S. Haneman - Joseph B. Perskie Scholarship [2342]

Personal Money Service **[9041]**

The Persons in or Affected by Recovery Scholarship [5233]

Persons Case Scholarship [303]

Gilberto and Lennetta Pesquera Medical School Scholarships [5001]

Pet Insurance U **[9043]**

PETA Foundation Law Internship [8979]

Peter DeWitt Pruden and Phyllis Harrill Pruden Scholarship [11202]

Peter F. Bronfman Entrance Award [12259]

Peter and Jody Larkin Legacy Scholarship [2806]

Peter and Malina James and Dr. Louis P. James Legacy Scholarship [1286]

Peter T. Steinwedell Scholarship [5341]

Larry A. Peters Endowment Fund Scholarship [1898]

Paul Evan Peters Fellowship [3452]

Ruth D. Peterson Fellowship for Racial and Ethnic Diversity [1420]

Kate B. and Hall J. Peterson Fellowships [497]

Captain James H. Peterson Memorial Scholarships [5290]

Herman Peterson Scholarship [12356]

William H. and Lena M. Petree Scholarship [12087]

Silvio and Eugenia Petrini Grants [5286]

Petro Law Firm **[9045]**

Petro Law Firm Scholarship Contest [9046]

Petroleum Engineering Scholarships [10473]

Petroleum History Society (PHS) **[9047]**

Petroleum History Society Graduate Scholarships [9048]

Petroleum Packaging Council (PPC) **[9049]**

Pew Charitable Trusts **[9051]**

Pew Latin American Fellows Program in the Biomedical Sciences [9052]

Pfafftown Jaycees/Lynn Canada Memorial Scholarship [12088]

William R. Pfalzgraf Memorial Scholarship [8867]

The Ruth Cook Pfautz Memorial Scholarship Fund [4782]

Pfizer Scholarship Fund [7055]

PFLAG Columbia/Howard County **[9053]**

PFLAG Howard County Scholarship [9054]

Carl H. Pforzheimer, Jr., Research Grants [6507]

PGM Graduate Scholarship [9152]

PGM Undergraduate Scholarship [9153]

PGSF Scholarship [9332]

PHA Research Fellowships [9449]

Pharmaceutical Research and Manufacturers of America Foundation **[9055]**

Pharmaceutics Post Doctoral Fellowships [9059]

Pharmaceutics Research Starter Grants [9060]

Pharmaceutics Sabbatical Fellowships [9061]

Pharmacology/Toxicology Pre Doctoral Fellowships [9062]

The PHD Scholarship [1954]

PHE Canada National Award for Teaching Excellence in Physical Education [9148]

PHE Canada Student Awards [9149]

J. L. Phelps Scholarship [12357]

Phi Alpha Theta **[9072]**

Phi Alpha Theta Doctoral Scholarship [9076]

Phi Alpha Theta Faculty Advisor Research Grant [9077]

The Phi Beta Kappa Society **[9080]**

Phi Chi Theta **[9083]**

Phi Delta Gamma Academic Achievement Awards [9095]

Phi Delta Phi International Legal Honor Society **[9086]**

Phi Eta Sigma Graduate Scholarships [9089]

Phi Eta Sigma National Honor Society, Inc. **[9088]**

Phi Eta Sigma Undergraduate Scholarship Awards [9090]

Phi Eta Sigma Undergraduate Scholarships [9091]

Phi Gamma Delta **[9093]**

Phi Kappa Phi **[9096]**

Phi Kappa Phi DissertationFellowships [9097]

Phi Kappa Phi Fellowship [9098]

Phi Kappa Sigma (PKS) **[9099]**

Phi Kappa Sigma Foundation Scholarship [9102]

PHI Research Fund Grant [9254]

Phi Sigma Epsilon Past National President Scholarships [9172]

Phi Sigma Pi National Honor Fraternity **[9103]**

Phi Theta Kappa Scholarship [5765]

Phi Upsilon Omicron Candle Fellowships [9119]

Phi Upsilon Omicron Challenge Scholarships [9120]

Phi Upsilon Omicron Diamond Anniversary Fellowships [9121]

Phi Upsilon Omicron Founders Fellowship [9122]

Phi Upsilon Omicron Golden Anniversary Scholarships [9123]

Phi Upsilon Omicron, Inc. (PHI U) **[9106]**

Phi Upsilon Omicron Past Presidents Scholarships [9124]

Phi Upsilon Omicron Presidents Research Fellowship [9125]

Phil Shykes Memorial Scholarship Fund [4217]

Philadelphia Bar Association **[9132]**

The Philadelphia Public Interest Fellowship Program [9133]

Philip Alston Scholarship [11203]

Philip F. Greco Memorial Scholarship [6960]

Philip F. Vineberg Travelling Fellowship in the Humanities [7184]

Philip H. Melanson Memorial Scholarship [11593]

Shoshana Philipp (Kirshenblatt) R.N. Memorial Scholarships [11063]

Philippine Nurses Association of America (PNAA) **[9134]**

The Walter T. Philippy Scholarship [7175]

Philips Lighting Continuing Education Awards [4353]

Philips Respironics Fellowships in Mechanical Ventilation [1358]

Philips Respironics Fellowships in Non-Invasive Respiratory Care [1359]

Phillip Guy Richardson Memorial Scholarship [6207]

Jean L. Phillips Auburn Scholarship Fund [3662]

Phillips Fund for Native American Research [1217]

Garry Phillips Scholarship [12358]

Lowell Phillips Scholarship [3705]

Ed Phinney Commemorative Scholarships [755]

Phoenix Pride Community Foundation **[9136]**

Phoenix Pride Scholarship [9137]

Photographic Historical Society of Canada (PHSC) **[9138]**

PhRMA Foundation Health Outcomes Pre Doctoral Fellowships [9063]

PhRMA Foundation Health Outcomes Research Starter Grants [9064]

PhRMA Foundation Health Outcomes Sabbatical Fellowships [9065]

PhRMA Foundation Informatics Research Starter Grants [9066]

PhRMA Foundation Pharmaceutics Pre Doctoral Fellowships [9067]

PhRMA Foundation Pharmacology/Toxicology Post Doctoral Fellowships [9068]

PhRMA Foundation Pharmacology/Toxicology Research Starter Grants [9069]

PhRMA Foundation Pharmacology/Toxicology Sabbatical Fellowships [9070]

PhRMA Foundation Post Doctoral Health Outcomes Fellowships [9071]

PHS Commissioned Officers Foundation **[9141]**

PHSC Publication Grant [9139]

PHSC Research Grant [9140]

Phycological Society of America (PSA) **[9143]**

PEN/Phyllis Naylor Grant for Children's and Young Adult Novelists [8952]

Physical and Health Education Canada (PHE Canada) **[9145]**

The Physical Therapy Faculty Scholarship Endowment [10846]

Physicians Group Management (PGM) **[9151]**

Physicians' Services Incorporated Foundation **[9154]**

Helen Edwards Summer Internship [11319]

Physiotherapy Foundation of Canada Research Grant [3096]

Pi Gamma Mu (PGM) **[9159]**

Pi Gamma Mu Scholarships [9160]

Pi Kapp Scholars Award [9162]

Pi Kappa Phi Fraternity **[9161]**

Pi Lambda Theta (PLT) **[9163]**

Pi Lambda Theta Scholarship [11743]

Pi Project 2000 Tali James Memorial Scholarship [6465]

Pi Sigma Epsilon (PSE) **[9165]**

Pichler Family Scholarship Fund [3393]

The Thomas R. Pickering Foreign Affairs Fellowship [11346], [12050]

Mary Pickford Scholarships [2248]

Peter L. Picknelly Honorary Scholarships [711]

Pidperyhora Eleonora Scholarship [9674]

Ronald C. and Joyce Pierce - Mobile Section Named Scholarships [1668]

Pierre Elliott Trudeau Foundation octoral Scholarships [11124]

Herschel H. Pifer Scholarship [8868]

Pignalberi Public Policy Scholarship [11489]

David Pilon Scholarships for Training in Professional Psychology [1271]

Pilot Project Grant [10456]

PIMS Postdoctoral Fellowship [8806]

The John Pine Memorial Award [9078]

Julia T. Pingree Student Scholarship [8252]

Pinnacol Foundation **[9175]**

Joseph E. Pryor Graduate Fellowships [379]
Cheryl White Pryor Memorial Scholarship [4012]
Phillis Brinton Pryor Panhellenic Scholarship [6466]
PSAC-AGR National Scholarship [9444]
PSAC - Coughlin National Scholarships [9445]
PSAC National Member Scholarship [9446]
PSAC Regional Scholarships [9447]
PSAI Scholarship Fund [9248]
PSF Research Fellowship Grants [9190]
PSGC/NASA Space Grant Fellowships at the PSGC Affiliate Institutions [8966]
PSHF Good Idea Grant [9441]
Psi Chi, The International Honor Society in Psychology **[9374]**
PSI Graham Farquharson Knowledge Translation Fellowship [9156]
PSI Healthcare Research by Community Physicians Grants [9157]
Psychology Association of Saskatchewan **[9377]**
Psychology Association of Saskatchewan Student Scholarships - Academic Achievement [9378]
Psychology Association of Saskatchewan Student Scholarships - Research Based [9379]
Psychosocial Research Pilot Grants [8201]
Psychosocial Research - Postdoctoral Psychosocial Fellowships [8202]
Psychosocial Research Studies and Demonstration Projects [8203]
Pt. Lay Memorial Scholarships [11462]
PTAC Crew **[9380]**
PTAC Crew Scholarship for HVAC Students [9381]
Public Accountants Association of Kansas (PAAK) **[9382]**
Public Agency Risk Management Association **[9384]**
Public Education Foundation **[9386]**
Public Health Informatics Fellowship Program (PHIFP) [11332]
Public Interest Environmental Law Fellowships [4415]
Public Interest Fellowship [797]
Public Library Association (PLA) **[9430]**
Public Relations Society of America Maryland Chapter (PRSAMD) **[9433]**
Public Relations Student Society of America (PRSSA) **[9435]**
Public Schools of Hawaii Foundation (PSHF) **[9440]**
Public Service Alliance of Canada (PSAC) **[9442]**
Public Service Fellows Internship Program - Center for Government Leadership [8904]
Public Service Fellows Internship Program - Education and Outreach [8905]
Public Service Fellows Internship Program - Government Transformation and Agency Partnerships [8906]
Public Service Fellows Internship Program - Human Resources [8907]
Public Service Internship Program - Communications [8908]
Public Service Internship Program - Development [8909]
Public Service Internship Program - Government Affairs [8910]
Public Service Internship Program - Research and Program Evaluation Focus [8911]
The Publicity.ai SEO & Content Marketing Scholarship [1694]
Pulaski Scholarships for Advanced Studies [827]
Eugene C. Pulliam Fellowship for Editorial Writing [10502]
Eugene C. Pulliam Fellowships for Editorial Writing [10086]
Pulliam/Kilgore Freedom of Information Internships [10503]
Pulmonary Hypertension Association **[9448]**
Harry B. Pulver Scholarships [5002]
Paul Pumpian Scholarship [1752]
Purdue University School of Mechanical Engineering - Ray W. Herrick Laboratories **[9450]**
The Purpose Challenge [9358]
Ross C. Purse Doctoral Fellowship [3049]
Doug Purvis Prize [2885]
PVA Research Foundation Fellowships [8820]
PWC Core Apprentice Program [9200]
PWIPM Professional Empowerment Grant [8038]

Harry V. Quadracci Memorial Scholarship [5209]
Qualcomm San Diego Science, Technology, Engineering and Mathematics Scholarship [9841]
Quality Bath **[9452]**
Quality Bath.com Scholarship [9453]
Quality Company Formations **[9454]**
Quality Company Formations Scholarship [9455]
Quarter Century Wireless Association Inc. (QCWA) **[9456]**
Quarter Century Wireless Association Scholarship Program [9457]
Queen Elizabeth II Graduate Scholarship [305]
Queens County Women's Bar Association (QCWBA) **[9458]**
Queen's University - Stephen J.R. Smith School of Business **[9460]**
Rosa Quezada Memorial Education Scholarships [3755]
Rosemary Quigley Memorial Scholarship [4442]
The Michael J. Quill Scholarship [11075]
Quill and Scroll International Honorary Society (QSS) **[9462]**
Quincy Brown Memorial Scholarship [9573]
Quincy Sharpe Mills Memorial Scholarship [11205]
AIST Judith A. Quinn Detroit Member Chapter Scholarship [2223]
Diamond & James Quong Memorial Scholarship [12360]
R. Garn Haycock Memorial Scholarship [9574]
R. Roy McMurtry Fellowship in Legal History [8772]
R. Tait Mckenzie Award [9150]
R. Wayne Estes Endowed Scholarship Fund [9025]
RAB Design Lighting Award of Excellence [4354]
Rachel Graham Memorial Scholarship [9575]
Natalie and Mendel Racolin Memorial Fellowship [12239]
Radio-Television Digital News Association (RTDNA) **[9465]**
Radio Television Digital News Association (RTDNA) **[9468]**
Radio-Television News Directors Foundation Canada (RTDNF) **[9479]**
Radiological Society of North America (RSNA) **[9481]**
RADM William A. Sullivan, USN (Ret.) Scholarship [8174]
The Raffin-Gathercole Scholarship [4873]
Railroad and Mine Workers Memorial Scholarship [6250]
Railway Tie Association (RTA) **[9488]**
Rain Bird Corp. **[9490]**
Rain Bird Intelligent Use of Water Scholarship [6652], [9491]
Rainbow Business Professionals Association (RBPA) **[9492]**
Rainforest Alliance **[9494]**
Rains - J.J. Rains Memorial Scholarship [3483]
Frederick Rakestraw Law Scholarship [8489]
Ivan & Dianna Raketti Scholarship [12361]
Raleigh Mann Scholarship [11206]
Tom D. Ralls Memorial Scholarship [4807]
Ralph and Josephine Smith Fund [4602]
Ralph Modjeski Scholarship [9240]
Ralph Silverman Memorial Scholarship [2362]
Rama Scholarships for the American Dream [975]
Rancho Bernardo/Smith Scholarship [9842]
Commander Newell S. Rand Jr. Scholarship Program [8828]
Helen F. "Jerri" Rand Memorial Scholarships [3715]
R&D Systems Inc. **[9496]**
R&D Systems Scholarship [9497]
R&E Foundation Education Scholar Grant [9482]
Jennings Randolph Peace Scholarship Dissertation Program [11380]
United States Institute of Peace Jennings Randolph Senior Fellowship Program [11381]
Randy Williams Scholarship [9843]
Edward C. Raney Fund Award [1484]
Rangel Graduate Fellowship [9499]
Charles B. Rangel International Affairs Program **[9498]**
Jeannette Rankin Scholarships [9501]
Jeannette Rankin Women's Scholarship Fund (JRF) **[9500]**
Raptor Research Foundation (RRF) **[9502]**

Marie Mathew Rask-Gamma Omicron Educational Endowment [6467]
James K. Rathmell Jr. Memorial Scholarship [905]
Ratinge **[9505]**
Ratinge Scholarship Program [9506]
Ratner and Sugarmon Scholarship [11612]
Lenny Ravich "Shalom" Scholarships [2054]
Rawley Silver Award for Excellence [503]
Rawley Silver Research Award [504]
Mary C. Rawlins Scholarships [5342]
Ray And Mary Bell Scholarship [9844]
W.B. Ray High School Class of '56 Averill Johnson Scholarship [3484]
The Ray, NØRP, & Katie, WØKTE, Pautz Scholarship [1956]
Ray and Pearl Sams Scholarship [12089]
The Shirley and Robert Raymer College Scholarship [6277]
Raymond A. Kent-Navy V-12/ROTC [11579]
Raymond and Augusta Klink Scholarship Fund [3397]
Raymond and Donald Beeler Memorial Scholarship [9576]
Raytheon Co. **[9507]**
Raytheon Scholars [9508]
RBC Medical Education Scholarship [8235]
RBPA Scholarship [9493]
Reach for Your Goal Scholarship [5174]
Read Carlock Memorial Scholarship Fund [1800]
Real Estate Elevated **[9509]**
Real Estate Elevated Scholarship [9510]
RealtyHop **[9511]**
RealtyHop Scholarship [9512]
William R. Reaser Scholarship [8869]
Reba Malone Scholarship [1305]
Rebecca Lee Crumpler, M.D. Scholarship [2070]
Carl C. and Abbie Rebman Trust Scholarship [5124]
The Recovery Village **[9513]**
The Recovery Village Health Care Scholarship [9514]
Mary K. Smith Rector Scholarship [8870]
Red Olive **[9515]**
Red Olive Women in STEM Scholarship [9516]
Redlands Baseball/Softball for Youth Scholarship [9577]
Redlands Community Scholarship Foundation (RCSF) **[9517]**
Redlands Community Scholarship Foundation Awards [9578]
Redlands Council PTA - Dorathy Jolley Memorial Scholarship [9579]
Redlands Evening Lions Club - Barbara Westen Memorial Scholarship [9580]
Redlands Footlighters, Inc. - Merle and Peggy Williams Scholarship [9581]
Redlands High School Academic Decathlon Scholarship [9582]
Redlands High School Aquatics Booster Club Scholarship [9583]
Redlands High School Boy's Varsity Volleyball Scholarships [9584]
Redlands High School Girls' Volleyball Boosters Scholarship Awards [9585]
Redlands High School Mock Trial Scholarship [9586]
Redlands High School-PTSA Scholarship [9587]
Redlands High School Softball Booster Scholarship [9588]
Redlands High School Spiritleaders Scholarship [9589]
Redlands High School Terrier Band Boosters Club Scholarship [9590]
Redlands High School Vocal Music Boosters Scholarship [9591]
Redlands Morning Kiwanis Club Foundation Scholarships [9592]
Redlands Rotary Club Foundation Discretionary Scholarship [9593]
Redlands Rotary Club Scholarship - Donald C. Anderson [9594]
Redlands Rotary Club Scholarship - Ernest L. Cronemeyer [9595]
Redlands Teachers Association Scholarship [9596]
Reedsy Ltd. **[9606]**
The Reedsy National Creative Writing Scholarship [9607]

Sponsor and Scholarship Index

Robert L. & Hilda Treasure Mitchell Scholarship [5176]
Robert L. Peaslee Brazing Scholarship [1671]
Robert N. Colwell Fellowship [2009]
Robert O. Wagner Professional Development Scholarship [2328]
Robert P. Ernest Scholarship [6208]
Robert and Patricia Switzer Foundation **[9720]**
Robert R. McCain Memorial Scholarship [8237]
Robert R. Palmer Research Travel Fellowship [1438]
Robert S. McNamara Fellowships Program (RSMFP) [12194]
Robert Sutherland/Harry Jerome Entrance Award [2599], [9461]
Robert Toigo Foundation Fellowship [11048]
Robert W. and Bernice Ingalls Staton Scholarships [11654]
Robert Winchester Dodson Scholarship [11208]
Clinical Scholars [6325]
Robert Wood Johnson Foundation Health Policy Fellows [6326]
Robert Wood Johnson Health Policy Fellowships [6327]
Paul V. Roberts/AEESP Outstanding Doctoral Dissertation Award [2165]
James H. Roberts Athletic Scholarship [8872]
Clifford Roberts Graduate Fellowships [4963]
Eugene L. Roberts, Jr. Prize [11209]
Thomas Warren Roberts Memorial Scholarship [8873]
Marion Roberts Memorial Scholarships [2360]
Elliott C. Roberts Scholarships [5815]
Actuary of Tomorrow - Stuart A. Robertson Memorial Scholarship [73]
A.D. Al and Maxine Robertson Memorial Scholarship [11463]
Robin P. Armstrong Memorial Prize for Excellence in Indigenous Studies [2087]
Robinhood Marine Center Scholarship [4920]
Gertrude J. Robinson Book Prize [2956]
Jackie Robinson Foundation (JRF) **[9722]**
Robinson G. Allen Athletic Memorial Scholarship [9599]
Helen M. Robinson Grants [6037]
Robinson Helicopter R22/R44 Safety Course Scholarship [12012]
Isobel Robinson Historical Research Grant [3081]
NKA Dr. Violet B. Robinson Memorial Graduate Scholarship [7978]
Jennifer Robinson Memorial Scholarship [1792]
Sara Roby Fellowship in Twentieth-Century American Realism [10218]
August M. Rocco Scholarship Fund [10788]
Rochelle Scholarship [6908]
Rockford Area Habitat for Humanity College Scholarship [3693]
Rockwell Collins Scholarships [190]
Rocky Mountain American Association of Collegiate Registrars and Admission Officers (RMACRAO) **[9724]**
Rocky Mountain Coal Mining Institute (RMCMI) **[9726]**
Rocky Mountain Coal Mining Institute Engineering/Geology Scholarships [9727]
Rocky Mountain Coal Mining Institute Technical Scholarships [9728]
Rocky Mountain Conservancy **[9729]**
Rocky Mountain Mineral Law Foundation (RMMLF) **[9731]**
Rodger Doxsey Travel Prize [684]
Paul W. Rodgers Scholarship [5925]
Rodney Williams Legacy Scholarship [11580]
Rodziny Krawczyk-Krane Family Scholarship [9676]
R.O.E.A. Dumitru Golea Goldy-Gemu Scholarships [1369]
ROFL Scholarship [9236]
Roger and Jacquelyn Vander Laan Family Scholarship [5177]
Roger and Joyce Howe Scholarship Fund [3400]
Roger K. Hughes Legacy Scholarship [2807]
Roger K. Summit Scholarship [9356]
Kimberly Marie Rogers Memorial Scholarship Fund [4603]
Red Rogers Memorial Scholarship [12365]

Roy Seymour Rogers and Geraldine Ruth Rogers Scholarship [11023]
William C. Rogers Scholarship [4937]
Roland E. Murphy, O.Carm., Scholarship [3186]
Sandra Journey Rolf Scholarship Fund [6469]
Ted Rollins Eco Scholarship [11158]
Rome Prize [476]
Ronald B. Linsky Fellowship for Outstanding Water Research [8159]
Ronald L. Schmied Scholarship [5253]
Ronald McDonald House Charities (RMHC) **[9733]**
Ronald McDonald House Charities Scholarship [9737]
Ronald T. Smith Family Scholarship [5178]
Dr. Orrin Rongstad Wildlife Scholarship [11510]
Charles and Ruth Ronin Memorial Scholarships [9600]
Dorothy Worden Ronken Scholarships [4042]
Roofing Industry Alliance for Progress **[9738]**
Doris Hardinger Roome Scholarship Fund [5411]
Susanna Stover Root Memorial Scholarship [6470]
The Roothbert Fund, Inc. **[9740]**
Roothbert Fund Scholarships [9741]
Rose Cassin Memorial Scholarship [8644]
Barnes W. Rose, Jr. and Eva Rose Nichol Scholarship Fund [322]
Rose Marie Princ Memorial Scholarship [9421]
Carl M. Rose Memorial Scholarship [8874]
Dr. Wayne F. Rose Scholarship Fund [4604]
Clarence J. Rosecrans Scholarship [1288]
Rosemary Cook Education Scholarship [5179]
Esther Katz Rosen Fund Grants [1289]
Jack Rosen Scholarship [6393]
Rosenberg-Ibarra Scholarships [9312]
Mandell and Lester Rosenblatt Undergraduate Scholarship [10434]
Walter A. Rosenblith New Investigator Award [5426]
Marshall N. Rosenbluth Outstanding Doctoral Thesis Award [1229]
Rosenfeld Injury Lawyers LLC **[9742]**
ASPPH/CDC Allan Rosenfield Global Health Fellowship Program [2284]
Harold W. Rosenthal Fellowship in International Relations [2264]
Jean and Tom Rosenthal Scholarship Program [3723]
Ross A. Wilson Science Scholarship [11024]
IADR Norton Ross Fellowship [5916]
S. Byrl Ross Memorial Scholarship [8875]
Ross/Nickey Scholarships [7422]
Ross P. Broesamle Education Fund [6667]
Colonel Jerry W. Ross Scholarship [1753]
The Bea and Harry Ross Scholarship Endowment [10847]
Ross Trust Future School Counselors Essay Competition [834]
Hon. Rudolph J. Rossetti Memorial Award [2854]
Rotary Club of Annapolis Scholarship [1719]
The Rotary Club of Cape Coral Goldcoast Scholarship [3149]
The Rotary Club of Charlotte Public Safety Scholarship Fund [4752]
Rotary Club of Corpus Christi Scholarship [3485]
The Rotary Club of Rancho Bernardo Sunrise Community Service Scholarships [9846]
The Rotary Foundation **[9744]**
Rotary Foundation Global Grant Scholarships Supplement [9745]
Rotary Peace Fellowship Program [4195]
Edward S. Roth Scholarship [10411]
Rothberg International School Graduate Merit Scholarship [2987]
Marjorie Roy Rothermel Scholarship [2002]
Hal Rothman Dissertation Fellowship [1458]
Theodore Rousseau Fellowships [7281]
Regie Routman Teacher Recognition Grant [6038]
Rove Pest Control **[9746]**
Rove Pest Control Scholarships [9747]
Rovelstad Scholarship [3871]
John Rowan Scholarship [12366]
Roy Rowan Scholarship [8789]
Rowe Family Fellowships [8752]
Leo S. Rowe Pan American Fund [8739]
Roy Anderson Memorial Scholarship [3536]
Robert Roy Award [2099]
Roy Cooper Memorial Scholarship [6758]

Travis Roy Foundation Individual Grants [9749]
Travis Roy Foundation **[9748]**
Roy H. Pollack Scholarship [11254]
Roy W. Likins Scholarship [1646]
Royal Bank Scholarships [2600]
Royal Canadian Regiment Association (RCR) **[9750]**
Royal Canadian Regiment Association Bursaries [9751]
Lucille and Edward R. Roybal Foundation **[9752]**
Lucille and Edward R. Roybal Foundation Public Health Scholarships [9753]
RPNAS Baccalaureate Level Program Scholarship [9620]
RPNAS Doctorate Level Program Scholarship [9621]
RPNAS Master's Level Program Scholarship [9622]
RRANN Program Scholarship [11491]
R.S. Williamson & Eliford Mott Memorial Scholarships [12007]
The RSA-Centre for Reformation and Renaissance Studies (CRRS) Grant (CRRS) [11818]
RSDSA Research Grants [9613]
RSL Funding LLC **[9754]**
RSNA/AAPM Graduate Fellowship [622]
RSNA/AUR/APDR/SCARD Radiology Education Research Development Grant [9484]
RSNA Education Scholar Grant [9485]
Research Scholar Grant [9486]
RSNA Research Seed Grant [9487]
RTDNF Scholarships [9480]
Kathleen and Winnifred Ruane Graduate Student Research Grant for Nurses [11582]
IPMI Richard Rubin Memorial Scholarship Award [6063]
Glen Ruby Memorial Scholarships [3122]
Joe Rudd Scholarships [9732]
Rudolph Dillman Memorial Scholarship [919]
Drs. Kirkland Ruffin & Willcox Ruffin Scholarships [5279]
Damon Runyon Cancer Research Foundation (DR-CRF) **[9756]**
Damon Runyon Clinical Investigator Awards [9761]
Ruppert Scholarship [2831]
Hermann G. Rusch Scholarship [847]
Russell Ackoff Doctoral Student Fellowship [11662]
Russell Athletics Scholarship [2336]
Russell C. McCaughan Heritage Scholarship [1199]
Dave & Laurie Russell Family Scholarships for Habitat for Humanity of Kent County Families [5180]
Russell & Lazarus **[9762]**
Russell & Lazarus Safety Scholarship Contest [9763]
Kenneth W. Russell Memorial Fellowships [729]
Russell Sage Foundation's Visiting Scholars Program [9774]
Russell & Sigurd Varian Award [2386]
Russian Brotherhood Organization of the U.S.A. (RBOUSA) **[9764]**
Russian Student Scholarship [11511]
NPELRA Foundation - Anthony C. Russo Scholarships [8057]
Lucile Rust Scholarships [9126]
Moti L. & Kamla Rustgi International Travel Awards [942]
Ruth Adams Memorial Scholarship [9601]
Ruth E. Jenkins Scholarship [9847]
Ruth K. Jacobs Memorial Scholarship [3317]
Ruth L. Kirschstein Individual Predoctoral NRSA for MD/PhD and other Dual Degree Fellowships [11337]
Ruth Liu Memorial Scholarship [3309]
Ruth M. Cogan Foundation Trust [10789]
Ruth McMillan Academic Excellence Student Scholarship [2836]
Ruth Messmer Scholarship Fund [10702]
Ruth Milan-Altrusa Scholarship Fund [6995]
Ruth Sager Scholarship [7056]
Ruth and Sherman Zudekoff Scholarship Fund [3593]
Alexander Rutherford High School Achievement Scholarship [307]
Rutherford Scholars [308]
IOIA Andrew Rutherford Scholarships [6055]
The Ryan Law Group **[9767]**

The Ryan Law Group Scholarship [9768]
Michael Clarkson Ryan Memorial Scholarship [2551]
Ryerson Scholarships [6219]
S. David Shor Scholarship Fund [3401]
S. O. Mast Founders' Scholarship [7057]
S. Penny Chappell Scholarship [9127]
Arthur C. Parker Scholarship [10270]
SABA NC - Public Interest Post-Bar Fellowships [10599]
SABA NC - Public Interest Summer Fellowships [10600]
Chester & Maria Sadowski Memorial Scholarships [9677]
SAEMS Environmental Scholarships [10645]
Safe Schools Coalition (SSC) **[9769]**
Safe Teen Driver Scholarship [4978]
Safer Athletic Field Environments Scholarships (SAFE) [10736]
Russell Sage Foundation (RSF) **[9773]**
SAH Study Tour Fellowships [10276]
Don Sahli-Kathy Woodall Graduate Scholarships [10960]
Sons and Daughters Don Sahli-Kathy Woodall Scholarships [10961]
Saint Andrews Scholarships [9776]
Saint Andrew's Society of the State of New York **[9775]**
St. Croix Valley Foundation **[9777]**
Saint Elizabeth Health Care Scholarship for Community Health Nursing [2170]
St. Francis Xavier Scholarship [12225]
St. Giles Young Investigator Award [8948]
St. James Armenian Apostolic Church **[9779]**
St. James Armenian Apostolic Church Scholarships [9780]
St. Joseph's Hospital School of Nursing Alumnae Scholarship [8876]
St. Louis Paralegal Association **[9781]**
St. Louis Paralegal Student Scholarships [9783]
St. Patrick's Day Scholarship [7444]
Saint Paul University Canada (SPU) **[9784]**
Saint Paul University Financial Aid Bursaries [9785]
St. Petersburg Personal Injury Attorneys McQuaid & Douglas **[9786]**
St. Petersburg Personal Injury Attorneys McQuaid & Douglas $2,000 Scholarship Contest [9787]
Saints Cyril and Methodius Scholarships [9766]
SAJA Student Scholarship [10604]
Sakura Finetek Student Scholarship [8113]
SALEF Health Career Scholarships [9791]
The Bill, W2ONV, and Ann Salerno Memorial Scholarship [1958]
Vincent Salierno Memorial Scholarship [468]
The Eugene "Gene" Sallee, W4YFR, Memorial Scholarship [1959]
Sally Beauty Scholarships for High School Graduates [9336]
The Sally Cole Visual Arts Scholarship Program [4753]
Salon Supply Store **[9788]**
Salon Supply Store Cosmetology Scholarships [9789]
Salvadoran American Leadership and Education Fund (SALEF) **[9790]**
Sam Bull Memorial Scholarship [269]
Sam J. Hord Memorial Scholarship [10629]
The SAMFund **[9792]**
Samfund grants [9793]
Burton MacDonald and Rosemarie Sampson Fellowship [730]
Margaret Jerome Sampson Scholarships [9128]
AIST David H. Samson Canadian Scholarship [2224]
Samsung American Legion Scholarship [1073]
Samuel H. Kress Foundation Fellowships [10277]
Samuel P. Hays Research Fellowship [1459]
Samuel Robinson Award [9267]
Samuel S. Wilks Memorial Award [1612]
ABS Amy R. Samuels Cetacean Behavior and Conservation Award [1717]
San Angelo Area Foundation (SAAF) **[9794]**
San Angelo Area Foundation Scholarship [9795]
San Antonio Paralegal Association (SAPA) **[9796]**
The San Diego Foundation (TSDF) **[9798]**
The San Diego Foundation Community Scholarship I [9848]

The San Diego Foundation Community Scholarship II [9849]
San Diego Pan-Pacific Law Enforcement Association (PANPAC) **[9867]**
San Francisco Foundation (SFF) **[9869]**
San Francisco State University Disability Programs and Resource Center **[9872]**
San Pasqual Academy Scholarship [9850]
Leo and Trinidad Sanchez Scholarships [10138]
Sand Plains & Lewis A. and Gurry F. Batten Education Scholarship [8877]
Bill Sanderson Aviation Maintenance Technician Scholarships [5459]
Leonard H. Sandler Fellowships [5636]
Sandra Jo Hornick Scholarship [6394]
Sandra Sebrell Bailey Scholarship [4043]
Amato Sanita Attorney at Law **[9875]**
Sanofi Pasteur Scholarships [3072]
Santa Clara County La Raza Lawyers Association **[9877]**
SAO Predoctoral Fellowship [5359]
Sarah Shinn Marshall Scholarship [4013]
Saratoga County Bar Association (SCBA) **[9879]**
Saratoga County Bar Association Law Student Scholarship [9880]
Frank Sarli Memorial Scholarship [7820]
SARP Professional Development Grant [9882]
Saskatchewan Association of Recreation Professionals **[9881]**
Saskatchewan Choral Federation Open Choral Scholarship [9915]
Saskatchewan Government Insurance (SGI) **[9883]**
Saskatchewan Government Insurance Actuarial Science Scholarship [9887]
Saskatchewan Government Insurance Anniversary Scholarships [9888]
Saskatchewan Government Insurance Corporate Scholarships [9889]
Saskatchewan Hockey Association **[9892]**
Saskatchewan Hockey Association Scholarships [9893]
Saskatchewan Music Festival Association (SMFA) **[9894]**
Saskatchewan Pulse Growers (SPG) **[9920]**
Saskatchewan Pulse Growers Undergraduate Scholarships [9923]
Saskatchewan Registered Music Teachers' Association Senior Romantic Music Scholarship [9916]
Saskatchewan School Boards Association **[9924]**
Saskatchewan School Boards Association Education Scholarships [9925]
Saskatchewan School Boards Association Graduate Student Award [9926]
Saskatchewan Trucking Association (STA) **[9927]**
Saskatchewan Trucking Association Scholarships [9928]
Roger C. Sathre Memorial Scholarship Fund [5680]
Sho Sato Memorial Scholarship [6251]
Satter Human Rights Fellowship [5366]
François J. Saucier Prize in Applied Oceanography [3045]
James A. Sauer Memorial Fellowships [731]
Curtis M. Saulsbury Scholarship Fund [3594]
Saunders – Kevin Saunders Wheelchair Success Scholarship [3486]
Save a Life Scholarship [448]
Save Mart Legacy Scholarships [2808]
Savoy Foundation Postdoctoral and Clinical Research Fellowships [4658]
John A. Savoy Scholarship Fund [4605]
Bill Sawyer Memorial Scholarship [6820]
Herbert M. Saylor Memorial Scholarship [10586]
SBE/Ennes Youth Scholarships [10287]
SBSE Ases Student Travel Scholarship [10291]
SBSE Student Retreat Scholarship [10292]
S.C. Johnson, A Family Company Scholarship Fund [3402]
SCA/IARS Starter Grant [10298]
Scandinavian Society of Cincinnati (SSOC) **[9929]**
SC&R Foundation Grant Program [10717]
SC&R Foundation Scholarship [10718]
SCBWI Work-in-Progress Awards (WIP) [10303]
SCC Full-Time Continuing Student Scholarship [10062]
SCC Part-Time Continuing Student Scholarship [10063]

SCCLA Fellowships [10647]
SCCLA Scholarships [10648]
SCDAA Post-Doctoral Research Fellowships [10074]
Wanda J. Schafer Graduate Scholarship [12177]
Schallek Award [7231]
Schallek Fellowship [7232]
Schatz Energy Fellowships for Graduate Studies [5640]
Abe Schechter Graduate Scholarships [9467]
Schedulers and Dispatchers Monetary Scholarship [7740]
Leopold Schepp Foundation **[9931]**
Schlegel-UW RIA Scholarship [2895]
Harold W. Schloss Memorial Scholarship Fund [3184]
Esther Schlundt Memorial Scholarship Fund [5754]
Schmeelk Canada Foundation **[9933]**
Julie Schmid Research Scholarship [2255]
Schmidt Family Scholarship [12367]
Schmidt Kramer Annual Scholarship For Academic Excellence [9936]
Schmidt Kramer Injury Lawyers **[9935]**
Bernadotte E. Schmitt Grant [963]
Schneider/Bingle PLTW Scholarship [10412]
Alan Schneider Director Award [11010]
Schneider Electric Student Merit Awards [4355]
Prof. George Schneider Scholarship [10413]
B.E. Schnurr Memorial Fund Research Grants [3097]
Stanley M. Schoenfeld Memorial Scholarship [8321]
Brown Schoenheit Memorial Scholarship [11492]
Lillian P. Schoephoerster Scholarships [9129]
Dale M. Schoettler Scholarship for Visually Impaired Students [9874]
Scholarship America **[9937]**
Scholarship Award of the Bell Aliant Pioneer Volunteers [3050]
Scholarship Contest from Dealroom [3981]
Scholarship for Disabled Veterans [6702]
Scholarship Foundation of the Pacific **[9946]**
The Scholarship Foundation of St. Louis **[9948]**
Scholarship Foundation of Santa Barbara (SFSB) **[9950]**
Scholarship Foundation of Santa Barbara General Scholarship Program [9951]
Art Competition Scholarship Program [9952]
The Scholarship Foundation of Wakefield **[9954]**
The Scholarship Foundation of Wakefield Scholarships [9955]
Scholarship for Indigenous Students [8148]
Scholarship from Law Office of Yuriy Moshes, P.C. [6699]
Scholarship-Leadership Awards [6499]
Scholarship in Medical Education Award [10339]
The Scholarship of the Morris Radio Club of New Jersey [1960]
Scholarship Program By My Weather Analyser [7525]
Scholarship for Students of Colour [8149]
Scholarships for a Cause **[9956]**
Scholarships for a Higher Education in Law [2683]
Scholarships for the Next Generation of Scientists [3144]
School Nutrition Association (SNA) **[9958]**
School Nutrition Association of Kansas (SNA-KS) **[9964]**
School Nutrition Association of Kansas Education Scholarship [9965]
Schools first Federal Credit Union Scholarship [9602]
Schrank Family Scholarship [11631]
Alice Southworth Schulman, Class of 1954, Simmons Scholarships for Unitarian Universalist Women [11255]
David and Jinny Schultz Family Scholarship [5104]
James F. Schumar Scholarship [1169]
Jeptha Wade Schureman Scholarship Program [3724]
Schurgin Family Foundation Scholarship [5982]
AIST William E. Schwabe Memorial Scholarship [2225]
Schwan's Food Service Scholarship [9961]
Frances M. Schwartz Fellowship [1171], [10026]
Musia & Leon Schwartz Scholarship [6299]
Fritz Schwartz Serials Education Scholarship [7560]

Sponsor and Scholarship Index

Society for Ethnomusicology (SEM) **[10325]**

Society of Exploration Geophysicists (SEG) **[10327]**

Society of Exploration Geophysicists Scholarships [10328]

Society of Family Planning (SFP) **[10329]**

Society For Industrial and Organizational Psychology (SIOP) **[10333]**

Society of General Internal Medicine (SGIM) **[10337]**

Society of Georgia Archivists (SGA) **[10340]**

Society of Graphic Designers of Canada Adobe Scholarships [10255]

Society of Graphic Designers of Canada Applied Arts Scholarships [10256]

Society of Graphic Designers of Canada Veer Scholarships [10257]

Society of Health and Physical Educators (SHAPE) **[10345]**

Society of Hispanic Professional Engineers (SHPE) **[10350]**

Society for Historians of American Foreign Relations (SHAFR) **[10353]**

Society for the History of Technology (SHOT) **[10362]**

Society for Human Resource Management (SHRM) **[10366]**

Society for Imaging Science and Technology **[10370]**

The Society for Integrative and Comparative Biology (SICB) **[10372]**

Society for Judgment and Decision Making (SJDM) **[10376]**

Society for Linguistic Anthropology (SLA) **[10379]**

Society for Linguistic Anthropology Annual Student Essay Prize [10380]

Society of Louisiana Certified Public Accountants (LCPA) **[10381]**

Society of Louisiana Certified Public Accountants Scholarships [10382]

Society of Manufacturing Engineers Education Foundation (SME) **[10383]**

The Society of Marine Port Engineers of New York (SMPE) **[10420]**

Society for Maternal-Fetal Medicine (SMFM) **[10422]**

Society for Military History (SMH) **[10424]**

Society for Mining, Metallurgy, and Exploration (SME) **[10426]**

Society of Naval Architects and Marine Engineers (SNAME) **[10432]**

Society of Nuclear Medicine and Molecular Imaging (SNMMI) **[10436]**

Society for Obstetric Anesthesia and Perinatology (SOAP) **[10447]**

Society of Otorhinolaryngology and Head-Neck Nurses (SOHN) **[10449]**

Society of Outdoor Recreation Professionals (SORP) **[10453]**

Society for Pediatric Dermatology (SPD) **[10455]**

Society of Pediatric Nurses (SPN) **[10458]**

Society of Pediatric Nurses Academic Educational Scholarship [10459]

Society for Pediatric Pathology (SPP) **[10460]**

Society for Pediatric Radiology (SPR) **[10464]**

Society for Pediatric Radiology Research Fellows [10466]

Society for Pediatric Radiology Seed Grants [10467]

The Society for Pediatric Urology (SPU) **[10468]**

SPU Research Grant [10470]

Society of Petroleum Engineers - Evangeline Section (SPE) **[10471]**

Society for Photographic Education (SPE) **[10474]**

Society of Physics Students (SPS) **[10476]**

Society of Plastics Engineers (SPE) **[10482]**

Society for the Preservation of Old Mills (SPOOM) **[10499]**

Society of Professional Journalists (SPJ) **[10501]**

Society for Psychological Anthropology (SPA) **[10504]**

Society for the Psychological Study of Social Issues (SPSSI) **[10507]**

Society for Public Health Education (SOPHE) **[10512]**

Society of Punjabi Engineers and Technologists of British Columbia (SPEATBC) **[10517]**

Society for Range Management (SRM) **[10519]**

Society of Satellite Professionals International (SSPI) **[10521]**

Society for a Science of Clinical Psychology (SSCP) **[10523]**

Society for the Scientific Study of Religion (SSSR) **[10525]**

Society for the Scientific Study of Sexuality (SSSS) **[10527]**

Society for the Scientific Study of Sexuality Student Research Grant [10528]

Society for the Study of Reproduction (SSR) **[10529]**

Society for the Study of Social Problems (SSSP) **[10535]**

Society for Technical Communication Lone Star Community (STC LSC) **[10538]**

Society for Technical Communication Puget Sound Chapter (STC-PSC) **[10540]**

Society of Thoracic Surgeons (STS) **[10542]**

Society of Toxicology (SOT) **[10544]**

Society for Underwater Technology Houston **[10546]**

Society of University Surgeons (SUS) **[10549]**

Society of Vacuum Coaters Foundation (SVCF) **[10552]**

Society of Vacuum Coaters Foundation Scholarship [10553]

Society for Vascular Surgery (SVS) **[10554]**

Society of Vertebrate Paleontology (SVP) **[10558]**

Society of Wetland Scientists (SWS) **[10561]**

Society of Women Engineers (SWE) **[10563]**

Sociologists for Women in Society (SWS) **[10565]**

Sodowsky Law Firm **[10569]**

Sodowsky Law Firm Scholarship [10570]

Softer H2O **[10571]**

Softer H2O Scholarship Program [10572]

SOHN Allied Health to BSN Degree Scholarship [10450]

Louis B. Sohn Fellowships in Human Rights and Environment [3219]

SOHN Graduate Degree Scholarship [10451]

SOHN RN to BSN Degree Scholarship [10452]

SOKOL U.S.A. **[10573]**

Dale and Betty George Sola Scholarships [4219]

Solano Law Firm **[10575]**

The Solano Law Firm Scholarship Contest [10576]

Soldotna Chamber of Commerce (SCC) **[10577]**

Solid Waste Association of North America (SWANA) **[10579]**

Carrie Fox Solin Blow Molding Division Memorial Scholarships [10494]

Solvable.com **[10583]**

Solvable.com Debt-Free Scholarship [10584]

SOM Foundation Architecture, Design and Urban Design Prize [10159]

SOM Foundation Structural Engineering Travel Fellowships [10160]

SOM Foundation Travel Fellowships in Architecture, Design and Urban Design [10161]

David C. Sommerville Memorial Scholarship [9852]

Sonepar Canada Scholarship Awards [4357]

Sonia Morgan Scholarship [8292]

Sonja S. Maguire Outstanding Scholastic Achievement Awards [10897]

Dr. Kiyoshi Sonoda Memorial Scholarship [6253]

Sonoma County Mycological Association (SOMA) **[10585]**

Sons of Confederate Veterans (SCV) **[10587]**

Sons of Norway Foundation (SOFN) **[10589]**

Sons of Scotland Benevolent Association (SSBA) **[10592]**

Sons of Scotland Past Grand Chiefs Scholarship [10593]

Sons of Union Veterans of the Civil War (SUVCW) **[10594]**

Sony Pictures Scholarship [2249]

SOPHE/ATSDR Student Fellowships in Environmental Health or Emergency Preparedness [10513]

SOPHE/CDC Student Fellowship in Unintentional Injury Prevention [10514]

SOPHE/CDC Student Fellowships in Child, Adolescent and School Health [10515]

Soroptimist International of Chambersburg Fund [4783]

Soroptimist International of Redlands Scholarship [9604]

Paul and Daisy Soros Fellowships for New Americans (PDSFA) **[10596]**

Paul & Daisy Soros Fellowships [10597]

Soros Justice Advocacy Fellowships - Track I [8666]

Soros Justice Advocacy Fellowships - Track II [8667]

Soros Justice Media Fellowships - Track I [8668]

Soros Justice Media Fellowships - Track II [8669]

SORP Student Conference Scholarship [10454]

Eastman Kodak Dr. Theophilus Sorrell Fellowships [8032]

John Soto Scholarships [3756]

South Asian Bar Association of Northern California (SABA-NC) **[10598]**

South Asian Bar Association of San Diego **[10601]**

South Asian Journalists Association (SAJA) **[10603]**

South Carolina Association for Financial Professionals (SCAFP) **[10605]**

South Carolina Association for Financial Professionals Certified Treasury Professional Scholarships [10606]

South Carolina Association for Financial Professionals College Education Scholarships [10607]

South Carolina Law Enforcement Officers Association (SCLEOA) **[10608]**

South Carolina Public Health Association (SCPHA) **[10610]**

South Carolina Public Health Association Scholarships [10612]

South Carolina Restaurant and Lodging Association (SCRLA) **[10613]**

South Carolina Scholastic Press Association (SCSPA) **[10616]**

South Carolina Tourism and Hospitality Educational Foundation Scholarships [10614]

South Carolina Undergraduate Scholarships [10615]

South Central Modern Language Association Fellowships [8383]

South Central Power Co. **[10620]**

South Coast High School Senior Honors Scholarship Program [9953]

South Dakota Division Scholarships [7375]

South Dakota Nurses Association (SDNA) **[10622]**

South Dakota Retailers Association (SDRA) **[10624]**

South Jersey Golf Association (SJGA) **[10626]**

South Jersey Golf Association Scholarships [10627]

South Kentucky RECC High School Senior Scholarship Program [10630]

South Kentucky Rural Electric Cooperative Corp. (SKRECC) **[10628]**

South Texas Unit Scholarship [5490]

Southeast Alabama Dietetic Association Scholarships [221]

Southeastern Library Association (SELA) **[10632]**

Southeastern Theatre Conference Inc. (SETC) **[10634]**

Southeastern Theatre Conference Secondary School Scholarship [10640]

Southern Appalachian Botanical Society (SABS) **[10642]**

Southern Arizona Environmental Management Society, Inc (SAEMS) **[10644]**

Southern California Chinese Lawyers Association (SCCLA) **[10646]**

Southern California Lambda Medical Association (SCLMA) **[10649]**

Southern California Lambda Medical Student Scholarships [10650]

The Southern California Research Center for ALPD & Cirrhosis **[10651]**

Southern Conference (SOCON) **[10653]**

Southern Nursing Research Society (SNRS) **[10657]**

Southern Regional Education Board (SREB) **[10662]**

Southern Scholarship Foundation (SSF) **[10665]**

Southern Scholarship Foundation Scholarships [10666]

Southern Section A&WMA Scholarships [10668]

Southern Section Air and Waste Management Association (SS-A&WMA) **[10667]**

Southwest Florida Community Foundation **[10669]**

Southwest Florida Community Foundation College Assistance Scholarships [10703]
Southwest Florida Deputy Sheriffs Association Fund [10704]
Southwest Movers Association (SMA) **[10706]**
The Southwest Native-American Foundation (SWNAF) **[10708]**
Southwest Native-American Foundation Scholarships [10709]
SouthWest Sun Solar $500 Scholarship [10711]
SouthWest Sun Solar Inc. **[10710]**
Southwestern Rugs Depot **[10712]**
Sovereign Nations Scholarships [984]
SPA/Lemelson Fellowship Program [10506]
Kathy Spadoni Memorial Scholarships [9313]
Amy E. Spain Memorial Scholarships [11614]
Betty Spalton Scholarships [2454]
Spangenberg Shibley & Liber LLP **[10714]**
Spangenberg Shibley & Liber Video PSA Scholarship Awards [10715]
Sparking the Future in Healthcare Scholarship [26]
Nathan Sparks Memorial Scholarship [3664]
SPE Foundation General Scholarships [10495]
SPE Student Awards for Innovations in Imaging [10475]
SPE Vinyl Plastics Division Educational Grants [10496]
SPEATBC Entrance Scholarship [10518]
Special Events Internship- New York [4987]
Special Events Internships - Los Angeles [4988]
Specialized Carriers and Rigging Association (SC&RA) **[10716]**
Specialty Equipment Market Association (SEMA) **[10719]**
Specialty Equipment Market Association Scholarships [10722]
Specialty Nursing Scholarships [4792]
Beatrice Drinnan Spence Scholarship [4268]
The Kennett Y. Spencer Memorial Scholarship [11524]
Spice Box Grants [848]
SPIE **[10723]**
SPIE Student Author Travel Grants [10729]
Phillip A. Spiegel IASP Congress Trainee Scholarship [5945]
The Lawrence Alan Spiegel Remembrance Scholarship [5546]
Spinal Cord Injury BC (SCIBC) **[10730]**
Spirit of Anne Frank Scholarship Award [4813]
The Spirit Square Center for Arts and Education Scholarship Fund [4754]
Spokeo Connections Scholarships [10733]
Spokeo Inc. **[10732]**
SPOOM Research Grants [10500]
Sports Internships - Los Angeles [4989]
Sports Turf Managers Association (STMA) **[10734]**
Sporty's/Cincinnati Avionics Scholarships [192]
Spouse Tuition Aid Loan Program (STAP) [8181]
SPP Young Investigator Research Grant [10462]
Dr. William E. & Norma Sprague Scholarship [5183]
SprayWorks Equipment Group **[10738]**
Spring Forward Scholarship [39]
Springer - Jim Springer Memorial Scholarship [3489]
Springfield Family Scholarship [11615]
SPROWT Scholarship for Women [5201]
SPS Future Teacher Scholarships [10480]
SPS Leadership Scholarships [10481]
SPSmedical CS Scholarships [5928]
SPSSI Grants-In-Aid Program [10511]
The Square Up Scholarship Program [6616]
Blanche Squires Memorial Senior Brass Scholarship [9917]
SRC Master's Scholarships Program [10001]
SREB-State Doctoral Scholars Program - Dissertation Award [10663]
SREB-State Doctoral Scholars Program - Doctoral Award [10664]
SRF Post-doctoral Fellowships [9982]
SSCP Dissertation Grant Award [10524]
SSF Research Grants [10154]
SSF Student Fellowships [10155]
SSHRC Doctoral Fellowship Program [3797]
SSHRC Postdoctoral Fellowships [3798]
SSOC Scholarship [9930]
The SSPI Mid-Atlantic Chapter Scholarship [10522]

SSSP Racial/Ethnic Minority Graduate Fellowship [10537]
The Charles B. Staat Memorial Scholarship [10741]
The Charles B. Staats Memorial Foundation Inc. **[10740]**
Stacey Scholarship Fund [7822]
Stained Glass Association of America (SGAA) **[10742]**
Stand Watie Scholarship [10588]
Standard and Poor's Award for Economic and Business Reporting - S&P Scholarships [8791]
The Standard Recognition of Excellence Awards [4358]
Alexander Standish Memorial Scholarship [3749]
Stanford Advanced Materials **[10746]**
Stanford Advanced Materials $1,000 College Scholarship [10747]
Lasek Stanisław and Aniela Scholarship [9679]
A.R.O.Y. Stanitz Scholarships [1370]
Stanley Moore FUI Foundation Regional Scholarships [8464]
Stanley Moore National Scholarships [8465]
Stantec Scholarship [1644]
Thomas J. Stanton, Jr. Scholarships [10029]
Star-Ledger Scholarships for the Performing Arts [8280]
Stark Community Foundation (SCF) **[10748]**
Stark County Bar Association Scholarship Fund [10793]
Stark County Dairy Promoters Scholarship Fund [10794]
Stasiuk Master's Research Fellowship [3032]
State of Idaho Board of Education **[10804]**
State of New Jersey Department of Health - New Jersey Commission on Brain Injury Research (NJCBIR) **[10806]**
State of Wisconsin Higher Educational Aids Board (HEAB) **[10811]**
Taylor Statten Memorial Fellowships [11698]
Staunton Military Academy Alumni Foundation (SMA) **[10815]**
Minnie Patton Stayman Scholarships [8968]
STC Canada West Coast (STC) **[10817]**
STC-Lone Star Chapter Traditional Education Scholarships [10539]
STC-PSC Scholarships [10541]
STC Scholarships [6884]
The Stanley H. Stearman Awards [8080]
The Robert P. Stearns/SCS Engineers Scholarship Award [10582]
Sheri Stears Education Scholarship [11494]
Tom Steel Post-Graduate Fellowships [9322]
Steele Family Memorial Scholarship [12373]
Cecilia Steinfeldt Fellowships for Research in the Arts and Material Culture [11000]
Stella B. Johnson Scholarship [12092]
Stelpro Scholarship 360: Energizing Potential [4359]
John & Doris Stenbraten Scholarship [12374]
Stephen Gates Memorial Scholarship [11211]
Stephen J. Brady Stop Hunger Scholarships [636]
Stephen K. Hall ACWA Water Law and Policy Scholarship [2078]
Stephen Lankester Scholarship [5184]
Stephen Schwartz Musical Theatre Scholarship [5624]
Stephen T. Marchello Scholarship [7030]
H. H. Stephenson, Jr. Oxford Cup Scholarship [2557]
Hugh E. Stephenson, Jr. Oxford Cup Scholarship [2558]
Mike Stephenson Legal Scholarships [7199]
Elizabeth Coulter Stephenson Scholarships [4044]
Sterbenz-Ryan Scholarship [9778]
H.H. Stern Award [2100]
Charles Sternberg Scholarship [2048]
Raymond H. Stetson Scholarship in Phonetics and Speech Science [63]
Steuben County Community Foundation (SCCF) **[10819]**
Steve Dearduff Scholarship Fund [3587]
Steve Hymans Extended Stay Scholarship Program [976]
Steve Kaplan TV & Film Studies Award [1412]
Steve Mason Sports Media Scholarship [7991]
Steve Petix Journalism Scholarship [9853]
Steven A. Stahl Research Grant [6039]

Steven L. Coffey Memorial Scholarship [4259]
Steven Titus & Associates PC **[10836]**
Christine K. Stevens Development Scholarship [1139]
Stevens Doctoral Award [5986]
Benjamin F. Stevens Fellowships [7153]
The Zachary Taylor Stevens Scholarship [1962]
H.L. Stevenson Fellowship [8792]
Richie Stevenson Scholarship Fund [3645]
Stewardson Keefe LeBrun Travel Grant [139]
Paul A. Stewart Grant [12056]
Allegheny Branch of Mid-America Chapter - Nancy Stewart Professional Development Scholarships [1588]
Mary Stewart and William T. Covington, Jr. Scholarship Fund [4755]
Stickler Involved People (SIP) **[10838]**
Dell Chenoweth Stifel Scholarship [6476]
Edward W. Stimpson Aviation Excellence Award Scholarship [4886]
Judith Gold Stitzel Endowment for Excellence in Women's Studies Teaching and Learning [11977]
The Richard Stockton College of New Jersey Foundation Alumni Association Graduate Awards [10848]
Stockton University **[10840]**
The David Stockwood Memorial Prize [97]
Louis Stokes Health Scholars Program [3742]
Louis Stokes Urban Health Policy Fellows Program [3743]
Ralph W. Stone Graduate Fellowship in Cave and Karst Studies [8128]
Ralph W. Stone Graduate Fellowships [8129]
Glenna Stone Memorial Scholarship [2999]
Stonewall Community Foundation **[10849]**
Stop-Painting.com Scholarships [5791]
William V. Storch Student Award [1632]
Stout Law Firm Family Matters Scholarship [10854]
The Stout Law Firm PLLC **[10853]**
Martin L. Stout Scholarships [2162]
Herb Stovel Scholarship - National Trust Conference Bursaries [8142]
Herb Stovel Scholarship - Project Research Bursaries [8143]
Strada Education Network **[10855]**
Robert "Bob" Strahan Memorial Scholarship [5210]
StraightForward Media **[10857]**
George A. Strait Minority Scholarship [600]
Jay A. Strassberg Memorial Scholarship [2855]
The Donald A. Strauss Scholarship [11532]
The Carole J. Streeter, KB9JBR, Scholarship [1963]
Stanley W. Strew Scholarship [2785]
STRI Short-Term Fellowships [10226]
Striving for Greatness Accounting & Finance Scholarship [9214]
The Norman E. Strohmeier, W2VRS, Memorial Scholarship [1964]
Robby Strong Cancer Survivor Scholarships [7472]
Stuart Cameron and Margaret McLeod Memorial Scholarship (SCMS) [5850]
Mark and Karla Stuart Family Scholarship [9854]
Stuart L. Bernath Dissertation Research Grant [10360]
Stuart L. Noderer Memorial Scholarship [9855]
Stuart Silverman Scholarship [9027]
Stuart/SIM Northern Education Scholarship [12375]
Student travel awards [30]
Student Entrepreneur Scholarship [5355]
Student Essay Contest [1683]
Student Fellowship [7530]
Student Illustrator Scholarship [10304]
Student Investigator Research Grant - General Audiology/Hearing Science [433]
Student Investigator Research Grant - Hearing Aids, Clinical Protocols and Patient Outcomes [434]
Student Investigator Research Grant - Vestibular [435]
Student Loan Relief Scholarship [7445]
Student Osteopathic Medical Association (SOMA) **[10864]**
Student Research Foundation Personal Achievement Scholarship [4309]
Student Researcher Award, From the Behavioral Gerontology SIG [2064]
Student Summer Research Fellowship [436]

Teacher.org's Inspire Our Future Scholarship [10925]
Teachers Insurance and Annuity Association of America (TIAA) **[10926]**
TeamMates Mentoring Program Scholarship [5125]
Tear Film and Ocular Surface Society (TFOS) **[10928]**
Tech Mastery Scholarships [9635]
TechChecks **[10930]**
TechChecks Business Leadership Scholarships [10931]
Technical, vocational or associate's degree programs [10621]
Technical Scholarship [8592]
Technical Women's Organization Education Scholarship [10933]
Technical Women's Organization (TWO) **[10932]**
Technology First **[10934]**
Technology First / ROBERT V. MCKENNA SCHOLARSHIP [10935]
Technology Student Association (TSA) **[10936]**
Technology - Students Scholarship Program [4246]
Ted Ousley Scholarship Endowment Fund [4759]
Teddy Wilburn Scholarship Fund [3646]
Telacu **[10939]**
Telecommunications Association of Michigan (TAM) **[10943]**
Telecommunications Association of Michigan - Category II - IV Scholarship [10944]
Maria Salit-Gitelson Tell Memorial Fellowship [12240]
Telluride Association (TA) **[10945]**
Telluride Association Summer Program Scholarships [10946]
Telugu Association of North America (TANA) **[10947]**
Temecula Valley Wine Society (TVWS) **[10955]**
Dora and Mayer Tendler Endowed Fellowship [12241]
Tenge Law Firm LLC **[10957]**
Alan and Grace Tenn Scholarship Fund [5414]
Tennessee Education Association (TEA) **[10959]**
Tennessee Learner's Scholarship [3888]
Tennessee Trucking Foundation Scholarship Fund [3647]
Mary L. Tenopyr Graduate Student Scholarship [10336]
Terra Foundation for American Art **[10962]**
The Terra Foundation Fellowships in American Art [10220]
Terra Foundation Fellowships at the Smithsonian American Art Museum [10963]
Terra Foundation Postdoctoral Teaching Fellowships at the Institut National d'Histoire de l'Art, Paris [10964]
Terra Foundation Research Travel Grants [10965]
Terra Summer Residency Fellowships [10966]
Terry Linda Potter Scholarship [5111]
TESOL International Association **[10967]**
The TESOL/TEFL Travel Grant [10970]
Marc Tetalman, MD, Memorial Award [10444]
TEVA Canada Survivor Scholarship [3292]
Texas Association of Community Schools (TACS) **[10971]**
Texas Association of Developing Colleges (TADC) **[10974]**
Texas Computer Education Association (TCEA) **[10976]**
Texas Counseling Association (TCA) **[10980]**
Texas Health Information Management Association (TXHIMA) **[10982]**
Texas Music Educators Association (TMEA) **[10986]**
Texas Music Educators Association Past-Presidents Memorial Scholarships [10988]
Texas Mutual Insurance Co. **[10989]**
Texas Mutual Scholarship Program [10990]
Texas Scholarship of Academic Excellence [1708]
Texas Society of Professional Engineers (TSPE) **[10991]**
Texas Space Grant Consortium **[10993]**
Texas State Historical Association (TSHA) **[10995]**
Texas State Technical College Scholarships [194]
Texas Telephone Association (TTA) **[11001]**
Texas Telephone Association Foundation Scholarships [11002]

Textile Care Allied Trades Association (TCATA) **[11003]**
Text=Wrecks Scholarship [4968]
TFC Edward A. Plank, Jr. Memorial Scholarship [3579]
TFI Latin America Media Arts Fund [11110]
TFOS Fellowship Awards [10929]
Jim and Pat Thacker Sports Communication Internship [11212]
ThanksUSA **[11005]**
ThanksUSA Scholarship [11006]
Theatre Communications Group (TCG) **[11007]**
Theatre Guild Scholarship [11012]
Theatre Guild of Simsbury (TGS) **[11011]**
Theatre for Young Audiences USA (TYA/USA) **[11013]**
Thelma Cardwell Scholarship [3082]
THEO WILSON SCHOLARSHIP [8794]
Theodore C. Sorensen Research Fellowship [6533]
Theodore E.D. Braun Research Travel Fellowship [1439]
Dr. Peter A. Theodos Memorial Graduate Scholarship [5468]
Thermo Fisher Scientific Antibody Scholarship [11016]
Thermo Fisher Scientific Inc. **[11015]**
Thermo Scientific Educational Scholarships [8115]
Thermoforming Division Scholarship [10497]
Thermoplastic Elastomers Special Interest Group Scholarship [10498]
Thesaurus Linguae Latinae Fellowship (TTL) [10312]
THFC Medical Research Grants [5454]
Werner B. Thiele Memorial Scholarship [5211]
Elizabeth R. Thomas Alumni Nursing Scholarship [10065]
Thomas Arkle Clark Scholar-Leader of the Year [9092]
Thomas B. Grave and Elizabeth F. Grave Scholarship [7059]
Barbara Thomas Bursary [6221]
Thomas D. Coffield Scholarship [5185]
Thomas and Don Hatton Memorial Senior Grade B Male Voice Scholarship [9918]
Thomas E. Shown, M.D. Memorial Scholarship [12094]
Thomas F. Black Jr. Memorial Scholarship [9686]
Thomas and Glenna Trimble Endowed Scholarship [9028]
Thomas J. Emery Memorial Fund Scholarship [3404]
Thomas J. Watson Fellowship [11939]
Thomas More Scholarship [5038]
Thomas and Ruth River International Scholarship [12201]
Charles C. Thomas Scholarship [1754]
Cheryl M. Thomas Scholarship [27]
C.R. Thomas Scholarship [8882]
Edith & Victor Thomas Scholarship [12379]
The Rev. Chuck and Nancy Thomas Scholarship [11256]
Thomas W. Gallagher Scholarship Fund [10797]
Thome Foundation Awards Program in Age-Related Macular Degeneration Research [5444]
Thome Foundation Awards Program in Alzheimer's Disease Drug Discovery Research [5445]
J. Walter Thompson Co. **[11017]**
The Honorable Raymond Thompson Endowed Scholarship [9029]
Karen Thompson Memorial Scholarship [8539]
Katrina Thompson Scholarship [9856]
Matilda B. Thompson Scholarship [5555]
Thompson Scholarship for Women in Safety [1573]
Barbara and Howard Thompson Scholarships [6209]
Ken Thomson Scholarship [2109]
Thornberg/Havens Scholarship [4045]
Thomas P. Thornton Scholarship [5731]
Arthur A. Thovmasian, Jr. Memorial Grant [1904]
Thunder Bay Community Foundation (TBCF) **[11019]**
The Thurgood Marshall College Fund [10856]
Thurgood Marshall College Fund (TMCF) **[11025]**
Thurgood Marshall Fellowships Program [8301]
Dorothy J. Thurston Graduate Scholarship [5186]
Tibor T. Polgar Fellowship [5613]
Tidwell Law Firm **[11027]**

Tien Bui Memorial Scholarship [12095]
Tiftickjian Law Firm, P.C. **[11029]**
Tiftickjian Law Firm, P.C. Juvenile Justice Law School Scholarships [11030]
Tikvah Center for Law and Jewish Civilization **[11031]**
The Tikvah Fellowship [11034]
The Tikvah Fund **[11033]**
Pat Tillman Foundation **[11035]**
Tillman Scholars Program [11036]
The Jack Tillson Scholarship Fund [6164]
Timeshares Only **[11037]**
Tingen & Williams PLLC **[11039]**
The Tingen & Williams Undergraduate Scholarship [11040]
Titan Web Agency **[11041]**
Titan Web Agency Bi-Annual Scholarship Program [11042]
T.L. Conlan Scholarship Fund [3405]
Tobi **[11043]**
Tobi's Scholarship [11044]
Mario J. Tocco Hydrocephalus Foundation Scholarships [5667]
Tocris **[11045]**
Tocris Scholarship Program [11046]
Michael W. Toennis Scholarship [2559]
Robert Toigo Foundation **[11047]**
Daniel B. Toll Memorial Award [2856]
Tom Bost Scholarship [11213]
Tom Cory Scholarships [1787]
Tom Gifford Scholarship [5112]
Tom Hanson Photojournalism Award [6622]
Tom Taylor Memorial Scholarship to Spartan College of Aeronautics & Technology [195]
William Tomar Memorial Award [2857]
The Adelle and Erwin Tomash Fellowship in the History of Information Technology [11641]
John L. Tomasovic, Sr. Scholarship [906]
Tommie J. Hamner Scholarship [9131]
Tommy Douglas Scholarship [8150]
Sally Kress Tompkins Fellowship [10278]
TonaLaw **[11049]**
TonaLaw Veteran's Scholarship [11050]
Took Trust Point Scholarship [9232]
The Toolsy **[11051]**
The Toolsy Scholarship: The Importance of Craftship [11052]
Top Ten List Scholarship [11235]
Top10bestbudget Annual Scholarship Award [10013]
Toptal, L.L.C. **[11053]**
Toptal Scholarships for Women [11054]
TopTechGiant **[11055]**
TopTechGiant $1,000 Scholarship [11056]
Torchia Scholarship in Public Relations [3104]
The Toro Company **[11057]**
Evald Torokvei Foundation Scholarships [11699]
Toronto and Region Conservation Authority (TRCA) **[11059]**
Toronto Rehab Scholarships in Rehabilitation-Related Research [11064]
Toronto Rehabilitation Institute **[11061]**
Toronto Rehabilitation Institute Graduate Student Scholarships - Ontario Student Opportunities Trust Fund (OSOTF) [11065]
Ferdinand Torres Scholarships [920]
Tourette Association of America **[11066]**
Tourette Association of America Research Grant Awards [11067]
Dr. Harry Jeffrey Tourigian Memorial Grant [1905]
Touro Synagogue Foundation (TSF) **[11068]**
Tower Cancer Research Foundation (TCRF) **[11070]**
The Town and County Club Scholarship [5346]
Charles A. Townsend Scholarship [8883]
Toyota Point Scholarship [9233]
Toyota Tapestry Grants for Science Teachers [8070]
Toyota/TELACU Scholarships [10942]
The Joyce Tracy Fellowship [499]
TRALA Industry Scholarship Awards [11119]
Vera Tran Memorial Scholarships [11825]
Reuben Trane Scholarships [1476]
Trans Issues Internships - New York [4990]
Transatlantic Fellows Program [4947]
TranscriptionServices.com **[11072]**
The TranscriptionServices.com Scholarship [11073]
Translational Research Professorship [3784]

Sponsor and Scholarship Index

VSCPA Graduate and PhD Accounting Scholarship [11849]
W. Eldridge and Emily Lowe Scholarship [10148]
W. Kaye Lamb Award for the Best Student works [2701]
W. Philip Braender and Nancy Coleman Braender Scholarship Fund [5347]
W. Stull Holt Dissertation Fellowship [10361]
W. Wesley Eckenfelder Graduate Research Award [2168]
Jane and Gregg Waddill Memorial Adelphe Scholarship [6477]
Joseph W. Wade Memorial Scholarship Endowment [8542]
Robert & Barbara Wade Scholarships [6834]
Percy W. Wadman, M.D. Scholarship [4815]
Wadsworth African Fellowships [11964]
Wadsworth International Fellowships [11965]
WAEPA Scholarship Program [12207]
Alan D. Waggoner Sonographer Student Scholarship Award [1423]
The Gary Wagner, K3OMI, Scholarship [1965]
Jack H. Wagner Scholarship [7350]
Wagner-Torizuka Fellowship [10445]
Dorreene & Herb Wahl Scholarship [12384]
Wakeford Gelini **[11865]**
Wakeford Gelini Driver Safety Scholarship [11866]
Wal-Mart Foundation, Inc. **[11867]**
Laramie Walden Memorial Fund [4762]
Sue Walicki Nursing Scholarships [6210]
Helen Zick Walker Adelphe Scholarship [6478]
Myrtle & Earl Walker Scholarships [10417]
Wallace House - University of Michigan **[11869]**
Bruce A. Wallace Memorial Award [2858]
Wallace Vail Scholarship [8293]
Gordon C. Wallis Memorial Senior Piano Beethoven Scholarship [9919]
Walmart Associate Scholarship [11868]
Walta Wilkinson Carmichael Scholarship [10125]
Walter C. Winchester Scholarship [5192]
Walter "Doc" Hurley Scholarship Fund of Greater Hartfort [5348]
Walter & Elsie Carr Endowed Scholarship [6823]
Walter and Lucille Harper Transfer Scholarship [6516]
Walter and Marilyn Bartlett Scholarship Fund [3407]
Robert E. Walter Memorial Scholarship [6958]
Patty Walter Memorial Scholarships [3537]
Walter Samek III Memorial Scholarship [3598]
Lynn McNabb Walton Adelphe Scholarhship [6479]
Shih-Chun Wang Young Investigator Award [1240]
War Memorial Doctoral Scholarships [7760]
WarFighters Motorcycle Club, Captain John Odber Chapter **[11871]**
Louis Dreyfus Warner-Chappell City College Scholarship [1413]
Warner Norcross and Judd L.L.P. **[11873]**
Warner Norcross & Judd Minority Scholarships [11874]
Warren M. Anderson Scholarship [5766]
Warren and Rosalie Gummow Endowed Scholarship [9030]
Marjorie Rose Warren Scholarship [9863]
Colin Wasacase Scholarship [8661]
WASBO Safety, Security and Wellness Grant [12111]
WASBO Scholarship Program [11883]
Washburn University School of Law **[11875]**
Washburn University School of Law Business and Transactional Law Center Scholarships [11880]
Washburn University School of Law Child and Family Advocacy Fellowships [11881]
Washington Association of School Business Officials (WASBO) **[11882]**
Washington City/County Management Association (WCMA) **[11884]**
Washington City/County Management Association Scholarships [11885]
Washington College Grant (SNG) [11919]
Washington CPA Foundation Scholarship [11899]
The Washington Group (TWG) **[11886]**
Washington Hospital Employee Association Scholarship [11892]
Washington Hospital Healthcare System (WHHS) **[11890]**

Washington Indian Gaming Association (WIGA) **[11893]**
Washington Library Association (WLA) **[11895]**
Washington Society of Certified Public Accountants (WSCPA) **[11897]**
Washington Space Grant Consortium (WSGC) **[11900]**
Washington State Association for Justice (WSAJ) **[11903]**
Washington State Business Education Association (WSBEA) **[11908]**
Washington State Lake Protection Association (WALPA) **[11911]**
Washington State Nurses Association (WSNA) **[11913]**
Washington State Nurses Association Foundation Scholarships (WSNF) [11914]
Washington Student Achievement Council (WSAC) **[11915]**
Chancellor's Graduate Fellowship [11923]
Washington University Law School Olin Fellowships for Women [11924]
Washington University School of Law **[11920]**
Water Environment Federation (WEF) **[11926]**
Water and Sewer Distributors of America (WASDA) **[11928]**
Waterbury Bar Association **[11930]**
Waterbury Bar Association Scholarship [11933]
J. B. C. Watkins Award [2873]
Watson-Brown Foundation **[11935]**
Watson-Brown Scholarship [11936]
Dr. James Watson Fellowship Program [5034], [11058]
Thomas J. Watson Foundation (TJW) **[11937]**
Matthew Watson Scholarship [12385]
George Watt Prize [6865]
Wayne County Bank Scholarship [8543]
Wayne County College Fund [11952]
Wayne County Foundation, Inc. **[11940]**
Wayne G. Failor Scholarship Fund [8969]
Wayne-Meador-Elliott Scholarship [8884]
WBA Paralegal/Legal Assistant Scholarship [11934]
WDHOF Undergraduate Scholarships in Marine Conservation [12137]
Richard M. Weaver Fellowships [5886]
Monica M. Weaver Memorial Fund [4606]
Web Design Scholarship [2665], [6917]
W.E.B. Du Bois Program [7944]
Webb Family Grant [3200]
Webb – Faye and Rendell C Webb JR Scholarship [3491]
Websauce Studio **[11953]**
Websauce Web Design Scholarship [11954]
Matthew Webster Scholarship [12386]
Webster Society Scholarships [11925]
WEDA Scholarship Program [11979]
John V. Wehausen Graduate Scholarships for Advanced Study in Ship Hydrodynamics and Wave Theory [10435]
The Arthur and Lila Weinberg Fellowship for Independent Researchers [8385]
Bertold E. Weinberg Scholarship [793]
Joel A. Weinstein Memorial Scholarship [6308]
The Bee Winkler Weinstein Scholarship Fund [10852]
William E. Weisel Scholarship [10418]
Susan C. Weiss Clinical Advancement Scholarship [10446]
Weiss & Paarz Annual Rising Star Scholarship [11956]
Weiss & Paarz P.C. **[11955]**
Weissbuch Family Scholarship [9864]
Welch Scholars Grants [1200]
James R. Welch Scholarship [2050]
Rob and Bessie Welder Wildlife Foundation **[11957]**
Wells Fargo American Indian Scholarship Program [996]
Wells Fargo Career Scholarship [11506]
Wells Fargo Point Scholarship [9234]
Wells Fargo Scholarship Program for People with Disabilities [9944]
Wells Fargo Veterans Scholarship Program [9945]
Ida B. Wells Graduate Student Fellowship [3831]
Jean Hess Wells Memorial Adelphe Graduate Scholarship [6480]

Jean Hess Wells Memorial Adelphe Scholarship [6481]
Donald M. Wells Scholarships [5193]
Wellstone Fellowships for Social Justice [4484]
Peter R. Weitz Prize [4949]
Judy Kay Wendland-Young Scholarship [6279]
Francis X. Weninger Scholarships [12226]
Wenner-Gren Foundation (WGF) **[11959]**
Wenner-Gren Foundation Dissertation Fieldwork Grants [11966]
Wenner-Gren Foundation Post-PhD Research Grants [11967]
John R. and Joan F. Werren Scholarships Fund [10801]
Wes Burton Memorial Scholarship [12097]
WESCO International, Inc. **[11968]**
The WESCO Student Achievement Award [4361], [11969]
Wesley C. Cameron Scholarship [8177]
Wesley R. Habley Summer Institute Scholarships [7569]
West Michigan Nursery and Landscape Association Scholarship [5113]
West Virginia Coal Association (WVCA) **[11970]**
West Virginia Nurses Association District No. 3 Professional Nursing Scholarships [8885]
West Virginia PTA (WV PTA) **[11972]**
West Virginia PTA Scholarship [11973]
West Virginia Space Grant Consortium (WVSGC) **[11974]**
West Virginia University - Center for Women's and Gender Studies **[11976]**
Western Equipment Dealers Association (WEDA) **[11978]**
Western Golf Association (WGA) **[11980]**
Western Governors' Association (WGA) **[11982]**
Western Governors' Association "Celebrate the West" High School Art Competition [11983]
Western Michigan Society Of Health Systems Pharmacists (WMSHP) **[11984]**
Western Social Science Association (WSSA) **[11986]**
Western Society of Criminology (WSC) **[11988]**
Western Society of Weed Science (WSWS) **[11992]**
Western-Southern Foundation Scholarship [3408]
Western Thoracic Surgical Association (WTSA) **[11994]**
Western University - Endourology Fellowship [4385]
Western Washington University Alumni Association **[11996]**
Weston Family Awards in Northern Research [11999]
Weston Brain Institute International Fellowships in Neuroscience [12000]
Weston Brain Institute Rapid Response Program [12001]
W. Garfield Weston Foundation **[11998]**
William Weston Research Award [10457]
Mary Elizabeth Westpheling - Long Beach (Calif.) Alumnae Association Memorial Scholarhip [6482]
Wexner Foundation **[12002]**
Wexner Graduate Fellowship / Davidson Scholars Program [12003]
Weyburn Credit Union **[12004]**
Frederick K. Weyerhaeuser Forest History Fellowship [4682]
WFMC Ride for the Fallen Memorial Scholarship [11872]
Dr. William "Tim" Whalen Memorial Scholarships [8476]
Whan Memorial Scholarships [9174]
Haemer Wheatcraft Scholarship [4175]
Stan Wheeler Mentorship Awards [6728]
Jerry Wheeler Scholarships [10625]
Nellie Yeoh Whetten Award [2387]
Whidbey Island Giving Circle Scholarships [9317]
WHIMA Established Professional Development Scholarship [12119]
Whirly-Girls Helicopter Add-On Flight Training Scholarship [12013]
Whirly-Girls International Women Helicopter Pilots **[12008]**
Whirly-Girls Jean Tinsley Memorial HELI-EXPO Scholarship [12014]

The Whistleblower Lawyer-Louthian Law Legal Scholarship Award [6920]
Whitaker-Minard Memorial Scholarship [8886]
Law Office of David D. White Annual Traumatic Brain Injury Scholarships [6687]
White Collar Defense Diversity Scholarships [9286]
Bradford White Corporation Scholarships [9209]
Alma White - Delta Chapter, Delta Kappa Gamma Scholarship [5415]
The Brian J. White Endowed Law Scholarship [9031]
White Glove Moving **[12015]**
White Gloves Scholarship [12016]
White House Fellows [9271]
Mary Kean White Memorial Scholarship Fund [10802]
Bob Evans And Wayne White Scholarship [4708]
Portia White Scholarship [2602]
Paul D. White Scholarship Program [2409]
Whitehorse Business & Professional Women's Club Bursary [12387]
Whitehorse Copper Mines Scholarship [12388]
Whitehorse Glacier Bears Swim Club Scholarship [12389]
Whitehorse Shotokan Karate Club Scholarship [12390]
Whitfield Bryson & Mason LLP **[12017]**
Ann Cook Whitman Scholarships for Perry High School [4964]
Ann Collins Whitmore Memorial Scholarship (ACWMS) [3098]
Jane and Morgan Whitney Fellowships [7284]
Helen Hay Whitney Foundation (HHWF) **[12019]**
Why Decor Matters Scholarship [10713]
Why Get Your Blue On? Video Scholarships [11997]
Flo Whyard-Holland America Line-Westours Scholarship [12391]
The L. Phil and Alice J. Wicker Scholarship [1966]
Tom Wicker Award [11216]
Larry B. Wickham Memorial Scholarship for Graduate Studies [7487]
Wicomico High School Class of '55 Schloarship [3580]
WIEA Scholarships [12121]
Robert L. Wiegel Scholarship for Coastal Studies [9865]
Elmo Wierenga Alumni Scholarship [5194]
Elie Wiesel Foundation for Humanity **[12021]**
Elie Wiesel Prize in Ethics [12022]
Fred Wiesner Educational Excellence Scholarships [2301]
WIFLE Regular Scholarship Program [12139]
WIGA College Scholarships [11894]
Wigs.com **[12023]**
Hair Loss Scholarship [12024]
The Fred C. Wikoff Jr. Scholarship [4763]
The Wilbert L. and Zora F. Holmes Scholarship [4764]
Ernest Wilby Memorial Scholarship [5805]
Wild Felid Legacy Scholarship [12026]
Wild Felid Research and Management Association (WFA) **[12025]**
Wilder Dimension Scholarships for Advanced Study in Theatre Arts [4178]
Wilderness Medical Society (WMS) **[12027]**
The Wilderness Society **[12030]**
Wilkinson & Company L.L.P. **[12032]**
Wilkinson and Company LLP Scholarships [12033]
Willa Beach-Porter CTBA Music Scholarship Fund [3246]
Willamette Chapter Scholarship Awards [8713]
Willamette University **[12034]**
Willard & Spackman Scholarship Program [1182]
James B. Willett Educational Memorial Scholarship Award [11426]
William A. and Ann M. Brothers Scholarship [1673]
William A. Fischer Scholarship [2011]
William A. Friedlander Scholarship Fund [3409]
William B. Howell Memorial Scholarship [1674]
William B. Martin East Carolina University Scholarship [6395]
William and Beatrice Kavanaugh Memorial Scholarship [6211]
William "Buddy" Sentner Scholarship Award [629]
William C. Ray, CIH, CSP Arizona Scholarship [1575]

William and Clara Bryan Scholarship Fund [3648]
William E. Parrish Scholarship [9079]
William E. Wilson Scholarship [10641]
William F. Vilas Merit Scholarship [11752]
William G. and Mayme J. Green Fund [5349]
William Goldberg Scholarship [4883]
William H. Andrews/HAWS Scholarship [12098]
William H. Davis, Jr. Scholarship [3599]
William J. Rielly/MCURC Scholarship Fund [3410]
William J. Tangye Scholarship [5974]
William J. Yankee Memorial Scholarship [1263]
William L. Brown Fellowship [8754]
William L. Graddy Law School Scholarship Fund [10705]
William M. Fanning Maintenance Scholarship [7742]
William P. Elrod Memorial Scholarship [10938]
William P. Van Wagenen Fellowship [608]
William Pigott Memorial Scholarship [3694]
William R. Bowen Scholarship [3581]
William R. Durham Drama and Theater Scholarship [3695]
William Randolph Hearst Educational Endowment [7060]
William S. Richardson Commemorative Scholarship [8934]
William "Sully" Sullivan Scholarship [11864]
William T. Burbage Family Memorial Scholarship [3582]
William T. Hartzell Memorial Scholarship [9605]
William Verbon Black Scholarship [228]
The Williams Chorale **[12036]**
Williams Chorale Bacardi Fallon Scholarships [12037]
Sidney B. Williams, Jr. Scholarships [4698]
BM1 James Elliott Williams Memorial Scholarship Fund [8936]
Alice Hinchcliffe Williams, RDH, MS Merit Scholarship [11833]
Dr. Anne Williams Scholarship [12392]
John G. Williams Scholarship Foundation **[12038]**
The Leon And Margaret Williams Scholarship [9866]
Maxine Williams Scholarship [605]
Shirley Williams Scholarship [12393]
Williams – Dr. Dana Williams Scholarship [3492]
Lippincott Williams and Wilkins Scholarships (LWW Scholarship) [3440]
Mary Katherine "Kathy" Williamson Scholarship Fund [3665]
Willie T. Loud scholarship [7894]
Beverly Willis Architecture Foundation Travel Fellowship [10279]
Willis W. and Ethel M. Clark Foundation Investment in Community Fellowship [3432]
Wilma Motley Memorial California Merit Scholarship [862]
Wilma Sackett Dressel Scholarship [10126]
Gary S. Wilmer/RAMI Music Scholarship [3696]
The Harriet Glen Wilmore Scholarship [4765]
The Ronald P. Wilmot Scholarship [6280]
Wilshire Law Firm, PLC **[12040]**
Wilshire Law Firm Scholarship [12041]
Dr. Alice E. Wilson Awards [2976]
Glenn Wilson Broadcast Journalism Scholarship [8887]
Woodrow Wilson Dissertation Fellowship in Women's Studies [12051]
The Wilson Fellowship [11677]
Woodrow Wilson International Center for Scholars (WWICS) **[12042]**
Pete Wilson Journalism Scholarship [9478]
Saul T. Wilson, Jr. Internship [11301]
Bob Wilson Legacy Scholarships [2810]
Arthur N. Wilson, MD, Scholarships [1113]
Ted G. Wilson Memorial Scholarships [9338]
Woodrow Wilson National Fellowship Foundation (WW) **[12044]**
Wilson Ornithological Society (WOS) **[12053]**
Robert Wilson Scholarship [12394]
Michael Wilson Scholarships [151]
Wingate, Russotti, Shapiro & Halperin LLP **[12057]**
Winston Build Your Future Scholarship [9963]
David A. Winston Health Policy Scholarship [2307]
Winston-Salem Foundation **[12059]**
The Winston-Salem Foundation Scholarship [12099]
Winterthur Museum, Garden and Library **[12100]**
Winterthur Research Fellowships [12101]

Wire Reinforcement Institute (WRI) **[12102]**
Wirefly.com **[12106]**
Wirefly.com Scholarhip: Wireless Technology and Society [12107]
Albert E. Wischmeyer Scholarship [10419]
Wisconsin Association for Food Protection (WAFP) **[12108]**
Wisconsin Association of School Business Officials (WASBO) **[12110]**
Wisconsin Athletic Trainers' Association (WATA) **[12112]**
Wisconsin Broadcasters Association (WBA) **[12116]**
Wisconsin Broadcasters Association Foundation Student Scholarships [12117]
Wisconsin Health Information Management Association (WHIMA) **[12118]**
Wisconsin Indian Education Association (WIEA) **[12120]**
Wisconsin Laboratory Association (WLA) **[12122]**
Wisconsin Laboratory Association Graduate Student Scholarships [12123]
WLA Scholarships [12124]
Wisconsin Laboratory Association Undergraduate University Student Scholarships [12125]
Wisconsin Lawton Minority Retention Grants [11753]
Wisconsin Minority Teacher Loan [10812]
Wisconsin Nursing Student Loan [10813]
Wisconsin Teacher of the Visually Impaired Loan [10814]
The William B. Wisdom Grants in Aid of Research [12130]
W. L. Shattuck Scholarship [5681]
WLA Conference Attendance Grants [11896]
WLALA Scholarships [12144]
WMSHP Scholarship [11985]
WOCN Society Accredited Educational Scholarship [12216]
WOCN Society Advanced Educational Scholarship [12217]
Woksape Oyate: "Wisdom of the People" Distinguished Scholars Awards [986]
Paul R. Wolf Memorial Scholarships [2012]
Emil Wolf Outstanding Student Paper Competition [8680]
The Wolf Trap Accounting Internship Program [12127]
Wolf Trap Foundation for the Performing Arts **[12126]**
Wolf Trap's Grants for High School Performing Arts Teachers [12128]
Nona Hobbs Wolfe Memorial Scholarship [6483]
Thomas Wolfe Society (TWS) **[12129]**
The Thomas Wolfe Student Travel Grants in Honor of Richard S. Kennedy [12131]
Eleanor M. Wolfson Memorial Scholarship Fund [4607]
Wendy Y. Wolfson Memorial Scholarship Fund [4608]
Woman's Club of Nashville Scholarship Endowment Fund [3649]
Women in Cancer Research Scholar Awards [536]
Women in Coaching National Coaching Institute Scholarships [3448]
Women in Defense, a National Security Organization (WID) **[12132]**
Women Divers Hall of Fame (WDHOF) **[12134]**
Women in Federal Law Enforcement, Inc. (WIFLE) **[12138]**
Women In Defense HORIZONS Scholarship [12133]
Women In Need Scholarships [4306]
Women In Rural Electrification Scholarships (W.I.R.E.) [10631]
Women In Transition Scholarships [4307]
Women Lawyers' Association of Greater St. Louis (WLA) **[12140]**
Women Lawyers Association of Los Angeles (WLALA) **[12142]**
Women Marines Association (WMA) **[12145]**
Women Marines Association Edith Macias Vann Southern California Chapter CA-7 **[12150]**
Women & Politics Fund [1261]
Women Techmakers Udacity Scholarship [5048]
Women of Today's Manufacturing Scholarship [3697]
Women of WSAJ Bar Preparation Scholarship [11904]

Sponsor and Scholarship Index

9 780028 670362

7